'Weekly boarding at Headington is the best of b... ...ou can spend the week at school with all your friends and take ...t in so many activities. Then you get to relax at the weekend with your family. I love it.'

Weekly boarder, aged 13

'EXCELLENT' IN ALL CATEGORIES, LATEST ISI INSPECTION

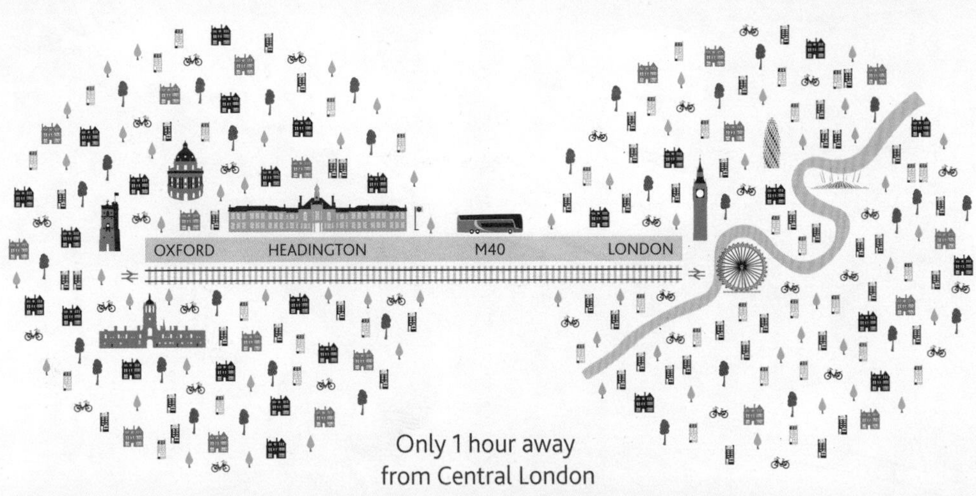

- Outstanding academic results
- Extensive extra-curricular programme
- Weekly boarding
- Half weekly boarding

Termly Open Events: **www.headington.org**

Headington School is a leading educational charity.
Registered Charity No. 309678 (1942)

PRIOR'S FIELD

GODALMING SURREY

GSA Girls' Boarding and Day School 11-18

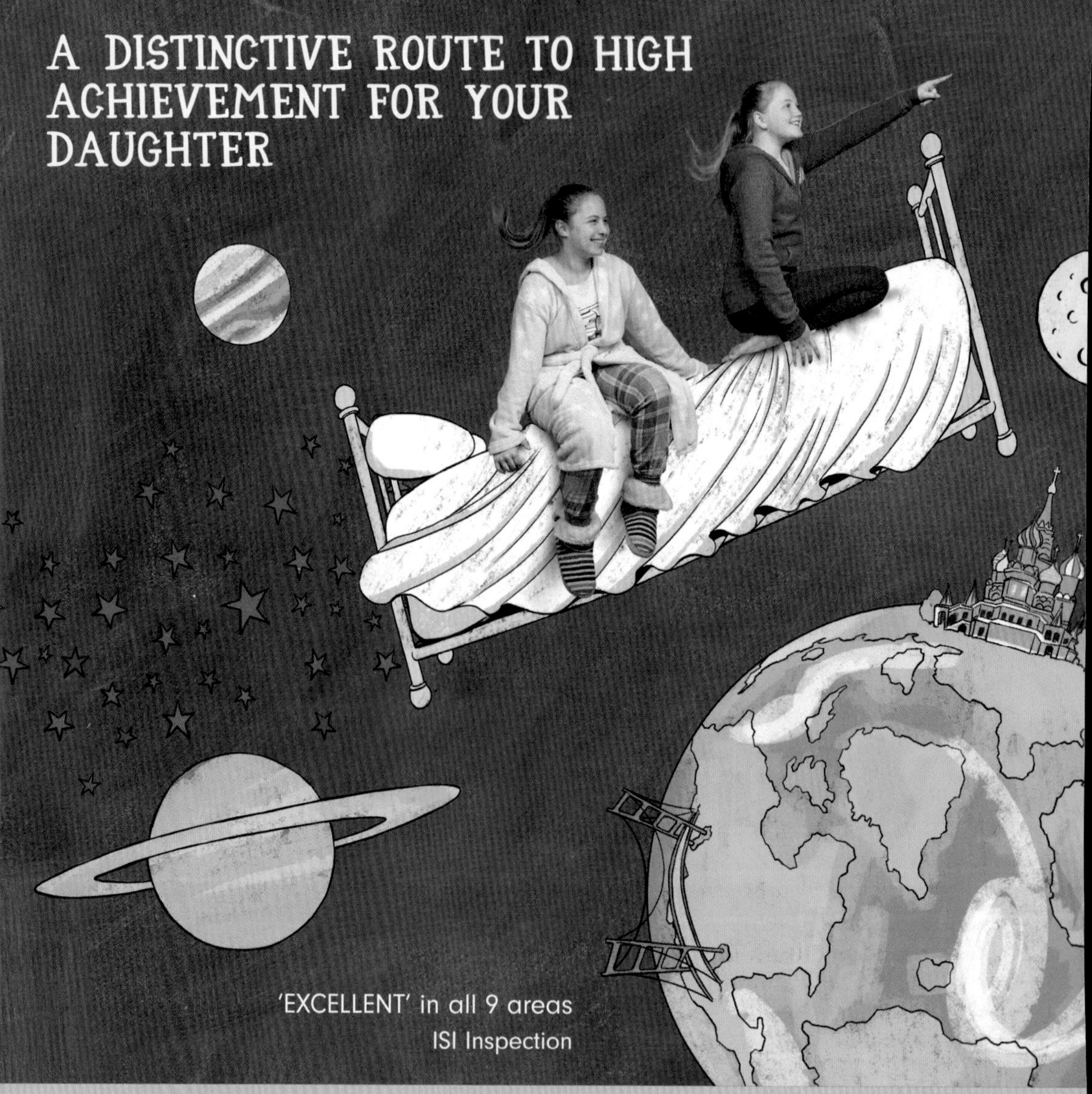

Full, weekly and tailored boarding options

11+, 13+ and 16+ entry

Call now to book your place at our next Open Event:

01483 810551 www.priorsfieldschool.com

Registered Charity No. 312038

THE GOOD SCHOOLS GUIDE

Boarding Schools

www.goodschoolsguide.co.uk

The Good Schools Guide is a registered trademark

"Probably what a boarding school should be: not oversized, caring, happy and successful across all ability levels."

GOOD SCHOOLS GUIDE

Caring for over 320 happy boarders, our dedicated staff display a genuine desire to do the very best for each child.

CLAYESMORE

DORSET

- Excellent pastoral care promotes and enhances the well-being of every girl and boy
- Bright, cheerful bedrooms and delicious healthy meals make boarding a home from home.
- A whirlwind of exciting actvity to broaden horizons
- A sense of stability leads to lasting friendships and the confidence to succeed.

Prep 01747 813155 • www.clayesmore.com • Senior 01747 812122

Second Edition published 2018 by Lucas Publishing Ltd
Good Schools Guide, 10 Greycoat Place, London SW1P 1SB
www.goodschoolsguide.co.uk
ISBN 978-1-909963-16-0
A CIP catalogue record for this book is available from the British Library
Copyright © 2018, Lucas Publications Ltd
Printed by Cambrian Printers Ltd

All rights reserved. No part of this publication may be reproduced, stored in or introduced into a retrieval system, or transmitted in any form, or by any means (electronic, mechanical, photocopying, recording, or otherwise) without the prior written permission of the publisher. Any person who does any unauthorised act in relation to this publication may be liable to criminal prosecution and civil claims for damages.

Every care has been taken to ensure that all information was correct at the time of going to press. The publishers accept no responsibility for any error in detail, inaccuracy or judgement whatsoever.

Acknowledgements

Writers

Alison Cooper
Anne Hadley
Anne Prendergast
Ashley Cavers
Bernadette John
Beth Noakes
Carolyn Murphy
Carolyn Thomas
Catriona Prest
Charles Cowling
Charlotte Obolensky
Charlotte Phillips
Charlotte Simpson
Claire Kingston
Debbie Reed
Denise Roberts
Elizabeth Coatman
Elizabeth Moody-Stuart
Elsa Booth
Emma Lee-Potter
Emma Vickers
Faye Monserrat
Fenella Douglas Miller
Godfrey Bishop
Guy Canning
Grace Moody-Stuart
Janette Wallis
Janita Clamp
Judith French
Juliet Austin
Kalantha Brewis
Kate Hilpern
Linda Tanner
Lisa Freedman
Lucy Heywood
Mary-Ann Smillie
Mary Bremner
Mary Langford
Mary Pegler
Melanie Bloxham
Melanie Sanderson
Nicky Adams
Patrea More Nisbett
Phoebe Bentinck
Ralph Lucas
Richard Field
Rosemary Taylor
Sarah Evans
Sandra Hutchinson
Susan Hamlyn
Suzanne Everest
Zoe Bing

Design: David Preston, Harriet Plyler

Typesetting: Theresa Hare, Optima Information Design

Editorial review: Beth Noakes and team: Janita Clamp, Kathryn Berger, Amanda Perkins, Helen Croston

Advertising sales: Charlotte Hollingshead, assisted by Jo Dodds, Publishing Matters

Project management: Katja Lips

Everything held together by: Shari Lord

Photography: Thanks to all the schools who supplied photographs.
Cover photos:

Heathfield School; St John's Beaumont School; Uppingham School; Gresham's; Merchiston Castle School

M
MONKTON

Find your inspiration

A co-education school in Bath, England
Pre Prep | Prep | Senior | 2–18 years
www.monkton.org.uk

Individual thinking. Amazing results.

MERCHISTON STORY

WHERE YOUR SON COMES FIRST

**EVERY BOY IS AN INDIVIDUAL. EVERY BOY HAS A STORY.
LET US SHAPE HIS FUTURE STORY.**

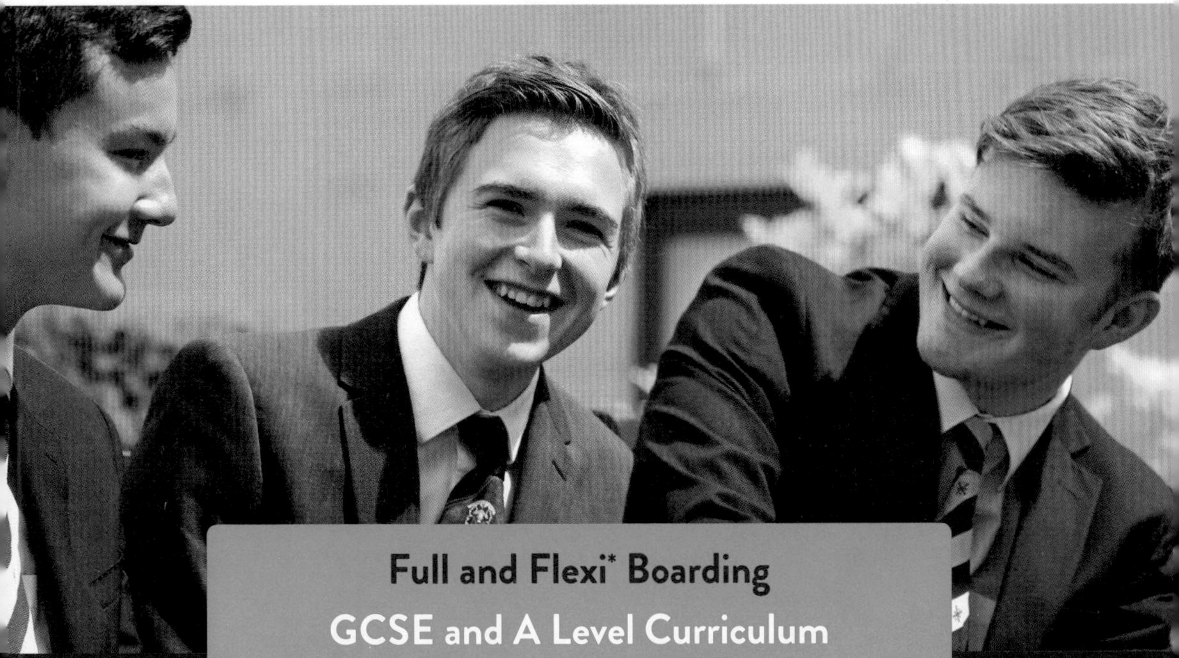

Full and Flexi* Boarding
GCSE and A Level Curriculum
Personal Tours Available All Year

A BOARDING AND DAY SCHOOL
FOR BOYS AGED 7-18
MERCHISTON.CO.UK

admissions@merchiston.co.uk +44 (0)131 312 2201

Means-Tested Financial Assistance Available *Merchiston Juniors (Year 4 – 8)
Recognised by the Inland Revenue as a Charity, number SC016580

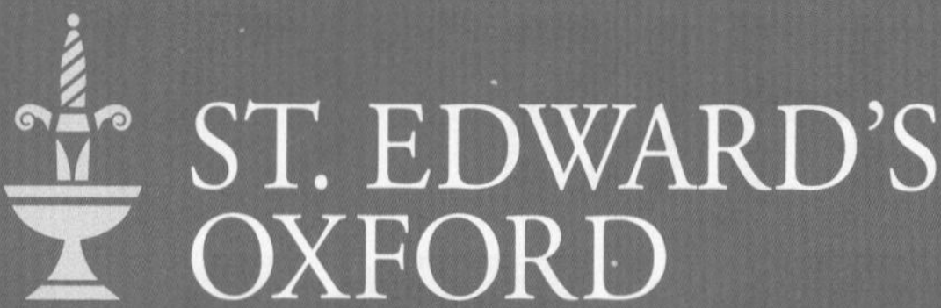

New school coach between London and Oxford every weekend

FROM SEPTEMBER 2018 | VIA BEACONSFIELD

'The spires of Oxford and the 100 acres of green loveliness make St Edward's a winning co-ed boarding ticket.'

TATLER SCHOOLS GUIDE

13 – 18 | A Level & IB

www.stedwardsoxford.org

Registered Charity No: 309681

The Good Schools Guide charter

We take our independence very seriously and the separation of commercial and editorial content is absolute. No school can pay to be included in (or choose to be excluded from) The Good Schools Guide. We do not charge schools for reviews.

We defray our costs by selling advertising space and licensing schools to reprint their own reviews for a fee. We make these offers only to schools that are already in the Guide on merit. Whether or not they choose to advertise has no bearing on their inclusion in the guide nor on the content of their review. Schools we have not chosen for inclusion in the Guide are not allowed to advertise.

Our printed guides and our website offer advice on a vast range of education matters. We also have a fee-paying consultancy service for parents (The Good Schools Guide Education Consultants). We receive no commission or any other payment from any school for these services. If you have any questions or concerns about our commercial policy, please contact editor@ goodschoolsguide.co.uk.

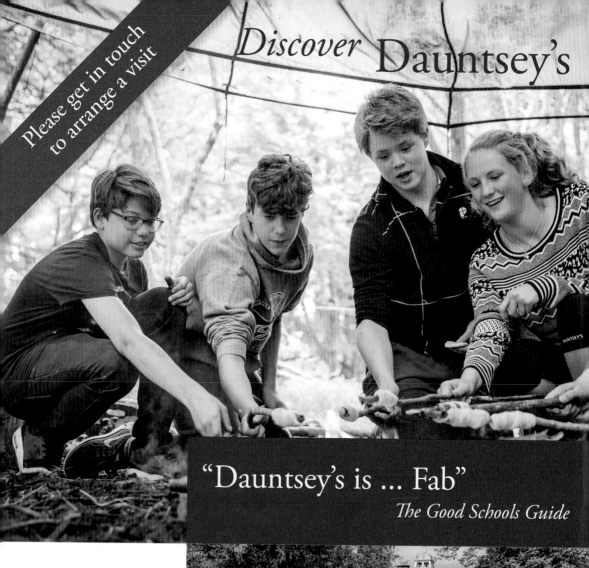

Please get in touch to arrange a visit

Discover Dauntsey's

"Dauntsey's is ... Fab"

The Good Schools Guide

Boarding & Day School
Co-educational 11-18

www.dauntseys.org

Wiltshire, Southern England, SN10 4HE - 150 km from London T. +44 (0)1380 814500

Contents

What makes them so successful?

A team of dedicated inspiring teachers, a nurturing and supportive atmosphere, good friends, their hard work, over 150 extra-curricular activities weekly, amazing facilities and a £100m investment.

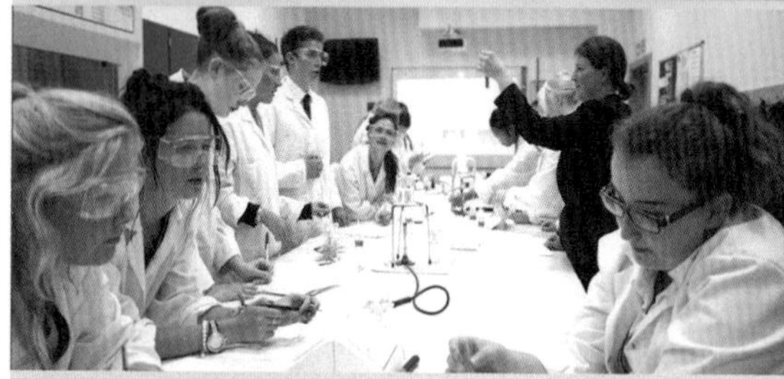

If you are interested in an independent education for your child and wondered how Queen Ethelburga's Junior, Middle and Senior Schools offer a non-selective pupil intake, yet by Year 13 achieve academic results well above all other schools in the region, with academic and sporting facilities unlike anything you will have seen anywhere else, with over 150 extra-curricular weekly activities, low fees and a large area covered by our daily bus service - then please either come along to an Open Day, or if you would rather come at a different time, simply phone our Admissions Dept. Tel: 01423 33 33 30 or email us on: info@QE.org

Amazing Sports Success - Yes
With dedicated inspiring sports coaches, a nurturing supportive atmosphere, amazing facilities and an on-campus £30m Sports Village - unrivalled in the North.

Chapter House Junior School	Nursery to Year Group 5	Day or Boarding - Boys & Girls
King's Magna Middle School	Year Groups 6 to 9	Day or Boarding - Boys & Girls
Queen Ethelburga's Senior Schools	Year Groups 10 to 13	Day or Boarding - Boys & Girls

Queen Ethelburga's College :
- 1st Northern independent school
- 3rd UK boarding school overall
- 5th UK independent school - all types

Faculty of Queen Ethelburga's :
- 2nd Northern independent school
- 5th UK boarding school overall
- 17th UK independent school - all types

(Based on % A*/A A-Levels 2017. Daily Telegraph)

- Pay by 12 monthly direct debit payments at no extra cost.
- New Sept 2018: Family Sibling award: 5% of fees for 2nd child, 20% of fees 3rd child and 35% of fees for subsequent siblings.
- Academic Scholarships for students entering Sixth Form with outstanding GCSEs and above average entering Year 6 to 10.
- Sports Scholarships for proven success at County, Regional, National and International Level
- First Term Free for Day Children entering Nursery to Year 5.

UK Termly Fees - 2017/18

Day fees paid monthly	Year Group	Boarding fees paid monthly
£474	Nursery	
£624	Rec	
£699	Year 1	£2,493
£699	Year 2	£2,493
£724	Year 3	£2,493
£881	Year 4	£2,678
£894	Year 5	£2,678
£979	Year 6	£2,832
£1,174	Year 7	£2,832
£1,174	Year 8	£2,832
£1,174	Year 9	£2,832
£1,281	Year 10	£2,970
£1,281	Year 11	£2,970
£1,371	Year 12	£3,115
£1,371	Year 13	£3,115

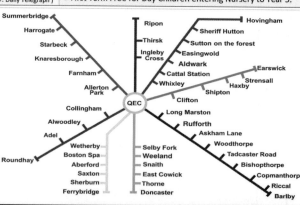

QEC
Summerbridge, Harrogate, Starbeck, Knaresborough, Farnham, Allerton Park
Ripon, Thirsk, Ingleby Cross
Hovingham, Sheriff Hutton, Sutton on the forest, Easingwold, Aldwark, Cattal Station, Whixley
Earswick, Strensall, Haxby, Shipton, Clifton
Long Marston, Rufforth, Askham Lane, Woodthorpe, Tadcaster Road, Bishopthorpe, Copmanthorpe, Riccal, Barlby
Selby Fork, Weeland, Snaith, East Cowick, Thorne, Doncaster
Wetherby, Boston Spa, Aberford, Saxton, Sherburn, Ferrybridge
Collingham, Alwoodley, Adel, Roundhay

Open Days
- Sat 18th Nov 2017
- Sat 20th Jan 2018
- Sat 10th March 2018
- Sat 28th April 2018
- Sat 9th June 2018

10.30am to 3.30pm
Meet the staff, tours by students + free buffet.

Queen Ethelburga's Collegiate.
Thorpe Underwood, York. YO26 9SS.
Telephone: 01423 33 33 30
Email: info@QE.org Web: www.QE.org
UK Independent Day & Boarding School - Girls + Boys - All ages

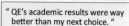

" QE's academic results were way better than my next choice. "

" The best sports and facilities. "

" Across the entire time my child will be at school, QE will cost me less than the other local independent schools. QE it is. "

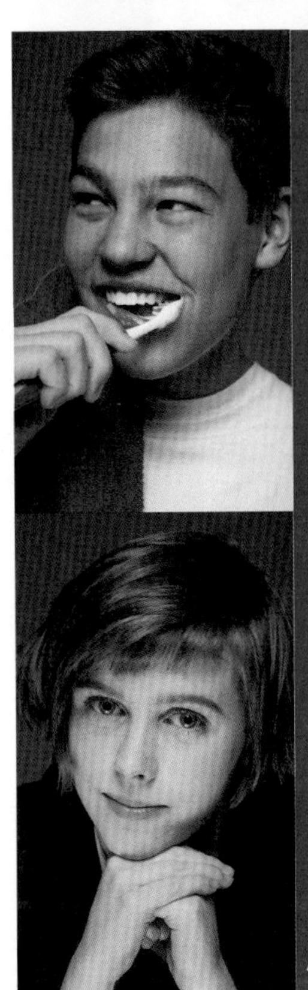

Achieving your child's personal bests

Ideally situated in the Sussex countryside
between Haywards Heath and Brighton

Hurst

HURSTPIERPOINT COLLEGE

A truly co-educational school with a strong community where pupils are known, nurtured and challenged to the best of their ability

Students in their second year of Sixth Form move into a co-educational Upper Sixth hall of residence, designed to provide a bridge between Sixth Form and university. As 'trainee undergraduates' every student – day/boarding – has his or her own study

Day, flexi and weekly boarding

hppc.co.uk

Admissions: 01273 836936 or registrar@hppc.co.uk

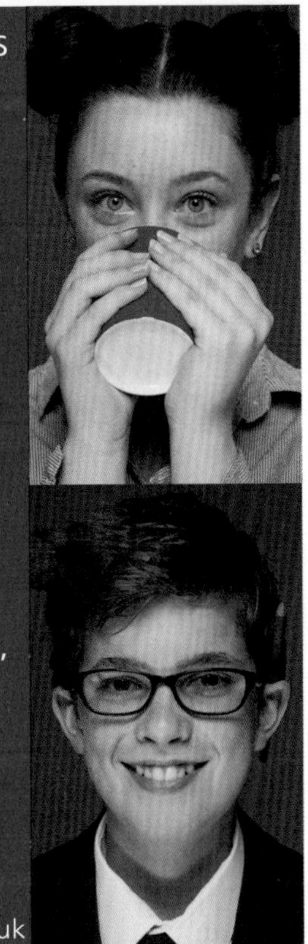

Haileybury
Creating bright futures for over 150 years

We are a co-educational boarding and day school for 11 to 18 year olds on an historic 500 acre campus in Hertfordshire, just 20 miles north of London.

We offer outstanding pastoral care, exceptional co-curricular activities and a strong academic track record in GCSEs, IGCSEs, A Levels and the International Baccalaureate Diploma.

To attend an Open Day or to book an individual appointment please contact the Registrar, Mrs Michele Metcalfe.

admissions@haileybury.com 01992 706 353

@HaileyburyUK HaileyburyUK
haileybury.com Hertford Herts SG13 7NU

Registered charity number 310013

extraordinary

days

Come and see what Stowe has to offer at one of our Open Mornings!

Stowe

Stowe is an independent co-educational boarding and day school inspiring pupils aged between 13 and 18.

e | admissions@stowe.co.uk t | 01280 818205 w | www.stowe.co.uk

CRANLEIGH
EX CULTU ROBUR

Cranleigh is a leading co-educational weekly boarding and day school on the edge of the Surrey Hills. Pupils lead busy lives now, exceeding academic and sporting expectations, while preparing for lives beyond our beautiful rural location. Cranleigh provides a breathtaking range of opportunities in a school small enough for everyone to know and support each other.

Registering now for 2020

To book a visit contact: admissions@cranleigh.org

www.cranleigh.org | admissions@cranleigh.org | 01483 276377

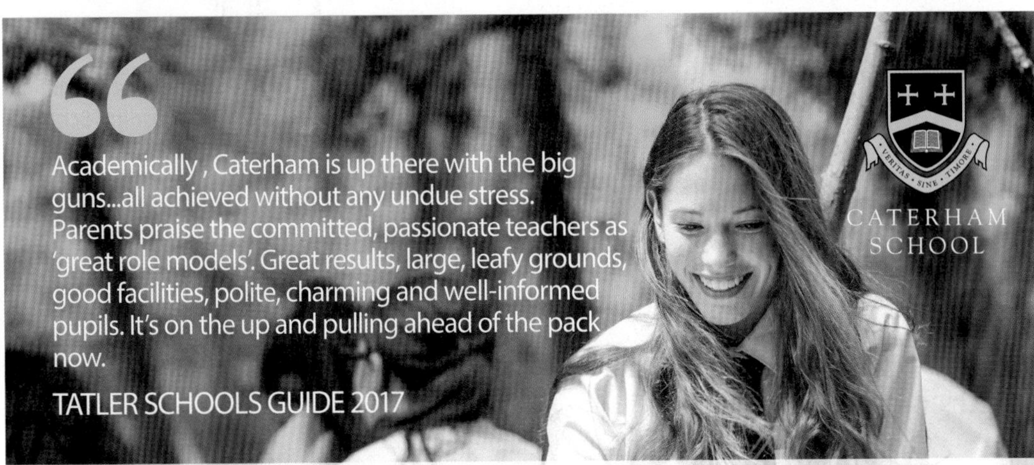
Academically , Caterham is up there with the big guns...all achieved without any undue stress. Parents praise the committed, passionate teachers as 'great role models'. Great results, large, leafy grounds, good facilities, polite, charming and well-informed pupils. It's on the up and pulling ahead of the pack now.
TATLER SCHOOLS GUIDE 2017
VERITAS SINE TIMORE
CATERHAM
SCHOOL

HMC Independent Day, Weekly and Full Boarding School for boys & girls age 3 to 18 years. One of the top co-educational schools in England with a unique, award-winning approach to Learning & Teaching, where all pupils can be successful in an environment which is caring, optimistic and encouraging.

Caterham School is easily accessed from London, Surrey, Kent and Sussex, and our extensive coach network includes mainline train connections and evening late bus services.

caterhamschool.co.uk | 

Catholic independent day
and boarding school for
boys and girls aged 2 to 13

"Jolly common rooms with
properly comfortable sofas
and cushions for film nights,
quizzes and meetings"
Good Schools Guide

Goring Heath, South Oxfordshire, RG8 7SF
email: office@oratoryprep.co.uk website: www.oratoryprep.co.uk tel: 0118 984 4511

Independent Catholic
Day and Boarding School
for Boys aged 11 to 18

**"Highly successful in
creating an atmosphere of
friendship, cheerfulness
and collegiality"** ISI Report

The Oratory School, Woodcote, Nr Reading, South Oxfordshire, RG8 0PJ
T. 01491 683 500 **W.** www.oratory.co.uk

HANDCROSS PARK
A BRIGHTON COLLEGE SCHOOL

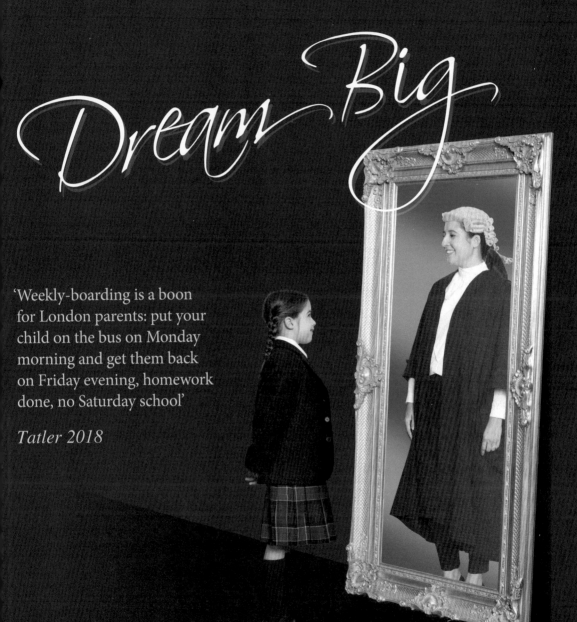

'Weekly-boarding is a boon for London parents: put your child on the bus on Monday morning and get them back on Friday evening, homework done, no Saturday school'

Tatler 2018

CO-EDUCATIONAL | DAY AND BOARDING | AGES 2-13

TEL: 01444 400526 WWW.HANDCROSSPARKSCHOOL.CO.UK
Handcross, Haywards Heath, West Sussex, RH17 6HF

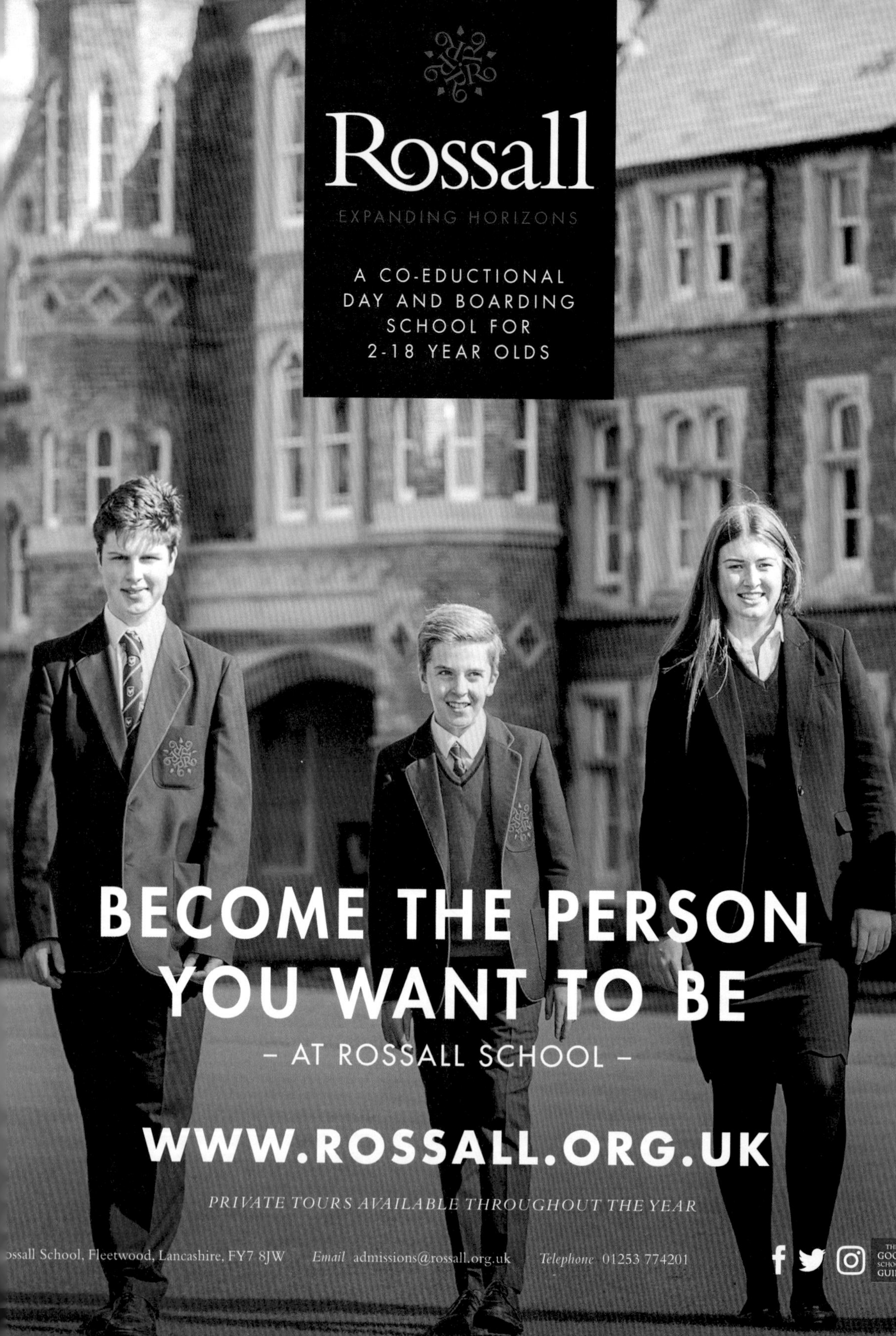
Rossall
EXPANDING HORIZONS
A CO-EDUCTIONAL DAY AND BOARDING SCHOOL FOR 2-18 YEAR OLDS
BECOME THE PERSON YOU WANT TO BE
– AT ROSSALL SCHOOL –
WWW.ROSSALL.ORG.UK
PRIVATE TOURS AVAILABLE THROUGHOUT THE YEAR
ossall School, Fleetwood, Lancashire, FY7 8JW Email admissions@rossall.org.uk Telephone 01253 774201
THE GOOD SCHOOLS GUIDE

Key to symbols

The age range of a school is shown by the colour of the title bar.

Junior School

Senior School

Girls' school

Church of England school

Boys' school

Quaker school

Co-ed school

Roman Catholic school

Boys' school with co-ed sixth form

Girls' school with co-ed sixth form

Co-ed pre-prep, then boys only

Co-ed pre-prep, then girls only

Vinehall

DAY & BOARDING SCHOOL IN EAST SUSSEX FOR GIRLS & BOYS AGED 2-13

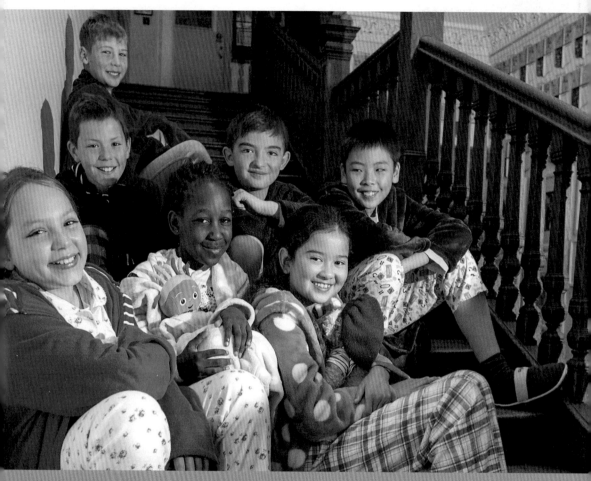

AN OUTSTANDING EDUCATION IN AN IDYLLIC SETTING

Flexible boarding options. An escorted train service from London.

Please contact Karen Cooper to arrange a visit or boarding taster session on **01580 883090** or at **admissions@vinehallschool.com**

Vinehall School, East Sussex, TN32 5JL
Tel: **01580 880413**

www.vinehallschool.com

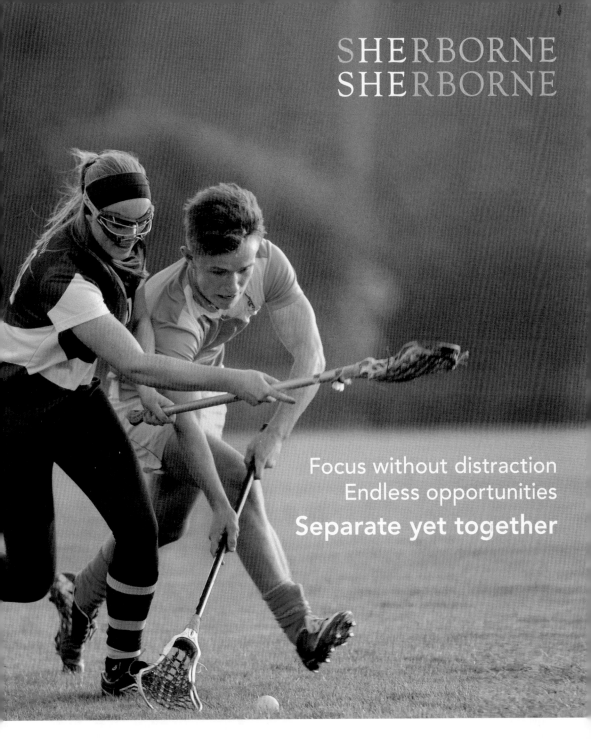

SHERBORNE
SHERBORNE

Focus without distraction
Endless opportunities
Separate yet together

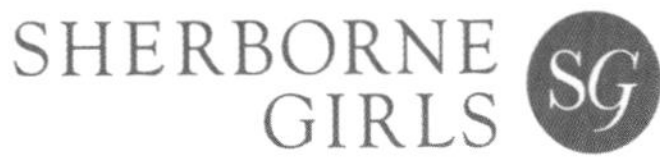

01935 810403
admissions@sherborne.org
sherborne.org

01935 818224
registrar@sherborne.com
sherborne.com

Boarding schools overview map

For UK-wide map of state boarding schools see p.1284

WINDLESHAM HOUSE SCHOOL

Independent Boarding & Day School for Boys & Girls Aged 4 - 13

- Excellent rating received in 2017 ISI Report
- Record number of scholarships gained to senior schools this year
- Outstanding pastoral care & extra curricular programme

Windlesham House School, West Sussex, UK | Call +44 (0) 1903 874701 | 40 mins from Gatwick | 1.5 hr from Heathrow

Email admissions@windlesham.com | visit windlesham.com

The Pilgrims' School, Winchester

Day and boarding for boys aged 4 to 13

Winchester to Waterloo: 1 hour. Escorted travel available

Please contact the Registrar for more details or to arrange a visit of the school

www.thepilgrims-school.co.uk | admissions@pilgrims-school.co.uk | 01962 854189

Incorporating the Winchester Cathedral Choristers and the Winchester College Quiristers

Junior King's
Canterbury

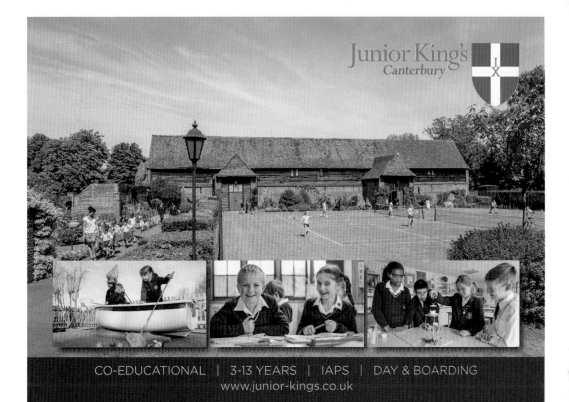

CO-EDUCATIONAL | 3-13 YEARS | IAPS | DAY & BOARDING
www.junior-kings.co.uk

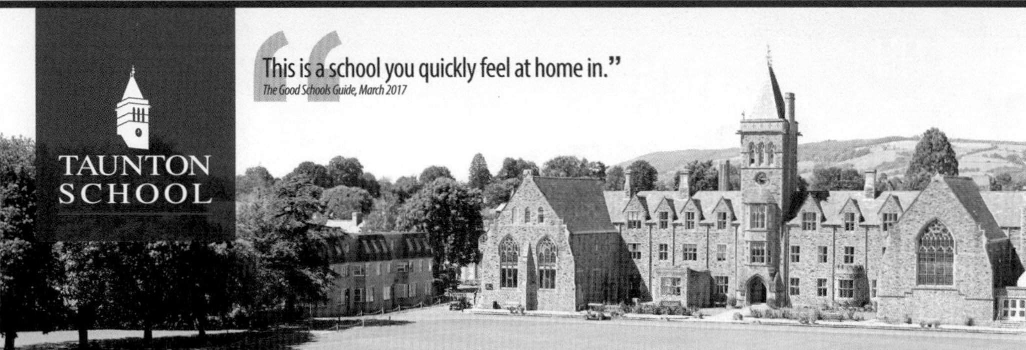

A School for every boy and girl

Taunton School offers outstanding education to boarding and day pupils from 0-18 as proven by our recent Independent Schools Inspectorate (ISI) report.

Boarders, who can join us in the Prep School from age 7, enjoy a varied and active life on our safe and spacious 56 acre campus, in the beautiful Somerset countryside.

Discover Taunton School at one of our Whole School Open Mornings
See the website for details.

Alternatively, contact us on registrar@tauntonschool.co.uk to arrange a personal visit.

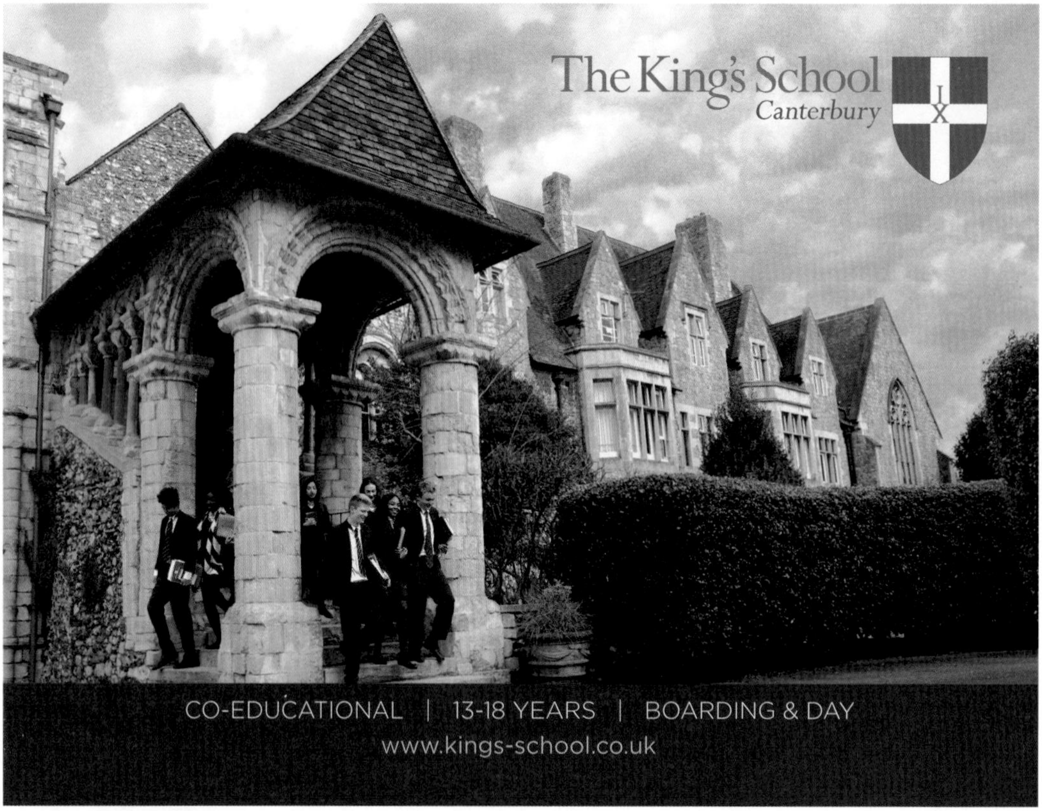

The King's School
Canterbury
CO-EDUCATIONAL | 13-18 YEARS | BOARDING & DAY
www.kings-school.co.uk

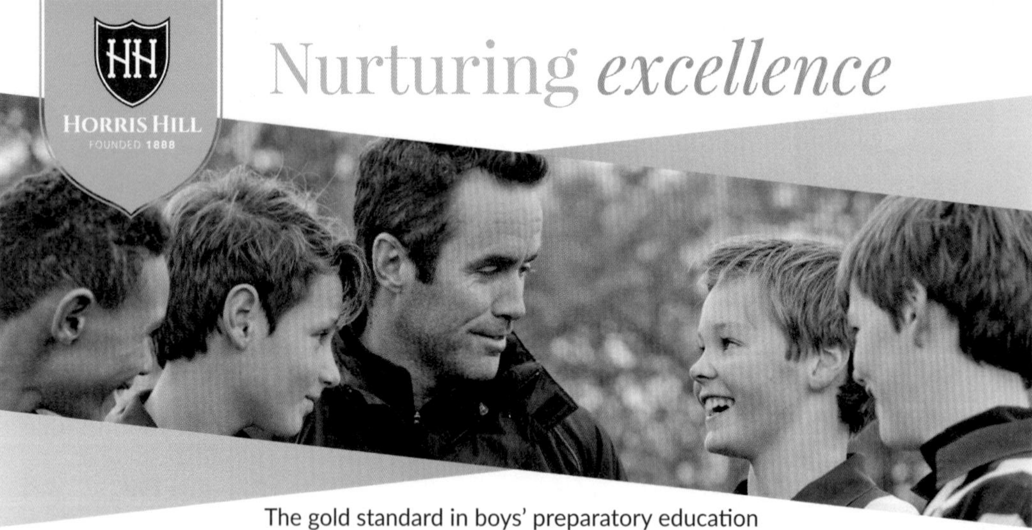

HH
HORRIS HILL
FOUNDED 1888
Nurturing excellence
The gold standard in boys' preparatory education
Excellent top senior school entry and scholarship track record
Wonderful rural setting with easy access to M4/London
Outstanding academic reputation
Huge breadth of co-curricular opportunities
horrishill.com

Introduction

Why boarding? Why indeed. Almost no other educational topic provokes such vehement and polarised opinions. But while the clichés of Dickensian cruelty remain deadlocked against St Trinian's and Hogwarts in the court of public opinion, a quiet revolution has taken place. Boarding schools have changed beyond measure in the last 50 years, not least because all schools, and society, have done so too. Traditional full boarding schools remain, albeit in much reduced number, but for many children today 'boarding' just means staying at school a couple of nights a week.

Boarding school heads tell us that the boarding family profile is much more varied than it used to be. It's likely that both parents are working – sometimes abroad or a long commute away. While boarding is still a tradition in some families, others come to it for the first time for a variety of reasons. Maybe your child has a particular aptitude – specialist boarding schools have the facilities and specialist staff on hand to develop sporting or musical talents. Families with several children may opt for flexi or weekly boarding because it's preferable to hours in the car on multiple school runs. Sixth form boarding is particularly popular and a great preparation for university – although some may find the accommodation at university a little less salubrious than school. In other circumstances a small, nurturing boarding school can provide stability and a haven for a child with an unhappy home life. Forces personnel posted abroad have always been a core group for whom boarding schools are essential. The allowances have become considerably less generous in the last few years but many state and independent boarding schools give priority and some financial assistance to children from these families.

One thing that hasn't changed for the better is the cost of sending a child to boarding school, now running closer and closer to £40,000+ a year. This hasn't discouraged applications from wealthy international families, but there are real concerns that the middle class British parents, who for years have just managed to afford private education by scrimping, saving and remortgaging, are being priced out of the market. Places at state boarding schools where parents only pay for the boarding element (usually around £12,000-£15,000 a year) and tuition is free, are consequently more sought after than ever.

Some years ago, possibly as a result of the economic downturn, the boarding demographic in some schools was not well managed. While this may have secured short-term benefits, bursars quickly realised that parents – whether they come from Beijing or Bognor – want their children to be part of a diverse and well-integrated boarding community. These days you will find that schools take great care to ensure that this is the case.

This book contains over 300 of the Good Schools Guide's highly informative and famously frank reviews. Every single school has been visited by our writers, who check out everything from dorms to food and weekend activities. We also speak to parents and, most important of all, pupils.

Boarding, twenty-first century style, is flourishing. The number of families choosing boarding schools for their children is increasing and the decision to board is, as often as not, made by children themselves. Whether you're interested in big names, local treasures, state boarding schools or country preps where your daughter can board along with her pony, this book is your unbiased guide to all that's best in British boarding.

What type of boarding – full, weekly or flexi?

If you're reading this you've probably already decided that boarding might suit your son or daughter. If so the next step is to consider the arrangement that best suits your family. Unlike the old days, when youngsters were packed off to school at the age of 7 or 8 and didn't see home again until the end of term, today's boarding schools offer parents a choice of full boarding, weekly boarding, flexi boarding or even a combination of these. For instance, flexi boarders may wish to weekly board during exam times or become full boarders in the sixth form. Whichever option you choose, there's no doubt that boarding schools are more skilled than ever at helping their charges settle in and feel at home. They may run taster weekends, get new pupils to start before the rest of the school arrives and appoint buddies and mentors to guide them through the first few weeks and beyond. Pupils are encouraged to keep in regular touch with their parents – and it's not just a handwritten letter hastily scribbled before church on Sunday mornings either. Children can email, Skype and – if mobile phones are allowed – text or phone home when they wish.

Full boarding

Full boarding schools are in the minority these days, but if you're looking for a school where everyone boards and there isn't a mass exodus at weekends, you still have quite a few options.

Boys' full boarding schools

These include some of the most famous names in British education such as Eton, Winchester, Radley and Harrow. Historically, boys from the English upper classes were sent here to be educated as future leaders, statesmen, bishops and military commanders. These days, boys from many different

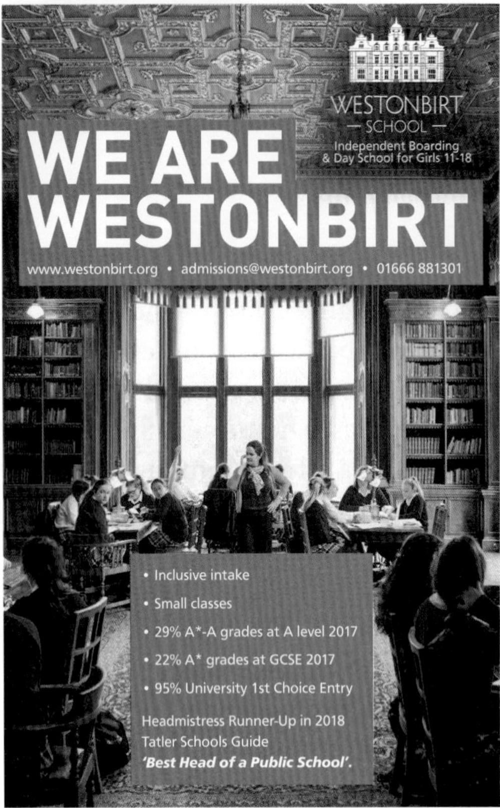

NURTURING
POTENTIAL
SINCE 1860

PREPARATORY DAY SCHOOL | FLEXI AND WEEKLY BOARDING
CO-EDUCATIONAL 3-13

'Lambrook is a lively and unstuffy prep school in an idyllic pastoral setting where boys and girls are educated to the best of their potential. Lambrook is a Good Thing'

GOOD SCHOOLS GUIDE

Winkfield Row, Nr Ascot, Berkshire, RG42 6LU
Telephone +44 (0)1344 882717 **Email** info@lambrookschool.co.uk
www.lambrookschool.co.uk

Do you see what we see?

LEARNING FOR LIFE

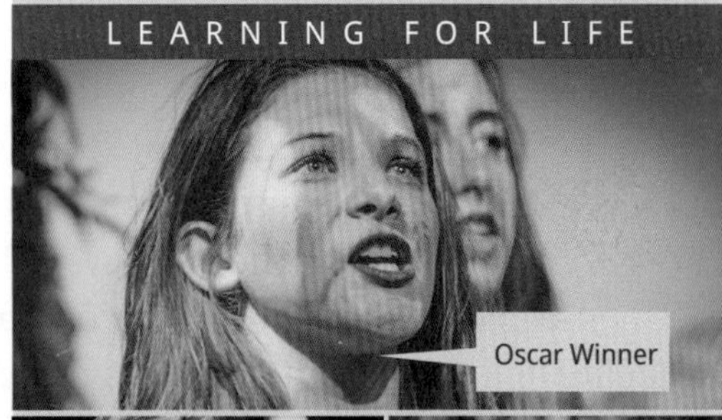

Excellent academic results

Fully co-educational 3-18

Easy Access to International Airports

Day and Boarding

Generous Service Bursaries

Ranked in the Telegraphs '10 Best value for money UK Boarding Schools'

Academic | Sport | Music
Drama | Art / Design

www.wellington-school.org.uk
admissions@wellington-school.org.uk
01823 668800

OUTSTANDING EDUCATION

BROMSGROVE SCHOOL
Founded 1553

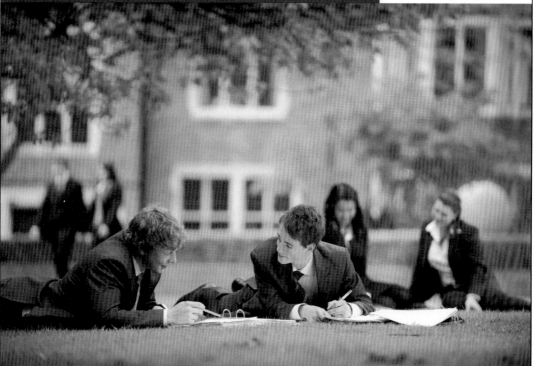

One of the UK's leading day and boarding schools.

Over 500 boarders aged 7 - 18.

The Good Schools Guide says:
"...Bromsgrove manages to combine the feel of a local family day school with an international boarding school, attracting pupils both for its sporting reputation and also its academic offer and results. The arts side of the school is definitely in ascendency."

Individual visits welcome, please contact Admissions

01527 579679 admissions@bromsgrove-school.co.uk
bromsgrove-school.co.uk
FLAIR • DISCIPLINE • ACADEMIC RIGOUR

ISI Inspection 2016:
Excellent in every category

Outstanding results
at IB and A level

Academic excellence coupled with a wealth of sporting and extra-curricular opportunities

Co-educational,
Day & Boarding

Over 500 boarders aged 7 - 18

930 pupils aged 13-18
500 pupils aged 7 - 13

backgrounds compete for places from all over the world. Nor do you necessarily have to come from a wealthy family. The former head of Eton, Anthony Little, believes schools like Eton should be 'needs blind'. He told the Good Schools Guide, 'We do not want to be a finishing school for the titled and rich.' Noble sentiments and ones that schools such as Eton and many others are trying to live up to with scholarships and 100 per cent bursaries. However it is fair to say that with fees heading for £40,000 pa the average pupil is not going to come from a family of modest means.

At these schools all the boys board and may go home only for exeats, usually two per term, Saturday pm to Sunday pm. However, parents are more involved with school life than formerly; those who live close enough attend matches, concerts and plays and technology enables much closer contact over long distances too. Boys at these senior schools may well have attended full boarding boys' preps such as Cothill House and Horris Hill or preps where boarding is compulsory for all in the last two years (7 and 8) such as Caldicott and Papplewick.

'We do not want to be a finishing school for the titled and rich.' Noble sentiments to live up to

Girls' full boarding schools

Benenden and Heathfield are among the very few exclusively full boarding schools for girls. Downe House, Wycombe Abbey, Sherborne Girls and Tudor Hall are essentially full boarding (no flexi/weekly) but also take a few local day pupils. Hanford School in Dorset and Sunny Hill in Somerset are two of a tiny handful of girls only boarding preps.

The best known girls' boarding schools such as Roedean, Badminton and The Cheltenham Ladies' College were established in the mid- to late-19th century by formidable pioneers of women's education. This makes them relative newcomers compared to the likes of Winchester College, believed to be Britain's oldest school, which was founded in 1382. It also explains why most girls' schools lack the extensive property portfolios and endowments held by their brothers.

Co-ed full boarding schools

If you want your sons and daughters to attend a full boarding school together there are quite a few co-ed choices including Oundle, Uppingham and Marlborough College. Because of its proximity to London, Wellington College is de facto weekly boarding since so many pupils go home for Saturday night, nevertheless all boarders must spend two Saturday nights in school per term. All these schools also take a small number of day pupils but don't offer weekly or flexi boarding options. Girls and boys live in separate boarding accommodation with clear rules about what is out of bounds to visitors of the opposite sex. Some schools have co-ed sixth form boarding houses, but boundaries are in place. See Sex and drugs and homesickness, page 27 for more information on this.

Weekly boarding

Weekly boarding is growing in popularity, particularly for children who live too far away to be day pupils or whose parents work long hours and/or frequently travel abroad. Weekly boarders either go home on Friday evenings or Saturday afternoons and return to school on Sunday evenings or Monday mornings. For many children, this offers the best of both worlds: they can enjoy school during the week, work hard and spend lots of time with their friends, then relax at home with their parents on Saturdays and Sundays. Parents are keen on weekly boarding too. They like the fact that they don't have to nag about homework or getting up on time in the morning and feel that home time is 'quality time.'

Many opt for boarding schools within an hour's drive so they can still turn up for sports matches, concerts and drama productions during the term.

Flexi boarding

Flexi boarding gets a mixed press; parents are generally in favour but for some schools it's a step too far. One prep headmaster describes it as 'a bit of a nightmare, like glorified hotel management.' Unlike full and weekly boarding, one school's definition of 'flexi' may not be the same as another's. It's certainly never going to be bed and breakfast at the drop of a hat. Most schools require parents to book boarding nights at the beginning of each term, with Thursdays and Fridays being the most popular. Not surprising if it means parents can enjoy a night out without having to find a babysitter (and not have to get up for the Saturday morning school run). While it can be complicated for schools to manage, flexi boarding could be just the ticket if your child has to stay at school late for sport, music or drama one or two nights a week, or if you want to dip your toe in the water and see if boarding suits your family. Schools that offer flexi boarding will inevitably have some spare beds and many told us that they will always do their best to accommodate a pupil at short notice if there's a family emergency.

BRAMBLETYE

Leading Pre-Prep and Prep School for Boys and Girls aged 2½ to 13

"...the place is always filled with laughter"
Good Schools Guide

"Brambletye magic is alive and working wonders"
Current Parent

Brambletye, Lewes Road, Sussex, RH19 3PD | www.brambletye.co.uk | +44 (0) 1342 321004

Escorted Weekend Train Service to London

"PUPILS' ATTAINMENT IS **OUTSTANDING**"

ISI Inspection Report March 2017

FIND OUT WHAT PUTS QUEENSWOOD "... AT THE **PINNACLE** OF HERTFORDSHIRE'S **VALUE-ADDED** TABLES"

Good Schools Guide

Lancaster Royal Grammar School

State day and boarding school for boys 11-18

A fantastic alternative to the independent sector

OUTSTANDING

Founded in 1472 we are one of the UK's top grammar school for boys offering:

- **Academic and sporting excellence**
- **An outstanding, well-rounded education with free tuition**
- **Warm pastoral care creating a community where all pupils feel valued**
- **Boarding provision rated 'Outstanding in all areas' (Ofsted 2017)**

www.lrgs.org.uk 01524 580542

Best Ever Results at GCSE
50% A* & 75% A*–A

67th at GCSE
Telegraph League Tables

ROEDEAN

'Excellent in all areas'
ISI Inspection 2016

Top Girls' School in Sussex
Telegraph Jan 2017

A UNIQUE EDUCATION – WHY NOT COME AND SEE FOR YOURSELF?

Register for an Open Day

roedean.co.uk

64 girls in Year 7
Sept 2017
570 girls on roll

SAINT RONAN'S SCHOOL

@saintronans

/SaintRonans

www.saintronans.co.uk

Book an appointment on **01580 752271** or e-mail **emmatv@saintronans.co.uk**

Boys & Girls 3-13 years | Founded 1883 | Hawkhurst, Kent | 01580 752271

State boarding schools

If you think your child would benefit from a boarding school education, but are put off by the high fees and consequent limited social mix of a typical independent boarding school, you may find that a state boarding school is the answer. These have seen a surge of popularity in recent years, partly due to increasing numbers of families with both parents working long hours. 'We all work hard during the week, and get together at weekends,' said one father. 'It's much less stressful than trying to oversee homework and music practice after a long day at work and travelling, and my daughter is happy to spend week nights at school with her friends.' Those schools offering full boarding are popular with families working abroad, in the Forces, the diplomatic service or with international companies.

Many day pupils stay for after-school activities with the boarders – 'boarding minus the bed'

What do they cost?

State boarding schools are comparatively cheap – mostly somewhere between £12,000-£15,000 a year in boarding fees – because the government foots the bill for tuition. The majority of pupils in most state boarding schools are day pupils, but many stay for after-school activities alongside the boarders – 'a boarding experience minus the bed,' as one school put it. Some of the schools, such as Gordon's in Surrey, levy a 'day boarding' fee of several thousand pounds to all day pupils to cover after-school activities (though bursaries are available for low income families). Others, such as Hockerill Anglo-European, have free day places for normal school hours attendance, but charge a day boarding fee to those who wish to arrive for breakfast and stay for activities, supper and homework.

Who can apply?

As with other state schools, these are open to British citizens, EU passport holders and anyone with a right of residence in

Steyning Grammar School

— Day & State Boarding in West Sussex —

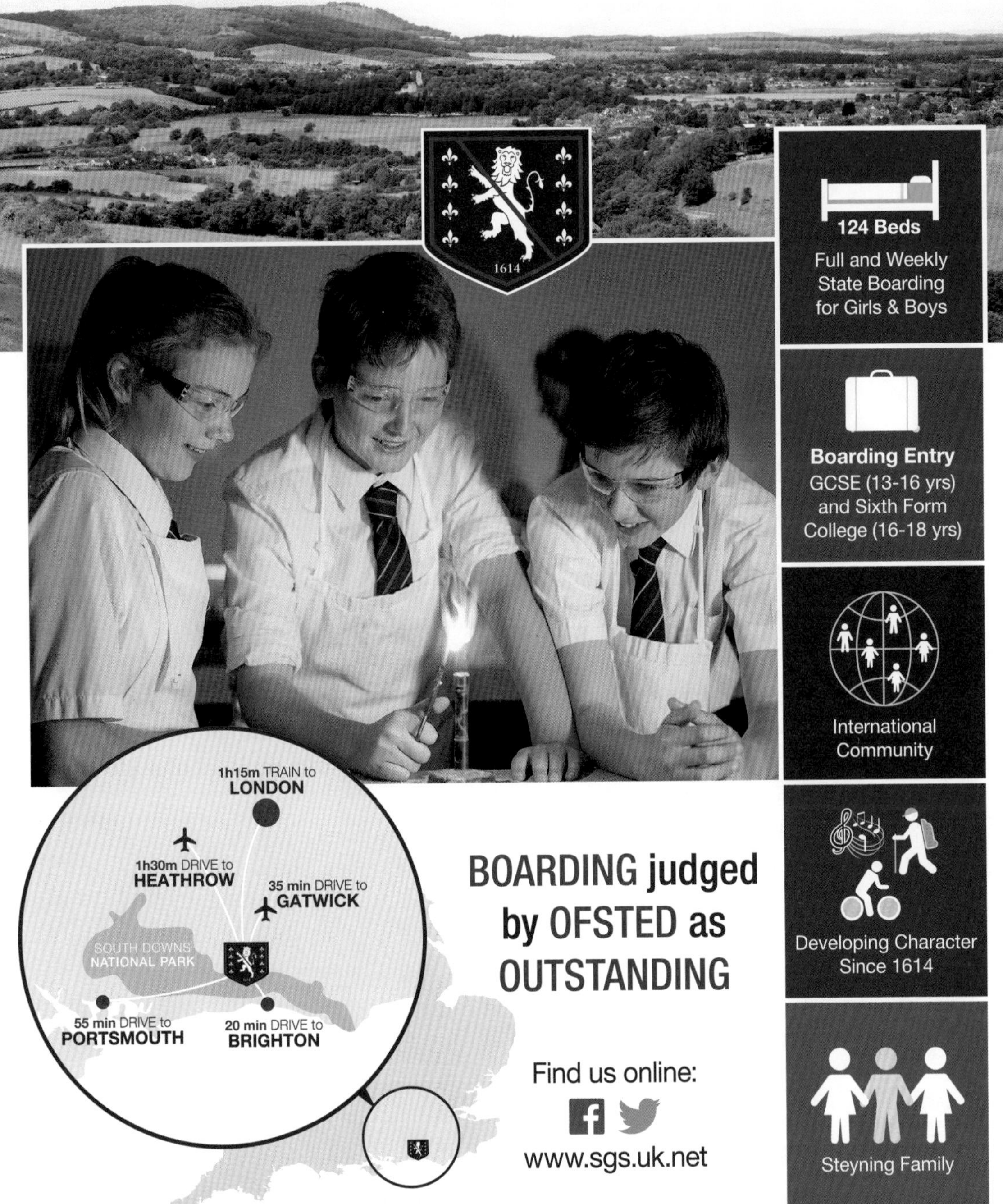

For further information please contact us: sgsboarding@sgs.uk.net / +44 (0) 1903 817601

the UK. It is not yet clear how, or if, admission arrangements will change for EU passport holders post-Brexit (see page 42). Some are academically selective, some are single sex, and they are permitted to interview pupils (which other state schools are not) in order to ensure they are suitable candidates for boarding.

How many are there?

There are 38 in England, including one in the Scilly Isles and one in Scotland – the latter for children from Forces families – with a total of some 5000+ places. Some offer full boarding, others only weekly boarding, some have boarding for sixth formers only and one is a specialist sixth form college run by the Ministry of Defence.

What to consider

As with any other school, read prospectuses, school magazines and newsletters, inspection reports and reviews such as those in this book. We review about half of British state boarding schools, and have extensive data for all of them on our website. See page 1283 for our reviews of state boarding schools.

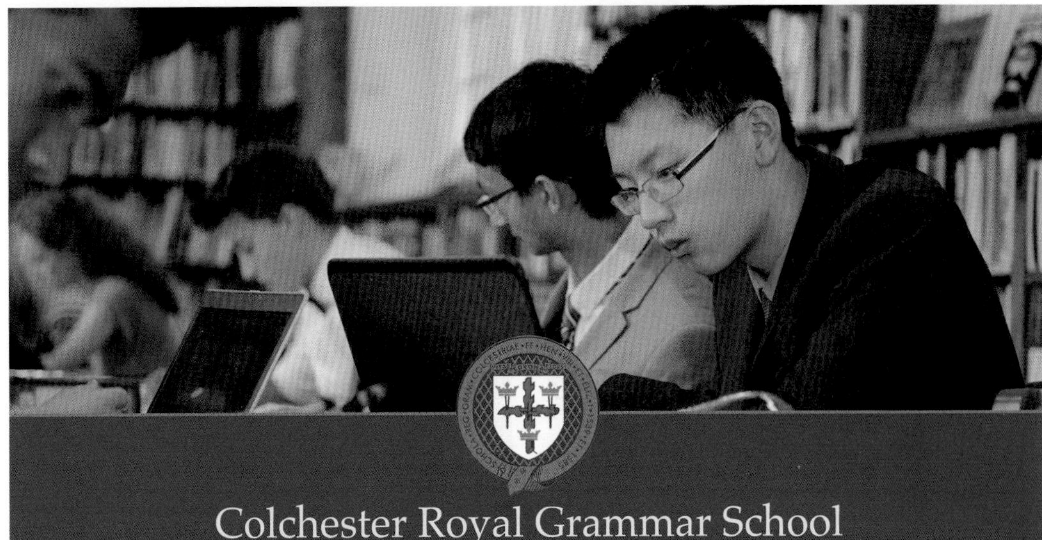

Colchester Royal Grammar School
• Top school at A Level in the government league tables for nine out of the last 11 years
• Named 'The Sunday Times Parent Power East Anglia State Secondary School of the Year'
• Over 235 Oxbridge offers in the last seven years
• Over 60 medical offers in the last three years
• Boarding fees only £4,400 per term - there are no tuition fees
For further information visit our website
www.crgs.co.uk

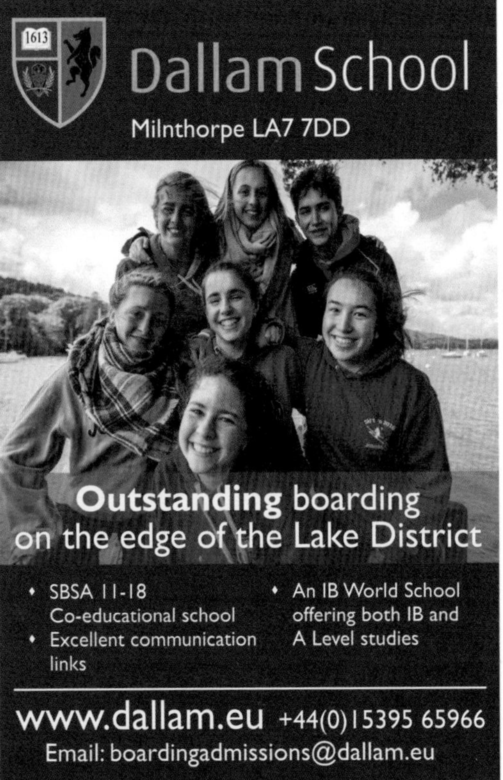

1613
Dallam School
Milnthorpe LA7 7DD
Outstanding boarding on the edge of the Lake District
• SBSA 11-18 Co-educational school
• Excellent communication links
• An IB World School offering both IB and A Level studies
www.dallam.eu +44(0)15395 65966
Email: boardingadmissions@dallam.eu

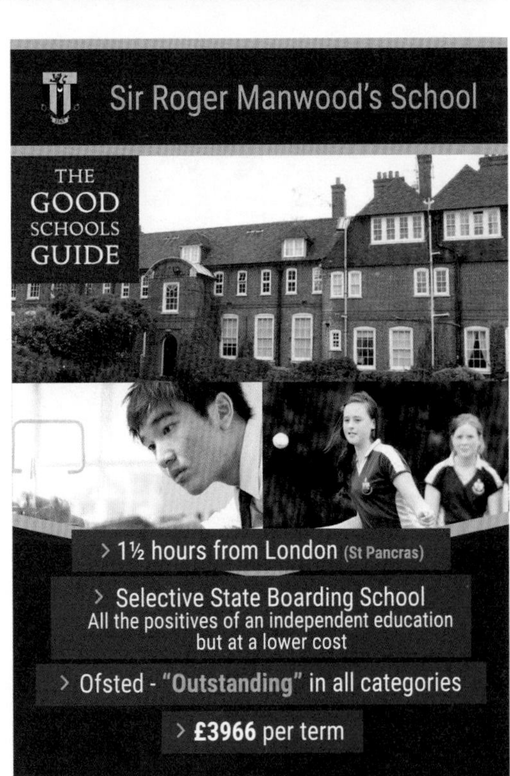

Sir Roger Manwood's School
THE GOOD SCHOOLS GUIDE
> 1½ hours from London (St Pancras)
> Selective State Boarding School
All the positives of an independent education but at a lower cost
> Ofsted - "Outstanding" in all categories
> £3966 per term
www.manwoods.co.uk
+44 (0)1304 610200

Opening doors
to affordable boarding

- A selective state grammar school with boarding for £3,800 per term.
- A stunning home with acres of grounds to explore.
- Excellent academic results – 80% A*-C at A-level last year.
- Extensive choice of sports and extra-curricular activities.
- Rated 'Outstanding' by Ofsted in all four categories.
- Boarding places available for Years 7-9 and Sixth Form entry.
- New purpose-designed senior boarding house now open.

T. 01952 953810
www.adamsgs.uk

What age to start boarding?

Most children start boarding at the age of 11 or 13. At this age children themselves tend to have a say in the matter. Some prep schools admit boarders under 10 and make special provision for them with bedrooms that look much closer to how things are at home (rather than dorms) and, because numbers will be small, an evening regime that is flexible. At Horris Hill, for example, where they have a few boarders under the age of 10, 'if it's hot they can have a swim, if everyone's exhausted they go to bed early.'

The sixth form is another entry point for first time boarders. We visit many schools where there are more boarders in the sixth form than lower down the school – largely because 16 to 18-year-olds are keen to concentrate on their studies, socialise with their friends in their spare time and get a taste of living away from home prior to university. Sixth form boarders will generally have their own study bedrooms in separate accommodation with well-equipped kitchens (Ocado will deliver to boarding schools!), washing machines, even yoga studios. At Westonbirt school where over three quarters of sixth formers board, one girl told us, 'there aren't so many distractions, it helps us stay focused on our studies.'

Groups of sixth formers take turns to stay for five days in the school flat in the nearby village

At Heathfield, an all-girls' boarding school in Ascot, Berkshire, girls in the upper sixth live in their own bungalow on site while Burford School, a co-ed state boarding school in Oxfordshire, has created a flat within the boarding house for a group of sixth form girls – to get them ready for the university years. At Rendcomb school in Gloucestershire groups of sixth formers take turns to stay for five days in the school flat in the nearby village. They are given housekeeping money and (apart from lunch at school) must manage this and the chores. Apparently sometimes it runs like clockwork, sometimes 'mummies deliver food parcels and help clean up at the end.'

THE GOOD SCHOOLS GUIDE

North or South?
We've got it covered

Our compact London guides are available in 'North' and 'South' editions and come with over 200 full colour illustrations in each volume.

Order now from our website:
www.goodschoolsguide.co.uk

Sex, drugs and homesickness

Given that the majority of boarding school pupils are aged from 13 upwards, some parents might think school fees a small price to pay for letting trained professionals steer their hormonal offspring over the turbulent waters of adolescence. Even so, we all know that risk taking, underage drinking, drugs, sex, cyber-bullying, self-harm, anorexia and the other ills that teenage flesh is heir to can occur right under parents' noses. What then should you expect boarding schools to do to keep young people safe?

Pastoral care and well-being are now up there with academic results as key measures of any school's success and as closely monitored as exam performance. In addition to the normal school inspection visits (Ofsted for state schools, ISI for independent schools), government inspectors visit all boarding schools to check every aspect of provision from fire escapes to mattresses and they also talk to staff, pupils and parents. All schools should have a link to the latest boarding inspection report (and their response to any issues raised) on their website. But knowing the number of locks on a dormitory window won't tell you if someone will notice your child staring miserably out of it.

They are your first point of contact, you should be able to ask anything and expect prompt answers

All schools provide copious information on how they ensure pupils' safety (usually termed 'safeguarding') and well-being (if they don't, make your excuses and leave). It's up to you to attend the open days, go to the talks, read the literature and then weigh up whether the regime will suit your child. See page 54 for more details about child protection.

Houseparents

Houseparents, as the name suggests, will be most closely involved in your child's day to day life at school. They are your first point of contact and you should feel able to ask them anything and expect to get prompt answers to your questions. This is a highly professional and responsible job and to a great extent your child's happiness will depend on their (and your) relationship with these people.

Many, but not all, houseparents are married couples, often with children – and pets – of their own. One (or very often both) is likely to teach at the school. They live in the boarding house along with several other adults such as 'gappies' (young people, often from Australia or S Africa), matrons and/or tutors. The nomenclature and precise arrangement will depend on the school and the number/age of boarders, but there's generally at least one resident adult per corridor/floor.

Most schools have 'vertical' (mixed age) boarding 13-16, with sixth formers accommodated separately; they may also keep year 7 and 8 boarders in a separate house. Some smaller schools have 'horizontal' (year group) boarding houses. In either case, there will be separate bed times, rules and such like that are appropriate to the age of the children.

Which house?

Parents often ask us how to get their child into a particular house – maybe they've heard on the grapevine that 'x' is the 'sporty' house or 'y' is the 'best' house. While it's true that the character of the houseparents or housemaster/mistress is inevitably going to have an influence, schools tell us that they work hard to ensure every house has a good mix of types. It's also worth bearing in mind that during your child's years at the school house staff may leave, so it's best not to pin all your hopes on someone you happen to particularly like. Families are encouraged to look round several, if not all, boarding houses and apply in order of preference – but school has the final say.

House or home?

While people are always more important to the ethos of a school than buildings, architecture can have an influence. Girls at Westonbirt School sleep under the high ceilings of grade 1 listed state rooms and our reviewer found 'priceless silk wallpaper, preserved under Perspex, rubbing shoulders with One Direction posters.' Boarders at Cheltenham College live in elegant town houses – one advantage of this is that it puts a little distance between school and 'home'. Modern, purpose built boarding houses, while less characterful, are likely to have better plumbing. All in all, boarding accommodation seems to be improving year on year, no doubt keeping local building trades very busy over the summer holidays. In most schools, pupils sleep in dormitories (usually about three to five beds in a room) until years 10 or 11 when they move into single or double study bedrooms. Sixth formers almost always have individual study bedrooms.

Pupils with physical disabilities

Historic buildings rarely make for easy disabled access and if your child needs special arrangements you must to discuss these with the school well in advance. This won't just apply to boarding houses; classrooms may be up several flights of stairs and there can often be a fair way to walk between lessons. That being said, we know of many schools who have done all they can to accommodate pupils in wheelchairs or with visual or hearing impairments.

Food glorious food

You will be relieved to hear that our reviewers, who always try and have lunch in the schools they visit, have never been faced with the grim fare endured by the likes of Oliver Twist and Jane Eyre. Nor, we hope, will today's boarders find themselves afflicted in adult life with 'boarding school eating'. This not entirely polite style of consumption, which stems from parsimonious portion control at schools in the 1960s and 70s, is characterised by rapid scoffing of everything in sight before someone else snaffles it.

Wonderful cooked breakfasts, delicious vegetarian options, salad bars, in-house coffee shops and locally grown produce are almost standard these days. Most schools have a central dining hall, but at some, such as Repton, Oundle and Malvern College, boarders eat all meals in their houses. This may be a practical arrangement if houses are a little distance from the main school building, but it also has a beneficial influence on table manners as well as making it easier for staff to spot a child who isn't eating. Boarders will also have access to house kitchens with toasters, microwaves etc and fresh fruit is always available. Nor have tuck boxes been consigned to history; full boarders still use them to keep favourite treats under lock and key.

At Tudor Hall School sixth formers told us they like to buy bacon and eggs from the nearby farm shop and make their own breakfasts at the weekend. Boarders at town schools will find that the local takeaways are more than happy to deliver; this is particularly popular with boarders from overseas who might fancy an (albeit Anglicised) taste of home.

Playing by the rules

Even in the sixth form it's unlikely that your son or daughter will enjoy the freedoms they have at home. Parents and children will be expected to agree to and abide by the school's policies on everything from uniform, energy drinks, alcohol to PDAs (public displays of affection – kissing, holding hands etc) and random drugs testing. These policies (all of which will be on the school's website) have been drawn up to ensure not just your child but the whole boarding community is safe.

Some schools allow 18 year olds to visit 'approved' pubs or restaurants in the nearest town, but such freedoms are a privilege instantly rescinded if abused. Others – perhaps in more rural areas – have a sixth form bar where alcohol is dispensed under supervision and always with parents' consent. At some full boarding schools older pupils may apply for permission to host parties in designated areas. What happens under the radar is, inevitably, another matter – as it often is at home.

Relationships between pupils at boarding schools are a concern for parents and, we imagine, a chronic headache for staff – especially at co-ed full boarding establishments. At most schools 'intimate or explicit sexual relations' are classed as 'misconduct' that can lead to suspension or expulsion. Some schools ban any public display of affection; some don't. However, as with drink and drugs, banning sex doesn't mean it won't happen. Parents of girls in particular may want to get a feeling for the state of gender relations in the school. Is there any suggestion that girls are second class citizens while (say) rugby captains are gods?

Sixth formers told us they like to buy bacon and eggs from the nearby farm shop and make their own breakfasts at the weekend

Rules about what happens on school premises are fair enough, but it's a much greyer area when full boarders attend private parties at, for instance, a day pupil's house. Parental permission must be obtained to attend this kind of event, but responsibility for policing pupils' behaviour under these circumstances cannot be the school's.

You should feel able to raise questions and discuss concerns about this or any other matter with the school. Talking to parents with older children at the school is also a good idea if you want to find out just how intimate the relationship is between policy and reality. The 'Pastoral care, well-being and discipline' section of our reviews covers these issues.

If your own domestic regime is more Liberty Hall than Dotheboys Hall you will need to discuss potential schools' disciplinary policies with your child and be realistic if you think the worlds are too far apart.

Googling a school may lead you to press reports about historic sexual abuse, expulsions for drug use and other stories guaranteed to make a parent's blood run cold. The measure of a school is not so much that these things happened (they do, though thankfully very infrequently), but how such serious and unfortunate incidents are handled. If a school declares, for instance, that possession of drugs will lead to immediate expulsion but fails to expel those who break this rule, you should make your own judgement. (Some schools will allow pupils to return to sit public exams.)

Schools manage this by keeping their charges busy, busy, busy during the first few weeks

Remember, too, that although occurrences like this are surprisingly rare, just because a school has a squeaky-clean record is no guarantee that something won't happen in the future. You will have to take much on trust, just as the school will trust your child not to break the rules.

Homesickness

Homesickness is almost always a short-term problem that the school, the parents and the child can weather by working together. It's not a universal affliction, but many children away from home and family for the first time are likely to have a bout. Schools manage this by keeping their charges busy, busy, busy during the first few weeks and being ultra vigilant. Several have told us that managing parents during this time is equally challenging and that, depending on circumstances, it can be more settling if children aren't chatting to anxious mummy every night. Some children sail through their first term but come down with a nasty case when they return to school after the Christmas holidays. No school will want to keep a child boarding if they are profoundly and persistently unhappy, and in these relatively rare circumstances parents are advised accordingly. Sometimes it's a case of trying again after a few terms, but sometimes a different type of school is the only answer.

Celebrating 150 years
1867 - 2017

A CO-EDUCATIONAL INDEPENDENT DAY AND BOARDING SCHOOL IN ABERDEEN FOR PUPILS AGED 2-18

THE TOP INDEPENDENT SCHOOL IN SCOTLAND FOR HIGHER EXAM RESULTS
THE HERALD, 2017

ALBYNSCHOOL.CO.UK
FEES ASSISTANCE AVAILABLE / CHARITY IN SCOTLAND (SC008392)

THE DOWNS
MALVERN

Co-educational • 3–13 years

A day and full boarding Prep School, with weekly and flexi options

For more information, please contact
Katherine Cox, Registrar
01684 544108
registrar@thedowns.malcol.org
www.thedownsmalvern.org.uk

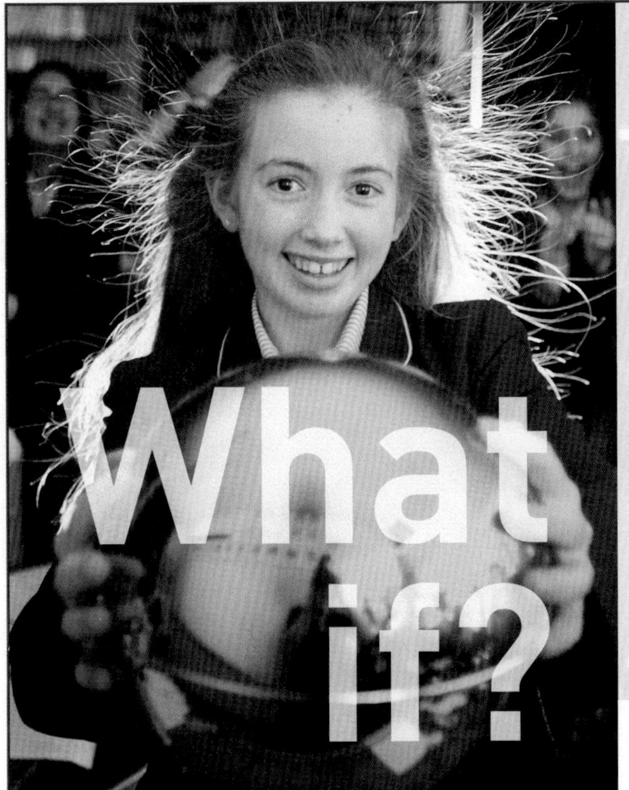

Boarding

Age 8-18

What if there was a boarding school that did things a little differently?

That really understood each girl and put her at its heart.

That found her individual talents and inspired her.

Yet challenged her to achieve the best possible results.

What if your daughter went to that boarding school?

RMS girls think differently
Learn more at RMSforgirls.org.uk

The Royal Masonic School for Girls,
Rickmansworth, Hertfordshire, WD3 4HF
01923 773168

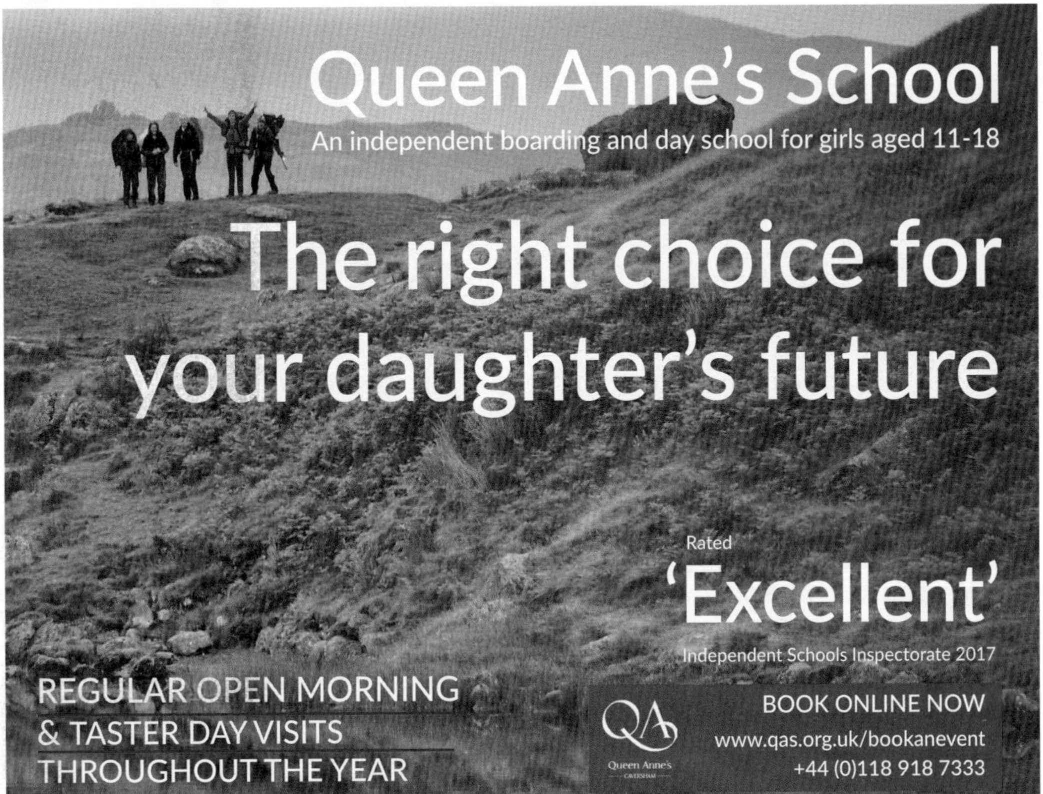

Queen Anne's School

An independent boarding and day school for girls aged 11-18

The right choice for your daughter's future

Rated
'Excellent'
Independent Schools Inspectorate 2017

REGULAR OPEN MORNING
& TASTER DAY VISITS
THROUGHOUT THE YEAR

QA
Queen Anne's

BOOK ONLINE NOW
www.qas.org.uk/bookanevent
+44 (0)118 918 7333

CASTERTON
SEDBERGH PREPARATORY SCHOOL

NURSERY - 13 YEARS

CO-EDUCATIONAL

Day, Weekly, Flexi,
Full Boarding Available

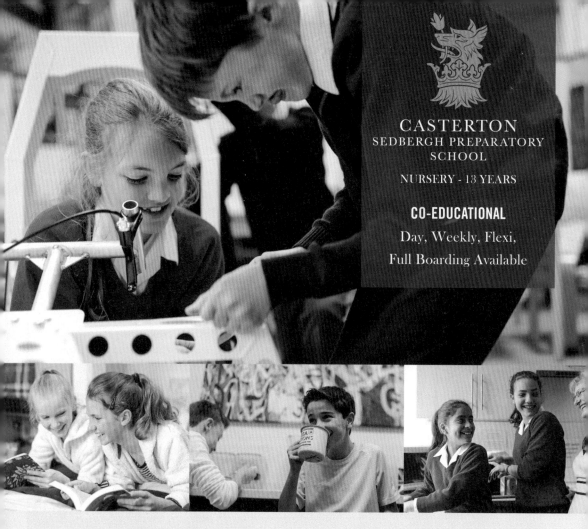

Boarding at Sedbergh Prep.
Your Child's Journey Starts Here.

A school where learning is brought to life, where children embrace every opportunity and follow their dreams.

Take the first steps towards your child's future, contact Mrs Mandy Marshall to organise a personal visit at ajm@sedberghprep.org or call 015242 79200

WWW.SEDBERGHSCHOOL.ORG

Sedbergh Preparatory School, Casterton, Kirkby Lonsdale, Cumbria, LA6 2SG

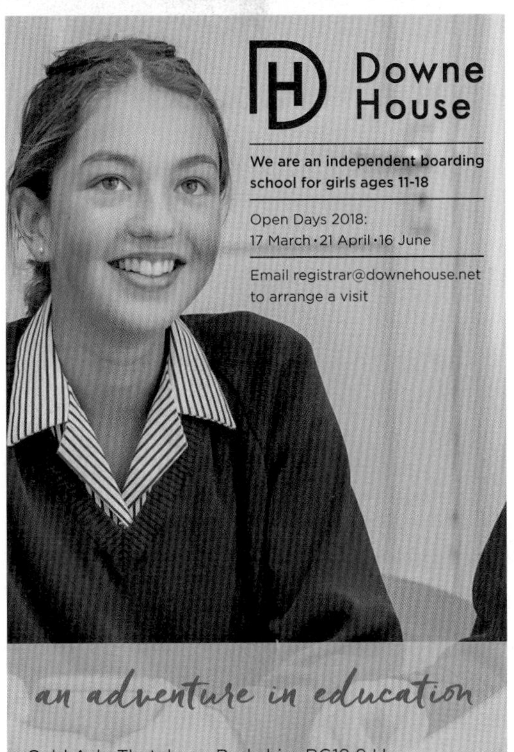

Feltonfleet

PREPARATORY SCHOOL

01932 862 264

BYFLEET ROAD COBHAM SURREY KT11 1DR

www.feltonfleet.co.uk

WHERE INDIVIDUALS REALLY MATTER

Advice for international applicants

British boarding schools have never enjoyed a higher standing abroad and each year thousands of pupils from all over the world pile in for a taste of the boarding experience. In fact, roughly five per cent of the UK's boarding school pupils are from abroad – that's 20,000 children from around 100 different countries.

Pastoral care is now given as much prominence as academic standards. Newly refurbished accommodation is bordering on luxurious (but don't expect many en suite bathrooms) and the transformation of school food is nothing short of miraculous, though fish and chips and custard – separately, of course – remain culinary fixtures. But before completing your registration form and paying the deposit, it's worth checking that you know what you are buying and whether it will suit your family.

English language support

The vast majority of international pupils follow a mainstream curriculum and work towards standard 16 and 18 plus qualifications. For those whose English isn't yet quite good enough or whose previous education puts them behind others of the same age, extra support from teachers who specialise in EAL (English as an Additional Language) may be needed.

Some schools run separate classes in key subjects, structured to allow more time for the language component so that maths and science students, for example, have sufficient understanding to decode word-based problems. A growing number of boarding senior schools also run International Study Centres that offer a range of specially structured courses in what is effectively a school within a school. Pupils may board or play sport with their 'mainstream' peers but will follow a largely separate and slimmed down academic

The transformation of school food is miraculous, though fish and chips and custard remain culinary fixtures

programme, working towards a smaller number of GCSEs with a big emphasis on learning English. These are covered in more detail on page 51.

Social life

While the academic side of boarding is undoubtedly important, the social dimension is just as vital. Good Schools Guide reviewers regularly hear of enduring friendships that span religious or cultural divides, or of lessons enriched by pupils on opposite sides of wars, sanctions or economic policy.

Things work less well if a school operates a monoculture policy. A large number of pupils from one nation in a single year group may help fend off homesickness, but can also reduce the motivation for pupils to speak English socially or immerse themselves in their host country's way of life – an opportunity lost rather than gained. It's okay to ask admissions staff for numbers if you're at all concerned.

Similarly, a school where the number of overseas pupils is so small that they are swamped by the prevailing culture can also lead to a miserable experience – particularly if they are the only full boarders in the place at weekends while everyone else goes home. It's essential to find out just how many pupils of your child's age are actually around over the weekend; many schools start off with a packed house for Saturday morning lessons or matches but empty out seconds after the final whistle (or bell) sounds.

Exporting education – big names abroad

Finally, for those happy to ditch some of the trimmings and all of the British weather, it's increasingly possible to get the ethos, results and teaching quality of a traditional British education without travelling anywhere near the UK. Over the past few years, some of the most famous names in education have opened offshoots overseas. You can get a

NURSERY 3-4 PRE-PREP 4-7 PREP 7-13 BOARDING 7-13 BOYS 3-7 GIRLS 3-13

Please contact the Registrar, Mrs Annie Bird, on 01494 429006 or email registrar@godstowe.org
if you would like information about our Open Days or to book an appointment to visit the school at any other time.

Godstowe Preparatory School, Shrubbery Road, High Wycombe, Buckinghamshire, HP13 6PR t: 01494 529273

www.godstowe.org

THINK BIG

- State of the art 'STEAM' Hub ready for April 2019 visit www.talbotheath.org/school-life/our-vision.
- Voted in the top 5 boarding schools for girls in the UK. *Study International, Oct 2015*
- Forest School in our own beautiful woods.
- One to one iPads from Y3.
- Official Apple Regional Training Centre.
- National finalists in sixteen sports.
- UK No.1 Tennis School for Girls, No.4 in the World.
- Superb achievements in Music, Drama and STEM subjects (science, technology, engineering, maths).

Talbot Heath

Independent School for Girls aged 3-18

Rothesay Rd | Bournemouth | 01202 761881 | www.talbotheath.org | Search @TalbotHeathSch | Day and boarding | Private buses to London / airports

Harrow education in Bangkok, Beijing or Hong Kong, become a Haileybury pupil in Kazakhstan and or sign up for Brighton College in Abu Dhabi. In 2017 Westminster School announced it was setting up no fewer than six schools in China (teaching the Chinese curriculum the Westminster way). Ethos and teaching standards are recognisably the same even if the facilities (sport is often air-conditioned and inside, for example) aren't.

Remember

- Distrust any educational firms offering to find your child a place in a UK school. If free to you, they may well be getting a commission. Similarly, a bill for securing you a 'guaranteed' school place should also sound alarm bells. Speak to the school yourself.
- The key entry points into UK schools are at age 11, 13 or 16. Many schools will look at potential pupils outside these times, but bear in mind that it's often on a one in, one out basis – places become available only if another family leaves.
- Look past fabulous exam results. Top schools do well because they select top pupils. What it proves is that parents of the brightest children send them here. It doesn't necessarily tell you how well it teaches them.
- Check how EAL provision (if required) is organised. Ideally, ask to sit in on some lessons to give you an idea of the standards/commitment and enthusiasm you'll be getting – and try to talk to similar pupils.
- Consider applying for scholarships if your child is outstanding (academic, musical and sporting excellence are the norms) and ensure that your idea of excellence is the same as the school's but...
- Don't be won over by worthless scholarships, sometimes offered as an incentive by schools to seal the deal.

- Check how often a child won't be boarding. Half terms, bank holidays and occasional weekend exeats all add up to a considerable chunk of time when pupils aren't in school and will need somewhere else to stay. Most schools require parents who live abroad to appoint a guardian for their child (see page 47), but you may also want to ensure family visits coincide with these dates.

A word on Brexit

There are around 4,500 pupils from the European Union at UK independent boarding schools and a further 500 at state boarding schools. At present EU residents do not need a visa for their child to come to a boarding school in the UK, but what the arrangements will be post-Brexit is unclear. If there is a free movement agreement then the status quo may not change, if not then it's possible that EU families, like those from outside the EU, will need to apply for 'Tier 4' visas. That's a lot of paperwork.

DOVER COLLEGE

Independent, co-educational, boarding and day, 3 to 18

- Set in idyllic surroundings of a 12th Century priory
- Only 1 hour from London by train
- Easy access to all London airports
- At the heart of the Garden of England, just minutes from the coast

dovercollege.org.uk

@DoverCol

BEDE'S EXTRAORDINARY

Archie
Lower Sixth
Scholar

To book a personal visit please contact:

admissions@bedes.org
T 01323 843252

HMC – Day, weekly and full boarding
Boys and girls 13 to 18

Bede's Senior School
Upper Dicker
East Sussex B
N27 3QH

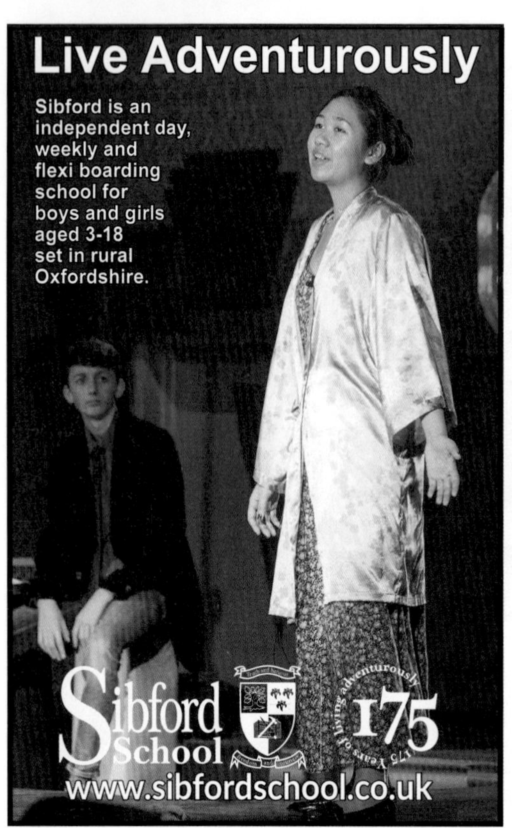

Live Adventurously
Sibford is an independent day, weekly and flexi boarding school for boys and girls aged 3-18 set in rural Oxfordshire.
Sibford School
175
www.sibfordschool.co.uk

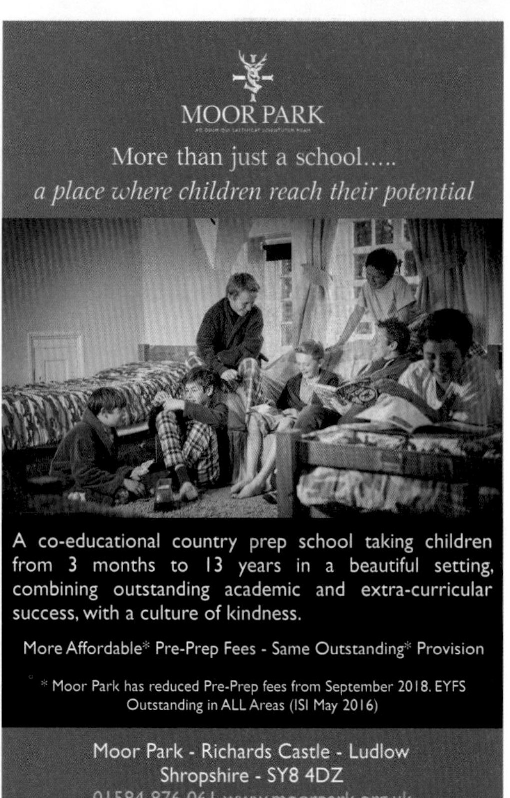

MOOR PARK
More than just a school.....
a place where children reach their potential
A co-educational country prep school taking children from 3 months to 13 years in a beautiful setting, combining outstanding academic and extra-curricular success, with a culture of kindness.
More Affordable* Pre-Prep Fees - Same Outstanding* Provision
* Moor Park has reduced Pre-Prep fees from September 2018. EYFS Outstanding in ALL Areas (ISI May 2016)
Moor Park - Richards Castle - Ludlow
Shropshire - SY8 4DZ
01584 876 061 www.moorpark.org.uk

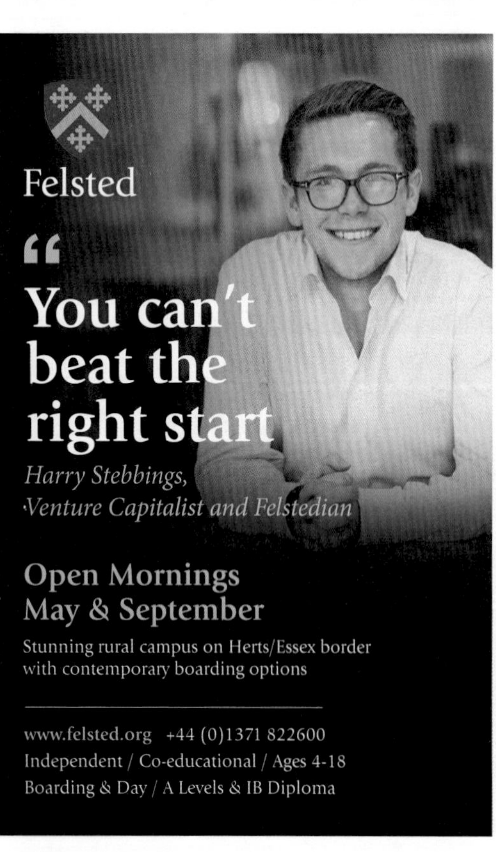

Felsted
“You can't beat the right start
Harry Stebbings, Venture Capitalist and Felstedian
Open Mornings
May & September
Stunning rural campus on Herts/Essex border with contemporary boarding options
www.felsted.org +44 (0)1371 822600
Independent / Co-educational / Ages 4-18
Boarding & Day / A Levels & IB Diploma

PRO PATRIA POPULOQUE
Blundell's
www.blundells.org

HAZLEGROVE - *prep school boarding at its very best.*

'Boarders are confident and exuberant in their appreciation of boarding at the school.'
Independent Schools Inspectorate

Making the most of education, opportunity and childhood and establishing long-term friendships in a home from home...

Call +44 (0)1963 442606 to find out more Hazlegrove, Sparkford, Somerset BA22 7JA

Bloxham School

Co-educational Boarding and Day School for ages 11-18

A country school around an hour from London

Scholarships & bursaries available

Please contact admissions@bloxhamschool.com to find out more

ORWELL PARK SCHOOL

Celebrating
150
YEARS

Independent Boarding and Day School 2½ to 13
Nacton, Ipswich, Suffolk IP10 0ER
Tel: 01473 659225 Email: admissions@orwellpark.org www.orwellpark.co.uk

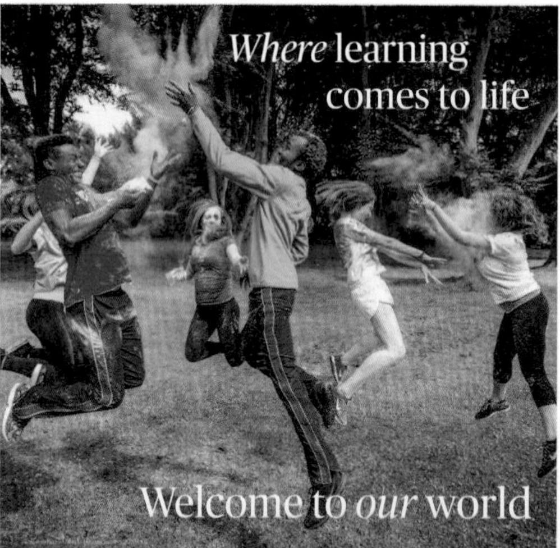

Welcoming boys and girls aged 9 to 18 yrs

Boarding and day

Scholarships and bursaries available

For more information or to arrange a visit please contact 01738 815003 or admissions@strathallan.co.uk

Strathallan School, Forgandenny, Perth, Scotland, PH2 9EG

STRATHALLAN SCHOOL

Opportunities for *all* to excel

strathallan.co.uk

MARYMOUNT
INTERNATIONAL SCHOOL LONDON

International Catholic Day and Boarding School for girls aged 11 to 18

Education that is formed from our past and transforms for the future.

LONDON • PARIS • ROME • NEW YORK • LOS ANGELES

Please contact: admissions@marymountlondon.com
www.marymountlondon.com Tel: 020 8949 0571
George Road, Kingston upon Thames, Surrey KT2 7PE.

Guardians

If a child is starting school in the UK and their parents live abroad, it makes sense to have another adult in the frame, someone who can act as a stand-in parent and become a trusted presence in their lives when they need someone to turn to. This person is known as a guardian (or education guardian). Sometimes the role is taken by a relative, but if the family has no relatives in the UK a professional guardian can be appointed.

Guardians meet and greet their charges from the airport at the start of term and do the reverse when it ends. In addition, they may sign forms, attend parent teacher meetings or sort out things such as mobile phone contracts and dentists' appointments. Guardians may also need to step in at very short notice at times of crisis, for instance if a child hits a problem and is excluded, suspended, or needs urgent medical treatment.

Despite what you may read online, there is in fact no legal requirement to appoint a guardian and education guardians have no formal status. Aegis (The Association for the Education and Guardianship of International Students), which is the closest the industry comes to a trade body, confirmed that it is not a legal requirement for an international student to have an educational guardian when studying in the UK. However, while failure to appoint an education guardian isn't against the law, it may tax your relationship with a school and severely impede the chances of your child being offered a place (it's often made a condition of acceptance).

It makes sense to have someone who can act as a stand-in parent and become a trusted presence

Guardianship firms

These are businesses that charge fees of up to £1,000 a term for basic support that includes round the clock emergency help, at least in term time. Many firms also give families the option of paying more for a premium service marketed variously as gold, platinum and – for the status conscious – VIP and royalty.

Guardianship firms come in every conceivable shape, size and cultural direction. Some specialise in one particular nationality, others are cannily expanding into new areas such as day school packages, where children board with a host family in term time. All guardianship firms should recruit and vet host families, ensuring they lead blameless lives, have squeaky clean records and, importantly, live within easy travelling distance of your child's school.

Unfortunately, membership of Aegis, which runs its own inspections, remains optional. The organisation is campaigning for safeguarding to be tightened and inspections made mandatory, but with only 10 per cent of schools currently working with Aegis members, it still has a lot of convincing to do. In the meantime, there are other ways of finding a guardian. Schools sometimes recruit – very sensibly – through their own parents. Other families prefer to make their own arrangements, turning to friends or relations as stand-in, and stand-by, mums and dads. This will only work, however, if they live in easy reach of the school.

For overseas pupils, a compatible guardian who cares about your child's well-being and happiness almost as much as you do can be an essential part of the educational experience.

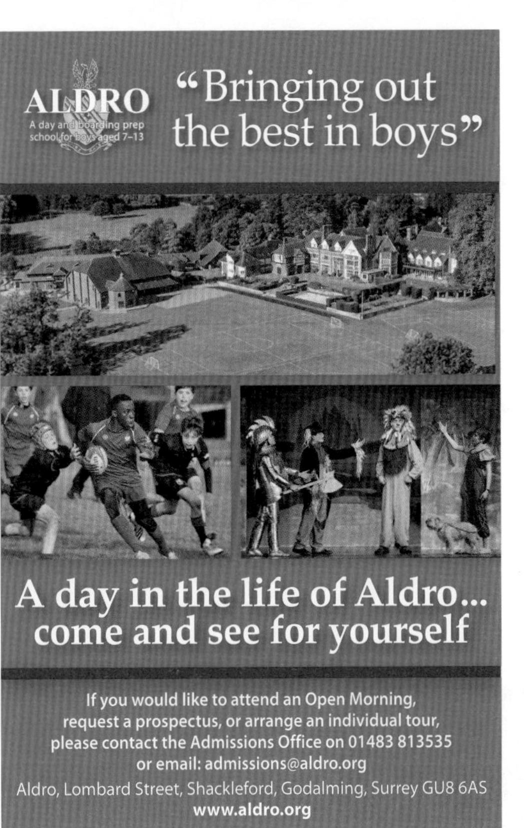

Outstanding boarding and day school
for boys and girls, 4 to 13 years

The Dragon School, Oxford

"Exceptional"

"The quality of children's achievement and learning is exceptional"
Independent Schools Inspectorate Inspection Report

You are warmly invited to attend
Dragon School OPEN MORNINGS
For Day and Boarding Children
held throughout the year, at both
the Prep and Pre-Prep sites

TO BOOK A PLACE OR ARRANGE A VISIT
Please contact the Admissions Team
T: +44(0)1865 315405
E: admissions@dragonschool.org
Dragon School, Oxford

Dragon School Oxford www.dragonschool.org

St Edmund's School
Canterbury

Be all you can be

St Ed's is a school where every pupil is connected by a love of learning, the pursuit of possibility and the challenge of being the very best they can be.

01227 475601
www.stedmunds.org.uk

Because no-one ever said

'I want the second best school for my child'

Call our consultants to find the right school for your child.

The Good Schools Guide Education Consultants

0203 286 6824 | goodschoolsguide.co.uk/consultants | consultants@goodschoolsguide.co.uk

International study centres

International Study Centres are to be found all over the UK in both the most obvious and the least expected places. These centres serve as a means of teaching young people (usually from age 11-16) academic English and introducing them to English culture and English education. The aim of most of these schools is to provide a gentle transition for foreign (non-English-speaking) adolescents into life in an English school, often as boarders, and to prepare them for either A levels or, in some cases, the IB diploma, which then leads to university entry. In some cases GCSEs or IGSCEs are offered alongside intensive English language programmes to facilitate this preparation.

A growing number of independent boarding and day schools have seen the income potential of attracting foreign national pupils and some have opened international study centres as what might be described as adjunct 'feeder schools' within the main school.

If you are thinking of sending your child to an international study centre, here's a checklist of the things you should consider

- What are the admissions criteria? How does the school assess the pupil's level of English language and other learning? Are the teachers trained in EAL teaching, and used to working with children from all over the world?
- How does the school welcome new pupils, make them feel at home and integrate them?
- Is there a good mix of pupils? Too many from one country may tend to talk amongst themselves rather than learning English and mixing with others.
- Are pupils encouraged to celebrate and share their culture?
- Are diverse diets and religious practices catered for?
- Can pupils keep up their own language to a high academic level?
- How much interaction do international study centre

pupils have with those at the mainstream school? Do they mix for sport, clubs, evening and weekend activities?

- What percentage of international pupils move into the mainstream school? What happens to those who are not admitted, and how much help do they get with finding a place elsewhere?
- Does the centre have the authority to issue CAS letters for those who need a visa?

If you are working with a third party agent, make sure that all financial agreements are transparent and reasonable.

TOP gizmos & gadjets for KIDS

STAND OUT Schools

Advice from the EXPERTS

The hottest educational DEBATES

Family HOLIDAYS

CHALK & CHAT

Subscribe FREE

All this and more in our termly digital magazine:
goodschoolsguide.co.uk/chalk-and-chat

The British student's guide to great universities in the USA from Harvard to Yale

Tells you how to choose, how to apply and how to pay

£18 for the book or 12-month subscription

goodschoolsguide.co.uk/university

UNI IN THE USA
THE GOOD SCHOOLS GUIDE

Child protection

Any parent preparing to entrust their child to a school – whether day or boarding – will rightly expect that child's safety and well-being to be a priority at all times. Such expectations are nearly always fulfilled but in a sad minority of cases that is not what happens.

We have all read news reports of bullying and abuse and shuddered to imagine the horror felt by the children and families involved. A flood of historical allegations against schools and subsequent court cases, not to mention mobile phones, flexi-boarding, more parental involvement and heightened awareness have together helped usher in some sunlight and fresh air.

Child protection policies, found on every school website, now make explicit reference to the possibility of abuse at schools – something rarely contemplated a generation ago.

Boarding schools in particular can be very closed worlds but abuse can occur at any school, anywhere. Fame is no protection, and nor is obscurity. Some kinds of school, though, need to take particular care – and how they do this should be obvious to you when you visit. International schools have transient pupil populations, and teachers whose histories may be overseas and hard to research. Specialist music teaching necessarily involves a good deal of physical contact with the teacher and the pupil alone in a closed room. Religious schools may have a system of authority that serves to keep abuse concealed. Special schools may have to deal with a large range of communication and emotional difficulties.

What can you do?

Parents should talk to their children – gently but seriously – about the dangers, however remote these may be. It is worth pointing out that abuse can come from anyone – including a teacher or an adult they know well, or from another child at the school. Having this discussion will make it easier for a child to come to you with anything they're worried about.

When visiting a school, inquire about the steps taken to safeguard children in the same way you might ask about bullying or learning support. As always, much can be gleaned from the head's attitude when questions about child protection are asked. Is he or she ill at ease or happy to engage and proud of the steps their school has taken? Openness is what you're looking for.

You could also ask about how a child or parent would go about reporting an incident. Schools make this possible in a variety of ways; what matters is that passing on concerns is a routine thing (children and parents do it about lots of things all the time), and is welcomed by the school. Doing this should be low-stakes, in other words the person registering the concern knows that they are not putting their relationships within the school at risk, let alone threatening someone's place in the school. That may seem an odd thing to say, but if you fear to report, say, careless management of a museum trip because it could harm an otherwise much-loved teacher, you might choose to keep quiet. An environment that seems hostile to raising such concerns may mean you never pass on those troubling observations that may be the outward indication of serious problems. To be safe, schools need to hear the little voices, not just the shouting.

And finally, do not think less of a school because a case of abuse has been brought to light there. Tabloid coverage can be the price the school has to pay for handling a case of abuse or bullying openly. It is inevitable that abuse will occur somewhere. What matters is how well the school deals with it, how well it performs in bringing the abuse to light and how open it is on the subject with current and future parents.

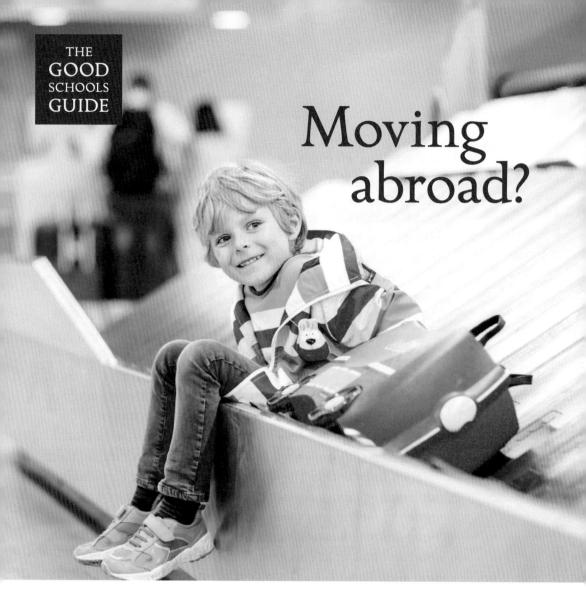

THE GOOD SCHOOLS GUIDE

Moving abroad?

 Tickets

 Passports

 Visas

 Schools

Still need to sort your schooling?

Go straight to The Good Schools Guide International.

The first class guide to world class schools.

goodschoolsguide.co.uk/international

Scholarships and bursaries

Boarding schools, like all schools, want clever children. Children who will shine in arts and sports, children who will be excellent all-rounders and who will contribute generously to the academic, cultural and social life of the school. To this end they will offer considerable financial help to families with children who meet this description but who would not otherwise be able to attend because of high fees. Many good boarding schools offer scholarships and bursaries in order to attract able and talented pupils. Scholarships are now usually worth more in glory than in fee reduction but bursaries can be worth up to 100 per cent of fees plus supplementary help for trips and equipment, if needed.

But how do you find out what financial assistance could be out there for you? Often, the information on schools' websites is hazy and unhelpful and you have no option but to call up and, perhaps, tell more about yourselves than you feel ready to with so little information.

The GSGEC Scholarships and Bursaries Service

The Good Schools Education Consultants has created a unique central resource for parents. We now hold information on the fee assistance available at more than 500 schools in The Good Schools Guide and, increasingly, at other good schools.

We won't be able to tell you exactly what – in raw financial terms – a school might offer you in terms of bursarial help, as this will depend on many things, such as your income, your financial commitments and the number of children you have – but we will be able to tell you about the school's criteria for scholarships and bursaries. We also know of odd and unusual awards eg for the children of clergy or sailors or children whose parent has died. We will be able to explain to you how a scholarship might be topped up by a bursary and answer any other questions you may have.

The Good Schools Guide Scholarships and Bursaries Service is a fee-paying service but we keep those fees as low as possible. Our charges depend on the number of schools or the breadth of the area you would like us to research.

Far more parents apply for fee assistance than get it. Schools' resources – even the rich ones – are limited and they disburse money with great care. Your child may be top of everything at his primary school and your family income may be low, but this does not entitle you to a place or help with fees at any school. Informing yourself, getting the timing right and applying realistically is the best approach and – as around one third of all children at fee-paying schools now have some fee remission – it has to be worth a try.

The Good Schools Guide Educational Consultants

The Good Schools Guide has been trusted by generations of parents to provide expert, honest and unbiased information about schools. Our educational consultancy provides the same high standards of expertise, independence and professional integrity to individual families.

Every day our highly-experienced consultants successfully help clients from all over the world find the right schools for their children. However urgent the deadline, however complex the circumstances, call 0203 286 6824 (UK) or +44 203 286 6824 (international) to find out how we can solve your educational dilemmas.

Our consultants

All our consultants have personally visited and reviewed countless schools for our website and publications; many also have professional backgrounds or specialist qualifications in education. Between them they have direct experience of every aspect of both the British and international education systems, not to mention invaluable local knowledge about schools in London and all areas of the UK. Our team includes experts in SEN, school appeals, scholarships and bursaries, grammar schools and relocation to the UK from abroad.

Consultancy built around your needs

Our consultancy packages range from a 30-minute telephone consultation to a fully bespoke service tailored to meet complex, urgent or other specific circumstances. Additional services include accompanied school visits, providing translators and educational assessments and arranging specialist tuition. For full details please visit our website www. goodschoolsguide.co.uk

Contact us

Phone us on +44 (0)203 286 6824 or send a brief email to: consultants@goodschoolsguide.co.uk outlining what you need. Tell us the age of your child and where you live plus your contact details. We will contact you within 48 hours, discuss how best to help you and ensure we match you with the right consultant. Consultations can be by phone, email or face to face, and we can find a consultant to speak to you within an hour if necessary.

How much?

Ours is one of the most competitively priced tailor-made education consultancy services in the UK. Check our website for current fees.

Our guarantee

The Good Schools Guide has an international reputation for providing unbiased, independent advice on educational matters. We have no commercial links whatsoever with any school. This gives our education consultants the freedom to consider a huge range of schools in order to find the best one for you. You can have complete confidence that if our consultants recommend a school it is because, and only because, they consider it to be suitable for your child. You can also be assured that we maintain the highest possible standards of privacy and all dealings with clients are completely confidential.

South West

City of Bristol
Cornwall
Devon
Dorset
Gloucestershire
Somerset
Wiltshire

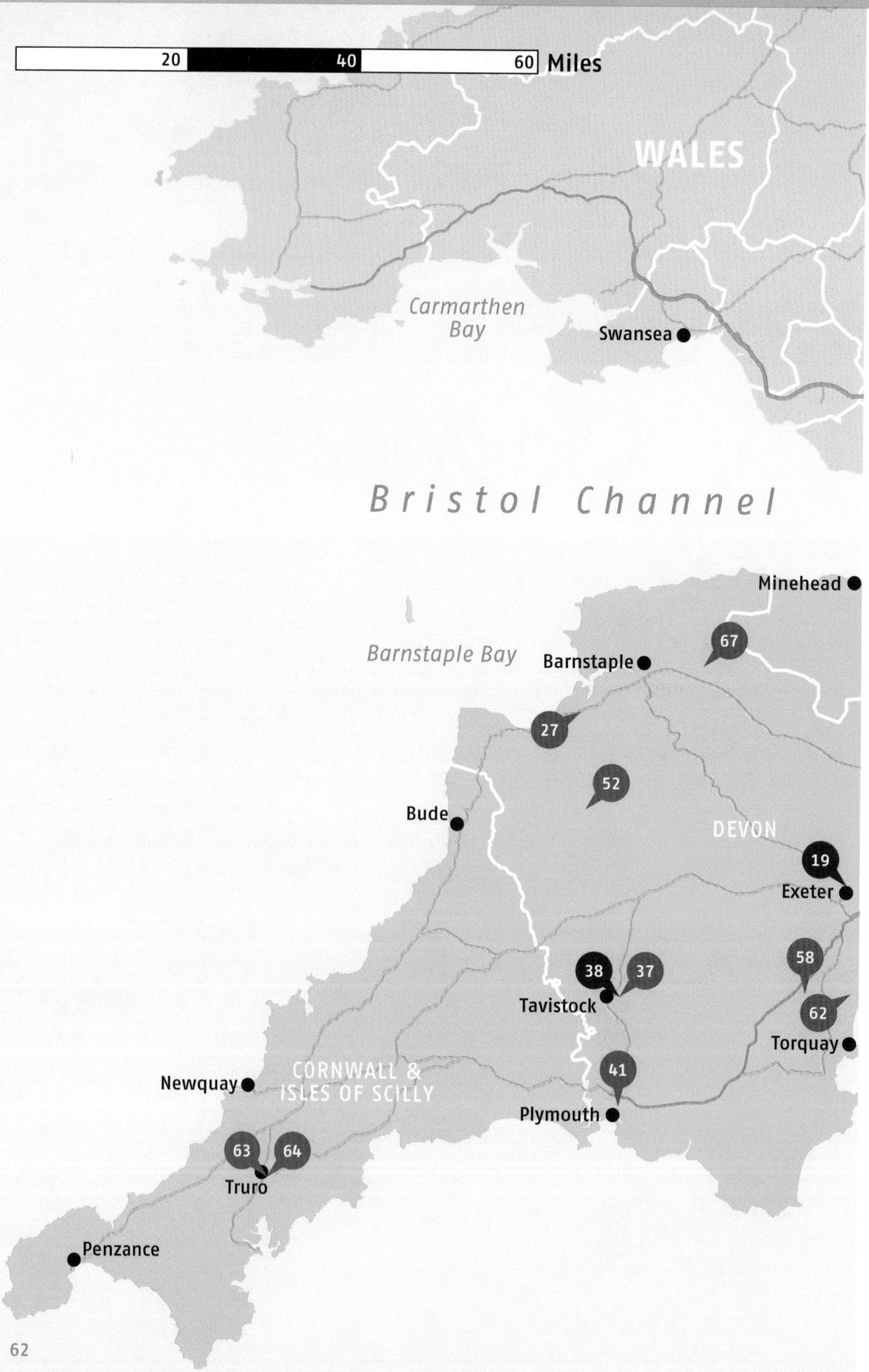

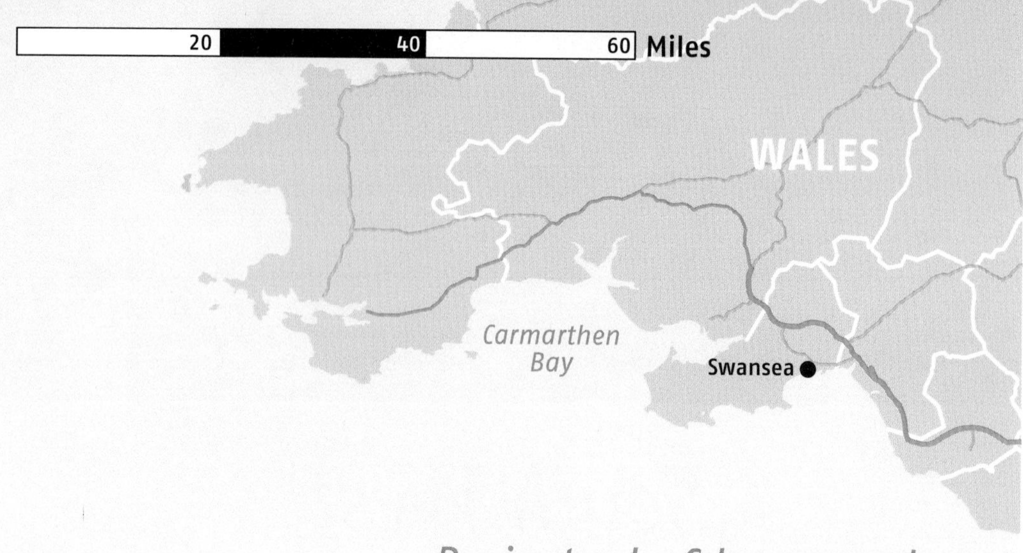
20
40
60 Miles
WALES
Carmarthen Bay
Swansea
Bristol Channel
Minehead
Barnstaple Bay
Barnstaple
67
27
52
Bude
DEVON
19
Exeter
38
37
Tavistock
58
62
Torquay
41
Plymouth
Newquay
CORNWALL &
ISLES OF SCILLY
63
64
Truro
Penzance

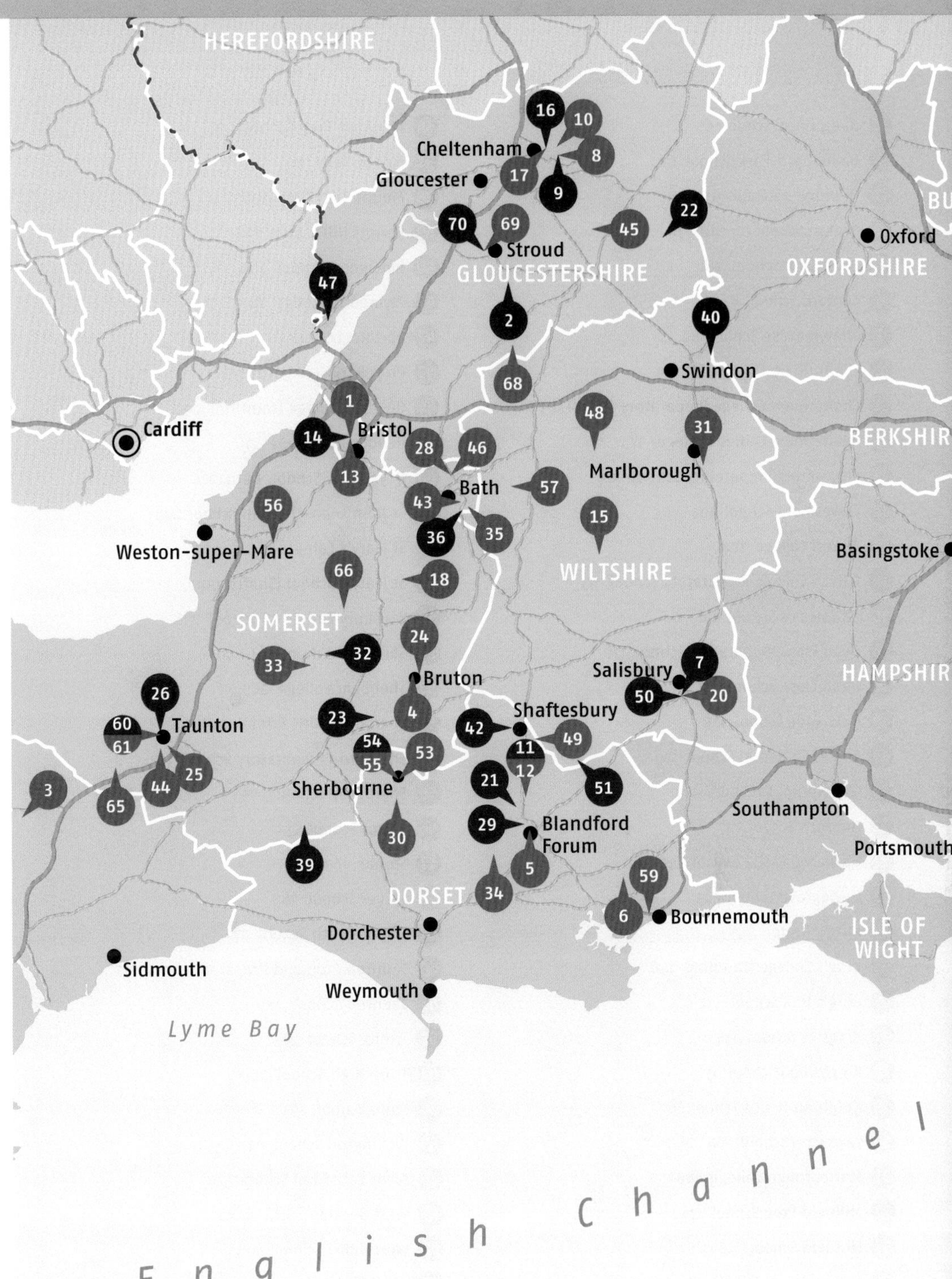
HEREFORDSHIRE
GLOUCESTERSHIRE
OXFORDSHIRE
BERKSHIRE
WILTSHIRE
SOMERSET
HAMPSHIRE
DORSET
ISLE OF WIGHT
BU
Cheltenham
Gloucester
Stroud
Oxford
Swindon
Cardiff
Bristol
Bath
Marlborough
Weston-super-Mare
Basingstoke
Bruton
Salisbury
Shaftesbury
Taunton
Sherbourne
Blandford Forum
Southampton
Portsmouth
Bournemouth
Dorchester
Sidmouth
Weymouth
Lyme Bay
English Channel

SOUTH WEST

Badminton School

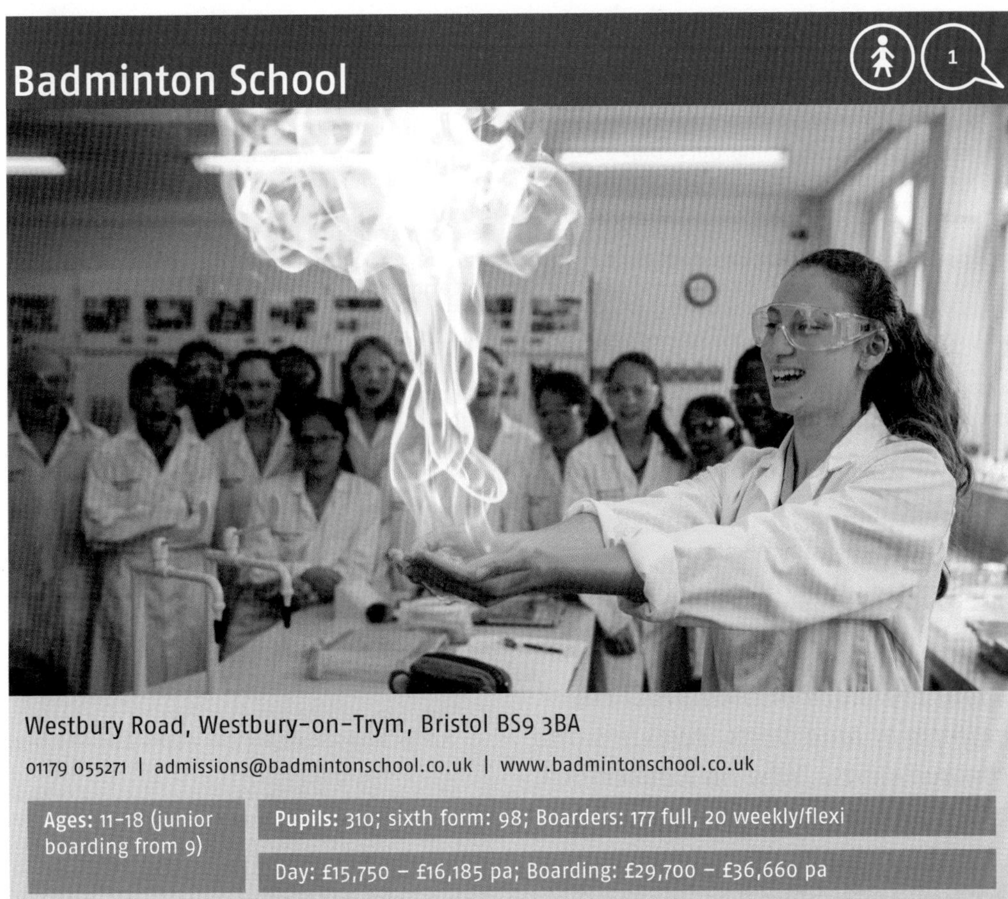

Westbury Road, Westbury-on-Trym, Bristol BS9 3BA

01179 055271 | admissions@badmintonschool.co.uk | www.badmintonschool.co.uk

Ages: 11-18 (junior boarding from 9)

Pupils: 310; sixth form: 98; Boarders: 177 full, 20 weekly/flexi

Day: £15,750 – £16,185 pa; Boarding: £29,700 – £36,660 pa

Headmistress: Since 2012, Mrs Rebecca Tear (40s) BSc MA PGCE. Her degree in chemistry from Exeter preceded a career in teaching science almost exclusively to girls, and which included other significant responsibilities eg head of sixth form and deputy head at Wycombe Abbey, taking in a masters in leadership in education along the way. An unequivocal believer in single sex education from her early teaching practice, where she saw how the less confident girls needed bringing out in lessons, she says, 'Teaching girls by themselves breaks down any preconceptions, barriers or stereotyping; when subjects don't acquire masculine or feminine connotations, girls tend to make more realistic personal choices.'

Somewhat jolly hockey sticks in manner – she strode across the drawing room, extending a hand and introducing herself as 'Bex' – we warmed to her no-nonsense and open personality; staff describe her as a real hit with the girls. For her part, Mrs Tear has made strenuous efforts to bring parents and guardians into school more: new ventures like the summer fair and fireworks night have been welcomed. 'I don't want the first time I meet a parent to be in a bad news situation', she says.

Married to another chemistry teacher, she has two young sons who doubtless counterbalance all those girls. Passions include outdoorsy things like running, ski-ing and cycling with her family, and she is a keen cook – though at home she regrets the lack of a lab technician to wash up for her.

Academic matters: Selective entry, rigorous exam preparation and small classes (averaging 14 until GCSE) all the way through the school make for stunning results, and a reputation as Bristol's most academic school. A level results in 2017 saw 61 per cent A*/A (84 per cent A*-B) grades, with the majority of girls taking four subjects. At GCSE, 81 per cent A*-A/9-7 grades in 2016. Options are (unusually) not blocked, so virtually any subject combination is possible; new A level subjects include psychology, business and PE, with a creative writing course for lower sixth. SAT training also provided for those hoping to go to American universities, plus the first ever opportunities fair, which featured a talk on world class university applications.

Girls greatly encouraged to take on all manner of academic challenges outside school; two girls were recently invited to go to a UK Mathematical Trust Olympiad training camp, out of only 22 youngsters in the country, and external essay prizes are frequently awarded. Everyone does English Speaking Board exams, which, for the year 8 class we visited, involved learning, reciting and discussing chunks of poetry – a Shakespeare sonnet in one case. Years 8 and 9 are also offered a 10 week STEM experience with engineering or manufacturing companies with Go4SET. Global Thinking Skills course for year 9 'which combines enhancing the girls' knowledge of the world they live in alongside developing their ability to think critically'. 'They push them, but not in any way too much,' said one mother, who also appreciated the way teachers go over work with individuals when they find it difficult. EPQ added to sixth form enrichment programme.

Groups of girls scurry purposefully about the place in their practical uniform of blue shirts, sweaters and checked skirts. 'Why no trousers?' asked one mother

SEN provision is modest – not much call for it here – and mostly delivered by 'flexible in-house support'. Weekly sessions at Bristol Dyslexia Centre to improve skills in English and maths are laid on for more severe cases: whilst some parents accept this, others resent the extra time expended, and the stigma associated with leaving the school by taxi, and feel that daily intervention would be a darn sight more use. More emphasis is given to extending the gifted and talented – a term the school avoids. EAL is also offered in school to support overseas girls.

Games, options, the arts: Games and sports are well catered for (Astro, tennis courts, netball courts and a 25m pool, plush new sports hall under construction) on the school's site, unlike so many of Bristol's schools, whose playing fields are a bus ride away across the suspension bridge. Hockey, netball, tennis and swimming are the main sports, but an innovative range of activities including kick-boxing and water polo means that no-one has an excuse to be idle. Badminton's riders enjoy considerable success: one was selected for the Prince Philip cup – the height of mounted athleticism. Hockey and netball players are regularly selected for the county. One parent was unhappy that only top players were ever picked for teams, and that mediocre participants barely got a game; also that the (beautiful) pool was used very little by the girls 'because it was always being hired out'. The absence of swimming teams or even a swimming club is an oddity.

Artistic life flourishes too, with top notch music, drama and art. Much is rightly made of high calibre musicians (one to the Royal College on Saturdays, two to the National Children's Orchestra, several playing in city orchestras, a recent leaver in training for The Sixteen) and school is fortunate to perform in St George's Bristol, a national concert venue. Most girls learn one instrument if not two, and school is proud of the number and scope of ensembles it lays on for musicians of all standards and persuasions. New music building has enabled school to bring all of its music teaching and practice activities to a single location and created a new focus for the department. The building includes teaching and practice rooms, a new music library and a generous classroom for curricular music lessons. Drama reasonably prominent too, with six productions a year plus a staff pantomime, as well as collaborations with outside initiatives at local innovative theatre the Tobacco Factory and Garden Opera, recently as a chorus of urchins in Carmen. Several notable actresses are OBs: Clare Bloom, Phyllida Law and Rosamunde Pike.

Art is housed in a most appealing setting, where mannequins dressed in creations fit for a Milan catwalk grace the entrance. Textiles, ceramics, painting, digital media (aka photography) and all types of artistic endeavour go on here. Badminton girls gain places at prestigious colleges such as Central St Martins.

Boarding: From age 9 although there's only a handful of junior boarders. Boarders accommodated in three houses grouped by age – Bartlett houses girls from years 5-8, spanning both junior and senior schools. Sanderson is the newest build for the middle girls; sixth formers are separate. One parent reported a tendency to cliques among the girls, which she felt the school did little to address, and that it 'feels like a boarding school which day girls attend'; another felt that integration was fine.

Weekends fairly relaxed for those who stay in school: girls might be involved in sports or drama, off on a surfing trip, going out for a meal or to the theatre. As elsewhere boarders from abroad are required to have a guardian, but here they do so much more than that rather dry word suggests and are more like surrogate mums – we applaud this.

Background and atmosphere: Founded over 150 years ago, Badminton is older than most girls' schools of its type and was set up to provide the same educational opportunities for girls as their brothers enjoyed. That sense of academic seriousness, courage, confidence and an international outlook still prevail – girls here

Boarders' weekends fairly relaxed: girls might be involved in sports or drama, off on a surfing trip, going out for a meal or to the theatre

tackle any academic challenge head-on. Originally sited in Badminton House in nearby Clifton, it moved to its present premises on the edge of the downs in Bristol, arguably the greenest and most desirable part of the city. Main building is Georgian and gracious (we were ushered in to a warm and luxuriously carpeted drawing room, where Classic FM played discreetly); over the years the site has been filled in with all sorts of additions of varying degrees of beauty, making the school compact, rather than crowded. Nestling on the edge of the Badminton site, the junior school is certainly the senior school's little sister and firmly under its wing.

Groups of girls scurry purposefully about the place in their practical uniform of blue shirts, sweaters and checked skirts. 'Why no trousers?' asked one mum. Sixth form dress is much less restricted than in some schools: torn jeans and strappy tops are out, otherwise more or less anything goes. Overseas girls are welcome here and come in droves, mostly from Hong Kong but a good few from Russia and Nigeria; a sprinkling from the rest of the world. Bristol's own ethnic and religious mix well represented and catered for too: any dish containing pork was firmly labelled at lunch. Old Badmintonians include Indira Ghandi and Princess Haya Bint Al Hussein of Jordan.

Male company is provided mostly by QEH, Bristol's only remaining boys' school (which now admits sixth form girls) – academic and social interactions, we gather, which include a shared minibus from Chepstow.

Pastoral care, well-being and discipline: Discipline, in as much as it is needed in this high-achieving environment, works on girls' general desire to please, and dislike of letting people down, so the head might well say, 'I am rather disappointed that I have to speak to you, Jemima', on the rare occasions that girls come before her. Smoking, alcohol and drugs will lead sinners straight to her study. Achievement of all kinds is recognised, but interestingly there is no honours board, and school's annual open day is as much about displays, demonstrations, music, drama and food than interminable speechifying; the only prize awarded is the Iris Murdoch (another OB) prize for creative writing.

Pastoral care reads as well as one would expect for a school like this, with a tutor assigned to each girl, a vertical house system and peer mentoring, but one mother told us her daughter's confidence had been undermined by too great an emphasis on academics, and too little on making supportive friendships.

We loved the way the bigger girls supported the littler ones: at the end of our visit, they were snuggled up on beanbags looking at books with year 6s. One little dot could not stop yawning at the end of her busy day; another could hardly be torn away from her riveting story to talk to us. Vertical tutor groups lie at the heart of these close relationships and are a feature of the school.

Pupils and parents: Quite mixed socially and ethnically, but united by high academic expectations and aspirations. We found the girls friendly, unpretentious and open-minded – and were pleased to see some tucking into the sponge pudding we are probably no longer allowed to call spotted dick. 'The school does not turn out a mass product,' said one mother with several years' knowledge

Entrance: Most arrive in year 7, but everyone below sixth form is required to sit papers in English (English as a foreign language for those who have been at school in the UK for less than two years) and maths and to do an online reasoning test. The transition from the junior school is not automatic and girls do exactly the same assessments as those coming from elsewhere (in practice, the vast majority are accepted). Sixth form hopefuls must sit papers in two of the subjects they intend studying at A level, plus a general paper. All applicants are interviewed, via Skype when necessary.

Exit: Some fall-out after GCSEs (around 20 per cent) from day girls wanting pastures new, and perhaps boys in particular. Those who stay go not only to our

most prestigious universities, but also to top notch international ones in Asia, Europe and the US eg English in Dublin, medicine in Hong Kong, liberal arts in New York, culinary arts in Switzerland. London is the most popular destination, followed by Durham, and a good handful to Oxbridge each year (seven in 2017). Wide choice of degree courses, more sciences than arts; five medics in 2017.

Money matters: Fees are much in line with comparable schools, though boarders from outside the EU pay over £2000 more per year to cover the cost of escorted journeys to UK international airports – and of the boarding travel co-ordinator. Scholarships are awarded to a maximum of 20 per cent of fees; bursaries are means tested. New-ish regional award for girls 'who will bring something special to Badminton'; the school intends this as a way to recognise wider achievement and potential than the range of scholarships currently on offer.

Remarks: Undoubtedly a distinguished Bristol institution, yet its size, compact site, high proportion of boarders and fearsome academic reputation (which frightens some off) mean it enjoys a lower profile than it should in the city. The head describes it as a hidden gem, so her mission, should she choose to accept it, is perhaps to polish up all its facets so it shines a brighter local light. Badminton Junior is a great choice for bright, organised and confident girls, where they will receive excellent opportunities in the classroom, on the pitch and on the platform. The diffident, disorganised, dyslexic, dyspraxic or ditsy should look elsewhere.

Beaudesert Park School

2

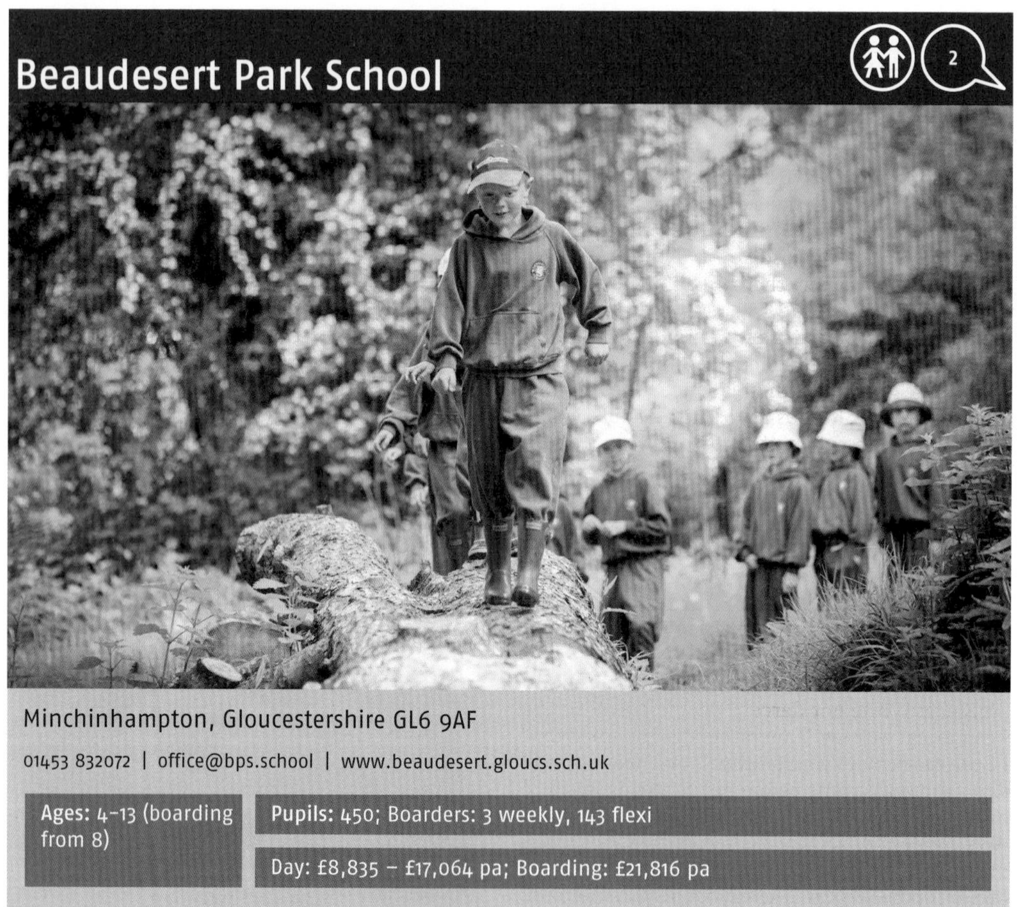

Minchinhampton, Gloucestershire GL6 9AF

01453 832072 | office@bps.school | www.beaudesert.gloucs.sch.uk

Ages: 4–13 (boarding from 8)

Pupils: 450; Boarders: 3 weekly, 143 flexi

Day: £8,835 – £17,064 pa; Boarding: £21,816 pa

Headmaster: Since 1997, James Womersley (50s). Educated at The Dragon and St Edward's Oxford, studied economics, history 'and rugby' at Durham, PGCE from Oxford. Came to Beaudesert after Eagle House, Emanuel London and nine years at his old prep school. He cites this time at the Dragon, where he became a housemaster, as a formative influence.

Mr W and his wife, Fiona, make a prep school power couple. Parents can be assured that whatever (or whoever) comes their way, the Womersleys have probably seen it before. Mrs W comes from a prep school family, although she claims it was the 'last thing I thought I'd find myself doing'. Nothing daunted, she takes care of marketing, catering, pastoral and safeguarding – and somehow manages to look groomed and elegant at the same time. The Womersleys are a great advert for the youth-enhancing properties of prep school life – fizzing with energy and joie de vivre. Certainly not ready for retirement, 'not while we're still enjoying it'. Their three sons all went to Beaudesert and St Edward's Oxford.

The Womersleys' job satisfaction must be infectious; they've created a school with a strong sense of identity and 'real soul', as one parent put it. The atmosphere is professional and collaborative, everyone we met was relaxed and friendly (well, it was near the end of term...). Mr W speaks of his teaching staff with pride – several current heads and deputy heads cut their teeth at Beaudesert.

He describes Beaudesert as 'virtually independent', by which he means that paths to schools such as Marlborough and Cheltenham College are well maintained – after all, it's the reason many families choose this prep. Nonetheless, parents can be confident that advice about senior schools is unbiased by anything apart from their child's best interests.

Although Mr W no longer teaches he does take cover lessons. And what job would he do if he hadn't become a prep school head? He ponders – perhaps he never thought of doing anything else. 'An art historian' he says finally.

You might think that the indefatigable Womersleys spend their leisure time having a well-earned sit down, but you'd be wrong. They play golf and tennis and enjoy skiing. Phew.

Leaving in July 2018. His successor will be Chris Searson, currently deputy head at Highfield School in Hampshire, where he has also been head of English and boarding houseparent. Married to Harriet; two young children.

Entrance: While not fiercely selective, Mr W says Beaudesert attracts a 'generally high level' and 'families with bright children'. Pupils come from local nurseries or the school's own. Transfer from pre-prep generally straightforward.

Exit: Majority in roughly equal numbers to Cheltenham College and Marlborough, then St Mary's Calne, Badminton, Cheltenham Ladies' College, Downe House (girls) and Eton, Radley, Winchester, Sherborne (boys). Also Bradfield, Malvern College, Stowe and St Edward's Oxford. Good spread of scholarships every year too (nine in 2017).

Remarks: Beaudesert Park School was founded in Warwickshire in 1908, moving to its mock Tudor Cotswold folly 10 years later. That folly has been joined over the years by buildings in a variety of architectural styles, the latest being a superb performing arts centre. Any deficit in architectural coherence is more than made up for by character – round every corner is a different view, whether it's terraced lawns and playing fields or the free-range cattle on Minchinhampton Common, who look as though they could wander into the car park (they can't, thanks to a grid). Towers, curved walls, covered outside staircases and walkways – it all looks rather like an animated Escher drawing as pupils go busily up and down between lessons.

Part of the charm of Beaudesert, according to parents, is that it's a proper 'outdoors' school: 'It's a real country school', 'the children are connected to their surroundings'

Although Mr Womersley regrets the dominance of exams in schools today, he's a champion of CE and believes it gives children a worthwhile goal. 'They work hard and get the joy of success', he says. But as several parents told us, at Beaudesert the balance between academic work and the myriad other activities on offer is skilfully maintained. Those who have moved their children from London preps really notice the difference and value the unpressurised environment – even more so when their children go on to gain places at top senior schools. 'They challenge the children academically by keeping them engaged,' said one. Homework is sensible too, certainly not hours every night. Nursery and pre-prep have their own mini-school with all the facilities including a hall and stage.

Pupils setted for maths, English and languages (French, Latin from year 6, optional Greek for scholars). No separate scholarship stream. Well-equipped labs where legendary 'screaming jelly baby' and other spectacular experiments are staged – obviously science is not impervious to Mr W's performing arts campaign. Old-fashioned values do not extend to technology and there's a full complement of whiteboards, iPads and the like. Delightful, bright art studios with separate ceramics room and proper kiln. SEN provision received mixed reviews. Pupils told us the help they'd received was 'brilliant', but parents raised concerns. Several thought that a school with a relatively unselective intake should have wider in-house experience to identify specific learning needs early on.

Part of the charm of Beaudesert, according to parents, is that it's a proper 'outdoors' school: 'It's a real country school', 'a proper all-round education', 'the children are connected to their surroundings.' Several made the distinction between country preps that are 'sporty' and Beaudesert, where, in addition to plenty of sport, there's free range tree climbing, den building, night camps, forest school for the little ones and bushcraft ('It's mainly about knives', a Just William character told us).

In defiance of Noel Coward's advice, school believes that everybody's daughter or son benefits from taking to the stage. Music and drama are enthusiastically pursued

Main sports arranged along pretty traditional lines, rugby, football and cricket for the chaps, netball and rounders for the girls. Both do hockey (girls very successfully) and there's some overlap with cricket coaching. Athletics for all in the summer, plus tennis and cross-country. We didn't hear any grumbles about teams and matches, most parents thought the arrangements were fair enough and that pupils in the B and C teams enjoyed their games just as much as those in the As. Swimming is a real strength – all Beaudesert pupils learn to swim and indoor and outdoor pools mean year round training. The school regularly qualifies for IAPS national finals and swimmers compete in local and national teams. This being Gloucestershire, there's a fair amount of equestrian activity – school team recently won national junior

Everything clean and homely. 'I love boarding, you get to sleep over with all your friends,' said one of our guides

polo championships. Golf, fly fishing and mountain biking also on offer. Pupils can bring their own bikes and learn cycle safety and maintenance.

In defiance of Noel Coward's advice, Mr W believes that everybody's daughter or son benefits from taking to the stage. Even before the opening of the new performing arts centre, music and drama were enthusiastically pursued by the majority. Minutes after the builders left preparations were under way for the inaugural concert, featuring school choirs, orchestra, ensembles and soloists. This glass and Cotswold stone building sits, appropriately enough, at the centre of the school and hosts plays, concerts, assemblies, parents' evenings, music and drama lessons and exhibitions. The exterior features distinctive cedar planks, rather like xylophone keys, positioned to deflect the light.

Pupils can board from year 4 and most will have some experience of boarding by the time they leave. Options are flexi or weekly – everyone goes home after Saturday school (lessons until 12.30) or matches. Boarders up to year 6 can work towards bronze, silver and gold Beaudesert Badges – activities include first aid, cookery, gardening, outdoor skills and charity work.

One boarding house with boys' and girls' sections up different staircases. Jolly kitchens and comfortable shared areas for 'TV and talking'. Brightly decorated boys' dorms run into each other (no doors), girls have separate (shared) rooms. Everything clean and homely. 'I love boarding, you get to sleep over with all your friends,' said one of our guides. Houseparents plus matrons, nurses and gappies oversee proceedings. 'There's always someone to talk to,' we were told. Food gets a big thumbs up, especially pulled pork buns and good old treacle sponge.

Year 8 girls informed us proudly of the small privileges of seniority – white shirts in winter, benches in assembly, 'senior snacks' (cereal and squash at 8pm on a Friday) and, best of all, 'senior supper' with the Womersleys – none typical 12 year olds' aspirations. Advocates of the 'real world' undoubtedly educate their children elsewhere and even its biggest fans concede that there is a Beaudesert bubble, but how many parents would wish their children to grow up more quickly?

Houses, we were told, are 'no big deal', thus rather suiting their prosaic names: A, B, C and D. No head boys and girls, instead all year 8s have duties and responsibilities. Newish school council has achieved victories including modifications to the year 8 uniform. 'Boys can choose their own socks, but they mustn't be luminous or white.' What else would improve their school, we asked? Modest proposals included golf buggies to transport pupils to games fields over the common, flattening the bump in the Astro, compelling teachers to sit their own exams, and 'unlimited ice cream'.

According to Mr W, the parent profile has changed in the 19 years he has been at the helm of Beaudesert – these days both parents are probably working, often weekly commuting to London. He welcomes the fact that parents are 'in a lot more' and encourages their involvement. Families all fairly local – few alternatives in the immediate area and weekly boarding only see to that. No PTA but active Friends of Beaudesert who organise fundraisers and socials. No class reps either – they don't really feature in the boarding model – but most parents happy with home-school communications, prompt replies to enquiries and general delightfulness of front of house staff. High praise, too, for pastoral care and teachers' 'genuine concern' for pupils, 'Nothing's too much trouble. You can't fault it', we were told.

Beaudesert and its lucky pupils continue to thrive under the expert custodianship of the Womersleys. Mr W has no need of educational jargon; his philosophy is a simple one: healthy, happy children learn best. Happiness isn't a subject to be taught, it should be the founding principle of any school – it certainly is at Beaudesert.

Blundell's School

Blundell's Road, Tiverton, Devon EX16 4DN

01884 252543 | registrars@blundells.org | www.blundells.org

Ages: 11–18

Pupils: 598; sixth form: 205; Boarders: 213 full, 187 flexi

Day: £13,725 – £21,750 pa; Boarding: £15,870 – £33,855 pa

Head: Since 2013, Nicola Huggett (40s) MA PGCE (Oxon). Educated at St Gabriel's and Marlborough, she read PPE at Oxford before embarking on a brief career in advertising with J Walter Thompson – brief because she soon realised it was not for her. 'Why did no-one tell me about teaching before?' she says of her experience shadowing a teacher in a comprehensive near her home. Since then her career has taken her via Haileybury, ultimately as head of boarding, during a time when the school went fully co-ed and introduced IB, and Downe House as deputy head, before being made the first female head of Blundell's since its inception in 1604.

Only moderate harrumphing greeted her appointment, and those foolish enough to do so must now be eating their words, such has been the wave of approval from all quarters. 'A wow appointment,' declared one mother. Mrs Huggett is clearly superwoman – as well as running a school, where she still teaches four lessons a week, she also runs marathons, rides – oh, and raises four children of her own, all at Blundell's. Husband Spencer runs a car dealership in Barnstaple and has always moved around with her. 'Blundell's appealed to me because there's an honest and unpretentious feel about the place – and I'm a country girl,' she says. 'Though when I saw the sign that said Headmaster's Visitors, I said "That'll be the first thing to go!".'

Leaving in July 2018 to head Cheltenham College. Her successor will be Bart Wielenga, currently senior deputy head here. Degree in economics from the University of Natal in South Africa and postgrad qualification in human resource development from the Rand Afrikaans University in Johannesburg. Also taught at Michaelhouse in KwaZulu-Natal and was a housemaster and head of economics at Wellington College before joining Blundell's in 2012.

Academic matters: Traditionally not the brightest star in the firmament of south west schools, but there's a determination on the head's part to make the school as academic as it is sporty. ('She'll have her work cut out for her,' remarked one parent.) To that end she has made some key appointments since she arrived, such as a head of learning support, who is an ed psych, and a switched-on academic deputy from Wycombe Abbey, as well as introducing a proper tutor system, which has gone down well with parents. A level results are sound, with 69 per cent graded A*/B and 42 per cent A*/A in 2017; sciences, geography and maths – good take-up of further maths too – are most popular, languages lamentably not, though it is impressive to note that the school has run Spanish, Russian and Latin for sole takers. Parents reckon that student aspirations are being raised under the current regime; many already take EPQ in sixth form alongside A levels. The brightest sparks are invited to join the scholars' club, which 'offers stimulation for rapid progress' in the dry language beloved of inspectors.

At GCSE, 51 per cent graded A*-A/9-7 in 2017. DT enjoys a big take-up: we would have been happy to give house-room to many of the items of small wooden furniture we saw. Students with a wide range of intellectual gifts are catered for: at GCSE science for example, school offers choice between IGCSE or less demanding boards. Everyone does French and Latin from the start with the choice of German and Spanish in year 9. Just over a fifth of students receive SEN support, including plenty of help for those whose first language is not English.

Games, options, the arts: Make no mistake, this is a very sporty school, and might not be the place for a pale aesthete. That said, there is masses on offer for those with little or no eye for a ball, as well as the usual fare of rugby, hockey (both huge here) netball and cricket (for girls too, plus football, tennis, squash and fives): CCF, D of E, Ten Tors and the Devizes to Westminster canoe race keenly pursued. In the spring, the whole school participates in the (frankly bonkers) Russell – named for the eponymous Jack (of terrier fame and an OB) – a hotly contested cross-country race for which local landowners open their land. We had never seen quite such cheerfully muddy girls as the ones we met just back from a practice. General heartiness extends to an outdoor pool only – 'reassuringly heated,' says school – though an indoor one is on everyone's wish list, and keen swimmers can use the indoor facilities in Tiverton. Riding strong here too – Blundell's riders regularly compete at events in the south west and recently won the National Schools Jumping-with-style contest – but it's not the kind of school where turning up with a horsebox is de rigueur; no equines on site.

We had never seen quite such cheerfully muddy girls as the ones we met just back from a practice. General heartiness extends to a (heated) outdoor pool only

Activities range from aerobics to yoga; everyone is expected to sign up for a minimum of two. Boarders are offered an adventure and leadership programme over eight weekends comprising gorge-walking and survival training along with other feats of derring-do. But Blundell's isn't just good at the strenuous stuff: a long tradition of debating both in school and beyond was crowned by winning the ESU national final recently. Artists in all media compete and show their work far beyond the school, with success at the Tate, in the Saatchi Art Prize for Schools (online but also, more excitingly, in the Kings Road) and more locally in Tiverton and Exeter. We were gutted that an art scholar's rendition of the Mona Lisa in peanut butter and chocolate spread had (presumably) been eaten before our visit. Music facilities have just been brought bang up to date with an editing suite and composition/technology studio, but

Crowning glory of boarding has to be Westlake, the co-ed sixth form house where students get as close a feeling of university life as possible

there has long been masses of music both sung and played: concerts and recitals, plus recently Grease, Cabaret and open mic night on the lighter side. In the last couple of years groups have been to Prague, Brittany and Venice, as well as prestigious venues nearer home. Drama takes places in the Ondaatje Hall, named for its generous donor, the notable philanthropist, brother of the author and an OB; plenty of backstage and technical experience on offer as well as acting, plus visits and workshops from French and Spanish theatre groups – a great initiative which other schools would do well to emulate. A long tradition of house and year group plays means there are opportunities for all budding thespians.

Boarding: Relationships between staff and students seem extremely good, with house staff coming in for particular praise – some email parents with photos of boarders' activities and high jinks just about the moment they happen. The seven houses accommodate a mix of all kinds of boarders (full, weekly, flexi) and day pupils, divided into two co-ed at the beginning and end of a student's time at Blundell's, two girls' and three boys'; all are known by their initials – NC, SH etc. The latter, School House, for years 7 and 8, was one of the first matters the head tackled on arrival as a result of considerable parental dissatisfaction: all now report huge improvements.

Twice as many boys as girls are full boarders and parents of full boarders rather wish more kids stayed in at weekends, and that the food was, on occasion, more girl-friendly. Some of their accommodation could do with a bit of tlc too. The crowning glory of boarding has to be Westlake, the co-ed sixth form house where students get as close a feeling of university life as possible before they get there, yet where girls and boys respectively can retreat from the hurly-burly to their own part of the house.

Background and atmosphere: Four-square Victorian red-brick buildings face more modern additions across Blundells Road in Tiverton – such is the importance of the school to the town that it has a road named after it – set off by gracious green spaces and a distinctive clock tower; though the school was founded by the generous legacy of one of England's wealthiest cloth merchants, Peter Blundell, over 200 hundred years earlier, it moved to its permanent home only in the 1880s. The values of that time persist in some measure today with the school's emphasis on 'distinguished performance in those games which the Victorians [had] developed to replace the rude sports of earlier centuries'. No more cock-fighting then. Definitely a traditional feel about the place, with a bewildering number of ties, though certainly not fuddy-duddy, with boys below sixth form wearing tawny tweed jackets, the colour of autumn bracken on Dartmoor, and girls red ones. Even the sixth form wear uniform; their jackets are navy blue, striped for those who have been awarded full colours – given not only for sports, but all manner of accomplishment.

What in other schools might be called assembly takes place in Big School and is called Latin prayer, concluding as it does with the Lord's prayer in Latin; chapel on other mornings in the school's own beautiful chapel. The first girls arrived in 1975 and the school went fully co-ed in 1992. We are delighted that the last head girl exercised her right to keep a pig at school for her final term, something conferred on the head boy from the start.

Parents love the friendly and inclusive feel of the place, the lack of arrogance among the students and the resilience the school instils in them. 'Absolutely non-stop programme of extracurricular activities means my children are absolutely exhausted by the time they come home – perhaps they need more soothing down-time at weekends to recover,' observed one mother of boarders. Great affection and loyalty for the school from past and present students and staff – one finally took retirement after 30 years' service; terrific and longstanding network of events for OBs, not just the 'winter lunches' in Devon, but all over the world.

Pastoral care, well-being and discipline: Discipline appears to be kept with a lightish touch – parents of drinkers and smokers can expect 'to be invited

in to discuss a way forward', according to the head. Drugs weren't even mentioned, and bullying gets zero tolerance. 'There's a sexting issue every year in year 9,' said one mother phlegmatically, 'but the school just deals with it'.

Pupils and parents: Mostly local but a good handful (about 15 per cent) from abroad, giving the school a more cosmopolitan feel than mid Devon might otherwise manage. Among the farmers, local professionals and the military, there are boarders from Cornwall, where there is little on offer, and of course refugees from London in search of a better life; some first time buyers of independent schooling too, one of whom said, 'My son is having the kind of education that I work for and dream of him having'. Pupils are as grounded and unpretentious as any you will find at a UK boarding school, the kind who will have a go and take a risk; we suspect that the rebellious, the precious and the show-off would not thrive here.

Entrance: Mostly at 11, by means of papers in English, maths and non-verbal reasoning in the January preceding entry; at 13+ via common entrance or the school's own entrance test in English and maths in June. At sixth form, hopefuls have to satisfy relatively undemanding entrance requirements of a minimum of five GCSEs at a C/5 or above with at least a B/6 in subjects to be taken to A2, plus interview

Exit: Up to 20 per cent leave after GCSEs. The vast majority to university and traditional ones at that, up and down the country. 'No-one goes to Exeter – too close to home,' sixth formers informed us. Recent Oxbridge successes (five in 2017, plus five medics) may well boost applications in that direction. Popular universities include Durham, Imperial College, Warwick, Reading, Bristol, Leeds and Manchester. Degree choices again tend towards the conventional and/or vocational, such as medicine, geography, economics, biochemistry, law and business management.

After that, Old Blundellians fan out across the globe, to the extent that there are OB gatherings in South Africa, Japan, Germany and Hong Kong. An extremely busy development office ensures strong links with the old school tie. Famous OBs include RD Blackmore, (the hero of whose chef d'oeuvre Lorna Doone was a fictional pupil), 40s actor Gerald Hamer and his director son Robert (Kind Hearts and Coronets), defence correspondent and author Robert Fox, organist Peter Hurford, TV journalist Claire Marshall and the drummer of The Vamps, Tristan Evans.

Money matters: For the first 300 years of its existence, Blundell's was maintained by the profits from its properties in Tiverton and estate in south Devon, but these days fees charged are in line with comparable schools. Decent range of scholarships for sport, music, art, drama, all-round as well as academic; only music and academic at 11+. Peter Blundell Foundation bursaries are awarded in cases of financial need where 'Governors wish to reflect the spirit of Peter Blundell's vision'. The school is innovative in attracting an array of corporate sponsors to fund events.

Remarks: Ancient and distinguished Devon institution preserving traditional values and feel, yet turning out considerate and balanced young people all set for careers across the globe. Not perhaps for those seeking exclusively to scale the heights of academia or social cachet, but deserves far higher prominence than the lowish profile ('Not in the west country!' protests school) it currently assumes.

Bruton School for Girls

4

Sunny Hill, Bruton, Somerset BA10 0NT

01749 814400 | admissions@brutonschool.co.uk | www.brutonschool.co.uk

Ages: 11–18 (junior boarding from year 4)

Pupils: 200; sixth form: 40; Boarders: approx 60

Day: £16,995 pa; Boarding: £26,415 – £31,350 pa

Headmistress: Since 2012, Nicola (Nicky) Botterill BSc MA NPQH FRGS FRSA (late 40s). A geographer by academic discipline, with a first degree from Middlesex Poly and a masters from the Institute of Education, Mrs Botterill has taught in girls' schools for her entire career, except for one stint in a mixed state school, ascending through the hierarchy as

far as the deputy headship of St Mary's Calne, from where she was appointed head of BSG.

'I felt immediately at home here and found the girls grounded and unstuffy', she says. Early exposure to travel and living abroad as a child imbued her with a love of adventure and foreign climes; the fact that she took a mid-career gap year has done it no harm at all.

Bruton is small girls' school in a part of south west England that is richly populated with good schools. Mrs Botterill was brought in to increase numbers but has achieved rather more than that since her arrival – her work supporting newly qualified teachers within the Girls' Schools Association was recognised by their award for 'an outstanding contribution from a recently appointed head' in 2014 – and has garnered approval from all quarters. 'She did not grab the reins, but took the time to get to know people'; 'But you know she's in charge,' say parents. In her trademark fuchsia jacket and pashmina, we found her engagingly warm, frank, chatty, approachable – all reiterated by parents and girls. Any free time she might have could be spent doing arts and crafts, such as pottery and stained glass, even DIY on occasion.

Academic matters: School scores highly on value-added. Fifty-seven per cent of GCSEs were graded A*-A/9-7 in 2017; 23 per cent of A levels taken came in at A*/A, 75 per cent A*-B. Before GCSE, the curriculum includes compulsory classics (including Greek and Latin), DT and 'home technology'. In sixth form, Leiths certificate in food and wine is popular – we would happily have stayed in any ski chalet catered by BSG students, judging by what was being made in the kitchen. Typically, girls take nine or 10 subjects at GCSE, to include separate sciences, but no language, ancient or modern, is compulsory; a choice of French, German, Spanish or Latin is offered. Flexible and enlightened enough to allow girls to take certain GCSEs (eg French and maths) two or three years early, in exceptional cases. Twenty-one subjects to choose from in sixth form.

Hockey and netball the main games here, with no fewer than 17 netball teams. Sporty activities include quidditch and tchoukball (truly – we wished we'd seen either)

Small class sizes, averaging under 10, hard work and the 'enthusiastic, effective teachers – the kind you get in a grammar school,' according to one parent, contribute to the school's academic success and high praise is given to SEN diagnosis and support: 'My daughter's in-house plan is tailored to her', said another, whose daughter had fled the local comprehensive. The wide ability range 'has meant my girls have learnt to tolerate all levels of ability, which is much more like real life,' commented one thoughtful mother of clearly bright girls. Stand-out subjects are English, drama, art and biology; some report that maths is currently in flux. Our impression was of interesting subject matter (West Side Story being used to demonstrate the realities of immigration for Hispanics, capital punishment v the safety and protection of prisoners) being delivered with IT as support rather than as a substitute for honest-to-goodness teaching, to a very compliant, quiescent flock – just for our benefit?

Games, options, the arts: Hockey and netball the main games here, with no fewer than 17 netball teams. An impressive fixture list where BSG looks more like David up against local Goliaths Sherborne Girls and King Edward's Bath. Several netball courts doubling up for tennis, a delightfully sunny Astro where strenuous hockey practice was taking place when we visited, plus an athletics track behind the main group of buildings. At present the swimming pool is an outdoors, solar-heated, summer only affair; the five swimming teams use opponents' indoor facilities for matches at less clement times of year. An indoor pool is top of the parental wish list. Although there is a riding team, this is not the kind of place where girls bring their own steeds, and the ability to pilot a horsebox is not a requirement for entry. Sporty activities include quidditch and tchoukball (truly – we wished we'd seen either).

'It's slightly Enid Blyton, with cocoa and biscuits at break,' said one mother. We liked the fresh air and heartiness about the place – the gaps between buildings necessitate a breather between lessons, through the beautifully tended grounds

Music comes in for high praise – deservedly so, judging by the singing practice for the director of music's own composition that we heard, the recital at assembly and admissions to national and county youth choir and orchestra. A school orchestra, smaller ensembles for brass and strings inter alia, a Baroque group, theory classes for those taking grades and plenty of opportunities to play beyond the school gates make for a rich musical offering: we enjoyed the CD (and cookies) we were given on departure very much.

Drama takes place in the Hobhouse theatre: although it is a popular option, outside the devised and scripted requirements of public exams – when we witnessed genuine belly laughs and dramatic talent in the GCSE piece we saw – the scope seems limited to one musical per year, but 'Please please don't make us play boys again,' beg the girls. The art department is truly vibrant – a crammed creative space where girls seem to be able to pursue any artistic fancy: the series of photographs resulting from one girl persuading an obliging friend to immerse herself in milk in a variety of poses was memorable. Good links with the arty town of Bruton enrich the life of the school – the installation by a local artist of felt poppies suspended on threads to commemorate the First World War was innovative and moving. Plenty of trips to local and not so local theatre, concerts and galleries complement the lively arts scene within school.

Boarding: Boarding (officially from year 4 in Sunny Hill Prep, but occasionally younger in the case of one small girl we met whose elder sisters all board and who was determined not to miss out) takes place in the cosy old vicarage where all junior boarders (just a handful from the prep) up to year 9 are housed. Day girls are free to join in with weekend activities and intermittent sleep-overs. Two other boarding houses for senior school boarders. Accommodation is homely and not obsessively tidy: a couple of sixth form girls had transformed their room into a Christmas grotto, complete with glitter and a snow scene, without attracting the wrath of the domestic staff. Intra-school allegiance, which might attach to houses with full vertical boarding in a bigger school, is created by assigning each girl (day and boarding) to one of four halls named for local stately homes.

Background and atmosphere: One of a disproportionate number of schools in Bruton (owing to the beneficence of Hugh Sexey, an auditor of the Exchequer in the early 1600s), a small charming Somerset market town of golden stone, BSG sits on Sunny Hill, certainly so the day we visited, with distant hazy views of Glastonbury Tor. Established in 1900 and known originally as Sunny Hill School (the name retained by the prep), it has mostly been independent but spent 30 years in the maintained sector early in the last century. It is possibly this which gives the school a delightful lack of pretension and snobbery, 'a place where the teachers don't parade like cockerels, but where they get a remarkable amount out of the girls,' in the words of one mother. 'It's slightly Enid Blyton with cocoa and biscuits at break,' said another. We liked the fresh air and heartiness about the place – the gaps between buildings necessarily mean a breather between lessons, through the beautifully tended grounds and eccentric pop-up garden, with its giant chessmen.

Boarding accommodation is homely: a couple of sixth form girls had transformed their room into a glittery Christmas grotto

Proud and unapologetic to be a girls' school, where both the girls and their parents choose to be: 'My daughter was offered the chance to move at sixth form and declined,' one parent told us,

Girls are awarded 'Honourables' for exceptional work, 'hallmarks' for acts of courtesy and community-mindedness, and colours for sporting prowess

another recounted a story of her daughter taking refuge from the local state offering and finding sanctuary at BSG. 'We landed on our feet here', said yet another satisfied customer. The school's size means that girls form friendships across year groups, and we felt a genuine sense of community over a delicious lunch of steak pie and fresh veg. 'Friendly' kept popping up as the most common adjective used to describe the school: 'My daughter took all of two days to settle in,' reported one happy mother.

Pastoral care, well-being and discipline: The pastoral side and the immense care the school takes over every girl in it are hugely appreciated by parents. Hot on friendship issues, a perennial subtext in girls' schools. 'Bruton stood out over other local schools,' in one parent's view, 'and the school is not afraid to tackle issues head on, yet sensitively'. Tutor groups are mixed age until sixth form (these meet daily), and between tutors and heads of halls, no-one appears to fall through the net. Relationships between staff and students and between the students themselves are sound and supportive, 'but we do teach them resilience and that things going wrong isn't necessarily a problem,' adds the head. 'Honourables' are awarded for exceptional work, 'hallmarks' for acts of courtesy and community-mindedness, colours for sporting prowess. Discipline is not a matter which seems to rear its ugly head very often: rudeness, lateness and wilder interpretations of uniform do not go unremarked; smokers and drinkers can expect a sliding scale of punishment, whilst druggies and persistent offenders face exclusion. 'Fluffy and lenient we are not,' states the head.

Pupils and parents: 'Confident without being arrogant' – that overworked phrase to which every school aspires – is echoed by parents. We found the girls, who arrive in anything from helicopters to old bangers, cheerful, unpretentious and very happy to be at this school. 'This isn't the place for hair-flicking city types, but for well-grounded families, wanting the best for their girls. Our parents aren't flashy but aren't without aspiration either'. A welcoming parent community helps to reassure first time buyers that they have made a wise choice. About one fifth of girls is from overseas.

Famous old girls include Clarissa Farr, ex-high mistress of St Paul's Girls' School and journalists Viv Groskop, Imogen Sellars and Catherine Davies.

Entrance: Via online verbal and non-verbal reasoning tests to assess potential, plus interview. At sixth form the bar is higher, at five GCSEs at grade C/5 or above, with B/6s at subjects to be taken at A level. Termly open days and visits by arrangement. Main feeders at year 7 are the prep and local primary schools, at year 9 local preps. Several buses serve surrounding area within 20 mile radius.

Exit: Sixth formers to a wide range of universities and an equal variety of courses. Most girls get to their first choice: everything from astrophysics at Liverpool to creative events management at Bournmouth Arts to medicine at Sheffield.

Money matters: As independent education goes, good value for money, at about 25 per cent cheaper than its most expensive competitors. 'Bruton offers everything academic and holistic a parent could ask from a 21st century girls' school, without charging the ridiculous fees that most other schools charge', so said one mother. Scholarships, awarded for the usual range of talents, are nominal, but governors' exhibitions are awarded in cases of means-tested need to a maximum value of 40 per cent of fees.

Remarks: 'It's just not very BSG to promote itself,' one father remarked, but if we were expecting an apologetic little school lurking in rural Somerset, we did not find it. Hidden gem is more like it – a place of unpretentious endeavour where girls can be girls and achieve as much as they are capable of. 'Follow the gleam,' may be the school motto, but in our view it could be time for a spotlight.

Bryanston School

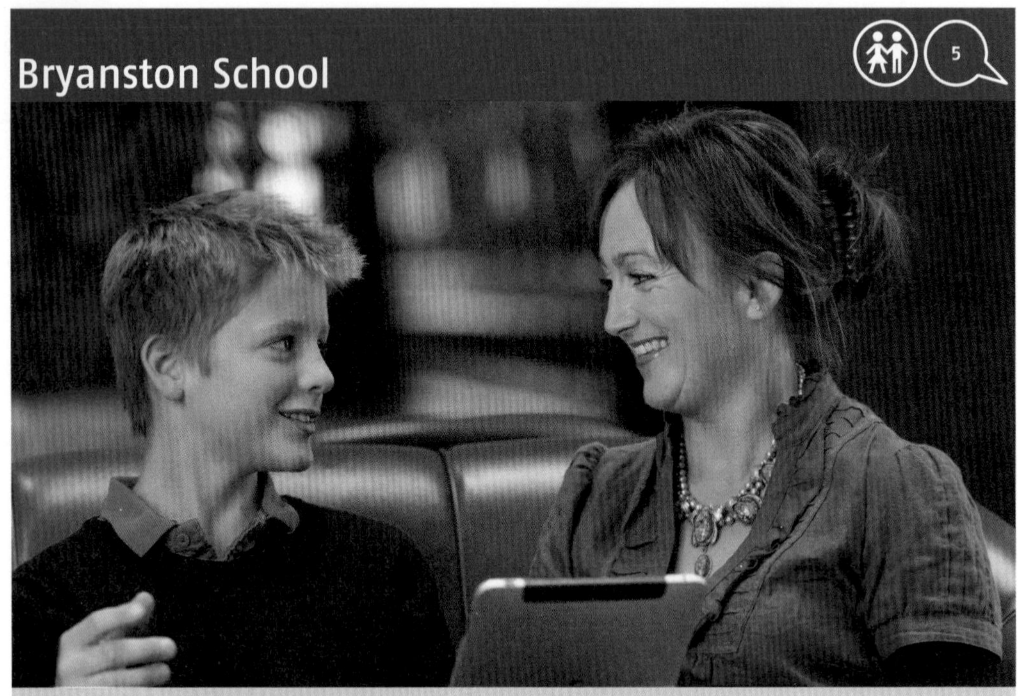

Bryanston, Blandford Forum, Dorset DT11 0PX

01258 452411 | admissions@bryanston.co.uk | www.bryanston.co.uk

Ages: 13–18

Pupils: 673; sixth form: 287; Boarders: 581

Day: £29,229 pa; Boarding: £36,984 pa

Head: Since 2005, Ms Sarah Thomas (50s). A GDST girl hailing from Birkenhead and proud of it, Ms Thomas read Lit Hum (classics – the proper kind with Greek) at Oxford, before becoming an articled clerk to a notary public. Both her parents taught, but their entreaties not to follow in their footsteps clearly fell on deaf ears, for she left the law to do her PGCE at King's College London, before longish stints at Sevenoaks and Uppingham. All that formative experience of co-ed boarding has equipped her admirably for Bryanston. 'A female head is just a part of who we are, and the best part of my job is recruiting outstanding staff', she says. We found her a (charming) force to be reckoned with, whom we can imagine causing stuffier members of HMC to choke on their sherry. 'Splendid', say parents, '100 per cent approachable, with fine powers of judgment'. Ms Thomas makes a point of keeping her hand in at the chalk-face – everybody has to do Latin in the first year, and a fair few take it on to GCSE; a brainy minority do Greek as well.

Ms Thomas' husband teaches at nearby Hanford and writes children's books and plays; they have two daughters at university. In her precious time off? 'Reading – for its peaceful aspects and the opportunity to lose myself in other worlds', she says, plus walking her dog and cooking.

Retiring in July 2019.

Academic matters: Not desperately selective, with an expectation of 50 per cent for each subject at CE – but what marks this school out is the way academic life is structured. The timetable contains assignment periods for each subject alongside lessons, where prep, further study or one-to-one sessions with the subject teacher take place – the latter ominously named 'correction periods'. In the first three years, assignment periods are supervised by the subject teacher, providing access and extra help outside lessons. Academic progress is tracked more tightly here than in any school this editor had seen: weekly assessments are provided by each subject teacher and entered on the e-chart, the online mark-sheet to which parents also have access. All assignments (prep) are set to be handed in a week later, so being organised and learning to manage a workload is a skill learnt early. 'The tutorial system ensures success,' says the school: each student is allocated a tutor for the duration of his/her time at the school – so far, so conventional – but these individuals do so very much more than that somewhat over-used term suggests. 'We tutors deal with the academic, spiritual, moral and act as a kind of PA', said one. Parents greatly value this and tutors' accessibility both to students and parents. SEN provision supports what goes on in class: each department appoints a staff member to liaise with learning support. One-to-one tuition is available; all help offered is discreet and without stigma. School claims to 'deliver for every child we admit.'

So does it pay off? At I/GCSE in 2017, 43 per cent A*/A grades and in some years, school is on a par with local independents such as the Sherborne schools, where entry requirements are higher. 'My daughter got results beyond our wildest dreams', raved one mother, who also reckoned that Bryanston had been perfect for all three of her children, with differing abilities and interests. Visual arts of all kind very popular and successful, as is Latin and Greek; results suggest as much enthusiasm as aptitude for Latin, but it is heart-warming to see such a resurgence in classical languages. School keeps a Greek theatre tucked away in its extensive grounds, and the JACT summer school in Greek – of formidable repute – for all-comers is held here. At A level, nearly 67 per cent graded A*/B and 38 per cent A*/A in 2017, but value-added shows up strongly against comparable schools. Business studies and English are the most popular choices, sciences hot on their heels, followed by art and design in its various forms. History and geography have a moderate following; modern languages surprisingly little, along with music and drama. Average 35 IB points in 2017.

Games, options, the arts: The scope is amazing – clearly something for the most idle couch potato. All the sports and facilities one would expect in a school of this type feature (rugby, hockey, netball, cricket, tennis, rowing) and both hockey and lacrosse are on offer in consecutive terms. Luscious grounds stretch down to the river Stour, where rowing of increasing seriousness takes place out of a beautiful new boathouse designed by an OB and keen oarsman (sadly we weren't shown this). New arrivals learn navigation skills and how to survive a night in the open – useful for those times when they get lost in the grounds. A carousel of adventurous options takes place in the second year, comprising (amongst other things) falconry, canoeing and rock-climbing (new climbing wall a great hit). Riding might seem quite mundane; we were bemused not even to be shown the stabling, indoor and all-weather schools, or cross-country course on our visit. Keen riders can bring their own steeds. Sailing in the school's own fleet of Lasers in Poole harbour. School is notable local and national player in a variety of sports. OBs include Phil de Glanville.

The art at Bryanston hits you between the eyes as you walk in. Enormous canvasses adorn the long walls of each of the central corridors in the main building: the scope of the department and amount of available hanging space, plus the skills and dedication of teachers and students, mean the most ambitious projects can be executed. The art department is divided into 2D and 3D; both aspects enjoy a passionate following and are fabulously resourced. Best work of both past and present pupils has thrice been showcased in London galleries (no less). School's reputation for a creative curriculum is well deserved, and fulfils the aspiration for 'the joy of the abundant life' which an early headmaster articulated.

Luscious grounds stretch down to the river Stour, where rowing of increasing seriousness takes place out of a beautiful new boathouse designed by a former pupil

Music and drama (both excellent and ambitious in scope) tend to be avidly pursued for the love of them, rather than chasing yet another GCSE. The 600 seat Coade Hall measures up as well as any school theatre facility, indeed visiting theatre companies stage performances here. Usual musicals (Cabaret, Guys and Dolls in recent years) sometimes include a showing for prep schools – canny marketing! Annual play for each year group (eg The Crucible, Pride and Prejudice in a specially adapted version). Much student-led drama, and our guides enthused about house drama, where even the most reluctant performers tread the boards. New Tom Wheare Music School (named after retired head) includes stunning 300 seat concert hall with huge stage designed to hold a large-scale symphony orchestra, plus, inter alia, large numbers of practice rooms, recital rooms, recording studios, soundproofed band rooms and courtyard area for outdoor performances (plans for performances and masterclasses from renowned musicians). Let's hope they are generous with it. Again, any musical whim can probably be accommodated – if not here, then where? Over a fifth of students sing in a group or choir: we heard the first rehearsal of one of mixed age and mixed ability during the lunch hour, and tuneful and enthusiastic it was too. Musicians perform all over the place, including London and abroad – the dance band to Paris, the chamber choir and orchestra to Florence. All students have to learn a musical instrument in the first year, which may be where the enthusiasm and lung capacity to play the bagpipes starts – there is even a pipe band. 'What the musicians did in the hols' was an interesting little aside in the school's extensive literature; one boy's attendance at a course at Berklee College in Boston helped him gain a place on its coveted degree programme.

Extracurricular activities are taken seriously here in pursuit of the abundant life – there is everything from Accessorise (jewellery) to yoga, and a choice of four out of more than 100 is compulsory in the first two years.

Boarding: Three boarding houses are contained within the main building, the rest scattered over the grounds immediately around the main building. Accommodation is comfortable rather than de luxe. Everybody eats centrally in the delightfully refurbished dining hall, and the food is all it's cracked up to be: we sampled the excellent salad bar but the hot choices and puddings all smelt and looked scrummy too. Rather cool café in lieu of tuck shop sells smoothies, cookies, pizza and other appealing fare; houses also have kitchens for making snacks and drinks. When we asked about the long walk into Blandford, students looked slightly blank – why would they need to do that when everything is at school?

On whole school weekends, all pupils stay in school and work together towards a common goal, eg a charity fundraising event, pupil-led arts festival, sponsored walk etc, but on open weekends they may go home after Saturday morning lessons/ any match commitments.

Rather cool café in lieu of tuck shop sells smoothies, cookies, pizza and other appealing fare; houses also have kitchens for making snacks

Background and atmosphere: Exceedingly long drive through woods leads eventually to a baby château perched on a rise overlooking the river Stour. Modelled on Menars in the Loire valley by Norman Shaw, the house had to be sold to meet the death duties of Viscount Portman after the family had lived there for just 30 years. In 1928 a young Australian school master bought it and founded the school on traditional and modern principles – et nova et vetera, as the motto says. Going co-ed in the early 70s was well ahead of the trend, and Bryanston has kept its reputation for blazing a trail – 'Just don't call us progressive,' said the head, with a visible shudder.

Acres (400) of grounds and beautiful bold modern additions surround the house, which make a harmonious whole. Inside, two long parquet-floored corridors dotted with sofas in the main house give the continuing impression of being fortunate residents of a mansion, though everyone looks more purposeful. Even the staff and visitors' loos were contained in a spacious cloakroom with leather armchairs in which to retreat from the fray.. Teaching spaces are high spec, particularly the science labs, with their wet and dry areas in the newish Sanger building, named after a double laureate biochemist and OB.

Pastoral care, well-being and discipline: Exceptionally good care is taken of all students. Newbies meet their tutors on arrival at school, and the team formed between him/her and the housemaster or mistress (known as a hsm, to rhyme with bosom) is a tight one. It seems as though it would be hard for any unhappiness or falling off in performance or morale to go unnoticed. Each house has a distinct character and students are placed in them according to a process 'akin to Hogwarts' sorting hat', according to the head. Boys spend a year in one of two junior houses; girls go straight into the house in which they will spend their whole time at the school.

We liked the understated but definite sense of a spiritual life at Bryanston, led by the chaplain. As well as the church in the grounds, there is a dear little chapel in the vaults of the main house which acts as a calm retreat from the hurly burly of life going on outside its open doors. One parent told us her son had 'quietly gone off and got himself confirmed', slightly to her surprise (but pleasure).

The persistent reputation for unchecked behaviour and general licence, drugs in particular, has been slow to die, but one parent briskly dismissed it as 'quite unmerited'. According to the school and the parents we spoke to, any involvement would result in immediate expulsion – and the kids know it. A civilised and age-appropriate view is taken of alcohol for sixth formers, 'carefully monitored under adult supervision,' says school. Any misdemeanours are 'harshly dealt with,' a mother confirmed. The school rules and regs fit on one side of paper and are unequivocal and up to date, eg 'Computers/iPods/MP3s must not be used to watch films, play games, listen to music in lessons, prep and after lights out'. For a school with a dress code rather than uniform below sixth form, we found the students tidier than at many other schools: the drill is a coloured polo shirt with a sweater with black or navy trousers or skirts; more leeway for sixth form.

Pupils and parents: When asked if she could sum up a Bryanston pupil, the head said no she couldn't, though one hallmark would be 'someone comfortable in their own skin', who would enjoy being a part of things. We were actually allowed to meet very few, just the head boy and girl who showed us around, who were of course charming and very much on-message. As for the parents, quite a range professionally from doctors to financiers to creative types, but they struck us as exceptionally thoughtful about their children's education. The geographical spread, in common with many schools, has contracted so that Bryanston is really a south west school, though with a significant minority coming from London and the south east, and a handful from the furthest reaches of the UK. A few from overseas.

On whole school weekends, all pupils stay in school and work together towards a common goal, eg a charity fundraising event, pupil-led arts festival, sponsored walk etc

Notable OBs include Lucian Freud, all the Conran boys, Mark Elder, John Eliot Gardiner (who sent his daughter too), Ben Fogle and Emilia Fox.

Entrance: There are 130 places at 13+ via ISEB pretest in the autumn of year 7; however, aware that some children develop later – ' It is very important

to us that we do not lose some of the very talented late developers that make Bryanston the school it is.' Close links forged with preps and prospective parents; instead of open days with a cast of thousands, the school arranges group visits for 12 or so families, as well as individual visits. Registered pupils are also invited to various events in the two years before they arrive. Between 25-30 new students arrive at sixth form for which 50 points at GCSE are required, after a day of tests (maths, English and abilities) and interviews at the school. Existing pupils also have to meet the points requirement, waived only in very exceptional cases.

Exit: Ten per cent left after GCSEs in 2017. Nearly half of upper sixth leavers apply to university once they have their results. The head of sixth form is all for this, and has tweaked the school's UCAS process to accommodate it. University strategy starts with tutors early in lower sixth and the vast majority of students do go on, whenever they apply. 'Less formal relationships between staff and students mean they are confident enough to bounce up to them and ask for what they need,' he says of the application process.

Degree courses, interestingly, tend to be conventional choices (business in various forms, engineering, architecture, history and English – but classics too – hurrah!) in conventional places: Bristol, Leeds, Oxford Brookes and UWE. Three to Oxbridge in 2017 and two medics; seven to art foundation courses and two to music colleges.

Also several off overseas including Dublin, Leiden, Amsterdam, Toronto, Zurich and a few to the US

A few gripes about careers and higher education guidance from parents; while they like the rather unpressured approach to UCAS, they feel alternatives should be more clearly spelt out. Newish head of sixth form appointment is grounds for optimism, however.

Money matters: Fees in line with comparable schools but some items (stationery, art and DT materials) appear on the bill as extras. Scholarships across a range of disciplines including DT and ICT to a maximum of 25 per cent of fees. Bursaries on application.

Remarks: Stunning school with unrivalled facilities and a great deal of latitude and encouragement for students to explore any aspect of academic, sporting and artistic life which takes their fancy. Too much too young? Possibly. A great deal more traditional than its reputation would suggest, but myths can take a long time to break down. We could not find any detractors, try as we might!

Canford School

6

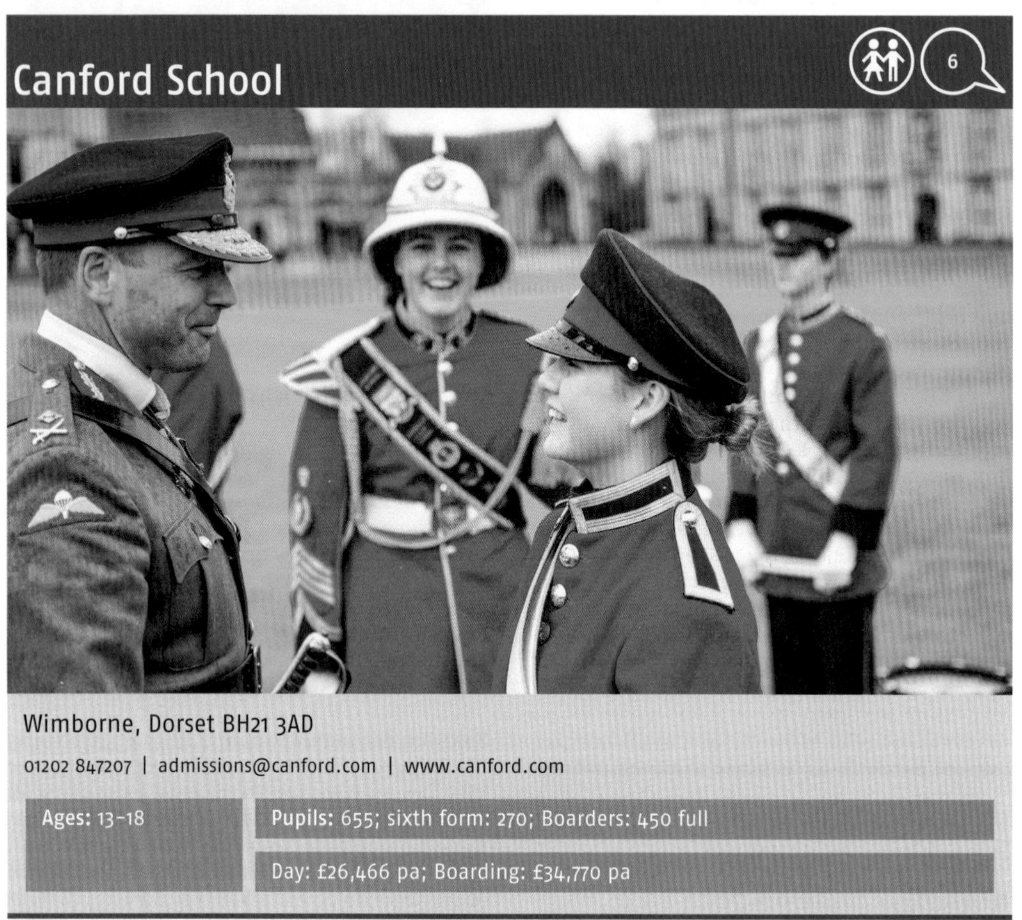

Wimborne, Dorset BH21 3AD

01202 847207 | admissions@canford.com | www.canford.com

Ages: 13–18

Pupils: 655; sixth form: 270; Boarders: 450 full

Day: £26,466 pa; Boarding: £34,770 pa

Headmaster: Since 2013, Ben Vessey BA MA MBA (40s). Educated at Magdalen College School, Oxford, then read history at Southampton. Intended to join the army but after tearing both knee ligaments playing rugby worked as an oil and gas broker for five years in the City and on placement in Texas. 'But when I came back from the US I realised that it wasn't what I wanted to do,' he says. Applied to Dauntsey's, who snapped him up to teach history. Became head of history and housemaster there, followed by four and a half years as head of history, politics and law at Millfield. Spent six years as senior deputy head at Christ's Hospital – 'it was a great apprenticeship for headship,' he says. Along the way he did an MA in history, a PGCE and an MBA in education management.

Loves teaching and teaches five periods a fortnight to a year 9 history set. 'I write reports and do parents' meetings and it keeps me in touch with the rhythms of teachers' busy routines,' he says. Much in evidence around the school and makes a point of dropping in on lessons to see colleagues in action in the classroom. Has lunch with pupils and staff as often as possible and supper with them twice a week. 'I leave them alone at breakfast,' he jokes.

Energetic, enthusiastic and impressively focused, he lives and breathes the school. He loves Sounds of Canford (the school's informal concert series), watches as many concerts, plays and sports matches as he can and catches up with Year of Genius, an innovative enrichment project launched by the school, as he cycles on his spin bike. Lives in a house on-site with his wife Harriet, their three sons (the eldest of whom started as a day boy at Canford at the same time as his dad) and two black labradors. In his spare time he plays golf, cycles and reads (he's a fan of Bernard Cornwell's Sharpe novels and other historical fiction). Winston Churchill is his hero and a bronze miniature of the legendary PM left to the school by old boy Terrence Cobden Pike has pride of place in his study. Churchill was a relation of the Guest family who owned Canford before it became a school and apparently he spent many summer holidays there.

Academic matters: Results are easily as good as other co-ed schools with illustrious names. In 2017, 48 per cent A*/A at A level and 76 per cent A*-B (figures include Pre-U for art and languages). At GCSE, 65 per cent A*-A/9-7. Considering the breadth of intake this speaks volumes for the first-rate teaching. Maths and chemistry are the most popular A level subjects but many pupils do a mix of sciences, arts and humanities subjects. EPQ on offer too. Sixth formers we spoke to were full of praise for the support in the run-up to A levels and the study skills workshops on offer. Study leave is awarded on an individual basis but most sixth formers opt to stay in school, keen to make the most of timetabled lessons, past papers and one-to-one help. 'Everyone works hard here,' a sixth former told us while another said: 'The teachers want you to do well and they really support you.'

All year 9s do French and Latin, as well as German or Spanish. Most take 10 subjects at GCSE, including at least one language and two sciences. Pupils are set for maths and languages from the word go. Computer science has been introduced throughout the school and is increasingly popular – 16 taking it at GCSE when we visited, 11 at AS and three at A2. 'Prep schools should be trying to embed computer science in the curriculum, rather than just IT,' we were told. Year 9s curriculum focuses on developing 'habits, skills and literacy' with plenty of cross-curricular projects. Good provision for those with learning difficulties, mostly dyslexia, mild dyspraxia and language attention difficulties. Learning support housed in the Lovell Building, along with the humanities department. Year 9 pupils who need additional support can take extra English instead of Latin, while in years 10 and 11 learning skills are offered for a number of pupils instead of one GCSE subject, with focus on developing study skills. One-to-one tuition available when the need arises. Average class size is 15 in years 9 to 11, nine in the lower sixth and eight in the upper sixth.

Canford pupils have achieved the highest Pre-U grades for art for two years running and up to eight students a year go on to do art foundation courses

Facilities throughout the school are second to none. Glorious library (complete with oak panelling, chandeliers and 18,000 books, DVDs and audio CDs, plus thousands of virtual resources). Excellent science labs. We liked the fact that every classroom and office has an inspiring and appropriate moniker – Roddick (after Body Shop founder Anita Roddick) for economics and business and Olympus for classics are just two examples. Even the book cupboard in the classics department gets its own name – Hades, of course.

Pro-active careers department organises advice on GCSE and A level subjects, annual careers symposium and interview experience. Work experience isn't compulsory but a growing number of students are applying for internships and work placements. REcently, sixth formers gained places on two of the UK's top corporate career programmes.

Games, options, the arts: Sport is a big deal here and Canford teams score notable successes at every level. Main sports are rugby, hockey and cricket for boys, hockey, netball and tennis for girls and athletics and rowing for both. Rowing VIII were Henley finalists recently. Acres of pitches, floodlit AstroTurf, real tennis court (there aren't many of those around), fitness suite and a 25m indoor swimming pool. In years 9 to 11, four teams regularly fielded per year group so everyone gets the chance to represent the school. Other options include cross country, sailing, dance, basketball, golf, squash, badminton, canoeing and fitness. Sports facilities and pool are used by local community at allotted times. When we visited a keep fit class for the elderly was in full swing in the sports hall.

Art is stunning – and in many cases highly original and ambitious. We were particularly taken with a vast oil painting (3.5m x 1.5m) of a turtle family. Canford pupils have achieved the highest Pre-U grades for art for two years running and up to eight students a year go on to do art foundation courses. Music is terrific, with a large number of choirs, orchestras, strings groups and jazz band. Around half of pupils take individual music lessons. Two major concerts a year, one at Canford, the other at the Lighthouse in Poole, home of the Bournemouth Symphony Orchestra. Lots of drama, with opportunities on stage, backstage and in technical roles. Several pupils have won National Youth Theatre places in recent years. Productions, house plays and an annual school musical take place in the Layard Theatre, opened by film and theatre director Sir Richard Eyre in 1999. Theatre used by professional companies too.

CCF isn't compulsory but is very popular. In 2015 nine cadets from the Royal Marine section beat the likes of Harrow, Winchester and Shrewsbury to win the Pringle Trophy, the premier inter-schools' cadet competition. Others opt for D of E, adventure training and/or community service programme. Seniors work in local primary schools and with disabled groups, run drama workshops and coach sport while juniors work as conservation volunteers. School is the lead sponsor of The Bourne Academy, a secondary school in Bournemouth. Canford pupils act as teaching assistants for languages, computing and science and sign up for book clubs and quizzes.

School is full of bright ideas – everything from Radio Canford to Connections, a general studies programme that challenges pupils to think beyond the curriculum and links different academic disciplines. Another innovation that caught our eye was Yellow Hour, an hour set aside twice a term for pupils and staff to perform in front of an informal audience. Recent highlights included the director of studies performing a maths equation and the head reading a short story he'd written. Year 9s do a carousel of activities every Wednesday – sculling, mixed lacrosse, bell ringing, even etiquette. A plethora of academic, sporting and cultural trips abroad as well as community projects in Argentina, Ghana and India. The Canford Partnership was set up following the discovery (and sale) of a £7 million Assyrian Frieze in the school tuck shop in 1994 and supports worthwhile community projects in the UK and Third World.

School is full of bright ideas – everything from Radio Canford to Connections, a programme that links different academic disciplines

Boarding: Full boarding only, no weekly boarding. Flexible exeat system means pupils can spend several Saturday nights a term at home if they want but on average two-thirds of boarders stay in school at weekends. Seven boarding houses – four for boys and three for girls (plus three mixed day houses). Each house has a married houseparent, three tutors and at least one matron (described by one teacher as 'the heart and soul of the boarding house'). Houses are modern and well equipped. In Beaufort, one of the girls' houses, youngest girls are in dorms of four, year 10s and 11s in twos and sixth formers get singles. When pupils arrive at 13 they are assigned a mentor from the year above and are so busy that they settle in quickly – weekend activities programme includes an assault course, pizza nights and trips to the beach. Beaufort housemistress has two cats and two dogs – 'they're brilliant therapy for anyone who feels homesick,' she says.

Most boarding houses are close to the main school buildings but Court and Franklin, two of the boys' houses, are a scenic seven-minute walk from the main school. Boys told us they enjoy the stroll and some bike or skateboard back and forth. Youngest pupils hand their mobile phones in at night but a housemaster we spoke to says pupils are so busy that electronic devices aren't generally a problem. Boys in his house prefer to play Connect Four and chess than stare at screens in their spare time. Very refreshing to hear.

Background and atmosphere: Canford is one of the most beautiful schools in the country. Located in 250 acres of parkland beside the River Stour, it even has its own Victorian arboretum, complete with 350 tree species and one of the largest sweet chestnut trees in the UK. A building of some sort has stood on the Canford site since the Domesday Book. The oldest parts are a pretty Norman church, used for services but too small to take the whole school, and the early 15th century John O'Gaunt's kitchen, used for debates, meetings and receptions. The stunning 19th century main building, originally known as Canford Manor and designed by Edward Blore and later Sir Charles Barry (architect of the Houses of Parliament), is grade I listed. Lord Wimborne sold the manor in 1923 and the school was founded the same year. It first admitted girls into the sixth form in 1969, went fully co-ed in 1995 and is now 60 per cent boys, 40 per cent girls.

School is a mix of grand, historic buildings and ultra-modern, but stylish additions. Dining hall, known as the Great Hall, where Edward, Prince of Wales danced in 1890 following a ritual slaughter of birds at a shooting party, is particularly magnificent. These days a modern cafeteria system is in place. Food is cooked in-house and gets the firm thumbs-up from pupils. All meals eaten in the Great Hall but there are kitchens with tea and toast-making facilities in every house, plus a tuck shop known as the Grubber.

The whole place fizzes with activity from dawn till dusk. Youngsters we spoke to said there's so much going on that it can be 'a bit overwhelming' at first but they quickly learn time management skills. Day pupils must be in school by 8.15am and leave at 6pm, although many stay on later. All look smart – blue jumpers and tartan skirts for girls up to year 11, tweed jackets and ties for boys, sixth form girls in navy. Everyone has to be presentable, we were told. No heavy eyeliner for girls – the look is 'healthy and glowing.'

Pastoral care, well-being and discipline: Parents told us that there's plenty of support via the tutor system. Doctors' surgeries held every weekday and confidential counselling services available on site. Pupils describe the chaplain, known as 'Rev Jack,' as 'really charismatic' and praise him for the way 'he involves everyone.' Midweek chapel for all, plus compulsory service for boarders on Sundays.

Zero tolerance on drugs. If pupils are caught smoking outdoors they get detention and parents are informed. If caught smoking indoors they are suspended. School aims to educate pupils about 'sensible, social drinking under controlled conditions' and sixth formers are allowed to have maximum of two drinks (wine and beer) with food at Saturday evening socials in the sixth form centre. 'It is very closely monitored,' we were told by a group of upper sixths.

Pupils and parents: Most pupils live within a 90-minute drive of the school. A sizeable chunk come from Dorset, Hampshire, Sussex, Surrey and Wiltshire and a smattering from London and further afield. Around three per cent of boarders are international students – from places like Hong

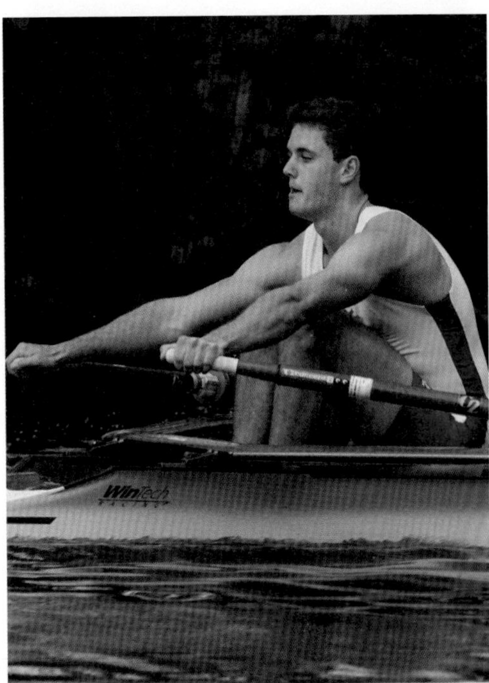

Kong, Poland and Bulgaria. Quite a few sons and daughters of Old Canfordians and lots of siblings and cousins. Day pupils come from all directions. School puts on 50-seater coach from Bournemouth and Poole, plus minibuses from Dorchester, Blandford and Wool to the west and Christchurch, Ringwood and Fordingbridge to the east.

Weekend activities programme includes an assault course, pizza nights and trips to the beach

The pupils we met said personalities of all types thrive at Canford. 'If you are a quiet sort of person the teachers will help you gain confidence,' one girl told us. Those we met were enthusiastic, full of appreciation for the quality of teaching and delightfully unpretentious. Parents (who include lots of medics) praised the place for its academic results, good communication and down-to-earth atmosphere. 'It's not stuffy at all,' one said. Their only criticism was that no building is big enough to hold the whole school for the Remembrance Day service.

Entrance: ISEB common pre-test is the first sift. Pre-assessment in years 6 and 7 (literacy, numeracy and reasoning, plus interview, group activities and prep head's report), with offers made to more than 60 per cent for conditional 13+ places. Registrar says school is looking to identify 'attitude and a have a go mentality as much as raw ability.' If you don't register early, 'the door isn't closed'; a few places usually come up in year 8. CE benchmark is 55 per cent, although vast majority achieve higher. Candidates who haven't attended prep schools take entrance exam in year 8 (this aims to spot academic potential rather than test knowledge). Around 125 places for year 9 cohort (known as Shells), including 30 to 35 scholarships. Pupils come from around 100 prep schools. Large numbers of boarders from Twyford, Port Regis, Highfield, Chafyn Grove, Walhampton, Westbourne House and Forres Sandle Manor. Day pupils often from nearby Castle Court and Dumpton.

Twenty-five to 30 join in the sixth form – assessment test in November the year before plus minimum of 42 points on students' best seven GCSEs (A* equates to eight, A to seven, B to six etc). A grades expected in subjects to be studied at AS level and at least Bs/6s in English and maths. Highly competitive at this stage – around four applicants (slightly more girls than boys) for every place.

Exit: Around 10 to 15 a year leave after GCSE (eight per cent in 2017) – for academic or personal reasons or for a change of scene. After A level, more than 95 per cent to university. Bristol, Cardiff, Durham, Exeter and Manchester perennially popular, with courses ranging from biochemical sciences and medicine to history and business. Four to Oxbridge in 2017, and 12 medics/dentists/vets. Interest in US universities is growing and school has its own international university adviser, with four to the USA in 2017 and others to study medicine in Cork and business in Norway.

Money matters: A range of 13+ and 16+ scholarships, plus means-tested bursaries worth up to 100 per cent of fees.

Remarks: As we said last time, a very special school and one that can easily hold its own with the most popular in the country. With its first-rate teaching, stunning setting and innovative ideas, Canford is definitely at the top of its game.

Chafyn Grove School

Bourne Avenue, Salisbury, Wiltshire SP1 1LR

01722 333423 | office@chafyngrove.co.uk | www.chafyngrove.co.uk

Ages: 3–13 (boarding from 8)

Pupils: 280; Boarders: 59

Day: £6,990 – £16,872 pa; Boarding: + £6,435 pa

Headmaster: Since September 2016, Simon Head, previously headmaster of Moreton Hall School in Suffolk. He held a short service limited commission with the Royal Green Jackets before studying classics at Cambridge, where he also acquired his PGCE. He has taught at Dulwich College Prep and Pembroke House in Kenya, and was then deputy head at St John's Beaumont in Windsor before becoming head of Moreton Hall. He is married to Sarah, also a teacher, and they have two young sons.

Entrance: Children join at all ages and stages and from all over the area. Entry is non-selective. After registration, places are offered two terms before joining and children are invited to spend a day at the school the term before they begin. Scholarships of up to 15 per cent are available in year 6 (academic, sport, music, art and drama). Forces discounts are available (normally 10 per cent day and minimum 15 per cent boarding), and sibling discounts from five to 15 per cent are also offered. Means-tested bursaries typically range between 10 and 40 per cent of the combined tuition and boarding fee.

Exit: Canford, Dauntsey's and Millfield top the list of 'next schools', followed by other relatively local choices, eg Bryanston, Clayesmore, Marlborough and Winchester. Otherwise pupils disperse to a range of schools, eg Charterhouse, Clifton College, Godolphin, Hampshire Collegiate and Monkton Coombe. Sports and all-rounder awards dominate the scholarship lists, but academic awards are on the up with a scattering of art, DT and music scholarships and exhibitions (six scholarships in 2017). Around 10 leave at 11 each year for the Salisbury grammar schools and independents.

Remarks: A 1914 school photograph shows just 17 boys and three members of staff sitting in the grounds of a large Victorian building. Today, that solemn handful of Edwardian scholars would be

very surprised to find nearly 300 pupils at Chafyn Grove, including over 100 girls.

Founded in 1876 as Salisbury School and changed its name in 1916 following an endowment by Lady Chafyn Grove. Although it caters for a wide ability range, there is a work ethic firmly in place. Has taken the unusual step of dropping history, geography and RS from the common entrance syllabus to focus on maths, English, science, French and Latin. This doesn't mean that pupils don't study these subjects, just that teachers can be more flexible in their approach, eg lessons on early history topics such as the Crusades and medieval life and geography lessons on South America. French is taught from year 1, Spanish in years 4 and 5 and Latin from year 6. Latin is strong and some pupils get to near GCSE standard. The odd truly hopeless linguist is allowed to drop languages rather than self-destruct in CE. Maths is set for everyone from year 3, top sets are streamed for all subjects from year 5 and lower sets in the last two years. Scholars aiming for the likes of Eton are educated separately, with extra lessons and lots of practice papers. This is certainly a change from times past, when 'Eton, Winchester and Harrow were not Chafyn's remit.'

Sessions in thinking, presentation, research and current affairs freshen up the timetable. Year 8 also studies business skills, involving Dragon's Den-style pitches and advertising campaigns to create and market a product for sale at the end of the year. Teaching body is very stable, with several married couples and long-standing staff members. 'You only realise how well they're being taught when they get to the next school.' At the time of our visit, there were 42 pupils on the SEN register. Taught by five members of staff in two dedicated rooms, there is a broad sphere of activity which includes study skills, spelling and learning support alongside help for dyslexia, dyspraxia, EAL etc. One-to-one sessions once or twice a week are free and school is honest about which conditions it can support.

Bushcraft weekends for seniors involve building shelters and campfires, as well as catching, gutting and cooking their own fish

School has the strongest sport in Salisbury and its reputation gives the opposition food for thought before walking out against Chafyn Grove. Everyone plays in a team and with so many – up to 20 on match days – school can send its top teams further afield to other seriously sporty schools, eg Sandroyd and Port Regis, whilst B and C teams play elsewhere. All the usual sports on offer; boys and girls can also take part in archery, riding, sailing, cross-country and steeplechase. There is an equestrian and a sailing team, both of which compete successfully. Outdoor swimming pool used in summer. In addition to the regular tally of match wins by all teams throughout the year, all four first hockey teams reached the national final recently, which school promptly won. Lots of individual success in athletics, eg U13 Hurdles National Prep Schools Champion. A team of coaches fosters everyone's talent (not just the superstars) on school's pitches and Astroturf, which spread out behind the school up to (distant) railway embankment at edge of school grounds. There's enough space for a gym, squash and tennis courts. Phone app keeps parents abreast of sports fixtures. 'I try to tone down sport a bit as the children do win a lot – they have to get used to the fact that it isn't all about winning,' said a parent. Saturday school (from year 4) is often taken up with matches.

Art department is roomy and light, with plenty of quality work on display including some excellent papier mâché creations. We noticed a good reference library for art and DT. Drama has long been of a high standard and parents rave about the quality of the annual spring production. 'The singing is always very good in these.' Years 3 and 4 put on their own play in the summer term. In music, we'd award a merit. One third of pupils were learning an instrument at the time of our visit and school teaches up to ABRSM grade VI. Some parents feel this isn't enough, although we feel that given the excellent sport and academics, school does a pretty decent job since many serious musicians are likely to head for the Cathedral School. Singing is very popular and there are three choirs, as well as a school orchestra, training orchestra and jazz band. Large performance hall has good acoustics, a grand piano and an organ. Practice rooms are small but masses of space for storing instruments and music. Instrumental lessons rotate through the timetable and practice sessions are scheduled for boarders.

Lots of trips, including the usual, eg Normandy, London, the theatre and skiing, and the less usual – a visit to a Sikh temple. Activities during the last two periods on Monday and Thursday are intended to 'give children room to breathe' and include gardening, cookery, golf and Mandarin. In a nod to childhoods of yesteryear, year 4s go on annual Pioneer Camp and learn to put up tents, tie knots and stalk. Bushcraft weekends for seniors involve building shelters and campfires, as well as catching, gutting and cooking their own fish. Chafyn Challenges for all age groups range from 'make a paper boat' to 'climb a mountain' to 'be good company at a table' to 'deliver a lamb'.

Boys and girls can also take part in archery, riding, sailing, cross-country and steeplechase. There is an equestrian and a sailing team

Boarding accommodation is comfortable and homely; parents speak very highly of boarding houseparents and matrons. 'They are totally on top of who, where, what and why.' Rooms are shared (6-8 per room) and boarding life is well organised, with shower rotas and different items of clothing collected daily for laundering. Year 8 girls have an ensuite shower room which, though clean, is crying out for new tiles. Boarders' sitting room and green room where children can Skype parents. Mobiles are allowed in free time but must be handed in at night. At the time of our visit, there were 26 full boarders, 20 boarding three nights a week and 40 casual boarders, averaging 40 to 50 per night. One third stay in on weekends and there is a full programme of activities, eg bowling, shopping, cycle rides in the woods and trips to London and the beach.

The original Victorian building is still home for the boarders, but most of the teaching takes place in modern buildings which seem to flow into one another on school's compact site. Children were engaged and interested in academic lessons; traditional classroom seating with everyone facing forwards. 'Children like their teachers and don't want to disappoint them.' However, atmosphere is neither old fashioned nor very strict (no standing for visitors). Our two student guides were polite, confident and very honest in their answers to our questions. 'It's a great school if your child is confident and outgoing and knows who they are,' said a parent.

Pupils feel comfortable about reporting any problems to teachers, who do their best to resolve unkind behaviour. 'They name names and know exactly who is doing what.' Likewise parents feel that they can turn to the staff. 'They are very likeable and approachable and they're always in the playground at pick-up times.' School will summon parents and children and rap heads together if a situation appears to be escalating. There is a seven-point system to discourage bullying and extra mentoring sessions in place for girls in years 5 and 6. Every pupil belongs to an Eight (house) with appealing names – Wasps, Frogs, Birds and Knights. Food is prepared in the school kitchen by the chef and served cafeteria style; meal times are informal and children sit where they like. Lunch was good on the day we visited with plenty of fruit and veg. Day children can arrive at 8am if parents work and stay on for supervised prep until 7pm.

Lovely modern pre-prep with bright, spacious classrooms, own hall and play area. Reception starts small, after which numbers gradually increase. Children in pre-prep can stay until 5:30pm and have their own after-school club and activities including paper craft, football, netball and hockey.

Like most Salisbury schools, there is a mix of local professionals, Forces, business and London commuters. Only a handful from abroad, mostly Spain and a few English with parents working overseas. 'We can't distinguish parents' wealth and professions.' Parents confirm that atmosphere is 'not snooty or overpowering'. A quick snoop along Bourne Avenue at pick-up time confirms that cars are mostly common or garden.

A busy, happy and academically sound school which still retains a friendly, family atmosphere. Will suit confident children who are happy in their own skin. Needless to say, sporty children are in their element here, although parents of the very talented might need to keep small feet firmly planted on the ground. Is, without a doubt, the go-to school for sport in Salisbury.

Cheltenham College

8

Bath Road, Cheltenham, Gloucestershire GL53 7LD

01242 265600 | admissions@cheltenhamcollege.org | www.cheltenhamcollege.org

Ages: 13–18

Pupils: 683; sixth form: 282; Boarders: 553

Day: £26,760 – £27,735 pa; Boarding: £35,700 – £36,675 pa

Linked school: Cheltenham College Preparatory School, 93

Head: From September 2018, Nicola Huggett (40s) MA PGCE (Oxon), currently head of Blundell's School in Devon. Educated at St Gabriel's and Marlborough, she read PPE at Oxford (where she was captain of her college boat club and president of the university riding club) before embarking on a brief career in advertising with J Walter Thompson – brief because she soon realised it was not for her. 'Why did no-one tell me about teaching before?' she says of her experience shadowing a teacher in a comprehensive near her home. Since then her career has taken her via Haileybury, ultimately as head of boarding, during a time when the school went fully co-ed and introduced IB, and Downe House as deputy head, before being made the first female head of Blundell's since its inception in 1604: and, indeed, she will be the first female head at Cheltenham since it was founded in 1841. Clearly a superwoman, she also runs marathons, rides – she has competed in several international three day events – and raises four children. Husband Spencer works for an automotive software development business.

Crispin Dawson, senior deputy head, is holding the reins until September.

Academic matters: In 2017, 58 per cent A*/A at GCSE. IGCSEs are offered in maths, English literature and science and were recently introduced for history and geography. Maths, English, DT, music, history and science results are particularly impressive. At A level in 2017, 55 per cent A*/A grades and 81 per cent A*/B. School has no time for the excuse 'you can't do all things well', and while there are no plans to become more selective or chase league table rankings, there is a strong drive to enrich the academic opportunities for all students via a broader approach to the curriculum and programmes that enable pupils to learn more effectively.

Children don't have to grow up too fast here; they're down-to-earth, polite and confident without being arrogant. 'It's not a London school', one parent said approvingly

Lessons are 35 minutes long and the new two-week timetable is, apparently, much less confusing than its eight-day predecessor. We saw thoughtful group work (boys and girls at separate tables) in Latin and a biology class where all but one were learning to love leaf mould and get to know its inhabitants.

The sixth form has received considerable attention with the introduction of an independent learning project for the lower sixth designed to extend and deepen subject knowledge (offered in addition to the EPQ). The college is also the first UK independent school to run an innovative accredited leadership and life skills course in the sixth form based on Sean Covey's book 'The 7 Habits of Highly Effective Teenagers'. Pupils can choose from 24 A level subjects including textiles, theatre studies, history of art and Latin and Greek. Critical thinking can be taken as an AS.

One of the assurances staff give is that no pupil is allowed to 'slip under the radar'; academic problems are tackled promptly via an 'academic support plan' drawn up with the pupil, parents, housemaster, tutor and subject teachers. The school is also very keen for pupils to learn from each other: disorganised pupils are assigned a buddy to help them on the path to order; older and wiser pupils give talks along the lines of 'Things we wished we'd known ...'

EAL pupils attend an induction programme prior to the start of the academic year and are supported by two EAL specialists. Learning support department caters not only for those with mild dyslexia, dyspraxia, ADHD etc but also ensures the gifted and talented are suitably challenged. The role of this department extends to the whole school, overseeing initiatives to develop the learning potential of all pupils.

Main school library has just been completely revamped, its wonderful tiers of gothic windows pour light onto new shelves and lounging readers. Banished with the old furniture is conversation; a kind of un-modernisation which, according to our guides, has been welcomed by all. Even more enticing than golden silence are the iPads mounted on black metal plinths that pupils can use to search the library catalogue which does not, we are told, extend to Angry Birds.

Games, options, the arts: Dr Edward Wilson the Antarctic explorer was educated here and no fewer than three intrepid members of staff (one of whom is director of activities) have climbed Everest – surely some kind of a record. While the hills and fields of Gloucestershire offer little to challenge explorers or mountaineers, pretty much everything else is available to fortunate Cheltonians. The first ever inter-school rugby match was played on the school's splendid pitch in 1844, overlooked no doubt by the confection of a pavilion that resembles a miniature Brunel railway station. In the summer this perfect pitch, which won the college's groundsman Groundsman of the Year award, plays host to the venerable Cheltenham cricket festival.

County and national triumphs in rugby, hockey, cricket, tennis, rowing and polo; coaching for all abilities is now 'much more professional' and even third and fourth team matches are keenly contested and enthusiastically supported. Rackets (a forerunner of squash) is one of the more arcane sports on offer and the college has won the national championships three times and is consistently in the top four. Golf, swimming, water polo, dance and fitness are part of the exhaustive (and

Hymn singing is such a feature of college life that some upper sixth leavers asked to record themselves in the chapel as a parting memento

exhausting) sports programme as is yoga, a surprising hit with the boys; apparently it is very effective for rugby injuries.

CCF, Young Enterprise and D of E are all enthusiastically tackled, the latter being offered in its less common cycling, horseback and ski-touring options in addition to the usual walking challenge. Service activities take place every Wednesday and volunteers give their time locally at schools and residential homes. Longstanding links with Kenya see college pupils working on projects there, often carrying this on into gap years.

Art, music and modern language teaching takes place in the rather grand neo-classical surroundings of Thirlestaine House, a former gentleman's residence. Its original features – huge mirrors, chandeliers, ornate cornices and radiator covers – have survived generations of school children (just) and create a suitably bohemian home for the creative chaos of art and pottery studios. The long gallery is venue for exhibitions, lectures and public events. Two students have gained places at RADA for costume design and backstage training courtesy of the outstanding DT department while another gained a place for acting.

Nearly half of pupils learn a musical instrument, a lower uptake than comparable schools but the figure is increasing. Chapel and chamber choirs plus orchestras, bands and ensembles must keep that 40 per cent pretty busy. Performing arts centre complete with dance studio, green room and, less predictably, a plaster frieze of the Parthenon uncovered during refurbishment. School and house plays and reviews are hugely popular, everyone is encouraged to get involved either performing or backstage.

The college also plays its part in Cheltenham's cultural life, participating in the annual festival fest. The combined choirs of the college and Dean Close opened a recent music festival. Harmony with nearby Dean Close and the Ladies' College is described as 'cooperative' with pragmatic sharing of visiting speakers, careers events and collaboration between international students' societies. Pupils are more forthright, acknowledging and enjoying the rivalry.

Boarding: Houses are in residential roads just outside the campus perimeter – separating 'home' and school is considered very important: the staff encourage pupils to adopt a professional attitude to school, 'it's a place of work', whereas houses are a home from home, informal and a place for relaxation. Parents are encouraged to join in with weekend or social events and are pretty much in agreement with Ofsted's conclusion that boarding provision at the college is 'outstanding.'

In addition to a matron, each house has a resident tutor who hosts academic 'clinics' outside school hours. Christowe, one of the original Victorian boys' boarding houses, has been beautifully decorated by the current housemaster and his wife (an interior designer) and there's not a whiff of the institutional in the first floor family rooms. As with all the boys' houses, 60 or so boys live here, sharing for the younger and single rooms for sixth formers. The common room and library are full of house memorabilia (house names a constant in the college); fascinating archive photos and a mini museum all foster a sense of continuity and house identity. Wonderful cushions decorated with the piratical house insignia of skull and crossbones were a gift from a parent. Clubby red-painted snooker and games room much admired. Ashmead, one of the girls' houses, was built round a garden quad with secure key pad entry system, lovely light bedrooms and civilised socialising areas. Boys are allowed to visit for film evenings and the like – apparently rom-coms are rather favoured. The housemistress heads off cliques by splitting up prep school groups and changing room-mates each year. All residents meet twice a day – a practical

system that also enables staff to observe shifting dynamics. House staff and prefects alert to meal skipping and similar warning signs when 'faddy could tip into eating disorder.'

Background and atmosphere: Beautiful mellow Victorian gothic buildings along Cheltenham's busy Bath Road, having undergone a major re-vamp – grade 1 listed status an expensive headache but good news for Gloucestershire's stonemasons and other master craftspeople. It's easy to see why visiting Americans (NATO base nearby) get a touch of the vapours; it's every inch the English public school. Public areas certainly getting the five star treatment though classrooms remain workaday and well used (all have requisite IT and smart boards). Stonework not the only area revamped: newish additions are a duo of deputies, one pastoral, one academic, a director of learning, a new head of sixth form and 30 new members of teaching staff. Numbers, like results, are rising and a modest increase in places (about 40) is planned, as is another girls' boarding house. Students and parents tell us that much has changed for the better, not change's sake. Singled out for mention were improved home school communication and relations between teachers and pupils. Interestingly, members of staff said that they thought this had always been one of the strengths of the college but our sixth form guides were very certain that things were different and teachers were 'much more involved and friendly'. The staff we met

First ever inter-school rugby match was played on school's splendid pitch in 1844. Pavilion resembles a miniature Brunel railway station

lived up to their billing and were indeed friendly, funny, charmingly young fogeyish in a few cases, and clearly enjoying both the teaching and strong sense of community at the college.

Pastoral care, well-being and discipline: Pupils start each day in the glorious chapel, no doubt energised for study by the famously enthusiastic hymn singing. This is such a feature of college life that a recent group of upper sixth leavers asked if they could record themselves in the chapel singing favourite hymns as a parting memento. The house system is everything here, for boarders and day pupils alike; each is a community within a community and fiercely competitive. Every house has its own character and distinguishing traditions such as prefect blazers and boaters (worn with pride apparently).

Houseparents first in line for problems whether academic or social, and liaise very closely with teaching staff to ensure 'joined up' care. Older pupils train for peer mentoring responsibilities and can often pick up on wobbles before they become serious. Mobile phones (aka 'the biggest headache') only allowed in houses and, along with laptops, must be handed in before bed. If a houseparent overhears parents being berated or harangued – not uncommon in a school population that is totally teenage – they will challenge (hooray!). The writing of proper thank you letters (to former prep schools, weekend hosts and the like) is another courtesy expected of pupils. While most pupils come from similar backgrounds, staff are alert to potentially insensitive displays of conspicuous consumerism – affording one the unexpected chance to ask a parent to 'take back the mink'.

Some pupils disgruntled about tightening up on trips into Cheltenham town centre – now only Sundays unless there's a legitimate need. School has responded to parents' view that since it offers so many activities, 'hanging around in town' need not be a supplementary option. Bath Road still in bounds for banks, supermarkets and cafés, not that the last should be necessary – food is plentiful with lots of choice: salad bar, curries, carvery and good puds served in the former chapel and 'legendary' bacon rolls and snacks dispensed by the very friendly ladies in the tuck shop. This is a town school and necessarily takes firm line on drugs, drink and similar misdemeanours. Sixth form privileges are realistic – at 17 pupils can go out for a meal at an 'approved' restaurant; at 18 they may visit a similarly endorsed pub. The sixth form social room in the main school has a café/bar; 'we have to prepare them for life beyond school', one housemaster told us.

Pupils and parents: Good mix of first time buyers, second generation Cheltonians, Forces and international. Around 18 per cent from outside UK – 30 countries represented. Not snobby or excessively label conscious. Many boarders are from local area or within a few hours of Cheltenham. Children don't have to grow up too fast here; they're down-to-earth, polite and confident without being arrogant. 'It's not a London school', one parent said approvingly. Uniform of navy and cerise plus usual complexity of ties generally adhered to, all pupils wear own choice of pastel shirts; boys' individuality expressed mainly via hair.

OCs include Rageh Omar, journalist; Tim Bevan, film producer; General Sir Michael Rose; Nigel and Jack Davenport, actors; James Whitaker, royal correspondent; James Stout, world rackets champion; Sir Alan Haselhurst MP, The Right Hon Lord Anthony Colwyn CB and the Norfolk coroner, William Morris. Several events marked the centenary of Dr Edward Wilson who died with Scott in the Antarctic in 1912.

Entrance: Increasingly competitive. Most via common entrance, 40 per cent from own prep school, others from plethora of localish preps including Beaudesert Park, Abberley Hall, Pinewood, St Hugh's, Hatherop Castle, The Dragon, Bilton Grange, Moor Park and St John's on the Hill. Entrants from state schools take exam (papers in English, maths and, where appropriate, French); sixth form candidates require at least five B/6 grades at GCSE and must sit papers in subjects to be studied.

Exit: Around 10 per cent leaves after GCSEs. Almost all sixth formers to higher education. Handful to Oxbridge (six in 2017, plus six medics and two vets), most to top universities, huge range with Bristol, Exeter, Cardiff Bath, Durham and Edinburgh amongst those currently favoured. Some to overseas universities, including Madrid, Berlin, San Francisco Art Institute, University of California, Berkeley. Most popular subject choices: biological sciences, psychology, economics and management, history, engineering.

Money matters: Scholarships (up to 25 per cent) and exhibitions (10 per cent) offered at 13+ and 16+ in academic, art, DT (13+ only), drama, music and sport. All-round award may be made at college's discretion. Additional means-tested bursaries also available.

Remarks: Radical modernisation does not always fit easily with old traditions, whether architecturally or educationally, but Cheltenham College has emerged refreshed and ready for a new era. This school is a happy, spirited community inspiring real affection and loyalty in its members.

Cheltenham College Preparatory School

9

Thirlestaine Road, Cheltenham GL53 7AB

01242 522697 | theprep@cheltenhamcollege.org | www.cheltenhamcollege.org

Ages: 3–13

Pupils: 372; **Boarders:** 39

Day: £7,920 – £17,775 pa; Boarding: £17,700 – £23,085 pa

Linked school: Cheltenham College, 89

Headmaster: Since 2013, Jonathan Whybrow BEd (50s). Educated at St Paul's School and 'loved every minute.' Joined the Royal Marines and then studied for a BEd in physical education and geography at Exeter. Much of his early career was spent at schools in or near London including Latymer Upper, Emanuel School, Devonshire House Prep (where he was deputy head). Previous headships at City of London Freemen's School, Ashtead and then Beachborough School, Northamptonshire. Married with two daughters, one at the school.

The headship of Cheltenham College Prep has been through a rather uneasy time but, cross everything, Mr W is a keeper. He set his sights on the school as early as 1999 when he attended a conference here and 'fell in love.' He says that he knew there and then that he 'wanted to be part of one of England's great schools.' The stars didn't align in his and the school's favour until 2013, but does he ever mean business. His mantra comes courtesy of the Royal Marines: Don't be late; don't ask your troops to do what you wouldn't do yourself; concurrent activity (aka multitasking).

Parents we spoke to were very, very happy. Several were in awe not only of his energy but also his mysterious capacity to be all places at once. 'He's everywhere,' said one, 'and he sorts things out straight away. We're so lucky.' Pupils equally impressed, 'He knew everybody's names by the end of the first week,' we were told.

When he's not being omnipresent at school Mr W enjoys golf, skiing, supporting West Ham and holidays in his house in France. He proudly showed us the 'burnt orange' 1977 MG tucked away in a garage – a recent acquisition and one he hadn't quite got round to telling his family about. (He has now.)

Retiring in July 2018. His successor will be Tom O'Sullivan, currently head of Old Buckenham Hall. Educated at Pate's Grammar School in Cheltenham and Durham University where he read law; people always said that he would become a teacher but, for a while, he resisted, spending an extra year at Durham as JCR president before deciding that a career spent in a quest for silk was not for him. Work began in a variety of roles: as a graduate trainee for WH Smith, for a recruitment firm in Singapore, and in drug education for a pharmaceutical company. He then followed his destiny, taking a PGCE, specialising in science, at Homerton College, Cambridge. Here he discovered in the first 10 seconds of his first lesson that 'the buzz from teaching' was better than anything he had previously experienced in his working life. Appointments at Beaudesert Park and a deputy headship at Mowden Hall followed, before he assumed command of Old Buckenham Hall.

Small classes, subject specialist teaching and plenty of individual attention enable pupils to progress at their own rate

Entrance: Taster day for entrance to nursery and up to year 3. For years 4-6 it's a taster day and entry assessments in maths, English and non-verbal reasoning. More choosy later on to ensure pupils are up to CE at 13. Discount available for third and subsequent siblings. Generous discounts for Forces families; means-tested bursaries available. A further 20 or so children arrive at 11+ and at this age scholarships of up to 30 per cent of fees in a variety of areas may be awarded. These are valid throughout Cheltenham College.

Exit: 'Four or five' leave at age 11 for local grammars or girls' schools. Majority stay on until 13 and then move over the road to senior school. Those who don't stay go on to (recently) Eton, Harrow, Marlborough, Radley, Wellington and Cheltenham Ladies'.

Remarks: School has been on present site – friendly jumble of Edwardian red-brick and newer additions in extensive grounds just across the road from senior school – since 1908. It was founded in 1863 as the College Juvenile Department and spent a couple of years squashed into a corner of the big school. Parents might be interested to learn that boarding fees in 1865 were 50 guineas (£52.50) a year and it was an extra £1 for a seat in the chapel. Smart rebranding has seen the name change from Cheltenham College Junior School to Preparatory School, with typography emphasising the Preparatory School part of the name. 'It's about trust,' says Mr Whybrow; 'parents must be confident that we will do the same job as a stand-alone prep. If Cheltenham College is not the right senior school for your child then we'll say so.' Understandably, he would prefer pupils to remain until age 13, but the local education market is a competitive one and realpolitik extends to what Mr W calls 'help' for children applying to grammar schools. He's not quite so generous when it comes to the occasional cheeky bit of poaching by a certain nearby girls' school, crisply describing his relationship with The Cheltenham Ladies' College as 'businesslike'.

This has always been a popular prep but parents' loyalty has been tested in recent times by the drift that inevitably results from a rapid turnover of leadership. It's not often that we hear a pupil describe their headmaster as 'the best we've had.' Mr Whybrow is candid about the effect that time of 'uncertainty' had on the morale of pupils, parents and staff. Bringing with him a wealth of experience from leading stand-alone and linked preps, he implemented some changes straight away that were visible on the first day of term – new signage, a general freshening up – small things that make a big difference. In consultation with parents he has reinstated French classes for the youngest children, brought back 'proper' prize-giving (we saw the new trophies in his study), revived the very popular school musical which had 'got lost' and appointed a director of co-curricular activities to beef up this aspect of provision.

High-ceilinged classrooms, old wooden desks and iPads – teaching and learning at Cheltenham College Prep is a creative mix of the best of traditional methods and the latest technology. Small classes, subject specialist teaching and plenty of individual attention enable pupils to progress at their own rate – something parents really appreciate. 'The teachers are very encouraging, it's made such a difference to my child's confidence' and, 'they make time to follow a child's interest in a subject and take teaching beyond the curriculum.'

Pupils learn French as soon as they start in the Kingfishers and between years 6 and 8 pupils can opt for French or Spanish. Most are expected to

take Latin – the class we saw looked like so much fun we wanted to stay and decline a verb or two – and there's also the option of 'off timetable' Greek. There are currently lessons on a Saturday morning but Mr W says that this is 'under discussion.'

Learning support has its cheerful offices in the Coach House; there are two full-time members of staff plus a team of part-time assistants. All children are screened and extra support is mostly given in small groups or parent funded one-to-one sessions. EAL is also based here; Cheltenham may not strike the observer as excessively multicultural but the headquarters of ARRC (NATO Allied Rapid Reaction Corps) is close by.

Today's parents might be interested to learn that boarding fees in 1865 were 50 guineas (£52.50) a year and you could pay an extra £1 for a seat in the chapel

Pre-prep, known as Kingfishers, occupies low-rise chalet, not an architectural gem but more than compensated for by the fresh air facilities, including forest school. Information boards outside let parents know what their children have been doing each day – great for conversations on the way home. During our visit Mr W reduced a class of 3-year-olds, their elegant ballet mistress and this reviewer to hysterical laughter by his attempts at 'naughty toes' and 'good toes'. We're sure he wouldn't mind us observing that he is not built for the ballet.

Whether it's sport, music or drama, 'inclusion' is the starting point – there are teams from A to E and bands and choirs 'for all'. Every child has the opportunity to play in a competitive sports team from year 3. Lively house competitions – not just the usual sport but creative stuff too such as poetry, photography and music. Plenty of matches; pupils claimed that the win/lose rate with nearest rivals is pretty even. National winners in schools' rugby recently; finalists in national comps for hockey, netball and also skiing.

Teaching and learning here is a creative mix of the best of traditional methods and the latest technology

Everyone is enjoying the extended range of after-school clubs – 30 or so options including polo, equestrian, archery, chess, street dance and the enticingly named 'Grow your own money.' In addition to termly calendars the school now produces a what's on of events for the whole year – much appreciated by busy parents – with dates for everything from school photos to 'try boarding' nights and theatre visits.

As we walked through the grounds in golden autumnal sunshine, Mr W (who in another life would be a farmer) stops at a muddy pen to scratch the backs of the Gloucester Old Spots, two of which would be attending bonfire night in sausage form. He's keen to extend the forest school provision to include more animals: lambs are next and also chickens who will take up residence on an island in the lake – we hope Gloucestershire foxes can't swim.

Improvements to the school's rather convoluted layout are next on Mr W's to do list – he wants to consolidate teaching into departments. A consequence of this has been a sad farewell to the atmospheric DT room with its parquet floor, wooden cupboards and historic sawdust from thousands of bird boxes – the new DT block opened in 2016. Outside in the corridor are glass cases displaying beautiful model boats made by a former teacher (they used to be sailed on the lake) and a drop-down model railway track. Art room similarly characterful but will be spared the same fate, not being located in the path of progress. The music department has a rather grand home, Lake House, with baronial fire places and wood-panelled walls. Nearly all pupils learn at least one instrument and there are plenty of opportunities to play or sing – whether it's chapel choir, jazz band, guitar group or, as on our visit, to compose and perform at a polyphone (surprisingly tuneful blue plastic tubes) workshop.

Mr W is a great believer in what he calls 'prep school world', in other words junior pupils should be self-sufficient when it comes to facilities. Fortunately this prep occupies a large site and any sharing is by choice rather than necessity. A new science block, full size rugby pitches, Astros and a sports hall that's about to get a £7m makeover are all at the disposal of the juniors.

One parent told us that 'children are encouraged to express their own opinions,' so we put this to the test and asked a few what they thought about their school. 'There are loads of new activities', 'We have a proper roast on Sunday, everyone sits down and is served at the table.' 'Mr Whybrow is amazing.' Yes, yes, but how about some constructive criticism? 'I wish they hadn't stopped us playing football in the car park. There's not enough time at lunch to change into a tracksuit and go out on to the field.'

One central boarding house on two floors (girls below, boys above, shared common room) and dorms divided into rather charming old style curtained cubicles with notice boards and cabin beds – those we saw were not over tidy, just comfortable, with soft toys, photos and the ubiquitous bunting. All freshly painted and carpeted, new bathrooms too. Lots of staff on hand – house parents, a matron and five gappies. After activities in the evening there's 'properly supervised' prep – overseen by the head or deputy head. School is aware that even very young children are under increased pressure these days and the head and teachers are vigilant to ensure that pupils keep things in perspective. 'School can be pretty full on, we need to be sure there's a good balance', says Mr W.

Music department has a rather grand home, Lake House, with baronial fire places and wood-panelled walls. Nearly all pupils learn at least one instrument

Boarding reasonably flexible but school can no longer accommodate 'drop of the hat' requests, especially at the end of the week. At around £35 a night we're not surprised it's so popular – the majority of prep parents are both working (medics, GCHQ, Forces, not so many farming families these days) and this certainly helps.

A few unsteady years would dent the confidence of any school so it's testament to staff and parents' faith in Cheltenham Prep that they've come out of the experience bigger, brighter and bolder. It's heartening to see this historic school under dynamic leadership facing the future with energy and optimism.

Cheltenham Ladies' College

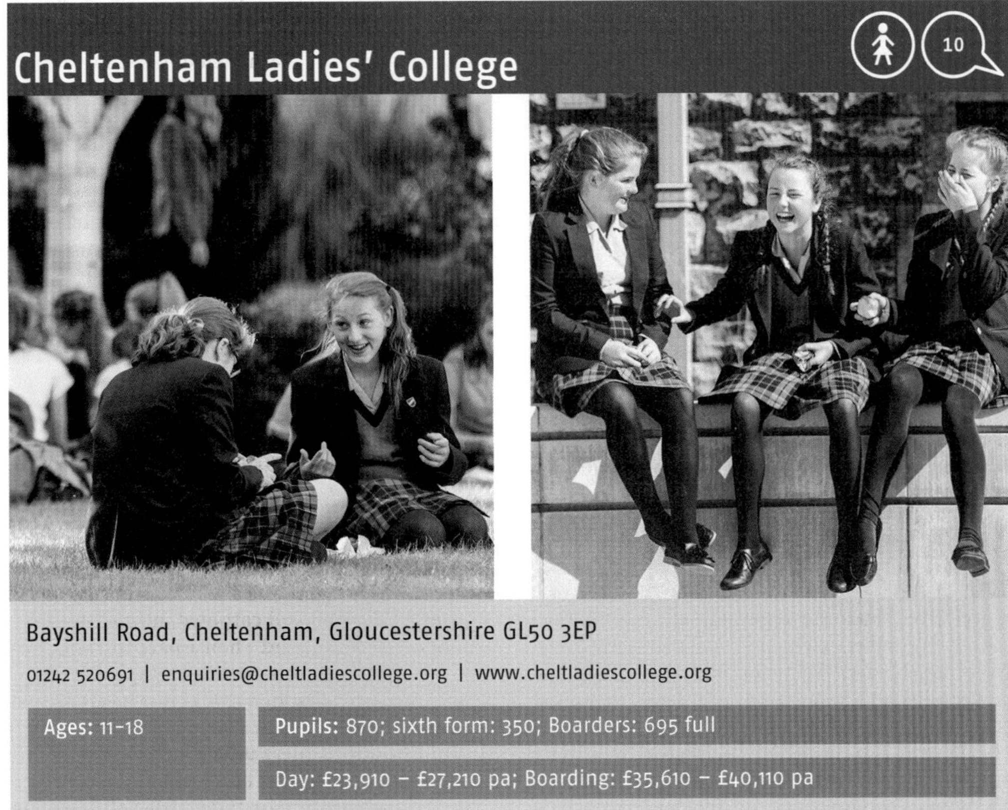

Bayshill Road, Cheltenham, Gloucestershire GL50 3EP

01242 520691 | enquiries@cheltladiescollege.org | www.cheltladiescollege.org

Ages: 11-18

Pupils: 870; sixth form: 350; Boarders: 695 full

Day: £23,910 – £27,210 pa; Boarding: £35,610 – £40,110 pa

Principal: Since 2011, Eve Jardine-Young MA (40s). Educated in Malawi, won a sixth form scholarship to the school she now leads, a place she credits with 'changing her life profoundly.' After graduating in engineering from Cambridge she worked for Ove Arup (structural engineers) before moving into teaching. Taught economics at Radley, moved to Epsom College where she was housemistress and head of sixth form, thence to Blundell's as director of studies. Married, her husband also works in education. Hobbies include reading, music (she is, apparently, rather a good pianist) and gardening.

Her appointment surprised some, but the CLC Council has a record of selecting left field candidates although they've only had to choose 11 since the school was founded in 1853. Ms Jardine-Young described the protracted recruitment process as: 'Extraordinary, the Council is very involved and take their responsibility extremely seriously.' Ms Jardine-Young lives up to her name and looks scarcely old enough for such a heavy mantle. When first asked if she felt the weight of history on her shoulders she said she saw her responsibility as 'stewardship, not of buildings but of tradition and future potential.'

So far Ms Jardine-Young has kept her head down and only turned up in the press a few times, including hitting the headlines for suggesting schools need to tackle mental health issues head on and that wellbeing should be put on an equal footing with academic achievement. She is, however, a keen blogger for the Huffington Post UK, taking on subjects such as whether single-sex or co-education offer the best preparation for 'real life' and girls' participation in sport and engineering, two areas of the curriculum that have been reformed during her headship. The words most often used by parents and girls to describe the principal are 'friendly,' 'approachable' and 'sincere,' and indeed she is; talkative she may be but she is not a loose cannon, so we wondered why a marketing person sat in on our interview. Apparently it was for 'training purposes.'

Ms Jardine-Young is her own woman and, in the best possible way, has not developed a headish persona. She isn't fixed, she likes exploring ideas and thinking aloud, but don't be fooled, she brings a formidable intellect to her alma mater. Nostalgic talk of a Proustian flashback courtesy of the smell of varnish is followed by discussion of the school's institutional 'meta language'...'while we rightly praise girls who achieve, do we give enough thought to what it means to be a winner? Do we articulate other values frequently enough?' She brims with excitement and vigour and her commitment to and passion for the school shine through.

Academic matters: League tables may come and go but CLC's academic record remains mostly mighty. In 2017, 90 per cent A*-A/9-7 at GCSE. At A level 55 per cent of passes were at A* or A, 83 per cent A*-B. Sciences, maths, economics, history and English by far the most favoured subjects but there are plenty of options and small numbers take Japanese, physical education, theatre studies, classical Greek and history of art. IB was introduced in 2008 and results are extremely strong: points average of nearly 40 (out of 45) in 2017. Regular national achievements and awards for science, maths and the arts and now also engineering, thanks to new engineering, enterprise and technology department. It must be said that, as in similar schools, pupils from the Far East raise the bar considerably in subjects such as maths and music. We have also heard from several sources that for some a popular summer holiday activity is subject extension classes in Hong Kong. The principal says, 'We're not producing clones, the model of exam grades at any cost leads to mental brittleness.' Try telling that to the tiger mothers.

The year 7 music lesson we observed was pretty serious, girls working at a high level, keen to answer questions, otherwise quiet and diligent. IB French – a debate on the uses of philosophy – was a bit livelier. The science labs looked like those in a university, girls in white coats utterly engrossed in their experiments. Parents tell us that while the prevailing mood is indeed serious there are 'inspirational' teachers and the girls enjoy their lessons. Average class size is 16 (seven in the sixth form), progress is monitored closely and girls move up or down through sets as necessary. The brightest may take one or two subjects early but most do 10 or so GCSEs at the normal time and in their stride. Parents impressed by proactive way in which teachers identify any problems and put solutions (extra lessons etc) in place swiftly. Pupils must learn to manage their time from day one – not only do they have to get to and from house to school promptly but they also have free periods for music lessons/practice and homework.

Small numbers with EAL or SpLD, mainly dyslexia. Specialist support for girls who need help with study skills, literacy and mathematics, but clearly CLC is not the place for those with significant problems and the school is frank about this. Most areas of school fully accessible by wheelchair but distance of houses could preclude all but a day pupil in these circumstances.

Games, options, the arts: Full programme of music and drama – size of school means there are opportunities for all who wish to perform; impressive results in LAMDA and music exams. Up to 50 music scholars must delight the ears at concerts and lunchtime recitals. College's jewel in the crown is its arts centre, the Parabola (it's in Parabola Road). Just across from main school, it has a 300-seat theatre, dance rehearsal rooms and small gallery primarily for school use but also hosts public shows and exhibitions. Cheltenham's many festivals also provide plenty of opportunities for cultural enrichment and school is 'strategic sponsor' for four: literature, music, science and jazz.

The sixth form house we visited was originally the indefatigable Miss Beale's teacher training college, it's intended to be a 'halfway house to university'

Impressive plate glass and metal arts building, school often has artists and writers in residence too, most but not all, women. Super art dept (school produced designers Katharine Hamnett and Amanda Wakeley) and a cornucopia of extracurricular options as one would expect, but school is explicit in warning girls that academics must come first. Strong tradition of charitable volunteering and fundraising – each year pupils nominate and then vote on which four charities to support, these are in addition to St Hilda's East, the charity established in 1889 by the 'Guild' (alumnae association, now 10,000 strong) in London's East End. 'Of what,' we asked naively, 'is Hilda patron saint?' Answer came there none but a few red faces and a Google later we discovered that she is saint in charge of learning. Old girls who work at City law firms also do pro bono work for the charity. We doubt Miss Beale would recognise today's East Enders but the area served by the charity is still very deprived and there remains much for the Cheltenham Ladies to do. Closer to home there is a well established community links programme and girls from year 11 upwards are to be found all over the locality helping out at homeless shelters, animal sanctuaries, primary schools and retirement homes.

Sports acreage and facilities (partly open to public) are pretty good and about to get even better when the brand new health and fitness centre opens. This will enable sports such as hockey, tennis and lacrosse to be played all year round. Notable individual achievements in athletics, tennis, skiing, riding, netball; team sport triumphs more frequently at county level although recently CLC has got through to national finals in hockey, cross country, swimming and riding. Most agree that sport not in premier league with few opportunities for the C,D,E team players to turn out (given size of school there must be a fair number of these). Physical activity compulsory all the way through with zumba and pilates for the less sporty, but the sixth formers we saw were hardly rushing to the gymnasium. On the other hand we hear of considerable efforts made to find something for the keen but not so able to participate in. The school is most successful at national level in hockey, netball and equestrian sports, with a girl in the GB under 16 team and talented riders competing internationally. Not sure the school can take direct credit for this – Gloucestershire with its links to the European riding scene may have been a deciding factor. No stabling at the school but girls may keep their mounts at a stables nearby. Polo is played at Birdlip.

Boarding: Younger girls' dorms spacious and very jolly with home duvets, under-bed storage and lots of photos and personalisation. At the foot of every bed was a brightly coloured tuck box. Single rooms for older girls are small but characterful, many with inspiring views. A place in one of the old-fashioned 'cubs,' dorms where beds have a curtain around them, highly coveted.

Parents full of praise for pastoral care whether for boarders or day girls – house mistresses in particular singled out for responding to email/telephone calls by return. Incidents – friendship issues or bullying – nipped in bud equally promptly, we hear. Girls bring their own laptops but internet use is heavily monitored. Boarders may use social networking sites from year 9 up out of school hours. The sixth form house we visited was originally the indefatigable Miss Beale's teacher training college. With its elegant library (plus wireless of course), it is intended to be a 'halfway house to university.' Girls may come and go with more freedom but the academic tutors and house mistresses liaise to minimise girls pushing themselves too hard and staff on each floor listen out for late night working.

Background and atmosphere: Miss Dorothea Beale led the school (including a nursery and a teacher training college) from 1858. She was a suffragette who pioneered women's education at a time when biology had to be code-named 'human geography' to stop irate fathers taking their girls home, because to learn about such things would make them unmarriageable. Not content with revolutionising women's school education, the astonishing Miss Beale also founded St Hilda's College, Oxford. What would she make of today's Cheltenham Ladies as they sweep all before them, outperforming most boys and becoming leaders in their chosen careers? Ms Jardine-Young says that the college has become 'more open, less introspective,' since she was a pupil there. Her aim is to take that forward and enable girls to 'become more adventurous learners, prepared to succeed but resilient enough to cope with failure.'

Parents tell us that while the prevailing mood is indeed serious there are 'inspirational' teachers and the girls enjoy their lessons

The main entrance to the college is on one of Cheltenham's wide boulevards. If it weren't for girls in PE kit massing on the steps it could be mistaken for a corporate HQ and, with 800+ pupils and over 600 employees, in one sense that's what it is. Behind lies a glorious quad, three parts Victorian gothic creeper-clad grandeur, one part grim 1970s concrete modernism. Miss Beale wanted her girls to learn in surroundings as beautiful as those boys had been favoured with for hundreds of years. The original fabric of the college, with its wonderful chequerboard marble corridor, grand library, mullion windows and arts and crafts frescoes, was thus as much a political statement as a seat of learning. The teaching rooms we saw were in the main functional and surprisingly anonymous. You couldn't tell you were at such a legendary school unless you happened to be daydreaming and looked out of the window (and we're sure that never happens).

On the day of our visit there had been something of a non-story in the national press about 'draconian guidelines' issued to ensure that 'mufti' (or home clothes) were sufficiently modest. Parents say they resented the tone of the letter rather than its content (some outraged by both). Uniform is

pretty dreary though – the most enthusiasm we could elicit from parents was that 'it does the job.' The good people of Cheltenham may have nicknamed the girls 'greenflies' but something a little less evolved, 'algae', perhaps, would more precisely describe the shade of the green skirts and jumpers. Sixth formers may wear navy pin-stripe trousers although to this reviewer the effect of these with regulation shirt and jumper is a curious half-bank worker, half-schoolgirl centaur. But away with such frivolous concerns; we feel the disapproving shade of Miss Beale urging us to look at the bigger picture. She's right, of course.

Pastoral care, well-being and discipline: This is a big school and the house system works well by breaking it down into manageable units – roughly 60 girls per house. In 2015, CLC introduced a whole-school wellbeing programme, complete with sessions in healthy lifestyles, coping with stress, study skills, self-defence and mindfulness. School meets every day in the Princess Hall for prayers, notices etc. Houses, most substantial and Victorian, but pleasingly not too unsympathetically subdivided, are scattered in nearby leafy residential roads and strings of Ladies' College girls walking to and fro are one of Cheltenham's perennial sights. Some houses are quite a hike away, conveniently making sensible footwear a must. Fair bit of road crossing necessary and this concerns new parents as girls travel in unaccompanied groups. Girls eat all meals in their house, a buffet lunch is available

Dorothea Beale was a suffragette who pioneered women's education at a time when biology had to be code-named 'human geography'

in the main school for those taking exams or with commitments that use up travelling time. Each house has its own chefs but meals are planned centrally – economies of scale no doubt, also cuts down on lunch envy – girls get to choose favourite menus. Eating environment and food seemed pleasant enough in the houses we visited. A significant boarding refurbishment is underway and to enable this a new junior boarding house has been built into which each house will 'decant' in turn.

Pupils and parents: So sorry to undermine a popular cliché but we encountered no braying Henriettas or snooty aristos, just normal girls – friendly, unaffected and full of fun. Our year 9 lunch companions were sweetly excited about how much they 'loved going to Waitrose' (store has wisely established itself as the nearest supermarket) and triumphant that they had persuaded the local ice cream van to call at their house. Some observe (as did we) that nationalities tend to stick together both in and out of lessons – inevitable perhaps – and a look at the results lists in the excellent school magazine tells its own, by now familiar, story of the formidable Chinese work ethic.

We hear whispers on the GSG grapevine that the school is not quite as fashionable with metropolitan parents as once it was, but London is still the home city of boarding majority. In the main, parents are the usual spectrum of by no means rich professionals who choose the college because of the opportunities it offers their bright daughters. Several mentioned that they valued the school's relative conservatism and high expectations in a world of declining standards. All said that the pace is fast; too fast for a few.

Entrance: Entrance exam at 11+ (English, maths, VR). 'Please don't coach,' the school begs parents. 'We can spot the child who has been coached.' We imagine most parents have their hands over their ears and are singing loudly. At 13+ exams in maths, English, science, VR and French (if previously studied). For entry to the sixth form girls must sit exams in the subjects they wish to study.

So what exactly, we quizzed the head of admissions, does CLC look for? All girls take the same exam, thus candidates from outside the UK must have a very high standard of English. Every admission is considered on an individual basis; a girl's extracurricular interests are an important factor. The message from parents is, if you think it will suit your daughter, have a go. One told us, 'my daughter wasn't top in her prep school but she got a place and is loving it.' CLC wants girls who 'accept that they are joining a community.' Families are strongly encouraged to visit several times so that they know 'what they are getting.' Indeed families are under nearly as much scrutiny as girls themselves. Great importance is attached to what the school calls 'generosity of spirit' – interpret that as you wish. Roughly 25 per cent from outside the UK (expats as well as foreign nationals), many from the Far East, and the IB programme attracts strong candidates from Europe. The 200 day girls keep school's Gloucestershire roots strong.

Exit: A few leave post-GCSE but most stay on and benefit hugely from the higher education and careers advice provided by the school's Professional Guidance Centre. Support includes subject mentors to aid with further reading and personal statements, interview training and the opportunity to talk with Guild members about university and career choices.

In 2017, 16 Oxbridge places and eight medics. Rest to top universities at home (eg Edinburgh, Durham, UCL, Bristol, St Andrews) or abroad. US increasingly popular with offers in 2017 from eg Harvard, Dartmouth and UCLA, and others off to Hong Kong, Queensland and The Hague. Careers of old girls give a flavour of what Cheltenham ladies do next: heaps of lawyers, MPs, medics and scientists. They include Nicola Horlick (financier), Cheryl Gillan (Conservative MP), Rachel Lomax (first woman deputy governor of the Bank of England), Dame Mary Archer (scientist), Lisa Jardine (historian), Rosie Boycott (journalist) and Amber Rudd (Home Secretary).

Money matters: Plenty of 'merit based awards' and scholarships for eg academics, art, sport and music. 'Limited amount' of funding for means-tested bursaries and some help for families of current pupils in financial difficulties. Bursaries intended to widen access to college are 'carefully awarded' to girls who would benefit from a college education. Principal very keen to extend opportunities in this area.

Remarks: A top flight school with strong traditional values and a clear sense of purpose. For the bright and energetic all rounder this school offers an exceptional education that is both broad and deep, with endless opportunities for fun and enrichment along the way.

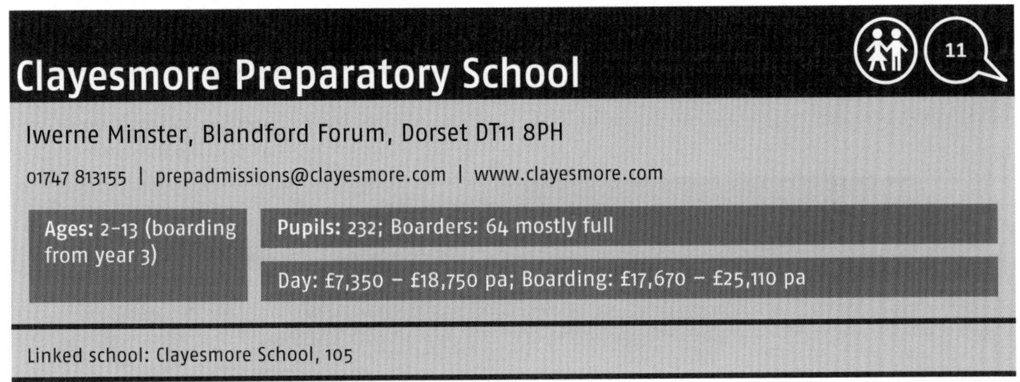

Clayesmore Preparatory School

Iwerne Minster, Blandford Forum, Dorset DT11 8PH

01747 813155 | prepadmissions@clayesmore.com | www.clayesmore.com

Ages: 2–13 (boarding from year 3)

Pupils: 232; Boarders: 64 mostly full

Day: £7,350 – £18,750 pa; Boarding: £17,670 – £25,110 pa

Linked school: Clayesmore School, 105

Head: Since 2014, Will Dunlop (40s). Previously at Kingston Grammar School after 10 years in the army. Enjoyed teaching map reading to other CCF recruits at school, interest in education consolidated as an army trainer with realisation that so many school leavers – particularly with undiagnosed learning needs – were being failed by the system.

Move into teaching in 2006 was 'a big step into the dark – had to put papers in before I had a job to go to,' though serendipity helped. Was on night duty when TES fell open at ideal job – CCF contingent commander and 'any subject' teacher at Kingston Grammar School – deadline 9am the following morning. Hit the fax machine with minutes to spare and got the job. Became a year 7 form tutor then, two years on, head of prep form and year 7, won over by curiosity and creativity of younger pupils along the way.

A former pupil here (features with brown mop and corduroy shorts in 1980s school photograph), was bowled over when returned as prospective parent – strength with SEN the clincher, even before saw job ad.

Noted for enthusiasm. 'Gets really excited,' reckoned a parent. 'You get this impression that he's the most amazing teacher first and foremost.' 'Mr Dunlop has tons of energy and made our time there very enjoyable, knows everybody,' said senior pupil, rather more primly. Thoughtful and erudite (peppers conversation with literary quotes), he's well liked by parents though wife pips him to the post. 'One of the genuinely nicest people I have ever met,' said parent.

'Kids absolutely adore him,' said one mother – and it's a red-letter day when he eats with them. 'My son came back very excited to say he'd had lunch with Mr Dunlop and couldn't quite believe it,' said mother. It's a similar high spot for Mr D – 'shows me how far they've come,' he says.

Sensibly, he's good at delegating and ensures that staff get the credit for own initiatives and support to develop them (by no means always the case). No killer questions for prospective staff (unless he wasn't letting on) – he's looking for creative people who understand difference 'between being a teacher and doing teaching.'

Bar slight boarding blip (2016 inspection found flaws in vetting of prospective staff, now corrected), it's all been – largely – plain sailing.

Happiest in the classroom, boarding houses or on the pitch, there's not much he doesn't love about the job, bar the emails ('the thing I would uninvent'). Sees sense of pastoral care as vital aspect of his role. 'If you don't understand where the children are coming from and what affects their feelings then you really have to ask if you're doing the right thing.'

Entrance: Pre-prep numbers, which had dropped off recently, now growing again, no doubt helped by free come and play toddler and parent sessions. Plenty of well-connected locals, but don't expect huge amounts of socialising as many work full time. 'Some parents...think they'll get into a niche little coffee club but it doesn't happen,' said mother.

Other nice touches in this compact and reassuring world range from perk of ringing large, wall-mounted bell when it's supper time and school's own Brownie pack

Further up, healthy levels of prep applications, particularly in top years, but don't be fooled into thinking this is school for all comers. Do take from wider ability range than competition, but pupils need to be able to access curriculum. Will ask for reports and may observe child at current school/nursery (avoids shattering of expectations if attend taster day here and aren't offered a place). Will only accept in top junior years if confident that can make transition to senior school and 'at least get some GCSEs'.

Unusually wide range of scholarships (academic, music, art, sports and all-rounder) awarded to year 7 pupils, though value – between 2.5 and 10 per cent off the fees – isn't going to take much of the edge off that chunky termly invoice.

Best to recover equilibrium by reciting routes of the school buses – who wouldn't be drawn

to Compton Acres, Sturminster Marshall and Spetisbury? (Though Limberlost Layby/Woodland Burial Ground Car Park lose a little bit of the bucolic magic).

Exit: Currently 90 per cent plus move up to senior school but transition from year 8 not prescribed, stresses school. Will happily accommodate anyone preparing for entrance exams elsewhere including grammars and other independents (Canford inevitably takes a few) though generally fewer as 'our reputation moves away from SEN focus,' says school.

Once here, however, families tend to stay on, often after completing compare and contrast round of open days. 'I suddenly thought "I love it but need to look around," so did all the local ones and came back,' says mother. 'Has just got the most amazing feel to it.'

Only time pupils have been asked to leave (single figures in the time Mr Dunlop has been here) is down to bullying. 'We do everything we possibly can but there comes a point where it's not viable,' he says.

Remarks: Set in a generous corner of school's 62 acres, this is a comfortable, home-like place to grow up in. Operationally run as a separate school with own uniform (the girls love their long tartan skirt, less for aesthetics than functionality. As one senior pupil said, nostalgically, 'It keeps your legs warm and the stains don't show – had food all over mine').

Where resources are shared with senior school, they're clearly delineated (path from main building to music block marks the division between play areas 'like Mexican wall though more porous,' says Mr Dunlop). Pupils go across to main hall for lunch – use other facilities too (swimming pool, forest school). Memories of original prep school site in nearby Charlton Marshall reside in impressively proportioned cedar of Lebanon, busily taking over middle of turning circle – planting dominated by sentiment rather than species. ('One of my successors will have difficult decision to take,' says Mr Dunlop).

Easy to overuse words like 'idyllic' when you hear tales of year 8 pupils still enjoying school's adventure playground. 'In an 11+ school they wouldn't because they're trying to be adult,' points out Mr Dunlop. Other nice touches in this compact and reassuring world range from perk of ringing large, wall-mounted bell when it's supper time to links with the community – Brownie pack, run by staff, is the only one 'in the valley' and includes local children as well as pupils.

Low rise buildings house the very youngest, with nursery and reception/year 1 in big, bright and open plan classrooms, amid plentiful greenery and the odd unexpected touch ('spaceman' sculpture by a sixth former, with humanoid appearance,

arrived overnight when reception pupils were studying aliens). 'The classes feel small but are large enough to feel like joining a class rather than a family,' says Mr Dunlop.

Given push on standards that's filtering down from the senior school, no surprise that Mr Dunlop is also felt to be giving teaching a gentle shove. Nothing that will cause resettlement of its axis, mind you – and not that most teachers (bar the odd one who 'should be moving on,' said one parent) need it. Current prospectus (being redesigned) may state firmly that 'every child achieves academic success', but more about realising individual potential than trailing clouds of glory for all.

Focus is on encouragement and thoughtful planning, such as visual timetables in boarding houses – sun for wake up 'good for reluctant readers'

Plenty to enjoy including path that winds round the back wall, taking in glasshouse (once used to grow melons, now used for ceramics). Out front there's the Everett Building (2008) – very attractive – and 70s teaching and boarding block building that isn't, though disguised with cotoneasters and – if nothing else – user friendly. 'A well functioning machine if not a beautiful one,' says Mr Dunlop, with consummate diplomacy.

Currently half a dozen part time boarders alongside the full ones, mainly in year 4 and up, though one pupil in year 3 having a great time courtesy of year 6 mentor – 'very kind and does

French plaits for me.' All happens above the shop, in large, generally bright and very clean rooms, if a tad low on ambiance with some bareish walls. Loads of underbed clothes storage (much empty thanks to almost non-stop and highly efficient laundry system).

Gentle approach to rewards and sanctions keeps things home-like. Spickest, spannest dorm gets 'muck' surprise (school jargon for afternoon break treat) which tends to be supermarket sourced (cupcakes a favourite). Individual winners get slap up meal at head of boarding's house. For older boarders, perks include moving closer to the bathroom (later to bed so keeps noise down for the rest) while Saturday school helpful in keeping bustle going well into the weekend.

Focus is on encouragement and thoughtful planning, from the visual timetables in boarding houses – sun for wake up 'good for reluctant readers' – to description of mini adventure playground as 'confidence equipment' (Mr D's words). Seems to work (two boys tearing around on crutches during our visit).

Girls love their long tartan skirt, less for aesthetics than functionality. As one pupil said, nostalgically, 'It keeps your legs warm and stains don't show – I had food all over mine'

Deliberately keep work pressure to a minimum (no prep until year 5, for example) – sensible given range of activities done by some pupils that makes homework an unenviable late evening prospect. Other sensible rejig of timetable is to move tutor time from start to end of day ('means more effective learning time').

Specialist teaching in all subjects from year 5, and in art, music and DT from year 2. (Latin added in year 7). Much setting and streaming (English and maths from year 3, most other subjects by year 6) so can cater for broad ability range.

Throughout, there's emphasis on sensible learning habits. Youngest 'plan, do and review' while new Clayesmore Compass emphasises – among other things – collaboration (permeates other areas – contribution award has replaced man or woman of the match), plus risk taking, challenge and (from year 6) creativity.

Not that pupils appear to need much telling. Macbeth witches inspired poems (from previous academic year but about to be replaced) were enjoyably big on yuck factor – 'sprinkle in fly vomit so grim...'; an autumn dragon with '...hurricane breath.' All helped by librarian, full of initiatives to get pupils reading things they wouldn't otherwise – our favourite, book spine poetry (pile up the titles and see how they sound): 'The railway children/ bowl like the devil/into battle/a wrinkle in time.'

Plenty of high tech resources as well, courtesy of Google Classroom – now in use across the school – 'helps children become responsible for own learning'. While not everyone was convinced ('I don't like reading, it's boring – have to sound out the letters and do it at home,' thought one little lad in reception) we couldn't see much in the way of deprivation, judging by universal enthusiasm for recent task – delights of windmills they'd just created. 'Had to make the sails turn.'

Learning support praised by all and accredited by CReSTeD (specific learning difficulties) and NACE (gifted children) though felt to be poorly understood in wider world. 'There is a misconception that school specialises in SEN. It doesn't specialise, it just does it amazingly well,' said mother.

Currently around 90 pupils with SEN – most SpLD but also ASD and ADHD, support courtesy of learning resource centre in middle of school, staff able to do just about anything, one working with pupil to pick out describing words for teeth – 'mysterious, tiny, heavy...' In class, gap year students are not so hidden weapon – one looks gangling next to the pupil he's supporting (though doesn't look so very much older) – a particular asset with behaviour management.

Upwards pressure on ambition translates into other areas – such as sports – though not excessively so. Mr Dunlop reckons that rival teams who used to be drawn primarily by the location and the quality of match teas now come because 'they'll get a good game as well as all the trimmings.'

Main sports rugby, hockey plus soupcon of football though most successful tend to be cricket (U13 county champions) and cross-country – school organises major inter-school event for 20 schools or so. Most pitches grass though plus Astro shared with senior school.

Bar desire for slight pepping up of sports generally (less rounders, more football), few mega grumbles from parents who feel that there's a decent number of matches. 'There is an A, B and C team and they do ensure that they have fixtures,' said parent. 'Quite a variety – and can do horse riding,' agreed another.

Arts generally very highly rated. Music team ('the noise department,' says Mr Dunlop) housed in what was once the trophy room with must-have zebra heads would be all the better for purpose built performance spaces – chapel, currently main venue, just too small.

Otherwise, impressively successful, with over 130 pupils learning at least one instrument, numerous ensembles and assorted competitions across the school.

Clayesmore School

12

Iwerne Minster, Blandford Forum, Dorset DT11 8LL

01747 812122 | mmccafferty@clayesmore.com | www.clayesmore.com

Ages: 13-18

Pupils: 466; sixth form: 182; Boarders: 245 full

Day: £26,220 pa; Boarding: £25,730 pa

Linked school: Clayesmore Preparatory School, 101

Head: Since 2016, Joanne Thomson BA MBA 940s). First headship. Previously joint deputy head for eight years at Christ's Hospital School, preceded by 13 years at Aiglon College. First post after finishing degree was at Repton Prep as English teacher, assistant houseparent and sports coach.

Model of modern marriage offers cheering example of give and take. Husband Frank, also a senior teacher, is head of PSHE here, has worked at most of same schools and is happy to let Mrs T take the lead. 'There's never a power struggle,' she stresses. Two children, both at young adult stage (younger attending sixth form here).

Parents at Christ's praised her 'industriousness and conviviality'. What comes across above all is calm, understated kindness (the only head this reviewer has ever met who physically booked a cab back to the station – though could be a subtle way of ensuring we actually left the premises...).

Never envisaged being a head and 'it's not about the power but making a difference.' She's succeeding, says a parent, by effective delegation. 'Doesn't have a finger in every pie but lets the school get on with it which is better for the staff.' Senior pupil praised her 'interaction' with pupils. 'Clear to see philosophy,' said year 10 guide. Particular strength is thought for the day speeches. 'I was like "How is she able to be so relatable?"' How, indeed?

Spent first year tied to desk, working on systems and structures that were creaking under the pressure of increased pupil numbers. 'Time-consuming but necessary and meant that some parents felt they didn't see quite enough of her. That's now being rectified. Also – somehow – managed to complete an MBA over the school holidays. Sent out questionnaire and is implementing suggestions – including extending autumn half term to two weeks (from 2018).

Like other schools she's worked at, this one is notable for exceptional pastoral care – she wouldn't join a school without it. Isn't planning drastic change but sensible rethinking designed to ensure that school does its best by all pupils throughout the ability spectrum. Inclusiveness is in but will be helped along with greater focus on tailored learning and monitoring, supported by extensive, joined up digital technology. Small but beautifully designed booklet serves up changes with strong dose of reassurance.

Her younger (state educated) self wouldn't be happy with independent school career and informs her desire to share resources as widely as possible. Community-related activity is important – pupils work at local special school, local elderly are regularly invited in for events and pipe band – goes with school's name, rather than location – 'is out and about' (not as threatening as it sounds).

Of the major sports (played three times a week) strongest are tennis, athletics and, especially, cricket, where school has made it into Wisden's top 100

Best part of the job? No surprises that it's the pupils. 'They keep you grounded, especially ours, they're very open and tell it like it is, they're great.'

Academic matters: Everyone – not just teachers and pupils but their parents and our taxi driver (a past parent, whose daughter is now well on the way to being something massive in the City) stress that families don't need to divide and rule, sending most academically able child elsewhere – school will do wonders with them all. In 2017, 37 per cent A*/A at A level; nearly 28 per cent A*-A/9-7 at GCSE.

Particular strength is whole-school commitment to SEN. Around 130 pupils have needs such as SpLD, mild ASD and ADHD/ADD and school ensures that training and regular insets extend to all staff, including rugby coaches. Differentiation is 'staggering,' says head. 'I've never been in a place where teacher are so united and committed to the cause.'

All pupils have CAT test in year 9 designed as 'stress free screening' to establish 'range of possibilities.' Those needing extra support can attend informal drop in maths sessions or may swap languages for extra classes in teaching and learning centre – (TLC, geddit?) which is located slap bang in middle of school – 'no wooden hut in the grounds,' says head – and universally rated as phenomenal. Separate classrooms for those needing EAL support.

Specialist staff, some full, some part time, many with teaching responsibilities, all with post-grad qualifications, are also regularly consulted by other teachers wanting to know eg how to support the very able. Accreditation from NACE (gifted children) and CReSTeD (specific learning difficulties) reflects school's strengths in both areas.

'Still marked as being a school where they do a fabulous job with learning support but they're brilliant with everybody else as well,' said parent. Not everyone will get A*s and As but 'what you will see is people who nobody ever expected it doing well.' Even inspectors (so relaxed they've not been back for over five years) could only pick on the consistency of marking as in need of improvement.

Teachers hold frequent meetings about pupils. 'Try get beyond the label,' agrees deputy head – and are equally good at winkling out hidden staff talent. One member of support staff, outed as successful published novelist, now runs creative writing workshops.

Class sizes drop steadily down the years, average 16 in year 9 (maximum 17), 11 in years 10 and 11 (max 19) and just eight in sixth form (13) with a pupil/teacher ratio of eight to one. Teachers 'young and dynamic,' says school – average age is 41, so perhaps more young-ish, but definitely committed (16 at the school for more than a decade).

Do the range, from facilitating A levels plus others – economics to psychology, photography to textiles as well as (very unusually) six BTecs (IT – most popular – plus sport, music technology, hospitality, travel and tourism and performing and production arts). Were sniffed at by Russell Group unis but things are changing, says school – though pupils are encouraged to mix with A levels.

Mega A level subjects are business (most popular) followed by geography, maths and photography – an eclectic mix that says a lot about the diverse interests and enthusiasms of pupils.

Fair few D and E grades in tough subjects at GCSE and A level– eg nearly a third of history GCSE entries and three of the six chemistry A level entries in 2017.

Not much that's outré – though unusually offers both computer science and ICT as an IGCSE. Over 50 – half the year group – currently taking DT, no surprise given rave reviews from teacher and range of goodies produced – papaya chess board a highlight mentioned by parents; though (perhaps surprisingly) very few for drama – single figures, just ahead of Latin.

Teaching is fun and animated. We watched maths lesson with year 10 teams working on probability problems, chains of different coloured arrows climbing up the whiteboards. Maths teacher is 'best I've ever had,' testified pupil. 'Understands how to have the class gripped as well as learning.'

Sensible use of technology, so joined up it must have created a virtuous circle, is now a feature of all subjects. Former head of drama, heavy Twitter user who's 'really into pedagogy,' says head, is clearly loving new role as digital learning supremo – now runs regular insets on the wonders of podcasting (many staff do their own), one of many options that come with Google Classroom (fabulous and free to schools – what's not to like?).

Other fresh ideas include the new Clayesmore Courses, for example, covering areas like history of art. No assessment pressure. Instead, 'we're starting to show kids that school can be quite fun.'

For those in need of reassurance, you'll hear (lots) about school's most successful pupil (astrophysics at Cambridge – ideally need a couple more to ring the changes). The bottom line is that this is learning without tears – an exceptionally happy and successful school that does well by all its pupils.

Games, options, the arts: 'Don't have to be good at activities to have fun,' said pupil. 'I'm not specially good – I just like to get involved.'

If the grounds and activities weren't enticement enough (D of E, CCF so popular that one year 11 pupil spent major chunk of summer holidays with them), school also invites pupils to complete 100 activities in 10 categories including sport and arts – as well as academics. Need to show leadership and participation and (our favourite) passive involvement (watching stuff). One year 13 pupil won (external) debating competition and watched inauguration of President Trump. Completion had been recognised with chunky cash prize and membership of Clayesmore Centenary Club, handed over on prize day though currently being rethought. 'I want pupils to participate for intrinsic reasons rather than monetary reward,' says head.

Single rooms for some lower and all upper sixth, who also get more advanced cooking privileges and own meeting areas

Of the major sports (played three times a week with option to add individual favourites from year 10 – featured successes include, eg, Jemima and Buttons doing fantastically well in dressage championship) – strongest are tennis, athletics and, especially, cricket, where school makes Wisden's top 100. Behind the scenes, the head, sporty herself, is keen to ensure more excitement for girls in particular who have own rugby and football teams. Cricket may also be on the agenda (if worthy opponents can be found) and staffing levels are being bumped up – girls' PE teacher recently appointed.

Parents positive but realistic. 'We go to win but it's a numbers game. It's a very different culture.' Consolation provided by exceptional match teas, renowned in the area – scones, cheese straws, sandwiches and 'massive cakes,' said pupil.

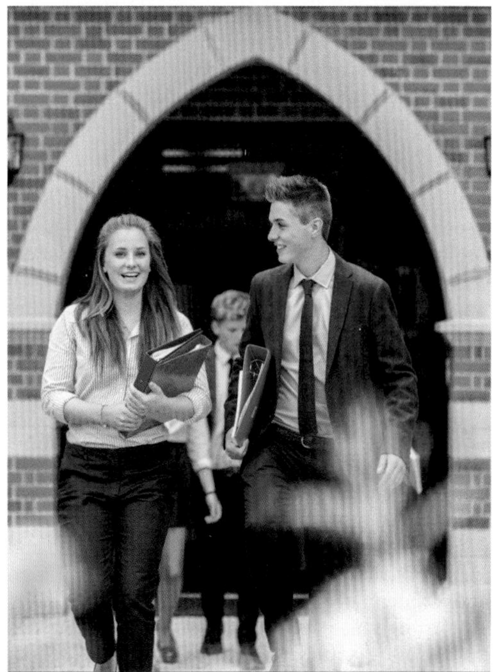

Small size means that sports results can vary, sometimes dramatically, between cohorts (not necessarily ideal for families fixated on winning at all cost) but has its benefits, too, not just in sports but elsewhere, with different year groups often working in same space (art and drama), for example. 'Gives them positive role models,' says art teacher.

Bar school-wide desire for bigger and better performance space (delightful but bijou chapel with electric – though not, sadly, solar-powered – organ is currently a major venue for whole school), music and drama both highly praised and on everyone's radar, including parents whose children aren't performers. Dedicated head of music felt to be upping standards across the board – particularly for choral music, though range of opportunities for instrumentalists (to grade 8, a few at diploma level) – concert band, jazz and brass ensembles, for example – also highly rated.

'Might not have the sportiest or the most academic reputation but it does all of them to a very good level and includes everyone in that,' said parent.

Boarding: Five boarding houses – three for boys, two for girls, each housing up to 50 pupils and strictly segregated (sight of boy boarder briefly wandering, shirtless, down corridor, reduces female tour guide to helpless giggles). Bar occasional stray corner it's all basically fine, especially now Devine (in the village, short walk from school) has been revamped and pupils given day room at school, though downside can be lack of space for day pupils.

Appearance ranges from the grand (Wolverton – girls – approached up impressive staircase in the main house) to the homely (Gate – boys – prettily set around former stable yard. Varying dorm sizes, some sleeping of six or more in junior years, though a couple of spares kept unoccupied for emergencies. Otherwise boarding full with waiting lists in most year groups. Nicest (girls' rooms) are elevated with wardrobes at the end. 'We lean up on the wardrobes and chat,' said girl. Single rooms for some lower and all upper sixth, who also get more advanced cooking privileges and own meeting areas.

No official weekly boarding but locals are allowed to go home after Saturday school. Some overseas Brits – FO, MoD, expats – though fewer than you might think (currently less than 20) given substantial presence of army bases in the area. Others from all over including Germany, China and Russia, with a few others from USA, Italy, Japan and Sweden.

Strong sense of community. Boarders and day pupils 'all mix and match,' said a parent. 'School is really lovely if you want to have a boarder for the weekend.' Pain of staying in eased by dogs (owned by staff in three out of five boarding houses), hot chocolate and plenty of talking therapy for homesickness, plus luxurious lie in to 10.45am on Sunday morning with potato cubes (chip off-shoots) and bacon and egg sandwiches the star attractions on the brunch menu.

'Suits people who like to be busy,' said pupil. 'You'll be joining in without realising it.' What with regular off site outings – shopping bus, cinema, spectacular coastline – and onside delights of, among others, squash, archery and kayaking, pupils reckon 'there's just not enough time to fit everything in' (no doubt the reason for copy of The Times, lying, untouched, in boarding house reception).

Background and atmosphere: School was founded in 1896 in Enfield, leading somewhat peripatetic existence, settling first in Pangbourne, then Winchester before final landing here in 1933. House, Iwerne Manor, was rebuilt in peak Victorian perpendicular gothic style by local squires (whose goodness to villagers extended to equipping each house with red blinds).

Main house floats like an island in a sea of grass, in the centre of 62 acres, commanding splendid views – crescents, one blue, one green, which feature on girls' blazer crests represent meeting of land and sky. (Traditionalists may prefer double headed dragon – still sported by boys – over corporate minimalism.)

Many attractive original buildings survive, though with substantial additions and rebuilds. Change has accelerated recently, with add-ons ranging from striking new DT extension to three separate blocks of classrooms. Ample space ensures that large sports hall, swimming pool, multi-surface pitch don't detract from lake, fountain and scenery. With exception of grimly functional 70s prep block, new builds generally fit into place rather than attempting to dominate it, a tribute to good architect ego management.

Strong sense of community. Boarders and day pupils 'all mix and match – shool is really lovely if you want to invite a boarder for the weekend,' said a parent

Doing bit for the environment, too, with biomass boiler installed 2016 plus big solar panels on three of the roofs (now produce almost 10 per cent of energy – as well as pepping up temperature and pressure to delightful levels in boarding house showers).

Pupils – some here with considerable sacrifice from parents – do count their blessings. 'Everyone feels very lucky to be here – it says something that you realise it now,' said thoughtful guide.

Pastoral care, well-being and discipline: Fabulous and A-Z. Starting point is (relatively) small size of school – 'can spot quickly if things aren't quite right and get in early,' says head.

Strong tutor system, supplemented with pupil mentoring and low levels of cynicism – house loyalty, we were told, stays at fever pitch levels even at the top of the school. Lots of house competitions – organised by upper sixth who 'choreograph dances, pick song, arrange music, lower key if pitch too high.'

Fully aware of how issues (such as eating disorders) can escalate and potentially shattering consequences if not spotted in time. 'So far, no transgender pupils but would go all out to make sure needs met,' says school. Approach geared to individual needs – haven created for one pupil, for example, who found classroom environment overwhelming and went on to achieve top exam grades.

Currently developing digital journal where pupils record, in images or writing, their emotional journey through school. 'Will help them think about times in their lives where they've made real leaps forward or had setbacks....could be so powerful when they look back,' says Mrs Thomson. Aim is to help them get out of groove of seeing social media as more than just mass transmission of selfies but tool for future reflection.

Pupils and parents: When it comes to socialising, spirit is willing but, with both parents working in many families, flesh and timetables are weak and coffee morning slots often elusive. When they do meet up, mood is correspondingly jolly. 'Gifted chaps' and 'all-round splendid fellows' pop up at intervals in annals of Clayesmore Society (open to all), and retiring nurse is a 'vision in waterproofs and wellies.' Translates into mixed bag of alumni from artist Edward Ardizzone to Beatles manager Brian Epstein and top surgeon Sir Rodney Sweetnam.

Locals and neighbouring counties (Dorset, Hants and Wiltshire) dominate – inevitable army contingent – though London is also on its patch (have had some families fleeing terrorism as well as its hothouse atmosphere). Low sterling value has upped interest from overseas, though long term Brexit impact yet to be seen.

Though a fair few parents arrive from state sector, there's plenty of dosh about, with school events ranging from clay shoot (a tenner a head) to a reunion with lavish canapés and fizz (free, but you have to get yourself to Guernsey).

Entrance: The normal battle over semantics. School says 'non-selective' when what it means is 'as non-selective as you can be,' says head. Bottom line is that all prospective pupils must be able to access the curriculum and be capable of achieving 'some' GCSEs (numbers will vary fairly widely but will include core subjects).

Around half of senior entry comes from junior school plus local preps (Forres Sandle Manor, Castle Court, Dumpton, Walhampton, Durlston Court, Salisbury Cathedral. Increasingly fed by families from London and the south east. Boy heavy – 100 or so more than girls. Evenly split day and boarding

Take around 90 in year 9; handful in year 10 and around 20 into the sixth form (with at least five A*-C/9-4 passes at GCSE).

Exit: Occasional departure for drugs but more humane than most: instant expulsion for dealing and hard drugs, potential for discussion at least for cannabis, though 'only if it's a first offence and then followed up with regular testing to ensure no repeat,' says school. Around five pupils leave after GCSEs, usually to state schools or because of relocation, others where demands of curriculum would simply be too much – preceded by plenty of discussion. Most to uni or apprenticeships – vast range of courses and destinations: arts and acting foundation to business studies and engineering everywhere from Loughborough to Southampton. A few on gap years. No Oxbridge in 2017.

Money matters: Generous sibling discounts – ask as not easily discoverable on website. About a quarter of senior school pupils receive means-tested bursaries (some substantial) and though generous, head would like to extend 'for talented but needy.'

Scholarships, in contrast, are available (10 per cent off fees) but head isn't a big fan, feeling that labelling the talented can impose unnecessary pressure at an early age and ignore talented late developers, who very often go on to scoop the glittering prizes. Children 'should just be enjoying time at school for the right reasons.'

Remarks: Lovely location; warm, inclusive ethos. Ignore dinner party chit chat about SEN focus and do all your children a favour by seeing it for yourself.

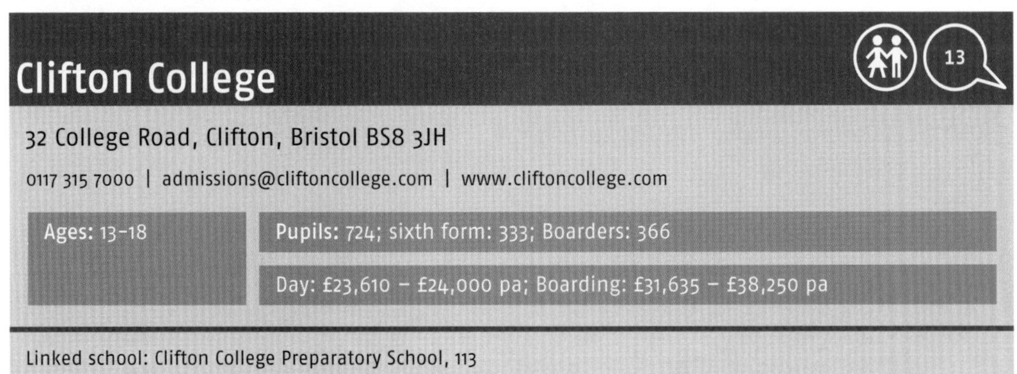

Clifton College

13

32 College Road, Clifton, Bristol BS8 3JH

0117 315 7000 | admissions@cliftoncollege.com | www.cliftoncollege.com

Ages: 13–18

Pupils: 724; sixth form: 333; Boarders: 366

Day: £23,610 – £24,000 pa; Boarding: £31,635 – £38,250 pa

Linked school: Clifton College Preparatory School, 113

Head: Since 2016, Dr Tim Greene MA DPhil (Oxon), who was interim head during the spring term before being appointed head in March 2016. He came to Clifton as head of chemistry in 2006, becoming deputy head (academic) in 2013. He read chemistry, took his DPhil and subsequently became a senior research fellow in inorganic chemistry at Oxford. In 2001, he joined the chemistry department at Exeter University, moving into secondary education at Queen's College, Taunton, in 2005 as head of chemistry. He is married to Lydia Massiah and they have three sons.

Academic matters: Academic profile of the school has sharpened, resulting in dramatic improvements in GCSE and A level results. 'We have established a new benchmark in terms of expectations,' said head. In 2017, 76 per cent A*-B, 48 per cent A*/A at A level. At I/GCSE, 68 per cent A*-A/9-7 grades. Success attributed to tougher entrance requirements at all levels and recruitment of very high calibre teachers, including an Oxford don and a research fellow. 'We have some fantastic young subject specialists among our staff. This is a competitive neck of the woods – we have to be on our mettle.' As well as keeping up with Bristol day schools, Clifton now feels it can match many of the top independent schools. Science has always been strong – several Nobel Prizewinners among alumni. Excellent facilities over three floors of the school science building, including the Stone Library, with more than 5,000 science titles. Classics also enjoying a resurgence.

English has been something of a poor relation, but changes expected since the opening in 2015 of a new centre for the subject and for modern foreign languages. Aim is for it to have a university atmosphere, with seminar rooms and a cafeteria. Broad range of subjects on offer in third form (Y9) and fourth and fifth forms (Y10-11). Thirty A level subjects as well as a range of supplementary subjects (sector E) to further develop strengths and interests. Sixth form growing rapidly – now makes up half the school. EAL lessons are provided where needed and additional classes can be purchased. Individual support for students with dyslexia and other specific learning needs is provided to improve literacy and numeracy and exam skills. Independent learning department, with its own head, is in a separate building to ease stress.

'Music is seen as a cool thing to do.' Outstanding facilities for recording and practice in the Joseph Cooper Music School

Games, options, the arts: 'There's a breathless hush in the Close to-night, Ten to make and the match to win' – lines written by Clifton former pupil Henry Newbolt in 1881 about the beautiful Clifton cricket pitch. Seven years later, AEJ Collins scored 628 not out there in a house match, and WG Grace also played on the turf. No wonder cricket is still a major draw: 'Watching my son play cricket on the Close is just incredible,' said one father. 'He is so proud to wear the kit.' Four ex-county cricketers on the staff providing high-standard coaching for boys and girls, and school has firm links with Gloucestershire CCC. School is the site of the the oldest English interschool contest in the game of rugby, Clifton College vs Marlborough, the Governor's Cup. Clifton won the 150th anniversary contest recently; trophy presented by Old Cliftonian John Inverdale. It was noted that the rules of the game might have changed since the original 20-a-side fixture, but the rivalry had not.

Swimming pool, gym and other sporting facilities on site but most of the games provision is over the Clifton suspension bridge at the school's 90-acre Beggar's Bush grounds. These include a water-based hockey pitch, 3G rugby pitch and a netball and tennis dome. Hockey for girls and boys also of high standard; Lily Owsley won first full international cap while still at the school and was part of the gold medal-winning GB team at the Rio Olympics. Real tennis, racquets, fives, water polo, chess, fencing ... the list goes on. Lots of outdoor pursuits, CCF, trips, expeditions 'developing the whole child'.

Music is also integral – 'It's in the fabric of the school, embedded, starting in the Pre (prep school). We have an absolutely brilliant music department. Music is seen as a cool thing to do.' Outstanding facilities for recording and practice in the Joseph Cooper Music School. More than half of pupils take instrumental lessons, and they have a wide range of opportunities to perform – chapel, recital hall, theatre – in classical, jazz, blues and many other styles, both solo and in orchestras and ensembles. Alumnus violinist Julia Hwang, BBC Young Musician of the Year finalist, won a scholarship to Cambridge and recently two students won organ scholarships to Oxford. Singing prominent too; chamber choir one of many opportunities. Links with Bristol Old Vic Theatre School provide opportunities for students, as does the Redgrave Theatre, named after former pupil Sir Michael Redgrave. Annual college musical and Shakespeare play are highlights of the school year. New dance studio with sprung floor. Students have talents in art too; Clifton has won the annual Bristol schools' art competition for six years out of nine. DT has been transformed and is now 'more girl-friendly, linked to art rather than a subset of engineering', including graphic design, CAD-CAM and resistant materials. Photography (school has its own darkroom), sculpture and ceramics also popular.

Staff are very sensitive to individual needs and provide a listening ear, and the pupils support one another. 'It's like an extended family, with sisterly relationships.' Houseparents also celebrate personal achievements as well as academic – one has initiated a 'Good Egg' honours board. The dorms are equipped with robust, good quality furniture that can also be used to provide some personal space. Younger pupils are in rooms of up to six, while GCSE students are in threes and sixth-formers in twins or singles. Children swap rooms every term. The houses include kitchen and laundry areas and pupils are encouraged to be increasingly independent.

Boarding: The school offers day, flexi and full boarding, with the latest trend towards full boarding, often even for those whose family homes are nearby. A total of 11 day and boarding houses for the upper school – with more girls' houses now because of increasing demand. There's a continual programme to upgrade the boarding houses, with the girls and boys often given a say over décor and furnishings. Even parents get involved, helping to upgrade a garden area, for example. Spacious communal facilities, with lots of games and activities. House singing competitions and plays keep them all pretty busy. 'It's full on; you never get bored,' a pupil told us. Some pupils complained to inspectors that there were too many evening and weekend activities, but it was judged that there were 'appropriate facilities to be alone or to mix informally with friends should they so wish'.

Background and atmosphere: Describes itself as a traditional British public school with modern teaching values. Founded in 1862 as a 'public school for the people of Bristol' and housed in imposing Victorian buildings. German and Russian families particularly attracted by the 'English boarding school experience package – and we certainly tick the Hogwarts box'. Each day begins in the impressive chapel with a hymn and an assembly led by a different department. Although robustly Anglican, there's also a synagogue as part of the school's Jewish heritage and students of all faiths or none are accommodated. You can wander the cloisters and see team sheets posted on carved wooden boards – though, crucially, the information is also available online. There's a sixth form common room in the Crypt – and how many schools have their own Armoury? The Percival Library is the highlight

– 15,000 books on carved wooden shelves, some adorned with fairy lights. A whole wall of titles about or by Old Cliftonians from John Cleese to Earl Haig. During our visit there was a wonderful Alice in Wonderland theme, including a curtain of playing cards, but the 21st century is represented too, with a 3D printer in the library and some excellent DT creations on display in modern cabinets. Dictionaries in many languages are a necessity. Three full-time professional librarians manage physical and digital stock and periodicals and run activities including film clubs, book clubs, creative writing clubs, competitions and events. Lessons still take place on Saturdays, followed by matches. Saturday brunch, a recent innovation, has gone down well with pupils. All food is tasty and ample and the catering operation is impressive.

'There is a perception of Clifton as "the toffs on the hill" and I think we have softened that image,' said Mr Milne. He is determined to continue to break down barriers and ensure his pupils realise how fortunate they are and how important it is to care for others. 'We are very much changed, more engaging and more accessible. We can't afford to follow what we did 50 or 70 years ago. The thing I am most proud of is the way social impact has taken off in the prep school,' he said. 'We have always been charity minded but we are taking a step further than cake sales.' As well as working with organisations such as Fairbridge and Prince's Trust, the school runs a unique project called 'Colour My Life' in which staff, parents and some children redecorate and refurbish a home for an underprivileged family, Changing Rooms-style. 'It is one of the most meaningful things we have done. It changes children's outlooks dramatically.'

Pastoral care, well-being and discipline: House masters and mistresses are the lynchpins, leading a team of tutors, matrons and support staff. Pupils of all ages know exactly where to go if they need help or advice and are hugely appreciative of the way they are looked after at school. The school has its own medical centre too. Parents seem happy with the systems in place to let them know what's happening. A comprehensive handbook outlines rules, sanctions and guidelines for so many eventualities. To an outside observer, it's a fascinating mix of ancient and modern: rustication, exeats and removing hands from pockets when passing through the Memorial Arch through to policies on the use of 'legal highs' and dietary supplements. Changes in ICT require all schools to be constantly on the alert; while Skyping mum and dad from the other side of the world is an obvious boon, the use of Wifi enabled devices also presents many challenges.

And, sadly, it's nothing new. Clifton was rocked by the arrest in 2014 of a housemaster who had been downloading indecent images. He was jailed and the school described his actions as an 'unforgivable breach of trust' and an 'affront to our values'. Specialist education lawyers were appointed to ensure best practice over safeguarding and child protection, partly in response to an unannounced ISI inspection in July 2015 that found some written procedures were not up to date, but a reinspection in January 2016 gave it the thumbs up. Parents we spoke to all said they were satisfied with the way college had responded to the matter. 'I think they've handled it well – changes are visible but not obtrusive,' said one.

Pupils and parents: More than 40 nationalities in the school. No one overseas group is dominant. China is the biggest – not Russia, as sometimes perceived. The Russians that do come are from wealthy but not oligarchical backgrounds. Hong Kong has always been strong, these days from both expat Brit and Chinese families. Biggest growth is in children from Western Europe – often with parents working at Airbus in Bristol or EDF in Somerset. Reputation of Bristol as a lively European city, with a wide mix of entrepreneurs and innovators, is a draw. Proximity of the airport makes the school accessible from around the globe. Very able students from countries such as Ukraine are being drawn to Clifton by word of mouth: 'It's a quality rather than a quantity argument for us. Our brand recognition is higher in some countries than in the UK, maybe because we are not inside the M25.'

As one pupil said, having native MFL and Mandarin speakers is a great help when it comes to homework and practising for oral exams. 'We have friends from all over the world.' one pupil observed. This is seen as an asset by many Bristol parents, including doctors, lawyers and other professionals. Proportion of girls in the school continues to increase – now around 40 per cent.

Spacious communal facilities, with lots of games and activities. House singing competitions and plays keep boarders all pretty busy

Sixth form has mushroomed; big demand for places, especially for girls. Parents see it as a conduit to the top universities. British families love the life-enriching experience of mixing with brilliant young people from around the world and gaining a global address book. 'The education is excellent, but it is the contacts and opportunities the children are getting that make Clifton stand out,' said one father. Students from some countries struggle a bit with cricket, but football proves a lingua franca and there is a multinational team. 'Our international dimension is one of the great strengths of the school.' Diverse, eclectic. Broader mix of social and economic backgrounds than in some similar schools, thanks to 100 per cent bursaries, which enable sons and daughters of taxi drivers to mingle happily with wealthy offspring of Old Cliftonians. Day and boarding is about a 50/50 split. This, coupled with the position within walking distance of the city centre, enables the school and its staff and pupils to be closely linked with the community.

Alumni include John Cleese, Simon Russell Beale, W G Grace and Sir Arthur Thomas Quiller-Couch.

Entrance: Most join the senior school from the prep school, after taking an entrance exam of the same standard as common entrance. Some bring scholarships awarded at 11+. Additional scholarships available at 13+. External candidates for common entrance or common scholarship at age 13 now pre-tested in year 7. Entry to the sixth form usually conditional on achieving three A/7 grades and three B/6 grades at GCSE, plus an English language paper for overseas students.

Exit: Around 20 per cent leave after GCSEs and others join. Four Oxbridge places in 2017 and four medics/vets. Small number to overseas universities. Other destinations include UCL, Imperial, LSE also London School of Fashion, Central St Martins and the Vienna Conservatoire.

Money matters: Academic, art, music, organ and sport scholarships and awards for up to 25 per cent of fees are offered on merit at 13+ and for sixth form and means-tested bursaries up to 100 per cent of fees are available.

Remarks: Visiting Clifton on a sunny day, the setting is almost too perfect. Among Bristol residents, the college is often viewed as full of rich, rugby kids with little grasp on the realities of life. But these stereotypes go nowhere near telling the story of the school. Whatever their backgrounds, the students are aware that the privileges they enjoy go way beyond the material. They are courteous and respectful – and modest about their frequently incredible achievements. Many of them are fluent in two or three languages. We met a brilliant young Somali boy from a disadvantaged area of Bristol who loves astronomy, intends to become an inventor and has settled in wonderfully to the school. Excellent prospectus gives a flavour – but explore the extensive website to get the widest perspective on life at Clifton College in the second decade of the 21st century.

Clifton College Preparatory School

14

The Avenue, Clifton, Bristol BS8 3HE

0117 315 7503 | prepadmissions@cliftoncollege.com | www.cliftoncollege.com/prep

Ages: 3–13

Pupils: 515; Boarders: 45 full, 10–12 flexi

Day: £12,825 – £16,965 pa; Boarding: £16,965 – £27,900 pa

Linked school: Clifton College, 109

Headmaster: Since January 2018, Jim Walton, previously head of Elizabeth College Junior School on Guernsey. He was educated at Warwick School before going on to Sheffield to read business studies. Has taught in both prep and senior schools, including Clifton High School and Cheltenham

College Prep, where he was a housemaster, and part of the senior leadership team, for 11 years. He is married to his wife Melanie, also a teacher, and they have two young sons.

Entrance: Informal assessment in literacy and maths for Y1, Y2, Y3 (none in EYFS). Entrance tests in English, maths and general ability for Y4-8, Minimum requirement usually appropriate national curriculum Sats level for age group.

Exit: Majority (between 90 and 95 per cent) take scholarship exam and move on to Upper School. Some sit common entrance for other major public schools such as Winchester, Marlborough and Cheltenham.

Remarks: Restructured from three separate schools – nursery, pre-prep and prep school (popularly known as the Pre) – to an all-through school, aligned with Clifton College upper school, allows for a more seamless curriculum and learning experience for children and for families. School admits it has been hard for staff – 'not without its issues' – but everyone realised it was being done for the right reasons. 'Some were initially territorial but are now seeing tangible benefits.' In the transition, seven staff with a total of 198 years' experience left. Those who remain are 'reinvigorated', enjoying the challenge of being responsible for curriculum progression from Y1-Y8.

Children benefit from being taught by specialists for music, science, technology, languages, and from access to improved facilities for art and IT. 'There can't be many pre-prep schools that have these kind of facilities at their disposal. We have found subtle ways to keep the best bits and give each part of the school its distinct identity. We were braced for a reaction but parents have embraced it. They were confident the merger would work. They now feel part of one college, not a piece of a big jigsaw. They buy into the Clifton lifestyle and ethos.' Term dates and exeats aligned too. One parent confirmed: 'There was a lot of difference academically between Butcombe (the pre-prep) and the Pre – that's not the case now.' Parents are impressed that the school has sought their views and acted upon them. 'There has been a real willingness to listen.' 'It's a sign of a school that wants to move forward.'

Firm links with near neighbour, Bristol Zoo: 'It's not every school that has a zoo in its back garden'

Very strong EYFS provision with nursery and reception in own building, fabulously equipped for child-led learning. Messy room was a beach when we visited – one child had insisted on bringing her swimsuit. Children love the smart table, with age-appropriate games and apps, which encourage collaboration. Wonderful early years library. Lovely outdoor area with willow tunnel, fake grass, sandpits, spider frame. Three reception classes. Forest school – every week – an integral part of the curriculum. Lots of feedback for parents – interactive learning diaries, including video and audio, with mums and dads encouraged to add photos and information from home.

Y1 and Y2 follow a topic-based curriculum, with plenty of innovative and imaginative activities to suit all types of learners. Children use iPads increasingly. Four Y3 classes, learning mainly with their class teachers. Y4 has science lessons with specialist teachers; more specialist teaching in various subjects as children move up the school. Scholarship class for high fliers in Y8. Standards and expectations high, but parents and staff adamant that school is not a hothouse. One parent said she specifically chose the school because she felt it would not 'push them to hard too quickly academically' and would develop the whole child. One-to-one support from specialist teachers where needed for children in pre-prep found to have dyslexia, dyscalculia or dyspraxia or other specific learning needs. Prep school has its own specialist learning centre, the Coach House, where short and long term needs are addressed 'as part of the school, not an added extra.' Parents feel that communication has improved. 'Previously reports were a bit vague. A really positive change is that we can access achievement points online through the parent portal. It means I can give my children immediate praise and feedback.'

Music very strong from the start. Every child in Y2 learns violin and in Y3 recorder. Singing, composing, choirs, individual instrumental tuition encouraged. Art is of exceptional quality. Dance and drama are very popular; children relish the opportunity to stage shows in the school hall and in the Redgrave Theatre. Five thousand books in the library. Design technology facilities are better than many a secondary school.

Pupils have swimming lessons in the college pool from reception onwards. A host of other sports both on site and at the college's sports ground at Beggar's Bush, including rugby, hockey and football. 'My boys absolutely love the sport, even though they are not A-team kids,' said one mum. Saturday school from year 4 now sports activities only, no lessons. Years 7 and 8 have two lessons followed by matches.

'It's not every school that has a zoo in its back garden.' A firm link has now been established with Bristol Zoo education centre. Positive relationships with state primaries too, and not just in the middle-class area near the school. Music projects and teacher exchanges have been set up with inner-city schools and those on deprived estates and there are aspirations for more local schools to be able to make use of the Beggar's Bush facilities.

'There is a perception of Clifton as "the toffs on the hill" and I think we have softened that image,' says school. They are determined to continue to break down barriers and ensure pupils realise how fortunate they are and how important it is to care for others. 'We are very much changed, more engaging and more accessible. We can't afford to follow what we did 50 or 70 years ago. The thing we are

most proud of is the way social impact has taken off in the prep school. We have always been charity minded but we are taking a step further than cake sales.' As well as working with organisations such as Fairbridge and Prince's Trust, the school runs a unique project called Colour My Life in which staff, parents and some children redecorate and refurbish a home for an underprivileged family, Changing Rooms-style. 'It is one of the most meaningful things we have done. It changes children's outlooks dramatically.'

Families value the pastoral support from matrons, houseparents and their teams. 'I feel like they are surrounded by people who care. There is always someone to talk to'

Another factor that helps pupils realise 'that Britain is not the centre of the universe' is the international nature of the school. Contrary to popular perception, it's not full of rich Russians. Biggest growth area is western Europeans, some of whom attend for a few years while their parents are working in aerospace or energy industries in the west country. Because they arrive speaking Spanish, French or German, their English is not always good enough to hit Sats level 5, meaning Clifton misses out in league tables, but that's a small price to pay. And, as one pupil said, having native MFL and Mandarin speakers is a great help when it comes to homework and practising for oral exams. 'We have friends from all over the world,' one pupil observed. This is seen as an asset by many Bristol parents, including doctors, lawyers and other professionals. Proportion of girls in the school continues to increase – now around 40 per cent.

There's a day house and a combined day/boarding house each for girls and boys. Children join the houses from Y4; Y3s have a common room where they can start to feel more independent. Families value the pastoral support from matrons, houseparents and their teams. 'I feel like they are surrounded by people who care. There is always someone to talk to.' 'It is a very nurturing environment.' 'So many people get to know your child, each from a different perspective.' Houses, mostly in Victorian buildings, are well maintained and continually upgraded. A major investment in recent years saw the £3.5 million development of 1 The Avenue, which contains a girls' and boys' day house and a dance studio.

Most full boarders are Y7 and Y8, although some are younger. British boarders largely from Forces families. 'School is 24/7 even for day pupils.' Weekly boarding and flexi-boarding options popular with busy local families, as are early start and late pick-up wraparound care. Sleepovers for day pupils popular. 'Still a critical mass of boarders around at weekends.' Recognition that children (and adults) get tired and possibly tearful from busy school day and need TLC. Emphasis on supporting families – 'one stop shop, we take care of everything'.

Incredible range of clubs and activities for children from dawn until beyond dusk, seven days a week. 'We want everyone to find their niche; discover their passion.' Older children also encouraged to take on responsibilities and to celebrate the achievements of their peers. 'Everybody has a chance to shine here,' one said.

Dauntsey's School

West Lavington, Devizes, Wiltshire SN10 4HE

01380 814500 | info@dauntseys.org | www.dauntseys.org

Ages: 11–18

Pupils: 815; sixth form: 254; Boarders: 300 full

Day: £18,450 pa; Boarding: £30,540 – £33,450 pa

Head master: Since 2012, Mr Mark Lascelles (40s), previously lower master, and temporary acting head of King's School Canterbury – something of a rough ride. He was educated at Shrewsbury School and Durham, where he read geography and was keen and proficient in cricket and football to county level and beyond. Now he only plays social cricket – frustrating, as he is very competitive. Back at Shrewsbury for a further 17 years, he became a housemaster and coached many of the Shrewsbury teams before joining King's School in 2009. He is married to Amber, a teacher and graduate of Durham, who was a national level canoeist. They have three young daughters.

Mr Lascelles is stunned by 'the quality of pupils' at Dauntsey's, not just their academic level but their genuine niceness and the energy injected by having an intake at 11: something he had 'missed out on before'. He sees Dauntsey's as a collegiate school, for families who understand about good education, and are not blinded by fashionable pretension.

Both the curriculum and the classrooms are quite traditional but the stunningly high level of pupil satisfaction registered in the recent ISI inspection bears witness to the excellence of the teaching. Parents like him and say he is accessible, listens and takes a personal interest in all pupils, meeting the school bus every morning and being a friendly presence at most activities. He had a hard act to follow and is very different to his predecessor, 'but has finally mastered the art of feeding biscuits to paddling canoeists as they pass in the Devizes to Westminster race!' Out of school he enjoys travel, skiing, reading and theatre – and is rapidly developing a taste for musicals, which is just as well as at the time of our visit Dauntsey's was about to put on Sondheim's Into the Woods followed by Mamma Mia.

Academic matters: Over the last few years Dauntsey's has come up quite a few pegs in the academic stakes and has a pretty impressive record for a 'not overly selective' school – though of course success breeds demand which ups the ante. In 2017, 49 per cent A*/A grades at A level and 71 per cent at GCSE – mostly IGCSEs which, pupils say, 'prepare better for A level'.

Big Cheeses of the school world locally should look to their laurels or Dauntsey's might pip them at the post. Curriculum includes a four language carousel of French, German, Latin, and Spanish for the first year from which two or three languages may be chosen. Other languages – Mandarin, Russian, Japanese, Greek, Arabic etc – are done in extracurricular time. Native speakers are encouraged to take exams in their own languages.

Three science IGCSEs for two-thirds of the year group; the rest do dual award science (three sciences taken as two GCSEs). Spanking new science labs full of GCSE groups practising practicals. A spectacular full-size skeleton monoplane hangs in the hallway and the charming courtyard with super bosky pond has raised beds crammed with Japanese anemones.

No limits on choices at A level. Pupils can now take three plus an additional AS, the EPQ, sport or Dauntsey's own leadership qualification. DT (resistant materials), in a whizzy new class room, with new courses in psychology, history of art and English language starting. Outstanding in maths and further maths and more than sound across a very wide board including theatre studies, music technology and class civ as well as the mainstream stuff.

Recently acquired Mercers' field has extensive pitches, 'levelled by computer,' pupils say. Huge range of 'strenuous pursuits' available in the 'long break'

Class size around 16 in GCSE years. Busy SEN department with three full-time staff providing help, within the timetable but at extra cost. Mainly helps mild dyslexia and offers a safety net for the organisationally challenged but, 'If pupils pass the entrance exam,' says the head, 'it is rare for us to say we can't cope with their special needs'. Impressively wheelchair friendly (even disabled wetroom showers) for a school with no current need for it. Thirty or so need and get EFL tuition, which is thrown in as part of the special enhanced international fees. Efficient IT taken for granted, having virtually reached IT saturation point, though pupils are pretty impressed that free standing printers at convenient points access and print from their personal files activated by thumbprint. Pupils register by thumbprint too for afternoon school, but house staff like to lay eyes on everyone in the morning.

Games, options, the arts: Sport is definitely big and timetabled three times a week. Boys' and girls' hockey, rugby and cricket doing pretty well at county and regional level. Football played in senior years, tennis, for all, and netball, for girls, all tackled competitively. A smart-looking rugby pavilion graces the grassy expanse in front of the main school and a new pavilion with lecture facilities was recently completed.

Girls regularly send a hockey team to South Africa to match the triennial rugby tour of the Australia, and there is no shortage of opportunity. The recently acquired Mercers' field has extensive pitches, 'levelled by computer,' pupils say. Archery happens there but was elusive on our visit, though we spotted the coach's van. A huge range of 'strenuous pursuits' available in the 'long break'.

Situation alone gives Dauntsey's a whiff of bracing contact with the great outdoors, focussed, during our visit, on the whole school cross-county race. The delightful lower school guides, when asked what happened to non-sporty people, didn't think there were any. Some parents feel that the less talented enthusiasts need more chances to play in teams, even against each other. Masses of expeditions like the Brecons Challenge and a long distance canoe race from Devizes to Westminster. Moonrakers, a third year programme, offers all sorts of outdoor adventure challenges (at no extra cost), and the more ambitious Dauntsey's Mountaineering and Expedition Society travels to the orphanage they have adopted in Romania or visits their contacts in Bhutan. Lots do D of E though they skip silver because of exam pressure.

Solid rather than spectacular facilities – indoor swimming pool, two handsome Astros, sports hall, new dance studio, athletics track a hike away – a source of grumbles for a few; macho fitness area with scary weights and levers has had a facelift and a bit more space. Too unusual to omit is the sailing club. No Optimists or Fireflies on a pond for Dauntsey's, instead school has bought a 100 year old tall ship, the Jolie Brise. Pupils have competed in the Fastnet (she actually won the first in 1925); they also cruise more lazily off the Isle of Wight. Everyone gets a go in mixed teams of eight and parents are envious.

What the music department lacks in size it makes up in enthusiasm – multitudinous groups of every genre happily play away, certainly more than 20 groups timetabled – choirs, orchestras bands. It needs a bit more space. A good take up of instrumental tuition on every instrument ever invented makes for plentiful concerts with some mature and accomplished performance. Practice sessions timetabled for junior boarders.

There is serious drama – King Lear is probably as serious as it gets – when enthusiastic performers can be weaned away from everyone's first love, the many enormous school musicals and 'extraordinary performances' which sometimes even make it to London theatres. Smashing A level results in theatre studies. The multi-function 'memorial' school hall has really good lighting and equipment thanks links with the West End. Plans are a foot to refurbish it with better seating (sinking into the floor) though it would be a pity to end such bizarre juxtapositions as the stately school altar, sanctuary and organ at one end and a stunning full size white puppet cow at the other. Annabel's, the well-equipped drama studio, has everything needed to launch careers via the Edinburgh fringe and such venues. Good and popular dance studios too – it's in the curriculum – with a few boys taking part.

There's not much you can't do at Dauntsey's, which is probably just as well for 300 or so boarders residing in a leafy backwater

Across the playing field, the chimneyed art block has a deceptively arts and crafts look but is full of all the relevant IT and pottery things. It's about to get an upgrade to make more space and dark room for photography planned for A level. Head of art keen on observational drawing. Bags of school trips – modern languages to Spain and France, geography to Iceland, RS to India, Adventurers to Bhutan, skiing in Italy

There's not much you can't do at Dauntsey's, which is probably just as well for 300 or so boarders residing in a leafy backwater.

Boarding: One advantage of being almost at the back of beyond is that Dauntsey's has plenty of room to spread itself – a seven hole golf course at the Manor House (co-ed boarding for juniors) who undoubtedly get the prettiest building. Some choose to ramble home through a lovely mile of so of woodland path, from which their Victorian mock Tudor mansion welcomes them at 4.30pm into a spacious galleried hall with inviting sofas round blazing fire in winter, to take tea and delicious looking scones and cake. It's a spick and span version of Hogwarts, with its long oak tables and panelled common rooms smelling of furniture polish rather than 60 small boys and girls. Dormitories are functional but spacious with lovely views, weekends full of well planned, child friendly activity, mostly on the spot.

Boarding houses (single sex), both old and new are exceptionally spacious, some with en-suite facilities and all have kitchens, workspace and proper recreation area. A sixth former described it as 'certainly better than adequate but not quite luxury'. Day houses get everything the boarders have except the bedrooms and the juniors have their own similar on-site day centre.

Background and atmosphere: Founded in West Lavington in 1542 on the deathbed largesse of William Dauntsey, master of the Worshipful Company of Mercers, the school opened in 1895. Mercers' Company still provides six governors, occasional generous financial help and annual knees-up for its associated schools which include an unlikely spread from St Paul's Schools in London – both boys' and girls' versions – to Peter Symonds College (state sixth form in Winchester), two new academies and The Royal Ballet School.

Lawns and trees enhance the setting of the handsome main school building, and the recently redesigned reception area is reminiscent of a five star hotel with its glass topped tables, comfortable furniture and well lit pictures changed regularly by the art department – and it is nice to see the artist's names. Other facilities are more functional, but very well maintained. Perhaps a bit countrified for some hardened Londoners – until 1930 the school was known as Dauntsey's Agricultural School.

Dauntsey's has mushroomed, to the extent that buildings jostle haphazardly with an increasing number of lawned and planted milling-about spaces between buildings, so the brightly coloured maps at every corner are necessity not decoration. A young pupil claimed to have taken only a week to find his way about. What impresses is that it has absolutely every facility a school should have but nothing extravagant.

It's a spick and span version of Hogwarts, with its long oak tables and panelled common rooms smelling of furniture polish, rather than 60 small boys and girls

The most spectacular feature is a superb bright and airy new library – which must say something about academic priorities. Some exposed desks/computers down the centre of the building may not be everyone's cup of tea (where do they hide the sweet packet?) but more sheltered study space is available upstairs plus round tables and comfy chairs for a good read. Fooling around can be done in the cyber café or in the tuckshop. Lessons finish at 4pm and it is technically possible for day pupils to creep off then, but most stay on for prep or take part in clubs or sports until the mass bus exodus at 5.30pm. Boarders have two hours of prep in the evenings, one just before and one after supper.

Uniform is as expensive but not more than most. Girls have a rather limp blue check skirt with blue blouse and pullover. Boys in blue shirt and grey-blue jacket. No uniform in sixth form but

smart-ish dress required (suits or chinos, tie and jacket for boys and at least a nod towards formality for girls) – quite widely interpreted. The reversible black and white rugby shirts are just being phased out for smart though less popular mainly white ones which wash better but get smelly very quickly. The busy school shop has an endless supply to lend to those who forget games things. The san is modern and inviting with quiet places to sit and suffer and comfortable looking bedrooms. Pupils definitely value the care given there, including counselling.

Pastoral care, well-being and discipline: Much less privilege orientated than many schools, so apart from the 17 Club, which is the hub of sixth form social life, and biscuits at morning break, sixth form and prefects live and work alongside the upper school and take a full part in house life. Relationships between year groups are definitely flexible. The pastoral system functions through the houses, in which the house staff and at least four assistants act as tutors to about 60 pupils. Parents say problems are handled successfully and with great sensitivity.

Breakfast provided for all-comers in the pleasant dining hall. Boarders have to be there by 8.15am. Buffet service with spectacular and popular 'live cook' every day and all meals in on the fees though not compulsory. Staggered sittings to manage flow of hungry diners but a few choose to use the house kitchens if the dining room is full.

Responsibilities taken seriously by prefects and captains of houses, who are selected by head and staff. Drugs get immediate expulsion and pupils know it. Apart from that, 'rules are', pupils say, 'a matter of common sense', though a new rule book is issued each year. The comments they made on 'how far into the opposite sex house' they are allowed showed they had a pretty shrewd idea of what is and is not acceptable. They also emphasised the trust between pupils and staff.

Pupils and parents: Not toffs on the whole, more local families, farmers and small businesses, with quite a number from state primaries or first time buyers. Lots of professional families with two parents working to earn the fees. Being just over an hour from London, Bristol and Southampton makes boarding pretty accessible from UK or abroad. International intake widening from Hong Kong and Russia to a wide spread of countries: Europe and beyond. Fifteen bus routes from Salisbury (south), Swindon (north), west to Frome and east to Hungerford and Andover, which puts them into competition with a number of good grammar schools as well as some top independents.

Entrance: At 11+, from state schools and a few preps, entry is by Dauntsey's own exam (maths, English, VR and optional music auditions). Selective in that they accept about the same standard of candidates as Salisbury Grammar, according to the head. At 13+ they take mainly boarders from prep school and some from abroad via 13+ CE or scholarship exams in November, with very few day places at this stage, adding an extra two forms. Feeders include Chafyn Grove, St Francis (Pewsey) and St Margaret's (Calne), All Hallows and Thorngrove plus many local state primaries. Everyone sitting an exam at 11+ is automatically considered for a scholarship and around 15 pupils out of 80 admitted get some sort of award.

Some 50 pupils join the school for sixth form, around a third from abroad – a minimum of three A*-A/9-7 and three B/6 grades at GCSE is required from UK pupils, plus interview.

Exit: A trickle – some 10-15 per cent – leave after GCSEs, mainly for local sixth from colleges. Large proportion to solid science, medicine, languages etc courses at good unis (Exeter, Bristol, Birmingham and Cardiff popular recently) and a respectable number to Oxbridge (five in 2017, plus six medics/vets, and one off to the US).

Money matters: Much more aware than many schools that parents' resources are not infinite. The vibe from parents is that day fees here particularly good value for money. A few nice touches: music lessons cost the full whack for first instrument but less for second and subsequent ones; a 10 per cent reduction for siblings who are boarding at the same time (a very sibling-friendly school). Mercers' connection is a help when it comes to funding building projects but not a bottomless pit.

Remarks: It's in there competing with the heavies but still unpretentious, with feet firmly on the ground. Parents value its special atmosphere, rooted in being reasonably non-selective, both academically and socially. Steadily improving results and facilities are putting Dauntsey's among the front-runners in the area. Its friendliness, breezy campus and outdoorsy image belie a focussed academic purpose, which encompasses arts and sciences, though it doesn't inhibit the pupils from having a pretty good time. Dauntsey's is fab.

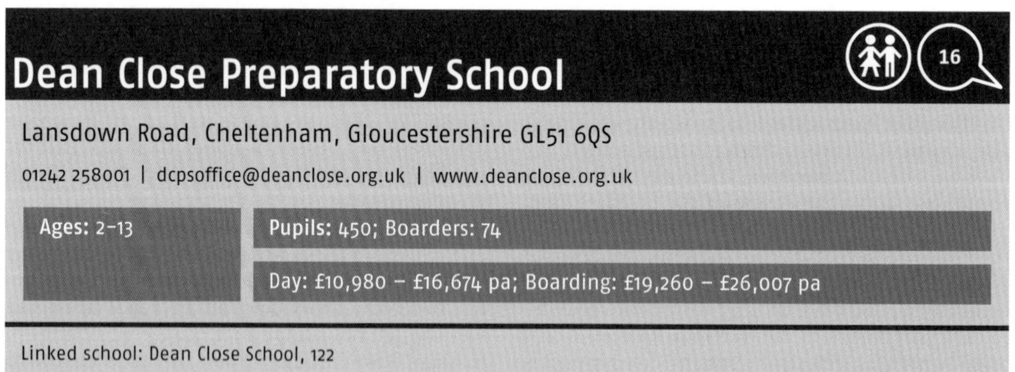

Dean Close Preparatory School

16

Lansdown Road, Cheltenham, Gloucestershire GL51 6QS

01242 258001 | dcpsoffice@deanclose.org.uk | www.deanclose.org.uk

Ages: 2–13

Pupils: 450; Boarders: 74

Day: £10,980 – £16,674 pa; Boarding: £19,260 – £26,007 pa

Linked school: Dean Close School, 122

Head: Since 2015, Paddy Moss, who was previously head of St Andrew's Prep School, Turi, in Kenya. He attended the school himself in the 1970s and was head of the prep between 2006 and 2015. His wife, Julie, is also a teacher and they have three daughters.

Entrance: Admission to pre-prep by taster day including information assessment. From year 3 by cognitive ability and English papers plus interview and school report. Year 3s mostly from own pre-prep, but roughly a third more come into year 7 from local preps and primaries. School makes

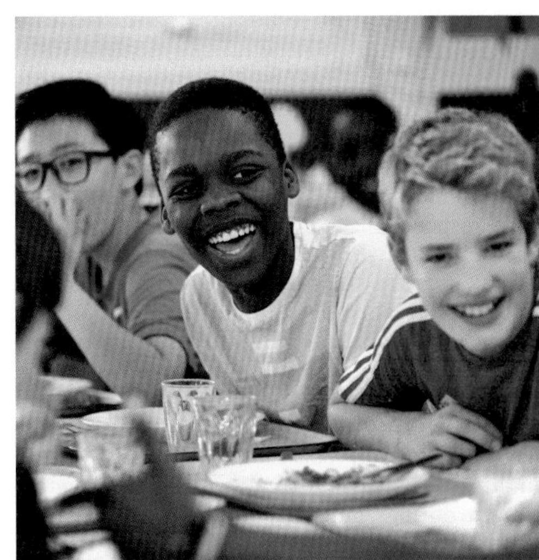

the test as unthreatening as possible – on our visit we saw one girl enjoying chocolate and having a fuss made of her in the office, having finished her paper. Choristers (boys only) auditioned between 7-11 years.

Exit: Nearly all to Dean Close School. Some five per cent go on to a mixture of other schools – Malvern, Eton, Marlborough.

Remarks: Pre-prep, fondly known as The Squirrels, headed since 2011 by Dr Carolyn Shelley. Early years' focus on developing children's senses, to prepare them for learning in prep and beyond. Plenty of hands-on activities, positive reinforcement and encouragement for achievement of all kinds, not just academic. These Squirrels are fortunate enough to have their own forest school in the extensive grounds – regular visits allow them to experience the changing seasons, go on expeditions and meet small invertebrates. Back indoors, facilities are just as appealing: great library and ICT suite – all designed for this age group – plus ground floor classrooms linked by creative areas. Sports facilities shared with prep and main school (swimming pool, tennis courts). Plenty of singing and music; all learn recorder with option of lessons in violin, viola, cello (in their reduced sizes) and piano. Dance classes also available. Burgundy sweatshirts with squirrel logo, tartan tunics for girls.

The prep school has opened a newish £4.5 million building which includes a reception area, theatre, music suite, hall for drama, concerts, assemblies and exams, plus IT suite, drama rooms and classrooms. The new classrooms are arranged to aid cross-curricular work. Prep is separated by playing fields from big school but with use of seniors' specialist sports facilities, such as dance studio and pool, in addition to their own considerable outdoor and indoor provision. At least four sessions of timetabled sport a week plus the option to join clubs and try out shooting, climbing, dance and golf. The floodlit, covered play area is a great asset, a huge space for pupils to race about, kick balls and even roller blade in, no matter what the West Country weather throws at them.

Around a third board – the vast majority are full boarders, meaning plenty of company after school and at weekends. A few 'day' boarders stay up to three nights a week

The school aims to 'fire the imagination and enthusiasm of every pupil', and children here benefit from subject specialist teachers, increasingly as they move towards common entrance. Setting from year 6 onwards based on individual learning plans. Subject knowledge boosted by frequent trips and plenty of hands-on activities – the emphasis is still on fun and teamwork. Those with mild dyslexia, numeracy or specific curriculum needs are supported in groups or one-to-one by specialist SEN staff; EFL also offered.

Dean Close is the Schola Cantorum for Tewkesbury Abbey, educating the boy choristers who sing there (four evensongs and Sunday services). Several other choirs, orchestras, ensembles and bands give ample opportunities for young players and singers to perform in house and at public events such as the Cheltenham festival of performing arts. Speech and drama thriving, with both timetabled and extracurricular sessions – great for confidence building. The list of clubs, many set up by the children themselves, runs from the predictable Warhammer to the gloriously unexpected Norman Wisdom film club, and takes in Fun with Wool, Start Greek, gymnastics and riding along the way.

In senior prep (years 7 and 8), pupils are given more responsibilities in order to develop independence and leadership skills, ready for senior school. All take part in community action projects and trips are further afield – Snowdon, camping in Devon and fencing in France, for example.

Approximately a third board – the vast majority are full boarders, meaning plenty of company after school and at weekends. In addition a very few places for 'day' boarders, who stay up to three nights a week. Of course many structured activities and outings, but equally important is free time to play outside and explore the extensive grounds, woods and brook. Three boarding houses: one for boys, one for girls and Wilton, a mixed house for the youngest; each is presided over by houseparents – a married couple with children, resident matron, two tutors and non-resident staff. Common rooms with televisions (weekends only), Wii, games consoles etc, plus table tennis, craft and model making areas, baking, a graffiti wall and milk shake nights are just some of the temptations on offer.

No chance for backsliding in instrument practice – one of the tutors in each boarding house is a musical (grade 8 minimum) gappie whose job is to oversee scales, accompany on the piano and encourage young singers and players. Boarders' rooms are bright and full of home comforts; we liked the customised carrels in the girls' prep room – all feathers and glitter. Children can speak to family via Skype and text, but no personal laptops allowed. Parents receive a Friday evening email from housemaster telling them what's been going on, so they can chat knowledgably with their offspring – a boon for those with uncommunicative young.

Seems to have the balance just right, providing a secure, caring environment in which pupils receive a first class academic grounding and explore their own talents and interests. As one parent put it, 'The school doesn't expect them to grow up too fast – it lets them enjoy just being children.'

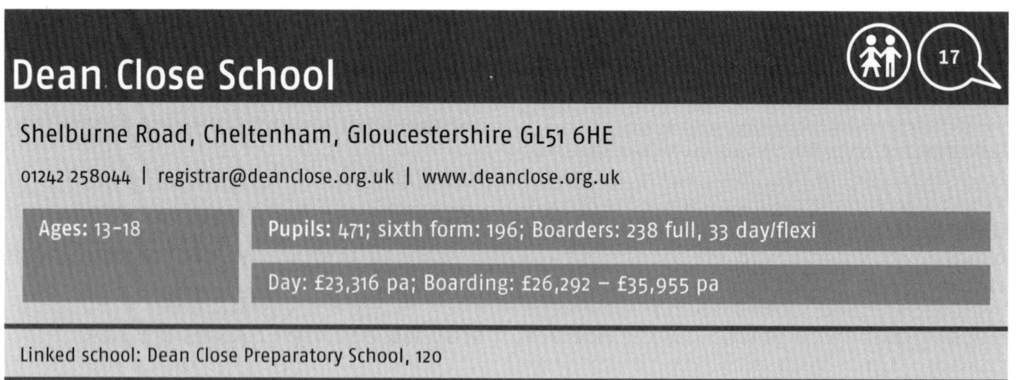

Dean Close School

17

Shelburne Road, Cheltenham, Gloucestershire GL51 6HE

01242 258044 | registrar@deanclose.org.uk | www.deanclose.org.uk

Ages: 13–18

Pupils: 471; sixth form: 196; Boarders: 238 full, 33 day/flexi

Day: £23,316 pa; Boarding: £26,292 – £35,955 pa

Linked school: Dean Close Preparatory School, 120

Headmaster: Since 2015, Bradley Salisbury MEd PGCE, deputy head at the school since 2009 and a successful acting headmaster. After studying at University of Leeds (completed part time masters at Bristol), taught religious studies at Gordano School before moving first to Bristol Cathedral School as head of department and head of years 10 and 11 and then to Wells Cathedral School where he was head of religious studies and a housemaster.

Academic matters: Solid results for all at GCSE and A level and though year groups vary, the trend is upwards. The head says that the school looks for 'attitude as well as aptitude', a statement that demonstrates his confidence in the school's proven ability to develop and boost its pupils.

In 2017, I/GCSE: 54 per cent A*-A/9-7. Twenty-two subjects offered, with most taking 10 or 11, smallish numbers for classics, Latin and Greek. Separate sciences, excellent maths and physics results. At A level, 73 per cent A*-B, 36 per cent A*/A. Once again the mathematicians are light years ahead with A*/As – whatever it is they put in the water in the maths department should be bottled.

Classes are small, between 15 and 20 (12 in the sixth form) and teachers, according to one parent 'work with each child's individual abilities', and, according to another, 'achieve miracles'. Mild SEN (dyslexia, dyspraxia) catered for and EAL is taught in individual lessons or groups.

The head is proud of the extension programme for sixth formers designed to help them develop critical thinking skills, engage with different ideas

and 'confront non-standard stuff'. A critical essay competition open to the whole school is judged by an external adjudicator and keenly contested.

Games, options, the arts: Hockey is the game here for senior boys and girls, with seemingly every team vanquishing all comers, including the likes of Millfield, to become county champions and national finalists. One of our guides was a rugby fanatic but realistic about his school's performance against the big names: 'We're probably not near the top'. Emphasis is on everyone getting a game – at least three and up to five teams for every year group. A pool, gym, rifle range, dance studio and climbing wall and, in addition to acres of playing fields, a large covered pitch so the younger children can play outside whatever the weather.

Equestrian sport is an increasingly popular option – this being Gloucestershire, a handy polo club in nearby Birdlip where riders can learn this sport from scratch. Teams take part in schools show jumping, cross-country, eventing and dressage competitions, with individuals competing at national and international level in all disciplines. No stabling, though, so you'll have to leave the pony at home.

Music here was described by one parent as 'second to none' – all are encouraged to take up an instrument or sing. Practice sessions are not timetabled but schedules are agreed with music tutors, which apparently results in more productive practice. The music school houses teaching and practice rooms and the Prince Michael Hall, used for concerts and public speaking. Hosts of chamber ensembles, rock bands, choirs and orchestras and musicians perform locally and nationally. Regular tours have taken them to Paris, Venice and New York. A strong tradition of Oxbridge organ and choral awards; the boy choristers from Tewkesbury Abbey's Schola Cantorum (stars of many a CD) are educated here. In residence is the new head of strings, the celebrated Carducci Quartet.

Art, too, has its own purpose built 'school' and exhibition space. Results at GCSE and A level are strong, a good proportion go on to continue their artistic education in some of the country's most acclaimed art colleges, including Central St Martin's, Chelsea, Camberwell and The Slade, and further afield such as the Charles Cecil Studios in Florence. Sixth form artists have allocated spaces where they can leave out works in progress. The art school's BonBernard Gallery is used to display both pupils' and professionals' work.

Parents we spoke to described the school's pastoral care as 'fantastic', 'The staff genuinely care about the children'

In addition to a studio theatre and a large amphitheatre in the grounds, fortunate thespians can also tread the boards of the Bacon Theatre, a 550 seat venue that wouldn't look out of place in small town. Named after former headmaster, Christopher Bacon, it hosts at least eight school plays a year, a major musical such as Les Misérables or Guys and Dolls every two years, as well as numerous professional productions; lecturing luminaries including Judi Dench, Samuel West and Peter Hall. In addition to GCSE and A level theatre studies, pupils are prepared for the RADA and LAMDA examinations up to diploma level. The school theatre company, Close Up Theatre, has performed sell-out plays at the Edinburgh Fringe for several years.

Add to the above a huge choice of clubs and societies, CCF training, D of E and a community action programme where pupils work on projects locally and abroad (building a school in Uganda) – it's no wonder boarding (or 'day' boarding, two nights a week) is so popular with local pupils: they don't want to miss out.

Boarding: The senior girls' boarding house we visited was light and modern with glass brick floors in the corridors. Rooms were reassuringly untidy (inspections on Sundays), customised with posters, photos and plenty of home from home clutter. 'Keep calm and carry on' seems to be the motto de choix on many walls. Sixth formers have single rooms with linked ensuites and plenty of Cath Kidson bunting. Fourth form prep is done in separate study areas and monitored by sixth formers. Downstairs are squashy sofas with bright red cushions, board games, puzzles, a Wii, DVDs and music. Saturday night is film night. Boys' boarding similar standard but less bunting, and sofas evidenced rougher treatment.

Background and atmosphere: One parent described the atmosphere at Dean Close as 'relaxed yet achieving' and that just about sums it up, rather more succinctly in fact than the colour printing fest of promotional literature – considerably more quality photography, paper and gloss than other schools we've visited and needing its own Dean Close carrier bag. School mags, The Decanian and Young

Equestrian sport is an increasingly popular option – this being Gloucestershire, there's a handy polo club in nearby Birdlip where riders can learn this from scratch

Decanian, are similarly shiny and flawless and perhaps just a little corporate. The school is more humane and down to earth than its brochures let on; the pupils we met were charming and grounded – one said that the best thing about school life was being part of a 'community of individuals'.

Occupying 50 green acres just beyond the centre of Cheltenham, it could be quite a daunting place but somehow keeps the protective ethos of a small school on its big site. The main school is a familiar mix of Victorian and later additions – although it is by no means short of the latest smartboards and ICT equipment, we were delighted to see a well-stocked library like an upturned boat and a wonderful high ceilinged history classroom with piles of books, walls covered in posters and a makeshift display of shells (exploding variety) and a tin helmet. And was that chalk dust floating in the shaft of sunlight coming from the tall windows? Probably not. The head has plans for a major redevelopment in the heart of the school, 'a radical approach to teaching space' (plus a new swimming pool) – we hope the history classroom's days aren't numbered.

The dining hall serves hearty home-cooked food with plenty of choice, pupils and staff eat at refectory tables with a fine view of the grounds. Boys and girls we spoke to were generally positive about the meals – several said they thought the food had improved while they had been there. Boarders can supplement with toast, hot chocolate and other snacks they prepare in the kitchenettes.

Pastoral care, well-being and discipline: The principles of Christianity form the moral heart of the school and for some this is a deciding factor, but 'no pressure' to get involved beyond cultural Christianity. One parent, not a churchgoer, was positively evangelical about what he identified as the 'spirit and energy' of the school. Our guide, who was very involved in this aspect of school life, said, 'It's not uncool to be a Christian here.' A whole school evensong in the chapel every Friday and voluntary communion and Bible studies plus a pupil-run Christian Union. The popular female chaplain organises various programmes to develop pupils' spiritual awareness.

No significant behaviour problems – main challenge, according to the head, is day pupils, who very occasionally get into trouble 'off-site' at Cheltenham's seedy dives. (Are there any?) Testing for any suspected of substance abuse; immediate dismissal for dealing. School takes a 'cultural approach' to bullying and staff vigilant for anything, even if it's just chit-chat, that may make a child feel isolated. Head very hot on challenging what he feels is a contemporary fashion for sexist put-downs. Prefects trained to look out for anyone feeling wobbly. Parents we spoke to describe pastoral care as 'fantastic', 'The staff genuinely care about the children'. A few grumbles from parents of day pupils, who wanted more opportunities to discuss their child's progress than the termly meetings with staff, but all agreed teachers were approachable and quick to respond to queries.

Pupils and parents: A good number of boarding parents are first-time buyers – the lack of old boy snobbery is a big draw. Significant numbers of Forces and diplomatic families are delighted to find a school where all their children can be educated together. School keen to stress its 'local' character, but even pupils whose parents live within bus distance elect to board when they get older (both our guides fell into this category). Mix of established families and London defectors has energised population in recent years. Roughly 15 per cent from overseas but no dominant nationality.

Famous Old Decanians include Tom Johnson and Pete Brown, rugby players; Hugh Quarshie, actor; George Adamson, author of Born Free; Francis Bacon, artist; Lord Bernard Ribeiro, former president of Royal College of Surgeons.

Entrance: 'Quite accessible,' according to head, but two applications for every place; he adds that one of the qualities Dean Close looks for is curiosity, children who will 'have a go' and embrace every opportunity the school offers. Pupils enter at 13 from the school's own prep and after common entrance from others such as Pinewood, Beaudesert Park, Hatherop Castle, Prior Park, St John's-on-the-Hill. Sixth form entrants are accepted on the basis of three subject-based papers with VR or EAL.

Exit: Over 60 per cent to Russell Group, handful every year to Oxbridge (five in 2017, plus three medics), plus a few to art college, drama school and music conservatoire. Popular subjects: engineering, economics (no surprise there, given calibre of mathematicians) and classics; favoured institutions currently Bristol, Bath, Durham and Exeter.

Money matters: Described by more than one parent as 'value for money'. Scholarships and exhibitions for 13+ and 16+ entry awarded for excellence in academics, music, sport, art, drama, DT, plus a few for 'all rounders'. Small number of 100 per cent bursaries for those who 'could benefit from a Dean Close education'.

Remarks: Dean Close is a warm and welcoming school, aspirational without being snobby and secure in its strong moral and social values. As one of our guides said, 'You don't have to be a type to fit in here – you just have to be keen to give everything a try.'

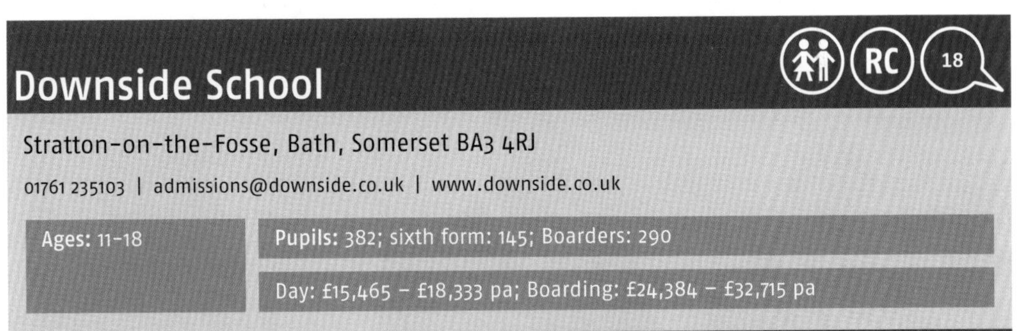

Downside School
RC
18
Stratton-on-the-Fosse, Bath, Somerset BA3 4RJ
01761 235103 | admissions@downside.co.uk | www.downside.co.uk
Ages: 11-18
Pupils: 382; sixth form: 145; Boarders: 290
Day: £15,465 – £18,333 pa; Boarding: £24,384 – £32,715 pa

Acting head: Andrew Hobbs, deputy head, is holding the fort until a new head takes over.

Academic matters: Results have come on leaps and bounds in recent years. In 2017, 35 per cent A*/A and 60 per cent A*/B at A level and 47 per cent A*-A/9-7 at GCSE. Usual subjects at A level, plus business studies, economics, history of art, PE, photography and psychology. History department offers the Pre-U – head of history says the qualification involves 'good, old-fashioned essay writing' and enables youngsters to study topics such as monasticism in the 9th century and the Gregorian reforms of the 11th century as well as more recent fare.

Most pupils take 11 GCSEs. English, maths and RS are compulsory and all are encouraged to take at least one language, a humanity and a creative subject. French, German and Spanish are the main languages, but Italian, Mandarin, Russian, Polish, Chinese, Portuguese and Arabic can be arranged. Most pupils do three separate sciences. Director of studies says the school believes in setting 'ambitious realistic targets' and tracks and monitors pupils' progress throughout. School's intake is 'selective, but broadly mixed ability' and its value added scores are particularly impressive. Maximum class sizes of 20 up to GCSE and 16 in the sixth form but classes are often smaller than this. Pupils are set in maths and science up to GCSE. A variety of academic societies, including the Knowles, where Oxbridge candidates present their own research papers.

Learning support department now in the heart of the school (it used to be housed in a separate block). Support given to 30 pupils, either one-to-one or in small groups, but department also offers drop-in sessions for anyone needing additional help. EAL is also available.

Games, options, the arts: With 500 acres of grounds to run around in, fresh air and exercise are an integral part of Downside life. As well as rugby, hockey, football and cricket for the boys and hockey, netball, tennis and rounders for the girls, there's a wealth of other sports on offer, including aerobics, athletics, badminton, cross-country, fencing, squash and swimming. Pupils have three games sessions during the week, plus matches on Saturday afternoons, but many do far more than this. Sixth formers get just as much sport as their younger counterparts – everything from boxercise to circuit training. When we visited, a group of older girls were in the middle of an energetic zumba class, music blasting across the courtyard. Sports facilities include an indoor pool (donated by a family whose son tragically died in a Naples swimming accident in 1925), rugby pitches galore, football pitches, cricket squares, Astroturf, a glorious 1930s sports pavilion and a sports centre with a weights room and fitness suite.

Downside has a rich cultural heritage. The abbey's Monastic Library, housed in a 1970s building, is one of the largest private libraries in the UK

Parents report that the music is outstanding. Half the pupils have instrumental lessons and there's a multitude of orchestras, chamber ensembles and choirs (the Schola Cantorum is the oldest Roman Catholic school choir in the UK), along with jazz ensembles, a barbershop ensemble, pipe band, brass band, even an open-mic night. Art department has been refurbished and is equipped with Macs, photographic studio, 3D printers and glass making facilities. Printmaking, textiles, oil painting, landscapes, portraits, graphic illustration, photography, fused glass – you name it, Downside does it. 'I'm a firm believer that everybody is creative in some shape or form,' the dynamic head of art told us. School has strong links with Hauser & Wirth Somerset, the contemporary art gallery in nearby Bruton. Busy drama department. School puts on a whole school play and musical every year, plus a host of other performances in refurbished 500-seat

theatre. Refurbished performing arts centre with recording studio, editing suite and 18 practice rooms circling around a 500-seat performance space is inspiring musicians, dancers and thespians.

All year 9s are expected to do CCF for at least part of the year. Many carry on while others opt for D of E and Ten Tors expeditions across Dartmoor. Action-packed co-curricular programme includes chess, astronomy, Model United Nations, Young Enterprise, sewing, contemporary dance and fly fishing.

Boarding: Most pupils board – boarding is 'part of our USP'. Four boys' houses and two girls' houses. All junior boys (years 7, 8 and 9) start in Powell, a boarding house located in the main school, with open plan dorms and bunk beds for the youngest and a homely kitchen where boys get to cook (and eat) cookies, crumbles and pizza. A parent said some of the boys' dorms could do with a bit of updating but her children think they are fine as they are. Junior girls go straight into Isabella or Caverel, the two girls' boarding houses.

House staff are adept at helping children to settle in. 'No one gets lost here,' we were told. A housemother reckons that Ovaltine, warm wheat bags (the modern answer to hot water bottles) and talking helps to stave off homesickness. Pupils are kept occupied at weekends with lots of trips and inter-house competitions. Up until the sixth form pupils hand in their mobile phones at night so they get a good night's sleep and aren't distracted by Facebook, Snapchat and the like. Parents thoroughly approve.

Although technically doesn't offer weekly boarding, boarders can go home on any bar four of the weekends each term. These are 'closed' weekends, the ones immediately after or just before holidays or half terms. Otherwise, pupils are welcome to go home after they have completed their sports involvement on a Saturday afternoon, which is some time between 3:30pm and 5:30pm, on other weekends. They then return to school for the Sunday evening.

Background and atmosphere: The magnificent Downside Abbey adjoins the school and is visible for miles across the rolling Somerset landscape. The school has been on its present site in the village of Stratton-on-the-Fosse since 1814 but dates back more than 400 years. The Benedictine community of St Gregory the Great was founded in France in 1606 by English and Welsh monks living in exile because of the penal laws in England against Catholics. By 1617 English Catholics were sending their boys across the Channel to be educated there. When it became safe in the early 19th century for Catholics to provide education once more the school moved to England. Downside's monastic

community (currently 12 monks, some of whom teach) has been in residence for 200 years. Members of an apostolic community from Chile – the Manquehue Apostolic Movement – have a base at Downside too. The school went co-ed in 2005 and the boy/girl ratio is now 60:40.

Most recent inspection report commented that 'pupils of all faiths and none possess an inner confidence, and a strong sense of their own identity'

Downside has a rich cultural heritage. The abbey's Monastic Library, housed in a 1970s building, is one of the largest private libraries in the UK and has a collection of more than 400,000 books and papers, many of them very rare. 'It's like having an Oxford college library on the campus.' The school's atmosphere and setting are traditional, with historic corridors (the science corridor is lined with pictures of old boys who died in the First and Second World Wars), parquet floors and pupils hurrying to classes in their eye-catching uniform. Worn by all (including the sixth form), the uniform comprises mid-length kilts and red or black jumpers for the girls and black jackets and pinstriped trousers for the boys. The pupils' maroon and gold game kit is particularly jazzy – good for spotting players on the games pitch.

School food much improved following the appointment of new caterers (manager formerly worked for River Cottage Canteen Bristol, part of Hugh Fearnley-Whittingstall's culinary empire). A stylish café serves cappuccinos, cookies and toasties during breaks and evenings. Fifty per cent of teaching staff live on site or in Stratton-on-the-Fosse.

Pastoral care, well-being and discipline: A strong sense of spirituality pervades the school. Around 80 per cent of pupils are Catholic but children from other Christian denominations are welcome. School has a distinctively Catholic and Benedictine character and incorporates the eight aspects of a Benedictine education – welcome, listening, reverence and humility, teaching and learning, personal discipline, concern for the individual, building communion and stewardship of gifts.

School's most recent inspection report commented that 'pupils of all faiths and none possess an inner confidence, and a strong sense of their own identity.' Everyone is expected to participate in the school's spiritual life. Sunday mass in the abbey is compulsory, as is hymn practice on Friday afternoon. While Downside's monastic community prays formally six times a day, each boarding house has prayers in the morning and evening. School chaplains visit each house at least once a week and the school chapel is always open for those who want to go and pray. A third of the school takes part in voluntary prayer groups but it's very much up to individuals. A father with two children at Downside emphasised that religion isn't forced on the pupils – 'it's a gentle, subtle part of what is there,' he said. A mother we spoke to praised the school's ethos. 'There's an emphasis on the whole person,' she said. 'Everyone is made to feel welcome.'

You can spot an Old Gregorian at a dinner party, we were told, because they always offer to do the washing up afterwards. 'It's that blend of good manners and service'

Excellent pastoral care and tolerance for the individual produces happy children. Each pupil has a tutor to oversee academic matters and there's a raft of people to talk to if they encounter problems – tutors, housemasters and housemistresses, housemothers, the chaplaincy team, health centre staff and a school counsellor who visits twice a week. Pupils generally well behaved. Policies on smoking, alcohol and drugs are very clearly spelled out. Smokers are enrolled on a smoking cessation programme in the health centre. 'Responsible' drinking permitted at the sixth form bar.

Sixth form has its own study centre (very quiet and studious when we visited). UCAS coordinator guides pupils through their university entrance. Pupils are prepared well for life after school via spiritual, moral, social and cultural education (SMSC) – topics covered include how to set up a bank account, relationships, even mortgages. School also runs themed weeks on issues like e-safety, alcohol and drugs.

The Independent Inquiry into Child Sexual Abuse is looking closely into historical, and relatively recent, cases of abuse by monks at Downside, and at the Benedictine practices which appear to have made them more likely. If/when you visit, it might be worth asking questions because, at the very least, whilst pupils may well remain unaffected, these will almost certainly have proved a distraction internally.

Pupils and parents: Boarders (28 per cent international students) come from all over. At the beginning and end of term school buses ferry pupils to London, airports and local stations. Day pupils tend to live within a 30-minure drive – places like Shepton Mallet, Frome, Bruton and the Chew Valley.

School says that while some of the pupils are from very privileged backgrounds no one is materialistic or showy. A parent with three boys at the school concurred. 'A lot of schools are quite flash these days,' she said. 'Downside isn't like that at all. The pupils are very well mannered and the school gives them really good values. They know what is right and what is wrong.' An old boy with two children at the school told us that while his daughter was 'almost surgically attached' to her mobile phone before moving to Downside she hardly uses it these days. 'The school is very good at keeping them busy,' he says. 'In my day Sunday was a quiet day but now there are coaches going off all over the place.'

Alumni (known as Old Gregorians) include writer and journalist Auberon Waugh, hotelier Rocco Forte, scriptwriter Peter Morgan and interior designer David Mlinaric. You can spot an Old Gregorian at a dinner party, we were told, because they will always offer to do the washing up afterwards. 'It's that blend of good manners and service,' explained the director of pastoral care.

Entrance: Pupils must be able to cope with the school's 'traditional academic curriculum.' At 11+ and 12+ entrance is via the Downside Junior Assessment Test (English and maths), plus reports and references from pupil's current school. At 13+ most applicants take CE (required mark of 50 per cent but the average is 65 per cent). At 16+ pupils sit tests in subjects they are planning to take at A level. B/6 grades at GCSE required (A/7s for maths and the sciences if they are planning to study these at A level).

Quite exceptionally helpful and welcoming admissions staff. A real sense – not found everywhere – that they will take the time and care each applicant deserves.

Exit: A handful leave after GCSE, usually for day schools or to study vocational subjects. At 18 the vast majority head to university (gap years not so popular these days). Yorks, Exeter, Durham, Edinburgh and UCL current destinations; one off to study medicine in Poland and one medical biochemistry in Germany in 2017.

Money matters: A 'substantial number' of scholarships and exhibitions are available (the number and size are at the discretion of the head). Means-tested bursaries, discounts of 2.5 per cent for children of Old Gregorians and 10 per cent for siblings.

Remarks: A boarding school with a strong moral compass. Downside is a great choice for Catholics and those seeking strong spiritual direction in a school. Its unpretentiousness, happy atmosphere and keen academic focus give pupils the chance to concentrate on acquiring their own intellectual and spiritual toolkit and to grow up in their own time.

Exeter Cathedral School

C of E 19

The Chantry, Palace Gate, Exeter EX1 1HX

01392 255298 | registrar@exetercs.org | www.exetercs.org

Ages: 3-13 (boarding from 8)

Pupils: 256; Boarders: 16 full/weekly, 54 flexi

Day: £6,915 – £11,535 pa; Boarding: + £7,200 pa (£8,724 pa overseas)

Headmaster: Since January 2016, James Featherstone (30s). Previously head of lower school at the Perse School in Cambridge. Studied French and Spanish at Durham, then did a PGCE there, and was a choral scholar at Durham Cathedral. He later joined the choir of Jesus College, Cambridge and became part of the professional quintet at St-John-at-Hampstead, London.

James and his family live in Hall House, the pre-prep school, and have embraced life in the southwest, making the most of nearby moors and beaches. Julia, his wife, was previously assistant director of music at the Stephen Perse Foundation and now teaches music part-time at ECS. Both are well-suited to this lifestyle; James is son of a headmaster so grew up living in boarding schools, and Julia spent her childhood living in vicarages.

To date, James has made significant improvements at ECS with his ambitious makeover plans, plus he has appointed new staff and repositioned older ones. Parents have been kept up to date with his newsletter and are so far impressed. 'I think he has exactly the right attitude for ECS,' one told us; 'a breath of fresh air,' said another. One added that he 'is dynamic, accessible, enthusiastic and ambitious for the school with a passion for nurturing the best in all his pupils and ensuring that they understand that success is not just based on grades but being a good person too.'

Entrance: Taster days with informal assessment, plus interview with headmaster. Voice trials for choristers (boys and girls). All special needs considered, although the school only supports mild needs currently. Children will only be turned away if their behaviour is not up to scratch on taster day (most are given a second chance). If a child doesn't fully meet academic standards, school may offer places as long as a learning support plan is agreed. Choristers must be above the baseline academically. Choristerships worth 25 per cent off tuition fee; there are currently 36 choristers at the school.

As well as taster days there are 'Come and be a chorister for a day' and 'Taste of boarding' sleepovers for prospective and current pupils alike. The entrance process and settling in is seamless. The school has a tea party for all new children and their teachers in Hall House just before term starts. Parents said, 'We were impressed with the staff, and the general warmth of the place.' Several told us that they chose ECS as it was the most natural step on from a small village primary school so suited their children best. Another parent told us, 'It was very much what the school could offer them, rather than whether the [children] would assist their results. Very refreshing compared to some of the other schools!'

Exit: Majority stay on to 13. In 2016, all year 8s gained places at their first choice school, some with scholarships, several with multiple offers. The head has recently appointed a head of scholarships, to guide pupils and parents through the process. Destinations include Sherborne, King Taunton, Taunton School, Exeter school, Maynard, Torquay Boys Grammar and Blundells, among others.

Former pupils include 14th century theologian Boniface; more recently, bass player Orlando le Fleming; Chris Martin – lead singer of Coldplay (who apparently once said, 'ECS is where it all began'); Hampshire CCC manager, Giles White and Dave Webb, ENO.

Remarks: Founded in the 12th century as a choir school, ECS is one of 35 choral schools in the UK, and the only independent boarding school in Exeter. As one parent put it, 'ECS is a rare kind of school,' and we agree. The Chantry, the prep school, and Hall House, the pre-prep, are on either side of the magnificent Exeter cathedral; an impressive backdrop to learning by anyone's standards. Although the multiple sites mean there is a lot of to-ing and fro-ing, it also means that the school feels very much part of the city. In fact one of the opening clips on the local news shows a line of happy children in royal blue tartans and sunny sweatshirts snaking across Cathedral Green.

Hall House is a former canonry and houses reception up to year 2. Securely enclosed by ancient Roman walls (and keypads), it is welcoming, bright and playful. A new 'spongey' all-weather playground separates the main building from the nursery, which was purpose-built in 2015. This is a fantastic area, free-flowing from inside to out. From the cosy keyworker areas and rooms, little ones (all in uniform) can play under awning in an area that leads to the shared playground one end, and the Woodland Garden at the other. This is a child's dream. Centred around a huge hawthorn oak tree, there's a mud

kitchen, a bug hotel and The Hide, their very own shed to bird watch, play games or make dens with pipes, tarps and crates. Beyond this there is a terraced garden with allotments for each class and the gardening club. Worried about noise from the city's neighbours? Next door is the bishop's garden.

Classes are small, between 11-18 pupils. And the classrooms are imaginatively set up; we saw one with a zoo area, another with a bakery café. The creativity continues into The Bookwormy, the library, that has a car for a bookshelf and bug beanbags. On our visit, pupils were just back from swimming and were settling down in comfy tracksuits, devouring healthy snacks, ready for storytime. The balance feels just right here; 'there is an expectation for children to do their best and give their all at any task, and there is an academic push, but it is a gentle, perfectly pitched push,' parents said. 'My son has only been at ECS for a year but the school has made him more inquisitive and he has learned so much already,' said one. 'Even this morning, at the age of just 4, he was explaining to me why he could hear building work echoing as he walked across Cathedral Green.'

Woodland Garden is centred round a huge tree, there's a mud kitchen, bug hotel and bird hide

Pupils walk to the Chantry for lunch or to the cathedral for worship. For sport they are minibussed around the city; there never seems to be a dull moment here and it adds to the charm of this inner-city school. School begins with daily morning worship in the vast cathedral chapter house. This includes spiritual readings, hymn practice and a chance to 'just be'. The Chantry houses the offices, plus years 3 and 4. Other buildings including Evans for years 6, 7, and 8 are dotted around nearby in spaces requiring passcodes. It feels like a maze but it's not; it's full of character. Walks between buildings are across pedestrianized walkways, and glimpses of the cathedral, pretty cobbled courtyards, small peaceful gardens and cleverly planned playgrounds areas make it all feel really rather special.

The boarding accommodation is made up of three Georgian houses with 22 boys' beds and 18 girls' beds for 7-13 year olds. Currently there are six full-time boarders, 12 weeklies and a large number of flexi-boarders. All are from the UK, most live within an hours drive, and around half are choristers. Girl and boy choristers sing on alternate evenings so pupils do get downtime, but this adds to the irregularity of the boarding numbers throughout the week. One parent said, 'The girls are

at home there and I know they are happy.' The large dorms have three bunkbeds each and a piano, or in some cases, a harp. Older pupils can have the privilege of a double room with two single beds. Decent showers and toilets. Efficient laundry system; even flexi-boarders get their own clean laundry basket. There's a comfortable common room, a TV room, a classroom to do prep, and the Cosy Club in the basement with sofas, DVDs, a games table and a crafts area. The boarders also have three gap students from Australia to keep them company. One parent said, 'To my eyes, parts of the boarding house could do with a lick of paint!' and this is true, but the new housemistress is on a mission and is gradually upgrading the whole place. After supper, prep, choir practice and Mrs Jolly's Hot Choccie Trolley, there's not much time for activities during the week. At weekends there can be anything from a handful of pupils to 25, and activities include trips to Haven Banks, Dartmoor or beaches. Recently boarders learnt to make sushi and hosted a Spanish tapas evening and an Irish evening.

As you would expect music plays a big part at ECS. One parent told us, 'Her music has gone from strength to strength and she has gone from a child who never stopped singing to a violinist, pianist and a member of Devon County Junior Choir with a place as a cathedral chorister. Yet the music hasn't taken over and she is developing a real love of hockey and netball.' Plans are afoot to create a music centre 'that is befitting of the standard of music that we're known for,' says the head. There is planning permission to pull down or extend the current music and drama building to make this happen. The design technology room has also recently been refurbished and the food technology room is equipped with a large and sunny kitchen. Most classrooms now have smart whiteboards or projectors. And there is talk of moving the ICT suite to a more central part of school and converting the current room into a hub, fully equipped with iPads and beanbags.

Mornings are for core lessons with form teacher and afternoons are for specialist lessons and sports. We were told, 'The English department in particular has exceeded our expectations – my eldest son has studied TS Eliot, Roald Dahl, Ted Hughes, Seamus Heaney, Shakespeare, Michael Morpurgo and Michelle Paver in the past three years with compelling lessons and homework that have both stimulated and stretched him.' Specialists teach science as separate subjects. French, from reception, is very popular. As is the teacher's dog. This is not unusual at ECS; there are several dogs. We met Ted, a rather floppy puppy who was thrilled to have tickles as pupils made their way between lessons. Latin is taught from year 6. The arts are just as impressive; we saw some fantastic (and huge) decorative masks on display in the art studio. Pupils are encouraged to think big and express themselves. For drama, year 4 recently performed Splash, a musical based on Noah's Ark. And every year 8 performs their leaving review. During a week of camping on Dartmoor, pupils work on sketches, singing and dancing (in-between other activities).

Learning support can cater for mild needs including dyslexia and dyscalculia, at extra cost. Small classes are also very beneficial and a real selling point to many families. Parents told us that ECS 'has offered an exceptional level of carefully selected and special, additional help specifically for my children. We are encouraged on a nearly daily basis with progress.' Another parent of boys with very different abilities and needs said, 'We were amazed at how quickly and accurately the teachers understood what made each of our boys tick and used the knowledge to help them both move forward.' In fact we were told several times over how pupils really do receive 'an all-round education.' One parent told us, 'her love of reading, spelling, maths and sport have all been developed at the school but I have also seen her become a kinder and more considerate child.' Another parent suggested that a school counsellor would be a welcome addition, but pupils can contact the independent listener who visits the school, if they wish.

Around half of boarders are choristers. The large dorms have three bunkbeds each and a piano, or in some cases, a harp

The school doesn't have its own sports facilities but makes good use of some of the best facilities in a traditionally sporty city. All-weather surfaces at the main university campus, other facilities at St Luke's and outside the city at Pinhoe complete the mix. Cricket is played at the county ground whilst judo, squash, swimming, cross-country and athletics are all catered for. Climbing, kayaking, cross-Dartmoor walk and annual expedition add to the excitement. As do the additional inter-house competitions. A new innovation this year was the introduction of U7 festivals for netball, soccer and athletics. As well as some pupils playing county-level hockey and taking part in the National Prep Schools Athletics Championships, one girl was selected as part of the GB sailing team in the Cadet world championships. And another was accepted into the England Pathway Netball Satellite programme. To manage these budding sportsmen and women, and the 60+ fixtures per term, the head is on the hunt for a new director of sport to, quite literally, up their game.

All sports clubs are after school, and all musical activities take place throughout the school day. The library is open to all at breaks and lunchtimes. The librarian reads with all year 3's to get to know them and their abilities and tastes. She recently ran a library Olympics reading competition that pupils have already asked to happen again. Judo after-school club is currently very popular and other clubs include fencing, ukulele, indoor cricket nets, maths, drama and poetry, bell ringing, tennis and cooking. Equestrian club takes place at weekends. Parents are very happy with the activities on offer, one saiying, 'After-school clubs cover an incredible variety (and are inexpensive) – but if you're running late for pick-up even after this time, ECS happily keeps them for prep and supper if needed. As working parents this has been perfect and takes the stress out of being stuck in a meeting and unable to contact the school.' Local trips make the most of the local area with Roman walks and trips to local museums and interests. Years 5, 6 and 7 go to France for a week every two years, year 8 goes camping on Dartmoor, plus there's a Buckfast Abbey choir camp, and hopefully some sports tours soon.

The only real grumble we heard from a number of parents was that 'The food is not great,' and 'the school dinners are very unappetising.' We have no doubt that the head and his team will be onto this with a fix straight away. This city prep school isn't perfect but it's definitely doing it's best to head that way. It's full of charm, balances academia and childhood brilliantly, and most importantly, it gives pupils and their parents exactly what they want and need.

Godolphin, Salisbury

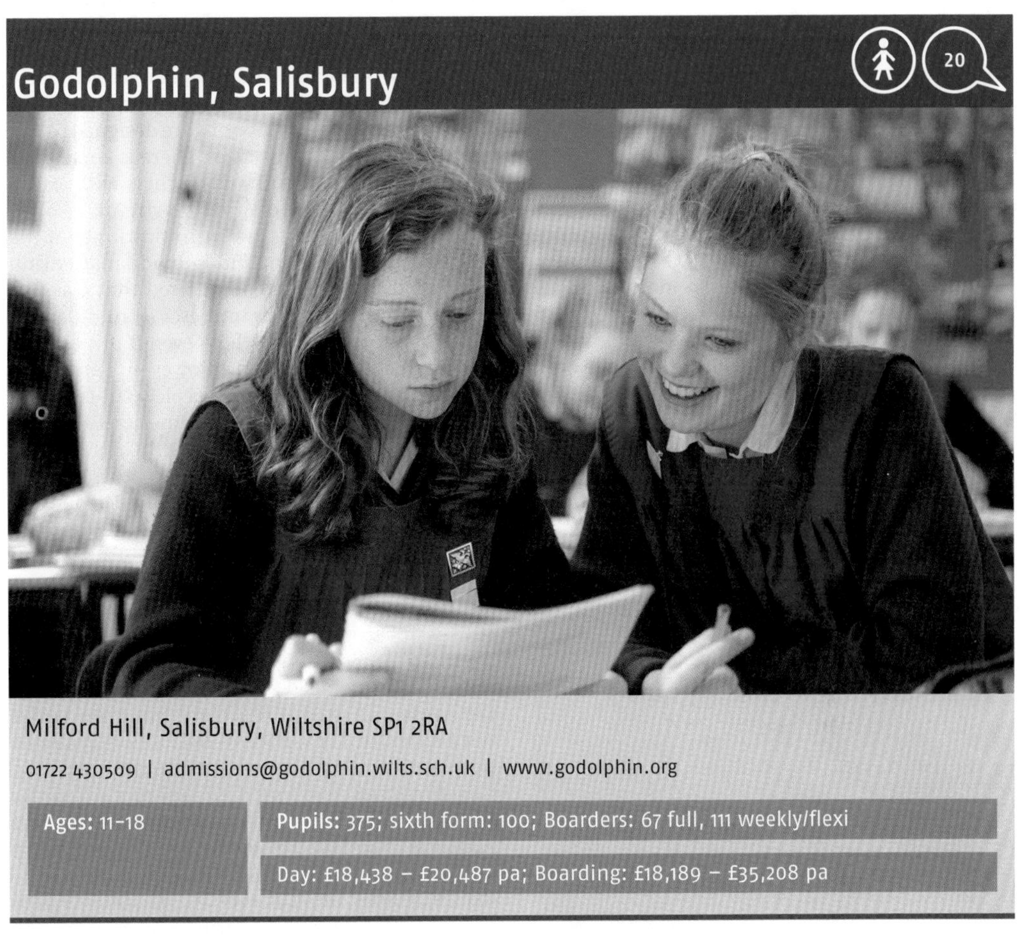

Milford Hill, Salisbury, Wiltshire SP1 2RA

01722 430509 | admissions@godolphin.wilts.sch.uk | www.godolphin.org

Ages: 11–18

Pupils: 375; sixth form: 100; Boarders: 67 full, 111 weekly/flexi

Day: £18,438 – £20,487 pa; Boarding: £18,189 – £35,208 pa

Headmistress: Since 2014, Emma Hattersley, previously deputy head, pastoral, at Sherborne Girls, before which she was a housemistress at Canford School. Mrs Hattersley trained as an opera singer at the Royal Academy of Music and has a music degree from Durham. Married with three children, she says she took her career break early so that now, in her early 50s, with her children pursuing their own careers, she is able to devote her time entirely to Godolphin. Her actor husband is immensely supportive, to the extent of running 'speakeasy' communications and other workshops in school.

Her calm, unthreatening exterior deceptively understates the determination beneath. Since arriving at Godolphin she says she has identified needs for brightening up areas of the fabric, developing staff and increasing opportunities for charitable activities. In fact she has already started on a programme of new showers, 'nice enough to make the girls feel good', surveyed parents of all leavers, consulted girls and produced her vision document for the future. She has also initiated the Elizabeth Godolphin Award for sixth formers, which gives focus to a programme of self-development and preparedness for work/life demands.

She says she believes in the Godolphin ethos: happiness, warmth, development which is aspirational but 'absolutely not at the expense of well-being'. 'We are not a hothouse' she says, but aim at 'the best we can possibly be in each girl's own style, celebrating diverse talent' and encouraging everyone to 'succeed at the level right for them'. Having taken on a school a little stunned by losing its new head to 'higher things' after three years, she has restored confidence and won parents' and girls' respect with her ability to perceive and develop what is best at Godolphin. A parent commented that 'under Mrs Hattersley staff can really develop their own teaching and pastoral skills.'

Academic matters: Definitely academic, with Latin up to A level and Greek on offer, though not taken up much for exams. Spanish, German and French also on offer though with a few following through to A level. Spectacular results in maths and art at both A level and GCSE. Other results certainly respectable, with 45 per cent A*/A at A level in 2017 and 36 per cent A*-A/9-7 at GCSE. Results have been slightly less stellar since the boards tightened up on top grades, but the latest results show that the top tranche of really able girls can achieve a sheaf of four A and A* grades at Godolphin.

French, German, Spanish and Latin taught from first year with Mandarin via a club. All available up to A level except currently Latin, and classical Greek done at GCSE via an 'Academic Society', Girls do either double award science or three individual subjects. The usual subjects are offered plus PE, design and food technology, economics, business studies and drama. Godolphin will put on an A level course for one or two students if necessary, so there's not much you can't do, and options are designed round each girl's requests every year. There is a real buzz of enthusiasm from girls and teachers with excitement about geology coming on-stream as an A level next year. Parents are enthusiastic about the level of encouragement and individual attention given by teachers. One commented that teachers support girls' particular interests by finding articles and information for them even if it is outside the curriculum. Able girls enjoy events put on by the scholars and 'Alpinists' (Accelerated Learning Programme) activities, though sometimes the compulsory ones are 'a bit groan-worthy'. Girls say most are really interesting and attract lots of non-scholars too. The REBEL (Recreational Enhancement for Bright Energetic Learners) scheme provides appreciated stimulus for year 9.

All the creative forces come together in drama, typified by recent Oklahoma – spectacular and full of home-grown music and dance

The few SEN students have plenty of help organised by SENCo/ed psych much praised by parents. Help is one-to-one, in groups, or takes the form of advice to teachers about learning styles of individuals. EAL is managed by SEN department – up to three lessons a week if necessary. Not many pupils need support, but advice to teachers is available from occupational therapist and maths specialist. Godolphin can cope with mild Asperger's. Healthy, friendly respect and affection between teachers and girls abundantly evident.

Games, options, the arts: Art has a huge and impressive building bursting with stunning work in every medium and hugely talented and enthusiastic staff. Very professional looking fabric design work on display as well as fascinating mixed media landscape work and spectacular studies based on work done in the cathedral. Two spacious studios for drawing/painting, with separate rooms dedicated to textiles, ceramics, photography and 3D; another smaller room full of iMacs for graphic design. This a truly brilliant department, making creative use of visits to and by local artists, who regularly initiate GCSE projects, and welcoming parents and visitors to view two floors of really breathtakingly exciting work – smashing results too. DT is no less impressive, with lots of colourful and innovative constructions in wood and plastic on display. It's not surprising academically gifted girls take up art or history of art here and a record number go on to art related courses at uni.

An attractive rotunda houses the performing arts centre with lovely in-the-round theatre, plenty of entertaining space and good practice rooms. Music is very well served, with the head running a popular junior orchestra of girls from prep and senior schools, a head of music who is as encouraging as he is talented, and the meticulous Mrs Sparkhall, who inspires the girls in a choral tradition that wins them the Barnardo's School Choir of the Year and other accolades. Individual lessons still in the unprepossessing and unreconstructed Rose Villa, but pupils and parents don't seem to mind and there's plenty of chamber music, though not much evidence of pop..

All the creative forces come together in drama, typified by recent Oklahoma – spectacular and full of home-grown music and dance. Girls also perform with Portal Theatre, a small, professionally run theatre group. Masses of LAMDA exams and smaller performances.

Lacrosse dominates amongst a total of 90 different teams covering all the usual girls' winter and summer sports. Netball actually fields 23 teams, and tennis 14 teams as well as teams in all the major girls' school sports – quite a feat for a smallish school. All sports reach a pretty high level considering the school's size, swimming aided by a sleek 25 metre indoor pool. Highly competitive equestrian stars, and lacrosse and netball high fliers get to county and regional teams. Achievements include equestrians getting into top three at Windsor Horse Show, U13 netball team winning county championships and one girl selected for England U18 lacrosse squad. One hockey lover's parent commented that perhaps it came second best to lacrosse, but acknowledged that there is plenty of opportunity, even so. No lack of outdoor and other related activities. One girl reported enthusiastically on taking part in the Dartmoor Ten Tors expedition after thorough training through CCF (quite unusual in a girls' school).

Boarding: Girls can start boarding from 7 or 8 in the prep, when they join the junior house. Boarding is about as flexi as it goes, with everything from full time to weekly to flexi (one or more nights per week). One parent commented that though full boarding had been ideal for her daughter because they were not too far away, it tends to focus a bit much on activities for foreign students. Current flexibility is dependent on there being some beds available.

Accommodation is simple, modern and not unnaturally tidy, with two senior (13-16) houses and

a very friendly well organised sixth form centre over the road via a pedestrian bridge. Complete refurbishment of boarding is still in progress; study bedrooms are comfortably spacious with plenty of storage and common areas. Parents commented on a lot of changes, probably referring to the recent restructuring of the separate prep boarding to be part of junior house.

Head says she believes in the Godolphin ethos: happiness, warmth, development which is aspirational but 'absolutely not at the expense of well-being'

Shared dining hall adjoins junior and senior houses. Sixth form house has its own dining room, kitchen, study areas, often with staff at hand, careers advice and leisure space with a proper Café Aroma serving the obligatory coffee shop range of expresso etc. Health provision is supervised by the indomitable Sister Gill, who creates an aura of calm, unfussy friendliness much appreciated by all.

Background and atmosphere: Unusually for a girls' school Godolphin has a long history, dating from a bequest made in 1726 by Elizabeth Godolphin, eventually resulting in the establishment in the cathedral close of a school for 'eight orphaned gentlewomen' who followed a remarkably enlightened curriculum for their day. It moved to its present 16 acre site in Milford Hill in 1891, retaining its links with the cathedral, with the bishop and chapter still represented on the governing body. Skilful use of space and the site still has a gracious feel, generated by the mellow red brick of the original building and the lovely open grass pitches with views of the downs enhanced by banks of lavender at the time of our visit. One has to look quite hard to find the few scruffy corners that Mrs Hattersley is determined to clear. The huge gothic school hall has the dusty feel (it certainly isn't, as the school is exceptionally clean and fresh) which old wood, high ceilings and portraits of ex-heads inevitably evoke. Road access is made awkward by several right-angled bends in the road, but efficient planning of parking helps, though parents report it can still be a bit of a maelstrom at pick up time.

Uniform is unremarkable: pale blue shirt, plaid skirt and navy blazer enhanced by stylish boater with crested red ribbons, known as a 'board'. All, however, is concealed by coverall old fashioned pinafores in royal blue for seniors (except sixth who wear own clothes, plus suits for going to the cathedral), red for preps and gingham for nursery. Oddly, girls seem to like this antiquated touch, while one parent attributed the school's exceptionally friendly and unthreatening atmosphere to the fact that no ultra-trendy girl would be seen dead wearing one. This is certainly a school where those who have been bullied elsewhere find general acceptance and support. An exceptionally happy place with few exclusive 'in groups', where the occasional 'falling out' is sympathetically dealt with by friendly staff, evidently liked and trusted by pupils. With its historic cathedral links, this is an overtly Christian school with a chaplain, using the cathedral for services and confirmation, though one parent regretted that it had to be on a Thursday to ensure parent availability.

Pastoral care, well-being and discipline: Pastoral care is delivered to day girls – known as 'Sarums' – and boarders together through the residential houses, which all have provision for day girls and welcome them to work and relax with the boarders. Lessons end at 4pm, but the myriad of school activities and prep run in three sessions after tea. School houses involve all ages from nursery to sixth form for competitions, fundraising and social events. Personal development is delivered in the PERSIL programme (another quirky Godolphin acronym representing Personal, Ethical, Religious and Social Issues in Life). In the sixth form the Elizabeth Godolphin Award encourages activities aimed at preparation for life after school. Truly all-embracing, it includes Prue Leith cookery (expensive), banking and finance, with car maintenance,

One girl reported enthusiastically on taking part in Dartmoor Ten Tors expedition after training through CCF (quite unusual in a girls' school)

emotional literacy, women's boot camp and dawn visits to Stonehenge all part of the bigger picture.

Firm, friendly, no-nonsense discipline leads to an atmosphere in which girls and teachers are at home with each other. The best is expected of everyone. Rules are few but clearly stated, and parents say problems such as drugs, smoking or alcohol are 'simply not part of the culture'. Girls rarely abuse the freedom they have to go into Salisbury attend socials with other schools, or entertain guests in the sixth form. 'Staff seem to care as much as I do', one parent commented

Pupils and parents: Mostly middle class with a total of about 14 per cent international students, mainly from the Far East. Not a 'toff' school, though pupils are not averse to joining up with Eton and Winchester for social events. Huge day catchment area has bus routes (some shared with Leaden Hall School) from every direction. In an area with ambitious state schools, art and music still attract pupils, as does the excellent pastoral care. Parents are pleased at how open pupils seem, speaking easily to adults and confident in public, but also that younger ones still behave like children.

Past pupils (with houses named after them) include the full spectrum of women writers, Jilly Cooper, Minette Walters and Dorothy Sayers as well as prolific novelist Amanda Brookfield. TV personalities include Dragon's Den businesswoman Deborah Meaden, Katie Knapman of Countryfile, presenters Helen Bishop and Louise Beale, sportswoman Ruby Smith, yachtswomen Hannah White and Nicola Rodriguez as well actress Charlotte Longfield.

Entrance: At 11+, 12+, 13+ and sixth form. Registered 11+ pupils invited for a preview day and night in the autumn term, before taking entrance exams in the spring term. Uses its own 11+ entrance test – maths, English and verbal reasoning, plus interview and team building exercises. Organises its own 13+ assessments 18 months prior to entry (13+ CE only used for setting purposes).

Exit: Around 30 per cent leave after GCSE, to local state schools and sixth form colleges. Most sixth formers go on to higher education, plenty art related, and a good proportion of Russell Group universities. One to Oxbridge in 2017; lots of bright hopes for the future.

Money matters: Scholarships at 11+ and 13+ for outstanding merit or promise in academic work, music, sport or art. Awards are worth 15 per cent of boarding or day fees. In sixth form, scholarships awarded for all of the above plus drama. Additional bursaries may be awarded to scholars in case of financial hardship. Six Foundation Bursaries (worth 70 per cent) are offered to orphans in need of financial support, when one parent has died or whose parents are separated or divorced. An Old Godolphin Association Bursary (25 per cent) is occasionally available to the daughter or granddaughter of a former pupil at the school. Entrance bursaries are available to all eligible candidates (including at 14+) in order of registration – so it may pay to get in early.

Remarks: It seems an idyllic school, almost too good to be true, and there is no doubt that it offers the very best of single sex education. For all its gentleness and Railway Children look, teaching is tip-top, especially now a real effort has gone into IT. Art and music are about as good as you can get and drama and games exceptional for a small school. Girls can really be themselves and the eccentric and the sociable are equally accepted. A very special place to grow up in.

Hanford School

21

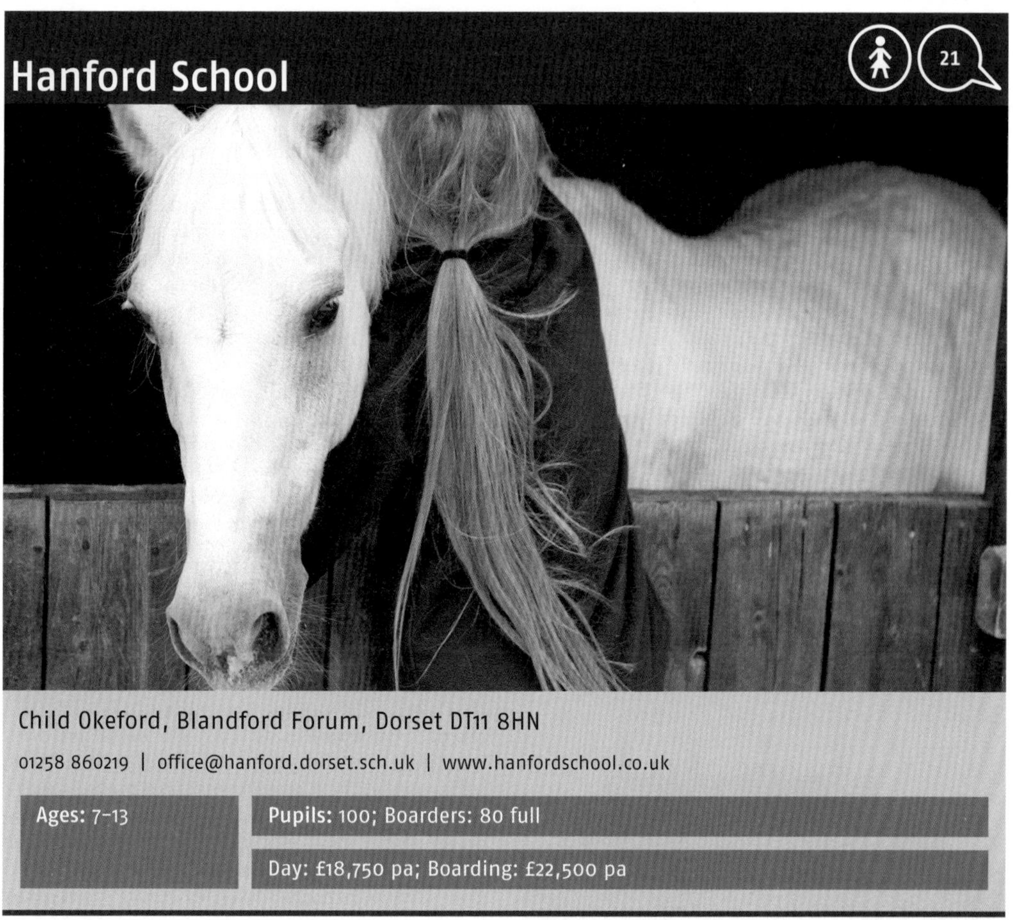

Child Okeford, Blandford Forum, Dorset DT11 8HN

01258 860219 | office@hanford.dorset.sch.uk | www.hanfordschool.co.uk

Ages: 7–13

Pupils: 100; Boarders: 80 full

Day: £18,750 pa; Boarding: £22,500 pa

Headmaster: Since 2014, Mr Rory Johnston BA (Cantab), Mr J to the girls. He's a classicist, a good fit for a school which has always excelled at classics. He's also a chartered accountant, a good fit for a school whose finances needed some grip – he's already upped the numbers and restored balance. Parted company with the City after 20 years and followed the hunch of a friend who reckoned he'd make a good teacher. Previously head of classics and boarding housemaster at Horris Hill. Wife Georgina, Mrs J to the girls, George to parents, works alongside him and heads up pastoral care. Very highly rated. Rory and George have two children.

Sarah Canning, daughter of the founders, head and owner since 1959, handed over to a charitable trust in 2003. She died in 2017. Her legacy lives on: Hanford remains very much the school she made.

Entrance: Informal, non-selective, girls can come at any time if there's room (lately a big if). Some at 7, most as 8 or 9 year olds, a few at 10 or 11. Locals, Wessex girls, Londoners (regular coach to Battersea) and numerous families posted or working abroad (especially popular with Forces and FCO families). A smattering of Europeans from Spain, France, Poland, Belgium and Germany. Parents as ever unshowy and unsnobby, new money prefers anywhere blingier. Some bursaries and a good deal for Forces families.

Exit: All over, most to boarding seniors – Bryanston, Sherborne Girls, Marlborough, St Mary's Calne and Ascot, Downe House, Benenden, St Swithun's, St Mary's Shaftesbury, Clayesmore.

Remarks: Ask any former parent or pupil about Hanford and you'll be bombarded by passionate paeans in celebration of its glories: its quirkiness, its changelessness, its quintessential Englishness. Evocations of Malory Towers and Hogwarts will ensue, together with a reverent inventory of the school's more bonkers traditions – the manners system which grades girls from Piglet to Royal Guest and the nutty names of the branches on a cedar tree that girls are encouraged to climb. You'll get the sense of a school that has somehow lain undisturbed for aeons, a time capsule, a girly Neverland; a place of butter-coloured sunlight, blissful children, long shadows, honey for tea, the whole timeless-idyll schtick. And to be sure, all of this grabs you when you go and see for yourself.

Pretty much everybody rides, but no worries if you don't. In the summer you can enjoy a gallop before breakfast

The school's location is paradisal, the manor house beyond beguiling. Stand and be captivated by the genius loci. Blandings Castle must surely be on the other side of the hill.

The cold reality, back in the days before overarching regulatory frameworks, didn't fall far short of this arcadia. This was the school where Tara Palmer-Tompkinson remembers, 'After swimming we used to run naked round the gardens because it saved the bother of tumble-drying the towels.' But Hanford needs to keep moving somewhat with the times; you can't do that sort of drying-off thing any more. Your typical Hanford parent is change averse, though. They expect a head to be a worthy guardian of the Sacred Flame, bringing as much of the past with them as possible while at the same time enabling the school to earn its keep, propitiate inspectors and prepare girls for the world of things as they are. It's a darn difficult trick to pull off.

The problem is not aims, it's means. It always is. Mr J's mission statement contains nothing that Sarah Canning didn't also sign up for, which, actually, every school in the country signs up for – fulfilling potential, nurturing talent, all that caboodle. But here's the rub: in a changing demographic where parents' needs, expectations and above all values are moving on, how can Hanford go on being Hanford?

Hanford has always had a free-radical feel to it. When the Rev Clifford Canning, newly retired headmaster of Canford, founded it with his wife in 1947, they decreed no uniforms and no prefects – which raised eyebrows back then. But the thing that's especially made the school brilliantly different is the spirit in which it's done things, with idealism, creativity and joy, wholly unselfconsciousnessly. The name for this spirit is eccentricity, and eccentricity is hard to perpetuate in process-driven times. Well, Hanford's heritage behaviours are underscored by strong seriousness, they're integral. They're loveable but they're not cutesy. Any head who fails to understand this must answer to those who feel exceedingly strongly about this school, ie, every single person who's ever known it. In the short time he's been at the school Mr J is winning high approval ratings.

His fans like the way he has committed to ensuring that girls enjoy rich, low-tech childhood in the core heritage Hanford way, out in the fresh air, playing, riding their ponies, making up games, tending the chickens, climbing trees, looking after their gardens (they get around a square yard each). They like the way this builds self-reliance and develops friendships; the way it instils, as one parent put it, 'gumption' – these are decidedly not snowflake children. Hanford parents like the adventurousness and muddy knees. They want their daughters to enjoy what they call 'a traditional upbringing' and that's exactly what they get, watched over at an unobtrusive distance, never fussily superintended. A notably horsey school from way back, pretty much everybody rides, but no worries if you don't. In the summer you can enjoy a gallop before breakfast. Ancient, lovely stables, grade II listed – 'more listed than the manor', a groom told us.

Hard to say the same about the sports hall complex, performing arts centre, design tech centre or indoor swimming pool, all of which the school has not got. But it gets by very well with what it does have – a perfectly serviceable outdoor pool, for instance, a halfway decent gym and some terrifically nice grounds. Okay, so a couple of the classrooms have been temporary for the last 30 years; what matters most is who's standing in front of the girls. Hanford's triumphant lack of state-of-the-art facilities does not, mostly, denote a lack of anything indispensable to the raising of 21st century children; indeed, it very much reflects the unmaterialistic mood music here and effectively – to be brutal – deselects the wrong sort of parent. Mr J does entertain architectural daydreams, mind, but wants to build beautifully.

The school's location is paradisal, the manor house beyond beguiling. Stand and be captivated by the genius loci. Blandings Castle must surely be on the other side of the hill

In the meantime, it's amazing what the girls achieve without benefit of stuff. By dint of excellent coaching and that indefinable Hanford spirit the girls are at the very least a match for the schools they play against with their fancy floodlights and their electronic scoreboards. All the usual sports here plus pistol shooting. Yes, pistol shooting. The time, though, has finally come to lay some Astroturf because other schools are reluctant to come and play any longer on Hanford's grass. So that's very much towards the top of Mr J's shopping list.

Masses of music, instrumental and choral – especially choral. Almost everyone plays an instrument. Dedicated music block. Drama very strong as you'd expect of a school which sets such store by play and imagination. Annual homemade production every summer performed outdoors, everyone has a part, natch. Art another heritage strength, seriously good, very well taught. The teacher told us 'The girls are amazing, they just get stuck in to whatever I give them'. Well, uninhibited spontaneity is very much a Hanford hallmark.

Academically tip-top – 'excellent,' as the inspectors express it. Recent influx of new teachers reckoned to be a shot in the arm. ICT now on course and high time too; next stop, please, DT and some engines to play with. The school bangs on an awful lot about scholarships won, around half a dozen a year, and hats off to that, fair dos, but what if your wee lassie isn't a likely Nobel shortlister? Our judgement: what the school is doing for the brightest it's doing for the rest. Just as the brightest are beneficiaries of extra attention (not special sets), so are the strugglers, because this is a very personal school. One parent who had switched her daughter here from somewhere glitzier described her learning as 'transformed'. Good library, newly beefed up. Around 10 per cent of the girls have a SEN and are attended to by specialists. Interventionist support given to anyone needing it as and when. Physical disability not easily accommodated here owing to the insurmountable architecture, wheelchair sadly a no-no. Not the right school for 'substantial' SENs.

If you want the full seclusive, immersive experience of Hanford – because shared experience and the joyous intensity of living together with your friends are what the school is all about – then you board, and that's what four-fifths do. But boarding doesn't suit everyone, nor the fees, so some don't. They have a bed all the same and can stay overnight more or less at the drop of a hat for free up to 20 days a year. Day girls go home after prep at 6.35pm. Dormitories are upstairs in the manor house, hugger-mugger, in rooms that adapt remarkably congenially to the purpose. They were once famous for their super-spartan furnishings and absence of lavatory doors, so we braced ourselves for a spot of memory lane and were almost disappointed to discover that they are cheery, snug and utterly unobjectionable even if, here and there, yes all right, a dab of paint wouldn't go absolutely amiss. Okay, so one prospective parent said she wouldn't expect her pig to live up here, but that only goes to show how much she just didn't get it. Perhaps she had a very fastidious pig. Whatever, we pictured only happy faces having heaps of fun – and reflected on how self-selecting Hanford parents are. What did concern us were the perils of pressure-cooker factors – girls getting on each others' nerves and being beastly to each other. But the quality of supervision by Mrs J, the matrons, including gap year students, is, we find, up to the mark and quickly onto this. One girl (her dad's in the Forces) protested under strong questioning, 'I've been to several schools and this one's easily the kindest.' So there. Mr J is keen to integrate the boarding and teaching staff more closely. Yes, all for that. In year 8 you graduate to a separate house, Fan's, where you get TV and feel more grown-up. A recent visitor reckoned the showers there resembled 'a 1970s campsite block, complete with soggy towels left on the floor. The tack room in the stable is tidier.' It happens.

A lot of people think that Hanford is an alternative sort of school. Couldn't be wider of the mark. Kindness matters most here. Close on its heels comes old-fashioned courtesy, hence the quaint manners league where you begin as a Boa Constrictor and earn your way up through Squirrel, Primrose etc, but risk plummeting to Piglet. It's aspirational, so there's very little Piglet-shaming. By all accounts it works. The same goes for the committee system, which takes the place of prefects. It's designed to bring out the helpfulness in girls, not the bossiness. Mr J, having watched its workings in his first year, finds it works extremely effectively. Both systems contribute to what one parent described as the school's climate of 'support, positivity and warmth' – a place where 'no one thinks they're better than anybody else'. All agree on this but no one can give you the full formula. One teacher said 'We just don't know how it works'. Being single sex has got to be a factor. That and the ban on mobile phones (but not email). Testimony to the extraordinary happiness of the place comes from the same parent: 'I'm sometimes mortified by how keen they are to get back to school'. None of the potential competition issues you might expect from a school without uniform. Why not? A girl explained 'If you wear something nice, it's probably just going to get dirty.'

If Hanford merely recreated a (mythical) 1930s childhood it would be no more authentic than one of those living history TV programmes in the mould of Wakey-Wakey Campers. It's nothing like that. It has judiciously preserved all those abiding elements which nurture the wonder of childhood at the same time as giving girls a good academic grounding and teaching them how to behave. Sounds simple, but who else does it this well? In a market where schools are increasingly differentiated by nothing more than geography, Hanford retains its measurable quality and its elusive magic. The Sacred Flame is alight and well.

Hatherop Castle School
22
Hatherop, Cirencester, Gloucestershire GL7 3NB
01285 750206 | admissions@hatheropcastle.co.uk | www.hatheropcastle.co.uk/
Ages: 3-13 (boarding from 7)
Pupils: 220; Boarders: 20 weekly and flexi
Day: £8,175 – £13,931 pa; Boarding: £18,435 – £20,985 pa

Headmaster: Since September 2017, Nigel Reed MEd BSc PGCE (30s). Formerly deputy head of Wallhampton School, Hampshire. Educated at Trinity School and Kelly College, both in Devon, and boarded from the age of 10 ('I loved it'). His father and grandfather were both in the navy and so, nearly, was he, but a taste of sports coaching while studying for his degree precipitated a sharp about turn into teaching. He started at Dulwich Prep in Kent where he taught PE and was a boarding house tutor, thence to Wallhampton where he was director of sport and, ultimately, deputy head.

Mr Reed met his wife, Jo, at Wallhampton – she's a forest school leader and a qualified teacher of mindfulness and meditation to children. She is also trained as an emotional literacy support teacher and has introduced emotional literacy to the school's pastoral care team, 'We already do a huge amount to promote physical well-being so we're keen to give the same attention to emotional literacy – offering support to parents, as well as children.' The couple have two boys at the school; 'It's a great adventure for us all.' We think they make a great team – relaxed, cheerful and full of energy.

Mr Reed is only the second head since the school started in its present guise as a prep in 1992 (before that it was a girls' school). We imagine that stepping into the shoes of Mr Easterbrook, who ran the show for 26 years, must have been a little daunting, but all seems to have gone very smoothly. Mr Easterbrook himself continues to work for the Wishford Group, who have owned Hatherop since 2014. Parents seem to agree, 'The transition was managed really well; we saw him (Mr Reed) quite a few times before he started and knew he was just the right fit.' The rapport was mutual; Mr R told us, 'I loved the feel of the place at once.'

He favours a collaborative style of headship and has appointed two new deputies, one academic, one pastoral. Of course, he has other plans – what new head doesn't – but parents who adore Hatherop because, not in spite of, its faded grandeur and old-fashioned courtesies have nothing to worry about on that score. 'Good manners are so important. We sit together at meals and all pupils from reception to year 8 shake a member of staff's hand at the end of the day.' Building up the boarding has been one of the school's priorities and London parents keen to 'educate their children out of the rat race' are catching on.

Mr Reed teaches computing and coaches rugby and girls' hockey. Since knee problems forced him to give up football, golf and cycling have become his recreational sports. He likes the fact that golf 'turns frustration into a positive' and that you can 'have a game at any age.' When he's not outside, Mr R enjoys reading crime novels and autobiographies – Douglas Bader's Reach for the Skies 'inspired him as a child'. And if all this sounds a bit hearty, he's also a huge fan of musical theatre and loves a good, old fashioned panto. He says he 'always wanted run his own school' and now finds himself doing just that – and king of a castle to boot. 'It's fabulous, I'm loving every minute.'

Entrance: No formal entrance tests; prospective pupils are assessed during the course of a taster day and on the basis of reports from previous schools. Exams and assessments for academic, art and music scholarships take place during the lent term. Some means-tested bursarial support available.

Little Owls Nursery takes from age 2 and there's a toddler group on Friday mornings where parents can bring their children (6m upwards) to familiarise them with nursery life.

Exit: At 11+ to Gloucestershire state schools and grammars. At 13+ mainly to local-ish day and boarding schools including Marlborough College, Dean Close, Cheltenham College, Cheltenham Ladies' and Abingdon School – up to half with scholarships and awards.

Remarks: Hatherop is recorded in the Domesday Book as 'Etherope', which means 'high outlying farmstead', and 900 years have not diminished the name's descriptive accuracy. To reach village and school requires a delightful meander through the lush meadows of the River Coln, followed by a steep ascent of its eponymous valley. At the height of summer this is a vision of quintessential English pastoral; what it's like on a dark winter's evening may be another story (imagine less romantic, more slippery); we hope it's on the council's gritting lorry route. The approach through classic estate parkland is hardly likely to disappoint, but the building that rises to meet you is definitely more stately home than fortified residence. If you happen to have any back-seat passengers who demand crenellations and a moat of their castles you may need to manage expectations (but only until you get inside).

Parents love the fact that every child is known as an individual, 'teachers work on developing each child's strengths – each finds their place and all progress is celebrated'

For the youngest pupils at Little Owls nursery, the emphasis is on creativity, outdoor learning and imaginative play, embodied by the delightfully sticky 'mud kitchen' and wooden pirate ship outside. Pirates and mud chefs were having 40 winks when we crept round but we spied nothing amiss. Like much at Hatherop, nursery facilities are spick and span, if somewhat make-do and mend. Friendly, dedicated staff and nurturing atmosphere more than make up any lack of superficial glitz and parents we spoke to were verging on evangelical; 'It was the nursery that sold the school to us,' said one. Several said that for them, the fact that the nursery is run along 'traditional' lines was a deciding factor. 'There's a caring, family ethos and they're brilliant at slow, but sure, nurturing.' Specialist teaching from 'transition' (age 3-and-a-half) onwards in French, music, and gym. Little Owls is open for 50 weeks a year. From the nursery buildings in their walled garden just off the yew walk, pupils move to the stable yard for reception and pre-prep. A serious game of Castle Vet was under way when we dropped in here (we very much hope the blue snake has recovered). Reception pupils may not yet be 5, but it's never too early to have a taste of work experience and they enjoy the chance to 'help' school maintenance or kitchen staff.

This is a small, inclusive school and parents love the fact that every child is known as an individual, 'teachers work with parents on developing each child's strengths – each child finds their place and all progress is celebrated.' The learning support department says school can accommodate children with 'mild to moderate SEN.' Staff will work with pupils who may just need a 'couple of terms' catch-up' and longer term one-to-one help is also available at extra cost. Study skills sessions are provided for pupils in years 7-8 to help them prepare for entrance exams. Our pupil guides took us in and out of lots of lessons and we saw quiet individual study, energetic teamwork, eager questions and answers, role play and great pupil teacher rapport. One parent told us, 'I've yet to meet a teacher here who regards their work as "just a job"; they all give so much time and energy.' School has won the Lego robotics regional finals for the past two years and last year came eighth nationally.

Parents told us it was the pupils who made the biggest impact when they visited, 'I saw the year 8s and just thought how much I wanted my own child to turn out like that'

An Astro was high on everyone's wish list and one is now destined for the newly acquired market garden site. It will make a huge difference to the sports fixture programme, enabling school to host home matches. Head wants to build up girls' sport – not just hockey but also football, with girls' rugby 'a possibility.' Other sporting ambitions include developing school's own equestrian team – riders currently put through their paces at the local riding stables – and introducing golf. Fencing is one of Hatherop's strengths – the high-ceilinged ground floor reception rooms must make excellent salles. Also on offer as clubs are judo, gymnastics, cross-country, ballet, Scottish dancing and yoga. The new performing arts centre is a well-designed modern venue that sits comfortably in the grounds. Drama and music programme is busy and ambitious, pupils of all ages and abilities are encouraged to take part in plays and concerts.

School offers full, weekly and flexi boarding; numbers aren't huge, but they're growing as parents from further afield 'discover' Hatherop. There are currently about 30 beds but scope for expansion in this area if necessary. Small regular contingent of short-term boarders from Spain and other, mainly European countries, dilute the Anglo-Saxon mix just a little. No Saturday school means everyone gets a proper weekend and weekly boarders from London can return home by train, accompanied all the way to Paddington on the Friday Cotswold Flyer (Kemble/Swindon stations are both close by), homework done and with a packed supper provided. A member of staff will meet them at Paddington on Sunday evening for the return journey. There's a programme of castle fun and excursions for boarders who stay at school for the weekend and weekly boarders can join in at no extra cost. Things are flexible enough that pupils can be scooped up in a crisis and one-off bed and breakfast option is very reasonable £35 per night – better value and more convenient than a babysitter. Working parents love the 8am-6.30pm wrap-around care option too.

Head describes the Hatherop boarding vibe as 'homely' and we'd agree. Boarders sleep in large, comfortable rooms up in the eaves – apparently the children 'prefer to be together in a big dorm' together rather than smaller rooms. We were impressed by the decoration of both boys' and girls' rooms – there was a competition to redesign them and parents judged the entries. Home duvets and lots of quirky touches, not to mention stunning views over trees and honey coloured Costwold stone cottages, more than make up for paintwork and carpets in the corridors that are showing inevitable wear and tear. A recent ISI inspection declared the boarding provision (and pretty much everything else at Hatherop) to be 'excellent' and we concur. Apart from the library, that is. Girls who studied here in the 1940s had the use of the house's original grand ground floor library. Today Hatherop's pupils make do with a fairly dreary kind of box-room cum book store – let's hope that new library comes after new Astro Mr R's to-do list.

Parents told us it was the pupils who made the biggest impact when they visited, 'I saw the year 8s and just thought how much I wanted my own child to turn out like that.' Another said how impressed she'd been with pupils' good manners and confidence: 'that's what sold the school to me.' Our guides were charming, thoughtful and very proud of their school, telling us with some nostalgia about 'cross-country runs through the woods', 'wonderful' Christmas activities and the disco in the front hall; 'Pupils from all the Wishford schools come here for that.' The tradition of year 8 leavers jumping into the outdoor pool in uniform on their last day was being eagerly anticipated.

Food got the thumbs up, particularly fish and chips, roast chicken and brownies. Parents say it's much improved over the last few years with increased use of local produce and sensible efforts to reduce sugar. We certainly enjoyed a delicious roast when we visited.

Like many stately homes, Hatherop (and its charming adjacent church) has been owned, sold, built and rebuilt over the centuries. In the 1860s it was leased by a Maharajah – there are tales of elephants on the lawn – but he didn't stay long because the railway authorities refused to give the estate its own station. It first became a school (of sorts) in the 1920s when the owner's wife, Mrs Francis Cadogan, offered to educate a handful of her friends' daughters alongside her own. One of those girls was Nancy Mitford, who recalls enjoying her time at Hatherop apart from the cold – morning wash with an icy sponge, anyone? When Mrs Cadogan's children had all flown the nest the school was moved to Cambridge where it became known as Owlstone Croft (hence Little

Owls Nursery and school owl mascot), under the governance of a Mrs Theodora Fyfe. By 1946 the school had outgrown its Cambridge premises and returned to Hatherop where Mrs Fyfe was known for producing girls who 'finished very well and debbed beautifully.' Mrs Fyfe and her successor, Dr Pandora Moorhead, sound like redoubtable characters; apparently Dr Moorhead installed a carousel on the lawn to provide relaxation for the girls. Her idea of discipline was 'come to the drawing room for a sherry darling and we'll talk about it.' Those were the days.

Hatherop was acquired by Wishford Schools in 2014, joining a group of seven preps located in Kent and along the M4 corridor. Prior to this the school was suffering as a result of changes to Forces school subsidies (RAF Fairford and Brize Norton are nearby), not to mention the financial burden of upkeep to a historic building. Let's be frank, if it's flash you're after then Hatherop isn't the place for you, but parents say that investment from Wishford has made a real difference, citing improvements to everything from food to communications.

Venerable trees, an Italian garden, rumours of secret passages, mullion windows and acres of green space – Hatherop feels like the setting for the kind of storybook childhood most parents, above all urban parents, want their children to have. It's an idea the school has taken and run with – their interactive prospectus is even called 'The adventure of childhood' and references Narnia, Enid Blyton and, of course, Harry Potter. Cynics may scoff, but if your school happens to be a castle in glorious rural surroundings, conjuring such visions is hardly a liberty. Any resident dragons and fairies must have made themselves invisible when they heard The Good Schools Guide was visiting, but we still caught a whiff of magic in the air.

Hazlegrove School

Hazlegrove, Sparkford, Yeovil, Somerset BA22 7JA

01963 442606 | admissions@hazlegrove.co.uk | www.hazlegrove.co.uk

Ages: 2–13 (boarding from 7)

Pupils: 355; Boarders: 95 full, 20 flexi

Day: £8,529 – £17,292 pa; Boarding: £20,058 – £25,593 pa

Linked school: King's Bruton, 145

Headmaster: Since September 2017, Mark White, previously deputy head (academic) at the Dragon School in Oxford. Educated at Eton and read politics and modern history at Edinburgh. Worked in retail for five years before turning to teaching and a PGCE in history from Bristol; taught in a 1,800 pupil comprehensive school in Cheltenham for 10 years, becoming assistant head, before moving to the Dragon School. Married to Serena.

Entrance: Broadly non-selective. All hopefuls are invited for a trial day at which reading/spelling ages and mathematical ability are assessed, plus any need for additional learning support identified.

Exit: To a panoply of greater and lesser public schools at 13+, majority in south west England. Between 40 and 50 per cent to the Sherborne schools, Marlborough, Bryanston, Millfield, Winchester, Eton, Oundle and Wells. Around half to its own senior school, Kings Bruton. The array of awards year after year impresses. A recent parent was delighted by the school's efforts in researching a senior school where Hazlegrove pupils do not usually go. Former pupils include Peter Wilson (Olympic gold medallist in shooting), Maddie Hinch (GB hockey goalie), sculptor Will Newton and author Tobias Jones.

Remarks: A long drive through glorious parkland – we narrowly avoided cows and 4x4s en route – leads to a fine example of 18th century domestic architecture, enhanced by formal gardens. Less sightly parts of what is undoubtedly a well-resourced and purposeful school are mostly hidden away, but facilities and space abound: super indoor pool, two Astros, tennis courts and acres of pitches satisfy the most sporty. Recent additions include new girls' changing rooms and upgrades to swimming pool including new viewing area and additional entrance. Pigs and chickens enthusiastically looked after by pupils, and there's no ducking their eventual fate either. Full use appears to be made of this bucolic setting (faintly marred by the services visible on the A303), recently enhanced by the planting of a five acre Jubilee Wood.

All these lucky children benefit from exciting and innovative ways to learn, such as a Skype call with astronaut Nicholas Patrick in which the whole prep school participated

We were enthralled and impressed by a scholarship English class of 13-year-olds who were getting to grips with the complex themes in William Blake's poetry. Parents recognise and greatly appreciate the fine teaching that goes on at Hazlegrove, and acknowledge the school's insistence in recruiting staff only of the highest calibre: 'The quality of the discussions at parents' evenings is phenomenal,' said one mother. But Hazlegrove is no hothouse, though the children are 'pushed enough,' say parents, and does very well by the breadth of ability it admits. About 15 per cent of pupils receive learning support. All these lucky children benefit from exciting and innovative ways to learn, such as a Skype call with astronaut Nicholas Patrick in which the whole prep school participated, and the millionaires' club which encourages children to read 1,000,000 words in the course of a term. The latter is part of the Accelerated Reader programme, where books are carefully graded to eliminate unsuitable choices. The librarian gets rave reviews.

Sport, music and drama ditto. There's an extensive fixture list with other schools and plenty of silverware in the trophy cabinet. One parent articulated the common tension between winning at all costs/sport for all, and wondered if there could be more chances for less skilled players to represent the school at matches. (School defends its record on this.) As for the music, well, our socks were knocked off by the impromptu marimba recital (we had not met one before either) the head asked a boy to perform when we happened upon him jamming with a couple of other pupils in the music department. Masses going on of all standards, from absolute beginners to one already at grade 8, and a clutch taking grade 5 theory – plus giant outdoor chimes in pre prep playground. Conventional choices for drama, such as Wind in the Willows and The Wizard of Oz put on in purpose-built theatre and much enjoyed by performers and audience alike; pupils also take LAMDA exams. Mandarin club has proved hugely successful and Mandarin introduced for year 5 pupils.

About a third of pupils board routinely (around 10 per cent of these are international pupils), and there is scope for occasional boarders too. Accommodation is fine (quite big dorms with a strong smell of disinfectant in the boys' quarters) with a bit of recent pepping up (includes a new common room) though rules are quaintly old-fashioned: no mobiles, letter-writing on Sundays and proper shoe-cleaning once a week. That said, activities are myriad and sometimes rather trendy: we were shown the film the boarders had devised, scripted and made the previous weekend. The feel of an extended family is palpable, enhanced by the fact that half the staff live on site. In the evenings, seating for meals is rearranged into family-style groups so boarders get to know everyone; a black tie dinner with five sets of cutlery enlivens proceedings from time to time.

Hazlegrove is quite smart and not a typical country prep school. A broad cross-section (says school) of local and not-so-local families drive or bus their kids in from all over the place up and down the A303, and it's the school of choice for many families making the big move out of London. The school defined parents, when asked, as the 'sort of people who don't look in the mirror before they come to pick up'; their occupations include farmer, lawyer, doctor, plumber, cheese-maker, helicopter pilot, entrepreneur, designer, author and chef. There is an active and welcoming social scene and parents, mums in particular, take up the exercise classes and tennis coaching with enthusiasm. Try as we might, we could not find anything to fault about this super one-off school.

King's Bruton

24

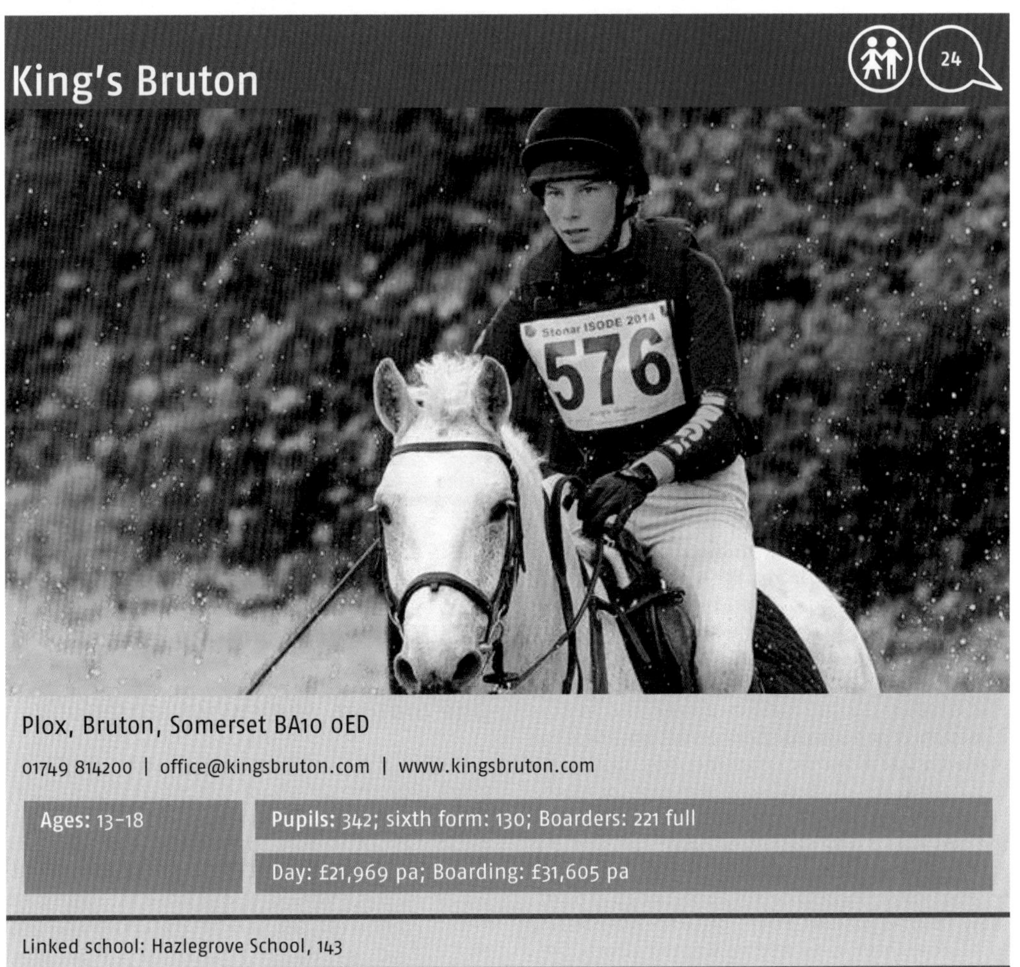

Plox, Bruton, Somerset BA10 0ED

01749 814200 | office@kingsbruton.com | www.kingsbruton.com

Ages: 13–18

Pupils: 342; sixth form: 130; Boarders: 221 full

Day: £21,969 pa; Boarding: £31,605 pa

Linked school: Hazlegrove School, 143

Headmaster: Since 2009, Mr Ian Wilmshurst MA PGCE (early 50s). A Scotsman by birth and, in his own words, born into and schooled in the Edinburgh educational mafia (his father taught at the Edinburgh Academy, even now his sister is deputy head at Fettes), the last thing he was going to do was teach. But wind the clock forward a few years, after reading geography at Cambridge and the briefest of flirtations with the army, he returned to his old college for his PGCE, after two terms' trying teaching out at the Dragon School. The roll call of schools where Mr Wilmshurst has taught since then is impressive: Highgate, Merchiston Castle and Royal Hospital where, as the sole deputy head, he had terrific exposure to the top job.

On arrival at King's Bruton, he had cause to call on that invaluable experience: at several years' safe distance, he candidly admits that he had plenty of work to do on appointment. Seven years on, he has increased numbers (it's now full for girls) so setting it on a secure financial footing, without sacrificing the welcoming and cosy feel of the place, revitalised the sport and brought the alumni on board. A very different place indeed – and one whose merits he was determined to show us, after spending some time rubbishing what he considered our previous lukewarm and out of date write-up.

Though initial impressions are of unremitting seriousness and focus (no lazy national stereotyping here), we uncovered a compassionate and reflective side, not afraid to discuss the seamier side of education. Not only easy to chat to on the touchline, according to parents, but also 'approachable and kind,' according to one mother whose family had been through a very rough patch. 'Not pretentious – what you see is what you get,' opined another. By his own admission, Mr Wilmshurst is not at all musical (though he certainly appreciates it): his hobbies revolve round sport – a sometime rugby player and cricketer, he now enjoys golf and cycling in particular. Married to Helen, who is a tutor here, he has two daughters, both in the school.

Academic matters: Not very selective, King's prides itself on accommodating all academic abilities: 'One of my priorities is to keep the balance between SEN and Oxbridge,' says the head. No room for slackers, though: everyone is expected to achieve all they are capable of and the whole sixth form does the EPQ. 'We reckon our top 30 per cent is comparable to academically selective schools,' he told us. All assessed for SEN on arrival, then setted in maths and, interestingly, French; classes are then compiled on ability.

Twenty-four subjects on offer at (I)GCSE with particularly strong languages, in scope and in grades, though this may well reflect the numbers of overseas students wanting an almost effortless GCSE. In 2017, 36 per cent A*-A/9-7 grades at (I)GCSE.

At A level, 58 per cent A*-B and 35 per cent A*/A grades; maths, further maths and history consistently good performers. Small numbers can make results fluctuate considerably, and mean that classes are all mixed ability except for maths. Voluntary EPQ. Sixth form timetable allows for the odd maths and English GCSE retake, and it is extremely rare that anyone would be thrown out for poor grades either then or at AS – not unknown, sadly, in other schools. BTec – 'after A levels reverted to a linear format, we felt we wanted alternatives for our less academic students,' the head told us – also offered in health & social studies, sport, hospitality and enterprise & entrepreneurship. We were lucky enough to sample the (delicious) edible submissions at tea time the day we visited, complete with immaculate napery and serving staff. Initiative generally reckoned to be a success, providing access to good universities: Exeter, Bath, Portsmouth inter alia.

SEN was described to us (in a wonderfully mixed metaphor) as the engine room where difficulties are unravelled. The staff of three, plus other prominent teaching staff with SEN qualifications, address a range of special needs: mainly dyslexia and dyspraxia, but also processing difficulties. Speech therapist and ed psych visit routinely. Two dedicated EAL staff to support the 40 students for whom English is not their mother tongue.

Games, options, the arts: 'Everything we touch turns to gold,' we were told, with not a little chutzpah – but it is true that the hockey in particular (girls' and boys') scales heights which would be remarkable for a much bigger school, such as reaching national finals eight times in the last four years and the U16 girls third in the national schools final. But, joyously, everyone gets a game and to represent the school, and are coached from the start by the hockey pro and director of sport to identify any burgeoning talent – 'but we manage expectations in the minds of pupils and parents', we were sagely assured. Rugby, netball and athletics also prominent and successful. No pool, but school makes use of the 25m pool at Hazlegrove; two élite swimmers currently train in Yeovil. Sport phobes accommodated with a range of recreational options, including volleyball and frisbee. Facilities fine (eg floodlit Astro) but not extensive, owing to the limitations of the school site; plans are afoot to develop underused parts of it.

'There's a good critical mass staying in at weekends and my children like Saturday nights and the chance to chill on a Sunday at school,' said one mother, somewhat regretfully

Music, likewise, is of a scope and standard befitting a much bigger school, and the complementary talents of voice and instrumental heads of music mean a fruitful cross-fertilisation of choral, jazz and orchestral music. From the military band, whose stirring strains and precise marching we were witness to on the most impeccably diagonally striped lawn we had ever seen, to the intense practice of a self-directed trio of violin, cello and piano, there truly is something ancient or modern for everyone. Music tech offered at A level: a handful of students have gone on to study the highly specialised Tonmeister degree course at Surrey. Fifty concerts a year give even beginners a chance to conquer performance nerves. Music scholars receive Kodaly and Alexander technique lessons. The new music school to be built to mark King's 500th anniversary will provide a more fitting home for it all.

Drama well provided for in Fitzjames theatre, where everyone – not just those studying GCSE or A level theatre studies – is encouraged to get involved, whether treading the boards or backstage in lighting, sound or set design. Two house plays per year on rotation, alongside whole school, sixth form and junior productions, in close collaboration with the music dept. Recent shows include Twelfth Night and Oliver! (yawn) but we were impressed that current theatre manager also writes new material. Annual trip to London takes in workshops as well as several shows.

'Not everyone is going to be a painter,' says the head of art, whose department – housed in a stunning former mill, complete with new gallery opened in 2016 – offers an exceptional range of media (3D design, sculpture and digital media, for example) to students who might go on to take a GCSE in art, craft and design. New students experience the whole enchilada, and enjoy the annual team video competition. Unusually, history of art is laid on as an A level – with outstanding results. Of course it does no harm at all to have the internationally renowned Hauser and Wirth gallery just down the road, with its education director keen to be involved. Former students have made waves in innovative artistic careers all over the world, to include a commission to beam multicoloured images onto the Sydney Opera House.

Trips (historians to Poland, linguists and musicians all over Europe, adventurers to Costa Rica) and all manner of physical and artistic exploration abound, with strong showings at CCF, D of E (where expeditions can now be done on bicycles) and that perennial west country ordeal, Ten Tors.

Boarding: Two-thirds of students (13 per cent from overseas) board in seven single sex houses where day students are fully integrated. The school's long history – all 500 years of it – means no homogeneity in houses: Old House is where it all began, whereas the girls of Wellesley House occupy an elegant Georgian mansion of cream stucco several minutes' walk from the main school. Dorms of up to four to start with; most have single rooms at sixth form. Parents rate the care given to their children, both pastorally and health-wise, and appreciate the option of flexi-boarding. 'There's a good critical mass staying in at weekends and my children like Saturday nights and the chance to chill on a Sunday at school,' one mother reported, in tones of faint regret. More space in the girls' houses would be welcome, but school tells us that places for girls have all been filled. One local pub will deliver late night cheesy chips to boarding houses on request.

Background and atmosphere: Very ancient (sits on the site of a Benedictine monastery dissolved in 1537; one wall survives), but doesn't shout about it; much will be made of the 500th anniversary in 2019, however. One of several distinguished schools in Bruton, where three generous benefactors born in this small Somerset town built of golden stone decided to found the first of them. Varying fortunes meant it was down to just one boy in 1812, but the first half of the 20th century saw it increase in numbers approximating the ones it has today, and take over buildings the other side of the busy road to Castle Cary and elsewhere in Bruton. Charming and quaint but not posh, the school works with its venerable buildings, not against them, using the parish church for whole school services, but its own simple beautiful memorial hall for assemblies.

Parents and students love its size, praising the friendliness and the fact that no-one appears to slip, drift or hide. 'Everyone is valued,' one mother told us; 'even if they aren't especially good at anything, they can just jog along'; another liked the fact that fewer students meant that her children would have to get involved in everything. The school cites its strong Christian ethos and celebrates major festivals and rites such as confirmation, but we did not get the sense that religious belief is imposed upon the unconvinced or the agnostic (respect is non-negotiable, that said): the exuberant chaplain is so down with the kids that his weekly and legendary TGI (Friday) sessions attract many comers and make the deeper exploration of faith voluntary and fun. 'It's not your belief in science that holds you together when tragedy strikes', as he puts it. A handful of Catholics and Muslims fit in comfortably and lend diversity.

Pastoral care, well-being and discipline: No adverse remarks about pastoral care whatsoever, and the tutor system, with its overview of the whole child, came in for high praise from parents; likewise health care and communications with houseparents, meaning that many problems are nipped in the bud. Though King's students might seem a biddable lot, transgressions are treated seriously – and publicly: drinkers can expect to wear uniform at the weekend, for example. We liked the sound of the relationship

policy, which cleverly omits any assumption of gender in these more enlightened times.

Pupils and parents: 'Not arrogant, good company and unassuming,' says the head – and we could not disagree. Most day pupils arrive from immediate vicinity; boarders from southern England, Europe, SE Asia and Kenya. All integrate so well that day pupils often come or stay in at weekends to join in with whatever is going on; we picked up some discontent from day parents at the long days and six day week which is more suited to boarders than their daily counterparts. More likely that one would find a child of a (successful) cheese farmer here than of a merchant banker, though the head claims to attract the same day pupil market as Millfield.

Entrance: For 13+, places offered in year 7 based on standardised test scores, school reports and interview with head. Sets in year 9 allocated from this and from common entrance results. Scholarships are awarded on the basis of papers in six subjects, plus a cognitive ability test. About 40 per cent come from Hazlegrove, the rather smarter prep school linked to King's; others from anything up to 15 other prep schools and secondaries. At sixth form, the bar is lowish at five GCSEs with a B/6 at subjects to be taken at A level, plus interview and references. Places in other year groups occasionally come up. The welcome extended to all new pupils was praised.

Exit: A handful go elsewhere after GCSE on economic grounds. Of those who stay for sixth form, only about three-quarters get to their first choice university. One to Oxbridge in 2017, and two medics (one of these at Madrid) plus one off to Boston. Some criticism was voiced about support for UCAS preparation, specifically that the school cut up rough on occasion about Saturday commitments clashing with university open days. Famous alumni include some heroes (Hugh Sexey, auditor to Elizabeth I, RS Blackmore, author of Lorna Doone), one villain (William Dampier, 17th century buccaneer) and one comedian (Marcus Brigstocke). The affection between the school and its former pupils is mutual: a higher than normal proportion of OBs come back to work at there – in proper jobs, after the school got rid of gappies. Since 2006, 150 leavers have been to work in their gap years at the Indian orphanage where the school has established strong links.

Money matters: Not a wealthy school in terms of its own assets or the families who come there, but restored to sound financial foundations under current head. Scholarships available to a maximum value of 20 per cent of fees; bursarial help available on application.

Remarks: A down to earth, unpretentious, happy school for virtually all comers in increasingly trendy Bruton (one might run into Mariella Frostrup or other celebs down from London) 'where no-one is ever made to feel second class,' according to one mother, but achieving remarkable success in the sporting arena. 'You get all the big names – then there's li'l ole us!' marvelled a proud hockey player.

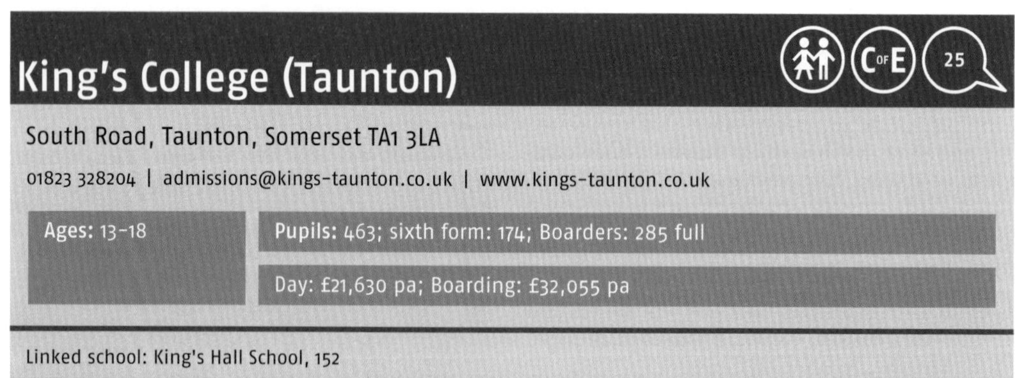

King's College (Taunton)

C of E | 25

South Road, Taunton, Somerset TA1 3LA

01823 328204 | admissions@kings-taunton.co.uk | www.kings-taunton.co.uk

Ages: 13-18

Pupils: 463; sixth form: 174; Boarders: 285 full

Day: £21,630 pa; Boarding: £32,055 pa

Linked school: King's Hall School, 152

Headmaster: Since 2007, Mr Richard Biggs (early 50s) BSc MA, a product both of the UK's and South Africa's finest: his first degree (physics) from University of Cape Town, his masters (maths and philosophy) from Oxford as a Rhodes scholar. Some barely discernible vowels hint at his upbringing in South Africa; his subsequent career has been entirely in the UK, at Magdalen College School as teacher of maths and physics then director of studies, from where he was promoted to deputy head at Lancing, thence to King's. Now into his eighth year of headship, he can look back with justifiable satisfaction at his achievements since he started, mainly an increase in numbers and improvements

to facilities. 'We can really concentrate on academics now, without being over-selective – the market in this part of the world wouldn't stand for it', he says.

Much liked by parents and students alike, who find him 'very bright, approachable and friendly', but we imagine he fixes miscreants with the eye of a basilisk when required. 'Runs a good ship,' remarked one mother succinctly, and writes a jolly good blog. A musical challenge to pass grade 1 on an unfamiliar musical instrument spurred him on to grade 8 proficiency on that most recalcitrant of instruments, the French horn ('a bit of a devil to play') and a seat in the school's wind band. He is married to Sarah, who edits the school magazine and oversees boarding house design, and has two sons in the school. When term ends, he escapes to his cottage on the north Cornish coast with his family for some rugged maritime r'n'r.

Academic matters: Academically inclusive, as attested by recent A level results, 31 per cent A*/A in 2017 (60 per cent A*/B) and yet do not quite achieve 100 per cent pass rates in all subjects. A sprinkling of U grades perhaps indicates that students are permitted to pursue their dream subjects, even if they are unlikely to get top marks; several popular and rigorous subjects (eg chemistry, biology, maths) receive grades from superb to dire, via mediocre. At GCSE, it is a similar story. In 2017, 50 per cent of grades at A*-A/9-7. A modern language is expected at GCSE; many study two, and minority languages (German, Japanese, Latin, Russian, inevitably Chinese) laid on for just one taker on occasion. Sciences can either be taken separately or as a dual award. Good range of SEN catered for, and 70 pupils currently receiving extra support; highly praised by a mother of four very different children whom we spoke to: 'My dyslexic child did as well here as anywhere; he received massive support, which meant he exceeded his predictions'. A BTec in sport in collaboration with Exeter City FC and Exeter Chiefs Rugby Club recently introduced.

Boarders are offered a good range of weekend activities; some of the students seize the advantage of being near-ish to the coast to surf and sail

Games, options, the arts: Make no mistake, this is a sporty school. Masses going on, and no exeat weekends mean a full programme of fixtures against other titans of the west country: Millfield is the one to beat. Football and rugby top sports in the winter terms, cricket the undoubted Queen of the May in the summer; school is a centre for cricketing excellence as befits its location in Taunton, home of Somerset county cricket with which the school has close links. Year round facilities (as well as beautiful pitches in the heart of the school and new indoor performance centre) mean this is truly a top school for cricket. Hockey and netball also popular with plenty of opportunities for matches (and new indoor facilities). We thoroughly applaud girls' football, cricket and hockey being promoted and resourced as well as the boys' games.

Minority sports include tennis, swimming, golf and athletics, whilst riders' lives are made easier by the offer of stabling near school for boarders' mounts, and the possibility of integrating riding into the school day for day students. Again, chances to compete and bring home the silverware are legion. Usual range of outdoor roughy-toughy stuff like D of E, Ten Tors, CCF and its precursor, the Chindit programme for year 9.

About half the school learns a musical instrument, brass especially popular and school has notable jazz band. Some grade 8 and diploma level players among senior students. Singers abound, their repertoire from the popular to the high-brow, from rock bands to the chapel and chamber choirs, via the new barbershop quartet, Quartones. Performance of whatever standard is encouraged.

Musical talents useful for annual school musical too: recently Guys and Dolls, Les Mis and The Wizard of Oz. One significant play per year, sometimes Shakespeare, many other less elaborate productions in school's own theatre, black box drama studio, recently built amphitheatre – or, memorably, in a pod of the London Eye.

Four floors of art school, including new art studio with doors onto the terrace, mean there is room enough for a gallery as well as studio space, where visiting artists can exhibit; one created a willow sculpture of the school's emblem, a pelican. Fine art is the basis of work here but digital media such as film and photography also laid on, and textiles GCSE is a new addition. We were especially taken by the newspaper tutu. King's has stand-out DT, which has won Arkwright scholarships and GSG awards on several occasions. A car in varying states of (dis)repair lurks in the DT studio for budding mechanics and designers to get their hands on, but the range of objects emerging from

School welcomes parents new and existing (but perhaps not vegetarian) with a hog roast at the start of every year

this studio combine beauty and functionality in equal measure: the tree-hung beehive is definitely on our wish list.

Despite the wealth of extracurricular activities on offer, 'the school does not push the kids into doing things, but once they sign up, they are expected to commit', according to one parent. 'Some parents don't like this, but the kids can then take credit for the activities they do, which makes them into secure self-starters'.

Boarding: Nearly two-thirds of students board, and it's the real deal: no flexi or weekly, they either board, or they don't. Busy and obligatory Saturdays mean a short weekend, during which a good range of activities is devised and offered by a designated co-ordinator; some of the students seize the advantage of being near-ish to the coast to surf and sail, some might choose to relax, swot or pop home instead. However, pupils may sign out on certain weekends as long as they don't have prior commitments. Around 12 per cent of boarders come from abroad: Chinese and Germans predominate, but the head actively explores different markets and will cap the overseas quota at 15 per cent. Military families now have their own liaison officer. Boarders stay in touch with home by email, Skype or Facetime. Devices belonging to younger students get handed in at night but enforcement varies from house to house, we were told. Boarding houses were, in our view, so-so: the girls' house we saw had a bitty lay-out separating year groups, but at least some baths still remain for muddy hockey players to soak it all off. Boys' boarding appears to be more integrated between year groups and definitely fewer frills – communal space boasted but some grubby leather sofas ('Eek!' said school. 'Not typical') and a huge TV. Day students get one night a week boarding included in the day fee.

Background and atmosphere: A Woodard School, one of about 30 founded by a visionary Victorian cleric, where, these days, Christian values of understanding, diversity and tolerance – 'religious literacy' in the words of the resident chaplain – are inculcated without a whiff of evangelism. The chapel (white, light, beautiful with a decent organ and great acoustic) and collective worship are big parts of school life; all faiths and none are made welcome. But the roots of the school go back to an ancient boys' grammar, founded in the 16th century, but relocated to its current Victorian gothic pile in the 1860s.

It's fair to say that it still feels and looks quite traditional, with conventional uniform with designer tweed jackets and blue shirts, and neatness being identified as a virtue. The dining hall boasts not ancestral coats of arms, but sporting achievements painted on shields all over the walls. We did not have the chance to sample its wares, as we were instead treated to quite the grandest lunch we had ever been offered in the headmaster's dining room: curried monkfish followed by fig beignets washed down with pink bubbly – reader, we succumbed. Not surprising to read that 'the art of tying a bow tie has been revived' at King's: its reputation as being Taunton's smartest school seems entirely deserved, and its parents are disparaging about the others, their attitude on the sports fields in particular. Whilst the façade is impressive, some of the other buildings hit low points of British school architecture – with the exception of the new library whose modern touches integrate wonderfully with the warm reddish Somerset stone.

Pastoral care, well-being and discipline: Highly rated, particularly in the person of the deputy head pastoral, and a sine qua non of Woodard schools. 'Pastoral scaffolding,' as the school explained it, includes tutors, house staff and the school chaplain, who doubles as an additional school counsellor (as well as coaching several sports); parents can raise any concerns they have through the parent portal. Considerate touches include a Facebook page for Chinese non-English speaking parents. 'Any breach of good manners and good sense' will attract censure; punishments range from detention to more community-minded activities like litter-picking, but not in orange jumpsuits. The ultimate sanctions of suspension or exclusion are rarely, if ever, necessary. Commendations are given for all manner of good works and we liked the sound of the Ferrett Prize for 'all round unobtrusive contribution by a member of the 4th form' – if you can spot it.

Pupils and parents: Unpretentious, happy to be there and grateful for all the opportunities the school offers. A boy from Hong Kong told us that he and his family had 'looked at every school in the country and chosen this one'. Families come from a wider geographical area both in the UK and abroad than the other Taunton schools, and inevitably some parents use the fast railway line to London to commute; the professions, the military, agriculture and the county set are all represented. The school welcomes parents new and existing (but perhaps not vegetarian) with a hog roast at the start of every year.

Entrance: Ninety arrive in year 9 by means of common entrance (passes expected in all subjects but school a bit coy about revealing pass mark), or by school's own papers in maths, English and verbal reasoning. Many, but not all, come from King's Hall, the school's associated prep school; others from prep schools in the south west or from overseas. A handful come into year 10 to start GCSE courses, where space permits. Twenty-five new into the sixth form after 'satisfactory performance at GCSE' or school's own papers for those without GCSEs.

Fair to say that it still feels and looks quite traditional, with conventional uniform – designer tweed jackets and blue shirts. Neatness considered as a virtue

Exit: About a dozen peel off after GCSE, some to the very good and free sixth form college across the road, Richard Huish. Leavers' destinations in recent years include a sprinkling to Oxbridge (six in 2017, plus one medic) and a bunch of conventional destinations up and down the land, around half to Russell Group, including Bristol and Durham; three off to the US in 2017. Some less orthodox choices like the Philip Green Academy for retail and the Academy of Contemporary Music. Several students apply post A level. All become Old Aluredians in any event – surely in the running for the most arcane alumni title. OAs of note include sportsmen/women (cricketers Jos Buttler and Roger Twose, hockey player Maddie Hinch, rugby player Tom Voyce), broadcasters Jonathan Meades and Dominic Wood and actress Juno Temple.

Money matters: The difference between day and boarding fees is closer than at the other Taunton schools but broadly in line. Scholarships for academic, sporting and artistic prowess plus DT, to a maximum value of 20 per cent of the day fee, are awarded at 13+ and sixth form. Academic scholars are expected to contribute to the intellectual life of the school, not just pulling in stonking exam results, but also attending weekly meetings at which papers are presented.

Remarks: Look no further for a traditional public school with distinctly sporty leanings sited in a county town. A Somerset institution housed in a suitably imposing stone monolith and serving its environs.

King's Hall School

26

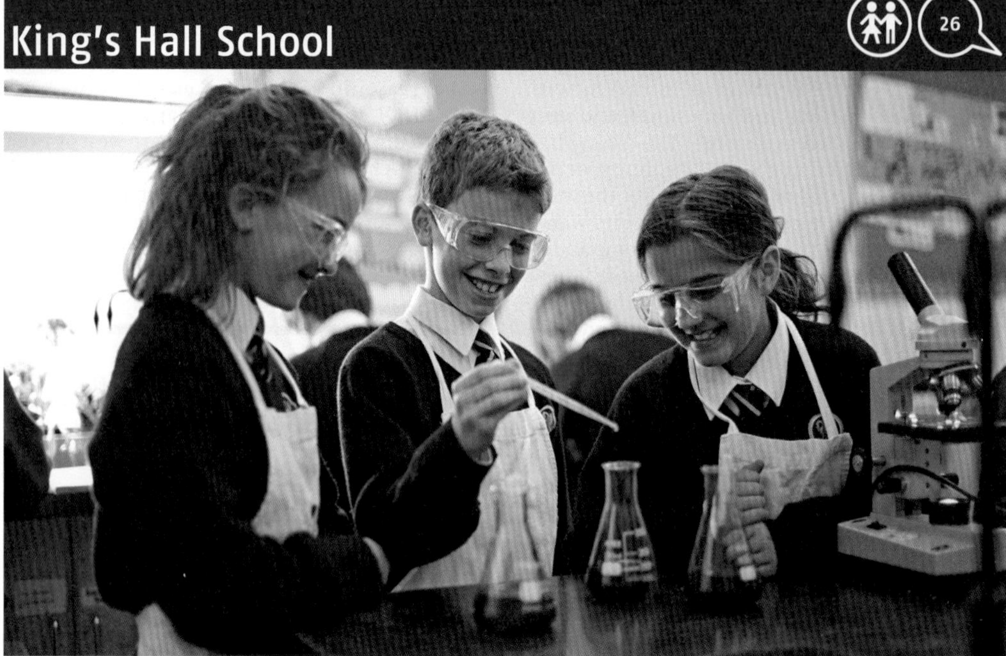

Kingston Road, Taunton, Somerset TA2 8AA

01823 285920 | admissions@kingshalltaunton.co.uk | www.kingshalltaunton.co.uk

Ages: 2-13

Pupils: 331; Boarders: 32 full, 12 weekly/flexi

Day: £7,485 – £15,990 pa; Boarding: £17,775 – £23,115 pa

Linked school: King's College (Taunton), 148

Headmaster: Since 2009, Mr Justin Chippendale BSc (late 40s). His education and subsequent career have caused him to shuttle between Oxford and Taunton, starting at the Dragon, thence to King's Taunton, back to Oxford Brookes for a degree in biology, exercise and health, a stint as housemaster at the Dragon, a detour to Chafyn Grove as deputy head, then back to Taunton. Affectionately and inevitably known as Mr Chips, he works hard to put the child's experience (of personal development, academic stimulus, physical challenge, artistic exploration and so on) as top priority at King's Hall, closely followed by the quality of relationships: between staff and pupils/parents/each other. 'I work on the invisibles and immeasurables', says he. But that's not to endanger academic expectations: 'It has to be cool to work, and ok to talk about work here,' he adds, and makes it his business to ensure that his charges (and their parents) make well-informed suitable choices for their next schools, even when the majority go on to King's Taunton.

Mr Chips is a keen sportsman and retains the physique of a rugby player, still occasionally coaching. Married with three children at the school, he enjoys entertaining parents 'in order to understand each family's own context' (though a few grumble about not being on the head's dinner list), and he is generally well-liked by both pupils and parents. 'He knows everyone, takes a real interest in us, and we love the Chips Challenge,' opined pupils, who might be asked to research an arcane matter, solve a puzzle or achieve a physical feat.

Entrance: Many join the pre-prep (school also comprises a nursery from 2), but some come from local primary schools and London at 7+. From years 1-4, new children are informally assessed during a welcome day; from years 5-8 they are tested in maths, English and verbal reasoning for which special preparation is not required, says school. Quite an intake also welcomed into year 7 for the final two years before moving on at 13+.

One busy mum told us her youngest had boarded just for a night at the age of 5 – and loved it. I board to relax!' one boy told us

Exit: The majority (74 per cent) to King's College at 13+, but a good sprinkling to the Sherborne schools; also the likes of Wellington College, Blundell's, Millfield, Canford and Beechen Cliff. Every child gets into the school of his/her first choice, apparently; 'We didn't get the hard sell for King's', said one mother with a sigh of relief. Famous ex-pupils include actress Juno Temple, founder of Everyday Sexism project Laura Bates, and mad adventurers Ross and Hugo Turner.

Remarks: Sited in the mellow golden former home of the Yea baronetcy Pyrland Hall, dating from 1760, and surrounded by 50 acres of parkland and woods, this is an idyllic setting just minutes from Taunton. But it's not precious – pupils here make the most of the space, freedom and mud to pursue a terrific range of activities and outdoor pursuits beyond the school day which finishes at 4.30pm, mountain biking and archery being just two. Some 15 acres of pitches, an astroturf and a sports hall mean all major sports are well catered for and fulfil all expectations, but an indoor pool is undoubtedly on the parental wish list; as it is, swimming is an extracurricular activity until the school's outdoor pool is opened in the summer term. But it all amounts to a slice of gracious enough living for the young.

King's Hall is reckoned to be Taunton's smartest and most academic prep school, partly because it's the only place which prepares children for common entrance (and scholarships) at 13+, still the measure and starting point for the most prestigious public schools. From year 3, children are taught in classes of about 15 by specialist teachers. All begin French in year 1 but there's the opportunity to pick up Spanish from year 5 or Latin from year 6. Science and geography get thumbs up from pupils, but 'We don't go to any lessons and think 'Oh no!', said one. Prep amounts to two half hour subjects per night for the oldest: 'It's ok to make mistakes and they will be explained to you again,' said another. One mother observed that some children are held back until they have learnt some basics by rote, and wondered if there should be more 'aspiration and challenge before they have everything right'. Both prep and pre-prep have own library. Some 49 children are currently on the learning support register; school has policy of not withdrawing children from vital lessons to have their two half hour individual sessions per week.

Pastoral care for the children highly rated; class teachers assume pastoral responsibilities in year 3, tutors with mixed horizontal tutor groups thereafter. The newly formed Friends of King's Hall provides purely social events for parents, and is working on extending its reach to everyone. We liked the enshrining of the school rules into six positive exhortations, such as 'do work hard, and do be honest'.

About 50 children board (four per cent of boarders from overseas) in a variety of arrangements; school entices children with regular year group boarding nights and film nights for the whole prep school. One busy mum told us her youngest had boarded just for a night at the age of 5 – and loved it. The sole boarding house has separate areas for senior boys, junior boys and girls, each with its own common room and quiet areas. 'It's fun and as homely as possible – I board to relax!' one boy told us, and all reckoned that boarders of all persuasions are well integrated. Parents tell us that facilities have improved, but the school 'doesn't have that horrible bling-tastic feel that the other Taunton schools have'. Well, thank goodness! Day pupils are welcome to join in the weekend activities with boarders, which might include dry ski-ing or making the most of the beautiful Quantock Hills nearby for a 16 mile orienteering exercise; facilities at King's College are also on offer at weekends.

Not precious – pupils make the most of space, freedom and mud to pursue a terrific range of activities and outdoor pursuits, mountain biking and archery being just two

The arts are well catered for too. Pupils' art was displayed everywhere we went and the design side has facilities for 2D and 3D design. Three major productions a year for years 4, 6 and 8 put on in the school's theatre or outside in the rose garden are complemented by prizes for acting and poetry recital at local festivals. About half the children learn a musical instrument, achieving grade 6 or 7 in rare cases, and the new director of music has gone down well.

So what's it really like? A question probably best answered by the pupils: 'I look forward to going back'. 'The weeks pass really quickly'. And to sum up? 'I don't instantly feel like the walking dead when I arrive'.

Job done, Mr Chips.

Kingsley School

Northdown Road, Bideford, Devon EX39 3LY

01237 426200 | admissions@kingsleyschoolbideford.co.uk | www.kingsleyschoolbideford.co.uk

Ages: 11-18 (junior boarders from year 5)

Pupils: 268; sixth form: 58; Boarders: 83 full, 1 weekly

Day: £12,465 – £13,185 pa; Boarding: £20,685 – £25,785 pa

Headmaster: Since January 2017, Mr Pete Last, previously deputy head pastoral, senior housemaster, head of boarding and housemaster of a boys' house at Stowe School. Educated at Alleyn's School, London and Cambridge, where he read geography, Mr Last has also completed a masters in educational leadership at Buckingham University. Married to Debs, an art specialist. Both from Kent but met in India while working at Hebron International School in Ooty. Returned after six years to teaching posts at Lord Wandsworth College in Hampshire, also running a boarding house, before moving to Stowe after nine years there. Mr Last is passionate about education (and Arsenal) and 'is looking forward to helping to lead Kingsley forward into a new and exciting chapter of its history.'

Academic matters: In 2017, 30 per cent A*-A/9-7 at GCSE and 39 per cent A*/A at A level. Fourteen A levels on offer, plus BTecs in outdoor education and performing arts, a Cambridge Technical in sport, a diploma in food, and the Extended Project Qualification (EPQ). French, Spanish and theatre studies offered if sufficient demand. Maths is strong and around 60 per cent opt for it at A level. Other top performing subjects include English and geography. A language is compulsory up to Year 9. BTec in engineering is available at GCSE level, replacing DT.

Kingsley School admits 25 per cent dyslexic pupils. Other SENs are catered for, mainly those associated with dyslexia, like behavourial issues, but nothing too complex. The Grenville Dyslexia Centre is on the school campus. The centre has just been refurbished and apart from classrooms, there's an ICT suite and a colourful common room. Pupils are taught English and maths in dyslexia-only classes, by qualified SEN teachers. Classes are small, 5-10 pupils. One-to-one tuition, and support in after-school prep sessions is also available. One parent commented, 'My younger child who is dyslexic has been given strong support from the dyslexic centre staff and enjoys attending it. It is a friendly and inviting place to be and recently had extras added to entice the pupils, such as tea and toast! We (both parent and pupil) have been asked (questionnaire form) how the centre could improve on the support and teaching and so I can see that they are striving to keep up and ahead with pupils' and parents' expectations.'

Following comments from recent inspections, the school has addressed the way the school staff and Grenville staff share information. There are now regular and formal meetings where teachers exchange information on individual pupils, and discuss how best to teach them. Teachers use visual aids for all lessons, for example, and reminders of current topic or homework tasks are clearly displayed on the wall. IEPs are followed and individual attention or needs are highlighted. One teacher told us this is all done in a subtle unobtrusive way 'without anyone blinking an eye.' One parent said, 'It is a friendly school and the staff seem to work well together for the good of the pupils and the school as a whole.'

Brilliant pastoral care. One parent said, 'He felt immediately at home and still appreciates the warm-hearted atmosphere of the school'

The results are good, the value added is impressive; SEN pupils do well, they are given good support in classrooms and also exams. One pupil who left recently with A level grades A*, A and B had been told by his previous school he would never amount to anything. With hard work and the specialist support of the dyslexia centre he has more than proved them wrong. Pupils are given the chance to opt for fewer subjects, sometimes dropping a language, if it helps them to focus. There is 'no stigma' at Kingsley and children are given the confidence to learn. One parent said, 'Kingsley School has positively changed our son from a child who found school life very difficult. He was a boy who was very passive and feared failure, he felt that he was not an achiever and his contribution was of little value. The reason for this is that our son is profoundly dyslexic, but in the six years that he has attended Kingsley School, we have seen him grow into a very confident and happy young man.' We heard similar stories from several parents. One parent of an overseas boarder said, 'He identifies completely with the school and we are very happy to see his progress in developing self-confidence and regaining fun in learning.'

The centre's mantra is 'Don't make dyslexia an excuse.' This approach relies upon a nurturing, safe-to-learn classroom environment, and interactive, hands-on, multisensory and memorable teaching methods. In year 7 they focus on spelling and touch-typing. In years 8 and 9, the focus is reading, using a scribe and learning to use software like Dragon Dictate and Read and Write gold. And in years 10 and 11, it's speed-reading, exam strategies and dealing with exam stress. One parent confided, 'Before he started at Kingsley School at the age of 9 years, we had very little expectations for [him], but now we have a son who is a year away from taking his GCSEs and we are approaching them with a confidence for his future and that is solely down to Kingsley School.'

Games, options, the arts: In line with the school's 'quirkiness', the main sports are judo, handball and surfing. Judo is up to Olympic standard, one pupil plays handball in the U19 England team, and another is a member of the GB surfing squad. Surfers and windsurfers do well in local, regional and national competitions and pupils regularly win national titles in gymnastics, netball, judo and biathlon. The U15 girls' football team reached the finals in the North Devon schools championships, and there are regular weekend fixtures for rugby, cricket, hockey, athletics, table tennis, swimming and cross-country. Golf has just recently been introduced, too. There are three sports fields, an all-weather pitch, tennis and netball courts, a sports hall and a gym. Local sports clubs use the school's facilities out of hours, including a fencing club and Bideford Football Club.

The music centre is sufficiently equipped with Apple Mac technology plus a rehearsal room and recording studio. There's a choir and a small orchestra – numbers are limited so quartets and ensembles are more common. Regular performances like 'An evening of ...The Bare Necessities...Pie Jesus... My Favourite Things to Guns and Roses...' End of term concerts and annual collaborations with the drama department include A Midsummer Night's Dream, and more recently Alice in Wonderland. Kingsley has a drama studio plus a fantastic theatre with seating for around 400 (also used by the local film club). It links to the library that is occasionally used for functions – like the Mad Hatter's Tea Party before this year's production of Alice In Wonderland. Kingsley also participates annually in the National Theatre's Connections programme and has been lucky enough to perform at the Theatre Royal, Plymouth and the Bristol Old Vic.

Art department commands the whole of the top floor of the main building, School House. Two huge studios, plus photography facilities. As a department, they specialise in portfolio building. Some great, and very large pieces on display, with plenty more space to fill. Sixth formers were taking advantage of the lunchtime peace on our visit. Annual exhibition at the local Burton Art Gallery.

Surfers and windsurfers do well in local, regional and national competitions and pupils regularly win national titles in gymnastics, netball, judo and biathlon

After-school clubs and activities run Monday to Thursday from 4pm-5pm. Activities offered includes choirs, Mandarin Chinese, judo, trampolining, sports, debating, drama, science, orchestra, surfing, yoga, gardening and the Duke of Edinburgh Award scheme. The local scouts and cubs are based on the school campus and are very popular. Plenty of local trips to places like the Eden Project, Cheddar Gorge and Exmoor. Senior school pupils have cultural trips to London, Paris and Iceland.

Boarding: Currently a 70:30 boy:girl split amongst boarders, 65 per cent from overseas (two-thirds Asian and a third European). Majority board full time, but some short-term boarders from Spain and Germany, usually to brush up on their language skills for a term or two.

Three large, well looked after boarding houses on the school campus. Belvoir House, just a short walk from the main school building, is the girls' boarding house and is surrounded by sports fields, with views over the woods. Carisbrooke (junior boys) and Longfield (senior boys) are beside each other.

The houses are run by houseparents plus assistants. Most have children attending the school. There are also gap students and two house prefects, which adds big brother or sister role models to the mix. Brilliant pastoral care. One parent said, 'He felt immediately at home and still appreciates the warm-hearted atmosphere of the school and the boarding complex.' The houseparent we met in the younger boys' house really does run the house like a mum: she was friendly, welcoming and has created one of the best family homes we've seen. The fairy lights are always on when the kids come home, there's bowls of fruit and plants in the lounge, two dogs and even a boyfriend/girlfriend sofa. Next to the huge lounge there's a pool table and table tennis table. Nestled amongst the fun is an open-plan office, cleverly tucked away but also allowing an adult to be around at all times. Decent kitchen; they would like to upgrade it but the boys don't want this: they love it the way it is, apparently. Rooms are doubles or triples, the odd single for older pupils. Smallish rooms but the communal areas more than make up for them. Only one dorm, sleeps six, used for flexi-boarders or short-termers. Decent wet rooms.

No Saturday lessons but there are sports fixtures or shopping trips in the afternoons, and activities like quad biking, combat zone, climbing and local city trips on Sundays

Plenty of activities and opportunities to get out and about, at weekends and in the evenings. But pupils are also given the time and space 'to be kids,' including downtime and fun, just like home. No Saturday lessons but there are sports fixtures or shopping trips in the afternoons, and activities like quad biking, combat zone, cinema, bowling, climbing, theatre, zoo, theme parks and local city trips on Sundays. Chapel is held on the first and last Sunday of each half of term. As soon as the weather brightens up, surf's up, and as much time as possible is spent making the most of north Devon's beach life. Awesome. One parent told us, 'He enjoys it very much. He likes living in this big family.'

No set exeat weekend, a real plus for Forces families. Kingsley also runs its own guardianship scheme so overseas boarders can now stay at school, in their own rooms, during half-terms. Around 50 boarders are currently taking advantage of this scheme and enjoying the extra activities on offer for them.

Background and atmosphere: In January 2009, Edgehill College and Grenville College came together under the aegis of the Methodist Schools, to create a new independent school. Previously there were three independent schools in Bideford; Edgehill College was founded in 1884, Stella Maris Convent in 1929 and Grenville College in 1954. Edgehill and Stella Maris were girls' schools, while Grenville was for boys until its merger with Stella Maris in 1994.

Now there are around 250 in the senior school and 150 in the junior. School House is the main building, an inviting white building with a 'Kiss and Drop ends here' sign cheekily sending parents on their way. Inside a stairwell and lift run up the centre leading to recently refurbished science labs, classrooms and the art department. Northdown block is a separate building with classrooms and junior common rooms predominantly for younger boys. The school is 'device free' for years 7, 8 and 9. The sixth form centre is separate, in another spacious building. Well-equipped with a modern café area, social area with pool table, table football, piano and large dining table. Several study rooms for small groups, all being well-used on our visit. No uniform but there is a dress code, loosely described as 'business dress'. Sixth form social events take place throughout the year culminating in the summer ball. Leadership opportunities and positions of responsibility are available as prefects, sports captains, competitive house captains and within the boarding houses. Students are also encouraged to act as mentors to younger students. Work experience opportunities are available in the junior school.

Pastoral care, well-being and discipline: Not formally rigid, 'but clear red lines.' There is an open, and perhaps laid back approach to life at Kingsley, but that does not mean that things get overlooked. Parents said, 'We welcome very much the straight rules concerning for example, smoking, leaving the school ground and so on.' This is a small school community and along with good pastoral care including form tutors, heads of years, house parents, school sister and the chaplain, pupils are given the 'confidence that they will be heard' and 'can have their say,' even if the school doesn't always necessarily agree. As a Methodist school, Christian ethos and values are embedded into life here in a subtle rather than preached way. One parent believed, 'Pastoral care and academic encouragement are key points to the school and are their strengths I feel.'

Pupils and parents: Day pupils come from a wide local area and school buses go as far as Croyde to the north, Blackmoor Gate to the north east, North Molton to the east, Winkleigh and Torrington to the south, and Kilkhampton and Holsworthy to the south west. Termly airport buses for overseas boarders.

The school communicates well with parents with the usual channels of emails, letters and reports. Queries or concerns are responded to quickly, 'usually within a matter of a couple of hours. This has always impressed me,' one parent told us. They went on to say, 'We also have phone calls (at the start of the school year and sometimes throughout the school year) from the form tutors to make sure that there are no concerns.' Another said, 'Show my homework is brilliant for keeping up to date on homework that is due. We have regular contact with the dyslexic centre and in fact any teacher is readily available to speak either personally or via email.' Another parent went on to say, 'The teachers all seem professional and friendly and I feel that they care for the well-being of my children. I feel that they act as a team and alongside of myself, as a parent, want to encourage my children/all pupils to achieve their best.'

Entrance: Open days, plus taster days and nights available. Entry by entrance test and interview. Entry at sixth form is a decent set of GCSE results (some subjects have their own minimum requirement), school reports, and the right attitude.

No problems with settling in: 'From day one he absolutely loved it! For a child who finds learning so difficult we have never heard him say he doesn't want to attend,' said one parent. Another told us, 'The invite to attend school the day before school started in the autumn term was a good idea as it gave the children a chance to meet some teachers/form tutors and others from their class. When school started, the children seemed to settle in quite quickly and find their way around the school easily. I felt that the teachers took time to get to know them.' There is also a boarding induction programme which includes a local activity like climbing followed by afternoon tea and sightseeing.

Exit: Some 50 per cent of day pupils leave after GSCEs to go the local free colleges. Most boarders stay on to the sixth form. Nearly all go to university, with a wide range – from Cambridge (one in 2017) to UCL to Cardiff to Oxford Brookes – to do subjects varying from creative writing to neuroscience to business management. Some take a gap year, go into employment, or return to their home country to continue their studies.

Money matters: Academic, performing arts or sports scholarships available at 11 and 13. Sixth form scholarships are based on GCSE performance, or excellence in music, drama, art and sport. Means-tested bursaries offered, plus bursaries to Forces families, and sibling discounts. In the senior school, the fees for the dyslexia department and EAL are additional.

Remarks: What teenager wouldn't want to combine school life with that of beaches, surfing and friends from around the world? That may all sound too much like fun rather than education, but Kingsley has got the balance right; a great campus, an open, caring approach, and specialist teachers. The dyslexic children at Kingsley progress further than anyone's expectations and so it's not surprising that one parent told us, 'We can honestly say it was and will remain the best decision we have made for his education.'

Kingswood School

Lansdown Road, Bath, Somerset BA1 5RG

01225 734200 | admissions@kingswood.bath.sch.uk | www.kingswood.bath.sch.uk

Ages: 11–18

Pupils: 780; sixth form: 239; Boarders: 165 full, 30 flexi/weekly

Day: £14,814 pa; Boarding: £23,286 – £31,929 pa

Headmaster: Since 2008, Simon Morris MA PGCE NPQH (early 50s). Educated at Ipswich School (he is one of three current HMC heads – the others are Mark Bailey, high master of St Paul's, and Nick Gregory, head of Wycliffe College – to have attended the school). Read modern and medieval languages at Cambridge, then went into the City, where he qualified as a chartered accountant with Arthur Andersen. He grew up in a boarding school (his father was deputy headmaster of The Royal Hospital School) and admits that 'the call of teaching was pretty strong'. PGCE at Canterbury Christ Church University, followed by first job at Warwick School (he became head of German after a year). Head of modern foreign languages, then housemaster at The Leys. Deputy head at St John's, Leatherhead for seven years prior to Kingswood headship. 'I'm not saying that every day is easy but I have never regretted my change of career,' he says.

First-ever non-Methodist head of Kingswood. Intensely proud of the school – particularly its sense of community and breadth of opportunity. Passionate about instilling high but attainable standards in every individual and results have risen under his leadership. School isn't highly selective but head says pupils have to be 'academically able'

– or as he puts it, 'doers who want to get stuck in and have a go at things'. Supported by two deputies (one academic, one pastoral). Taught languages when he first arrived but now teaches PSHCE to year 7 pupils. 'It's a brilliant way to get to know them,' he says. Visible around the school, approachable and easy to talk to – 'a round peg in a round hole,' as we said last time.

Wife Caroline teaches modern languages at Kingswood (she has lots of state school experience too) and they have three children. Elder two were pupils at Kingswood and are now at university (one doing medicine at King's College London, the other reading geography at Sheffield) and the youngest is still at the school. A keen sportsman (cricket and golf), he also enjoys travel and reading. Lives in a house on-site but family (plus labrador) decamps to their house near Axmouth in the holidays.

Academic matters: Results are as good as some other co-ed schools with illustrious names. In 2017, 49 per cent A*/A at A level. At GCSE, 56 per cent A*-A/9-7. School says it does brilliantly on value-added – apparently in the top 20 nationally. Masses of subject choice, with 24 subjects on offer at A level and more than 20 at GCSE. Most students take three A levels (some add the EPQ) and a few, particularly mathematicians, do four. Impressive deputy head (academic) has focused on academic development and says the school does everything it can to give students 'total free choice' of A level subjects. 'We don't pigeonhole anyone here,' she says – a claim borne out by a talented artist who at the time of our visit had just won a place to study medicine yet had managed to do A level art too.

Unusually, there's an improvisation event for budding comics called Exit Stage Right, loosely based on Whose Line is it Anyway?

At GCSE the majority take 11 subjects, with all doing English, English literature, maths, three separate sciences (a few do double award) and religious studies. Most take at least one language (French, Spanish or German) although some requiring study support may not. Study support department has three full-time staff and runs an informal drop-in centre for students needing help with anything from managing their time to learning how to revise. Independent support programmes in place for those with specific learning difficulties such as dyslexia and dyscalculia. One mother told us: 'The school isn't just interested in the kids who are going to get three A*s at A level. They mean it when they say they are interested in children with all kinds of talents and skills.'

Games, options, the arts: Sport is a big deal here and there are lots of unbeaten teams. Main sports for boys are rugby, hockey, cricket, tennis, athletics and swimming while girls do hockey, netball, tennis, athletics, rounders, cricket and swimming. School fields at least two teams per year group, with 30 fixtures against other schools each week. Up until year 10 all pupils do a double period of PE every week, plus games. From year 11 some opt for

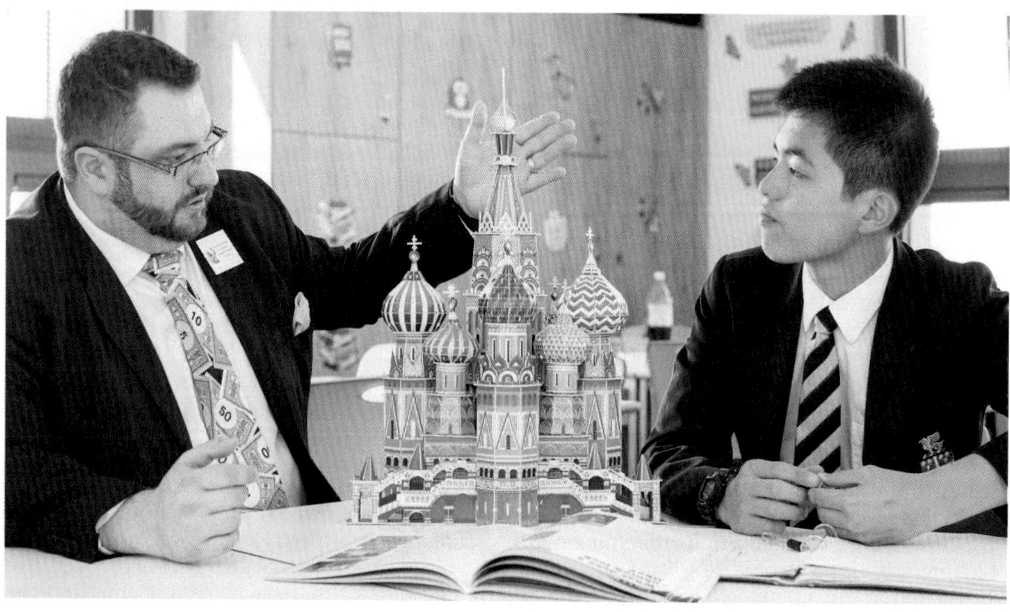

social sports, including aerobics (80 pupils doing this when we visited), cycling, cross-country, multi-gym, orienteering, equestrian sports and more. 'We try and give them more options as they go up the school,' explains the director of sports and PE.

Great facilities, including eight rugby pitches, three cricket squares, two Astroturfs, sports hall and new pavilion. Some pitches are a half-mile walk up the hill but it keeps everyone healthy. School a tad defensive about its 100-year-old swimming pool but says it is 'a great pool to teach in'. Strong links with Bath Rugby Club and the University of Bath.

The arts are outstanding and there is an annual award ceremony for artistically talented pupils in art, drama, DT and music. A third of pupils learn a musical instrument and there's something for performers of all styles and standards. Recent highlights include a performance of Fauré's Requiem, the jazz orchestra playing at the opening event of the Bath International Music Festival and the annual Kingswood Voices Festival, which celebrates the contribution that singers make to the school life.

Drama department has two spaces – a 366-seat theatre and a drama studio. Up to 30 students take drama GCSE each year and between six and 12 do drama and theatre at A level. Three major productions a year and pupils are encouraged to get involved in lighting, sound, stage management and scriptwriting. Unusually, there's a comedy improvisation event for budding comics called Exit Stage Right, loosely based on Whose Line is it Anyway? Art is glorious. Housed in a three-storey arts and crafts style building, it boasts top-notch facilities for drawing, painting, printmaking, sculpture, ceramics and photography. Annual summer art and DT exhibition is a highlight and we saw some breathtaking work, including a vast wire sculpture of a birds' nest by year 8s, a portrait made from tights and pins and a 12-ft long drawing of hands. Sadly, the pupils' monogrammed smocks of old have given away to smart grey aprons embroidered with the Kingswood logo – 'the smocks were too hot,' says the head of art.

Boarding: Even though day pupils outnumber boarders, Kingswood feels like a co-ed boarding school with day pupils. Seven day/boarding houses, some of which are in the process of being updated. The first to be completed, Hall House (for 42 year 9 to 13 boys), is one of the most stylish boarding houses we've seen in a long time, complete with outdoor decking area, wholesome bedrooms (12 en-suite), the housemaster's prized vinyl collection in the common room and views across Bath to the Mendips. We particularly liked the kitchen rules painted on the boys' kitchen wall: 'If it smells, throw it away. If it's dirty, wash it. If you get it out, put it away. If it's on, turn it off.'

Westwood, for year 7 and 8 pupils (some 170 day pupils and 30 boarders), provides a gentle introduction to the big school. Homely and sprawling, the four-storey building is a hive of activity, with the housemaster's friendly border collie running around with the children after school. Girl boarders live on the second floor, boy boarders on the third, all in dormitories of six to eight and out of bounds to day pupils. The Westwood pupils are allowed to grow up in their own time and, rather sweetly we thought, are read a weekly bedtime story – Ted Hughes's The Iron Man has been a particular favourite. Boarders love the place. 'I'm an only child,' one boy told us, 'so being here is like having lots of brothers'. No Saturday school for anyone these days but a vast array of weekend activities. Sports matches on Saturdays and trips to places like Drayton Manor and Legoland on Sundays.

Background and atmosphere: The only school founded by John Wesley, who believed that education should engage the heart as well as the head, and the first Methodist one. School opened in 1748 for the sons and daughters of Wesley's friends but was soon restricted to the sons of Methodist preachers and leaders. Went co-ed again in 1974.

School moved from Bristol to its current site (just across the road from the Royal High School) in 1852 and has occupied an imposing collection of purpose-built Victorian gothic buildings on the steep northern slopes above Bath ('Satan's throne', according to Wesley) ever since. Even on a grey day, the views from the school are magnificent. Pupils from all denominations and faiths.

School is ideally placed – a 20-minute walk down the hill into the city, but with a country feel about it. Other buildings of varying age and beauty are dotted around the school's 214 acres of manicured grounds, including the chapel (too small these days to house the whole school, which gathers for religious and secular assemblies in the theatre).

Central dining in splendid gothic hall, with pupils allowed to sit where they like. Food is good, with plenty of choice. We much enjoyed the Moroccan potato salad and lemon couscous with pumpkin seeds on offer when we visited. Uniform is tidy and businesslike, with girls in black blazers, white blouses and tartan skirts and boys in black blazers, charcoal trousers and school ties. Sixth formers wear dark suits – girls in years 12 and 13 are allowed to wear natural make-up, nail varnish and modest jewellery. Sixth form housed in The Dixon, slightly scruffy but much loved sixth form block, completely with cabin-like studies, kitchen and chill-out space.

Pastoral care, well-being and discipline: Head says school is 'non-confrontational' and that discipline structures are clear. 'We are quite prescriptive in terms of what is acceptable and what isn't,' he adds. 'I refuse to be complacent but we don't have a huge discipline issue. We educate pupils to make sensible choices.' Pupils and parents agree. Parents describe pastoral care as 'outstanding' and say communication between school and home is excellent – high praise for the head's regular drop-in sessions and the school's weekly newsletter.

'What I love about Kingswood is that the pupils are an eclectic lot. I wanted my children to grow up kindly and nicely and they really have here'

Impressive support structure from year 7 up. Pupils are in house-based tutor groups of around 10 (tutors change in years 8,10 and sixth form). Tutors have day-to-day responsibility for pupils but there's a raft of people to help if issues arise. These include housemasters and housemistresses, head of boarding, medical centre (open 24/7) and chaplain. PSHCE for all, often linked to assemblies. Clear system of sanctions, with emphasis on support and redirection rather than chastisement.

Prefect body is known as PR, with head boy and head girl, deputies (one deputy head boy and two deputy head girls recently) and senior prefects. School council meets once a week – recent topics of discussion range from school menu suggestions to exam timetabling issues. 'We want them to air their views,' says the deputy head (pastoral). Very comprehensive pupil and parent handbook details everything from the school's philosophy and aims to behaviour, health and dress.

We liked the rules painted on the boys' kitchen wall: 'If it smells, throw it away. If it's dirty, wash it. If you get it out, put it away'

Pupils and parents: Moderately to exceedingly affluent families, but not particularly posh. Lots of medics, lawyers, business people and an increasing number who have relocated to Bath from London. Around 10 per cent of pupils from overseas (more than 20 different nationalities represented).

Pupils are polite, friendly, unpretentious and confident. A mother whose two children are weekly boarders told us: 'What I love about Kingswood is that the pupils are an eclectic lot – you've got the city children, the country children and the overseas boarders. I wanted my children to grow up kindly and nicely and they really have here, while at the same time being stretched academically.' Most day pupils come from the north side of Bath (crossing the city during rush hour is horrendous and there are plenty of schools south of the river). Pupils come from as far afield as Calne, Chew Valley, Wiltshire, south Gloucestershire and north-east Bristol. Famous alumni include actor Tim Curry, director and writer Jonathan Lynn, the historian and writer EP Thompson and Reggie Tsiboe, one of the lead singers of pop band Boney M.

Entrance: Increasingly competitive, although year 7 recently expanded from four form entry to five form entry. 'More are applying but we are taking more,' says the head. Main intake is in year 7. Around 50 per cent join from own prep school (they share the same site). Others from 20 preps and primary schools (St Stephen's down the road is a major feeder). Maths, English and non-verbal reasoning tested, plus report from current school and interview. Coaching discouraged. Up to 20 pupils start in year 9, with applicants taking exams in English, maths, non-verbal reasoning, science and a foreign language, plus report from current school and interview. At sixth form stage (20 to 30 newcomers arrive in year 12) students need a minimum of four B/6s and two C/5s at GCSE or equivalent.

Exit: Virtually all stay for sixth form. A handful leave, usually due to financial reasons. Almost all to university (three to Oxbridge in 2017) – Leeds, Exeter, Birmingham, Warwick, Durham, Cardiff and Oxford Brookes popular. A few to US universities. A high achieving pupil recently opted to do an apprenticeship with Barclaycard.

Money matters: Academic and special talent (art, DT, drama, music and sport) scholarships offered at years 7, 9 and lower sixth. John Wesley awards available to boarders in year 9 and sixth form – for 'candidates who show the potential to offer a significant all-round contribution to the life of the school'. Head is keen to increase bursary provision throughout.

Remarks: A terrific school, with a culture of creativity, kindness and academic hard work. Kingswood has a strong sense of community, achieves fine results and is definitely on the up.

Knighton House School

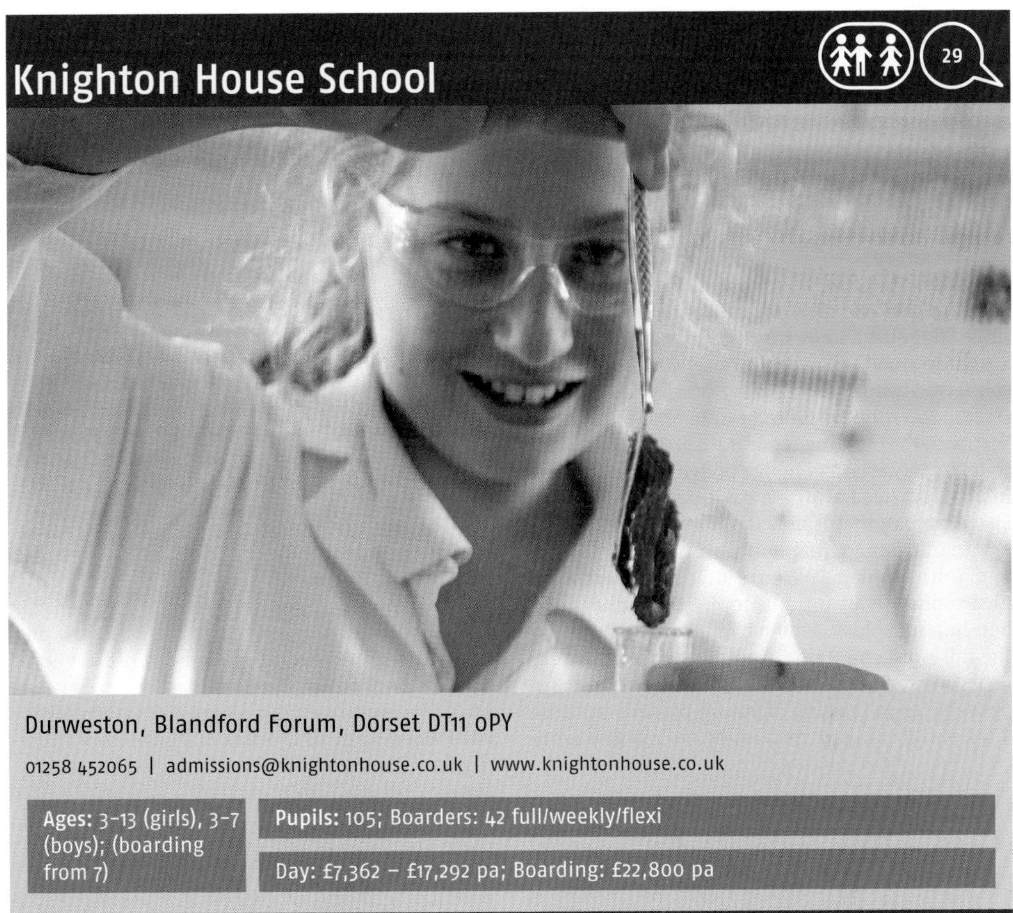

Durweston, Blandford Forum, Dorset DT11 0PY

01258 452065 | admissions@knightonhouse.co.uk | www.knightonhouse.co.uk

Ages: 3–13 (girls), 3–7 (boys); (boarding from 7)

Pupils: 105; Boarders: 42 full/weekly/flexi

Day: £7,362 – £17,292 pa; Boarding: £22,800 pa

Head: Since September 2017, Robin Gainher BSc. Educated at King's Bruton and the LSE, he's a historian who also teaches some maths. He's sporty, too. A lifelong teacher, he rose to be deputy head at Cranleigh, then head for seven years of Beeston Hall. Left to found an international school in Casablanca. Returned to England when he became concerned about the project's backers. Married to Ali, three daughters. Chair of governors promises 'a raft of new ideas and initiatives'. We grilled Mr Gainher about this. He's not a firebrand, neither does he have a manifesto – 'I'll take it as it comes', he says. So he's a pragmatist. His values? 'Giving children confidence is key. Schools are for children; everything we do should be to make their experience more enriching.' He also believes in 'working closely with parents to share the same philosophy and values'. What may raise eyebrows is that, shock horror, he has never in his life sat astride a horse, nor has Ali. The good news is that they are both devotees of lifelong learning and faithfully undertake to leap into a saddle soonest and embark on their new chapter at a rising trot.

Entrance: Non-selective. Come any time so long as there's room. Invariably an ongoing swelling of numbers by children unhappy at their present school. Taster days. Scholarships. Bursaries (Greenwood Awards) for families who wouldn't otherwise be able to afford it. Parents local, Forces and expats. Not much of an ethnic mix, this being Dorset, but it wouldn't be an issue in the slightest. Always a horizon-broadening contingent from Spain, France, Italy, Belgium.

Exit: Most to independent seniors, some to state schools. Experts at matching children to the right one. Dorset offers a full range of choice from highly academic to those offering learning support. Bryanston especially popular, plus Canford, Clayesmore, Lewiston, Milton Abbey, Sherborne Girls, St Mary's Calne and The Thomas Hardye School. Trickier if you're looking for a boyish doppelganger post-pre-prep. Sandroyd, Clayesmore, Port Regis popular.

Remarks: Standing on rising ground above the floodplain of the river Stour in the hushed and tiny village of Durweston (very pretty church), Knighton stands apart from busy world yet is well connected by road to all parts Dorset – and beyond. Once a dower house on the estate of the viscounts Portman, the building is domestic in scale, not a bit stately, a wisteria-clad hodge-podge. The toffs (back in the day) lived a mile away up in the Norman Shaw chateau that is now Bryanston school.

A still-young school founded in 1950 by Peggy and John Booker (parents of controversialist Christopher) as an antidote to their own character-building schooldays which had been defined by all the miseries, chilblains, iron bedsteads, splintery floors and random acts of discipline reckoned indispensable to the raising of young persons in those days. Knighton was instead to be a home from home where girls could be girls, play in the fresh air to their hearts' content, learn kindness, love learning and develop what a present parent identifies as 'bedrock confidence'. Romantic and gently revolutionary in its time, this is mainstream stuff nowadays; everyone else has played catch-up. There's quite a lot of retro-country boarding around just now, done somewhat self-consciously via artful marketing – prospectuses read like fashion shoots for Boden, and look, there's the head in the just the right country casuals, accessorised by a dog. Knighton, a governor told us, is forward-looking, 'we're not seeking to return to the 1960s'. At the same time, it remains recognisably the Knighton everyone remembers. A parent who was a pupil there in the 80s told us the school 'remains exactly what it's always been'. Not a lot of schools could have pulled that off.

No danger of Gradgrind values; the mother of a very bright 8-year-old told us, 'They are definitely stretching her, but not in ways she's really aware of'

The Bookers' greatest legacy was that, unlike so many schools created by reformers in their own image, Knighton never developed the sort of captivating idiosyncrasy (cultishness, if you like) that makes the job of successors so difficult. Captivating, yes, idiosyncratic, no; progressive yes, offbeat never. So the school has enjoyed a remarkably steady and howl-free evolution. This played to its advantage in 2013 when some of the school's governors almost made a strategic misstep of existential proportions. A proposal to merge with a nearby school was swiftly strangled by a coalition of parents and there have been no aftershocks, but it was a crisis that wasn't allowed to go to waste – indeed, one parent described it as 'the best thing that ever happened to us'. The episode focussed minds on the intrinsic qualities that make Knighton so distinctive and precious. It awakened awareness of the school's uniqueness and value and reinvigorated the parent body. Other happy outcomes include the purchase of the school's freehold and the appointment of a very bright, eclectic board of governors.

Parent power is one of those things that can go either way. Knighton parents have not by any means taken to throwing their weight around; on the contrary, they're a supportive lot. Notably unpretentious and dressed down, not the sort ever to be wowed by your new Evoque or leather trouserings, sorry. They range from what one parent described as 'heavy duty aristocracy' to members of the armed forces, expats, local professionals and farmers, businesspeople, creatives and other members of the digital diaspora. In the words of one parent, 'They're not remotely flashy, they're cheery, low-key and I have no idea who's rich and who isn't'. They find the school 'brilliantly supportive of working parents', 'wonderfully accommodating of late-to-collect crises'. Significantly, Knighton is very much the school of choice of teachers (who know a thing or two about schools) at local independents; there's always a tranche from Bryanston. Nice touch: grandparents' days.

Single sex important for some, not so much for others. What chance the school will accede to some parents' preference for one school for all their children? Don't rule it out. But standalone girls-only boarding preps in the UK are up there with the snow leopard and the black rhino on the endangered species list; they're down to the last three. Quite a USP.

Academically hearty. Until the merger-most-foul episode the school had been falling off the pace. Gaps have been plugged, below-par staff eased out and there's a continuing focus on the quality of teaching. Rising numbers of scholarships testify to this, and they'll let you know about it. It's not all about getting the best out of just the brightest, though, and non-schol girls don't feel at all like also-rans. Small classes play their part, and teachers who really know the children. No danger of Gradgrind values; the mother of a very bright 8-year-old told us, 'They are definitely stretching her, but not in ways she's really aware of.' The overall philosophy remains 'in your own way, in your own time' – but definitely not 'when you feel like it', or as one mum put it another way, they're 'challenged and encouraged'. A parent who moved down from London reckons his daughter got to the same place academically that she would have reached in her mirthless pressure-cooker; another said, 'People are once again sending their bright girls to Knighton'. Senior schools confirm this.

Conventional curriculum, maths 'brilliant', Latin from year 6, art superb and there's a fine personal enrichment programme that goes off-piste into history of art, public speaking, you name it. Surprisingly well-resourced across the board, classrooms in converted farm buildings. Careers talks for years 7 and 8 because 'there are no limits to what girls can achieve'. Yep, there's an empowerment agenda here, check out their KED talks programme. Special needs a strength as you've every right to expect of a non-selective school. Learning support spans short-term interventions – everything from reinforcement to gifted and talented – to long term SENDs: dyslexia, ADHD, ASD, etc. No wheelchairs when we called but, says the school, 'We'd do what we needed to do'. Something you don't notice til it's pointed out: no ungainly school bags being lugged, swinging, from class to class. They're banned. Take just what you need from your locker. Amazingly civilising.

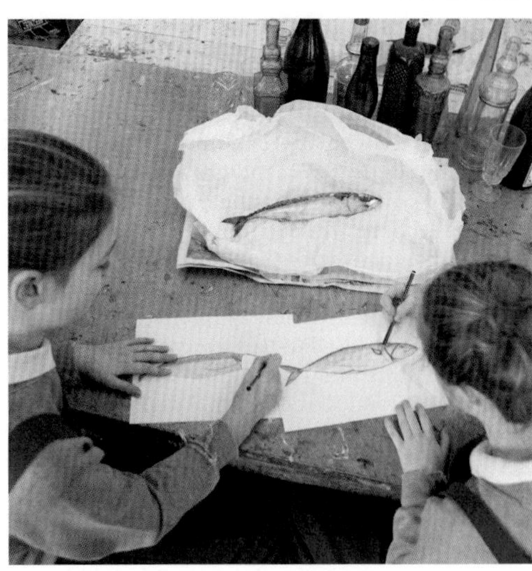

Knighton girls are mostly outdoorsy types so it's no surprise they're a sporty lot. There's been a focus on quality of coaching in the last few years and the best go on to county and national levels. If you're bookish or not sporty that's fine but you'll be expected to join in. Riding is huge and maybe why you're reading this. Knighton is one of Horse & Hound's 'Six dream schools for horsey children' and ponies have been at the centre of school life forever. Around half the children ride. They're good, too, up there with the best.

Overnight and weekend boarding joyously popular because the boarding staff are lovely and make it such fun

A lot at Knighton happens in fresh air. They play outside in their dens, make up games with bits of sticks, climb trees and converse with ponies, goats, hamsters etc. We watched them at it. A delight. What they (arguably) do best indoors is sing. The music-making tradition here is as old as the ponies. Instrumental practice begins before breakfast (yes, seriously) and most girls play something. Lots of ensembles and an orchestra. Singing compulsory for years 3-5 and if you're top-drawer you can audition for the super-elite chapel choir which sings at, no less, professional standard in some really nice venues. Music is a big part of Knighton's identity; it's a bigger deal to be head chorister than head girl.

Around 25 full-time boarders plus all the flexi options. Overnighting and weekending joyously popular because the boarding staff are lovely and make it such fun, and the head of boarding is a force of nature who lives and breathes her job and is amazing, and has to be marched off the premises on her days off otherwise she'd never have one. It took the school a while to find her and on the way it parted company with a few who didn't make the grade – a reminder that extraordinary kindness in any regime is achieved only by rigour and, yes, steel.

Universal praise for pastoral care. Teachers are 'very accessible and always give you time'; 'they really understand the children'. Knighton has long been noted for this; in the words of a former pupil it's 'deeply ingrained'. Wherever we questioned we got the same responses: 'nurturing', 'loving', 'home from home'.

Unanimous and, dare we say, fervent praise for the pre-prep, the Orchard – 'exceptional,' in the words of a mother you wouldn't want to get on the wrong side of. Girls and boys 3-7 plus babies and toddlers every Thursday.

Knighton judiciously makes sure its pupils outgrow the school by setting them slightly above and apart in their final year in the Alpha flat. They swap dungarees for a grey skirt, get some more independence and turn their eyes to what comes next. It's well done.

By their bright red dungarees ye shall know them, for this is the school uniform. They're not about aah-factor, though they are certainly not deficient in that; they're just the job for playing out and doing horses. They can be spotted by teachers if the occupant strays too far or climbs too high. Above all, they're democratising. Red dungarees are just one of the elements that create the rare social atmosphere you find at Knighton, the unaffected friendliness, the way the girls look out for each other, older ones for tiny ones. Single sex may be a factor; the school's small size definitely is: girls feel they belong here, this isn't just a school they go to. Another factor is the example set by the staff, because nothing good happens in a school that does not derive from role modelling by adults who care deeply about their work.

While we were in the head's office we scanned the books on the coffee table. One was by Christine Pullein-Thompson, author of wildly popular pony books for girls. For us it provided the vital clue to what Knighton is all about. The PTs (there were three of them) created a world whose values are wholeheartedness, pluck, resourcefulness and good humour. They invented a genre which has been described as 'feminist way before its time': in their own words, 'we convinced girls they were as good as chaps'. Their spirit lives on here not as creed nor affectation but in an internalised way – eg, in the annual award for Gumption. Triers are rewarded, exemplifying a culture of 'you can do anything' which is borne out by the estimation of senior schools, one of which told us that their Knighton girls 'are amongst the most rounded academically and socially'.

Knighton has never blown its own trumpet other than understatedly and is free of the sort of marketing machine that blights so many other schools. Hurrah. The school is clad in values and practices that make it very current, unencumbered by trad baggage, financially strong and blessed by a once-and-future ethos which makes it, in the words of a parent, 'very happy in its own skin'. Is there magic in the air? Yes.

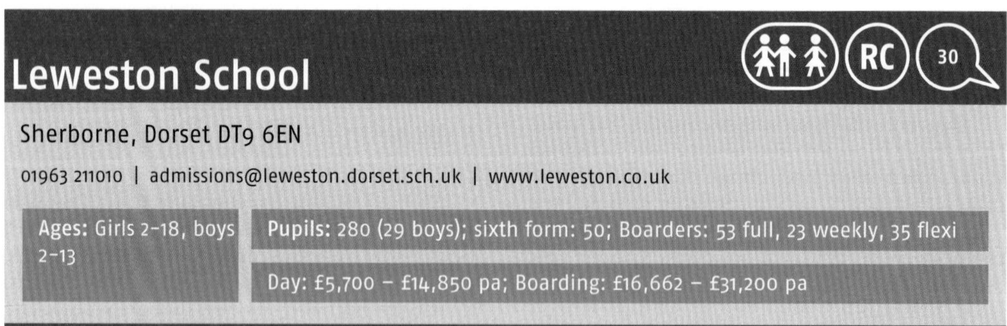

Leweston School

Sherborne, Dorset DT9 6EN

01963 211010 | admissions@leweston.dorset.sch.uk | www.leweston.co.uk

Ages: Girls 2-18, boys 2-13

Pupils: 280 (29 boys); sixth form: 50; Boarders: 53 full, 23 weekly, 35 flexi

Day: £5,700 – £14,850 pa; Boarding: £16,662 – £31,200 pa

Head: Since 2015, Mrs Kate Reynolds MEd LLB PGCE (early 50s). Educated at St Mary's Ascot and Wellington College (where she met her husband). Read law at Bristol, followed by two years at a top London law firm. She then did 'the best thing I ever did' and decided to become an English teacher. After a PGCE at Bath Spa University she taught English and drama at Gillingham School, then Sherborne School. Joined Leweston in 2002, became head of EAL in 2013 and was appointed as head two years later. 'It was one of those serendipitous things,' she says. 'Leweston is so much part of me, as is the local area.'

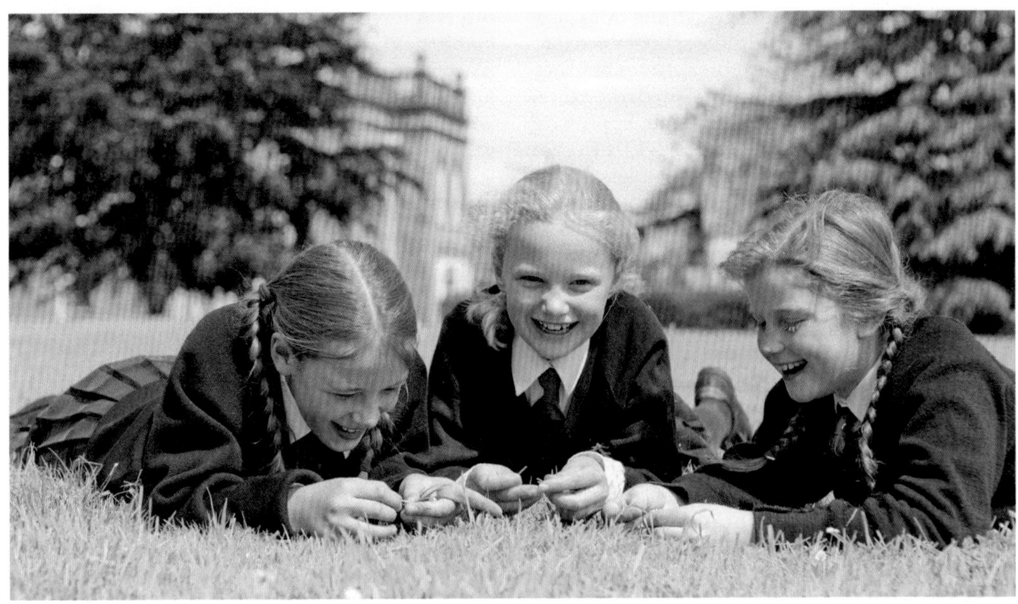

The head is very proud of the girls. 'There is no homogenous product,' she says. 'They are very individual, with a real "can-do" attitude, and they smile all the time. We never pigeonhole them.' She cites the example of a shy girl who wanted to clarify a theological question so emailed every bishop in the country on her own initiative to ask their views. Armed with her findings, she then led assemblies at both the prep and senior school. Asked who the school is right for, the head says: 'It's a decision parents make with their hearts. We are not shiny – some call us shabby chic – but what you get is a fantastic, supportive environment.'

Warm and approachable, she loves teaching and still teaches six periods of English a fortnight. Married to Giles, head of history at nearby Sherborne School, with four sons (one studying materials science and engineering at Imperial College, two at Sherborne School and one at Sherborne Prep). They live in a house on site with their collie-labrador cross. In her spare time she plays the piano and cello, runs and swims. She's often in the pool at lunchtime with other staff but wisely leaves the 6.30am swim training to the pupils.

The new junior department head is Alanda Phillips BA PGCE MEd, former head of the school's early years foundation stage.

Academic matters: Results are good, particularly so since the school is non-selective. In 2017, 52 per cent A*-A/9-7 at GCSE, 43 per cent A*/A at A level or Pre-U equivalent. The school currently holds Good Schools Guide subject awards in English and LAMDA. Most girls take 10 subjects at GCSE, including English, English literature, at least one language (French, Spanish or German), maths, RS, history or geography and either combined science or three separate sciences. The school regularly excels in STEM Olympiads, with one pupil representing Team GB last year.

Head is very proud of the girls. 'There is no homogenous product,' she says. 'They are very individual, with a real "can-do" attitude'

When it comes to value-added, performance at GCSE consistently ranks Leweston in the top 10 per cent of schools nationally. Pupils are able to choose almost any combination of 21 A level subjects. Also offers BTecs in health and social care, hospitality and sports and exercise science. Small A level classes (often three or four for less popular subjects so lots of individual attention) appreciated by the girls, who also have the option to do the EPQ. Around 16 to 20 girls in year 7 (including 11 who move up from the prep school) and 35 to 40 in year 9 and up (but classes are far smaller than this). EAL is compulsory and included in the international fees; learning support available to those who need one-to-one help. A sixth former praised the support she'd received when she struggled to memorise poetry for her English literature GCSE.

Co-ed prep school is housed in a separate building and fizzes with activity. Pupils are proud to show off their badges – awarded for everything from picking up litter to taking part in the school's eco day. Fidget spinners all the rage at break-times but they aren't allowed in class. When we visited, the year 6 teacher was showing the first edit of an impressive 20-minute film of A Midsummer Night's Dream made by his pupils. Most girls move seamlessly from the prep to the senior school. When we visited the prep our sixth form tour guide told us nostalgically: 'It still has the same familiar smell.' Separate nursery takes girls and boys aged 3 months to 4 years.

Games, options, the arts: Leweston is a very sporty school, with a 25-metre covered pool, eight netball courts, 15 tennis courts, sports hall, fitness suite and Astroturf. Besides the conventional hockey, netball and tennis the school is also one of only eight pentathlon academies in the country, offering opportunities in the triathlon, biathlon, tetrathlon and modern pentathlon. Ten pupils qualified to represent Team GB at the European Triathle Championships in 2017 and a year 6 girl holds four national titles in her age group – for pistol shooting, biathle and the triathlon. 'We have got some gutsy pupils,' says the director of sport. 'Despite our size, we really punch above our weight.' Ballet, zumba, kickboxing, fencing, shooting and sailing (at nearby Portland Olympic Sailing Academy) on offer too. It's possible for boarders to stable their horses at a livery yard nearby.

Around a third of pupils play a musical instrument and there are choirs, orchestras and bands galore to join. Senior girls also take part in the Sherborne Schools' Sinfonia and Symphony Orchestra. Up to four girls take GCSE and A level music each year. Art is very popular, giving girls the chance to try their hand at everything from portraiture to graphic design. The school also offers A level textile design (including a fashion component). Year 12s are encouraged to do work placements and in recent years girls have worked at Boden and Cath Kidston. Lots of drama, from Aladdin at the prep school to The Ash Girl, 'a darker version of Cinderella', performed by the seniors.

Older girls are allowed to go into Sherborne several afternoons a week, to meet friends and have coffee. There are socials with Sherborne School too

All pupils do practical cookery and many opt to take home economics (cookery and nutrition) GCSE. A group of girls were busy making sweet potato and shallot quesadillas and Viennese tartlets when we visited. One young pupil, completely unprompted, sweetly gave us one to take home. School is one of only 12 in the country to offer Leith's basic certificate in food and wine, a professional qualification designed to run alongside the school timetable at A Level. Around 10 girls a year do this – not surprisingly, they are far better equipped than most to cook for themselves at university.

A plethora of clubs and activities on offer, including den building in the woods for year 2s and up, with a new accredited forest school. Lots of opportunities for community work, including mentoring younger pupils and visiting the elderly and young mums. One of our sixth form guides was just off to teach Spanish in a local primary school, a voluntary activity she'd fixed up off her own bat. Sixth formers also have a programme of enrichment activities, including public speaking, art appreciation and politics and debating.

Boarding: Girls can board from year 3 onwards. Very few at this young age but the boarding numbers increase as the girls progress up the school. By the sixth form most girls board, on a weekly or full basis. Flexi-boarding available too. Three boarding houses, all within the main school – one for years 3 to 8, one for years 9 to 11 and one for sixth formers. Pretty dorms with views across the lush green countryside – eight in the youngest dorms, four in year 9 dorms and single rooms for older girls.

New head of boarding is a registered nurse with a background in school nursing and interest in adolescent mental health (as well as being the school's lay chaplain) so is well equipped to deal with any problems. Sixth formers act as peer mentors and the head girl told us that as Leweston is a small school and everyone knows each other so well they are often the first to spot anything amiss.

Background and atmosphere: The school is set in 48 acres of beautiful parkland, at the end of a long drive and three miles outside Sherborne. Founded in Sherborne in 1891 by the Religious of Christian Instruction, a group of nuns from Ghent. Moved to its present site, a Palladian manor house, in 1948 (the house was bought from the Rose family, of lime cordial fame). Lots of later additions to the sprawling site, some visually pleasing, others less so. No nuns these days but the chapel is central to school life. Daily prayers, masses and other school services are held there and pupils, staff and parents can visit when they wish. The tiny 17th century Trinity Chapel, one of the first post-Reformation Catholic churches in the country, seats 50 and is used for smaller services. A palpable sense of Catholicism still prevails but girls of any faith and none are welcomed.

The school day starts at 8.15am and ends at 4.20pm, followed by clubs, activities and after-school care for the youngest. Uniform is distinctive – tartan skirts and blazers for girls up to year 11, plus sailor dresses for juniors in the summer. Boys wear grey trousers, navy jumpers and blazers. No uniform for sixth formers but they are encouraged to look smart – definitely no denim. We didn't spot anyone flouting the rules although a girl once turned up in slippers as a joke. Older girls are allowed to go into Sherborne several afternoons a week, to meet friends and have coffee. There are socials with Sherborne School too. The girls we met reckoned they have 'the best of both worlds' – studying in a single sex environment but being able to socialise with boys outside their classes. Sixth formers also have their own sixth form area, complete with comfy Chesterfield sofas, outdoor courtyard and dedicated study centre.

Atmosphere everywhere is friendly, yet purposeful. As one parent put it: 'We wanted somewhere that would stretch our girls, whilst giving them the confidence to be themselves. We didn't want a product.' Pupils eat all their meals in the dining room but spill out onto the outside picnic tables in good weather Plenty of choice, with vegetarian and gluten-free options.

Pastoral care, well-being and discipline: Pupils say the school is warm and welcoming and like the fact that they are encouraged to achieve their potential. 'Everyone is kind to you here,' a year 6 girl told us. When pupils arrive they are each given a peer mentor to help them settle in and everyone knows everyone.

Head girl, two deputies, heads of the four houses and other prefects in place. They all keep a weather eye out for each other and for the younger girls. Pupils can turn to tutors, houseparents, chaplain, counsellor and the two health centre nurses for help if they need it. The head of boarding,

mindful of the pressures on today's young people, says: 'One of the things that Leweston does very well is helping the pupils to develop a sense of balance.' PSHE covers everything from e-safety to tolerance.

Pupils and parents: Day pupils come from within an hour's drive away. School minibuses ferry pupils in from as far afield as Wincanton, Beaminster and Dorchester. Boarders mostly from the south west but a sprinkling from London. Around 17 per cent of pupils are from overseas – including mainland China, Hong Kong, Mexico and Europe – and the head says they integrate well. No Saturday school but around 80 girls stay at school every weekend so there's plenty going on. A third of the pupils are Catholic and everyone is expected to attend church, whatever their faith.

One of our sixth form guides was just off to teach Spanish in a local primary school, a voluntary activity she'd fixed up off her own bat

Currently 13 boys in the junior school but school expects the number to grow. They can now stay at Leweston till the age of 13, a move the school says is driven by parental demand and to avoid boys having to change schools twice. No provision for boys' boarding yet.

The girls we met were enthusiastic, unpretentious and charming, with a sense of fun. 'They're comfortable in their own skin,' agrees the head of boarding. Unlike peers elsewhere they aren't alarmingly sophisticated – the head loved it when the head girl gave a speech on open day about the sixth formers playing hide and seek in the corridors at night. Old girls are known as Old Antonians and include Dame Kristin Scott Thomas, Erin Pizzey, founder of the UK's first women's refuge, former TalkTalk CEO Dido Harding, entrepreneur Sarah McVittie and sculptor Serena de la Hey among their number.

Entrance: Non-selective. Pupils join at multiple points so it's always worth contacting the school. Leweston accepts all-year-round applications and when we visited after the summer half-term, two girls had just started in year 9 and one in year 10. Girls join the senior school from state primaries and preps like Perrott Hill and Hazlegrove. Prospective pupils take part in a taster day – juniors have an informal assessment while seniors take academic, numerical and perceptual reasoning tests. New sixth formers require six good GCSE passes.

Exit: Around a third of girls leave at 16, sometimes for financial reasons. Some head to local state schools like The Gryphon School in Sherborne and The Thomas Hardye School in Dorchester while others go to independents like Hurtwood House. The head says that a few miss Leweston so much they 'boomerang back' after a few weeks. At 18, most progress to university. A vast array of destinations, with one or two to Oxbridge most years (one in 2017). Recent choices include veterinary science at Bristol (three in 2017), drama at the Royal Central School of Speech and Drama, Chinese and German at Edinburgh and architecture at UCL. 'They aim high,' smiles the head.

Money matters: Mindful of the tough economic climate, the whole school recently took the decision to reduce its fees substantially. 'Our parents are very down-to-earth and many make sacrifices to send their children here,' says the head. The school has done this by a raft of measures, including getting some senior teachers to teach subjects like Latin in the prep school too.

Prep school offers scholarships for entry into year 5 – academic, music and sports. At senior school level there are scholarships for academic attainment, art and design (13+ and sixth form only), drama, music and sports, including equestrian and pentathlon.

Remarks: Leweston is a hidden gem in a stunning setting, definitely worth a look by parents looking for a small, friendly school that achieves good results. The pupils work hard, make lifelong friends and absolutely love the place.

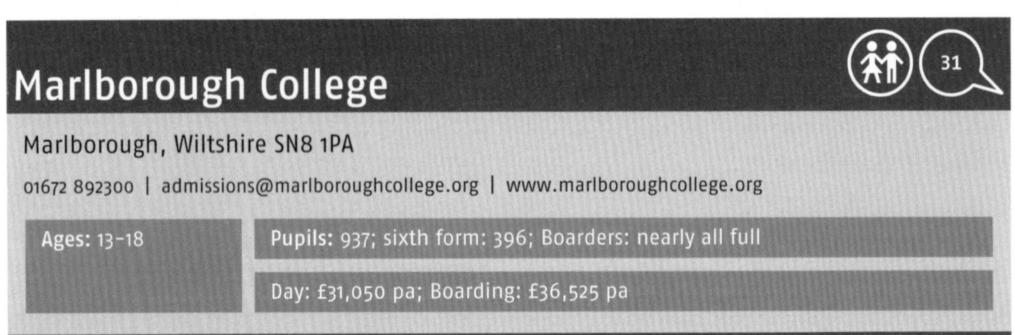

Marlborough College

31

Marlborough, Wiltshire SN8 1PA

01672 892300 | admissions@marlboroughcollege.org | www.marlboroughcollege.org

Ages: 13–18

Pupils: 937; sixth form: 396; Boarders: nearly all full

Day: £31,050 pa; Boarding: £36,525 pa

Master: Since 2012, Jonathan Leigh (60s), previously head of Ridley College, Canada and before that head of Blundell's School and second master of Cranleigh School. Married to Emma, also a Cambridge history graduate, they have two grown up children and the obligatory black lab. Educated at St George's Windsor where he was a chorister, thence to Eton. Degree in history from Corpus Christi College, Cambridge, where he was a choral exhibitioner. He still sings (tenor) and on leaving Cambridge thought seriously about going professional, but instead 'drifted' into teaching and consolidated this drift with a PGCE.

Mr Leigh seems to be the go-to chap if you want to do something structural and potentially controversial at a school. He took Blundells co-ed and taught Canada to love the IB at Ridley College. He is a great advocate of the IB but for some reason the qualification (brought in by previous master) failed to 'take root' at Marlborough and, pragmatically, he de-introduced it here. 'It's very hard to run a dual system', he told us, 'especially since A levels have been toughened up. You need a critical mass to make the IB work and it didn't attract the take up at Marlborough that it has elsewhere.' Under 20 candidates is indeed very far from a critical mass – it's a shame though, the results were pretty good.

Since accepting the post of master, at a time when he might have been contemplating retirement, Mr Leigh and his wife have thrown themselves into Marlborough life and society, much to the admiration of parents (Marlborough parents, we have discovered, don't hold back) who describe him as 'charming and user-friendly.' He's perhaps a little shy at first,' we were told, 'but he's a modest and gentle man who's terrific with the children.' Mrs Leigh is equally popular: 'she's brilliant at fundraising events' and 'great company'.

Marlborough is a big school but the master is diligently applying himself to meeting all its pupils, having breakfast or lunch with groups of four to six at a time. He also 'teaches a bit' – an upper sixth elective course on his specialist subject, Middle Europe 1400-1715.

Most sports including fly fishing and clay pigeon shooting take place within the college grounds

Unsurprisingly, Mr Leigh is an opera lover; his favourites are Samson and Delilah and The Magic Flute. Somewhat more surprisingly he's part of a 50 strong flat racing syndicate and has shares in two horses (both winners, apparently). Syndicate is called The Fifty, horses are called, wait for it, Fifty Shades of Grey.

We found Mr Leigh thoughtful, diplomatic, quietly humorous and without the hubris that is sometimes par for the head course. He has provided Marlborough with much more than a 'safe pair of hands' and parents agree that the College is extremely lucky to have him. 'I only wish I could have started here 10 years earlier,' he says.

Retiring in July 2018. His successor will be Louise Moelwyn-Hughes (40s), currently head of St Edmund's School in Canterbury. Previously senior deputy head of The Perse in Cambridge, and has already spent 13 years in various roles from year head to housemistress here at Marlborough College, following a degree in classics at Cambridge. Now immediately dismiss the picture you've formed, because she's far from the Cambridge to public school head you're imagining. Still has the accent from her humble but bookish Belfast background, and says she didn't really know what Cambridge was when a teacher suggested that her schoolgirl love of ancient Greek could be a ticket there.

Two young children are currently curbing her hobbies of squash, running, walking and reading.

Academic matters: In our last review we remarked that what with A levels, the pre-U and IB, Marlborough offered something for everyone. But clearly everyone didn't want quite that much choice. IB has quietly expired and 2015 leavers were its last takers. Academic head hadn't turned his IB poster to the wall (maybe he never will) and delivered a touching eulogy about the bountiful legacy of the qualification's brief life. Its general goodness will float around like educational ectoplasm, enriching the remaining qualifications. He didn't actually say that. He did say, 'Marlborough already offers much of what the IB contains, more so now that A levels are returning to the linear format.'

College motto is Deus dat Incrementum ('God gives the increase') but steady advance of exam results may have less divine origin. Admissions criteria are now somewhat more academically demanding (although prep school head's reference is still crucial). CE result mainly used to 'keep them on the boil and help us with setting'. In 2017, 49 per cent A*/A grades at A level and Pre-U equivalent; at GCSE, 69 per cent A*-A/9-7 grades. Stand out results in A level art, drama, sciences, geography and maths but good tail of non-vowel grades as well. Astronomers fare well, but then they do have the famous Blackett Observatory to aid their star-gazing – local schools also get their turn to view the cosmos from a field in Wiltshire. Parents singled out teaching in philosophy as 'inspirational', and its popularity at Pre-U, not to mention the results, endorse this. We know, we know, it's not all about exams and comparisons are invidious, but just out of interest that puts Marlborough some way ahead of many co-ed rivals.

Exam syllabi excepted there seems to be an (admirable) ideological aversion to the churning out of standard curriculum fare at Marlborough. Shell (first year)'s first taste of their new school's academic approach is Form, a multi-disciplinary enquiry into the 'origins of human civilisation', no less. These lessons take the place of separate English, history and RS lessons. Run in parallel with this is the Artemis PHSE course: new pupils take part in guided discussions within their boarding houses. All do two modern languages and Latin, some may also take ancient Greek. Sixth formers can choose from around 35 'electives', mini courses that teachers – including the master – devise to impart specialist knowledge on subjects from cryptic crosswords (now that's a life skill) to special relativity or conducting – the baton, not electrical,

Exam syllabi excepted there seems to be an (admirable) ideological aversion to the churning out of standard curriculum fare

kind. These must be as much fun for the staff who run them as they are for pupils.

Average class size is 15, eight in the sixth form. Approximately 100 students have learning difficulties such as moderate dyslexia, dypraxia and ADHD. School says a great deal of thought goes into assessing pupils with SEN to ensure Marlborough is the 'right learning environment' before places are offered. Learning support department works one-to-one and provides a programme of support appropriate to the individual's needs. School also helps a number of students with planning and organisation.

Games, options, the arts: It's no surprise that we filled an entire notebook and ran out of ink during our visit to Marlborough; there's so much on offer beyond the academic timetable. Lest we also deplete our stock of superlatives, suffice it to say that art, drama, sport and music are all very, very good. Generous facilities and 'inspirational' specialist teaching help every pupil, from the most talented to the least coordinated, play, sing, throw or create something to be proud of.

The college may have been co-ed for nearly 50 years, but on the sports field rugby is still king. Four England captains and 38 internationals is indeed a noble heritage. 'The first X1 get clapped onto the pitch at the start of the season,' one parent told us. 'They are the undisputed heroes,' said another. These were observations rather than criticisms and everyone agreed that there are so many fixtures everyone gets the chance of a good match. Besides, the girls are doing just as well: the U14 hockey team recently retained the Wiltshire County Championship and several girls have been picked to represent their county and country in sports such as netball, sailing, lacrosse and athletics. Long tradition of excellence in shooting. Most sports including fly fishing and clay pigeon shooting take place within the college grounds, but there's also a off-site programme that offers beagling, canoeing, caving, coasteering, mountain biking, mountaineering and sub-aqua.

Seemingly universal admiration for 'amazing' drama and music, although the former gets more takers at A level than the latter. Performances and teaching take place in the Bradleian studio theatre and on the flexible stage of the Ellis Theatre that seats up to 400. There are three ambitious audition-only main school productions a year, a musical every two years and a house play festival each summer. Nearly half of pupils take individual music lessons and house music competitions get everyone doing something tuneful. There's a symphony orchestra, choirs, loads of ensembles and plenty of opportunities to perform in the college as well as nationally and internationally. Chapel choir has made several recordings and recently returned from a tour of France. Organ scholars get to learn on the beautiful and recently restored Van Beckwith teaching organ. The department also has an impressive concert programme of visiting professionals and partnerships with the Southbank Sinfonia and individual musicians including Julian Lloyd Webber and Ioan Davies, head of chamber music at the Yehudi Menuhin School.

The college is a founder member of the CCF and has 300 cadets and a 25m indoor range. Those who choose not to join the CCF take part in a variety of service activities, working at primary schools, with younger children in the homes of local families or at a school for children with learning difficulties in Swindon; another group helps at a local riding for the disabled group. There are also opportunities to work with the elderly or on conservation projects.

There's a real energy and buzz at Marlborough; you can feel it. Pupils are busy, busy, busy. Maybe too busy, sometimes. Sensible advice comes from several parents: don't try and do it all, especially in the sixth form. You can't star in the play, play in the firsts and come first in the tests. 'You can do your academic work and one other thing well,' we were told. School says most do more than one thing well but they are vigilant about possible overload. Girls especially can feel the strain: 'The boys are more laid back but girls put themselves under tremendous pressure,' said one mother.

Boarding: Sixteen boarding houses (six boys', six girls' – with another under construction, four mixed ie boys plus sixth form girls) are run by housemasters or housemistresses who live there with their families; they are supported by resident tutors, dames and other members of the pastoral and support staff. Vertical (mixed age) boarding promotes cohesion between year groups and house loyalty is fierce. 'It's really competitive,' several parents told us. Plenty of opportunities to do battle – house shouts (singing), plays, matches and so on.

Every house has its own character, dictated as much by its position and architecture as the team running it. In Hermitage, one of the older houses, we admired a wonderful ground floor bedroom with huge marble fireplace. This prize billet is given to the chap (it's a boys' house) the housemaster thinks is the hardest working, and its occupant looked very proud to have been chosen.

While we did spy some distinctly less than fancy corners as we ran behind a very long-legged housemaster, most boarders at Marlborough seem to get a pretty good deal. Some of the recently refurbished accommodation we visited looked fit for an interiors magazine – walls painted in the sort of modish shade that might be called Vole's Whisper – and, in one, a spectacular glass wall in the kitchen/dining area that overlooked playing fields.

Shells (first years) sleep in four or five bed dorms, graduating to twin and then single rooms from Hundreds (fifth year) up. Occupants are moved around every half term or so. Shell have supervised prep (no gappies, house prefects do this job), Removes (second year) have separate shared studies, after that pupils work in their own rooms. Pupils may Skype their parents (or vice versa) any time apart from during prep; 'we are flexible because of time zones'. Sensible rules re mobiles etc. Meals are taken centrally but continental breakfast, snacks and drinks available in houses.

Pupils are busy, busy, busy – Marlborough is an educational, creative and cultural challenge to teenage apathy and we can only stand back in admiration

Although we didn't inspect all 15 houses, we very much liked those we saw. Considerable thought and expense is going into boarders' surroundings and we're sure the refurbishment programme will eventually transform even the ugliest corners. We often say that boarding school accommodation is of a higher standard than university rooms, but at Marlborough some would surely outclass many homes.

So we asked, how can parents ensure their son or daughter is in the 'right' house? Short answer is, you can't. 'There is no 'best' or 'right' house', we were told firmly. What, no sporty house? No musical house? No. 'Parents must come to house open days and visit as many as they can – at least four; some end up seeing six or seven.' Applications are then made to three but school is in charge of mix and has final say. And parents, while you are inspecting the houses you can be sure members of staff are giving you a surreptitious once over.

Background and atmosphere: Marlborough has both in spades. Surely there is no other school on earth where one can walk out of a glorious Victorian gothic revival chapel (stained glass by Burne Jones and former pupil William Morris, sculpture by Eric Gill) and come face to face with a neolithic mound. Merlin's Mound, as it was dubbed by the 12th century tourist board (complete with 17th century poetic grotto at its foot), is the second largest man-made mound in Europe. 'Mound,' though alliteratively effective, doesn't really describe its stepped shape: it looks more like a fancy Victorian pudding mould. In the 10th century the mound was recycled into the motte of a motte-and-bailey castle – its moat flows beneath the performing arts centre.

Take a few paces more and you will see the Memorial Hall, a neoclassical theatre and assembly hall built in 1925 to honour the 749 men who fell in 1914-1918. Constructed upon a floating 'raft' over the water meadows, the 'Mem' no longer holds the whole school (actually it could, but not if school wants to stay on the right side of health and safety legislation). Apparently the acoustics are excellent and the beautifully preserved interior remains very evocative. The hall is to be restored in time for the centenary of the end of the Great War in 2018. Peeping out from behind the Mem is the 'most architecturally important building in the school', a white painted 1930s concrete science block with ocean liner style aluminium windows and topped with a gourd (head of science at the time was Mr Gourd). It is hoped that this building can be converted into a new design centre.

Forgive all this talk of bricks and mortar – we know schools are about people – but somehow the eclectic mix of ancient and modern across the school estate embodies the breadth and quality of a Marlborough education. We were fortunate enough to be shown around by the head of admissions, an architectural historian. He describes the college site as both 'its greatest asset and a glorious problem' and knows the provenance of every wall and window. If ever a chap was in his happy place...

Marlborough College was established in 1851, the Church of England's response to a shortage of vicars. It wanted to provide a good, affordable education for clergymen's sons from the south west of England on the assumption that these young men would go on to take the cloth. List of clerical OMs testament to success of this operation. School was established in an 18th century mansion and former coaching inn which was gradually joined by Georgian, Victorian and Jacobethan buildings including the former town gaol (now converted into a gym). The master's garden looks down to the River Kennet but alas, the Tennyson tree, a glorious copper beech planted by the poet laureate (his son, Hallam, was a pupil), is no more. Its huge canopy of leaves proved too heavy to bear and crashed down during a summer storm.

Marlborough claims to be the first public school to go co-ed (sixth form only, 1968). Surely Bedales, founded in 1893 and fully co-ed in 1898, should get that prize. But let's not quibble, it'll be 50 years in 2018 and even if boys still outnumber girls in the lower years it definitely doesn't feel like a boys' school. Marlborough College Malaysia was established in 2012 and has already doubled in size. This is not a franchise but a 'genuine expansion of the home school', with linked management and governance.

It's impossible to cover everything that goes on at Marlborough in this review. The school is a 24 hour educational, creative and cultural challenge to teenage apathy and we can only stand back in admiration. 'We ask a great deal of our staff,' the master told us; 'during term time there's no such thing as working hours.'

Pastoral care, well-being and discipline: All food is prepared in house and eaten in the large communal dining hall. Lunch is staggered between 12 and 1pm, an arrangement that we hope has improved the lot of Shells who we hear sometimes used to go hungry, elbowed out of the way by older children. Pupils eat with their friends at long wooden tables, there's plenty of choice and what we tried was delicious. Breakfasts and lunches get full marks but (and we heard this from several quarters) supper could do better – not an uncommon complaint at boarding schools, must be something to do with leftovers. Former pupil John Betjeman wasn't a fan of this meal either, although we're sure it's much nicer than what he got in the 1920s.

So what about discipline? It hasn't always had a robust reputation at Marlborough, although our impression is that it is now an extremely well run school. A rummage through the college's many 'policies' leads somewhat circuitously to chapter and verse. Suffice it to say that 'explicit or intimate sexual relations' will get you suspended or excluded. Likewise drugs, alcohol, bullying, theft, use of weapons and a whole load of other nasties. Prefects can go to some of the town pubs but on the whole partying is an in-school affair (there's a policy about it on the website) or – and this sounds like more fun – takes place at friends' houses during the holidays or on exeats.

Relations between boys and girls seemed friendly and relaxed, more best mates than Romeo and Juliet. 'There's great banter between the girls and boys,' a father told us. 'There's the odd bit of snogging in the bushes but nothing serious,' said another parent. While we can't comment on the activity we can confirm that the school grounds are well supplied with shrubs of all kinds.

Every house has its own character, dictated as much by its position and architecture as the team running it. Plenty of inter-house competition – shouts (singing), plays, matches

Great praise for houseparents, tutors, dames and all others directly involved in pastoral care. Parents like the 'clear' chain of command and felt that anxieties or problems were dealt with swiftly. Good medical care, plenty of joined up thinking and sharing of information (where appropriate) in cases of illness, stress etc. Medical centre or 'Sanny' looked rather forbidding and was described by one parent as 'grim' (building, not people).

House identity is great for bonding but there are still a few grumbles about pupil hierarchy and the lot of the youngest. Efforts are being made, there's a mentoring system and older children write to new pupils before they start, but maybe there's still room for improvement here.

Pupils and parents: Traditional full boarding families broadly sums up the type you will meet here but school doesn't (and doesn't want to) feel like the 'default outcome of a dinner party conversation.' Yawn. It's sparkier and quirkier than that – fish pie and a decent Muscadet at the kitchen table with slightly naughty friends perhaps, rather than 'faine daining', competitive parenting and house prices. Less country than schools further south but 'not too London' either. Some very local day pupils, six per cent international students.

Pupils are a great advert for co-education – self-assured, good company, the sort you could see fitting in anywhere. Many parents get to know their children's friends socially at weekends (exeats, privis) or during holidays. 'They're a great bunch', we heard, 'the sort who always help clear up after a party.'

In addition to ranks of clerical and military worthies, notable former pupils include artists: William Morris, Graham Shepard, Lauren Child; writers: John Betjeman, Louis MacNeice, Siegfried Sassoon, Bruce Chatwin, Frances Osborne; actors: Wilfrid Hyde White, James Robertson Justice, Michael Pennington, Jack Whitehall; politicians (and their spouses): Hallam Tennyson, Rab Butler, Christopher Chope, Mark Reckless, Sally Bercow, Samantha Cameron; plus Sir Francis Chichester, Mark Phillips, Simon Fanshawe, Mark Tully, Frank Gardner, HRH Princess Eugenie of York and HRH Duchess of Cambridge (she was a prefect). Quite some school reunion that would be.

Entrance: Parents are advised to start the process (visiting boarding houses etc) at least three years in advance. According to the director of admissions, 50 per cent of the decision to admit a child rests with the prep school head's reference, 10 per cent on the ISEB test (to check the academic part of the head's reference) and two interviews in a boarding house by HM and a tutor to verify other aspects of the reference. CE's biggest use, he maintains, is to help with setting once a child joins. Important part of the interview is to discover whether a child will be boarding by consent or 'compulsion'. No one wants the latter. Nor do they want children who have been tutored, 'we're looking for potential for happiness.' Someone will be offering to coach children in that soon.

Consensus from many parents that Marlborough is a great family school. School says it does its best to accommodate siblings, but warns it's not automatic. 'We can't be a closed shop and sometimes this isn't the right place.' Pupils come from over 100 preps but main suppliers are Beaudesert, Cheam, Cothill, The Dragon, Farleigh, Highfield, Lambrook, Ludgrove, Pinewood, Twyford and Windlesham.

We have in the past heard from parents somewhat bruised by Marlborough's 'brusque' response to admissions enquiries. School horrified to learn this: 'we go out of our way to be welcoming and give people time'. Certainly all the front of house staff we met could not have been more charming and less intimidating.

Exit: Very few leave post-GCSE; certainly no kicking out for under par results. Influx of girls in sixth form swells numbers. Big improvements in careers advice; we loved the huge signposts showing all the directions OMs can take. As previously, Edinburgh, Manchester, Bristol, Exeter, Durham and Leeds popular destinations; much the most popular courses are in history, art history, modern languages. Eleven Oxbridge places in 2017, five medics, several off to the US/Canada plus one to Madrid and one to Maastricht.

Money matters: Fees on a par with other similar schools. Still lots of scholarships (more honour than hard cash) but before you bask in the warm glow do check small print and talk to your child about the expectations that go with these.

Means-tested bursaries of up to 100 per cent available and school may assist in individual cases of hardship. Marlborough is one of 'very few schools' who have followed the Charity Commission's advice and transferred all scholarship funds into bursaries. College is currently raising an appeal for substantial additional bursary provision.

Remarks: The college defines its 'triple foundation' as 'rigour, respect and responsibility', an ethos that is at once modern and yet in keeping with its Anglican traditions. Pupils at Marlborough are part of a diverse, creative and academic community – 21st century co-ed boarding at its very best. To paraphrase lines John Betjeman wrote after revisiting his old school in the 1960s, Marlburians 'Live in a world as rich as is a king's. How sweet are tastes to them, how deep their dreams. How hopeful and how possible their schemes.'

Millfield Prep School

32

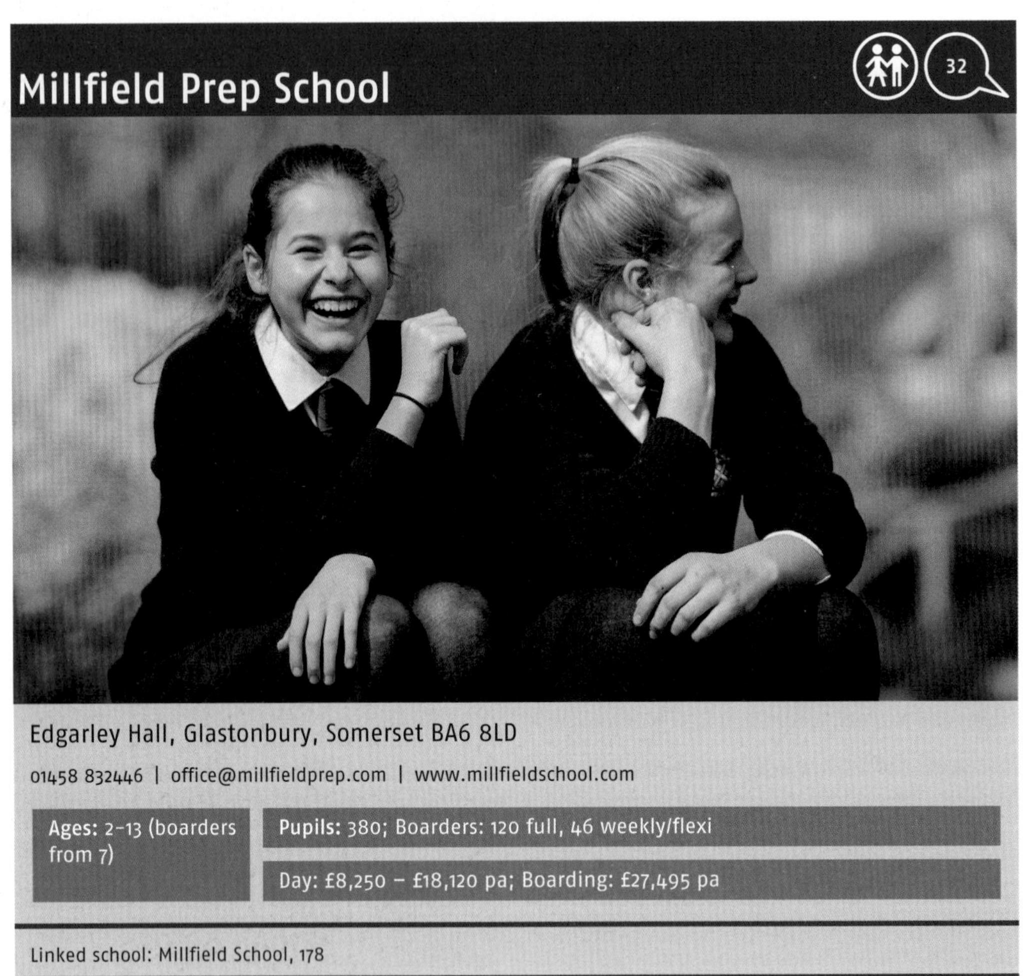

Edgarley Hall, Glastonbury, Somerset BA6 8LD

01458 832446 | office@millfieldprep.com | www.millfieldschool.com

Ages: 2-13 (boarders from 7)

Pupils: 380; Boarders: 120 full, 46 weekly/flexi

Day: £8,250 – £18,120 pa; Boarding: £27,495 pa

Linked school: Millfield School, 178

Headmistress: Since 2010, Mrs Shirley Shayler MEd BSc PGCE. Educated at Carrickfergus Grammar School, Northern Ireland, degree in biology from the University of Stirling, PGCE from Queen's University, Belfast, masters in educational management. No stranger to Millfield, having taught biology at the senior school 1989-2002 and undertaken an impressive spread of pastoral and extracurricular roles including coaching first XI girls' hockey and being a houseparent. Deputy head of Taunton School for four years then head of Stonar for another four plus years doing much to expand and improve the sixth form. Lives on site with husband Gary, biology teacher and head of careers at senior school, and daughter, Caragh, who attends Millfield Prep and rides a school pony.

'Delightful' and 'caring' but steely when need arises. Parents we spoke to all thought she was 'a good head who works hard' and commented on how 'she has won respect through not being afraid to stick to her guns.' Loves being back at Millfield: 'a way of life rather than a job,' she commented to us. Really believes in educating 'whole child' and in releasing children's potential. Often seen walking family labrador. Still involved in hockey and also enjoys swimming, cycling, skiing (annual family ski trip is a highlight for Shaylers), reading and the theatre. Vision for future includes providing more enrichment à la Dragon's Den-style enterprise activity, more involvement in the local community and further developing pastoral care.

Entrance: Many admitted via interview and report from previous head (eg from prep schools finishing at 11). Some arrive from pre-preps or local primaries and others from as far away as Venezuela or Hong Kong (we have seldom seen such a varied list of feeder schools). Learning development centre tutor involved at interview where there are special learning needs. Can be flexible – will always make the effort to take pupils and has been a sanctuary for pupils unhappy or failing to thrive elsewhere: 'IQ not the only arbiter; we need to see the child, not just a collection of data.' Can and will take when space available; means tested bursaries available in cases of genuine need and a number of scholarships (all the usuals plus chess) for entry into years 6, 7 and 8. The former depend on success in the scholarship exams which can be sat each January.

Exit: Most proceed to senior school. Dozen or more scholarships won annually to senior school: academic, art, music and sport. Transfer automatic subject to good behaviour and satisfactory academic standard. A small number move elsewhere, mostly to other independent schools.

Remarks: Millfield provides a top notch experience in almost every sphere. Lively boarding community which doesn't high tail it home at weekends (apart from exeats) – around 40 per cent of boarders are from overseas – and still includes Sunday chapel. Boy and girl numbers pretty equal throughout. Many sign up for complete (2-18) Millfield experience. Parents underline how school 'instills confidence and maturity' and how it 'has brought a global dimension to rural Somerset.' Prep campus benefits from more acreage than its senior partner. Centrepiece is an elegant Victorian home of former local landowners. Oak-panelled hall leads to head's capacious study (now made over to suit her taste) overlooking grounds. Internal standard of classrooms, sports and other facilities more than compensates for lack of architectural cohesion on a site that has grown like Topsy. Unusual external

touches include a huge outdoor chess set and the multi-coloured climbing wall. Children seem quite content, scurrying around like worker bees under the queen's command. Main entrance sits on a bend of A361 on the Pilton side of Glastonbury opposite (and safely accessible via footbridge over main road) school's small chapel, nine-hole golf course and Edgarley Manor (a boys' boarding house) at the foot of the famous Tor.

Many sign up for complete (2–18) Millfield experience. Parents underline how school 'instills confidence and maturity' and how it 'has brought a global dimension to rural Somerset'

Show starts with Millfield Minis, a three-day-a-week event for local parents and toddlers using pre-prep hall from 10.00-11.30am. There are even Minis' swimming, tennis and trampolining. Pre-prep department caters for pupils aged 2-7. Safe, ideal location within former walled garden. Reception area shouts creativity and fun; classrooms are flexible learning spaces with eye-catching displays, live animals and loads of interest. Outdoor raised beds for veggie growing, safe play and exploration including Forest School (two teachers trained leaders) nearby. Pond includes underwater camera for pupils to watch submarine activity on linked computer screen. We liked the three little pigs guarding the gazebo and outside quiet area. Cosy library to make reading fun and indoor tumble room for scrapes without scratches. Read Write Inc a favourite phonic approach, number games abound and we saw some beautiful progressions of pupils' cursive handwriting on display. Humanities and science themes run alongside core learning. Music, art and drama all play a big part.

Children coming into pre-prep are automatically assessed for learning support: one-to-one groups and lessons for those who need extra help from two specialist teachers who work closely with school's learning development centre. Parents appreciate the experience of many long serving teachers and the extent to which it is 'an inclusive environment' rather than pushy.

Most of the prep school buildings are modern (if not of any particular architectural merit) and provide well for a community of around 400 children. The large, refurbished assembly hall serves for school's frequent drama productions and activities such as fencing and gymnastics. The well stocked library is above the dining complex (probably the best we've seen in a prep school: all shiny service counters and friendly staff). Food is plentiful and varied.

We observed versatile teaching across a broad curriculum in small classes (maximum is normally 16) from an experienced and friendly staff. Years 3-5 are taught by group tutors for most lessons. Setting from year 3 in English, maths and languages with mixed ability tutor groups. From year 6 all lessons

Powerful presence in major sports at county and national levels, but meets stiff competition on the prep schools circuit

are taught by subject specialists, with tutors continuing to have pastoral oversight. Academic standards are reassuringly high. Despite many children needing extra English, the school's 'language for all' policy ensures that every child can take Spanish as part of their programme. French and Latin are on the main menu with some linguistic side orders also available (eg Mandarin, Russian and Japanese).

The five science labs are still housed in very adequate temporary accommodation close to the main teaching areas, and teachers we spoke to were in no rush to move into a new building. Young number crunchers perform well in competitions such as UK Maths Challenge and we were told that children particularly enjoy using MangaHigh software. Splendid IT suite where we saw some pupils operating robots they had programmed; good use made of smart boards and digital projectors in all subjects. Scholarship group starts in year 7 and we saw some year 8 scholars preparing for Salters chemistry festival at Bath University. Strong eco bias (Green Flag holders) with regular focus on environmental issues (eg switch off fortnight) and annual eco day. Pastoral team overseen by experienced deputy head: each child is watched over by group tutor, responsible for welfare and progress, and first port of call for anxious parents. Reports are termly, with grades for effort as well as attainment. Parents contacted every half term regarding progress.

Millfield is not a special school, but it attracts pupils with a range of problems from mild literacy difficulties to those with a diagnosis of dyslexia and/or speech and language difficulties. The language development centre (LDC) is a centre of excellence with five full time and four part time specialists plus a classroom assistant. Strong liaison throughout between LDC, pastoral and academic staff as well as with senior school. If reading or spelling is more than a year behind chronological age, this is flagged up, 'But data is not the only aspect taken into account when determining a pupil's current needs.' Speech and language therapist works closely with both the prep and pre-prep. Parents praised how their daughter, previously in a specialist school, was now 'blossoming' at Millfield through the combination of specialist help and 'an emphasis on the positive side of everything.' Group help at both ends of the spectrum included in fees but one-to-one support and recall to therapists are chargeable. Special programme (Potential

Academic Curriculum Excellence or PACE) undertaken by super bright. EAL teacher uses academic lesson time with over 30 international students to immerse them in English before they are progressively fitted into mainstream curriculum.

Sport is a big deal here and a pull for many parents: five PE specialists and a number of ex-international coaches. Sixty pupils in swimming squad alone, partnership with LTA to provide top class tennis coaching, and bubble over one of nine courts on site (pupils go to senior complex if necessary) ensures practice continues through winter. Stonking sports hall (includes large spectator area and four squash courts – two of which are glass backed), equestrian centre with extensive stabling and arenas for dressage and show jumping, a nine hole golf course just for Millfield prep, a fine 25 metre pool (ditto), new sports pavilion and all sorts of courts, pitches and fields to cater for every conceivable sport and activity (seven county champions in athletics alone).

Rising stars can miss a regular PE lesson to receive individual coaching (eg from ex-first class cricketers). U13 girls had just won national (not just preps) cricket title at Lord's when we visited. A powerful presence across all major sports at county and national levels. School is not invincible and meets some stiff competition on the prep schools circuit. Individuals star in many disciplines: fencing, tennis and golf being recent examples. Even the chaplain has a sporting seam running through him (he was going off with a golfing group when we met him). Millfield brain does as well as its brawn with chess teams defending an enviable reputation in tournaments at all levels.

Cracking music department under long serving director: attractive modern recital hall (seats 200), classrooms and practice rooms; wide range of instruments, 350 individual lessons, 29 music ensembles and 18 annual concerts. Junior baroque chamber orchestra plus four choirs and a chapel choir. Pupils selected for national children's choir and orchestra. Annual highlights include home grown Young Musician of the Year competition and a rock and pop concert. Drama lessons lead to many pupils becoming involved (on stage or behind the scenes) in one of four major productions held annually. Staff sometimes have to write plays to suit Millfield's large casts. Parents have been amazed at positive effect of school drama on their children. Art (including popular after lessons clubs) is strong as evidenced by displays around school, from print making to ceramics via ICT, with critical discussion an integral part of its teaching. Good environment in both drawing and painting studios; innovations downstairs included an ex-government printing press bought for a song and stone carving taught in warmer months by talented working artist and done under a lean-to adjacent to art department. Picture of the week chosen from pupils' artwork for insertion in school's newsletter. Design facilities are more akin to a senior school and include CAD design and a laser cutter. Products range from torches to clocks. Textiles aplenty downstairs and food science upstairs encourages innovative cooking which even includes an inter-house competition.

House system is used for internal competitions of all kinds (not just sport). Apart from Edgarley Manor (boys' boarding house) across A361, remaining four boarding houses are on main site: all modern with capacity for 38 boarders each. No large dorms: boarders either in two, four or six bed units (early swimmers kept in rooms together to avoid disturbing others when they get up to train). More of a home from home than an institutional feel and bright colours help keep spirits high. Year 8 allowed to do prep in rooms; otherwise, boarders are supervised in school between 5pm and 6pm. Well-equipped common rooms and cosy kitchens for snacking and chatting. Extra tuck part of house reward system. Boarding houses have outside play areas including tennis court and enclosed field. Medical staff available 24/7.

Staff sometimes have to write plays to suit Millfield's large casts. Parents have been amazed at positive effect of school drama on their children

Minibuses ferry day pupils (early rises for some) from outlying villages in time for 8.25am start. Younger ones can leave at 3.45pm but majority stay for activities until 5pm. Great choice includes sailing at Durleigh, sub-aqua group aiming at PADI junior qualification and caving on Mendips. Weekday activities include Airfix modelling and touch typing, as well as sports from pop lacrosse and indoor go-karting. Diverse theme days and stimulating educational visits to destinations as distant as Rome or as close as Glastonbury Abbey all add to broad mix. Charity fundraising and activities within the local community are also given importance.

We liked the way that so many year 8 pupils get leadership roles on a rotating basis and how 20 of them trained with Kidscape to become peer mentors. Former pupils include 10 current first class cricketers (including half of Somerset CC first XI), rugby stars: Matt Perry and Chris Robshaw, Olympic hockey brothers: Simon and Richard Mantell, Euan Dale (Scottish swimming medallist), Joey Barrington (squash international), Ruth

Kelly MP and Max Milligan (photographer, author and explorer).

Happy school with genuine excitement at every level. Pupils find their niche here (be it academic, sporting or creative) and 'want to do well.' Facilities to take your breath away but school produces well rounded individuals rather than arrogant know-it-alls. 'My daughter was dancing with the daisies before she joined Millfield,' said one mum, 'and now the change is unbelievable.' Parents testify to extent that 'academic and less academic pupils can flourish alongside each other.' Hard to do better than this if the package suits.

Millfield School

33

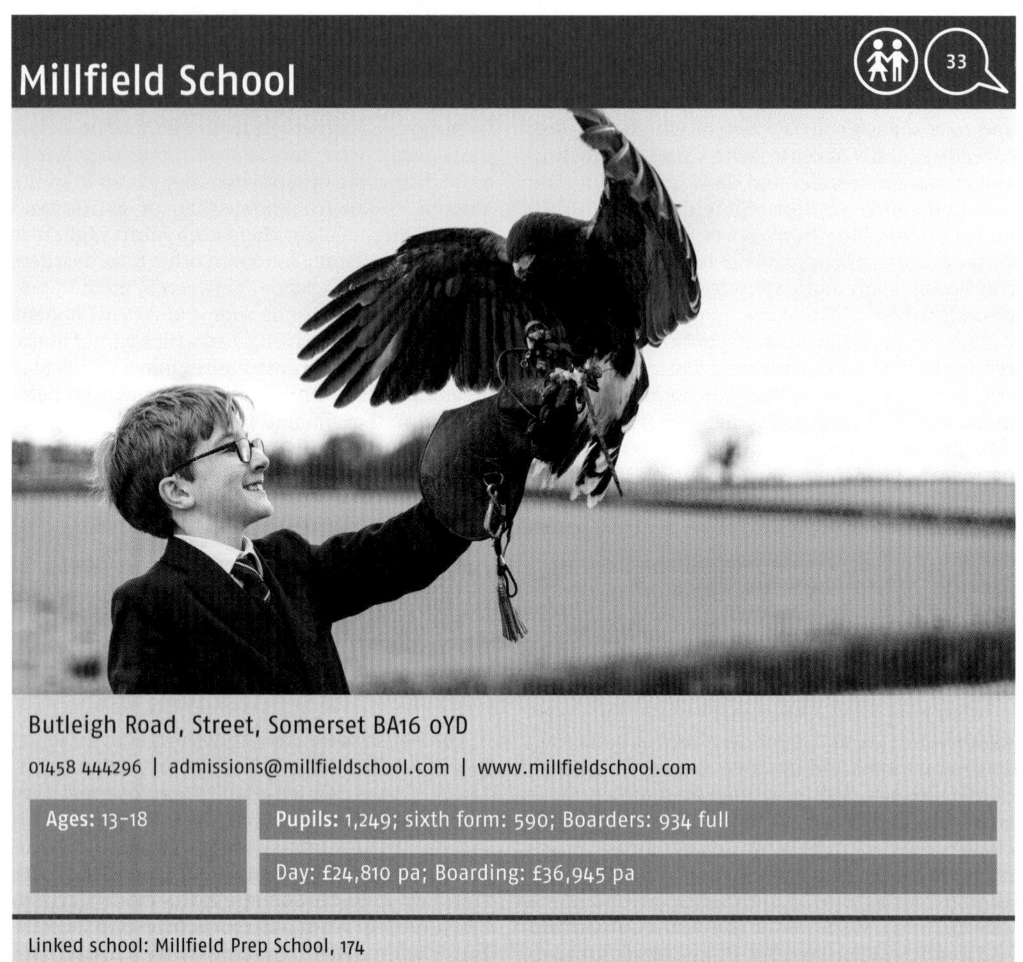

Butleigh Road, Street, Somerset BA16 0YD

01458 444296 | admissions@millfieldschool.com | www.millfieldschool.com

Ages: 13–18

Pupils: 1,249; sixth form: 590; Boarders: 934 full

Day: £24,810 pa; Boarding: £36,945 pa

Linked school: Millfield Prep School, 174

Head master: Since 2008, Mr Craig Considine MEd (mid 50s). Firmly rooted in the southern hemisphere until his appointment to Millfield – a degree in applied science in human movement (that'll be sports science then), a masters in educational leadership from Melbourne's top universities, director of co-curricular at Geelong then head of Wanganui Collegiate School in New Zealand – he brings some welcome Antipodean directness to one of 'the big names – not one of the old names', as he puts it. A previous (British) head of Geelong had suggested Mr Considine could do worse than look at Millfield for ideas for sports facilities; along with those, he was also aware of and intrigued by Jack Meyer's (Millfield's founder, of whom more anon) work on word blindness, as dyslexia was then called, and its links with top flight cricketers. In the ensuing years, Mr Considine has concentrated on improving academics and dispelling perceptions of Millfield as a place for the well-heeled, dim and sporty, but keeping, nay enhancing, the remarkable scope of activities outside the classroom. 'It's all about balance,' he says, 'We can be all things to all people, but it's still about results – and the school needs to be on more prep school radars'. He is proud of the successful attempts to work ever more closely with each student through increased staffing levels: 'We've increased the number of resident staff to take some of the responsibility from houseparents – I could possibly be lampooned for the burgeoning management team', he admits.

A considerable athlete himself – he represented Australia in the decathlon and played professional Australian rules football – his study overlooks the hockey pitches, and his love of sport is still evident in his physique and Twitter feed. Family consists of five grown up children, including two daughters sometimes based in Australia. 'This is a not a job you can get away from,' he asserts, but he loves the proximity and cultural richness of Europe. We found the mix of Antipodean directness with insight and deep appreciation of matters ancient and modern (Avalon meets the iPad) very refreshing in this unexpectedly thoughtful head, who generally meets with parental approval, and was variously described as approachable, willing to listen, humble and not very polished; 'he doesn't work the room,' one parent remarked. Might he be content with being summed up as 'a good bloke'? Very probably.

Leaving in July 2018. His successor will be Gavin Horgan, currently head of Worksop College. Classics degree from Oxford; worked in schools in Sri Lanka and Argentina before returning to the UK as depute rector of Glasgow Academy. He gathered headlines for organising a Worksop school trip to climb mountains in Greenland, believing that risk is essential to children's development. He is married to Alison and they have a young family.

Academic matters: Our previous review said that 'academics will never be the point of Millfield' and that remains true, but the head has devoted considerable efforts to beefing up the intellectual offer with, amongst other initiatives, an enviable programme of academic enrichment, including a lecture series and subject conferences which any young person would be foolish to miss, given the calibre and repute of speakers (scientific colossi Robert Winston, Maggie Aderin-Pocock and Jim Al-Khalili on the same platform!). Brainboxes are invited to join Eureka! or Think Tank, mixed aged groups which meet fortnightly 'to develop the skill of argument analysis'. 2017 GCSEs 43 per cent A*-A/9-7 ; depending on ability and aptitude, students might do any number between six and 12, including core subjects but not necessarily a foreign language. A level results 52 per cent A*/B, 25 per cent A*/A, with a staggering 33 subjects to choose from, including world development and classical Greek.

Onward destinations are manifold, both in the UK and North America in particular; just two to Oxford in 2017 'but then we don't have a lot of kids saying Oxbridge is where they want to go,' the head remarked. One parent was critical of Oxbridge preparation – or lack of it, feeling that the school was much more interested in and geared up for applications to American universities; the school is a SAT centre, but that same father reckoned that the top results at Millfield are as good as anywhere. But it is heartening to see the range of qualifications on offer at Millfield: for the less academically inclined, BTecs attract growing numbers, along with the British Horse Society's Preliminary Instructor's certificate and the ever popular Leith food and wine course – just the thing for running that chalet in Verbier in one's gap year. Judging by the longevity of some teachers' careers there, teaching at Millfield can be a job for life, leading to some dissatisfaction with the calibre in some quarters, and a sense that some old timers could usefully be moved on. The head is addressing effective recruitment at least by providing the kind of accommodation designed to attract top notch staff. Class sizes noticeably small here, max 14; the staff pupil ratio is the lowest this editor had ever seen, at just 1:6.5. Students are generally grouped into ability bands via literacy tests, then into sets within those bands, but some A level language and science classes are taught across the ability range.

BTecs attract growing numbers, along with the British Horse Society's Preliminary Instructor's certificate and the ever popular (and always useful) Leith food and wine course

School's website cites 'sophisticated use of digital technology for learning' but this greatly understates the almost total integration of iPads throughout the school (closer at the younger end). Every student must have one, and through it, almost everything flows, in and out of the classroom. That said, it does not replace live teaching, but aids it: we were privileged, if not faintly repelled, to witness the dissection of a horse's lung, where the lesson went on to explore human lung capacity at rest and after exertion via an iPad app, one boy gamely leaping up and down outside as a live experiment. Unhelpful chatter from Facebook, Instagram and Twitter is blocked in lesson time, and there's a tracking system which monitors any reprehensible activity. 'But what about old-fashioned skills like note-taking?' we asked – and received a somewhat prickly assurance that these were also taught. 'We're about adapting, not adopting' the head said pithily.

SEN provision underpins much of Millfield's successes and its appeal. When we asked the head about Millfield's being viewed as a haven or magnet for SEN, his response was unequivocal: 'Well it is! We make strong assessments of SEN which we normalise here, and occasionally have to say no to those whose learning we cannot support'. Just over a third of students have an identified need, addressed and supported by a team of SpLD experts in the exceptionally well-resourced learning support centre (no fewer than four educational psychologists on the staff), sited right at this rambling school's heart. Support is based on literacy, the key to the entire curriculum, but help is available for all manners of barriers to learning including dyscalculia (sometimes delivered to milder cases among younger students by sixth formers alongside the maths tutor), dyspraxia and organisation skills. Just about everyone gets GCSE English and maths at grade C/4 (90 per cent in 2017) – hurrah – but retake classes are run in year 12 for anyone just missing that important hurdle. The sheer numbers receiving support means a total lack of stigma: our delightful young guide came straight to the point during our tour: 'I am very dyslexic and here I get all the help I need'. Close liaison between teachers, house staff, tutors and SEN staff provides continuity and reassurance.

Games, options, the arts: Genuinely exceedingly difficult to know where to start! This is unquestionably the place for your budding Olympian, and the fact that it has produced so many top flight athletes and sportspeople is no accident. Both provision and facilities abound, from the famous 50m Olympic swimming pool with all the wizardry and coaches associated with training future national champions to the recent acquisition of a stretch of the Huntspill river (a world class water facility, apparently) and Swingulator which trains oarsmen/women on dry land. It is typical of the Millfield seriousness of purpose that, having only introduced rowing a few years ago, investment in a year-round programme including nutrition, video analysis and diverse training has resulted in this Jonny-come-lately beating many established rowing schools and even universities. But whatever Millfield does – and it does almost everything – it does exceptionally well, devoting considerable sums, land and care in recruiting top coaches to its unequalled sporting offer. We could wax rapturous about the provision for riders, comprising a polo ground, cross-country course and gallops, or about the fencing salle, but the more usual school sports are outstandingly provided for also. The school's level of commitment has to be matched by that of the students': a daily 5.40am reveille is quite common for élite swimmers, for example. Parental opinion about the school's attitude to sporting élitism varies: clearly some send their offspring here exactly for that, others feel that the push for excellence has rather meant other kids being 'left to get on with it', in the words of one father. At junior levels, by contrast, we found some frustration that previous top prep school players (rugby, but maybe other games too) were regularly substituted, meaning that they played less often/for less long than they were used to, demotivating them at times.

School's level of commitment has to be matched by the students': a daily 5.40am reveille is quite common for élite swimmers, for example

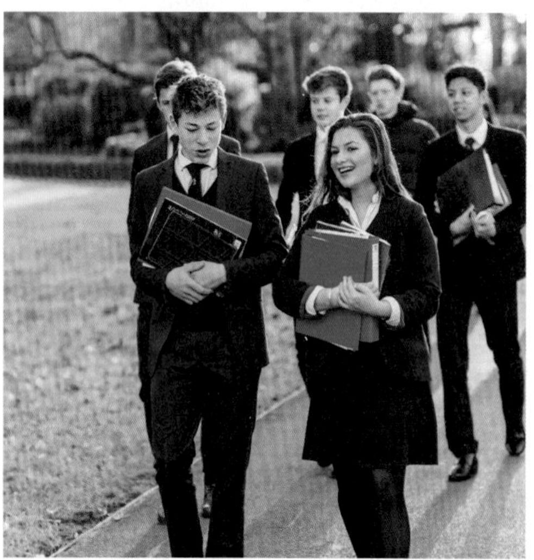

Art and DT all happen in the same gorgeous spacious block; needless to say, all equipment is bang up to the mark and, claims school, equals some university facilities. The nationally known Atkinson Gallery hosts four major exhibitions a year; when we visited, the most innovative work coming out of the UK's top art schools was on show. We wished we had taken more note of the Millfield sculpture trail as we trotted about the extensive site: new work is regularly commissioned or purchased. Music facilities marvellous – lots of it, very high spec too – and the exposure to the musical life a part of every Millfieldian's first year, when learning an orchestral instrument is compulsory. Major concerts often take place in the sublime contrast of Wells Cathedral, where the choir sings also regular services. It was an unexpected delight to happen across a member of the music staff practising Poulenc for his own pleasure. Drama is popular and very well-resourced, with several studios as well as the Meyer Theatre. Just one whole school production a year but a ton of other things, such as a sketch show and a Spanish play, and opportunities to get involved in all goings-on back stage. Applications to drama school are exceptionally well supported here, and success rates high in this competitive area.

The Millfield Activities Programme (MAP to its friends) offers 100 different pursuits for all students up until year 12, and is intended to offer breadth – alongside élite sport, for example. French cinema, German card games, skiing race training, silversmithing – it's all there for the taking. Local volunteering opportunities with a range of charities provide an outlet for altruism and perhaps a chance to reflect on all that privilege.

Boarding: Three-quarters of students board in 19 boarding houses scattered across the 240 acre campus. We were whisked around a selection of them in a golf buggy, on account of the sheer scale of the place (not because we had visited unsuitably shod in stilettos). Year 9s have their own houses for that vital first year, to ensure solid friendships across the year group and to integrate the large numbers who arrive from Millfield Prep. After year 9, students have a say in their final house, but staff are careful to try to avoid the forming of cliques. Most rooms are twins, singles further up the school, some with ensuite shower rooms; all was clean and functional rather than luxurious, and we noted the congenial common room space with pool tables and ping pong, rather than more screens; all i-anything is handed in at night to a named charging compartment. Pleasant outside space specially designed for barbecues and summer socialising. House staff come in for praise: one housemaster was described as a 'cracking bloke', and parents like the high staff:student ratio and the 15 bed medical centre, with physio clinic. We did, though, pick up a sense of social divide between the day students and boarders, and one father said bluntly that the former are 'disproportionately bright'. Boarders and day students alike eat in the magnificent cafeteria, where the range of choice is enormous, not say bewildering; menus embrace all sporting diets. The tortilla and salads we chose from the Spanish counter as part of the world food bar was delicious, and it was made even more authentic by the Spanish staff jabbering away on the next table. Further flung boarding houses have the occasional dinner in their own dining rooms on special occasions.

Background and atmosphere: For one of the UK's most successful boarding schools, Millfield is really quite a new kid on the block. Just over 80 years ago Jack Meyer, a bright young civil servant and accomplished cricketer, went out to work with the Indian Civil Service. Attracting the notice of a passing maharajah as a jolly good chap, 'Boss' Meyer, as he became known, returned to the UK in the mid 1930s at his request with seven Indian boys, six of them princes, to found a school – Millfield, initially set up in a private house of that name rented from the nearby Clark family (of shoe fame). Innovation was the name of the game from then on: co-ed from 1939, as much emphasis on excellence and opportunity in sport and the arts as on academic success, and from 1942, an interest in and commitment to overcoming dyslexia and other barriers to learning, following the arrival of the 'word blind' son of the then deputy PM, Martin Attlee, who (most unusually for dyslexics of the time) went on to higher education.

This is unquestionably the place for your budding Olympian, and the fact that it has produced so many top flight athletes and sportspeople is no accident

These three markers have defined the school ever since, sometimes unfairly, but the feel and look of the place is fresh and contemporary – no hallowed portals here. Instead, buildings of all materials, types and function ('No great architectural merit,' said one father, drily) are scattered across the huge site, more akin to a small university campus, whose grassed areas were strewn with crocuses at the time of year we visited. A culture of entrepreneurship still prevails: on the school's part, ambitious plans for a new enterprise centre, on the part of one new sixth former, encouragement and plaudits for setting up his own charity club to raise funds for less fortunate youngsters. No overwhelming sense of entitlement, privilege or history among the students either; all the ones we spoke to expressing in forthright terms their good fortune at being there. Uniform unexceptional – standard issue navy suits with the finest of pinstripes and v-necked jumpers for the girls below sixth form, but boys get to buy their own suits: we saw one dandy clad in immaculate Prince of Wales check. 'Not fair,' opined one mother – but the fact that it's cheaper than designer options doubtless chosen by some boys must compensate.

Pastoral care, well-being and discipline: The head is concerned that no-one gets lost, overlooked or presumably away with too much in this big school, and has increased house staffing levels considerably to ensure none slip through the net. The general levels of affluence and huge geographical catchment might cause some to make simplistic links with illicit contraband like drink and drugs, but this passed unmentioned by all those we spoke to. Parents are mostly happy with the way in which their concerns are dealt with, and students feel that punishments are fair and appropriate; sixth form gating is a particular deterrent to wrongdoing. The fact that academic work is commended both for achievement and effort goes down well also. What most schools call PHSE has been redesigned as Positive Education – a through-going programme covering, inter alia, resilience and emotional intelligence; this is reinforced in day/boarding houses as well as in class. A dedicated email address exists to report any incidents of bullying.

Pupils and parents: Everyone, nay everyone, talked of the diversity of families – the much-vaunted Millfield Mix – and given the range of bursaries on offer, this is not as fanciful as it might appear (OK, OK, a few children arrive by helicopter, but others in much humbler hatchbacks). 'We work on the Robin Hood principle,' says the head. Maybe its sporting prowess, international clientéle (20 per cent come from overseas but no one nationality predominates) and openness to a wide intellectual spectrum create the 'egalitarian feel of a southern hemisphere school' that the head is keen on, but there's certainly 'a lot less tweed on the touchline than there is at Radley,' as one dad put it. The students we met looked us in the eye and shook us firmly by the hand – 'confident in the qualities that make them wonderful,' in the words of the head. Worth noting that there are roughly 60 per cent boys.

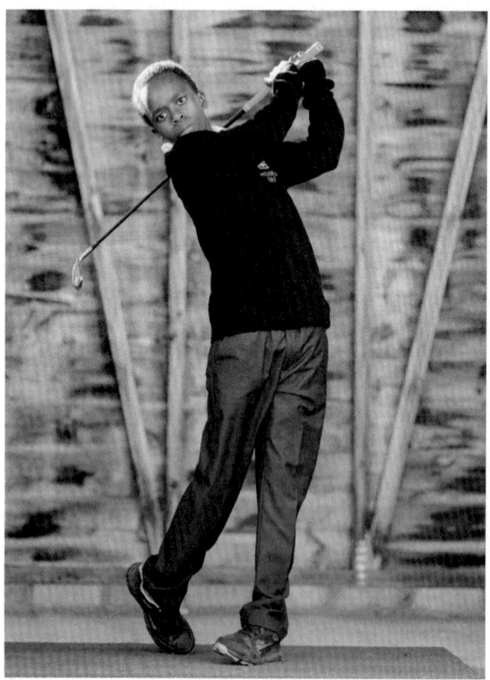

Whatever Millfield does (and that's almost everything), it does exceptionally well, devoting considerable money, land and care

Entrance: Mainly into year 9, many from its own large prep school, but from 120 other prep schools all over the world. Thirty-five places are available in year 10. Places are offered on the basis of an interview with a senior member of staff and a computerised verbal and non-verbal reasoning assessment for which it is not possible to prepare. Overseas applicants sit the UKiset test. Sixth form entry for the 130 who join at this point depends on a minimum of six passes at GCSE including English and maths for those doing A levels; just four for those doing BTecs

Exit: A handful seem to leave in the first couple of years, about 20-25 per cent after GCSE and, unusually, a scattering at the end of year 12. Those who stay for the duration praise the quality and administration of the support given university admissions, whether in the UK or abroad. Two to Oxbridge and one medic in 2017; Cardiff and Oxford Brookes currently top of the pops in the UK, and American universities leading the field by miles for study abroad, some awarding sports scholarships, particularly in hockey and tennis. Surprisingly few gap years. Famous alumni, especially sporting ones, too numerous to list, but stand-outs are Gareth Edwards and Chris Robshaw (rugby), Duncan Goodhew, Joanne Atkinson and James Guy (swimming). Eight Old Millfieldians competed at Rio 2016 and won four medals between them (swimming, rowing and rugby). But Old Millfieldians are also to be found at the top of their game in journalism, finance and even one medieval history don among the dreaming spires.

Money matters: In the past it enjoyed the reputation of being the most expensive school in the UK, but at the moment it comes in at less than Eton. It would, however, be easy to go large on the extras (endless racks of monogrammed house team kit etc) in the school shop, where items can be bought and bunged on the bill with the houseparent's permission. Some activities are chargeable where outside staff are brought in (eg polo); specialist therapy such as speech and language and vision, EAL, individual learning support also. Scholarships (including for design & innovation and chess) awarded to a maximum of 15 per cent of fees, but a generous 50 per cent for exceptional all-rounders into year 9. Extensive bursary provision which goes to 100 per cent in cases of phenomenal hardship

Remarks: A big open-hearted school welcoming all talents but not, we think, none. Only the best will do, in terms of facilities and IT and its ambition seems boundless, as the head turns his attention to the academics and the new centre for enterprise. Besides, where else would you meet princes and paupers?

Milton Abbey School

34

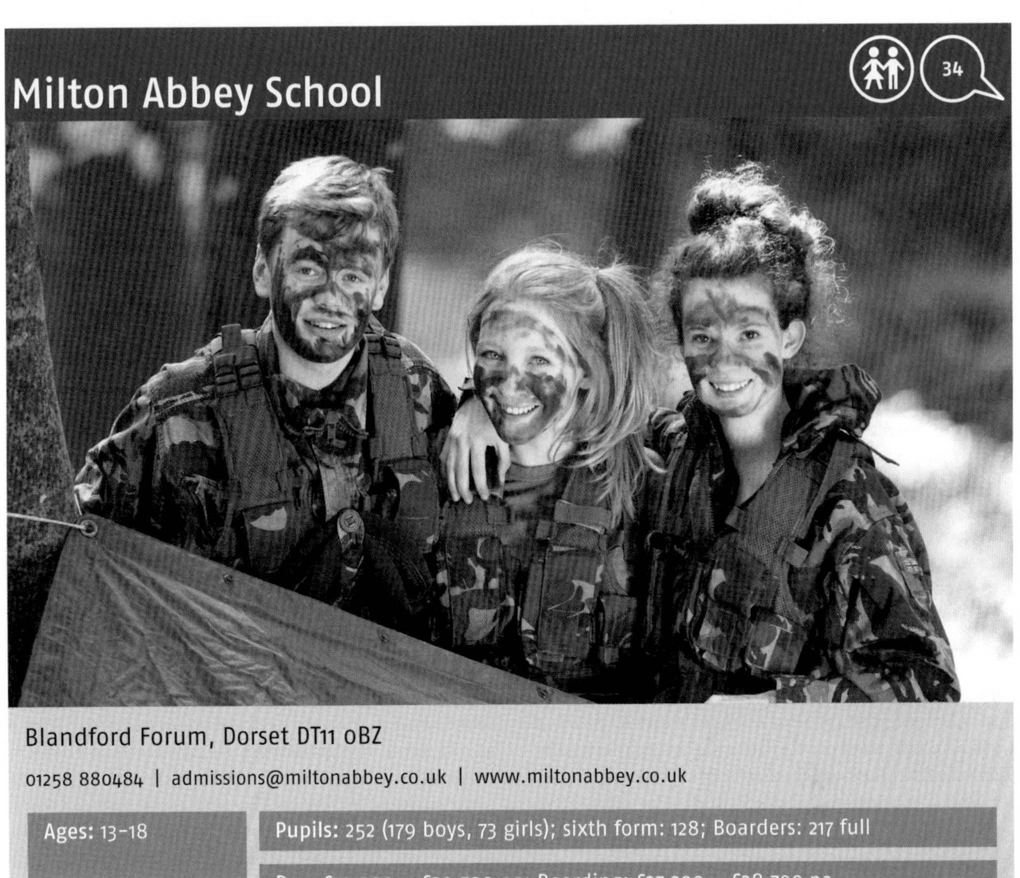

Blandford Forum, Dorset DT11 0BZ

01258 880484 | admissions@miltonabbey.co.uk | www.miltonabbey.co.uk

Ages: 13–18

Pupils: 252 (179 boys, 73 girls); sixth form: 128; Boarders: 217 full

Day: £19,500 – £20,700 pa; Boarding: £37,200 – £38,700 pa

Headmaster: Since 2014, Magnus Bashaarat MA PGCE (40s), previously deputy head of Stowe. Educated at The King's School, Canterbury (he and Stowe head Anthony Wallersteiner were contemporaries there), followed by University of Edinburgh, where he read English. After work experience at the York Evening Press he decided to become a journalist and worked for the Observer and Evening Standard for a while. He changed direction after taking a course in teaching English as a foreign language – found he loved 'standing up in front of a class and helping people to learn.' PGCE at King's College London, followed by two years at Sherborne and a 15-year stint at Eton, where he taught English and drama and was a housemaster for seven years. He also did a year at Sydney Grammar as part of a teaching exchange with Eton. Moved to Stowe in 2009 and spent five years as deputy head. He says Milton Abbey is similar to Stowe – 'just on a different scale' – and that its size means 'everyone is seen as an individual, everyone is valued and pupils have a very good relationship with staff.'

Mr Bashaarat is dynamic, forward-thinking and hit the ground running when he arrived. He didn't teach during his first year at Milton Abbey but now teaches an English GCSE retake set. 'It's lovely to have contact time again,' he told us. He's adamant that a head shouldn't be a remote figure and makes a point of seeing the pupils as much as possible, chatting at lunch, running a school cycling group and popping into the boarding houses in the evenings. 'This place has a very honest, nurturing ethos and pupils are very well looked after,' he says.

His wife Camilla used to work in communications for the NHS and now runs Milton Abbey's parents' association, or MASPA as it's known (everything from a yoga retreat in Norfolk to a trip to Champagne in France). They have three children – sons at Stowe and Eton and a daughter at Sherborne Girls. In his spare time, he cycles (his road bike is propped against the wall of his study), rows at nearby Canford and goes to the theatre as much as he can. He likes 'serious drama' and if he can't get to London drives to Poole, Salisbury and, a new find, The Tobacco Factory in Bristol.

Moving on in July 2018 to head Bedales. His successor will be Judith Fremont-Barnes, currently head of Duke of Kent School in Surrey. English degree from Oxford; first teaching post at JAGS, then spent five years in Japan where she lectured at Kobe Kaisei College for Women and Kobe University, as well as bringing up a family. On her return to the UK, joined King Edward VI School and then Radley College, where she became head of English, was involved in boarding and a member of the school's academic planning group. Next post was deputy head at More House School in Surrey; she moved to Duke of Kent in 2011. Leisure interests include long walks with her border terrier and time spent with her family: her husband Gregory, a military historian, and their two grown up sons.

Academic matters: Milton Abbey's strengths lie in its value-added. School doesn't publish its GCSE and A level results (though 14 per cent A*-A/9-7 at GCSE in 2017, the best result since 2012), taking the view that students have such a broad range of ability that their achievements wouldn't be accurately represented by what the head calls the 'crude mechanism' of league tables. 'The value added we get for our pupils wouldn't be represented by the league tables,' he says. Students range from a boy who got three A*s at A level and headed to Oxford to read archaeology and anthropology to those who find formal academic learning 'really difficult' and opt for a more vocational route. The school talks a lot about 'parallel learning pathways' and prides itself on tailoring an academic programme to suit individual students. At sixth form, a third of pupils take A levels, a third take a combination of A levels and BTecs and a third take BTecs. In year 11 youngsters attend an options evening, when they discuss individual sixth form choices with tutors and heads of department. Pupils' GCSE profiles are taken into account and subject combinations are based on advice from tutors and teachers (no chance of doing physics A level and a BTec in hospitality). Pupils are encouraged to pursue their passions and interests and all the usual A levels are on offer, plus economics, politics, history of art and music technology.

Ahead of the curve when it comes to vocational learning. School says it offers the broadest range of BTecs in the independent sector

The school is ahead of the curve when it comes to vocational learning. Milton Abbey says it offers the broadest range of BTecs in the independent sector and is one of the few schools to offer BTecs at extended diploma level – equivalent to three A levels. BTecs (available in countryside management, performing arts, enterprise and entrepreneurship, equine management, hospitality, creative media production and sport) aren't an easy option though. They are made up of continued assessment, with a small percentage of the course assessed by exam at the end of two years. The school's 2015 ISI report commended its approach, saying that 'pupils, who come with widely different educational backgrounds and needs, often suffering a negative experience of education elsewhere, are enabled to rebuild the foundation of their knowledge and skills, as well as the self-confidence needed to progress.' The assistant head (academic) concurs with this. 'We're all about getting the best out of our pupils,' she says.

Pupils take between seven and nine GCSEs, with everyone doing English, maths and a science. Class sizes are small – average of 12 up to GCSE and six at A level. 'The small class sizes mean that we have much better outcomes for learners,' says the head. Pupils are streamed by ability for the core subjects. Lessons are now one hour long – school says this helps pupils to concentrate better.

Milton Abbey is resolutely mainstream but learning support, with four teachers and six teaching assistants, is the biggest department. Some pupils are screened before they start and around two-thirds access learning support in some way – for a wide range of difficulties, including dyslexia, dyspraxia, dyscalculia, mild Asperger's). Learning support assistants provide additional help in lessons and there's one-to-one or group support outside lessons too (charged on top of the fees). EAL support and study skills support on offer. Some pupils have learning support lessons instead of doing French or Spanish. The department is very welcoming, with its door permanently open to help anyone who wants to drop in for revision tips, essay planning and time management. 'Quite often their self-esteem and confidence is low and it's our job to raise that,' says the head of learning support.

School library has 9,000 resources and pupils are encouraged to read books for pleasure as well as for study. Robert Muchamore and Meg Rosoff are two current favourites – 'we like to get the pupils in the habit of reading,' the school librarian told us.

Games, options, the arts: Sport is taken seriously here but the emphasis is on enjoyment and there's loads on offer. Rugby, hockey, cricket and football predominate but golf (there's a course in the grounds), sailing and polo have a strong take-up too. The fixtures list and results show the school punches above its weight on the sports field. Relatively small number of girls means everyone gets the chance to represent the school at hockey, netball and lacrosse during the winter and tennis and rounders during the winter. Facilities include a 25-metre swimming pool, two gyms, squash court, all-weather pitch, sports hall and outdoor pitches galore. Everyone does games on Tuesdays, Thursdays and Saturdays but the sportiest do far more. Wednesdays are given over to CCF or community service (including visiting the elderly, taking dogs for walks and cleaning the local church). There's all manner of country pursuits, like fishing, ferreting (you can bring your own ferret, although none were in residence when we visited), clay pigeon shooting, beagling and mountain biking.

It's possible to combine a burgeoning equestrian career with school life. Pupils can bring their own steeds – many of the keenest riders take a BTec in equine management and keep their horses at the school stables (each individual stable is labelled with the inhabitant's name – Sparky, Dolly and the like). They manage the day-to-day care of their horses and can choose to ride instead of playing other sports.

Art is a popular subject and we saw artwork that was easily on a par with larger schools. A year 12 boy showed us an astonishing oil painting inspired by renaissance art that he'd worked on over the summer. School puts on a big drama production in its theatre every year and there's a vast array of music. Hymn practice is held in the Abbey every Friday, when the whole school gathers to sing at the tops of their voices. 'The volume creeps up bit by bit and it sounds wonderful,' a sixth form boy told us.

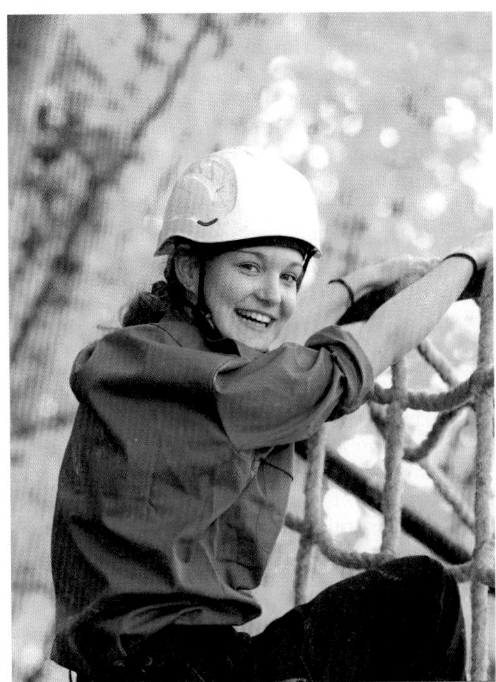

Milton Abbey runs the innovative Entrepreneurship in Residence competition, aiming to inspire pupils with ambitions to launch their own business. Top-notch designers like Anya Hindmarch, Johnnie Boden and Cath Kidston and Carphone Warehouse founder David Ross have all fronted the scheme. Unlike some boarding schools, students do work experience – usually with school alumni (an Inner Temple barrister and a Coutts banker were among those who volunteered this year). Other activities include D of E, farm club and the Ten Tors expedition across Dartmoor. School is a member of Round Square, a worldwide organisation that encourages young people to broaden their horizons and gain greater understanding of the wider world through exchange trips, community work and themed activities within school.

Boarding: Milton Abbey offers full boarding or day places – 'we don't have anything in between,' says the head. Two three-day exeats a term to allow for longer journeys home. Five boarding houses – four for boys and one for girls. We visited the two newest houses, both wholesome and welcoming, with disabled access and underfloor heating. Each has a housemaster or housemistress, resident tutors and two matrons, who take charge of laundry and cleaning, offer support to pupils and help them to prepare for life beyond school. One matron told us she'd just taught a boy how to iron his shirt – 'it was important he learned how to do it himself.'

Common rooms in the boarding houses are equipped with TVs but these aren't allowed on during the day. There's no mobile phone signal on much of the site so phones are less of a problem here than at other schools. Most use the old-fashioned landlines in the boarding houses to phone home.

Background and atmosphere: Milton Abbey, with 76 acres of rolling countryside, is one of the prettiest schools in the country. You can't fail to be enchanted by the ancient abbey nestling in a wooded Dorset valley, one of the finest Capability Brown landscapes in the country, 15 minutes' drive from Blandford. 'It's deeply rural, but not remote,' is the head's description. We visited on a sunny day but were assured that it looks lovely in the rain and mist too. The school was founded in 1954 and occupies the converted monastery buildings. The vast abbey belongs to the Diocese of Salisbury but the school has full use of it, with services four times a week. Milton Abbey also has its own farm (complete with pigs, sheep, goats, turkeys and chickens), makes its own honey and grows flowers, fruit and vegetables.

Pupils eat all their meals in the Abbot's Hall, a grand dining room complete with stags' heads and a huge mural of the school painted by a parent to commemorate the school's 50th anniversary. Pasta, salads, wraps and paninis on offer at lunch-time, as well as hot meals, plus snacks at break, fresh fruit and cake in the afternoons. 'No one goes hungry,' grinned one boy. Uniform is smart. Younger girls wear tartan skirts and blazers while sixth form girls are clad in grey skirts and tweed jackets of their choice. Boys wear tweed jackets, grey trousers and ties.

Pastoral care, well-being and discipline: Pupils keep the same tutor from year 9 to year 11, and see them two or three times a week. In the sixth form students get a say in their choice of tutor – often someone who teaches them or whom they have a good relationship with. School operates a system of rewards and sanctions when it comes to behaviour – awards given for good work, sporting achievements and acts of kindness.

Good communication with parents – school has introduced a new parent portal where parents have access to weekly notes on everything from a missed prep to an academic triumph. Pupils told us that 'there aren't hundreds of rules. They give you a degree of trust.' Student voice is considered important. Head boy and head girl (who meet the headmaster every morning), heads of houses and a raft of prefects – called 'pilots' here.

Pupils and parents: Pupils come from 120 or so prep schools and from all over the country – quite a few from London and from as far afield as Northumberland. International students from France, Italy, Germany, Italy, Kenya and the US. Day pupils ('our day fees are really competitive,' says the head) tend to live within a 30-minute drive. School minibus service covers Blandford, Wimborne, Poole, Dorchester, Shaftesbury and Salisbury. Day pupils leave at 6pm but there's the option to stay on for activities and prep if they wish.

Milton Abbey also has its own farm (complete with pigs, sheep, goats, turkeys and chickens), makes its own honey and grows flowers, fruit and vegetables

Despite such privileged surroundings, the pupils we met were outgoing, enthusiastic and delightfully unsnobby. Sixth formers summed the school's appeal up in a nutshell. 'For the people it's right for, this is the best school in the country,' one boy declared. 'I love it. My sister's at Millfield and her year group is as big as this whole school. Here, everybody knows everybody and the support you get is second to none.' A girl said she liked being 'a big fish in a small pond' while parents told us they love the family atmosphere, plus the fact that their children get loads of country air and aren't glued to their phones, tablets and laptops.

Former pupils include Professor Jonathan Freeman-Attwood, the principal of the Royal Academy of Music, photographer, screenwriter and TV director Harry Hook, restaurateur Oliver Gladwin, sculptor Robert Rattray, documentary maker Anthony Geffen and Professor Alastair Bruce, royal, religious and constitutional affairs commentator for Sky News.

Entrance: School is 'inclusive and non-selective.' Around 70 per cent of pupils do CE – pass mark is around 50 per cent but school is flexible on this and says 'there's no hard and fast rule.'

Applicants attend a taster day to see if the school suits them. Usual entry points are 13 and 16 but a handful of pupils start in year 10, often because they didn't settle at their original choice of school. Milton Abbey doesn't chuck pupils out if they don't make their GCSE grades either. Head believes that when a school accepts a youngster at 13 it should stick with them for the duration.

Exit: School loses around 10 per cent of pupils after GCSEs – largely due to relocation or for financial reasons – but larger numbers choose to join from other schools. At 18 or 19 pupils choose a plethora of routes. In 2017, destinations included Newcastle University, King's College London, Oxford Brookes and the Royal Agricultural College as well as Aston, Goldsmiths and the Royal College of Drawing. School has strong links with international catering colleges, such as Glion and Les Roches in Switzerland, and several pupils have headed to these in the past.

Head points out that 'a degree isn't a guarantee of a job' these days and is keen on courses that 'will facilitate future employment.' He admits that if he was choosing a degree now he would probably go for vocational journalism and media rather than English. School has forged a close relationship with The Arts University Bournemouth, which specialises in art, design, media and performance across the creative industries.

Money matters: A range of scholarships at 13+ and 16+ – academic, all-rounder, art, DT, drama, music and sport. All worth 10 per cent of the fees, although these may be increased 'where financial need is demonstrated.' School also offers means-tested bursaries, plus scholarships for day pupils living in Dorset.

Remarks: Milton Abbey's setting, countryside expertise and innovative mix of qualifications give pupils, some of whom may not have thrived elsewhere, a host of opportunities to shine – both inside and outside the classroom.

Monkton Combe School

35

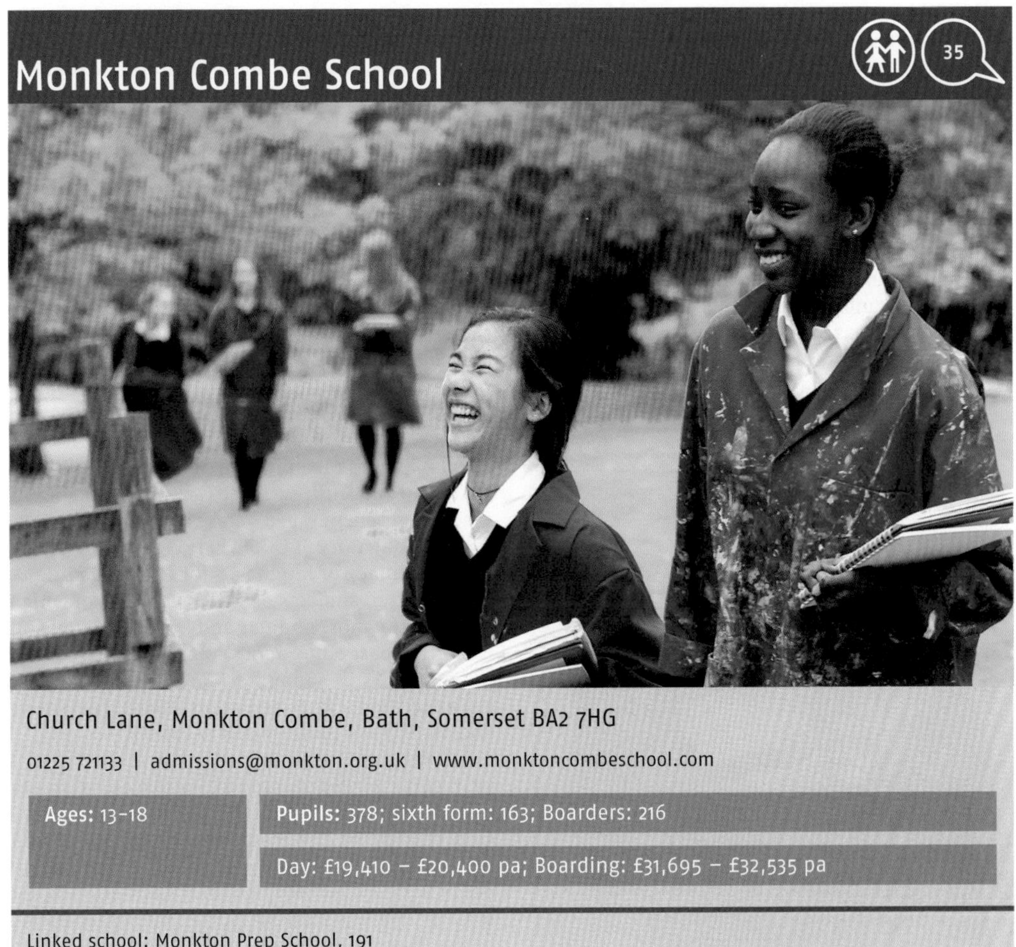

Church Lane, Monkton Combe, Bath, Somerset BA2 7HG

01225 721133 | admissions@monkton.org.uk | www.monktoncombeschool.com

Ages: 13–18

Pupils: 378; sixth form: 163; Boarders: 216

Day: £19,410 – £20,400 pa; Boarding: £31,695 – £32,535 pa

Linked school: Monkton Prep School, 191

Principal: Since 2016, Christopher Wheeler BA PGCE (early 40s). The son of a general and educated at the thoroughly pukka institutions of Winchester, Durham (where he read English and philosophy) and Bristol (PGCE), Mr Wheeler started his teaching career at St John's Leatherhead, where he left as head of English to take up several roles (head of English and drama, registrar, deputy head – where did he find the time??) at Peponi School in Kenya. Since then, his working life has ping-ponged between the UK and Kenya, never staying anywhere very long and combining teaching with the usual climb up the managerial ladder with spells as a housemaster at Brighton College, head of its prep St Christopher's Hove and, latterly, principal and CEO of Hillcrest International School in Nairobi. 'Africa gets under your skin' he says – something he discovered during his gap year in Zimbabwe – but now as a father of three young children, he is conscious of security concerns in Kenya, prompting a move back to the UK.

Very different from his cerebral predecessor, Mr Wheeler has something of the showman about him: one might even say show-off, with the remarkable breaking into a rendition of One Day More (that stirring number from Les Mis) in the middle of his address at Speech Day 2017. (It went viral and the school has been shortlisted for a social media award.) But he has taken the place by the horns since his arrival with the introduction of the notion that Emotional Quotient (EQ) is a more helpful measure than IQ, and of the growth mind-set, developed by Carol Dweck, where students are encouraged to believe that intelligence is not fixed but malleable, and that improvement and achievement are therefore very much in their own hands. More controversially, he has brought in peer review of staff; several key members of long standing have left.

First and foremost a boarding school, with late evenings (10pm pick-ups) for day students and compulsory Saturday morning lessons

Improbably boyish for such a senior role, he bowled us over with a flood of exuberant verbiage: future plans include repositioning the entrance to befit 'a proper public school' and creating an equestrian centre on site in a redundant part of the extensive grounds. 'After all, riding, rowing and reeling are life skills, aren't they?' says he (reely??). Students find him approachable and charismatic: he has made a point of weekly lunches with different groups and take-up of his morning dog walks was so popular that he was begged to reinstate them after discontinuing them in the winter. He reckons they provide a brilliant opportunity to chat to teenagers without discomforting eye contact. Parents broadly positive, staff possibly less so. Married to Georgie, who teaches sport and is a keen horsewoman, Mr Wheeler doubles as action man during the holidays, enjoying paragliding and snowboarding in the Alps.

Academic matters: Not particularly selective, though the previous principal upped the academic ante and there appear to be no plans to change this, so the 2017 results (of 60 per cent A*-A/9-7 at GCSE, 73 per cent A*/B and 40 per cent A*/A at A level) are more than respectable, especially at sixth form. Two languages taken in year 9, which can include Mandarin and Latin – why no German? – and pupils are strongly encouraged to take a modern language but not obligatory at GCSE. Extra English or maths takes the place of languages for those needing it. Twenty-seven subjects on offer at A level, of which maths is the most popular and DT (3D Design) and Latin the least – but good that the choices of the minority are still honoured. Monkton sixth formers are expected to start and complete three A levels and an EPQ. No IB nor plans to offer it.

Good handful to Oxbridge (six in 2017) every year. Our visit fell during exam season, so much of what we saw was rigorous preparation and revision classes; of the teachers' commitment and dedication including at weekends there can be no doubt whatsoever: 'My daughter's ambition to get to Oxbridge was fully supported by her teachers,' one mother told us, adding that the school had also suited her dyslexic sibling. Small class sizes averaging at 15 or so below sixth form and around nine at A level must help. 'Inspiring academic ambition is a key priority,' intones the website, an aspiration underpinned by the importance placed on growth mind-set (see above) and the instilling of a good work ethic by one-to-one tutoring; students have some discretion to change if the allocated tutor does not work out. Well-stocked library for all ages with limited computer facilities: the vast majority of students doubtless have their own laptops. Though the bright and modernised classrooms and labs we saw were all suitably equipped with interactive whiteboards etc, we did not sense that this was a school where technology was, refreshingly, the be-all and end-all.

Monkton used to be something of a refuge for SEN students, but it no longer has CReSTed status, catering only for minor difficulties these days. The learning support department is right at the centre of the school and staffed by two SpLD teachers. Difficulties in organisation and processing as well as exam technique are also addressed, and all students are assessed on entry. Most of the site has been made accessible for wheelchairs.

Games, options, the arts: Surely something for everyone here, with acres of pitches including, according to Wisden, one of the most beautiful cricket grounds in the country, with its views of the perfect honey-coloured viaduct carrying the busy A36 out of Bath. Rugby, hockey, netball and tennis (hard and grass courts, plus Astro) all onsite, though swimming takes place in the delightful indoor pool at the prep school just up the hill, since Mr Wheeler had the old outdoor pool filled in. Rowing is a big deal here: with a good stretch of river just yards from school and Olympian oarsmen Steve Williams and Rowley Douglas, plus GB single sculler Olivia Caesar among former pupils. Senior rowers benefit from a splendid new boathouse and a (better) stretch of the Avon at Saltford (about 20 minutes away), used also by the university crews of Bath and Bristol. Lots else to do too, though, such as fencing, dance, riding – and yes, CCF, D of E and Ten Tors of course. More sedate extracurricular choices include baking, knitting and chess.

Surely something for everyone here, with acres of pitches including, according to Wisden, one of the most beautiful cricket grounds in the country

It's the upgrade to the arts facilities, though, which is astonishing. Both art/DT and music have had sensational new (or hugely enhanced) buildings, creating pleasing contemporary touches to quite a traditional campus. Visitors to the art school go straight into the gallery, filled when we saw it with enormous textile print hangings using beetroot juice. Textiles a particular strength and the specialism of the current artist in residence. The art dept is proud of the numbers getting places at Central St Martins. Huge dark room and industrial printing facilities (busy with a school promotional banner when we were there) complete a superb set-up. As for music – it's just 'Wow!' Jewel in the crown must be the concert hall, quite an intimate space with acoustic design and its requisite mosaic (non-technical term for technical necessity) ceiling, but the more hi-tech musicians are thrilled with the recording facilities all linked to a central studio. It's not just the surroundings though: the head of music is widely lauded for his 'desperate enthusiasm', and his innovations like the choir who can't sing (mostly boys) and the choir who won't sing (mostly girls). The vast majority who can and do play and sing, however, gain merits and distinctions in their music exams; accomplishment a rigorous counterpoint to enjoyment. Monkton has had a long tradition of jazz and the Longmead jazz festival attracts the general public, who can enjoy a smart picnic in a spectacular setting. Drama facilities fall behind those for art and music (on the list for improvement), but commendably less usual fare produced, such as Arabian Nights, Swallows and Amazons and After Mrs Rochester recently. Informal drama evenings give aspiring writers as well as actors a chance to participate.

Boarding: First and foremost a boarding school, with the late evenings (10pm pick-ups not uncommon for day students and their long-suffering parents) and the only compulsory Saturday morning school in Bath. All age single sex houses are presided over by married houseparents, who go out of their way to create a homely and welcoming feel, with their own families and pets. Just as well really, as the boys' accommodation we saw was, shall we say, functional rather than luxurious. Girls are reckoned to need more 'talking time' – to house staff, rather than each other – so school has policy of making girls' houses smaller by around 10 students. A new girls' house has just been opened. Each year group has a kitchen for making snacks, toast and hot drinks; pizza, curry and Chinese food can be ordered in no more than three times a week. What with and a good supply of fruit and tuck, no-one appeared to miss nipping into Bath for comestibles. School food ok (not the most inspiring menu we've seen), but 'definitely improved and breakfast is the best meal of the day,' say students. Everyone eats in the beautiful light dining hall, with its huge windows and high ceilings. Five and four night boarding options exist alongside full boarding, and day students get 10 nights' free boarding thrown in each year.

Background and atmosphere: In the lusciously green Midford Valley just outside the golden city of Bath snakes a narrow lane lined with the honey-coloured buildings of Monkton Combe. The school, founded by the evangelical Revd Pocock in the 1860s, takes up much of this idyllic village, and still attracts many families wanting an overtly Christian setting for their children's education. Although it's definitely not a faith school, the Christian underpinnings exert a palpable influence: 'It's a very kind place,' we kept hearing. 'Even if you're not a fervent Christian, you're not made to feel bad for that, and it teaches you a way to behave,' one mother told us. Mutual respect for personal faith (of whatever kind – a few Muslims also attend Monkton) or a lack of it seems to be the (commendable) watchword. 'There is rigorous questioning in RE lessons, and we're taught all about comparative religions,' students told us, alongside a very active student-led Christian Union.

Each year group has a kitchen for making snacks, toast and hot drinks; boarders can order in pizza, curry and Chinese food but no more than three times a week

It struck us as a tolerant place – tolerant of difference and celebrating all kinds of achievement, not just academic. Its relative isolation outside Bath and general feel suggest somewhere where children don't have to conform quite as rigidly, or grow up quite as fast – fondly referred to as the Monkton bubble at the school, disparagingly so by other Bath institutions. School held in great affection by students and parents alike, and much made of the Monkton family, something that persists long beyond school days with a very strong alumni network: the school was way ahead of the game in developing links with former students (and doubtless tapping them up for funds).

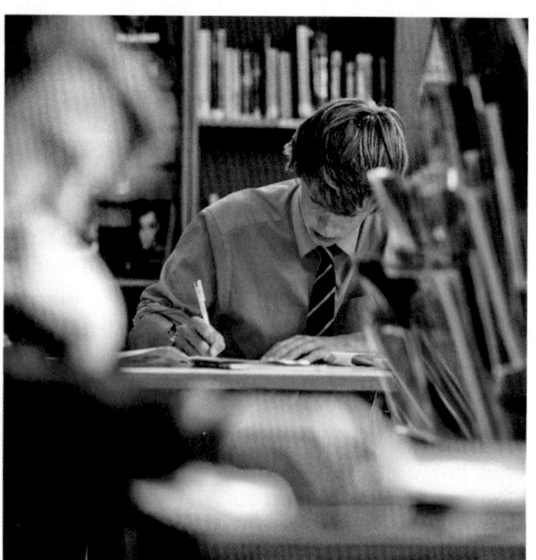

Pastoral care, well-being and discipline: Traditionally a great strength and the reason many families choose the school – and an aspect much touted by the principal and registrar. Transition arrangements and welcome praised by parents, and the efforts houseparents and academic staff go to to get acquainted with each new student. 'Pastoral care is integral to creating academic success stories,' we were told; parents describe it as 'standout' and 'unparalleled'. This school goes one step further with its recent introduction of Affective Social Tracking: a twice yearly online questionnaire taken by all students as a gauge of their emotional well-being and 'areas for development'. No outright opposition to this from the biddable flock of Monkton students; we heard some cynical mutterings about it being a ridiculous waste of time, but none about what struck us as the slightly sinister intrusion into the adolescent mind with its growing need for independence and privacy. Discipline is not a concept that looms large here: the emphasis is much more on celebrating achievement and intrinsic rewards. Bullying is tackled through the lens of restorative justice, where appropriate. 'The kids feel safe here,' we kept hearing, one mother adding that 'as the students have no fear of cruel ridicule, they are not afraid to make fools of themselves'. Our last review talked of 'unfailing support for the troubled' – and we see no change. But we sense that the principal would not hesitate to get tough with miscreants if required, even if he thought very hard before throwing them out.

Pupils and parents: Kind, thoughtful and nice to each other (we liked the easy way in which students from different year groups interacted over our shared lunch). Some might say unworldly, but that would be to undersell the extent to which these kids think about the profound problems of the world such as hunger and poverty, albeit from a largely Christian perspective. Parents 'do all they can to send their children here,' according to the principal, 'and the car park is full of Land Rovers and Audis, not Maseratis.' Many drive considerable distances to get to school; boarders, unless from overseas tend, to be no more than an hour and a half away. Monkton family dynasties still exist.

Entrance: At year 9, half come from the prep school by means of common entrance, provided hopefuls have come through broad assessment, taken in year 6 and 7. Overseas students are required to sit

Appeals to those wanting a truly Christian education for their children. Atheists, agnostics and humanists with open minds also welcome

UKiset and, if English is not their first language, an English Placement Test. A few students come straight into year 10 by means of the CAT 4 test. For sixth form entry, at least five GCSEs above a C (new grade 4/5) with an average of a B/6 across them all is required from the 30 or so new students who come. Maths and sciences require an A and languages a B. Monkton reserves the right to restrict entry to year 13, if AS results are not up to what the school considers snuff.

Exit: About a dozen leave after GCSEs, possibly for greater freedom and post-16 choices, possibly for financial reasons. After A levels, the vast majority go to university – a range of degree courses at institutions old and new up and down the land. One recent student has embarked on a degree apprenticeship in logistics at Rolls Royce. We picked up some dissatisfaction about guidance on university choices from one parent, however.

Notable alumni include Antarctic explorer Eric Marshall (school has his sledge from Shackleton's expedition of 1909), author Bernard Cornwell, musical funny man Richard Stilgoe, former head of MI6 Sir Richard Dearlove and Olympic oarsmen Stephen Williams and Rowley Douglas.

Money matters: Fees are comparable with similar schools and the full boarding makes this arguably better value than those schools with a shorter week. Scholarships amount to a maximum of 25 per cent of fees but bursaries go as far as full fees in exceptional cases; special consideration is given to the offspring of clergy or missionaries. For many years the school has cultivated a highly effective development office, so its financial health is, we are sure, rude.

Remarks: An appealing option in an idyllic location for those wanting a truly Christian education for their children, or at least one that embraces its values and where they do not have to grow up too fast. Atheists, agnostics, humanists with inquisitive and open minds also welcome. New principal pushing the exceptional pastoral care, but seems to be buffing up its social cachet and media profile too.

Monkton Prep School

36

Combe Down, Bath, Somerset BA2 7ET

01225 831202 | admin@monktonprep.org.uk | www.monktonprep.com

Ages: 2–13 (boarders year 3)

Pupils: 335; Boarders: 30 full, 40 weekly

Day: £9,495 – £16,710 pa; Boarding: £22,335 – £24,090 pa

Linked school: Monkton Combe School, 187

Head: Since January 2017 Martin Davis, previously deputy head at Hazlegrove Prep. He has also been deputy head at St Andrew's Turi in Kenya. An old Montonian (he went through both junior and senior schools), he teaches maths and coaches a wide variety of sports teams. A committed Christian, he is married to Nicola and they have three young children.

Entrance: Essentially non-selective. Parents pleased that the entry policy allows a wide range of abilities and types, though they're even more pleased that the standards achieved at Monkton Prep rival schools that select. 'The best prep school in England,' one told us. Boarding numbers have doubled over the past few years, so the feel is definitely of a boarding school with day pupils, especially as there is a significant tranche of pupils from abroad (some 25 per cent of boarders). Informal interview for pre-prep. For the prep at age 7, interview plus tests (English, maths and verbal reasoning). Parents are mostly local professionals and businessfolk, and a few Forces' families too – an easy mix of the churched and the un-churched. New year 7 scholarships for academia, art, music, sport and drama.

Exit: Some 70 per cent to the senior school at 13, but others to eg Marlborough, Sherborne, Prior Park, Canford and King's Bruton.

Remarks: Fiendishly hard to find down a genteel residential cul de sac, school has a dramatic hilltop setting with great downland views. The stunning sweep of the cricket pitch and leafy lawns isn't spoilt by the mish-mash of school buildings tacked onto the back of the manor house.

Academically sound and according to our pupil guides offers a stimulating and enjoyable education. Despite its non-selective ethos, a parent told us that there are plenty of 'incredibly able' children about. Two-form entry in years 3, 4 and 5; streaming from year 5 and an extra scholarship stream added in year 6. Saturday morning school for year 4 and above. Smallish classes (16 to 17). Lots of emphasis on finding out what a child has to offer. Masses of reading lays a foundation for this, with a programme of author visits and a library offering books, board games and beanbags. Long established learning support staff – 'a cracking team' – offer in-class support, handwriting and spelling groups.

Children carry journals and too many negative entries result in Saturday detention – but slates are wiped clean every quarter term. The worst sanction, exclusion for disruptive behaviour, is hardly ever needed. Tutors know children well enough to sense when something's wrong so potentially bullying is picked up quickly but 'children do fall out' and need a 'chat.' Enthusiasm for school meals and even more for the three nurses who care for boarders (and day children when needed).

Plenty going on at weekends including trips to Wales, Dorset coast, rock climbing, cinema and shopping in Bath

New pre-prep and nursery building which links to the prep school and includes new play spaces.

Plenty of sport. Classy pool and new Astroturf hockey pitches (used by senior school too). Great opportunity for competition in top years as the corresponding years in senior school play friendlies against them. Music of every genre – a culture of singing and oodles learn instruments. Some top notch music scholarships to senior schools for the best. Art and drama, with a plethora of expert staff and a chance for everyone to join in. Bags of time for play (not sure how they fit it all in) but even on fine days they are not forced out at break.

Boarders live in Hatton House which overlooks the golf course and has views across the valley. Boarding numbers have increased in recent years as has the number of pupils from abroad. Up to 70 pupils stay during the week with around 30 or so in at the weekends. Plenty going on at weekends including trips to Wales, Dorset Coast, rock climbing, cinema and shopping in Bath. After church on Sunday there's roast dinner and time to relax. Computers rationed for boarders, but with dedicated daily Skype time for keeping in touch with home.

The school's evangelical Christian ethos underlies all aspects of education here. A happy place,

where much is expected and much achieved. Staff, and therefore pupils, work to the highest Christian principles of honest work, self-discipline and concern for the needs of others. 'It teaches how to be a good person,' said one firmly non-Christian parent, 'and allows children to be accepted and to make their own minds up.' Pupils come first, education next but never as second best. Though open-minded, and progressive in the ways which matter, this is an unashamedly and all pervasively Christian foundation.

Mount Kelly

37

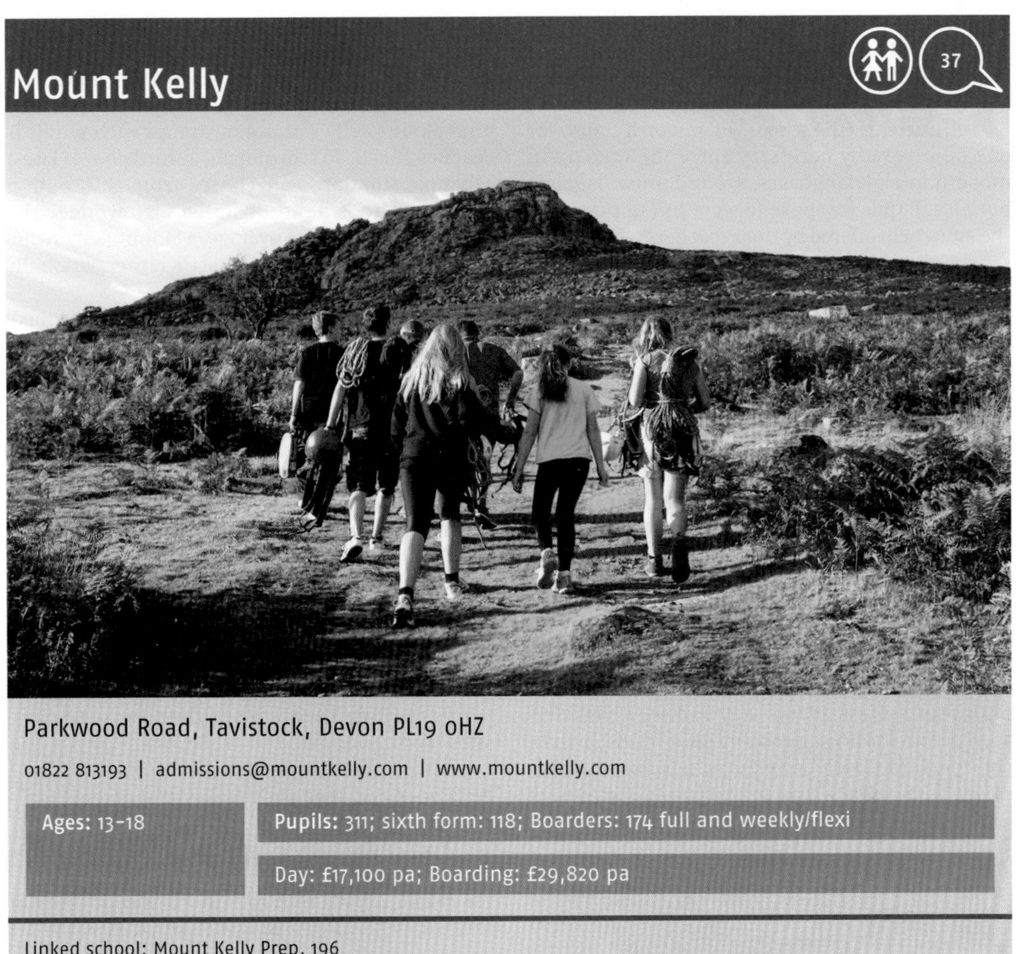

Parkwood Road, Tavistock, Devon PL19 0HZ

01822 813193 | admissions@mountkelly.com | www.mountkelly.com

Ages: 13–18

Pupils: 311; sixth form: 118; Boarders: 174 full and weekly/flexi

Day: £17,100 pa; Boarding: £29,820 pa

Linked school: Mount Kelly Prep, 196

Head master and principal of Mount Kelly Foundation: Since 2014, Mark Semmence, previously assistant head at Rugby School. An economist with degrees from Durham (BA and MBA), London (PGCE) and Warwick (MA), he taught at Ludgrove Prep, then worked in international sports marketing before returning to teaching. Played cricket for England Schools U19 and Durham University; a member of MCC Youth Cricket Committee. Married to Alison; they have two young daughters. Mr Semmence cites architectural history as one of his interests, which is probably just as well as he has inherited a building whose Victorian architect clearly thought that the naval officers it aimed to produce required a medieval monastic training.

He is certainly equal to the challenge, having managed to pull off a universally excellent Independent Schools Inspectorate review within six months of taking the merger of Kelly College and Mount House into the Mount Kelly Foundation. This has involved a restructuring of both staffing and of the way the prep and the college relate. Parents comment that he has been 'ruthless about upping academic teaching standards'. Masses of 'rebranding' has been done to tempt both local day pupils and traditional 'public school' boarding. He must have done a remarkably thorough and well-planned job, as ISI normally requires 'embedded values': hard to achieve in six months. He has also acquired a swimming pool left over from the London Olympics. Wow!

Academic matters: A level results commendable, especially for a school which is not academically selective, with maths definitely impressive at all levels. In 2017, 35 per cent of grades were A*/A and 53 per cent A*-B; at GCSE 39 per cent A*-A/9-7 grades.

Class sizes are small – sometimes very small at A level. Currently the school will put on a course for one pupil – sadly necessary since the take up in modern foreign languages, art and music is select but able. Pupils we spoke to were full of praise for the extra help offered by their teachers when necessary. A good range of solid academic subjects on offer, with excellent language and IT areas. Parents spoke of the expert and sensitive advice they had had from staff when trying to help their children choose the most suitable subjects for them. Perhaps fewer now feel the urge to go further afield for a 'real academic education'. Parents and pupils speak very highly of the help given to those with special needs.

Games, options, the arts: Mount Kelly is rapidly becoming synonymous with swimming. Its reputation, built up over 30 years, is currently growing under the tutelage of Robin Brew, ex-pupil and international and Olympic swimmer, who heads a team of coaches of similar calibre running a comprehensive coaching programme for swimmers with competitive ambitions. The programme is built round the academic day and so is considerably less stressful and probably less expensive than the constant travel, early mornings and compromises with school that many young swimmers

Clever planning means that day pupils and boarders have plenty of well-equipped work and milling about space on the ground floor

have to make. A parent commented that only one or two British schools have anything like comparable swimming and coaching facilities, and that Mount Kelly's pastoral care for such pupils is leagues ahead. To crown it all, a third pool to latest Olympic standards purchased from the London Olympic site is being installed. No wonder the school boasts that, on average, a Mount Kelly swimmer a year has represented the UK either nationally or internationally.

Non-swimmers, however, are far from sidelined. Pupils spoke with enthusiasm of music, debates and outdoor activities, and there are myriads of curriculum supporting events. It's a lively place but also cheerful, friendly and definitely not frenetic, even at exam time. It is old fashioned enough to insist on school blazers with ribbons and badges festooned all over athletic gods and goddesses, but musicians, artists, thespians and prefects can be equally decorated – the school is just good at celebrating and acknowledging. The pitches and grounds in both prep and college areas are superbly managed and the acquisition of the Mount House School site has brought the one missing element, a fantastic sports hall. School has planning permission for a bridge across the River Tavy between the prep and college sites. Sport plentiful but traditional – rugby and cricket for boys and hockey and netball for girls. Both girls and boys play hockey and compete in a mixed summer league.

A splendid and most interestingly designed performing arts centre with superb facilities for music, drama and debate – to say nothing of interval entertainment – is close by, as is the art building with evidence of creative painting and pottery. Since the college snuggles into a valley on the edge of Dartmoor, it's hardly surprising that outdoor education, D of E, CCF and all those sort of things are available and popular. Huge numbers of girls as well as boys complete the 125 mile canoe marathon from Devizes to Westminster and the Ten Tors expedition, as well as training as divers, rifle shots and mountaineers.

Boarding: Despite its monastic appearance, the renovated sections of boarding are exceptionally well done. Clever planning means that day pupils and boarders can socialise on the lower floors with plenty of well-equipped work and milling about space, while the bedroom floors above remain private. We were not taken to the 'unreconstructed' areas but, since two out of four houses are already redesigned and the others proceeding apace, most pupils entering now will not see them either. The four houses are divided into girls' sixth form, boys' sixth form and two co-ed houses for years 9-11, each managed by housemasters with a team of tutors drawn from academic staff as well as non-teaching matrons. Full medical service on hand. Boarders spoke enthusiastically of the sixth form centre and the activities arranged at weekends. Flexi boarding is very flexi.

Background and atmosphere: The buildings, tucked under the edge of Dartmoor just outside the pretty little town of Tavistock, have historical connections with the Duke of Bedford, who donated the land for the college, founded in 1877 by an Admiral Kelly. Despite its gentle lawns and lush green pitches, it's a craggy looking place, all gothic arches, dark wood and stone staircases, echoing corridors and lots of pointy bits. Academic mustiness, however, is banished by skilfully placed features of interest, pictures, honours and information about the school's past and the pupils' futures. Handsome library presided over by enthusiastic librarian and dusty looking (actually it isn't) chapel still exuding

The pupils we met and observed were open, friendly and trusting, and we noticed how much family-like interaction existed between the different age groups

an odour of past sanctity, used four times a week.

Attractive new buildings higher up the hill behind the Victoriana, one of them the delightful Conway House, where the younger boys and girls live in comfortable harmony before joining the senior houses. Co-ed has been going here for nearly 40 years, so it all feels very relaxed and natural.

Pastoral care, well-being and discipline: Lunch in the dining room (masses of choice – cooked meals, salads and faster-looking stuff – particularly delicious lemon posset) was a good insight into the relationships between staff and pupils. Enough mutual respect and genuine affection to allow friendly banter on occasions. The pupils were forthcoming, friendly and honest in their conversation with us, though we were not shielded from meeting the odd awkward customer – treated with helpful sympathy and understanding. While accepting that bullying was always a possibility, they felt that the tutorial system in place was a good safety net and protection – always someone to talk to; above all they said they genuinely like the staff. Pretty common sense school rules result in very little indiscipline. Pupils all looked smartish, though lots dressed in mufti or sportswear towards the end of the day.

Pupils and parents: Parents come from a broad spectrum. Mount Kelly is trying to bridge the gap between being a good local option for the West Country and an upmarket public school. Boarding is boosted by swimmers from England and abroad (around 25 per cent of boarders are from overseas). One parent commented: 'My son can swim but hates it. But he gets stuck into lots of other things and that's the point. I take the view that excellence breeds excellence.' Others praise the community feel among parents, stressing how welcoming they are to families who move to Tavistock for schooling. The pupils we met and observed were open, friendly and trusting, and we noticed how much family-like interaction existed between the different age groups. Though there is definitely a sense that Mount Kelly is on its way to joining the league of 'top schools', it still feels a friendly, relaxed place where children can be children as much as is possible in this day and age.

Entrance: At 13+, about 75 per cent of entries come from the prep. Academically, the emphasis is on literacy and numeracy, with as much attention paid to potential as to knowledge. Entrance at sixth form is based on GCSE results (or equivalent) – normally about 20 new sixth formers joining each year. The important thing is to be alert, bright-eyed and willing to be taught. That applies as much to rugby players as potential Nobel Prize winners.

Exit: Three-quarters go on to the sixth form. Nearly all of these to university. A sensible number to well established ones all over the UK (and occasionally USA) to do old fashioned academic subjects, with the occasional one or two to Oxbridge, proves they can do it.

Money matters: Scholarships and bursaries are available. Forces families may receive 10 per cent discount – don't be afraid to ask.

Remarks: Definitely worth watching. The signs are that it may succeed in providing an excellent environment for girls and boys set on local schooling as well as building up a boarding clientèle based on academic success enhanced by the lure of swimming. A sound, progressive place, where effort is rewarded and friendships flourish, unhampered by snobbery or over-sophistication, and on its way to giving the West Country a really fantastic school. Numbers up in the college with more boarders this year, so the signs are positive.

Mount Kelly Prep

38

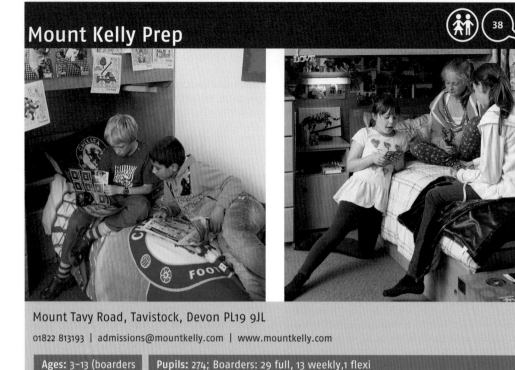

Mount Tavy Road, Tavistock, Devon PL19 9JL

01822 813193 | admissions@mountkelly.com | www.mountkelly.com

Ages: 3–13 (boarders from year 3)

Pupils: 274; Boarders: 29 full, 13 weekly,1 flexi

Day: £7,050 – £13,710 pa; Boarding: £15,900 – £23,400 pa

Linked school: Mount Kelly, 193

Head of prep: Since September 2016, Dominic Floyd, previously assistant head at Hazlegrove. Geography degree and PGCE from London University; taught geography at Cothill House and Westminster Under School; director of studies and deputy head at Polwhele House; head of Ashdown House. He and his wife Maria have three young children and his interests include micro-adventure, hiking, tennis and golf.

Entrance: Wide ability range – tests in English and maths 'more for benchmarking than selection,' says head. Most entrants attend a taster day in February prior to admission. Majority join the pre-prep at start of year 3, but growing numbers delay start until year 7, transferring automatically to the college at 13.

A few means-tested bursaries available.

Exit: Pupils prepared for 13+ transfer to the College at Mount Kelly or elsewhere. Presumably any pupil wanting to 11+ transfer elsewhere is prepared for this. The hope is for the majority of prep children to move into the main college at 13 and about 80 per cent do so.

Remarks: In the merger which established the Mount Kelly Foundation in June 2014, Kelly Prep children moved into the sumptuous Mount House facilities, which are conveniently adjacent to the main Mount Kelly College buildings. The prep benefits from the college's Olympic size pool and college pupils gain access to the prep's sports hall, extensive grounds and other impressive facilities.

Stunning grounds include a trout stream (ideal for fly fishing) and a beautiful lake (great for science) bordering on Dartmoor National Park. A recent team of inspectors dubbed it 'an inspirational learning environment'. The prep is based in and around an elegantly proportioned, stone-built Georgian manor house with an assortment of additions, some historic and some ultra-modern purpose built. The attractive hall, accessed rather curiously through an office rather than its lovely glass doors, fulfils a variety of functions including regular assemblies and church services. The head's oak-panelled study leads off on one side and the school dining hall on the other. Upstairs are all the boys' and girls' dormitories in separate areas plus the sick bay. Dormitories of between four and eight are extremely well designed, with bathrooms between each pair of dorms. Boys' rooms are clean, fresh and pretty tidy, while the girls obviously like to express themselves more freely via plenty of pictures, and personal touches.

A plethora of buildings cluster behind the main house, some old and definitely unusual – the original stables have been converted in a variety of ways, including the 'giraffe house', which features a climbing wall, plus some really impressive purpose built facilities: the modern sports hall (with two squash courts), two large science laboratories and impressive music school. Music had a bit of a hiatus after the merger but seems to have recovered to 'even better than before', partly thanks to the 'best singing teacher in the universe'. 'Proper' church choir contributes to festivals and music is definitely 'in'. Full orchestra, jazz band, woodwind, choir, rock band all perform regularly. The school has a record of music and art scholarships, and the inviting art department had work on display which more than explained this.

Prep schools with such an array of enterprising ventures are few and far between, especially in deepest Devon. Recycling motivates the highly organised CDT department, where self-sufficiency and sustainable technology become second nature, and everything from day-old chicks to bicycle wheels finds a use. It is masterminded by an enthusiast who also runs a small farm in the school grounds. All ages contribute and 'truly love it'. Amongst animal and other agricultural activities, pupils are building a sustainable hut which even provides it own electricity (solar micro generators) while the tractor runs on the kitchen's recycled vegetables and the water supply comes from a borehole.

Stunning grounds include a trout stream (ideal for fly fishing) and a beautiful lake (great for science) bordering Dartmoor National Park

Most of the classrooms are an extension of the main building: attractive internally – some with stunning displays – and all with high level of equipment (smartboard in every classroom). Eighteen PCs in IT suite and staff are mostly IT savvy. 'Some fantastic teachers with a wide variety of styles from formal and well organised to lots of fun' – but all of them kind and good at building confidence. The recurring theme from parents, however, is that teachers are kind while children enjoy lessons and are happy. 'Mix of old timers and new blood on staff works well,' commented one father. Average class size is about 16. Curriculum is designed to allow pupils to go off piste and generate individual enthusiasms. High quality of written work wherever you look; motivational French lessons was another strong point noted.

Most pupils spill out into grounds after prep but there are also hidey-holes in the library for dedicated bookworms, and a lovely decked space for quiet relaxation

Director of studies acts as SENCo with some 35 pupils on special needs register. Pupils are screened for dyslexia and a dedicated education psychologist will develop an IEP if required. Two part-time SpLD staff give one-to-one help where required.

Pre-prep in purpose-built, low level accommodation for 60 children up to end of year 2 with discrete outside area. High level of care and individual attention – most pre-preps transfer seamlessly aged 7. Lots of fun and outdoor experience for this end of the school, as well as developing strong foundations in the classroom basics.

Boarding ethos is all-important, especially to day pupils. One who begged to do a term's boarding loved it and found it problem free. No cliques or bullying and the occasional loner supported and encouraged. The new régime has relaxed some of the compulsory weekend elements but includes Saturday evening pick up after activities, then low key, on site Sunday programme. Ten couples/families live on site and rotate weekend duties. All staff stay here until 6pm every day; prep finishes at 7pm for older pupils (younger ones have clubs) and duty team of staff remains until dorm staff take over at 8.30pm. Most pupils spill out into grounds after prep but there are also lovely hidey-holes in the subterranean library for dedicated bookworms, and a lovely decked space for quiet relaxation complete with multi-lingual telephone box.

Five days a week sport here – facilities include fine pitches, heated outdoor pool (very popular) and full size astroturf; national/regional successes principally in rugby, cricket and girls' hockey. Boarders love to play in the nets or swim after prep in the summer. Pony mad pupils get a look in with the local hunt and inter-school equestrian events. The Shackleton Award scheme (junior D of E award type project aimed at building confidence) was in full swing doing splashy things down by the enchantingly beautiful lake during our visit. The exceptionally beautiful grounds with waterfall and sloping lawns are meticulously managed by a groundsman who is endlessly kind to pupils, and even to parents with engine trouble or no petrol.

Pupils are well turned out – variety of dress according to age and season; they come mainly from Devon and Cornwall, professional, farming and Forces' families plus a few from London or elsewhere (very few overseas). Twice-termly lectures, alternating between the prep and the college, for parents and pupils across the Foundation, tap parental know-how: recent outside speakers have included explorer Pen Hadow and yachtswoman Tracy Edwards. Lots of local visits for all ages, annual trips to Northern France for the older pupils and regular ski trip to Alps. Former pupils include Phil de Glanville (England rugby captain), Adrian Lukis (actor in Pride and Prejudice), former foreign secretary and SDP co-founder, Lord David Owen, and explorer, long-distance swimmer and environmentalist, Lewis Pugh, to name but a few.

This combination of traditional prep and local junior schooling has given the far west a potentially remarkable school. One parent commented that the last few days of summer term are a triumph and say it all. Pupils leave, some to take up academic, sporting or artistic scholarships at the college itself, or other schools, able to 'catch a fish, thread a sewing machine and bake a cake', full of the confidence to face the next step eagerly.

Perrott Hill School

North Perrott, Crewkerne, Somerset TA18 7SL

01460 72051 | admissions@perrotthill.com | www.perrotthill.com

Ages: 3-13 (boarders from 9)

Pupils: 184; Boarders: 15 full, 97 weekly/flexi

Day: £9,510 – £15,750 pa; Boarding: £19,200 – £23,850 pa

Joint acting heads: Deputies Bryan Kane (academic) and Will Silk (pastoral) are holding the fort a after the sad departure of previous head Tim Butcher due to family illness.

The new head from September 2018 will be Alexander McCullough, currently head of Polwhele House prep near Truro. Music degree from Durham; after his PGCE, he became a primary school deputy head whilst still in his 20s, moving on to Foremarke Hall as academic director. His wife, Helen, is a pre-prep teacher and they have two children, who will be joining the school.

Entrance: Non-selective, entry is at the discretion of the head following an interview with the parents and consideration of previous school reports. Scholarships awarded for academic, sport, music, drama and art/DT excellence. Means-tested bursaries also available. Overseas pupils should be at Basic Level A1 in English and are expected to complete a minimum of one term and preferably three terms; no short study programme. The EAL specialist teacher can offer two weeks intensive tuition to bring pupils up to speed. The school will consider all children, but may not offer a place if any special educational needs cannot be supported.

Open mornings every term. 'As soon as we saw Perrott we were bowled over by the warmth of the teaching staff and parents, the happy positive and politeness of the children as we looked around and the stunning setting of the school and grounds.' There's a taster day plus a test day. Test day is a short academic assessment to ensure the school can meet all educational requirements. According to parents, these days are far from daunting. 'They are seamlessly arranged for the new little person to snuggle into the class: the experience is homely, smiley, personal and fun.' There is also a 'new pupils' day' at the end of the summer term and lots of help to settle in once started; 'The settling process was great, they had two buddies, they were there to meet them in the car park on any settling days and the first week of starting. They also wrote them welcome cards.'

Exit: Nearly all stay until 13. To a wide range of destinations including Blundell's, Canford, King's College Taunton, Leweston, Millfield, Queen's College Taunton, Sherborne Girls, Sherborne, Taunton School and Wellington School.

Remarks: Founded in 1946, Perrott Hill is situated in 28 acres of beautiful grounds and woodland close to the Somerset-Dorset border. It is a traditional prep that embraces its surroundings and promotes good country living, a big selling point for many parents. One told us, 'They love the outdoor opportunities; double woods sessions, golf before lunch, farming in the afternoon – they didn't get to do that in London!'

Nestled under the trees is forest school with a newly built roundhouse and large fire-pit. When we visited, it was alive with activity

The school day is long, from 8.20am-5.45pm, but all the (many) activities on offer are fitted into these hours. One parent told us, 'There were many opportunities for the children, the hours of care suited us and the nurturing environment suited our children.' Activities include ballet, karate, fencing, riding, gymnastics (at extra cost) and unpaid activities such as art, sports, eco-club or playing in the woods. From year 5, there is school on Saturdays until 4pm (for day pupils and boarders). There are lessons, sports fixtures and the highlight of the day is the French lunch. Not all pupils and parents are enthusiastic about the extra day but they all agreed 'you soon get used to it.' During the school weekday there are two long breaks of 40 minutes, one in the morning and one after lunch. Pupils are not only encouraged to rest or play in these periods; they are given the chance to read or to work on an art project. We saw plenty of these projects in the small but very productive art studio. One pupil, inspired by his recent travels, had created a collage of a world map showing flight paths. A class trip to Lulworth Cove was another inspiration. Art is obviously very popular and the teacher sets up still life projects and even life drawing sessions – the last one was a geisha. Parents are invited to take workshops too. One parent who used to work for John Galliano ran a 'punk' workshop recently, another ran a photography session. One parent said, 'The art department is fantastic at school and with the resources it has bats way above other schools, but we would love there to be a bigger art room and facilities as it is such an amazing department.' We will definitely second that.

The school is planning on creating a similarly creative environment for science. Now the new sports hall is complete, the old changing room will be refurbished as a 'science suite'. The labs will be set up with movable benches and storage to allow room for experiments of all kinds and flexible teaching. There will also be a 'tinker room' full of Lego, Meccano, BBC micro-bits and anything else that can be used for 'free-flow projects' at break times. Although many parents love that screens are few and far between at Perrott (fibre-optic broadband only reached them last summer), staff feel it's important to find a balance and prepare children for the real world. This is a creative and fun way to do it.

The location and outside environment are stunning; in fact it's hard to believe that anybody could have a bad day here. At the back of the main school building the library opens out on to a terrace, a rose garden, the monkey woods (a maze) and fields for as far as the eye can see. There are playing fields with an athletics track, cricket pitches and nets, rugby and football pitches and a pavilion. Plus two hard courts, a climbing wall, an Astroturf, a sports hall, a heated swimming pool, and not one but two golf holes and a practice putting green. Nestled under the trees is forest school with a newly built roundhouse and large fire-pit. When we visited, it was alive with activity; one group was rubbing flints to make fire, another was learning to saw and a thride group was making donuts – normal and gluten-free, of course. Other culinary delights have included wild garlic bread and nettle soup, all foraged and picked themselves.

Not far from the forest school is the new music centre. Fundraising for this has included staff taking grade 1 music exams, and an auction to become head for the day (head becomes a pupil, of course). Environmentally sensitive, it sits in the natural slope of the hill, clad in cedar. Concertina doors open out onto the decking looking across the Somerset hills. Fantastically inspirational. The department is run by 'an excellent music teacher' who has set up a good-sized string orchestra for such a small school (all year 2s learn violin for a year), and a choir that has been to Venice, Prague, Rome and London. As well as musical performances, there are plenty of drama productions too, all taking place in the well-equipped theatre. Recently year 6 performed Why the Whales Came, and the leavers' production will be Beowolf.

One parent said, 'We live only 15 minutes away and the older boys choose to weekly board and flexi board. Sometimes they don't want to come home!'

Class sizes are small, average of 12 to a class, with two classes in most years. Years 6 and 7 are streamed in preparation for common entrance. Excellent learning support department, highly praised by parents. One told us, 'My child, having received learning support for a few years is now leaving with scholarships, has been made a prefect, his confidence has increased and his academic ability has improved enormously.' Another told us, 'He had lost his confidence and with the individualised teaching and fantastic learning support it is like Pandora's box has been opened, it is so wonderful to see.' The head of SEN is a literary specialist and there is an in-house team of five assistants plus an external team, Sound Thinking, who provide speech and language therapy and educational psychology. The school provides good support for dyslexia and dyscalculia and extra tuition can take place instead of Latin or French, at an extra cost.

The school offers full, weekly and flexi-boarding. Boarding has become increasingly popular, especially for those planning to go on to board at senior school. There are six pupils from Spain, one from France and the rest are from the UK. In fact a large number are fairly local. One parent said, 'They love it! We live only 15 minutes away and the older boys choose to weekly board and flexi board. Sometimes they don't want to come home – they have a lot of fun!' Flexi boarders must book regular days; the school is keen not to be used as a hotel. Flexi or weekly boarding is available from year 3, and although numbers are currently low, interest is growing in the lower year groups. Full boarding available from year 5. Due to the high demand (there is a waiting list) the school is converting the old music suite into two senior boys' dorms and a shared common room over the summer. Dorms are a good size and there are decent separate common rooms. Parents said, 'The boarding house is very family orientated and they have a lovely time in the evenings when the houseparents are very involved with activities with the boarders.' Evening activities include reading, music practice, watching TV, art, ICT, games in the sports hall, tennis, football, skateboarding, rollerblading. There are 'family weekends' spent with the houseparents and then there are 'activity weekends' when day pupils can join in too (up to 40 pupils). Past weekend themes have been Inspector Gadget, Indiana Jones (with an assault course), Harry Potter and Making a Musical. 'The boarding staff are fantastic; my children have always been very happy to board, although we tend to build it up over a few years as they get older, and have more stamina,' parents told us.

The best thing about this school is that the pupils love it, something we couldn't help but notice on our visit. One parent said, 'She will not hear a bad word against it or anything to do with it and cannot under any circumstances be persuaded to stay at home if she is under the weather.' And the academic results are undeniably impressive. But the most important thing for many parents is self-belief and confidence and the school does a great job here. One parent told us, 'My eldest was very shy and within a year was in the final of the school poetry recital performing in front of the whole school and parents – in less than one year!' With confidence and self-belief you can go far.

Pinewood School

40

Bourton, Shrivenham, Wiltshire SN6 8HZ

01793 782205 | office@pinewoodschool.co.uk | www.pinewoodschool.co.uk

Ages: 3–13 (boarding from year 5)

Pupils: 398; Boarders: 28 weekly, 92 flexi

Day: £8,970 – £17,250 pa; Weekly boarding: Supplement £4,215 pa

Head: Since 2002, Philip Hoyland BEd (60s), educated at The Downs, Malvern, followed by Cheltenham College. Read English and education at Exeter; previously housemaster, then deputy head, at The Dragon. Married to the warm, compassionate Henrietta; they met at Ludgrove when she was under-matron and he a rookie teacher (they have three grown-up children). Very much a partnership – she is head of girls' boarding and central to much of school life, particularly the pastoral side.

Eloquent, charming, a gentleman, he has a great sense of humour and even greater sense of adventure, wanting education to be both explored and enjoyed and for children to learn through taking risks. 'Let them be children, I say – there's plenty of time for stress in adulthood.' Old-school in demeanour, but thoroughly modern in outlook, he embodies exactly what he seeks for the school: 'old-fashioned values, coupled with innovative learning.' More than a sense that his Quaker heritage (his great grandfather was businessman and philanthropist George Cadbury) shapes his views. Says, 'I'm more detached from daily school life than I used to be – more of a CEO these days, with much of my time taken up with compliance, strategy, recruitment, staff and showing parents round.' But a remote figure in a suit he is not, still having breakfast, lunch and supper with the pupils, as well as giving regular assemblies (wearing jumper not jacket). A kind of grandfatherly dignitary, he circuits the school to a flurry of waves and excitement from animated youngsters, eager to tell of their day,

show off work, badges, awards – and while older children stand to attention, he's ready to joke with them, and they joke back. His office, a relaxed, homely first floor room with stunning views, is regularly inhabited by pupils showing off their work, 'and checking if they're due their packet of skittles, which they get once they've shown me three outstanding pieces.' Parents say they have more to do with him the further up the school their child goes and call him 'kind,' 'a strategist' and 'fantastic with the children,' who in turn describe him as 'lively,' 'funny' and 'really nice.' All that's missing is the obligatory labrador – he has one, of course, but keeps it at home 'as you never know if children will take to dogs.'

Entrance: Mainly via nursery and pre-prep; register early (many do so at birth). Unselective, but prospective pupils come in for a taster day. Deliberately takes broad-ish ability range, 'deal with what we get,' with very rare exceptions. Assessment for entry into prep. Most years full with waiting lists, though movement, especially of day children, and flexibility for additional groups, means places materialise.

Exit: Primarily Winchester, Marlborough, Radley, Cheltenham College, Wellington, Sherborne, Sherborne Girls, Dauntsey's, Cheltenham Ladies' College, St. Edward's Oxford, Stowe, Bradfield, St Helen and St Katharine, Bryanston, St Mary's Calne, Tudor Hall and Abingdon. A clutch of scholarships (art, music, sport, academic and all-rounder) to a range of schools is the norm most years.

Remarks: Founded in 1875, moved to current pretty Victorian Cotswold stone house in 1946. Noughties, and the arrival of the Hoylands, saw shift from a school languishing in the doldrums ('bad headships,' say parents) to one riding a wave, albeit with a few choppy interludes.

Expect a home-from-home welcome as soon as you enter the oak panelled hall, complete with squidgy sofas and open fire – in full use (to our delight) by the children at break times; definitely not just a showpiece for prospective parents. The main house is also home to other recreational rooms, dining hall, dorms for borders, admin and head's office, as well as some year 5 and 6 classrooms (although there are plans to move them to a swanky new building). Nursery and pre-prep in former stable block with fantastic play area in old walled garden. Super performing arts centre, modern sports hall, outside swimming pool, library rehoused in the Orangery and newish science labs packed with test tubes, microscopes, Bunsen burners etc ('We dissected an eyeball last week,' one boy told us, elatedly) – a real world of discovery and experimentation.

Think greenhouse not hothouse; tender plants (and tough weeds) will be nurtured, but not pruned

Be sure to pack your children's wellies if they get a place here as outdoors is as important as in, with 86 acres of land for the children to enjoy – and enjoy it, they do. Pinewood is one of the country's leading outdoor schools, so besides the astro and sports pitches you'd probably expect, there's a treetops adventure playground, outdoor classroom, fairy garden, super sensory gardens, polytunnel and lawn after lawn. 'I have a tonne of conkers in here,' one excitable young boy with a heavy tub called out to us; 'Yes, but look how many pinecones

I've got!' pitched in another. The children couldn't wait to tell us how they 'break the ice' at the start of every summer term in the outdoor pool – not literally, but an annual event that usually sees the head dive in first, followed by a posse of pupils. They also enthused about spotlight, a unanimously favourite (and don't panic – it's risk assessed) pastime in which children try to get from one point to another outside in the dark without being caught in the teacher's torchlight. And don't even get them started on the list of Thursday afternoon outdoor activities (indoor ones also available) unless you've got a spare half-hour on your hands. In fact, the only thing stopping us from saying this school is all about getting outside and climbing trees is pupils' claim that this where the limit is drawn – 'health and safety means no tree climbing,' one told us disappointedly, with other grumbles of some out-of-bounds woods that 'we keep being promised access to, but it never happens.'

Most teachers are head's own appointments; admits he has taken a few risks, going for the fizzy or alternative to encourage excitement and develop a joy of learning. Big on teaching the children how to learn and how they learn, a strategy that hasn't been lost on the youngsters, with pupils eager to talk us through how they got from A to B when showing us their work – and there wasn't a single classroom we saw that wasn't ablaze with gusto. 'Why do the French only ever eat one egg at a time?' the headmaster called out to a year 8 French class who were just about to embark on role-play of a French restaurant. 'Because one egg is un oeuf!' responded a boy, reflective of the humour and laid-back vibe that defines this school.

Between 42-48 pupils per year group, split into three forms of 16, until year 5 when pupils are taught in three sets, with an extra scholarship set added from year 7. French from age 4, Latin or classics from 10, enrichment for anyone who will benefit. History, geography and RE recently dropped at common entrance 'to free the children from the treadmill of exams and subjects that just require children regurgitating facts'. RE replaced with theology, philosophy and ethics. Clear focus on teaching collaboration, problem solving, independent learning, presentation skills, linking ideas etc. Lessons recently lengthened to 45 minutes – 'It's made us all a bit less frantic,' says head. Computer science important for all, even wee ones are encouraged to Google. Saturday school unpopular with pupils and parents alike, but head has 'no plans to stop it.'

This is a country prep, with more mud-splattered four-by-fours than flashy Ferraris. Expect relaxed rigour, not blazers and caps; cobwebs on windowsills, not spic and span

Solid learning support is well integrated, not an add-on. A genuinely multi-sensory approach mean those with mild dyslexia, dyspraxia, ADD (Bluetac et al for fiddlers), high functioning ASD are well served. OT, speech and language therapy, play therapy, plus one-to-one or small groups if required (most incur additional fee) but not the place for those with moderate or severe needs.

Usual plaudits for art; DT replaced with graphic design for older ones; lots of applause for drama (year group performances, not whole school, with plenty of Shakespeare) and music thrives (includes ensembles, jazz band, a chorus of choirs and inclusive performing opportunities, with around three quarters of the children learning an instrument). Daily sport for all, plus Thursday activities which include touch rugby, girls' football, ballet, clay pigeon shooting, archery, sketch and paint, yoga, mindfulness, drama, mountain biking, model making, camp building and more. Main school sports are rugby, football, hockey, cricket and tennis (girls' hockey and boys' cricket the strongest performers). A hardy bunch who practise in all weathers and of course play to win (which they often do) in weekly fixtures but, as one parent says, 'It's not the kind of school that gets in the best rugby coaches to help them win the most matches – it's more a case of making sure every child gets a chance to represent the school and have fun doing it.' Trips generally within the UK ('so everyone can go'), the highlight of which (to the pupils anyway) is the annual PGL-style Pinewood Adventure Weekend for year 4s upwards.

Think greenhouse not hothouse; tender plants (and tough weeds) will be nurtured, watered but not pruned, though delicate darlings might flounder: 'You need a have-a-go attitude,' pupils insist. Concentrates on extending childhood, Enid Blyton-style – the pre-pubescent 'make-up and manicure' brigade would either roll up their sleeves and regain their innocence – or, likely as not, hate it. But for those happy to don a boiler suit, roll down a hill, play hide and seek or chase through a meadow, it's a blast. 'I don't get hung up about untucked shirts – a smiley face is much more important,' says head. Small-scale transgressions are dealt with swiftly and discreetly, although pupils told us 'some teachers are a lot stricter than others.' Bullying not seen by anyone as an issue; school is a mobile phone free zone ('none of us minds,' a pupil told us); recent appointment of head of wellbeing and mental health.

Parents consider this a local school, majority live within an hour's drive; ethnicity (mainly Caucasian) reflects that. Boarding (from year 5) popular, though, and on the wish list for most pupils – 'We beg our parents to board,' one pupil told us. Opt for either regular boarding (sticking to set nights per week, often increasing as children go up the school) or weekly boarding (particularly popular for year 8s). Comfortable, homely accommodation ('the girls' accommodation has recently given the Hotel du Vin uplift,' jokes head about the new carpets, door frames etc; boys, equally as shiny but a little cramped under the eaves), with between four to nine beds in a dorm and great food – 'better than the lunches,' say pupils. Prep finishes at 5.30pm, after which 'there's plenty of activities and free time – it's like a huge sleepover every night,' say pupils. Squabbles usually sorted over a mug of hot chocolate in Mrs Hoyland's kitchen; no complaints from anywhere on that score. Reading room (much loved by youngsters) and old chapel provide quiet spaces, with games room (table tennis, air hockey, snooker) for the active.

Pre-prep suits the worms, germs and stones brigade; aims for children to fall in love with learning, which extends well beyond the regular primary diet. Parents genuinely welcome to spend time with their child at beginning and end of the day; no classroom barriers here.

This is a true country prep, with more mud-splattered four-by-fours than flashy Ferraris. Expect relaxed rigour, not blazers and caps; cobwebs on windowsills, not spic and span. If you could recreate the secret garden you'd probably do it here; active children fizz with enthusiasm, happily maintaining the innocence of a bygone era but with the benefits of modern technology and teaching. A genuinely wholesome school that emphasises cooperation rather than competitiveness, confidence not arrogance and team before me. These are children that showed as much interest in our lives as we did in theirs (believe us, that's rare) and, best of all, they seem completely at ease with themselves and who they are. Especially good for the creative boy or girl with boundless energy, sporty or not, and limitless curiosity. One parent sums up, 'They go in happy and come out even happier.'

Plymouth College

41

Ford Park, Plymouth PL4 6RN

01752 505100 | mail@plymouthcollege.com | www.plymouthcollege.com

Ages: 11–18

Pupils: 475; sixth form: 149; Boarders: 129 full/weekly

Day: £13,425 – £15,900 pa; Boarding: £21,375 – £30,675 pa

Headmaster: Since 2015, Jonathan Standen, originally from Tunbridge Wells, studied ancient history at Nottingham University. Previously head of The Crypt School, Gloucester. He has also been deputy head at St Augustine's Catholic College and Bishop Wordsworth's School and assistant head at Hardenhuish School, all in Wiltshire. Lives on site with partner Suzie and their son. In days gone by he has been a ski instructor, a rugby coach and a cricket coach, but these days he enjoys a round of golf.

Some positive parent reviews: 'I'm impressed with the new headmaster and I feel he's keen to improve the standards at the school,' said one. 'There has been a shake up of staff and he's good at communicating with parents – via a newsletter – and keeping us informed of changes.'

Academic matters: In 2017, at A level, 65 per cent A*-B and over a third A*/A grades. At GCSE, 41 per cent A*-A/9-7 grades. Twenty-two options at A level offered. Top performing subjects are maths, science, economics and business studies. Most do three A levels plus one elective subject eg EPQ or a BTec in sports leadership, ICT, performing arts. A one year IGCSE course is available in year 11, popular with international students. Also offers the sport baccalaureate, which is based round the BTec level 3 extended diploma in sport (outdoor adventure), and includes topics such as fitness, nutrition, coaching and leadership. Plymouth College is well known for producing top athletes including swimmers, modern pentathletes, fencers and divers. For the last seven years, the college has been the top swimming school in the country. All athletes are supported through their rigorous training programmes as well as their academic studies. One parent told us, 'We chose Plymouth College because it gave the opportunity for her to develop her swimming (she had swum competitively from a young age) whilst also stretching her academically.'

Class sizes are small, around 13 per class. Setting or streaming in maths, science, and English from year 8. As well as the standard GCSE options, the school offers some that can be studied as an after-school activity, including philosophy, Greek, computing and film studies. Most pupils study two languages of French, Spanish or German. Extra support in maths and English can be provided for those that only take one language.

The head of the learning support department is a qualified educational psychologist. In-class support and individual tuition is provided for mild needs including dyslexia, dysgraphia, dyscalculia, and dyspraxia, though some parents felt that 'earlier identification and intervention' would be helpful. One parent, who had eventually organised her own child's assessment, commented: 'The SEN department has improved hugely since then, but integration in teaching and lessons as well as regular SEN feedback still needs improving.' All comments on teachers, including SEN, were positive; 'supportive and communicate well' and 'very committed and enthusiastic.'

Games, options, the arts: As expected, top sports facilities here. There's a large sports centre, a cardiovascular gym, two squash courts, a weights room, a climbing wall, Astroturf, playing fields and cricket nets. Plus a fantastic 25 metre indoor pool (the elite swimmers use the Life Centre facilities in Plymouth). As well as swimming lessons the pool is used for inter-house galas, water polo and lifesaving competitions. Around 50 pupils swim at national level. Past pupils include Tom Daley, Olympic diver and Cassie Patten, Olympic swimmer. However, it's not just in the water that the college succeeds. Other former pupils include Henry Slade and Paul Ackford, both England rugby international players. Two current pupils play football for Plymouth Argyll, another plays cricket for the Surrey county professional team, and one girl was selected for the U15 south west England rugby team. No problem if you're not a top sportsperson: 'He has not felt out of place among elite sports people even though he is an amateur,' a parent told us. Other sports offered include basketball, badminton, hockey, netball, gymnastics, cross-country running, golf and equestrian.

For the more arty types, there's a new drama studio (recently opened by ex-pupil Michael Ball),

Activities take advantage of school's location; sailing in Plymouth Sound, and adventures on the moors including the Ten Tors

and plenty of productions to get involved with. A recent whole school production was Beauty and the Beast. And a recent house drama was Scrooge – each house had to adapt the original story giving it a modern twist or unexpected makeover. Most pupils learn a musical instrument; even the harp is offered. As a traditional school, there are plenty of formal music concerts but informal guitar and piano evenings are popular and recently there was a woodwind, vocal and brass evening. Clubs and groups include choir, chamber choir, rock school, flute group, orchestra and string orchestra. One talented pupil recently won a place at the prestigious Royal College of Music for vocal studies.

The art department is split across the site. There is a small sixth form classroom adjoined by a computer suite for photography and graphics. Plus there is the Art Haus, a small two-storey cottage, hidden by trees, appropriately decorated with a graffiti-type mural. One classroom downstairs, and another upstairs with a handful of PCs and a dark room. Department produces good results.

Extensive list of extracurricular activities. Many take advantage of the school's location; sailing in Plymouth Sound, and adventures on the moors including the Ten Tors and Duke of Edinburgh schemes. Plus there's caving, climbing, mountain biking, sea kayaking, SCUBA diving, canoeing, white water kayaking, mountain and hill walking, camping, bushcraft and gorge walking. Then there's the Combined Cadet Force; from year 10 onwards students can opt for navy, army or RAF. Other clubs include activities such as archery and snooker, music clubs such as school of rock and samba club plus there's a model railway club and a Young Entreprise group. With around 40 activities on offer each term, there's something for everyone. An activities fair is held at the beginning of the autumn term to find out what's on.

Sixth formers have their own enrichment programme. They can choose from D of E, CCF, Ten Tors challenge, financial studies, politics, cookery, journalism, photography or volunteering placements. The latest addition has been a pre-med course. Medicine has been a popular university course choice in recent years and the new enrichment course prepares students for their medical school applications alongside studying for their A levels. It is heavily supported by parents and ex-pupils, many of whom are GPs and consultants.

All pupils benefit from regular local trips to the theatre, art galleries, ancient castles, plus field trips to south Devon beaches and Dartmoor. Further afield there are day trips to France and London, overseas residential trips to Ireland and Greece, German trips to Berlin, physics trips to Switzerland, ski trips and language exchanges. Recent sports tours include South Africa with Rugby and a cricket tour to Sri Lanka. Annual charity expedition to Malawi. The prep school has local day trips throughout the year plus year 6 goes to France for a week and year 5 goes to an eco-camp in Cornwall for a night.

Boarding: Currently, 150+ boarders in six boarding houses, a row of large villas dating from the mid-19th century. On the main school site is a boys' house, a girls' house and three smaller houses/annexes for sixth formers. The Captain's House, specialist accommodation for the elite swimmers, is on the prep school site, 10 minutes away, housing around one third of boarders. One parent told us, 'The boarding facilities were initially disappointing but have improved dramatically....A tremendous amount of work has been done to improve the accommodation.'

Around 50 per cent of all boarders are from the UK. Other boarders are from over 40 countries around the world including Germany, China, Hong Kong, Australia, the Caribbean, Estonia, Bangladesh, Bolivia, Italy, Russia, South Africa, to name but a few. Some pupils come from military backgrounds, but not as many as expected: just three in the girls' house when we visited. Weekly boarding is available, but we were told the majority of boarders are resident at weekends these days. Flexi boarding is offered for up to 14 nights per term. If your child is going to be a full boarder, do check how many of their age group will be around at weekends, particularly in the lower years, to ensure they have plenty of company.

Boys and girls are free to socialise between the boarding houses, cooking food in the kitchen, playing games, chatting or watching TV

Currently, some 40+ boarders in the girls' house. Fifty per cent are athletes – swimmers, divers, pentathlons etc. The house is run by a friendly, approachable housemistress who lives in the basement with her husband and three young children. Parents told us, 'The current boarding staff are exceptional in creating an environment in which both our girls are currently thriving.' Rooms are mostly doubles and a few triples, with older girls together at one end of the house. One room has been specially adapted for a disability but there is no wheelchair access available. All the newly refurbished bedrooms and bathrooms are lovely. The housemistress is now looking forward to updating the common areas – one room will be a games room and the other a large lounge. There is also an arts and crafts room and a homely office area with sofas for girls to pop in for chats any time. There are regular (and impromptu) informal discussion groups to chat about current issues or 'things on their minds'. This is a busy house; some athletes start training from 4am and others are training until 9pm. There are a lot of comings and goings and the housemistress does a great job staggering food times and everything else in this house. She says it keeps the house alive and interesting, buzzing. Boys and girls are free to socialise between the houses, cooking food in the kitchen, playing games, chatting or watching TV.

'Mr Tippetts is the head of boarding and an impressive man,' parents told us. 'He's a calm but effective leader.' He has been been at Plymouth College for some 20 years and lives there with his wife and dog. Popular with the boarders; one told us that many boys, him included, have found that Mr Tippet has fitted into the father figure role perfectly for them. He runs the boys' house with a good balance of discipline and fun. If he finds a bed unmade, he will hide the duvet as punishment, so beware. Plenty of common areas including a TV room with projector, table tennis room, pool table room, music room with table football and a prep/study room with PCs. The junior kitchen is new, but the best makeover of all is the sixth form area. There is a fantastic new kitchen with a stunning

Active school council 'gets things done.' Members planned and created the outdoor classroom, set up and now keep a flock of rare chickens at the school and installed a wildlife pond

open-plan lounge, wooden floors, sofa and large dining table. The annexe, or the Boat House, is also new and provides sixth formers with very small but private single rooms. Great for the transition to university life.

In the Captain's House, boys are on the ground floor and the girls on the first floor. The staff are experienced in the training and needs of elite athletes; it is a unique environment supporting over 40 performance swimmers with high levels of pastoral care, specialist nutritional needs and complicated logistics. There is a regular minibus service between the boarding house, the pool and school. One parent whose child swims for GB said, 'The boarding house dedicated to swimmers is ideal.... The only problem [my child] sometimes has is the transport arrangements from school to the boarding house.'

In the evenings and at weekends, the boarders can use the school facilities. Most evenings there is a game of football or dodgeball in the sports hall, or games on the Astroturf. The swimming pool is open at weekends. Other weekend activities include trips to the beach for surfing or paddle boarding, or days out to Adrenaline Quarry or the Eden Project. Regular trips to the cinema, 10-pin bowling, ice-skating, paintballing, boat trips, pitch and putt golf, moorland walking, and dry-slope skiing. No exeat weekends but the school closes at half term.

Background and atmosphere: Founded in 1877 as Plymouth High School for Boys, the school moved to its current site at Ford Park in 1880, changing its name to Plymouth College three years later. The prep school moved to a different site in Hartley Road in 1947. There have been a number of mergers with girls' schools (the school became fully co-ed in 1995), and most recently with St Dunstan's Abbey School for Girls in 2005. It was then that the prep school moved to its current site in The Millfields, the old naval hospital, three miles away.

The site is tucked behind the hustle and bustle of Mutley Plain in Plymouth. It is surprisingly big considering its urban position. The main buildings are grand Victorian villas, very impressive from the outside, in need of a little attention inside. However, work is underway and it's looking as if these original family homes will be restored to their former glory. The main building is huge. With its high ceilings, stone steps and beautiful ornate windows it's stunning, but in places it feels cold. The library is grandiose and the classrooms are traditional; original wooden benches in the science laboratories, everything you'd expect in a school as old as this.

Decent sixth form centre with bistro and lounge area to socialise or work. Very small and uninspiring quiet study area upstairs. Sixth form social life is thankfully much more vibrant and fun with a freshers' ball to kick it all off, followed by a Halloween ball, quiz nights, DVD and pizza nights, and an end of year ball.

The active school council 'gets things done.' Members planned and created the outdoor classroom, set up and now keep a flock of rare chickens at the school, have installed a wildlife pond, and successfully campaigned for a salad bar and pasta bar. Their latest project is the Gutter Grow system for cultivating fresh herbs, vegetables and fruit on the roof of the school canteen.

Pastoral care, well-being and discipline: Very good pastoral care. Parents told us, 'Staff work hard to integrate the different nationalities and the welfare and medical support is outstanding. Both our [children] have had medical issues that have been dealt with comprehensively and with compassion.' There is a school nurse plus a day matron in each boarding house, also in charge of physio for the athletes. Out of hours, responsibility lies with the boarding staff, all first aid trained. For athletes there's a 'playground to podium' ethic, which involves regular communication between boarding and pastoral staff, parents, coaches and the athletes themselves. Sixth form course includes coping with stress and mindfulness as well as eg money management.

At a small school with a strong and very competitive house system, pupils have opportunities to make friends across the years. Boarders, athletes and day pupils live, study and train together well; pupils seem to make good lasting friendships that continue beyond their school years. Plymouth College has a Christian ethos but it is 'understated,' the head told us.

Pupils and parents: As well as Plymouth itself, day pupils come from south east Cornwall, west and mid Devon and the South Hams. The school provides a daily bus service. Parents are doctors, surgeons, teachers, business owners, engineers, members of the Royal Navy, RAF and the army. Parents of all pupils we spoke to said they were happy with communication between school and home. One said, 'Communication has always been superb with easy access to teaching, boarding and support staff with prompt responses to issues. This has been tremendously important in living at some distance from the school.'

Entrance: Non-selective, but entrance exams in maths and English 'to maintain minimum standards,' and for scholarships. Around 50 per cent of intake is from the prep school. One parent told us, '[Our child] settled in well into year 7 with a great head of year leading the team and a weekend away in Whiteworks, Dartmoor. It's a good thing to do in the first few weeks of term.'

At a small school with a strong and very competitive house system, pupils have opportunities to make friends across the years. Boarders, athletes and day pupils live, study and train together well; pupils seem to make good, lasting friendships

For sixth form entry, pupils are expected to achieve at least six GCSE passes at grade C/5, including English and maths, and three passes at grade B/6 or higher. International students are assessed for English speaking and writing skills.

Exit: On average, 25 per cent leave after GCSEs to go to local colleges or grammar schools. The same number (around 20 pupils) will join the sixth form. Some sixth form boarders are particularly attracted by the sports programmes on offer, others by the fact that nearly all sixth form pupils go on to university. Several have gained sports scholarships at American universities in recent years. Other popular university destinations include Bristol, Cardiff, Exeter and London. Most popular courses include architecture, business, economics/accounting, engineering, law, medicine and sports science.

Money matters: Scholarships offered include all-round, academic, art, drama, music, performing arts and sport awards. Means-tested bursaries also available, as well as discounts for siblings and military families.

Remarks: Elite athletes plus day pupils and boarders of all abilities and nationalities study, train and live together harmoniously. Pupils are able to develop at their own pace, and most importantly gain confidence. One parent confirmed, saying, '[My child] is now oozing self-esteem, loves going to school.'

Port Regis

42

Motcombe Park, Shaftesbury, Dorset SP7 9QA

01747 857914 | admissions@portregis.com | www.portregis.com

Ages: 3–13 (boarding from year 3)

Pupils: 295; Boarders: 78 full, 25 weekly, 15 flexi

Day: £8,670 – £18,600 pa; Boarding: £25,800 pa

Headmaster: Since 2016, Mr Stephen Ilett (50s). Educated at Rossall School in Lancashire, where his father was a housemaster, and Lincoln College, Oxford, where he read history and played rugby for the university's first XV. Spent 18 years working in the City (for Lloyd's of London) before moving into education. Reckons his early career equipped him well for headship. 'I held positions of responsibility in the City and ran teams of people so I'm used to keeping all the balls in the air,' he says.

First post was teaching French and coaching rugby at Caldicott. He was promoted to director of studies within two years. After eight years at Caldicott he became head of Milbourne Lodge, the Surrey co-ed prep. Five years later he took the reins at Port Regis. 'Port Regis has the reputation of being one of the best schools in the country,' he says, 'and when the headship came up it was too tempting to turn down.'

A keen linguist, he taught modern foreign languages at Milbourne Lodge – 'I love teaching French,' he says. He believes Port Regis' stand-out qualities are its facilities ('which are genuinely acknowledged to be second to none') and the high calibre staff.

Married to Amanda, who is Port Regis' marketing manager, and they have five grown-up children between them. They are passionate believers in the benefits of boarding and are keen to show that Port Regis is 'very friendly, very caring and very nurturing'. In his spare time the head likes cricket, golf, travel, reading and walking his two dogs. They live in a house on site.

Entrance: Main entry points are nursery and year 3 but children join all the way through the school. Pre-prep is first come first served, while entry to the prep is via an interview with the head, assessment (verbal and non-verbal reasoning) and report from previous school. Children join from a raft of preps and from local state primaries (including Motcombe, Semley, Wardour and Ludwell). Virtually all pre-prep children move up to the main school (no assessment required).

Exit: Port Regians go on to a wide range of co-ed, single sex, boarding and day schools. Most popular destinations in 2017 included Sherborne, Sherborne Girls',Bryanston and King's Bruton. A total of 18 scholarships awarded, including two to St. Edward's, Oxford, two to Bryanston, two to St. Mary's Calne and two to Sherborne Girls.

Senior schools tell Port Regis that Port Regians are children who are 'resilient, self-reliant and know how to get on with things'. Most pupils stay until 13 (one or two girls leave at 11 for schools like Wycombe Abbey but school doesn't encourage this).

Remarks: Located in 150 acres of sweeping Dorset parkland, yet only a couple of miles from the hilltop town of Shaftesbury. Visitors gasp at the setting – it could easily be mistaken for a senior school, with its long drive, stunning architecture, modern classrooms, central lake, huge treehouse and extensive playing fields and grounds. Main school building is a Victorian mansion built in 1894 by Baron Stalbridge but it is surrounded by a collection of stylish, purpose-built additions. School was founded in London in 1881 by Dr Alfred Praetorius. It was later bought by a couple called Mr and Mrs Roderick, who moved it to Folkestone. When they retired it was incorporated into a school at Kingsgate, Broadstairs and named Port Regis (Latin for 'Gate of the King'). It moved to Motcombe House in 1947 (via stints at Bryanston and St Albans). First admitted girls in 1972.

Mildly selective – head says the school is 'a broad church' – but academic results are very good. Setting from year 5, with scholarship sets introduced in the last two years (year 8 scholarship group is called Alpha, year 7 scholarship group is Beta). Maximum class size of 15 throughout. French taught from the start and Latin from year 6. Spanish on offer from year 6 and there are opportunities to study Italian, Russian and Mandarin outside the main curriculum. Ancient Greek is taught as an after-lunch club for children in years 6, 7 and 8. Staff give it a try too. When we visited the director of studies had just signed up.

Pupils have a form teacher till the end of year 6, then get the chance to choose their own tutor for years 7 and 8. Excellent learning support department led by dynamic head (who used to be head of science and also teaches mindfulness). A fifth of pupils access learning support, mainly for dyslexia, dyspraxia, ASD, mild ADD and speech and language therapy. School has produced a senior school guide to help parents choose the next schools for their children and head meets parents to discuss choices when children are in year 5.

Well-known far and wide for its sporting prowess, school offers a plethora of sport. Boys play rugby, football, hockey and cricket while girls do hockey, netball, rounders and tennis. As well as acres of playing fields there's an astroturf, nine-hole golf course, rifle range, heated swimming pool and impressive indoor sports complex that serves as a national centre for junior gymnastics. School does particularly well at hockey, rugby and athletics (11 pupils qualified for 15 different events at a recent IAPS national athletics championships).

Girls' boarding house is stunning, with disco lights on the hall ceiling and a double tier sofa to snuggle up and watch movies at weekends

Art, DT and pottery (there can't be many prep schools with a whole room devoted to ceramics) are amazing. We were particularly taken with a vast sculpture of a pear core created by a 13-year-old pupil. The year 8 guide who showed us round the DT department told us: 'This is a place where ideas can be formed.' Many senior schools would give their eyeteeth for facilities like these – everything from a 3D printer to a laser-cutting machine (great for making stickers). The children really let their imaginations run riot here. We saw an iPod speaker inspired by an old-fashioned toaster, a hanging chair and a lamp that projected a bat-shaped shadow on the wall. 'They surprise me all

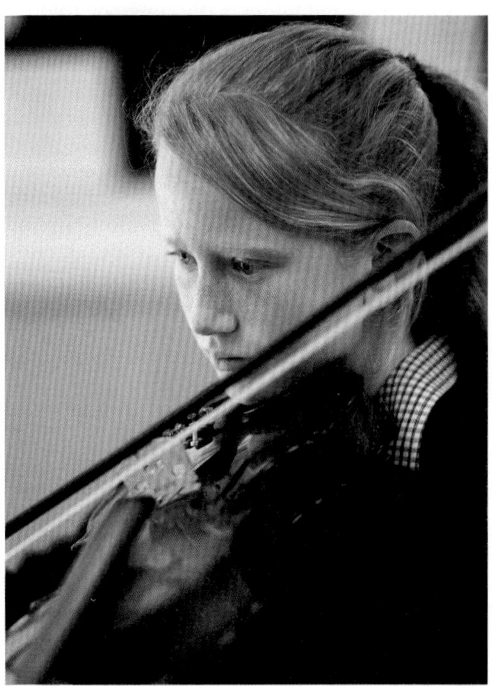

the time with their designs,' beams the head of DT. Annual summer exhibition gives pupils a chance to show off their creative flair.

Music is top notch too. Every 7-year-old learns the recorder and how to read music and every 8-year-old learns the violin. Music is taught in the striking Farrington Music School, an octagonal-shaped building overlooking a small lake known as 'Bob's Pond'. It boasts a 132-seat recital hall, music technology room and 17 teaching rooms. Wind, brass and string ensembles, school orchestra, senior and junior choirs, samba band, swing band and lots of other groups, all of which put on regular concerts. Plenty of drama. Each year group puts on a play and there's a leavers' show at the end of the summer term. More than 70 activities and hobbies (we'd love to do them all), including aerobics, backgammon, beekeeping, film animation, computer coding, friendship bracelets and trampolining. Debating, or 'persuasive talks', are very popular, with children encouraged to discuss the issues of the day.

As well as acres of playing fields there's an astroturf, nine-hole golf course, rifle range, heated swimming pool and impressive indoor sports complex

School is firmly committed to boarding. 'It feels like a second home really,' one boy told us. Around 60 per cent of children board in some way, whether it's full boarding, flexi-boarding or the odd night here and there (via an efficient online booking system). 'We have tried to listen to what our parents want,' says the head, who introduced flexi-boarding on his arrival. Apart from half term and holidays, the school never shuts. While some boarders go home at weekends, 70 to 80 children (around a third of the main school) stay at school. Around 35 per cent of boarders are from overseas (17 per cent of the school community). Lots on offer for the boarders – staff and 12 gap students put on activities like face painting, cooking, weekend walks and trips galore. Most staff live on site.

Boarding facilities are top notch – way better than some senior schools we've seen. Junior boarders (years 3 to 6) are housed in the main school building – girls on one side, boys on another. Dorms of four or six, each with a dorm captain. Older boys and girls have separate boarding houses in the grounds. The girls' boarding house is stunning, complete with disco lights on the hall ceiling, a double tier sofa to snuggle up and watch movies at weekends and breakfast bar stools made from riding saddles. Each girl has her own 'cubie', with a bed, desk and wash basin – separated with a stylish bead curtain at the door. There's even a retro caravan in the garden (the enterprising bursar snapped it up on eBay). The senior boys' house is pretty nifty too – the games room ceiling is decorated with real surfboards. A lot of thought has been given to helping new children settle in. New pupils get a shadow to guide them through the early weeks.

Year 8s given responsibility – there's a head boy and head girl, plus dorm captains for boarders. No prefects. 'We don't think it's good to single out children at this age,' says the head. Children encouraged to be children for as long as possible. No electronic devices or mobile phones (apart from pupils whose parents live abroad). Boarders can Skype their parents on the boarding house computers. Pastoral care is very much at the forefront, with form tutors and houseparents the first port of call when problems arise. Very few behaviour issues here. Indeed, Port Regis is hot on manners, pleases and thank yous and holding doors open for visitors. Boarders write letters home every Tuesday. School is also planning a kindness day – 'we want children to understand that it's cool to be kind,' says the head. 'It's not to be derided. It's a real strength.' Slightly more boys than girls but school has appointed a head of girls' games and a senior tutor, who is effectively head of girls (she is also head of classics, has a PhD from Cambridge and has written two critically acclaimed books).

School food is among the very best we've tasted. Head chef (whose family runs a local restaurant) and his five-strong team cook up to 1,000 meals a day – breakfast, lunch and supper, using fresh locally sourced ingredients as much as possible. We happily tucked into a lunch of fillet of sea bass (freshly caught off the coast of Brixham) topped with caper and lemon sauce, spinach and roasted new potatoes. Salads and vegetarian options always on offer – avocado and chargrilled peppers, quorn wraps and lentil soup when we visited.

Pre-prep (with 52 pupils) is housed in a stable block, just a few minutes walk from the main school. Idyllic setting, complete with forest school, enclosed playground, rose garden for imaginary play, loads of outdoor space and plenty of scooters and helmets. When we visited children had been picking apples and were about to cook their own apple crumble. Head of pre-prep is a former Team GB underwater hockey player and is passionate about outdoor learning.

Pupils are chirpy, enthusiastic and refreshingly down-to-earth. We saw a group of year 4s, all dressed up as chimney sweeps, street children and lords and ladies of the manor, throw themselves with relish into a Victorian Day workshop led by a guest speaker. Parents say there's 'a buzz about the school' and like the way it treats every child as an individual. A mix of local families and those who have moved to the country in search of a healthier, less pressurized lifestyle. Some from London – school is only two hours from the capital and Heathrow by train. Day pupils come from as far afield as Sherborne, Salisbury, Bruton and Warminster, mostly places within a 40-minute drive. School is building up a network of minibuses for day pupils. Parents are very involved in the school, attending quiz nights, balls, the Christmas fair, debates and lectures.

Illustrious alumni include the abstract painter Adrian Heath, former Press Council chairman Sir Louis Blom-Cooper, fashion designer Jasper Conran, singer/songwriter Bo Brudenell-Bruce, Olympic medallist horsewoman Zara Phillips and historian Jonathan Gathorne-Hardy.

As we've said before, it's difficult to find fault with Port Regis. It has sometimes been seen as the preserve of the very rich but in reality children come from a wide variety of backgrounds. Scholarships and means-tested bursaries on offer too. The pupils we met clearly love the place and as a parent told us: 'If anyone is going to bring out what your child is good at, Port Regis will.'

Prior Park College

RC 43

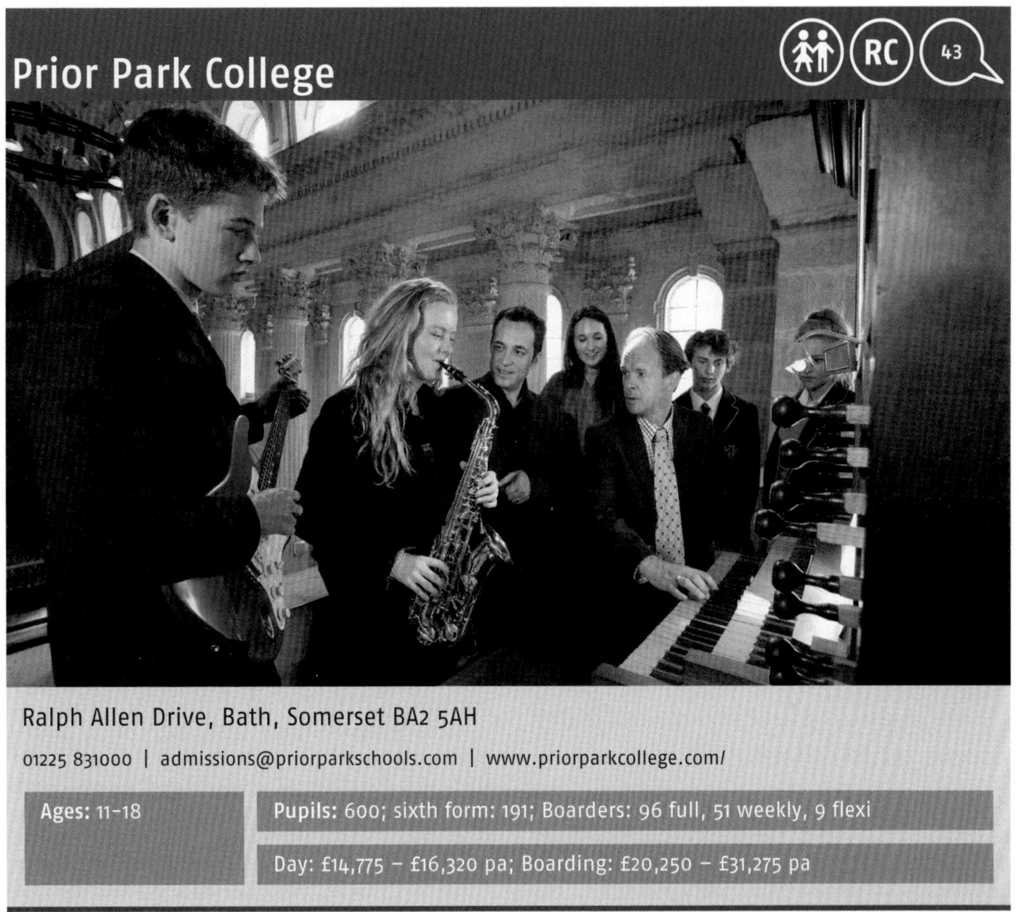

Ralph Allen Drive, Bath, Somerset BA2 5AH

01225 831000 | admissions@priorparkschools.com | www.priorparkcollege.com/

Ages: 11-18

Pupils: 600; sixth form: 191; Boarders: 96 full, 51 weekly, 9 flexi

Day: £14,775 – £16,320 pa; Boarding: £20,250 – £31,275 pa

Head master: Since 2009, Mr James Murphy-O'Connor MA (Oxon) PGCE (40s). Historian. Educated at St Benedict's, Ealing. Degree at Greyfriars Hall, Oxford, PGCE at Peterhouse, Cambridge. Thence to Stamford followed by Sherborne, where he was a housemaster. First headship was the brand new Sherfield. Says 'Prior Park is in my DNA' and justly, for his father, Jim, was educated here along with his four brothers. Jim played rugby for Ireland, his younger brother Cardinal Cormac is the retired Archbishop of Westminster and still engages with the religious life of the school. James is married to Ali, four children, all former or current students. Keen on the arts, fan of F Scott Fitzgerald and Thomas Hardy, plus Picasso's 1920s art. Passionate Tottenham Hotspur and Ireland rugby fan. Enjoys retreating to family cottage amongst the mountains and wild Atlantic beaches of his beloved Mayo in Ireland where dalmador (dalmatian x labrador) Holly runs free.

By present day standards Mr Murphy-O'Connor's has already been a longish innings, but he's not ready to move on yet and talks like a man with an as-yet unfulfilled vision for the school. His focus is the human level, improving the school experience of all students, making sure they are nurtured, safe and throwing themselves into everything on offer. Often to be sighted out and about at the start of the day, 'chatting and welcoming', students note admiringly that 'he knows your name and things about you from day one'. Well-being issues come first in his book – not that the snazzy new sports centre is anything to sneeze at. Scorelines from academic through to sporting have risen measurably on his watch but his legacy will be the emotional health of the school community – which is inaccessible to units of measurement. This isn't a bandwagon response to recent alarm bells about teenage mental health issues, it's where his and his school's heart have always lain. At the time of our visit the big news was a fledgling peer mentoring scheme, a give-something-back enterprise originated by sixth formers intended to enable them to offer discreet advice and emotional support to their younger fellows. Rather than take ownership of the initiative, Mr Murphy-O'Connor was characteristically taking the route of empowerment. This is what his school is all about and all parents we spoke to said it was the pastoral care and evident happiness of the community that got them reaching for their registration form.

Amazingly posh architecture notwithstanding, the social climate here isn't the least snooty; this is a down to earth place where ordinary people go to school

In a Catholic school whose roll numbers 65 per cent non-Catholics, Mr Murphy O'Connor unabashedly decrees Catholic values of kindness, service and 'being the person God wants you to be' – he says 'every child is precious'. No lip-service here. None of these values is objectionable to parents of a broadly secular disposition, to whom they are also humanist values which they want their child to imbibe. Discussion of topics like abortion and homosexuality hears out and respects all points of view. Non-Catholic students express no uneasiness.

Prior Park delivers, says the head, a rounded education. Lots of heads say this. When they do, cock an eyebrow – we did – for this is an inexact term. It can mean an educational philosophy, it can mean that the students here aren't terribly good at exams or, when employed by a school that is terribly good at exams, can mean all too little. Which is the case here? The way to find out is to investigate whether, down on the shop floor, teachers and students are walking the talk. What we found by dint of interrogation is that they most emphatically do. Yes, they echo and act out what their head says, and never in a dutiful, parroty way. It is highly unusual to visit a school and hear the words of a head made flesh like this, the more so given the disposition of young persons to subject the exhortations of authority figures to ruthless due diligence. But they like what their head wants, they really do. They want it too. Work matters most, but everything else matters too. One parent told us that your typical Prior Park student is 'accomplished, compassionate and humble'. No divergence here from Mr Murphy-O'Connor's primary purpose. Another said, 'Each student, honestly, matters to him.' Another: 'He's passionate about encouraging pupils to become rounded.'

Academic matters: No point in looking at Dept for Education performance tables for raw data and comparison tables because the school, along with others, is boycotting them. Why? Because in the head's book there's more to education than exam results, performance tables take no account of 'creativity and inspiration', and the only true measure is how far a school raises its students. So he'd happily sign up for value-added league tables.

Headline figures vary little from year to year. In 2017 at GCSE 56 per cent A*-A/9-7 grades; at A level 38 per cent A*/A, 66 per cent A*-B. So: the school does consistently well by its broad-ish intake. This is not an exam factory because there is no relenting in the commitment to all-round personal development, neither is roundedness achieved at the expense of best-possible exam results – a neat trick which the school pulls off adroitly. There's pressure all right, but it's judiciously applied and it works because – this is the culture of the place – teachers know their students very well as people, they pick up on stress, lethargy and waywardness just like that and make time to support. One student said, 'They always help when you're finding it difficult and get you back for a bit of tuition to help you through.' Another said, 'No teacher here would ever turn down a request for help'. Call this rigour through kindness if you like, there's a lot of mutual respect going on here. The PHSCE programme is substantial and delivered with purpose.

Prep (homework) is supervised up to sixth form. The relatively long day here (no Saturday school) means that you can break the back of it before you get home. Parents like this: 'There's usually not all that much to do at home so we can relax together as a family'. As you age it increasingly spills over, of course.

Fabulous Julian Slade theatre (1993) largely funded by Cameron Mackintosh's Foundation – he's a former student

There's currently a curriculum review in progress which aims to fine tune already estimable value-added scores. Having rejected the International Baccalaureate, they aim now to offer a bespoke version. The outcome the head seeks is 'an educational framework that enshrines our values.'

No statemented students accepted, but SEND provision supports milder SENs and intervenes when disparity emerges between a student's potential and ongoing achievement, or a student needs, say, organisational strategies or exam-stress support. Extends to students who develop mental health issues. Parents speak well of the expert sensitivity of the support given to their children. Mobility impaired students accepted where possible, but the school's architecture is a constraint.

Games, options, the arts: Sport, says the head, is 'one of the things we do'. Puts it in its place nicely, neither bigging it up nor doing it down and underlining his commitment to celebrating achievement in all areas equally, each student according to their lights. Parents like the way the school 'encourages everyone to give it all a go regardless of ability.' Hockey's what they do best in shop-window terms (national champions 2016). Netball is strong, rugby has an ex-England international coach, the rest competitively respectable given the size of each year's intake. Spacious playing fields, plentiful Astroturf. Sport for all, they say, greatest involvement by the greatest number, borne out by number of teams per sport sent forth to battle for their school every Saturday – around 10 on good day. Individuals regularly play at regional and international level. One of the lessons we learn from sport, they say, is humility. That's so Prior Park. No, it's emphatically not a philosophy of loser takes all, they love to win. Sports centre, source of great pride, includes multi-sport gym, fitness suite, you name it. It's been a boon for the less gamesy types.

Art and design happen in and around a refurbed dorm. Fine art good, photography especially strong just now as is textiles. Healthy numbers, decent results. Design technology in a good place, partnerships with local industries, lots of energy input from staff. A bit boy heavy but efforts being made to bring in the girls.

Music universally praised. Inspirational head of music also performs with singing group Opus Anglicanum. No elitism here when it comes to genre: anything goes from Gabrieli to grime. In cases of indie genres his smart ploy is to offer 'hands-off facilitation' thus enabling students to retain ownership of their sounds. High-end choral tradition longstanding and outstanding, biennial opera, multiplicity of ensembles, concerts formal and informal, for they love to go live and give others 'an experience of the sublime'. Two, yes two, musicals every year, all singing, all dancing – one parent said, 'Never a duty date, I simply can't believe the standard they reach'. 'Blows my mind,' said another. Music here reaches all parts and catches up those who never knew they could. There's an inter-house music competition including student-rehearsed house song in which everyone sings and thereafter dwells on, marvelling fondly, for the rest of the year. A level numbers small, but of these a good number go on to top music colleges. Chapel choir is 90 per cent day students who come in every Sunday to sing at mass. What does that tell you?

Drama's right up there with music (let's call it a dead heat). Up to 14 productions of all sorts a year, much of it high-end stuff. Staff (superb) all come from professional theatre, that's what makes the difference. Fabulous Julian Slade theatre (1993) largely funded by Cameron Mackintosh's Foundation – he's a former student – palpably redolent of the magic created in it down the years by dint of passion, sweat, discipline, creativity and self-discovery. It's the real thing all right. Mackintosh also funded the excellent dance studio.

You get to do your after-school activities in school here. Recreational options, both lunchtime and after lessons, are multifarious and eclectic, embracing a diversity of endeavours from tricky physics to knit-and-natter. More than 60 to choose among. There's a Saturday (morning) Active programme whose breadth spans street dance and cookery. There's a CCF – voluntary sign-up from year 8 upwards – and there's D of E. There's even an equestrian team.

Sixth formers have their own after-school (ad) ventures. They concoct a social programme – film nights, music nights, BBQs etc. The charities committee coordinates competitive fundraising for good causes and the best house wins a cup. Then there's Prior Concern, which sends forth students to do their bit for the homeless, nursery-age children and the elderly. Catholic values in action.

Boarding: Some 160 students board from age 11, around a third of them girls. Of these, around 50 are weekly and flexi boarders. Roughly 60 full time boarders are international students. Stopover beds for day pupils. We had reservations about the boys' accommodation in St Paul's. Gorgeous as the building may be on the outside, its bigness seemed inimical to snugness on the inside. This is an adult perception; the students reckon it does very nicely. Boys live alongside residential staff and their families. Girls occupy the unarguably cosier Priory nearby. Prep is supervised by a teacher. Weekend activities, the bugbear of any boarding regime, continually addressed. Mass on Sundays compulsory. To be honest we wondered about the head of boys' boarding being an ex-Marine – until we met him. Bit of a martinet? No way. He's a man who understands the vital importance of addressing individuality in all its manifestations.

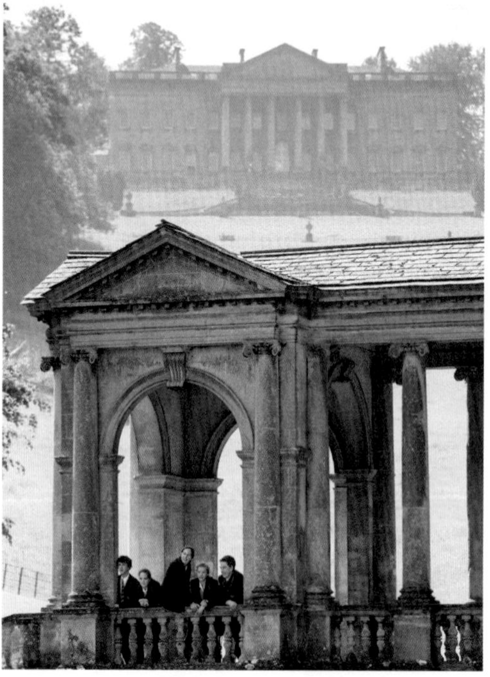

Background and atmosphere: Run by the Christian Brothers 1830-1981. Palladian mansion built by quarry owner Ralph Allen to advertise the golden glories of Bath stone. This a grade 1 listed building standing two miles from the centre of a UNESCO World Heritage city. Stunning view down from the portico stops all the clocks. Inside, architectural grandeur doesn't always adapt readily to the needs of a 21st century school and can play the part of an awkward host. 'Don't agree,' say the students as you fight for breath up an endless spiral staircase; 'it's quirky, it's part of the charm'. A parent concurred: 'Yes, all right, it's a bit shabby in places but in the nicest way – a bit basic but kids love it.' Lovely chapel, lovely name, Our Lady of the Snows, used also for weekly assemblies – all get in, just. Science block purpose built. Years 7 and 8 in their own standalone house, Baines, overseen by greatly-liked housemistress and team. Compulsory residential course early in year 7 and team building day for year 8 students underpin community values.

Amazingly posh architecture notwithstanding, the social climate here isn't the least snooty; this is a down to earth place where ordinary people go to school, a place whose unpretentious personality answers the values of the sort of parent who celebrates 'a school that doesn't set itself apart from the city but participates in local events.'

Pastoral care, well-being and discipline: There's a culture here of looking out for each other, teachers for students, older students for younger ones – one parent said, 'they got to know my daughter very quickly and genuinely appreciated her as a person.' It's a palpable culture, one you pick up on as you tour and chat. Intervention is prompt. One parent said, 'It is a fantastic strength of the school that they are so diligent with the students' well-being.' This doesn't all come about by wishing it so or generating policy docs, it derives from expectations, watchfulness, example-setting and buy-in. It works because it's hard work and it conditions behaviour because it is underpinned by tenacity. Above all, it's what the students want. So, said one parent, 'There is no room for anyone to bend the rules. Boundaries are set and are the same for everyone. This has created a school of pupils who take pride in how they are being perceived by everyone.' Another said: ''We are constantly amazed by the school's ability to encourage and maintain an exquisite level of behaviour and compliance without the need to instil enormous amounts of discipline.' Concern for well-being shirks no issue raised by social media, a major concern;

sexting, by way of example, is a regular assembly topic and parents join in the discussion. We asked one parent if social media was a regular discussion topic. 'No, it's a constant conversation.'

Pupils and parents: Co-ed since 1982, almost 50:50, boys slightly more numerous. Common rooms are same-sex, lessons and dining mixed. Some 35 per cent of students are Catholic. Year 7 entrants from, equally, local state schools and Paragon Junior. At year 9 a wodge from the prep school in Cricklade plus a smattering from other preps and international schools. Sizeable contingent of parents are dahn-from-Londoners, who have colonised Bath in recent years – yes, even raggle-taggle Walcot Street has capitulated to the hipsters. This monocultural tendency is mitigated by the school's international students, never more than 10 per cent of the roll. To cope with demand from overseas the school has just launched Prior Park Gibraltar. With two outstanding (Ofsted) state schools and four rival independents in Bath alone, the education market locally is working well, with competitive pressures driving up standards and heightening distinctiveness.

For day students, buses from all corners up to 30 miles away. Parental involvement welcomed: twice-monthly coffee mornings hosted by PoP (Parents Of Prior), which even has its own private Facebook page. Regular parent forums with the head so he can hear what you think. Weekly newsletter from the head. Listings of parent phone numbers by year group (voluntary) a nice touch. Businesslike, highly functional website. Parents really like the 'wonderful feeling of community'.

Entrance: Selective. Don't miss the application deadline – details on the website. Tests for 11+ entrants; CE and scholarship at 13. At any other time, report and interview. Around 20 join post-GCSE from other schools, telling you something about the strength of the sixth form, whose entrants need a minimum six GCSEs with As in A level subjects preferred.

Exit: Small exodus post-GCSE, most to vocational courses. Sixth form leavers are Russell groupies, most of them, Exeter, Manchester and Cardiff especially popular. Good and varied balance of arts and sciences. One to Oxbridge in 2017 (usually three or four), plus two medics.

Money matters: Customary range of scholarships up to a value of around 25 per cent, more in deserving cases. Bursaries can be standalone or added to a scholarship. The head says he likes to help where he can, and in another clear-cut case of walking the talk an examination of the accounts reveals that the school awards roughly half as much again in bursaries (as a percentage of income) as other Bath independents. Some carry-over scholarships from prep school. Discounts for siblings. Lunch bundled with fees but not transport. Taking account of the long school day and the 4-6pm activities programme, good value for money. The head says, 'We recognise that we have a lot of working parents who stretch themselves to afford the fees. We don't want to let them down.'

Remarks: Confident in its Catholic values, happy in its own skin and distinctive in its commitment to a genuinely all-round education, this is a school which inspires esteem and affection in equal measure.

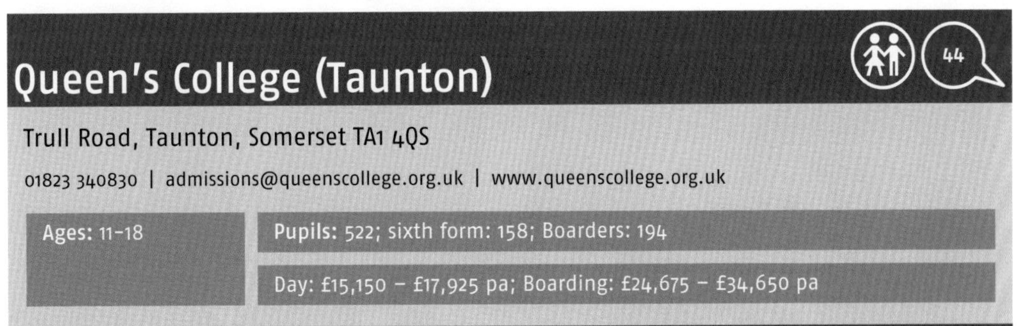

Queen's College (Taunton)
44
Trull Road, Taunton, Somerset TA1 4QS
01823 340830 | admissions@queenscollege.org.uk | www.queenscollege.org.uk
Ages: 11-18
Pupils: 522; sixth form: 158; Boarders: 194
Day: £15,150 – £17,925 pa; Boarding: £24,675 – £34,650 pa

Head: Since September 2016, Dr Lorraine Earps, previously deputy and then acting head here (following the resignation of previous head Chris Alcock in May 2016, following allegations that he had breached the school's code of conduct). Degree in chemistry and biochemistry from Southampton, plus a doctorate in protein chemistry; taught in the state sector for six years; has also been head of chemistry at Stockport Grammar and director of studies at Withington Girls. Married with a son.

Academic matters: One of the top of the Taunton schools pops for A level results in 2017, at 62 per cent A*/B, and 33 per cent A*/A, plus a respectable 51 per cent A*-A/9-7 at GCCE, suggesting sound value-added at sixth form. But they appear to achieve this without excessive pressure: 'I spend more time taking the pressure off, than laying it on', said the previous head. That said, he had, during his time, concentrated on the middle band, moving Cs to Bs, and Bs to As, as well as catering to different learning styles – testament to his success is a severely dyslexic boy now reading law at Exeter. He also binned Saturday school – 'The kids at the other Taunton schools are tired!' he asserted. Class sizes average 17, and there's a choice of 24 subjects for GCSE and A level. A modern foreign language is compulsory at GCSE; business studies and ethics & philosophy more unusual options. Students are grouped by ability for core subjects but mixed for options. At A level, option blocks are changed yearly in an effort to accommodate individual subject choices and the school's flexibility at the start of sixth form while A level choices bed down is appreciated. Critical thinking, EPQ and TUG (top universities group) offered alongside these. One parent we spoke to chose Queen's specifically for its academics, another because her child 'did not shine academically, but has not been made to feel inferior by staff or pupils'. Stand-out subjects for the students are geography, chemistry and maths – 'but the sport and music are also amazing', our guides reported.

SEN support is provided through an integrated approach with the learning development unit (sic), where an electronic register shared with teaching staff records and tracks the needs of the high-ish proportion of SEN students. 'We haven't and don't wish to acquire dyslexia-friendly status,' says school, but it appears to serve its SEN population well, maths support in particular provided by the same teacher throughout the school, using traditional methods. Active EAL programme for the 100 or so overseas students.

Founding Methodist values still in place today: tolerance, friendliness and a lack of pretension, underpinned by Christian principles

Games, options, the arts: Sport is important – more a question of a game for all than winning at all costs. Just the place for sportsmen and women, but 'equally OK for incredibly anti-sports daughter,' according to one mother, who added that it is 'much more geared towards music, drama and the arts than the other Taunton schools'. Nonetheless, Queen's excels at sports and has just opened academies for both hockey and cricket (for which Taunton is famed), not just for its own promising players, but also for high flyers locally. Thirty acres of pitches, two Astros, an indoor pool – swimming is a strength here – and well-equipped sports hall make for a comprehensive offering. 'Rugby and hockey have been fundamental to my son's time here,' stated one mother. Off site, riding, sailing, canoeing, climbing and caving in nearby Mendips

suits those with less of an eye for a ball, but everyone is encouraged to explore the great outdoors: almost all do at least bronze D of E, and a high number complete gold.

Performing arts shine too – school boasts largest performing space(s) of any school in the south west: two theatres and a studio big/smart enough for more intimate productions, and uses expertise of Somerset College's specialist film and TV make-up course. Recent shows include Seussical, Coram Boy, Macbeth and Storm Boy, adapted from the book by the head of drama, a published playwright. A massively ambitious arts festival, Quartz, takes place at school each October, which brings in actors, musicians, dancers and artists of all persuasions for performances and workshops. Dancers extremely well looked after in terms of facilities and the school's own academy of performing arts, which attracts the likes of Birmingham City Ballet to give classes; strong on contemporary dance too, such as street jazz. Musicians jolly fortunate, too, to have a dedicated concert hall as part of the music school, complete with Steinway and 30 stop organ, plus music tech facilities. Choirs and ensembles abound – we were intrigued by the 'exuberant arrangements' apparently played by Sound School, a sax ensemble. Trips for local and international (recently Germany and Italy) performance and trophies from Taunton Festival round off an extensive, if traditional, musical offering.

A massively ambitious arts festival, Quartz, takes place at school each October, bringing in actors, musicians, dancers and artists for performances and workshops

Art of all kinds is housed in a gorgeous art school overlooking the cricket pitches; students are exposed to all media, techniques and materials so that they are well prepared for GCSE art and design. Painting, ceramics and textiles are areas of particular expertise, but all benefit from trips here and abroad (Barcelona and New York, inter alia) as well as the influx of visiting practitioners at the annual Quartz Festival. But despite the range of diversions to choose from, some parents still feel it's too narrow, and that a shove could usefully be applied to the idler students to sign up to more of them.

Boarding: More than a third of students board, and some parents, at least, appreciate the finishing time of 4pm, which suits those who come daily. The absence of Saturday school does not

mean a fallow day, however: au contraire, there's a full programme of activities or rehearsals in the morning, with sports fixtures and expeditions in the afternoon.

We felt some of the senior boarding accommodation was on the cheerless side of acceptable; doubtless legally compliant, but the bare walls and lack of personal touches in some of the dorms was a bit bleak – and a bath list a relic from an earlier age. The continuing refurbishment cannot progress fast enough. That said, the evident warmth of the staff and close friendships between year groups compensate for any dreary living quarters awaiting tarting up. Food generally reckoned to be good: a tasty choice of stew with Yorkshire pudding, cheese and onion pie, breaded chicken or salad bar the day we visited is not, though, perhaps enough to satisfy every palate, witness the group of Asian girls we saw tucking into noodles in one of the house kitchens... The boarding community enjoys eating together in the evenings and the tweaking of boarders' teas with extra carbs and meat to suit sportsmen/women is appreciated.

Background and atmosphere: Originally and fabulously named the West of England Wesleyan Proprietary Grammar School and founded in 1843 by local Methodists dissatisfied by the kind of schooling accessible to nonconformists, Queen's was renamed for Queen Victoria's golden jubilee in 1887. A run of imposing Victorian gothic buildings redolent of the timeline along a stretch of road leading out of Taunton to the village of Trull; modern additions are concentrated behind the original buildings, leaving a view across the extensive sports facilities to the distant Quantocks. A super sixth form centre has been created from a former rather ugly civil service club, now greatly appreciated by its new occupants who enjoy areas for silent study, as well as space to chill, chat and rustle up those staples of British education – toast and coffee. In the view of one parent, it gives students 'independence, self-respect and responsibility'. Sharing the same stretch of road and major facilities as Queen's College, if not its architectural merits, is the junior school.

More than a third of students board, but the absence of Saturday school does not mean a fallow day. Au contraire, there's a full programme of activities or rehearsals in the morning, with sports fixtures and expeditions in the afternoon

Founding Methodist values still prop the place up today: tolerance, friendliness and a lack of pretension underpinned by Christian principles and practice define it; a full time chaplain is on the staff. Individuals are valued, quirks and diversity welcomed: 'We looked at several schools,' one mother told us 'but this one had a good feel and was right for both my very different children. My son was initially shy but has really grown into himself'. Other parents praise the school's 'gentle approach' which builds confidence in the diffident, as well as 'the lack of social/wealth/class issues'. Hurrah for that.

Pastoral care, well-being and discipline: Pastoral care highly rated by students and parents alike, from the tutors to the house staff. Close attention is paid to every child – 'We notice if anyone is off-colour'. No in-school counsellor, as staff feel that students would be 'naturally suspicious of anyone from inside school'; the view from one girl we spoke to was that she wouldn't know who to talk to if she had a problem – 'there are just so many options'. An extensive reward system recognises not only achievement but also students who have triumphed over adversity in some form. Discipline was not a word we heard much – we suspect that it doesn't rear its head that often – but 'to incur the disappointment of the head is a crushing blow,' one mother told us. Prefects have the power to administer 'fatigues' for minor infringements of rules or poor behaviour.

Pupils and parents: Mostly pretty local (Somerset, Devon and Dorset), augmented by a contingent of overseas boarders such as Forces' children and an array of nationalities, with Russian and SE Asian predominating. 'Queen's wouldn't suit very competitive sporty, hearty, Sloaney families,' we were reliably informed. Parents tend to be loyal and to involve themselves in the life of the school, but some think school communications need a kick in the posterior: poor grammar, six copies of the same email just two examples.

Entrance: About 60 per cent of senior school entrants come from the junior school without let or hindrance, unless they are trying for a scholarship or have specific learning difficulties. Others arrive from local primaries at 11, yet more from the odd prep school at 13+ and all sit tests in English, maths and verbal reasoning. At sixth form, the bar looks quite low at five GCSEs above a C/5 with 'preferably A*-B/9-6' for subjects chosen for A level, but hopefuls are also required to take two papers in their likely A level subject choices. Children from overseas take a paper in English as an additional language.

Exit: About 30 leave after GCSE, many to local excellent (and free) sixth form college in Taunton, Richard Huish. Almost all sixth form leavers go on to their chosen degree courses up and down the land – Warwick, Cardiff, Swansea, Bristol and Southampton popular. One to Oxbridge in 2017 and three medics, with four off overseas. Some gap years. Notable alumni include Sir Nick Harvey (long-standing MP for N Devon), Lord Widgery (former Lord Chief Justice of England and Wales), and clutch of other luminaries across the professions, armed forces and arts, including a prime minister of Newfoundland and Elephant Bill, an army officer known for his work in Burma in world war two.

Money matters: Fees about 10 per cent lower than comparable schools for UK students, but work out about the same for those from overseas. Lunch is charged separately for day students; learning support, EAL and any kind of extra tuition cost extra. 'Singing lessons are a bit steep,' remarked one parent. Usual range of scholarships on offer, more bountiful than many at a maximum of 25 per cent for a major academic award. Sibling discounts more generous than some we have seen, too.

Remarks: A Taunton institution which distinguishes itself from the local competition by its family feel, yet continues to cut the academic, sporting and artistic mustard year after year, Queen's is a welcoming, inclusive, unpretentious place which could sell itself better. A lick of paint here and there wouldn't go amiss either.

Rendcomb College

Rendcomb, Cirencester, Gloucestershire GL7 7HA

01285 831213 | admissions@rendcombcollege.org.uk | www.rendcombcollege.org.uk

Ages: 3-18 (boarding from year 7)

Pupils: 370; sixth form: 90; Boarders: 140

Day: £5,850 – £22,650 pa; Boarding: £21,750 – £31,500 pa

Headmaster: Since 2015, Rob Jones, previously deputy head at Shiplake College. Educated at Swansea (economics), Worcester (PGCE) and Buckingham (MEd). After a brief period mixing banking with elite rowing, he became a teacher in 1994. Rob has taught economics and business at Canford, Clifton College, King's Worcester and Dauntsey's, as well as coaching rugby and rowing and running day and boarding houses. Teaches business economics to sixth formers at Rendcomb.

A keen sportsman, an Ironman medal is proudly displayed in his office, he is a regular supporter at school matches. Lives in the college with wife, Pippa, a singer turned teaching assistant who leads the staff band, and children, a son in year 8 and daughter in year 6. Rob is immediately likeable; parents say he is 'an excellent head teacher,' 'so fabulous with the students; they respect him completely,' and 'great with parents too.' One explained, 'When we first met he told us that if there wasn't a lot of noise and laughter in the corridors there was something wrong! He hasn't disappointed in that regard and runs a caring, happy, pupil-focused school.' Another added, 'He has a compelling vision for the future of the school, with the interests of the students at its heart, and isn't scared to innovate and modernise.'

Head of junior school since 2017 is Mr Gavin Roberts, previously deputy head at the school from 2014. Before that he was senior tutor (academic) at Cathedral School, Llandaff, for 11 years. Lives in the village with his wife Jen, also a teacher. A rugby man, he is a qualified WRU referee. Gavin teaches year 5 English and is 'warm, down to earth and approachable,' parents told us. It was clear to us that he loves this school and as a result, 'the children absolutely love him to bits; he allows them to be who they are.... There is always a lot of fun when Mr Roberts is around.'

There is a One College approach at Rendcomb, one ethos and one vision for the whole school, both juniors and seniors. The two heads are very much united on this and we get the feeling that this fairly new team are steering Rendcomb College towards a bright future.

Academic matters: In 2017, at A level, 66 per cent A*-B grades, and 43 per cent A*/A grades. At GCSE, 37 per cent A*-A9-7 and 63 per cent A*-B grades.

Twenty-three A levels offered including a new design and technology option. Another recent addition is a travel and tourism BTec. If this is popular, a business BTec will follow. EPQ optional. Consistently strong subjects are the sciences and maths. Oxbridge applicants are supported well with external business experts conducting mock interviews and providing feedback. Bespoke courses for overseas pupils available.

French is taught from nursery along with some Latin and German in the later years of junior school. French, Spanish and German are the main languages in the senior school. Specialist teachers teach art, music, drama, PE, and English and maths from year 3. Any child in the junior school showing particular talent or aptitude will be encouraged to take part in senior school activities. One parent told us, 'Our son has gone from struggling/being somewhat disenchanted with school to really finding himself. His academic side has picked back up extremely well and he has taken up new hobbies (rock band, film club) and the school has been great at helping him open up and grow.'

Boarders' committee helps decide on evening and weekend activities: dance, yoga, baking, craft nights, playing laser tag in the grounds or canoeing down the River Wye

Technology is taken seriously. Computers are upgraded every three years; the current Macs are being donated to the music technology department and the replacements are equipped with facial recognition and touch screens. The enthusiastic heads of department both have industry backgrounds, from Tesco and Microsoft respectively. The department has a maker-space full of old bits for pupils to reuse; game consoles were under construction on our visit and 3D printed prosthetic limbs operated by Raspberry Pi computers have been created in the past. There is also a computing laboratory, 3D printer and Oculus Virtual Reality headsets. Computing lessons are delivered using real-life examples. This forward-thinking department won the ICT Facility Award at the Education Business Awards in 2017 and were shortlisted for the ICT Innovation category for the use of technology across the school's 230-acre campus. Numbers at A level are on the up and the heads of department are well positioned to help with industry links and advice. But it's not just for the seniors; the juniors have been crowned Gloucestershire's Coding Champions and are ranked first place in the Discover Education Coding League Table.

SEND department caters for the whole school. Provides one-to-one support as well as catch up programmes in small groups. Needs include dyslexia, dyscalculia and dyspraxia. Specialist dyslexia teachers teach pupils from 4 to 18. The department also has a quiet room. More complex needs are considered on an individual basis.

Games, options, the arts: Not the sportiest of schools. As it is small, teams are mixed ability and often mixed year groups. However, the school ethos is that everyone tries their best and everyone gets the opportunity to represent the school. Outdoor facilities, including the 10-acre sports park known as Top Pitch, are excellent but parents would like to see indoor facilities to match. Top Pitch alternates each term as rugby/lacrosse pitches, cricket pitches, football pitches, a hockey pitch and an athletics track. Plus there is a permanent clay pigeon shooting ground. Other facilities include an Astroturf (to be replaced soon), an outdoor swimming pool (to be covered one day, hopefully), squash courts, indoor cricket nets and a climbing wall.

'Rendcomb is probably not going to be first choice for the highly competitive, sports-mad child,' we were told, but several parents would still like to see more opportunities and activities on offer. Major sports for boys are rugby, hockey and cricket (football in the junior school). For girls it's hockey, lacrosse (coach is part of the England Lacrosse squad) and tennis (rounders in the junior school). Badminton and basketball fixtures are arranged throughout the year but these are minor sports (offered as clubs) as are athletics, fencing, golf, netball, rounders, sailing and cross-country. Equestrian club and clay pigeon shooting are offered from year 5. Shooting teams apparently 'hold their own' against larger and more experienced schools like Harrow, Eton, Millfield and Cokethorpe. An athlete development programme supports a number of pupils in training and competing for district, county and national level teams. Junior pupils have swimming lessons in Cirencester Leisure Centre from reception. From year 5 pupils use the outdoor swimming pool in the summer.

Forest school is one of the stars of the show at Rendcomb (the other is The Griffin Theatre). The site has been in the grounds for 10 years, run by four fully trained staff and used by everyone. Every week nursery pupils have two sessions and juniors have one afternoon up to year 4. After that it can be chosen as an extracurricular club. Nestled amongst the trees they have a fire pit, several dens, rope swings and an eco toilet. Senior pupils have their own dedicated space as part of the outdoor education curriculum.

Shooting teams apparently 'hold their own' against larger and more experienced schools like Harrow, Eton and Millfield

Art, music and DT are in one building, purpose-built in 1967. This is a good space with art studios, textiles and a design technology studio. The latter is equipped with a laser cutter and 3D printer plus CAD suite. A small exhibition area at the entrance confirms the standard is high. Upstairs is the music department, under refurbishment on our visit. Plenty of practice rooms and pupils told us they can come and practice whenever they like. Four concerts a year include both staff and pupils, plus regular informal lunchtime concerts. Around 50 per cent of pupils learn an instrument. Plenty of music clubs for all and particularly talented juniors are welcome to join senior groups.

In 2017, the £3.3m Griffin Theatre opened, the first development in almost 30 years (Godman boarding house in 1989 was the last). An impressive building, it will undoubtedly inspire pupils to take part in performing arts. Available for external events too, it has a 350-seat auditorium plus a dance studio and drama classroom. A drama lesson was underway on our visit with pupils rehearsing on the stage and in the foyer. First production in The Griffin was Agatha Christie's And Then There Were None, next will be Les Misérables. Recent senior productions include One Man, Two Guv'nors, Macbeth, Jerusalem and Footloose, whilst the latest junior production was Porridge. All juniors get a part, (even the head), and all year 6s get a speaking part. Next up is Pirates of the Curry Bean.

Rendcomb also offers classical ballet from 3 years and contemporary dance from 11 years. Royal Academy of Dance and Contemporary Dance Association exams and grading. Stretch and tone classes offered to grade 3 pupils and above. Performance group club encourages pupils to choreograph pieces and enter dance competitions such as the great big British Dance Off and Cheltenham Festival of Performing Arts.

Other extracurricular clubs include debating, dissection, martial arts, military fitness, theatre, Lego, nature and gardening. Juniors can opt from a range of activities including mixed year and ability sports or music clubs, knit and stitch, scrabble, or clay pigeon shooting (ammunition is extra, we were told). For sixth formers there is an in-house leadership programme, a buddy scheme and D of E to choose from.

Head is conscious of the cost of trips so funds for expeditions to places like Patagonia must be fundraised by pupils. Other trips are kept affordable, including a trip to Norway for hiking and trekking, a sports tour to Netherlands, language exchanges and outdoor challenges in the UK. Junior trips include a year 6 outdoor challenge residential, and a biennual French trip for years 5/6. Day trips include Bristol and Cheltenham Literature Festival.

Boarding: From year 7. Around 45 per cent of pupils board either on a full, weekly or flexi (up to three nights a week) basis. Only about 10 per cent of years 7 to 9 board, meaning numbers at weekends are low (four to 12 in each house). However, numbers increase in the older years with around 55 per cent of years 10 and 11 boarding and 70 per cent of sixth formers. At weekends there are around 30 to 40 pupils in these houses. Some 75 per cent of boarders are from overseas, from a range of 14 countries worldwide. Year 11 studnets from Germany come on short stays.

There are five houses, all on the campus. House system is horizontal rather than the traditional vertical. All have common rooms with pianos, table football, projectors, TVs, X-Boxs, private Skype rooms and kitchens. We were impressed with the homeliness of the houses; rooms are well looked after and the houseparents are friendly and caring. Gap students help out in the younger year boarding houses.

The Old Rectory is a grade II listed building with plenty of character and has been housing year 7-9 boys since 1966. The girls are in Godman. Dorms are a good size, for threes or fours. Phones and such are removed at lights out. Both houses have prep rooms, but year 9s are given a separate room away from younger ones. They have a main common room to share with day pupils plus their own boarders' common room. Year 9 girls also have their own

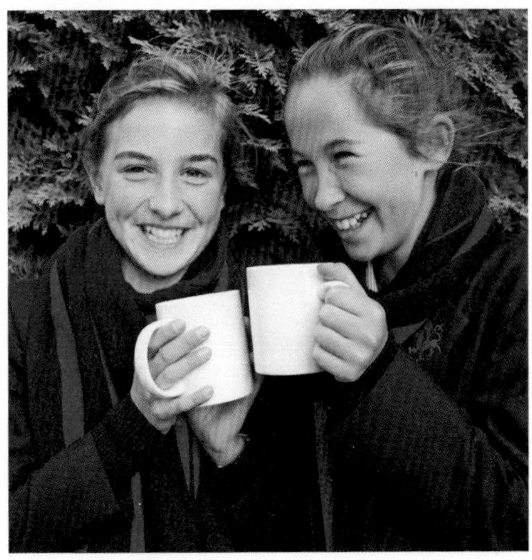

lounge that they recently redecorated in a particularly grown up design of greys and velvets. Kitchens are used for cooking as a family if numbers are low at the weekends. Both houses have gardens that boarders can spill out onto during good weather.

Years 10 and 11 boys are in Lawn House, and the girls are in Stable House. Here, boarders have individual bedrooms with a study space. In the boys' house there is a large media room for quiet study, and in the girls' there is a library, a hobbies room and a gym. Plus two house dogs.

Park House is the mixed sixth form house. Again, all rooms are individual with a study area. Common room and a well-equipped kitchen (two large cookers and a dishwasher) looks out onto the outside seating area. A smaller quiet room is available for more private chats. In addition there is Garden House, a cottage based in the village, within walking distance. All sixth formers have the opportunity to spend two separate weeks here and the idea is that they budget, shop, cook, wash and get to school on their own as an introduction to university life. Some fare better than others, we were told, but the excitement around this was ubiquitous.

A boarders' committee helps decide on evening and weekend activities. These include dance or yoga, baking, craft nights, playing laser tag on the grounds, using the climbing wall, going shopping, cinema trips, roller discos or canoeing down the River Wye.

There is plenty of socialising between boys and girls and across year groups. Social areas include The Barn for years 10-11, and the sixth form bar, open twice a week. This is tucked away in a basement with sofa snugs, a snooker room, pool room and a dance room. Think, no windows, flashing lights, graffiti walls – every teenager's dream; they absolutely love it. No place for parents, but rest assured this is a fully supervised, responsible zone.

Head is looking to reorganise the houses in the near future. He hopes to renovate the junior boys' boarding house and turn it into a sixth form centre. The other boarding houses would then be re-jigged and extended (planning permission underway) so that years 7-9 would become mixed. Years 10-11 would remain single sex houses and the sixth would remain co-ed.

Background and atmosphere: Founded in 1920 by Frederick Noel Hamilton Wills as a boys' school with just 12 pupils; girls were introduced into the sixth form in 1972 and the school became fully co-educational in 1992. The junior school was added in 2000 and the nursery five years later. There are now some 280 seniors and 90 juniors, with around 30 per cent from overseas.

Set within 230 acres of parkland in the Gloucestershire Cotswolds, the school is in, and very much part of, the small village of Rendcomb. Cheltenham and Cirencester are nearby. Within the beautiful grounds lies a deer park, home to over 70 fallow deer and classified as an 'ancient tree hot-spot' by the Woodland Trust. This is an 'outdoor' school that makes the most of its setting, with regular events like treasure hunts for the juniors and laser tag days for the boarders. 'Our children come home with pink cheeks and muddy trainers and yet still excel in the classroom,' parents told us.

This is a traditional school steeped in history and it takes great pride in the 'Rendcomb family'. Not just a marketing strapline, we were told by parent after parent; 'Rendcomb has an amazing community spirit'; 'an all-round, family inclusive, friendly feel.' 'The children all mix and play together regardless of age and everyone knows everyone,' they told us. Pupils often to be seen chatting sociably with teachers over lunch or walking between lessons. 'A place where character comes first and superficiality is correctly dismissed,' we were assured.

The main house is stunning inside and out. The staircase has stained glass windows that beautifuly illustrate the Aesop's fables. The school recently held a concert here (yes, this is no ordinary stairwell), taking full advantage of the acoustics and backdrop. Heating and maintaining a building like this with its huge windows and stone corridors must be challenging and the school reflects this; it is practical and far from flashy.

The grand dining hall is used solely for dining, no moving of chairs and tables on a daily basis. Diners are staggered according to age. Huge floor to ceiling windows and ornate ceilings give a sense of tradition and old-fashioned splendour. Next door a large reading room is used for overspill at lunchtimes or for events and meetings. Beyond that is a

'We love the way the school not only provides pupils with academics, but teaches them manners, confidence and to be all round great children'

library with a 150 year history; it doesn't get more authentic than that.

Daily assemblies after lunch are run by 'the very funny' head of juniors, and are popular with both pupils and parents. Year 6 requested that storytelling be part of assembly so the head is now working his way through Broccoli Boy with an audience from reception to year 6 listening attentively. Friday's assembly is longer to celebrate achievements. Parents are welcome and they told us, 'when they have been awarded a distinction they go up and tell the school and the parents why they were awarded it.. a clever way to get used to public speaking at a very young age!' Happy birthday is sung en masse to all who celebrated that week.

Junior school is attached to the main building. Juniors have the luxury of sharing all the senior facilities including dining in the same hall, using the sports facilities and the new theatre, plus being taught by some senior teachers. Classrooms are based around a quad with the nursery ('excellent,' according to parents) tucked snugly in the middle with its own courtyard. Rooms are large, overlooking the outdoor swimming pool or extensive gardens, and class sizes are small (16 max). Large art, design and technology classroom is upstairs next to a brand new science lab. With its white benches and stools, it is a modern and rather grown up lab. Juniors are also treated to science lessons in the senior school labs once a term. The playground and adventure playground are just by the sixth form boarding house. In fact the sixth formers are probably the most likely to see the juniors during their day, building on the brother and sister ethos that is a way of life here.

Both boarders and day pupils share the same boarding houses, ensuring there is no split and everybody gets to know each other. All pupils register at their houses to 8am daily. This includes Saturday school (currently under review), which is followed by sport. Most day pupils are still on-site at 4pm.

Pastoral care, well-being and discipline: 'We have had call to rely on the pastoral care of the tutors at Rendcomb during some challenging health issues and can honestly say that the children now view the school as a part of their extended family,' one mother told us. Another parent explained how the school had allowed her son to pursue his rugby passion and 'offered him all round support and care away from crazy commitment levels of an athlete and a chance to be a sixth former too!' The excellent pastoral care has resulted in a nurturing environment that 'brings out the best in each pupil regardless of their abilities or likes/dislikes. It instils confidence, encourages and builds an all round sense of respect for fellow pupils and staff.'

Pastoral care is further reinforced by the family ethos, including big sister and big brother events when younger pupils are shown around the houses. This sense of 'looking after each other' is not exclusive to these events, we were told. 'I am really impressed with how many students across all years know each other and support one another,' they explained.

Services once a week in the listed St Peter's Church on site are conducted by the school chaplain, Reverend Bob Edy, an old Rendcombian himself with many a story to tell.

Pupils and parents: Day pupils commute from Gloucester, Swindon and Stroud and some from as far as Oxford. Some parents went to the school themselves and one family we spoke to are saving up to send their new granddaughter there. 'The parent community is really friendly, refreshingly unpretentious and richly diverse,' one new parent confirmed. Another added, 'The teachers and students have very strong relationships and the parents are welcomed into the community as well. '

The staircase has stained glass windows that beautifuly illustrate Aesop's fables. The school recently held a concert here (yes, this is no ordinary stairwell)

Smart blue uniform with a touch of red for all except sixth formers, who wear business dress. 'We love the way the school not only provides the children with academics but teaches them manners, confidence and to be all round great children.' Based on the pupils we met, this is definitely true. Interests and passions are encouraged rather than stifled, resulting in a real mix of children here.

Rules are of course in place, but this isn't a strict school in the traditional sense. More of a place where pupils will be 'steered by conversation' as a parent would at home. Communication with parents has improved under the new head.

Entrance: Nursery from 3 years old. For junior school entry, shadow/taster days plus assessments in English, maths and verbal/non verbal reasoning plus reports from current school. Children are teamed up with a 'buddy' on these days.

For senior school entry, entrance exam and interview with the head. Automatic entrance for juniors, but all pupils must sit the exam for assessment purposes. The school looks to see if the child would thrive here and any needs are discussed with the family on an individual basis. Entrance day tests include exam in the morning followed by an outdoor education session. This is a fantastic way to observe children working in teams in a more relaxed, fun environment. Overnight stays available.

Transition is seamless as the senior school continues with the junior school's ethos, parents told us. One added, 'New pupils settle in quickly and are not judged by whether they are good at maths, music or throwing a ball. All are genuinely kind, polite and (very importantly) full of character.'

Sixth form entry is based on GCSE results, an interview with the head and school reports. As a small school, they can be flexible, the head told us. One pupil is studying engineering at Chippenham College as well as A levels at Rendcomb. If students have a passion or talent, the school will support them and work with other organisations so they can compete and train.

Exit: Around 80 per cent of juniors go on to senior school, others to Pate's Grammar, Marling School, Cotswold School and Stroud High.

Around 75 per cent stay on to sixth form with 90 per cent then going onto university. Destinations include Exeter, Bath, Imperial College, King's College, Swansea, Royal Holloway, Birmingham, Cardiff and Nottingham. Subjects include geography, medicine, politics, drama, law, accounting and finance, chemical engineering and physics. One to Oxbridge in 2017.

Notable Old Rendcombians include Issy Bailey, Paralympian (shooting); Jonathan Suffolk, technical director at the National Theatre; Richard Dunwoody, jockey; David Tyler, chairman of Sainsbury's.

Money matters: One parent told us, 'With its Noel Wills ethos of offering an inclusive education – even to a child who would not otherwise be able of afford it – we felt much less intimidated and genuinely welcomed and valued in the Rendcomb family, something we still feel today. We love catching up with staff and pupils at the many family events.' Many pupils are not from very rich families, so although scholarships and bursaries are limited, they are welcomed. In 2015, the school reduced sixth form day pupil fees. Numbers have since doubled.

Academic, art, music, drama and sport scholarships are awarded each year at 11+, 13+ and 16+. Noel Wills Scholarship and the Rendcomb Scholarship are offered at 11+. Pupils joining year 3 from September 2018, are eligible to apply for a 7+ scholarship.

Remarks: A small family-focused school where everyone knows everyone. One parent summed it by saying, 'When it comes to kids, nothing top trumps the development of character, and on this metric I haven't seen a school in the area that comes close to Rendcomb.' Set in amazing grounds, this outdoorsy school is traditional with some modern twists – an impressive performing arts centre and a forward-thinking ICT department. Not for competitively sporty types, but Rendcomb is a bit of find if you're looking for a school that nurtures individuals.

Royal High School, Bath

46

Lansdown Road, Bath, Somerset BA1 5SZ

01225 313877 | royalhigh@rhsb.gdst.net | www.royalhighbath.gdst.net

Ages: 11–18

Pupils: 481; sixth form: 141; Boarders: 120

Day: £13,053 – £13,626 pa; Boarding: £25,221 – £29,649 pa

Head: Since 2015, Mrs Jo Duncan MA PGCE (40s). Previously head of Princess Helena College in Hertfordshire. Grew up in Northern Ireland, where she attended a girls' grammar school. Studied English and theology at St Andrews, with the intention of working as a lawyer or teacher. After stints working in schools in Hungary and Romania during her university years she realised she felt 'very at home in the classroom' so opted to do a PGCE at Homerton College, Cambridge. First teaching post was at The Latymer School, a high performing state school in north London, where she taught RS for four years. Then moved to Benenden, where she spent seven years and 'fell in love with boarding

and its community feel'. Encouraged by the then Benenden head Claire Oulton to apply for the Princess Helena headship – and was appointed at the relatively young age of 33. Spent seven years at Princess Helena – 'a nice length of time' – but was attracted to the Royal High by its bigger size, boarding (it's the only Girls' Day School Trust school with boarders) and the fact that it offers the IB as well as A levels. 'The quality of the teaching really struck me,' she says, 'and being part of the GDST is exciting. It's the most fabulous network for heads, teachers and pupils and the opportunities are amazing.' Parents are impressed by her energy and drive. 'She has very good ideas,' one told us, 'and she has really improved the boarding facilities.'

Asked to describe Royal High girls, the head stresses that the school is 'not a hothouse', with pupils ranging from the highly academic to those with a 'much broader academic profile'. As you'd expect, she's a firm advocate of single-sex schools and says the Royal High 'focuses on how girls learn' and helps them achieve in all aspects of life, from lessons to leadership. Coincidentally, on the day of our visit, the papers featured apposite comments from Ofsted chief Amanda Spielman, saying that single-sex schools help to cut gender stereotyping and encourage girls to explore 'typically male subjects'.

Married to Murray, a London lawyer. They have two children – their son is a pupil at Kingswood, just over the road from the Royal High, and their daughter is a pupil at the Royal High's junior school – and live in a house on the school site. In her spare time she enjoys travel, skiing, theatre, ballet and reading.

Academic matters: Excellent teaching and very good results. One parent praised the Royal High's teaching as 'the very highest calibre' while another told us that girls achieve their potential without the element of pressure sometimes found in girls' schools. 'They are expected to do well but they don't seem to be stressed about doing well,' she said. In 2017, 72 per cent A*/A at GCSE and 50 per cent A*/A at A level. School has offered the IB since 2008 and girls achieved average score of 37 in 2017. Lots of help and guidance about the respective merits of the IB and A levels, including an IB/A levels-themed Any Questions event. Sixth formers are encouraged to take the EPQ too. Most girls do 10 or 11 subjects at GCSE, including two or three sciences and at least one language.

Boarding houses are comfortable, homely and chic, so much so that day girls jump at the chance to do the occasional sleepover. Older girls are allowed to walk into Bath

Strong focus on STEM (science, technology, engineering and maths) subjects, with impressive numbers choosing sciences at A level (when we visited, a quarter of the sixth form were taking chemistry). 'We do lots of experiments and practicals,' a year 10 girl told us. 'My favourite lesson was when we made toy helicopters and flew them off the balcony. Science is so much fun.' Maths is the most popular A level subject, with year 13 girls giving extra help to younger pupils during their lunch break. Languages are particularly strong – French, German, Italian, Spanish and Mandarin on offer, plus Latin from year 7. Head girl told us she did four languages at GCSE, as well as Mandarin AS. Pupils are keen on Vocab Express, an online vocab learning challenge, and at the time of our visit a group of year 10 and 11 girls had been placed eighth nationally. Lots of language and exchange trips. A sixth former waxed lyrical about a recent trip to China, where she'd taught English in a primary school.

School is broadly selective, but probably not the place for girls with extensive learning needs. Learning support ranges from in-class support to one-to-one help (girls are never withdrawn from core curriculum subjects). As the school says: 'The majority of girls we currently support are those with specific learning difficulties such as dyslexia. We also have some girls with ADHD, autism and a few girls with sensory impairments such as hearing difficulties.'

Games, options, the arts: Pupils are proud of the school's sporting successes, notably in hockey, netball, athletics, swimming, fencing and taekwondo. 'We hold our own,' says the head. At the time of our visit a year 13 had just been selected for Bath Rugby Ladies team after a year of playing the sport. Sports

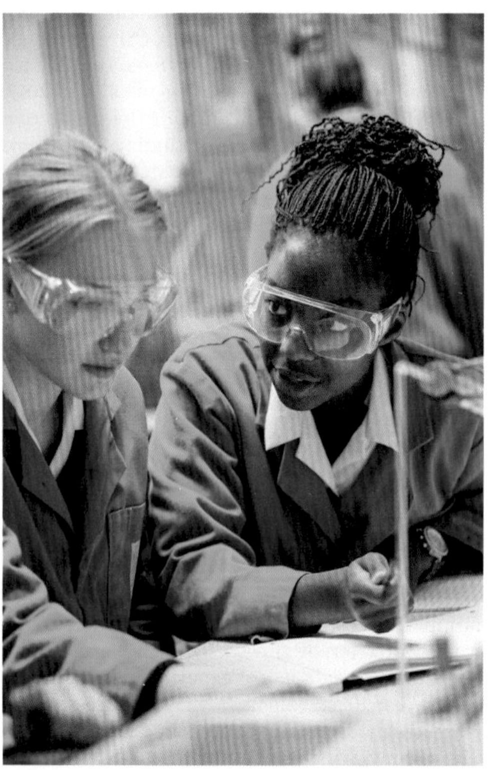

Strong focus on STEM (science, technology, engineering and maths) subjects, with impressive numbers choosing sciences at A level (when we visited, a quarter of the sixth form were taking chemistry)

facilities include sports hall, outdoor swimming pool, fitness suite, hockey pitches, netball courts and new Astro opened by Olympic gold-medal winning hockey player Kate Richardson-Walsh. The school also uses the University of Bath's sports pitches.

Performing arts are big at the Royal High. Dynamic director of music (a composer who previously worked for EMI and the BBC) encourages musicians of all standards and abilities to have a go. All-inclusive music programme features 35+ events a year, performed by five choirs, orchestra, swing band, strings group, woodwind ensemble, rock bands and more. Carol service at Bath Abbey is the highlight of the year for many parents. All year 7, 8 and 9 pupils get an hour's classroom music a week, learning about different styles of music, performance and composition, plus taster lessons to help them decide the instruments most suited to them. Around 300 instrumental lessons per week, with 14 girls a year taking GCSE music and up to eight doing A level. We met a talented sixth form singer who has already released two EPs of her own.

Wonderful art produced in the light, airy art school, with four studios and panoramic views to inspire girls' creativity. We particularly admired a sculpture made of wire, tights and teapots representing pattern and rhythm and a remarkably accomplished series of countryside paintings by a sixth former who brought in bags of twigs, sticks and leaves for inspiration. Up to 40 girls a year take art GCSE, 20 take A level and four or five take art as part of the IB. Well-equipped DT department has an ultra-sophisticated 3D printer and a four-axis router. Head of DT says he's 'constantly surprised' by the girls' ideas, showing us a student's stunning faux-leather backpack inspired by an armadillo. Drama and dance in the Sophie Cameron Performing Arts Centre and school's dance studio. Loads of successes in the Mid-Somerset Festival and LAMDA exams. Year 13 girls run a drama club for year 7s and there's a plethora of school and house productions throughout the year. Recent shows include The Tempest, The Wizard of Oz and The Crucible, with rehearsals for Oliver! taking place when we visited.

School has a strong international focus and links with schools as far afield as New York, Kenya and Sydney. Year 9 girls get the chance to do a five-week exchange with Australian girls – 'the most fantastic experience,' a parent told us. An enterprising sixth former set up a charity project, designing and producing cards and gifts to raise money for a school in Kenya. Year 8s take part in an enterprise day with nearby boys' state school Beechen Cliff and older girls do Model United Nations debates with Kingswood and King Edward's School, Bath. There's also the Aspire programme, an academic enrichment programme featuring after-school lectures, activities and debates.

Boarding: Boarding numbers are growing steadily. New head of boarding joined from Benenden in 2016 and is responsible for the development of boarding at the Royal High. Around two-thirds of boarders are from overseas – from China, Hong Kong, Spain, Germany, Brazil, Kenya (30 nationalities in all). Boarding from year 7 (also available to year 5 and 6 girls from the junior school). Two boarding houses – School House for younger girls and Gloucester House for sixth formers. Full and weekly boarding only. Flexi boarding is available subject to availability of beds. Lots of weekend activities, including pottery painting, baking, zumba, spa days, expeditions to places like Harry Potter World and theatre and cultural trips. Girls are allowed to walk the mile down the hill into Bath – year 7s are escorted while year 8s go in groups of four.

Boarding houses are comfortable, homely and chic, so much so that day girls jump at the chance to do the occasional sleepover. Youngest girls are in wholesome dorms of four or five while sixth formers get doubles or singles. Sixth form boarding house is 'a stepping stone to university', with girls able to cook and do their own washing if they wish. Sixth form café attached, where day girls and boarders can relax and chill.

Background and atmosphere: Bath is a Unesco World Heritage Site and the first glimpse of the school is an impressive Victorian stone monolith at the top of a steep drive off the city's picturesque Lansdown Road. Extensive refurbishment programme in progress when we visited on a blustery October day but the school's listed Grade II buildings are stunning, especially when viewed under a glowing orange sun. Many of the classrooms, dorms and the head's office boast panoramic views across the school's 11-acre site to the city and beyond. The Royal High has blazed a trail as the only GDST school to offer boarding – a legacy from the amalgamation between Bath High School and the Royal School back in 1998. It admitted boys for a brief period but has been all-girls since 2010.

Sixth formers wear business suits rather than uniform. Younger girls are very happy with their new navy blazers and tartan skirts. Unlike some schools, no over-the-top make-up – 'we don't do contouring here,' grinned a year 9 pupil at lunch, to the merriment of her friends. Food, provided by catering company Holroyd Howe, is very good. Lots of choice, including vegetarian and gluten-free options, all carefully labelled, pasta, salads, sandwiches and hot meals.

Pastoral care, well-being and discipline: Girls are well looked after and look after each other well. No behaviour problems – just the occasional social media or friendship issue typical of girls of this age. Parents like the school's size ('not too big, and not too small so everyone knows everyone') and say that if an issue arises the school 'is on it very quickly'. 'We talk to the girls all the time about who they are and what they want to achieve,' says the head. 'As a girls' school we want to be a positive place where girls can flourish and grow.' All pupils have a one-hour PSHEE (personal, social, health and economic education) session per fortnight and school also runs Your Daughter, a programme of talks for parents on topics like developing resilience and happiness, surviving social media and the dangers of illegal drugs and legal highs. When suitable, girls attend these talks with their parents or hear their own version in school.

Parents come from all backgrounds, including business people, medics, media types and ex-Londoners. Sixty per cent of day pupils live in Bath, others commute from Somerset and Gloucestershire by bus and train

One of the most popular members of the school community is Spitfire, an 18-month-old black lurcher, who belongs to the student welfare co-ordinator (she also teaches biology and is known as 'Spitfire's mum'). A well-being dog, Spitfire is a comforting presence when girls feel stressed, worried or tired. When the registrar announced to a group of year 9s that Spitfire had just become a father to seven puppies, a unanimous 'aaaaah' went round the room. He even got a round of applause on a recent open day.

School is keen on encouraging leadership and responsibility. It hosts the annual GDST Young Leaders' Conference, where year 13 student leaders from all 25 GDST sixth forms get the chance to network, take part in teamwork challenges and hear a host of inspiring speakers. The sixth formers then feed back to the rest of the school in assemblies. Head girl, boarding deputy, day deputy and four additional prefects – all voted in by staff and pupils (year 10s and up). Year 13s mentor younger girls and everyone takes pride in belonging to one of four houses named after impressive women – Austen, Bronte, Wollstonecraft and Du Pré.

Pupils and parents: The pupils are sparky girls who throw themselves into lessons, music, sport and extracurricular activities with enthusiasm and panache. We particularly enjoyed lunch with a group of chatty year 9s, who, with the amused registrar in attendance, talked about everything from the 'great' integration of boarders and day pupils to the 'reasonable' amount of homework they get. They were funny, charming and keen to extol the virtues of their school. 'We feel like we can be ourselves here,' said one girl. Another said that that everyone was 'so accepting' and she didn't feel any peer pressure.

One of the most popular members of the school community is well-being dog, Spitfire, a black lurcher, he's a comforting presence when girls feel stressed, worried or tired

All agreed that the Royal High is not a snobby school. Parents come from all backgrounds, including business people, medics, media types and ex-Londoners. Sixty per cent of day pupils live in Bath, others are from Somerset and Gloucestershire – some walk to school, some commute by bus and train. Famous alumnae include baking supremo Mary Berry, Baroness Elspeth Howe and entrepreneur Emily Brooke, who designed a pioneering laser bike light.

Entrance: Competition for year 7 places is less intense than you might think. Around 100 girls a year apply and the school offers 80 places. The entrance assessment takes place in January – an interview first, then English, maths, verbal reasoning and non-reasoning tests a few days later. Around 95 per cent from the junior school progress to the senior school via a transfer test.

Up to 15 girls join in year 9 and 35 or so in year 12. Sixth formers need six Bs at GCSE, including As in subjects they want to study at A level or the IB.

Exit: Up to a quarter leave after GCSEs, either for a change of scene or to do other subjects. A few (two last year) change their minds and return to the Royal High in double-quick time. At 18, around 98 per cent go to university, virtually all to their first choice destinations. A healthy smattering of medics and engineers, plus a few to art foundation courses and drama school. Seven to Oxbridge in 2017 (six to Oxford and one to Cambridge). An eclectic mix of subjects studied at university, from aeronautics and astronautics at Southampton to psychology and linguistics at Oxford.

Leavers join the GDST's Alumnae Network, which offers mentoring for GDST alumnae and sixth formers, university advice, career development and networking opportunities. The Royal High encourages former pupils to inspire and mentor their younger counterparts – old girls return to talk about their careers and many offer work experience.

Money matters: Good value for money, especially as textbooks, stationery, most extracurricular activities and sixth-form laptops are included. Boarding fees are cheaper than many other boarding schools due to GDST economies of scale. A raft of scholarships and bursaries available, including academic, art, dance, drama, music and sport. STEM scholarships offered in year 9 and year 12. Means-tested bursaries (up to 100 per cent of the fees) for students demonstrating 'outstanding all-round academic ability'.

Remarks: A happy, high achieving, very go-ahead school with a distinctive ethos, sense of community and impressive results. For parents looking for a single sex-school (day and/or boarding) we can't think of any girl who wouldn't thrive here.

St John's-on-the-Hill School

Castleford Hill, Tutshill, Chepstow, Monmouthshire NP16 7LE

01291 622045 | Office@stjohnsonthehill.co.uk | www.stjohnsonthehill.co.uk

Ages: 4–13	Pupils: 186; Boarders: 10 full, 20 flexi
	Day: £7,980 – £13,140 pa; Boarding: £18,663 pa

Head: Since 2016, Ruth Frett, previously housemistress at Cranleigh School. After reading English at St Andrews, she studied music at Trinity College performed all over Europe as a professional singer. Enjoying giving school masterclasses led her into teaching in London primary schools after having four children, eventually becoming head of RS and middle school and chaplain at Cranleigh Prep. Married to American Dan, who is curate in the local parish church as well as working for a software company. Her four children are now past school age but her fifth, a foster child, is at St John's.

Dean Close, the owners of St John's, are wisely leaving her a free hand to put St John's back on the map. Filled with enthusiasm and energy, she has transformed the look of the school with new paint and much-needed refurbishment of boarding and other areas, though there is still a long way to go. Plans are afoot for a range of new facilities, including an art room, and already there is lots of new equipment. The curriculum now includes reading time as well as a renewed emphasis on IT, with keyboard skills for everyone. Though staff turnover has not been huge, Mrs Frett has appointed has a new director of studies – 'impressive,' say parents – who is overhauling curriculum content and delivery, plus new heads of music and boarding. She has also taken on a fully qualified nurse, who not only looks after boarders' health and everyone's minor accidents and ailments but also coordinates monitoring of day pupils.

Endlessly enthusiastic, Mrs Frett clearly loves her school and her pupils visibly blossom in response. She evidently relishes the challenges of St John's, and numbers, which had dipped, have already started to rise.

Entrance: Entry is by gentle taster day assessment. Children come from Newport, the Wye Valley, Cardiff, Monmouth and Forest of Dean, both sides of the border. Lots of minibuses make this work. St John's runs two nurseries off-site in Newport and Chepstow as well as the on-site Hedgehogs, which provide about half the reception intake.

Exit: St John's has maintained its long-established reputation for scholarships and common entrance to secondary schools, and in 2017 over half of the leavers gained awards, with some impressive academic scholarships as well as sports, music and drama awards. Clifton, Dean Close, Monmouth School, Monmouth Girls and King's Gloucester are popular, with a dribble to a huge range of others including Wycliffe College, Talbot Heath in Bournemouth and Millfield.

Mrs Frett says that she does not believe in cramming for secondary school entrance because the senior schools know and value the results of a St John's education. A few leave at 11 but Mrs Frett, who is exceptionally good at maintaining links with senior schools, says that most schools value the extra confidence the last two years at St John's give their 13+ intake.

Remarks: Perched on an idyllic site above the River Wye, St John's is jumbled into a pretty little Georgian manor with a scatter of other houses and purpose built school facilities. Work is still clearly in progress and the overall impression fluctuates from the gracious Embassy Room and black and white flagged passage through a few darkish corners brightened with child-created murals to some really up to date buildings like the pre-prep. School has been in situ since 1923, under a number of guises, and as a co-ed educational trust since the 60s. The Dean Close Foundation took over when the school got into financial difficulties in 2015. Under Mrs Frett, it is recovering from a stormy interlude of acute money shortages and anxious parents, leaving a few year groups with uneven numbers of boys and girls. Bustling and friendly with confident children, there's masses going on. A full court hearing with real judge and magistrate advising the pupil barristers and officials was in progress on the day of our visit.

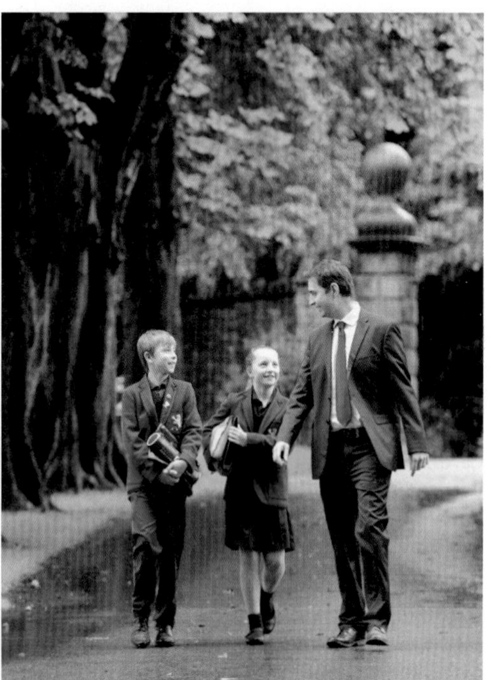

Much loved by parents, pupils and staff for its exceptionally friendly and supportive atmosphere, and for the sporting and academic traditions it strives to maintain

Lovely pre-prep department with private gardens for each class, delightfully muddy and enjoyable forest school and exceptionally attractive and well-planned modern buildings. Classes were quietly enjoying reading time in our visit but there was evidence of academic progress all around, with joined up writing from the very beginning. Oodles of work on display and really up-to-date IT.

Prep years are in less luxurious but cheerful classrooms with small classes (16 maximum) with good science areas and recently updated IT. One parent said staff had been a little slow to 'get behind' a reluctant learner but everything is now tightening up. The curriculum, currently offering French, Spanish and Latin, is being overhauled for 'modern needs' which may include another language in future replacing Latin. After pre-prep there is a gradual transition to specialist teaching in all subjects and gifted children get the chance, for instance, to tackle GCSE maths. Learning support is for high flyers as well as strugglers. The non-selective intake means some need quite a lot of help, mainly in class but occasionally one-to-one. All pupils are tested with a battery of CATs etc. Regular reports are now electronic. Plenty of inspiring trips and in-school one-offs to enhance learning like the visit to St Fagan's Iron Age farm, or entering the competitive maths challenge, with some pretty impressive results. A particularly enjoyable English department inspired bout of typoglycemia (being able to read a word with the letters wrongly ordered) spawned some cunningly misspelt notices around school – which believe it or not is a great way to reinforce spelling and reading because pupils have to think.

Plenty of sport, in keeping with school's distinguished past record, and they had already notched up several rugby wins in September when we visited. Enthusiastic girls were practising hockey and clearly delighted with Mrs Frett's knowledgeable support. One mother was thrilled that children were getting extra coaching and games skills from Dean Close specialists. Good sports hall and lovely covered pool with doors opening in summer to outside viewing areas which also give a view of Astroturf. Acres of grassy grounds with a lovely treehouse project under way for year 8s to learn practical skills on. The music department has some ambitious musical projects: audition processes and organisation being licked into shape by new head of music. All children are encouraged to take up instruments (at the time of our visit, 97 pupils were learning an instrument). Encouraged by Mrs Frett, choirs are beginning to take off. Year 7s have and love a three week trip to South Africa including time on safari and a day in a township school, and there is an annual sports trip. Those we spoke to really appreciated the opportunities they get here and the kindness of the staff.

Now the battle for listed building planning permission has been won, a new art block and dining area are promised to replace the current art hut (full of exciting work) and cheerful but cramped and noisy cafeteria. Boarding accommodation, in a rambling town house on site, has been freshened up and is spruce and welcoming. Currently it is very flexi, though some children with distant, military or expat parents stay for weekends with matron or go to guardians. Separate boys' and girls dorms' but everyone mixes in together, and like everywhere at St John's a family feel is the key. Regular influxes of groups from China and Spain each year bring an international flavour as well as taking up current spare places, though boarding has already expanded a little. Wraparound care possible for day pupils with supervised after-school homework and masses of activities and sport, sustained by biscuits and fruit. No charge for any activity run by the school though some – such as dance – requiring outside tuition have to cover their costs. Parents can drop off children early for breakfast though few do. Mrs Frett says her staff are exceptionally dedicated and all take on after-school or weekend duties and activities.

Parents say that the smallness of the school means that it has a truly family atmosphere and that staff know children exceptionally well, though the downside of this is that one or two year groups are have very small groups of either boys or girls. Friendliness and a happy atmosphere seem to extend to all parents and visitors as well. Poor behaviour is sensibly dealt with and bullying picked up quickly and effectively, though it seems to be rare. Food is pretty good and children like it. The house system is largely social, since the main pastoral care for all pupils is via the form. Lots of responsibility for year 8 pupils with head boy and girl as well as house and sports captains, who speak confidently of their duties and ambitions.

Supportive parents' association provides activities like fireworks parties for school and raises funds. Parents from all backgrounds, mostly within the large catchment both sides of the border, and they hope for more from Bristol when the toll on the Severn Bridge is removed. A few military families. Past pupils include Richard Mead, Olympic show jumper, and Welsh rugby player Marc Batten.

Much loved by parents, pupils and staff for its exceptionally friendly and supportive atmosphere, and for the sporting and academic traditions it strives to maintain. The school is part of the Dean Close Foundation and plans to increase numbers to about 250, which should mean it is financially viable in the future. Certainly a school well into recovery and worth watching for the future.

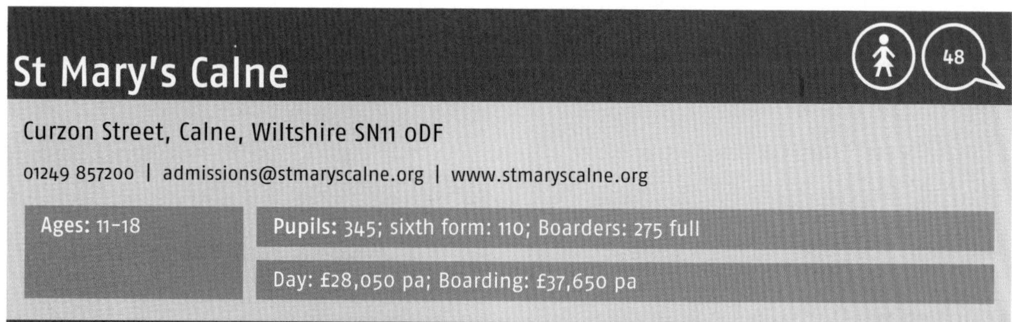

St Mary's Calne

48

Curzon Street, Calne, Wiltshire SN11 0DF

01249 857200 | admissions@stmaryscalne.org | www.stmaryscalne.org

Ages: 11-18

Pupils: 345; sixth form: 110; Boarders: 275 full

Day: £28,050 pa; Boarding: £37,650 pa

Headmistress: Since 2013, Dr Felicia Kirk MA PhD (early 40s). Born and raised in Maryland, USA, Dr Kirk's distinguished academic career in languages, both ancient and modern, took her to the École Normale Supérieure in Paris, where she met the Brit she would later follow to England and marry, leaving the groves of academe for the real world of teaching children. Her first job was at the Royal Hospital School in Suffolk, followed by a move into girls' education as director of higher education at Wycombe Abbey, then latterly as head of sixth form at Ipswich High School. Of her move to Calne, she says, 'I missed the boarding, and I liked the fact that the school is small, yet ambitious'.

Totally committed to girls' education, she intends to build on breadth of opportunity at Calne 'unencumbered by gender stereotyping'; building both literally and figuratively, that is, with an ambitious 10 year development plan to squeeze every last square inch (OK, centimetre, then) out of this school's compact site, with increased provision for arts, sports, a new library and more science labs. Any faint question marks about an American leading this very British institution are utterly dispelled on meeting her – she's hardly even mid-Atlantic in accent, and elegantly clad in a tweed jacket with velvet collar the day we visited. Parents appreciate the richness brought by experience from elsewhere, as well as her plans for the place: 'The school needs more than academia to keep it at the top table,' said one mother. Try as we might, it was impossible to break through her professional, though charming, veneer. Her girls describe her as enthusiastic and easy to talk to, are pleased to see her walking her dog in trackies and to receive a birthday card in their first year. 'Plus she's innovative,' said one. What does that mean again? 'It's new stuff like introducing company jumpers,' said a helpful friend.

Dr Kirk is married to an accountant. Her home is in Suffolk, where she also keeps her retired eventer.

Academic matters: Undoubtedly what the school is about, but not all it's about. At A level, 70 per cent A*/A grades in 2017. Stand-out subjects are maths, history, Spanish and Latin, sports science and computer science are new additions.

At GCSE, results have crept up over recent years to the point where 86 per cent were A*/A in 2017. Geography, Latin, art and music excel here. Results are more exciting than the classrooms which produce them, and teaching does not appear to be as reliant on IT as is the case in many schools we see; that said, refurbishing the labs cannot come a moment too soon. Library provision too is good but scattered, and will be consolidated under the development plan.

School skiers take part in the quaintly named but deadly serious British Schoolgirls Races in Flaine each year, to some acclaim

Enrichment week – inter alia, gung ho girls in camouflage crawling enthusiastically under netting taking orders from an army officer – was in full swing when we visited, but we were pleased to note an A level history class of about six discussing Mary Tudor's relationship with the clergy, rather than the apparently ceaseless rehashing of the two world wars. Ditto Northanger Abbey read in its entirety in year 9 – none of these bite-sized chunks beloved of modern exam setters. Recent success enjoyed in prestigious maths and German Olympiad competitions too.

SEN provision is as expected at a school of this calibre – definitely the mild end of dys- spectra – though everyone is tested on entry. About eight per cent of girls have an identifiable educational need catered for; provision equally is made for EAL and the very brightest sparks too.

Games, options, the arts: An astonishing amount of sporting facilities is crammed into this compact site, with more planned. A full-sized Astro and new netball/tennis courts (all floodlit) opened in the few days

before our visit form part of an ambitious upgrade of the sports offer, which has already seen the leasing of pitches plus track and field facilities a short distance away, making the hosting of fixtures with other schools easier. New sports complex, including dance studio, under construction with opening planned for summer 2018. Lacrosse is the winter sport on offer, alongside netball, which is played against schools not offering lax; hockey is played in the spring term. The youngest girls all represent the school early on; later, team practice becomes optional and from year 10, girls can drop ball sports altogether, as long as they do something to get them off the couch and away from the toaster. Tennis, swimming, fencing happen all year round, rowing and sailing in summer. Though no horses reside at school, show-jumping and eventing are a successful part of the sporting calendar. Skiing is prominent too: as well as the usual ski-trip, school also takes part in the quaintly named but deadly serious British Schoolgirls Races in Flaine each year, to some acclaim.

The arts take centre stage. Huge portraits adorn the entrance (colloquially known as the goldfish bowl), and paintings most of the walls. Sculpture is big here too – long before art becomes a GCSE option, junior girls experiment with life-sized figures. A full size war horse and cavalry officer in the early stages of construction out of wood and chicken wire has to be built in a gazebo outside the art school: 'I can't wait for the new studios,' remarked one member of staff with feeling. Drama a high point too: an inspirational head of drama who retired a few years ago left a legacy of adventurous excellence, which is not limited to an annual musical, Shakespeare (recently an all-female Hamlet), performances at the egg theatre in Bath and at the Edinburgh Fringe. Tess of the d'Urbervilles was on the week we visited – we were charmed by the hay and ancient agricultural machinery strewn throughout the foyer of a somewhat tired theatre. Quite the glossiest programmes we had ever seen.

Much of the singing harks back to its roots in the English choral tradition, to be expected in a school where chapel is still central to its life, but its reach extends to the charitable, profitable and glittery: a concert at Chelsea Old Church with a sideshow of celebrities raised £19,000. A symphony orchestra, jazz band, opera, string and flute groups complete the offering, which both brings top performers into school, takes musicians out of school (not only in the UK but abroad to Paris and so on) and music to local venues and primary schools as part of its community outreach. Generously resourced and imaginative in scope, the music department recently commissioned an opera to commemorate the start of WW1.

Boarding: The majority board, housed in year groups and moved into accommodation of increasing luxury each year as they progress up the school; day girls belong to houses along with their boarding counterparts and integration seems seamless. The new lower sixth house with its en-suite bathrooms and groovy décor (not sure about the bilious green chairs, however) will surpass anything likely to be encountered in most freshers' lodging, or even at home. House unity, as generally understood, is generated through 'companies', five groups of girls of all ages named after former bishops of Salisbury; a coloured band on the regulation navy jumper denotes it, and the company shout (known elsewhere as house music) loudly affirms it.

Tennis, swimming and fencing all year round, rowing and sailing in summer. Though no horses reside at school, show-jumping and eventing are successfully pursued

Background and atmosphere: Founded in 1873 by the then vicar of Calne, as a place where girls would receive an excellent academic grounding and would be able to develop their individuality within an Anglican foundation, the school still delivers on all three fronts. Its compact site right in the small somewhat undistinguished (yes, the last entry said that, but we agree) Wiltshire town means a lack of rolling acres and constant improvement, redevelopment, refurbishment rather than expansion of existing facilities, resulting in a startling mix of architectural styles redolent of the time they were built. No pretty gardens or places to escape to for a quiet cig, that we could detect – maybe that is why

vice seems so notably absent. Parents like the fact that the school is not London-y, though there is a posse from London and buses run at the start and end of every term and half-term.

It all feels quite cosy and its size is frequently mentioned as a positive by both girls and parents. Uniform is ubiquitous kilted skirt and light blue blouse. Sixth formers' dress code is quite relaxed, and perhaps because there are no boys, make-up is minimal. Unquestionably a female preserve or possibly a refuge, but not a nunnery: 'It's easier and less distracting not having boys around,' said one little scrap, though the junior dorms were full of pictures of boys (and ponies), known or dreamed about. Older girls regret the lack of socials with boys' schools, though the mixed lacrosse match is possibly a less stilted encounter.

House unity is generated through 'companies', five groups of girls of all ages, named after former bishops of Salisbury. Allegiance denoted by coloured band on jumper

It all feels rather traditional, despite the 14 per cent from overseas, partly on account of daily chapel, not always religious, but serious and, when the occasion demands it, reverent.

Pastoral care, well-being and discipline: Highly rated by both girls and parents. Each girl is allocated a tutor (who can be changed in the unusual event of it not working out) and has a weekly individual meeting. Between the housemistress and tutor, 'it's like having a mum and dad at school,' said one. Plenty of avenues to seek help if ever things go wrong, and generous provision for anyone needing medical attention, with a fully equipped, permanently manned medical centre. Not only is good work (both absolute and relative) rewarded by 'blues', but so are other virtues such as kindness, punctuality and tidiness. A 'good egg' prize is awarded each year for the sort of qualities which make a community run joyously. Miscreants who talk after lights might be made to do the house washing up the following day; major sins attract an escalating scale of punishment. Smokers' fines are donated to cancer charities.

Pupils and parents: Well-mannered and forthright with plenty of get-up-and-go. 'If you want something started, ask a Calne girl,' said the head. The ones we met were certainly privileged but not in the slightest bit tiresome. One mother said she chose the school because she wanted confidence not arrogance instilled in her daughters; something the girls in Grosstete company might be particularly mindful of. The school appears to run on old money, rather than new – 'The car park is full of Audis, Volvos and battered old Fords,' one parent observed – with a tangible affection from its former pupils, some of whom send their daughters. Considerable camaraderie on the lacrosse touchline too.

Entrance: Registration is advised three or four years ahead of proposed entry at year 7 (LIV in school parlance). Places conditional on entrance exams (either CE or school's own 11+ exam) are offered after an assessment day held in the September one year before entry. Process for 13+ (year 9, UIV) starts a year earlier; assessment day held almost two years before entry. Bright sparks are invited to apply for scholarships. Girls come from the smarter prep schools in the south and south west, some from London, some from school's own prep, St Margaret's, and a few from local primaries.

Around 15 new into sixth form with good GCSEs, sparkling in subjects to be taken to A level.

Exit: A handful – some 10 per cent – leave after GCSE in search of (in no particular order) boys, brighter lights, wider subject choices, more freedom; the rest to top notch universities up and down the land or art foundation. A handful to Oxbridge every year (four in 2017, plus one medic), the majority of the rest to Russell Group. School takes great care over the next stage: hosting a higher education conference for GSA, Oxbridge aptitude testing in school and Futures, a new half termly publication covering exclusively university applications, developments and more adventurous overseas options, plus alumnae experience. Increasing number of gap years. Famous OGs include Laura Bechtolsheimer, Olympic dressage medallist, and writer Lucy Hughes-Hallett (plus David Cameron's sister).

Money matters: Not a rich school, but one husbanding and developing its resources to ensure its place amongst the UK's top girls' schools. Usual range of scholarships offered, including a choral scholarship at 13+. A nominal five per cent fee reduction is given, but up to 40 per cent depending on means-testing. Two sixth form scholarships to internal candidates and one to external on offer too. A foundation scholarship of up to 100 per cent of day fees at both year 7 and sixth form is aimed exclusively at state school pupils for whom 'reasons of financial restriction' would otherwise preclude going there.

Remarks: A school for clever girls? Certainly, though 'it doesn't matter if they're not – they're usually good at something else.' Quintessential English girls' boarding? Absolutely. Social cachet? Unquestionably.

St Mary's School (Shaftesbury)

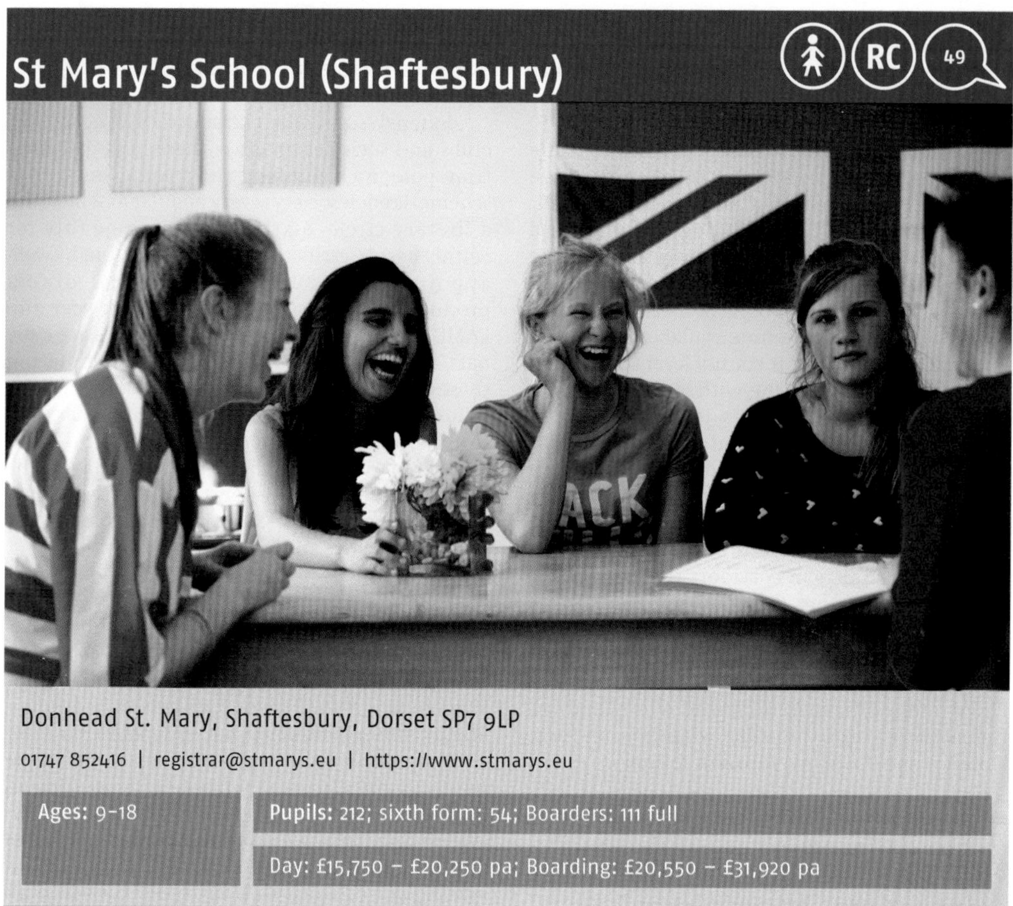

Donhead St. Mary, Shaftesbury, Dorset SP7 9LP

01747 852416 | registrar@stmarys.eu | https://www.stmarys.eu

Ages: 9–18

Pupils: 212; sixth form: 54; Boarders: 111 full

Day: £15,750 – £20,250 pa; Boarding: £20,550 – £31,920 pa

Acting headmistress: Sarah Matthews is holding the fort following the resignation in October 2017 of Mary Arnal 'for family and personal reasons'. Mrs Matthews 'has significant experience in leading schools through significant change, having worked as part of the senior leadership team at Harrow Hong Kong to stabilise the school and significantly increase numbers.' Originally a philosophy and RS teacher, she worked for 12 years at Stamford High School for Girls prior to her role at Harrow.

Academic matters: Popular A level subjects include English literature, history and history of art, geography, fine art and photography. Steady uptake of science, economics, business studies, maths and modern languages. For a small school with pupils of mixed ability, results are consistently good. In 2017, 61 per cent of A levels graded A*-B and 41 per cent A*/A. Drama AS level continues to broaden the range of subjects available.

GCSE results also good with 56 per cent A*/A and 7-9 in 2017. Girls do well in English literature, modern languages, science, the humanities and art. Languages department has introduced iGCSE exams throughout and runs a language 'circus' where girls can try Spanish or German for a term; six-week taster sessions in Italian and Portuguese also on offer. French exchanges for those interested.

Parents praise 'very experienced teaching staff' for their dedication, openness and lack of pretension. Some have been there for years, but head says the average age is beginning to come down. General consensus is that self-motivated girls are very well supported. 'If you do want to be bothered [with work], the teachers will bend over backwards.' One commented that the school 'hides its academic light under a bushel', although all agreed that 'the teaching shines'.

Three dedicated SEN rooms at the top of humanities block helps those with mild learning difficulties (dyslexia, dyspraxia) as well as running revision sessions and helping girls to improve their grades in maths and English. At the time of our visit, 46 pupils (up to three at a time) were receiving EAL coaching.

Games, options, the arts: 'Sport for all' is school's aim and girls play all the usual sports up to GCSE plus a few less common, eg water polo, yoga, pilates and zumba. School will lay on an activity if there is sufficient interest, eg scuba diving. In years 10 and 11 girls have access to the school's fitness suite and can begin the sports leaders programme which continues in sixth form for those taking A level PE. Circuit training and conditioning machines used for school's elite athlete training programme. Large sports hall and 25m pool sit side by side, surrounded by Astroturf pitch, netball and tennis courts. Swimming and tennis available year round. A few girls play hockey at county level and train at the county netball academy, with some year 10 girls put forward for LTA tennis league each year. Regular match fixtures and swimming galas throughout the year; teams hold their own and win against much larger schools.

Stunning, spacious art block opened in 2014; the creative arts are a real strength here and evidence of this hangs in corridors throughout the main school building. 'Art is outstanding and all visual arts are very good.' Busy textiles room with lots of sewing machines humming; textiles and design taught in six-month blocks, fine art all year. Photography offered at GCSE and A level and textiles at GCSE. Trips abroad to exhibitions in Paris, Florence and Barcelona for sixth formers.

Strongly underpinned by school's Catholic faith, pastoral care is 'brilliant'. 'Somehow the school makes the girls very caring and respectful'

Excellent music block, with 25 individual practice rooms, small concert space, music technology room and dedicated classroom, plus a well-stocked music library with archive material and CD recordings. Some 60 per cent learn a musical instrument, 15 per cent study two and some learn two instruments and singing. Each term, around 40 girls take ABRSM and Trinity Guildhall practical exams. Instrumental lessons rotate through the school day up to year 9, after which they are fixed; practice is timetabled. Ensembles include school orchestra, percussion and wind bands plus a rock band; others are formed depending on instruments and girls are encouraged to take the initiative. Everyone sings each week, either in class or as a form. Young maths teacher runs a GLEE club. 'The school needs a bit more singing outside the chapel choir.' Two school choirs, one of which is the 'awesome' chapel choir which rehearses three mornings a week for chapel assemblies, Sunday mass and tours abroad. St Cecilia's pupils' concert takes place each year. Regular outreach to primary schools and local choirs, including annual Choral Day.

Extensive range of extracurricular activities, clubs and societies on offer; these include equestrian polo, rock climbing and a young enterprise scheme. French society is very popular and includes a literary circle. Sixth formers can qualify for Leith's Basic Certificate in Food and Wine in well-appointed cookery school. Several drama productions across the age range each year and LAMDA exams are popular. D of E awards are a big part of school life, with two-thirds completing these every year. In keeping with school's Catholic ethos, girls fundraise and lead charitable expeditions to countries such as Rwanda, Chile and Zambia to work with schools and orphanages. The Mary Ward Lecture Series encourages girls to think through listening to speakers on topics such as war theory, bioethics and religious pluralism.

Boarding: Boarding arrangements work well; years 7 and 8 board separately in individual 'cubies'; day girls are welcome to visit the boarding house. After this, girls move into one of four houses where they sleep in single, double or four-person bedrooms. Some bedrooms are small, but each house has a spacious common room and a kitchen. Rooms rotate regularly and day-to-day housekeeping is efficient. 'A brilliant woman runs the laundry and the shift system for washing clothes works.' Parents full of praise for sixth form housemistress. 'She's seen everything and can deal with anything.' Girls in sixth form are given independence, eg preparing their own breakfast and entertaining outside friends to dinner parties.

Two-thirds are full boarders, so school doesn't empty out on weekends, though flexi-boarding is available. Day girls can go home after lessons, but many choose to stay on for clubs, homework and supper. Supervised prep sessions on Saturday mornings and plenty to do on weekends. Long, wrap-around green kilts up to year 11 are very popular with the girls; sixth form uniform phased out in favour of smart home clothes.

Boarders are escorted to and from various airport terminals by school minibus on exeat weekends, at half-term and at the beginning and end of term; those going to London on exeats can travel by escorted coach to Richmond. Parents confirm that school is very aware of where girls are.

Background and atmosphere: St Mary's was founded in 1945 and can trace its origins back to Mary Ward, an English Catholic nun who championed the rights of girls to receive an education, despite living in hostile Tudor times. Imprisoned

Two thirds are full boarders. Day girls can go home after lessons, but many choose to stay on for clubs, homework and supper

for her beliefs, she succeeded in establishing a school for girls in York before her death in 1645.

With the school set in 55 acres of parkland and approached down a winding, tree-lined drive, there is a sense of leaving the outside world behind as one arrives at an imposing early Victorian mansion. Sensitive efforts have been made to modernise the interior, with glass screens to let in light. Spread around the main house is a collection of buildings ranging from ultra-modern to slightly frayed labs and other older classrooms. New and old nestle side by side and somehow manage not to look incongruous, but the impression is of much brown and green.

In contrast to the school's cooler colours is its warm, family atmosphere. Teachers, parents and girls alike champion it as safe and nurturing. 'It's a very caring school which fosters life-long friendships.' Walking round, we were struck by the genuinely supportive relationships between girls of all ages. 'If you could bottle the atmosphere at St Mary's, it would be invaluable.'

School has reinstated years 5 and 6.

Pastoral care, well-being and discipline: Strongly underpinned by school's Catholic faith, pastoral care is 'brilliant' and 'house assistants are excellent'. 'Somehow the school makes the girls very caring and respectful.' Full-time chaplain lives on campus, with school's own priest in residence from Thursday to Sunday. Anglican minister visits once a week to lead the Eucharist. 'The school operates more on praise than sanction,' said one parent. Any misdemeanour earns the culprit a lavender ticket, 'lavvies' to the girls. Punishments range from parental meeting to suspension. 'The girls want their community to work – we have to deal with so few sanctions.' Strict on smoking and alcohol, the odd suspension has happened for having one too many at socials with boys' schools.

Despite being 'in the sticks', parents insist their daughters don't feel cut off as school allows enough freedom. Thirteen-year-olds don wellies and stride off in small groups over the fields for Saturday afternoon shopping in Shaftesbury; older girls catch the train to Salisbury. School puts on a bus to Bath if enough girls wish to go.

School meals served in cafeteria with staff on hand to supervise; good food with several choices including a vegetarian option, plenty of fresh fruit, cheese and puddings.

Girls are allowed mobile phones, but no Skype or Facebook until year 11. School Wifi switched off at night. School says that trust between staff and pupils forms the basis of school community; 'older staff are very good at dealing with any minor teasing or bullying'.

Pupils and parents: Girls joining in years 5 and 7 come from local primaries, London day schools and boarding preps, eg Leaden Hall. Intake doubles at 13+ from prep schools such as Farleigh, Sandroyd and Port Regis. Some foreign nationals join the school later. Average year group numbers 55, with 70 per cent of families within an hour's drive. Some 15 per cent from abroad, mostly Mexico, Spain and Hong Kong, with a few from Nigeria, Japan and the rest of Europe. There are 25 military families, though no extra bursaries for Forces. Parents are a mixed bunch, some wealthy, some not, whilst girls are natural, unspoilt, polite and articulate. 'The girls like themselves, know themselves and are very confident in their own skins.'

Entrance: Main entry points are at nine,11 and 13, although girls can join in any year. Entrance examination day takes place in January and includes tests in maths, English and verbal reasoning plus an interview. At 16, girls need a minimum of eight GCSE C grades. Families must be 'sympathetic to the Catholic ethos' of the school.

Exit: Up to half leave after GCSEs. Most sixth formers to Russell Group universities throughout the country, eg Bristol, Exeter, UCL, Manchester, Newcastle and Edinburgh. Oxford Brookes also popular. A good handful to art college each year, eg Bournemouth, Falmouth and Plymouth. Most choose arts degrees; good to see that a sprinkling of

girls opts for the sciences, eg anatomy, biomedical sciences, physics and nuclear astrophysics. A small number pursues practical courses such as agriculture, publishing and events management.

Money matters: Usual range of 9+, 11+, 13+ and 16+ music, academic, sports and art scholarships on offer together with one 11+ Catholic Local Primary Scholarship. Head's Scholarships 'for excellence' plus means-tested bursaries worth up to 50 per cent of school fees are available at school's discretion.

Remarks: In the past we have described St Mary's as 'a jolly nice girls' Catholic boarding school' but this belies its true character. A reasonably pacey school, St Mary's is performing pretty well on all fronts, albeit with great modesty. 'They don't blow their own trumpet enough,' remarked a parent. With lower fees than many independent schools, this school is quietly delivering excellent value. Girls wanting to be educated with boys and/or dolled up to the nines should look elsewhere, but those looking for a warm and caring environment where they can achieve and be themselves will be right at home.

Salisbury Cathedral School

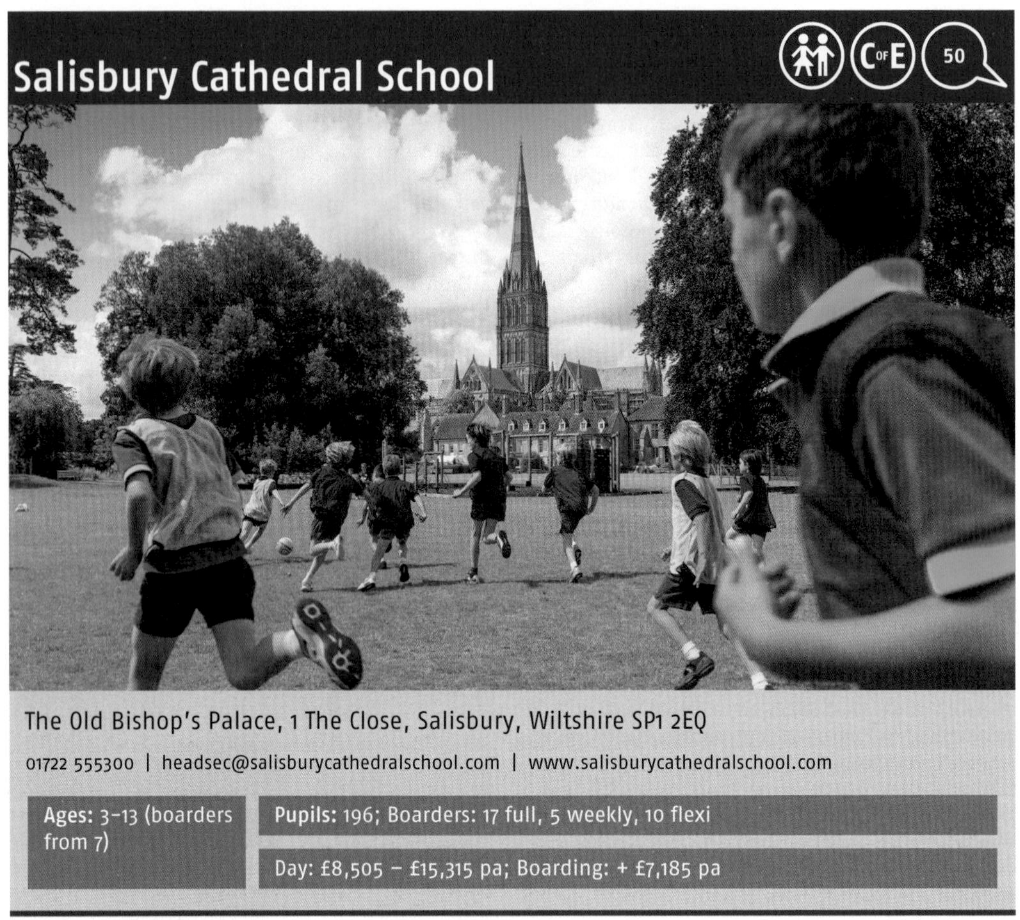

The Old Bishop's Palace, 1 The Close, Salisbury, Wiltshire SP1 2EQ

01722 555300 | headsec@salisburycathedralschool.com | www.salisburycathedralschool.com

Ages: 3–13 (boarders from 7)

Pupils: 196; Boarders: 17 full, 5 weekly, 10 flexi

Day: £8,505 – £15,315 pa; Boarding: + £7,185 pa

Head Master: Since 2013 Clive Marriott MA BEd. Single. Raised and schooled in Crediton (Haywards and Queen Elizabeth's), finished at Winchester (geography). Just the one string to his vocational bow from earliest consciousness: to be a primary teacher. After eight years in a state primary at Landscore, Crediton he was for 14 years deputy head at St Paul's Cathedral School where he made a name for himself for, especially, pastoral care. Work-life balance seesaws between total immersion in school during term times and full-on recreation in his holidays at his home in Devon. Loves walking and sailing, French culture and cuisine and urban design. Keen musician, interests span church music and musical theatre.

First impression: tremendously nice. With him, children come first, they're his primary avowed motivation. (Next in order of precedence, fyi, come 'parents, then faith, then teachers'.) Children first, that's the key, each and every one. When in their midst he either sinks to his knees or adopts a sort of walking crouch that brings him level – 'Hello Isobel, having fun? Bless you!' They are drawn to him. Bubbling with bonhomie, he scatters greetings and benedictions wherever he goes – there's something of the Michael MacIntyre about him. Knows everyone of course. We only hope all this ducking and blessing is not storing up future lumbar problems.

Subsequent impressions reinforce a sense of grip and capability. A parent warned us: 'He doesn't stand for any messing'; another said he's 'both soft and tough'. Consensus parent view: 'We all adore him ... simply the most wonderful headmaster'. Could well be the most unspun head in Britain, preferring at all times candour to flannel. Our probing enquiries among teaching staff concerning what looks like a low-ish number of academic scholarships were met by loyal fog, but Mr Marriott came straight out with it: 'Yes, I know, I've been working really hard on that.' Not the sort of head you ever have to hunt down if you've something on your mind; you'll find him out and proud every morning at drop-off time, an easy catch. Some parents have questioned whether this is a good use of his time. If the sort of head you like is one who puts himself about, prioritises people over paper, gives it to you straight and fixes stuff, Mr Marriott's your man.

Putting children first has equipped him with the resolution to do what he's needed to do. Of that, to understate it massively, there has been a lot. He's now well on his way to overhauling teaching by restructuring, raising professionalism and increasing accountability – there you are, he's good at paperwork and back-office stuff, too. There have been astute new key staff appointments and overdue departures. Oversight of pupils' well-being has been beefed up. Sports coaches have raised their game. The logic he has followed has been impeccable, but the machinery of education is human beings and letting them go can be a sanguinary, not to say lachrymose business calling for firmness of purpose. Never a man to harden his heart, Mr Marriott's simple, implacable focus – and probably the saviour of his sanity – has been: children first. So academic attainment is very much on the up here, but never, never at the expense of general and individual happiness.

There have been events of the 'events, dear boy, events' kind, not single spies but battalions. In Mr Marriott's second year the dean of the cathedral, also chair of governors, proposed to move the school out of the bishop's palace, which it had occupied since time out of mind (aka 1947). Cue Trollopian hullaballoo followed by diocesan climbdown (praise be). Then, in 2016, the school 'merged' with (ie absorbed) a dwindling girls' school in the cathedral close to a backing track of wailing and gnashing of teeth. For the following year the school operated from split sites. All in all a massive and distracting shemozzle ending up – this is what you need to know – with everyone back safe and sound in the bishop's palace, status quo ante. Mr Marriott has arguably not been well served by those who ought to know better – our unsparing verdict, we emphasise, not his: he doesn't do high politics. We reckon the governors owe him one.

Entrance: Non-choristers – a term Mr Marriott greatly dislikes; he prefers scholars – come at any age. Academically non-selective. Informal test from year 3 on to ensure your child can keep up. Parents mostly local and include, says one, 'an awful lot of doctors'. Boarding numbers swelled by Forces children, an occasional Spanish or Swedish pupil and two or three South African exchange students. Gender balance: roughly 60 per cent boys. Scholarships discretionary, currently under review.

Around 95 per cent learn an instrument; the best of them to an unbelievable (literally) standard. No pressure to be a musical genius, there's just a very wide ability span

For those in pursuit of a cherished choristership, highly selective. Consider an informal pre-audition and get a steer on whether your child is in with a chance. Consider also the open taster day. White-knuckle voice trials for boys in years 2, 3 and 4 and girls in years 3 and 4. Places awarded

'regardless of financial circumstances'. A choristership is worth 30 per cent of day fees. Around a half of all choristers receive additional means-tested top-up bursaries. Boarding is not obligatory.

Exit: Most stay to 13 and go on to local favourites – eg Bryanston, Canford, Clayesmore, Godolphin, Warminster, Dauntsey's – or further afield. Up to a third leave at 11 and go on to South Wilts or Bishop Wordsworth's grammars.

Much pride in scholarships won, most of which are for music. Given the elite standard of choristers, no surprise there; the test is the quality of the choirs they go on to. Other scholarships growing in number, academic still a bit thin on the ground and impacted by bright children leaving at 11, but decidedly on the up.

Remarks: Abounds in kerb appeal, tucked away as it is in the privacy of the close against the backdrop of the cathedral and chapter house. Masses of green space – 27 acres – for sport and play; who'd have thought the close was this big? When you learn that cricket teas here are renowned, you get the vibe (the scones really are excellent). Founded by an actual saint, St Osmund, in 1091 up the road in Old Sarum, origins traceable back to a druidical henge school established in the early Iron Age. We made that last bit up. The bishop's palace wasn't of course built with classrooms in mind, hence the (genuinely) Hogwartsian aura – origins 1220s, lovely creaky staircase, portraits of po-faced divines gazing down

Bishop's palace wasn't of course built with classrooms in mind, hence the (genuinely) Hogwartsian aura

with worldly piety. Fit for purpose? Very much so in the eyes those of the right sensibility. We quoted to a parent the words of the (now ex-) dean: 'many of the rooms within the Bishop's Palace are unsuitable for modern teaching methods'. The testy response was 'They're children, for heaven's sake!' Quite so. They're fine. However, the dean was unquestionably less wide of the mark in observing: 'the external classrooms are in temporary or dated buildings ... the need for the school to have modern facilities ... is as true today as it was in 2008 – perhaps more so'. She's right. Shabby chic is good, shabby ad-hoc ain't. We asked for a statement and got this: 'It is the governors' intention to push forward with plans as quickly as possible.' Our view importance critical.

Here's how it all works. The school's short name is SCS. There are 220-odd pupils. Of these just 16 boys and 16 girls are choristers. Their fees are subsidised by an endowment fund established as recently as 1314. When they're at the palace the choristers are schoolchildren just like anyone else, no difference. The school does not swirl around the choristers, the choristers are part of the swirl. When called upon to sing, gowned and ruffed, they form up two by two and enter under the auspices of the cathedral. Two separate but conjoined entities. Mr Marriott links them by attending evensong in the cathedral pretty much every day – his PA says 'it's his Zen'. Governors are appointed by the cathedral and non-C of E parents should note that other denominations and religions are indulged (but not accommodated) because the charitable object of the school is to 'promote and provide for.. the advancement of religion in accordance with the practices of the Church of England'. The girls' choir was established 900 years after the school's foundation to quite a bit of bahing, now abated. It is 100 per cent equal opps.

Academically improving across the board under the head's push for professionalisation. Google classroom. Enhanced progress tracking in development overseen by deputy head, a recent appointment. We saw some really good teaching. Regard for what Mr Marriott is trying to accomplish is a motivator; one teacher said: 'He trusts us and we trust him'. We happened upon some superbly marked English essays, full of advice and encouragement together with a full audit of grammatical errors. DT not all that well endowed with T, but ('They're children, for heaven's sake!') we admired a freshly made array of really excellent wooden automata whose construction called for sophisticated 3D conceptualisation plus craft skills requiring a hands-on understanding of the properties of wood. Art is well taught but in too small a space, with the curious result that all the finished work is small, too. Recent investment in IT well spent. No scholarship class, but extra challenge from teachers who know you inside out. Humane touch: no institutional bells at the end of lessons. Learning support brilliant, marvellously led. Includes gifted and talented. Focus very much on the whole child, not just the administration of remedial tweaks – big crossover with pastoral care. Around one child in five in receipt of support and 10 per cent of pupils at any time are being monitored closely with an eye to intervention. Some dyslexia, some ADHD, some Asperger's, some mental health issues.

Never had much of a name for sport, SCS. At a schools' jazz festival, which SCS creamed, a parent was told: 'Well of course, the Cathedral School is a music school'. But things are changing. At a hockey tournament, where her daughter's team ran out winners, the same parent was informed: 'Well of course, the Cathedral School is a hockey school'. This is new and testifies to improved standards of coaching. Good artificial pitches. Girls and boys play cricket on equal terms up to 1st XI. On match days, so many teams do they field, it's all hands to the pump. That's the spirit. Well chosen selection of after-school activities including, how civilised, calligraphy. Day pupils can do their prep instead.

Around 95 per cent learn an instrument; the best of them to an unbelievable (literally) standard. No pressure to be a musical genius, there's just a very wide ability span. Full range of ensembles and every genre of music. Jazz band just one much admired public face of the school's music. Informal concerts, where your friends drop in to support you, very much part of the mutually affirmative ethos here. One parent told us her son 'struggles to find a quiet place to practice'. Performance happens in what was the bishops' 18th C drawing room. It's splendid, it's roomy (very bright acoustic) but it's not, we wistfully think, a patch on the purpose-built auditorium the dean proposed. Parents agree: 'it would be good to have a dedicated hall'. Annual festival features ensembles involving pupils, staff, parents and grandparents. Drama ambitious, sometimes way outside the children's cultural experience, teacher passionate. All good, but would benefit from a dedicated performance space. Yup, that auditorium would be just the job.

Pastoral care is simply superb. There are systems and frameworks but let's cut to the chase: people here – children, teachers, support staff – really care about, and look out for, each other. Over and above formal structures, children tend to identify their preferred adult; for one or two that's the head's PA. Choristers especially closely monitored for upcoming crunch points. They learn to be, ahem, 'very organised'. When they cross over to the cathedral they are accompanied and watched over by – new appointment – the chorister tutor. No wonder parents tell us that years 7 and 8 here promote 'huge levels of growth' and personal development. Around 30 board in their own house in the close. Lovely houseparents, walled garden, homely. Best place to take the social temperature of the school is the undercroft at lunchtime. See how they chatter. The food's great, too, all cooked fresh including sauces, meat from a local butcher. The catering manager – he loves his job – and his staff keep an eye on eating patterns and report concerns.

School inspectors haven't the instruments to measure anything as soft as a school's loveability factor but we can because we trust our intuition. On our scale, SCS scores a max 10. There's a naturalness about the children here that gives the school a timeless feel. This is not a workplace school, it's a fellowship school, a little band of friends. It's an admirable school, too, and it's on a roll.

Sandroyd School

Rushmore, Tollard Royal, Salisbury, Wiltshire SP5 5QD

01725 516264 | office@sandroyd.com | www.sandroyd.org

Ages: 2–13 (boarders from 7)

Pupils: 205; Boarders: 100 full, 40 weekly/flexi

Day: £8,460 – £20,250 pa; Boarding: £19,410 – £24,540 pa

Headmaster: Since September 2016, Alastair Speers (early 40s), previously senior housemaster at Oakham. Alastair and his wife Alice (an English teacher) grew up in Dorset and have strong links locally. Alastair attended Sherborne School, whilst Alice went to Bryanston. He has a degree in building engineering and management from the University of the West of England; worked for six years in architecture as a consultant engineer, before completing his PGCE at Cambridge. Has recently completed a masters in education leadership at Buckingham. Keen on rugby, cricket, skiing, sailing, squash and performing arts. They have two young daughters who both attend Sandroyd.

Entrance: Pupils join at all stages, although school policy is to keep numbers below 200, hence there is a waiting list in some year groups. The Walled Garden (pre-prep) takes children from the age of 2. Many join the main school in year 3 from local primary or pre-preps (mostly in Wiltshire and Dorset) and the first full boarders start in year 3, when the school doubles in size. Some come at 10 or 11 from further afield, specifically for senior boarding. Not selective, but all those joining aged 7 and above have an informal interview with the head and are assessed in reading and reasoning. School stresses that tests are not pass/fail exercises.

Means-tested bursaries are available on an annual, case by case basis. Single 100 per cent bursary from year 7 (joint award with Bryanston) is awarded to one child. A further 100 per cent bursary (in conjunction with Radley, St Mary's Calne and Downe House) is available for children of servicemen or women killed or wounded on operational tours.

Exit: Most leave at 13 for eg Eton, Harrow, Radley, Downe House, Marlborough, Winchester, Bryanston, Canford, St Mary's, Sherborne, Downside, Clayesmore; otherwise to schools far and wide. A good handful leave with sport or all-rounder scholarships or exhibitions and some win academic, music and art awards (12 scholarships in 27, awarded to a quarter of leavers).

Remarks: Founded in 1888 by the Rev Wellesley Wesley as a 'small coaching establishment' for aspiring Etonians at his own home, the school quickly flourished. It moved first to Surrey and in 1939 to Rushmore House (the Pitt-Rivers' family home) on the Wiltshire/Dorset borders. School purchased the house and 57 acres within the 400-acre Rushmore estate in 1966. Like most elegant country houses, it sits at the end of a long, winding drive in solitary splendour, surrounded by playing fields, woods and parkland.

Beautiful entrance hall with open fireplace, cosy sofas and lovely wood panelling; head's study is bigger than some studio apartments and has a stunning view of open countryside. Entire school (except pre-prep) is in the original house, although there have obviously been significant additions and alterations, eg theatre, chapel, classrooms and girls' boarding wing. Everything connected by lots of passages (even our pupil guides managed to miss out half the school first time around) but there is an order to the layout once you get the hang of it. Bright, spacious classrooms on the far side of the house are mostly ranged along two main corridors and also have marvellous views. Still feels very much like a country home in the boarders' quarters (sitting rooms and comfy sofas) where houseparents have apartments. Although it is now less traditional, we were pleased to see that some 'old style' disciplines remain, eg shoe polishing, letter writing and good manners.

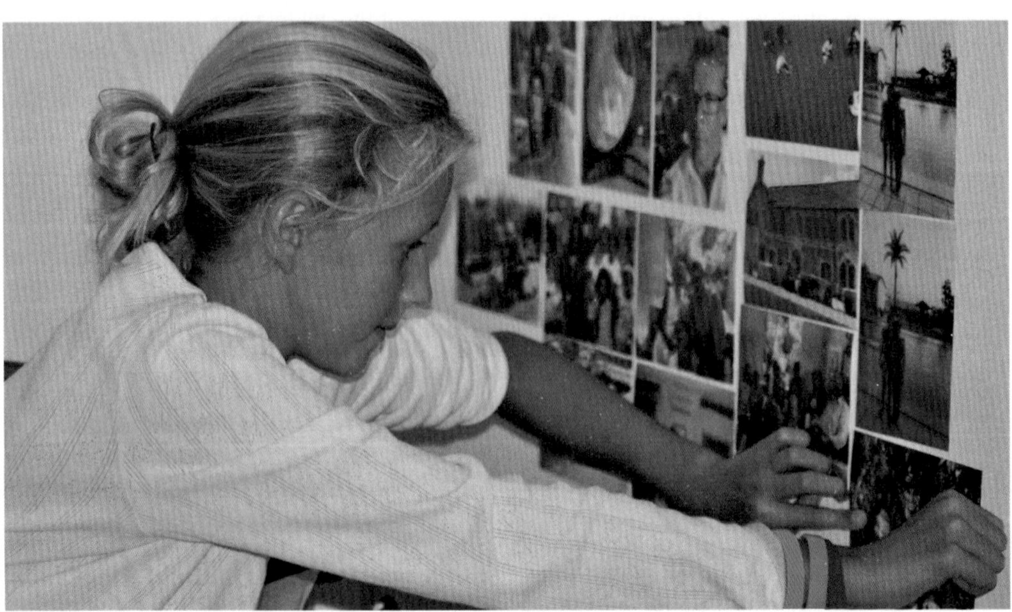

Still true to its original purpose, the school fosters a 'cool to work and achieve' ethos and parents confirm this. 'If you are destined for Eton, you will get there.' Children get lots of support along the way, with each child assigned to a personal tutor who monitors academic progress and keeps an eye on extracurricular activities. 'Tutors always have time to talk to parents and seem to know the children very well.' Strong in most areas of the curriculum thanks to good teaching and positive attitudes, together with small classes of no more than 16. Saturday morning lessons start in year 4. Teachers reward effort and achievement with 'alphas' and discourage slacking with 'omegas'. Pupils collecting enough alphas are treated to an outing and tea with the headmaster's wife.

Maths is set in years 7 and 8; able mathematicians in year 6 join advanced classes. French from year 4 and Latin from year 5. Year 3 also gets a taste of French, German and Spanish, whilst year 8 is introduced to Greek. School has a scholarship set from year 7. Year 7 pupils go on an annual residential trip to a château in Burgundy.

Although it is now less traditional, we were pleased to see that some 'old style' disciplines remain, eg shoe polishing, letter writing and good manners

Two very well-appointed ICT suites and an excellent, bright, modern science laboratory. STRIVE educates beyond the classroom, eg study skills, art appreciation and career skills for older pupils, financial literacy and European culture sessions for younger ones. RATS (reasoning and thinking skills) culminates in a GCSE in year 8. General knowledge questions set for whole prep school every week and tested every Friday. At the time of our visit, there were 32 pupils in the learning support unit and nine pupils with EAL requirements – mostly Spanish pupils at the school for one year. SEN classrooms are welcoming, light and bright (with those brilliant views again).

A very sporty school – games every day and Wednesday and Saturday afternoons devoted to matches and sport. Lots of boys' teams, eg four senior boys' rugby teams with an A and B side at every level, means everyone gets the chance to play for the school. All girls play in competitive fixtures too – including the girls' cricket team (and this year, for the first time in its history, a girl played in the school's first XI).

As well as the usual prep school sports for boys and girls, there is tennis and squash coaching, plus

archery, shooting and clay pigeon shooting, plus a girls' cricket team. School surrounded by acres of green space for games and has wide expanses of grass pitches, plus an all-weather pitch, cricket pitch, new netball and tennis courts. New sports hall. Many individual sporting accolades, eg finalists in IAPS national swimming and athletics championships; some selected for Wessex rugby and U14 and U13 county hockey and cricket teams.

New all-singing dance studio under construction and new curriculum includes everything from ballet to street dance.

A third of the pupils have riding lessons, either on school's ponies or their own (ponies are welcome to board) – eager beginners up to advanced equestrians. In our enthusiasm to see the whole school, we vaulted a stile and strode off across the paddock to watch a lesson. Naturally, the pony promptly morphed into a Thelwellian devil and refused to jump anything (much to the chagrin of both pupil and instructor, to whom we apologised profusely). Since joining the head has decided he really ought to give it a go, so he can keep up with his charges' conversations and appreciate just how good they are. And so he should, as the school is renowned for hosting an incredibly popular tetrathlon, and the senior boys' show jumping team has competed in the National Schools Equestrian Association finals.

Arts appear to be in rude health; music is on the up with newish head of music. The chapel choir, which now practises several times a week, sings Sunday morning service in the school chapel and has sung evensong in Salisbury Cathedral. There are two further choirs, a school orchestra, string ensembles, brass and saxophone groups, a jazz band and the School of Rock. There are concerts every term and an annual school musical. Eighty per cent play an instrument and music lessons are rotated through the timetable; practice sessions are timetabled and checked. All the usual instruments on offer, plus some less likely, eg tuba, banjo and bagpipes. Music theory and aural training are also available. All pupils in year 4 receive free tuition for one term on an instrument of their choice.

Fantastic theatre, probably the best we've seen outside senior schools, used by all ages from reception upwards. Every year group in the prep school puts on a play and reluctant thespians are encouraged to help out with lighting, scenery and sound. Lovely bright art studio affords plenty of space and light; next door is a small exhibition space for art scholars to display their work. Very well-equipped DT studio, with computers for designing projects (doubles up as a bike repair shop on Wednesday evenings). Lots of activities on offer during designated 'hobby' afternoons, after school and at the weekend, including astronomy, philosophy, scuba diving, pony care, survival skills and den building in woodland belonging to the Rushmore estate. Great climbing wall perches at the back of the main house.

Older pupils have desks in their bedrooms and can do prep here if they wish. They also have their own common rooms and kitchens, where they can make toast and cocoa

Boarding provision is very well organised, with a junior house for boys and girls, middle house for boys and senior boys' and girls' wings. Senior girls' wing accommodates those in the top two years. All year 7s and 8s board, and a busy programme at the weekend means most do stay in, but there are no restrictions. Every house and wing has its own houseparents as well as a team of matrons. Pastoral care is 'fantastic' and parents praise swift communications between home and school. Any unkind behaviour is stamped on quickly; a parent commented that 'school culture provides very little room for bullying.' Girls' dorms are probably the prettiest we've seen, with lots of pink and attractive lampshades and curtains. Boys' dorms are plainer and slightly more spacious in the senior wing, with three or four to a room. Older pupils have desks in their bedrooms and can choose to do prep here if they wish. They also have their own common rooms and kitchens, where they can make toast and cocoa (and learn to wash and tidy up). We were amazed to learn that school washes day pupils' sports kit as well as all the boarders' clothing. The laundry room resembles a commercial operation – rows of machines and banks of shelves for clean towels, shirts etc.

School lunches are generally good and served in a large bright, airy dining room; snacks of fresh fruit are available throughout the day. Some mothers felt school teas could be healthier, but supper seemed wholesome enough (milk, cereal, bread and fruit). Mobile phones are not permitted in school; overseas boarders are allowed to Skype their parents and others can buy phone cards to call home. There are two obligatory 'weekends in' per term, but on most Sundays children are allowed out for lunch with their parents after chapel. Many choose to remain at school with their friends to join in afternoon activities, eg football, cycling, cookery and hacking across the Downs. 'My only concern about boarding is that my children would rather be at school than at home,' said one mother wistfully.

The Walled Garden (pre-prep) is built on to an original wall surrounding the formal gardens to one side of Rushmore House. A sympathetically designed, unusual curved fibreglass ceiling lets in plenty of light without spoiling the existing aspect. Children are taught in small classes, often by a specialist teacher, with a strong focus on numeracy and literacy. The Walled Garden has its own hall for drama and assemblies (which doubles up as an art studio). A new library has recently been opened. Pre-prep pupils use the main school computers and swimming pool, walk up to the dining room for lunch and can stay on to take part in after-school activities. The playground is packed with activities such as sandpit, musical instruments, bikes, trikes, chickens, wormery and a recently opened Bug Café.

School is 'a happy mix of local and less local folk', with students from all over – a few Spanish there to learn English, with others from Germany, Norway, Japan and Mexico, plus a few expats from Hong Kong, Nigeria etc. School escorts pupils on the train to London on exeat weekends and at half-term, it arranges taxis to airports for overseas pupils. Pupils are uniformly polite, display excellent manners (standing up for the head and visitors to the classroom) and perhaps more important, are utterly unpretentious. A luminary roll call of former students includes Sir Terence Rattigan, Sir Ranulph Fiennes, Lords Carrington, Gladwyn and Wilberforce, Archbishop Ramsey of Canterbury, Rt Revd Roger Wilson, Bishop of Chichester, Professors Hawkes, Godley and Dummett, Randolph Churchill, Ian Gow and many other British and foreign dignitaries.

A very happy school, offering a well-balanced education in spectacular surroundings. Not a hothouse, but prepared to 'push when necessary' to prepare for senior school. There is lots of sport, so those allergic to games might not feel totally at home here. Has retained the best of traditional boarding school values and consigned the outmoded to the dust. We'll watch the top scholarship tally in years to come with interest.

Shebbear College

Shebbear, Beaworthy, Devon EX21 5HJ

01409 282000 | info@shebbearcollege.co.uk | www.shebbearcollege.co.uk

Ages: 11–19 (junior boarding from 7)

Pupils: 275; sixth form: 60; Boarders: 77 full, 20 flexi

Day: £12,585 pa; Boarding: £14,835 – £25,050 pa

Headmaster: Since 2013, Simon Weale MA (Oxon). Previously deputy head at Brentwood School and before that, head of sixth form at Reigate Grammar School, head of year at Latymer Upper School, London, and history teacher at Judd School, Tonbridge. He has relocated from the south east to one of the most rural areas in Devon. Married with three children ranging in age from tot to teens. A keen sportsman, he has played cricket for Oxford University and was captain of Teddington Cricket Club. He played rugby for London Cornish RFC and hockey for the London Schools Hockey Association. Still plays cricket. In fact he can literally step from the headmaster's house in his whites straight onto the cricket field to play, something he can't wait to do again this summer.

The Old Shebbearians and governors seem to have a tight rein over the school's developments; it is 'their baby.' The aim is to 'preserve but improve through careful change.' One parent said of the headmaster, 'I feel he has a good long term strategy for the school but at times does not sell himself or the school as well as he might.' Another said, 'I like the headmaster enormously. He has a great sense of humour and is happy to listen to issues and pass them on appropriately. However, he appears somewhat shy and I believe is seen as being unapproachable by some parents due to this.' What do the pupils think we asked? 'I know my daughters have the utmost respect for him while having no qualms if they needed to speak to him. That is just as it should be,' we were told.

Academic matters: In 2017, at A level, 26 per cent of grades were A*/A and 46 per cent were A*/B. At GCSE, 32 per cent A*/A grades in 2017. Parents are happy with the teaching, progress and results, saying, 'Academically I feel the teachers understand both children's strengths and weaknesses and work with them so they achieve their best.' Another agreed, adding, '[My children] may not be grade A students, but they are encouraged to give it their all.'

Seventeen subjects offered at A level. Maths and science are strong at this level; at least half of sixth formers opt for maths or a science. One pupil was recently ranked number one in the country at the Maths Challenge UK, and another is now studying at Cambridge. Art and music have produced top marks at both levels. Now offers BTecs in creative digital media and sport. Religious studies and a language are compulsory at GCSE. Spanish is taught from year 7 and French from year 8. As an international school, some pupils take qualifications in Italian, German, Russian and Cantonese. EAL also offered.

'We chose Shebbear because it had such a homely feel and the head of boarding made a lasting impression on both of us. Facilities for the boarders are very good'

All pupils are annually assessed for reading comprehension, spelling and writing skills. Learning support is then provided as needed, at an extra cost. A foreign language can be dropped if extra tuition is needed. One parent told us, 'She needed some additional help, but wasn't bad enough to get any at the state primary school. Shebbear offered, gave, and are still giving her the additional support she needs.' The learning support department produce Individual Teaching Plans (ITPs) twice a year and Individual Education Plans (IEPs) for all pupils with a statement/EHC plan. The department uses a number of tried and tested methods to help pupils, including a handwriting scheme using music, coloured reading rulers and overlays to help dyslexics. For pupils that find it difficult to retain information and to concentrate, they motivate them using multi-sensory techniques, educational puzzles and computer programmes. This provides structured learning, in a playful, fun way. Assistance during exams is also available, including reading, scribing, word processing, prompters, transcriptions and extra time. Nurses assess pupils too, and any seen to be showing signs of fine motor skill difficulties can take part in exercise classes designed for neuro-developmental delay. The school can also provide a number of resources including special pens and grips to help.

Games, options, the arts: All the traditional sports are played here. For boys, the major games are rugby, hockey and cricket, and for the girls there's hockey, netball and rounders. Other sports on offer include basketball, football, surfing, horse riding, hiking, table tennis, badminton and trampolining. There are several playing fields, an all-weather floodlit pitch, cricket nets, a dance studio, a gym overlooking the sports hall, and a weights room. For a small school the teams do pretty well; the U15 and U14 rugby teams are strong (an ex-head-girl now plays in the England women's rugby team), and the U14 cricket team recently won the Devon Cup. Latest sports tour travelled to Barbados and St Lucia where the boys and girls played football, netball and cricket. Next tour is a trip up to London for matches and tournaments. Swimming lessons start in year 3 and some prep pupils play in senior school teams.

When we were there, preparations were underway for the upcoming performance of Oliver! Two casts performing over four nights. The art teacher was busily working on a very impressive set in the main hall; he definitely has a great eye for design, and a passion to match. Past performances include Sweeney Todd and The Rocky Monster Show and, more recently, An Evening of Music Drama and Readings from the First World War. Prep school productions have included Joseph and His Amazing Techicoloured Dream Coat, Panto Pandemonium and Pirates of the Currybean. The senior pupils here have even been lucky enough to take part in a drama workshop with actor Joseph Fiennes.

No school on Saturdays, just sports fixtures. Plenty of social events throughout the year including the summer ball, discos, themed parties and talent contests

Shebbear has a strong musical reputation and the music department is run by a husband and wife team. Brand new music centre with recording studio and Steinway concert hall. Several budding musicians have gone on to top music colleges, some with scholarships. There are plenty of musical activities and groups – choirs, orchestra, flute group, saxophone group, brass ensemble and a string group. Plus regular performances such as informal chamber concerts for the younger ones, gig nights for the teenage rockers, and formal concerts for ensembles, choirs and orchestras. Recent visits by professional musicians have included Voces8 and Festive Flutes.

The art department is on two levels in the main building, with separate pottery, woodworking and food and technology areas on the ground floor. The top level has a large studio for sixth form use, as well as an ICT suite (for all pupils). The downstairs level has another large studio. There is screen-printing equipment as well as a cylinder and roller press, plus a kiln room. Artwork is displayed everywhere, no wall is left uncovered, and good use is made of the ceiling, too, with plenty of pieces dangling overhead. The art teacher is keen on pupils being able to compare and contrast their work, learn from each other, and be able to go back to pieces and give them more attention. We felt this approach gave the space a real creative edge, a great way to motivate and improve. Standards of work were in some cases very high. Regular visits to art galleries, local cathedrals and museums for all, plus A level students can visit London, Barcelona and Paris. Weekend workshops and some evening classes are on also offer, including life drawing. In 2017, five out of seven A level artists got A*.

Extracurricular activities include the usual array of sports, science, drama and arts clubs, plus a few more unusual offerings such as archery, shooting (rifle range is just behind main school building), Minecraft, wildlife studies and gardening. Given the location, outdoor pursuits like Ten Tors, Duke of Edinburgh and army cadets are also readily available and very popular. There are other projects like World Aims and Eco-Schools, which pupils can get involved in events like the Global Student Forum and Model United Nations, campaigning for War Child, Amnesty International and Christian Aid. There are also Fairtrade events such as the recent fashion show, plus a daily Fairtrade tuck shop. Recent trips abroad include a trip to Poland visiting Auschwitz, and a sixth form charity expedition to Uganda.

Boarding: Just over a third of boarders are from Hong Kong and China, a third are from the UK and the rest are from Europe. A large number of the UK boarders – including four 7-year-olds – are from Forces families. One parent told us, 'We chose Shebbear because it had such a homely feel and the head of boarding made a lasting impression on both of us. The location was and still is stunning, and the facilities for the boarders are very good. I also felt that the school really understood the needs of military children and in this I haven't been mistaken.' They went on to to say, 'When asking for time off in special circumstances eg bereavement and holiday when dad was back from Afghanistan,

Set in 85 acres of the North Devon countryside, this is as rural as it gets. In fact it's surprisingly rural, so be prepared

the school have been understanding and always honoured my request.' One girl, who recently left the sixth form, boarded here for 12 years.

The older boys' boarding accommodation, Pollard, is in the main school building and currently houses the majority of boarders. Pyke House, which has recently been reopened, is for the 11 to 13 year old boys, and is above the prep school kindergarten and lower years classroom. There are currently 12 boys there. The girls' house, Ruddle, is across the campus and has around 25 boarders at the moment. Most rooms are doubles or triples; sixth formers are offered singles if they would prefer. All rooms have internet connection and are good sized, well maintained and homely. Common rooms or lounges are also decent sizes with power hockey and snooker tables in the boys' houses and a decent kitchen in the girls'. The girls often invite the boys over for meals and cooking evenings. Parents said, 'I have always been completely happy with the rooms, the pastoral care and the general facilities. My girls have been properly cared for and helped if feeling homesick or angry or just plain miserable. I have been able to ring the houseparents if I've been worried and within minutes they have been with my child and then calling me back with an update.' The majority are full-time boarders but families do make use of the flexi arrangements occasionally. Weekly boarding is becoming more popular and some are opting to do so during the summer term so they can revise at school during the week.

School facilities including the sports hall and library are open to boarders in the evenings and at weekends. Swimming is on Mondays, there are shopping trips at weekends, plus visits to National Trust places, theme parks, cinemas, theatres, paintballing, surfing, cycling, and horse riding by arrangement. Summer is when the school really comes into its own, lovely light evenings and sprawling countryside, perfect for barbeques, picnics or evening sports. There is no school on Saturdays at Shebbear, just sports fixtures. Plenty of social events throughout the year including the summer ball, discos, themed parties and talent contests. In the summer holidays the school is used as a language school.

Background and atmosphere: Founded in 1841, Shebbear College is one of the oldest schools in Devon, currently celebrating its 175th year. Originally set up as Prospect College by Bible Christians in 1829 (the emblem PC still remains on the main gates today), it was re-founded by the Bible Christian Church as Shebbear College over a decade later, and eventually became part of the Methodist Church. It became co-ed in 1992. Set in 85 acres of the North Devon countryside, this is as rural as it gets. In fact it's surprisingly rural, so be prepared. Nearest cities are Exeter and Plymouth, both about an hour away, nearest big town is Barnstaple, half an hour or so away. The school rents out 65 acres of the land to local farmers but has plenty of room left for the main campus, several playing fields and a good cross-country course. The campus itself is very flat, open to the elements, ensuring any cobwebs are blown away as pupils make their way between buildings. The main building used to be an old printworks and some of the original 100-year-old tables are used in the dining area.

Great science block; all the laboratories have been updated in the last 18 months. Lovely, modern, bright classrooms; we particularly liked the biology lab, equipped with a hamster colony and tubes for them to run across the ceiling. There's also a resident python.

New sixth form block is open to all pupils on the ground floor, but sixth formers have exclusive use upstairs. Downstairs toilets have underfloor heating, much to the delight of girls here who regularly take their shoes off on a visit. There are also changing rooms and a kitchen. The building opens out onto the cricket pitch so the ground floor is used for cricket match teas in the summer. Upstairs, the sixth formers can look out across the Devon countryside on all sides. There's a modern kitchen, sofas, a study room and a quiet area. It's all open-plan, divided by glass windows rather than walls. There are separate tutor rooms and a small classroom too. The large viewing balcony runs all along one side of the building, looking over the cricket field. This is no doubt well used in the summer.

Sustainability is high on the priority list at Shebbear. As an Eco School they have been awarded a Green Flag award. They have two biomass plants that provide heat and hot water to the main buildings, and solar panels that provide around five per cent of the electricity. A wind turbine was opposed by locals, but Shebbear is undeterred; they are now planning electric car charging points. Even the minibuses are eco-friendly: all run on biodiesel made from oil from a local pasty company.

Pastoral care, well-being and discipline: Polite, well-behaved children, standing when an adult enters the room and opening doors is standard here. One parent said, 'It is very important that our children should be kind and have good manners and these values are constantly reinforced through example.'

Good pastoral care, as well as tutors (each pupil has a designated tutor who is responsible for overseeing both academic and social progress), houseparents and nurses, there is also a full-time resident chaplain. Chapel is every day except Wednesday, and although the school's Methodist roots are central to the school's ethos, students of all faiths and none make up the community – less than 10 per cent of pupils are Methodists. One parent commented, 'Both of my daughters have and are excelling themselves academically and I have to put this down to the quality of the teaching staff and the environment they live in. They are happy, cared for and have a fantastic group of friends around them.'

Pupils and parents: There is no school gate life at Shebbear; pupils come from a very wide area, so free buses are provided. Destinations include Tavistock, Bude, Holsworthy, Launceston, Okehampton, Bideford, Dolton, Bridestowe, Hartland, Merton, Petrockstowe and Torrington. Buses leave at 5pm daily Monday to Thursday so everybody gets the chance to participate in after-school clubs. One parent told us, 'Our daughter was not getting on very well at the local school, always came home very tired, grumpy... Despite a longer day at Shebbear she still comes home tired, but is happy and achieving lots.'

Chapel nearly every day, but although the school's Methodist roots are central to its ethos, less than 10 per cent of pupils are methodists. Students of all faiths and none make up the community

The school keeps parents updated with regular newsletters. 'The school is good at communicating to parents. We have email addresses for all the teachers, who are very approachable and are good at coming back with answers to any queries,' parents told us. The only grumble from parents was around sports fixtures – 'Organisation at times could be better – particularly with regard to matches where the children don't know until the day before whether or not they are playing.' One parent added, 'Often it is left to the children to communicate changes, which they do not always do.' And the only grumble from pupils, 'The food is the only thing which our children occasionally complain about!'

Entrance: Entry to Shebbear is not selective but there is an entrance exam to the senior school for assessment purposes and scholarships. Open days and taster days, including boarding, are available, plus induction days once accepted. Smooth transition from the junior school, which makes up nearly 50 per cent of the senior intake. Others come from local primary schools including Bradworthy, and also from St Petroc's in Bude.

On settling in, one family told us, 'The entrance process was slightly daunting for our elder son who is not particularly confident. It took him a whole year to settle but we had a lot of help from the pastoral team who went to great lengths to try and make him feel comfortable; they even established a new club based on his main interest.' A parent of a boarder told us their story: 'The entrance process was simple and straightforward. The settling in time was awful for me as I felt like I had lost a child. The boarding mistress and staff were incredible and made my daughter feel immediately at home. They also gave me regular updates as to how she was doing which made me feel a million times better.'

Exit: Some 66 per cent stay on there for sixth form. Many pupils come from farming families so some pupils leave to go on to vocational colleges to study land-based courses. Most sixth formers go on to university. Popular destinations include Exeter, Plymouth, Bath, Falmouth, Durham and York. Two to Imperial to read engineering in 2017 and two off to Hong Kong. Some boarders return to their home country to study.

Money matters: Shebbear offers academic, all-rounder, music, art, drama and sport scholarships at year 7, year 9, and sixth form entry. The Boarding School Allowance (BSA) is provided to help children of service families, plus there are means-tested bursaries, a college bursary scheme, a Methodist church bursary scheme, siblings discounts and allowances for old Shebearians, families in the parish of Shebbear and Methodist ministers.

Remarks: Shebbear is a traditional, historic school set in rural countryside. Pupils come from far and wide, and particularly for military families, Shebbear is a good choice. It is small and many parents praised its family atmosphere. The school makes the most of its rural setting with its sustainable approach, good sports facilities and outdoor pursuits. The new buildings are great assets; hopefully this is just the beginning and Shebbear will continue to develop and move forward. Parents commented, 'We did look at other schools but chose Shebbear because of its excellent reputation for pastoral care, the very good relationship between the teachers and children based on mutual respect, and the lovely family atmosphere.'

Sherborne Girls School

Bradford Road, Sherborne, Dorset DT9 3QN

01935 812245 | registrar@sherborne.com | www.sherborne.com

Ages: 11–18

Pupils: 485; sixth form: 179; Boarders: 421 full

Day: £20,460 – £25,170 pa; Boarding: £27,810 – £34,500pa

Headmistress: Since 2006, Jenny Dwyer BEd (late 40s), formerly head of Prior's Field. Educated at Bradford Girls' Grammar and then read maths at Homerton College, Cambridge. First job at Benenden (teaching/housemistress), then went on to Queen Anne's School, Caversham, where she was deputy head responsible for pastoral care. 'Glad to be back in full boarding', she asserts that 'all girls, not only the very brightest, should have a chance of a seriously good education'. Boarding numbers are up by more that 20 per cent since her arrival and the school is nearing completion of a huge development programme of new buildings and thorough refurbishment of old.

Married to a 'very supportive man', they have two sons (educated at Charterhouse and Milton Abbey). Keen on maths, hockey and dinghy sailing at her home on the Norfolk coast. Pastoral care is her particular passion. Vivacious and easy to talk to, she appears full of creative energy and very stylish. Her most obvious attribute, apart from the ability to negotiate stairs and rough ground at speed on needle thin three-inch heels, is the ability to get people talking freely and confidently. She also listens to what they say.

Stepping down in July 2018. Her successor will be Dr Ruth Sullivan, currently deputy master (sic) at Haileybury. Educated at City of London Girls and Sherborne Girls, she has a geography degree from Edinburgh and a PGCE from Moray House (Edinburgh), a masters in population and health and a PhD in non-communicable epidemiology, both from the London School of Hygiene and Tropical Medicine. Her first teaching job was at St John's Leatherhead, where she was head of outdoor pursuits and a housemistress as well as teaching geography; she moved to Glenalmond (head of geography) then queen's School Chester (head of sixth form) before joining Haileybury as acting head of geography.

Ruth coaches netball, is a qualified MLTB mountain leader, a computer software trainer and has taken numerous Duke of Edinburgh gold award expeditions to such places as the USA, Morocco, Scotland, Iceland and Norway. She also trained the first-ever all-girls Scottish Islands Peaks team (a 72-hour sailing and fell running event), has run several marathons for charity, taken part in iron-man competitions, climbed Mount Kenya and Mount Kilimanjaro and trekked in the Vietnamese Highlands, Argentinean Andes and around Bolivia.

Academic matters: The number of girls taking IB has grown. Sherborne Girls now offers it as the boys' school dropped it from their curriculum (boys can still do IB with the girls). Mrs Dwyer says girls thrive on its rigour and staff return from IB training courses full of enthusiasm which filters down to everyone. Evidently it's horses for courses, as one girl said she had started it but found she preferred A levels. Results generally pretty impressive, with average point score 35 in 2017.

Weekend workshops offered on juicy topics eg book-binding, stained glass, paper or jewellery making. Overseas trips made jointly with history of art dept

At A level greatest uptake is art history and maths. Wide range, including Russian, Japanese, theatre studies and DT reflects broad curriculum. In 2017, 45 per cent of A level entries were graded A*/A. IGCSE now used for sciences, maths, and English. Mandarin recently introduced. Sciences amongst strongest results. In 2017, 65 per cent of GCSE papers were graded A*-A/9-7. One parent commended the school for being hot on picking up and remedying any weakness in the curriculum.

New labs, each with practical and teaching areas, don't even smell of chemicals and announce their purpose to the world via curious sundial on the squat turret. Adjoining is the bright, refurbished language department with lots of lovely language IT. When Sherborne refurbishes it's root and branch, not just a lick of paint. French, German, Spanish (plus Latin) on offer and native speakers of other languages can study them to GCSE. New languages, including Russian, introduced in second year – they also get a Prue Leith Cookery School course (the sixth form can brush up on Prue Leith too).

There is flexibility to take subjects jointly with Sherborne Boys' at A level and IB. Theatre studies is genuinely a joint enterprise but has quite a small take-up.

Much setting and streaming from age 13. No form tutors; girls meet individually with personal tutors moving to a new one approximately every two years. The Junior Diploma is an initiative to keep girls consciously reflecting on their own competencies in the foundation areas of knowledge, learning skills, personal attributes and contribution to the curriculum. About 20 per cent of pupils have mild special needs; they may get extra lessons outside hours.

Games, options, the arts: Sport has a high-ish profile now at Sherborne and girls' teams are definitely up with the best in Dorset. They are old hands at the increasingly popular lacrosse and have hosted ELA lacrosse finals for 1st and U15 teams throughout UK. The girls are proud of their record and Sherborne holds pop lacrosse tournaments for prep and primary schools. Even the less sporty get encouragement.

Hockey (county champions and have provided England team members) and netball seriously competitive. All levels of players have access to good coaching. L4 and U4 have sport every day, L5 to U5 have at least three sessions per week, plus activities. The Oxley Sports Centre, with indoor pool, fitness suite, gym, dance studio plus floodlit Astro is getting a facelift, and offers first class facilities to girls and to the town in a smooth-running shared arrangement. Plenty of grass pitches and 27 tennis courts (eight floodlit), mostly artificial.

Bags of other sporty things. Riding team does well in National Schools' Show Jumping at Hickstead, polo, ski trips, various martial arts, dance etc and opportunities via Sherborne Boys for things like rifle shooting as well as everything (almost) put on for the town in the Oxley Centre.

Art block with libraries, photography and printmaking has cunning wooden bars across the wide stairwell and entry, allowing for effective display of textiles etc. There are ambitious plans to link this with a new performance centre in the next development phase. Masses of accomplished architectural studies all over the school as well as a few landscapes that might be mistaken for one of the modern masters. Head of art is an inspirational teacher. Good studio space for A level candidates who appear virtually to live here. Weekend workshops offered on juicy topics eg book-binding, stained glass, paper or jewellery making. Overseas trips made jointly with history of art dept. Computer-aided design and manufacture suite.

The lovely singing from above when we arrived was Friday choir practice. Several choirs sing in the abbey and even Salisbury Cathedral and benefit from having accessible boys' choirs. Sherborne Choral Society runs jointly with boys' school, one area in which their proximity really enables girls to keep up in an area notoriously hard for girls' schools to build a good tradition. Sherborne Schools' Symphony Orchestra skims off the cream of musicians from Sherborne Girls, Sherborne Boys and nearby Leweston to produce two joint orchestras. Singing, chamber orchestra, jazz band, senior choir, elite madrigal choir etc etc. Girls enjoy music and even take up instruments when previous experience has been off-putting. Current music building bursting out of its breezeblocks into huts alongside, so the new performing arts centre (due in January 2019) is eagerly awaited. Joint musical theatrical productions with Sherborne School and some separate drama.

'A plethora' of societies and clubs for intellectuals (from astronomy to current affairs), the arty crafty (life class – gardening), domestic goddesses (cookery – all sorts) or sporty types (ballet – yoga). D of E gets about 150 and 40+ go on to gold.

Lots of charitable activities including a lovely project for the juniors in the New Aldhelmsted West (just say West) with past pupil Camila Batmanghelidjh CBE, who opened the house. Trip to Nepal exploring and helping in an orphanage – plus all the usual exchanges and field trips such as sea kayaking and trekking in the Spanish Picos. School exchange links with Toronto and Tasmania.

Boarding: Sherborne is one of the few true boarding schools remaining with only about 40 day girls (seven per cent). Day girls are allocated to boarding houses and given their own space (some even their own bed) there. They can stay for the occasional night. No flexi-boarding and there is Saturday school. The majority want to be in on the weekend activities. Ideal for expat parents. Day girls allowed home at 6pm but some stay to do prep until 8pm.

Massive refurbishment of boarding houses means all have pleasant meeting, working, library and dining areas plus 'drawing rooms', for entertaining or watching Downton Abbey. Some girls sleep in cubicles (partitioned compartments in a dormitory – they claim not to make a habit of vaulting the partitions) but most in double or single rooms. Upper sixth girls move into Mulliner with individual study bedrooms and bit of independence. After February of their final year they are allowed into Sherborne pubs.

Background and atmosphere: Founded in 1899 by the Wingfield Digby family – local bigwigs owning Sherborne Castle – the main building is a rambling Victorian warren in the pretty local hamstone. Meticulous planting makes an attractive site with the main boarding houses and teaching facilities forming a crescent round a green expanse of playing fields and lawn on the edge of the town. Still a few 'huts' for drama and music but the five year development plan is nearing completion.

Recently completed Aldhelmsted West is a fabulous environment for the first two years with sunny dining room, laid out for birthday tea on our visit, work rooms for homework, lots of comfortable play space and room for music practice. Parents get involved in sports as West positively encourages

them to get to know one another. Several live-in staff and a housemistress' house attached with openings onto all three floors. Good big bedrooms, mostly for four, with loo and shower en suite.

There is flexibility to take subjects jointly with Sherborne Boys' at A level and IB

The undoubted advantage of an all boys' school in the same small market town means the girls can share entertainment and have sensible and reasonably safe access to town life, a situation envied by similar girls-only schools in the area. Younger girls can go into town at weekends. Lower sixth can go as far as Yeovil, Exeter, Salisbury. Upper sixth girls allowed into the sixth form bar at Sherborne Boys. Common features include coordinated term dates, some A level courses, IB, social events, two joint plays, the Academic society and Epicurean society as well as music.

Pastoral care, well-being and discipline: School rules are straightforward, based on 'keep safe and consider others'. Exclusion for dealing drugs; experimenters can 'expect' to go but 'touch wood no issues' and smoking not really a problem. 'Robust' attitude to alcohol, shared by boys' school, includes possibility of breathalysing. Daily living still done the old school way with all meals in houses with their own separate kitchens and dining rooms. Formal lunches (sixth form do table plans, staff at each table), but cafeteria-style suppers. Hot drinks machines for girls to entertain friends, male and female, in the downstairs areas. Afternoon tea at 5pm and supper at 7.30pm means sensible pre- and post-supper time for supervised prep and activities. Girls say food's pretty ok.

Upper sixth girls move into Mulliner with individual study bedrooms and bit of independence. After February of their final year they are allowed into Sherborne pubs

Resident housemistresses, some with families and pets (one house is pet free for allergy sufferers), run the houses like homes with minor medical help and a friendly ear available during the day. Proper school san. The popular school chaplain teaches, offers confirmation etc and keeps an eye that all denominations get spiritual support. Has the right balance of welcome and warmth with respect for girls' views, say parents. Teams of house tutors give personal and academic support on an individual basis. Issues (homesickness, cliques, etc) do crop up but they are very well resolved, said one parent.

Pupils and parents: Still lots of old west country families but also Forces families, diplomats, Londoners with south west connections (Sherborne is on the main line to Waterloo). About 10 per cent come from Hong Kong and elsewhere: Dubai, Nigeria etc plus Europe since IB was introduced. Around 25 need EAL support of one lesson per week. Recently awarded the DfE International School Award in recognition of the international dimension being a key part of school ethos. Sixth form are let out of uniform but have regulation black tailored suit (with a quite skimpy skirt) worn with their own accessories.

Old girls – Camila Batmanghelidjh, soprano Dame Emma Kirkby, violinist Ruth Rogers, writers Sophie Kinsella, Santa Sebag Montefiore, Dames Deirdre Hutton of the Trading Standards Institute and Juliet Wheldon, who was legal advisor to the Bank of England. Sherborne old girls are exceptionally efficient: organised into regional circles, they support all sorts of school initiatives, their own charitable causes and a careers information network. Such benevolent networking may lie behind the remarkable collections of speakers who visit Sherborne – AC Grayling on the day of our visit, Germaine Greer, recently, Becky Anderson of CNN, Matthew Pinsent, Simon Weston, Ann Widdecombe, Griff Rhys Jones.

Entrance: Visit, registration, 'at work days', taster weekends, deposit paid, then scholarship exams, common entrance papers or own entrance exams in maths, English and reasoning plus an interview. One form enters at 11, a few girls join at 12 but the majority (three forms) enter at 13. Mainly from Hanford, Port Regis, Hazlegrove, Knighton House, Sherborne Prep, Leaden Hall, Perrott Hill, Cheam, Bute House, Newland, Thomas's, Mount House Farleigh, Forres Sandle Manor, Twyford and Sunninghill. About 20 join for sixth form – at least five grade B/6 or above GCSEs required for A level or IB.

Exit: A few leave after GCSEs, mainly to sixth form colleges. After A levels, practically all go on to university to read a wide variety of courses (modern languages, theology, lots of sciency things including medicine). Edinburgh, Exeter, Durham, Newcastle, Bath, Warwick, King's College London, Sheffield, Cardiff and Bristol currently leading the pack. A few to Oxbridge most years (seven in 2017, plus five medics/vets) and several to art schools or to study academic art history.

Money matters: Boarding fees about what you would expect, on a par with co-ed fees for boarders though less than the boys. New fee structure for day students with two options: day boarder (with the option for overnight stays) or day girl (no overnight stays, but her own space for storage and study in a boarding house). The school hopes the new cost structure will offer a competitive day fee to local families whilst still ensuring that day girls feel fully involved in the busy life of a boarding school.

Scholarships generous for a girls' school. Academic, art and music awards pay up to quarter of fees, plus bursaries based on need. Music scholars get up to three lessons per week – more than at most schools. Nearly 100 girls are receiving some sort of award or bursary. Currently appealing for bursary fund. School has also introduced elite swimming programme for which scholarships are offered.

Remarks: No longer the stuffy warhorse of girls' education, though its academic standards are undiminished. Parents appreciate that its good teaching avoids hothousing and encourages a balance of activities. A real gem amongst the girls' only full-boarding schools with all the advantages of its symbiotic proximity to Sherborne School.

Sherborne Preparatory School

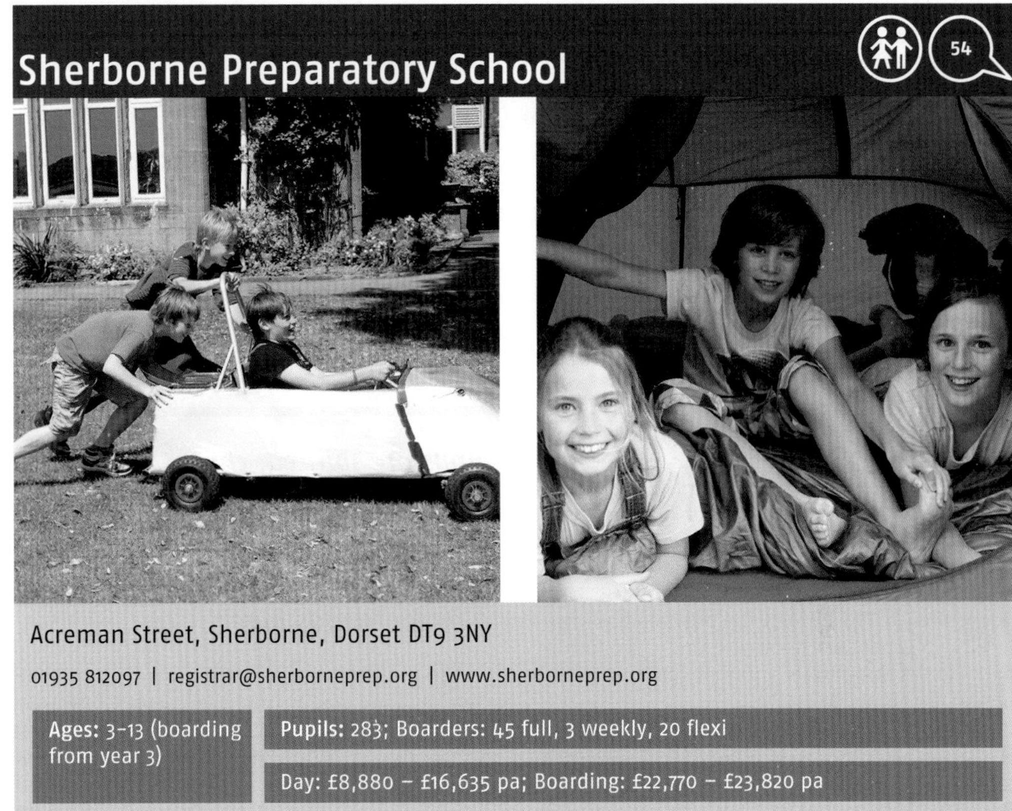

Acreman Street, Sherborne, Dorset DT9 3NY

01935 812097 | registrar@sherborneprep.org | www.sherborneprep.org

Ages: 3–13 (boarding from year 3)

Pupils: 283; Boarders: 45 full, 3 weekly, 20 flexi

Day: £8,880 – £16,635 pa; Boarding: £22,770 – £23,820 pa

Headmaster: Since 2015, Nick Folland (50s). Educated at Exmouth Community College, one of the largest comprehensives in the country, and Loughborough University, where he read PE, sports science and geography. Worked with deaf children for three years, did a PGCE at Loughborough and then moved to Blundell's. Played professional cricket for Somerset for three years before taking a housemaster's post at Blundell's. Appointed as inaugural head of Blundell's Prep and after a decade there took on the headship of St John's on-the-Hill prep in Chepstow, where he spent four years.

Married to Di, a charming Australian speech and language specialist who is immersed in school life. They live in a house owned by the school, a five-minute walk away, and have two children. Head is go-ahead, energetic (his wife describes him as a 'can-do person'), refreshingly down-to-earth and popular with parents. 'I'm a pretty open book,' he says, 'and if there are things to improve then I get on and improve them.' Very proud of the fact that the school is not selective yet gets excellent results. 'I'm really enjoying the job,' he says. 'The children are what it's all about and they are wonderfully positive and really want to achieve.' His hectic schedule means he doesn't teach these days but he's very visible around the school, lunching in the dining hall, chatting to children in the corridors and coaching the under 9s rugby team. Plans are afoot for him to coach netball in the coming year. He isn't in the least fazed by taking on a new sport – 'I'm a gamesy person,' he says. Enjoys sport, film and travel in his spare time.

Entrance: School is non-selective and unpretentious. Entrance is by interview with the head and previous school report, plus informal assessment when pupils come in for a taster day before joining, to ensure that the school is the right fit and can meet child's needs. Most pupils start in the pre-prep or year 3 but there is a steady trickle joining from years 3 to 7 and at least 10 new starters arrive in year 7. School is happy to consider new pupils all year round, not just those starting in the autumn term. Academic, music, sport, art, DT and all-rounder scholarships available – school says 'talent and enthusiasm are especially sought'.

Exit: Sherborne Prep is independent of Sherborne School and Sherborne Girls but has strong links with both, and around half of the pupils head to one of these. Others go to Bryanston, Canford, Kings Bruton, Winchester, plus a few to Eton, Harrow, Cheltenham Ladies, Marlborough, Blundell's, Dauntsey's, Radley, Rugby, Downside, Milton Abbey, more than a third with scholarships. Some to local state schools The Gryphon or Thomas Hardye at 13+.

Remarks: Founded in 1858, the school moved to its present location, just off a quiet Sherborne side street, in 1885. Went co-ed in the 1970s. The school site combines the best of both worlds – it's five minutes' walk from the centre of town but has 12 acres of grounds (including five acres of sports fields) for children to play in.

Despite its traditional exterior, Sherborne Prep is impressively forward thinking. The dynamic head of teaching and learning (she's also the head of languages) helps children to work out what type of learners they are (visual, auditory, kinaesthetic) and has brought in a self assessment programme that encourages pupils to give themselves scores for collaboration, participation, conduct and independence. The head of the pre-prep has introduced a Singapore maths programme called Inspire Maths to develop pupils' number confidence and mental arithmetic skills.

Teaching is excellent throughout. Teachers are a dedicated bunch, full of ideas and enthusiasm. A parent described them as 'outstanding, with a diversity of styles and approaches'. We met the deputy head (academic), who attended the school herself and had such happy memories that she decided to return, and a humanities teacher who has been at the school for 41 years. Exam results are first rate but a member of staff emphasised that the school isn't an exam factory. 'Exams aren't the be all and end all,' she said. 'They are part of the journey. People get so focused on exams and it's important to realise that they are just a stepping stone.' As well as their form tutors, who they see every day, the children get to choose their own independent tutors – anyone from the teachers to the head of maintenance.

Classes are mixed ability, apart from scholarship sets at the top of the school. Maximum class sizes of 18, but rarely more than 16. Three classes per year group in years 6, 7 and 8 and two per year group for younger pupils in the prep. Learning support (accessed by 13 per cent) is provided by the Learning Hub. Children receive one-to-one help or work in small groups.

Pupils are spirited, chatty and polite. Asked what they liked best, one said: 'The teachers. They understand you as a person.' Another said, 'it's easy to make friends here'

Languages are a particular strength of the school and are taught from the pre-prep upwards. Reception children do a bit of Italian (learning through music, drama and cultural aspects) while year 1 and 2 pupils learn Mandarin. 'The idea is to give them a foundation in the idea of appreciating languages,' says the head of languages, who has developed a website called Language Prep to make languages fun and accessible (it's used by other schools too). Years 3s do German, year 4s Italian (with a focus on ICT and cooking) and year 5s and up French and Spanish (ready for their senior schools). Latin is taught from year 6. Debating and public speaking are notable. When we visited a year 8 boy had just won the local round of the Youth Speaks competition, speaking without notes about finding strength through adversity. No lessons on Saturdays. School runs an optional programme of activities – children come into school in their home clothes and take part in three-hour clubs (everything from forest school and pond club to circus skills, cartoon character drawing, LAMDA and sport). Saturday lectures for year 7 and 8 children and parents tackle a raft of unusual subjects – the history of salt to 'is levitation possible?'

Newish head of sport (previously at Glenalmond) is keen for every pupil to get the chance to wear a team shirt during their time at the school. Main sports for boys are rugby, hockey and cricket and hockey, netball and cricket for girls (rounders less popular these days). Hockey is particularly strong, with under-8 and under-11 girls winning a string of tournaments in recent months. Sportiest pupils get pro cricket and hockey training but school also has a 'team of the week' award, where individual children are commended for their efforts in promoting school values on the games pitch. School mainly uses its own playing fields but also has access to the facilities at Sherborne School, just over the road, and the swimming pools there and at nearby Sherborne Girls. The children get loads of fresh air, running off steam in the grounds at break and lunchtimes. Pupils enjoy playing conkers (a previous head thoughtfully planted a row of chestnut trees for precisely that purpose).

Parents are full of praise for the school's music, drama, art and DT. A father with two older children and two at Sherborne Prep said a year 7 play he'd recently seen was 'creatively delivered and outstanding', far better than productions he'd seen at senior schools. Music is integral to the prep and the school provides 14 choristers for the choir at Sherborne Abbey. More than half of the children play a musical instrument and the new director of music reckons numbers will rise to 75 per cent before long. A host of opportunities for budding young musicians, including full orchestra, senior choir, junior choir, chamber choir, brass ensemble, jazz ensemble and piano trio. The art room is a vision to behold – light and airy, with views of Sherborne Abbey and the children's work proudly displayed everywhere. Head of art is a successful artist from Spain who encourages the children to explore different art forms, including drawing, painting, sculpture, film and experimental media. 'They never have the same lesson,' he says. He allows children to use the art room at break times, on the proviso that they clear up afterwards, and also teaches art to parents during the spring term.

The pupils are spirited, chatty and well mannered. They stand up when visitors enter the room and are keen to talk about their school. Asked what they like best one said: 'The teachers. They understand you as a person.' Another told us that the teachers have 'a fun way of teaching' while a third described the school as 'small and cosy'. A boarder waxed lyrical too. 'It's easy to make friends here,' he said. 'It's more like a family.' They all gave the Sherborne Prep uniform the thumbs up (especially the navy blazers with jaunty green trim and assorted badges), but the school's sweet and sour chicken wasn't quite so popular. Senior schools say Sherborne Preppers are mature, independent and like 'having a go'.

School has 45 full boarders but offers flexi and occasional boarding too. Boarding from year 3 upwards but few board before year 5. Seventeen international pupils when we visited, from France, Japan, Thailand, Korea, China, Russia and Spain. Two boarding houses – one for boys, the other for girls. Both very homely and friendly, with a plethora of weekend activities to sign up for. Day pupils come from Sherborne itself and from as far afield as Dorchester, Shaftesbury, Shillingstone, Langport and East Coker. Five minibus routes at present. Parents range from architects and business people to writers and directors, many of whom have swapped London for the wilds of the West Country. A mother told us she 'couldn't sing the school's praises highly enough.' She added: 'It's a very warm, unsnobbish, lovely place.'

Pre-prep (completely refurbished) and nursery housed in a separate building on the main site. Head of the pre-prep says there's an outdoor ethos, with children spending lots of time outside (clad in wet weather gear on rainy days). 'You don't know until you try' is her motto and there's a plethora of after-school activities, including recorder club, ballet, golf and cross-stitch.

Sherborne Prep is an exciting school. Full of character and great ideas, it's friendly, unsnooty and fun – and achieves top-notch results.

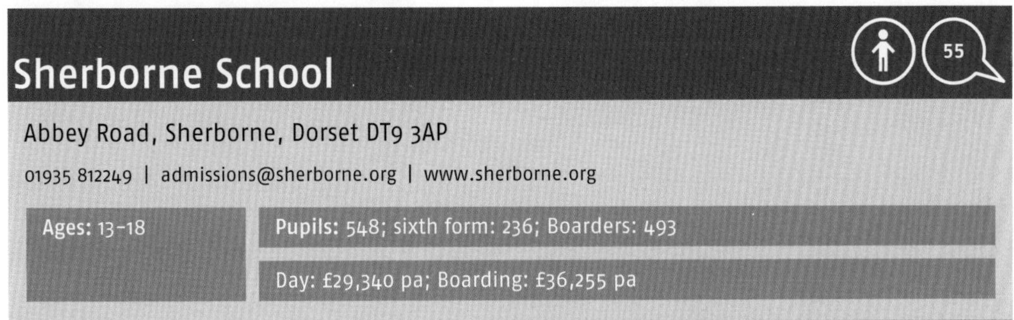

Sherborne School

55

Abbey Road, Sherborne, Dorset DT9 3AP

01935 812249 | admissions@sherborne.org | www.sherborne.org

Ages: 13–18

Pupils: 548; sixth form: 236; Boarders: 493

Day: £29,340 pa; Boarding: £36,255 pa

Headmaster: Since January 2016, Dr Dominic Luckett (early 50s), previously head of Mill Hill School. Educated at King Edward VII Grammar School (now King Edward VII Academy) in King's Lynn, the University of Leicester, where he gained a first in history, and Magdalen College, Oxford, where he did his DPhil in early Tudor history. Encouraged by an inspirational history teacher, he was the first of his family to go to university. 'I suspect that if it hadn't been for him I would have ended up working in Sainsbury's,' he says. Taught for 11 years at Harrow School, where he was head of history and an assistant housemaster. Barnaby Lenon, head of Harrow at the time, suggested he should apply for a deputy headship and he subsequently moved to Worth School as deputy head. In 2007 he became head of Mill Hill School and chief executive of the Mill Hill School Foundation. He is an ISI inspector and a member of the University of Leicester's governing body.

His wife Cara is a barrister and they live in a school house with their two young daughters (the elder is a pupil at nearby Sherborne Prep). Head loves the fact that Sherborne is 'a proper boarding school' and 'doesn't empty out at weekends'. When he first visited Sherborne he was delighted to see boys in their early teens playing tag in the school grounds. 'You don't get boys in north London playing tag,' he says wryly, adding that boys at Sherborne get 'a year to 18 months more childhood' than their London counterparts.

Parents and boys talk about him in glowing terms. They say he has upped the academic ante, put an emphasis on kindness and smartened up the uniform. In turn, the head is full of praise for the pupils. 'The boys are interesting, engaging and decent,' he says. 'They know their own minds but there is a reservoir of kindness there. People say that you never meet an unpleasant old Shirburnian and it's true.' He often mentions acts of kindness in assemblies. 'It's very easy to celebrate a first XV victory or a university place but if you aren't kind you're not a proper Shirburnian, however much you achieve.'

Oldest boys act as mentors. We liked the subject guru system – pupils flummoxed by their prep can consult a sixth former for help

A thoughtful, likeable man, he clearly loves his job and is delighted by Sherborne's sense of community. He is determined to raise Sherborne's profile and is proud of the fact that the school is in the top one per cent in the country for value added scores at GCSE and A level. 'We haven't been very good at banging our drum but it's an extraordinary school,' he says. In his spare time he enjoys paragliding, music ('the music here is incredible') and collecting clocks. He points out his 'third favourite clock' in his drawing room – a late 18th century long case clock.

Academic matters: Results are good – and on the up. In 2017 at GCSE, 58 per cent A*-A/9-7 grades; at A level, 50 per cent A*/A grades (74 per cent A*-B). Art, further maths, geography and physics are the best performing subjects. EPQ on offer to sixth formers. Most boys take 10 subjects (a mix of GCSEs and IGCSEs), including maths, English, English literature, theology, a language, a humanities subject and science (most boys do all three sciences). French, German, Spanish, Latin and Greek are taught across all year groups. Boys can

learn additional languages, including Arabic, Italian, Japanese, Mandarin and Russian. All the usual A levels on offer. The school also pools its teaching expertise with nearby Sherborne Girls to extend A level subject choices and overcome timetable clashes. So Sherborne gives girls the chance to study A levels in PE and music technology while Sherborne Girls takes boys for photography and history of art.

Teaching is praised by boys and parents alike, many commenting that lessons are stimulating and inspiring and teachers go the extra mile to help. School takes a forward-thinking approach to technology. When we visited a lower sixth English class some boys were writing notes by hand, others were tapping away at their laptops and phones. Learning support is housed in its own building (West Lodge). All boys are screened on arrival and sessions on learning styles and study skills are timetabled. One of our guides told us he had suffered anxiety during exams and the school had organised for him to take his exams in a separate invigilation room. 'They are so helpful,' he said.

Games, options, the arts: Sport is a big deal here and there are lots of unbeaten teams. Acres of playing fields (just a 10 minute walk away), plus tennis courts, sports hall, fitness suite, two Astroturfs (one floodlit), 25-metre indoor swimming pool, four squash courts, five fives courts and an indoor shooting range. Main sports are rugby, football, hockey, cricket, tennis and athletics but the school offers 26 sports in total. All new boys play rugby but they can switch to another sport later on if they prefer – choices include sailing, swimming, equestrian sports, fives, cross-country, squash, water polo and cycling. A sixth former relished the fact that he could spend two afternoons a week on his road bike rather than on the rugby pitch. County champions in rugby, hockey and cricket, and ski team won gold in team and individual competitions at the British Schoolboys Ski Racing Championships in 2017. Other notable successes in sailing and judo and Sherborne boys have represented GB in the modern tetrathlon, pentathlon and sailing.

Music is astounding, up with the very best. The music school is in the middle of the campus, complete with soundproofed rehearsal rooms, a 120-seat recital hall, swish recording studio and a large foyer where boys congregate and chat. The choir sings in Sherborne Abbey twice a week, boys give free lunchtime recitals at Cheap Street Church (lucky locals) and there's a host of orchestras and bands. When we visited a swing band rehearsal was in, yes, full swing, led by the exuberant director of music. The boys looked like they were having the time of their lives. Two-thirds of pupils play instruments, some at grade 8 and ATCL diploma level. The school sets aside an hour after lunch each day

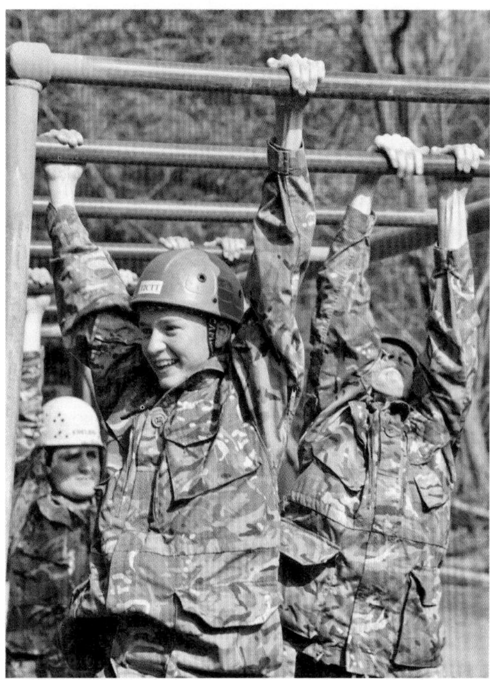

for rehearsals, known as Q Time. The result is that boys don't have to choose between music and sport. It's quite usual for at least half the first rugby XV to be in the choir. The school has also produced a number of rock musicians, including Chris Martin of Coldplay and more recently, New Carnival, an indie dance band.

You don't get boys in north London playing tag,' head says wryly, adding that boys at Sherborne get 'a year to 18 months more childhood' than their urban counterparts

Sherborne counts a plethora of top actors among its alumni, including the late John le Mesurier, Jeremy Irons, Hugh Bonneville, James Purefoy, Charlie Cox and Charles Collingwood (Brian Aldridge in The Archers), as well as the director Sir Richard Eyre. School hosts two major productions each year, plus four house plays and a junior school play, most of these in the school's 220-seat Powell Theatre. Some joint productions with girls from nearby Sherborne Girls and Leweston.

Art studio, designed by the architect Sir Reginald Blomfield, is open seven days a week and offers painting, life drawing, sculpture, printmaking and digital media. Around 30 boys take art GCSE each year (doing the course in one year rather than two) and 16 to 18 take the subject at A level. We particularly admired a huge golden eagle with a three-metre wingspan, made entirely of cardboard and hanging from the art studio ceiling. An art teacher, an old Shirburnian himself, had given his year 10 group a pile of cardboard and a hot glue gun, challenged them to make something 'life-size' and this was the result. 'It was an opportunity for them to be creative and have a bit of fun,' he told us. DT is popular too, with the emphasis on coming up with ideas, making prototypes and considering whether they have the potential to be commercially successful.

Vast co-curricular programme, including D of E, CCF, Amnesty International, the Ten Tors expedition and Young Enterprise. Academic societies include classics, debating and philosophy, as well as scholars' societies for each year group.

Boarding: The overwhelming majority of boys board, joining one of eight boarding houses. Around 70 boys per house (13 or so in each year group). The houses are dotted around the campus and are wholesome and comfortable rather than luxurious. We visited The Green, a homely house with a large garden that's perfect for kicking a ball around in. Youngest boys in dorms of four or five. Sixth formers get their own rooms. Oldest boys act as mentors to younger ones. We liked the subject guru system, whereby pupils flummoxed by their physics or maths prep (or any other subject for that matter) can consult a sixth former for help. 'And we do,' said an appreciative year 9 boy.

Background and atmosphere: A beautiful school in the heart of a charming, well-heeled Dorset market town. Sir John Betjeman once described the town as looking 'like a junior university city, with every

Pupils we met loved living in the heart of town and being able to pop into shops and cafés. 'It's nice to have a bit of freedom,' one said

other house an old college'. Some school buildings date back to the 12th century but the school itself was refounded in the mid-16th century under the auspices of the monastery at Sherborne. It survived the Reformation to become a free grammar school during the 17th and 18th centuries and has been a boys' boarding school since the 19th century. At the heart of the school are The Courts, a vast quad surrounded by ancient golden stone buildings – 'our beauty spot,' said a sixth former. The Courts boast two cloistered walls and share one with Sherborne Abbey. Later additions to the school, such as the Pilkington science labs, are sensitively designed and blend in well.

When boys pass a wall bearing the names of Old Shirburnians killed in the First and Second World Wars on the steps up to the chapel they fall silent as a mark of respect. It's very moving to witness. School chapel plays a key role in the boys' lives. Every morning starts with an assembly or a chapel service and the whole school attends services at Sherborne Abbey on Wednesdays and Sundays. There's also a candlelit service in the school chapel on Fridays. 'It isn't excessive,' a sixth former told us. 'Some come for the prayers, some come for the peace and quiet.' As the school puts it: 'While we welcome boys of other faiths, and no faith, to the school, we hope these moments of calm will bring structure to their routine, and nurture their spirituality.'

The pupils we met loved living in the heart of town and being able to pop into shops and cafés during their free time. 'It's nice to have a bit of freedom,' one said. 'Some schools are in the middle of nowhere but I prefer being in the middle of things.' Sixth formers wear smart suits and ties, while younger boys are kitted out in practical navy shirts and trousers, known as 'blues'. Breakfast, lunch and supper are eaten in the central dining room. Food gets the thumbs up, especially the breakfasts, and the boys say there is plenty of it.

Pastoral care, well-being and discipline: Sherborne prides itself on being 'boy-focused' and is quick to respond if and when problems arise. Tutors keep a close eye on pupils, meeting them at least once a week. 'They've always got your back,' a boy told us. A sixth former whose tutor had moved to another school said his former teacher still emailed to see how he was getting on. Youngest boys are allocated a tutor from their houses but sixth formers can choose their own.

The boys have plenty of people to talk to, including housemasters, tutors, a counsellor and the (female) chaplain, known as Rev. Two head boys appointed each year, plus deputies and a raft of prefects. Sixth formers also act as peer mentors. PSHE is delivered by housemasters to year 9 boys and by specialist teachers after that. A broad range of topics covered, from coping with bereavement and divorce to the stress of exams. School has a sensible attitude to mobile phones. The youngest boys all hand their phones in before bed while some houses organise device-free weekends.

Pupils and parents: All the boys we met were down-to-earth, full of fun and clearly enjoying their busy lives at Sherborne. Pupils come from more than 40 prep schools. Around 10 per cent from overseas (including sons of expats and Forces families). Many come from the south west, plus a smaller proportion from London. Sherborne is only 140 minutes by train and South West Trains lays on trains for pupils from Sherborne, Sherborne Girls and Leweston at exeats and half-term.

Parents from a mix of professions, the Forces and local gentry. Some boys from long-established Shirburnian families (one of our guides was a third-generation Shirburnian and proudly showed us the names of his forebears on his house board). Other famous old boys include Enigma codebreaker Alan Turing, John le Carré, Major General Patrick Cordingley DSO and ITV News journalist Tom Bradby.

Entrance: Boys looking to start in year 9 (third form at Sherborne) are tested at an assessment day in January of year 7. They sit verbal and non-verbal reasoning tests, take part in a group task, complete a piece of creative writing and have an interview with a senior member of the academic staff. The head then offers guaranteed places for entry in year 9 although boys still take CE for setting purposes. Impressive induction system in place. Deputy head (pastoral) writes to parents of new boys asking how the school can help their sons settle in and 'hit the ground running'. Around 20 new boys join in the sixth form each year. At 16, entry requirements into the sixth form are the same internally and externally – an average of at least grade 4 across all GCSE subjects, plus grades 8 or 9 in subjects boys wish to study at A level.

Exit: Almost all stay on after GCSEs and most head to university at 18. The majority go to Russell Group universities, including Durham, Bristol, Exeter, Imperial College and the LSE. Seven to Oxbridge in 2017, plus three medics. Growing interest in US universities. One boy recently won a highly prized Rolls-Royce apprenticeship.

Money matters: A range of scholarships. Academic scholarships and exhibitions with a maximum fee remission of 20 per cent. Closed awards available to sons of serving or former officers in the armed services or for sons of Royal Navy officers. All-rounder awards, plus art, drama, DT, music and sport awards. Means-tested bursaries, some worth 100 per cent of the fees. A third of boys receive some financial assistance.

Remarks: A terrific boys' boarding school in a breathtaking golden setting. Sherborne, with its strong sense of community, good academic results and opportunities galore on all fronts, succeeds in combining the best of ancient and modern without diminishing either. For parents debating the merits of single sex versus co-ed schools for their sons, it offers the best of both worlds.

Sidcot School

Q 56

Oakridge Lane, Winscombe, North Somerset BS25 1PD

01934 843102 | admissions@sidcot.org.uk | www.sidcot.org.uk

Ages: 3-18 (boarding from year 7)

Pupils: 573; sixth form: 131; Boarders: 148

Day: £7,650 – £17,130 pa; Boarding: £25,710 – £32,430 pa

Head: Since 2012, Mr Iain Kilpatrick BA Med FRSA PGCE, a former RBS banker who saw the light and turned to schoolmastering in the mid-90s, by way of a degree in English from Stirling and a PGCE from Edinburgh. Though English-born, Mr Kilpatrick's upbringing, education and career until Sidcot has been north of the border, but 'Much as I love Scotland, there's not a huge diversity of schools. IB was quite a draw, plus the mix of day and boarding, the area and the size and atmosphere at Sidcot'. Having thrown himself wholeheartedly into the holistic life of Strathallan and during his first headship of Beaconhurst, an all-through day school, he has shown himself ready to do the same at Sidcot, and is often to be seen around school, at its performances and indeed away matches.

Parents reckon he has smartened up the place and the people in it, made it 'more corporate' (for good or ill), and on occasion let technology obfuscate the message – some parents would be perfectly happy with good old-fashioned letters or emails, rather than having to download an app to check what's going on. Some also suspect that he is eyeing the academic performance of the Bristol independents with which Sidcot competes for Bristol families – with a view to upping Sidcot's game. Personally, he is dapper and articulate – 'Not to be messed with,' said one mother – and possessed of a good firm handshake. His students find him 'Scottish, smiley, interested in everything you do, with the power to make things happen'. Married to Katrina (a pharmacist), he has a son and a daughter in the school, and is very family-minded: 'children are an endless source of optimism, humour and entertainment'. Though he admits to being that kind of annoying person who always enjoys their job, he takes much pleasure in the countryside (walking and golf), as well as theatre.

Head of junior school since 2012, Ms Claire Lilley (early 40s). Educated at Tunbridge Wells Grammar and Homerton College, Cambridge, where she did a BEd in music. She worked at Sidcot as a year 5 teacher and after a foray down a different career path realised that teaching was what she truly wanted to do: 'I felt as though I had come home when I came back to Sidcot in 2009,' she says. A rapid ascent through the hierarchy culminated, after a proper selection process, in her appointment to the headship.

Tall and blonde, with an infectious laugh – 'you can always hear Ms Lilley,' said one boy – she is described by pupils as friendly, cheery and 'really in control but does not have to shout to get her point across.' Has a young daughter.

Academic matters: Non-selective at junior and senior level and no Sats – 'we think labelling children according to their intellectual ability is counterproductive,' says the junior school head. But that is not to say that the teaching lacks rigour or focus. 'We follow the national curriculum, but are not slaves to it, and we certainly don't expect children to come in and conform to the way we teach. We look for a learning style that suits each child.'

Closer tracking to monitor progress continues to be introduced in the junior school (not that the children are necessarily aware of it). Languages are strong: there is even a competition to recite a poem in a foreign tongue. Now a forest school from the nursery onwards, whose benefits include managing risk, getting up close and personal with nature, teamwork, cross-curricular learning and making an Iron Age round house. Phew! Alongside the three Rs, children here also learn emotional intelligence, to have a voice and to learn independently: each pupil has to research a topic to present on a double page spread in any way which appeals – writing, pictures, photographs, diagrams. Anything goes and is peer-reviewed. Work is often marked by two stars and a wish – the stars for things done well, a wish for something to be done better next time. The friendliness of the school is noted and appreciated by the children and SEN support is extensive and totally without stigma.

Size of the school causes some parents to bemoan the strength and depth of rugby talent, but naked aggression is not the Quaker way

Results are solid if not stellar, with 37 per cent of GCSEs graded A*-A/9-7 and 42 per cent A*/A at A level in 2017. That said, maths is acknowledged as being exceptionally well taught. Year 11 Pathway (up to seven GCSEs taken in a year) scoops up students who need GCSEs, and fast – perhaps because they have bombed elsewhere, perhaps because they plan to do A levels or IB and need the ground work, or because their English requires a shot in the arm. IB (taken up by about one in five) average score was 28 in 2017. Resolutely not an academic hothouse, which is a large part of its appeal – 'Being force-fed academically just because she is bright would not suit my daughter,' remarked one mother – yet parents are confident that bright children will be sufficiently inspired and well enough taught to achieve all of which they are capable.

Mr Kilpatrick is keen on breadth, and has introduced the Sixth Form Passport, comprising the CAS elements (creativity, action and service) of the IB syllabus for all sixth formers, plus 'post-school survival skills'; EPQ is also encouraged. SEN students with mild to moderate learning difficulties, as well as social and emotional issues like anxiety and (a lack of) social skills, are well provided for by well regarded and qualified staff in a light and colourful room; school has CReSTeD status, and staff work closely with English and maths depts. Integration and acceptance are total here – everyone is screened on entry, and periodic assemblies on dyslexia to raise awareness mean it's just part of school life. The undiagnosed are also welcome to ask for support, for example at exam time, and

'Everyone who needs support, gets it,' according to one parent. 'The teachers will help you hundreds of times till you get it right,' affirmed one child.

Games, options, the arts: Twenty acres of pitches, including new all-weather pitch, and a multi-purpose sports hall with the nicest school pool we have ever seen – lifeguarding and kayak tuition also happen in it – mean there is plenty on offer at Sidcot. The size of the school causes some parents to bemoan the strength and depth of rugby talent – but naked aggression is not the Quaker way. Sidcot is not, perhaps, the place for an élite sportsperson – more serious players often belong to local clubs – although a pair of sisters have achieved considerable regional and national success at swimming, both in the pool and open water. The equestrian centre has opened to the public for livery, Pony Club and equestrian studies. Its purpose for the school seems to be more to provide qualifications (BTec, BHS) and opportunities for students to ride (some boarders bring their own steeds) than to identify and kick on young, promising riders. All benefit from an indoor and outdoor school (floodlit) and 160 acres of glorious country to hack in. Plenty else for those unmoved by ball games or horses, such as trampolining, archery, TV production, debating and so on. Newish sports development director giving increased focus on life skills acquired through sport.

Quaker half hour is held every week and presided over by sixth form elders, at which teachers and students have equal rights to speak and to be listened to

Arts are housed in a new light, airy centre which accommodates visual arts, drama and music. Visual arts astound in particular. We witnessed the most controversial A level art exhibit we had ever seen, depicting the conflicting duality of Muslim women, the siren beneath the burqa. Ceramics and textiles also noteworthy. All manner of artistic media are on offer, and those not studying art are welcome to scratch any creative itches at a club or society. DT and product design stand out too: from a man-powered bushfire extinguisher to an iPhone-powered record player – a range of practical, aesthetic and downright eccentric projects are realised. Seven drama productions a year; recent ones include Into the Woods and A Midsummer Night's Dream (directed by students) performed in the grounds; facilities exist to make film and radio also. International students are encouraged to take part, partly to improve their English – but Struwwelpeter in Chinese was surely not to be missed. School takes a show to Edinburgh every other year. Sidcot's music, the school readily admits, would appeal more to fans of One Direction than the Endellion Quartet, resulting in some of the school's most talented classical musicians choosing to take their lessons in Bristol, rather than at school – but they don't half sound impressive at concerts. The auditioned choir (all girls, necessarily limiting the repertoire) tends towards 'the Gareth Malone end of the spectrum', quite possibly because there has never been a tradition of church music. Facilities and tuition designed rather for music tech, creativity and composition.

Outdoor stuff on offer such as D of E, and good use is made of the extensive grounds for gardening, beekeeping and the construction of a nature trail, inter alia. Trips include a French exchange, Tanzania, Vienna for culture/art/language. PASS – Programme of Activities for Sidcot School – 'a co-curricular initiative based on our key values of integrity, stewardship, self-reflection, adventure and community'.

Sports and music are junior school favourites: everyone adored composing music for Tom and Jerry on the computer and the pop choir is – well, popular. Separate PE for girls and boys from year 3. Trips, laid on every year for each year group, also get thumbs up: a camp-out in the grounds for the littlest, progressing all the way to outdoor pursuits camp in Okehampton for year 6.

Boarding: Majority full but a few flexi boarders; around half from overseas. The five boarding houses are sprinkled through the grounds, facilities are clean, tidy yet homely; we were struck by the warmth and knowledge of each boarder displayed by the house staff. Three or four share a room in the younger years; sixth formers in ones or twos. Usual range of sporting and artistic activities after school and at weekends, plus trips to eg cinema, ice skating rink, local festivals.

Background and atmosphere: Sidcot's USP: everyone, nay everyone, we spoke to singled out the atmosphere at the school as being the reason for being there. The school's proud Quaker origins (dating from its founding in 1699), history and traditions are lived out every day, giving it a curiously contemporary feel which is so much more than lip service. The school's first ever founding director of peace and global studies has recently been appointed, with a brief to 'bring 21st century Quakerism to life' right through the curriculum, weaving in themes such as social justice, conflict resolution and global responsibility. Sidcot is now a 'change-maker school', as a member of the Ashoka movement, which aims to 'empower the next generation to lead social, environmental and economic development'. Specifically, the atmosphere is one of respect and tolerance – for those of all faiths and none, for different nationalities, for different gifts, skills or shortcomings, for each individual. Quaker half hour is held every week and presided over by sixth form elders, at which teachers and students have equal rights to speak and to be listened to.

Five boarding houses in the grounds, facilities are clean, tidy yet homely; we were struck by the warmth and knowledge of each boarder displayed by house staff

We had never met a more thoughtful bunch of young people. 'The children look out for each other, and the school does its best to bring out well-rounded young adults'; 'a home from home for your child, with similar principles as the ones we have brought them up with at home'; 'the teachers are accountable to the children' were just some of the views we heard. One mother described her daughter as a 'bruised and tender plant when she arrived at Sidcot', but who 'had turned into a strong, forthright and confident young woman, which is moving to see'. We heard about several instances of parents choosing Sidcot for its ethos (dread word) over other schools whose academic, sporting or musical prowess was more notable. Learning is conducted in a calm and conducive environment, where 'punishment is not a word we use,' said one member of staff; some parents though feel on occasion that the benign Quaker view of children needs to be tempered with a dose of realism when it comes to high jinks in class.

The Quaker foundations and conventions are not lost on the juniors, either. 'The elders are year 6 and we sit silently in a circle with our teachers at our Wednesday assemblies. We think about stuff like keeping secrets.' Perhaps because the children and their achievements in every field are fêted, there is no need for anyone to feel undervalued, 'We absolutely do not brag at this school,' said one perceptive year 6

Conveniently situated just beside the A38 running south from Bristol (thankfully with a bridge over it to get to the sports fields), the school's main façade is a pleasing white stucco building, with the inevitable less sightly additions behind it. The main complex of buildings is compact and extremely well signed, but there are some charming gardens in among them, covered in brightly coloured gazebos on the scorching summer day we visited, to represent each of four virtual houses. Sidcot has no physical house system, though there are (of course) five separate boarding houses sprinkled through the grounds, plus the meeting house: a little oasis of calm and quiet just metres from the main building. We were enchanted by the ponies grazing beyond the fence bordering the garden to one of the girls' boarding houses, with a tantalising glimpse of the Mendips behind.

Pastoral care, well-being and discipline: Respectively, exceptionally good and deploying the lightest of touches. We did not uncover any rebels, tearaways, lads or ladettes, and when quizzed, students listed acts likely to attract reproof as 'not listening, disobedience, laziness, doing what you want'. Hardly hanging offences. Censure from one's peers would be a greater deterrent, we sense. According to parents, the head is adamant about drink and drugs in school – one strike and you're out. Sidcot has no bar, unlike most boarding schools with a vibrant sixth form.

Pupils and parents: An intriguing mix of individuals conforming to shared expectations and outlook, but card-carrying Quakers a small minority. Though the students look conventional enough, with uniform on the posh side (striped shirts, blazers), we suspect that Sidcot families conform to fewer than usual independent school stereotypes. When asked what sort of parent would send a child to Sidcot, the head replied, 'Guardian readers indifferent to sipping sherry on the lawn on speech day, whose children see diversity as a strength, who are prepared to stand up for what they believe in'. According to the junior school head: 'The kind of parents who send their children to us are normal, down to earth and just want the best for them – some make considerable sacrifices for them to come here.' A few locals, refugees from Bristol schools and nearly 20 per cent from overseas thrown into the mix. Notable alumni include Sir George Trevelyan (dubbed the hippies' champion), geologist Robert Shackleton, founder of Macmillan Cancer Support, Douglas Macmillan, Zoe Wanamaker, Justin Webb, and Deborah Warner.

Entrance: All junior school hopefuls attend a two-day taster session, including assessments in maths, reading and spelling, non-verbal reasoning plus an informal interview with the head – but the policy is non-selective. Children are welcomed in at all stages; quite a few arrive in year 5 instead of starting middle school as they would under Somerset LA. Scholarships on offer from year 1, 'both talent and academic.'

Sidcot is academically non-selective so transfer is automatic (and highly praised) from the junior to the senior school; otherwise applications are taken at any stage except into years 11 and 13, and places offered on the basis of previous school reports and interviews at the school to 'children who will benefit from an academic education and activities at Sidcot and who will contribute to and benefit from the ethos of our school community', to quote the admissions policy.

Exit: The majority of juniors to the senior school (around 80 per cent), whence entry is automatic. Baseline assessments are done for setting and monitoring purposes. Some 40 per cent move on after GCSEs for a change if they have been there since nursery, some to a greater range of courses and subjects post 16, and quite possibly the brighter lights of Bristol. Destinations comprise old and new universities up and down the land to do an array of courses, with a leaning towards art and design; some gap years. One medic in 2017.

Money matters: Fees are stepped according to year group, and a loyalty discount (about 12 per cent for boarders, seven per cent for day) applies to anyone staying on to sixth form. In general, fees are noticeably lower than local boarding competition in Bristol, but more expensive than the Bristol day schools which have no boarding infrastructure to fund. Ten per cent sibling discount. Quaker families on occasion receive 100 per cent remission of fees. Scholarships awarded for academics or talent; level of funding is discretionary.

Remarks: A school more likely to produce the head of an NGO than a merchant bank. For those untroubled by notions of social pretension or academic snobbery, yet for whom a considerate altruistic atmosphere really matters, this is just the place

Stonar

57

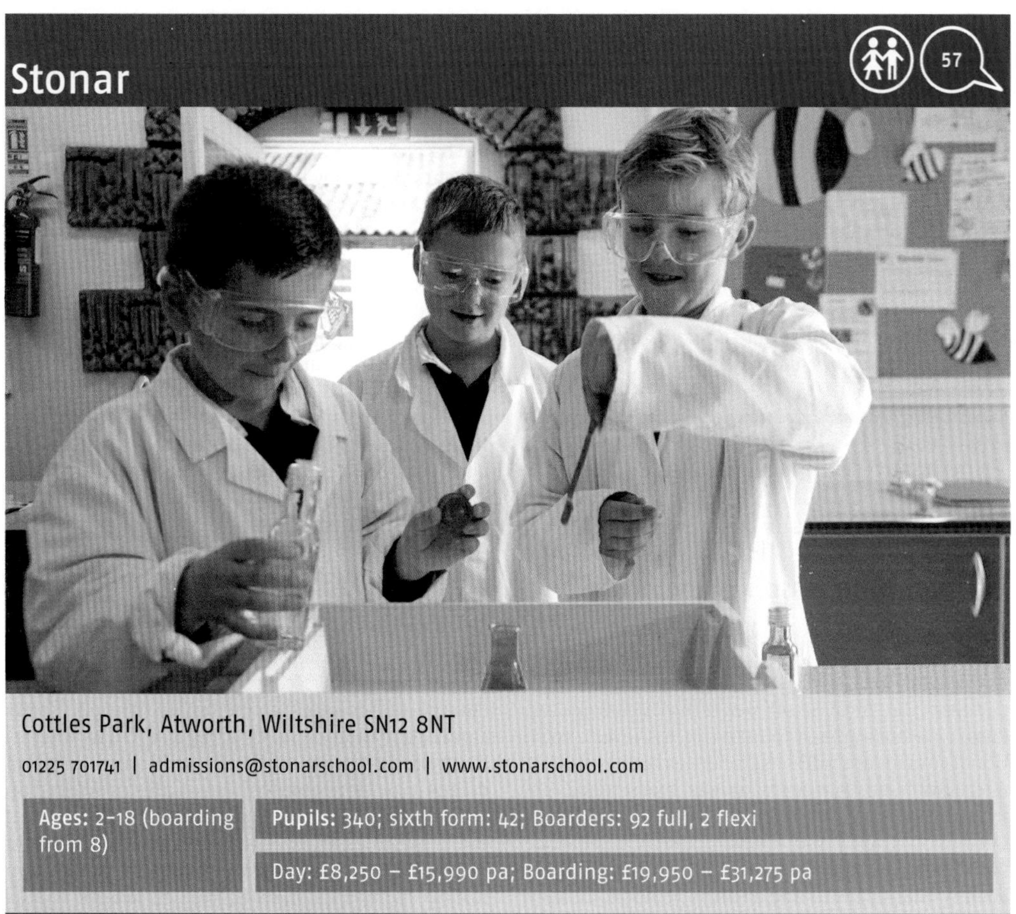

Cottles Park, Atworth, Wiltshire SN12 8NT

01225 701741 | admissions@stonarschool.com | www.stonarschool.com

Ages: 2-18 (boarding from 8)

Pupils: 340; sixth form: 42; Boarders: 92 full, 2 flexi

Day: £8,250 – £15,990 pa; Boarding: £19,950 – £31,275 pa

Head: Since 2015, Dr Sally Divall MA PhD PGCE, previously deputy head academic. Originally from north London, Sally gained a PhD in natural sciences at Cambridge before working at BP, the Bristol Exploratory, as a visiting lecturer at UWE and as a research fellow at Bath University. As a scientist she was inspired by the 'hands-on approach to learning' and teaching seemed to be a natural progression. Sally joined Stonar as head of physics in 1999 and has absolutely no intention of leaving. Parents are more than happy about this, one telling us, 'Dr Divall is an inspiring head-teacher and very approachable.'

Head of prep since 2008, Mr Mark Brain BA (Ed), formerly deputy head of Kelly College Prep (now Mount Kelly Prep). Also an independent schools inspector, Mark lives on site with his young family. His wife is a teacher in the senior school. Originally from the Cotswolds, Mark studied education at Exeter University and has taught in both state and private schools. He was director of sport at Repton and sport will always be his 'first love,' he told us. Still teaches PE as well as coaching local junior football and cricket teams outside of school. Parents told us, 'He has a calm and gentle manner with the children and has introduced a sound ethos having implemented 'growth mindset' across the school.'

Since 2013, Stonar has been part of the NACE schools group, an international educational group with 21 schools across five countries. Stonar is the only English school; others are in Spain, France, Italy and India.

Academic matters: Head prefers 'broad academic intake' rather than 'non-selective'. Value-added scores are more important than grades alone and the school uses the Yellis system from Durham University to keep track. The aim is to develop each individual pupil to help them reach their full potential, whatever that may be.

Parents told us, 'The equestrian staff are highly knowledgeable.' Horses can be loaned or pupils can earn a riding lesson by working as a stable help

In 2017, at A level, 48 per cent A*-B grades, 29 per cent A*-A. At GCSE, 48 per cent A*-A/9-7 grades. Pupils are encouraged to take three A levels; vocational courses are 'add-ons.' Sciences are popular at A level with most opting for at least one science subject or maths or psychology. The arts are also strong with photography and art particularly popular at both levels. Vocational courses include British Horse Society qualifications and a Leiths Toolbox Cookery Course. These courses allow pupils to indulge in their passion of riding (or cooking) and help to develop 'personal attributes' as 'academic qualifications are just not enough these days', says head.

With a staff to pupil ratio of 1:6, classes are small, usually around 15 or 16, and no more than 20. Girls we spoke to all agreed this is one of the advantages of Stonar, especially at A level when some subjects are one-to-one. Parents told us the teaching staff are 'incredibly supportive and inspiring,' and 'understanding and encouraging.' One mother added, 'Both my husband and I are educators and we are delighted with the standard of teaching and the sheer quality that Stonar offers.' The 'individualised support' that the school provides was mentioned several times. And sixth formers agreed, telling us how all their A level choices were fully supported by the school. High praise too for the careers advice; one aspiring doctor told us the career advice had been 'amazing'.

At the prep school, 'Getting the children out of their seats, out of their class and indeed out of the school makes learning more memorable and this is a driving force,' the head told us. Lessons are often linked to trips and activities. The curriculum focuses on improving not only the children's learning but also their understanding of what learning means. Parents are invited into the school at the end each topic and the pupils 'teach' their parents what they have learnt. The head has introduced a culture of 'growth mindset' across the school. The theory is that when children believe they can get smarter, they understand that effort makes them stronger. Therefore they put in extra time and effort, and that leads to higher achievement. A large part of this is rewards, which are celebrated in assemblies and the weekly newsletter. Pupils are taught in mixed ability classes and not streamed. 'We want to nurture a love of learning, not turn them off and create reserved, demoralised children,' the head told us. They benefit from the expertise of the languages and music staff from the senior school.

The learning support centre is in a separate house opposite the health and well-being centre, set around a cobbled courtyard. Prep pupils receive learning support in the form of extra maths and English lessons and/or a TA in class. In the senior school, around a fifth of pupils have TA support, though one-to-one not currently offered. Needs catered for include ADD, ADHD, ASD, Asperger's, dyspraxia, dyslexia and speech and communication difficulties. More complex needs are considered on an individual basis. One parent told us, 'they treat each [pupil] as an individual.' However, learning support is not just about special needs; one pupil told us she was having extra maths lessons to support her through her physics A level.

Games, options, the arts: For horse-lovers this is a dream come true. The new equestrian centre (British Horse Society approved) opened in March

Latest exciting addition is the new social area fitted with a bar (older pupils are allowed two ciders over a week), a projector and a Wii

2017 and is most impressive. There are stables for 65 horses, BSJA jumps, a floodlit, outdoor all weather manège, a cross-country schooling field with a wide variety of different fences, a large indoor school with viewing gallery and a lecture room. The Olympic-sized outdoor arena with seats is used for jumping and dressage as well as Christmas and Easter shows. Competition squads regularly compete on and off site including National Schools Equestrian Association competitions and Stonar's own inter-schools one day event championships.

Parents told us, 'The equestrian staff are highly knowledgeable.' Pupils with horses are up at 7am to muck out. Horses can be loaned or pupils can earn a riding lesson by working as a stable help. Around 50 per cent of pupils ride, but at various levels; some may own a horse, take qualifications and compete, others may just have a weekly riding lesson. And it's not just about the riding; stable management skills are taught too. However, the main priority at Stonar is academic studies and pupils told us that however passionate they are about horses, they are never allowed to let school work suffer.

Other sports include athletics, rounders, tennis, netball, hockey, rugby, football, badminton, swimming and cross-country. One parent suggested that additional PE options rather than just the traditional sports would be welcome. All the usual sports facilities including a swimming pool; lessons from pre-prep all the way up to year 12 when pupils can choose to do zumba or fitness instead. NACE Sports Olympics annually (hosted at Stonar recently). Plus an annual awards dinners for sports including riding – one pupil told us they're campaigning to get the same recognition for the arts.

In the prep school there is a progressive sports programme: pupils have sports lessons up to four times a week including basketball, tennis, rugby, athletics, swimming, gymnastics. New sports performance programme for older talented pupils, who receive specialist small group coaching in football, hockey and cricket.

Art is popular. Main art studio is above the sixth form centre, kitted out with kiln and adjoining photography studio and dark room. Separate sixth form studio. High standard of art and photography on display.

There's a new head of drama who sounds as if he may be shaking things up a little. One girl told us excitedly that he used to run a theatre company in London and has some more 'contemporary' ideas. Traditionally, the school has alternated the main annual production between musicals (Guys and Dolls, Oklahoma) and Shakespeare plays. This year something different may be on the cards, we were told. Speech and drama available as well as LAMDA and RADA qualifications. The prep school has a classic nativity play every year as well as a large summer production for all of years 3-6; last year it was Scheherazade.

Plenty of music groups including choir, chamber choir, wind band and orchestra and plenty of opportunities to perform, including at regular lunchtime rotary club concerts for local people. The annual NACE music festival is a highlight, bringing pupils from around the world together to perform. A fantastic opportunity and great fun, by all accounts. In the prep school there are termly musical assemblies and larger theatre performances twice a year. Formal carol concerts take place in Bath Abbey (a Christmas service and a summer service), plus musical concerts in the Wiltshire Music School.

Extracurricular activities aplenty. Sixth formers must do at least one club, younger years at least two, either at lunchtime or after school – everything from sports to debating to music to drama. D of E popular. Younger pupils can also turn to their elders for help with their studies – sixth formers run lunchtime clubs, Science Base and Maths Base.

Plenty of trips including ski trips and exchanges. One parent said, 'My two daughters have had opportunites to visit other NACE schools with sports, academic and choir groups.' There's a biannual trip to a sister school in Barcelona for years 5 to 8. Pupils stay in a 'very posh' hotel and go to the partner school every day, immersing themselves in Catalan life and, last year, studying Gaudi. Other trips include outdoor challenge residentials for years 3 and 4. Sixth formers have the opportunity to take part in charity expeditions. Last year one group built a polytunnel in Romania while another went to Borneo. This year a trip to Kenya is planned. All expeditions are funded by the sixth formers themselves with innovative fundraising events; baths of jelly particularly caught our attention.

Boarding: Stonar offers full or flexi boarding, no weekly, and the vast majority are full boarders. Very few board below year 7.

Some 65 per cent of boarders are from overseas, including pupils from America, Australia, Belgium, China, Holland, France, Germany, Nigeria, Russia, South Africa, Spain and Switzerland. Around a third of these pupils (mostly those from France, Germany and Spain) are short stay boarders, usually staying for just one term (occasionally for the year). Parents and pupils all very positive about this; one parent told us, 'My younger daughter spent a half term holiday in Madrid at the invitation of a boarder from Spain. It really is one big happy family!'

Three boarding houses, all of which have had a makeover (thanks to NACE). Ganbrook is above reception and houses younger pupils. York is the sixth form girls' house and is very much part of the school campus. Hart is a grade II listed farmhouse which now has a new boys' boarding wing. It is a short stroll away, set amongst the teachers' houses and slightly separated from the campus. This, we can imagine, would feel more like 'going home' at the end of the day. All houses have decent sized rooms in doubles or singles for sixth formers, and dorms of four for younger pupils. Common rooms all large with plenty of sofas and a TV but lacked decoration or homely touches on our visit. Perhaps this was because it was the beginning of the year? Hopefully the boarders will be able to put their stamp on it now (absolutely, yes, the school confirmed). Good kitchens for snacks. Latest exciting addition – still under construction – is the new social area fitted with a bar (older pupils are allowed two ciders over a week), a projector and a Wii.

Parents spoke highly of houseparents and 'the caring environment'. Plus, they told us, there's a great deal of fun; 'baking cakes, playing games, talent shows, movie and pizza nights. All the pupils are very supportive and encouraging of each other. Even when we relocated to be closer to the school (we are now 20 mins away) they still wish to board as they love school life so much!' Day pupils often stay for the evening activities (mocktails night, canapes night and ploughmans and science night all firmly in the diary for our guides) and everybody gets two free sleepovers per term.

No exeats; pupils are free to go home any weekend. For those at school, weekends are filled with trips to Bath, Laser Quest or Cotswolds Water Park. Whilst younger pupils have no choice but to join in, older pupils are given more freedom. Sixth formers can go out for up to five hours alone, and from year 10 groups of four can go to Bath in a taxi for the day.

Background and atmosphere: Stonar was originally established at Stour House in Sandwich and can be traced back as far as 1895. The school relocated to its current location in Wiltshire at the beginning of the second world war. Cottles Park is a grade II listed mansion set in rural countryside about eight miles from Bath. Riding was firmly established back in 1934 when the first pony, Tuffy, arrived and it now has a strong reputation in the horse world.

Since 2013 NACE has been funding Stonar as its flagship English school and new buildings and refurbishments have transformed it, giving it a modern edge. And a welcome international feel. Pupils now have an exciting programme of cultural and academic exchanges and events with schools in the NACE group.

As the number of boys grows, more upgrades and developments are inevitable. But the head aims to keep the school 'family-sized.' This is without doubt a strength and enables them to be adaptable and provide individual support. One pupil may be passionate about riding, another an aspiring musician, another may need learning support; all can be looked after well at Stonar, the head told us. The prep school has been fully co-ed for a number of years now, but the addition of boys to the senior school (it will be fully co-ed by 2019) will undoubtedly change the dynamics of what has always been 'a traditional girls' school.' On our visit we felt the change was being fully embraced by pupils and teachers alike.

Parents spoke highly of houseparents and the 'caring environment'. There's a great deal of fun; baking cakes, playing games, talent shows, movie and pizza nights

Parents say, 'The school is a good mix and has a nice feel to it. The size of the school and community gives it a family feel and it's not too overwhelming.' Prep school and nursery are very much part of the school on the campus; the building is separate but that's where the separation ends. Facilities are shared and little ones can be seen playing out on the front lawn of the main house every break and lunchtime. Inside, the main hall, used for assemblies, performances and drama, is central, with classrooms adjoining. Upstairs on a mezzanine level is the library, fitted out with cosy beanbag areas under the wooden rafters. Outside there are playgrounds, a play area with sandpit, a nursery sensory garden and a forest school for the younger years. The whole school comes together for celebrations such as carols at Bath Abbey and the Stonar summer fete.

'The grounds are amazing and my girls go for lovely hacks around the school parkland,'a parent enthused. The actual campus is a mix of old and new. It's easy to navigate and compact. Traditional wooden-style chemistry labs contrast with the newly upgraded physics laboratories. Library is a good size, equipped with PCs and used for lessons as well as after-school prep sessions. Sarum, a new cedar-clad classroom block opened in 2017, houses humanities and languages, along with a brand new ICT suite. The sixth form area has also been treated to a refurb with a plush new café and their own decked outside area. Years 7 and 8 can play on the Astroturfs and senior pupils have a designated 'side' for break times.

Technology has improved dramatically in recent years. Wi-fi now works well across the whole site and mobile signal has improved (not that phones are allowed). Several ICT suites with 3D printers, plus iPads available for use in language and science lessons. Recent addition of Show My Homework App is 'brilliant' according to sixth formers. In the prep school, the ICT suite is used for a computer science curriculum that involves programming and robotics – 'the children love it,' the head told us.

Large modern dining room, also used for awards dinners. Stonar is a 'no-nuts' school; pupils told us, 'Veggie options are always tasty; never an afterthought.'

There are hymns and prayers in assembly but pupils told us this is 'not a particularly religious school'. It is, however, a traditional school, and a strong house system carries pupils from prep to senior school. Lots of events including inter-house tug-of-war, cross-country, drama, music and sports, all led by sixth formers. As to be expected there is also a prefect system – our guides were all donning cloaks for our tour. Plus a school council and 'committees for everything' we were told. Pupils most definitely have a voice here and meetings are popular.

Pastoral care, well-being and discipline: We heard 'nurturing environment' from a number of parents. And pupils agreed, telling us that Stonar is a very supportive environment and teachers are approachable and helpful. Plus, 'everybody knows each other' and it has 'a personal feel to it'. One mother told us that her daughter, who had been bullied at a previous school, felt reassured by teachers who not only worked her hard but let her 'play hard and, most importantly, be herself.'

Discipline is based around asking pupils to question their actions and consequences. One parent told us, 'I really like it that there aren't reams of ill-thought-through rules; rather, the children are really encouraged to think about values instead.'

Nurses (very popular for chats, according to our guides) hold daily drop-in sessions at the health and well-being centre – a very well equipped centre with girls' and boys' rooms plus showers. Counsellor available once a week.

Pupils and parents: The prep school is fully co-ed and the senior school first accepted its first 11 boys in 2016. However, there are now 38 boys in the senior school, some 18 per cent of the total. It's expected to be fully co-ed by 2019.

Pupils we met were happy to be back at school after the summer holidays. They were enthusiastic about Stonar, well-spoken, and confident without a trace of arrogance. One girl told us, 'it really isn't a case of just going to school and then going home at the end of the day; it's a whole community thing – there's much more going on than just school.' Another girl said she was sold on Stonar after reading Mallory Towers books.

Parents of both day pupils and boarders are pleased with communication with the school.

One said, 'I have even had same day responses sent at the weekend!' Another added, 'Be it from the head to the tutor and everyone in between, we feel we have had all matters dealt with quickly, professionally but in a friendly, supportive and helpful manner.' There is a weekly newsletter plus the head holds informal weekly drop-in breakfast sessions for parents.

Entrance: Open days and taster events available. For entry to the prep school, teachers discreetly assess literacy and numeracy as well as social interactions and natural approach to learning. The head of prep told us, 'Judging whether a child approaches learning with a growth or fixed mindset is an important part of our process.' If there are learning issues a child will be invited for a second taster day and the learning support department carry out more formal assessments. Entry to nursery, open all year round, at 3.

For entry to the senior school, entrance exam to assess strengths and weaknesses – Stonar is a non-academically selective school. For sixth form entry, school reports and an interview with the head. If English is a second language pupils must take an EAL exam and a maths paper.

Parents told us, 'The site makes transition much less stressful between prep and senior...it is not daunting.' One parent whose child started mid-year said they were 'happy from day one.'

Exit: Around 80 per cent of pupils move from the prep school to the senior school, and 60 per cent stay on for the sixth form after GCSEs. Some 80 per cent of sixth formers go to university.

University destinations include Bath, Durham, Exeter, Imperial College London, York and University of Hong Kong. To date, pupils have gone on to become journalists, doctors, actors, officers in the armed forces, international riders, barristers, designers and authors. Old girls include big names in riding such as junior and young rider gold medallist Georgie Spence, and twice Olympic short-lister Lucy Weigersma; actor Romola Garai and controversial author Gitta Sereny. Boys soon to be added.

Money matters: Scholarships offered for entry into years 7, 9 and 12 for academia plus art, drama, music, sport and riding. Sixth form scholarships are based on GCSE results, school reports, an assessment paper, plus an interview by the head.

Remarks: Stonar is transforming itself from a traditional girls' school into a modern co-ed with a strong international influence. New buildings keep popping up and makeovers have been swift; this school is definitely embracing change. However, it isn't losing sight of what makes it special: it's a small school that treats pupils as individuals. You don't need to be horsey to go here, but with facilities like this you will probably end up having the odd lesson – why wouldn't you?

Stover School

58

Stover, Newton Abbot, Devon TQ12 6QG

01626 354505 | registrar@stover.co.uk | www.stover.co.uk

Ages: 3-18 (boarding from year 5)

Pupils: 356; sixth form: 70; Boarders: 50 full, 5 weekly, 5 flexi

Day: £7,872 – £12,729 pa; Boarding: £16,695 – £26,076 pa

Head: Since 2014, Richard Notman BSc. Studied finance and stats at Birmingham University but soon discovered he was not made to be an auditor. After taking his PGCE in Manchester, he spent the next eight years in inner-city comps before teaching maths at Withington Girls School and then becoming head of maths at Alderley Edge School for Girls. From there he went to Longridge Towers, Northumberland as deputy head, and finally Cundall Manor School, Yorkshire as head teacher before he swapped the moors for the Devon hills.

'A breath of fresh air', said one parent. He is more than up for the challenge and is excited to be at Stover. He says he 'can cherry-pick the best of state and independent practice' and feels he now has the experience, knowledge and confidence to take the school forward. Plus it's rural, small, non-selective, 3 to 18, and co-ed; everything he wants in a school. It's not just a new life for him though; his wife and young family live in the school grounds, and his two children are in the prep school. He's keen to make this a family venture, and one parent

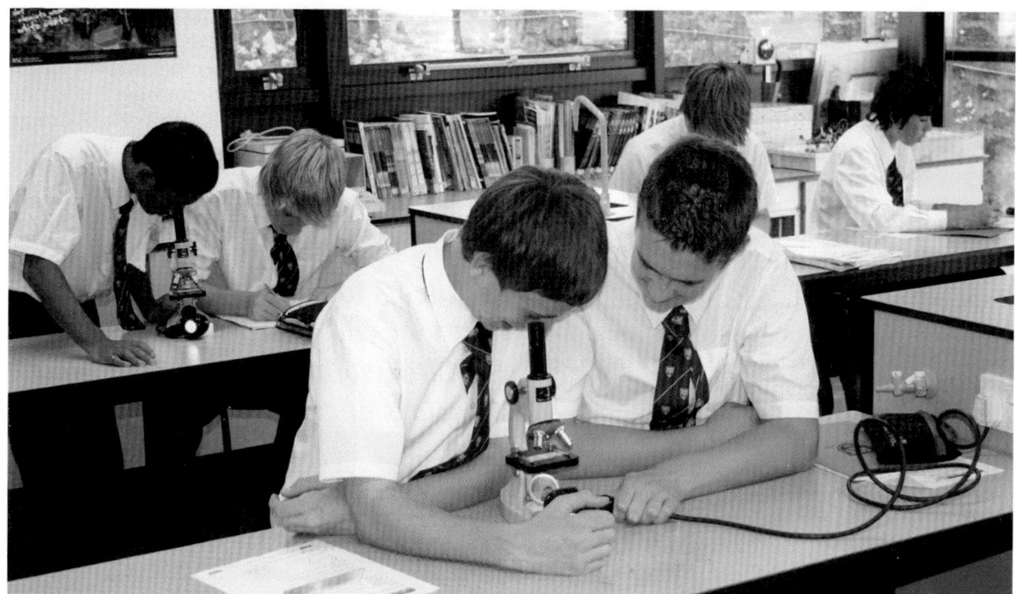

told us, 'Both Mr Notman and his wife Helen have done everything they can to integrate their family into the school and make themselves known and accessible to all. They are a tremendously friendly family, and have placed emphasis on getting to the root of what the parents and children of Stover want changed and improved.'

Some major changes (or 'tweaking' as he calls it) are under way and parents have been impressed so far. 'Communication from the school has been excellent in this matter,' they say. Research-based learning has been introduced and teachers have all taken it on board enthusiastically. Parents said, 'He has focused the staff on the bigger picture and has given a renewed energy across the school.' Pupils are 'very inspired by his assemblies and messages he is getting across.' His to-do list includes major makeovers for the sixth form and boarding; getting parents more involved; and making as much use as possible of the extensive grounds. One parent told us, 'The head has been fantastic at attracting new children, as Stover was good but too small.'

Head of prep school since 2016, Mr David Burt, previously head of primary at Compass International School, Madinat Khalif, Qatar. He has a degree in geography and sociology and a PGCE in primary education. Originally from the Isle of Wight, his hobbies are based around the outdoors and the sea: he is a keen fisherman who likes nothing more than spending a few hours on a beach or in a boat attempting to catch fish. He also enjoys watching and playing a wide range of sports and is an avid gym-goer. He is married and has two small children.

Academic matters: At GCSE in 2017, 30 per cent A*-A/9-7 grades. At A level, 32 per cent A*/A and 58 per cent A*-B. Recently introduced vocational qualifications: BTecs in home economics, sport, ICT and performing arts. Maths is a strong subject with top grades at both levels. Stover has performed well in recent Regional Maths Challenges. Chemistry another strong subject with three students recently winning places at the prestigious Salters Chemistry camps. Photography very popular at A level. Spanish is taught from reception and French from year 3.

Extracurricular activities include table tennis (big here), fencing, clay shooting and more recently a Stover riding team. D of E and Ten Tors are very popular and a part of life here

Stover welcomes pupils of all abilities. One parent said, 'It's a non-selective school and does very well in terms of exam results given its mixed ability (and after the grammar schools cream the top academics off).' A boarding school with 15 per cent of overseas students, and English is not everyone's first language; this is sometimes reflected in the grades. Parents speak highly of the learning support department, and a whole range of learning difficulties are well looked after here, with one-to-one specialist support for autism or Asperger's. One said, 'When extra help is required they have the staff to support your child and our daughter was given her own "adult" in maths to sit with her and help her on a one-to-one basis, which helped hugely.'

Along with the introduction of research-based learning, Stover is setting up 'bring-your-own-device'. It is planning to invest heavily in a new (and safe) server instead of upgrading equipment. This will give teachers a new teaching aid, encouraging pupils to research online and become more tech savvy on their own computers. The ISI inspectors reported that 'teaching was excellent,' but we heard some concerns from parents about its quality. One said, 'I think there should be a review of the current teaching staff to ensure any weaker members of the team receive up-to-date training to help them improve their methods.'

Games, options, the arts: Extensive grounds and good sports facilities. Pupils 'relish the 60+ acres at Stover.' There are six all-weather floodlit tennis courts (some recently resurfaced), netball courts, a gym, plus football, rugby, hockey and cricket pitches. The only drawback is that Stover is a small school and there aren't always enough players of the same standard to make winning teams. One parent said, 'They seem to punch above their weight and have won hockey and netball leagues recently against much bigger schools.' However, other parents agreed that there's room for improvement: they would like to see 'a bit more sport and a few more fixtures in the senior school,' as well as 'investment in a school swimming pool.' Extracurricular activities include table tennis (big here), judo, fencing, clay shooting and more recently a Stover riding team. With the school on the edge of the moors, D of E and Ten Tors are very popular and are a part of life here. The head has linked up with Devon Schools Sports Partnership so that other local schools can make use of the grounds too. They hosted the Devon Schools' Area Athletics Cross-Country Championships recently with over 350 competing athletes.

Good music department. One parent said her daughter 'has been inspired by the head of music.... they have nurtured her talent; she was very disengaged with it when she first joined.' Most pupils learn an instrument – the ukulele is popular in the prep school – and there's plenty of concerts and groups to join: the orchestra, brass and jazz bands and choirs. Another parent said, 'Stover has several choirs and is very good at singing and music. They win almost everything in local and regional competitions. My son's year even went to Bruges Cathedral after winning one competition.' Productions, assemblies and concerts all take place in the dome-shaped Jubilee Hall which also houses a recording studio and practice rooms (more rooms recently added).

As well as music, performing arts and public speaking are strong themes throughout the prep and senior school. Regular productions and plays, including one each year for the prep and the pre-prep. 'The ones I have seen are very well produced. I went to Bugsy Malone the other year and the Match Girls last year. So, very different ones,' said one parent. Stover also offers LAMDA speech and drama lessons with Stagecentre plus performance exams.

Pupils 'love being able to go outdoors to learn – in science and art they will often make use of the natural world around them.' Great displays and some impressive work

The art department has a building to itself. It's well set out with art downstairs, a separate sixth form area at the back, and photography upstairs. Art studio the latest add on. Pupils 'love being able to go outdoors to learn – in science and art they will often make use of the natural world around them.' Great displays and some impressive work including a John Lennon mural, and large fish sculptures inspired by a recent trip to the aquarium. We were particularly impressed by the photography upstairs, including some portraits taken on a trip to Brick Lane. Good take up for A level art.

Clubs or daily activity sessions take place at lunchtime, with a late-ish school finishing time of 4.30pm. Mixed messages from parents on this. It suits some, but not all. When we were there we saw the Ukulele Club doing karaoke, and the Ready Steady Fry club had just finished making dough in the well-designed home economics room. Other activities, apart from the usual offerings, include bush-craft, astronomy, Dragons' Den, the Raving Reporters, Knitting Club and Man Choir. There's also plans to make more use of the grounds and set up horticultural and farming activity clubs.

Day trips from reception, residential trips from year 4, with a night away, then a three-day trip to Cornwall in year 5, three days in Mount Batten for year 6. As well as language trips abroad, there are regular theatre trips, art trips to galleries locally and in London, field trips to Dartmoor, history trips to Flanders, and a recent sixth form expedition to Tanzania.

Boarding: The head sees Stover as different, not as 'regimented' as other boarding schools; he says it's ultimately 'a school, that has boarding provision.' Admissions criteria have been changed and there is now much more focus on language (interviews by Skype). There is also a more varied mix of nationalities (currently 17), with pupils coming from Bulgaria, Serbia, Russia as well as China, Vietnam, Spain, Germany and Cuba, though Brits now in the majority in both houses. The plan is to recruit mainly full boarders and offer the flexi option in a very limited and controlled fashion – they don't want it to 'feel like a motel.' Short stays will still be offered during the summer as these serve as good tasters, and day pupils will still be able to take advantage of the wrap-around care.

Girls board on the opposite side of the main school building to the boys. Both areas have been recently refurbished. The boys are lucky to be in the original part of the building with high ceilings, ornate cornices, huge bay windows with shutters, original fireplaces, domed ceilings, arched hallways and great views. It's very tidy; the military background of their houseparent keeps them in check, apparently. He's also well known for getting the boys together for regular evening chats round the dining table. Cheerful rules boards dotted around – live, laugh, love etc – make it feel homely. The large dorms feel light and spacious.

The girls' side, without the original features, is less impressive. The common room felt stuffy, and although it was equipped with PCs, a Wii, a drinks area and dining table, it didn't have the same inviting feel as the boys' room. On the plus side, the girls do have single, double and treble rooms as well as dorms. When we were there the girls were obviously getting ready for the prom, dresses proudly displayed on most wardrobes. Good-sized showers and bath facilities. In fact all the facilities are good – kitchen areas, drinks area and laundry facilities all promote independent living as much as possible.

Usual rules for mobile phones and such, but all seemed pretty relaxed. The boarders here really get to know each other, and the staff, well. Parents say it has a 'friendly, family atmosphere.' Some students even come back for more. Gap year students help out with admin duties, evening activities like football or tennis, and weekend trips to the cinema, the beach, shopping and just recently Stonehenge and Thorpe Park.

Background and atmosphere: Stover School is set in beautiful grounds, 64 acres of parkland located between Dartmoor and the sea. Founded in 1932 by two sisters on the Stover Estate, the object was to help pupils lead independent lives. Boys and girls have been in the prep school since it started in 1996, and boys in the senior school since 2005. The Clock House, built in 1843 and housing the prep, was originally stables and is set around a charming cobbled courtyard. Several of the classrooms have interconnecting doors and are linked by very narrow hallways and stairs. It's small, some would say it feels cramped; others would say it's full of character.

The main house, built of granite ashlar, is an impressive sight as you drive in. With its double flight of portico steps it wouldn't look out of place on a film set. Inside, the grand entrance hall continues to impress with high ceilings, beautiful plasterwork and ornate fireplaces. The school is proud of its heritage and cups, plaques and photos adorn the corridors. The rest of the school is housed in various well-designed buildings and wooden outbuildings in the perfectly manicured grounds.

The Millennium building is modern and bright with science labs downstairs, and maths upstairs. Floor to ceiling windows, new equipment and colourful murals by a teacher make the labs cheerful and inviting. Small class sizes also mean that there is always enough equipment. Fish, gerbils and even an adopted stray ginger cat add to the happy vibe here. Recent trips include The Big Bang and the Eden Project. Upstairs are two bright and sunny maths rooms, linked by a large balcony, also used as form rooms.

Separate wooden buildings or cabins are used for English, humanities and modern languages. All freshly painted; we could still smell the paint – something else the head has done to freshen up the school.

Amongst the acres and acres of land, there's a large playground with a sandpit, a wooden pirate ship, a football pitch and even an outdoor chess board. The new outdoor classroom has replaced the forest school that was destroyed by bad weather. There's a pond, a fire pit and parents have recently planted fruit trees. They are keen to make as much use of the grounds as possible with activities like bushcraft and gardening club. The nursery is next to the playground and is a homely space for toddlers from 8am to 4pm. The school provides wrap-around care from 7.30am until 6.30pm for prep school pupils from 6 years old.

All pupils agree full-heartedly on two things at Stover. Firstly, it's friendly. And secondly, the food is excellent. We saw long queues of hungry pupils

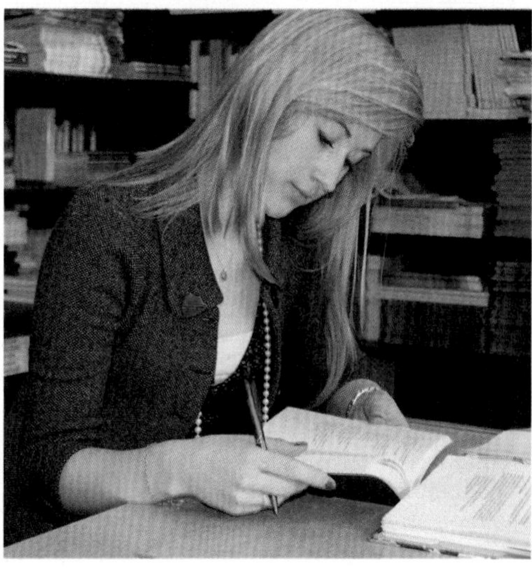

looking forward to the curry of the day. One said, 'I love Roastie Wednesday and Fishy Friday!' and apparently lots of pupils happily get dropped off early in time for the boarders' breakfast.

Parents like 'the friendly, family atmosphere.' One told us, 'We chose Stover for a number of reasons – yes, the grounds are lovely and the buildings beautiful but a school needs to give more than that. We were inspired by the ethos of the school as a whole. You don't have to get the highest scores in maths and they aren't going to force your child into a shape they don't naturally fit. [Stover] helps them to excel in the areas they have a passion for.'

Pastoral care, well-being and discipline: Well-behaved, well spoken and polite. Good behaviour is part of life here and is instilled at a young age – walk into any prep class and they will all stand. The pupils we spoke to seemed happy and proud of their school. Due to its small size, problems are spotted quickly and dealt with swiftly. Everybody knows everybody, but there is a solid support network of house parents, tutors, the school nurse, the school counsellor and the school chaplain if needed. The chaplain takes an active role in school life as well as regular collective worship and running the Christian Union Group.

All pupils agree full-heartedly on two things at Stover. Firstly, it's friendly. And secondly, the food is excellent. One said, 'I love Roastie Wednesday and Fishy Friday!'

The house system runs all the way through the prep and senior school and helps to give the pupils a sense of belonging. It's also great to bring out the competitive streaks. There are three houses, but strangely they are then split into boys and girls, making it six houses in all. The pupils we spoke to had no idea why it was like this as the only aspect they are separated for is sport. Presumably this is just a hangover from days gone by when boys and girls didn't mix. Strange that it hasn't changed with the times.

Pupils and parents: Day pupils from Newton Abbot, Exeter, South Hams, Torbay, Bovey Tracey, Plymouth. Boarders mainly from overseas. Parents mostly in professional occupations. Good bus service, or parents can take advantage of the wrap-around service from 7.30am to 6.30pm.

Communication is good, there's even a parents' app for news, events and photos. Plus Soundcloud to access all the latest music. Friends of Stover are always busy fundraising, and the upcoming Summer Ball was causing a bit of a buzz. 'There is also a monthly Friend's of Stover coffee morning where parents meet with the headmaster and his wife, and can exchange information, chat and generally catch up, which is lovely,' said one mother.

Entrance: Main entry points at 4, 7 and 11. By interview, school reports, and a taster day where academic ability and attitude to learning are assessed in an informal manner. One parent told us, 'They focus a lot on getting big friendship groups and not allowing cliques in prep school; new pupils are embraced.' Another said, 'We all found the entrance process very good. The older two started half way through the year but, they didn't seem to have any problems fitting in and finding their feet. The staff were welcoming, helpful and informative and communication with us was good. Since starting we have not had one single morning that they haven't wanted to go to school.' The school also has a system of parent class reps to help the new parents settle in – 'one parent per class keeps a database of details so that round-emails can be distributed with details of coffee mornings, birthday parties and play-dates – you soon feel like part of the furniture even when you've only been at the school for a matter of months!'

Exit: Most prep school pupils move up to the senior school, with a few peeling off to local grammars. Around 60 per cent leave after GCSEs, mostly to non-fee-paying alternatives. Popular university choices are Plymouth, Exeter, Bristol, Cardiff and Falmouth; one off to study medicine and surgery at Plymouth in 2017. One leaver worth a mention is Debra Newbury, awarded the MBE for her services to transatlantic rowing.

Money matters: Academic, music, art and sport scholarships available at most ages up to 20 per cent of day fees. Two means-tested scholarships at year 10 and sixth form, the Maurice Key and Laurus scholarships offering up to 100 per cent of day fees. There's a maths scholarship available to international sixth form students covering 25 per cent of fees at Stover and 10 per cent of fees at Plymouth University. Armed forces and the police force are offered a 10 per cent discount.

Remarks: Stover is a small, friendly school. It's for mixed abilities, and for those that wouldn't suit a larger mainstream setting. It's undergoing some major changes. For the better. Everyone agrees there are 'exciting times ahead'. As one parent put it, 'It was a good school in many ways, but now I think it has the chance to be really outstanding.' And having met the heads, we think this is just the beginning. One to watch.

Talbot Heath School

59

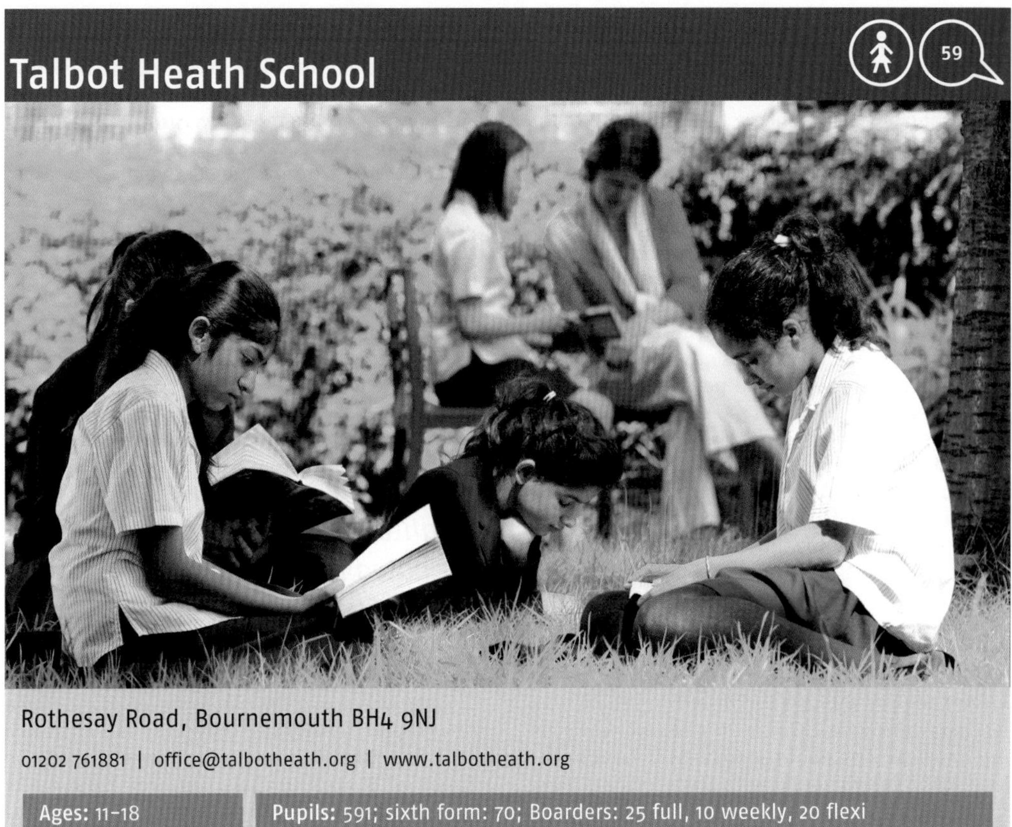

Rothesay Road, Bournemouth BH4 9NJ

01202 761881 | office@talbotheath.org | www.talbotheath.org

Ages: 11-18

Pupils: 591; sixth form: 70; Boarders: 25 full, 10 weekly, 20 flexi

Day: £13,857 pa; Boarding: £23,397 – £24,546 pa

Head: Since 2010, Mrs Angharad Holloway, previously head of MFL and IB at The Royal High School, Bath. Married, with two girls at the junior school. Mrs Holloway has made some 'fantastic changes,' said a parent, who described the the previous head as somewhat old fashioned. Not so Mrs Holloway, who is gently updating school, curriculum and thinking with a largely conservative constituency of parents. Lively energy – 'enthusiastic all the time,' said one mum. Not goaded by Jeremy Paxman on his visit, so unlikely to be shaken by much.

Keen her girls should have coping strategies for life, and teaches women and leadership to her 12 year olds, who end the course understanding not just about leadership, but also work/life balance and the right to flexible working. Teaches international politics to 11 year olds to broaden their horizons. Most desired quality for her girls on leaving school – resilience. Quite.

Academic matters: 'A first class education for girls,' say parents, who expect results – '[the] priority's always academic,' said one. And they achieve good results. In 2017, 76 per cent of A levels were A*-B (44 per cent of these A*/A). GCSEs – 58 per cent A*-A/7-9 grades. 'We do it well,' says the head. 'We are not a hothouse, but [we] do wish each girl to give of her best.' This is strongly felt in the atmosphere of this school. It's not a school where it is cool to muck around. Girls are very aware of why they are there and the importance of exams – 'all the girls want to achieve,' said a parent – but there are light touches. One mum described how her daughter had the school webcam – situated in a nesting box in the woods – on while she revised, so she could keep an eye on the babies.

A great school for value added. Entry requirements not stringent, so the high standards achieved in exams are all the more remarkable. At least in part due (says the head) to being an all-girl environment where girls can flourish – there is not that 'second's hesitation' before a hand goes up. Attracts a number who didn't make the grammars, who do very well – 'I think it's because...the staff genuinely care that the girls do well. Parents' evenings are very businesslike – this is what we need to do for your daughter, and this is how we will do it.'

'Subjects are traditional,' said a parent, 'nothing weird.' It is a conventional and fairly short list (classical civilisation finds a natural home here), but with Mrs Holloway at the helm, with her aim of holistic education, parents can be confident the girls are not being limited. Good take up (around 40 per cent) for A level chemistry and biology – the girls say the teaching of biology is outstanding. Physics is not so popular (just 10 per cent), and the results are less stellar. The head has set up a number of projects with local universities: music, drama – even forensic science; and of course there are her own pet subjects – international politics and women and leadership. Extended Project is also available. Languages are limited to French, Spanish and Latin, and some would like to see German back on the curriculum (it was dropped due to low uptake). But extracurricular Italian was implemented to assist a girl who wanted to study modern languages at university, and attracted a number of other takers, all enthusiastic about achieving GCSE Italian in a year. 'They provide extra if they can,' said a parent.

Sixth formers spoke with great enthusiasm of coming into school with extracurricular questions about favourite subjects and discussing them with teachers during lunchtime – 'It's like we're exploring and learning about it together.' Lunchtime lectures are very popular with sixth formers – one spoke eagerly about listening to Professor Frances Ashcroft talking about ion channels – 'they suddenly fitted in to life.'

Good computer provision: science block has dedicated space for computers, CAT block has a computer room for younger seniors, and lower and upper sixth each have a computer room.

Learning support gets a thumbs up from the girls – apparently no stigma here. 'They help a friend with her spelling every week,' said one matter of factly. Unusually, extra sessions from learning support are free here. Around 10 per cent have support for a range of mild learning disabilities, and they can drop a subject to make life easier. Girls have the highest opinion of teachers, who apparently go out of their way to help those who are struggling. One pupil, who had what she described as a 'maths crisis', spoke with enormous praise and affection about the maths teacher who devoted so much time to helping her regain skills and confidence. Lunchtime maths and science clinics available for those who are struggling.

One mum described how her daughter had the school webcam – situated in a nesting box in the woods – on while she revised, so she could keep an eye on the fledglings

Girls who speak English as a second language are welcome, providing they pass the entrance exam. Specialist in-house EAL lessons, and will be supported by staff in class. Children from many countries, including Russia, Spain, Germany and Jordan.

Lots of change in the staff – around 50 per cent in the last four years (but largely due to retirement). Three classes in each year. Small class sizes (maximum of 20) please parents, who believe they promote good relationships between staff and pupils – and of course get those results.

Games, options, the arts: Dedication to sporting excellence described by parents as 'second to none'. Special tennis programme designed with the nearby West Hants tennis club. About 10 girls are enrolled on the programme, and it is pricey, although the school awards a scholarship to tennis players, so that they are not paying overall more than a regular full fee payer. There is no wish to expand numbers of elite tennis players, so competition to get a place is fierce.

Specialist programmes are not limited to tennis: Talbot Heath has 20 girls at national level in 14 sports, including tennis, netball, rowing and badminton, and there are Youth Olympians among the pupils. This school is small enough to tailor-make education for individual girls, and flexible teaching accommodates the need for elite athletes to train and travel around the country to tournaments, whilst still providing a rigorous education.

But although there are the elite – and yes, they are cool – genuine efforts are made to encourage all: there are some 56 rowers and 70 netball players of all abilities who turn up to training sessions. One parent said they are always coming up with weird and wonderful sports to keep the girls engaged.

'[Sporting] facilities are not as good as at more expensive schools,' said a parent, 'things need to be bigger and better.' In particular, a new pool to replace the 'tired' existing outdoor pool, or at least a cover so year round swimming would be possible, said another: an indeed an indoor swimming pool will be part of a 600 seat auditorium about to start construction. The pavilion on the sports field is a bit ropey (and match teas 'could be a bit nicer' too), but although facilities are not as 'fantastic as they could be...it doesn't really matter,' said one. 'The staff are the thing, and they're amazing, and they work really long hours.' The level of sporting excellence at this school suggest their facilities are indeed secondary to success.

Excellence here is not limited to sports: there are members of the National Youth Ballet, the National Youth Choir, the National Children's Orchestra, the National Youth Orchestra and Wessex Youth Orchestra. Those outstanding in certain areas can drop a subject and have a reduced timetable to accommodate their specialist subject. Many win classes at the Bournemouth Music Festival, and there are monthly informal concerts for parents and friends, as well as more formal affairs.

Drama is popular: and although the drama block is a bit scruffy, it is clearly well loved, with an effective (if claustrophobic) curtained black box space. There are five productions a year, using the black box or the decent sized stage in the school hall. Girls often write their own adaptions – The Lion, The Witch and The Wardrobe was in dress rehearsal when we visited, written by 14 GCSE drama pupils. At another recent production, a parent described things as being '... stuck together...Heath Robinson style,' but the parents we spoke to appreciated the team spirit and the 'all hands on deck' feel, and pupils certainly have a wonderful time.

There's a well-attended debating society, very popular with girls after their stint with the head in international politics. Art is a strong department, say parents, although conditions are rather cramped. The CAT block includes a room with a battalion of sewing machines – certainly the warmest in the school (everywhere else kept at a fairly brisk temperature; no falling asleep in muggy classrooms here); there are old but well-preserved cookers in the food technology room, where lower sixth is taught a range of low cost dishes in preparation for university.

Boarding: Glossy new facilities in St Mary's boarding house (after a mediocre report from Ofsted).

Spacious shared dormitories for those in years 6, 7, 8 and 9, with a cubicle effect (giving semi privacy) created by desks and cupboards, all in crisp new pale wood. No bunk beds. Own rooms from year 10, which increase in size considerably for those in upper and lower sixth. The boarding house has a rather clinical feel at the moment (it has only recently been finished), but the art department is going to provide some pieces to make it feel a bit more homely.

Bathroom facilities clean and new – 'the shower's better than home,' said one girl feelingly. Food varies from average to good, depending on the chef that day, say boarders. Practice room with a piano, and comfy lounges with TV and Wifi. Boarders can have laptops, Kindles and phones – although latter removed at night.

The 40 or so boarders mix across age groups – which creates a family feel, says the housemistress. Boarders seem very happy and well cared for. Most stay at school for the weekend, and are kept busy with a variety of activities, from ice cream making and adventure days to archery and shooting, evena pamper afternoon with homemade facial scrubs (inspired by a trip to Lush).

Background and atmosphere: School formed in 1886 by Mary Broad to provide a first class liberal education for girls. She shocked the locals by exercising her girls on the local common and taking them on trips around Europe.

'Traditional' is a word which comes up a lot when speaking to parents (although the current head is certainly blowing away any remaining dusty elements). Curriculum, staff, behavioural expectations – all traditional, and parents like it. Attractive to one parent for being 'well structured, organised and friendly, [with a] structured discipline.' It is a disciplined environment – although it didn't feel stifling. But rebellious and disruptive girls would certainly stand out; and if their behaviour continued, would need to find a home elsewhere. C of E school, but focus primarily on fundamental values, so those of all faiths fit comfortably. Don't have to attend faith assemblies, but most choose to.

Rather foreboding buildings in the pine woods (but what a lovely smell). Some 30s charm, particularly a gorgeous gym which looks as though it has been perfectly preserved since the building's inception (there's a modern sports hall too). Even has original WW2 bunker classroom, complete with toilet buckets bearing TH emblems. Flags festoon the ceiling of the language corridor. There is art, and it's very good, but it's not spread lavishly around the place (apart from a few entrance displays: a sleepy china pig in bed with many covers, pop art shoes, and the school birthday quilt which all pupils embroidered). School is extremely well ordered, with tidy notice boards.

Chosen by one parent who moved to the area for the selective grammars, but fell for Talbot Heath. She 'loved the calmness...the silence during lessons, and the sense of purpose [in the school]'. One pupil, who chose the school after looking at three in the area, did so on the basis that it was the most welcoming, and said they 'focused on me as an individual.' The individual point is one frequently mentioned by parents, particularly in the context of the local school options: the grammars are big and impersonal, you're just one of the crowd; here teachers treat girls as individuals and want them to succeed. The grammars expect 14 GCSEs. Only nine or 10 taken at Talbot Heath, to make time for the rest of life – for sport, music and drama. One sixth former said she felt she had learnt that you need to spend time doing things just because you enjoy them.

Navy uniform, with a super blue cloak for the juniors (or coat alternative for the self-conscious). No uniform for sixth formers, and although there is the standard no-denim rule, girls succeed in looking very relaxed in skirts and leggings. More comfortable than smart, but these girls have a tremendous sense of purpose. Sixth form common rooms with kitchen facilities, with which they are tremendously pleased. The girls appreciate being treated more like adults in the sixth form, and like the tutorial feel of some of the lessons – cosy further maths lessons for two at the moment. The sixth formers we met were friendly and articulate, but didn't have that public school confidence bordering on arrogance.

Communication good – they do take notice of feedback, said a parent who had protested about the large amount of homework expected of year 9 compared to other independent schools. Another said 'food...is the biggest moan,' but she thought the school was trying to address the issue (on the day of our visit it varied from average pasta to excellent sticky toffee pudding). Parent Staff Society (PSS) meets every three months and responds to every point raised: apparently the PSS works hard to try and keep parents involved after the increase in independence expected of the girls after the move to senior school. Parent portal has got better recently, and the school is proud of its new website.

Glossy new facilities in St Mary's boarding house. Bathrooms clean and new – 'the shower's better than home,' said one girl feelingly

Pastoral care, well-being and discipline: This is a strong community, and there is a great feeling of vigilance here. Teachers will go out of their way to support pupils, and parents had high praise for their efforts. It's a very supportive environment, and several parents commented on the girls' tendency to encourage and care for each other – 'they positively want each other to succeed'.

Senior school head says there is a strong ethos of respect and care, so those who don't follow this stand out a mile, fitting with school motto – 'honour before honours' (one does feel a hint of Malory Towers here). The school aims to resolve any issues rapidly, and through discussion: 'this is a talking school,' says the head. Differences of opinion are usually sorted by consultation. One parent described how a personality clash between her daughter and another child was sorted out amicably and quickly by coming in to discuss it. Staff are very approachable, say parents, and it's easy to come in and talk.

Usual system of sanctions for unsatisfactory work or behaviour. No one we spoke to had come across drug taking of any sort – of course they experiment at some point, said one parent, but the strong school culture militates against it, at least on school premises.

Pupils and parents: Pupils both from the immediate area and further afield, by bike, train and school buses. About three-quarters of boarders from overseas, and Forces parents – also the tennis whizz kids, who work long days and find it helpful to be on site.

Some comfortably affluent parents, but most feel it's a big decision to pay for education, and those who fork out have academic results as their main priority. Typically both parents work, and they don't have elaborate holidays. Wouldn't suit one-dimensional girls, suggested one parent; nor, with its academic emphasis, those looking for a more vocational education. Not a posh school.

Former pupils include Judge Cosgrave, Lady Faithful (social worker and reformer), Charlie

Lee-Potter (journalist), Pat Smythe (show jumper), Natalie Clein (cellist), Dame Shirley Williams (politician), Kate Royal (opera singer), Nicole Faraday (actress), Caroline Gledhill (engineer) and Frances Ashcroft (geneticist).

Entrance: Own exam at 11+ – maths, English and verbal reasoning. Waiting lists for some years, currently 10-12. Most juniors pass the exam to progress to the senior school.

Exit: Lose some to the grammar, mostly for financial reasons, although around 25 per cent depart before sixth form to study something more unusual. They depart after sixth form to universities all over eg London, Exeter and Southampton. Subjects range from medicine (one in 2017) and law to animal behaviour.

Money matters: Parents say the school is cheaper than many independent schools in the area, and very good value for money. 'Prices could go up, and we would still go,' said one parent with enthusiasm. 'Bargain,' said another. Around a quarter of pupils are on scholarships or bursaries of around 10-20 per cent.

Remarks: Does what it says on the packet: a first class education for girls, provided with a great sense of purpose and vigour. Though academic, sport also strong, and excels in accommodating sporting and other extracurricular specialists. Feels like a very safe and caring environment. Better introduce boys yourself along the way though, suggested one parent, or some girls could go a bit crazy at university.

Taunton Prep and Pre-Prep School

60

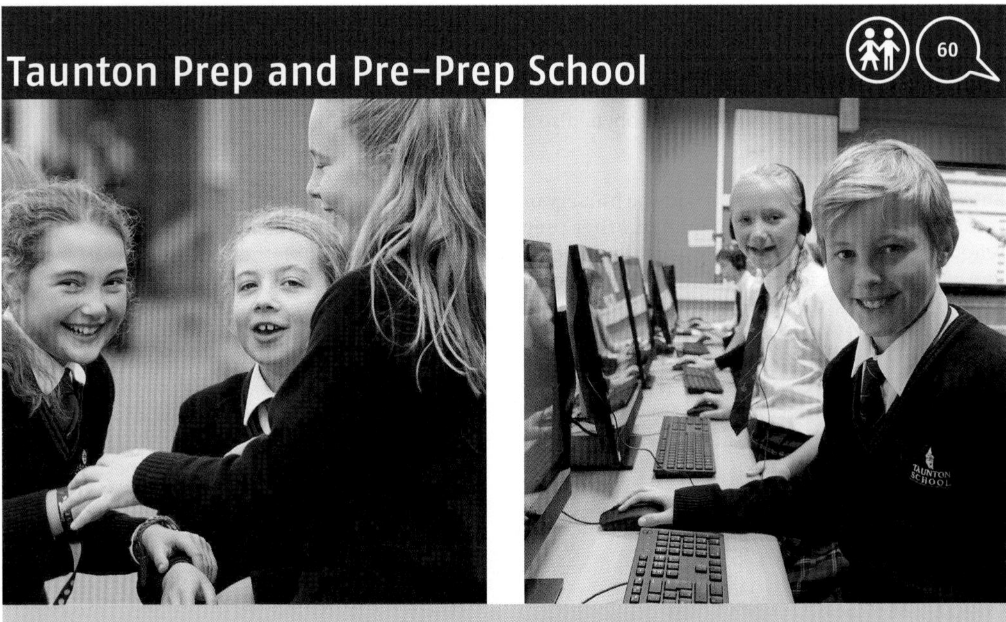

Staplegrove Road, Taunton, Somerset TA2 6AE

01823 703307 | admissions@tauntonschool.co.uk | www.tauntonschool.co.uk

Ages: 0-13 (boarders from 7)

Pupils: 457; Boarders: 22 full, 2 weekly

Day: £7,125 – £14,925 pa; Boarding: £14,250 – £24,750 pa

Linked school: Taunton School, 280

Headmaster: Since September 2017, Andrew Edwards BA PGCE. Early 50s. Also an all-rounder: degree in French and German, coaching qualifications in football, tennis and cricket, cellist to diploma standard, school inspector – and solicitor. Two years of lawyering in the City just didn't do it for him so he pluckily bundled sports kit, French text books and a cello into the boot of his disreputable Nissan Cherry and went peripatetic until snapped up by Cottesmore. Here he is 20 years later having done time at Port Regis, Dumpton and Castle Court. Previously head of Park School, Bournemouth for the last six years.

He likes things just the way they are here, so no major engine rebuild planned, fine tuning only. Not a believer that an eye-catching USP is everything – 'There's nothing wrong with doing what other schools do, the important thing is to do them extremely well' – so no hey-look-at-us joy-riding, either. Not so much a continuity candidate, more a continuous improver. Parents feel that following recent restructuring and staff departures – for the best, all agree – a period of calm is in order. Mr Edwards is a believer in rigour, challenge and respect, but his educational philosophy has it its heart the s-factor. Smiles. The more the merrier. Sound a tad, we don't know, mawkish? Okay, so what better way to measure a school? Our view: Mr Edwards is a Good Thing, a good fit. As an all-rounder, he's exactly what his new school is. Following two relatively quickfire headships here parents will be pleased to know that he has his eye on a decent innings. Married to Robyn, also a teacher. Two boys.

Entrance: Non-selective. Start at 0 in the nursery or come any time from a local school or other prep schools if (big if) there's room. Overseas students join when they're ready from Taunton International Middle School. Taster days on request. Range of scholarships at 11+ for entry to year 7.

Exit: Pretty much everyone to the senior school, a natural progression and for most parents the whole point. No one is de-selected; this is a cradle-to-adulthood school.

Remarks: Taunton isn't one of those towns that tops any tables for loveliness, well-being or up-and-comingness. Closer inspection reveals that it's no one's best kept secret, either. When you discover that the town is the beneficiary of a regeneration scheme your expectancy levels may droop some more, leading you to suppose that its schools aren't necessarily going to be anything to write home about. And there you'd be bang wrong. Just as we were. The town is home to a couple of blisteringly good state schools ('outstanding' in Ofstedspeak) and three independents. When it comes to education, the good people of Taunton and environs are spoiled for choice. So how do you choose? One parent we spoke to chose Taunton Prep School – TPS they call it in everydayspeak – because 'We liked the way it made us feel.' Much to be said for that.

TPS occupies its own self-contained campus bang next door to the senior school in the leafy northern outskirts of the town, bounded by the railway to the south and the A358 to the north. It has none of the huddledness of so many town schools, while the spacious playing fields further mitigate any urban vibe. It feels like its own place. Buildings a mix of Victorian and later, nicely maintained. That's not all: we have never seen a cleaner school nor have we met cleaners who so much enjoyed their work. Shares its chapel with the senior school. Established to educate the sons of dissenters but not Methodists. In place of foundational sectarianism we found only indulgent broad church values. An international contingent, around 10 of them, feed through from the international middle school – TSIMS (tee-sims) – when their English is up to it.

Demographically there's no pinning TPS down. It's popular with hardworking local entrepreneurs and businesspeople wanting the best for their children and for whom this is their first experience of private education. They told us that the school didn't talk down to them like others they looked round, it's not 'grand and intimidating'. TPS is also attractive to parents for whom private is second nature and who like the (relatively) wide social spectrum here. TPS has long been attractive to Forces families, for whom the school very much sets out its stall – to officers and other ranks equally. The draw for them, as for other nomadic families, is that TPS, together with the pre-prep and the senior school, gives them a fixed point from 0-18. So: not a muddy-wellie school, nor a set apart school, but a modern school very much part of, and involved in, the local community. To use a word du jour, inclusive.

Academically a very safe pair of hands across the board – just the right blend of extra-mile dedication and judicious professionalism. Every subject is well resourced. Parents of bright children tell us their child is stretched but not to snapping point;

Academically a very safe pair of hands across the board – just the right blend of extra-mile dedication and judicious professionalism

parents whose children need support tell us that's what they get, and never in such a way as to make them feel like dawdlers. Lots of praise for the teachers. One parent said, 'You fire off an email last thing at night and get an almost instant reply – it can be embarrassing'. Plenty of celebration of achievement according to your lights – a word oft-repeated by parents is 'nurturing'. One pupil told us she'd really taken off at the school and showed us written work which demonstrated sound understanding of the parenthetical comma. You don't see them very often these days. Maths exceedingly strong – terrific showings in Maths Challenge and an inspirational head of department who left one of your profoundly innumerate reviewers feeling there may still be hope. DT especially strong. Thinking skills a new addition to the academic mix. The head speaks of the children being on a 'GCSE continuum' which makes sense when pretty much everyone goes on the senior school. Lots of dialogue with the senior school and, big strength, some teacher sharing, especially in languages, classics and sport. Currently working on a joint IT strategy with senior school, a bring-your-own-device scheme 'the intention for the future'. IT has just enjoyed a £600,000 investment. Good blend of male:female teachers, roughly a third male. Saturday school til lunchtime for years 7 and 8. Special educational needs addressed by a team headed up by a head of learning success (neatly standing a downside on its head). The full spectrum of SENs, mostly, note, on the mild side – 10 per cent on the register. Architecturally wheelchair-unfriendly but they're willing to put themselves out for visually and hearing impaired children and wobbly walkers – head expresses a willingness to 'address the needs of any prospective pupil and see what reasonable adjustments could be made'.

Former England batsman Marcus Trescothick coaches cricket here and former England netball team manager Lisa Manley coaches netball so yes, this is a school that takes its sport seriously, generates good stats and crowns a sportsperson of the week at every Monday morning assembly. A very few parents feel sport is taken a bit too seriously, worry that it distracts from the academics and don't relish traipsing in of a Saturday evening and collecting their child from a bus. But maxing out every daylight hour in the week is what a good prep school does; it's all bang for your buck, and busy children who do lots, studies show, get the best results. Around a dozen of the best children rise to county level. No also-rans if they can help it: they try to give everyone the chance to play for their school at least once. It doesn't matter a bit if you're not sporty, if a thing's worth doing, it's worth doing inexpertly, it's meant to be fun. Decent mix of other sports on offer. Facilities are on the amazing side, many their own, some shared with the senior school.

Not many prep schools have their own performing arts centre but TPS does. Not many prep schools have quite such a passionate head of performing arts, either. We were particularly beguiled by five little French hornists parping away pluckily. The French horn is a frightfully difficult instrument at any age and to see so many seemed to set an aspirational benchmark. One mum we spoke to was taken by surprise when her son, having previously evinced neither interest nor aptitude, suddenly took to the trumpet, and this after a daughter had been identified as having an unsuspectedly good voice – 'They spot talents you never knew they had'. Here's a thing: in years 4, 6 and 8 everyone plays a part in a musical for which a whole week of all-day rehearsals is set aside. Everyone. The whole week. Don't parents march on the school demanding proper lessons? No they don't, they reckon the benefit outweighs any academic impact, they trust the school completely. Given that this is not a school whose parents are the sort to allow it to play fast and loose with scholastic attainment, what does that tell you? Lots of performance opportunities, formal and informal, at some of which parents join in. Senior choir sings in churches abroad. All in all, a rich and very classy mix. Heaps of lunchtime and after-school activities on offer. Go home at 4pm or stay to 5.30pm for clubs and prep (homework) periods.

One pupil showed us written work which demonstrated sound understanding of the parenthetical comma. You don't see them very often these days

Parents praise pastoral support and rapid response to glitches arising. First port of call is the form tutor. Head's door is ever open – stride on in. No prefect system; it was abolished by the previous head to universal crossness and dismay – a parent told us, 'It's the only time I went to the school and complained' – and replaced by year 8 councillors. Senior pupils apply for a role in writing then stand for election by everyone, including teachers. All are trained in peer mentoring. And it has all come good, making for a kinder environment with higher mutual respect levels and without saying goodbye to leadership opportunities. Parents praise the way the school celebrates kindness and 'is quick to support self-esteem'. You quickly pick up on the social atmosphere here because everyone is so naturally nice and courteous, welcoming of strangers, and that's not something you find everywhere by any means. Try this: flip through the photos in the school magazine – the unstaged ones. Don't all parents want their children to look like these?

Some 20+ children are full boarders, around 10 per cent of the roll, a number small enough to make you justly jittery. Aren't these simply left-behind children? Lots of schools couldn't make this work, not with so few. But TPS does. The accommodation is clean and snug. There's access to senior school facilities. The staff are brilliant, that's key, and the children are clearly well looked after and happy. Our misgivings evaporated. In the course of the year around a third of all pupils board. All flexi options available down to sleepover, and if you're caught late at work the boarding staff will look after your child till you come to collect.

The nursery and pre-prep is self-contained on the prep school site. None of the higgledy-piggledness that characterises some pre-preps, no sense of being an architectural afterthought. Described by one parent as 'the jewel in the crown'. Lovely atmosphere, really good staff, brilliantly led. Intelligent use of teaching materials, the best of the new plus golden-oldie classics. Huge pride in their forest school – outdoor areas where the children can play, hunt for bugs and bumble about. Aftercare til 5.45pm at no extra cost.

Marmite schools are schools with a highly distinctive personality and probably a stand-out specialism. These are schools that some children love and others don't. TPS is not a Marmite school. So, a very good ordinary school, then? Well, if you want to put it that way, yes, this is a school for every child, a place where values of humanity come first, where happy children find out who they are and what they can do and then go on and play out of their socks. Ordinariness at its best, then. Extremely personable. A terrific all-rounder.

Taunton School

61

Staplegrove Road, Taunton, Somerset TA2 6AD

01823 703700 | registrar@tauntonschool.co.uk | www.tauntonschool.co.uk

Ages: 13-18 (boarding from 7)

Pupils: 519; sixth form: 243; Boarders: 232 full/flexi

Day: £18,825 pa; Boarding: £32,100 – £35,100 pa

Linked school: Taunton Prep and Pre-Prep School, 277

Headmaster: Since 2015, Lee Glaser MA BSc PGCE, deputy head since 2009. Educated at his local comp in Blackpool and Liverpool University (maths). Qualified as a chartered accountant with Coopers & Lybrand, then turned his back on bean-counting and trained to be a teacher. Millfield for 14 years, maths teacher, senior master and director of sport; he's a diehard sports enthusiast rather than a dead good player. By general agreement he has made a very decent fist of taking over from a bouncy, charismatic head with a silver tongue and a penchant for continuous change. There's been enough of that; Mr Glaser's here to get the trains running on time and bed things down. Doesn't mean innovation is off the cards by any means, mind. Spent his first year appointing a new senior management team and agreeing vision and strategy which is expressed graphically by five pillars – see website – and is, we find, very definitely not a confection of buzz words and blah. If 'challenge, inspire, nurture' is what you want to hear, Mr Glaser is right behind them. A realist (as well as an accountant) he's a big believer in sound finances. Everyone likes him – he's 'approachable', a wysiwyg kind of a guy, 'good sense of humour', 'accessible, a good listener', 'right person at the right time', 'a nuts and bolts person', 'sticking to the knitting'. Very visible, his door is open to students first thing every morning. Oratorical skills reckoned to be improving. When he eventually steps down he hopes the consensus view of his bottom line will be that he 'improved everything'.

Wife Liz is a practising accountant. Two girls, both at the school. Chocolate lab, Lola. Mr Glaser

enjoys music and drama. Faced with shipwreck on a desert island he would lunge for Sympathy for the Devil (Stones) and Sebastian Faulkes' Engleby.

Academic matters: Results are sound considering the non-selective intake: 32 per cent A*/A at A level or equivalent in 2017, 49 per cent A*-A/9-7 at GCSE. IB diploma average score was 36. GCSE results broadly strengthening. Good range of subjects offered in the sixth form resulting in some very small class sizes. In terms of national averages strong in maths, history, biology, geography. Fewer top grades in physics, economics, business studies and psychology but signs of recent improvement. Curriculum well judged to accommodate a relatively wide range of abilities. Subject range embraces the usual suspects and includes, classy touch, Latin to A level. Open-minded about adding vocational subjects to the mix if sufficiently broad-based to act as a springboard to a spectrum of career choices – hence the BTec in sport and exercise science, equivalent to three A levels and laying the ground for a variety of employment sectors. Just under half of the first cohort achieved three triple starred distinctions. Performance table data shows expected progress at A level and BTec while IB students do rather better. Saturday school popular with working parents.

Classrooms bright and well equipped, students engaged even as lunchtime became imminent, teachers giving it plenty. A good number of teachers here did something else first. Lovely library – the new name for a learning resource centre – staffed by specialists and open til 9 every evening. Design technology blinking brilliant, masses of kit – oscillating spindle sander, inverted trend router, plasma cutter, you name it.

Huge efforts to retain students post-GCSE, all of which redound to their benefit – ah, the joys of a highly competitive market. Outstanding guidance in opting between A levels, IB and BTec, choosing the right subjects and thereafter making university and careers choices.

Learning support – 'educational progress', they call it – delivered by a staff of five who also support children in the prep school, offering continuity for long-haul students. The customary range of interventions spanning long-term SLDs to short-term study support. SLDs on the mild side – you've got to be able to keep up. Typically professional, all learning assistants are graduates. Head of department told us it's all about 'celebrating the differently gifted'.

Games, options, the arts: 'This is a school that really values breadth,' a parent told us. Another: 'Taunton students have absolutely no understanding of boredom'. All parents agree that when lessons are over there's masses to do. Sport, for example. This is a sporting hotspot that takes a characteristically professional approach to maxing out the talents of all students. Cop these coaches: Pete Sanderson, ex-Somerset CCC first team coach; Marcus Trescothick, ex-England opening batsman; Nic Sestaret, ex-France, Exeter Chiefs and Toulouse rugby player; and Lisa Manley, ex-England netball development squad manager. Yes, blimey. If you're any good you'll go all the way. That's not all. For students whose enthusiasm outruns their innate gifts there are B and some C teams where you can do your bit. Famous victories and lean spells alike are recorded in the Courier, the excellent weekly e-mag that records dash and enterprise in all areas of school life. Exhaustive coverage allows for the greatest number of students to be namechecked, a source of pride and joy to doting parents. As well as progressing to regional and national levels, students also play for local clubs, with some of whom the school shares facilities. All in all, impressive.

Some parents say the focus on sport has got a bit much, others disagree. One said, 'If your child is not in one of the top two teams [As or Bs] you don't get value for money'; others disagree. One said that there's a danger that a sporty child will do nothing but sport and miss out on everything else on offer; others point to manifold achievements on a broad and eclectic front by their own child. Given the strength of the sporting culture here, what is the fate of the non-sporty? Do they shiver on the wing only to be hooted at on the rare occasions the ball reaches them? We spoke to the parent of a resolutely non-sporty child. After popping in for a constructive talk with the right people, a personal fitness programme was agreed. Very civilised, all happy, no stigma. Putting this in context, another parent remarked: 'This is a school which is far more interested in the welfare of every one of its children than it is in looking good to the outside world'.

The school's minibuses carry the strapline 'Offering more'. There may be something in it. The music offer is multifarious, everything from chamber music ensembles to big musicals – in recent years Phantom, Evita, Cats. There are choirs, overseas tours – in short, around 40 public performances a year. The busy drama department offers courses at GCSE and A level in addition to productions for which anyone can audition. The art studio is similarly open-house and evidence of the quality of work made here surrounds you. Students spoke glowingly of working relationships with their teachers as we gazed.

Zero sock odour in the boys' houses, testimony to regulated lifestyles and the care of terrific support staff whose pastoral role is crucial. 'One big family,' say teachers

Outside the classroom there are heaps of clubs and activities on offer, many of them student-generated. There's a fully fledged rationale behind the co-curricular programme – Horizons, they call it. It's all about reaching out beyond the confines of the classroom, it's self-directed and it embraces all abilities. There's a CCF, compulsory for years 10 and 11. And for fresh air fans there's a thriving D of E scheme. Is there enough range? Students told us unanimously yes; parents told us that their children are operating at the outer extremes of busyness, and cited by way of verification the way they sleep for much of the first week of every holiday. One parent said, 'They are trained to cope with lots to do'. Lots of cultural, sporting and exchange trips worldwide reflecting the school's global outlook.

Boarding: Around 45 per cent board, of which roughly the same percentage are girls. House system in discrete houses, visitors need permission, so privacy (which tends to be in short supply in boarding schools) is safeguarded. Not a hotel school awash with pampering and fine fittings (though refurb ongoing) but students perfectly content with comfort levels, girls' dorms softer and tidier than boys', it goes without saying, for most chaps are strikingly insouciant in matters of interior decor at this age. Zero sock odour in the boys' houses, testimony to regulated lifestyles and the care of terrific support staff whose pastoral role is crucial and, well done Mr Glaser, officially recognised. Happy campers, all. 'One big family,' say the teachers, as they do; 'home from home'. When you hear the children say this too you give it credence. Eventide hunger pangs, long the bane of boarding, sated by after-prep snacks – we liked that. Busy weekend activities programme. Big boys look after little ones. Young people these days really are so much kinder to each other (sigh), the more so when vigilantly and benignly overseen as these are.

Background and atmosphere: Began life in 1847 as the West of England Dissenters' Proprietary School supported by the Wills family, Bristol ciggie kings, who built the chapel. Original neo-gothic flagship building imparts an image of tradition at modest cost. Target market was nonconformists – manufacturers, industrialists, tradespeople. Within 40 years the sectarian rationale had largely evaporated, denominational differences not being what they were, and the school moved into the public school mainstream, competing directly with, eg, the two other Taunton indies, Queen's and King's. Never a supertanker sort of school, the sort that can sail serenely through economic bad weather, it has looked disaster in the face a few times, most recently the late 1990s. Existential peril has arguably been the school's greatest friend, compelling it to look repeatedly to its wits and jolly well deserve to exist, denying it the doubtful luxury of complacency. Ever-adept at identifying new markets it went co-ed in 1976 – one of the first – and has offered IB since 2007. Business savvy – in the holidays there's a thriving venue hire business including weddings.

A legacy of this adaptive mindset is the global outlook of the school today built on an admirably enterprising business model. Two separate international schools between them take overseas students aged 8-17, bring them up to speed and feed them into either the prep or senior school – somewhere around 45 different nationalities. This makes Taunton fundamentally different in spirit from schools that look abroad opportunistically to top up ad hoc. There's a fully developed rationale behind this in tune with that of other international schools, yet Taunton remains essentially British because that's what its overseas parents want. Another stand-out feature of the school is that it will take your children and educate them from 0-18. Their market research tells them this is what parents want, and parents we spoke to concur – 'I didn't want my son to lose all his friends at 13'. One parent, new to town, was only looking for a nursery. One thing led to another; her third child has just started as the eldest gets ready to leave. Taken together, the cradle-to-adulthood model and the international model account for the fact that the head girl who showed us round had been at the school for 16 years, the head boy for just two (he's Russian). Striking for us, perhaps, not a big deal for them. Point is, it works. 'The friendships my daughter has made,' said one parent, 'have made the world a smaller place.' How chill a wind Brexit is going to be is yet to be seen. Taunton students emerge as global citizens, definitely not citizens of nowhere.

The campus, on the northern outskirts of Taunton, embraces also the prep and the pre-prep. The 15-17 year-old international students are semi-detached, just over the A358; the 8-14s are 10 mins to the north in Kingston St Mary. None of the crammedness you get in many town schools, the spacious playing fields and unnecessarily blue artificial pitches of the 50-acre site give way to agriculture. Architecturally there's nothing

here to take your breath away, though the Loveday building may elicit a low whistle. At the same time, there's absolutely nothing to make your heart sink. No, there's one of everything and everything's eminently fit for purpose – deceptively so in the case of the theatre which, as performing arts spaces go, is a piece of work. It's all at one with the down-to-earth nature of this place, a school that has no truck with servicing bank loans or wowing have-yachts. One parent said, 'The facilities meet its needs. In real life most people don't have pots of money to spend.' Another said 'One of the best things about the school: it's not in the least up itself.' Our observation: this is a school you quickly feel at home in.

Eventide hunger pangs, long the bane of boarding, sated by after-prep snacks – we liked that. Busy weekend activities programme

Very much a part of its local community, the school issues invites to university fairs, talks, etc. There's a community choir. The head enjoys good relationships with local state schools and sixth form college. Townsfolk come in and use the fitness suite. Taunton parents highly approve; they definitely don't want their children growing up aloof and apart. Confident in its identity and values, very much its own place, wholly free of minor public school hangups.

Pastoral care, well-being and discipline: Of all the school's greatest hits, pastoral care stands at

Number one. However hard we tried (and we did, we did) we could lure no one into uttering a bad word. First up, this is, in the words of one parent, 'a school where teachers really like kids' – which, interestingly enough, is exactly what the teachers told us when we asked them why they love working here. There is praise for rapidity of response times and sensitive, effective nipping in the bud of problems as they arise. One parent, worried about an unsupervised party planned for a weekend, went to share her misgivings with the deputy head. Sorted. Discipline is reckoned judicious and firm; a parent praised the way the school 'doesn't pander to parents' in this respect. Another parent observed, 'Family values are important to Taunton parents'. A new parent was rung by a teacher in the first fortnight to tell her how well her son was doing, point being this teacher didn't even teach him. We fielded countless 'extra mile' plaudits and enjoyed 'this is the biggest family ever'.

If the school looks big, 'it's not when you're there; the house system divides it into manageable chunks'. There's praise for the way year groups mix, look out for each other and integrate the newbies. There's peer mentoring. Year 9s share their space with year 11s. One parent told us they reckoned the house groups socially too small. All parents see this as an open door school, they'll always make themselves available and listen to you. You can drop in and taste the food anytime. It's an inclusive sort of place; a parent told us 'You'd struggle not to fit in'. Another said 'There's never been a day when my children have not wanted to go to school'. It's an open-hearted sort of a place, too: there's a pupil-led feminist society open to the full spectrum of LGBT students.

Pupils and parents: Especially popular with hard-working local entrepreneurs, businesspeople and professionals for a number of whom this is their first experience of private education – a higher proportion than you'll find at many independent schools. Not so different, then, in terms of values, from the school's original nonconformist parents – attributes of enterprise, thrift and social responsibility score high with them. They're looking for a return on investment, they like the school's groundedness and professionalism – and they bust a gut to pay the fees. We also encountered a number of seasoned veterans of private education who'd always seen themselves sending their child to a major-brand flagship school but, having found Taunton – in one case because their child was unhappy at a big-name school – count their blessings and have become passionate, even fierce, advocates of the school's virtues. Worth noting the relatively high proportion of state educated teachers here, too, including the three most senior managers. Most children come up from the prep school, some from local preps, some from state schools. Longstandingly popular with Forces families. Buses bring day students from a 30-mile radius from all parts of the compass – Yeovil, Exeter, Weston-super-Mare.

It's an inclusive sort of place. We fielded countless 'extra mile' plaudits and enjoyed 'this is the biggest family ever'

Entrance: Essentially non-selective. Assessment test and interview. Years 9 and 12 the customary boarding points but any other time if they've got room. Go to an open day or schedule a personal visit.

Exit: Pretty much everyone to university, half of them Russell Group. Given the international intake there's expert advice available for all students looking abroad. Some British students go on to Harvard, UCLA, etc and the school is a national SATS centre. Plenty of support for anyone opting for vocational training or apprenticeship – eg, hospitality, design at NABA Milan. Up to a fifth leave but reducing year on year after GCSEs, lured by the excellent local sixth form college. A number of these, missing the nurturing, find their way back to the mothership, postponing installation of the new dream kitchen back home for another two years. School prides itself on parity of support for all routes from academic to apprenticeship. Three to Oxbridge in 2017, plus two medics and a vet. Others to Australia, Canada, Germany, Italy, Netherlands, Spain and the USA.

Money matters: The usual range of scholarships for year 9 entrants. Same for sixth form entrants plus IB scholarships up to 100 per cent of fees. Extras include books, food, daily bus and some trips. Big ongoing investment in bursaries. Application process as far as possible businesslike, never an ordeal. Help for students at all ages who exhibit 'talent and determination'.

Remarks: Most of Taunton's hard-headed, analytical parents choose the school because it 'feels right', something that leaps out at them. It does. You quickly pick up on the professionalism – the admin systems are superfast. Never a school to fall in love with its own reflection, the new senior team, with its 'improve everything' agenda, is tweaking underperforming areas with precision. What makes the school so likeable, so agreeable, is its individuality: kind, hardworking, ambitious, terrific fun, very much its own person – a great fit for everyboy and everygirl.

Trinity School

62

Buckeridge Road, Teignmouth, Devon TQ14 8LY

01626 774138 | registrar@trinityschool.co.uk | www.trinityschool.co.uk

Ages: 11–19

Pupils: 167; sixth form: 50; Boarders: 58 full

Day: £11,940 pa; Boarding: £24,525 – £26,625 pa

Headmaster: Since September 2016, Lawrence Coen BSc Hons (Aberystwyth), PGCE (St Lukes, Exeter), NPQH. A science teacher, specialising in biology, Mr Coen was previously senior deputy head and spent time as a residential boarding master, as well as being involved in sport and co-curricular activities at the school.

Academic matters: In 2017, 38 per cent A*/A grades and 57 per cent A*-B at A level. At GCSE, 11 per cent A*/A grades. Trinity is a non-selective school, catering for a wide range of academic ability and results vary considerably from year to year. Classes are very small – rarely reach double figures. At all levels in recent years, girls have achieved far better results than the boys, although this may be a secondary effect of SEN/EAL currently being more heavily represented amongst the boys.

Nineteen options at GCSE, 18 A level subjects offered, plus BTecs in performing arts, music, sport and travel & tourism. BTecs were introduced in 2014 and are becoming popular; 51 per cent D* grades in 2017. Strong subjects across the board include maths, business studies, economics, art and psychology. A language is not compulsory at GCSE; psychology can be taken instead. RS is compulsory; everyone takes ICT at KS3 but can drop it at KS4 if taking single sciences.

Some 22 per cent of pupils have special educational needs, double the national average. Experience with dyslexia, ADHD, pragmatic and semantic disorders, autism spectrum disorder, non-verbal language difficulties, dyspraxia and general learning difficulties. Complex needs and some behavioural issues may not be catered for. The school is aware that they cannot cater for too many pupils with special needs, therefore some may be turned away after assessments. One-to-one specialist tuition with qualified SEN teachers is charged by the hour. All staff are given on-going training in-house and updated on individual pupils' IEPs. When we were there a deaf scriber and BSL signer were supporting a profoundly deaf student in a biology class.

One parent told us, '[My child] has language delay and needed educational support... They have adjusted the teaching materials according to his abilities.' Other parents explained how Trinity has helped their children to become more confident. We hoped [my child] would work hard, have fun and meet new people and develop confidence. [S/he] is developing in all ways already and we have seen a huge increase in self confidence.' Providing a supportive learning environment for children that lack confidence, or have had a bad experience of learning, seems to be what Trinity does best. A parent of an oversea boarder told us, 'He had shut himself off from learning; he just lost interest in school totally. Confidence completely drained away from him.' Now, he is 'happy' and 'interested' in school again; 'teachers have been excellent at supporting him.'

Every member of staff we spoke to said they had been at Trinity for a long time, several more than a decade. Parents say, 'The teachers are extremely dynamic, passionate and enthusiastic about their topics and are always available to communicate with parents.' For some, Trinity's size is a great benefit, particularly the small classes, but sometimes this can be limiting. One parent mentioned this to us: 'For its size I think it does an excellent job but I think a larger year group, particularly in [my child's] year would be beneficial. This is not the fault of the school.'

Games, options, the arts: Great opportunities for sporty types. For such a small school they celebrate a good deal of success. Medals aplenty for the last two years in national ISA swimming and athletics championships. Tennis is a major sport and several play at county and national level, one even at international. The U13s are Devon county champions. Trinity came second in the SW schools climbing championship, and U16 runners up in the netball ISA SW finals. One family with two children at the school commented, '[Our children] are both extremely sporty and have represented both Trinity and the south west in the ISA championships (daughter – netball, cross-country, athletics and swimming; son – cross-country, athletics and aquathon). My daughter also embraced all extracurricular activities available and was a member of the CCF and took the D of E Award.'

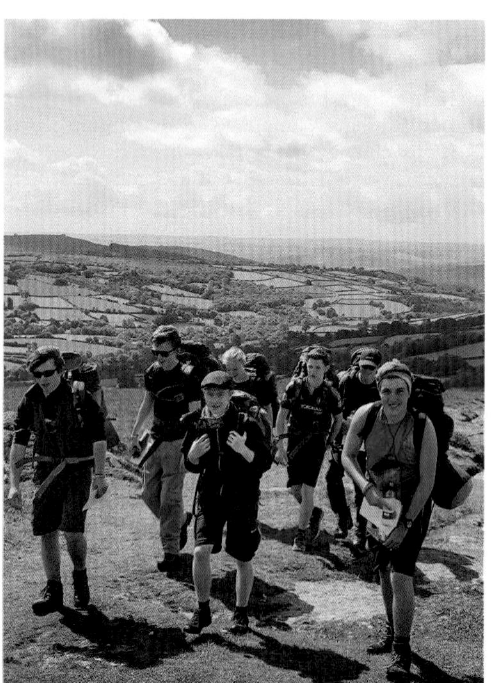

At the national surf lifesaving championships, Trinity won two golds, one silver, and one bronze. One pupil has been selected for a GB sailing squad

Facilities on site include an outdoor pool and indoor and floodlit tennis courts; they use local sports hall, swimming pool and Astro. There is a tennis academy on site, run by former junior international player Mark Syms, plus an indoor cricket academy. Pupils can sign up for individual, group or squad training in both. Trinity takes full advantage of its coastal location and pupils can take part in surf lifesaving, rowing, sailing and other watersports. At the national surf lifesaving championships, Trinity won two golds, one silver, and one bronze. One pupil has been selected for a GB sailing squad. However, table tennis is not on offer competitively and one parent from the Far East said, 'it is a real pity that this sport is left out at Trinity.'

Combined Cadet Force is compulsory in year 9. Very popular. Activities on the cards the week we visited were sailing, a powerboat course, and helicopter rides over Teignmouth. CCF meets once a week, and there are also weekend activities and holiday camps. Cadets take part in Ten Tors and the Duke of Edinburgh's Award scheme. Plus they can play in the National CCF Band, and last year the CCF team raced in the Tall Ships' Race from Falmouth to Greenwich, coming in second out of 50 ships. Cadets can also take a level 2 vocational award called BTec Public Services First Diploma. This equates to four GCSEs.

Good art facilities including a kiln and a printing press. Fantastic studio which was the star of the show for us. Unlike much of the school, it is large and spacious. A huge diamond shaped window almost fills one end of the room. The art teacher says the mix of nationalities creates an 'international flavour.' Some of the sixth form pieces on display were particularly abstract and demonstrated thinking beyond their years. No surprise that Trinity won two golds, two silvers and two bronzes at the recent ISA national art competition. One recent leaver has had her first exhibition of art work open at Living Coasts in Torquay.

Music department is well-equipped with the latest Apple computers, a grand piano, drum set, keyboards and electric guitars. The senior school choir has been named South West choir of the year – again, they've won three out of the last four years at Torbay Festival. Individual music lessons available, plus clubs including Big Band and a recorder club.

Recent major senior drama production was Les Misérables. Rehearsals were underway for Joseph and the Technicolour Dreamcoat in the drama studio. The band accompanying were BTec music students. Plenty of after-school clubs for aspiring thespians, including theatre workshops and public speaking. Recently four pupils won at the poetry recitals at Paignton Festival. Other options for extracurricular activities include anything from chess to salsa dancing to public speaking or judo, fencing or even cross-stitch.

Regular trips to Normandy for French and history classes. Geography students to Iceland. Plus cultural trips to Berlin, and skiing in the Alps. In the UK, there's an adventure and challenge week in Wales. For sixth formers there are volunteer opportunities on the Grass Roots Project in South Africa. The students work in township schools teaching, developing sports fields and building vegetable gardens. There's now a second project choice, an orphanage in Johannesburg.

Boarding: 'The boarding staff provide excellent pastoral care in a safe, loving and caring environment. They also encourage each individual with both their school studies and extracurricular activities,' said one parent. Boarders currently range from 10 to 19 years. The majority are full time, there are occasional flexi-boarders and some European short-termers to brush up on language skills. Some 75 per cent are from overseas, a third from the Far East, a third from Europe and a third from elsewhere. Around 50 per cent of the sixth form are boarders. A parent of one told us, 'He was homesick the first night, but the houseparents kept him busy so that he didn't have time to think too much. He settled down very quickly, much quicker than I expected. The houseparents are simply the best. They looked after him so well. He loved them. They would send me emails to tell me how he is doing without me asking.'

Two mixed gender houses – one for year 11 and below, one for sixth formers, with university-style

accommodation. One parent said, 'We looked at a few schools and liked the homely atmosphere at Trinity.' The boarding accommodation is part of the school building and as such pupils don't leave school 'to go home'. For some this may make a difference. Rooms are nearly all doubles. Only sixth formers are allowed to study in their room, but all boarders are allowed back to their rooms at lunchtime. We saw quite a few taking advantage of this rather than socialising with fellow pupils over lunch.

Occasional evenings out are allowed if arranged in advance with set home times. Church on most Sundays in Teignmouth for everyone

Activities in the evenings and weekends can be 5-a-side football, cinema, climbing, go-karting, paintball, or anything the pupils' request. Each house votes for their house captains who then assist the boarding staff in the running of the house. All activities are compulsory for the younger ones. From year 9, pupils can go into Teignmouth, and from year 11 they can go to Exeter, back in time for supper. Occasional evenings out are allowed if arranged in advance with set home times. Church on most Sundays in Teignmouth for everyone.

Regular Skype calls to parents, plus updates from houseparents. One parent said, 'Houseparents are simply the best. They looked after [him] so well. [He] loved them. They would send me emails to tell me how [he] is doing without me asking. They are really excellent.' Other parents told us, 'Very safe environment with a lot of activities.' And 'he made a lot of friends.' Plus, 'Clear rules help the boarders to orientate.' All parents agreed their children settled well; one told us, 'He settled down very quickly, much quicker than I expected, in fact since day two at Trinity he didn't need help from his guardian at all except during exeats and term breaks.' Exeats in the middle of each half term, one being compulsory in the autumn and spring terms.

Background and atmosphere: Founded in 1979, the school used to be a girls' convent school. Set in a stunning location in Teignmouth, the school has views over Lyme Bay and the English Channel. Not far from the rugged moors of Dartmoor and the surf beaches of South Devon, Teignmouth is a traditional English seaside town. It is a quiet town, not known for nightly rowdiness like other nearby hotspots. This is part of the attraction for parents; it's safe. 'The smaller size of the boarding school in a safe area was attractive given [he] was travelling on his own,' said a parent of a boarder.

The school's motto is 'Optimism, Confidence, Charity.' They have raised over £4,500 for local, national (mainly British Heart Foundation) and international charities

The main building is old; narrow corridors, even narrower wooden winding stairs, and panelled wood. The red library on the red corridor is in the oldest part of the building. Induction sessions for all newbies. It's set on two levels, with a reading room to one side and a large teddy in residence in the middle. The reading room is also used for lunchtime films plus the girls' and the boys' (separate) 'brew clubs'.

Up the stairs is the chapel and the boarding accommodation. At the very top of the building, aptly named The Attic, is the sixth form area. Here there is a (very warm) study room, a quiet zone and a common room. The head of sixth form also has his office here. Basic and functional, but ideally located at the top of the school away from everybody else. The new building links into the original building with a courtyard in middle. In the new part is a DT lab with laser cutter and CNC cutter, four science labs and three ICT suites.

The school's motto is 'Optimism, Confidence, Charity.' Recently they have raised over £4,500 for local, national (mainly British Heart Foundation) and international charities like the one in South Africa. Annually there is a Giving Nations' Day when pupils set up stalls and sell their wares for charities around the world. Students are also encouraged to volunteer to help in the prep school or work in a local elderly home. Trinity has won the school float contest in the Teignmouth Carnival for the last two years.

For sixth formers, there's quite a social calendar to keep up with. They kick off the year with a disco or gig night, followed by quiz nights, a fancy dress party and a film festival. That only takes them up to the Christmas festivities. Then it's the Valentine's ball, a prefect dinner, a summer barbeque, a beach barbeque, and finally the sixth form summer ball.

Pastoral care, well-being and discipline: 'The head teacher and all of the staff involved in pastoral care have been excellent,' said a parent. Another told us that they chose Trinity because 'I wanted a caring supportive environment which I felt was important as I am a single parent.' Form tutors, key stage heads, boarding staff, two qualified nurses, the school chaplain, and a school counsellor are all available to support the pupils. The school also runs pastoral review meetings every half term to share information amongst staff, and discuss any potential issues or support needed.

The prefect system, including the pastoral prefects and the mentors, provides peer support and ultimately friendships across the years. The house system also gives pupils the chance to make more friends throughout the school – and it is taken very seriously; pupils love the competitiveness. There are regular sports competitions, talent shows, science and maths challenges.

Trinity is a Christian school built on a joint Anglican and Roman Catholic foundation. The school chapel is central to the spiritual life of the whole school community. Mixed year chapel services throughout the week plus hymn practice every other week. Employs a full-time chaplain, a C of E priest. As well as formal celebrations, chapel and assemblies, his role includes the pastoral care of pupils and staff. He also teaches PE and looks after the boarders a few nights a week; he is keen to get to know everyone. He is also keen that the school becomes a part of the local community and that pupils 'don't live in a bubble.' He encourages them to 'look outward' and participate in local charitable events. Pupils we spoke to were happy with the school's approach to religion and said 'it's not pushed, it's a way of life' at Trinity.

Zero tolerance on drinking, smoking and drugs. Persistent smaller offences lead to detentions. Further persistence leads to suspension and expulsion. Trinity works with pupils and parents as much as possible to prevent this.

Pupils and parents: Parents of day pupils are mainly local professionals. Recently many more people are relocating to Devon and commuting into London. Some pupils come from as far as Totnes, Paignton, Ivybridge and Honiton. This is the advantage of having a train station on the doorstep; pupils can catch the train to school and jump on the school shuttle. The Dartmouth bypass should also help bring more pupils from that part of Devon. Escorted airport bus service for boarders. Parents all agreed, 'Communication is good, proactive and responsive. No complaints.'

Entrance: Entrance test and interview. Copies of school reports if applicable. For sixth form entry five GCSE passes at grade C/5 or above. Overseas students must complete a personal statement and English skills assessment. Only those with good use of the English language are accepted onto the standard curriculum from year 10 upwards, but there is a pre-A level course enabling those with weaker English to enter the sixth form. At this level there are usually 10 new European boarders, 10 new international boarders and six UK pupils, usually two of which will be boarders. Parents commented, 'The school was very helpful in helping the children settle in. I could not have asked for more.' Another confirmed, 'The children now feel at home at the school.'

Exit: Around 40-45 per cent leave after GCSEs to go to the local grammar schools or vocational colleges. Around the same number of new pupils join the sixth form. Around 65 per cent to university. A good number of pupils go to Russell Group universities; some overseas students return to their home countries.

Money matters: Sport, music and performing arts scholarships available, mostly at 11+, offering up to 50 per cent off fees. The Notre Dame Award is an all-rounder scholarship. Limited number of means-tested bursaries. Armed forces discounts available plus sibling allowances.

Remarks: Trinity School is a small school that provides a safe and supportive environment for pupils of all abilities – particularly those who may have struggled to learn in the past, or lacked the confidence or support to reach their potential. Trinity ticks all the boxes, but it doesn't push any boundaries, it just does what it does well. Sport is a good example of this. One parent told us that they chose Trinity as 'We were amazed by the fact that every pupil is treated as an individual and they recognise their strengths and weaknesses, and Trinity view these (as we do) as just as important as academic prowess.'

Truro High School
63
Falmouth Road, Truro, Cornwall TR1 2HU
01872 272830 | registrar@trurohigh.co.uk | www.trurohigh.co.uk
Ages: 11-19
Pupils: 250; sixth form: 50; Boarders: 45 full, 5 flexi
Day: £13,233 pa; Boarding: £24,336 – £26,337 pa

Headmaster: Since 2014, Dr Glenn Moodie, early 40s. Originally from New Zealand, he studied classics and ancient Greek at university before coming to the UK to study a PhD in classics at Bristol, and a PGCE at Leicester. This is his first headship; he was previously at Wycombe Abbey as director of studies, and prior to that, had teaching roles at Uppingham School and Clifton College. Currently teaches Latin and history of art to sixth formers. Married to Vanessa, a primary school teacher; their daughter attends the prep. He says the drive to school often evokes nostalgic memories of New Zealand, which makes him smile. What he loves about Cornwall is that many people are there because they have made a choice; they want a better work/life balance and their perspective on life is different – health and well-being are paramount.

Truro High School is the only single-sex school in Cornwall. The school says, 'An all-girls education is liberating with students able to be themselves and take on challenges without fear of censure.' However, the co-ed idea was thrown into the ring just as Glenn started and it definitely stirred up the parents, many of whom are 'more wedded to the idea of single-sex education.' One parent sympathised, saying, 'Dr Moodie had a tricky start with the whole co-ed question – which we believe was essentially down to the governors. Everything has settled now.' In the end, the governors decided to stay all-girls, as they have been for 135 years.

Another parent told us, 'The co-ed idea was very badly handled, but communication has been much better since. I would like the head to be much more visible, especially at events where parents are in school. It is his school, he should be there "pressing the flesh".'

In years gone by, there was a co-ed sixth form at Truro High, and although this could be suggested in the distant future, the whole co-ed matter has now been parked indefinitely. Things have without doubt settled down now, and confidence is improving. 'We feel the head teacher is extremely diligent, approachable and non-judgmental and that he puts the interests of the school first and foremost.'

Academic matters: In 2017, 42 per cent A*/A grades and 82 per cent A*-B at A level; 47 per cent A*-A/9-7 at GCSE. The school is regularly top of the county league for A level and GCSE. Twenty-one subjects on offer at A level. Maths and physics are strong, and all girls take separate sciences at GCSE. English is consistently good at both A level and GCSE. Latin holds up very well at GCSE and is still there at A level. MFLs include Spanish, French and German, as well as EAL and a Japanese club. Religious philosophy is compulsory. Has opened the first solar observatory on mainland UK. New Aspiring Medics programme has already produced a Cambridge medic and a Nottingham vet.

With so few pupils, all classes are small, and at A level some are even one-to-one. Very low turnover of staff but a few recent retirements have made way for some welcome new blood. Parents told us, 'We are impressed by and have every confidence in the head teacher and all the other teachers who have been involved in our child's education.' Another was a bit more critical: 'I think the teachers are pretty good, but listening to the girls talk about them, I think covering illness etc could be better handled. I still feel there is a lot of stuff which goes unchecked, spelling errors in work displayed on the wall etc, errors in reports.'

According to the ISI inspection report, the school 'provides a good education....the curriculum is good, successfully providing for the needs of all pupils including those with EAL and SEND.' All staff are trained in assessment techniques and the school provides extra study support for those pupils in the prep and the senior school with dyslexia or dyspraxia. The small class sizes enable regular monitoring and support.

Games, options, the arts: Facilities are pretty good. There's a 25 metre heated indoor swimming pool, full sized Astroturf, a playing field, two netball/tennis courts, and an athletics area for long/high jump, javelin, discus etc. There's also a separate dance studio building, historically only used for ballet, now packed with yoga classes, and street and lyrical dance ensembles.

Netball and hockey fixtures are weekly and the school has won 37 county team sport titles over the past five years. Twenty-five girls represent the county and nine play either hockey or netball for West of England. Girls' football and tag rugby are now included in the curriculum and the new rugby club on Mondays was hot news of the day. Proper rugby, not tag, we were informed. They even had the Cornish Pirates in for a session. Swimming is popular, as is horse riding; they have their own

team. Outdoor pursuits like D of E and Ten Tors are a part of life here. Third fastest all-girl team in Ten Tors challenge on Dartmoor recently.

Most girls learn an instrument and there's a 120-strong choir and a 60-strong orchestra. The new music building has six individual practice rooms and a large main room set up with instruments aplenty and 10 iMacs. Groups include a jazz band, samba band, flute choir, chamber choir and a ukulele club. Recent choir trips and tours include Belgium and Hong Kong.

The performing arts centre has a small theatre used for presentations, as well as larger productions. Rehearsals were under way for Into The Woods, the year before it was The Importance of Being Earnest. Girls are keen on debating and participate in competitions organised by the ESU and the Cambridge Union. Large numbers doing LAMDA qualifications and Rotary public speaking competitions. One parent told us, 'I think Truro Hugh ultimately gave my daughters self belief. My youngest became the member of the youth parliament for mid Cornwall; she had been taking extracurricular lessons in speech & drama, and debating society. These little extras can make a huge difference to one's future.'

Trips for all boarders on Saturdays and Sundays. Treasure hunts in town, beach trips, horse-riding, shopping in Exeter and visits to the Tate in St Ives and the Eden Project

Art is set in yet another outbuilding; rooms are a good size and sixth formers have their own area. Plenty of girls go on to do the prestigious Falmouth foundation course. Textiles also popular and former pupils have gone on to get firsts in design courses, and land jobs at Mulberry or Karen Millen. Head of department once worked for Laura Ashley and knows not just the creative side, but also the logistics of production and manufacture. On our visit there was a lot of excitement about the fashion show that night. Proceeds going towards The Mermaid Centre at Royal Cornwall hospital and purchase of a laser cutter for the department.

Up until GCSEs, girls alternate terms of textiles and food & nutrition. The latter includes food science and is popular, with some even taking it at degree level. One sixth former told us she's signed up for a Cooking for Uni course as one of her enrichment options on Wednesday afternoons. Other options include ceramics, life drawing and photography.

Football, rugby and engineering are also available and enthusiastically taken on board. The school is adamant that there is no pressure, and girls are given the space and confidence to choose. There has been a big drive towards engineering, with guest speakers and events on Women In Engineering. The school also has its own racing car team with five cars. With help from the local community, the girls are raring to go and compete in national racing events.

Boarding: 'The fact that both girls loved weekly boarding had a huge bearing on their success at school.' Majority of full boarders are from abroad but the school promotes its flexi facilities so families can use them whenever necessary. No plans to change the boarding; the head says it provides the school with some essential cultural diversity, something Cornwall rather lacks. The German students tend to come just for a term to improve their English, but other boarders from Russia, China and Australia and the local islanders from the Scillies are more permanent.

Two boarding houses – Dalvenie (years 8-10) and Rashleigh (years 11-13). Trips for all boarders on Saturdays and Sundays. Treasure hunts in town for the new girls, beach trips, horse-riding, shopping in Exeter and visits to the Tate in St Ives and the Eden Project. For nights in, there's swimming, plus pool parties with inflatables, barbeques, baking and movie nights. Boarders all participate in after-school clubs, and the older girls are allowed into town in pairs – back for supper at 6pm.

The younger girls are four to a room with communal showers and toilets. The older girls can opt for either two in room, or individual rooms, all with ensuites – very much like university rooms (actually a little better). In Dalvenie the common room has a TV, Wii, a pool table, piano, PCs, a dining table and a comfy sofa area. Rashleigh was refurbished a few years ago and the lounge is really rather grown up, set out like a large apartment with sofa/TV area and a fully fitted kitchen. Next door is a quiet room with pianos, a room for the girls to be able 'to get away from it all'. Girls do their own laundry and have a council and regular meetings. Houseparents live on site with their families (and cat). Their daughters also attend the school, so it really is a family affair here.

Background and atmosphere: Founded in 1880 by Bishop (later Archbishop) Benson (first Master of Wellington College) who built Truro cathedral and gave Henry James the idea for The Turn of the Screw. Situated close to the centre of Truro, the school has been on the same site since 1896. The aim was to provide an academic education for girls within a Christian community. The school retains its founding links with Truro Cathedral and commitment to a Christian ethos but welcomes girls of all faiths or none. Hymns are sung in assembly once a week, girls attend services at the cathedral threes times a year, plus twice-termly church services at the local parish church have recently been introduced.

The main building is partly castellated and made of Cornish granite, not a grand entrance but a welcoming one. Inside, narrow corridors, wooden staircases, plaques dating back to 1800s, fairly antique toilet facilities, in need of a lick of paint here and there. Outside, the site is very well-maintained, the gardens are lovely, but overall it feels a little disconnected as outbuilding after outbuilding appears, as do seemingly ad-hoc extensions. Shining stars are obviously the most recently built language centre, music block and performing arts building.

'Boarding here really worked for my girls, it's fun, friendly, relaxed.' A pupil said, 'Coming to Truro High was the best thing I've ever done'

The library seems well-used and well-resourced, with a separate sixth form area. School is definitely not overrun with computers, but given its size maybe this is reasonable. Best IT resources appeared to be suite of iMacs in the music room. Wireless internet is available in certain areas of the school and to sixth formers. All social media is blocked until 4pm, when the boarders can log on.

'The sixth form building is fantastic,' say parents. Both floors have workstation rooms with individual carrels – the girls call these 'caroles' and personalise them as much as possible. Most amusing was the fact that the girls were using wine glasses for water (it was definitely water); young ladies at work. Shared common room opens out onto garden. Kitchen with dishwasher, toaster and coffee machine. Girls seemed happy and relaxed, chatting away over a mountain of toast. Lunchtimes in town are allowed but they rarely go, occasionally on birthdays.

Pastoral care, well-being and discipline: Discipline problems are rare and pastoral care is led by the form tutors and houseparents. There is also a nurse on site. Good mentoring and prefect system means that girls of all ages get to know each other – lots of impromptu hugging on our tour as our guide saw her younger friends. This is a small, friendly and unintimidating school. One girl told us how she was bullied in her last school and that she couldn't have felt more welcome when she started Truro High. She made friends easily and says she has never looked back: 'Coming to Truro High was the best thing I've ever done.'

One parent of a boarder told us, 'Only last week my youngest, now in upper sixth, was not feeling very well, but a quick call to the boarding house reassured me. One of the senior members of staff has been there many years and I have formed a good relationship with her. Boarding at Truro High really worked for my girls, it's fun, friendly, relaxed.'

Pupils and parents: Parents are professionals, company directors and the like; many have relocated and now commute by plane or train to London. One told us, 'We are not particularly enamoured of the attitude which is common amongst some of the children and parents of the top tier private schools so were looking for a "third way" of excellent schooling without some of the arrogance, stress levels etc found elsewhere.' They went onto to say, 'We wouldn't have moved to Cornwall if it wasn't for Truro High.'

Others said, 'We were delighted by the atmosphere of the place. The wit and dynamism between children and teachers, the warmth between the girls – the spark was exactly what we were looking for (and what was lacking at the other schools).' Communication from the school to parents is good. 'There is a huge amount of information to share and parentmail does the job well. Teachers are approachable and helpful when required. Communication regarding the general management of the school has improved.'

Uniform up to year 11 is a Balmoral tartan skirt and green pullover. Sixth formers could easily be mistaken for staff – very mature, not a rebel in sight. Parents enthused, 'Can't speak highly enough of the culture of Truro High. Our girls come home at the end of the day with a smile on their faces. They look forward during the holidays to going back to school.'

The school has recently had a publicity makeover thanks to the director of marketing, a former ITV Cornwall news presenter. Smart promo packs, new-look magazines, local news articles, radio plugs and a Facebook page that is updated several times a day. An old girl herself, she has two daughters at the school and continues to fly its flag by setting up events like the fashion show in conjunction with local businesses, and letting parents use the grounds – one recently put on a refugee in crisis event.

The school is also strengthening its relationship with local community and parents with events such as 'family swim days' at weekends. Anyone is welcome for a small token that is then used to pay the (qualified) sixth formers to lifeguard.

Old girls include Dame Lynne Brindley (master of Pembroke College, Oxford), TV presenter Hannah Sandling, comedien and writer Morwenna Banks and mezzo soprano Anna Burford.

Entrance: Entrants mainly from own prep plus Polwhele House, Roselyon, St Piran's, Bolitho and Truro prep. A decent number are from local state primaries. Biggest overseas market currently is Hong Kong; others from Russia, Germany, Spain and Australia.

Applicants for the senior school are invited to a taster day (boarders have a trial night), then sit an exam and interview before admission. For sixth form entry, GCSE grade A*-A/9-7 in proposed A level choices, plus interviews for UK candidates and test papers/school assessments for overseas students.

Exit: On average half leave at 16 to go to (free) Truro College up the road, Truro School or co-ed boarding elsewhere. One off to study biomedical engineering at Imperial in 2017, others to eg Exeter, Bristol, Manchester and Hartpury College.

Money matters: Academic, music, drama, sports and art scholarships available, plus means-tested bursaries at year 7 entry, and into sixth form.

Remarks: Truro High School is unique in Cornwall. It's a small, all-girls school that delivers on qualifications, but nurtures and cares. One parent said, 'We wanted all girls, so it was a no-brainer.' But most have been overwhelmed by the 'spark' and 'atmosphere' of the school. A few minor grumbles about teachers' spelling and communication, but all we saw were happy, well-behaved girls. One parent said, 'I thoroughly recommend Truro High, for sciences and humanities, for quieter children and more vocal – I have one of each!' It's the type of school that needs to be visited; parents will know immediately if it's right for them or not.

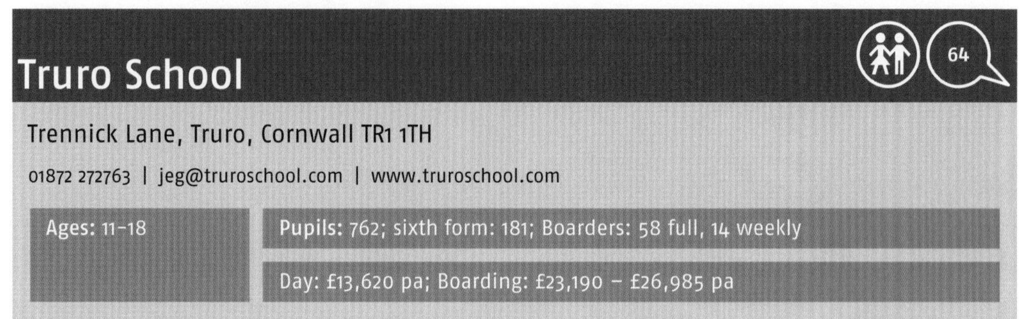

Truro School

64

Trennick Lane, Truro, Cornwall TR1 1TH

01872 272763 | jeg@truroschool.com | www.truroschool.com

Ages: 11–18

Pupils: 762; sixth form: 181; Boarders: 58 full, 14 weekly

Day: £13,620 pa; Boarding: £23,190 – £26,985 pa

Headmaster: Since 2013, Andrew Gordon-Brown BCom MSc QTS (40s). Educated at Hyde Park High School in Johannesburg, read commerce at University of Cape Town and then qualified as a chartered accountant. He rowed for South Africa in the 1992 Olympic Games (team came a creditable eighth) and set his heart on rowing for Oxford or Cambridge. He achieved his dream when he completed an MSc in agricultural economics at Keble College, Oxford and picked up a rowing blue along the way (he rowed for Oxford in the 1994 Boat Race). After 12 years in banking and financial services, working for blue chip companies such as Deloitte, UBS and JPMorgan Chase, he had a 'Damascene conversion' and decided to become a teacher. 'I turned my back on the big bucks,' he told us with a smile. Achieved his QTS via the University of Gloucestershire, taught economics and rowing at Radley for four years and then spent five years as deputy head at Stonyhurst College in Lancashire.

Dedicated, energetic and charming, he has always loved Cornwall (his family owns an old farmhouse on The Lizard) so jumped at the chance to take the reins at Truro School. Keen to use his business background to help pupils, he teaches careers guidance to year 11s and runs financial literacy classes as part of the sixth form's enrichment programme. Has a very global outlook and tells students they should see the world 'as their labour market.' He holds regular lunches for year groups and describes pupils as 'wonderfully unpretentious.' 'Unlike in bigger conurbations, they don't have an edge to them,' he says. Discipline isn't a problem either. As he puts it: 'The teachers teach, the pupils learn and the parents are very supportive.'

His wife Harriet (who was on the same MSc course as him at Oxford) is very involved in school life and they have three children, the eldest at the senior school, the younger two at the prep. They live in a house on the school site.

Still a keen sportsman, he enjoys running, cycling and going to the gym. His family has recently bought a boat – 'but I'm a novice sailor' – and he sings whenever he can (most recently in the Truro School Choral Society performance of Faure's Requiem at Truro Cathedral).

Most lower sixth pupils do a 16-week peer counselling programme led by the chaplain (who's known as the Rev)

Academic matters: It's cool to work hard here – and the pupils do. Fifty-nine per cent of GCSEs were A*-A/9-7 in 2017, with English lit, maths and physics all strong performers. At A level, 41 per cent A*/A, with maths leading the field. The sciences and maths are particularly strong and many go on to be medics, dentists, engineers and, perhaps not surprisingly given the location, geologists. The school is one of only 230 in the country to offer geology – 'we've got a department that isn't far off a small university department.' School runs more than 20 subjects at A level, including business studies, economics, PE and psychology. Thanks to a bit of timetabling wizardry, students can take any combination (for options submitted in the preceding spring term). EPQ on offer too.

Everyone does at least one language at GCSE and some take up to three (students can study a third language from year 9 in extra twilight sessions first thing, at lunchtime and after school). Mainly French, German and Spanish but the school will do its best to accommodate requests for others

(students have taken Chinese, Dutch and Russian in recent years). Exchange trips for younger pupils and work experience in France and Germany for older ones, with CVs written in French and German of course. Music is offered to talented musicians off-timetable as an extra GCSE.

Learning support department with full-time head and two part-time staff. School caters for students with moderate learning difficulties – dyslexia, dyspraxia, dyscalculia, dysgraphia and Asperger's. All students are tested during their first year at the school – extra support given individually or in small groups (no extra cost).

All pupils are encouraged to be the best they can (school motto is 'To be rather than to seem to be') and they get regular progress reviews, on attitude in lessons, ability to study independently and organisation skills, as well as academic achievement.

Games, options, the arts: A very sporty school, with county champions in rugby, hockey and netball. First XV regularly gets into the last 16 of the NatWest Schools Cup and a sixth former was recently selected for the England U18 XV. Teams often have to travel long distances to compete but pupils don't seem to mind. The school has 40 acres of playing fields, Astroturf, eight tennis courts, cricket pavilion and grounds, climbing wall and a 25m pool, but the jewel in the crown is the new Sir Ben Ainslie Sports Centre, opened by the man himself, which boasts an eight-court sports hall, two squash courts, fitness suite and dance studio. It's used by the local community too – 400 members signed up in a flash when it opened. The days of the school being regarded as 'the rich kids on the hill' have long gone. The school also excels at fencing and runs an elite academy programme. Several youngsters fence at national and international level and are aiming for the 2020 Olympics. A girl in the upper sixth was recently ranked fifth at senior level in the GB. As the head reminded us, 80 per cent of Cornwall's county border is sea, so the school makes the most of the plethora of water pursuits on the doorstep – like sailing, surfing and snorkelling.

The music department buzzes with activity from dawn till dusk. A third of pupils takes instrumental lessons and there are orchestras, choirs, bands and jazz bands to join. Pupils frequently selected for National Youth Orchestra and National Youth Choirs. Around three or four a year take music at A level. School has a strong relationship with Truro Cathedral – girl choristers aged 13 to 18 can now join the cathedral choir and get a 25 per cent scholarship from the school.

Drama is top notch. When we visited, the school was gearing up for a production of Sweeney Todd, complete with an ambitious two-storey revolving stage. Theatre was opened by Sir Tim Rice, and as well as school productions and Friday lectures for the sixth form, it opens its doors to touring companies. Art is superb – everything from oil paintings and life drawing to sculpture and ceramics. The head's study, corridors, boarding houses and art department are lined with stunning artwork. School has strong links with nearby Falmouth University and with local artists (some of their work is exhibited at school's new Heseltine Gallery). We loved the graffiti-style mural painted up the side of the gallery steps – pupils came up with ideas and street artist Cosmic spent five days on a cherry picker creating it. Theatre studies and art are popular at A level. So is DT, which is taught in a proper workshop. Many of the pupils' creations are inspired by the sea. We spotted model yachts, a gadget for cleaning boat chains and a rocking hammock.

Lots of activities organised at weekends, particularly for the youngest – kayaking, coasteering, surfing, barbecues. Older pupils get time to socialise with friends

Wednesday afternoons are given over to extra-curricular activities – everything from sport and music to surfing and war games. Truro pupils certainly don't lack fresh air, that's for sure. D of E is huge here (over 100 take part each year) and there are always school teams in the gruelling Ten Tors Challenge across the wilds of Dartmoor. World Challenge on offer, plus a raft of expeditions at home and abroad.

Boarding: Small number of boarders but head says that he has 'given boarding a bit of a push', and recently opened an additional boarding house for girls. There are now four boarding houses (two for girls, two for boys), all small and homely and each with a resident housemistress or housemaster. Boarders do 90 minutes prep a night in the library, overseen by staff and sixth formers. Lots of activities organised for them at weekends, particularly for the youngest – kayaking, coasteering, surfing, barbecues etc. Older pupils get time to socialise with their friends – 'it's important not to timetable every part of their day,' said a housemistress. Some flexi-boarding available.

Background and atmosphere: Gloriously situated on a hill overlooking the River Truro and the cathedral (you get tantalising glimpses of it as you walk between the buildings). A Methodist school founded in 1880, it opened with 35 boys and two teachers in a schoolroom in the centre of the city and moved to its current site in 1882. Original gothic building in local stone has been much added to – it's 'a bit of a warren,' said a parent – but it adds to the charm. School went co-ed in 1990 and these days 40 per cent of the pupils are girls. Buildings include a lovely 1920s chapel (year 7 and 8 pupils attend twice a week and year 9s and above once a week) and library with 18,000 resources. Whole school assembly every Tuesday. Library staff are dynamic – they produce own reading for pleasure guide, say John Green (The Fault in Our Stars) is the most requested author right now and invite the likes of Meg Rosoff and Patrick Gale to do author events.

Food gets the thumbs-up – 800 lunches served up every day, payment by lunch cards and lots of choice. Boarders eat in the main school, although they can make toast, pasta, hot drinks etc in boarding house kitchens. Sixth formers have to be in school every morning but if they haven't got lessons, they are allowed out after 12 noon. They also have their own café and sixth form centre, complete with common room, study area and thumping music at break time.

Pastoral care, well-being and discipline: School has clear expectations of pupils but everyone we spoke to reckoned it's a fair, equitable place. Prefects are trained to play a big brother/sister role to younger counterparts – all adding to the friendly atmosphere. Most lower sixth pupils do a 16-week peer counselling programme led by the chaplain (who's known as the Rev). When we asked if the school is strict, a year 7 pupil told us: 'There are lots of rules but they are reasonable ones.' Homework is pretty sensible too – starting at 20 minutes a night per subject (up to three subjects a night) and rising as youngsters get older. Good support for new pupils – sixth form prefects look after younger pupils and maps doled out to help them navigate their way round the site. The only improvements year 7s and 8s could think of would be a mini-buggy or ski lift to transport them around the campus. We can't see it happening any time soon.

Deputy head is responsible for pupil progress and welfare. Tutor groups organised by year and tutors are pupils' first port of call if there are any problems (they can also go to their head of year, chaplain, medical centre, school counsellor and sixth form peer counsellors). Head boy and head girl, plus deputies and a raft of senior prefects, and a house system in place. Current head is said to be stricter on uniform than his predecessor and pupils are well turned out. Sixth formers wear business dress – 'we have our own fashion sense but we have to look smart,' said one. No jeans and trousers must have a crease.

Pupils and parents: The youngsters we met were down-to-earth, motivated and refreshingly modest about their individual achievements. Our guides included a talented 800m England schools champion and a jazz singer who's in the National Youth Choir, but we had to drag the information out of them. 'Anyone can fit in here – even if they are quite shy,' we were told. Pupils come from all over Cornwall – around half from Truro itself, but others from up to an hour away and as far afield as St Austell, Bodmin, St Ives and Penzance. Many travel long distances by train (a fleet of double-decker buses ferry them from the station) and parents have organised minibuses from places like Helston.

Parents said they approve of the way the school treats youngsters as individuals and seeks to discover everyone's talents

The boarders include weekly boarders who live in the Scilly Isles, children of expats and a small number of international students from countries like Germany, Spain, Italy, Hong Kong, China, Nigeria, Georgia and Ukraine (around 40 with EAL requirements). Everyone mixes in together – 'it's a really friendly place,' a sixth former told us.

Parents are an eclectic group – lots of doctors, accountants and lawyers plus farmers, holiday park owners and entrepreneurs. Just like their children, they are genial, unpushy and appreciative of the school. As we said last time, there's 'nothing flash or lah-di-dah here.' A mother who'd moved from Surrey told us: 'The teachers are incredibly supportive and down-to-earth – questions and queries always get dealt with, and unlike my son's old school, I never come home grumbling.' Parents also said they approve of the way the school treats youngsters as individuals and seeks to discover everyone's talents.

Distinguished former pupils include former M&S chairman Lord Myners, actors Robert Shaw, John Rhys Davies and Nigel Terry, baritones Benjamin Luxon and Alan Opie, sopranos Lynette Carveth and Saffron Jones, quadruple Olympic gold medallist sailor Ben Ainslie, chess grandmaster Michael Adams and Queen drummer Roger Taylor.

Entrance: Around 40 per cent of the pupils come from the school's own prep, the rest from a host of state and prep schools. School is moderately selective (around 110 applications for 85 year 7 places) and main entry points are at 11, 13 and 16. Admission before sixth form is by entrance exam, school report and interview. For pupils joining sixth form, predicted GCSE grades, school report and interview.

Exit: Around a third leave after GCSEs, either because they want a change or to do subjects not offered by Truro School (many head off to the mighty Truro and Penwith College four miles away, although new head says he is determined to increase retention). After the sixth form most go to university (80 per cent straight from school), including a handful to Oxbridge – six in 2017. Maths, sciences and geology are the most popular subjects and Cardiff, Exeter and Bristol the most popular destinations over the last five years, with a few off to Europe or the US. The school offers a specialised careers programme for budding medics, dentists and vets.

Money matters: Academic, art, music, drama, fencing and sport scholarships worth five to 10 per cent of the fees offered. Not a rich school – no endowments – so relies on prudent husbandry and strives to be as inclusive as it can afford to be. Some means-tested bursaries and headmaster's boarding awards (fee discount of 25 per cent) for boarders.

Remarks: A friendly, high achieving school with a real sense of purpose. It combines the best of old and new, makes the most of the bracing Cornish sea air and encourages pupils to find their own niche, whatever it may be.

Wellington School

65

South Street, Wellington, Somerset TA21 8NT

01823 668800 | enquiries@wellington-school.org.uk | www.wellington-school.org.uk

Ages: 11-18 (boys board from 11, girls from 13)

Pupils: 583; sixth form: 165; Boarders: 122 full, 16 weekly

Day: £13,161 – £14,784 pa; Boarding: £22,245 – £30,495 pa

Headmaster: Since 2014, Henry Price MA. Eton and Oxford (classics). A career teacher, first post at Sydney Grammar, Australia, next Sherborne then Rugby for 13 years where, in addition to being head of classics and a housemaster, he was involved in all manner of extracurricular activities. Married, four young children. Circumscribed cultural and recreational hinterland just now, given the demands of his large family. In holiday time enjoys the beaches and mountains of Wales from his base in Anglesey.

Mr Price was guarded in his responses to our questions, leaving us with a lot to find out for ourselves. We did learn that he is fiercely proud of his school, its values and attributes. If it has a USP, he said, it is that it is 'grounded'. And he gave us a valuable insight into his philosophy of education. Our ears pricked up when he spoke of Wellington's teachers as 'schoolmasters' and 'schoolmistresses'. You don't hear those heritage words very often these days. What does he mean by them? To understand, we must blow the dust off the seminal work on the subject written by AC Benson waay back in 1902. He defined the role of the schoolmaster/mistress as: 'to curb, to correct, but also to encourage and to lift' by 'the personal interest which they take in all that concerns the [students] for whom they are responsible'. In sum, 'there should be a conscious consecration of self to work'. The modern tendency in education is towards specialisation; the plum roles are in management. So teachers who want to get on nowadays are more likely to be found in suits at exam board meetings, not charging about in short trousers refereeing the U14 Bs. Is Mr Price's ideal of the teacher as all-rounder massively behind the curve? Or is the richness of the school's pastoral and co-curricular provision a testament to his, and his predecessors', vocational, holistic approach? We suspect the latter. And we applaud his focus on supporting the development of his teachers both in and out of the classroom. A parent told us, 'He has refocussed on work and sport without losing the essential decency of the school'.

The overwhelming majority of parents we spoke to like their headmaster. Even after correcting for choice-supportive bias, he gets good chitty – and that's after taking into account those who say 'I wish he had more presence' and 'more sense of humour'. His fans are vigorously protective and speak with strong affection, for they have got to know him and acknowledge that yes, he can come over as reserved, and no, 'he's not an in-yer-face head'; he's the sort who 'quietly sees what's going on and takes it all in'. 'He's shy and may have felt burdened by the step up to headship, but he's growing in confidence'. 'Heads at Wellington learn on the job.' 'He's the softly-softly sort.' 'He's a thoroughly humane, decent man with a strong sense of justice'. Also clearly bright and scholarly, his interests span philosophy, modern lit fic and medieval history. His speeches on formal occasions are highly esteemed and contain a lot of heart – together with some rather good jokes. Plainly a man who enjoys honing a sentence.

Doesn't score five stars for luxury, more like a solid three. The point is the students like it, enjoy their relationships with house staff and express contentment

Hosts a sticky bun club for students every Friday break where he gets to hear what they think. Teaches Latin – 'I'm still a schoolmaster'. Sends all students a birthday card. One of his students, we learned from their mum, really likes his warmer, funnier classroom persona.

Academic matters: Typical grammar school curriculum, all the subjects you need for a top university and the right ones to suit the full range of students here – 24 of them. Actually, more than enough, uptake varying from 40+ to, in one or two subjects, 0, so some very small class sizes. Four modern languages including Chinese and two ancient ones (Latin and Greek). No vocational courses eg BTecs. Maths and sciences an enduring strength. Results in 2017 commendable by any standards, and that's without factoring in the ongoing lurch to 'reformed' A levels. Seventy-eight per cent A*-B and 50 per cent A*/A grades at A level. Value added score shows the school in the top 12 per cent nationally, an achievement flattered a little by the absence of GCSE maths from the calculation (students here do the IGCSE), but nonetheless admirable. Best of the best: geography, maths (historically strong), Eng lit and classics. Less strong: business studies, economics and physics (improving). Notable: the number of B grades attained by students who might otherwise have got Cs. At GCSE the 2017 harvest was 47 per cent A*-A/9-7 grades. Broadly, strong on all fronts, physics especially so. Sixth form foundation course for international students.

Exceptional special needs provision addresses everything from classic special needs (dyslexia et al) to support for students who have hit a wobbly patch, to a few with mild behavioural problems. Some of these (120 when we visited) have an eye kept on them remotely (they don't know), monitoring mechanisms having registered a blip. Hugely impressive SENCo, masses of experience, wise and thoughtful. He told us: 'Our relationship with our students is key; there's a pastoral element to this. Our department is a good place for a time out, especially for those struggling with sociability'. Big believer in empathy exercises for teachers to give them some idea what dyslexia feels like.

Careers counselling and course guidance highly rated. You see the evidence for that in the well-chosen universities students go on to, from the highly academic to the best of the rather more doable. As a flagship achievement this is as impressive us as Oxbridge triumphs: they're bringing out the best in all their students. Head of sixth form much admired and strongly liked by students and parents.

Games, options, the arts: Novel approach to physical exercise – may even be trend-setting. Well-being, they call it. Potentially confusing, too, when you're told, in the school's words, that 'The well-being programme ... replaces the subject that schools have traditionally called physical education'. Acting on a perhaps understandable misunderstanding, The Sunday Times shouted 'zumba puts team games on the bench at top school ... Wellington School in Somerset has abandoned traditional PE lessons ... and replaced them with "well-being" classes'. But it's simply not true. The new and pioneering look for PE here is, in the head's words, 'evolved'. He explains: 'There is plenty of physical activity but also classroom sessions based around nutrition, mindfulness and leadership, which links into our PSHE programme. Our aim is not only to increase fitness and confidence at school, but also teach pupils how to look after themselves long after they leave school.' In other words, there's as much traditional team sport here as there ever was (heaps), but also a recognition that 'it is.. important that an increasingly sedentary generation understands the importance of physical fitness in their working lives'. We can testify that the splendid sports hall was not reverberating to a chant of ohm when we visited, and while some might regard the way the school addresses mindfulness as a tad narrow, we were struck by the benevolence of the PE staff, their borderline-messianic dedication and their concern to find something for everyone. One mum told us that her daughter had become sporty for the first time in her life. Strong girls' cricket and rugby. Head of sport is an ex-pro rugby player and ex-county cricketer. Team sports are compulsory to year 10; thereafter you get to choose. The one thing you can't choose is nothing. To the gratification of many parents, mainstream sports have been boosted by Mr Price: 'Wellington needed to up its game'.

Music exceptionally strong, much raved about by the mother of a scholar: 'The head of department is inspirational'. Rich range of ensembles and styles and a choral tradition that spans all-girl a capella group and a chapel choir that sings choral compline in local churches. Drama 'could be bigger,' said one parent. Happens in the converted old school hall, ideal for big musicals; also in the South Side studio theatre opened by alumnus David Suchet. Director in residence, thesp background, aims to drum up numbers for GCSE and A level, presently on the low side. Club for techies under the watchful eye of a BBC-trained overseer. Art department buzzy as can be, lots of big ambitious work in progress, everything from paint through ceramics to digital. Well impressive.

Heaps of extracurricular activities likely to render students paralysed for choice. On offer Saturday mornings too, but only compulsory for boarders. Head very keen on outdoor ed, so D of E has enjoyed a recent shot in the arm. CCF hugely popular – very Wellington, this; it's an esprit de corps sort of school. Attractive adventurous activities on offer including arduous Ten Tors trekking event. CCF comes with enhanced outcomes here: you can put your service towards a BTec level 2 diploma in uniformed public services or an Institute of Leadership and Management qualification. Lots of holiday expeditions home and abroad, some educational, some recreational and some downright gruelling. Brilliant initiative, student generated, enables boys and girls to get their Amateur FA basic refereeing badge. Absolutely not the sort of school that lets anyone skive off but, as a student told us, 'They try really hard to cater for what you want to do'.

Boarding: Around 150 board, roughly 50 per cent of them international students from all over, mainly Russia, China and Europe – 25 nationalities when we called in – numbers of any one nationality limited in order to spur integration. So buoyant

is boarding that there are plans to open a new house. Good systems for boarders to make their views heard. Weekend activities, always a bugbear in boarding schools, have been beefed up under the impetus of the head. A parent we spoke to who'd sent her son elsewhere entertained a lasting sense of regret that she had not opted what she described as 'Wellington's smelly-socks boarding'. She may have been misinformed. No odour of hosiery when we dived in, everything clean and gleaming. Doesn't score five stars for luxury, more like a solid three, though we hear five star things about brand new girls' boarding house. The point is the students like it, enjoy their relationships with house staff and express contentment.

Background and atmosphere: Founded in 1837 as Wellington Academy, offering a commercial, mathematical and classical education. That 'commercial' tells you something about the target clientele, still a sector today. In 1879 it rebranded as the West Somerset County School. During WW1 the pupils grew vegetables on the playing fields and made munitions for the front line in the school engineering shop – and the name was changed to Wellington School. In 1945 it became a direct grant grammar school. On the abolition of that scheme in 1976 the school's application to join the state sector was refused, so it went independent. As it has grown it has spilled over into a hodge-podge of handsome buildings bisected by a traffic-calmed road. The main campus is altogether more unified, blessed for space and recognisably public-schooly with its chapel and commodious playing fields. Well resourced throughout, money carefully spent. Never the sort of school to be seduced by the spirit of the present age and blow cash on fancy-pants prestige buildings. Opened its doors to international students in 1904 and girls in 1979.

The school sits squarely in the midst of the architecturally handsome market town of Wellington, once a wool town, now more of a dormitory for Taunton. Nice Georgian town houses, a branch of Waitrose and a Wetherspoon pub named in honour of the Iron Duke whose link to the town is in fact notional. He visited just once. His brother chose his territorial title for him when he got his dukedom – the great man was tied up with the Peninsular war at the time – and plumped for the name Wellington for no better reason that that he thought it sounded a bit like Wellesley. A lofty if decayed obelisk celebrating Waterloo stands just outside the town. The town itself nestles on the banks of the M5, enjoying excellent transport links, so much so that some parents to the east of Taunton find it easier to get to Wellington than its competitor schools in Taunton itself. Not to be confused with the namesake college in Berkshire, obviously, except that a surprising number do. The realisation dawns at some point

Careers counselling and course guidance highly rated. You see the evidence for that in the well-chosen universities students go on to

when they're looking round, by which time they have lost their hearts and signed up.

The social climate of the school is influenced by the level at which it sets its fees – some 20 per cent or so lower for day students than local competitors (the difference for boarders is less than 10 per cent). This broadens its social base, opening it up to local families who would otherwise be unable to afford an independent education. It also opens it to sneery jibes, eg 'the state school you have to pay fees for', precisely the sort of remark that makes it attractive to affluent folk who don't want their children to be infected by hauteur. We spoke to a number of such parents who had chosen Wellington rather than the sort of school they had been to themselves, who spoke of their pride in the down-to-earth, unpretentious nature of a school whose students go out into the world with an ability to relate to people of all sorts with absolutely no sense of entitlement. We spoke to a working mum for whom finding the fees is a heroic struggle. She told us, 'I never feel intimidated when I go up there', and rejoices that when her daughter leaves 'she will be sure of herself, not full of herself'. One parent talked of a 'school happy to be itself' and there's no doubting its strong sense of identity; we've rarely encountered such ardent loyalty from both students and parents.

Parents also like what one described as 'a thoroughly traditional ethos' and 'Christian values unashamedly proclaimed'. Another said, 'It's the sort of school where it's cool to work hard and make something of yourself'. This is widely endorsed: 'Wellington is good at finding out what your child is good at'. Yes, this is a meritocratic environment whose grammar school inheritance lives on.

Pastoral care, well-being and discipline: Sound and recently reinforced systems for pastoral care. Principal guarantor of well-being is good relationships among students and between them and staff, whether 'teachers, who really care' or support staff. Some intermingling of year groups; sixth formers pretty good at looking out for the youngest. Parents report rapid response to problems and feel their views count. Though this is a school notable for its camaraderie it is, in the words of a parent, 'not overly conformist'. A student told us 'character is valued; some need more leeway'. For all that the climate is notably orderly. A problem with good schools is that there's so little to rebel against.

Pupils and parents: Most day students come in by bus from Exeter and Chard to the south, Minehead and Dulverton to the north west and beyond Bridgwater to the east. Good social spread of down to earth parents. 'Not a posh school by any stretch of the imagination', one told us. Another: 'No one judges you by what car you drive, only by how nice you are'. And another: 'A good solid cohort of decent parents. Lots of doctors.'

Entrance: Main entry at year 7, everyone sits school's entry test in January. At year 9, tests in Eng, maths + paper of own choice. Post-GCSE they'll have you as long as you got three B/6s and three Cs/5. So, not fiendishly selective. International students from year 7.

Exit: Varying numbers leave at the GCSE watershed. Of these, most to vocational courses, especially Taunton's Richard Huish College: 'Outstanding' – Ofsted. Some parents make a strategic decision to fund just years 7–11. Majority of leavers go on to uni. Usually three or four to Oxbridge, two in 2017.

Money matters: High value, especially for day students. Fees what they say on the tin, none of the mum's-the-word discounts you can haggle at other schools and no sibling discounts either. Scholarships up to 20 per cent. Top-up bursaries to 40 per cent subject to means test. The school is committed, according to its means, to educating local boys and girls. Notably astute money management.

Remarks: Down to earth. Punches above its weight. No sense of entitlement. Good value for money. Not our words, those of a parent. Says it for us, too.

Wells Cathedral School

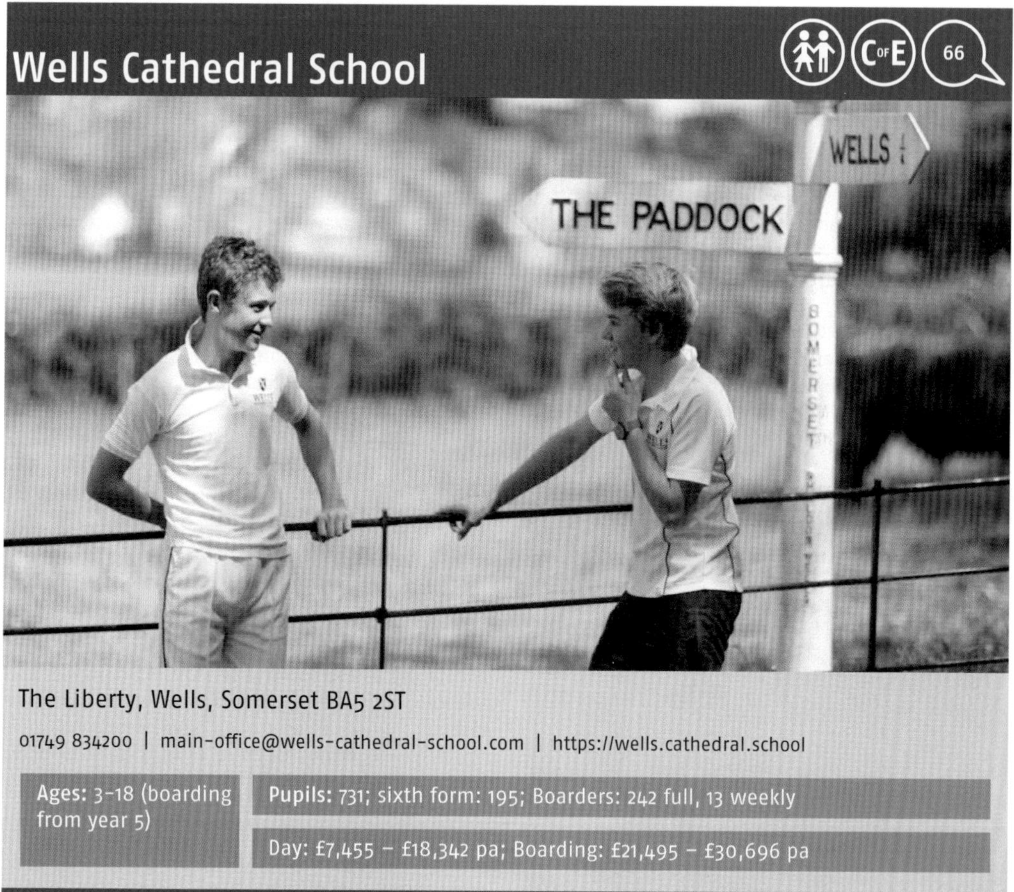

The Liberty, Wells, Somerset BA5 2ST

01749 834200 | main-office@wells-cathedral-school.com | https://wells.cathedral.school

Ages: 3–18 (boarding from year 5)

Pupils: 731; sixth form: 195; Boarders: 242 full, 13 weekly

Day: £7,455 – £18,342 pa; Boarding: £21,495 – £30,696 pa

Head: Since September 2016, Andy Kemp, previously deputy head and maths teacher. Several degrees and postgrad qualifications from Warwick in maths and maths education, plus an MBA in educational leadership from the Instutute of Education. Taught maths and ICT at Warwick School and moved to

Taunton School as HoD; joined Wells as director of studies before moving upwards.

Head of junior school since April 2014, Mrs Julie Barrow. A longstanding member of the junior school staff, and still very much involved in the day to day delivery of the curriculum at all levels of both pre-prep and prep. Her appointment has delighted parents. 'The school is thriving under her care,' wrote one parent, 'she is down to earth, has a great sense of humour and clear leadership skills. She also has a truly professional and committed team around her.' Another grateful mother added, 'Mrs Barrow is the most wonderful, kind and caring head teacher. She is always approachable, and in every instance the child comes first.'

Previous senior school head, Elizabeth Cairncross, is now principal of the whole school. Read English at London University (Bedford College, now joined with Royal Holloway College). Formerly deputy head of Christ's Hospital, Horsham, where she had been a teacher since 1986. A passionate believer in co-education, and radiates calm confidence in the school. Not an elite musician herself – a useful asset here, she believes – but came to Wells because 'the Wells way is to look at what's the best way and it was that creativity that attracted me.'

Impresses as a true scholar, who thinks hard about life, the universe and everything; and as a modernizer who is nonetheless at home with tradition. Hugely popular with parents, who queued up to give praise: 'An inspirational leader, who doesn't take any flannel, is very focused, and manages to juggle the many facets of the school with skill and aplomb'; 'Clearly not a head who rests on her laurels, and there is a definite sense of a school wishing to explore new ways of working and not being satisfied with the status quo'; 'An excellent role model with high academic standards'; 'What I love is that the children absolutely and 100 per cent come first for her' – etc.

Wells is one of five UK schools accorded specialist music school status by the government's Music and Dance Scheme

Academic matters: Wells's unique selling point is flexibility. The school goes out of its way to address individual needs and preferences, and the results are highly creditable. In 2017, 55 per cent of GCSEs A*-A/9-7 and 47 per cent of A levels were graded at A*/A. Compared with the other specialist music schools, offers a broad and challenging curriculum, with a good range of languages on offer: French, German, Spanish, Italian, Mandarin and Latin. Really excellent maths provision, owing to the innovative Specialist Maths Scheme, which allows able students an extra three hours of maths per week and aims to turn out creative mathematicians who can think beyond the syllabus. Why maths in particular? School says, 'It grew out of the music – we already knew how to specialise and be flexible.' Science labs endearingly shabby, but science teaching is 'very good, one of the strengths of the school,' according to a parent, and the pupils we spoke to – one of whom was off to Edinburgh to read medicine – agreed. Humanities also popular: one mother wrote, 'The school is now providing some really exciting and interesting history, philosophy, etc.' No IB – head dislikes the amount of assessment involved, and prefers the depth of A levels (Cambridge Pre-U also offered in history). Everyone praised the teaching staff's willingness to give students the support they needed and to work constructively with all pupils, including those for whom music came first. Small class sizes and kind, knowledgeable staff, many of whom have been here for years and have a huge loyalty to the school.

SEN well catered for, with specialists in both the junior and senior schools ('second to none,' according to the mother of a dyslexic pupil), and school excels at adapting its provision to the individual student, an approach head clearly relishes: 'In 10 years' time, all schools will have to offer bespoke programmes for everybody.' One mother ran out of superlatives when describing the way the staff had worked with her to draw up a care plan for managing her child's epilepsy. At the other end of the scale, parents rated the way their bright children had been stretched and challenged: 'The teaching is really good for an able child, and the maths has been wonderful.'

Given that Wells isn't overly selective in terms of academic ability, we were much struck with the school's achievements in this area and asked how it was done. 'By tailoring, by playing to people's strengths, by being can-do, and by having staff prepared to put the grounding in place,' was the answer. Parents agree: 'The children do incredibly well there, but it comes without the hothousing stress that other nearby schools create,' said one. 'They're really, really good at getting the best out of their pupils, no matter what their level is,' wrote another.

Games, options, the arts: Wells is one of five UK schools accorded specialist music school status by the government's Music and Dance Scheme and, as you'd expect, the music here is very special indeed. We heard a stunning young violinist rehearsing Korngold's violin concerto with the school's equally stunning symphony orchestra, which pretty much set us up for the day. For those who love music, there's a pulse-racingly good range of ensembles and other opportunities offered by the nine performance faculties: brass, composition, choristers, jazz, keyboard, percussion, strings, vocals and woodwind. The new Cedars Hall offers a world class concert venue within the school grounds, adding to the school's already-top-notch music facilities. Quirkier aspects of music also catered for: the percussion suite includes a World Percussion room, complete with its own Indonesian gamelan – other specialist music schools, please take note. All children in year 1 are offered free violin lessons, and the lovely end-of-year performance we heard testified to their impressive progress in this area. Fantastic and inclusive junior choir performs in concerts and all children aged 3 to 11 are involved in the school shows. For the specialists, there are two highly-regarded sets of junior choristers, one for boys and one for girls.

'The real and very special feature of Wells,' wrote a father, 'is that it manages to make highly skilled musicians feel normal and grounds them in real life'

Parents and students alike praised the inclusivity of the music provision at Wells, saying that all pupils had the opportunity to take part and to excel if they wished, and many felt that the music benefited pupils in ways beyond the music itself: 'I think that being in a place where musical excellence is encouraged has inspired excellence in other areas,' wrote one mother, and others made

similar comments. May not suit young musicians seeking the hardcore, all-or-nothing ethos of the other specialist music schools, but the parents we spoke to felt this was a strength: 'That's the real and very special feature of Wells,' wrote a father. 'It makes highly skilled musicians feel normal and grounds them in real life.'

Better sports than at any of the other specialist music schools, and pretty good for any school. Lovely new sports pavilion, all blond wood and glass, fronts the tree-dotted cricket pitch that boasts 'one of the best wickets in Somerset,' according to proud students. Teams are fielded in cricket, rugby, hockey (boys and girls), netball, rounders, tennis, swimming, soccer and basketball, and everyone who wants to participate will get the chance. Again, inclusivity is the watchword. 'I love that the emphasis is not on winning at all costs,' wrote one parent. 'Sometimes the order will be changed to ensure that the lower order players get to play the key positions, even if that means we are likely to lose the match. I think this is brilliant, although not all parents agree!' It's not all losses, either: remembering a recent victory against Millfield clearly raised our tour guides' testosterone levels. Excellent covered swimming pool used all the year round. Dance studio is home to compulsory dance for both boys and girls up to year 9.

Flourishing drama with at least two productions per year, and remarkably good art and photography, reflecting the very creative ethos. A huge programme of clubs and societies, everything from jewellery making to CCF. School embraces the forest schools initiative – children in years 1 and 2 learn to eg build shelters and cook on open fires.

Boarding: The boarding provision was given the thumbs up by everyone we spoke to, with all boarders confirming that they enjoyed their time here ('It's really nice! Lots of activities at the weekends,' said a sixth former who joined in year 12). Very small numbers of boarders in junior school (currently nine), all of them housed with the older pupils – didn't sound ideal to us, but no complaints of any kind reached us. Boarding houses are frankly dilapidated – the ones we saw, at any rate – and numbers to a room rather high for this modern age, with four or five being fairly normal. Living in one of the country's prettiest and oldest towns has its flipside, perhaps. But the students seemed cheerful enough about it, and although we dug hard, we couldn't unearth any complaints. Appraisals of the food were mixed. 'Like the food I had to endure when I boarded 25 years ago!' said one parent, while another countered loyally, 'I'm told it's amazing!' But again the students, all of whom seem to radiate good health, seemed happy with it. We ourselves were served a pleasant and wholesome lunch, so can't comment on this further.

Background and atmosphere: Tracing its roots back to 909, Wells is one of the world's oldest schools, and wears its age beautifully; there surely can't be a lovelier place of learning anywhere. Whether picking our way down the cobbled Vicar's Close, where we heard mellifluous treble recorder playing drifting out of the mullioned windows, or wandering about the many elegant Georgian buildings cocooned in greenery, we thought that growing up here must be a gift. 'I am not sure our children yet realise just how lucky they are,' agreed one parent, 'and when I visit I do have to pinch myself sometimes.'

School motto is 'Be what you are' ('Esto quod es'), and all parents commented how confident and happy their children were and on the good friends they'd made

Co-educational since 1969, and a specialist music school since 1970, and remains the only such within the setting of a normal school, something which parents clearly value. Music department housed in gorgeous – if rather cluttered – medieval building directly opposite the cathedral. We liked the library with its stock of 2,000 vinyl records plus turntable, although it did seem too small for quiet study, and one parent said that this was a problem throughout the school, describing the boarding houses as noisy. Junior school on a cloistered, lovely, leafy, tree-dotted site with a very nice games courtyard and a delightful early years play area. All rooms made attractive and colourful, and when we visited on a blisteringly hot day, they were refreshingly cool.

This is undoubtedly a very happy community; everywhere we looked we saw a kind of upbeat tranquility blended with lively creativity. One mother spoke for everyone when she wrote, 'What I love about Wells is the happy and welcoming atmosphere. Everyone has a smile – and it is really infectious!'

Pastoral care, well-being and discipline: Highly praised by everyone. The school motto is 'Be what you are' ('Esto quod es'), and all parents commented how confident and happy their children had become since starting at the school, and on the good friends they'd made there. Indeed, we spoke to parents whose children had previously been miserable – in one case at a top academic school, in another at a different specialist music school – but were now simply loving life after transferring to Wells. School communications on pastoral issues rated by parents as prompt, efficient and helpful. (Exception to this appeared to be some of the music teaching staff, who, some said, were reluctant to keep parents in the loop and clung to an outdated 'what goes on in my lessons is my business' attitude.) One parent wrote, 'We love this school. It expects high standards of behaviour and achievement but allows children good levels of independence and autonomy in reaching these. The children learn to motivate themselves. They are supported and nurtured and helped with strategies and tools, but they are not micro-managed.'

Focus is on 'mutual consideration, respect and courtesy,' and discipline problems are few. Children are charmingly polite, but very much themselves: 'Hullo, Mrs Cairncross!' exclaimed a 6-year-old lad with grave propriety as we walked by, 'I looked away and when I looked back again you'd popped up!' Older students showed the same style of courteous assurance, duly matured.

One parent, whose child had moved to the junior school after an unhappy time at another school, commented, 'My daughter is now the happiest child you could ever meet. She goes into school smiling and comes out so excited about her day.'

Pupils and parents: Day pupils drawn from large local radius – school operates bus routes to bring children in from Bristol, Bath, Taunton, Yeovil and comparable. Boarders come from all over, but a significant proportion still from the south west, perhaps because Wells remains off the beaten track: the nearest train station is Castle Cary, some 13 miles away. International students bring cultural diversity: they are welcomed into the purpose-built International Centre and offered very good EAL support. Parents mostly hardworking professionals, keen for their children to turn out right on all fronts – many families choose to send all their children to Wells for their entire education. Pupils are well-mannered, well-spoken, well-adjusted, well-turned-out, and very likeable.

Entrance: A broad church academically and, as always with Wells, flexibility is key. Informal assessment for the pre-prep plus meeting with its head, Janet Bennett. At junior level, more formal tests but still 'friendly'. Chorister auditions held in January each year.

Children can join the school at any point in their school career, even year 13 – the school works to make it a success. At the usual senior entry points of age 11 and 13, however, a formal entrance assessment is held in maths and reasoning, and satisfactory report from previous school is required. Entry to sixth form is subject to interview and at least six grade C/5 passes at GCSE, with grade B/6 or above in subjects to be taken for A level. Auditions for music places currently held in November (sixth form) and January (all age groups) after a pre-audition meeting.

Exit: Almost all juniors move up to the senior school, after sitting an entrance test to gauge academic levels. Some 10 per cent after GCSEs. At 18, almost all to higher education, with a high proportion to Russell group universities, or to music conservatoires in the UK or abroad, many with scholarships. Others off to study eg environmental science, history of art, psychology or engineering. Eight Oxbridge places in 2017 and three medics.

Money matters: Historically, not a wealthy school, but Wells has made what it's got go a very long way. An unusually wide variety of scholarships on offer: maths, music, sports, creative arts, academic and all-round. Most of these worth no more than 10 per cent, but a sliding scale of means-tested bursary assistance is also available, and school is working overtime to build up its endowment and reach a 'needs-blind' point of admissions. Funding of up to 100 per cent available for some 'elite' specialist musicians via the government's Music and Dance Scheme. Special provision pupils – children who are musically gifted but want to follow the full academic curriculum and keep their options open – often receive financial support for their music tuition.

Remarks: As one parent summed it up, 'We really love this school, and believe that by sending our children here we are giving them the best possible start in life.' A magical place, where children grow into kind, confident and accomplished young adults.

West Buckland School

West Buckland, Barnstaple, Devon EX32 0SX

01598 760000 | headmaster@westbuckland.com | https://www.westbuckland.com

Ages: 3–18 (boarding from year 7)

Pupils: 600; sixth form: 118; Boarders: 99

Day: £7,800 – £14,550 pa; Boarding: £23,520 – 29,685 pa (UK boarders), £25,785 – £32,520 pa (international boarders)

Headmaster: Since 2016, Mr Phillip Stapleton BSc MA Ed MBA (40s). Educated at Bishop Stopford School in Kettering, followed by Durham University, where he read biochemistry and immersed himself in music, drama and sport. Several university friends became actors (including Alex Macqueen of Peep Show and The Inbetweeners fame), but he modestly says: 'I wasn't good enough'. Initially set on a career in molecular genetics, he stayed on at Durham to take part in a show, embarked on a PGCE and discovered he loved teaching. 'It brought everything together – working with inquisitive minds, a passion for my subject and the chance to perform,' he says. First teaching post was at Stonyhurst, followed by Charterhouse, where he taught chemistry and became a housemaster. Then moved to Ardingly, where he was deputy head for five years. He is also an ISI inspector.

Head was struck by West Buckland's friendly atmosphere and beautiful location the instant he arrived for his interview. 'The sun was shining and a group of students were setting off for a run,' he says. 'It was a breath of fresh air to see their sense of enjoyment. There was a real buzz of opportunity and potential.' The school is selective but he's determined that the school should cater for children from all backgrounds. He's very proud of West Buckland's decision to offer 100 per cent bursaries to local youngsters whose families don't have the financial means to send them to the school (there are currently 17 children benefiting from this programme). During his first year at the school he focused on teaching and learning, observing every teacher in the classroom and broadening the extra-curricular opportunities on offer. He's determined to raise the school's profile, citing its academic results, musical prowess and emphasis on character development.

Energetic and approachable, he still teaches (many heads don't). This year he's got a year 12 A level chemistry set. Married to Jules, who teaches maths at West Buckland. They live in a house on-site and have three children, all pupils at the prep. Keen on sport (he once ran four ultra-marathons in a year – respect) and has recently taken up the double bass.

Sixth form boarders have their own en-suite rooms – far more salubrious than many university rooms. They're encouraged to do their own laundry and learn to cook

Prep school head is Andrew Moore BEd, who's retiring in 2018 after 18 years at the school. He joined West Buckland from The Pilgrims' School in Winchester, where he was head of the 'quiristers', the boys who sing in the Winchester College chapel choir. New head of the prep school will be Nick Robinson MSc PGCE, deputy head of Dunhurst, Bedales's prep school.

Academic matters: Results are good. In 2017, more than 60 per cent A*-A/9-7 at GCSE (with four pupils gaining the much coveted new grade 9 in maths) and nearly 41 per cent A*/A at A level. Most pupils take 10 subjects at GCSE, including at least one language (French or Spanish) and two or three sciences (the majority take three). School is the highest performing sixth form in north Devon, with around 20 subjects on offer at A level. Chemistry, maths and biology are the most popular A level choices, followed by geography and economics. A small number took the EPQ in the past but now AS exams have been ditched all pupils will do it. Other options available to sixth formers include a BTec in applied science and core maths (a new level 3 qualification). No Saturday school.

Unusually, the school doesn't charge extra for learning support (now called personalised learning and development). Around 100 children have help in some shape or form and the dynamic new head of department has brought in a wealth of ideas and strategies, including coloured reading rulers to reduce visual stress, pencil grips, spell checkers, prep diaries and a quiet room for children who might be having a difficult day and want a bit of peace and quiet. Reading for pleasure is encouraged throughout the school. Imposing new library has 14,000 resources and pupils can use it whenever they like, whether they're studying or curled up with a good book. Favourite authors at the time of our visit included Sarah Crossan and Kim Slater for younger pupils, Emma Cline, Deborah Levy and Ta-Nehisi Coates for sixth formers.

Prep school is housed in a separate building. The head boy, one of our tour guides, reminisced nostalgically about his days at the prep and said he'd be very sad to leave the school. Prep teachers work closely with the senior school – children learn French from nursery and get the chance to use the senior school's art department and science labs (the prep has its own lab too). Ninety-five per cent of prep school pupils progress to the senior school. Pre-prep has its own building, with views across fields full of grazing sheep – no wonder parents race to get their children's names down. It's not all splashing paint and building sandcastles though. When we visited, a group of year 2 children had just learned the meaning of 'onomatopoeia' and were excitedly coming up with their own examples.

Games, options, the arts: West Buckland is a sporty, outdoorsy place, with acres of playing fields and excellent facilities. The sports centre (named after distinguished old boy and Olympic triple jumper Jonathan Edwards) boasts a vast sports hall, fitness suite and 25m indoor pool. Boys' main sports are rugby, hockey and cricket and girls' main sports are hockey, netball and tennis. Lots of pupils play for local and county teams. The school also offers specialist performance and development programmes in tennis and dance. Sport is compulsory till year 11 and optional after that ¬ but around 98 per cent continue with it, whether it's mainstream sports or activities like squash, swimming or dance.

Pupils are encouraged to get out into the fresh air as much as possible. The school has its own forest school, where pre-prep pupils – under strict supervision – play in the woods, build bivouacs, make fires and learn to tie knots. The older ones take on challenges like the gruelling Ten Tors hike across Dartmoor and the school's annual Exmoor run, once described by school archivist Berwick Coates as 'the oldest, longest, roughest, toughest, regular scheduled, compulsory school cross-country run in the length and breadth of England'. Around two-thirds of pupils do the run each year (the length of the run varies according to age), while others mark the course, administer the race and cheer their pals as they run across Exmoor's hilly terrain, through muddy streams and over rugged moorland. Staff, parents and old boys and girls take part too and as

School is rightfully proud of its stunning timber-clad 150 Building, built in collaboration with former West Buckland parent Damien Hirst

one of our young tour guides told us: 'The Exmoor run defines the school.'

Music is an integral part of the school, led by dynamic director of music Emma Kent, who's also musical director of the award-winning North Devon Sinfonia. Pupils and staff queue along the corridor to join her lunchtime choir rehearsals – we watched the junior girls' choir singing their hearts out before heading off to afternoon lessons. Music department comprises a recital room, teaching room, computer suite, recording studio and eight practice rooms. Everyone does music till year 9. Up to 25 pupils take the subject at GCSE and around six a year do A level music. Musicians get plenty of opportunities to perform in public – everything from Verdi's Requiem at Exeter Cathedral to Guys and Dolls in the Queen's Theatre, Barnstaple.

School is rightfully proud of its stunning timber-clad 150 Building, built in collaboration with former West Buckland parent Damien Hirst and opened in 2010. As well as the school theatre it houses the art and DT departments. Sixth formers have their own art studio – and their own individual space within it. 'If you treat someone as an artist, they'll work as an artist,' says the head of art. The standard of artwork is inspiring – we were particularly taken with a vast painting of the Exmoor run being painted by a sixth form art scholar as a gift to the school.

Lots of extracurricular options, everything from astronomy to jazz. Enterprising head of sixth form is keen to develop 'academic enrichment' and youngsters are encouraged to take part in the STEM Club, Phoenix Society (debating) and Aldiss Society (guest lectures). Outdoor learning is the jewel in the school's crown. Many youngsters do D of E (bronze, silver and gold) while CCF is compulsory for year 9 pupils (optional after that). New head of outdoor learning encourages pupils to challenge themselves. 'We've got enough tents to put 100 people under canvas,' he told us with a note of pride in his voice. Outdoor activities are voluntary but most take part, whether they surf after school or try their hands at coasteering. There's also the aptly named Adventure Society, which gives pupils the chance to experience new outdoor pursuits. Pupils excel at climbing, with two brothers gaining places in the GB bouldering team in recent years.

Boarding: Pupils can board from year 7, and occasionally younger ('we are always open to discussion,' a member of staff told us). Three boarding houses – one for year 7 to 11 girls, one for year 7 to 11 boys and a brand new sixth form boarding house, with separate wings for girls and boys. Sixth form house (Parker's) is very civilised. All sixth form boarders have their own en-suite rooms – far more salubrious than many university rooms we've seen. They're encouraged to do their own laundry and learn to cook. Stylish common room on ground floor is open to all sixth formers. Lots of activities for boarders at weekends, including cultural visits, shopping in Bath and Bristol, cinema trips, surfing, running, kayaking and paintballing.

Background and atmosphere: The school is set in 100 acres of idyllic countryside on the edge of Exmoor, 220 metres above sea level and eight miles from Barnstaple. Initially known as the Devon County School, it was founded as a boys' boarding school in 1858. The school's enterprising founder, the Rev JL Brereton, thought that the boys could do lessons in the schoolhouse in the morning and work on the school farm in the afternoon. They would then sell the produce and the income would pay for the school's upkeep. The school was renamed West Buckland School in 1912.

Imposing main building dates back to the 19th century but in recent years there have been many new additions, including the Michael Morpurgo Library (the celebrated War Horse author has a farm 20 miles away), the 150 Building and the sixth form boarding house.

Pastoral care, well-being and discipline: Universal praise for the school's friendly and welcoming ambience, with just the 'right balance of formality and friendliness'. One parent describes it as 'a hidden gem' while others say it produces 'grounded, socially aware and respectful individuals with a positive self-assurance'. Pupils particularly like the house system (everyone belongs to one of four houses and there are lots of inter-house competitions).

Plenty of people to talk to if problems arise, including personal tutors, housemasters and housemistresses, the school nurse and a school counsellor who comes in twice a week. School has its own chaplaincy team – a school assembly with a spiritual dimension takes place once a week and the carol service at South Molton Church, six miles away, is a highlight of the autumn term. Christian values are part of school life but students of all faiths or none are welcomed and encouraged.

Most day pupils travel to school by bus so they are allowed to bring phones to school but must put them away during lesson time, unless asked otherwise. Pupils' behaviour is excellent – murmurings about the occasional minor misdemeanour but that's all.

Pupils and parents: Day pupils come from within an hour's drive away, mostly from Barnstaple and North Devon villages. Some choose weekly or flexi boarding (parents can book online up to 24 hours in advance). A fleet of school buses ferry pupils (and sometimes staff) in from areas as far afield as Chawleigh, Tiverton and Winkleigh. Buses start as early as 7.30am to allow for the winding country lanes. Senior school day fees include travel costs but prep school fees don't. Around 20 per cent of pupils are boarders – a third of the boarders are from the Far East, a third from Europe and a third from the UK, mostly the south west.

The pupils we met were enthusiastic, unpretentious and refreshingly down-to-earth. No quibbles about the smart navy school uniform (sixth formers wear business suits) or the food, served in the newly refurbished dining hall. Parents range from families who've lived in the area for generations to those who've moved out of London in search of a better work-life balance – plus the chance to surf at nearby Putsborough Sands after work. Notable alumni include novelist RF Delderfield of To Serve Them All My Days fame, former Whitbread boss Alan Parker, science fiction author Brian Aldiss, triple jumper Jonathan Edwards, former England rugby players Steve Ojomoh and Victor Ubogu, and Somerset and England cricketers Craig and Jamie Overton.

Entrance: Entry into reception isn't selective. After that, those joining the prep higher up spend a taster day at the school and meet the prep school head. Entry into the senior school is selective, but not dauntingly so. Pupils joining in year 7 (from the prep and other schools) take English, maths and verbal reasoning tests in the preceding January. Children can start at multiple points so it's always worth talking to the school.

Some new pupils join in the sixth form (27 in 2017), many from local secondary schools finishing at 16. A minimum of five grade Cs/5s required by all, although it's not set in stone. Those aiming to do maths A level need at least a grade 7 in maths and a minimum grade B/6 is required for A level biology, chemistry, physics and modern languages.

Exit: Up to a fifth of pupils leave at 16, for a change of scene, to take the IB (not offered by West Buckland) or to do vocational subjects. At 18, around 90 per cent head to university, including one or two to Oxbridge most years (one to read physics at Oxford in 2017). Most popular universities are Bristol, Cardiff, Bath and Southampton, with subjects like engineering, geography, business, English and biology leading the pack. A few opt for apprenticeships and the world of work. Pupils get plenty of guidance about university and careers. Youngsters are encouraged to get some work experience from year 10 onwards – everything from working at local law, marketing and architecture firms to volunteering at a children's hospice in Barnstaple.

Money matters: Mindful of the tough economic climate, the school has kept its fees as low as possible, with learning support, travel, exams and books all included in the senior school fee. Academic scholarships available to year 7, 9 and 12 pupils, plus music, art and sport.

Remarks: A gem of a school in an exceptional location. West Buckland is an impressive all-rounder school with excellent facilities, great teaching and a real sense of community. Children work hard, get lots of fresh air and don't grow up too fast. Best of all, they seem to have a whale of a time while they're at it.

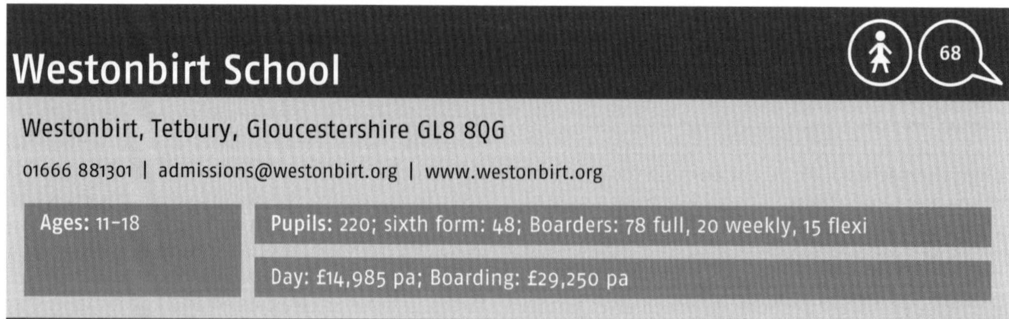

Westonbirt School

68

Westonbirt, Tetbury, Gloucestershire GL8 8QG

01666 881301 | admissions@westonbirt.org | www.westonbirt.org

Ages: 11–18

Pupils: 220; sixth form: 48; Boarders: 78 full, 20 weekly, 15 flexi

Day: £14,985 pa; Boarding: £29,250 pa

Head: Since 2013, Mrs Natasha Dangerfield BA (40s), previously deputy head and head of boarding at Harrogate Ladies' College. Also taught at North Foreland Lodge and Downe House and was director of pastoral care at Gordonstoun School. Mrs Dangerfield studied physical education and English at the University of Brighton and thought she wanted to be a physiotherapist, but while

working in sports camps she met teachers who inspired her to change direction. Parents describe her as 'dynamic', and 'approachable' and a great role model for the girls, 'she speaks their language.'

Westonbirt inspires fierce loyalty and we got the impression that any head who messed with the school's fundamental character would do so at their peril. Most agree that her changes so far have been the right ones – modernisation of some material aspects, gentle 're-booting' in other areas. The fact that she is a parent herself (she has three young children, two boys and a girl, who attend the prep) must be a good ice-breaker. Her husband works in the fire service.

The combination of over 200 lively girls and a grade 1 listed building must be a little worrying, we suggested to Mrs Dangerfield. 'This house is built so well that everything is in pretty good order,' she told us. Fortunately, the Westonbirt Trust takes care of historic preservation; 'To put Venetian silk back on the walls is not our responsibility.'

Lacrosse is Mrs Dangerfield's sport (back in the day she played for England) and she continues to coach – even taking pre-season training for her school team. 'I'm not very good at standing on the sidelines,' she confessed.

Academic matters: In 2017, a upswing to 29 per cent A*/A (56 per cent A*-B) at A level. At GCSE, 48 per cent A*-A/9-7 grades. Highs and lows in all subjects reflect the relatively non-selective intake. While there has certainly been a tightening up of standards and a review of the subjects on offer, head has no plans to change entrance requirements. Focus here is on helping girls reach their potential, whether that's 10 A*s at GCSE, or three 'good' A levels.

Parents have told us how well their daughters are doing and the University of Durham has put a number on it: Westonbirt is in the top five per cent of schools in the UK for value added. This objectively assessed measure calculates pupils' academic improvement between the ages of 11 and 16. Analysis by the University of Durham shows that girls here achieve almost a grade higher in each subject at GCSE than expected.

Many sixth formers like to remain in school over the weekend, because it 'helps them stay focused on their studies'

All learn French in year 7, Spanish, Mandarin and Latin 'tasters' in year 8 and all learn touch typing. In addition to academic subjects, girls in all years follow a 'skills for life' programme that focuses on practical (communication and study skills) as well as personal and social development. With an average class size of 10 (maximum 15), girls here receive what is practically customised teaching; the parents of several girls who had joined from large preps were astonished at their daughters' progress. 'She thought she was bad at maths and science but now she's so confident and doing really well.' Subject teachers set targets and academic progress is closely monitored by tutors. In a year 7 maths class the atmosphere was collaborative rather than competitive, girls attempting questions confidently, undaunted if they were wrong. Even we wouldn't have been scared to hazard an answer.

Choice of 25 A level subjects – all the usuals plus history of art, classical civilisation and business studies. School says that it is able to accommodate most combinations. Now offers a range of BTecs from performing arts to equine management to creative digital media production. Enrichment for sixth formers includes a lecture programme and weekly personal finance lessons.

Technology was somewhat prehistoric but is now much improved and used in lessons 'appropriately and with relevance,' although Mrs Dangerfield's announcement of the 'death of the handout' might be a bit previous. iPads now on kit list although school will lend if necessary. Great boon for dyslexic girls who can use the speech facility for essays. Apps etc stored in the 'Westonbirt cloud' and controlled by school. As we were visiting the science, art, design and technology block, we spied a classroom of very overgrown schoolgirls and boys, concentrating hard. 'Oh, that's the teachers,' our guide said. 'They're having an IT lesson.'

No shortage of running around space and opportunities to play for the school abound, whether it's lacrosse, netball, tennis, golf (there's a nine hole course), riding or polo

'Outstanding' learning support department caters for wide range of SpLDs including dyslexia, dyspraxia, dyscalculia and mild speech and language impairments. Gifted and talented programme also in place.

Games, options, the arts: 'There's so much drama at Westonbirt!' we heard. Ditto singing, dancing and playing of instruments. Emphasis is on enabling everyone to perform, whether it's in the intimate setting of the Camellia House – a charming venue, used for recitals, 'little plays' and socials – or in the 450 seat Orangery Theatre. Fresh air fiends can also tread the grass of the amphitheatre in the grounds. Music practice block suffers somewhat by comparison with the smart Marriott Centre, home to brand new recording and music tech kit. Three choirs and weekly whole school hymn practice keep everyone in good voice. Huge art studios looking out onto peaceful pastures, DT workshops with laser cutters and CAD equipment.

Mrs Dangerfield is applying her expertise to sport. Local opposition is formidable, and while no one expects Westonbirt to carry home the silverware at every match, there was room for improvement. Sensible trend in this and other girls' schools is a shift from privileging team sports to an equal emphasis on health and fitness – that way you can keep everyone doing something.

No shortage of running around space here and opportunities to play for the school abound, whether it's lacrosse, netball, tennis, golf (there's a nine hole course), riding or polo. In the £3m sports centre, opened by near neighbours the Prince of Wales and Duchess of Cornwall, there's a dance studio and fitness suite. Very popular is the new all weather wicket; 'now we can invite other schools to play at home.' All weather facilities for other sports still on school's and parents' wish lists. Parents tell us that there are plenty of fixtures and the school is more than able to take on and win against other, often larger, opponents. Or you could just take a book and find a secluded spot in the gardens.

As befits the alma mater of Baden Powell's daughter, the school has a girl guide troop – 1st Westonbirt Guides, although members tend to be from local villages rather than the school itself. D of E to gold level offered plus clubs and activities from app design, through gardening and poultry, to zumba.

Sixth formers have the opportunity to enrol on the very popular Leiths certificate in food and wine. Westonbirt was one of the first two schools to run this course, and to have Leiths on your CV is great for holiday and gap year jobs such as a spot of chalet girling. For those whose ambitions go beyond holiday jobs, there's the Young Enterprise scheme and a separate business school with office space and classrooms – A level business studies is taught here.

Boarding: Years 5-8, day girls and boarders, live together in Beaufort House. This junior house is a stepping stone between prep and senior school. There are three senior houses for years 9, 10 and 11 – Badminton, Dorchester and Holford – plus the sixth form. Girls in Holford sleep in what were the family state rooms on the first floor, little beds dwarfed by grand proportions (grade 1 listing is not at home to subdivision). Priceless silk wallpaper, preserved under Perspex, rubbing shoulders with One Direction posters. Beautiful painted panels on the wardrobes and tall wooden shutters instead of curtains. All day girls get one free night of boarding per term and sleepovers are very popular. Wonderful views over the park from common room 'perfect for moon watching'. We asked girls what they thought of the food and the general consensus was breakfast fab, lunch pretty good (we can vouch for that) but catering seemed to run out of steam by supper time. We hope this is on Mrs Dangerfield's to do list.

As we sighed over the Gentleman's Library, enjoying the irony, we wondered what the girls thought about their sumptuous surroundings

In the sixth form house every girl has her own study bedroom so day girls can decide at the last minute to stay overnight. There's a dining room, kitchen, laundry facilities, yoga room and bar/café. Not surprisingly, over three-quarters of sixth formers board. Many like to remain in school over the weekend, because it 'helps them stay focused on their studies'. An international student (around 20+ girls are from abroad) told us how much she appreciated learning in such 'serene and calm surroundings.' We loved the spacious common room, newly decorated in a modish putty colour ('seagull'), a simple vase of marguerites on the coffee table.

Background and atmosphere: Westonbirt is one of the Allied Schools, an umbrella body for eight Martyrs' Memorial Trust schools including Canford, Stowe and Harrogate Ladies' College. It was founded in 1927, acquiring Westonbirt House and 210 acres of park and garden from the Holford family who had lived on the estate since the 17th century. The house itself, built in Jacobethan style (later than, though not dissimilar to, Highclere Castle), was completed in 1871 and used by Lord Holford as a country retreat (his main residence was Dorchester House, Park Lane, now site of The Dorchester Hotel). Just over the road is the world famous Westonbirt Arboretum, another of Lord Holford's enduring projects. When the head told us the house was 'well built' she meant it – constructed around a steel frame, it had all the mod cons of its day (gas lighting, central heating), not to mention fire-proof cavities between each wall and floor. Interior décor was in the distinctly un-modern classical style, with splendid marble halls and corridors on the ground floor, richly gilded wood and plasterwork and intriguing architectural details wherever you look. Friday notices and vespers are held in the galleried great hall, and year 11s dine under a ceiling festooned with plasterwork goat skulls.

As we sighed over the refurbished Gentleman's Library, enjoying the irony, we wondered what the girls thought about studying in such sumptuous surroundings. 'It is a bit like Downton Abbey', one confided, and we would not have been surprised to see Hugh Bonneville and his arthritic labrador taking a constitutional in the Italianate garden. What a place.

Pastoral care, well-being and discipline: Pastoral care has always been one of Westonbirt's strengths. In a small community with a high staff to student ratio, problems become visible sooner. Parents say that friendship troubles and the like are dealt with fairly and swiftly. 'Everybody has to get along,' we were told, and 'the older girls look out for you.' Not really the place for 'tricky' personalities, observed one mother. We agree; Westonbirt girls are more likely to ride the horses than frighten them.

Girls are encouraged to take responsibilities such as organising social events – planning for a charity ball was under way when we visited. There's a 'much improved' programme of socials with boys from Abingdon, Radley and even co-ed Cheltenham College. A less welcome visitor is the school's lone peacock, Westy, who frequently has to be escorted off the premises. We hear that the class of 2014 bought him a friend, christened (you guessed it) Birty.

Pupils and parents: From all over the UK, although majority of families live relatively locally. Easy to reach from Bristol and Bath and handy for M4, Heathrow and London. Parents tell us it's 'not posh.' Hmmm. It is, but in a quiet way. Nearest places to spend pocket money are Cheltenham and Bath, although you could do some damage in Tetbury. Smallish cohort (some 25 per cent) of international students from all corners of the globe – as elsewhere, more attention being paid to the mix.

Former pupils include the Hon Mrs Betty Clay (Lord Baden-Powell's youngest daughter), Mercia MacDermott (historian); Anna Hornby (painter); Salma Sobhan (academic and human rights activist); Patsy Toh (pianist); Georgia Byng (author of the Molly Moon series of children's books); Lady Natasha Rufus-Isaacs (designer, founder of Beulah London); TV presenter Ruth Watson; TV producer

Patricia Llewellyn; Lady Jenny Bland; Jenefer Greenwood, OBE.

Entrance: Entry includes many from the prep, rest from wide range of preps and local primaries. Non-CE candidates sit school's own entrance exams in maths and English plus an online adaptive test. Head likes to interview everyone in person (or via Skype). For entry to the sixth form girls need at least five A*-C/9-4 grades at GCSE (including maths and English), with A/7 or B/6 in subjects to be taken at A level.

Exit: A few girls leave for pastures new after GCSEs but are replaced by others from elsewhere doing the same thing. Occasional one or two to medical school, likewise Oxbridge (though none in 2017); destinations range from Edinburgh (sustainable development) to Coventry (international finance and accounting) to the Conde Nast School of Fashion Design.

Money matters: Fees restructured fsince 2017, with flat rate boarding fees and day fees reduced by some 25 per cent. Academic, art, drama, music, sport, performing arts, organ and choral scholarships up to a maximum of 50 per cent of day fees. Means-tested bursaries may be available – applications considered on an individual basis. Fee reductions for siblings, Forces and clergy families. Girls transferring from prep also get a five per cent discount throughout their senior career. Sixth form bursaries offered to girls from local state schools.

Girls encouraged to take responsibilities such as organising social events – planning for a charity ball was under way when we visited

Remarks: Westonbirt has always been highly regarded for inclusivity and exemplary pastoral care, but perhaps its other strengths have been overlooked. Until now. Parents told us that 'there's a new energy, a real buzz' about the place; one described it as 'added sparkle', and they're right. Inside this solid Victorian stately home we found a vibrant and forward thinking community of young women, hugely appreciative of their beautiful surroundings but very well prepared to take on the world beyond Gloucestershire.

Wycliffe College

69

Bath Road, Stonehouse, Gloucestershire GL10 2JQ

01453 822432 | senior@wycliffe.co.uk | www.wycliffe.co.uk

Ages: 13–19

Pupils: 417; sixth form: 166; Boarders: 230

Day: £17,985 – £19,485 pa; Boarding: £32,970 – £34,320 pa

Linked school: Wycliffe Preparatory School, 317

Head: Since 2015, Nick Gregory, (40S) who was previously pastoral deputy head at Mill Hill School in London. He graduated in French and Spanish at Nottingham, then spent eight years at Barclays, including time in Madrid, before teaching modern languages, first at Barnard Castle School, County Durham, then at Merchant Taylors' School, Northwood. He then became boarding housemaster at Old Swinford Hospital, Stourbridge. He and his wife, Helen, have three sons, two of then at Wycliffe. He believes school needs to be more than a teaching machine, somewhere that gives a lived and valued experience which will lay a foundation for life. Despite the popularity of his predecessor, senior pupils say he has grasped the traditions and special nature of Wycliffe and that he knows them well as individuals.

He took over an already flourishing school and is mainly concerned to develop the good practice and vision he has found. 'No major changes planned' but there have been a few changes in staffing. He is 'nurturing boys' sport from the bottom up' to ensure that there are promising signs of success (girls are doing pretty well at present). He aims to support 'the gifted and talented pupils the school attracts, while maintaining access to all academic levels, and supporting bringing out the best in those with difficulties'. He expressed his

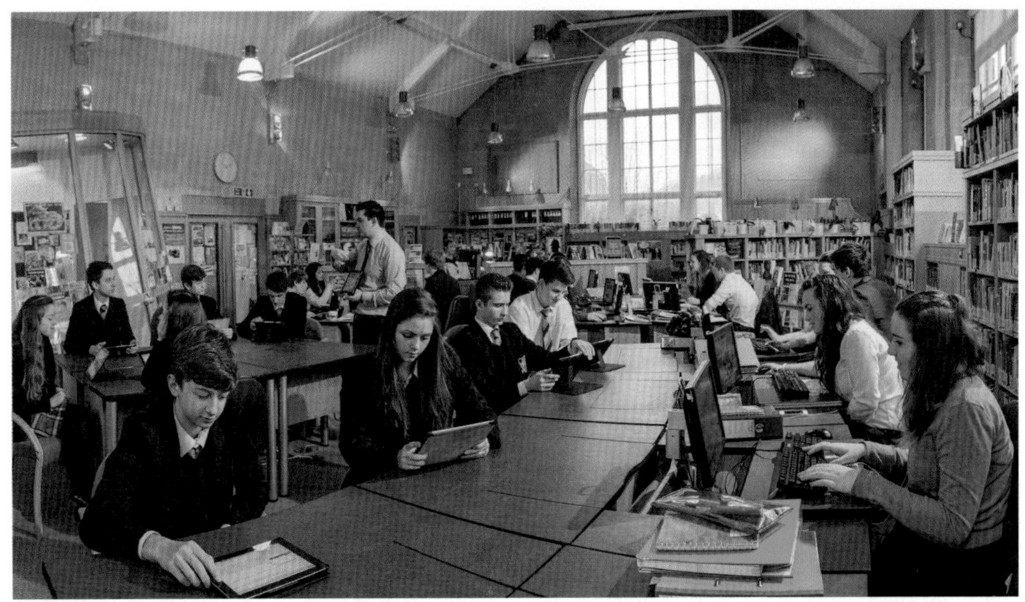

approach very simply as enabling his pupils 'to be good people'. His pastorally orientated philosophy works on the premise that young people learn and are motivated when they are confident secure and feel valued. If the these sound like 'soft' skills, he is also determined that the school will be supported by the best in teaching and technology, and have well structured opportunities from tutors, careers advice, business links and university access. Parents consider that he is bringing a needed touch of academic edge to the school. Exceptionally accessible and easy to talk to, Mr Gregory is also someone who works fast and gets things done quickly. 'A force of nature,' said one parent. He and his family live on the premises, and when he actually gets some time away he likes to spend it giving full time attention to his family life in their house in southern Spain.

Academic matters: Considering that the school has an open access policy with exams only used for purposes of setting or scholarships, GCSE and A level results are usually very respectable. There is no doubt that gifted pupils do really well, with the relatively few high fliers, including those who have been right through the Wycliffe experience and some more recently arrived from abroad, getting straight A*/A grades. However, a disappointing 11 per cent A*/A and 30 per cent A*-B at A level in 2017. Mr Gregory says the long-term aim is least a third of A levels A*/As and two-thirds at B or above. Choice is impressive with over 30 A level subjects including BTec equivalents in travel & tourism, digital production and sport, which have impressive results. Languages (French, Spanish, German, Russian and Japanese) have good take up as does maths, with a consistently sound record, though whilst economics and business studies are also much in demand, As and Bs are thin on the ground.

2017 GCSE results much more encouraging – 48 per cent A*-A/9-7 – despite the national downward trend. Some spectacular results here in maths, further maths, German, Russian and Chinese – the latter possibly accounted for by some native speakers.

Having pupils from all over the world, plus Brits who live some distance away, means that there is a solid core of boarders in school at weekends

Value-added is key to the school's approach and all the statistics indicate that this is impressive. (It is worth pointing out that value-added is particularly difficult to assess in very high achievers, and pupils and parent satisfaction is probably a much better guide.) Masses of help available when needed – with teachers exceptionally ready to go the extra mile with one-to-one and special help. Lots of careful supervision and expert help on subject choice. Study leave is only allowed at A level, and even then those who need guidance with revision are advised to stay in school. Teachers always keen to help even after exams have started. Boarding and day pupils have study space in their houses and the library, which is also a fabulous multimedia resource centre. Very popular, spacious and well planned, with plenty of help on hand; it was very full and had an extremely studious feel on the day of our visit. All this is underpinned by a careful tutorial programme and rigorous tracking of pupil progress which stops pupils slipping through the net. PHSEE provides life and study skills and every year group has courses such as teamwork, problem solving etc, aiming to develop skills as useful in life as they are in academic approach.

Newish labs, biology sporting a fish tank that wows prep school visitors. Classrooms jigsawed into every part of the buildings with plenty of the relevant IT etc, and without exception those we passed looked busy and purposeful.

Extensive remedial and special needs programme with lively, sensitive and fully qualified teachers who help and support. Pupils are automatically assessed on entry to the school, as much to identify gifted and talented as those with learning difficulties. Wycliffe has received accreditation and plaudits from both CResTeD (for SEN) and NAGC (for specially talented), which endorses the quality of teachers' work with pupils. Emphasis is on differentiated teaching as well as individual help. EAL support is on hand.

The 'development year' is a pre-A level course designed to give pupils from abroad both basic English and some GCSEs or equivalent on which to ground A level study. Some 30 or so pupils each year from all over the world benefit from this, with 15-20 staying on into the sixth form and contributing a range of sporting and other skills. Mr Gregory, parents agree, has certainly 'turned up the gas' a bit on the academic side but not, they also agree, at the expense of Wycliffe's happy and supportive community feel.

Opportunities to take up fencing or yoga, the staples of CCF and Duke of Edinburgh, and academic extensions such as robotics, studying newts or serious debate, are integral to what Wycliffe is about

Games, options, the arts: Sport is a vital aspect at Wycliffe and a number of parents cite it as their deciding factor in choosing the school. Facilities are excellent, with smashing new Astroturf and smart multipurpose sports hall (full of aspiring small cricketers avoiding the rain on our visit) with professional standard squash courts, fitness gym and viewing areas. The pool is on the prep site. Massive pitches and lawns surround the school. Teams in hockey, netball, rugby and tennis reach county level at least on a regular basis, while individuals perform at national level in a huge range of sports including rowing, biathlon and an abundance of all branches of athletics. Girls' teams have acquitted themselves particularly well recently, with recent district and county successes at netball, hockey, rounder and tennis. Squash is truly exceptional, with boys' and girls' teams winning national events, and the school has an internationally-renowned programme that pupils from across the world come to join as boarders, producing recent British and European champions.

Choral singing – with a 75-strong chapel choir and the upmarket Vox chamber choir for the real elite – is the heart of performance music, but a vast swathe learn instruments with a few getting to grade 8, and National Youth Orchestra or Choir standard. No full orchestra, but lots of thriving ensembles and an emphasis on music technology. Several take A levels in music and music technology each year, with some progressing to uni on the technology side. Fantastic support and inspiration from the two exciting musicians who head the department.

Strong drama boasts established theatre studies and emerging film studies, with pupils carrying both of these on to post-school study and ambitious school productions. The Sibly Theatre, named for the founder, now looks a little dated, so not quite as slick as the junior theatre, but bigger and very well equipped with studio spaces behind the stage.

Art inhabits its own building with a chaotic barn-like upper art room and pottery, classrooms and other media below producing some striking work, which reflects the team of professional artists. Sadly we missed the A level work, which had been packed up for dispatch, but there was some exciting painting and in most years the results are A* studded.

Not surprisingly for a school offering a whole life experience, the range of co-curricular activities is wide and diverse. Up to GCSE pupils have to opt into two activities weekly. Since the alphabet of activities starts with astrology, beekeeping and cryptology, continuing in the same vein, this is no hardship. Opportunities to take up fencing or yoga, the staples of CCF and Duke of Edinburgh, and academic extensions such as robotics, studying newts or serious debate are an integral part of what Wycliffe is about, and a chance for every pupil to excel – and they do.

Beyond this there is serious programme of exchanges, visits and expeditions: cricket to Barbados, squash to Canada, hockey and netball to Sri Lanka. Language visits include Japan and there are careers and education trips to theatres and museums etc, and year 12 is launching a charitable project in Costa Rica.

Boarding: Having pupils from all over the world, plus Brits who live some distance away, means there is a solid core in school at weekends. Some locals choose to stay as there seems to be a thriving social scene, so boarding really is a good bet for Forces families or expats.

Founded in 1882 and named for the pioneering Christian spirit of John Wycliffe, school now goes out of its way to make this spirit accessible to all denominations and races

Boarding houses with full and flexi boarders plus attached day pupils form the core of the social life. The system is a real mixture with a designated sixth form house but some sixth formers in the main school houses, and a day pupils' house, as well as some day pupils in the main boarding houses. Loosley (named after the third and most illustrious Wycliffe head) houses the sixth form – both boys and girls – with spacious common rooms, small kitchens and laundry areas for washing casual clothes and a campus feel for milling about. Sixth formers in mixed age houses can drop in on Loosley. The mixed day house, with generously broad corridors, brightly painted studies and common rooms with balconies overlooking the green sward, is clearly much appreciated.

Rooms (for two to four and the odd single for prefects or heads of houses) are fairly basic and include work space. Most boarding accommodation is utilitarian rather than palatial, though some

Sixth form boarders are allowed a pint or glass of wine at weekends and the occasional early evening visit to the pub in the neighbouring Cotswold town of Stonehouse, which despite its quiet atmosphere is conveniently on the main line from Paddington.

Background and atmosphere: The parkland feel of the huge grassy campus is created by wide, well-maintained pitches (cricket/rugby and some Astroturf) sited amid trees and well-kept garden. A succession of buildings, some inspired and some less, has divided the whole into a series of campus 'rooms', each with its lawns and distinctive buildings, ranging from the elegant Georgian Haywardsend House, though the bizarre exterior of the Sibly Theatre (really good facility inside) and the workmanlike labs to the inspired modern wood and glass of the huge curved dining area, serving delicious food with a tantalising variety. Sunday brunches 'are to die for'. The last looks out on a massive expanse of new, green Astro used for hockey etc in the winter and tennis in summer. It is spectacularly edged in dark purple, which echoes the head's penchant for this colour – which, conveniently, is the school colour, emphasized by the pale mauve of the large Wycliffe sign boards and, more attractively, by the wisteria which swarms over several of the buildings.

Founded by the Sibly family in 1882 and named for the pioneering Christian spirit of John Wycliffe, the school now goes out of its way to make this spirit accessible to all denominations and races. Pupils and parents set immense store by the Wycliffe ethos, friendly, nurturing and pupil centred. A sixth former commented favourably on Mr Gregory's evident efforts to know the school history. A busy campus with friendly staff and well-mannered but unaffected pupils strolling purposefully around. Inside and out there is seating dotted around inviting conversation with a sense of reasonable privacy. The school has been fully coeducational for more than 30 years and it feels absolutely right. The happy purposefulness of the place is most evident in the exceptionally user-friendly library, full of pupils working quietly and calmly (it was almost exam time) with help on hand. It is designed to divide into areas for quiet study, computer research, reading and even discussion and is clearly a real centre of academic life.

Pastoral care, well-being and discipline: The house system is the pastoral structure for both boarders and day pupils. The houseparent, matron, house staff and a team of house tutors are supported by prefects and responsible sixth formers, who provide the essential links between staff and pupils. Both pupils and staff give the impression that the relationship between them is free and easy. Students say there is little or no bullying, certainly nothing serious. 'It's just not what we do and absolutely not tolerated'. One parent reported that he was informed of a minor incident which his son had not mentioned because 'it was not a real problem'. It had clearly been nipped in the bud before it became serious. Communications are excellent and parents who want frequent updates are well satisfied. Pupils from abroad seem to mix in well – a table of very all-inclusive chatterers in the dining room proved on our enquiries to consist of a real mix of recent and new pupils, from both the locality and as far away as Latvia and the Ukraine. Awkward moments, like the transition from prep school, are extremely well handled, according to parents.

Sixth form boarders allowed glass of wine or beer at weekends and even occasional early evening visit to the pub in neighbouring Cotswold town of Stonehouse

All faiths catered for and the chaplain is very open and inclusive. Pupils evidently felt real affection for the beautiful chapel, and recounted its history with pride: rebuilt post war by pupils and staff incorporating wood from a pier on the Isle of Wight and stone from a bombed church.

All is underpinned by clear procedures and regulations. Support runs deep in the community, typified by the head, who after just under a year was able to give minute details of every pupil we met.

Friendly staff and well-mannered pupils. School has been fully co-educational for more than 30 years and it feels absolutely right

Houses do lots of social, competitive and charitable events, which give creative opportunities involving everyone in mixed age groups in cultural and aesthetic activities: singing, drama, film quizzes etc. Usual structure of prefects etc clearly relishing their responsibilities.

Pupils and parents: Plenty of army families but also lots of locals as well as a high proportion from abroad (30 per cent, which means about 60 per cent of boarders): Europe, ex-USSR countries and the Far East. The chair of the PA says parents who want to take a large part in their offsprings' education are given real support, but those with a less hands on approach seem equally satisfied. Head finds pupils refreshingly unaffected in comparison with the London set. Parents here are exceptionally supportive of each other, and those from further away say they get invitations to stay and offers to entertain their offspring.

Entrance: The majority of pupils joining in year 9 come from the school's own prep school, though recently increasing numbers come from other prep schools as well. Entrants sit exams but only for setting purposes. The school really prides itself on value added, which is one of its key aims, and only turns down those with learning difficulties too severe to be managed well at Wycliffe. Entry into the sixth form usually requires at least five GCSEs at grade C/5 or above, but they do consider, more carefully than many, the question of potential, and the variety of academic pathways post-16 allows pretty much anyone to be accommodated appropriately.

Exit: Just over one-third leave post-GCSEs to vocational courses and sixth form colleges. Over 97 per cent of the sixth form go on to university with a few Oxbridge places on occasion. A number apply successfully to USA and other unis all over the world, and when the specialist adviser on US places moved on, the replacement was expert in international university entrance. Some art foundation courses and drama school, otherwise business-related careers very popular, as are law and digital/creative courses.

Money matters: In terms of endowments, the school is not particularly wealthy, though it stresses that it is 'strong financially.' Scholarships are available at 13 and 16 for academic excellence, art, music, DT, ICT, drama and sport (10-20 per cent). This seems to be a particular draw in sixth form and there are a few pupils with exceptional circumstances who get pretty full financial support from the school, dependent on school reports and financial circumstances.

Remarks: A school which offers a way of life as much as an education. That the Wycliffe experience clearly breeds the confidence and openness is evident in its pupils. Definitely hotting up academically under the new head, but still faithful to its broad academic ability range. If success increases demand, will it be able to maintain an open admission policy? At present it is doing a remarkable job of being 'all thing to all men' – and women. A real gem of a school.

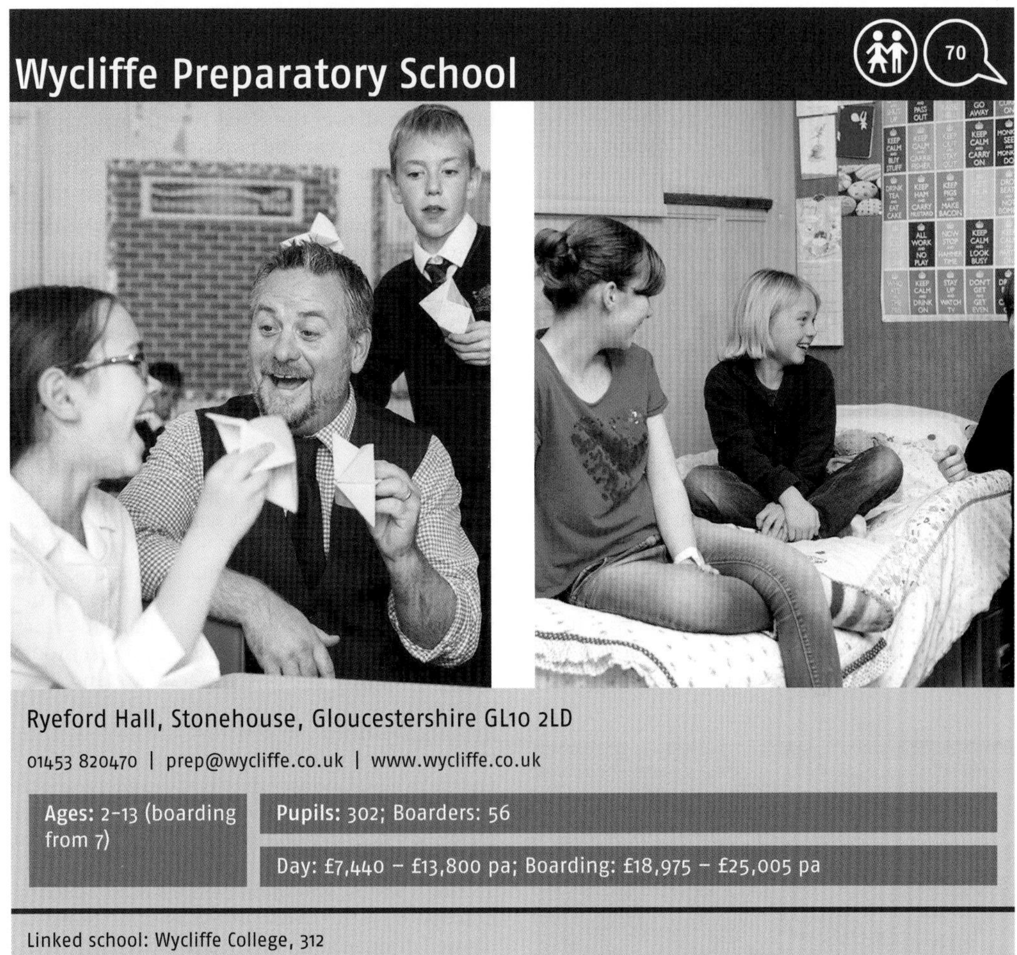

Wycliffe Preparatory School

70

Ryeford Hall, Stonehouse, Gloucestershire GL10 2LD

01453 820470 | prep@wycliffe.co.uk | www.wycliffe.co.uk

Ages: 2–13 (boarding from 7)

Pupils: 302; Boarders: 56

Day: £7,440 – £13,800 pa; Boarding: £18,975 – £25,005 pa

Linked school: Wycliffe College, 312

Headmaster: Since 2003, Mr Adrian Palmer BA (rapidly approaching 60 but with no intention of retiring). An ex-maths and PE teacher, he had a spell as head at Warminster Preparatory School then moved to Rendcomb, where he started the junior school and built up numbers rapidly before moving to Wycliffe. Though he works closely with Wycliffe College as part of the overall leadership team, he enjoys the freedom and respect accorded him by the new head of college, which gives him complete control of development in the prep school. Married to Julie, a lynchpin in the school, managing SEN and, as author of The Write Path, assisting everyone to develop legible handwriting; they have son and a daughter who both went through the prep and the college.

Exceptionally talented at inspiring children and setting them at their ease; they positively bubble with delight at his arrival, and are reluctant for him to depart. His office boasts masses of impressive artwork with a stunning pencil portrait of him done by a pupil. His 'persona' is emphasized by a lurid collection of over 200 ties, which are the source of endless discussion and delight to pupils. Though he does not teach, he is very much in evidence around the school at all times, personally showing round every prospective parent and aware of the individual needs of every child. He has developed a simple but effective effort grading system which pervades every classroom, based on skills like persistence, cooperation, organisation etc, which accounts for the confidence with which one pupil told me that coming top was less important than fulfilling potential and achieving a personal target grade. End of year exams for the top three years are intentionally tough with 'opportunities provided' for revision, so that children can learn to deal with this situation.

Utterly pupil-centred, Mr Palmer, and hence the school, believes in pupils enjoying their education. Responsibility appointments, prefects, etc are made 'when children are ready for it' throughout the final year, and head boys and girls hold the post for part of the year only so that leadership is shared out. He runs the school with a light and humorous touch, an example being the hanging model of a bee in the dining room, left after a food info project 'because it was fun'. While his approachability is clearly appreciated by pupils, staff and parents, his professionalism is evident everywhere. Everything runs like clockwork.

Entrance: Over 60 per cent from the nursery situated across the road from the main prep school, via a charming bridge built in the 1930s, which is 'the only way pupils ever cross this busy road'.

Main campus is an amazing hotchpotch, attractively united by some remarkably well-designed gardening and wonderful views

Pupils joining from other schools take a cognitive ability test and attend a taster day. (International students take the cognitive test and a skype interview). Moderate learning difficulties can be given appropriate help. An increasing number comes in at 11+, when scholarships and awards in music, drama, dance, sport and art are available. Fleets of buses from all over the place. Parents may apply at any time of the year and pupils may join whenever there is room.

Exit: Most pupils (some 85 per cent) from Wycliffe Prep go to Wycliffe College. Exams are for setting purposes as transition is very nearly automatic and the school gives plenty of warning to parents if the senior school would not be appropriate. Pupils who need to go elsewhere are prepared for CE etc. Destination schools include Cheltenham College, Marlborough and Wynstones.

Remarks: The campus is divided by a main-ish road with the prep, lower prep, teaching, drama, sports hall and pool (used by seniors as well) nestled tightly but comfortably on the smaller southern area. Nursery, boarding and massive playing fields are over the bridge to the north. Teaching facilities include bang up to date Etheridge Hall, an attractive modern and spacious class and subject room centre with latest high-tech facilities, and large common room for year 8 pupils (tea and toast making facilities). In contrast the largely unreconstructed original house, with its high ceilings and steep stairs, houses the library (undergoing recataloguing by the new real librarian) and lower forms. It's not very accessible, though the school will switch what's taught where to accommodate anyone's needs. The main campus is an amazing hotchpotch attractively united by some remarkably well-designed gardening and wonderful views. Early years have disguised portacabins, airy and well equipped inside with colourful enclosed outside soft play areas. Little sheltering pagodas with blue roofs harmonise the haphazard older buildings, which include a hugely impressive art room, full of deconstructed cubist guitar paintings and occupied on our visit by a class learning to make Egyptian cartouches.

Gym and good sized indoor pool are serviceable but undistinguished, and juxtaposed with a massive and essential boys' changing room in Tesco's

Toytown style, and a really state of art modern theatre building, much used for really exciting performances – Hairspray, The Lion King etc. Far better equipped than many a semi professional senior school theatre. A cunning portrait of the head done in string on the tennis court fencing typifies the friendly, quirky atmosphere of the school. An inspirational addition evidencing its serious core is the stunning sensory garden with open-air pavilion for either teaching or just sitting and thinking.

Everywhere is well equipped. ICT is taught as 'a discreet subject' and from the age of 7 each pupil has two lessons a week. Pupils talk enthusiastically and cogently about their activities. Good labs, French taught from tinies on and German and Spanish from year 8. The prep school provides carefully appropriate tuition for a very wide range of abilities and has demonstrated this by its affiliation to both CResTed, which confirms its good SEN provision, and NAGC, which accredits work for gifted and talented pupils.

Pupils genuinely believe that there is no bullying and that any potential problems can and will be sorted out by sympathetic but firm pastoral staff. Parents confirm that the merest sniff of trouble is dealt with well. A zero tolerance of bullying and a real sense in older pupils of their responsibility to take care of younger ones make it 'a bit like a family,' one said. A boarder explained that there was no need to be homesick because some members of staff are really like another mother.

A cunning portrait of the head (smiling as usual) done in string on the tennis court fencing, typifies the friendly, quirky atmosphere of the school

Lots of Forces' boarders and a few from abroad – occasionally short term visitors like it enough to want to stay on for the rest of their prep years. Weekends great fun and, though boarders are allowed out, there tends to be an inflow of day pupils staying for special activities rather than a general exodus. The boarding houses (one each for boys and boys and girls of all ages, with a connecting lobby) are at the top of the site and have splendid views. The large dormitories have been split into rooms taking two to four pupils with loos very near and showers – some definitely catering for privacy and some less so – and baths downstairs. Boys and girls are allowed to visit each other's common rooms under supervision. Lovely touches abound, like the heart-shaped 'memories' collage of photographs. All prep is done in school so work doesn't come home, but mobiles and computers are allowed during waking hours in the boarding houses – handed in at night and during lesson hours. It's all feels very secure, homely and not too tidy, with the inevitable bunk beds which children seem to like.

Early bird day children are welcomed into boarding houses and taken down to breakfast by helpful prefects

Food is 'pretty good now', especially breakfast with croissants and pain au chocolate. Pupils were anxious to assure me that there is masses of choice and all food groups represented. Dining is informal with a separate round table area for little ones. Early bird day children welcomed into boarding houses and taken down to breakfast by helpful prefects. At weekends boarders go up to the college for Sunday lunch – one parent said this was the only feature of the school she had reservations about, but not a serious one. Noticeably kind and motherly kitchen staff. Teachers sit with pupils. Saturday morning school (for years 6, 7 and 8) was one of the few things pupils could think of that they didn't like – but then they decided that actually it's fun 'on the whole'.

Sport is really important, and as well as the usual rugby/soccer/cricket for boys and netball/hockey/tennis and rounders for girls there are some distinguished athletes – one girl reached national biathlete standard, and other children who are interested in special sports or excel in any area are taken to local clubs in the evenings and get absolute top coaching, with some spectacular results. Masses of other activities after school, and day pupils can go home at 4.45pm or stay later for prep and activities.

The nursery is next to the boarding houses, surrounded by little secure areas for digging, outdoor play and exploration. More log-clad portacabins make a light-filled flexible space with all the nursery equipment imaginable. It is filled with small children absorbed in play activities or books, dressed in cheerful red tops or cardies with bright gingham dresses for girls, quite different to the smart jerseys and girls' kilts of the older pupils. Good library – 'the nursery eats books,' said one teacher. Other meals are taken in the nursery dining room. It all feels happy and purposeful, provides after-school care and has terms which are much longer than school ones to provide a consistent service. There are even beds available for occasional rest time.

Parents get a chance for input as Mr Palmer has parent forum groups, and one noted that several suggestions had been taken up and were working well. Those stationed abroad are particularly grateful for a parent community prone to scooping up boarding children with absent parents and ensuring they get to birthday parties etc, and being on hand to offer visiting parents a bed for the night.

The key feature of Wycliffe Prep is its happy atmosphere. Children and parents enjoy their experience of the school as well as getting second to none opportunities in sport, music and drama, combined with some exceptional teaching.

Home Counties West

Berkshire
Buckinghamshire
Hampshire
Isle of Wight
Oxfordshire

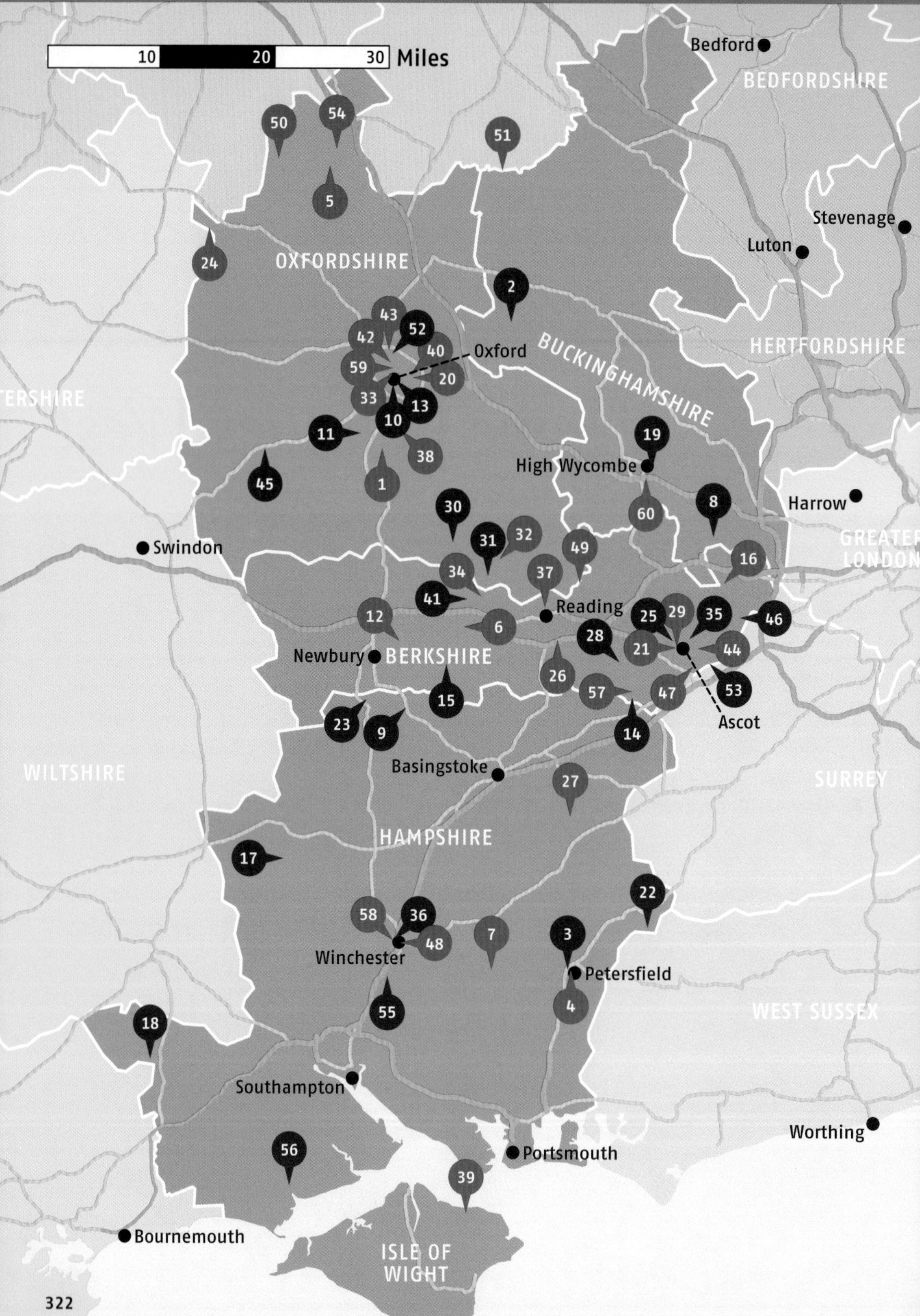

10
20
30
Miles
Bedford
BEDFORDSHIRE
Stevenage
Luton
OXFORDSHIRE
Oxford
BUCKINGHAMSHIRE
HERTFORDSHIRE
TERSHIRE
High Wycombe
Harrow
GREATER LONDON
Swindon
Reading
Newbury
BERKSHIRE
Ascot
Basingstoke
WILTSHIRE
SURREY
HAMPSHIRE
Winchester
Petersfield
WEST SUSSEX
Southampton
Worthing
Portsmouth
Bournemouth
ISLE OF WIGHT
1
2
3
4
5
6
7
8
9
10
11
12
13
14
15
16
17
18
19
20
21
22
23
24
25
26
27
28
29
30
31
32
33
34
35
36
37
38
39
40
41
42
43
44
45
46
47
48
49
50
51
52
53
54
55
56
57
58
59
60

HOME COUNTIES WEST

Abingdon School

Park Road, Abingdon, Oxfordshire OX14 1DE

01235 849041 | admissions@abingdon.org.uk | www.abingdon.org.uk

Ages: 11–18

Pupils: 1,001; sixth form: 331; Boarders: 108 full, 29 weekly

Day: £19,275 pa; Boarding: £32,550 – £38,970 pa

Head: Since September 2016, Michael Windsor, previously head of Reading Blue Coat School. The son of two linguists (his father was a lecturer at the University of Bristol and his mother taught French and German at Badminton School), he was a chorister at Bristol Cathedral School. Thence to Durham University and first-class honours in French and German. Worked briefly in publishing before heading to Bologna where he 'toyed with the idea of becoming a professional musician' and making a living from his double bass. That lasted until he got hungry, at which point although he 'knew he definitely didn't want to be a teacher', he gave up jazz for teaching English as a foreign language – and met his future wife. On his return he did a PGCE at the Institute of Education and then joined King's College Wimbledon to teach foreign languages and become the first director of its new IB programme. He describes his work introducing the IB as 'an amazing project' but has no such plans for Abingdon (we checked). Moved to RGS Guildford where he was deputy head (pastoral) and after five years there took up the headship at Reading Blue Coat. Has coached rugby, hockey and athletics and was involved in CCF and World Challenge expeditions. That's three academic boys' schools (okay, two have co-ed sixth forms) and Abingdon makes it four. Must be habit forming.

Mr Windsor also has an MA in modern German studies from Birkbeck and is an ISI inspector. He's a keen musician, plays the double bass in classical and jazz ensembles and recently surprised (and delighted) boys and parents with a guest appearance playing bass guitar in the school's Big Band (jazz). Married to Shanti, who works at Reading University; they have two daughters.

He says he 'felt drawn' to Abingdon, especially the culture of 'exceptionally high expectations' that pervades all aspects of school life. He's also enjoying working with the prep school. Even without the prep, Abingdon is much larger than his former school and he concedes his new role is 'less hands on' and he doesn't have time to do any teaching, although he says he would like to.

Abingdon has been through a period of significant growth – both in terms of pupil numbers and building projects – and Mr W feels that the school is now 'as big as it will get.' He does have plans; he's keen to 'develop more areas of collaboration' (academic, pastoral and extracurricular) with St Helen and St Katharine, the neighbouring independent girls' school (where his daughters are pupils). We wish him good fortune. There have been attempts in the past to take things beyond sharing actors, musicians and school buses, but as one boy put it, 'timetables never seem to match up.'

Academic, musical and sporty – Mr Windsor is such a good fit for Abingdon, embodying three of the school's great strengths. He's also down-to-earth, good humoured and at ease with himself – very much a head, rather than a figurehead. The boys think he's 'great' and love the way he seems to turn up and enjoy everything – quite an accolade considering just how much goes on at the school. We felt a genuine groundswell of goodwill and support for Mr Windsor – boys, staff and parents, even those parents we spoke to who have yet only 'seen him in the distance,' are right behind him.

Academic matters: Academics matter hugely, but not exclusively. I/GCSE headliners are English, maths and sciences, but A* is by far the most common mark in all subjects apart from art, RS and drama (where the As have it). In addition to IGCSE maths, boys in the top sets also sit the free-standing OCR additional maths qualification – and take it in their stride with the vast majority gaining top marks. French, Spanish and German are the core language options with Russian and Chinese offered as additional subjects. Healthy numbers and outstanding results for Latin, ancient Greek and ancient history (Latin is compulsory in years 7 and 8). I/GCSE results in 2017: 86 per cent A*-A/9-7. Only a very few marks at grade C or below, but the boy who gets a grade B in one or two subjects won't feel alone. Not a school that kicks unexpected underperformers out post GCSE either

A level results in 2017: 63 per cent A*/A (84 per cent A*-B). Most popular A level by far is maths (followed by chemistry and physics); over half of sixth form boys take maths and the vast majority get A*/A, further maths is an option. Parents generally very pleased with A level maths teaching, but one or two felt that boys in lower sets didn't always get sufficient support. Word on the local tutor grapevine confirms that some feel the need to buy in external help.

Large take up and excellent results too for history, economics and geography. Pre-U exams only for French, German and Spanish (results outstanding: 96 per cent A*/A equivalent), but as elsewhere, modern foreign languages are a minority interest – there are more takers for Latin. Indeed, classics department is thriving (described to us as 'inspirational'), sending annual small, but perfectly formed contingent of brightest and best to Oxbridge. High praise also received for history teaching. Music, art and DT don't attract huge numbers at A level, but are well resourced and get good results. Theatre studies offered in conjunction with St Helen and St Katharine, neighbouring independent girls' school, no doubt a mutually beneficial and practical solution to low uptake. Must also increase the repertoire of plays and parts considerably. Psychology has been a fairly recent introduction to previously 'ology' allergic A level menu. Jury is still out – as yet the subject's popularity and exam record are on a par.

Abingdon's pupils have been rowing on the town's stretch of the Thames for nearly 200 years and boys in their pink and black kit jogging to the boathouse are a familiar sight

Lessons are fast paced and challenging – setting for maths and science from year 9, but selective intake means all are working above and beyond. Good staff mix of male and female, old timers and recent graduates; sensible creative latitude given to non-standard teaching styles – much appreciated by boys, parents and (we assume) the teachers in question. Great engagement and rapport between boys and teachers in lessons we saw – lots of fun and sparky ideas in year 9 English where boys were coming up with literary foods: apple pie for Paradise Lost, Pina Colada for Robinson Crusoe and our favourite, a 'saucy stir-fry' for Chaucer's Canterbury Tales!

Abingdon is an academically selective school, but it's a broad enough church to accommodate bright boys with mild to moderate SEND (mostly dyslexia and dyspraxia). In-class, small group and one-to-one help provided by well-regarded learning support department. Pupils who are identified as needing short-term help with, for instance, study skills, receive six one-to-one sessions free of charge. Parents tell us that the department is 'on the ball' and that staff are extra vigilant at high pressure times such as school and public exams.

Games, options, the arts: Abingdon's sporting alphabet runs from athletics to water polo, taking in a wide range of team and individual pursuits along the way. The letter 'r' gets more than its fair share of kudos, with rugby and rowing being two of the school's chief glories, along with hockey. Full-on fixture list for these and other sports – regular opponents include Marlborough, Radley, Bradfield, Wellington and Eton. Fine sports centre with swimming pool, several grass pitches and popular climbing wall on site; more extensive facilities including athletics tracks and a 4G pitch (no, we didn't know what this was either – apparently it's the very latest thing in Astroturf) just down the road at Tilsley Park. Abingdon took over the management of Tilsley Park from the local council in 2014 and after considerable investment in facilities it is now used both by the school and the local community. Much success too in less mainstream sports such as fencing, cross-country, sailing and shooting.

Abingdon's pupils have been rowing on the town's stretch of the Thames for nearly 200 years and boys in their pink and black kit jogging down to the beautiful wooden boathouse are a familiar sight on summer afternoons. Rowing laurels have suffered a few soggy seasons lately, but boys told us excitedly that the coach was 'making huge changes.'

All boys, including sixth formers, must do at least two sessions of sport a week, but most do many more, including Saturday training and matches. Lots of tours and specialist development camps (some abroad). Boys who duck when they see a ball coming (yes, such boys do exist) are expected to have a go at different options and find something they enjoy – karate and canoe polo have proved popular recent additions to the sports mix.

Dynamic music department will seek out and nurture every kind of musical talent – from pipers, choristers and counter tenors to, famously, all five members of Radiohead. Every boy is encouraged to take up an instrument when they join the school if they don't already play one. Unsuspecting parents may find their son coming home drooping under the weight of a French horn or bassoon in an ever-optimistic effort by the school's director of music to uncover a virtuoso in these vital, but less popular, orchestral instruments. A plethora of choirs, bands, orchestras and chamber groups, plus an ambitious programme of concerts for all abilities, equals quite a few nights out for supportive parents. Regular organ and choral scholarships to Oxbridge and music colleges.

Annual drama productions for lower, middle and senior school boys plus house drama and joint ventures with girls from St Helen and St Katharine. Theatre design workshops, modern foreign language plays and a podcasting club add to the repertoire. Newly refurbished Amey Theatre is the main venue for concerts, plays and other whole school events. The addition of a projection screen and surround sound has made it a popular local venue for films, live theatre and opera screenings.

All the above and much, much more is included in the school's famous Other Half programme. You won't hear music, art, D of E, CCF, community service or the 120+ clubs and societies referred to as 'extracurricular activities' here. At Abingdon such things are not optional extras, but essential parts of a well-rounded education. Close harmony singing? Lego architecture? Ceramics? Entomology? Code-breaking? Take a look at the school's (excellent) website and you'll wish you could sign up for one or two options. Worthy of note are debating – the debating society is believed to be the school's oldest non-sporting society and the dinner debates with local girls' schools are a big draw – and Abingdon Film Unit (AFU). The AFU is quite possibly unique, a semi-autonomous organisation run by professional film makers to enable secondary school pupils to make short films – mostly documentaries and stop-motion animations. Since it was set up in 2003 over 120 films have been produced, a number of which have been screened at national and international festivals and won awards.

Boarding: Majority of international boarders are from Hong Kong and China. Small weekly contingent from local families. The three boarding houses (School House, Crescent and Austin), are home to roughly equal numbers of boarders and day boys – ensures good integration. Communal areas we saw were well cared for and rather clubby (pool table, stags' head on the wall); bedrooms are, well, just like those in all the other boys' boarding houses we've visited: two or three beds, floor garnished with huge trainers, lots of Lynx and stashes of snacks. Not overly tidy – always a plus point. Each house has a resident house master and his family, at least one resident tutor, and a matron. Other house tutors live nearby. School has its own health centre with a nurse on call overnight and an on-site counselling service. Four meals a day, plus a school cafe; sixth formers can cook their own lunch in the house kitchen or forage in Abingdon's shops and takeaways. Excellent range of joint and individual house activities and trips, making full use of Abingdon's proximity to Oxford and London. Socials and sixth form dinners with girls' boarding schools such

Excellent range of joint and individual house activities and trips, making full use of Abingdon's proximity to Oxford and London

as Westonbirt, St Mary's Calne and Headington. Boarding 'enrichment programme' aims to equip boys with vital life skills such as cooking, cleaning and ironing plus information about English law, taxes and applying for student loans. Attendance at boarders' chapel services is compulsory and we heard one or two polite grumbles about this ('a bit boring'). School says it has listened to boys' comments about this and services are now less frequent.

Background and atmosphere: One of England's oldest schools, Abingdon was 'officially' founded in 1256 when the Abbot of Abingdon, John de Blosneville, left money for the support of 13 poor scholars. Earliest references date back to 1100 when a school was likely to have been established alongside Abingdon Abbey. Having survived the dissolution of the monasteries its fortunes waxed and waned over the ensuing centuries, according to the generosity of benefactors and the quality of headmasters. School moved to its present site, adjacent to an elegant crescent around a park, in 1870 and proceeded to buy up more land and some of the crescent's houses. Architecture is sturdy Victorian red brick and running up and down stone staircases between lessons keeps boys and staff pretty fit, but could present a challenge to those on crutches (most of the school except Big School, the oldest part, is wheelchair accessible). Original library in Big School is a bibliophile's delight and the 21st century additions such as the arts centre, sports centre and the new Yang Science Centre have been thoughtfully designed and well executed. Work is underway on Beech Court which will house a new sixth form centre plus a library, UCAS resources and careers office.

The Yang Science Centre is a superb addition to the school – three floors of labs and work rooms with an extraordinary metal tree-like sculpture, the Fusion Tower, that fills the stairwell, ascending and morphing into a representation of the science pursued on each level. Apparently, the only drawback of this is that 'physicists have nowhere to drop things from.' (Surely they've got gravity sorted out by now?) At the sculpture's base are 1,256 discs, one for every boy in the Abingdon foundation at the time of the piece's creation.

On the ground floor is a large, dedicated 'outreach' laboratory where pupils of all ages from local schools and organisations such as Scouts and Guides can come for science clubs, projects and subject extension activities. The work tables and seats are designed so that they can be adjusted to fit proto-scientists and there are mini-lab coats and goggles too. Abingdon boys also go out into local primary schools to run science clubs as part of their service activities. This exciting and generously resourced venture has really taken off and the Abingdon Science Partnership (ASP) co-ordinator told us that the school is now a centre of expertise for science continuing professional development, running teacher training workshops for Oxfordshire and neighbouring counties. School has a burgeoning partnership with Fitzharrys, a local maintained secondary, and the classics department has a long-standing tradition of teaching pupils from other local secondaries too.

Abingdon itself is an ancient market town on the River Thames with insufficient parking and a fiendish one-way system that can leave the uninitiated driving in circles. School doesn't dominate the town, it's a little outside the centre, but is a significant local employer and those ever-hungry boys must boost takings in the local shops and eateries.

With three other independent schools in the immediate vicinity and several others very close by, this corner of South Oxfordshire is rather a hotspot for educational privilege. That being said, Abingdon School isn't regarded as snobby and despite impressive facilities seems to retain the faintest, pleasingly meritocratic whiff of an old-style grammar. Uniform is fairly standard (grey trousers, blue blazer) and most components can be bought from M&S; there's also a second hand uniform shop, run by the parents' association. Ties are another matter, almost 50 possibilities at the last count: house ties, half and full colours, scholars, societies, prizes, and so on. Boys know what they all mean, but parents usually lose track after the first few.

Pastoral care, well-being and discipline: Parents tell us that the house and tutor system works well to ensure all boys receive individual academic and pastoral attention – vitally important in such a big school; staff are 'very observant', a parent told us. Boys who arrive at age 11, many from local primaries, join Lower School, which gives them two years to ease in to things before another influx at age 13 from preps, including Abingdon's own. In common with other schools, much more attention is now paid to pupils' mental as well as physical health. Boys can book directly or through the health centre to see a counsellor (on site, four days a week). PHSCE sessions – in class or during tutor time – cover a multitude of age-appropriate topics including healthy eating and body image, bullying, drugs, alcohol and relationships.

High expectations, both from the school and parents, and long, busy days, generally ensure good behaviour. Rules are sensible and consistently enforced. There's a lot of 'banter', but boys tell us that most know 'how far they can go.' There's no stereotypical Abingdon boy and school has enough alternative milieux for the unusual or eccentric to find their tribe.

Pupils and parents: School buses (all morning and some evening routes shared with the St Helen's girls) bring pupils in from as far as Reading, Newbury, Fairford and Bicester. Parents are fairly typical Oxfordshire mix of medics, academics, IT professionals and business people – not conspicuously wealthy, probably because they're paying school fees. Active parents' association organises socials and fundraisers, runs a popular second hand uniform shop and a car share scheme. Boys themselves are the most persuasive advert for their school – prospective parents attending open days are allocated a current pupil as a guide and most are ready to sign on the dotted line by the end of their tour. Old Abingdonians include Francis Maude, former MP and cabinet minister, Sir Kim Darroch, British ambassador to the US, Tom Kempinski, playwright, Thomas Dolby, musician and producer, actors Tom Hollander, Toby Jones and David Mitchell, all five members of Radiohead, lots of rowers and rugby players and centuries of churchmen, soldiers, academics, lawyers and all round good chaps.

Entrance: At 11 candidates from local primary schools and some preps, such as Chandlings, are tested in English, maths and reasoning. On the basis of performance in the test boys are then selected for a 'friendly' interview. Year 7 pre-tests for 13+ entry. Most arrive at this stage from Abingdon Prep, Moulsford, New College School, Dragon and St Hugh's. For entry to sixth form a minimum of B/6 in all I/GCSEs, and A/7 in the subjects to be studied at A level (A*/8 for further maths) is required.

Exit: Nearly all sixth formers head for mainly Russell group universities to study serious subjects. Lots of engineers, chemists, economists and theoretical physicists as one would expect, but also historians, classicists and philosophers – it's that kind of school. Current favourite destinations are Bath, Bristol, Durham and Newcastle. In 2017, 19 to Oxbridge and 12 medics. Growing numbers to study abroad including one each to Harvard and Yale in 2017.

Money matters: Range of scholarships which confer more prestige (and ties) than dosh. Means-tested bursaries available for part or all of day fees.

Remarks: Bigger, yes, and even better. We were delighted to revisit Abingdon and see how it has skilfully managed significant growth and development without compromise to its traditions, ethos and humanity. An outstanding school for bright all-rounders.

Ashfold School

Dorton House, Dorton, Aylesbury, Buckinghamshire HP18 9NG

01844 238237 | registrar@ashfoldschool.co.uk | www.ashfoldschool.co.uk

Ages: 3-13 (boarding from 9)

Pupils: 281; Boarders: 45 flexi

Day: £9,255 – £16,365 pa; Flexi boarding: £19,605 pa

Headmaster: Since 1997, Mr Michael Chitty (50s). Educated at Clifton College, Bristol then Exeter University where he read economics before following generations of forefathers to Sandhurst. First bitten by the teaching bug on his gap year in Kenya, where he was a student teacher at The Banda School and later, following an army career that saw him rise to the rank of Captain in the Queen's Royal Irish Hussars via Equerry to HRH Prince Philip, when he returned to Sandhurst as officer instructor.

Landed squarely on his feet in his first teaching position at Stowe School, where he taught economics, politics and European studies, always with an eye to his main ambition of becoming a prep school head. Given role of 'adjutant' to ease communications between the head's office, bursary and staff common room before being appointed housemaster of Grenville House (after which he later named one of his two black labradors). Headhunted after six years to become head of Ashfold, which he transformed with his energy, enthusiasm and clear vision. No longer teaches, although he does share

boarding duties, but parents say he is 'very hands on' and he still coaches rugby, hockey and cricket teams, as well as clay pigeon and.22 rifle shooting teams, sits with children at lunch times and is always visible at matches and other school events.

Prospective parents unlikely to meet many heads whose former jobs include 'deployment of the British army worldwide' and Chitty does not disappoint, with his overwhelmingly positive, driven – and some might say military – approach to managing his school. An animated and dynamic communicator, he likes to keep up to date with car park chit chat via parents. Says he is running a 'very together school,' and is now 'in a position to do some very exciting stuff.' Appointment of a female deputy has boosted girls' numbers and brought fresh ideas.

Lives in a house on site – as do around 15 staff – with wife Louise, a barrister. Two grown up children, now working, come back for regular visits and often join their parents at their second home near Cirencester, where they enjoy spending weekends sailing, walking dogs and occasionally indulging a passion for cricket.

Retiring in July 2018. His successor will be Colin MacIntosh, currently deputy head of Beaudesert Park School. English degree from St Andrews; started his teaching career at Shrewsbury School, then spent 15 years in various prep schools before joining Beaudesert. He is a keen sportsman, playing football, cricket and golf. He is married to Anna and they have two children.

Entrance: Non-selective, with the majority joining reception from the nursery. Prospective pupils for all year groups invited to spend a day in school for assessment only. Head likes children from state primaries to join by year 2 and will hold places for them to this point. From year 3, places are harder to come by, with waiting lists for most year groups.

Exit: Leavers to a wide variety of schools, with about 50 per cent heading off to board most years. Popular choices include Stowe, Bloxham, Harrow, Rugby, Wellington College, Headington and St Edward's. Impressive scholarship record – on average, more than 40 per cent of leavers have won scholarships or awards to their senior schools over the last nine years. Head takes care to place less academic children in schools where they can shine. Very few to state maintained grammars (just a couple each year), with head discouraging 11 plus unless for financial reasons.

Remarks: The cross country drive through rolling hills and farmland and rising fear that the satnav is playing tricks on you is well worth it for the first sight of Ashfold's stunning Jacobean mansion set in 33 acres of fields and woodland. Rugby pitches in the foreground give the impression of a traditional boys' prep but behind the magnificent building are three hard tennis courts, a well maintained, heated outdoor pool, full size astroturf, netball courts and a lovely adventure playground, proving that that the girls who make up roughly 40 per cent of the school population are well catered for and now integral to the culture of the school.

Wood paneling, winding staircases and cobbled stable blocks bring Hogwarts to mind, and rosy cheeked, windswept and slightly disheveled children litter the grassy play areas, giving an overall impression of an idyllic country school – worlds apart from the urban London schools many of its commuter families have left behind. Lacks some of the dazzling showcase facilities boasted by many preps, but every part of the campus is put to excellent use (and in the words of one parent: 'you're a bit restricted with a grade I listing') and the overall effect is of an inspiring, functional and nurturing environment, which, in the head's words, 'celebrates children.'

Purpose-built pre-prep building houses nursery to year 2 in a light, spacious and colourful setting with its own well-equipped playground and large field, complete with bug hotel. Pre-prep children well integrated into the main school, sharing its assembly space (often the village church, situated on site), sports hall and playing fields. Junior department housed in main wing of house, while most senior lessons take place in recently renovated courtyard classrooms.

Largely rural catchment from surrounding villages, with majority of children from hard-working middle class families ('hardly any old money,' said one parent), who travel up to 30 minutes to school. Very few from non-Caucasian families. School keen to prove its country credentials with a flourishing veg patch tended by pupils and weekend challenges set for families, resulting in the presentation of the school's 'countryside certificate' on completion of all 30. Small number of scholarships, with the Stowe-Ashfold scholarship and the Tudor Hall-Ashfold scholarship covering 100 per cent of fees and other awards up to 30 per cent, available for pupils 'who show outstanding academic, artistic, sporting, musical or all-round ability' for the last two years at the school.

Girls have been part of the furniture at Ashfold since the 1980s and make up 43 per cent of the total cohort. Parents say that all children get the same opportunities, regardless of gender.

Whether arty, sporty, or musical, there's something for every child here ('they look at the child as an individual,' say parents) and academics are solid all round too. Class sizes are small. French with a specialist teacher from year 1 and Latin from age 9. Setting has been introduced in the core subjects. Pupils entirely specialist taught from year 4 and move around the school for different subjects from thereon. All children screened for dyslexia aged 7 or whenever they join the school. Currently around 12 per cent of pupils under the SENCo for mild needs (SpLD, dyslexia or dyspraxia). In class support and small group work with a learning support assistant covered by fees. One-to-one lessons with the school's SEN specialist charged as extra.

Parents find channels of communication excellent and are able to email class teachers – who they describe as 'a really talented bunch' – directly with queries or issues. Recent introduction of e-learning online assessments for all children from year 3 up have 'really freed up teachers to focus on creative lesson planning,' says head.

No mobile phones, iPods or other gadgets allowed with the exception of kindles – a very popular move with parents. Lights out at 9.30pm and cooked breakfasts are a hit

High standard of art on show in and around a lovely bright art room; 'you can't usually see the ceiling for work,' said the head of department when we visited (it was the first week in September), although it would be nice to see a bit more of the pupils' work festooning the walls around the rest of the school. A swanky art and design centre opened recently with facilities for DT, cookery, art, ceramics and textiles.

Almost 60 per cent of pupils learn a musical instrument. The new head of music introduced Music Masterclasses and lots of workshops with senior schools, as well internal events such as an instrument fair to introduce the children to all the instruments on offer at Ashfold. Collaborates with drama teacher to produce fantastic musical theatre – recent productions include the musical Honk! (performed outside in the walled garden) and The Canada Years (the true story of Ashfold's evacuation to Canada during WWII) as well as A Midsummer Night's Dream. Waiting lists for all choirs underscore the school's renewed collective passion in this area and all pre-prep children learn the violin and recorder from year 1. Lots going on in the drama department too, with productions including Sherlock Holmes and The Secret of Immortality and The Wind in the Willows.

Once children reach the prep school they have an extended day, ending at either 5 or 6pm, depending on age. This enables the curriculum to include daily sport for all, which although adored by most is 'a struggle' for some of the less sporty ones, according to parents. All the usual suspects played to a good level but head exceptionally proud of his U13 girls' hockey team which won the IAPS championship recently and the clay shooting team, also IAPs U12 and U13 champions and runners up at the British Schools and Young Shots Clay Shooting Championships in 2017. He puts this and other sporting successes down to a 'real focus on coaching' with specialist talent brought in to coach rugby, hockey, netball and football (with an ex-Oxford United coach). Gymnastics and indoor games take place in a good sized sports hall incorporating wonderful changing facilities – 'with hot showers,' the head assures. From year 6, those demonstrating talent in other areas are selected to join scholars' groups (academic, art, drama et al) in place of time allocated to games.

Boarding allowed from year 5, where children can stay for supper after games, then take part in one of a multitude of activities on offer (from rifle shooting or fishing to chess and cookery). Given that this takes them up to 8pm it's a bit of a no brainer for parents of children keen to sample boarding life, and up to 30 children board on any given night (up to three nights a week in year 5 and four nights in year 6). Dorms of up to seven beds have been recently revamped and provide spacious, comfortable accommodation in the mansion, girls at one end of the building, boys at the other. Head says, 'it's proper boarding, not a sleepover,' and boarders sleep in the same bed on their chosen boarding nights. Newly refurbed boarders' common rooms, complete with pool table, two flat screen TVs and comfy sofas, provide a home from home feel and open onto the houseparents' accommodation. No mobile phones, iPods or other gadgets allowed with the exception of kindles – a very popular move with parents. Lights out at 9.30pm and cooked breakfasts are a hit.

School has a Christian ethos but accepts other denominations. Rightfully proud of its pastoral care with parents reporting 'very clear lines of escalation' should things ever go wrong. Three houses (Gryphons, Lions and Dragons) compete in lots of eagerly contested competitions (parents describe the standard of work in the inter-house art competition as 'unbelievable') with the each term culminating in a house cup. Pre-prep pupils presented with star of the week awards for effort and attainment in weekly assemblies. Head boy and girl chosen at the beginning of year 8 amid great excitement; rest of year 8 are all prefects. Head clear that 'leadership is about serving others,' and says he won't have any arrogance in the school, on occasion passing over obvious macho choices for head boy for 'a lovely gentleman with outstanding manners.'

No school buses as head wants parents to bring children into school to keep lines of communication open: 'If a child has had a sleepless night, for example, we want to know about it,' he says.

Bedales Pre-prep, Dunannie and Bedales Prep, Dunhurst

3

Alton Road, Steep, Petersfield, Hampshire GU32 2DR

01730 711733 | admissions@bedales.org.uk | www.bedales.org.uk

Ages: Dunannie 3-8; Dunhurst 8-13; boarding from 8

Pupils: 269; Boarders: 39 full, 18 flexi

Day: £9,069 – £18,300 pa; Boarding: £21,669 – £24,318 pa

Linked school: Bedales School, 334

Head: At Dunhurst since September 2017, Colin Baty, previously head of Great Walstead Prep in Sussex. He taught at the prep, and his wife, Debbie, at the pre-prep, before moving to Moreton Hall, where he was deputy head.

At Dunannie since 2010, Jo Webbern, who worked before at Ibstock Place. 'Very lovely and approachable, great with children', said a parent. 'A look or a word from Jo means a lot to these children – they don't want to let Jo down'. Has 'commit-tea' every Wednesday with four of year 3, to discuss ideas – 'how about a zip wire in the orchard', suggested one. 'I've got a zip wire at home', said another. 'We'll all go around to yours then', said the head brightly. Jo is very careful to write everything down: she ensures the children here feel that their ideas are properly considered and valued. Leaving in July 2018.

Entrance: They are looking for children and families who like and understand the Bedales ethos, and this, and an intention to progress through the school, is all that is necessary for entrance into nursery and reception. For entrance to years 1-3, informal assessment of reading, writing and maths. At Dunhurst, English and maths assessments, non-verbal reasoning and interview. Prospective pupils are considered in the round, so although they are looking for average ability or above in academic terms, a pupil could be below average in some areas, with a spark in others.

Overall lower scores might be acceptable in a child who is a good worker who won't give up. Prospective pupils spend time with their peers to see how well they cooperate: three day assessments for 10+ and 11+ applicants. No waiting lists, but some classes close to full. Eight plus and 11+ are natural points of entry.

Exit: Nearly all progress on to Bedales, after sitting a maths and English test. A small number to other senior schools, including Canford, St Swithun's, Cranleigh and Bryanston.

Remarks: Pupils sitting on chairs, tables, leaning against radiators. Excited laughter, banter between teacher and pupils, the energy almost tangible. Were they perhaps discussing a forthcoming party? No: it was a lesson on longshore drift. Rare indeed that longshore drift generates such excitement; but this exchange of energy between teacher and pupils was replicated in other classrooms again and again. Pupils didn't leap to silent feet when we appeared – they were engrossed in learning. The point here is not neat quiet rows, but the work you are doing; and the pupils were fully and busily engaged.

No carrot or stick approach to learning here: it's not an awards assembly sort of place. Time is not wasted on the common entrance – years 7, 8 and 9 do a three year pre-GCSE curriculum. A parent commented that 'children are expected to raise questions which require discussion and debate'; another that 'lessons are rigorous and stretching'. Although one parent commented that a greater insistence on accurate spelling would be nice, most felt that high standards were expected, particularly of those with potential.

This school is about learning to live, and understanding yourself as something worthy of inquiry: '[It is] very challenging; not an easy way'

Parents agree that English, dance, music and art are outstanding, and that there has been a significant effort to raise the game in sciences and maths, which are now also strong – 'pupils do now routinely learn things by rote, such as tables'. One parent commented happily on the cross fertilisation between subjects, giving the example of a school trip where everyone had to make a snack for everyone else: a happy blend of maths, domestic science and altruism.

Class size is a maximum of 20. Years 4, 5 and 6 have a double in intake, with three or four classes a year in years 7 and 8. Children are only set for maths – they're keen to avoid any labelling here. Saturday morning school starts at age 12, in block 1. Parents aren't terribly keen on it, but the kids don't seem to mind.

Homework is integrated into the day, pupils having a number of free periods called Greens for homework, and any LAMDA or music commitments. Parents say it's great for those who are self-motivated and can organise themselves, and love the fact that prep gets done at school, so kids are free when they get home.

No competitive parenting here; one mum told us if people were heard talking about their child's

levels of achievement, other parents would raise eyebrows of horror: they were certainly at the wrong school.

Learning support both in and out of lessons – we spoke to a pupil who chose Dunhurst particularly for its SEN support, and to the happy parents of a dyslexic pupil who had regained lost confidence here.

The whole idea of jaw (a weekly lively discussion forum with a speaker) seems made for the self-assured to fly, reflected in a parent's comment that this is a school which would best suit those who know their own minds, are self-motivated, and not easily influenced by their peers. But this caring environment could also suit those who are more tentative. Development of individual rather than the mass is a focus which pleases parents, and shy children can find their feet and their confidence at Dunhurst.

Those seeking a traditional prep school education might be disconcerted here. 'If a parent has pigeonholed a child as just academic then it won't suit them,' says school. As a parent told us, 'It's not so much which child the school wouldn't suit, as which parents...'. They described a pupil, lacking self-confidence and happiness, who came from a traditional school; a recovery at Dunhurst; then subsequent return to the traditional school, and the surprise of the parents when the child fell apart again.

The pastoral care here is highly praised by parents – the clincher for this school. There's much emphasis on well-being; down time, such as meditation, is incorporated into the school day. The Friday custom of staff shaking hands with pupils stems from the idea that knowing the nature of each pupil's handshake means you can tell if something's wrong; it connects you with every child and gets rid of any bad blood before the weekend. 'It's totally unique', said a parent, describing his son's happiness, and his development of social skills, self-confidence and worldliness at Dunhurst.

Bullying not tolerated here, confirmed a parent, who said that older children have a responsibility to look out for the younger ones, and blow the whistle on any bad behaviour. This is mentioned frequently, as is the peer listening network and the school counsellor – to whom the children can self refer. '[The children are] all very tuned in and look out for each other', said a parent. The school says the approach will depend on the severity: if year 4s are getting a bit tetchy with each other, being a good friend might suddenly become a topic in PHSE.

In disciplinary terms, it's not so much which punishment fits the crime, as what can you give back to the community. Offenders might be put on beauty duty cleaning out the greenhouses; but bring your friends along, some other teachers might join in, and someone brings a radio.

First names between teachers and pupils, and the lack of uniform, might seem strange to

newcomers, but there is plenty of respect here – 'when kids talk to adults, they're not frightened', said a parent. Most kids chose to dress very casually – jeans, leggings and hoodies are the norm.

Head, heart and hand are the guiding principles here, and the head part is not just academic; there needs to be something for the soul too: time for stillness and thinking; opportunities to appreciate beauty and contemplate life. So there's lots of art, drama, and music; the divine smell of a room devoted to woodwork – 'Dunhurst pupils wouldn't go to B&Q to buy a shed'. An art room with views over the countryside; a colourful paper model village, with circuits underneath for night time lighting; a table of cupped pottery hands which look as though they are awaiting communion. All do outdoor work – a hand-painted gypsy caravan will become a small classroom. There's an outdoor hut with pizza oven, rows of wellies on pegs, mud and clucking hens; tasks range from building to planting to clearing bracken. There was schoolwide participation in RSPB Birdwatch.

Wednesday afternoon is activity time, which includes outreach for years 7 and 8 (visiting the elderly or helping at local primary schools), outside work, shopping in Petersfield, cooking in Scoffs (the pupil run café) or sports. Sport is not something which is overemphasised, and you can opt out of matches (as you might expect). There is plenty of sport available, with excellent tennis provision, and access to all the Bedales facilities, including the lovely swimming pool, but 'if you're not strong at sports, it's not a big deal', said a parent.

Communication is good, with a Friday report reviewing the week's events. Staff will contact parents by phone or by email if something is going wrong, and one parent described thorough and regular reporting of his child's medical condition. For parents who have experienced the fluid atmosphere of Dunannie, it is less easy to walk into Dunhurst to chat to teachers, said one parent, but they do always get back by email.

There are some 60 boarders, around 40 full, the remainder flexi, staying from one night a week. Most boarders are from years 7 and 8. Beds are singles, two to six per room. Comfortable clean facilities, showers and baths – the girls protested at the suggestion of segregating the triple bathrooms – apparently simultaneous bathing is a happy community activity (curtains can be drawn if the girls choose). Kitchen facilities are available at certain times, with cereal, toast and fruit on offer (but boarders must go to the dining hall for proper breakfast and supper). Tech must be put away at 8.30pm. Boarders can contact home by phone or email, and most use their own devices, but can use the phone in matron's room at any time. Very few overseas boarders, but pupils can stay at weekends, and trips are organised for those who do.

Dunhurst connects to Dunannie, the pre-prep, but the nursery is separately situated in an old barn, full of light and sunshine, a safe magical world. All the usual tiny person activities, with the addition of an area devoted to planting vegetables, which they subsequently enjoy making into soup. Outside, a large sandpit, and saucepans and frying pans to batter hanging on strings.

Dunannie children take learning outside for around a quarter of each day – 'it's not just an add on here', says Jo; all-in-one rain gear and wellies hang neatly in a boot room – the children learn how to change very quickly so they can maximise their outside time. Vegetable plots from nursery upwards, a willow pod (made by years 2 and 3) and a thatched Celtic hut (made by Bedales students) to play in.

Relaxed classrooms, children sitting happily on the floor, chatting with teachers. Lessons are practically based: year 3 are studying birds, filling paper bags with shells to make up the different weights of birds, following birds' migratory paths on maps, and making their own memory maps for trips around the grounds. Home-made willow bird feeders are hung outside the large windows so the class can appreciate visitors (how many schools would find these random interruptions to lessons acceptable?).

Individualised learning plans for each pupil, with no expectation that they will all progress at the same rate. A child can do a year again if seems advisable for their happiness and development. Very little homework, mostly spelling or reading. Dunannie can cope with quite a profound level of special needs, but will consider carefully how well a child will fit into a class before accepting them. Those with severe needs are unlikely to be able to progress to Dunhurst.

Class sizes up to 20, split into two at year 3, where class sizes are up to 15.

Pastoral care is very strong. The golden rules at Dunannie are to listen and be respectful, and they talk about these rules a lot. Pupils are very caring of one another: one parent told us that when one child made racially explicit comments about another, a classmate reported the issue. It was dealt with immediately, and the matter fully reported to the relevant parents.

Bedales School

4

Church Road, Steep, Petersfield, Hampshire GU32 2DG

01730 300100 | admissions@bedales.org.uk | www.bedales.org.uk

Ages: 13–18

Pupils: 468; sixth form: 186; Boarders: 360 full, 20 flexi

Day: £27,816 pa; Boarding: £35,397 pa

Linked school: Bedales Pre-prep, Dunannie and Bedales Prep, Dunhurst, 331

Headmaster: Since 2001, Keith Budge, married with three grown up children. Read English at Oxford, and came to Bedales via Loretto and Marlborough. His previous schools, says the head, did not have the child so much at their centre. Neither, presumably, did the pupils call him Keith. Children here

own and shape their education; the teachers, says Keith, are their collaborators. Who, indeed, would collaborate with Sir?

The head is deeply committed to the underlying ethos of Bedales (education of head, heart and hand). These are the ideals, says Keith, but 'idealism here has a strong thread of pragmatism running through it'. He also believes that a school needs to constantly reinvent itself: the head originated Bedales Assessed Courses (BACs) as an alternative to GCSEs, and also now offers enrichment as an option instead of a fourth A level – 'an intelligent, brave approach', said a parent. Others say he's 'intellectual and caring'; 'kind, understanding, firm where necessary'; 'tries to see others' point of view'. 'I'm a huge fan', added another parent, who says he does an incredible job with diverse parents and really varied students.

Leaving in July 2018. His successor will be Magnus Bashaarat MA PGCE (40s), currently head of Milton Abbey School and previously deputy head of Stowe. Educated at The King's School, Canterbury (he and Stowe head Anthony Wallersteiner were contemporaries there), followed by University of Edinburgh, where he read English. After work experience at the York Evening Press he decided to become a journalist and worked for the Observer and Evening Standard for a while. He changed direction after taking a course in teaching English as a foreign language – found he loved 'standing up in front of a class and helping people to learn.' PGCE at King's College London, followed by two years at Sherborne and a 15-year stint at Eton, where he taught English and drama and was a housemaster for seven years. He also did a year at Sydney Grammar as part of a teaching exchange with Eton. Moved to Stowe in 2009 and spent five years as deputy head.

His wife Camilla used to work in communications for the NHS and they have three children. In his spare time, he cycles (his road bike is propped against the wall of his study), rows and goes to the theatre as much as he can. He likes 'serious drama'.

Academic matters: Education is different here, its value much more in itself than the end qualifications – the qualification hoops to be jumped to get to the university to reach the gold-plated job. It's not that Bedales ignores these reasonable parental desires – most students end up at the same universities – but it tries as far as possible to make education of the individual the thing: 'to develop inquisitive thinkers with a love of learning who cherish independent thought'.

Parents refer to the unusual mutual respect between teachers and pupils – 'a powerful developmental thing'

Qualifications look different here too, to fit this more holistic vision of learning: 'the wonderful BACs' (as described by a parent) are a living alternative to GCSEs. They focus on cross-curricular, independent thought, with a range of assessment methods from written assignments to presentations and performances: an organic process of learning over time, with few make or break final day assessments. And universities are happy with them too, though Bedales retains a compulsory core of five IGCSEs in English, maths, modern languages and sciences. Parents and pupils like the mixture of assessment methods in the BACs, and they're done and dusted in time to leave a clear month to revise for IGCSEs.

At BACs/IGCSEs in 2017, 50 per cent A*-As. It's a classical looking curriculum, but a global awareness BAC is new and sports science is imminent. Philosophy, religion and ethics (PRE) is one of the most popular BACs, with nearly half of the students taking this option. 'It really makes pupils think, and they carry those skills and that knowledge with them. It's evident in their thinking at A level... a really impressive linking of ideas', said a parent. 'Star course', said another. Classics was also particularly highlighted by parents, who said the quality of teaching is 'superb'. '[students are] really stimulated and pushed to the limit'.

Uniquely at Bedales, there is no dead time after IGCSEs and BACs. Pupils start their A level courses immediately, so they have a month's A level taster before the summer holidays. If pupils don't like what they have opted for, they can change courses before starting A levels properly in September.

At A level, 33 per cent A*-A, 61 per cent A*-B in 2017. Maximum class size is 14 but often significantly smaller. On average seven per cent to Oxbridge over the last five years (five places in 2017). Enrichment, compulsory for those not taking four A levels, safeguards time to learn something just for the joy of it; it could include beginners' Russian, oak framed building, dance or astronomy. 'Education at its best', said a parent, another describing her child's delight at doing art again, having given this up to concentrate on academic subjects. Some parents are concerned that enrichment subjects won't be as rigorous as examined courses, and might be viewed by universities as wasted time. But the school believes that enrichment is valuable in itself (hear hear).

The counter-side of all this educational roaming is a strong and structured guidance system: there's a six weekly review by teachers of each student's effort and attainment, and students have a fortnightly one-to-one tutorial. The tutor's job is to get students to self-motivate and organise, and help them realise that what they put in to learning is what they get out. This 'got it' moment should happen earlier at Bedales because of the innate value placed on learning, but in the rare case that it hasn't clicked by the sixth form, they will put a military structure in place to try and help.

In this strong community, students are encouraged to help others academically: year 13s can be Badley seniors (from founder John Badley) and help year 9s with their work; others become dons – English dons, physics dons etc – and champion a subject to help others.

Homework is generally fitted into free periods during the day, one parent commenting on the different homework culture at traditional schools: her non-Bedales child swots all evening. Some teachers give loads of homework (don't worry if that leg injury's keeping you at home – you can be Skyped the French homework), others much less. A parent commented that his daughter feels the pressure a bit, but the Bedalian atmosphere helps: 'If she was surrounded by little Miss Perfects it would be much worse'.

Students at Bedales are generally highly motivated, owing, a Harvard study suggests, to a love of learning, and the level of autonomy and choice enjoyed by students here. But 'some don't bother at all', said a parent, who wonders whether a more pushy environment might galvanise the lazy. Here, the approach is to try to find out why children are not performing, and help them develop their full potential. And generally this works much better than an order from above: parents refer to the unusual mutual respect between teachers and pupils – 'a powerful developmental thing'. '[They're a] really gifted staff', said another.

Learning support (LS) is staffed by one full-timer and six part-timers, two of whom are maths specialists, and is charged as an extra. A speech and language therapist comes in as necessary. No in class support here, so students need to be able to cope with lessons on their own. Up to two sessions of support a week during free periods. LS rooms here are dotted around, so students don't have to leave a subject area to go to a particular stigmatised centre. There's close liaison between LS and subject teachers, with LS feeding into every year group review. LS emails home with progress reports, keeping in regular contact.

Around a third of students use LS at some point: the department is happy to provide spasmodic support for particular difficulties, although often short term problems can be mopped up by teachers and supervised study. LS generally supports mild learning difficulties (but can cope with severe dyslexia). Progress rates of dyslexic students are the same as others, with some doing exceptionally well.

'It's the ethos of boarding school with day pupils', said one parent. Even day students have to do activities in the evening, so can be at school until around 9.30pm

Several parents described dyslexic children who suffered from self-esteem issues while attending high achieving, pressurised schools, and the difference in their children once they started at Bedales: 'Bedales is outstanding in the support it offers pupils'; 'it's inspiring pastoral care'; 'they draw out the best in children'.

One couple with a dyslexic child were initially sceptical about Bedales – 'we're not celebrities, just ordinary middle class parents'. Four open days later, they decided to go for it, and describe an open and supportive atmosphere, and a child who now loves school and has regained her confidence.

Games, options, the arts: This must be the only school in the country which has 'appreciation of the beautiful' as one of its aims. 'There is an intense delight in seeing your work grow under your hand...It is the delight of creation, of shaping something that shall have use and beauty, the delight of an artist' (John Badley, founder). Outdoor work is a key part of the curriculum: from planting, to building a posh pig sty, to putting a new engine in an ancient Land Rover.

Parents eulogise about the music, arts and drama here – 'art is very, very good – they're really pushed and well prepared for A level'. Music receives similar accolades: the BAC is much more demanding than GCSE, dismissed by the head of music as a 'pub quiz': students go from the BAC to music Pre-U. Performances take place in the lovely timber-framed Olivier Theatre and there is an award-winning new art and design building with arching roofs and skylights. Bedales arts feels a thoroughly professional affair, from a display of Matisse, visiting theatre, music and dance, to in-house productions.

'Sport doesn't dominate the extracurricular', says Keith, although he adds that Bedales competes in the usual rounds of county, regional and national competitions. But sport is just one option in the compulsory activities programme, allowing pupils to choose from a range of cerebral, social and physical activities (heads up for the boys – this is not a big rugby school).

Plenty of charity initiatives, D of E, but no students marching around in combat gear – not a natural home for CCF. No noticeable community service either, which parents feel is an omission, and surprising since one of the school's aims is engaging with the local community.

Boarding: Pastoral care for boarders is excellent, agree parents, one saying that the housemistress 'did a better job than we would have done' with his anxious daughter: she 'knew instinctively' what would work.

Comfortable, well-kept single sex boarding houses, with mixed aged dorms, which are a big plus, parents feel. Year 12 pupils take the responsibility of running dormitories and caring for younger pupils, although one parent said her daughter opted out of boarding to avoid being dorm boss, which is a time-consuming post. No flexi-boarding, so those who aren't interested in boarding full time may revert to day pupil status. Year 13 pupils live in a separate, co-ed boarding house as preparation for university. Dorm size varies from two to six beds. To clamp down on over-use of technology, school Wifi is switched off at midnight and the Block 3s (year 9s) hand in their phones at night.

Dorms have a comfortable homely feel even during the day, students returning during breaks to lounge happily on beds and chat or work. Of the school population, 68 per cent are boarders and eight per cent are overseas students.

Laundry is done for younger children; year 13s learn to do their own. Kitchens in boarding houses are open 8.30-9.30pm, with pasta, bread and butter, and fruit available. Students do kitchen duty twice a week – 'a bit grim' said a boarder. There are activities on Sundays, which are not compulsory. 'Some just slump', said a student.

Students keep in touch with home by phones, text and email, most returning home on Saturday afternoon until Sunday evening. For those left at school – overseas boarders, or those who live further afield in the UK – things can be quiet at weekends.

'It's the ethos of boarding school with day pupils', said one parent, who feels this is a boon – even day students have to do activities in the evening, so can be at school until around 9.30pm.

Background and atmosphere: Nonconformist. No Sir or Miss, no uniform – unless the prevalence of hoodies could be described as such. Emphasis on development of the individual, and collaboration between individuals.

This school is in many ways quite extraordinarily lovely: you can feel the life and energy in the wood when you enter the oak-framed arts and crafts memorial library. It must be inspirational to study in: an 18th century timber-framed barn housing some outdoor work, donated, dismantled and carefully re-erected in a convenient spot. There is an integrity about these buildings, their construction and materials: a clear coherence with the school's ethos. Bedales sits comfortably in the surrounding gentle countryside: a world apart in many ways – a 'Bedales bubble,' said a parent – very gorgeous for the lucky students who attend.

The head wants this to be a protected part of life, but says there 'needs a breeze to come through from beyond'. This evident in the fortnightly Jaw, a more inclusive version of other schools' assemblies, with student or visitor led debate on matters of moral or spiritual engagement. 'It opens their horizons', said a parent; 'makes them feel they can do anything'. The breeze is also evident in careers advice, which aims to develop ambition and show horizons, old Bedalians playing their part by mentoring and networking.

'Not pressurised', said a parent, whose academic children benefit from being big fish in a small pond. 'Work is not carried out in a competitive fashion'. She sometimes asks herself whether more pressure might make them do better (her son just failed to get into Oxford) – '[but] the ethos of the school is very attractive, and of more benefit than attending a school which would have helped achieve Oxford. And socially Bedales is the best', the parent concludes. Another parent commented on this positive atmosphere: her daughter was lazy at her old school, but now never wants to be late, is really trying hard and working her best.

'Bedales doesn't do prizes', said a parent, 'it just doesn't believe in them'. An egalitarian, no marks on the wall sort of establishment. This means if you're not very good at something, no-one need know. Achievement is celebrated via a handwritten card, or email, with those doing really well being invited to a Keith's feast.

Pastoral care, well-being and discipline: Pastoral care is the real strength of the school, said a parent – 'if you're vulnerable, if you've had a terrible time, it's lovely'. Another said that 'people are understanding, friendly, kind, and very open'. 'They will find something good about you'. Understandably, in the light of this, Bedales does sometimes find itself receiving serial offenders from other schools. Sometimes it works; sometimes parents are not happy that these kids convince peers to follow them into 'naughty projects'; worth perhaps bearing in mind the comment from a parent that this school suits best children who know their own minds.

'Before we went to the school, we had the impression it was all about sex and drugs', said a parent, who was very pleased to find it was zero tolerance in many areas.'There are a fair number of pupils who smoke', she added, but the school firmly try and stop this amongst Block 3s (year 9); it is harder to control amongst sixth formers. 'They try to keep an eye out, but the kids need some freedom', she added. Parents are pleased that the head talks to them about his approach to drugs, taking into account their views. There are occasional incidents of bullying, said a parent, but they are dealt with appropriately – 'it's harder to get away with here because of the strong integration between the years'.

Many parents spoke of the strong relationships at this school: between pupils, and pupils and teachers – '[it's] as close to family as possible to get'. 'Pupils good at celebrating each other', said another, describing the time when her child had to wear sunglasses for an eye problem, and was teased by a couple of class mates. The housemistress sent out a carefully crafted light email: some kids sent apologies, and the next day all the kids in class turned up in sunglasses in support. The day mistress called the parents and kept them informed. Several parents commented on the unusual level of involvement: at other schools, the doors are closed, school knows best. Not at Bedales. Parents are very involved here. 'It's almost like being at primary school', said one, who said school is very welcoming to parents and 'very, very patient'.

Food was delicious on the day of our visit, though no meat Thursdays, the brain child of the vegan head boy a couple of years ago, is controversial with committed meat eaters, who don't see why they should be forced to abstain.

Pupils and parents: Parents include media, actors, business, celebrities, professionals, scientists, a few bankers ('with exceptional educational views', said a parent), trust fund kids, and a few from overseas. A broader range than there used to be, says the head, with more traditional parents reassured by good behaviour and academic records. 'Good alumni', said one parent practically – 'you're buying a network'.

Communication with parents is generally good: a weekly newsletter keeps parents up to date with what's going on; there are half termly reviews, and termly parents' evenings (not the usual siren when time's up – 'that would not be Bedalian', said a shocked parent). There are a few blips: one said that when a teacher has an issue, this can be slow to trickle through to the parent; another, that there are a few administrative issues: wrong half term dates and occasional typos on the school website, and they were once sent the wrong school report – it's 'sort of charming,' she said, but could be improved. On the other hand, another parent described the head's involvement of parents on the changes to A levels with shocked delight: she had never experienced such engagement at other schools.

Entrance: Maths, English and general ability test for 13+ entry in the January 18 months before entry. Just over half from Dunhurst, and most of the rest from preps in London and the south east, in particular Highfield. For sixth form entry, minimum of five B/6s, four C/5s at GCSE or equivalent points.

Exit: Around 15-30 per cent leave after GCSEs. Pupils depart for a variety of universities and art colleges, a small number of Oxbridge (five in 2017), and many to Russell group (eg Edinburgh, Bristol, LSE), plus some overseas: five off to do liberal arts (at Haverford College, US, Maastricht, McGill and Rhode Island School of Design) and one to Leiden to study liberal arts and sciences with global challenges. Only a handful to science-based degrees, including three medics in 2017.

Money matters: Scholarships are largely honorific in nature, but the school funds 70 bursaries at a cost of over £1 million per annum.

Remarks: Most children would thrive at this lovely school. Parents described the very clever, the quirky, the academic and those in the middle, all of whom are happy. Not perhaps for a child who needs lots of boundaries, or a large degree of privacy, thinks the head; and it wouldn't, perhaps, suit all parents, who need to be broad-minded about the purpose of education. But for most children, this would be a wonderful place to grow a rooted sense of self, and joy in life and learning.

Bloxham School

5

Banbury Road, Bloxham, Near Banbury, Oxfordshire OX15 4PE

01295 724301 | admissions@bloxhamschool.com | www.bloxhamschool.com

Ages: 11–18

Pupils: 430; sixth form: 150; Boarders: 200 full, weekly and flexi

Day: £17,565 – £25,125 pa; Boarding: £25,125 – £32,775 pa

Headmaster: Since 2013, Mr Paul Sanderson (40s), previously a deputy head and director of curriculum at Gordonstoun. Originally from Northern Ireland, he was educated at Banbridge Academy before studying evolutionary biology and genetics at St Andrews University. Postgrad qualifications from Oxford (PGCE) and Cambridge (MPhil). Taught at Lancaster Royal Grammar, Oundle and Carr Hill High before joining Gordonstoun as housemaster.

Drawn to the school's modest size, where children are 'less likely to disappear', he described his first year as a 'rollercoaster', and has made great strides in raising the academic profile of the school. Ambitious and determined, with a refreshing heart-on-his-sleeve honesty (a few watery-eyed moments when recounting the achievements of his pupils), Mr Sanderson's mission is to redefine what makes a Bloxham education.

A rugby enthusiast, with a passion for ice climbing and skiing. Runs a climbing wall class and recently took a group of students alpine climbing. Married with three young children.

Academic matters: In 2017, average A level grade C+; small numbers taking most subjects but business studies and maths top the popularity polls.

Almost half A*-A/9-7 grades at GCSE in 2017. No plans to introduce the IB. IGCSEs currently offered in English, geography and sciences.

Management restructure has introduced new deputy and five new heads of department and there's a definite sense that the bar has been raised when it comes to teaching standards. Staff:pupil ratio average is 8:1 and progress is measured across the year through a challenge grade system. Length of lessons has recently been increased from 35 minutes to an hour and music and drama have been shifted to the afternoon in response to latest research that children become more creative as the day goes on.

While Bloxham is quick to point out that it is not a special needs school, it does have a good reputation for nurturing able pupils with mild to moderate dyslexia who have become demoralised in more competitive arenas. A specialist dyslexia course is offered for up to six pupils a year in the third, fourth and fifth forms, focused on improving their reading speed and accuracy, spelling and study skills.

The Eunoia Society (ancient Greek for 'beautiful learning') provides an intellectual 'stretching' beyond the academic curriculum. As well as offering prep for Oxbridge entrance, it boasts an impressive programme of events, with trips to exhibitions, opera and ballet, and recent visiting speakers have included an art historian, a US diplomat, a professor of biophysics and a senior civil servant.

Games, options, the arts: While there's been some rebalancing of a historic bias towards sport, the school still takes great pride in its achievements. Rugby and hockey are particular strengths (girls reigning county hockey champions at time of visit). Regular rivals include Stowe, Warwick, Marlborough and Wellington and competition is taken seriously. Coaches use iPads to record games for post-match analysis.

Animal club is offered once a week for pupils keen to help look after the school's resident lizards, snakes, hermit crabs and beetles

Facilities are excellent. In addition to two all-weather pitches, the school boasts extensive playing fields, two squash courts, two fives courts, six outdoor netball courts (doubling up as tennis courts during the summer) and a 23m indoor swimming pool. The Dewey Sports Hall has a well-equipped fitness suite with yoga and an assortment of classes also on offer. Sailing takes place on a nearby reservoir. Recent national successes in both clay pigeon shooting and equestrian competitions (twice national schools eventing champions). No stabling at school but pupils may arrange to bring their own mounts for twice-weekly tuition. Those who don't own their own horses can arrange to hire from local stables.

Bloxham is fast gaining a reputation for its drama programme. Since his appointment in 2013, the director of drama has increased the number of productions from one to eight a year and all pupils are expected to take part, either front of stage or behind the scenes. The school recently staged its first

original production (about Bloxham boys who fought and perished in the Great War), selling out all four performances to rave reviews: 'as good as the West End', commented one enthusiastic parent. The Great Hall stages the major productions, with the rest at the Wesley Theatre (a former Wesleyan Chapel).

The music department is housed in the Sam Kahn Music School and there's a new orchestra – quite an achievement given the size of the school's population. Fifty per cent split across music and music tech subjects. We dropped in on a lesson about film scores and learned of an impending visit from an old boy who now works as a film composer in Hollywood – such 'value-added' is much in evidence. Lots of rehearsal rooms support a busy performance schedule and there's the added bonus of a school radio station, run by pupils. Art provision is equally impressive. Sixth form students benefit from dedicated personal workspaces in a charming room that resembles an artists' garret, complete with sloping eaves.

'We want kids who are hungry and ambitious inside and outside the classroom', says Mr Sanderson and Bloxham's enrichment programme is extensive. As well as the Eunoia Soc (see above), pupils can choose from clubs ranging from astronomy to knitting as well as a wine society for sixth formers. Animal club is offered once a week for pupils keen to help look after the school's resident lizards, snakes, hermit crabs and beetles.

Boarding: First and foremost a boarding school; day pupils (known as day boarders) make up half the population and can stay until 10pm, and the school opened a new day house in September 2017. There's also the option of flexi-boarding (pay per night). One local parent said her son doesn't want to come home for fear of 'missing out on the fun'. This flexibility was a big draw for a number of the parents to whom we spoke.

Seven boarding houses are clean and bright with large communal areas – a bit dated in places but a rolling programme of refurbishment is under way. Weekly and flexi boarding in years 7 and 8, with own lower school boarding house. Full boarding from year 9. Thirteen per cent of boarders from overseas. Maximum of three beds to a room, full boarders have their own room from year 10.

Background and atmosphere: With its picture-book cluster of buildings in honey-coloured Horton stone, manicured lawns and homely atmosphere the school blends harmoniously with beautiful Bloxham village. The lower school (Exham House) is actually situated in the former village pub.

Originally known as All Saints School, Bloxham was founded in 1860 by The Reverend Philip Reginald Egerton who wanted to establish a school that embodied the high church values

of the Oxford Movement. In 1897 it joined the Woodard Foundation, the group of schools founded by Canon Woodard to promote education in an actively Christian environment.

Food excellent (we took full advantage of visiting on Curry Thursday). Great choice and emphasis on healthy eating. Sociable lunchtimes with teachers sitting happily alongside pupils.

Pastoral care, well-being and discipline: Self-proclaimed 'gold standard' of pastoral care is justified. Multiple systems in place to ensure children's emotional welfare, including a team of 'peer listeners' – sixth form student volunteers with formal counselling training. Small size of school promotes healthy mixing and solid friendships between girls/boys and different year groups. Head meets daily with head boy and girl, helping to keep abreast of any grumbles or issues. School refreshingly honest about (infrequent) incidents of bullying; intervention swift and effective, according to parents. Keen sensitivity about emotional needs of pupils: 'let's face it, the teenage years are difficult', says head.

Holy communion for all once a week. School doesn't shy away from talking about the importance of spiritual development in education but head recognises need for religion to 'translate into the 21st century'. It's less about doctrine and more about getting children to think about their place in the world, 'To be a giver, rather than a taker'.

This ethos is reflected in service initiatives such as Reading Club, where older pupils help children from local primary schools with reading difficulties. According to head this has inspired at least one student to go on and train as a primary teacher.

Pupils and parents: Bloxham has long been a popular local option and is now increasingly so for London refugees looking for a smaller, more 'gentle' boarding school. Recent push to improve parent-school communications has been warmly welcomed. Very informative parents' handbook published annually; newly established parents' association. Saturday matches are well attended and there are plenty of opportunities for parents to get involved if desired. Former pupils include impressive numbers of high ranks from all three forces plus novelist Tom Sharpe and journalist John Sergeant.

Entrance: Candidates for lower school (age 11) via school's own exam (maths, English and verbal reasoning) and interview; CE for 13+ entry. Sixth form requires minimum six GCSEs at grades A*-C/9-5, with at least a B/6 in chosen A level subjects (A/7 grade required for maths and physics). Lower school intake is from state primaries or independents such as Carrdus; at 13+ pupils from preps including Ashfold School, Beachborough, Bilton Grange, Swanbourne House and Winchester House.

Exit: Small leakage (around 10 per cent) after GCSEs. Post-A level, varied subjects and destinations; Bristol, Nottingham and Loughborough currently popular.

Money matters: Parents say flexi-boarding option and late stay for day pupils represent value for money. Scholarships (20 per cent fee reduction) for academics, sport, DT music and drama. Means-tested bursaries can be combined with scholarships; limited number of full-fee bursaries.

Remarks: Successfully combines academic challenge with plenty of sport, service and practical life skills. A perfect environment for happy all-rounders.

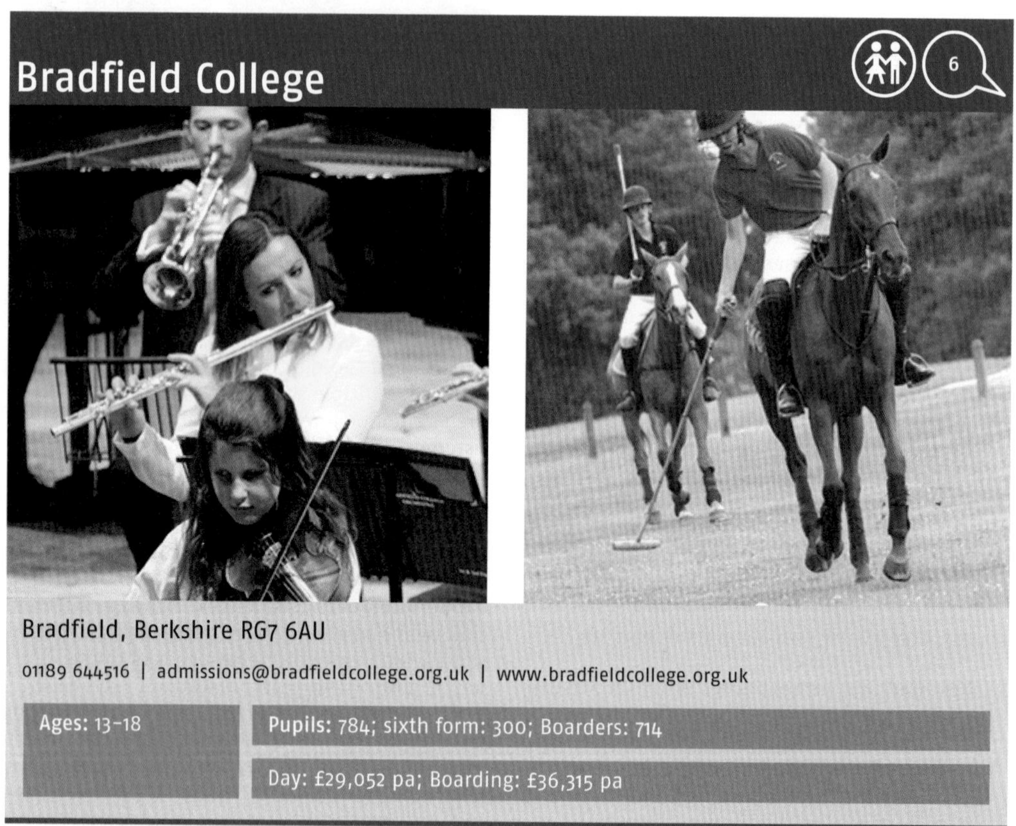

Bradfield College
6
Bradfield, Berkshire RG7 6AU
01189 644516 | admissions@bradfieldcollege.org.uk | www.bradfieldcollege.org.uk
Ages: 13–18
Pupils: 784; sixth form: 300; Boarders: 714
Day: £29,052 pa; Boarding: £36,315 pa

Headmaster: Since 2015, Dr Chris Stevens MA DPhil (early 50s). Previously second master at Marlborough College (from 2011), he started his career in prep schools as a (very) young man. Brambletye, briefly as a gap student, and then Ashdown House as a young master where he split the year in half, six months at Ashdown (where a lot of the time was spent establishing the Ashdown château in France) and half the year studying for his doctorate. He finally firmly established himself in the boarding senior school world in 1997 when he started at Uppingham, where he was master-in-charge of cricket and housemaster for nine years. Educated in an all boys' environment at Tonbridge School, Dr Stevens read modern and medieval languages at Caius College, Cambridge and researched Italian literature for a DPhil at Oxford. This is where he met Helen, now associate professor of English at Corpus Christi, Oxford. They have school age daughters.

A highly intelligent man; sometimes you have to run to keep up with Dr Stevens in conversation. He thinks fast and talks fast, everything spoken in a mellifluous voice, however, and everything considered and thoughtful. He made the decision to work in schools rather than devote himself to academia largely because, despite his intellect, he loves the rough and tumble of life in a boarding school. Thoroughly unpretentious, he scoffs at the hierarchies that can divide the prep and senior school worlds and values the time he spent with much younger children and the very different challenges that are found in prep schools. Both he and his wife missed the boarding house atmosphere while they were at Marlborough and both are relishing being back in the fray and at the heart of things. They are still in the process of getting to know all the pupils, which he is determined to do. Sixth formers are regularly invited to dinner at their house, and a privileged few in lower years are also invited to dine with him and his wife. Otherwise it's at breakfast in the dining hall that he seizes the opportunity to eat with the more junior pupils and get to know their views on life at Bradfield and beyond. 'Best insight into who are the best teachers are too', he confides.

The library is reassuringly old school and a refreshingly studious atmosphere prevails

The 'beyond' is something that he holds very important. An outward looking man, he celebrates the influence of families from different cultural backgrounds – often each parent from a different country, and shudders at what the landscape may hold post-Brexit. An international outlook and mindset he considers to be essential, particularly in the face of how easy it could be to reflect a pocket of little England, given the picturesque, chocolate boxy location of the school.

An inclusive man, he has changed the staff photo so that it genuinely incorporates the whole

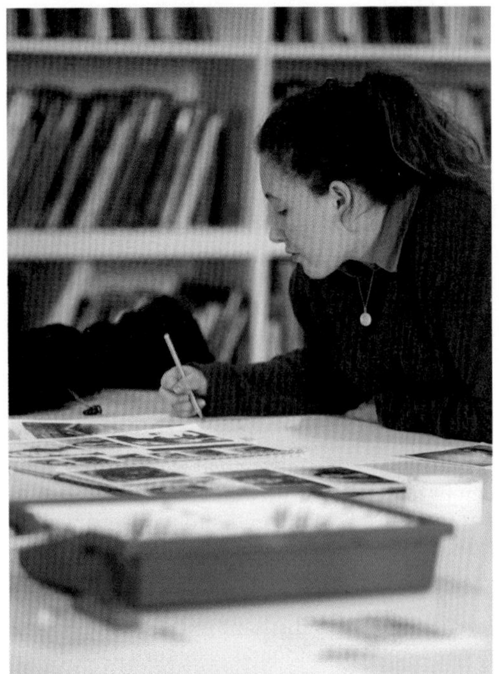

staff, not just the teaching staff. Everyone is invited for hog roast and ice cream in his garden. He is passionate about avoiding pretension and a sense of entitlement. While keen to maintain the sense that Bradfield is a warm, relaxed and caring environment, he is concerned that this should not be mistaken for a lack of ambition. Students here are to be challenged without becoming stressed. Stretched in order to be stimulated, alive and curious. Parents approve, while noticing a shift towards heightening the academic standards. 'Fabulous,' said one; ' very sensible,' another.

Academic matters: A school that is, without question, on the up. A real contender now, academically, and firmly on the radar of aspirational parents as well as those who have always wanted a rounded and broad education for their children. A levels disappointing in 2017, however, 59 per cent A*-B, with 23 per cent A*/A. IB cohort got an average of 36 points (out of a maximum of 45). Pupils normally take 10 GCSEs; in 2017, over 50 per cent A*-A/9-7 grades. Economics continues in popularity; business studies, film studies, textiles and photography all offered alongside the traditional subjects. One took Latin A level in 2017, none Greek (though a small number take the Latin certificate at GCSE, and an even smaller number do Greek) but five took Russian A levels. Large take up for EPQ; wide range of projects from 'Aid or trade in Africa, which is better for development?'; to 'To what extent is diversification the main reason for Apple's success?'; and

'Was the Lance Armstrong scandal beneficial for the sport of cycling?' Results 31 per cent A*/A.

The Blackburn science centre is a hugely impressive. As well as being eco-friendly and thoroughly up to speed with technology, it is beautiful to look at and ergonomic. Ten classrooms and laboratories, spaciously spread out on each of the two floors. What goes on inside is also impressive. Parents regard it as one of the stronger subjects. 'Fantastic,' they said. The library, on the other hand, is reassuringly old school. Constructed of the local flint and brick with diamond paned windows, it is properly stocked with books as well as decorated with looming portraits of former heads and wardens. Not a high tech environment, but a refreshingly studious atmosphere prevails, young men and women working and collaborating in here. Comfortable areas filled with smiley faced emojis to escape to with a good book.

Large study skills and support department (SSSD – SEN to you and me). About 150 receive support; caters for everyone from those who require minimal support to those who need a reasonable level, but no specialist unit to cater for extreme needs. Would not automatically turn away someone with specific difficulties but will always ask the question, 'will they be happy here?' says head. Vast majority who use the SSSD have had a history of provision in their previous schools, but teachers can refer individuals, initially to houseparent.

We only have them home from Saturday tea time until Sunday evening, but it's a much needed chance to recover,' said one mother; 'it's so full on during the week'

Help given across the board at key pressure points. 'Extra lessons to help with GCSEs have been phenomenal,' said a seasoned parent with children at other schools. However if a child is not responding to being pushed, then the pressure drops. 'You have to want to do well, and what is brilliant is that it's cool to work hard and to get good results,' confirmed another parent. Grades given each side of half term. Reassuring to parents who like to feel on top of how hard their child is working.

Games, options, the arts: Bradfield is a football school, no rugby here at all. They are good – and known to be good. A recent captain of the first XI played for England in an international match against Scotland, we were told by our proud sixth form guide (who was a water polo aficionado himself). 'If you're good,' he said, 'opportunities open up for you at international level, but if you just love to play you can play at any standard that suits.' A wide range of teams means everyone can take part but a competitive edge survives. Boys' major summer sport is cricket, for girls it's lacrosse (there is also mixed lacrosse, and girls can play in boys' teams) and netball in the winter, tennis in the summer. Hockey and swimming are also major sports for both boys and girls. 'There is a team for everyone who wants to play and the B and C teams will get the same rewards as the A team. No elitism,' said a parent. Lush facilities from acres of green sports fields as far as the eye can see, to splendid indoor tennis courts, as well as outdoor courts, dotted around the grounds. Lots of sports tours to as far afield as Sri Lanka (cricket) and Singapore and Malaysia (hockey).

One of the most enticing range of minor sports we've seen. The school website reads like a highly exclusive action-packed adventure camp. From clay pigeon and rifle shooting (school has its own ranges for both) to zumba and yoga, with fives, real tennis, dodgeball, sailing, canoeing and polo as well as water polo and golf. A nine hole golf course is nestled towards the end of the games pitches. Water polo takes place in the glistening 25 metre pool that forms part of the swanky sports complex. CCF compulsory for year 10; Duke of Edinburgh also has a high uptake – our guide had just achieved gold. Standards are high here – both in the quality of provision, the teaching as well as facilities, and in the quality of commitment and enthusiasm from the pupils.

A Bradfield flagship is its Greek theatre, Greeker, as it's known. Recent performances include Antigone (in the ancient Greek). Theatre has been carefully restored and is sheltered in a shady bower. It is well used, whether it be for Shakespeare (Midsummer Night's Dream), a rock concert, or the whole school prize giving, which involves the famous handshaking ceremony ('a chance to test my knowledge of each child,' winks the head).

Music thriving, as is the art. Music is housed in a spacious building with two large classrooms, a concert hall and plenty of practice rooms. 'I'm enjoying coming here to play and practice,' enthused one sixth former; 'everyone is so friendly here.' A plethora of groups and choirs, jazz and classical, some pupil led, some staff led. We watched year 9s having rowdy noisy fun with steel drums, shakers and tambourines. The art rooms are tucked away on the other side of a brook in a delightfully separate, rustic cottage-like building. Everything is tidy and organised here but without losing a sense of spontaneous creativity. Well-thumbed art books are scattered amongst the workstations. A welcome relief to see them here rather than neatly stacked and barely touched in the library. Art is popular; students like the teachers as well as the subject.

Pupils make the effort to stay in for particular events, like the famous Michaelmas Goose weekend – a riot of inter-house competitions

We saw monochrome butterflies on wire in the textiles department and an oil painted elephant on newspaper. Photography, sculpture and screen painting all in interconnecting rooms. One particular talented student had their work exhibited at the Tate Modern.

A plethora of societies from the religious (Swinbank) to philosphy, debating, drama and feminist (Neska).

With so much available you would have thought some students might become overwhelmed and not do anything at all. Not possible here. The Bradfield Diploma, a qualification pursued in years 10 and 11, involves pupils being assessed according to their co-curricular pursuits, and quite apart from that, affirmed one student, 'the Bradfield ethos is about getting involved; it is a family community and you get out what you put in.'

Boarding: Let there be no mistake, Bradfield is a boarding school. There are only 70 day pupils. However, with most families living within a 50 mile radius, only about 150 out of 750 pupils will be in on a Saturday night. 'We only have them home from Saturday tea time until Sunday evening, but it's a much needed chance to recover,' said one mother; 'it's so full on during the week.' Pupils will make the effort to stay in for a particular event, like the famous Michaelmas Goose weekend – a weekend packed with an interhouse riot of a competition which includes 'total wipeout' style water and inflatables obstacle course as well as dodgeball, debating, dancing and singing ('very raucous, and loud,' warned a student). The summer term sees more people opting to stay, and the further up the school they are the more they choose to enjoy the freedom to finish work and socialise with friends. Year group dinners are organised for Saturday nights and the unschooly feel to the place helps attract pupils into staying. Blundells Bar plays a large part in this, open in the evenings for sixth formers on Saturday nights (as well as two weekday evenings), this is the real deal with comfortable leather armchairs and pool table, doubling as a café in the day time for all year groups with proper coffee machines and muffins. With its decked terrace overlooking the cricket pitch, it's perfect for long summer evenings.

Faulkners – the mixed house for the whole of year 9 – is a Bradfield triumph. Not many schools do this, but the idea is to weld the year group together so that as they branch off to their different (single sex) houses in year 10 (all of which have been selected before they even arrive at the school), everyone will know each other and there will be less scope for cliquishness. There is the added advantage, suggested the super impressive and engaging housemaster and housemistress of Falkners, that the young 13-14 year olds don't have to navigate what can be an intimidating hierarchy of older boys and girls. Most parents remarked on how much their children's confidence grew throughout the year, although inevitably we heard the odd case of difficult relationships, particularly among the girls. The building itself is modern, functional but attractive. Neat little drawers with names attached for mobile phones to go to bed in at the end of the day, very comfortable and tasteful common rooms on each boys' and girls' side, and a place in the centre where they can all gather to play games and hang out.

First class boarding accommodation – some of the most comfortable we've seen. Many of the study bedrooms have ensuite bathrooms, two or three to a room, there is a kitchen on every floor, and the comfortable common rooms are not the tatty stinky ones of olden days. Well upholstered sofas, pool tables and table football in good condition with all the pieces still intact, and best of all, when we visited at least, a lovely fresh smell of clean laundry.

Attempts are made to avoid houses becoming stereotyped – 'the sporty one', 'the nerdy one', although those trends can creep in without some social engineering.

Background and atmosphere: Founded in the 1850s by Thomas Stevens, lord of the manor and local rector, as a choir school for his church, Bradfield

may not have a long sweeping drive, a grand central building, miles away in the middle of nowhere, but it is nonetheless a rural school. A picturesque one to boot, with its flint and brick buildings and sloping roofs. The village and the school are one and the same. There is no bank, post office or pub, but a fabulous arts and crafts manor house with stunning quadrangle and beautiful gardens, complete with astronomy hut for stargazing as well as the school chapel at the heart of the site. Here children have a chance to be children for longer, and there is not much to distract them from all that is available to do at school. Lots of walking to and from lessons, and that enticing sixth form bar is quite a hike. Faulkners eat in their house with some senior pupils. Others eat in the main dining room.

The art rooms are tucked away in a delightfully separate, cottage-like building. Everything is tidy and organised, but without losing a sense of spontaneous creativity

Plenty of quirky old fashioned public school traditions, including the many nicknames for things (glossaries are distributed on arrival arrive at Faulkners). Kitchens are Brewers, prefects, Beaks, Rux is the outdoor space near your house where you can kick a football around. The headmaster is the headman.

Day pupils fully integrated – sometimes leaving as late as 10 in the evening. They can leave after lessons but are encouraged to do their prep at school. In the sixth form they can get permission to drive themselves to school. All day pupils have a desk in a dormitory. Flexi-boarding arrangement is available, but not encouraged and not many take it up.

One housemaster (and ex-BBC sports commentator) observed that the fact that Bradfield is a football school, rather than a rugby school, allows it to lend itself more readily to a healthy, collaborative co-education environment. He may have a point. Relationships between the genders here certainly seem to be positive. Neither wary nor subservient but natural and enjoyable.

A strong community spirit, manifest in its educational partnership with Theale Green Academy, a local school which has gone from being in special measures to 'improving' and, 'we hope, to good,' says head. Pupils from Theale Green can come and learn science in the splendid labs here, but largely it's about sharing knowledge and expertise and providing support for their teachers. Continues to nurture the more than 100 year old relationship with Bradfield Club, a youth club in Peckham.

Pastoral care, well-being and discipline: Dr Stevens has a broadminded and sensitive approach to punishment. Highly experienced (chief disciplinarian was one of his major roles as second master at Marlborough), he recognises the difference between 'naughtiness' and 'nastiness'. As much of a concern as drugs now, in all schools, is the abuse of social media. While you need clear boundaries on the former, 'if you had zero tolerance with regard to social media you could empty a school,' he observes. One bad post may amount to stupidity, however three may well amount to bullying. Dr Stevens encourages an approach that helps pupils learn from their mistakes.

Faulkners students hand in their phones at night (quite apart from the threat to well-being caused by social media, the use of phones affects sleep, which is an even greater threat, he points out). Policies on phones and screens vary from house to house for year 10 upwards, but a heightened awareness of the effect – positive and negative – of screens is universal. 'The only criticism I have of the school is that they don't remove the phones of all pupils at the end of the day,' remarked one parent. Clear lines are drawn on intimate sexual relations as well as on using drugs in school – it's automatic expulsion. 'We don't have open season'.

Effective mentoring and support system between the sixth formers and newbies. Sixth formers eat lunch with year 9 in Faulkners and monitor their homework time. Complicated system of appointing head girl and boy, prefects, heads of house. Not all parents and pupils are fans, not least as some teachers can be indiscreet and partisan. It involves applications with references, an interview process, with some selection by the head boy and girl and some by the teachers. Within each house pupils are appointed to particular roles – head of academic, head of media for example, not difficult for the odd person to slip through the net and find themselves without a role.

Well-being is part of the curriculum for years 9 -11. This takes place in the Well-being Centre, a comfortable place among the roof beams where pupils can sit on beanbags, in chairs around a circle or at a large table to talk about difficult issues. A recent discussion was 'what does cancer mean to you?' They also do yoga, mindfulness and relaxation. The cynic may detect the influence of their grander neighbour up the road, but well-being is – or should be – firmly on the map in all good schools and this is just another indicator that Bradfield is keeping up with the times.

Tutors (all teachers also act as a tutor), attached to the houses, are assigned eight students. They will mentor, support and keep an eye on their progress – including their study skills and prep. Keen to strengthen and capitalise on this personal, focused support, Dr Stevens has freed up more time for tutors to meet their tutees so that as well as keeping a watching brief, they can take a more active, inspirational role. Some parents observed that their child had had four tutors since they started. Delicate balance struck between sticking with a tutor to form a solid relationship and moving on when the dynamic is not working.

We heard some reports that a high turnover of staff, particularly housemistresses and masters in the past, meant that not all holes were plugged soon enough when they appeared; however, it would seem that things are settling down now, and the atmosphere we experienced was purposeful, collaborative and stimulating.

On the whole a tolerant, unpressurised environment. 'You're always busy at Bradfield,' said a sixth former. 'If you're not doing something then something's wrong.'

Pupils and parents: Large London and local – Reading-Windsor-Ascot – contingent. About 10 per cent international families, based overseas. 'We keep an eye on numbers of particular nationalities, just to avoid cliques,' says head, but there is no quota at all, no missions to the East (or anywhere else) to recruit. Some Europeans – Spanish, Danish etc – but a more English flavour to it than many boarding schools. Certainly not flashy nor grand. Families here are pretty comfortable in their skin and with their lot. 'Impossible to pigeonhole,' commented one parent. 'There are foreign royalty, the odd celebrity, some very ordinary English folk and a few on full bursaries, a well-rounded community.' Boys still outnumber girls, about 60 per cent boys, but number of girls continues to grow.

Children have a chance to be children for longer, and there is not much to distract them from all that is available to do at school. Lots of walking to and from lessons, and that enticing sixth form bar is quite a hike

Within those parameters, the pupils too are diverse. This is not a sausage factory. Dr Stevens values what he describes as 'the integrity of difference – one of the great strengths of a boarding education.' Pupils come from 60 different prep schools. No one school ever sends as many as 20. Among the prep schools that send numbers in double figures are Cheam, St Andrews, Lambrook, Northcote Lodge and Broomwood. Siblings are welcomed and their assessment looked at favourably: 'it would be wrong to turn them away on the basis that they scored a few percent less than they should have,' says head. Bradfield remains a broad church and under the current leadership will continue to do so.

Former pupils include politicians, Lord David Owen and Sir John Nott, authors Louis de Bernieres and Richard Adams, cricketer and broadcaster Mark Nicholas, actor Claudia Harrison and astronomer Sir Martin Ryle.

Entrance: Main entrance point is into year 9. Selection criteria are 'attitude, character and potential for happiness,' says head. School increasingly selective as demand for places has shot up in recent years. CE pass mark is 55 per cent (no slippage). Introduction of a pre-test in year 7. School considers prep school heads' reports and on the basis of that invites pupils for assessment in years 6 and 7. All candidates interviewed and tested. School works closely with prep school head with borderline candidates especially. The main aim is to find candidates who will be 'net givers' to the school.

First step is to see the school. Tours every Saturday morning and head makes himself available for personal meetings at other times. Occasional places do arise in year 10 and between 50 and 60 places in the sixth form. English and maths tests plus two interviews in November before year of entry into year 12. Minimum of six B/6 grades with at least Cs/4-5s in English and maths GCSEs.

Exit: Up to 10 per cent leave after GCSE to sixth form colleges and day schools (though all stayed on in 2017). Practically all sixth formers go on to university. Current popular ones include Bristol, Exeter, Leeds, Manchester, Newcastle, Bath and Oxford Brookes. Two medics in 2017. Increasing numbers head for US universities and European ones, with 2017 leavers off to, inter alia, Parsons School of Design in New York, Florida Southern, Southern California and Virginia. A very few (though school feels this is likely to increase) go straight into employment or on apprenticeship schemes.

Money matters: Although lots of scholarships awarded – including academic, sport and music – a fee reduction is only available with means-testing. The school is a charitable trust and provides bursary support, from anything from 100 per cent of fees to one per cent.

Remarks: Thoroughly unpretentious yet with lots to boast about, Bradfield is a heavenly place to learn and to grow. Very difficult to imagine who would not thrive here. There's something for everyone and lots for all.

Brockwood Park School

7

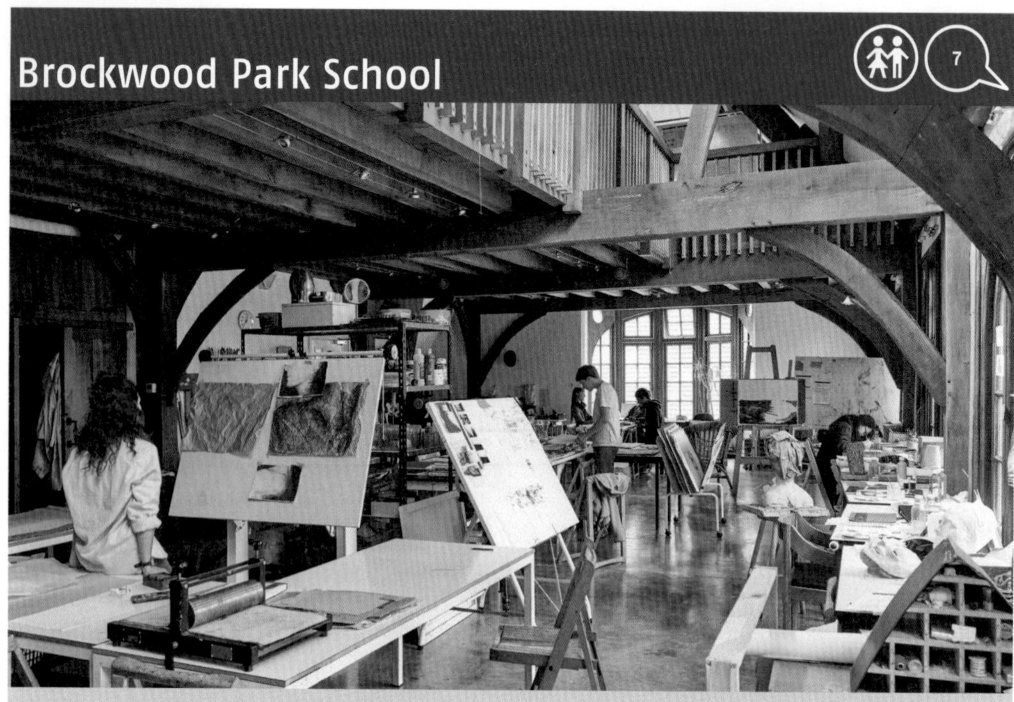

Brockwood Park, Bramdean, Hampshire SO24 0LQ

01962 771744 | enquiry@brockwood.org.uk | www.brockwood.org.uk

Ages: 14 –19

Pupils: 66; sixth form: 41; Boarders: all full

£21,400 pa

Co-principals: Since 2013, Gopal Krishnamurthy (PhD), and since 2015, Antonio Autor. They are principals by name only: there is no hierarchy here; everyone has a voice and is heard, and everyone has the same salary, from cleaner to principal.

Gopal has a warm, light vitality; his whole body seems a staccato of excitement when he thinks of something; here, personified, is the sheer joy of learning and finding out. He has been a student and teacher at Krishnamurti schools in India, the USA and the UK.

Antonio has the still presence of a mountain or deep water. Here is someone who seems remarkably free of ego or any sort of push; and yet, astonishingly, he had a previous life as a professional footballer. He has a BA in business and has studied English at Cardiff, Brighton and London. He joined Brockwood Park in 1987, and his jobs have ranged from gardener to teacher.

Students: 'love them'; 'above everything, you can go to [them] if out of control'; '[I'm] really comfortable talking to them – normal conversation without having to fake adult and know everything.'

Academic matters: 'A way of education which is rare and original', said a parent, and completely different to traditional education, dismissed as 'academic memorising'; or as Krishnamurti (founder) put it: '...education [is]...not merely transferring what is printed on a page to your brain. Education may mean opening the doors of perception on to the vast movement of life.'

No small task and certainly not an easy option for student or teacher. Students are encouraged not just to accept what they read or are told, but to inquire into it themselves: we saw a group of students on the lawn, attempting to get a solar panel working again so they could charge their mobile phones on a camping trip; we have never seen a teacher so alertly attentive, but silent, as students worked it out. 'Right education is a mutual task demanding patience, consideration and affection', said Krishnamurti, and this is evidently so at Brockwood Park.

The only compulsory courses here are inquiry time and human ecology. At inquiry time, the school meets to discuss the way we live our lives – '[my son] seems to find it valuable for sorting issues out'. Students said they felt listened to: 'space to speak,' said one. Human ecology is the study of our home in its broadest sense, recognising that we all share the responsibility to care for the planet. Students might work in the kitchen garden, eco building or observation: giving full attention to the world outside and, during inquiry time, to the world within.

There is a large element of personal decision-making in the curriculum, greatly appreciated by students: 'I learn something I want to learn; do what I want to do'; and to some degree by parents: '...students invest in what they are doing with choice', but 'I would like them to insist a bit more in academic matters'. Another said: 'I'm not sure [my son] is applying himself properly...I think he is challenged, but only if he is interested'.

At Brockwood Park they have their own way of getting people interested in things. If you hate maths, 'I would find out why you don't like it and what it means to you. I am not going to let go – my interest in your learning is non-negotiable', said Gopal, or as a parent put it: 'If a student doesn't want to study, they discuss and discuss and discuss...[The] question is whether immediate efficiency is a good thing, or [it is] better for students to take time to discover for themselves... Not to decide for them is the best thing I can do and have to do...'.

Those under 16 take three core courses: science and mathematics, humanities, and arts and crafts. The focus, in each, is on learning through firsthand experience. Described by the co-principals as being 'the roots of literacy...getting them to think for themselves...[where] not knowing is a vital point of departure'.

Topic courses are also available, which enable students to explore issues in much greater depth: the teacher introduces a topic, such as 'movement of humans', and after a few weeks, students determine their own specific area of exploration.

Languages are taught organically, depending on the skills of the staff at the time. There's always a lot of support for them in this international school: Italian, French, German and Spanish are being taught at the moment. English as an additional language (EAL) is highly successful: a French speaker told us he was confident in English after only three months at Brockwood Park. 'Learning English is easy here. Even if I make a mistake, I don't mind. If you say something stupid it doesn't matter'.

Lessons are usually with six or seven students, 10 at the most, with teacher and teacher apprentice present, which allows students to 'work more deeply in the subject', said a dad who felt that a big class would have no time to divert from the programme. There are no year groups: 'even young ones help older ones sometimes', said a parent.

Students can develop their own projects if their proposal is approved by the teachers' group, which will choose an academic adviser to support the project for the year. It's a bigger, tougher version of the EPQ with 'a sense of excellence for its own sake', said Gopal.

They have their own way of getting people interested in things. If you hate maths, 'I would find out why you don't like it and what it means to you' said the principal

Those coming here from traditional environments can have some 'unlearning to do'. 'They often have no original thought or vitality', said Gopal, and we were given the example of a student who arrived with a long list of A*s at IGCSE: 'It took a lot to get her to ask questions or disagree with me – but now she says "I don't want you to help me".'

They're not against traditional achievement here, but it's a byproduct. '[We] do think exams are important, but not as a reflection of worth or learning. They are what you've done, in a particular direction, according to certain criteria. Academic success should not be confused with excellence', said Gopal.

Some students take A levels and the mock exams are often the first exams students at this school have ever sat; they also have a pre-exam intensive study week with the aim of building a sense of confidence in their own work: 'It's a game – we want them to play it well'.

Students can take IGCSEs if they want to; although it was clear that the co-principals couldn't

really see why anyone would want to: 'an easy option', said one.

There are students here with dyslexia, dyspraxia and ADHD, but they do not like labelling students SEN: each student has their own programme, and the whole curriculum supports the special needs of each student. No extra charge for one-to-one unless help from outside is necessary.

Games, options, the arts: Exercise is important here, and students spend two afternoons a week playing games, but not games as you know it. Games are played for the pleasure of the movement, for the beauty of the shot, with 'heart [and] everything in the game', said Gopal, but not for the winning. So badminton is played with rigour but not with points; for what could the significance of points be, other than winning?

A couple of students who had tasted the joys of competitive sport missed the adrenalin, although they do play friendly football with local schools and the farmers. Netball, basketball, yoga (naturally) and hockey are also available. There are plenty of opportunities for long walks and orienteering: 'the need to finish together and take care of the team is a substitute for the team spirit of games', said a parent.

The art barn with its curved windows contains a pottery studio, darkroom and Mac suite. Textiles are popular – students used a Japanese manual dying technique on old sheets, before making them into clothes.

'Words have limitations', said Krishnamurti, so music, with the harmony it brings to body and mind is very important at Brockwood. Most students learn instruments; there are two grand pianos and a 30 strong choir of students and staff whose repertoire ranges from 15th century to contemporary. Regular informal concerts take place, which include both dramatical and musical performances.

Boarding: This small school is a boarding community, of whose 66 students 21 are British, the rest international.

'[It is] intense to live with people, but beautiful to share all your day. Your whole life in this amount shared with all these people', said a parent. Another said it is an 'intense social life. [My son] is thrilled at this'.

Girls board in the main house, with single rooms for older girls, and large rooms for two or three younger ones. Students arrange furniture how they like it, some making their views clear from their door decoration: next to a picture of a cow: 'Not your mum, not your milk'. Bathrooms are elderly but clean.

Boys are in the cloisters, a 70s add on around a square of grass and trees with teachers living on the corners; this accommodation was described by one parent as 'adequate': his son will opt for the pavilion next year. The pavilions are very grand indeed: oak framed with underfloor heating and glass topped roofs, fragrant herb gardens outside; a wing each for girls and boys.

Students have to be in their rooms by 9:30pm and are now allowed smartphones, but only in their rooms. TV is not much of an event here: there's one in the cloisters (under a stripy cover like a big bed sock when not in use), and another in the study, but students generally spend more time in the sitting room: a grand old room in the main house, with sofas, grand piano and wood burner in the old fireplace, for staff and students alike. Just outside is an herbal tea-making area, with cinnamon and honey in little pots.

Students may catch the bus into Winchester at weekends, and go away for the weekend if they seek permission first ('they're on top of their game for safeguarding', said a parent).

Wifi is in a particular corner of the school, and otherwise not easy to locate; apparently there's one spot up a particular tree, but use of devices is not encouraged...'beneficial to be starved of it for some time', said a parent hardily.

Background and atmosphere: '[It's an] interesting way of living – fantastically beautiful', said a parent, who was enchanted by his first visit to Brockwood Park – ' [We] discovered the ambience and the liberty of the students'. The school is run on the basis of collaboration, not competition: an atmosphere in which all sorts of students thrive: '[They] don't judge you here... [I] feel more open. Better for you: to love yourself and feel more confidence', said a student.

This school is about learning to live, and understanding yourself as something worthy of inquiry: '[It is] very challenging for the student; not an easy way', said a parent. Students have to learn about responsibility; or, as one parent put it: 'the capability of everyone to be response-able in a situation...

Students may catch the bus into Winchester at weekends, and go away for the weekend if they seek permission first

what [they can] do to contribute to the world'. It starts in small ways here: a student described how she has come to realise that washing up is part of life: at home, it just happens; at her old school, there were cleaners. Here, everyone has to pitch in, or it doesn't get done.

'[It's} very challenging for parents to have children at this school. Questions raised with the students touch the parents: about the future, human beings and existence...I am educated by my kids by their education at Brockwood Park... for some, it is difficult to accept this', said a parent.

The strength of community here is something students were keen to talk about: 'everyone is open to know you'; 'after only four months, I have found a way I like of having relationships – I enjoy them; even if I don't like the person'. A wide sociality is encouraged, both in terms of the Brockwood community (exclusive relationships are frowned upon), and in terms of being part of a worldwide community: time is devoted to exploring social and political crisis.

Different faiths are tolerated, but if you follow a particular religion, others need to be free to ask questions of it and you. 'If there is a God, find him for yourself', said Antonio.

Many of the buildings are beautiful: the elegant main house; the assembly room with its beautiful wooden roof and a grand piano; and the study with cream carpet and wood panelling: morning meetings take place there every day – 10 mins of quiet time to start the day. As you walk around, you can feel how much this school is cared for: it is not, here, just a collection of buildings which serve as a shell to house those within.

The school sits in 40 acres, including the original kitchen garden, where students have human ecology lessons, and the head gardener works with the head chef to grow seasonal produce for the kitchen. All food at Brockwood Park is vegetarian; on the day of our visit a delicious lentil bake, a fresh salad from the garden with flowers, and fruit, students spilling out of the dining hall to eat lunch on the lawn.

Pastoral care, well-being and discipline: Understanding discipline at Brockwood Park is best done by considering the words of Krishnamurti:

'After all, discipline means resistance...Do you think resistance will bring about understanding, thought, affection?... Discipline is always exclusive, whereas understanding is inclusive. Understanding comes when you investigate, when you enquire, when you search out, which requires care, consideration, thought, affection'.

There is, however, no absence of rules or agreements as to how to behave; students sign a contract on entering the school, committing to the curriculum and caring for each other, and agreeing not to smoke, drink alcohol or eat meat (no sneaky bacon butties in Winchester at the weekend either). Parents are convinced by the school's approach: 'Brockwood Park is the safest school to grow up a teenager that we know'.

Dealing with each breach of rules will be different, emphasised Antonio, but there will be a process, which will involve talking with teacher, student, tutor, and pastoral coordinator. It's an 'opportunity for learning', said Antonio, and much depends on how the student responds to the process. An action plan for drinking alcohol might be for the student to investigate how alcohol attacks the body and mind, and share it with the school. 'Troubles with kids doing forbidden things [are] dealt with in a peaceful way; [they] awaken responsibility in kids', said a parent.

The gentleness of this school does not mean that there are no consequences for actions. Students will be suspended if a habit needs to be broken. Expulsion can happen, and has, rarely, four times this year, for drug and smoking offences. '[I was] surprised at the number of expulsions, but understand that a firm message has to pass on to the children, and it is slowly dawning on [my son] that he cannot act in any way he pleases'.

Students sign a contract on entering the school, committing to the curriculum and caring for each other, and agreeing not to smoke, drink alcohol or eat meat

Another parent told us that his son had admitted to having an unsmoked joint in his room. The consequences were daily discussions with Antonio for 15 minutes every morning – for months. The parent had the impression both quite enjoy the chats now...

Agreements are settled between students and teachers about lesser matters, such as hairstyles and tummy rings; although a determined mohican lasted out his time without changing his hair: agreements are not rules, but students wishing to flout them should expect a lot of discussion.

Students, asked to describe the best thing about the school, described their relationships with teachers: 'teachers look at you like a person'; 'chat any time'; 'someone, always, has an ear for you. Always.'

Bullying is not a problem here, say students and parents. Students agreed that some people are popular; 'but not better, or of more consequence,' pointed out another.

Pupils and parents: Many students are ex-Waldorf, said a parent; have already opted for this sort of education, and are 'most thrilled at what's offered [here]'.

Parents receive two detailed observational reports a year. Communication varies, with dates for events sometimes communicated rather late in the day, but pastoral communications are good. Parents can come and stay in the area for the weekend, and meet their child's academic adviser and tutors.

Entrance: Students attend a prospective week before they sign up to the school, so they know what to expect. Non-selective.

Inwoods Small School, a 10 minute walk away, is a junior school run by the same Krishnamurti Foundation, but few children come from there.

Exit: 'You will leave education here with a set of questions – with uncertainty', said one of the co-principals. More reassuring is the fact that most students leave to continue their education somewhere in the world, previous destinations including Bennington and Vasser in the US, and Sheffield University and the Guildhall School of Music and Drama in the UK. Entrance is secured on a mixture of exams results, interviews and coursework/portfolios. Others depart for gap years or jobs: one student went on to train as a chef and works in one of the only vegetarian restaurants in Italy – she is 'well balanced; well in her basket', said her father.

Money matters: Bursaries are available from seven to (exceptionally) 100 per cent of the fees. Around 15 per cent of the fee income is available for bursaries.

Remarks: Parents think it wouldn't suit a very competitive child, or one who comes from a rigid background – 'where are the instructions?' 'Great for creative types, artists and musicians'; 'A child needs to be independent in character – you need to "be an actor in your learning".'

This extraordinary school is not for those who want to purchase an off-the-shelf education with the assurance of a clutch of academic certificates to match, but for families who are willing to risk exchanging the bland safety of traditional education for something more real and exciting.

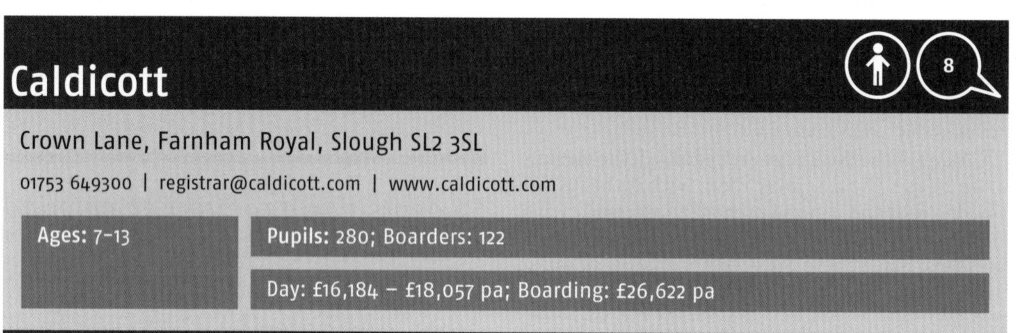

Caldicott

Crown Lane, Farnham Royal, Slough SL2 3SL

01753 649300 | registrar@caldicott.com | www.caldicott.com

Ages: 7–13

Pupils: 280; Boarders: 122

Day: £16,184 – £18,057 pa; Boarding: £26,622 pa

Head: Since April 2018, Jeremy Banks, previously headmaster of Beachborough School. His own mother was a headteacher, and having realised relatively young that he too had a way with children, he subsequently did a degree in education studies and geography at Warwick University and a masters in educational leadership (distinction) at Buckingham. Spent his first 10 years as a teacher at Dulwich Prep London, where he was director of studies and housemaster. Smiley, energetic and enthusiastic.

Married to Sophie, also a Warwick graduate (education studies and music) and also a teacher. They have three daughters.

Entrance: Two form entry in year 3 is joined by another two form entry in year 4 (legacy of Bucks middle school system). There is a short formal academic assessment plus an opportunity to meet other pupils and teachers. Head likes to show prospective parents round (several said they felt they were under as much scrutiny as their sons) and there is an open day in June.

Exit: Nearly all at 13, mainly to trad boys' boarding. Harrow gets the lion's share followed by Eton, Radley, Wellington, Charterhouse, St Edward's, Winchester and Stowe. Good clutch of scholarships most years (six in 2017), mostly sport, art and music. Definitely not a school for those with eyes on the Bucks grammars at 11.

Remarks: Caldicott sits on top of a wooded escarpment with views down to Windsor; 40 acres of prime Bucks real estate adjoining beautiful Burnham Beeches. The school was founded in 1904 by Heald Jenkins who named it after his new bride, a Miss Theodora Caldicott Ingram. The school and its wonderful Harrison Harrison organ (recently restored and residing in the chapel) moved from Hitchin to Farnham Royal in 1938.

Half the pupils are local, the other half come in from the capital on the 7.30am Caldicott express, 'the service is incredibly efficient'

Perfect pitches extend as far as the eye can see, busy with grounds staff rolling and mowing grass that already looks like a billiard table. We defer to one of our guides who observed, 'I can't think of a prep school with better pitches.' Cricket and rugby are a big deal here with up to eight teams (is there really an 'H' team?) ready to take on all comers at all levels. Oxford's Dragon School, as its name suggests, is their fiercest opponent. And what about that H team? Do its duckers and triers really get the same standard of coaching as the Olympians in the As? Certainly, says school. 'We want everybody to take part; the coaches aren't baby-minding. The challenge can be finding other schools ready to field as many opposing teams.' When it comes to sport for all, noble aims such as these are often at odds with the grass roots actualities. Not so at Caldicott. Parents of unsporty boys do not find them swinging round the corner posts while the A team triumphs on a distant pitch. 'If the A team is playing then so are the Bs, Cs and Ds.' And it's the same with other things, drama for instance, lots of groups (teams) at all levels to 'keep everyone improving'.

Music (once the school's weak spot) and the other performing arts are now highly valued and a significant part of life at Caldicott. Boys benefit from an experienced and dedicated teaching team of 15 professionals and the department delivers over 200 instrumental and singing lessons a week. All boys receive a class music lesson every week up until their final term. There are several choirs and instrumental ensembles which provide a variety of opportunities for collaborative music making, along with an abundant range of performing opportunities throughout the year from informal, small-scale beginner platforms to whole school occasions such as carol services, charity concerts, and instrumental recitals. The musical and educational experiences of the whole community are enhanced by regular visiting performers, collaborative projects and outings to public venues. Boys have recently gained music awards to Eton College, Radley College, Harrow School and Charterhouse.

Half the pupils are local, the other half come in from the capital on the 7.30am Caldicott express. School claims to have 'invented' busing in from west London – we hope the other busing Bucks preps pay a copyright fee. 'The service is incredibly efficient, the buses run like clockwork, they're travelling against the traffic,' we were told. Youngest

go home at 4.30pm but rest stay until 6pm – it's a long, active day, but at least there's no homework 'apart from a few spellings or a bit of reading' until the last two years (and the boys are all boarding then). Saturday school is 'proper' with lessons until 12.30pm for all and matches in the afternoon for the older boys. London parents just as visible on sidelines as locals. Is there a divide between the local and London boys, we asked? 'Not at all, the boys don't even notice,' said one mother, although she conceded that the London chaps seemed 'a bit more polished and prepared' when they joined.

All boys in years 7 and 8 board; it's an integral part of their preparation for senior schools such as Harrow, Eton, Radley and Winchester. Dorms are upstairs in the main school building – clean, bright with home duvets, photos and posters. Evenings and weekends are busy with dedicated clubs including fly tying and model making, and competitions and activities such as fondue nights (boys have to go and buy the cheese as well as cook it) and a Caldicott Bake-off. New boarders are given an 'uncle', an experienced boarder in the same dorm who will help him settle in. Senior houseparents live on site with their family and all full-time staff do boarding duty. Our sixth form (year 8) guides, almost ready to leave for senior school, were waxing nostalgic: 'There's so many people around, it's a community,' said one. What would they remember, we asked? 'Summer evening cross-country runs through Burnham Beeches; after-school swims in the outdoor pool; the boarders' Christmas party with carol singing around the huge tree.' Sigh.

Teachers are called 'sir' and 'ma'am' but that apart, education is firmly in the 21st century with bright classrooms, smartboards, well-equipped labs and lots of techy stuff. We loved the screens outside the DT studio flashing up individual photos of every boy proudly holding his finished work.

One way in which Caldicott is untraditional is its neatness – it's the tidiest prep we've ever visited. In fact it was a relief to see some naughty geranium cuttings sprawled muddily beneath a windowsill in the biology lab. Even the art room, usually reliable as a haven of creative chaos, was ship-shape. Parents describe the school as 'incredibly well organised' and it really does seem that no corner of the place is overlooked. Very reassuring.

Evenings and weekends are busy with clubs including fly tying and model making, and activities such as fondue nights (boys have to go and buy the cheese as well as cook it)

Boys are set in maths from the start and in other subjects later on. Apparently there's 'much less setting than of yore', but several parents commented that the system wasn't clear and didn't seem that flexible. Average class size is 16, there's a good mix of staff – old and new – and about a third of teachers are women. The lessons we peeped into were lively and interactive, boys bursting with ideas and eager to contribute. Some grumbles in the recent past that school was slow to pick up SEN but this no longer seems to be the case; several new parents said teachers had been very quick to act on potential problems.

Monitoring is generally regarded as good and communication as excellent; 'Teachers are all contactable by email and usually reply within a couple of hours.' Pastoral care and school counsellor came in for high praise; wobbly new boarders are ably helped through those tricky first few weeks. Several parents remarked how thoughtfully boys in different year groups (so often tribal) related to each other.

Boys say food is 'so much better'. Chicken Kiev is top choice, closely followed by the Thursday roast and cooked breakfast. We were, however, told to 'avoid Saturday lunch at all costs.' We couldn't find out exactly why, but you have been warned. On the wall of the school dining room we were shown the honours boards and there he was, Nicholas Clegg, the only head boy in the school's history to hold the post jointly. The Caldicott coalition – you couldn't make it up.

The word we keep reaching for is 'traditional', but in its best, unstuffy, sense. Parents who choose Caldicott told us they do so because it has secure values: courtesy, fair play, loyalty, regard for others. 'When the boys leave they are young gentlemen,' one said. All in all, this is a cracking prep that will play more than fair by any boy lucky enough to get a place.

Cheam School

Headley, Newbury, Berkshire RG19 8LD

01635 268242 | office@cheamschool.co.uk | www.cheamschool.com

Ages: 3-13

Pupils: 401; Boarders: 50 weekly, 150 flexi

Day: £11,535 – £20,655 pa; Boarding: £26,715 pa

Head: Since September 2016, Martin Harris BSc (50s). Previously head of Sandroyd for 13 years. Educated at boarding school then grammar for A levels. After missing out on the RAF – a natural, but too tall – started in the City only to realise that waiting in same place for same train every morning for 40 years wasn't for him. Coached children at holiday camp, realised he loved it, was accepted for PGCE and hasn't looked back since, with two spells at Ashdown House, first as teacher (1991-1996) returning first as deputy then acting head (1998-2003), and a stint as deputy head at King's Rochester in between.

Two children with wife Catherine, who traded career as physiotherapist for role here – own office, informal conduit for staff, parent and pupil concerns. Family completed by obligatory dog though ringing the changes with terrier rather than standard issue labrador.

With little time off (Sundays tend to be filled with paperwork and marking – Mr Harris is teaching history to top two years) school can be 'all consuming' – but all in a good way. Describes it in newsletter as 'exciting', staff 'passionate,' and pupils 'ebullient' (they're certainly polysyllabic). Even school's location and buildings are 'a great metaphor for prep school life.' We found them tangible enough, fortunately (it's hard enough reviewing real life schools, let alone ones that exist only as a literary device).

He's felt to be fair and approachable. 'Spends time with the children, not in his office and I feel closer to him,' said pupil. He's relaxed into the role, say parents – not an easy one given of massive popularity of predecessor.

Little in the way of drastic changes. 'One of the great schools in the country,' says Mr Harris. 'Like a jumper, you don't want to start unpicking a few areas and find that everything unravels.' So far, upgraded IT ('much needed,' says Mr Harris), addition of reasoning to the curriculum, a few tweaks to the uniform, more even distribution of coaches so Cs and Ds don't always get the gap students.

Also liberating staff to teach more creatively. 'Not going to be trendy or different but to open children's eyes so they're not just sponges regurgitating facts.'

Most commented on development relates to the food, where Mrs H is having her way and introducing healthier options. Parents we spoke to were very pleased with sensible balance – an avocado on toast short of the full Naturally Ella but a definite step up from previous stodge-heavy diet. (Decline of God's great chip, unsurprisingly, not as popular with pupils.)

Also cautiously repainting some walls white (keeping enough Cheam dull red to please the traditionalists) and stepping up displays (miniature dressing gowns, giant toothbrushes for boarding; hoops and tiny hockey sticks for sports) though school museum, complete with unsettling mannequin in vintage uniform, is staying.

'People are pleased,' we were told. 'Together, Mr and Mrs Harris are a considerable force for good. Very important for the pastoral side that you see the head and the head's wife together.'

Entrance: Very popular with waiting lists in every year group. Broadly selective – must be able to access curriculum but very few turned away. Entry by date of registration. Attend familiarisation day – reading, reasoning and maths and spending time in class before place is confirmed. Main entry points are at reception, year 3 (15 added each time), plus another 10 in year 4. A few places in year 7 but don't take many into years 5, 6 or 8. No feeders – mix of state primaries, London preps and relocators (quite a few parents grow up here, work in London for a bit and then head back home again, with evident relief). Most live within 20 mile radius. Currently no EAL or overseas pupils.

Exit: One size fits most. 'At Cheam we are preparing your child for their future senior school which will probably be full boarding,' says the school. Every top name, every year, with more even spread (Marlborough was previously biggest destination by far). Radley, Eton, Harrow for the boys; girls to St Swithun's, St Mary's Calne, Downe House, Sherborne Girls. Wellington, St Edward's Oxford and Bradfield among top co-ed choices.

Nice mix of awards spread evenly through the range, couple each for academics, music and art – though stand out success recently is DT (four awards in 2017).

Remarks: Easy to pre-judge clientele by nicely judged tweet congratulating 'former Cheam parents HM The Queen and Prince Philip on the birth of their Great Granddaughter.' That, and winning entry in sandcastle competition – a 'multi storey mansion' – plus prevalence of cast iron titles among the old boys. Viscounts, barons, HRHs (UK and overseas), politicians. (Also – our favourite – John Michell, 'writer and esotericist': ask for details).

Boasts (in poshly understated way) gold-plated 17th century provenance, founded in (then) quaint Olde World village of Cheam in 1645, numbers boosted by escapees from Great Plague 20 years later.

Swapped mock Tudor element for authentic countryside when moved to current 100-acre site in 1934, demonstrating that you can not only take the school out of Cheam but (name aside) take the Cheam out of the school as well. Were just in time to set up local Home Guard platoon and host 21st Tank Regiment in 1941 (business as normal except for after-class tank rides as a treat for the pupils).

Added girls and day places in the 1990s after facing and overcoming, as in 18th and 19th centuries, significant money troubles (one financial crisis per century isn't bad).

But despite all this (and the names of pupils, rich on Florences, Allegras, Orlandos and Fredericks as well as the normal flocks of Henrys and Georges), school community falls over itself to stress social mix. While not exactly drilling down into the deprived underbelly of the nation, rather more diverse – and infinitely more welcoming – than appearances might suggest. 'We came from state school – everyone is down to earth,' said parent.

Lots of earth, too, courtesy of splendiferous site with green vistas in every direction – lakes, formal gardens and fountains are 'an awesome sight,' said parent and big enough and to spare for the 400 or so pupils, with traffic noise well damped down, replaced by gentle smack of tennis of balls on the all-weather surface (pupils' complaints of running track deformed by slope, tree roots and 'little frogs' not substantiated by school...).

Green vistas in every direction – lakes, formal gardens and fountains are 'an awesome sight,' said parent and plenty big enough for the 400 or so pupils

Little of the original buildings remain (main house had two mega rebuilds in 19th and 20th centuries) and campus is now filled with many extras – most recently the Duke of Edinburgh building (powered by geothermal energy), home to pre-prep, art and DT and a new kitchen area.

Space well used. 'Something for everyone' boasts the website for the extracurricular activities section (most free) – including Greek and German as well as extra enrichment sessions for scholars.

Don't be fooled by online images of ballet club, apparently populated only by pink tutu-wearing girls. Gender stereotypes are being put to one side.

Plenty of interesting things to do in school, from hatching butterflies to investigating the contents of owl pellets

Currently, biggest success is former (boy) pupil, a rising star in classical dance. Similarly, membership of sewing, Sylvanians, Jedi and Lego – some of the (many) other clubs on offer – is (often) mixed.

Former sports inequality has also been largely addressed. Boys and girls play football and cricket, for example and there's a decent range of co-ed sports – cross-country (masses of prizes), athletics, shooting, fives, swimming (outdoor but no indoor pool – on the wish list), judo, fencing, horse riding, polo and golf and range of trips and tours.

Performing arts similarly varied, despite lack of purpose built spaces. Fab productions (regulars at Edinburgh Festival), wonderful selective choirs (junior and senior). Music lessons start with two sessions a week for all pre-prep pupils and tasters in recorder, strings and brass in year 2 (though only start individual lessons in year 3) – continues through the school and how, with well over half the pupils learning some of 17 instruments on offer, lessons and (for boarders) practice sessions timetabled – impressive string quartet whizzing, unsupervised, through repertoire including Pink Panther theme. Drama's the area to expand in top years – not taught in years 7 or 8; would be good as extra, feel some parents and pupils. Plenty of showcases for top two years in the meantime, says school, including soirées as well as full-blown shows.

Impressive emphasis on pastoral care – parents felt recently improved for all, and especially youngest; bullying minimal. Half the staff already have training in mental health first aid – more following. No detail left to chance: everything from staff mentors – pupils can request any teacher – to prominent displays and emotional tracking (repeat same, simple questions twice a year – helps predict child's levels of resilience). Appears to work. One pupil we talked to was movingly open about how school had supported him through family crisis.

Boarders, from year 4, up at 7am, lights out at 8.15pm for juniors and an hour later for the oldest. 'Sweet dreams' is last comment on the timetable. No mobiles allowed – contact by payphone and email. Weekly and flexi offered – no full boarding: everyone goes home on Saturday afternoons. Only drawback of fluctuating numbers means, said some pupils, that could be on their own. Mr Harris qualifies this as 'not with their friends...they would never be on their own in a dorm.'

Parents couldn't fault the recently revamped organisation or the 'super energetic' staff who make it 'so much fun that everyone wants to board,' though our girl guides who hadn't seen boys' quarters for themselves were vocal about inequalities, refrain of 'We don't have that!' prompted by everything from bigger hanging spaces for clothes to bed frames (some metal in girls' dorms, 'which rattle'). Even the disinfectant-filled jar for boys' combs got an envious look...

But it's the academic fare that really pulls in the families. School prides itself on work without tears. 'All learning should be fun,' they say under FAQs. Confirmed by parents who praised 'magical' teachers – recruitment boosted by staff housing in Cheamville. New recruits (several 'worryingly young' – though average age is 37) can arrive with ultra-serious outlook, but quickly encouraged to lighten up. 'All seem to get the same principle which is that...if you can't have a laugh in prep school years, good luck to rest of your life,' said mother.

Pre-prep head, Mrs Marriott, praised for warmth, ability (and dressing up costumes – 'have seen her in more than any teacher should have to wear,' said mother). She presides over attractive surroundings (bright classrooms with more fabulously inventive displays – teachers clearly arrive with A* skills in transformatory foil wrapping) and an admirable fusion of fun and learning for the youngest that, on day of visit, included reception pupils busily chalking planets on courtyard paving stones.

Homework isn't daunting, starting with a little light reading, emphasis on key words and writing practice in pre-prep. Twice-yearly reports (spring and summer terms for years 1 and 2), plenty of informal contact encouraged while colourful, detailed newsletters (pre-prep has its own) fill in any gaps.

Step up from year 2 to 3 relatively gentle. From year 4, from arrival for 8.15am assembly until finish of prep (everyone stays for it) at 6pm – later for top years – it's pretty much non-stop, particularly as there's also Saturday school for all from year 4 – a no concessions full day.

Well staffed (teacher to pupil ratio of one to six in prep and one to four in pre-prep) and smallish classes – 18 official max, smaller for French and maths, and setting generally left to year 5.

Plenty of interesting things to do in school, from hatching butterflies to investigating the contents of owl pellets (rather them than us) – and on numerous subject-related trips (history, geog, French) plus culture (theatre, ballet, museums) to sweeten the pill.

Main focus, though, firmly on CE preparation in key subjects (English, maths, science, French, Latin, history, geography and RS), though less academic are, say parents, never made to feel like lesser mortals and subject popularity spans the ability range.

Science – pluses the breeding colony of stick insects, deficits the paucity of labs, though more are on the wish list – and DT among favourites as well as history. 'I love the Black Death,' said cheery pupil.

'Behind the scenes they are pushing as much as they can but aren't making them feel that academics is the be all and end all,' reckoned parent. 'People say it's so competitive but haven't found that in any way shape or form.' Pupils agreed. 'So supportive about everything, in and out of lessons – may as well be my family,' said prep pupil.

If teaching is good – and despite inevitable tutoring, with or without school's blessing, that does go on – learning support is 'brilliant,' says parent. Issues quickly identified, up to two sessions charged for but anything extra normally isn't. Academic support also there if needed. Currently some 54 pupils receive some form of learning support in prep school, with one-to-one, group lessons and in-class support. 'Really good at helping the ones who struggle as well as the ones at the top end,' said parent. 'Half of these have a diagnosed condition (dyslexia etc) while the others need a little help with spelling, writing and maths,' says the school.

While growth in the 1990s was helped by mergers with two other less successful establishments, school's continued success – it's now pretty much at capacity – is down not to establishment credentials: plenty of schools with similar profile, including David Cameron's old prep, have failed to survive. Instead, it's about ensuring that excellent results aren't achieved at the expense of fun. 'A little piece of heaven,' said one parent. But definitely not a metaphor.

Christ Church Cathedral School

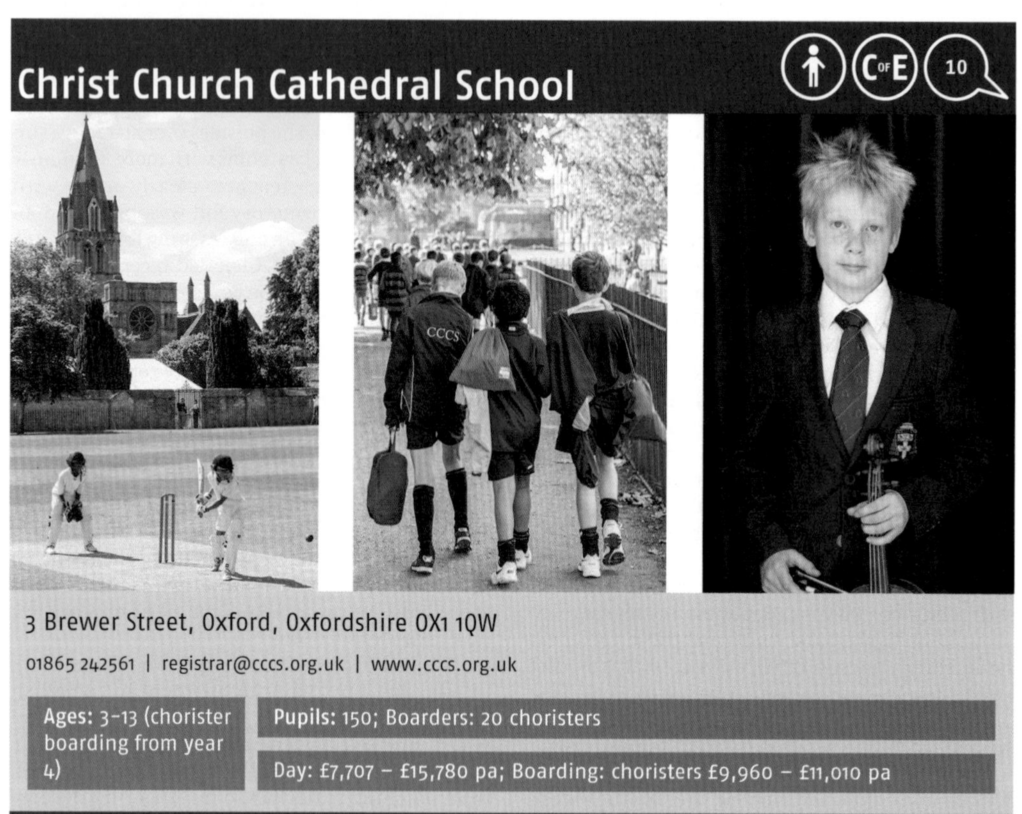

3 Brewer Street, Oxford, Oxfordshire OX1 1QW

01865 242561 | registrar@cccs.org.uk | www.cccs.org.uk

Ages: 3-13 (chorister boarding from year 4)

Pupils: 150; Boarders: 20 choristers

Day: £7,707 – £15,780 pa; Boarding: choristers £9,960 – £11,010 pa

Headmaster: Since 2014, Richard Murray BA MA (Durham), previously a housemaster and English teacher at St Edward's School in Oxford. English degree from Durham; has also taught at The King's School Gloucester and Rendcomb College.

Entrance: Most day boys are from the Oxford or Bucks area, and enter at nursery or reception; the single class grows as more boys join in year 3 and the majority stays until common entrance. A few girls in nursery only. Assessment is by participation in class for the younger boys and informal academic tests for the older boys. Four chorister places are available each year from year 4, selected by voice trial. Choristers come from further afield, board and receive a two-thirds fee reduction in a bursary established by royal appointment in 16th century. School benefits from recommendations by old boys, siblings and music teachers. The Cardinal's Scholarship is a new introduction, for up to three year 3s, who are expected to achieve well academically throughout the school. Parents of choristers are a particularly music-focused sub-set; others are local professionals, medics and academics

Exit: To a range of schools: in 2017, Our Lady's Abingdon, Radley, Cokethorpe, Eton, Abingdon, St Edward's, Charterhouse, The Oratory and King's Canterbury. Plenty of music scholarships and exhibitions, as one would expect.

Remarks: Described by one parent as 'the secret of Oxford', it is hidden in a historic corner of the town in the shadow of Christ Church Cathedral. Every available inch has been transformed, embracing the original Tudor residence of Cardinal Wolsey, a Victorian parsonage-type house commissioned by Dean Liddell, father of Alice in Wonderland, and a bright new block to commemorate old boy William Walton. The net effect is a warren of classrooms, labs and play areas combining traditional and modern. Henry VIII's charter of 1546 established the education of eight boy choristers and a master for Christ Church Cathedral. Shame it didn't stipulate a few parking spaces too, as staff parking on the playground is an issue, according to one parent.

Music permeates through the school, from music-stands among the pyjamas to treble clef murals in the corridors. The cathedral choristers' day kicks off at 7.30am to fit in their three hours of choir practice and daily services. In addition they all learn the piano and one other instrument. There are celebratory services throughout the year, including Easter and Christmas Day, as well as singing tours, recently as far afield as China, performing in the world's largest concert hall. The rest of the school has caught the bug too: with pianos in every corner and 140 individual music lessons per week, there are informal concerts which start with the smallest to encourage confidence, 'even if it's a recorder and they play the same note 10 times,' laughs one parent. However, having heard the choir sing like angels at evensong, we were struck by the skill and professionalism of even the youngest. Parents are welcome to watch the weekly service in the cathedral and some day boys are chosen for Worcester College choir. 'They see that older boys are doing it and it's fun'.

These are not just pretty voices: under the surplices there is an academic rigour to the school, starting with the tiny tots in the Montessori nursery. The historic cardinal's house now holds a climbing frame and zoo animal frescoes in the garden. Small class sizes in the pre-prep, approximately 16, rising to a maximum of 20 when choristers join in year 4. The pre-prep enjoys recently refurbished classrooms with play areas, music corners and piano. French classes in year 2. There is a conscious promotion to the prep, a separate building, a more formal uniform, and a more exacting curriculum, in which subjects are taught by specialists from year 5 and maths is set in year 6. We witnessed a vibrant Latin class and were invited to help judge the Roman legionary cut-out doll competition – it was a tough decision, but the joy of learning in the classroom was infectious. IT resources have multiplied and are used, among other things, for workshops on Sibelius (musicians' software, not the chap). Head sees all parents in year 6 to discuss future schools and makes prefects of all the final year boys. Teachers include alumnae of the college.

Named after the cathedral's organists, including John Tavener, boarders' rooms are decked with photos and teddies from home

The school makes good provision for a surprising variety of SEN children, with one full-time and two part-time staff. 'Some schools attract a uniform product and this is a school which attracts eccentrics'. One parent reported that a boy who was severely dyslexic won a top place in the annual poetry competition. 'That's part of the school's draw: it treats everyone with a lot of respect'. Oxford's fluid population means that there is often a handful of EAL children, which our guide appeared to relish as contributing to the school's rich tapestry.

Picture the most idyllic cricket field you can imagine – these boys play on it, overlooked by the dreaming spires of Magdalen and Christ Church, the sound of rare breed cows lowing by the river; a timber cabin of a cricket pavilion, now with modern additions, electricity and a loo. One parent criticised the school's outdoor areas – 'Boys don't have far to run in the playground' – but Merton field over the road more than makes up for it (there's also woodland school in Christ Church Meadow). No wonder the fixtures in rugby, football, cricket and athletics are successful and many boys make the renowned A teams in their next schools. Parents enjoy a summer fair here on sports day, a scene which is eagerly photographed by tourists, looking for a snap of old England. 'I've never seen so many cakes,' gasped a parent. The school is conscientious about all boys representing the school in sport at some stage – school also offers an autumn half term course with Premiership footballers. Inflatable sharks and papier mâché snakes in the art room testify that the creative child is catered for. Art and poetry are celebrated on Arts Day, by visiting professionals who run workshops in photography, fine art, music and poetry. This year's cartoonist helped produce some lively portraits of composers, one of whom looked suspiciously like the bursar.

Named after the cathedral's organists, including John Tavener, the boarders' rooms in the main building are decked with photos and teddies from home; the largest dorm sleeps eight cosily. The bright and tidy shower room confirmed our suspicions that these are no ordinary boys. 'We try to make it their home,' said our guide. The choristers' common room is in cardinal red, like their cassocks, and houses a computer to email home, TV and, of course, ivories to tinkle upon. Our noses led us enticingly to the dining room, lined with scholars' and house point boards – houses are named after dignitaries associated with the school: (Lewis) Carroll; (Cardinal) Wolsey and (Dorothy L) Sayers, who lived next door and whose father was headmaster. There's a traditional tie for the winners of the merit awards to wear each term; another system for poor behaviour culminates in a mild punishment of sitting outside the staff room. Good discipline is inherent in a musical training: 'It's not external discipline we're after, it's a means to self-discipline'. Lots of clubs after school, from knitting to furniture-making to amuse the boys, while parents fight with the city traffic: 'Bit of a pain to get to at 5.30 at night,' said a parent. Free after-school prep club until 6pm pleases working parents. However, not really set up as a boarding school; reports of choristers at school at weekends kicking their heels with no organised activities, and sometimes missing meals.

The school is proud of its reputation for good manners, and rightly so. Boys stand when visitors enter the classrooms, address teachers as 'sir' and learn to hold the door open at an early age. It is a conscious emphasis on courtesy which comes across as old-fashioned. As one parent remarked, 'I think we are paying for the education I received'. Parents are happy with the contact from teachers: 'They speak to you, and really listen to what you say'; office staff got particular praise, 'even with difficult parents they are very diplomatic'. It is no coincidence that in premises seeped in history the school play should be Old Father Time. He has certainly instilled character and sound traditional values here, from the daily Latin quotation in the head's study to the boys' charming Thomas More-style hats. The honest traditions are summed up by the bursar: 'Snowballing? Of course we allow it. I think being a boy nowadays is not as exciting as it should be'.

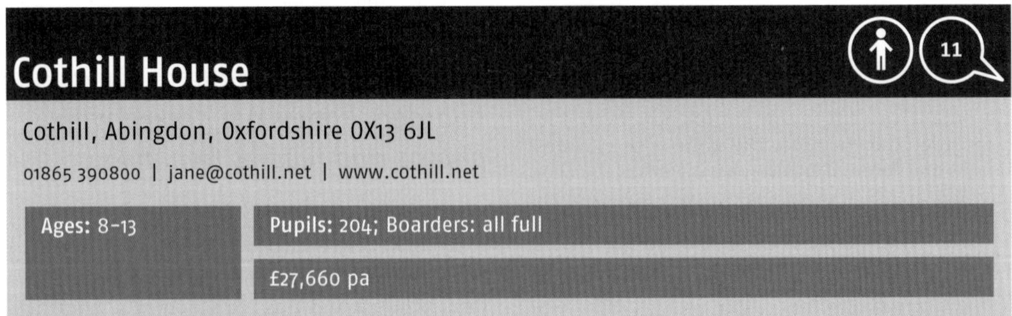

Cothill House

11

Cothill, Abingdon, Oxfordshire OX13 6JL

01865 390800 | jane@cothill.net | www.cothill.net

Ages: 8-13

Pupils: 204; Boarders: all full

£27,660 pa

Headmaster: Since 2011, Mr Duncan Bailey (30s). Educated at Cothill, followed by Eton and a gap year in West Africa, then Manchester University (French) and Vienna University (German). Bitten by teaching bug during his year abroad but harboured ambitions to nurture his passion for sport, particularly

Boys can build dens or bird boxes, go pond dipping or interpret Notre Dame Cathedral in clay to their hearts' content

tennis (he was a contemporary of Tim Henman) and moved into sports management. 'Fell into teaching' after being asked to stand in for the head of modern languages at Eton, where he spent two years. Prior to taking headship at Cothill, ran Sauveterre, the Cothill Trust's French outpost, for eight years.

Married to Maria (his 'secret weapon' according to parents), lives at heart of school with his two young daughters, currently schooled at nearby Chandlings. A hands-on couple, the Baileys are in true loco parentis – head says he is 'a parent above all things' – taking full responsibility for the four year groups housed in the main school building. Maria 'does everything,' from rolling up her sleeves to help with cooking, cleaning, teaching and running the school if required, right down to marching boys back to the salad bar if they don't have enough veggies on their plates.

Relaxed and approachable, with the chameleonic ability to switch between the persona of favourite uncle and respected leader, and not adverse to taking pupils on at table tennis or joining in with an after-hours skateboarding session, head says he 'likes boys to be happy, expects them to be busy and insists they are polite.' Parents consider him 'very dynamic, involved and committed to the school' and the few that were 'worried he might be a bit green' when appointed have climbed firmly back into their boxes.

Entrance: Recruits about 20 boys with a 'fairly broad brush' into year 4, with intakes in both September and April and numbers swelling to between 25 and 30 by end of year. Parents and boys interviewed together ('we choose the whole family') to establish fit rather academic ability. Boys assessed rather than tested, in English and maths. Majority at this point from London prep schools with just a few local boys in the mix. Good number of forces' children and between 10 and 15 per cent international (mainly Spanish and Russian with a few Chinese and Thai) although head insists on fluent English and no EAL on offer ('they have to be able to survive in the boarding environment').

Oversubscribed from year 5, with head looking for 'boys who are prepared to roll up their sleeves and get stuck in' above all else. Drop-out rate of less than one a year. A number join in summer term of year 5 to settle in before real focus on destination schools starts in year 6.

Exit: As in previous years, 20 to 25 per cent each to Eton, Radley and Harrow. Smaller numbers to Winchester, Marlborough and Wellington, plus Sherborne, Stowe, St Edward's and Malvern for less starry academic achievers. No fall-out to day schools. Huge focus on 'negotiating' places with destination schools with evidence of heart and soul going into making sure boys land in the best places. 'A good handful' of scholarships most years, most notably in art and music.

Remarks: Steadfastly traditional, Cothill is so discreet you could almost miss it altogether in its picturesque village setting. No grand buildings or flashy reception. Visitors arrive directly into the heart of the school (the dining room) – giving the first clue to school's substance over style ethos. Main building is a large country house with several later additions nestled in 26 acres of grounds, playing fields and woodland. Sports and leisure facilities include a super 15 metre indoor pool, six all-weather tennis courts, a nine-hole golf course, a somewhat shabby, albeit well used squash court cum table tennis room and a fleet of shiny BMXs for tearing around the woods. Equally appreciated by pupils is the wealth of retreats where they can spend as much free time as they like indulging creative passions such as woodwork (a real favourite with boys, guided by former police officer known as 'PC'), pottery and art. There's also a large, modern library and gleaming ICT suite for, amongst other things, Skyping home, although a handwritten letter once a week is compulsory.

No common rooms to speak of, bar a pool room, and no significant evidence of televisions (junior movie nights and major sporting events only are hosted in head's sitting room) or other passive distractions. Parents report boys roaring around on scooters in their pyjamas before bedtime rather than gluing themselves to screens. And therein lies the magic of the place. Macs and iPads do have a home here but what Cothill really offers is a Swallows and Amazons approach to education. It's a school where boys can 'have a childhood,' say parents. Boys can build dens or bird boxes, go pond dipping or interpret Notre Dame Cathedral in clay to their hearts' content. Parents and boys also firmly supportive of full boarding ethos (two exeats per term), which makes for fun-filled weekends jam packed with activities for all, not just those who live too far from school to make a weekly journey home. Broad geographical spread, from Scottish Highlands to Norfolk as well as overseas, makes for a collegiate bunch.

Majority of parents from upper echelons, most of whom have gone 'through the system' (read Eton, Harrow etc), with titles aplenty. Car park generally occupied by ancient mud splattered 4x4s rather than gleaming Maseratis on match days and supporters, who are encouraged and welcomed to visit twice a week, tend to be of the green welly variety, with the odd royal godparent thrown in for good measure. In the words of one mother, 'definitely not the facelift and white Range Rover crowd.' That said, head reports increasing numbers of professional, middle class London parents, keen to escape the hot-house London day school scene and allow their boys the space and roundedness offered by a country prep. One such parent reported that without exception the children are just from 'incredibly nice families who want the very best education.' Boys confident, smiley and polite with no sign of entitlement or arrogance and, with shirts untucked and ties askew, the slightest hint of Just William.

Action-packed weekends mean boys can become wistful when they are at home, missing the mix of activities and free time on their rollerblades or exploring the woods

Strong artsy feel around the place with examples of boys' excellent work festooning every spare wall and surface. Music, art and DT highly praised by parents and boys alike and head's bet with us that 'about 70 per cent' of boys would say their favourite subject was history appeared to be bang on the money. A visit to the history room demonstrated what teaching at Cothill is all about – getting boys out of their seats and experiencing things firsthand. A mini Battle of Trafalgar was laid out across pushed together tables, complete with tablecloth sea and stacks of wide, slim drawers opened to reveal other famous (mostly French) battlefields to enable boys to visualise and act out events. Another recent highlight for history department was the re-enactment of the Dambusters raid on the school field. No wonder it's top dog, although this kind of thing is apparently all in a day's work for most departments here, with teachers across the board described as 'inspiring' and often 'quirky – in a good way.'

The star draw though, has to be Sauveterre, Cothill's unique French chateau outpost near Toulouse where all year 7 boys spend a whole term immersing themselves in French language, culture, food and sunshine. Parents evangelise about the benefits of this, not only where tipping the balance at CE is concerned but in terms of an unforgettable life experience.

Boys 'loosely set' from the outset for all subjects with maths more tightly so, but flexible according to exam results. Class sizes between 10 and 15 at the bottom of the school, gradually shrinking to seven or eight from year 7 onwards, consistent with head's belief that 'success at common entrance comes from small classes at the top of the school.' Each subject teacher reports to head on every boy on a weekly basis, resulting in a score out of 10 read out in Friday's assembly. High running totals at the end of term lead to treats and trips. Although school not equipped to deal with serious SEN, superb support in place for those who need a bit of extra help with a highly experienced, passionate SENCo who spends time with every boy before they join the school.

'Spectacular' drama, with frequent plays and shows, including My Fair Lady, Mary Poppins and original works written by Cothill teachers. And yes, boys do take on the female roles ('mainly with enthusiasm,' they told us). Around 80 per cent of cohort plays a musical instrument and there are bands and choirs galore for them to showcase their talents. Sport every day, with a focus on health, fitness and everyone getting a go at representing the school. Lower teams celebrated as vigorously as superstars – a recent fixture saw the bottom football team allowed to wear the first team strip as a reward for thrashing the opposition in their previous match.

Parents moving 'overeducated' children out of London preps shouldn't be surprised if boys cruise a bit academically initially. Year 4 is all about getting to grips with boarding to set the foundations for future success and happiness. Tidy, basic dorms for about eight boys, adorned with all the usual football paraphanalia, house years 4, 6 and 7 in the main school and year 5s are split between here and 'the bungalow' – a cosy outpost across the games field where according to parents boys feel 'terribly grown up.' Action-packed weekends mean boys eventually become wistful when they are at home, missing the mix of organised activities – an optional trip out every week and free time on their rollerblades, ripsticks or exploring the woods.

All year 8s minibussed out after supper each evening to sleep at nearby Chandlings School, which looks disastrous on paper but in reality 'works brilliantly' according to parents and boys we spoke to and gives boys 'the space to be pre-teenagers.' Weekends also spent there, in the care of an 'extraordinary' house couple, with boys given their own activities and free run of Chandlings' facilities. Formerly sceptical parents now evangelise and are insistent that this part of Cothill life should 'never change.'

Unsurprisingly top notch pastoral care with parents reporting that school 'celebrates high spirits' and 'really understands each boy's potential and how to get him to reach it,' with more than one parent telling us their son had been 'turned around.' Very impressive, albeit informal, daily staff meeting where issues or concerns are raised (from which boys need to be reminded to wear their spectacles to who is struggling with the pressure of scholarship exams) leads to holistic care for every pupil. Boys know they can confide in whomever they wish, whether it's their tutor or junior matrons (usually gap year girls). Parents report boys returning to school 'without a backward glance' – and our guides themselves encapsulated the spirit of the school by telling us that the only kind of boy they could imagine not liking Cothill would be 'an iPad lover.'

Downe House School

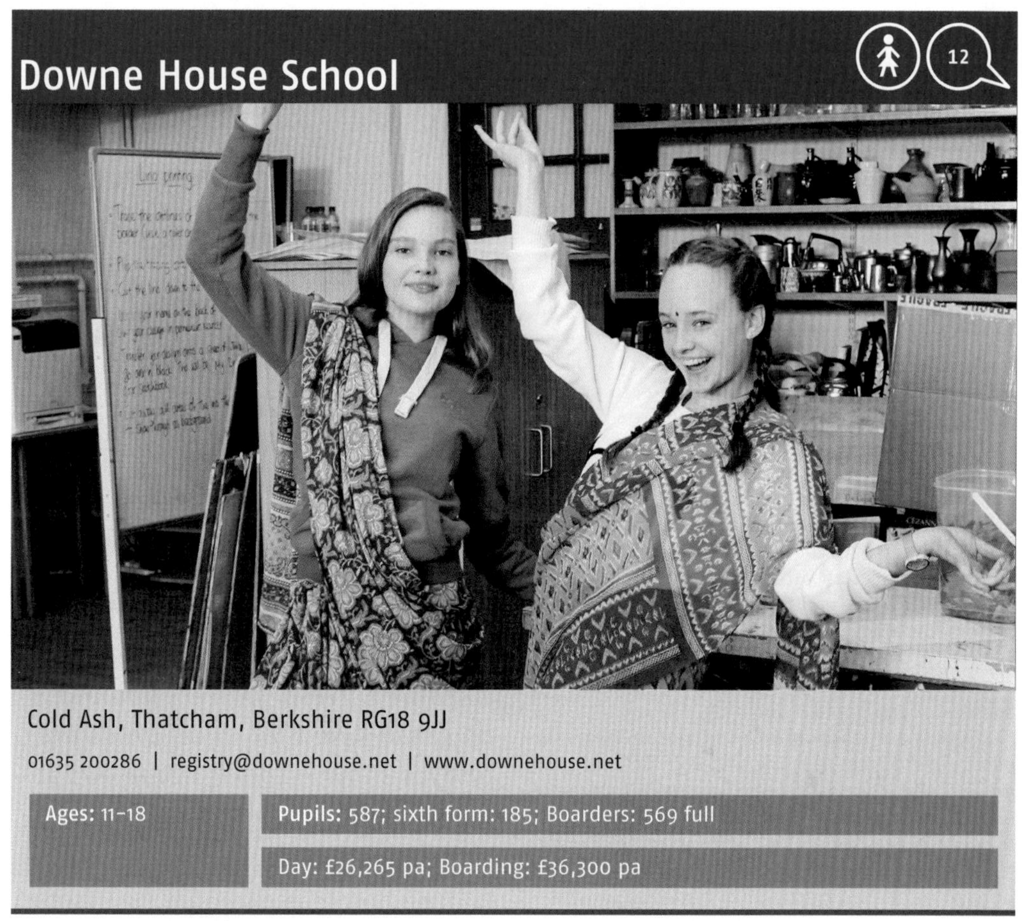

Cold Ash, Thatcham, Berkshire RG18 9JJ

01635 200286 | registry@downehouse.net | www.downehouse.net

Ages: 11–18

Pupils: 587; sixth form: 185; Boarders: 569 full

Day: £26,265 pa; Boarding: £36,300 pa

Headmistress: Since 1997, Mrs Emma McKendrick BA PGCE FRSA (40s). Educated at Bedford High and at the universities of Liverpool and Birmingham (German and Dutch). Previously at The Royal School, Bath, where she had been i/c careers and sixth form, a housemistress and deputy head before becoming head in 1994. Remarkably young when appointed to her first headship – that this was so is to the credit of the school's governors. She is soft-spoken, stylish, somehow very grown up, calm and relaxed. Her office and the room in which she receives visitors is a joy – windows on three sides so she can 'see everything', bright, light and tasteful. Parents – who tend to be deeply passionate about the school and many of whom are old girls – sigh with pleasure: 'She is excellent, on top of everything'; 'She is miraculous – I can say nothing against her. She is so professional, warm, and has a sense of humour. One cannot but be in awe of her, but you love her too'.

Academic matters: Had opted for Pre-U in preference to A levels in all but a few arts subjects – 'It really has made a difference to my upper sixth,' said the head. 'They are forced to be more independent. They are far better served by the Pre-U in terms of coping with what they will get at university.' However, with demise of AS, now returning to A levels for most subjects.

In 2017, at A level and Pre-U, 58 per cent A*-A, D1-D2. Maths very popular, with biology and English close behind. Good numbers for Latin and the odd taker for Greek. Politics, photography and economics offered along with history of art, plus all the trad subjects. Wide range of languages including support for home ones. Eighty-four per cent A*-A/9-7 at GCSE in 2017. Blissfully small classes – this is nurturing indeed.

Most teachers highly praised, many seen as 'inspiring'. Learning skills support given to those with mild dys-strata plus those who need extra help with organising themselves or time management. Also stretching help for the most able. Hopeless site for anyone in a wheelchair – the buildings are too scattered and the site is too up and down for this to be possible. EAL support given where needed – 35 in receipt of individual help when we visited.

Games, options, the arts: That the extracurricular life of the school is run from its own sizeable woodland cabin in the heart of the site with designated staff tells you everything. Every kind of opportunity is offered here – from trips to The Royal Opera House to playing lacrosse for Berkshire, to preparing soup for hungry people in South Africa from sackfuls of bones fresh from a slaughterhouse during a trip to a link school there. Lots of visits from outside speakers, who clearly inspire and motivate. Much lively and imaginative charitable activity – often with the boys from Radley. Excellent drama – again, often with Radley – generously supported by old girl Geraldine James, who opened the performing arts centre and has been known to take aspiring actresses under her wing. Two recent successful auditions for the National Youth Theatre. Successful and popular debating.

Sports are many and varied and include, for older girls, pilates, fencing and golf. Several girls are England lacrosse players – lax taken more seriously here than other sports. Internal competition between houses seemingly counting more than fixtures against other schools. Art is lively, though housed in the least attractive building on site – great range of activities: we loved the individuality of work in textiles, ceramics and woodwork, along with truly impressive painting. Ballet, modern dance, tap and hip hop on offer and around half the girls take speech and drama. Practically all of them learn at least one instrument. 'They all do so much extra,' a parent told us, half-admiring, half-concerned. 'They do whack on the pressure – the girls themselves, that is.'

Houses clearly of immense importance here – friendly but significant rivalry in all areas of school life. Lots of trips at home and abroad – all with sound educational or charitable purposes. Most exciting, memorable and generally aaaahed over is the term spent during year 8 at the school's own converted farm in the heart of Perigord. Those who join the school in year 9 seem to spend the next five years biting their lip at having missed an unforgettable experience. A seasoned sixth former told us – as if it were obvious – 'Oh, we never stop talking about it.' It's about French and French life, cuisine, charity work, community and living ensemble.

Boarding: All but a handful of local day girls are full boarders. One boarding school veteran told us that the boarding staff were much the best she'd ever come across. The boarding houses themselves are much loved. We relished the dressing up boxes in the junior houses.

New lower school house for all year 7 and 8 girls, providing a sheltered introduction to boarding life. Older girls are in mixed age houses – dorms are mostly spacious; singles and doubles for the older girls are homely and attractive. Everywhere is properly carpeted and curtained. Fresh flowers abound – no sense here that 'nice' areas are just for show – this is home and it feels like it. All houses either wireless or with network points.

Sixth form houses are exceptionally well designed and furnished. Pigeonholes for girls' post and newspapers; sofas, careers areas, meeting rooms, kitchens. Girls can be independent here, if they wish – no wonder so few leave after GCSEs. All have a personal safe in their rooms. Further extension to and enhancement of the boarding facilities planned.

Everywhere is properly carpeted and curtained. Fresh flowers abound – no sense here that 'nice' areas are just for show – this is home and it feels like it

Lessons until 12pm on Saturdays are followed by sports, so everyone signs up to the full boarding life. Saturday evenings are spent in rehearsal, at concerts, trips to theatres, cinemas etc. Sundays include trips, D of E activities and chillin'.

Background and atmosphere: Founded in 1907 by Olive Willis, its first headmistress, as an all-girls' boarding school. Its first home was Down House in the village of Downe, Kent – formerly the home of Charles Darwin. The school outgrew the house so Miss Willis bought The Cloisters in Berkshire – its present home – on a high ridge which provides occasional views over distant downs. The Cloisters – still at the heart of the school – comes as a surprise. Built by Maclaren Ross for an order of Spanish nuns, who named it The School of Silence, it has an arched walkway linking most of the classrooms which – with its white walls, arches and terracotta pantiles – is incongruously Moorish in the heart of Berkshire.

However, the school has grown many newer buildings – boarding houses, specialist blocks etc – around the main building and the site is now extensive – many buildings nestling amongst trees, woody areas and neatly planted beds. All maintained by 'little green men' who hover around the site on electric car-lets. No architectural gems here – nor any monsters – though a few blocks lack charm. The whole has a sense of modest purposefulness – described by one mother as 'almost spiritual'.

The uniform is standard school green skirt, shirt and jumper, though the sixth form still cling to their floor length black skirts – 'They wear them so they can keep their pyjamas on underneath,' one mum told us.

Pastoral care, well-being and discipline: 'Completely faultless,' a mother said of the pastoral care. 'The house staff are very responsive and email you back at once.' 'When people complain, things do get done,' another vouchsafed. 'We've been bowled over by the pastoral care,' said yet another. 'The attention to detail is extraordinary – almost obsessive. Nothing is too much trouble.'

The loveliest school dining room we have seen in over 100 schools – proper tablecloths on round tables seating six to encourage time over meals. Food – 'We make all our own bread and sausages and buy in the absolute minimum' – which occasions rhapsodies in the girls.

Some sense that the sixth form centre separates older from younger girls and work still to be done on integrating those who arrive after the first year, but this is tricky in girls' schools everywhere. Very few discipline problems – smoking sighed over as 'an occasional safe rebellion which one wishes they wouldn't do', and illicit drinking looked upon as a threat to a girl's personal safety – 'You need to be safe, to look after yourself and to preserve your dignity,' the head reminds them. No drugs incidents within memory and the very rare girl who 'cannot stop being unkind has to go'.

Pupils and parents: Girls from all over the UK and beyond; increasing numbers of daughters of alumnae. Seven per cent from overseas – mostly from the Far East but also the US, Nigeria, Kazakhstan. Parents solid middle class, usually with boarding backgrounds.

Exceptionally impressive list of notable alumnae includes: chemist and educator Rosemary Murray, Geraldine James, Clare Balding, Mary Midgley, Elizabeth Bowen, Priscilla Napier, Anne Ridler, Audrey Richards, Sophie Conran, Lulu Guinness, Fru Hazlitt, wildly different comics Miranda Hart and Laura Solon, Hannah Wright – pioneering barrister, Jenifer Hart – pioneering civil servant and Oxford don and Aileen Fox – pioneering archaeologist. Oh – and Kate Middleton. A rare

degree of loyalty amongst alumnae – few schools excite more affection, it seems, and many keep in touch. Mrs McKendrick fosters this in imaginative ways, enlisting old girls to support newbies in their professions, eg an established barrister mentoring a recent alumna in her pupillage. A considerable attraction to potential parents.

Entrance: Lists close at 110 applicants and head interviews all those over four days, during which all are tested in maths, English and reasoning. They also participate in drama and sports activities et al to see whether they're happy and likely to fit in with boarding life. Eighty then invited to sit CE for the 60 available places. At 13, around 65 are assessed similarly for the 35-odd places. Girls from 180+ preps/primaries have joined Downe in recent years – from all over the UK.

At 16, it depends on how many are leaving but usually around 8-10 places for the 'huge' number who apply. Applicants sit the school's own papers and the strongest are then interviewed, the best offered conditional places. Seven I/GCSEs at B or above expected including A*/As in sixth form subject choices.

Exit: Some 10 per cent leave after GCSEs, often for co-ed sixth forms. Most to top universities, eg Bristol, London, Warwick, Exeter, Leeds, Edinburgh; some to universities in the US. One to Oxbridge in 2017 and one to Harvard. Popular subjects include science/medicine, psychology, history of art, MFL, economics, politics, RS, business related degrees plus music and creative arts.

Money matters: Scholarships for sports, arts and academics more of an honour than a significant contribution to fees. Bursaries up to 100 per cent of fees plus additional help available for the right applicant.

Remarks: Archetypal traditional girls' full boarding school turning out delightful, principled, courteous and able girls who go on to make a significant contribution to the world. As one parent said, 'We couldn't be more thrilled.'

Dragon School

13

Bardwell Road, Oxford, Oxfordshire OX2 6SS

01865 315405 | admissions@dragonschool.org | www.dragonschool.org

Ages: 4–13 (boarding from 8)

Pupils: 813; Boarders: 212

Day: £11,640 – £20,520 pa; Boarding: £29,580 pa

Head: Since September 2017, Dr Crispin Hyde-Dunn MA (Oxon) PGCE MA (Ed) NPQH, PhD (40s). Read history at Oxford. Previously head of Abingdon Prep. Before that was deputy head of King's College School, Cambridge and earlier still was head of history at New College School in Oxford. Wife, Lucy, is a medical research fellow at Oxford.

Entrance: Register early – as early as you like post-conception. The school is full and there are waiting lists at all stages. However, spaces can be available at any time as pupils move away to another area or country. Potentially easier to get in as a boarder but this depends on the year group. Non-selective entry although the school assesses maths and English to check that a child will be able to cope. Up to 100 per cent means-tested bursaries are available from year 4 for the full five years. Not based on academic merit: the school states that they 'start with need' but have to be sure the family is able and willing to commit to the Dragon way of life – Saturday morning school, extracurricular commitments etc.

Exit: Frequent destinations include Abingdon School, Cheltenham Ladies' College, Eton College, Harrow School, Magdalen College School,

Marlborough College, Radley College, Rugby School, Stowe School, St Edward's School, Wellington College, Winchester College and Wycombe Abbey. No favourite school, but 'we have a strong working relationship with St Edward's', as the two schools have a similar ethos and are co-ed day and boarding. Pupils are supported but not intensely prepped for pre-test at 11 or entrance exams at 11 – would not want a child to get into a school on the basis of excessive prepping. Senior schools take note of the Dragon's reports and trust their judgement but this isn't a school whose priority is to get children into the most academic local seniors. Bucket-loads of scholarships won – 40 to 50 per year. Famous Old Dragons include Sir John Betjeman, Leonard Cheshire VC, John Mortimer, Antonia Fraser, Alain de Botton, Rageh Omaar, Hugh Laurie, Tim Henman, Tom Hiddleston and Emma Watson to name but a few.

Remarks: The Dragon, so named after an early school football team called Dragons, is as sought-after as ever. Originally founded as the Oxford Preparatory School by a group of dons who wanted a progressive, liberal school for their sons where learning would be fun. Once avant-garde, education and society have caught up with these principles so that today the Dragon can only aspire to unconventionality. It has resisted formality and retains the ethos of ordered disorderliness – a charmingly unpretentious, relaxed atmosphere. The school confesses they are relaxed about petty issues – untucked shirts, scruffy uniform and clutter – while concentrating on the things that matter, such as learning. Like an upturned swan – feet paddling busily on the surface whilst the underlying systems are serene and quiet. Unconventionality, or 'colouring outside the lines', has always been and still is encouraged, although school admits it is 'a balancing act' between risk-taking in schoolwork, striving for imagination and curiosity on one side, and discipline and toeing the line on the other. The Dragon aims for and encourages both.

Broad curriculum with a huge extracurricular programme including languages such as Mandarin, Japanese, Arabic and French as well as 'toast and translation' (a Latin club), music and drama etc. Most subjects are setted with scholarship classes at the top of the ability range. Learning support needs are screened in year 2 or on intake and help is available at extra cost. Dedicated learning support unit with five full – and three part-time members of staff who advise and update colleagues and draw up individual education plans. Additional groups provided at no extra cost for handwriting, reading comprehension and social skills.

Breadth is key at the Dragon with excellence across the board – outstanding sport with fantastic facilities and accolades too numerous to mention. Non-sporty children can find refuge in music – equally successful and receiving high praise from parents. Over two-thirds of pupils take individual music lessons. Fantastic art work in light airy art rooms and space in the Forum for the annual art exhibition – check out the school magazine – worthy of any secondary school. Facilities in general match those at many senior schools with science labs, impressive library (look out for dragons etched on the glass fronted mezzanine), 25m swimming pool and playing fields stretching down to the river and boat house. A mini-campus with happy free-range children roaming around, unrestricted by petty rules and health and safety, having a jolly time; play by the river still possible as long as a child can swim two lengths of the pool fully clothed. Traditions such as this survive along with others – female teachers are called Ma, bun break at mid-morning and tea in the afternoon. The blue cords of yesteryear have stood the test of time – for boys, shorts in summer, longs in winter plus polo shirt and jumper; for girls, a kilt and bright yellow shirt, summer plaid dresses.

Huge extracurricular programme including languages such as Mandarin, Japanese, Arabic and French as well as 'toast and translation' (a Latin club)

The Dragon is large (800+ including pre-prep, a mile or so up the road). Boys outnumber girls nearly two to one. Some grumbles about middle of the road children lost in the masses and unable to find a niche if not sporty or musical. School says that the children are separated into smaller units so that they operate within age-related spheres at any one time without being overwhelmed. Good pastoral care – children are discussed weekly and communication is paramount. The school takes its privileges with responsibility and is committed to raising money for charity through entrepreneurship which starts with the concept of the 'little society' and the teaching of philanthropy to children, and extends to ventures such as the locally renowned Dragon sale which raises tens of thousands of pounds. School is lead sponsor of a new multi-academy trust which includes three Blackbird Leys' primary schools. The primaries can use the school's science, art, music and sporting facilities, while Dragon teaching staff are developing initiatives within the new academies. The Café Dragón brand of ethically-sourced coffee is sold at school events.

Boarding houses, separated by sex and age, run by married couples with a homely atmosphere and individuality. Bun breaks and tea in the houses with supper in the dining hall. Children can pop in and out of their house during the day. Day pupils often invited back. Full boarding means that the boarders are 'the heartbeat of the school'. Weekends are packed with activities and many day pupils opt to board – one boarder walked from his boarding house past his family home every day. Day pupils easily fielded until 6pm, playing with boarders or participating in the huge number of extracurricular activities.

It was once established for dons, but they have largely been priced out of the market (in line with many independent schools). Lots of London money and business parents buying up north Oxford but professions also in evidence – many medics, lawyers, as well as a few academics (wealthy ones or few children). Lots of Old Dragon children. The Dragon remains the choice for the social elite of Oxford – if you want to be invited to the smartest dinner parties, this is your school. School says there is still plenty of mix and parents agree that everyone can find their level and this is not necessarily a school full of nannies in the playground. Boarders local and international, with no particular country in predominance. Currently 30 pupils have EAL lessons.

The Dragon is still the prep school in Oxford, in sound heart as ever, chosen by parents for breadth of education, good old-fashioned freedom and encouraging a 'can do' attitude. Lifelong friends and contacts start here.

Eagle House School

14

Sandhurst, Berkshire GU47 8PH

01344 772134 | info@eaglehouseschool.com | www.eaglehouseschool.com

Ages: 3-13 (boarding from year 3)

Pupils: 388; Boarders: 10 full, 40 weekly, 50 flexi

Day: £11,235 – £17,580 pa; Boarding: £23,610 pa

Linked school: Wellington College, 529

Headmaster: Since 2006, Mr Andrew Barnard BA (40s). Educated at Christ's Hospital, thence to Sheffield for a degree in archaeology (claims he 'still gets excited by a pile of earth'). 'Dabbled' in the restaurant business but was diverted to a PGCE via a stint helping out in various prep schools. Started at

Eagle House as head of history and English teacher, then housemaster and head of English and drama at Heath Mount School, deputy head at Winchester House and then back to Eagle House as head. He loves poetry, especially the Liverpool poets. Favourite author? Julian Barnes. Married to Sarah, who comes from a dynasty of teachers – no doubt it is from them that she has learned to embody grace under pressure: serving lunch to the nursery children, shepherding excited girls as they mass to play a rounders match against her old school, teaching French and EAL, taking care of front of house. They have three children, all at Wellington.

The Barnards have steered Eagle House successfully though some big changes. Their initial challenge was the move to co-ed and they admit that increasing the number of girls at the top end was, initially, 'hard to crack'. Intake is now 'robust' at about 40 per cent, with the few who leave at age 11 replaced and then some by girls joining for the last two years.

Living on site means the boundaries between home and work are pretty porous though the Barnards say that they and their children love every minute. This notwithstanding, sanctuary is a house in the Loire and all things French.

Entrance: Parents are advised to visit and register 12 months before their child is due to start. Pre-prep: trial day and usually automatic progression to prep. Prep: trial day, copies of reports and a reference from current head. Prep is relatively non-selective but pupils are 'expected to be able to cope with the school's academic course'. Year 7 entrants are tested in English, maths and reasoning.

Exit: Around half go to Wellington, the rest to Bradfield College, Lord Wandsworth College, Luckley House, Charterhouse, Radley, Bryanston, Millfield, Reddam House and Westminster

Remarks: Set in woods and heathland between Crowthorne and Sandhurst, Eagle House was founded in Hammersmith in 1820 and has been on its current 30-acre site since 1886. Owned by near neighbour Wellington College (the two schools share a boundary) and head says that these days, 'links are much better defined'. Being part of 'brand Wellington' includes teaching exchanges (each member of Eagle House staff is twinned with one from Wellington) as well as a definite trickle down (or up) of innovative approaches to education. For the past two years staff have attended life coaching courses at Wellington, there is a life skills club for prep pupils and now parents are snapping up taster sessions. We were particularly struck by how teachers of all ages were fired up by new ideas, welcoming change and educational debate – Eagle House clearly no place for moss gatherers.

Lessons are an hour long and those we saw were well-paced and active, pupils using hands as well as heads. Although Eagle House is not an official forest school, increasing use is being made of the grounds with lessons from science to English taking place outside. History comes to life in the Tudor House, a thatched replica where children dress up and learn about the past through workshops and activity days. Creativity is boosted by evening writing workshops and there are plans to continue with the school's literary festival after the success of earlier ones. Setting from year 3 in English and maths, and then for French and Latin in year 6. Latin for all from year 5, Greek for scholars. Four SEN staff support pupils individually with dyslexia, dyspraxia, mild ADHD (extra charge). EAL also offered.

We hear that as pressure to gain coveted places at Wellington builds a few parents are paying for extra tuition in years 5 and 6 to prepare for pre-testing in year 7, though when exactly their children fit this in is unclear. Not a reflection on the prep's teaching, rather more indicative of the holy grail a Wellington education has become. School is alert to this, saying that a few parents have unrealistic expectations, wanting their children to be 'brilliant at everything'. Some grumbles that the scholarship class (years 7 and 8) is 'divisive', citing detrimental effects on friendships. Scholarship exams are in February and March so the children in this class are 'off on trips' while the rest are studying for CE until June.

Eagle House differs with Wellington on one thing at least: books. The clean lines of big brother's splendid new library may not be spoilt by shelves and their dusty contents but for now at least, eaglets are still encouraged to curl up on squashy sofas with a good book. 'Over my dead body' were the young librarian's words when we asked if there were plans to defect to e-readers. Long may she reign.

In keeping with the school's 'learning for life' ethos, the golden eagle programme of activities introduces pupils to a rich mix of experiences intended to challenge and develop interests. Clubs such as golf, orienteering and Scalextrics run in the extended lunch break – a good example of making a virtue out of a necessity since limited size of the otherwise charming wood-panelled dining room means that it takes two hours to feed everyone. Years 3 and 4 can do optional Saturday morning activities and older children also have timetabled golden eagle session once a week.

'Brilliant' was the adjective most often used by parents to describe music at the school. Trial lessons and plenty of opportunities to develop talents great and small

The Eagle House journey starts, naturally enough, in the nest. Here in the nursery little ones (many of whom have older siblings in the prep) begin to learn through play. They are introduced to the big school and its curriculum via weekly sessions of swimming dance, music and IT. Delightful inside and outside spaces full of tempting toys, sand and water.

Pre-prep pupils gradually begin to explore the subjects that they will be taught once they move up, with specialist teachers for French, music, art and drama. Head of the pre-prep wants her pupils to have a 'happy start to school life, develop confidence and a love of learning' – we thought the kinaesthetic approach to numbers via 'maths stories' looked like a great idea. Literacy is taught using Read Write Inc phonics and the pre-prep is a model school for this scheme. No male class teachers, but music and football are taught by chaps borrowed from the prep. Dance is a popular activity and we enjoyed watching 5-year-olds' imaginative evocations of tarantulas – all part of the term's rain forest topic. Apparently playing medieval games in the Tudor house and visits from a 'real, live knight' are highlights.

A trio of energetic eaglets treated us to an access all areas tour. The dorms are on the first floor of the original mock Tudor house, rooms have large windows and high ceilings. The boys' (blue) rooms were predictably unadorned but the girls' (pink) rooms were as homely and sparkly as anyone could wish. Isn't this blue/pink cliché rather at odds with the progressive educational ethos of brand Wellington, we wondered? The eaglets told us gleefully that the showers and changing rooms in the new sports centre were similarly gendered, right down to the colour of the soap. Bathrooms, corridors and common room are clean and fresh, if towards the make do and mend end of the homely spectrum. The 15 or so pupils in over the weekend (or rather Saturday evening to Sunday evening) amount to, as Mrs Barnard pointed out, a 'minibus full'. Each member of staff does a Sunday stint so we imagine that minibus must go on a very interesting range of trips.

According to our guides, hockey and football are the main sports and nearby Cranleigh is the arch rival. The trophy cabinets show that boys do well at county level hockey and cricket but it's the girls' silverware that fills the shelves. Most recently the under 13s were national champions in hockey and the under 12s in netball. Such success is certainly celebrated but the Eagle House philosophy is not 'win at all costs' and the children we spoke to got huge enjoyment from their daily sport – whatever the result. Facilities are pretty good, with standard issue multi-purpose gym and an indoor swimming pool. Outside there's astroturf and all-weather pitches for hockey, netball and tennis, though boys told us they would like separate cricket and athletic fields. There's a lot of beautiful green space around the school but much of it belongs to venerable trees bearing preservation orders so, in the absence of a hurricane, cricketers and athletes will be sharing for many summers to come.

Music department resides in a deceptively spacious portakabin, though once inside listening to a superb impromptu performance of a Schumann Polonaise we wouldn't have cared if we were in a coal bunker. 'Brilliant' was the adjective most often used by parents to describe music at the school. Trial lessons and plenty of opportunities to develop talents great and small; lunchtime concerts allow new players to have their first experience of performing in a 'non-judgemental' environment. As we admired the beautifully decorated small organ in the charming chapel, choirmaster told us that organ lessons were just being established.

School may not have its own theatre (major productions are staged in Bracknell) but drama is big here. In the new performing arts studio we saw year 3 and 4 pupils belting out a song for their forthcoming show, not a single reluctant soul mouthing the words. On the walls of the foyer are larger than life photo canvases of past theatrical triumphs. So much for the stars, what about the tremblers in the wings? Everyone gets a chance to shine, school said; parents, while praising the 'wonderful' productions, weren't quite so sure.

Art and DT departments may be eagerly anticipating move to their new premises but no sign of a reduction in creativity. In art pupils were busy learning the patient craft of stop motion animation using 'indestructible' iPads and in DT they were dreaming up designs for boats. Work of a very high standard was on display everywhere.

Pastoral care generally praised and children we spoke to had a clear understanding of anti-bullying policies and what to do if they had a problem. Every child now has their own tutor from year 5 (prior to this form teachers are first point of contact) and the new system is intended to be more 'open and flexible', involving all members of staff in pastoral roles.

Most pupils are from 15-20 mile radius but increasing numbers from London. Handful from abroad, no dominant country. Small contingent of Spanish children come for a year or two – it's not an organised thing, more 'word of mouth', according to the head. Parents, the usual Thames valley mix of management and high-tech industry professionals, like the boarding ethos even if their children are day pupils. We're not surprised, pupils can stay until 6pm and by then prep has usually been done (older children may have to finish theirs at home). For most though it's the Wellington connection that makes this a first choice school and leavers' destinations over the last few years bear this out. Several parents told us they thought the school had changed, describing it as much more 'under Wellington's thumb'. However another said, 'We initially chose Eagle House because of its links with Wellington but now realise that's only one aspect. It's a great start, wherever your child goes on to'.

Eagle House is a happy, creative school. The atmosphere is eager and unstuffy – honouring the best of prep school tradition; nimbly assimilating 21st century educational thinking. Eaglets headed for Wellington and other eyries will find this a great place to learn to fly.

Elstree School

15

Woolhampton, Reading, Berkshire RG7 5TD

01189 713302 | registrar@elstreeschool.org.uk | www.elstreeschool.org.uk

Ages: Boys 3-13, girls 3-7

Pupils: 260; Boarders: 15 full, 95 weekly/flexi

Day: £11,220 – £20,160 pa; Boarding: £21,720 – £25,860 pa

Headmaster: Since 2013, Mr Sid Inglis BA (40s), previously headmaster at Ludgrove. Uncertain as to career until taught English in Chile (where met wife Olivia) and realised that as professions go 'there is no finer job.' Appointed at exciting if nerve-wracking time following wobbles in leadership, parent confidence and pupil numbers. It's now all go again, with school at capacity, no need even to contemplate going fully co-ed (girls leave at 8), scholarships back to full honours-board levels – and all right in world.

Mr Inglis's first name is unusual and, even more unusually, shared with last head but two. Would be karma except that real name is Andrew. All the other more predictable essentials are also in place: labrador ('though had her before we arrived,' says equally charming Mrs Inglis), three cherubic offspring (two still at the school) and website must-have – photograph capturing whole shebang smilingly disporting themselves on well-positioned, sunlight-drenched bench if human (and beside it if not).

Would take a mean-spirited reviewer to deny that Mr Inglis exudes winning headmasterly qualities of authority and personability. Out and about like nobody's business. 'Very much a figurehead,' said parent. 'I don't know how he can be in so many different places all the time. He and his wife go around like a pair and are very supportive of one another.'

Even slots in weekly story-reading session to different pre-prep class each week (we encountered him en route with book, wondering if would require 'funny voices'). While parent approval can reach adoration levels, pupils' response more down to earth. 'Lets us get on with life as long as we're sensible,' said one. 'Doesn't feel special – acts just like a normal teacher.'

Relaxed, too – when this reviewer turned up at the very last minute for an open day visit, he (and all colleagues) were genuinely welcoming (if there were any less positive feelings, were fathoms deep).

He thinks it's part and parcel of the ethos that made this a dream job. Does a spot of teaching (RS, his degree subject, has yielded to classics here) and loves it. Aim, as laid out in prospectus, is to discover 'how a child is intelligent rather than how intelligent a child is' – while still preparing them for range of senior schools.

Translated, means that 'don't want academic success at the expense of muddy knees,' he says. 'If a child is confident and happy in their own little shell, academics will follow.' School, he says, isn't for chest-beating alpha males, jostling for position (or females, either). Will have a few who struggle academically but exude sense of purpose elsewhere, shining on sports field or stage. Combination of variety, straight-talking pupils and enjoyable challenge of (successfully) giving school boost it needed makes this a role he relishes. 'Love being busy.'

He is passionate about sport, particularly rugby and cricket, and enjoys playing golf and fishing. He took over after the school spent a year under an acting head, after the abrupt and unexplained resignation of the previous head, and brought with him parental hopes for stability after troubled times.

Head of Home Farm School (the pre-prep), Mrs Kay Markides, arrived 2009. Graduated in science, married with a family (including a son who attended Elstree) before deciding to train for teaching young ones. Taught for a while at another school nearby. Thrilled to be involved with Elstree, and it shows. Warm and at ease with the children ('I love them') she is clearly not only very competent but also exudes calm dependability. Presides over a talented young staff who clearly relish the company of their young charges, patiently explaining things and then rushing around with them in the grounds of the prep school.

Entrance: Non-selective in Home Farm, the pre-prep (nursery to year 2), whose 60 pupils are accommodated in next door farmhouse and converted outbuildings, with own separate entrance and playgrounds but overlapping grounds. Co-ed but boy-dominated as 'people are signing up for the whole school,' points out amiable pre-prep head and former parent Mrs Kay Markides. No girls in current year 2 and a cheerful minority over in the prep for year 3.

Open to learning needs including ADHD. Key is ability to keep up academically and impress with right attitude: prospectus stresses that 'effort is king'. Growth of waiting lists (in almost every year group) means that while ability range is wide, 'we have become gently selective,' says Mr Inglis.

While teachers sometimes sorely tried, rare that won't make a go of it, helped by much-praised learning needs department. Will, though, review progress in years 4 and 6 when long-term compatibility of child and school will be weighed up, says headmaster. Thus far, nobody has been asked to leave.

Exit: Good links with Bradfield (former head, now at Eton, sent all his brood here), most of first rank southern staples represented. Bradfield, Radley, Pangbourne, Eton, Abingdon, Winchester, Stowe,

Marlborough, Sherbourne, Harrow and Wellington have all featured recently.

Year 3 girls to St Andrew's Pangbourne, Cheam, St Gabriel's, Marlston House and the Manor, Abingdon.

Remarks: School that likes life in duplicate. Pre-prep's 60 pupils have large magical woodland area (annexed from prep), paths canopied with intertwined branches or bordered with wild grasses (there's even a troll bridge) – and a second mini wilderness for everyday, star attraction a palatial roofed sandpit big enough for whole class to enjoy. Even Mrs Markides shares year 2 teaching duties with colleague (though second best rule undoubtedly doesn't apply).

Appearance, in pairs or otherwise, is winningly green and traditional. School's 150 acres include two lakes, one used for Elstree Award activities (like D of E but bespoke), croquet lawn with wire sculpture of (Lewis Carroll inspired?) flamingo, courts and pitches (including full-sized Astro), dog-walking parents and staff adding homely touch.

Though vibe is venerable (pre-prep uniform list specifies named napkin ring), mood is progressive. 'Lots of tradition and trust, but we're well aware it's a modern world,' says Mrs Inglis. Mr I stresses importance of charitable activities that open pupils' eyes 'to the wide world away from idyllic leafy confines.' Perhaps accounts for staff list hedging its bets – some male teachers are Esq, some are Mr, while headmaster, straddling both worlds, is bereft of any salutation at all.

Though vibe is venerable (pre-prep uniform list specifies named napkin ring), mood is progressive. 'Lots of tradition and trust, but we're well aware it's a modern world'

'Pushes children hard but pleasantly so,' thought prospective parent. 'It's not "you will learn 10 verses by Tuesday".' By way of proof, there's combined staff and pupil YouTube version of 'Happy' to mark departure of recent batch of girl leavers, treat for dad dancing (or teacher equivalent) connoisseurs and anyone needing lesson in chutzpah.

Full boarding the only traditional element that isn't faring so well, hanging on but only just. Now a minority occupation for 15 out of the 100 or so boarders, mainly overseas (Russians, sprinkling of Spanish) plus odd Londoner, though most stay for at least three nights a week. They 'get used to it,' thought pupil. Not most ringing of endorsements, even backed by run of grounds at weekend.

However when it comes to flexi or weekly stays, 'boys are clamouring to board,' the head told us firmly, reeling off vast list of evening activities on offer when they do – from bridge to fantasy football, debating and improvisation. School now so 'full to bursting' from Monday to Friday that it's a case of joining the queue with waiting list in operation. No quibbles with boarding logistics, which work a treat, year 4 to 6 dorms to the side – we liked their emergency cuddly toy cubby hole to keep homesickness at bay – while years 7 and year 8 have separate quarters in main building.

Dorms on large side – eight to 10 not uncommon – but with spacious, pleasant rooms and friendly, uncrowded feel. Décor variable, one room a shrine to Shoot! magazine, plastered floor to ceiling with pictures of footballers, another, the former ballroom, featuring stucco storks looking down from ceiling in gentle amazement at year 8 pupils' beds in formation on parquet floor. Possible setting for new reality TV show, 'Come boarding,' perhaps?

If full boarding continues to decline and parent vibe suggests it will – 'strong majority who like the day aspect,' thought one – Big Weekends could be the future, with 40 or so other pupils piling in for fun and games including Laser Tag and exciting Indoor Lions, inside version of Stuck in the Mud played in the dark for added thrills.

Extremely popular (currently free of charge, so no wonder) and means 'full boarders have more company,' says school. Also an organisational cinch as Saturday school – a full day with lessons and afternoon games – is in full force from year 4. Can be shock to the system (as is late weekday finish) for those coming from state sector, though 'only do easy subjects then,' said tour guide. Well, maybe – if you consider French and maths a bit of light weekend banter, though heavy-duty exercises are interspersed with the odd quiz, which helps. And without Saturday school, 'weekends are too long,' thought pupil.

Best teaching (and there's lots of it) combines humour and memorability. One English teacher (a school favourite) known for quick draw funny pictures – enthusiastic year 7 boys (like all other pupils smilingly standing up for adults) praising memorable stick person imagery that instantly conjured up poetic protagonist 'swimming against tide with heart sinking...'.

Impressively inclusive, say parents, with children's confidence boosted by lessons cannily pitched at challenging rather than daunting. 'My son thinks he's brilliant because they've given him the work that's appropriate,' said mother. Even less inspirational teachers – maths felt to be slightly variable – usually get the results in the end. 'If you get something right, you get a point. Didn't like it but it does work,' thought one pupil.

Heroic efforts elsewhere, with year 7 pupil in DT class who had elected to make sundial out of seasoned oak and, equipped with bow saw, was two-thirds of way through chunky tree trunk. 'Has taken an hour already,' was weary comment.

Sport equally strong and inclusive (goes down to E teams and 6th XIs). Fine summer evenings are an enthusiast's delight, with croquet on front lawn

Pre-prep pupils similarly keen on lessons and given undiluted praise from parents – staff 'can't do enough, there morning, noon and night, so happy and 100 per cent involved with the children' – no wonder. One small maths fan was full of praise for 'hard sums', another extolled virtues of recent pirate topic because 'they kill people' – before being gently shepherded into more wholesome approach by teacher. 'Our pirates wouldn't do things like that.' (He didn't look totally convinced).

Music 'absolutely thriving,' says head, with 200 individual lessons timetabled each week, top performers reaching grade 8, two recent scholarships (Radley and Charterhouse) and department 'always full of boys.' Prep choir (one of three) is 30-deep, recent delights including choral evensong at Bath Abbey. Music school now includes a rehearsal studio and music technology room.

Encouraged by many means, including piano located somewhat unusually on first bend of main staircase in prep school for impromptu concerts – one boy at a time, ban on James Bond theme tune (popularity led to aural repetitive strain injury risk for admin staff nearby).

Drama similarly successful with boys happy to take female roles and lack of self-consciousness that comes with single-sex environment. Parents thrilled with gentle encouragement that sees the formerly un-keen blossoming into performers. Talent search starts early with violin (free lessons for all in year 1) and recorder (year 2) – parents apparently thrilled with results, performers shining in end of year concert.

Sport equally strong and inclusive (goes down to E teams and 6th XIs). Fine summer evenings an enthusiast's delight, with croquet on front lawn. Lots more – from swimming to shooting, golf and judo, as well as school staples – athletics, football, rugby, hockey, cricket (coach, current Berkshire captain, also teaches pre-prep pupils, one mightily impressed to find his teacher known to Lord's).

Plenty of informal activities, too; one tree full of roosting boys, like giant navy blue rooks. Though staff presence seemed to us to be relatively hands-off, some parents and pupils feel free time can be over-supervised. 'Always a teacher walking round.' Reasons for adult presence well understood – 'it's so someone doesn't get hurt,' and by year 8, said pupil, things improve. 'They accept you need some time alone.'

Greta Garbo tendencies no doubt forgotten in excitement of table football matches and hotly contested corridor cricket. Boys very keen, though one thought teachers possibly less so when caught in path of oncoming cricket ball during evening rounds.

Gentle pace gets up speed through the school, senior school entrance exam pressure an inevitable fact of life for year 8 pupils, though teachers do best to defuse the tension, felt boys. Weekly form time used to air difficulties; friendly gap students a more informal source of support, comfort food – evening bowls of cereal – provided for boarders.

Pastoral care generally felt to be good, from daily staff briefings to half hour catch up sessions at lunchtime. Pupils urged to use common sense if someone is feeling left out of activities – 'they expect us to find something that fits,' said pupil. Bullying clearly well managed. 'Issues dealt with very quickly with children pulled in. If you overstep the mark there's a punishment and everyone knows that,' said parent. Pre-prep opts for circle time and golden rules. Staff had slight struggle to remember them but do appear to work, parents full of praise at absence of problems in any age group.

Highly organised parents notable for efficiency and ability sweep up newcomers – 'integration' events include lunches for the mums and curry nights for dads (or vice versa one progressive day?). Praise, bar mutterings about over influential queen bees from former parent, was universal, school community the icing on the cake. Attracts London exiles as well as locals, drawn by welcoming culture and lots to keep sporty and arty happy.

'Son has been pushed where would like to be pushed and pushed along where needed to be. An amazingly efficient school that continues to surprise me,' said mother.

Eton College

16

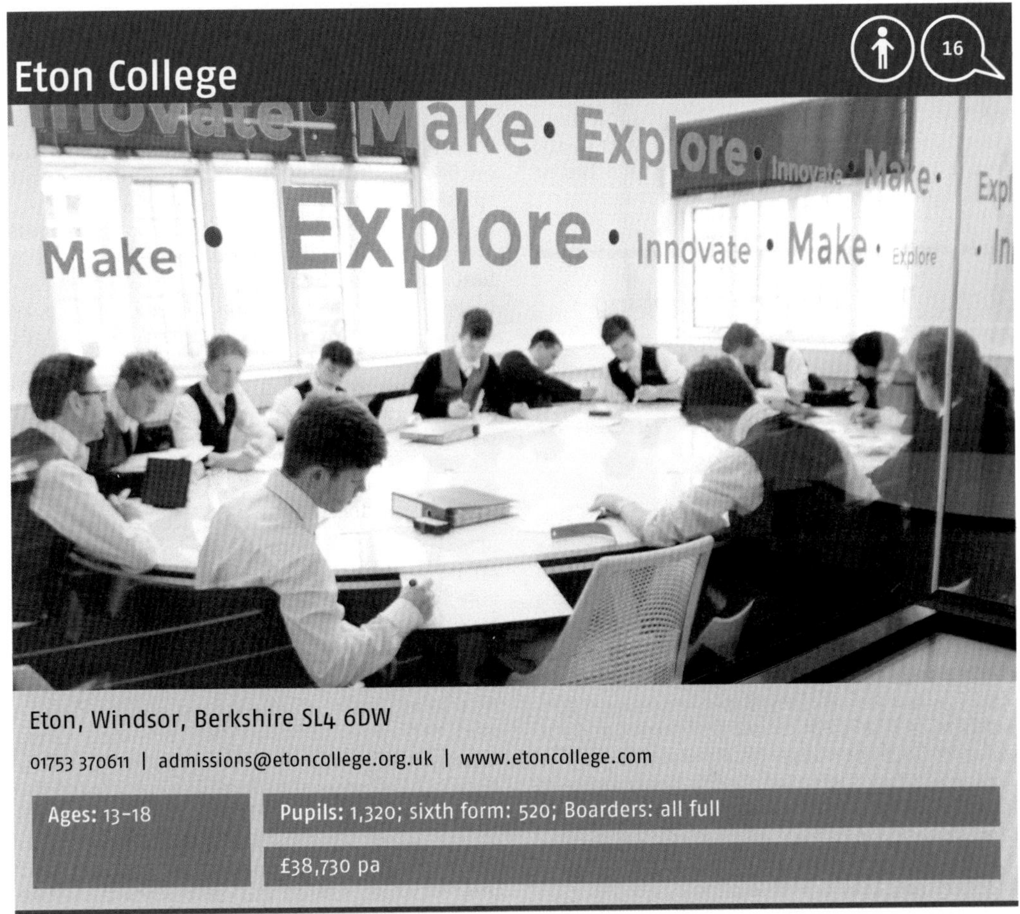

Eton, Windsor, Berkshire SL4 6DW

01753 370611 | admissions@etoncollege.org.uk | www.etoncollege.com

Ages: 13–18

Pupils: 1,320; sixth form: 520; Boarders: all full

£38,730 pa

Head master: Since 2015, Simon Henderson MA PGCE (30s), previously head of Bradfield College. Educated at Winchester College, followed by Brasenose College, Oxford, where he read history. Teaching career started at Windsor Boys' School, thence to Eton in 2001, where he was a deputy house master and head of history, and on to Sherborne School in 2009 as deputy head (academic). Married to Ali with four young children.

Mr Henderson has the impeccable manners, inscrutability and cerebral acuity generally alleged to distinguish the man who's been to Winchester, but in our experience also common to many heads of senior schools. But he has too the aura of serene composure and mastery of self that Betjeman mocks, gently, in his poem, The Wykehamist, 'It's something too to know your wants/And go full pelt for Norman fonts.' We strongly suspect that Mr Henderson's equivalent of Norman fonts is schools and teaching. Of his own education he says, 'I loved school – it was dynamic, exciting and vibrant.' His first experience of teaching was in South Africa on his gap year, 'I absolutely loved it.' His vocation was confirmed by a spell doing corporate internships in the City ('awful').

Does being head master of Eton leave any time for teaching? 'The unpredictability means I can't commit to any formal teaching, but I make guest appearances.' He says he has 'plans to get back into the classroom,' but in the meantime is making a 'conscious decision to be here as much as possible.' That must be hard when his presence is expected at so many events – 'I go to lots of dinners,' he says somewhat ruefully. 'Schools are big communities of people, it's so important to make personal connections.'

In any large boarding school it will be house master, rather than head master, who is pupils' day-to-day influence and whom pupils and parents know best, so it was perhaps unsurprising to find that almost all the many parents we spoke to had had no contact with Mr Henderson. 'He holds lunches after games on Saturdays but we haven't been to one yet.' 'My son says he sends cards to all the boys on their birthdays and they sometimes meet him if they've won a prize.' And what do the boys think of their 'head man'? 'He's nice, but he seems quite strict.'

Rather than headline-grabbing attempts on the superficial, one gets the impression that Mr Henderson has addressed himself to Eton's internal workings

When we met Mr Henderson, his mind was on the role of technology in the classroom. Eton's Tony Little Centre for Innovation and Research in Learning is at the forefront of developments in this field, working in partnership with education technology firms and also pursuing its own ventures. The centre's aims are to take this expertise beyond the school gates and make it available to its state school partnerships, local education authorities and the wider world. Interestingly Mr Henderson sees this as Eton's virtual version of other schools' overseas franchises. Eton itself, he believes, cannot be replicated, but the school's approach to education can.

Does he foresee a time when Eton's beaks (teachers) can stand down? 'Technology is changing what happens. For example, if there are 20 pupils of broadly the same ability in a maths set, computer programmes can be used to detect areas of weakness and generate questions that consolidate or extend learning, but they will never be a substitute for human interaction.' He believes that this kind of personalised learning will free teachers to concentrate on higher order work – spending more time with individuals rather than generating questions. 'Technology will enable teaching in schools to become similar to that in universities – with a mixture of small classes, online courses, set-piece lectures, time spent on individual study and more fluidity between year groups.'

Every Eton head appointed in recent years must surely have pondered at the start of his tenure whether or not he had the stomach to go down in history as the barbarian who consigned the school's world-famous uniform to the archives. Mr Henderson was touted as a moderniser, just the sort of chap who might actually do this deed. Not that he's ever said as much, naturally. In an early press interview his answer to this predictable question was, 'Well, I'm not getting rid of the uniform this week', accompanied by a photograph of him sporting chinos, a linen jacket and a slightly casual shirt (with tie, of course). Several years on, and despite moving headmaster HQ from traditional study to a studiedly modern office, in sartorial matters at least he appears to have gone native. No doubt the tailors at Eton town's four (yes, four) gentlemen's outfitters have decided it's safe to go ahead and splash out on new tape measures.

Mr Henderson is one of the school's youngest ever heads so perhaps donning the armour of the uniform each day makes it easier to inhabit such a huge role. Not that he seems to need any help, as anyone who heard him being questioned by MPs from the Education Select Committee inquiry into 'exam integrity', will know. Completely unruffled, his answers were eloquent and precise and there was no doubting his resolve that such a thing (boys seeing material that later appeared in exam papers) would never happen again.

So where, beyond his new office, is the evidence of Mr Henderson's promised 'modernisation'? After all, he taught here for eight years so must presumably have identified things that could be improved. He has made half term holidays longer to bring them into line with other independent schools and banned mobile phones for boys in F block (year 9). He told us that he wants to continue the school's work to broaden opportunities and access – long term commitments include sponsoring nearby Holyport College (a state boarding school) and the London Academy of Excellence, a state sixth form college in East London. Eton's famous Universities Summer School has been running since 1981 and provides expert subject tuition to pupils from state schools who are applying to top universities. Mr Henderson says that he shares his predecessor's ambition for access to Eton to become 'needs blind'. 'We spend around £7m on means tested bursaries and most of that money has been given by former pupils for this purpose.'

Access to Eton may one day become needs blind, but it's unlikely to become gender blind on Mr Henderson's watch. He told us, with just a hint of impatience, 'There's too much focus on whether a school is single sex or co-ed, what matters most is whether a school is good or not.' Adding, 'Young people feel under more pressure to conform to gender stereotypes at co-ed schools.' Women teachers are still in the minority at Eton, but the appointment of the first female lower master (the senior deputy head) is a good sign.

We were interested to get the head's take on the public perception of Eton and the way the school is portrayed in the press. 'We must not be defensive, we need to engage with our critics. Pupils who have been educated here should never feel guilty, but they must be aware of their good fortune and responsibilities.'

We doubt Mr Henderson has much in the way of spare time, but what he has is reserved for his family (he has four young children) and golf. And supporting QPR. Favourite writer? Thomas Hardy. Regrets? Giving up on the piano and clarinet

Rather than headline-grabbing attempts on the superficial, one gets the impression that Mr Henderson has addressed himself to Eton's internal workings, adjusting the calibration of its doubtless Byzantine ancient mechanisms. 'I think he's probably making subtle changes,' one father told us. 'Subtle changes' can be hard to spot, even for a Good Schools Guide writer, so thank you Eton parents for your help and all those insightful, robust and sometimes contradictory opinions!

Academic matters: Parents think teaching staff (known as 'beaks') are 'exceptional', but not without exception. Those we met lived up to this, ahem, billing – deeply knowledgeable about their school and delighted to tell visitors about its past and present. Eton must be a great gig – not just for the kudos of working in the world's most famous school and the resources and opportunities it offers, but also the intellectual challenge of teaching a carefully hand-picked selection of the (mostly western) world's sparkiest young men.

The deputy head (academic)'s introduction for new parents sets a certain tone, 'When all is said and done, a boy is not coming to Eton simply to earn a set of qualifications.' But exams are exams and even Etonians must jump these trifling hurdles. They do so hardly putting a foot wrong. IGCSEs for most of the core subjects; nine languages on offer in addition to French and Spanish including Mandarin, Russian, Arabic, Italian and Japanese. Considerably more opt for classical Greek and Latin than for drama, DT and music. Most boys take 11 subjects and gain top marks in all – 96 per cent A*-A/9-7 grades at I/GCSE in 2017 – only 15 grade Cs across the board. Interestingly, the only subject with a clean sweep of A*s is fine art and design, one of the harder subjects in which to achieve the highest grade.

Though still impressive, A level results spread a little beyond the first letters of the alphabet (or their Pre U equivalents) – in 2017, 79 per cent A*/A at A level and 82 per cent D1-3 at Pre-U but there are also Cs, Ds, Es – even, gasp, a couple of Us. Most popular subject by a considerable margin is maths, followed by economics, history (both of these offered as Pre U), religious studies, physics, further maths and chemistry. Further maths garners the highest percentage of A*s along with, once again, fine art. Only a handful of takers for drama and DT, much better news for the oft-beleaguered modern foreign languages – particularly Spanish – but more opt for Latin than French.

Small classes and setting for all in most subjects ensure teaching is precisely targeted and boys' progress is extremely closely monitored – any falling off is brought to the attention of tutors and house masters. Several parents thought it is the combination of great teaching and competition between the boys themselves that keeps academic standards flying, 'they learn so much from their peers.' Clearly understood and immediate sanctions for work submitted late or sub-par. Parents marvel at the beautifully written and minutely detailed termly reports – each arrives accompanied by a two – or three-page letter from the boy's house master and tutor.

Full boarding means a different shape to the school day, with lessons (known as 'schools') following afternoon sports activities at least three times a week. We sat in on several late afternoon sessions: computing, Spanish and F block (year 9) divinity. As they mustered and spread themselves out, waistcoats and hair somewhat dishevelled, the older boys could have passed for weary ushers at the end of a particularly gruelling society wedding. And notwithstanding all the high-powered goings on in the Tony Little Centre for Innovation and Research in Learning, the lessons we observed would have made perfect sense to any shades of beaks long dead – books, pens, questions, answers, discussion, testing, checking and a bit of good-humoured banter

(though we're not sure what they'd make of laptops, Google and interactive white boards).

Well-resourced and highly professional SEN provision and staff. Around 50 to 60 boys receive regular learning support for mild to moderate dyslexia, dyspraxia, dysgraphia – either one-to-one or in small groups (charged as an extra). All boys assessed during their first term and any whose results give cause for concern get extra help, either from their tutor or the SEN unit.

In 2017 Pre-U candidates in economics and art history had their marks disallowed by the examination board after evidence of questions being leaked in advance came to light. In the case of art history there was no evidence of Eton pupils or staff having done anything wrong, but this was not so for economics, where the revelations lead to the departure of the head of economics, who was also deputy head (academic) elect. The school dealt with these matters swiftly and openly, but it makes one wonder under how much pressure teachers feel to produce top results in their subjects.

Games, options, the arts: How long have you got? It is surely impossible for any boy to have a go at all the opportunities Eton offers in a five-year school career, but the message from pupils and parents is that the school does its utmost to foster and support boys' interests and ambitions. 'Whatever the talent or interest, school will do all it can to enable boys to make it their thing.' 'Eton encouraged me' was a phrase we heard several times, not necessarily in relation to extraordinary achievements but, for instance, performance opportunities for keen but far from concert level musicians. Co-curricular programme includes CCF – Eton's was founded in 1860 when the country was threatened by Napoleon, community service, and over 50 'societies', nearly all established and run by boys, including debating, comedy, Orwell (described as 'left wing'), cheese and wine (these last two are not held together). Meetings, many with visiting speakers, take place in the evenings.

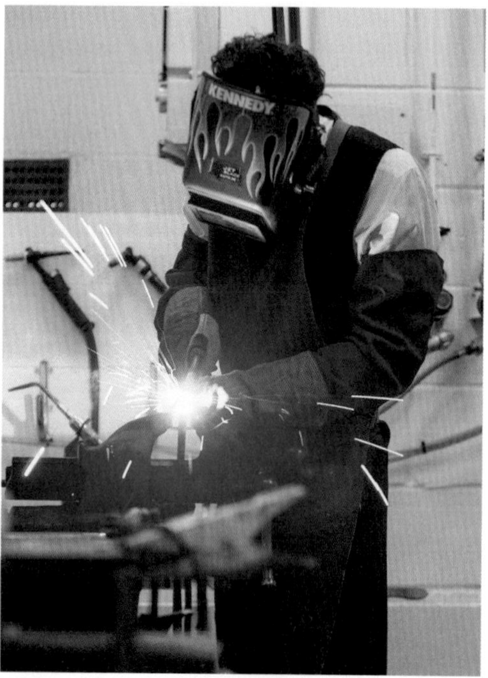

School playing fields, with evocative names such as Agar's Plough and Mesopotamia, used for football and rugby matches in the Michaelmas half (term), rugby and hockey in the Lent half and cricket and athletics in the summer. With up to 16 teams fielded for a particular sport at any one time, a parent told us that sometimes two opposing schools are invited so that everybody gets a game. On match days there can be up to 40 teams competing. Even the least sporty boys will play in house and inter-house competitions. A parent told us, 'Sport is important, but it doesn't dominate school life; it's just one aspect of the boys' development – like music and drama.' Another observed, 'Even if your son was in all the A teams at prep school, he probably won't be when he gets to Eton – it can come as a bit of a shock when they find out how many boys are better than them!'

Eton also has its own unique version of football, 'the field game', but since no one else plays it these matches are entirely home affairs. Another unique sporting tradition is the 'Eton wall game', a version of rugby played between Collegers (scholars) and Oppidans (rest of the school) on a narrow strip of ground adjacent to a brick wall. Nearly all matches, entirely organised by the boys, appear to result in goalless draws, but the rules and vocabulary are so esoteric and confusing we can't comment further. Suffice it to say that Boris Johnson was a keen player. Rowing takes place at Dorney, with superb facilities developed for the rowing and canoeing events of the 2012 Olympics. One or two parents (presumably not parents of rowers) thought that investment in Dorney had been at the expense of other sports. Huge range of minor sports including rackets, fives, golf, shooting and sailing. While lack of stabling means you can't bring a horse Eton, school has thriving polo and eventing teams.

Over 1,000 individual music lessons a week, splendid facilities for teaching and concerts, eight (yes, eight) organs, and a hierarchy of orchestras: symphony orchestra for the best, chamber orchestra for string players from the symphony orchestra, concert band for wind and brass players plus junior versions of all these. Smaller groups such as piano trios, quartets, jazz and rock bands get the chance to perform at events organised by the school, houses or boys themselves. Audition-only College Chapel Choir sings three times a week at services,

'Even if your son was in all the A teams at prep school, he probably won't be when he gets to Eton – it can come as a bit of a shock'

tours abroad and has produced nine CDs, but there are also plenty of opportunities for keen but less exquisitely musical voices to be heard.

Of all Eton's many strengths, it was drama that parents singled out for particular praise: 'stupendous', 'phenomenal', 'as good as West End productions.' The Farrer theatre has 400 seats and there are two smaller venues. 'It's not exclusive, there are so many opportunities to get involved – not just acting but on the technical side'. What with whole school plays, house plays, and productions written, produced and directed by boys themselves, it's perhaps understandable that relatively few boys feel the need to choose GCSE and A level drama.

Remember all those art GCSE and A level A*s? They're nurtured in the light-filled Drawing Schools, home to teaching expertise and superb facilities for painting, drawing printmaking, photography, computer graphics, sculpture and ceramics. Each year a different artist in residence is invited to set up an open studio, produce and exhibit their work.

Boarding: Eton has 25 boarding houses, mostly located in historic buildings throughout the town. Each is home to 50 boys (exception is the scholars' house, College, which has 70). Every boy has a single study bedroom – no dorms or sharing. Rooms we saw were pretty standard issue boys' boarding school – relatively unadorned apart from large shoes. Several parents mentioned that the quality of the mattresses left a lot to be desired.

Around half the houses have their own chefs and dining rooms; boys from houses with no catering have their meals at Bekynton, the college dining complex, eating in house groups together with their house master and other house staff. According to boys, the main pro of a catered house is 'not having to dash down the street for breakfast on a cold, rainy morning.' One parent suggested that because Bekynton offered a wider choice of food, a non-catered house could suit a boy who is a 'picky eater.' We enjoyed a delicious lunch in Bekynton's staff dining area where the food was, we were reassured, exactly the same as the boys were getting (but with added napery).

Mealtimes seem to be more formal affairs than at other boarding schools. A member of staff told us, 'eating in house groups is important for strengthening the relationship between staff and boys.' In addition to three main meals, all boys are provided with morning and afternoon drinks and snacks in their houses (breaks known respectively as 'chambers' and 'messing'). And if they're still hungry they can forage at the school shop or those in the town.

When it comes to choosing a boarding house the unanimous advice from school and parents is to keep on open mind, 'Don't get fixated.' Do your homework, visit at least three, rank them in order of preference and the 'vast majority' will get a place in one of their choice. Everything will depend on parents' (and boys') rapport with the house master and also the dame (responsible for domestic arrangements, health issues etc). One mother advised, 'trust your instincts, if you really don't think a house master is going to get the best out of your son then it's better to go back into the pool.'

House masters are in post for 13 years and in addition to the house master and his family, there will be a deputy house master and two assistants, the dame and her assistant, plus domestic staff. Boys also have responsibilities – every house has a house captain and a captain of games. Eton provides all teaching staff with accommodation, so boys' tutors will live only a short distance away.

In addition to standard holidays, boys can go home after commitments on Saturday until Sunday evening once a term (additional weekend leave is at housemaster's discretion).

While boys arriving from prep schools may at least be accustomed to boarding, message from parents is that the very long, full days are quite a 'gear change' for new boys – more so for those arriving from state schools. Some house masters hold events such as barbeques or football games over the summer for those joining in September. New boy integration is, apparently, 'very good' – house masters are 'incredibly observant and always contactable.' In addition to standard holidays, boys can go home after commitments on Saturday until Sunday evening once a term

It's perhaps inevitable that over 13 years a house master will shape the 'character' of his house and as a consequence houses may 'collect boys in the same mould.' Accordingly, some houses will become known as, for example, 'sporty' or 'musical'. Several parents thought there were ongoing 'power struggles' between senior management and house masters (such tensions are not uncommon in boarding schools). While everyone was overwhelmingly supportive of the 'federal' status quo and utterly loyal to their own sons' house masters (all 'fantastic', 'indefatigable' and 'inspirational' to a man), one or two conceded that 'a degree of uniformity' might keep accusations of fiefdoms at bay

Background and atmosphere: Eton is a small and charming Thameside town, not unadjacent to Slough and a bridge away from Windsor. It also just happens to have the world's most famous school attached. This makes it somewhat atypical, with its three art galleries, gunsmith, four gentlemen's outfitters and any number of restaurants and cafés. At least some of the latter should be applauded for having resisted the temptation to mine the rich and apparently inexhaustible seam of school related names. No one but tourists and the occasional nervous prep-school boy visiting with his parents looks twice at the tail-coated pupils and teachers as they stride up and down the high street between boarding houses and main school.

On arrival we were made very welcome in the porters' lodge, wood panelling decorated with framed personal photos of the royal family (princes William and Harry were pupils here – it is their local school after all!). Royalty or not, Eton's front of house staff are charming and friendly to deal with – in person or over the phone – quite an accolade when you consider just how busy the world's interest in its most famous school must keep them.

The school was founded by in 1440 by King Henry V1 to provide free education for 70 poor boys, but his ambitious building work stopped (the chapel, though fine and large, is considerably smaller than planned) and the school lost many of its original endowments when Henry was deposed by Edward 1V in 1461. Records from the 16th century show pupils had a pretty tough day – lessons finished at 8pm and there was only an hour of 'play'. The school's history lives on in its language – terms are 'halves' because there used to be only two three week holidays a year; 'oppidans', from the Latin for word for town, refers to pupils (originally from the nearby town) who, unlike the scholars, did not live at the school. Now it means all pupils who are not scholars.

Over 1,000 individual music lessons a week, splendid facilities for teaching and concerts, eight (yes, eight) organs, and a hierarchy of orchestras

Eton has two superb libraries, a huge collection of fine and decorative art including works by Sir Joshua Reynolds and J M W Turner, and no fewer than three museums. The Natural History Museum contains material from botanist and Old-Etonian, Sir Joseph Banks, who sailed with Captain Cook; the Museum of Antiquities has a particularly fine collection of ancient Egyptian artefacts and there's also a Museum of Eton Life. All three are open to the public on Sunday afternoons.

Until the late nineteenth century boys at Eton could wear pretty much what they liked, although the upper-class monoculture at that time probably ensured they all looked fairly similar. When uniform was introduced it appears to have taken its first breath and dived into a vat of aspic. Top hats and cropped jackets may have been shed along the way, but what message do tail coats and white collars have for the 21st century? Pride in tradition and the confidence to follow one's own path, or outdated fancy dress, preserved because it distinguishes the members of a privileged club? That depends on the politics of the observer.

Ironically, egalitarianism Eton style means boys and (male) teaching staff wear pretty much the same costume, with subtle distinctions of hierarchy such as patterned waistcoats and silver buttons for exalted members of Pop (sixth form prefects). Such uniformity may be why the issue of uniform is less pressing than one might imagine. Despite it being an outfit that flatters just about anyone who wears it, boys shed their uniform double quick once the school day is done.

Pastoral care, well-being and discipline: By all accounts the house and tutor system works powerfully well to ensure that despite the size of the school, no one is overlooked – 50 boys in each house means only ten of each year group. Boys are encouraged to discuss social and health issues; the house dame deals with minor medical problems and school has three doctors a psychiatrist, two psychologists and a counsellor. Honourable mention goes to the multi denominational chaplaincy team in this context too. We heard mixed reports of peer support – some say that there's a strictly observed hierarchy of age, but we also heard that members of B block (sixth form) are assigned to look after younger boys. Like so many things at Eton, this seems to vary between individual houses.

Eton is a demanding school, 'very much into the pursuit of excellence in every field', but it is also very good at choosing boys who will thrive in such an atmosphere – robust self-starters who want to take every opportunity offered, 'It puts a lot of trust in boys and treats them as adults from the word go.' Parents describe it as 'surprisingly meritocratic' and 'very comfortable with difference.'

While appearances would suggest that the school doesn't sweat the small stuff (things like hair etc), one parent sounded a word of caution, 'They have their own way of doing things which is fine when all is going well, but if you come up against the system it can be pretty inflexible.'

Pupils and parents: Cast your preconceptions aside, families from all walks of life can, and do, send their sons here. Name down at birth has long gone and now around 60 per cent of Etonians do not

Getting into Eton is tough, so it's reassuring to know the admissions department is equally rigorous in seeking out the 'right' candidates

have any family connection with the school. We heard from lots of parents who had plenty to say about the school they had chosen for their sons; they were as interesting, non-standard and off-message as we could wish, but all were convinced that though demanding, an Eton education was the very best choice they could have made.

As for Etonians themselves, many are super talented, most are charming, but once you become 'uniform blind' (and because nearly everyone is wearing it this doesn't take very long) they're reassuringly just schoolboys of the scruffy hair, doodles on hands and scuffed shoes variety.

The term 'old Etonian' has of late become something of a knee-jerk pejorative shorthand for posh, wealthy and privileged, indiscriminately applied to the relatively small number of alumni prominent in public life – from David Cameron, number 19 in the list of British prime ministers educated at Eton, to actors such as Eddie Redmayne, Damian Lewis, Hugh Laurie and Tom Hiddleston. The reality is that you're more likely to have encountered Etonians unknowingly as they quietly get on with doing their professional thing in journalism, medicine, education, law and the arts. Before them came centuries of soldiers, including 37 holders of the Victoria Cross, explorers, novelists, sportsmen, poets, politicians, academics, philanthropists and the odd ne'er-do-well (ancient and modern). Fictional OEs include James Bond (expelled), Bertie Wooster, Lord Peter Wimsey, Mark Darcy and that old crocodile-phobe, Captain Hook.

Entrance: You might think that all Eton has to do is to sit back and wait for the world to beat a path to its door, so when we met the director and deputy director of admissions we were surprised, and delighted, to find two scholarly Indiana Joneses. As they spoke we had a vision of them in pith helmets, enthusiastically navigating roads less taken to discover new talent for their school. With around five applicants for each of 250 places, you don't need us to tell you that getting a place at Eton is tough, but it's reassuring to know that the admissions department is equally rigorous in seeking out the 'right' candidates.

This is an academically demanding school, but a place depends on much more than getting all the right answers in tests. Eton looks for that extra je ne sais quoi – a quality that is more about character and personality than bolt-on achievements. Parents who believe they can play the system by forcing their son to memorise War and Peace, making him practice the harpsichord until his fingers bleed and drilling him to say that his favourite leisure pursuit is calculus, do not generally prevail. Of course, if your son willingly does this kind of thing he's probably in with a chance.

All applicants are assessed in year 6 – verbal reasoning, numeracy, perceptual potential, interview and school report. School recognises that pre-testing may penalise late developers, so stays in touch with school heads and gets feedback on near-miss candidates. Just think for a minute of the amount of work that assessing and interviewing 1,200 ten-year-old boys involves – a five-strong committee spends two days considering the candidates, and places offered are conditional on passing CE or, for boys at state schools, Eton's own exam in year 8. A further 80 names go on the waiting list.

And what about the prep school baccalaureate? We asked knowing that a kind word from Eton would cheer its champions in prep schools up and down the land. The Indiana Joneses morphed back into tail coated Etonians: 'We still like CE; CE is the right foundation, it covers all the core areas of the year 8 curriculum.'

Scholarship boys include 14 King's Scholars (decided on academic merit alone), plus New Foundation scholars (boys joining Eton from state schools) and many more.

Minimum of six A grades at GCSE needed for entry to sixth form, not much of a hurdle at a school where the majority get 10 or 11 GCSE A*s. Twelve sixth form scholarships a year for boys from state sector or independent schools lacking sixth form provision.

Exit: One or two may depart for co-ed or day schools post-GCSE, but after A levels almost every boy will be headed for university. Or so we imagine. Eton is peculiarly coy about its leavers' destinations. The record on the website is several years out of date because, 'many boys delay their higher education applications until after leaving Eton, [thus] there is necessarily a delay before an accurate statement can be provided'. Hmm, almost all other schools seem to have no problem at all keeping track of post-results applicants.

This deliberate obfuscation is not just unhelpful to prospective parents who understandably want to know which universities boys go on to and what they study there; even parents with boys at the school told us they were unable to get this information when they asked for it. Needless to say, rumours abound – is it to fend off negative publicity about 'too many' going to top universities? Ditto too few? Is it because Oxbridge applications are handled by houses, not coordinated centrally? We wish we could tell you. Several parents suggested that Cambridge University in particular does not look favourably upon candidates from Eton.

Ball park figure for Oxbridge is 80 or so a year (we hear that many boys get in second time around) and we'll stick our necks out and say that the others will head for Russell Group universities or to study abroad.

Money matters: Indeed it does, and school remains determined as ever that lack of it should not be a barrier to any boy who is offered a scholarship. Currently around quarter of boys receive some form of financial support – still a way to go before Eton reaches its stated goal of being 'needs blind'.

Remarks: As George Orwell definitely didn't write about his alma mater, some schools are more equal than others. Eton is an extraordinary place, like many of England's institutions it's a mass of contradictions – ancient and modern; exclusive and accessible; liberal and exacting; loved and hated; formal and eccentric; hierarchical and meritocratic. And though it sounds counter intuitive, somehow these traditions, formalities, rules and hierarchies harmonise, allowing 1,300 tail-coated flowers to bloom.

Farleigh School

RC 17

Red Rice, Andover, Hampshire SP11 7PW

01264 710766 | office@farleighschool.com | www.farleighschool.com

Ages: 3–13 (boarding from year 3)

Pupils: 458; Boarders: 91 full/weekly, 17 flexi

Day: £18,750 pa; Boarding: £21,990 – £24,405 pa (HMF Boarding £20,745 pa)

Headmaster: Since 2004, Father Simon Everson BA Cert in theology (50s). Educated at Caterham School, studied theology at Leeds Collegiate and Ripon College, followed by three year certificate in theology awarded by Oxford University. An Anglican curate and vicar in London for 14 years, he moved to Hurstpierpoint College as senior chaplain in 1996. Following his conversion to Catholicism, he was appointed as chaplain and teacher at Farleigh in 1999, then head five years later.

A modest, softly spoken and self-effacing man, he doesn't engage his inner salesman straight away – prospective parents take note and beware of making snap judgements. Current parents and pupils were falling over themselves to tell us how highly they rate him (one mother phoned three times) and that he is an outstanding head. Whilst watching over every aspect of his charges' development – spiritual, social, moral and academic – he endeavours to dispatch children to their senior schools as educated, fair, kind and generous human beings. Still teaches half the school each week and leads by example, setting high expectations for manners and behaviour. Positively lights up around his pupils. Firmly believes that the school is there for the whole family and encourages wholesale parental and sibling participation.

Head's wife, Gail, is involved at all levels – a qualified nurse, she works as a learning support teacher in the pre-prep, helps in the nursery, teaches swimming and organises school flowers. They have two daughters, both at senior school.

Entrance: Not selective, pupils join at all stages. In pre-prep, the majority join aged 3; a few more at 5 (mostly from local nurseries), leaving occasional places in years 1 and 2. No formal assessment in pre-prep. Most transfer to the prep, but entry is not automatic (parents are kept well informed). From year 3, pupils come from local primaries or London schools, eg Broomwood Hall, Thomas's, Newton Prep, Fulham Prep and Finton House. One-to-one assessments in reading, writing, spelling, vocabulary and maths ('get to know the child' sessions) and report from current school required.

Priority given to practising Catholics, boarders and siblings, plus children of past pupils. Usually oversubscribed. Means-tested bursaries at head's discretion, 15 per cent discount to boarding children of Forces families.

Exit: Most at 13 – more than a third leave with scholarships and exhibitions: a good tally across the board, with sport and art featuring strongly, plus a healthy scattering of academic, all-rounder and music awards. Catholic schools are obviously popular, eg Downside, Ampleforth, St Mary's Ascot and St Mary's Shaftesbury, although a good number opt for local choices, eg Sherborne, Sherborne Girls', Marlborough College, King Edward VI, Winchester College and Cheltenham Ladies'. A few boys go to Eton, Radley and Harrow most years. A small number (fewer than five) leave at 11, mostly to senior girls' boarding schools, eg Downe House, St Swithun's and Godolphin.

Remarks: Founded in 1953 by Jocelyn Trappes-Lomax as a prep school for Catholic boys, initially based at Farleigh House, residence of the Earl of Portsmouth. Moved to its present home in 1982, a magnificent 19th century Georgian house built by General Webb. Set in 60 tranquil acres of sweeping parkland and has a landscaped arboretum (for history buffs, trees were planted in the troop formation of the Battle of Malplaquet in 1709). It's hard to believe that the A303 threads its way past just five minutes' drive from the school gates (handy for London parents).

Some single rooms available for exam candidates, so they get a good night's sleep before a big day

The house has been sympathetically adapted to school life and some of its original charm remains in the elegant drawing room, used by the whole school as a common room in the evenings. Elsewhere the focus is on the modern and practical, both within the main house and without. All new buildings – including new science and food tech building – have been added to one side of the school, thereby preserving swathes of parkland on the other side and woodland to the rear.

Parents are full of praise for academic approach and achievement. One told us, 'Farleigh fulfils parents' ambitions and then some.' Children are taught by subject specialists from year 5 (French from year 2). Small class sizes – average 15. We observed plenty of sound teaching in core subjects. Maths is set from year 4 (for all other academic subjects from year 6) and parents say teaching is 'exceptional'. Able mathematicians given extra work and compete against other schools (a pupil in year 8 was current maths champion at Dauntsey's). English is also good – 'The teacher is wonderful, really old school' – and clearly effective, as a year 7 pupil won Marlborough's poetry competition. French good and looked like huge fun. Latin taught

from year 6 and plenty of it, so those needing higher levels in CE can get there. Whole school follows a course known as The Way, The Truth, The Life in RS (not limited to Catholicism).

Exam preparation for scholarships is excellent. We noticed lots of extra coaching sessions squeezed in for individual year 8 pupils in most subjects (some voluntary). Scholars also have taster sessions in Spanish and Greek. Gifted and talented group meets several times a week for extra activities, eg debating (school has won Marlborough's prep school debating competition several times). All are helped to discover how they learn best. 'Teachers go the extra mile for the children – if a child expresses an interest in something they'll use breaks to teach it,' said one parent. Another told us: 'A work ethic is instilled in year 7 and there are grades every four weeks, so any problems are picked up early.' ICT provision is quirkily good, with a room full of computers and iPads for classroom use. Well-stocked library is run by hugely enthusiastic librarian and pupils can borrow Kindles as well as books, newspapers and magazines.

Exceptional, free SEN provision provided by four members of staff with impressive qualifications (69 pupils on the register when we visited). A few Spanish nationals receive EAL tuition. No surprise that more than a dozen teachers have stayed at Farleigh for more than 10 years – 'Father Simon has created a very happy stable ...The school has a satisfied customer feel'.

Sport takes place on wide expanse of playing fields, including new all-weather pitch, bordering the front drive of the main house. Games on four afternoons a week and matches on Wednesday and Saturday afternoons. All the usual prep school sports on offer and staff put together three or four teams at the top of the school for boys' rugby, football and cricket and girls' hockey and rounders, with many more lower down the school. 'Everyone gets a chance at sport,' says the school. Annual rugby tour to France for boys in years 7 and 8; senior girls go on hockey and netball tours. Pre-season training is free of charge. Consistently good athletics results, with around 10 children each year representing the school at the National Athletics Championships. Unusual amount of competitive tennis on the calendar, eg house tennis, internal tournaments and matches against other schools. Pupils play tennis all year, with 80 per cent having coaching in the prep school. LTA Mini Tennis Awards scheme followed to year 6 and colours also awarded.

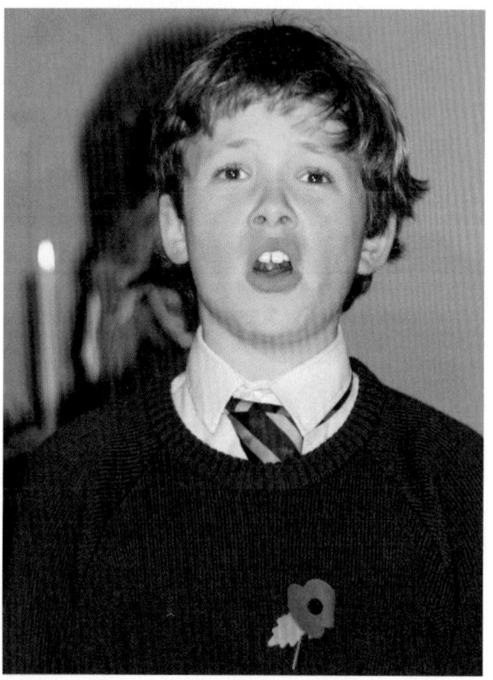

A good range of minor extracurricular sport played on two afternoons a week, eg girls' football, golf, squash, badminton, riding and fishing. Boys who don't enjoy rugby matches can choose to play hockey. School has a large gym and full size indoor swimming pool – boarders have access all week for free swimming. The best are invited to join swim squad; also weekly aqua fit and water polo sessions. Outdoor pool amongst the trees is used in summer.

The arts are thriving – modern, bright art block (two large rooms with high ceilings for painting, ceramics etc) doubtless contributes to the healthy number of art scholarships gained by pupils, who can use it whenever they like in free time. Well-equipped DT room next door.

New purpose-built music school including recital hall and recording studio. Some 300 pupils have private music lessons, with over 60 learning more than one instrument. Singing is a popular choice and nearly 80 have voice lessons (we noticed good exam results here, with half the total number of distinctions awarded for voice). Lots of singing on the timetable, eg daily in chapel, weekly hymn practice and in class music lessons. Chapel choir is auditioned and occasionally tours abroad. Individual music lessons rotate through the timetable (year 8 pupils don't miss academic lessons) and practice timetabled for all. All the usual instruments on offer, as well as harp and bagpipes. Two further choirs, a school orchestra and rock academy, plus around 20 ensembles which rehearse weekly and perform music from jazz to chamber repertoire. Senior jazz band, The Thundering Herd, has played twice at the Edinburgh Festival. School musicians give 17 formal and 20 informal annual concerts, including a jazz dinner night. Music theory is offered as an extracurricular activity. Father Simon even makes music part of his morning assemblies, eg listening to Maria Callas.

Gifted and talented group meets for extra activities, eg debating (school has won Marlborough's prep school debating competition several times)

School theatre is well equipped, with semi-professional lighting and sound and tiered seating (a good view of the stage at last). Two annual school productions include a year 8 musical (The Sound of Music, Bugsy Malone) and alternate productions by years 3 and 4 (Alice in Wonderland) or years 5 and 6 (Annie). LAMDA speech and drama lessons available and pupils can take exams if they wish. Optional creative activities include ballroom dancing, pottery and toy making.

Approximately one-third of the school boards, with flexi boarding available from year 3 up to the summer term of year 7, when families choose between day and full boarding. The majority choose to board in preparation for senior school. About 30 children stay in school every weekend and the full complement on the four 'all in' weekends every year.

Boarding provision is well organised (junior – recently refurbed – and senior dorms for boys and girls) and the houseparents are 'brilliant at instilling spiritual values and manners'. Bigger rooms with more beds for the younger ones, shrinking to doubles for older children, and quite the cleanest and most orderly bathrooms we've yet to see, with a place for everything and everything in its place (possibly for our benefit, but suspect probably not). A really lovely touch is that some single rooms available for exam candidates, so they get a good night's sleep before a big day. Not a lot of room for storing personal possessions in dorms, so most clothing is stored in communal (and very tidy) cupboards and drawers, which lead into large senior common rooms with lots of home comforts, eg computers, TV, squashy sofas and toasters (healthy bowls of fruit here too).

School food is excellent, served cafeteria style in a bright, welcoming dining room. Even though we were slightly late for lunch, still plenty of choice and the food was very good, with fresh fruit on offer for pudding daily. School chef is a bit of a local hero, we gather, not least because he treats boarders to Dinner Night twice a term – pupils dress up and sit down to a themed dinner, which can be anything from Indian to Spanish. Junior boarders get the chance to cook every Friday, when they become kitchen sous chefs and prepare supper for the whole school.

Masses to do during evenings and weekends (including for day children staying late), from cub scouts, zumba and tennis to band practice and street dance. Acres of space to play in outside, either at Fortress Farleigh (traditional play area on the edge of the woods) or deeper into the trees, where pupils are free to roam, build dens etc.

Pastoral care praised time and time again by parents, as was inclusive ethos – 'The school includes my family in their big family,' a parent said. Staff too are welcomed into the fold – all staff members (not just teachers) belong to a house. As well as fostering community spirit, head cares passionately about behaviour and standards – 'Father Simon instils good moral values..The children become self-regulating'. Pupils confirmed zero tolerance of bullying and that kindness to others is prized above intellectual prowess. Everyone is encouraged to 'look beyond themselves' by helping others, eg hosting children with severe learning difficulties in school each week, helping at a local food bank and actively supporting a charity for street children in Colombia – 'It keeps hearts large,' said a parent.

The Catholic faith is at the school's core and Sunday mass is open to all. As well as preparing for first communion and confirmation, children can go on (short) religious retreats; an annual gathering for Patronal Feast Day. Head aims to keep faith both enjoyable and contemporary, eg interpreting the book of Genesis through Holst's The Planets. Members of other churches stress they 'never feel discriminated against for not being Catholic' and 'there is no default setting to send children to Catholic schools'. Perhaps most important is that the school's caring side ensures 'every child will leave with the sense that they have a strength ... not always the usual – it could be something unusual'.

Pre-prep housed in a super building on the fringes of the main campus and is 'beautifully run and thoughtfully managed'. Kindergarten off to one side, away from the hurly-burly. Children looked happy and engaged. Head of pre-prep made us smile by wishing aloud for more room – in fact the building is positively spacious, with four classrooms for years 1 and 2, another for reception, its own library and four separate play areas, not to mention masses of storage space for wellies, bookbags, coats and trainers.

Children in pre-prep walk to the main school for lunch and use other facilities, including the swimming pool and tennis courts. Swimming lessons and ballet timetabled for everyone all year; tennis coaching and football from year 1. After-school clubs include football, cricket, hockey, rounders and woodland games. A free violin taster group each term. French taught from year 2. Staff put on an annual summer concert, spring term production and Christmas show. Father Simon takes assembly one day a week to present children with 'good worker' certificates.

Parents are a harmonious mix of Londoners, locals and some Forces – 'There is a real mixture of people, some Sloaney and some not so; the Forces families are taken very seriously'. Lots of siblings, a few Spanish nationals and overseas British complete the mix. School escorts London-based pupils on the train to and from town on exeats and at half-term. Overseas boarders often stay with local families on exeat weekends (matrons help to coordinate arrangements). Pupils are open, honest, thoroughly genuine young people who clearly love their school and have respect and regard for each other. The fact that the Farleigh Society (old boys and girls) publishes a 25-page newsletter every year is proof that strong bonds are forged here; these often continue on through senior school and beyond.

Former pupils include Lord Stafford, Marquis of Bute, journalist Craig Brown, actor Rupert Everett, rugby player Hugh Vyvyan, TV presenter Hugh Cordey and climber Tarka l'Herpinière.

Every so often, we visit a school which is enjoying a real purple patch and getting most things right. Parental plaudits say it more succinctly than we could – 'It hasn't sacrificed values for academic successes,' and 'They are unwavering in their advice, honest and direct.' When it comes to the head, parents can verge on the evangelical, such as, 'Father Simon is absolutely extraordinary ... on a pedestal with so many parents'. We'll let them off – were we parents here, we rather think we would say the same. Not perhaps for anyone unwilling to buy into school's ethos, but clearly most see the light, and we suspect that this outstanding prep school will become even more sought after than it already is.

Forres Sandle Manor School

18

Sandle Manor, Fordingbridge, Hampshire SP6 1NS

01425 653181 | office@fsmschool.com | www.fsmschool.com

Ages: 3-13 (boarding from 7)

Pupils: 203; Boarders: 75 full, 25 weekly

Day: £8,400 – £16,905 pa; Boarding: £18,940 – £23,550 pa

Headmaster: Since 2010, Mr Mark Hartley (40s), previously deputy head at Winchester House, Brackley, and before that housemaster at Mount House School, Tavistock. Studied biological sciences, now teaches PSHE to older ones and maths tutors those who struggle. Started his working life as an insurance underwriter, met wife Beth at a 21st birthday party and shortly afterwards discovered his true vocation – teaching. Three children later, Beth has returned to her former stomping ground with responsibility for marketing and promoting FSM – though we hear bottles of champagne, sent to parents, for recruiting newbies, are a thing of the past. Described as fresh, fun and funny by youngsters, Mr Hartley is something of an action man, enjoying hockey, cycling, kayaking and climbing. Inheriting a school that required fine tuning rather than wholesale overhaul, he has tinkered at the edges: tightening up reporting procedures, smartening the kids, introducing a parent portal and encouraging more competition via house events. So far so good on the parental front, 'He's livened things up, smartened up the children but not pushed things too far'.

Entrance: Most at age 3 or 8, boarders from 7. Non-selective but works from premise of 'Will a child be happy here?' Stomping grounds include New Forest, Avon Valley and environs of Cranborne. Predominantly white British with a handful of short-stay pupils from Norway and Spain. Boarders a 50-50 mix of expats, mostly Forces, and locals. Around half are first time buyers. Start when you like, if room (pressure on boarding places – must pay for full even if weekly board). Means-tested bursaries and discount for Forces.

Exit: Over 25 different schools in the last four years, including Canford, Bryanston, Sherborne, Sherborne Girls, Clayesmore and Dauntseys. Eminent old boys: Michael Foot (Forres), Alec Guinness (Sandle Manor).

Remarks: Set in child-friendly grounds, centred around an elegant Jacobean manor, a stone's throw from the New Forest. It's hard to imagine a more captivating environment for the tweenager. Delightful pre-prep with inspirational head who ensures learning is child-led, fun but pacey. Super pirate ship playground and forest school ensure year round fresh air and plenty of boisterous play.

All 6 year olds screened for reading delay – those found in need are given booster sessions till back on track. 'We never guarantee a child will improve but are yet to have one that doesn't.' Fans of Ruth Miskin's Read Write Inc, which promises every child a reader by age 6. Imaginative teaching and learning captivates the spellbound youngsters. We especially liked the 'naughty bus' that hides on a daily basis and had been found encased in ice on our visit. Even an errant bus can't compete with the excitement of making stinky, brown poo – a simulated investigation which begins with crushing of digestive biscuits (to mirror crunching of teeth), mixed with water (replacing saliva), washing up liquid and vinegar added (enzyme and stomach acid), then squeezed through grandma's stocking, simulating the intestine and final movement: learning at its gory, imaginative, and experiential best.

Fairly relaxed approach to learning in the prep school – not a soft option, but perhaps uniquely, youngsters say they'd like more prep sooner, 'The year 8 workload is a shock and we could be better prepared for it'. Gifted children pepped up via PACE activities; some, such as Green Giant, an eco project examining biodiversity and recycling with hands-on fun – chopping bamboo, mixing smoothies and making wool – open to all.

Ennui not an option – daily sport and afternoon activities as diverse as scuba diving, golf (even for the tinies) and banana boating

Learning support encompasses wide range of cognitive ability. 'We have children who cannot read/decode but are L4 and L5 national curriculum in some subjects, so we have to help and support'. Parents enthuse, 'My child struggled at his previous school, but since he came to FSM and got the support he needed, he has never stopped smiling.' Another added, 'It's a long day yet my child is never tired. Somehow they work it just right.'

Most teachers deliver multi-sensory lessons geared to active learning. English, drama and science top the popularity polls; 'Our science teacher respects us – he's not patronising, we do lots of experiments, it's fun and there is practically no writing,' cooed one boy. History, geography and RE depart from confines of CE, a conscious decision to develop skills of enquiry and investigation. Testing topics include Smuggling in Fordingbridge. Senior schools approve and see some seriously good work – not that fun doesn't come into it: we spotted a wall of history jokes, our favourite, 'Who built the Ark? I have Noah idea!' Post CE youngsters hone their practical and problem-solving skills – changing a tyre, wiring a plug, ironing shirts or finding the scariest ride at Thorpe Park.

Most lessons take place in The Barn with scattering of specialist buildings for art (we loved the bronze Olympian action sculpture), DT and music. Sports hall and climbing wall on wish list, but grounds contain heated outdoor swimming pool, courts for netball and tennis plus myriad of pitches. Ennui not an option – daily sport and afternoon activities as diverse as scuba diving, golf (even for the tinies) and banana boating, alongside annual trips and tours to everywhere from Iceland to Africa. Project week and cub-camp, with Boy's Own firelighting, knife-skills, cooking and camp craft, perennially popular. All lower school do ballet (a good way to spot potential dancers and dyspraxics) – optional classes for seniors. We listened to the fledgling Exterminators jamming and spotted imaginatively named groups, eg Flute Pastilles, and fabulous fiddlers. School has a competitive edge: thrice finalists in the Junior Memory Championships and recent debut as finalists in Kids' Lit quiz.

Seemingly parents equally competitive when it comes to teams, with boarder parents saying, 'Local parents seem to have everything sewn up – it can be difficult for the boarding fraternity to get a look in, especially for parent fixtures,' adding, 'Communication could be better – they're great at reporting on the kids but not on activities: we need time to schedule and plan'. Parents kept busy with quiz nights, football, hockey, plus 'maths for mums and dads', courtesy of Friends of FSM – hardly surprising they jest that an in-school Costa Coffee concession is on their wish list.

Meals are table served in one of two dining rooms, the mantra to always try a little, including experimental offerings such as beetroot brownies and soup concoctions dreamed up by the youngsters. Sports teas are legendary and, as we flicked the last melt-in-the-mouth crumbs from our lips, could only nod in heartfelt agreement as our trusty guide declared them 'outstanding!'

A boarding school that welcomes day children – 'It's a family-friendly community, flexible when we need it'. Fairly healthy weekend boarding numbers though parents of full boarders (75, compared with some 25 weekly) say to check the age and gender of those who stay, if this is important to you. Cheery boarding accommodation with ongoing renovations – though we were a tad overwhelmed by the swathes of bubble-gum pink adorning the girls' dorms. We loved the 'getting better bay' with healthy doses of TLC for the homesick and panaceas for the poorly. Seemingly all want to try boarding, so expect up to 11 per dorm and the odd grumble that it can be difficult to escape, 'Sometimes you need time or space but they can be hard to find'. Nothing too heavy-handed on discipline front: naughty boarders are red-carded and miss the coveted Wednesday special boarding night or put on dreaded laundry duty, sorting socks, folding shirts. Matrons praised, 'You can tell them things because they have seen it all before and know what to do', ground-staff lauded as cheery and fun, 'They have a nickname for everyone'.

Focuses on developing happy, confident children. Takes a broad range, delivers the goods, 'One minute you are watching a really talented child, the next someone who is just keen to join in'. Children are respected and 'feel part of the gang,' say parents. Children candid, 'It can be a bit difficult for those who are naturally loners or need quiet space.' Not posh or pushy. A happy, homely school with a sunny disposition, going from strength to strength. Turns out friendly, confident, quietly ambitious youngsters.

Godstowe Preparatory School

Shrubbery Road, High Wycombe, Buckinghamshire HP13 6PR

01494 529273 | registrar@godstowe.org | www.godstowe.org

Ages: Girls 3-13, boys 3-7 (boarding from 7)

Pupils: 455; Boarders: 95 full and flexi

Day: £10,380 – £15,975 pa; Boarding: + £7,825 pa

Headmaster: Since September 2017, Sophie Green, previously head of Herries School in Cookham. She has also been director of studies at St George's Windsor Castle, where she prepared pupils for scholarships and was involved in the demanding boarding life of the choristers. She is also an ISI inspector.

Entrance: Despite Godstowe's growing popularity, school is adamant that it will remain 'first come first served', non-selective. Entry to pre-prep The Lodge (boys and girls) at 3+; most girls move up to the prep, making up 80 per cent of its intake, with other girls joining all the way through to year 6 from a variety of local prep and state schools, and boarders joining from further afield in the upper years. Boarding can be full time or flexible with many day girls choosing to try it in years 7 and 8 as a taster for senior school.

Exit: Not a specific feeder, with alumni most years heading off to some 20 different senior schools notably Wycombe Abbey, Cheltenham Ladies, Queen Anne's and Downe House; others to eg St George's Ascot, Rugby, Wellington, Stowe, Haileybury, Tudor Hall, Oundle, Uppingham, Pipers Corner, St Edward's, Bradfield, Millfield, Headington and Marlborough. A handful leave for local grammars at 11.

Remarks: England's first girls' boarding prep school and Enid Blyton's inspiration (though not the only contender) for Malory Towers, purpose built in 1900. The grounds make excellent use of a hilly, if a little blustery, site overlooking High Wycombe, with the original pretty Virginia creeper-clad buildings now housing years 3 to 8, plus The Lodge and nursery buildings. The few boys in pre-prep, mostly siblings, move on at the age of 7.

The airy new double height reception building (buzzing at pick-up and drop-off times) is a modern addition to the more rustic Victorian buildings and has a gallery-like atmosphere, setting the tone for the rather artsy feel of the whole school. Other recent revamps include the dining room (we highly recommend the lasagne), early years centre, art room and food technology centre, opened in 2017 by Mary Berry. There's also a £2m sports hall for eg indoor tennis, hockey and lacrosse plus dance and gymnnastics. Old swimming pool demolished; new one due to open in 2018.

Definitely not a school placing importance on hushed tones, although good manners are notably present. Girls dash about chatting noisily between lessons, picking up considerable speed when heading to the dining room for lunch. Posters all over the school that indoctrinate pupils to be happy, confident and successful are clearly doing the trick.

Non-selective it may be, but success is in the air here. Minority (about 15 per cent) peel off at 11 to local schools (parents have to 'opt in' to 11+), but unlike many prep schools in the area which hothouse pupils for the sought-after Bucks grammars, this is a true 3-13 establishment, feeding its post-CE alumni into a heady mix of top day and boarding indies, many with scholarships. Which are pretty abundant, by the way, with the current record for one year standing at 26, to 17 different schools. School puts this down to 'quality teaching' and the fact that girls are 'led rather than pushed through the curriculum', and is proud not to share the pushy reputation of some of its competition.

Girls dash about chatting noisily between lessons, picking up speed when heading for lunch

French is taught from reception, Latin and Spanish from year 5 in creatively themed classrooms. Classes in pre-prep school 'subtly' streamed, with a maximum class size of 18. Formal streaming from year 6 for English, maths and French. Girls stay in form rooms for lessons in years 3 and 4, after which they start to move around the school for individual subjects.

General acceptance that everyone learns differently and SEN is all in a day's work rather than marginalised. Two dedicated SEN staff in place and an excellent EAL programme – mostly for those boarders from the Far East, Spain and Nigeria, with girls' needs assessed upon entry to the school and timetabled to meet their specific requirements. Boarders' prep takes place from 4.30pm to 6.30pm, although an hour of this is often taken up with an enrichment activity. Day girls report homework levels to be acceptable.

Creative pursuits are well catered for, with a dedicated sewing room in CDT where girls knock up the odd wedding gown for the year 8 fashion

show. Some 300 girls learn musical instruments and practise daily in bright, well-equipped studios. Pupils' artistic endeavours are displayed throughout the school – and with good reason. They look more like GSCE work, thanks to the inspirational head of art, who specialises in 3D work.

The art department, with its gleaming new extension, has the wow factor in terms of space and light, as does the work on show there, from glazed pottery meals on plates to life-size papier mâché humans – not a still life fruit bowl in sight. Taught by specialists from the word go, senior girls win art scholarships every year, but importantly parents report that a passion for creativity has been bred into the core of the school and latent talent is eeked out of those who didn't know they had it.

Parents say the standard of music is 'incredible', with one slipping in that the girls' achievements and public performances by far outstrip those at their brothers' schools. All pupils are encouraged to participate from the age of 3 in regular recitals and choir is compulsory in years 3 to 6. Revamped JK Theatre is used for music concerts, after-school clubs, art exhibitions, assemblies and parents' evenings.

Sports lessons are four times a week, with the usual suspects (netball and lacrosse) taking centre pitch – all to a high competitive standard. Athletics and rounders are also on offer, as are ballet, gymnastics and dance, and despite the current lack of swimming pool they do swim against other schools. Parents of children in larger year groups occasionally grumble that the A and B teams are a bit exclusive, with not everyone getting a go, but the school is keen to introduce more teams and by and large most girls are able to compete at some level, often with winning results.

Boarding facilities have a real home from home feel, with bedrooms (sleeping between four and eight) rather than dorms, cosy sitting rooms and homely kitchens. All have their own large gardens, with swings and other outdoor equipment. Housemistresses are non-teaching staff, leaving them free to focus on girls' pastoral care. Pupils are charming and poised without a hint of precociousness and describe their typical peer as 'kind and happy'. Some 40 per cent of boarders from overseas. Early drop-off plus breakfast (7.30am) and late pick-up plus supper (6.30pm) is available for day girls at low cost.

The mobile phone arms race was stopped by the clever acquisition of 100 bog standard phones (yes, these do still exist) into which girls can insert their own SIM cards to call home. Thursdays are 'no go gadget' evenings in the boarding houses to further encourage those old fashioned skills, reading, conversation and game playing. Girls say the best thing about Godstowe is 'everyone is happy all the time' – future careers in PR await.

The 'enrichment curriculum' – that's after-school clubs in old money – offers up to 50 free options for two hours a day from 4.30pm. These range from the traditional sports, LAMDA and wind band to the more diverse knitting, prop-making and cross-stitch, with up to 100 girls staying for these. Boarders benefit from a buzzing spectrum of activities at weekends too (rarely fewer than 50 girls in), many of which take place off site (bowling, skating, theatre, cinema etc).

Post CE, year 8s are given a lifestyle crash course to prepare them for a less cosseted existence. Includes classes in self-defence, internet safety and relationships, charitable works, trips out, visiting lecturers and, in a surprisingly retro twist, a hair and beauty day, which seems a little old fashioned but, hey ho.

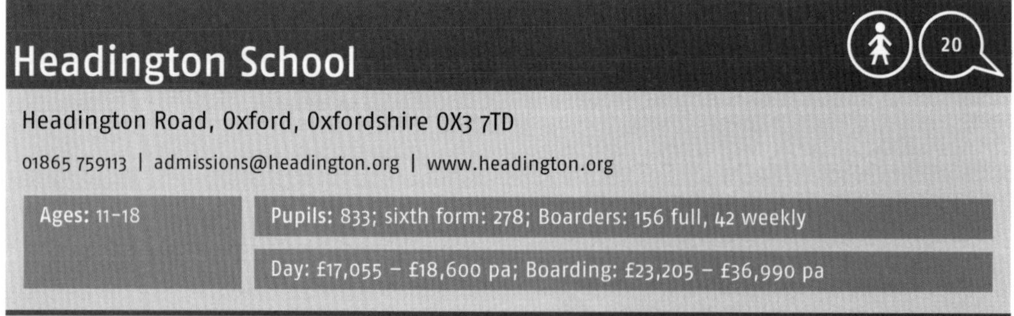

Headington School
20
Headington Road, Oxford, Oxfordshire OX3 7TD
01865 759113 | admissions@headington.org | www.headington.org
Ages: 11-18
Pupils: 833; sixth form: 278; Boarders: 156 full, 42 weekly
Day: £17,055 – £18,600 pa; Boarding: £23,205 – £36,990 pa

Head: Since 2011, Mrs Caroline Jordan (50s). A local girl, she was educated at St Helen and St Katharine in Abingdon, read geology at Oxford and did her PGCE (science) at Manchester. Previously head of St George's Ascot and before that spent 10 years at Wycombe Abbey where she was head of sixth form and deputy senior housemistress. Lives on site; married to Richard, a company director, one adult son, two border collies. Currently president of the Girls' Schools Association.

Before going into teaching Mrs Jordan ran her own business. She says that heads 'need those

skills'; they do, and indeed we could imagine her as one of the dragons on Dragons' Den – not that she's scary, but she is direct and, well, businesslike. As one parent said, 'definitely not fluffy'. She's forward thinking and ambitious, hyper alert to social and educational change and ready for whatever the future holds in these areas. Parents describe her as 'really on the ball' and 'ahead of the game' and are mostly in favour of the changes she's making. 'She's mad about rowing,' we were told; 'you should hear her shouting from the riverbank when her crew are racing!' Another was impressed by Mrs J's energetic networking when she accompanied crews to a competition in the US. 'She took the girls round as many universities as she could, making contacts.' We anticipate US college scholarship offers rolling in for Headington rowers.

Parts of the school are being seriously revamped – not just bricks and mortar but also Headington's Achilles' heel (rowing excepted): sport. Mrs Jordan is frank about this; historically lack of opportunities and support meant that girls had to join outside clubs to progress in team games such as hockey. A complete overhaul of facilities and teaching will see the 'inspirational' head of rowing become director of sport, no doubt expected to do his magic in other departments.

Favourite childhood reads were Dorothy Dunnett's Scottish historical novels but these days Mrs J enjoys quick crime thrillers on her Kindle. Down time is spent 'mixing concrete' – she and her husband are restoring a 500-year-old house in France.

Head of junior school since 2014, Mrs Jane Crouch BA MA (40s). Studied French and geography at Keele. Her masters, in educational management and administration, is from the University of London. Was previously head of Dame Bradbury's School, Saffron Walden and before that head of Ashford School, Kent and deputy head of Great Walstead, West Sussex. It was early days when we visited but Mrs Crouch had the confidence of parents we spoke to and her easy, friendly relationship with the girls already seemed well established. Tempting though the calm of her study must be, she told us that she 'loves getting into the classroom' and was 'determined to fit some teaching in'.

Special mention here for ICT – girls learn to code in Python and apply this and other skills to robotics

All possible building work having been done, we wondered whether Mrs Crouch wanted to redevelop any other aspect of the school. While not hatching plans for revolution, she told us that she hopes to set up a breakfast club, extend the range of after school activities and has her sights set on the prep becoming an 'eco' school. She's also keen to up the involvement of sixth formers from the senior school, 'helping with assemblies and other activities'.

Mrs Crouch and her husband are keen coastal walkers but, since coastline is in short supply in Oxfordshire, they are enjoying new vistas in the Chilterns. As if running a school wasn't enough she enjoys zumba, spin and step classes and visiting art galleries. On her Kindle you'll find Swedish crime fiction.

Academic matters: In 2017, nearly 83 per cent A*/A at GCSE. At A level, 62 per cent A*/A. Maths, economics, sciences, fine art and English literature notably successful. Languages don't seem to attract many (as is so often the case).

More than respectable IB average of 39 in 2017, with one girl scoring the maximum 45 points. Take-up for IB roughly 20 per cent and growing – Mrs J certainly thinks it is a more secure option at a time when 'A levels are up in the air.' She's particularly keen on the IB theory of knowledge course and this is now being offered lower down the school. We're sure the girls benefit but it's also a canny and not so subliminal bit of IB marketing.

Gone are the days when girls ploughed through up to 13 GCSEs; it's 10 now with increasing number of IGCSEs. Choice of one language from French, Spanish and German; surprisingly there's no Mandarin GCSE although it's offered as an after-school club, as is ancient Greek. All do Latin in first two years.

Twenty-nine subjects to chose from at A level including fine art, photography, computing, law, psychology and government and politics. EPQ encouraged but there's 'not much time' in term and research and writing during the summer holidays post year 12 can be a big ask. Oxbridge, medicine and veterinary hopefuls get application support and so do girls applying for architecture. The latter receive specialist lectures and help with portfolio preparation – must account for the unusually high number of Headington girls accepted to study this oversubscribed subject.

Special mention here for ICT – girls learn to code in Python and apply this and other skills to robotics. Not content with winning 'best rookies' and 'first moves' prizes at recent Student Robotics Competition, the Headington team (one of just two all girl teams) designed, built and programmed an autonomous robot from scratch to become champions. 'It sent a real buzz through the whole school,' the head girl told us proudly.

For those who don't go home on Fridays there seems to be plenty on offer – we saw sign up sheets for strawberry picking, a trip to Brighton and a make-up workshop

School says it makes 'reasonable adjustments' for girls with mild SEN including one-to-one weekly support for girls in the lower school and drop-in sessions for the middle school and sixth form. EAL tuition also provided.

Games, options, the arts: The 'inspirational' leadership of Headington's South African head of rowing has brought the school national and international success on the water (most recently the J8 crew won the Henley women's regatta). Girls start training in the summer term of year 7 and some parents think this is too young (boys generally don't begin until age 13); school says the programme is run in conjunction with Oxford Brookes and everything is very carefully monitored. Compared to the riverside facilities enjoyed by other notable Oxfordshire rowing schools such as Abingdon, Headington has it tough – they row out of a couple of portakabins shared with St Edward's School. 'Our success is all down to inspiration,' says Mrs Jordan.

School boasts over 30 different sporting activities (many are lunchtime or after-school clubs) including fencing, synchronised swimming, dance and cheerleading. It's also pretty horsey, despite the urban setting. 'It's a side branch of the Pony Club,' we were told. What if you don't have a horse? We asked. 'Oh, someone will lend you one,' came the airy reply. Girls compete in blue Headington silks and bring back plenty of rosettes.

Mrs J acknowledges that there's still work to do when it comes to 'sport for all'. 'Every girl should have her own regime to stay fit and healthy, whether or not that includes competitive sport. We should expect these things from a school.' She wants team sport to be 'for everybody', not just the chosen few. With this determination and the new facilities taking shape in the grounds, Mrs Jordan's ideal of 'scholar athletes' may soon be realised.

Singing and orchestral days are a great way for older players to workshop and develop ensemble skills. Budding artists, actors and musicians are spoilt for choice – facilities include a 240 seat theatre complete with box office and professional backstage team. The seriously well-equipped music school, opened by Brian Eno, a former parent, provides ample teaching, practice and recording space. Girls must participate in some musical activity during their first two senior school years – the emphasis is on taking part and most choirs, orchestras and ensembles are audition free. Music for all is the message with break and lunchtime concerts and, recently, a Garsington opera workshop.

Pupils' paintings of a very high standard are proudly displayed all over the school, including the head's office. A level results for fine art should also be put in a frame – almost every candidate is awarded A*. As we marvelled at the work in the splendid double height art building our guide confessed that it was 'a bit overwhelming for those who can't draw.'

CCF (from year 10 upwards) is 'huge' and girls love the camps – whether in Dartmoor, Scotland or the school grounds. D of E attracts good numbers too. Tempting range of trips from geography in the Alps and diving in the Red Sea to expeditions and charity work in Ethiopia, Kenya and Zanzibar.

Boarding: About a third of pupils board, either full time or weekly. Head is not a fan of flexi boarding (describes it as 'bed blocking') but school may accommodate pupils for one offs (plays, trips) or family emergencies. Year group boarding houses are cheerful with plenty of home comforts. Most have double study bedrooms with good storage and room mates are swapped around each term (sixth form can choose). For those who don't go home on Fridays there seems to be plenty on offer – we saw sign up sheets for strawberry picking, a day trip to Brighton and a make up workshop. Sixth form boarders have kitchens and may cook for themselves as long as they ask in advance – enables house parents to be sure girls aren't missing meals. They can also go to parties and stay over with school friends – parents are emailed for permission.

Background and atmosphere: Founded in 1915 by a group of evangelical Christians to provide a 'sound education for girls to fit them for the demands and opportunities likely to arise after the war.' Occupied various houses in the area, trading up as it grew from 18 to today's 1,000 (including 280 in prep school). Present main school was built in the 1930s in a sharp-edged, no frills style described (rather kindly) as neo-Georgian. Set in 23 acres just off Oxford's busy London Road, it's right next to the hospitals and ambulance sirens lend it an extra urban edge. Despite its town site there's a sense of space, and plenty of greenery remains undeveloped. Newer buildings are very well appointed, especially the Diamond Jubilee Building – home to large, modern teaching rooms, ICT and that award-winning robot.

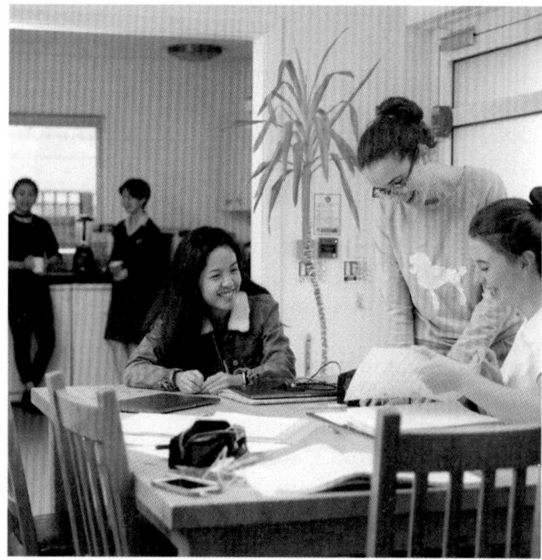

Lessons we observed were challenging but not intimidating, girls were contributing enthusiastically and seemed keen to have a go and share opinions. In an A level English 'taster' class we were impressed by how quickly students got to grips with new ideas. A brief introduction to the principles of critical theory and they were off, producing Marxist and feminist readings of Where the Wild Things Are. The library is all you could ask for and dedicated librarians also provide a cuttings service – filing cabinets hold the latest journal or newspaper material for over 250 subjects. This resource, hand in hand with Google, introduces girls – particularly sixth formers tackling the EPQ – to university style research techniques. 'They know everything here', said our guides.

Pastoral care, well-being and discipline: Parents and girls we spoke to were generally very positive about pastoral care, but the school is large and busy and we did wonder how quickly a quiet or unhappy child would be noticed. This is where the sixth form prefects come in. Each class of around 20 is allocated two prefects, whose job is not only to be a friendly non-teacher face, but also to get to know the girls and alert staff if they suspect a girl is struggling socially or in any other way. There is also a drop-in counsellor. Prefects are elected by peers and candidates for head girl and deputies have to make speeches at hustings before those on the chosen short list go before senior staff for final interviews. Win or lose, it's all very good experience. Sixth form common room was looking rather forlorn when we visited, but it's since had a make over and is now, apparently, much more inviting.

Some concerns expressed about the lunch arrangements – feeding 800 girls in an hour and a half must be quite a challenge. Sittings are by year group, but with only five minutes in between, one pupil acknowledged that lunch break was 'a bit of a mosh.' Staff 'bouncers' are positioned outside for crowd control and 'when it's raining you push.' All good fun when you're used to it but 'quite intimidating' for newbies. Once you're in, though, food is seriously good, varied and plentiful. We enjoyed a delicious meal in the large, modern dining hall decorated with huge canvases of old school photos – all the food is serve yourself and girls help themselves to as much as they like of everything.

Pupils and parents: 'Not too posh' – nice, swishy-haired girls who don't seem to kick too hard against uniform, skirt length and make up regulations. Most families from Oxford's private and public sector employers – medics, lawyers, academics, IT professionals. Head says, 'girls understand that parents are making an investment'. Growing cohort of weekly boarders commute from London on the Oxford tube (stops outside). International students from 47 countries – IB and rowing reputation are attracting more Europeans. Zealous overseas recruitment in the past led to large groups of one nationality (evident when we visited the sixth form Costa café). Parents say that this has been 'a big issue' and they would like to see better integration. Head acknowledges these concerns and says things are now being managed. OGs include Baroness Young, Julia Somerville, Lady Longford, Christina Onassis, Emma Watson and Lily van den Broecke

Entrance: Several applicants for every place (but bear in mind that girls will be sitting for other schools too). For entry at 11+ girls sit papers in English, maths and non-verbal reasoning and have an interview. Prep school candidates (13+ entry) come for an interview and taster day after the pre-test. Sixth form entrants sit exams at Headington in the November before their proposed entry.

Exit: Inevitably some girls depart post-GCSE, lured to local co-ed sixth forms, although we hear that it's not uncommon for there to be a return to the fold after a few weeks. Nearly all sixth form leavers go on to university, including usually several to Oxbridge – seven in 2017, plus eight medics, dentists and vets; LSE, UCL, Durham, Bristol, Bath, Birmingham trending currently, with 11 off overseas in 2017.

Money matters: Academic, music, art, drama and sports scholarships (£300 per year). Means-tested bursaries of up to 100 per cent of fees plus help for Forces and clergy. Of course there are extras but parents told us that these weren't unreasonable; they also said that they approved of the sensible and inexpensive uniform.

Remarks: This dynamic school is going from strength to strength. True to its founders' aims, nearly a century on it is still sending out girls ready and able to tackle whatever the future has to hold.

Heathfield School

21

London Road, Ascot, Berkshire SL5 8BQ

01344 898343 | registrar@heathfieldschool.net | www.heathfieldschool.net

Ages: 11–18

Pupils: 176; sixth form: 62; Boarders: 163

Day: £21,300 – £21,915 pa; Boarding: £34,348 – £35,220 pa

Headmistress: Since September 2016, Mrs Marina Gardiner Legge, previously director of studies. MA in English literature from Oxford and PGCE from the University of Hong Kong, where she started her teaching career relatively late, having previously worked in business marketing, the charitable sector and teaching horse riding to disabled children. Head of year and assistant head at Rutlish School, a boys' comprehensive in south London, before joining Heathfield in 2013.

Go-getting, no-nonsense, earnest, engaging and frank, she is on a clear mission to change the school's reputation (parents told us that girls are known as 'clotted cream' among some local schools – as in, thick and rich). 'I'm sick and tired of hearing people say this school isn't for clever girls. In the old days, I think possibly it did cater for some girls who weren't very bright from wealthy families whose brothers went to the likes of Eton. But what we're turning out now are girls who are movers and shakers – women who run successful businesses and achieve amazing things. We are easily comparable to Downe House, yet often seen as its poorer cousin.' With dwindling numbers in some year groups presumably reflecting her fears, it's no wonder her first job in post has been heading a mammoth marketing campaign, albeit with some hiccups as the school's introduction of a weekly boarding option caused such uproar among traditionalist parents that it was promptly reverted.

Girls claim she's a visible presence (often out and about; teaches English once a week) and that she 'commands respect while being incredibly supportive.' 'She's strict, but fair and is amazing at driving us to do well.' Parents seem keen too. 'She's picked the school up and is running with it – great to see.' 'She looks and feels like a proper headmistress and word on the street is that she's well liked.'

Lives on site (having previously commuted from Fulham). Has three grown-up daughters and hobbies include writing poetry and running. 'I ran a marathon, having never been a runner until after I got over two bouts of cancer 10 years ago. I'm all about perseverance and resilience.'

Academic matters: Aims high across the subject range, with parents certainly getting their money's worth when it comes to added value (Durham University research puts school in top 12 per cent schools nationally and in the top 17 per cent of independent schools nationally for pupil progress) and generous staffing levels (one to every four pupils), which result in small class sizes with average of 15 and maximum of 19, often single figures for sixth form.

Top line results good overall. In 2017, 54 per cent A*/A grades at A level. Spikier profile for individual subjects – strong in art and design, photography, psychology, biology, English literature and RS, but sprinkling of D grades in some facilitating subjects. Total of 24 subjects on offer, mostly traditional, with economics and film studies recently added. Slightly mixed results at GCSE, too, though achieve healthy percentage of top grades (58 per cent A*-A/9-7). Strongest GCSE subjects include RS, English literature, geography and history, with most popular subjects include history and geography.

A gizmo a year policy means toaster and kettle from year 10, dishwasher and sandwich maker a year later etc – causes great excitement

Setting? 'Absolutely!' exclaims head, clearly stunned by the question, although it only starts from form 3 (year 9) upwards in English, maths and science. Languages kick off with Spanish and French from form 1 (year 7), Latin from year 9. Current push on sciences, off to high profile start with Lord Winston opening new STEM building, boosted by lively lessons, although it's proving a slow burner, with A level take up improved but still some way to go.

'Standards have gone up a lot,' is the mantra here, with girls asked to set their own targets (under supervision), which are reviewed every half term. 'Teachers know you well, so they know what makes you learn best,' one girl told us. 'And there are subject clinics if you feel you are falling behind.' It's no exam factory, though – 'it gets great academic results

without being a pressure cooker,' summed up one parent.

SEN (15 per cent when we visited) well-resourced though Spectrum centre (an unfortunate name if ever there was one, although the name is intended to evoke rainbow shades of pupil diversity rather than autism) is widely used as drop-in service for walking worried, as well as those with identified need (headed by dyslexia). 'There's no stigma,' a pupil assured us. But SEN pupils must be able to follow the curriculum and cope socially and nobody misses lessons, with some in-class support from higher level teaching assistant as well as group or one-to-one sessions, some after school.

Games, options, the arts: Strong on sports, with an emphasis on team sports, matches often twice a week. Regularly attended by parents and staff, including head ('I go to as many off-site matches as possible'), with some of sportiest playing across several year groups – only drawback the minnow vs shark issue if facing opponents from far larger schools. As for those who aren't sporty, 'they're expected to get stuck in anyway, and it's a jolly good thing too,' one parent told us. 'My daughter didn't think she was much good at sport, but their "can do" attitude has made her realise she is.'

Lacrosse popular, no doubt helped by decent tours – USA, Canada among them – and pupil success (regular selection for county and regional squads and one girl picked for great glory with England's development squad). Netball, rounders, tennis and swimming do well and prominence also given to fitness, with one housemistress being trained up in zumba when we visited. Strong equestrian resources coordinated by dedicated staff member, adept at finding good livery stables and organising dashing events (like military riding with swords) – and the school has its own polo league too. Don't expect ponies on the front lawn, though – all off site. Everything else – including courts, indoor swimming pool, sports hall, fitness suite and playing fields – on site.

Outstanding art department, with some spectacular work dotting the walls (although the three most notable canvases 'have been there for years,' say pupils) plus impressive textiles adorning mannequins, including a ballgown made from intricate layers of denim, with red sequin Nike logo on the bodice. In fact, one of the things the school is best known for is nurturing BRIT style talent in the arts, bolstered by close ties with London College of Fashion, which provides proactive course and careers advice to interested sixth formers. We were particularly blown away by an impressive rail of avant garde garments ready for the school's annual fashion show (the hottest date on the school calendar, say pupils) which teams up with music and drama department (think actors juggling and live music). One girl talked us through her striking 'wealth' themed coat (part of GCSE project), complete with trapped pills ('representing addiction'), crime tape ('representing how the wealthy influence the law') and 'Just Kids' logo ('being influenced by money can start young'). Very well-resourced photography department (with two staff and a dark room).

Drama department thriving, with whole-school Christmas performance (the likes of Lady Windermere's Fan) and LAMDA is strong here too. Good at knowing who'd rather take a back seat, though nobody escapes altogether, with termly chapel reading for all, even the shyest accepting it as the norm. Gentle encouragement from school results in what parent describes as 'nice confidence'. Plenty of opportunities for the musical too, from audition entry chapel choir to choice of bands including orchestra and flute ensemble for instrumentalists. Sixty-four girls currently taking peripatetic instrument lessons. 'I hadn't expected the music and drama to be quite so marvellous and was left gawking like a goldfish,' said one parent.

No shortage of clubs – mainly sports, but academic and arts based also popular, plus debating. Head also keen on girls suggesting and running their own – recent examples include gardening club and new online newspaper called the Heathfield Hub. Plentiful day trips ('Tomorrow we're off to a climate conference,' one sixth-former told us) plus some residentials, including the form 3 'rite of passage' trip to Barcelona, part of a geography and classics syllabus.

Boarding: No boarding houses as such. Instead, the upstairs of the main building is dedicated to bedrooms – shared (up to eight girls) for younger years, then own rooms from form 3 upwards (en suite for head girl). The ones we saw were roomy, light, homely and tidy, but with reassuring pockets of clutter and little touches like teddy bears and blankets turning beds into dens – no military style scrutiny here. A gizmo a year policy means you get toaster and kettle from year 10, dishwasher and sandwich maker a year later etc – causes great excitement for the girls. But despite close proximity of bedrooms, girls encouraged not to use them during the day. 'We want them to feel they're going home after school.'

Levels of off-duty shrieking suggested that good times were demonstrably had by all, though 'not definitely not like a sleepover,' we were told by a pupil. (As one dorm is directly above head's study, probably just as well...)

Super-efficient and kindly housemistress manages it all, helped by team with background in childminding, nannying or youth work rather than academic background. 'You can talk to them about anything and they're so helpful,' a pupil told us. 'One girl in my daughter's room couldn't sleep and they got her a sleep therapist and yoga – nothing is too much trouble,' sayid a parent. Inevitable homesickness (it's always a bit rocky in the first few weeks,' sayid a sixth-former) is dealt with by hot chocolate, cuddle or 'on your feet, soldier' pep talk, depending on what's deemed most appropriate. Lights out at 9pm for form 1, reaching 10.30pm for sixth-formers.

Equestrian resources coordinated by dedicated staff member, adept at finding good livery stables and organising dashing events (like military riding with swords)

Two closed weekends a term, otherwise first two years who want to can go home after Saturday sport, returning Sunday evening – similar freedom of choice for sixth formers. If we'd have visited the school a month earlier than we did, the school sign would have also promised weekly boarding. But following the resistance from those parents who want it 'to stay as a boarding school – that's what we signed up to' (as one put it), the option was swiftly removed and a new school sign made. 'Parents feel like this is a proper boarding school and they want the ethos that comes with that,' explains head, with some parents also having worried it was a sign that the school was facing financial difficulties (hotly denied). One parent told us, 'The whole thing has been a shambles,' while another said, 'It's not as if the full-on boarding can last forever.' Many suspect it will eventually be phased in discreetly.

For those who do stay on, weekend activities mainly include sports (swimming pool, tennis courts and the sports hall 'in constant use,' says

school literature) and there's also dance and music, craft, cookery and discos, bands, quizzes and competitions in the evenings. 'The themed dinners are good too – everything from Alice in Wonderland to Harry Potter,' one girl told us. Outings as well – cinema, museums etc. Older ones do less, with licenced lazing about, along with some socials with local boys' schools.

Background and atmosphere: Heathfield is just one of a number of tiny, charming girls' schools in the area that, to the untrained eye, can seem pretty much indistinguishable. But what sets this one apart is a particularly happy and homelike feel with a dash of top school trimmings. (That and the penny-sized home-made biscuits and meringues served with tea to all visitors.) It's as if someone has carefully curated a best of boarding school experience, from the tiny, bow-fronted Harry Potter-esque tuck shop (where, said sixth former, 'hordes of first formers run to get strawbs and ice cream and eat them in little groups on the pitches') to the occasional water fight and spontaneous dancing, both popular exam pressure relievers. In short, it's a bubble – so much so that you might wonder how it's managed to survive in today's fast-living society. And there – explain parents – lies its appeal. 'I'm not saying it's cut off from the real world – it genuinely isn't – but these aren't streetwise girls and they stay children for longer, while getting an excellent academic grounding and holistic education. If you like the sound of that, this is the school for you.'

There's not a hair out of place (and if there were, it would be cashmere) on the 36-acre site; pupils wear their uniforms with pride; and we're met with a look of horror when we asked if there are assemblies on issues such as self-harm or anorexia ('We're all about prevention here – so we'd make sure they ate healthily in the first place').

Originally founded in London by Victorian educational bigwig Eleanor Beatrice Wyatt for the disadvantaged of South Ken (doubtless a more substantial group in 1882 than today), school moved to current site in 1899 when she decided to concentrate on training future educators in greener surroundings. In 2006, gained pupils and financial boost after merger with St Mary's Wantage, commemorated in attractive performing arts centre, old honours boards displayed in foyer. Wyatt would have no problem recognising the school today, down to high church accoutrements that include a termly candlelit mass once a term (white dresses on the uniform list) in tiny chapel, pews bearing engraved names of all leavers and heads. But that's not to say facilities are lagging behind – those of note including the dazzling shaker/Laura Ashley style fifth and sixth form common rooms leading off old assembly hall, plus well-stocked pristine white-shelved library, ubermodern science labs and playing field where groups of friends congregate in summer.

Pastoral care, well-being and discipline: The fact that every pupil and parent we spoke to raved about the pastoral care – but couldn't quite put their finger on what makes it so good – reveals how embedded the nurturing culture is here. 'But without the cotton wool,' adds the head firmly. When asked who the girls talk to if they're unhappy, the consensus was there was nobody they couldn't talk to. 'You could even go to the head if you wanted,' said one, with more common sounding boards including the housemistress, teachers, counsellor (two days a week), 'independent listener' ('hardly used, but important they are there,' says head) and the girls themselves (with an unfortunately named 'crush' system, whereby a sixth-former becomes a younger one's crush to help look out for them).

Head insists it's a more mixed bag than in the past. 'One of the questions we're often asked is, are there normal families here? And there are,' she laughs

Small size means school tends to function as a family ('including inevitable sibling rows') and careful pupil selection also seen as key to keeping the school happy, with friendships formed here generally for life. Alpha personalities probably better suited to larger school.

Traditionally, more carrot than stick when it comes to behavioural policies, although everyone agrees the current head has stepped up on strictness – with detentions now set for poorly worn uniform, lack of punctuality, misbehaviour in class etc. Parents clearly pleased that girls who see it as 'cool to continually misbehave' get their just deserts (22 temporary exclusions in just over two years). A number of girls have also been expelled or given the option of going quietly during the last few years, say parents, although school insists it's actually just one girl. Smoking in school grounds historically an issue – and some parents stay it still is, although school reports that current head 'has clamped down hard on it.'

Pupils and parents: Almost one in 10 mums are old girls, which adds to the already strong likelihood of being invited to socials (mass pub lunches before exeats), as well as to the fiercely strong school loyalty. Indeed, plenty of old money keeps on rolling down the generations as satisfied customers send on their daughters and granddaughters, although head insists it's a more mixed bag than in the past. 'One of the questions we're often asked is Are there normal families here? And there are,' she laughs. Balance is firmly in favour of 'British girls' (just under 80 per cent of total, a fifth from expat families, international pupils largely from Europe, Russia and Far East). Old girls include designer Nina Campbell, actor Sienna Miller, polar explorer Rosie Stancer and the late Isabella Blow. In fact, so many famous names that aren't so much dropped as infused into school literature. When you've so many celebs that 'Mrs Le Bon' judging the school fashion show merits only a (large) postage stamp-sized picture in the school mag, you've got nothing to prove about your connections.

Current pupils feature Emilies, Kathies, Charlottes, Daisies and Roses in abundance – a roll call of reassurance. These are the kind of girls who look you in the eye, who are confident, chatty and generally likeable.

Entrance: Offers (mainly in form 1 but quite a few in form 3) are conditional on passing school's own entrance papers (English, maths, science and non-verbal reasoning), taken in November with places offered in December. Not known for being overly selective, although school they turn away those who wouldn't cope. Handful of places in the sixth form – interview plus minimum five A*/C GCSEs with Bs in A level subjects. School is looking for girls who are good communicators, team workers and have creative potential.

Majority of pupils within 50-mile radius, mostly from country preps ('we are seen as a nice continuation – now that I've got my fire working, I just need the black lab,' laughs the head), although some from West London, with Hyde Park School, Knightsbridge Prep, Finton House, Fulham

Prep, Eaton Square, Pembridge Hall, Garden House, Broomwood Hall and the Thomas's trio – Clapham, Fulham, Battersea – the biggest feeders. Others from Surrey, Sussex and nearer bits of Hampshire (Ashdowne House, Cottesmore, Daneshill, Farleigh, Godstowe, Wellesley House). A few from East Anglia, Yorkshire, Scotland. Bright locals interested in day places also encouraged to get in touch – although only 10 day girls when we visited.

Exit: Some leave post-GCSE – 10 girls the year we visited. 'Co-ed is a big call,' admits head. Of those who stay on, vast majority go to university or college, with two off abroad in 2017 (Boston and Switzerland) and the rest to a range from RS at Edinburgh to sportswear at Falmouth to animal welfare at Harper Adams. 'Most of our girls get 2:1s or above – besides the obvious academic preparation, I think it's because we prepare them so well for independence through our boarding ethos,' says head.

Money matters: Discounts of 10 per cent for children from diplomatic, 20 per cent for armed forces families (five children max in each case) down to five per cent for siblings (flat rate).

Music, drama art and sport scholarships offered at 11+, 13+ and in sixth form. Also academic, by invitation – top 40 per cent of entrants sit extra tests. Confer lots of glory but, at £750 a year, little in the way of spondoolies. Also means-tested bursaries covering all fees ('The bastion of privilege is changing,' insists head). Helping hand extended to existing pupils if family finances hit a crisis.

Remarks: Enchanting and quintessentially British boarding experience with chocolate box-esque quality, though works hard to ensure that it never tips into cutesie. And while this small school produces rounded, ambitious and highly capable girls thanks to its good academic grounding and outstanding opportunities in the arts, one can't help but wonder about its long-term future unless the die-hard traditionalist parents are dragged kicking and screaming into the 21st century.

Highfield and Brookham Schools

Highfield Lane, Liphook, Hampshire GU30 7LQ

01428 728000 | headspa@highfieldschool.org.uk | www.highfieldandbrookham.co.uk

Ages: 3-13

Pupils: 449; Boarders: 120 full, 45 weekly

Day: £10,800 – £20,850 pa; Boarding: £23,023 – £24,600 pa

Head: Since 1999, Phillip Evitt, MA (Cambridge) and previously head of history at Dulwich College (50s). Brainy, articulate and a dead ringer for Tony Blair in his glory days, reckon a fair few parents (particularly the mums), some staff and probably pupils too, if able to connect with dim and distant political past.

Personable (head, that is – we can't comment on T Blair) with smile, voice, animation and epic hand gestures to the fore, but very much his own man. Attractively self-deprecating – 'It's very sweet of you,' he says when complimented. Emphatically not a spin doctor, he's 'totally genuine' thought a parent (coal-effect gas fire in his study was only non-authentic accessory).

He's good with the 'pushy, intelligent, successful parents,' said a dad and even better at cultivating highly effective relationships with senior school heads, securing places through 'amazing contacts to enable you to get what you want. If school's operating well, that's really what you need at the end.'

Leads a happy band of teachers who have 'a strong sense of unity – they're all good mates,' thought one, though it's taking a few turns of the wheel to secure uniform quality across the subject range. Maths and sciences 'excellent' but 'weaker in languages,' reckoned one parent, though 'not borne out in the sets the children are placed in at senior school,' says school.

Lyrical about post, for which he was head(master)hunted despite having no plans to go to the country and prepare for government. 'I never aspired to headship.'

Drove down 'on a profoundly unpromising late April day' battling new baby sleeplessness (last of four children, all – impressively – home births, now aged from teens to their 20s, who came through the school), and was instantly captivated by pupil élan as future charges played in the rain with evident enjoyment. 'I thought "how intriguing." These were children who felt comfortable being children, they didn't have that world weariness of the south London streetwise 13 or 14 year old.'

Modestly assumed he wouldn't suit. Of course, he did, and still does. Now well into his second decade, he's sixth head since school's foundation in Southampton in 1892, though far from being its longest serving (number two, member of family that still owns the school and responsible for move to purpose-built accommodation in 1907, clocked up a staggering 49 years).

Not much given to imposing his own world view, he lets school success (and its originators) speak for itself (we particularly liked school's weekly parish-style newsletters, featuring ads from local business amidst the reports of sporting and musical successes).

Relishes all that school has to offer in the way of tradition but is careful to keep the pace of innovation ticking over. Years 7 and 8 pupils have iPads which talk to school whiteboards and can store and file homework. May sound fancy but well in keeping with school's reputation for doing things earlier than most (it's been co-ed, and taken day pupils, since the 1970s).

He's taken difficult decisions from the off, starting by axing the 'madness' of compulsory boarding which was putting off many a parent who loved everything else about the school. To traditionalists, 'I was the hunter who'd shot Bambi's mother.' Many others approved and ultimately it proved a vote-winner. Now it's boarding because you want to, not because you have to – and, combined with sterling exam success, school is packing in the numbers, helped by increasingly popular pre-prep incubating the next generation.

Feels it's vital to listen to parents. Schools were 'conceited and arrogant' for too long, the experts in education who kept their customers at arms' length. These days, with successful, highly educated parents, 'you ignore what people have to say at your peril'.

Classrooms for older children, all interesting spaces and angles, were big on colourful, and up to the minute displays (including some gorgeous monster poems)

Suiting action to the word may make him 'possibly too accessible,' thought a parent. 'Does well to keep himself slightly aloof because otherwise, he'd end up having to get involved in every single micro issue that every parent had.'

Radiates clearly heartfelt belief in role of schools in providing not just rigour but also 'joy and wonder, enchantment, delight, challenge, excitement, fun.' Collect the set and learning becomes 'something you get out of bed to do, like turning a page in a book and wanting to move on to the next page.'

Despite rumours that he was considering his options as he approached his 10th anniversary, we weren't picking up any sense that he was off to scribe his memoirs (or indeed, set up a Peace

Foundation). Just as well, then, that there's no Gordon Brown figure lurking on the premises.

Best bit about the top slot? 'Genuinely, I want to make things better.' We feel a song coming on. Could it be D:Ream circa 1997? We think it could.

Head of Brookham pre-prep: since 2015, Sophie Baber BA PGCE postgraduate diploma in psychology, who previously taught at Marlborough College Malaysia.

Entrance: First come, first served until year 2 when school is 'sightly more cautious, as we need to ensure we can support pupils.' That said, there's not much that can't be handled in the way of learning needs, including one pupil statemented and fully LA funded – very much not the norm; school's deep regret that school is a postcode's throw from special needs switched on Hampshire.

Access all pupils largely down to owner says yes approach. Grandson of the founder, he has children at the school and what appears to be fairly substantial behind the scenes presence. 'When I first arrived, I asked, "Do you want me to be very tough in who we take on?" He said, "I want you to take them on and make a difference",' said previous head.

Most proceed from pre-prep to prep, though parents think number told they may not make the cut is rising (there's also no automatic rite of passage for siblings.) 'Definitely raising the standards,' reckoned one parent. 'When we first started, you had to have a severe problem not to get in.'

Most families within a 25 minute drive, Haslemere, Liphook, Liss and Petersfield the norm, Midhurst and Farnham at a stretch, augmented with influx of well-heeled Londoners, offspring increasingly the products of Thomas's and similar ultra-smart establishments.

Atmosphere is changing too. Once 'a bit chaotic and very friendly', it's now 'much slicker' – bemoaned by some though 'not necessarily a bad thing,' thought one mother. Though on the rise, the pushy, assertive contingent ('mums who wear hats at matches,' according to a local – we're keeping a watching brief on this one) is small enough 'to be squashed' by fellow parents. Tutoring, so far at least, remains a minority out of hours occupation 'and only if your child is really struggling.'

Exit: Move to prep is viewed as an exciting prospect by year 3s. 'It feels you can be free, because you get to walk around by yourself without a teacher following and there's much more playing area,' said one.

Prep school has opted for laissez-faire approach to departure age, loosening the ties by offering preparation for 11 plus (and even 12 plus) as well as common entrance. It's proved a smart move, parental freedom of choice coming down strongly in favour of staying the course, with what head describes as 'a small attrition rate' – as few as four leaving at end of year 6 and senior boarding for most. Widespread destinations, from Eton and Winchester, to Bradfield and Cranleigh, reflects ability range, Canford, Wellington and Marlborough amongst the perennial favourites. Scholarships, being pushed hard, thought parents, are going great guns.

Other local schools, wrestling the will they, won't they stay on beyond year 6 conundrum, must envy top years stability here. Though a few do leave early (some, reluctantly, because of financial pressures) seniors-only delights lure vast majority, headed by wonderful trips – voluntary year 7 trip to remote Scottish island to build own camp (look, no adults) one of the most memorable.

Parents feel breadth of talent and characters in top years something to celebrate. 'You've got people who are going to Eton, people who are struggling ...but who might be the best at sport or the best at music, and they can accommodate that,' said parent.

Remarks: Approached through prosperous Liphook, school looks a treat on a sunny spring day. Picturesque brickwork casts early morning shadows on a sea of green, pitches everywhere, side order of bluebell-carpeted woodland (provides fuel for new biomass boiler as well as home for achingly on-trend forest classroom), all 175 acres well-used by mothers who 'turn up in their lycra and go running with their labradors,' said former parent who also bemoaned the fact that 'it's easy to start feeling a bit smug.'

Top-up scenery fix every Wednesday when there's post-match 'car park time', families enjoying picnics together (courtesy of Messrs J Sainsbury – branch a short 4x4 schlep away), invitations to international boarders from local families ensuring nobody is left out.

Interiors are corridor heavy, twists and turns best tackled with an expert guide – star turns include attractive, solemn (but not sombre) chapel (nearby plaque commemorating school's founder must be touched if passed – brings luck, say older girls), nice, bright main music room (with a second for composition); excellent library, walls stuffed with reading lists, each personalised with jacket illustrations as effective aide-memoires – a time-consuming but worthwhile labour of love that ensures everyone broadens literacy horizons, say staff – and one of the small details that shows just why, academically, the school shines.

Guinea pigs and climbing frame in juniors' cosy cottage garden, as well as dress down Sunday morning breakfasts and highly rated cook your own supper sessions

Layout on Venn diagram lines, pre-prep largely self-sufficient but overlapping with prep when it comes to music, art and some sport, especially for older children. Cosily named nursery classes, Little Bears and Big Bears, lead a more self-contained existence, with attractive classrooms and separate, secluded and well-equipped play area. Integration starts early through treehouse families, small groups that span the age range and meet to share worries or good news, enjoyable sessions in forest school for all, and mealtimes, with older bruins having lunch in Highfield dining hall (Little Bears bring packed lunches instead), fajitas much enjoyed, 'salty' ham one of few dishes that wasn't.

Reception pupils start off in similar seclusion, though by the end of their first year, they're enjoying substantial tumbling about green space featuring gorgeous (though rather ignored) outdoor xylophone, as well as more conventional but attractive equipment, mad galloping in tentative sunshine seemingly the main amusement, though with behind the scenes staff presence to suggest games. Space gorgeous, only drawback ease of mislaying possessions: 'That sports jumper was there yesterday,' said pupil, with interest.

Inside, every inch of relatively compact and modern building is used to maximum effect. New and grandly named research area (library with computers – touch typing is taught in reception) was recently added, entrance area come assembly hall occupied by high flying and wonderful woven willow dragon spouting red velvet fire. Onesie design, though highly efficient, means some areas, such as nursery/reception music, are also through routes to somewhere else. Not a problem as remains '...a nice quiet place though sometimes people go through it,' said pupil.

Everywhere is extremely neat with not an inch wasted and loads to see and do, including rocket in reception class, less final frontier than cosy den, though strange lifeforms, courtesy of tank o'tadpoles, had already been discovered. Classrooms for older children, all interesting spaces and angles, were big on colourful, extensive and up to the minute displays (including some gorgeous monster poems).

Parents rate academics. 'We want our kids to have been pushed to the level where they can achieve either common entrance or scholarship to one of the major public schools,' said one. Achieved with no setting to speak of until year 3, maths the sole exception. 'If we have a big enough spread, might do it in year 2.' Anything but laissez faire, however, with lots of monitoring and no automatic move up between years, those who would benefit from 'spending extra time at a stage' as it's diplomatically phrased, doing just that. School also has a fair few of the extravagantly bright, who get fair share of extra support and encouragement – including peer socialisation (occasionally tricky for those punching above their weight conversationally).

Big thing is the creative curriculum, introduced some four years ago as a way of avoiding national curriculum ennui by adding all round oomph. Takes a theme such as 'Day at the sea', 'Knight in the castle' (pun intended), launches it with wow factor event (Sir Teach-a-lot knocking thunderously on pre-prep door to invite pupils to visit castle for a spot of princess rescuing) and ends similarly, with parents invited to share the fun by coming to medieval banquet or turning school into Brookham-sur-Mer, complete with donkeys and sand.

Subjects are knitted in en route, some national curriculum must-dos covered off-piste. While not everything can be shoehorned in (many science discoveries, for example, having inconveniently post-dated Round Table days) it's amazing how many dots can be joined. Would an exciting display of ultra-tactile rocks in year 3 classroom be followed by a snazzy volcanic eruption? Of course it would.

Huge staff enthusiasm provides a welcome outlet for pent-up creativity and they are encouraged to give full rein to creative instincts. Children are pretty sold on the idea (even if you did get the impression that overlaying a narrative element was even more popular with staff than their pupils) with activities, many hands on, doing wonders for confidence, one dyslexic child 'growing about three feet' after trebuchet improvement tip dramatically improved its destructive powers during siege weapon-making session.

With or without fun element, lessons are generally enjoyed, science for strong practical dimension, art at least in part because of resident dog, asleep in corner, music for charismatic teacher, whole-school favourite. Spanish, taught from year 3, seemed to be the only laggard – 'I just don't get it,' said pupil.

'What we do – I'm sure all schools say this – is absolutely aim to add value,' says prep head, disarmingly. Boasts 'unbroken record in getting everyone to first choice senior school'. Trickier these days because of the rise of pre-assessments, think parents, which has pushed up academic standards, and a tribute to what one described as 'fantastic' teaching across the ability range. So far, no sense of pressures feeding through to pupils, let alone creating the 'pale, wan' types that one parent reported seeing at other, more academically-focused hothouses closer to the capital. Indeed, this bunch were notable for good cheer (and delightful manners, too) though some parents felt that a few families have increasingly to be restrained from ramping up the anxiety levels at home.

Pupils, though reassuringly relaxed, have no doubts as to expectations, though lead-in is gentle, usually (though not invariably) mixed ability teaching for everything in year 4, maths set in year 5, when there's across the board specialist teaching, academics ramped up several notches in year 6 with three sets for everything, strengths in English, maths and science determining who you're with for everything else, including music and sport. Fourth set is added in year 7, and scholars identified. 'They try to give them other names,' say pupils, 'but we know exactly which group we're in.' (School, which sticks to 'obvious' one to four numbering, was slightly baffled by this.)

Staff, reckons one of their number, are 'lifers, not bolters' who '...all like children, and that's not always the case with some teachers,' says head (laughing, but we don't think he's joking). This lot include many clearly in love with their subject – head of maths was happy to deliver short tutorial on iPad geometry apps, their habits and haunts to this reviewer (only flaw the occasional unintentional transmission of scrawled notes to mothership whiteboard in classroom, visible to all).

Year 8 pupils, with impressive maturity, were quick to acknowledge that though some teachers were clearly more down with the kids than others (sports teachers and witty head of music particular favourites) even those with a less obviously child-pleasing style 'could turn a good pupil into an excellent one,' said one – and had the scholarship to prove it.

Most commonly school can cope with mild to moderate dyslexia, dyspraxia and dyscalculia, speech and language, auditory and sensory processing difficulties, fine and gross motor skills, Asperger's and mild ASD. Support one full time plus assorted specialists – ranges from study skills to specific help with literacy and maths. Seen as part and parcel of daily life by pupils – 'helps you write and read if you are having a problem,' reckoned one – support is regularly reviewed and, in the case of one rapidly progressing pupil with ADD, withdrawn altogether.

Though parent felt that SEN support could be even better, it's generally still felt, however, that full time SENCo, five other therapists and positive attitude from owner, a brilliant and dyslexic businessman (sister was a highly-rated teacher here until recently) creates haven for those with mainly mild learning needs. Children are 'never made to feel persecuted' and '...one of the great glories of the place in that we are a very broad church,' says head. Especially good with late developers, giving them the confidence to bloom in senior school – and many do.

With increasing numbers testimony to school's appeal there's the inevitable fraying at the edges. It's all change, however, with new sports hall planned, together with major surgery to senior teaching block including two additional science labs. Parents, while praising efforts, keen to see replacement of 'old fashioned' kitchens which, though good for terrific range of break time snacks and 'lovely' lunchtime fajitas as well as recently introduced salad bar, can be slightly over-reliant on stodge for afters.

Boarding has also had a fairly substantial shake up following period when lack of feedback made parents feel uncertain about pastoral care. New houseparents have 'definitely breathed new life and energy into our boarding.' Parents agree. Now 'hand on heart I'd say boarding is excellent whereas before I wouldn't have been able to recommend it,' thinks one.

With or without fun element, lessons are generally enjoyed, science for strong practical dimension, art at least in part because of resident dog, asleep in corner

Stalwart adult presence reassures – you're never more than two dorms away from a houseparent – as does good communication including separate boarding email updates and mobiles 'strapped to us,' says houseparent, whose cosy office becomes an informal meeting place for 'tea and gossip' and who has custody of special huggable piggy which 'slots round stomach' and is loaned out to ward off homesickness blues. Approachable matron, meanwhile, full-on mending session under way when we visited, is 'always here at breaktime for chats and spare clothes.'

There's considerable smartening up (showers in reds and pinks, girls' dorms very fetching – Tom

Daley pin ups adding final touch) with more to come. Loss of linen room, imminent, will be mourned by the heat-starved Spanish boarders who 'go in to soak up the warmth,' says houseparent. Biggest casualty, though, will be boys' shower golf, fondly imagined to be a secret from staff, ball propelled round vast, old-fashioned, Carry on Camping style washroom course, bonus points awarded for sinking hole in one into tooth mug.

Has all made boarding wildly popular. Pupils plead to start – 'mine were supposed to be day,' said one mother, resignedly – and is almost universal in top years. Who can blame them when evening cricket calls (there's always a summer term surge in numbers) and lures include guinea pigs and climbing frame in juniors' cosy cottage garden, as well as dress down Sunday morning breakfasts and highly rated cook your own supper sessions for years 7 and 8, run by Mrs Evitt who, though a vegetarian, gamely tackles hard core red meat dishes including 'delicious' burgers stuffed with mozzarella.

Day pupils, however, get fair share of the action, staff interests swiftly channelled by head into delightful range of clubs. School boasts of 'enough to experience something different every day of the week' – probably an understatement, given range extending from recently introduced Hyperdrive after school talks (history of flight the ambitious inaugural topic) to the remote control club which races model boats across smart swimming pool), as well as bushcraft group (one for the Bear Grylls wannabees, if ways with newly defunct wild rabbits anything to judge by).

Bonds are further strengthened by compulsory Saturday school in prep, well tolerated by all (marginally later starting time sweetens the pill – just – for sleep-starved parents), as allows five clear afternoons of sport a week, Thursdays reserved for

Highfield Keys – school's own D of E equivalent with 'spectrum' of activities ranging from 'charity outreach to outdoor pursuits.'

Big programme of optional Saturday sports undoubtedly helps, as do popular after-school clubs (majority sign up for at least one), judo, gymnastics and orienteering amongst the options, street dance, pottery and chess ringing the changes and 60 per cent of pupils also learning an instrument. Animated children also encouraged to look outside immediate surroundings, worthy swapsies with London multicultural Catholic school – a valuable eye-opener for all. 'I suddenly realised that there's all these other people like me,' said one of few non-white pupils.

House on house whomping is a big thing (not for nothing do their names commemorate famous English victories). Ranges from the big set piece pomp and ceremony of sports day, where knights set forth from separate marquees to do battle, to Bonfire Night guy contest, Lady Gaga a recent winner (Bradley Wiggins would have been a strong contender but 'his head fell off' – rarely a recommended tactic). If there's no house to duff up, 'we can turn anything into a competition,' said year 8 pupil, citing tidiest dorm, cleanest teeth and best veg plot by way of proof.

Officially, 'we aim to teach pupils that it's all about taking part.' However, 'Life is competitive.' And while prospectus may highlight 'development of fine and gross motor skills', pupils, organised on mainly traditional lines (cricket, football and rugby for boys, rounders and hockey for girls, swimming for all in decent pool) are in no doubt that purpose is to form ace teams and slaughter the opposition. 'We've only lost one match this year,' say 7 and 8 year-old football and rugby stars. Matches are, naturally, played to win with staff who are proud that their own teams regularly trounce those of other schools setting high class example. School says that it's emphatically not out 'to win at all costs' and stresses that all pupils shall have team games and represent the school in matches, whether endowed with athletic superpowers or not. Good sportsmanship comes with the territory and 'full respect is given to other teams in defeat and in victory. It's not personal.'

Parents agree that victory never comes shorn of good manners, which are emphasised throughout the school, year 8 monitors supervising younger pupils at break and lunchtime.

School, as a result, is a breeding ground for 'amiable killers,' says one parent, with netball stars known for pausing as they streak to victory to voice tender concern for opponents after collision. 'My daughter stops to say, "are you OK?" if she treads on someone's feet,' said mother. Boys' sport is 'excellent – I would say they win three-quarters of their matches,' reckoned dad. One parent felt girls' sport was a bit undernourished compared with boys'. Absolutely not so, says school, which puts it down to perceptions that girls currently 'don't win as many of their hockey matches because they are less experienced on Astroturf than other schools' teams,' though will all change when they get their own.

All in all, a super school that radiates enthusiasm and good cheer. Head says it's the happiest place he's ever worked in, felt previous GSG description 'tradition with a twist' summed it up to a tee. Aim is for greater cultural variety in the future, particularly in the top years, 'because it's good and healthy for the children.' Track record of all round success makes it a safe bet that it will add extra flavour to the mix.

Horris Hill School

23

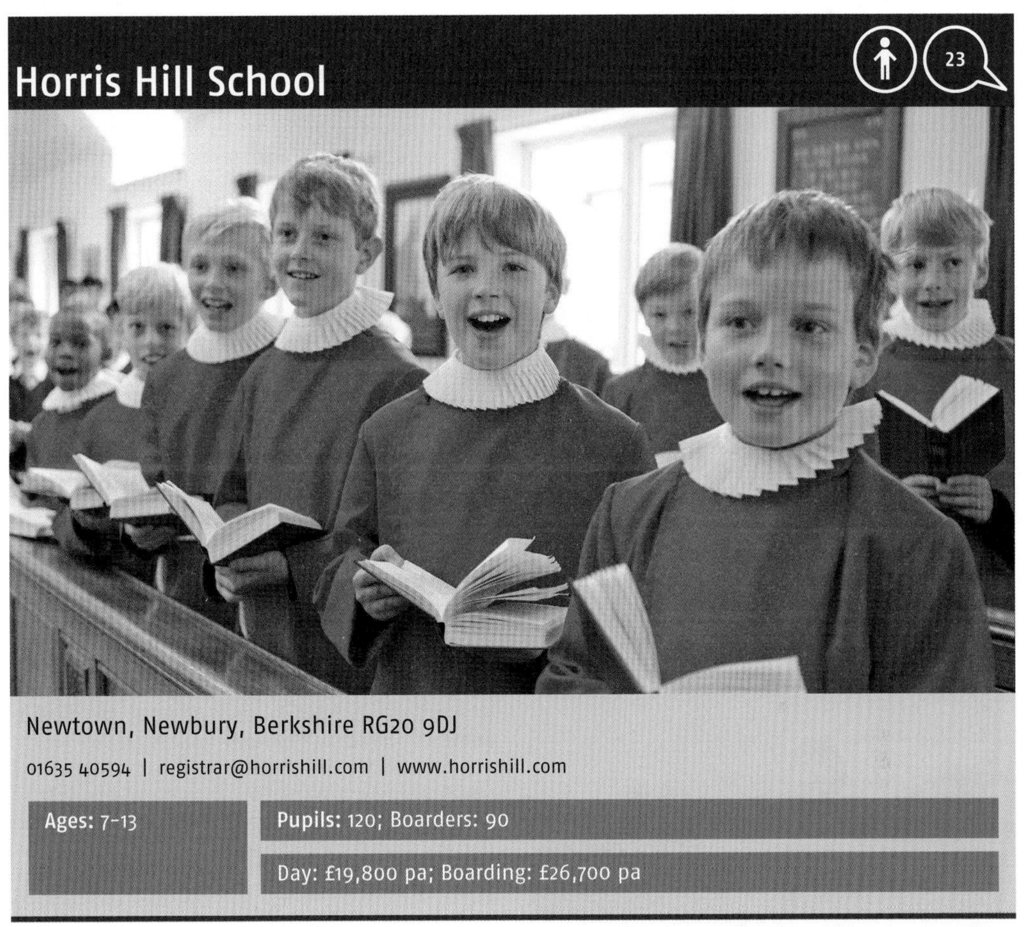

Newtown, Newbury, Berkshire RG20 9DJ

01635 40594 | registrar@horrishill.com | www.horrishill.com

Ages: 7–13

Pupils: 120; Boarders: 90

Day: £19,800 pa; Boarding: £26,700 pa

Headmaster: Since 2011, Mr Giles Tollit BA (40s). Tall and lean, reminded us a little of Bryan Ferry in his salad days. Seems reserved at first but soon unbends and shows a nice, dry sense of humour. Educated at Holmewood House in Kent and then Sevenoaks, where he was an academic scholar. Initially destined for a career in the military, he studied classics at Bristol on an army bursary. Took gap year job at a prep where he was expecting to teach Latin in a fairly junior capacity, but before term started found himself head of classics. Such a fiery baptism would have been enough to turn a lesser chap off teaching, but it had the opposite effect on Mr Tollit, and Sandhurst's loss turned out to be preps' gain. Ten years at Caldicott and thence to Bilton Grange as deputy head. He's 'delighted to be back in an all boys boarding school' (he loved his own time at prep) and certain about the positive benefits of a sector he believes suffers from outdated stereotypes. Not that he has to sell boarding to the parents he meets; they've all done it themselves. Describes school, memorably, as being 'not dissimilar to a cruise ship; doors close at the start of each term and off we go.'

Mr Tollit teaches Latin and Greek and helps the scholars polish their skills in debating, logic and philosophy, he 'mucks in' as necessary and takes year 8 camping at his house in North Wales after exams. Describes HH as a 'seven day a week' school and is unconvinced by flexi-boarding, which he feels is sometimes the worst of both worlds. A former UK shot, he has introduced clay pigeon shooting and a rifle range is planned. He's also a keen photographer and, because 26 miles just isn't enough of a challenge, an ultramarathon runner.

Married to Molly, also a classicist, whom he met at university. It seems that three young sons aren't enough for Molly, who has turned her energies to transforming part of a field in the school grounds into a thriving kitchen garden. Establishing one at their former school, Bilton Grange, taught her 'what works and what doesn't' and HH is reaping the rewards.

Parents think the Tollits have brought energy to the school and like the fact they have their own family. They have total faith in Mr Tollit, think he knows their boys incredibly well and praise his (and rest of staff's) swift response to calls and emails. Boys think head needs to be 'a bit more relaxed' but like the fact he's introduced clay pigeon shooting.

Entrance: From age 7. No exam 'as such'. Head meets all prospective parents. Boys have informal interview with the head, simple maths and English assessment and spend a day, a year before entry for those pre-registered. Mr Tollit says he's 'not looking for superstars'; boys are observed to see how they interact and whether they are comfortable being 'in the academic spotlight' of such small classes. Years 3-6 can be day or boarding; years 7-8 boarding only (does not take new entrants to year 8).

Exit: Nearly all to senior boarding schools. Recently: Winchester, Radley, Eton, Harrow, Sherborne, Marlborough.

Remarks: Founded in 1888 to prepare boys for entry to Winchester, Horris Hill is set in 80 acres of wooded heathland on the borders of Berkshire and Hampshire. You'll need your satnav first time round so as not to miss the quaint wooden signpost directing you down an unpromisingly narrow lane; it's almost as though only those who need to will find their way here.

One of Horris Hill's idiosyncrasies is that it doesn't do year groups, it does 'termly remove'. Boys are placed in small classes (average 12) according to the progress they are making and remain there until they have mastered all their subjects to the requisite level. It might sound like a nightmare to organise but head says the maximum discrepancy between similar age boys is 'a couple of terms either way'. A boy's performance is reviewed via 'form order' (mark, position and effort grade) every three weeks, and at the end of term he stays or moves up accordingly. It's an unusual (possibly unique) system and only feasible in a school of this size (max 130) and age group. Besides accommodating summer birthdays, advantages are no B stream, no individual subject setting and ongoing challenges for both brightest and less able. According to Mr Tollit, it's as close as you can get to an education that is customised to each boy's needs. Arrangement is only for academic work; boys are grouped by age for sport, dorms etc. Parents all in favour, say it's great both for confidence and humility as boys are usually towards the lower end during first term and nearer the top in the second. The consensus is that the system works, even if one or two parents admitted they didn't entirely understand it.

Lessons we observed were fun, inclusive and challenging – a hard trio to achieve but less so with a class of 10, perhaps. Subject classrooms are named after senior schools: Winchester, Harrow, Eton, Radley etc. It took a bit of getting used to seeing such an age range, but the boys' enthusiasm and rapport with teachers was inspiring. In geography, impressive answers to quick fire questions were rewarded with chocolate; in the next classroom we thought we'd come across boys being punished but discovered that immersion in French pop music is a great way to practise listening and vocab. In the DT workshop, small boys in enormous aprons were busy sanding and drilling – some with more finesse than others. Was there anything, we asked, that they would like to change at their school? Extra free time was one suggestion, as was getting rid of second prep (senior boys do this after supper). Most popular idea was being able to bring small pets to school, something we mentioned to Mr Tollit, who promised to consider the proposal. Few boys with SEN – dyslexia, dyspraxia – receive support but this isn't the place for those with more than mild problems.

The no mobiles, laptops, iPads (basically, no screens) rule is, as far as we could tell, no big deal and so much easier than trying to control limited access. Boys write weekly letters and may email/ Skype from the house computer. As a teacher observed, if the no screens policy were to change, 'it would mean more rules.' Boys accept the policy and parents love it. They're not quite so keen when, for instance, CE results come out and they can't talk to their sons because the boarding house telephone is engaged – surely room for a little more 21st century communication technology here? This is a school where 'live' notice boards mean that someone changes the pictures and display on the wall in the dining hall corridor several times a day. There aren't smartboards in every classroom, although those we saw were being creatively employed; boys treasure the one or two teachers who spurn their use. Science labs, art and DT rooms have all the necessaries in a charmingly scruffy, no frills style. By contrast, a high tech rooftop weather station relays the prevailing conditions to a screen outside the geography room.

Sensible uniform features navy blue cords – either trousers or shorts, boys can decide. Apparently 'some boys wear shorts even when it snows.' Sartorial democracy extends to choice of tie as well. Long morning and lunch breaks allow plenty of time to work in the kitchen garden, ride bikes (boys can bring own), play outside in the meadows, make dens and have adventures in their own bosky dominion (known as 'Spain' because it's roughly the same shape). Nowhere is out of bounds but pupils mustn't go off alone. Camping out and cooking in the woods is one of the ultimate post-CE treats. Juniors have their own wood, 'too tame for us,' said our super confident year 8 guides. One of the characteristics of HH is the amount of personal freedom pupils enjoy, finely balanced by the equivalent expectation of personal responsibility. Boys organise their own activities (or sign up), recording where they are on a notice board so that everybody knows.

Youngest boarders (age 7-9) have lovely rooms in the 'private side' above the head's family quarters, with teddies on beds and lots of posters. Evening activities include silent reading, film nights with popcorn, board games and even shoe polishing (try suggesting that at home...). Numbers are small so things are flexible; if it's hot they can have a swim, if everyone's exhausted they go to bed early. Gappies 'bridge the gap' between boys and staff and are, as always, very popular. What about the homesick, we ask? Of course it happens, but staff are vigilant and boys support each other, telling tutors if they're worried about someone. 'You feel awkward at first,' our guides said, 'but it only lasts a week.'

Lots of younger teachers with families live on site, married couples head up the boarding houses, but after the junior forms most of the teaching staff are men. This notwithstanding, the traditional boys' own atmosphere prevails and is what many, especially army families, treasure. There are a few local day boys who are 'building up to boarding', rest may go home after matches on Saturday until Sunday evening (except first and last weekend of term) but most stay, 'or you miss too much fun.' That fun includes cross country cycling, tree running, kite flying and ghost stories round the campfire. A parent praised the 'pater' system that pairs new boys with older boys and said that these cross age friendships are kept up throughout school. Older boys move on to one of two Edwardian houses a short walk across the playing fields. Four bed rooms are very comfortably furnished with home duvets, posters, beanbags and lovely soft carpet. Fruit bowl and toaster fill the gaps between meals, all of which are eaten in school dining room. Everyone, staff and pupils, sits down together at large tables, boys serve the food. Head v keen on benefits of 'interaction across a table'.

Sensible uniform features navy blue cords – either trousers or shorts, boys can decide. Apparently 'some boys wear shorts even when it snows'

Spacious and well designed music school can accommodate all for studio theatre or concert performances. Twenty six practice rooms means there's no excuse for not getting down to scales and arpeggios after breakfast. Parts for all in 'fantastic' music and plays. Main venue for drama, assemblies etc is rather tired windowless sports hall, not enhanced by pervasive whiffy trainer smell, but never fear, Mr Tollit is on the case and this part of the school is undergoing complete refurbishment. As he says, 'HH is not a flash school', but a shooting range, climbing wall and upgraded squash courts are on the way. Interestingly, it seemed to us that there was less of an obsession with organised sport and winning here than at other similar schools. Plenty of options: usuals plus hockey, squash, tennis, sailing, golf, fencing. Boys think cricket and football are what they're best at and all get to represent school in something. Parents come and watch matches, although it's a long round trip if you live in London. Swimming pool is outdoors (very) with wooden changing huts – all a bit basic but doubtless character building. One of the school's 'quite old fashioned secret things' is the modelling and train room, a glue and paint besmattered garret where Warhammer enthusiasts create their miniature worlds and model railway buffs of all ages can operate trains and signals.

With a maximum of 130 pupils, quite a few who are siblings, the parent body is small, self selecting and fiercely supportive. Although it's in a wealthy part of the country, HH is definitely not (outwardly at least), a smart school. Parents are welcomed to plays, concerts, matches and Sunday evening chapel and there are social events such as fathers' and sons' cricket matches and mothers' and sons' tennis, but there's no PTA, sports day or speech day. One father, who had considered London day schools for his sons, spoke of the way in which HH 'preserves innocence' – not just by absence of personal technology but also because full boarding means boys develop a camaraderie that is not influenced by each others' possessions or houses. On a more practical level, parents love the fact that all sports kit is provided, washed and maintained by the school.

Horris Hill is such a distinctive school it's unlikely you could choose it by mistake; proud to be different, it epitomises the very best prep school traditions without being pompous or rigid. HH boys are confident but not precocious; they think for themselves but aren't arrogant. There's room for big characters but a shy child won't be trampled underfoot; academic success is important but not to the exclusion of other talents. As another happy parent told us, 'it's a hidden gem.'

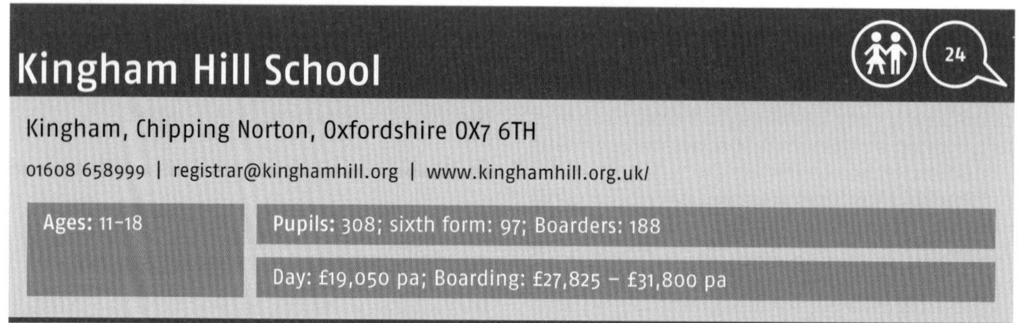

Kingham Hill School

24

Kingham, Chipping Norton, Oxfordshire OX7 6TH

01608 658999 | registrar@kinghamhill.org | www.kinghamhill.org.uk/

Ages: 11–18

Pupils: 308; sixth form: 97; Boarders: 188

Day: £19,050 pa; Boarding: £27,825 – £31,800 pa

Headmaster: Since 2008, Nick Seward MA BEng (40s). After a fairly international childhood, he boarded at Millfield School and went on to do aerospace engineering at Imperial College. His interest in the dispossessed and the homeless in particular, however, led him to work with homeless people in Blackburn and London; after a year travelling he went to Durham to study theology including a masters with a thesis on CS Lewis. He worked as a curate for four years but eventually moved to teaching at Magdalen College School (it was that CS Lewis connection that attracted him – Christianity with literature and deep intellectual curiosity). He was mentored and inspired by the head who 'celebrated eccentricity' and he saw that 'hard work, rigour and routine delivered challenges and results for the bright boys'. It must have been a transformative teaching experience, where he saw how school could encourage and channel individual interests.

He has brought the same ethos to Kingham Hill, which he joined because he was drawn to its 'Christian ethos, strong heart and the non-selective admissions policy', and he believed it was a school where he could make a difference. And it would appear he has. The parents, teachers and pupils are 'impressed' and 'adore' him for his commitment, his humanity and humility. Interests include go karting, sea fishing, camping holidays with his family and running the local football club. And this on top of teaching (economics) up to a quarter of a full teaching timetable and preaching or taking services in the local church.

He brought in big plans ('Realising our Vision') and has delivered well before schedule – increasing pupil numbers, improving exam results, raising funds to build fabulous new facilities (library, maths and science block), and all these improvements whilst sticking faithfully to an inclusive admission policy. He would like to increase bursaries and maintain the founder's intention to provide 'education for the poor'.

Married to 'the lovely Hannah – the clever part of the marriage'. She was previously a director of music (explained one child who is a chorister). She helps out as informal school matron and joins on the joint annual skiing trip with Magdalen College School. They have one daughter and three sons.

Academic matters: Small classes, traditional teaching, an emphasis on handwriting and ethical behaviour over technology, and a very individualised level of input gives pupils clear boundaries. It means that lessons are calm and directed. Some limited setting in classes; pupils learn tolerance and teachers manage to differentiate. Science and maths results lifting: wonderful light and airy new

building specifically for these subjects. Fantastic science labs – a science trip to CERN was a highlight for one student doing physics. Languages and humanities in the old school, wood panelled classrooms where history lessons referred to pupils from the First World War era who had sat in the same rooms and belonged to the same school houses.

The size of the school and close teamwork of teachers (several live on site) allows for some cross-curricular work – French/history trips, biology/sports, English/music. Evidence of interactive whiteboards but education here is more about discussion and explanation than technology. French or Spanish compulsory initially, but currently not a very high take up at GCSE or A level (nearly all A level linguists take Chinese or Russian). Good GCSE results – especially for a non-selective school. Forty-eight per cent A*-A/9-7 grades at GCSE in 2017. Popular subjects are maths, sciences and history. And very good and improving A level results – 45 per cent A*/A grades, with mathematics, government and politics, economics and business studies very popular and maths particularly successful. Students spoke of 'wide opportunities' and having 'more ways to choose' because of the breadth of opportunity.

The brightest children from each year are invited to join the Octagon society, where they are extended in an 'academic society'. Students felt that it 'allows us to really push our thinking' and teachers enjoyed the chance to 'motivate' and 'enrich outside the usual school curriculum'. It is about philosophical and ethical questions and encourages articulate explanations and leadership. Several pupils we spoke to felt very proud and privileged to be part of the Octagon society, which 'pushes me'.

The school has a successful learning support department with students given both individual and group support (sometimes instead of taking a foreign language), and some choosing to go along for extra homework help, study skills, revision help and advice about technological support for learning. In-house assessments possible and extra time for exams and laptop use for those with dyslexia where needed.

We saw a child leading a pony round the school, we met Casserole the rabbit, saw the new lambs being fed by bottle, were introduced to the one-eyed horse

This has the 'vibe of an international school but is still very British,' explained one student. It is accredited by New England Association of Schools and Colleges and is recognised by the US Department of Education. This means that US pupils can study in Kingham Hill and still gain American school credits and, if they stay to the end, can graduate with a US diploma. Perfect for students moving to and from the States.

Games, options, the arts: Acres of space for sports with both PE lessons and school team sports for all – we were pleased to hear from the girls that their sports are taken just as seriously as the boys'. Fencing, hockey, basketball, watersports, climbing, mountain biking (all those wonderful rolling hills and forests). Rugby very popular with boys we spoke to. Girls in the football teams. Lots of matches against local school teams, but room for those who want to pursue individual sports – swimming, gym, long distance running. The warmest school swimming pool we have come across with pupils also gaining certificates in lifeguarding and being able to earn money and experience doing this at weekends. The pool is open to pupils' families – parents reported using it regularly in the morning after dropping children off at school, and at the weekends.

Years 7 and 8 have the opportunity to learn a new musical instrument with free music lessons, and then often join the school orchestra or one of the ensembles. Singing is part of chapel service every morning ('it sets the tone for the day') led by school choir and backed by an organ scholar from Oxford. A 'taste of the Anglican choral tradition,' according to the head, as well as four different choirs including gospel.

Art is in an older workshop – creative chaos with many media including the rare treat of a pottery studio with kilns. DT (resistant materials) led by very long-standing teacher who clearly loves the fact that students explore and lead the learning. His own background in aeronautical engineering is evident from the many large model planes made by students as well as metalwork, 3D digital printing, woodwork. We saw garden benches that transformed into tables, book cases and finely jointed boxes. Hugely practical and creative.

Performing arts in a good drama hall – musicals, speech and drama, straight acting – any chance to perform welcomed and is the highlight of the school according to one pupil we spoke to. Drama scholarship pupil has 'new confidence since

Parents like the fact that the school is 'warm' and 'happier' than most and reckon that teachers must be better because it is not selective

joining the school', and drama awards announced in assembly alongside sporting achievements.

The school farm, run by the chaplain's wife, is a real asset – 'my son's favourite day is when he has farm club after school'. We saw a child leading a pony round the school, we met Casserole the rabbit, saw the new lambs being fed by bottle, and were introduced to the one-eyed horse. And this is a real little farm, not a petting zoo – pupils are taken to the abattoir when the time comes and learn about real agricultural practices, not just pet keeping. A touch of sanity and a chance to keep pupils' feet firmly on the ground and in the mud.

Boarding: Some 60 per cent of students board (almost entirely termly boarders, though a smattering of weekly boarders too) in a range of small houses. A maximum of 33 pupils to a boarding house with resident houseparents. These houses are their home, with clean, bright bedrooms and sitting room areas. A house for day pupils too, so they have a space to gather together each morning, leave their bags and get changed for sports. Boarding houses used in the morning for house meetings (aka checking diaries, reminding about music lessons and special notices), at lunchtime to collect themselves and their books, and after school for homework and recreation. Slightly more boys than girls board, but this is slowly equalising, especially with creation of the Lodge for more independent living for sixth form girls, which is a highly prized destination – day students stay occasionally too if they have evening practices or activities. Students in the Lodge do their own laundry and have more freedom than those in other boarding houses. Both parents and pupils reported that there was no division between day pupils and boarders. Local parents regularly welcomed boarders from further away for long weekends or exeats.

Background and atmosphere: Purpose built in 1886 by a philanthropist who wanted to educate the poor from the East End of London and get them out into the country, the wooden beamed chapel and mixed outbuildings still feel more like a country manor than a school. Well kept grounds and buildings, but not precious. It is set high in the Cotswolds with views all round of rolling hills and distant villages mid way between Stratford upon Avon, Cheltenham and Oxford. A hundred acres of grounds allows for wonderful playing fields and space to breathe. Chapel central to the school with daily services and the chaplain a big presence in the school. 'Atheists a minority at Kingham,' according to one parent, but pupils were encouraged to explain and discuss their points of view; 'free thinking encouraged' and 'no indoctrination'. Pupils expected to 'back up their ideas' rather than repeat dogma. Christian values 'core to the school' with prayer central too.

Pastoral care, well-being and discipline: Pupils call the close-knit community that exists at the school the 'Kingham bubble', and we can see why – set in some isolation in the countryside, with older and younger pupils mixing unselfconsciously and both adults and pupils 'treated with respect as individuals whose opinions are valued'. No teachers on first name terms, but no pupils called by their surnames either. Pupils 'on a par with teachers' who 'chat to them', and pupils say they 'feel listened to'. This school is 'more about the whole child' and is 'not pressurised'. The teachers 'find out about the kids' and 'interact with the children'. There is 'an ease between teachers and pupils, it is respectful but jovial at the same time'. Parents like the fact that the school is 'warm' and 'happier' than most and reckon that teachers must be better because the school is not selective but get such 'good added value in terms of academic achievement'. Parents spoke of pupils not being pushed but of being 'given opportunities and encouraged' and of choosing the school precisely for that reason.

Pupils and parents: Famous old boys include Andrew Adonis, Pink Floyd's Guy Pratt and even an air-vice marshal. This range of interests and careers sums up the school – space for pupils to be individuals. Approximately 15 per cent of students from families in the Forces or Foreign Office, with 10 per cent American students (state department or embassy families), some 70 per cent of students British and 20 per cent overall international. School works hard to ensure no large groups of international students so a medley of some 20 nationalities (we met a German student, a boy from Uzbekistan and a Chinese girl just for starters). British students primarily fairly local. There is no pressure to be a 'cool kid' at this school, which 'doesn't attract the more pushy parents'. Parents spoke of the joy at finding an alternative to the very academic and driven schools that abound in the area, where pupils have time and are encouraged to have extracurricular interests rather than focussing entirely on academic studies.

Entrance: No academic selection and the school will take children needing learning support but 'rarely' those with ADHD, autism or behavioural difficulties. Head meets all families when they visit and/or

apply and then there is an assessment in English, maths and reasoning, as well as sight of previous school reports. Assessment by agents if pupils from abroad. Taster days possible for prospective pupils – so reassuring for parents and pupils to know the school before committing. Applications for scholarships (up to 25 per cent of fees for academic, art, performing arts and sport and at sixth form, one 50 per cent organ scholarship and three 75 per cent academic scholarships) by October.

Exit: Around 20 per cent leave after GCSEs. Serious effort goes into career guidance provision throughout the sixth form, with presentations and careers evenings – attendance, needless to say, by MOD and agricultural colleges, but also a wide range of other career talks. Americans tend to go back home for university – in 2017 to Irvine (computer science), George Mason (government and international affairs), Gettysburg (sociology and international relations) and Shenandoah (elementary education). Other internationals mostly going back to their home countries – Maastricht (law), Vincenza (history and English), IED Istituto Europeo di Design (jewellry design) – but otherwise a fair number stay local and go to Bath and Bristol or Oxford Brookes. Many move to London – Imperial, Kings, UCL, LSE. One to Oxford in 2017 to study chemistry. The school is very proud of several past students who came from backgrounds in care to go on to Oxbridge.

Money matters: Fifteen per cent of revenue from the school is spent on concessions and school bursaries (means-tested bursaries of up to 50 per cent are available and a generous 100 per cent of school fees for able sixth form pupils). Scholarships of up to 25 per cent of fees for academic, art, performing arts and sport and at sixth form, one 50 per cent organ scholarship and three 75 per cent academic scholarships. The school has a proper set of 12 governors – rare and reassuring in a private school, as well as trustees who oversee Kingham Hill Trust. At present, building projects are funded from revenue, which appears solid.

Remarks: The overriding approach at Kingham Hill School is 'what can the school do for the pupil rather than what will the child bring to the school'. The Kingham bubble is a supportive community of pupils and teachers treating each other with respect and kindness in this area of outstanding natural beauty. A traditional English boarding school with Christian values and prayer at its core, giving a solid education in its widest sense to both English and International pupils.

Lambrook School

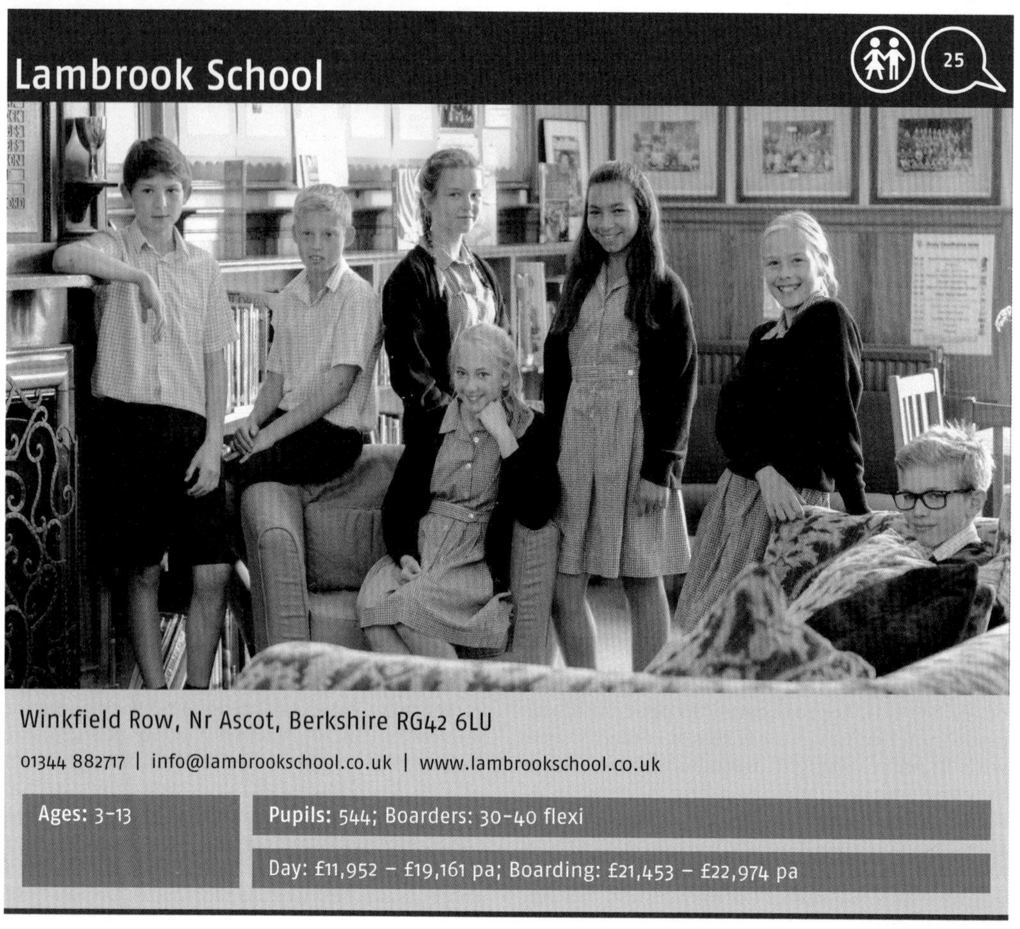

Winkfield Row, Nr Ascot, Berkshire RG42 6LU

01344 882717 | info@lambrookschool.co.uk | www.lambrookschool.co.uk

Ages: 3–13

Pupils: 544; Boarders: 30–40 flexi

Day: £11,952 – £19,161 pa; Boarding: £21,453 – £22,974 pa

Headmaster: Since 2010, Jonathan Perry, previously head of Kingsmead School in Hoylake, and before that senior housemaster at Monkton Combe, Bath. Degree in religious studies and history from Gloucestershire; PGCE from Cambridge. With a family made up largely of teachers and clergy (father was a bishop), public service is clearly in the blood.

Personable, chatty and very much a double act with wife Jenny, a gentle and hospitable woman who works one day a week as a clinical pharmacist at a nearby hospital; their own children attended the school and have since progressed to Wellington and Downe House. 'I only got the job because of Jenny,' he jests. 'But a headmaster's wife's husband, he is not,' points out Jenny; indeed, her role involves meeting prospective parents with him (most mornings), helping pastorally with the school nurses, overseeing the school's second-hand shop, match teas and liaising with the PTA.

Doesn't do any timetabled teaching ('I'd constantly have to find cover'), but does current affairs sessions for older pupils when he can. Says his door is always open, although pupils told us they 'wouldn't dream of going over to that side of the school unless invited'; they did add, however, that he's 'approachable,' 'fun' and 'often out and about' and it was noticeable how at ease in (and clearly used to) his company they were when we visited.

Described by parents as 'the perfect fit' and 'always willing to go the extra mile – the type of head who gets into costume on Greek day and who is the first to start clearing up after a social event.' And it is testament to his modesty that it took parents to tell us how he greets them every morning, is present at most matches and, as one put it, 'finds exactly the right school for your child to move on to.' Mixed feelings from parents about him having increased pupil numbers, but he promises 'no more.'

A keen sportsman, he enjoys golf, tennis and cricket, but more often these days from the sidelines. Cornwall is where the family go to get away from it all – sea being practically the only thing lacking in Winkfield Row.

Entrance: Mostly at 3, 4 and 7 years. School meets all prospective pre-prep families and there's a formal assessment day for entrance to the prep, up to a year before prospective entry. Assessment criteria include academic ability, wider interests, character and behaviour. With around four to five applications per place in some years and growing waiting lists, parents are advised to clock an interest a good few years in advance.

'It's not just the acting we get involved in, but the backstage tech stuff too,' pupils told us excitedly

Increasingly favoured by west London parents (for which school runs three minibuses, but is capping it there); while home counties parents hail from Ascot, Windsor, Eton and Henley, as well as villages right across Berkshire, Buckinghamshire and Surrey.

Exit: All to first choice senior schools including Wellington, Bradfield, Eton, St Mary's Ascot, Downe House, Harrow, Marlborough, Charterhouse, Radley and Stowe. In 2017, 25 scholarships – academic, all-rounder, sport, music and drama.

Remarks: If you're lucky enough to visit the magnificent white Berkshire mansion that is Lambrook on a sunny day, it is a glorious site. And if you pick a day to see the school's 52 acres of lush prime estate at their peak of green and pleasantness, expect to see children playing under distinguished trees, with the cricket pitch and nine-hole golf course (yes, really) looking like velvet and birdsong coming from every direction.

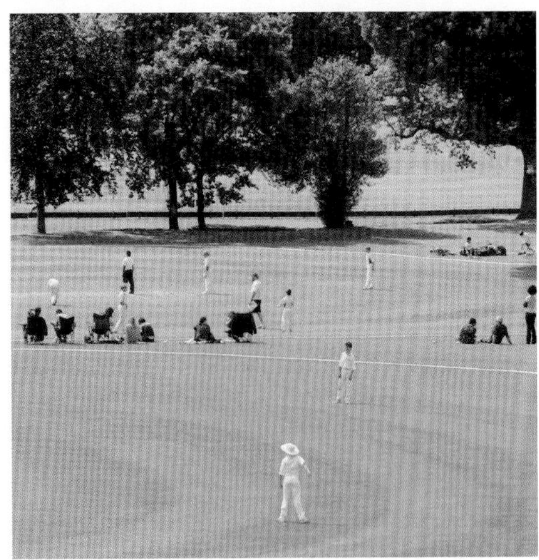

The front door of the original house leads to grand hall and staircase, with stylish reception area and headmaster's study; pupils and parents will (from summer 2018) enter through a modern foyer which bridges the old and new builds. The library is true gem, with gothic wood panels and shelves, plus huge sofa and armchairs which children can use anytime – and really do. Double glass doors lead from here into the spacious, conference style Churcher Room, where we saw pupils working away on iPads. The dining room, which could appear vast to younger children, somehow manages to stay homely and unintimidating. Here, as elsewhere, historic photographs of the estate's history and past pupils – teams, plays etc – form part of the fabric rather than separated into an archive. Founded in 1860, Lambrook is alma mater of, among others, Lord Alfred Douglas (Oscar Wilde's downfall), Queen Victoria's grandsons Prince Christian Victor and Prince Albert, W C Sellar and R J Yeatman, authors of 1066 and all that. More recent alumni include actor Alex Petyffer and rugby internationals Max and Thom Evans.

The fine chapel with its gleaming brass and polished pews can no longer accommodate everyone, so whole school assemblies and inter-house competitions (singing etc) take place in the performing arts auditorium (a 2013 building that is also home to swish music facilities), while other newer buildings of note include the sports hall and spectacular indoor swimming pool (2015). Classrooms, which are dotted around the site, are bright and welcoming, with pupils' work displayed on the walls and desks set up for interactive teaching.

The boy:girl ratio here is 60:40, but the feel is thoroughly co-ed. And despite the step up in academic rigour in recent years (including more testing), Lambrook lessons genuinely seem fun, with relaxed but respectful relations between pupils and staff, many of whom live on site. 'I can't think of a single teacher that has been substandard,' one parent told us; CPD certainly valued, with all teachers (65 per cent of whom were recruited by current head) invited to observe others, including those in different departments. Good mix of male, female, old and young; and the enthusiastic gappies are well-liked too. Many pupils (and some parents) give the impression, however, that they'd gladly give their right arm to give up Saturday school (compulsory for years 5 and above), although will have to grin and bear it as head says, 'I'm proudly holding onto it – it's what most will be doing in senior school so it prepares them well.'

Four form entry from year 3, with maximum of 18 to a class. Setting from year 3 in maths and English (five sets); from year 5 in French, Latin and science (four sets). Lots of fluidity, agree all, and there's some informal banding for humanities too. French taught from nursery; Spanish from year 7 (Saturday school); German for scholars; Latin from year 5; Greek for the most able year 7s. Mandarin due to return by popular demand as extracurricular. Homework on the heavy side – 40 minutes a night from year 3, moving incrementally up to an-hour-and-a-half by year 8, but with compulsory daily prep sessions that finish at 5/5.30pm, pupils don't usually have to take any home – 'such a boon,' said one parent.

'Always willing to go the extra mile – the type of head who gets into costume on Greek day and who is the first to start clearing up after a social event'

Milder cases of SEN well catered for, with support in the classroom where possible. No stigma, with pupils chatting away about their various needs, while parents rave about open minded approach: 'The school is very mindful that dyslexia is not one thing and are happy to try one thing and move onto another if it doesn't work, as well trying out approaches I've read about,' said one.

Music is flourishing; 85 per cent of children learn at least one instrument up to and including grade 8 (420 performing arts lessons each week) and there's a wealth of school bands and ensembles, as well as a full symphony orchestra. We were privy to choir practice in the chapel at lunchtime – such a sonic sensation that we could have sat there all day; no wonder they are regularly invited to sing at Eton College and St George's Chapel, Windsor and have also performed at Notre Dame Cathedral. Drama popular, with pupils having performed at the Edinburgh Fringe; recent school productions include The Railway Children, Macbeth and Annie. 'It's not just the acting we get involved in, but the backstage tech stuff too,' pupils told us excitedly. Art also flying; so much so that they were building a bigger department for art, design and technology.

Grounds and facilities are a sportsperson's paradise and while it must be tough to do them justice (and, apparently, the match teas), the boys' and girls' teams regularly bring home gold and silverware – school currently county champions at hockey and first 11 football team has been unbeaten for three years straight. Main sports (played four afternoons a week) are football, rugby, hockey, tennis, cricket (boys) and hockey netball, lacrosse, tennis, rounders (girls). 'But we don't just play to win,' say pupils, with A-E teams ensuring everyone gets to represent the school. And what of pupils who don't like sport? 'You still play!' one answered, incredulous we had asked. Breadth of activities thankfully mean most are lured by something – trampolining, skiing, basketball, fencing, diving, sailing, polo (well, this is Ascot). Impressive choice of clubs – creative writing, beekeeping, debating, astronomy etc – mean school is often busy until 8pm. Equally exciting range of expeditions, with highlights including canoeing in Sweden and bi-annual cricket tour to South Africa, all with a strong sense of public service included.

Pastoral care proactive rather than reactive, with form tutors and heads of year meeting with pastoral head every week to identify children in need of support – 'anything from a friendship group regularly falling out to someone whose father has just died,' says head. Matron, counsellor (visits every Thursday) and Mrs Perry also involved. 'It's a busy, pressured environment and we have to back that up with support,' she says, with staff themselves attending mental well-being courses. 'There's no teacher I don't feel I could talk to,' one pupil told us. High expectations (rather than lots of rules) set the tone for the good behaviour and most pupils go through school without a detention. 'There's room to slip up, with most teachers giving multiple warnings before you get a punishment,' one pupil told us. Two temporary exclusions in the last few years. 'Bullying doesn't exist,' pupils told us; head knew better than to make such assertions, 'but we're on the front foot, identifying and keeping a close eye on children with sharper elbows.' There's a clear no-phone policy.

We visited the nursery, separate from but close to the main school, just before lunch (meals on wheels from main school kitchen). Tinies sitting on the floor were engrossed in a singing session. At age 4 children move on to the pre-prep, not a huge step geographically but parents praised the way the staff prepare children for this transition. All downstairs classrooms boast fenced in outdoor areas to encourage freeflow, while outdoor classroom with tepees and a sensory walk is also used regularly. Pre-prep has its own hall, used for before (from 8.15am) and after (until 6pm) school care – a bonus for parents, especially if they have older children at the main school.

Boys' dorms (two to 10 beds per dorm) are located at the top of nursery, all with homely touches and contemporary colours, plus a common room packed with table football and other active indoor games. Girls' dorms (two to eight beds per dorm) are back in the main house, with similar set-up but far more pink and a common room more focused on seating ('We chat and watch telly more,' explained one girl). Boarders' kitchens are large, sunny and refreshingly un-institutional. Boarding (available from year 3 upwards) is either weekly or flexi; the latter is particularly popular at the end of the week – parents certainly appreciate it – with 220 different children having boarded during the last year. 'It's really good fun – you get a great mix of scheduled activities and free time with your friends,' one pupil told us.

Lambrook is a happy, dynamic and unstuffy prep school in an idyllic pastoral setting where children are educated to the best of their potential. Providing a fabulous range of opportunities to broaden horizons and instil new interests, it's best suited to the academically able and (ideally, but not exclusively) sporty boys and girls.

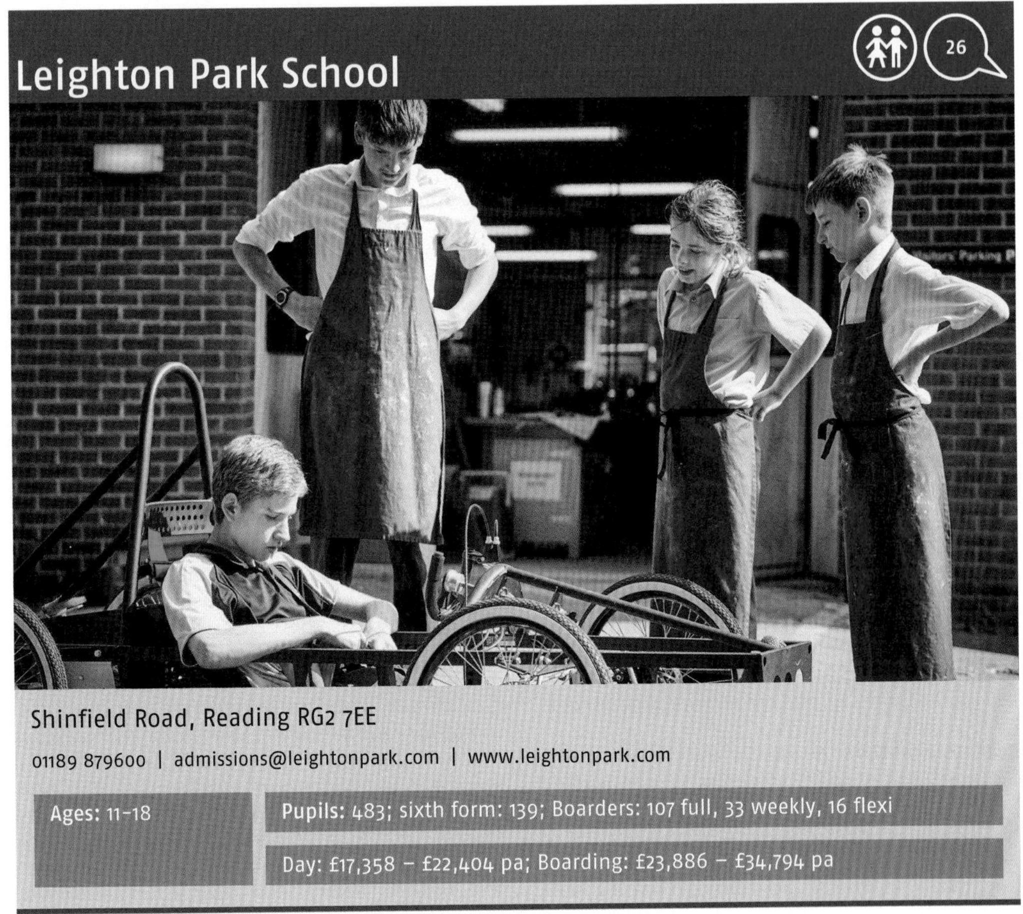

Leighton Park School

26

Shinfield Road, Reading RG2 7EE

01189 879600 | admissions@leightonpark.com | www.leightonpark.com

Ages: 11–18

Pupils: 483; sixth form: 139; Boarders: 107 full, 33 weekly, 16 flexi

Day: £17,358 – £22,404 pa; Boarding: £23,886 – £34,794 pa

Head: Since 2013, Mr Nigel Williams BA MA PGCE (known here – as are all staff – by his first name). Educated at Monmouth School, Nigel read history at Bristol and then a masters in Victorian Studies at University of London. Began career at St Albans, where he became head of general studies. Joined Leighton Park in 1994 as head of history and became, successively, housemaster, director of studies, deputy head: academic, deputy head: pastoral and then, with nowhere else to go – head. An unusual trajectory and represents a terrific vote of confidence from the school governors and community. Plus a recourse to stability and continuity. His tenure followed the lengthy reign of a highly-regarded predecessor with a brief hiccup in between when another appointee rapidly came and went. No scandal but a mismatch and no hard feelings thereafter, in a way that is characteristic of the school as a community.

Nigel – whose delight and surprise at his assumption of the headship is touching and genuine – is larger than life, colourful, smiley, warm and an easy man to talk to. He embodies his school and its values but is more than a safe pair of hands, having learned the place all through and having sound and sensible ideas of his own. This was a wise appointment. Leighton Park, already in stout heart, will be the better for it.

Although no staff and only penny numbers of pupils are Quakers, the school lives by and exudes those gentle, civilised and socially responsible values

Leaving in July 2018. His successor will be Matthew Judd, currently second master at Haberdashers' Aske's boys and executive head of its prep. Degree in geography from University of Wales and teaching qualification from Cambridge. Started his career at Habs in 1993, becoming head of department and housemaster; moved in 2005 to be principal at Mander Portman Woodward College in London before rejoining Habs five years later as second master and then later head of the prep and pre-prep. Also an ISI inspector and was motivated to apply for the job after inspecting the school. Grew up in Crawley and was the first person in his family to go to university, having attended the local comp in the shadow of Gatwick airport – 'if you were a boy, you went into baggage handling; if you were a girl, you went into duty free.' Will live on site with his partner Ian; a keen musician, and enjoys travel and fitness.

Academic matters: Academic work is taken seriously and pupils strive for success – as they should – although not, thankfully, a results-driven school. In 2017, 35 per cent A*/A at GCSE. A level and IB offered though IB numbers not yet on a par with A level takers. In 2017, 38 per cent of A levels gained A*/A. Overall IB average 33. IB retained partly because 'its values are so much those of the school,' explains Nigel. Useful cross-fertilisation – IB and A level languages often taught together in year 12 and all take an Extended Project Qualification for its educational value. Good languages. BTec in creative digital media available in years 10/11. Very good teacher:pupil ratio at 7.5 pupils to one full-time teacher and some sixth form classes with only one or two students. Small but well-stocked library and much praise for the range of visiting outside speakers. Interesting displays of work – we were moved by the WW1 montage of Old LPs fallen in battle which made it all pathetically real.

Parents, for the most part, praise the teaching – 'My son is enthused by everything – especially the Mandarin', while there is some sense that a little more rigour, vigour and initiative might not come amiss here and there. Probably not a school for workaholics, but then, they probably wouldn't come. Very much a school for joiners-in and those with breadth and brain.

EAL classes for small number of students who need them and school prepares them for FCE and IELTS exams. They don't take an additional language and use one of the class English lessons to boost their language skills. Some 15 per cent on the SEND register – surprisingly few for a school with such a good reputation for supporting those with an educational special need. Individual learning centre and all staff involved in support. No in-class assistants unless provided by the pupil's LA. Helpful and flexible approach, as parents attest, and 'they are quite relaxed about Ritalin, they take it in their stride'. A sense that the large and highly-regarded SEN team are there to make themselves less and less needed.

Games, options, the arts: Large and beautiful site, with fields, pitches, courts and tracks which positively set your muscles aquiver. 'My son is not sporty but they have really got him to love it,' a mother marvelled. Music is big here and no other house activity compares with the annual House Music, which is taken very seriously – 'almost too seriously,' we were told, 'as everyone gets really into it and the noise is louder than at a football match'. Good number learn an instrument in school and remarkable cohort of fine musicians – ie beyond grade 8 – practise here. Art exceptionally varied and imaginative. We loved the year 10 work on 'Surfaces, facades and veneers' and the sixth form studio was full of mind-stretching, clever creativity, alongside examples of the crucial skills of drawing and painting. Pottery, photography, textiles and DT work provide evidence of novel, individual ideas being fostered. DT provision newly enhanced by laser cutter, CNC router and 3D printer. Drama also lively – big productions, mostly musicals, in attractive, flexible theatre, its regular seating arranged, interestingly, in the guise of a Meeting. Also small drama studio in stand-alone brick building, formerly a squash court.

Lots to do. And lots of encouragement to try things out. Huge range of clubs and activities and masses of space for them all. Young Enterprise, D of E, trips of all kinds but no CCF, of course.

Boarding: School would not claim that boarding accommodation is up-to-the minute. Rooms are spacious enough. Most younger years share in 3s and 4s. Sixth formers in singles but not an en-suite or even a bedroom with basin anywhere on site – yet. All houses well-provided with table games, TVs and sofas – they feel like home only with more fun. Meals now eaten in Oakview dining room rather than in houses and pyjamas – to the regret of some. Many day pupils stay until 7.00pm or even 9.00pm, thus getting the best of two worlds.

Many staff live on site and have boarding duties. Head's modest house, also on site, all adds to the sense of community and pupils love that 'our tutors are in the boarding houses after school and we can just chat to them'.

Background and atmosphere: Situated in the centre of 'the park' – an apt name for this spacious, meadowed site with hundreds of mature trees, garden areas, large reedy pond, generous planting and low-rise blocks – is the main building, an elegant 1850s white house. It was bought by an earlier incarnation of the school in the 1880s and more land was donated by the Reckitt family – the aim being to educate Quaker children for Oxbridge. It remains a Quaker-run school as the majority of governors are Quakers and, although no member of the Friends remains on the staff and only penny numbers of pupils are Quakers, the school lives by and exudes those gentle, civilised and socially responsible values. Few who leave here take nothing of those with them, and many see them as a guide for a healthy life. A palpable sense of calm pervades the place – you feel it as you drive in and your shoulders drop as you step out of your car and breathe out.

This is not just another school and it is best not to approach it as such. Nor is it 'alternative', though the pupils and teachers being on first name terms can deceive you into thinking so. The Quaker philosophy is central and, although it is never pushed at you, its calm wisdom steals gently into one's consciousness. 'When you're in year 9, you don't really get the meaning of it,' one soon-to-be-leaver told us, 'but, by the end, especially when life is hectic, you really appreciate it. It helps you find quiet time to clear your thoughts.' Weekly Meeting for Worship and monthly Meeting are the overt Quaker practices but, in the diverse mix of today's population, no particular faith dominates and everyone brings to the sessions what they wish. In practice, this approach changes relationships. 'Calling teachers by their first names makes you treat them as people – you don't have to be on your best behaviour and it makes you more inclined to learn,' we were advised. And, of pupil:pupil dynamics – 'If we fall out we tend just to fix it and hug it out.' The 2015 Peace Pole – an extraordinary carved wooden column visible from most parts of the school – enshrines these principles, as do the many examples of pupil creativity – benches, tables etc carved from fallen trees on the site – around the place. Very much a school for joiners-in and those with breadth and brain.

Art exceptionally varied and imaginative. Sixth form studio full of mind-stretching, clever creativity, alongside examples of the crucial skills of drawing and painting

Lots of buildings of all eras, little of startling architectural merit though the recent Oakview restaurant is cleverly designed and a popular addition. We were very impressed by the food – its freshness and variety – and deeply regretted not being able to stay to sample it. 'Theatre Special is when they cook it in front of you – like a performance; pork baguette is a thing of beauty,' apparently.

Some splendid individual rooms, especially in the main building. New all-singing-all-dancing music and media centre soon to open, with rehearsal and performance rooms plus a fully-equipped media suite. We were repeatedly struck by the good order of the site – not an instance of peeling paint, a shabby carpet or a stained wall met our eye and, over an extensive tour, we saw not a shred of litter. Signing is useful and not municipal in style.

Houses, named after notable Quakers, matter but not too much – except at House Music. But the traditions and values of the place inspire spontaneous, unaffected loyalty.

Pastoral care, well-being and discipline: Discipline maintained with a light touch and some incomers given refuge after mishaps elsewhere become model citizens here. A great place for deserving second-chancers – 'The only people to get kicked out are complete idiots as they'll have had several warnings'. So – very occasional permanent exclusions, usually of those with more money than sense. A parent told us that 'they encourage them to become self-reliant and independent' and 'unlike at other schools, they can pick up their own clothes and make their own supper'. 'They are good at integrating kids who've been fish-out-of-water at their previous schools.' More rules than you might expect – no eating while walking around, no use of mobiles during the school day – but all designed to consider others and to maintain the peace. And Nigel is subtly stiffening the teacher-pupil dynamic to remind all that, in the classroom, work is what matters and discipline is there to protect that principle.

Pupils and parents: Day pupils outnumber boarders 3:1. Full boarders outnumber weekly/flexis by 4:1. And boys outnumber girls – as in most co-ed schools – by more than 2:1. Some 72 per cent are UK nationals, the rest from everywhere – 29 nationalities at time of our visit, so no cliques and enclaves. Vast majority of UK students are local or local-ish. Healthy 75 per cent of boarders in school at weekends. Old Leightonians: Sir David Lean, Sir Richard Rodney Bennett, Jim Broadbent, Laura Marling, Eliza Bennett, Michael Foot, Lord Caradon, Lord Frederick Seebohm and a fair clutch of MPs plus Rowntrees, Cadburys, Clarks, Reckitts, Morlands and Frys.

Entrance: Online entrance tests in English comprehension and maths, plus creative writing exercise and short interview in the January preceding entry for years 7-10. Entry to sixth form conditional on GCSE or equivalent results, plus interview. At 11+, 95 apply for 40 places; at 13+, 35 apply for 15-20 places. At year 10, 20 apply for 10-15 places. Year 11 is a 'pre-sixth' year for overseas students. There are six applicants for each of the 20-30 places in the sixth form. Second language speakers sit an EAL test.

'Theatre Special is when chefs cook in front of you – like a performance; pork baguette is a thing of beauty'

Exit: Around a third leave after year 11. Most who leave after sixth form go to a range of courses at respectable universities but, as one parent enthused, 'we liked the fact that alongside the leavers who read medicine at Oxford they celebrate those who go and learn circus skills'. Most, however, to eg Sheffield or Exeter to read eg engineering or philosophy. One to Oxbridge in 2017 and one medic.

Money matters: Not an immensely rich school but a decent amount of money available for bursaries. Emphasis on enabling those whose financial situation would not allow them to attend, to do so, so most recipients on awards of 50 per cent or more. Robust mean-testing and assessment of income/commitments/assets etc. Six on 100 per cent bursaries at time of our visit. Scholarships mostly worth 10 per cent.

Remarks: A school in which to grow. Not for hustlers, bustlers and takers but great for thinkers, makers, givers, be-ers.

Lord Wandsworth College

27

Long Sutton, Hook, Hampshire RG29 1TB

01256 862201 | admissions@lordwandsworth.org | www.lordwandsworth.org

Ages: 11–18

Pupils: 603; sixth form: 161; Boarders: 352 full, weekly and flexi

Day: £19,650 – £22,575 pa; Boarding: £26,550 – £32,100 pa

Headmaster: Since 2015, Adam Williams (40s). Born Down Under, he went to Bradfield then Durham University. Previous job was deputy head of Glasgow Academy; has also been head of geography at Bradfield and Oakham. A neat man with an open face and the hint of a twinkle, he honed impressive cricketing and golfing skills, making it into national teams at schoolboy and university level. Out of school he still keeps his skills up to scratch, preferably on some windswept Scottish course more easily

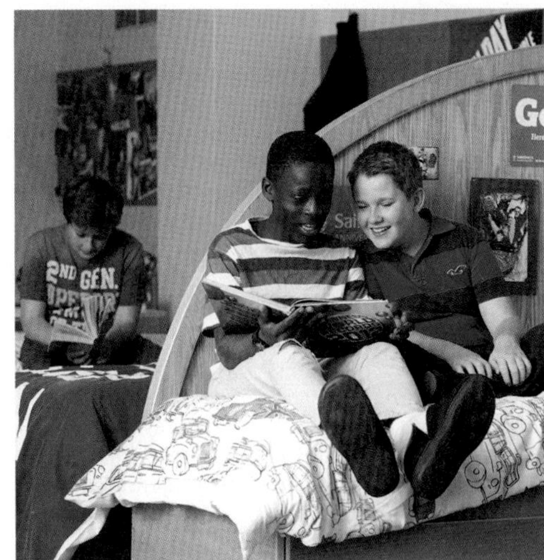

reached from his last job. His Australian start may have led to his love of travel and he rather endearingly admits to having used his geography classes as an excuse to bring out the holiday snaps.

Feeling that his first task on taking over was to thoroughly understand the school staff from groundsmen to departmental heads, he shed the suit and successfully donned the overalls. He was also pretty sharp over his pupil homework: one leaver last year was 'bowled over that he knew my name the first time he met me'. Described as an 'absolute legend' (a term more usually handed to brilliant steeplechasers), he plans to set this down-to-earth, country school firmly in the educational firmament, an approach that is steadily gaining appeal with local parents and is endorsed by his regular, witty, self-deprecating letters about life as a headmaster.

Married to Karen, a busy medic who tries hard to be on tap as much as possible; three children – the eldest offspring is soon to join LWC.

Academic matters: They work hard at the three Rs and it clearly pays off with GCSE results (53 per cent A*-A/9-7 in 2017) ranking in the top 250 on the Guardian independent schools list recently. The results at A level also solid but not stellar, 39 per cent A*-A and 65 per cent A*-B. However, bright children feel sufficiently stretched: for some Oxbridge is a definite possibility not a dream and the remainder speak confidently about reaching the next step, whatever it may be.

The 60:40 boy:girl split may partly account for maths and science having tended to be the school's forte, and the new building for the former backs up the quality of the teaching. One sixth former said he was so well taught that he'd moved from a doubtful pass at GCSE to a predicted A* at A level. A concerted move to change this bias is in progress and parents report that arts-orientated children are flourishing.

All pupils take one or two languages at GCSE and a new outing to France takes place 'pour encourager les autres'. Latin is compulsory for the first two years and either this or classical civilisation is taken by 35 per cent at GCSE. Language numbers at A level are quite small (19 last year) but in a French oral class a valiant attempt to explain why the French are so French was being combined with politics in the shape of Marine Le Pen.

There are chances to give almost anything a go at the beginning: 'All schools say that they try and bring out your strengths, but here they really do it'

Screening for dyslexia takes place in the first and third years and again in the lower sixth. All teachers are aware if there is a problem and the nine per cent who need it have weekly one-to-one sessions. Strong encouragement to hand in original work and not to succumb to the temptation of Wikipaedia is given to pupils and parents. There is also a popular tutorial system ('they become friends when you're in the sixth form and even stay friends after you've left').

Across the board the staff training budget has been doubled and the slight tendency to have brilliant sportsmen/women who can teach a bit is being reversed by sourcing teachers who are also sporty.

Games, options, the arts: Famously strong at rugby, they don't just pay lip service to a wide range of other sports but are winning prizes, particularly at girls' hockey and cricket. As well as providing several club and county level players on the turf, they have even managed to switch surfaces and pull an international ice hockey player out of the bag. There are plenty of teams across the sporting spectrum for the less starry, who can also choose anything from yoga to rock-climbing or riding. The system works well, parents happily reporting that they 'run them ragged on the sports field'.

There are chances to give almost anything a go at the beginning: 'All schools say that they try and bring out your strengths, but here they really do it'. Saturday morning clubs, including options for the arty, sporty and those keen to fill academic gaps, are so popular – particularly the destruction and reconstruction of electronic or electrical objects – that parents are prepared to make sure day children don't miss out. 'He might even be able to mend the Hoover at the end of it so it's well worth the drive.'

Lots of takers for D of E, and the possibility of taking to the sky in a glider is a strong card for the CCF, with the added draw of yomping in the wilderness far from tidy, cultivated Hampshire.

Art is important, both visibly around the school ('he tends to claim any empty space,' said a teacher wryly) and because it is a favoured subject for exams (nine taking A level last year) as well as a good fun co-curricular activity.

The new teaching centre topped by a mirrored dance studio for zumba fans and Strictly wannabes is run by a head full of energy and ideas, attracting an increasing number of students from senior scholars to shy first termers. Choirs cater for all abilities, 'even the tone deaf are encouraged to give it a go', an admirable if slightly worrying thought. The practice rooms are full all week and the department head 'beams with pride', not only at the mastering of Scriabin but also at the squeaky rendering of an Abba tune.

The new teaching centre topped by a mirrored dance studio for zumba fans and Strictly wannabes is run by a head full of energy and ideas

The drama department is flat out all year round, tackling everything from Sheridan to Lloyd Webber, plus clubs, technical workshops and sorties into the outside world. The only negative is the lack of a dedicated auditorium, richly deserved, according to parents.

Boarding: Enormous flexibility is the key, a policy very popular with hard-working parents whose life is made easier by the ability of the school to scoop up their children when necessary, rescue only an email away. The eight boarding houses, one co-ed for the first two years, three for girls and four for boys, are run by multi-tasking houseparents. A rigorously enforced tracking system prevents chaos and assures parents that their offspring's whereabouts are known at all times.

Background and atmosphere: The century-long transformation from farming orphanage to present day public school began in 1912 with the bequest of Sydney Stern (the one and only Lord Wandsworth), a wealthy playboy turned Liberal politician. For the son of a Victorian banker buried in the Balls Pond Road it was rather an odd choice as a memorial, but due to the financial ability of the foundation trustees it turns out to have been a wise one. The school motto, 'perseverantia vincit', was taken most literally by the redoubtable Scot Sandy Henderson, headmaster from 1943-1968 (25 years of perseverance), who inspired the metamorphosis from agriculture to academics.

Still surrounded by the original farm, the school may have a rustic setting, but once through a surprisingly pompous, arched entrance there is a view of neat brick buildings and a shiny tarmac drive bordered by expectant playing fields. This is not a school with architectural pretensions, and one of the boarding houses was described as a 1960s disaster. However, a flight of fancy that one might have stumbled onto a low budget film set is swiftly squashed at the sight of lively teenagers purposefully swopping classrooms. No slacking here, as one day pupil put it; in fact the only negative point she could raise was how tired they were at the end of a packed day.

There is now a firm, securely financed, 10 year plan for change in place, including the completion of all brand new classrooms over the next five years as part of a concerted effort to modernise the school. Part of the regeneration, the new maths block – kitted out with wickedly clever whiteboards – and an assembly hall are finished, and the creaking science block is next on the agenda. The junior boarding house has girly curtains and rows of cuddly toys in the dormitories, and although the senior houses seem a little bland, long on new bath and shower rooms but low on cosy clutter and smelly socks, reliable information reveals that they can also look as if 'regularly burgled'. Maybe it's all squashed into the huge cupboards when the GSG comes round?

The head is determined to stop it being pigeonholed as a rugby crèche (all the fault of poor Jonny Wilkinson, who heads a list of high flying alumni so long that it seems as if LWC rugby has seen more dramatic conversions than the road to Damascus).

Pastoral care, well-being and discipline: One parent described the pastoral care as 'second to none', a claim backed up by ubiquitous signs in a boarding house reading 'I am available 24 hours a day, in or out of term'.

Rules applied on a fair, case-by-case basis. No outward evidence of teenage rebellion – these are not students likely to sport green hair or facial piercings

Hot on bullying in every form with notices everywhere, and all pupils have to carry a laminated card with examples on one side and how to get help on the reverse. Practical emails about cyberbullying and internet dangers are sent to parents, giving detailed instructions that even confirmed Luddites can follow.

The rules don't come to parents as a surprise but are applied on a fair, case-by-case basis and not necessarily sticking entirely to the book. No outward evidence of teenage rebellion – these are not students likely to sport green hair or facial piercings. Some parents have a minor niggle that the younger ones can look pretty scruffy, particularly in comparison to the exceptionally tidy sixth formers.

A strong impression is created that most (not too wacky) ideas from the pupils will be seriously listened to, and that the head's statement 'their ideas and views are at the heart of the school development and planning' is no vain promise.

Pupils and parents: The distinction between day and boarding students is blurry as they seem to morph from one to the other pretty seamlessly, and lots of supposedly day pupils stay on to work or play long after the academic stuff is finished. Up to five per cent international students and the head plans to recruit more into the senior school. The Sternians' Association with its deliberately rustic (covered in tractors) website encourages parents to muck in and even make fools of themselves at the Santa Dash, a charity run started by the head.

Entrance: Almost all from prep schools including Yateley Manor, Eagle House, St Neot's and Hall Grove, with a few from local primaries. Selection at 11 through school's own tests in English, maths and reasoning, aiming to identify a bit above average pupils who will fit into this tight community. Thirteen plus candidates need 50 per cent at CE; mid-range GCSEs, a school report and an interview to join the sixth form. 'All along we are looking for pupils who will get stuck in and put their hand up.'

Exit: Some 20-40 per cent leave after GCSE to go to one of several excellent state sixth form colleges in Hampshire, usually for budget reasons. Three to Oxbridge in 2017 and one medic; the school is rightly proud that the remainder have left for destinations as varied as Aberdeen, York, Camberwell Art College, LSE and the Royal Agricultural College to read everything from archaeology to civil engineering via law and theatre studies. Also one to Florida (engineering) and one to The Hague (international relations). Good next step communication with students, who say that the well-informed careers advisor 'will always find out if she doesn't know the answer'.

Money matters: Eight per cent of pupils are supported by The Foundation; means-tested awards restricted to British children who have lost the support of one or both parents through death, divorce or separation, and whose surviving parent (if there is one) has not formed a new relationship. The order of priority is: 'children who have an identifiable boarding need, the need for pastoral care and support, the need for stability and security in a structured environment, the candidate's home and family situation, the ability to cope academically, integrate socially and contribute to the college community, the family's financial circumstances'.

Remarks: Until recently a bit under the radar but worth watching this spot. An impressive head, smarter buildings, improving results and a firm set of values should encourage more potential parents to key this postcode into their Sat Navs.

Ludgrove

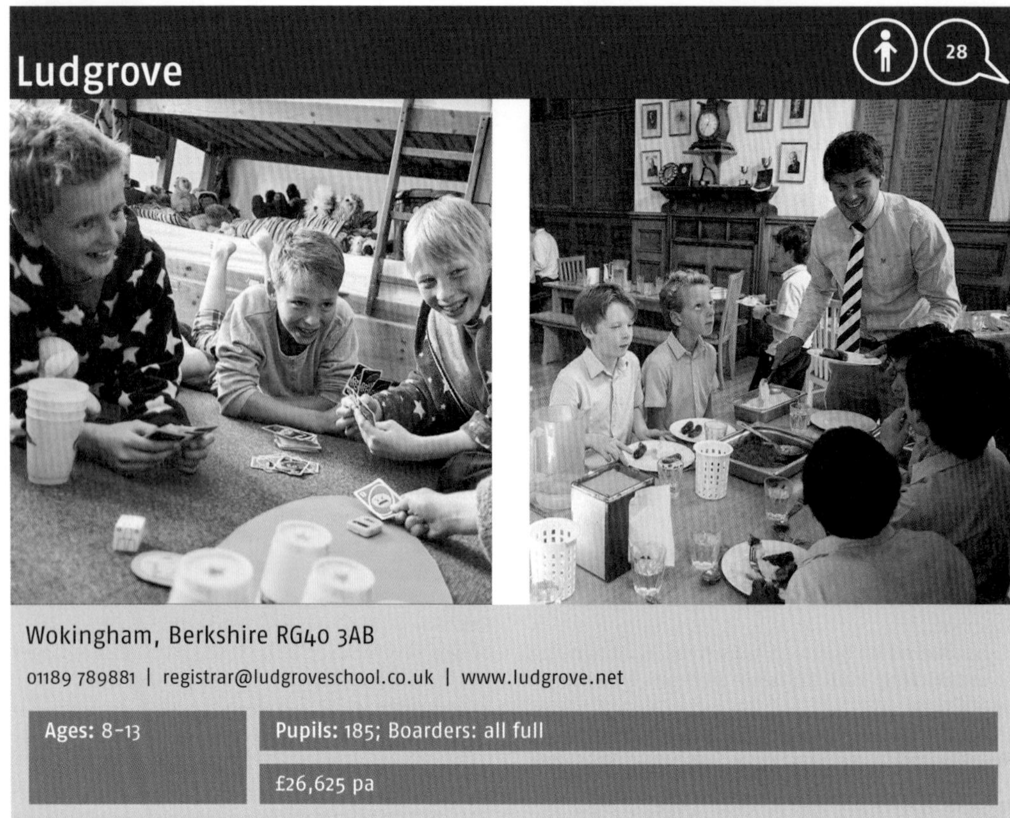

Wokingham, Berkshire RG40 3AB

01189 789881 | registrar@ludgroveschool.co.uk | www.ludgrove.net

Ages: 8-13

Pupils: 185; Boarders: all full

£26,625 pa

Headmaster: Since 2008 Mr Simon Barber BA (40s) following six years as a teacher here and, before that, at Ashdown House. Mr Barber, who grew up here (and has fond memories of watching cows being milked in what is now the art and carpentry block), completed teacher training at robust state school Cranford Community College with aplomb, tweed jacket and Eton education no barrier to pupil acceptance – when asked where he was at school 'I said, "down the road, just south of Slough".' Spell teaching geography at LVS Ascot was followed by short digression 'as junior squit' in corporate finance – quickly realised not for him.

Headship shared until 2013 when joint incumbent moved on to school of his own. After initial parental nerviness, Barbers now universally reckoned to be bit of all right, having grown into role. Mr Barber teaches Latin, PSHE and Greek myths – 'so important, you can see their little minds buzz.' He's nice but strict if necessary, thought pupil – 'if people are talking after lights out.'

Mrs Barber ('Sophie' to all) sorts domestics – 'kitchens, matrons, nurse, cleaners' – as well as being first point of contact 'for mothers' worries' and prepping boys for first phone calls home. '[Mr Barber] likes children, enjoys their company and knows how to make them feel good about themselves,' said one parent. 'As a team, they are superb,' agreed another.

Barbers' immersion in school life is almost total (though Mrs Barber does get short daily break to collect youngest child – they have two daughters and a son – from local school). Instead of separate house have own (though separate) quarters in the main building, but appear miraculously claustrophobia-free. Mr Barber, in particular, can go for days without leaving the building. 'I love walking round the school and thinking about creating an environment that is fun, safe and full of opportunities,' he says.

Entrance: Takes 30 in year 4 when it's completely non-selective – unless you count speed of registration as competitive sport. 'Don't believe in testing boys at 8,' says school. After initial enquiry (at birth) parents receive letter from head (handwritten) with registration form (printed). Two years before joining, there's a fun day for boys with confirmed places, followed by final make-your-mind-up time.

For occasional places (around eight in year 5, four in year 6 and even a couple in year 7 – generous bursary scheme helps bright boys fill gap between state primary and common entrance), hopefuls sit English and maths tests 'to be sure they can slot in easily.' Duvet changing and tie-knotting practice before start of first term also urged.

No official feeders, but road here well trodden by families moulded in traditional cast (plenty of second generation pupils or better). Around 40 per cent from well-connected pre-preps (Finton House, Thomas's Fulham, Eaton House, Knightsbridge and Broomwood Hall in London, Pinewood and Farleigh outside), many escaping competitive inferno of London school entrance.

Around half of places to country dwellers, most within two-hour commute (Wiltshire, Hampshire, Berkshire, Northants). A few from further away (East Anglia, Scotland). Remaining 10 per cent overseas, split about equally between expats (FO, MOD) and international pupils from all over – India, Thailand, Ukraine, Russia, Spain, China, Nigeria, Korea. A few arrive for year's immersion in penultimate year then head for home. DBS-cleared drivers (ideally same one both ways) on tap to do the airport run.

Exit: Given diverse input, rightly proud of output – reckon to get around three-quarters, sometimes more, into Eton, Harrow, Winchester and Radley. Mr Barber's expert knowledge of all four won't mean special treatment at CE, though word dropped in admission tutor's shell-like can't go amiss if results an unexpected disaster. Others to eg Marlborough, Tonbridge, Charterhouse, Wellington and Sherborne.

Best-known OBs are Prince William, Prince Harry and Bear Grylls (who recently waxed lyrical about his experiences in print). Very occasionally head may suggest specialist school. One dyslexic pupil has recently gone to Bruern Abbey, though 'welcome back at any time,' says Mr Barber.

Remarks: Mood is determinedly upbeat...'a belief that one should always look on the bright side of life,' says prospectus and reflection of Mr Barber's philosophy. May not sing the Monty Python song but lives it. 'The eternal optimist,' says Mrs Barber.

So at their best, teams 'are a match for anyone.' School trips – a range, from Devon (leavers and geographers) to Sauze D'Oulx (skiers) – return having learned that 'a sense of humour can see you through most tricky situations'. Torrential rain makes sports day 'a memorable occasion.' Breakages in Roman-themed pottery session 'added to the authenticity.' Boys ward off looming homesickness by 'thinking of funny things and looking forward to the next lunch,' said one.

Upbeat approach translates into academics. Teachers are 'amazing,' say parents, talking round subjects and knowing their pupils. 'They work you hard but within your ability,' thought pupil. 'I wasn't clever when I arrived – now I am.' 'Never gave up on my son...and he flew,' said parent.

Wobbles impressively dealt with. 'Support without throttling,' said parent. 'Nurtured from the start but guided towards independence as they get older'

Small classes (average 12, maximum 15, minimum eight) undoubtedly help. So does overall staff to pupil ratio of just under one to seven (and that's not including the nurse and six matrons; all live-in). Streaming in English and maths from the beginning, lessons lively – new boys attacking Venn diagram in geography with enthusiasm; ditto 11 year olds discussing perils of 16th century religious affiliation. (Can read on in cheerful, traditional library, popular titles enticingly face up in long rows, pupils trained in old-fashioned referencing using real encyclopaedias).

Boys go through order papers with division master (form tutor) so clear on how to improve. Ups and downs caused by small class sizes and narrow range of marks (can shoot from second to eighth place) can cause occasional jitters among success-focused parents who need lots of reassurance. 'Boys pick up on their hopes and fears,' says Mr Barber.

While coming top is well and good, the message that endeavour counts is received loud and clear. 'Trying hard is better,' said top year boy firmly. Workload in and out of lessons bearable, adjusted if necessary. No shame in saying you're struggling – teachers will set less and help with catch up, thought boys.

Individual excellence (good work) commended by head and rewarded with sweets. Plus marks also awarded, best performing house rewarded with special (and, needless to say, 'delicious') tea. The naughty get minus marks – occasional detentions. Boarding runs its own rewards system, giving angels, however dirty their downstairs wings, a second chance at redemption

Parents get emails summarising life in and out of the classroom and can phone child's class during a 40 minute slot at lunchtime to speak to son. Resulting free-for-all generally works (a bit of muttering about parents who go beyond allotted five minutes) though substantial redialling sometimes required. Alternative – giving boys mobile phones – felt by all to be far worse. Some – 'particularly sweet boys who want to make sure their parents are all right,' said mother – also send emails.

Daily staff meetings, attended by boarding nurse, ensure whole-school awareness of any issues. Wobbles impressively dealt with. 'Support without throttling,' said parent. 'Nurtured from the start but guided towards independence as they get older.'

Solid assistance for pupils with learning needs – around 30 or so in the school – includes academic support (booster groups for spelling, maths, reading) as well as help with handwriting, one-to-one EAL lessons and esteem and confidence-building sessions – we liked King of the Shelves award for better organisation skills. Four specialist teachers develop programmes for pupils with more complex needs – speech and language or specific learning

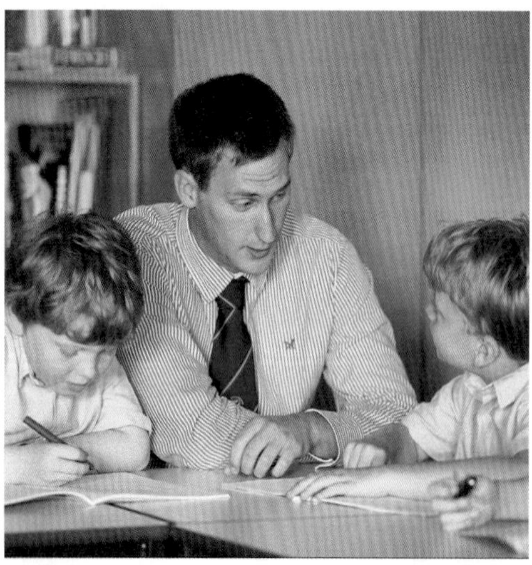

Every pillow adorned with loved, often dilapidated soft toy, resident seamstress ('crucially important,' says Mrs Barber) on hand to work miracles when teddies' arms come adrift or eyes go missing

difficulties – and ensure that subject teachers know how to implement it. 'Have been called a rottweiler,' says jolly but firm head of learning support. Younger pupils have support sessions during art, drama and music while older pupils can opt to miss occasional rest period or break so don't lose out on favourite subject.

Merely mastering school's year group numbering system must be considerable source of pride. 'Sixes are year 4; fours year 5, threes year 6, twos year 7 and top year is year 8,' says school handbook. And those missing fives? 'Not a year group but a game with a small ball and leather gloves,' it adds, helpfully.

Uniform options similarly quirky. In addition to giddy whirl of jacket choices (a tweed spotter's dream), school jumpers offered not just in navy, but rather more exotic pink and green, adding welcome flash of colour to massed gatherings.

Great outdoors spread over 130 acres includes usual playing fields as well as nine-hole golf course and plenty of space for building camps. Every parent commented approvingly on boys being out in all weathers. 'All is underlined and bold and caps,' said one. Sports rampant and not just for current pupils, either. Most recent alumni calendar featured five matches and just one drinks party.

However, quantity doled out can be varied to taste. Everyone, talented or otherwise, gets shot at glory of minibus trip and match tea. How much glory is a tad confusing to decipher, what with online match reports dating back to 2013 with tendency to linger on the glories of game well played rather than the score.

Deadline for posting team lists is 7.00pm the night before, seemed a bit tight in giving parents sufficient time to change all arrangements and rush up to watch their son score the winning try/goal/run – but felt largely to work as most teams, once settled, there for the duration. Parents in broad agreement, biggest issue we encountered relating to yawning gap between the keen and talented – who get lion's share of training and interest – and keen but less so, who don't and can be completely overlooked. More matches on the cards for every shade of ability, says school, while swimming notable for squad training that's open to all.

The less athletic joyfully opt for extra art, pottery or, top favourite, carpentry/DT, where Portuguese fishing dinghy, owl nesting box as well as enough chairs and tables to equip several classrooms are among impressive projects to have helped school to several DT scholarships in recent years.

Music busy, with choirs, open access music block, numerous ensembles and vast majority (85 per cent) playing at least one instrument (bagpipes, tuba and bassoon adding interesting new timbre to conventional choices). Not as busy as drama, however, now in impressive new theatre (none of that 'performing arts centre' nonsense here...) where according to prospectus, boys 'have been on stage non-stop...' Crumbs. Our visit clearly took place during one of brief periods of non-occupancy. (Drama teacher was having lunch at the time, explained school later, keen to ensure nobody got the wrong end of the stick, and theatre 'has had a tremendous impact on provision of music and drama'). No wonder exeats billed as a time to relax. Happen every fortnight, so not too punishing for the youngest recruits.

Attractive 19th century building was purpose-built as school and it shows. Dorms, all south-facing with attractive big windows and same gorgeous view over greenery as from head's study but a floor up, hold four to 10 pupils from single year group, some in bunk beds, each with top year monitor, honoured with different coloured laundry basket (vibrant pink in one case). Every pillow adorned with loved, often dilapidated soft toy, resident seamstress ('crucially important,' says Mrs Barber) on hand to work miracles when teddies' arms come adrift or eyes go missing – 'upsetting but it's the smell they like...' Matrons much praised. 'Never shout if you do something wrong,' said pupil. 'Say it doesn't matter, don't worry.' Occasional accidents sensitively sorted – boys squeeze matron's arm when woken up, signal for sheets to be unobtrusively washed and replaced.

Dedicated maintenance posse roams school, killing at least 99.9 per cent of all known germs dead and rounding up errant possessions. Basins, loos, baths in communal washroom all radiant; boys' clothes and towels a tribute to precision folding, cloakroom a thing of wonder, coats and shoes lined up as if on parade – a daily, 90 minute task undertaken with pride.

Not a job for the boys, though perhaps it should be, joining list of well-organised activities carefully balanced to ensure that everyone is just busy enough and thus avoiding too much time for introspection, particularly for newbies (who have dedicated matron and allocated 'shadow' to help them settle in), but ensuring 'can flop if they want to,' says school.

Saturday is the faster-paced weekend day, with lessons till lunch, matches afterwards followed by free time, film screenings and a spot of X-Factor if in season. Sunday has fixed slots: chapel and assembly to announce the day's happenings. Otherwise less structure, with activity staples (swimming, art, films) and specials (visiting climbing wall, circus workshop and – occasionally – ice cream van) but also potential for spontaneity – boys will organise own games of cricket, five-a-side football or make camps. Less official dorm raids and stair run (down one, up the other at night without being caught) also happen but 'I know nothing about it...' says Mr Barber.

Great outdoors spread over 130 acres includes usual playing fields as well as nine-hole golf course and plenty of space for building camps. Every parent commented approvingly on boys being out in all weathers

For youngest, there's comfort zone story time with Mrs Barber, 'special half hour when they're piled like puppies on the sofas and all over the floor.' Tuck, in the form of sweets, isn't allowed. Instead, school suggests packing 'useful and fun' – but inedible – items such as bluetac, string, stickers and playing cards.

School-supplied treats appeared attractive replacements for missing goodies, particularly birthday ice cream cake with choice of five flavours, multi-coloured remnants being solemnly enjoyed by small break time group on day of visit. Similarly colourful foodfests celebrate pupil nationalities (Ireland with mandarin, whipped cream and lime jelly...). Match teas a more restrained mix of sandwiches and cakes (parents) with doughnuts, crisps and juice for boys. Pupil committee gets unpopular dishes pulled and replaced (fish pie with scampi).

Other trad preps can feel as if saturated in own past. Here, though pride in history is evident, it's not overwhelming, with few pictures of ancient OBs. Instead, names of new boys are added to the honours board within a few weeks of start of first term – simple but effective way of generating pride and self-confidence and looking ahead.

'You've got to look at what you're doing – and how to do it better,' says Mr Barber. 'It's amazing,' said one parent. 'The camaraderie amongst the boys is one of the key things and they leave with lifelong friends. I couldn't fault it at all.'

LVS Ascot (Licensed Victuallers' School)

29

London Road, Ascot, Berkshire SL5 8DR

01344 882770 | registrar@lvs.ascot.sch.uk | www.lvs.ascot.sch.uk

Ages: 4-18 (boarders from 7)	**Pupils:** 823; sixth form: 160 (103 boys, 57 girls); Boarders: 178
	Day: £9,708 – £17,403 pa; Boarding: £24,846 – £30,576 pa

Headmistress: Since 2010, Christine Cunniffe BA MMus MBA. Three children, all at the school (husband goes to the parents' evenings). Personable, open, quietly assured and one of what seems like growing number (or should that be band?) of musicians to forsake lieder for leadership. Other careers have beckoned. After university, had close brush with the law (professionally speaking, that is) securing postgraduate traineeship with Slough-based legal practice only to succumb to alternative role as pianist to fashionistas and London high society (think white baby grands and late nights in plush hotels). Four years in, realised that though 'loved life, not what I wanted to do when I was getting older'. Putting aside renewed yearnings for law when husband-to-be pointed out years of study ahead, she tried her hand at teaching and loved it from the off, going straight in as head of music, first at a Stevenage school, then St Bernard's, a selective co-ed grammar school in Slough. Joined LVS Ascot as ambitious director of music in 2003 (school, which had no choir when she arrived, was performing Vivaldi's Gloria at Eton College Chapel just two terms later).

Overcame crisis of confidence in first year as head when numbers dipped (they're now on the rise again), confessing all in school magazine – unusual if not unprecedented openness for a head – which, she feels, sends useful message to pupils. 'You have self-doubt. I thought, the children are going to face problems in life, so why pretend it doesn't happen?'

Is considered by parents to be doing a good job though some would like a greater presence and more speechifying at major school events. 'She needs to be seen and heard a bit more...you've got to be the front runner, Ursain Bolt-ish and get up there if you're a head with over 1,000 pupils and fee-paying parents,' said one. Pretty visible during the school day though, the more so as job comes with house in grounds (she also has west London bolthole for change of scene). 'I'm not one of those people who hides behind a closed door; there's no point.' Doesn't teach but asks boarders to choose lessons for her to observe every week, and on day of visit was in gym encouraging sixth formers flagging half way through 56-mile sponsored row for charity. 'I said, "I'll be your Mrs Motivator".'

All parents have her email address, a useful barometer as 'they'll only bring something to me directly if they are really upset,' and doesn't shy away from taking criticism on the chin. 'I don't want people to tell me what they think I want to hear but to be honest.' Pleased, she insists, to get lots of 'forthright' comments when recently invited parent group in for dinner and presentation on proposed introduction of heads of year to help raise academic bar through better tracking and target setting.

Own experiences make her sympathetic to late developers. 'I experienced problems at about 13 and it's made me passionate about not giving up on a child until we have exhausted all areas,' though firm when line has to be drawn – handful of children have been asked to leave during headship. 'The boundaries are like an elastic band – you have to know when it's going to break.'

Like Mary Poppins, will go when mission is accomplished. 'I'm a realist. If, after five years, I think my job's done, I'm not going to stay around.' Not necessarily to another headship, either. 'I might just become a lawyer after all,' she says.

Academic matters: Though tolerant, school isn't the place for skivers. 'The school's a hard runner... and they want the exams. Non-selective doesn't mean an easy ride,' said a parent.

Mission in junior school is to ensure that no child is left to languish in educational no man's land; regular meetings picking out those 'falling below or zooming ahead'. Children give a high rating to all subjects, particular favourites being literacy (popular library-based reading scheme, which carries on into main school, tests comprehension rather than merely rewarding headlong dash for the last page) and science in year 6 – where, joy of joys, 'you get to light the Bunsen burner'. They're also unexpectedly appreciative of small teaching groups (average is about 12). 'In state schools you have 60 in a class,' said one horror-struck year 6 guide.

There's minimal setting (maths from year 3) and a pick and mix approach to national curriculum – used or modified where it works, ditched if it doesn't (children's progress well ahead of national averages). Everything is seasoned with welcome dash of carpe diem flexibility so teachers can go off piste if not-to-be-missed educational opportunities present themselves; recent stick collection and den-building exercise for reception was a case in point. Lots of popular outings, too, including the inevitable trip to Swanage.

Exam results compare well with local competition. In 2017, 30 per cent A*-A/9-7 at GCSE – reasonable for non-selective school, let alone one so large. Ten the norm though whittled down to nine for some students with learning difficulties who fill the time with extra English and maths support. Choice of around 20 subjects, nothing showy (there's no Latin or classics, for example). English, maths, French or Spanish and science/environmental science all compulsory with options including German, humanities, all the sciences, media/business studies, art and PE.

Sixth form options broad and getting broader, with law and psychology recently added to the roster of around 30 courses. Students will need GCSE B grades or better in chosen subjects though vocational courses such as ICT and sport also available for those of a more practical mindset. In 2017, 48 per cent A*-B and 16 per cent A*/A grades at A level.

Head on mission to ensure that ability is unearthed and nurtured earlier through advanced data crunching and addition of heads of year to management team. 'We haven't even scratched the surface with gifted and talented children,' she says (something also picked up in recent inspection). School's strength thus far has centred on bringing low achievers up to snuff (several heart-warming stories of pupils helped up the academic ladder to top exam grades) and parents like the approach, big on encouragement, small on class sizes – average teacher to pupil ratio of 12 to one – and low on hothouse forcing (definitely not the school's style).

Games, options, the arts: School's philosophy is that there's something for everyone and brave attempts are made (with help of extensive range of activities, all bar four included in the fees) to keep participation rates high all the way through the school. A dip in current year 10 and 11 girls' teams reflects lack of numbers rather than interest.

Sympathetic to late developers. 'I experienced problems at about 13 and it's made me passionate about not giving up on a child until we have exhausted all areas'

Approach, strong on inclusion and optimism – sports honours board runs to 2023 – is recognised by award of Sportsmark Gold and helped by cracking facilities including two games halls, the larger with climbing wall and cricket nets, the smaller with cushioned floor for happier landings in judo and high impact sports. Enticing heated pool is well used, offering all-ability training at 6.30am three times a week, while thumping pop music from upstairs broadcasts presence of well-equipped fitness suite, predictably popular with older boys. Has recently set up elite golf academy for sixth formers which combines coaching at a nearby club with a BTec in sports science.

With recent wins in judo, swimming and rugby, achievement counts but so does nurturing, for B as much as A teams so not seen as also rans. Felt by some parents to handicap the single-minded. 'Everyone gets a game which is to be encouraged but [can be] a drawback if you really want to excel at one sport,' said one.

Head would like greater take up of outdoor activities and has appointed ex-marine who 'doesn't sleep and likes to live in tents' to make it so. With rejigged timetable incorporating two additional sessions a week for all (year 9 upwards can do as part of D of E, open to as many as are interested) expect substantial increase in fresh air intake.

Vibrant artistic life is similarly wide ranging (though indoor-based) with ringing endorsement from award of Artsmark Gold to prove it and enthusiastic support from (literally) all-singing, all-dancing staff who aren't averse to taking to the boards as hoofers in zingy, highly regarded productions like Hairspray and Bugsy Malone. (By all accounts do a mean version of 'Teacher, leave them kids alone' too).

Year 3 teachers (and their classes) break into spontaneous song about Mothers' Day. 'It happens a lot here,' says one, who's also, as it turns out, responsible for junior school's huge, ambitious productions with 100-strong cast (all 'proper' parts: 'People don't want to be a third tree') and special

Staffed by team of affable universal aunt and uncle types who always have a giant jigsaw on the go and live for research

effects including ultraviolet bubbles and even an exploding shark – 'every gizmo I can get into it'. Every other summer there's a Dance for Fitness workshop instead – fun and worthy, no doubt (and considered sufficiently cool for embarrassment-free participation by older boys) though you sense teacher's regret that it can't be waterfalls of lights and smoke effects every year.

With five choirs, numerous ensembles including rock school, and around a third of pupils learning instruments, some to diploma standard, performance is shifting from niche activity to sizeable minority occupation. Possible that numerous pianos lurking in school nooks and crannies (some boarding houses have several) are conveying subliminal positive message; whizzy music tech studio probably better recruitment ad. Admittedly, boys in years 10 and 11 remain somewhat shy and retiring – 'Music's not a cool thing to do,' says pupil – but some at least are drawn in again to at sixth form (though the need to pep up UCAS forms with wholesome balance of activities is, they confess, also a factor).

Boarding: Four boarding houses – co-ed junior house, one each for senior boys and girls and co-ed sixth form house – are now plushness personified with full-size beds and colour-matched walls, carpets and curtains chosen by pupils. Palettes err towards predictable blues in boys' boarding house though biggest difference is in communal areas where girls arrange smart leather sofas close together to maximise eye contact and conviviality, boys in contrast opting for side by side seating for maximum cheering-on potential during pool matches.

Boarding house staff, particularly those with experience of compromise Victorian conversions, are enthusiastic. 'A breeze to run,' comments one. Experienced houseparents are experts at sidestepping homesickness and ditching superfluities like complex laundry rules – 'I'd much rather you were clean than worried about what day you need to put your washing in,' says one.

It's all about fine-tuning to achieve delicate balance between homely family feel (thoughtful inclusion of year 8 boarders with juniors for extra cosseting) and early detection of transgressions. Morning lethargy beyond normal teen parameters can signal OTT late night laptop/mobile use (enormous phone bills arriving at parental home the other tell-tale sign). Controlled independence, such as giving year 11s separate kitchen and TV 'so they don't have to watch the same thing as year 8s,' explains teacher, is carefully cultivated.

Keeping idle hands (and brains) busy is the priority. 'We don't want boarders sitting around, twiddling their thumbs,' says pastoral head. Steady but not relentless stream of activities from house talent shows to relaxed Saturday breakfasts in pjs. Weekend minibuses, booked by the hour, swap returning sports teams for boarders off on assorted excursions (shopping, films and bowling all popular) with departures and arrivals as precisely coordinated as flight control at Heathrow.

Background and atmosphere: Site was formerly home to Heatherdown, an ultra-traditional prep school for chaps and David Cameron's pre-Eton alma mater, with own miniature steam railway. It was demolished in 1982 after Licensed Trade Charity (LTC) – which runs school, founded 200 years ago to support drinks trade employees – made such an advantageous sale of previous premises in Slough to well-known supermarket chain that could fund construction of what prospectus claims is the 'most modern boarding school in the UK'.

It comes complete with LVS branded drainpipes and school houses named, delightfully, after major drinks brands, leading to such pleasing sentences as 'this year saw the introduction of many new staff and students to Guinness,' in school magazine.

And yes, lovers of mellow brickwork may need to recalibrate their aesthetic sensibilities when it comes to the exterior (think sheltered housing designer meets Etch a Sketch addict – prospectus sensibly avoids any full-on shots of the facade). However, it's well worth the effort as school lacks neither charm nor character and is stuffed with quirky touches from the formal (two back-to-back reception desks, one glitzy for corporate visitors to charity HQ, the other, smart but workmanlike, for school traffic) to the relaxed (skeleton of dolphin in science lab, Garfield soft toy clasped lovingly between jaws). There's tradition, too – the 25 acres of grounds with rustic bridge spanning small but perfectly formed lake prove the point – but exists primarily to serve a purpose (lesson bell all but abolished after it broke five years ago, ending mid-sentence rush for the door and making teachers so happy that was never reintroduced).

Thoughtful layout now past 30th birthday may no longer be at cutting edge of school design but fundamentals still apply, noticeably the way space-intensive subjects like performing arts get the room they need in central location rather than being consigned to outer reaches of site, while related subjects are housed together making navigation a breeze – at least if you're a pupil. 'It's the adults who struggle,' says passing teacher.

It's all well cared for, too – maths display board with cracked plastic cover is rare exception ('Children pick at it without realising they're doing it,' explains staff member) and nicely spruced up where required.

Add lively art room with wall-to-wall high quality work (intriguing bronze-effect sculpture floats above plinth), busy, popular DT department with more saws than you could shake a freshly trimmed stick at and fabulous learning resource centre; light, airy and staffed by team of affable universal aunt and uncle types who always have a giant jigsaw on the go and live for research – 'You need a bit up here and to love finding things out,' says one – and easy to see why purpose-built practicality gets parental thumbs up. 'Some private schools try to make the best of the [space] they happen to have, such as a former chambermaid's room being used as a biology class room, [whereas] LVS have great classrooms built to deliver good lessons,' said a father.

Junior school has good-sized infants' play area with buddy bench (hardly used, though, insist pupils 'because there's a bare minimum of people who feel sad') and lots of sturdy wooden equipment to climb and balance on. Year 3s and up enjoy scaled up versions in adjoining area, separated by unmarked but universally recognised boundary line. Reception also has smart new outdoor classroom and cheerful playhouse, starting point for innumerable let's pretend games. Eagerly awaited musical train complete with three carriages and bells (if no whistles) currently being built by senior school sixth former as part of DT A level is arriving soon.

Pastoral care, well-being and discipline: Highly regarded focus of pastoral care is the tutor group system with same teacher responsible for child's well-being throughout school career. Works well given high percentage of old-timers (figuratively speaking) on staff – 40 out of 340 have been there over 10 years – and is liked by parents and pupils. 'They have a vested interest in you as a person, you're more than just a pupil,' said 17-year old.

In contrast, tribal yin to sensitive tutor group yang is a house system that's far more than convenient administrative format. Pitting combined boarders – normally four houses strong – against teams of day pupils, it's a focal point of school life, with fiercely contested matches generating 'as much rivalry amongst the [teachers] as pupils,' says member of staff.

There's affectionate tolerance for teachers who, they say with preternatural (but approving) gravitas, 'want to have fun but in a sensible way'

Not as daunting as it sounds, however, given universal insistence that loyalties do not cross into lessons nor escalate beyond friendly rivalry ('It's just banter,' confirmed sixth former). Day pupils can also cross to other side by signing up for occasional one-off boarding sessions and there's added flexibility with extended day, including meal and the run of learning resource centre, popular with working parents.

School works hard to raise aspirations without upping the pressure, particularly at junior school level. Parental feedback – 'not sure what a hothouse is,' said parent, when questioned – suggests it's working.

Pupils and parents: A nice, un-showy and straightforward bunch, pupils are thoughtful rather than introspective, articulate but not glib, and fond of school (in touch with emotions, too – one burley and soon to be ex-sixth former admitted to welling up when contemplating imminent departure). Start of term, said one, 'feels like you're going home rather than just going back.' There's affectionate tolerance for teachers who, they say with preternatural (but approving) gravitas, 'want to have fun but in a sensible way'.

As in other schools, pupils on show to visitors usually the top dogs. Here, cheeringly, they may only recently have had greatness thrust on them and reformed Horrid Henries stand as much chance as card-carrying Perfect Peters of getting their day in the sun. 'Prefects aren't just the "right" people,' explained one of the current glorious band of brothers (and sisters).

Families cover socially and economically broad spectrum from royalty to socially deprived (borne out by range of parental cars at drop off – five and six figure off-roaders rubbing fenders with elderly mid-range saloons). Mix of working parents/career mothers, but either way are generally friendly and polite, though won't hesitate to come forward if there's a problem, though occasional hothouse impulses 'are squashed quite quickly by the school,' said approving mother.

Entrance: Most children arrive at junior school in reception (single form to year 2) or year 3 (two forms to year 5). At 11+ majority from school's own junior department with assorted state and private schools supplying the rest. Also small but significant international component, with 30 overseas students from as far afield as China, Russia and Korea and 40 or so from expat families, many in Forces.

Once settled, pupils tend to stick around. 'We were never going to take the boys out unless we needed to,' says mother. Locals form large proportion of the clientèle and, while job mobility means some degree of coming and going each year, there's not as much as you might suppose. Around 50 per cent of pupils stay on into sixth form ('places will only be offered where deemed appropriate by the head of sixth form, director of studies and head,' says admissions policy) with incomers, including first time boarders from local day schools, plugging the gaps. 'In my [elder] son's year, I'd say that 80 per cent went all the way through,' said parent.

Catchment area extends 15-20 mile radius or so to Reading in west and Maidenhead up north, compass points ably covered by seven school bus routes (some oversubscribed, so worth checking). Head is on a mission to spread the word elsewhere so expect increasing numbers of refuseniks from super-selective London fringes, deepest Berks and Bucks

Exit: As you'd expect given breadth of intake, pupils take corresponding range of university courses from the solidly academic – medicine, law, economics – to the more vocational, including photography and journalism. Many secure first rank university places (one to Oxbridge in 2017), roughly a quarter to Russell Group. Old boys and girls end up as community stalwarts, many as successful entrepreneurs or 'something in the City'. Few facts and figures to back this up though with-it marketing manager is making good the omission with 'where are they now?' campaign.

Money matters: Ten per cent discount for siblings (but only third onwards and then only while all three attend school), 15 per cent off for MOD and diplomatic service employees, including five per cent early payment discount and a 20 per cent reduction for anyone who has worked in the licensed drinks trade for five years or more.

Families are attracted by all-through co-education, cracking facilities, local reputation and complete absence of entrance exams unless you're after a scholarship, academic worth a not-to-be-sniffed-at 50 per cent off fees; music, art, drama and sport a slightly less headline-grabbing £1,000 a year, in which case standard hurdles apply.

School tries to keep budgeting simple with many senior school clubs and activities included in the fees – rowing, riding, sailing and ballet plus individual instrumental lessons and one-to-one language or learning support are the main extras. Means headline fees are just that, with minimum of extras buried in the frequently expensive small print.

Remarks: All-comers welcomed in this well-equipped, friendly and unpretentious school that combines non-traditional exterior with timeless values and makes non-selectivity the starting point for success rather than a justification for its absence.

Moulsford Preparatory School

30

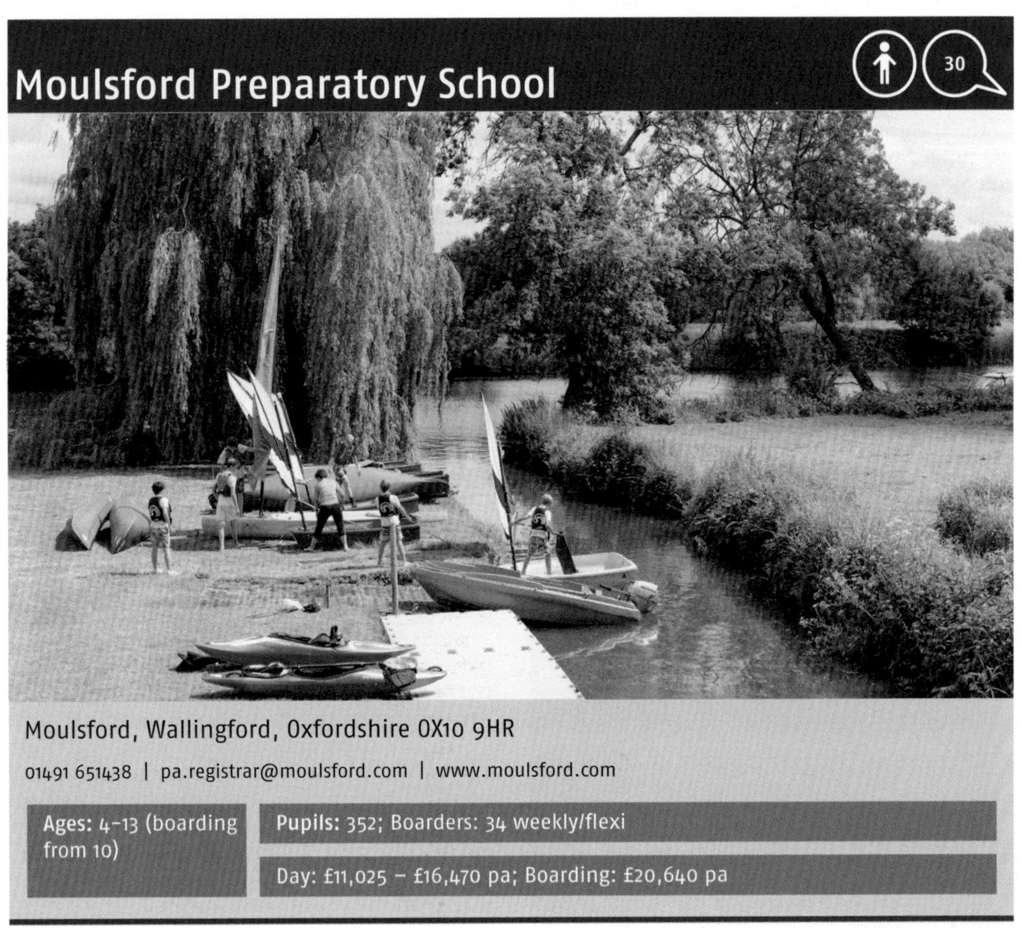

Moulsford, Wallingford, Oxfordshire OX10 9HR

01491 651438 | pa.registrar@moulsford.com | www.moulsford.com

Ages: 4–13 (boarding from 10)

Pupils: 352; Boarders: 34 weekly/flexi

Day: £11,025 – £16,470 pa; Boarding: £20,640 pa

Headmaster: Since 2014, Ben Beardmore-Gray (40s). Educated at Ludgrove (where his father taught) and Ampleforth. After history degree at Newcastle he trained as a lawyer and worked in the City, but the lure of the family business was too much for him and he succumbed to teaching. Back he went to Ludgrove where he gained his QTS, thence to Farleigh Prep as deputy head followed by seven years as head of Mowden Hall School in Northumberland.

Mr B-G is a huge fan of boarding. He and his wife, Sarah, have done a stint as houseparents and he also ran boarding at Farleigh. While the majority of pupils at Moulsford may be day boys, the small Monday to Friday boarding community is 'key to the school's ethos,' he says. He sees weekly boarding as 'dynamic' and 'forward thinking' and believes it could well be the future for schools like his.

Boarding also 'draws staff' who are enabled, courtesy of the school's staff flats and houses, to live in what could otherwise be a prohibitively expensive part of the country.

By all accounts Mr B-G had a job of work to do in his first headship at Mowden Hall, so he must have been glad to find his next school in such rude health. He pays tribute to his predecessor (who retired after 20 years) and says, with some relief, that he inherited a 'cracking school' that was 'running very nicely' and 'fantastic' staff. He also seems to have been bowled over by the support and dynamism of the parent community.

Having 'spent his first year observing' and consulting parents, Mr B-G has exciting plans for Moulsford's future. The school already has a deservedly strong reputation for sport; Mr B-G wants to raise its profile in other areas, particularly the performing arts. Hence forthcoming redevelopment of the theatre and music school – cue more plays, ensembles and concerts. He wants Moulsford boys to enjoy breadth of opportunity in as many different areas as possible. All this, we were assured, will not come at the expense of sporting excellence. Some parents we spoke to hoped that leadership change would also herald ethos change in this area. While no one wanted the school to be less successful on the sports field, quite a few wanted more opportunities for chaps who are never going to make the A teams.

Mr and Mrs Beardmore-Gray, who met at university, both hail from this part of the world. The couple have three children plus the standard issue black lab. Down time is for cricket, golf, tennis and cycling.

Entrance: Main entry points are reception (for pre-prep) and year 3 (for prep). One pre-prep class; expands to three in year 3 when boys join from schools such as Rupert House (Henley), Cranford House (just across the road), The Manor (Abingdon) and Harriet House (Frilsham), which all kick boys out after year 2.

Entry to reception is first come, first served. Assessment day in October for following September's year 3 applicants. School says it's not 'overtly academically selective' but paucity of boys' prep options in Henley area means a scramble for places.

Exit: Abingdon takes the lion's share of day boys followed by Readley, Pangbourne, Bradfield, Shiplake, Marlborough, The Oratory and Magdalen College School. Boarders to Radley, St Edward's Oxford, Marlborough, Wellington, Stowe, Harrow and Eton.

Remarks: Moulsford and its eponymous village sit on the banks of the Thames just outside Wallingford in south Oxfordshire. Fast rail links to the capital make this picturesque area attractive to London escapees with young families (and deep pockets). The school has always been popular with locals; its distinctive red blazers and caps give chaps a retro Just William charm and make for great free PR in Waitrose. The strange dearth of boys' preps in and around Henley is Moulsford's gain – about a third of the school's pupils come in from there by coach (about half an hour each way).

Before Moulsford took up residence in 1961 the Victorian red-brick building at its centre was a private house and subsequently the boarding accommodation for Cranford, the girls' school across the road. It sits, high and dry, on top of a steep bank overlooking the Thames. Lush water meadows at the foot of the bank do their job if the river floods and the rest of the time accommodate a fire-pit, camps and the school's fleet of river craft.

Head's study and front of house admin are downstairs and boarding accommodation is upstairs. The library occupies what must have been a delightful drawing room with bay windows overlooking the river. Room and contents have been completely refurbished and there's a new librarian to go with the new reading material.

No Saturday lessons but extensive programme of matches demands attendance. Boarding starts at age 10 and is Monday to Friday only. Flexi boarding parents must commit termly in advance to minimum of two nights a week. 'Day boarders' can stay until 8pm. Dorms sleep up to 13 and were, at the time of our visit, looking rather down at heel. We're pleased to report that these have now been refurbished from top to toe, including new mattresses (the latter were previously source of some parental grumbles). As we looked through the dorm windows we wondered if the occupants were inured by familiarity to the priceless view of river and water meadows so charmingly framed by Virginia creeper. We hope these lucky boys remain blithely ignorant for as long as possible of the hours they would have to slave in order to open the curtains onto such a vista as adults.

No 12-year-old should be without the ability to say 'There is a stain on the pillow' or 'The minibar is empty' and these could bandy such phrases with Gallic gusto

About 35 boys board at any one time and those we met were keen to tell us how much they enjoyed the experience. 'There's so much freedom. After prep and supper you can kayak or go in the pool and in winter there's movies'. Food – especially fish and chips – got the thumbs up apart from 'something like couscous'. We certainly enjoyed sharing the boys' riverside barbecue lunch.

General consensus from parents is that teaching is 'brilliant'. First on our tour was an inter-house maths challenge in the multipurpose hall with stage, retractable seating and very impressive lighting gantry. Small groups of boys, the 'top two or three from each house', were tackling maths problems in a relay. Later on the whole school (including staff) gets involved. Apparently it's very entertaining although we remain to be convinced by the dramatic potential of equations.

Next stop was a year 6 class in the rather swish ICT suite. Boys were learning how to select and export images for use in the picture books they were designing for young children. By way of contrast we also saw little year 2s who were learning to tell the time in a reassuringly hands on and low tech style.

Top set French was a hoot. An inspiring teacher, a bag of props and imaginative use of the interactive whiteboard kept everyone on their toes. No 12-year-old boy should be without the ability to say 'There is a stain on the pillow' or 'The mini bar is empty' and these chaps (according to our notes they were all called Henry or Monty) could bandy such useful phrases with Gallic gusto.

Science labs and art rooms are in good shape and we loved the new stand-alone classroom, all cedar and glass, topped by a living roof – it's been commandeered by geography, which considering the riparian views, seems fair enough. Music and drama are tackled with typical enthusiasm. There are currently two choirs and an orchestra; parents said that music had improved 'hugely' in recent years and all supported head's plans to raise the status of the performing arts.

Currently after-school clubs are limited to optional Hobbies, twice a week. This is something parents felt needed addressing, pointing out that compared to other preps the day is relatively short and they'd like a much wider range of after-school activities. Mr B-G says the 'structure of the whole school day is under review, including activities and the range on offer.' To that end a new 'head of activities' has been appointed.

We mostly heard praise for Moulsford's approach to SEN though there were one or two grumbles about cost and how out of class support timings didn't always fit in sensibly with lessons. 'Little and often' is the mantra and whether it's help with motor skills, speech and language or handwriting the school will provide support from in-house or external experts. 'Come and talk to us' if you're worried, the head of SEN tells parents.

And so to sport – acknowledged by everyone to be Moulsford's forté. Cricket, rugby, football, hockey, tennis – courts and pitches are tip-top. 'Rugby is our best sport,' boys told us, but added that the school isn't 'just about rugby'. School says all teams get expert coaching and plenty of matches against rivals such as the Oratory Prep, The Dragon and Caldicott. Some parents say this isn't the case for the boys in teams C-F and felt boys who weren't natural athletes not encouraged enough to try different sports such as hockey or tennis. Moulsford is also a top judo school (came joint first in recent IAPS championships) and offers trampolining, fencing, gymnastics, a climbing wall and 'wonderful match teas'.

Canoes, kayaks and dinghies are launched from the school's own creek for expeditions upriver to Goose Poo Island. Forest school, camping in the tepee, bows and arrows, fire building and whittling – plenty of opportunities to make the most of school's dampest asset. Not quite Swallows and Amazons though – participation is limited by the number of craft so not everyone gets a go. Nevertheless, by the time they leave boys should be pretty handy around boats of all kinds – great for those heading to rowing schools such as Abingdon, Eton or Harrow.

The legendary post-CE tradition of throwing each other in the river, beloved by former pupils (known as Old Moles), was retired with the last head. Now boys can enjoy multiple goes at hurling themselves down a huge water slide while parents drink champagne and try not to watch. We imagine most are secretly relieved that their sons are in no danger of a ritual ducking in the Thames

What did they think of the head, we asked a group of boys enjoying their riverside barbecue? 'He's lively,' we were told. And what should he do for the school? 'Make it more famous, not enough people have heard of it.' Other boys were keen to add to Mr B-G's to-do list with requests for a retractable roof for the outdoor pool (parents echo this one) and loos on the far pitches. The cricket nets are, apparently, fine for fast bowlers but too low for spinners. Several boys were very keen to see fishing reintroduced as a hobby. Greatest consensus was over the inverse relation between the expense and quality of the special school socks. 'Six pounds a pair and look!' (They fall down.)

With a loyal crew and new captain at the helm the good ship Moulsford is steaming ahead. Yes, things will change but from what we heard the head's plans are in harmony with parental consensus. Mr B-G told us his favourite book is The Great Gatsby but parents can be confident that under his leadership Moulsford will most definitely not be 'borne back ceaselessly into the past.'

Oratory Preparatory School

RC 31

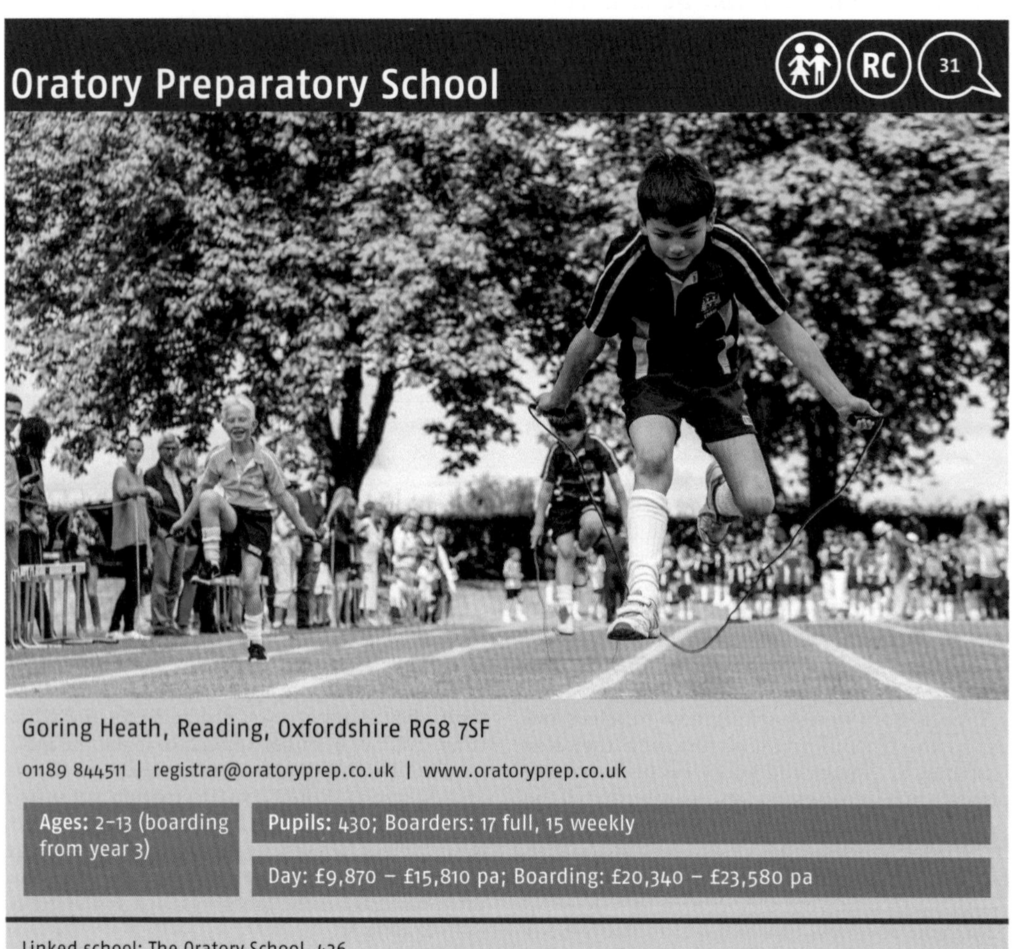

Goring Heath, Reading, Oxfordshire RG8 7SF

01189 844511 | registrar@oratoryprep.co.uk | www.oratoryprep.co.uk

Ages: 2–13 (boarding from year 3)

Pupils: 430; Boarders: 17 full, 15 weekly

Day: £9,870 – £15,810 pa; Boarding: £20,340 – £23,580 pa

Linked school: The Oratory School, 436

Headmaster: Since January 2017, Robert Stewart, previously housemaster and master in charge of Roman Catholics at Eton. Theology degree from Durham and PGCE from Cambridge, then taught for five years at Ampleforth, moving to Eton in 2001. During his stint there, he was head of the divinity department and took a masters in education management at King's College London. He is a keen sportsman who has played and coached rugby and cricket, and he loves running marathons. He enjoys watching Chelsea play football, and listening to the music of Bruce Springsteen. Rob is married to Sam, a GP (who was born in South Africa where she became a national qualified swimmer). Sam and Rob love using their holiday time to travel as a family. They have three children.

Entrance: No academic selection for prep, assessment morning and report from previous school. Observed visit for pre-prep entrants or else head of pre-prep visits them at current nursery.

Exit: At age 11 – handful of girls plus one or two boys. Rest leave at age 13. Around a quarter of boys to The Oratory, girls to Queen Anne's School, Caversham, St Mary's Ascot, St Helen and St Katharine. Others to Abingdon, Bradfield, Canford, Marlborough, Uppingham. Good number of scholarships to The Oratory, Bradfield, Wellington, Headington and Abingdon.

Remarks: Approach is down a quiet lane and through a riot of rhododendrons. The 65 acres of grounds are a real feature of this school with beautifully topiary, sunken lawns ideal for croquet or a marquee (recently hosted 300 for dinner and ball) and, when we visited, sculpture by a visiting artist. One parent commented that it's by no means a 'ritzy' school; this may be true but it's certainly easy on the eye. Looking out over another perfect view one couldn't help wondering whether the imperfections of the real world come as a shock to departing pupils.

Our year 8 guides (who were remarkably composed considering they received their CE results during our visit) started the tour in the chapel. Although neither was Catholic, both knelt respectfully and spoke warmly of the school's inclusive and welcoming attitude to non Catholics. When we asked what their stand-out memories of prep school were, for one it was 'all the hands-on science stuff and experiments'; for the other it was performing in the annual Shakespeare festival. The learning support department got a special mention, as did fish and chips and chocolate cake and custard.

Average class size 16. Latin from year 6, no Greek. We sat in on a year 7 maths class, impressed by the pupils' teamwork as they explored different methods of solving what seemed to us pretty challenging algebra. In history we enjoyed an enthusiastic and knowledgeable debate on arms escalation in the First World War – serious stuff enlivened by role playing and hammy French and German accents. Parents were full of praise for staff, from dinner ladies to teachers, particularly 'old hands' who might seem a bit old fashioned but were 'loved by children' and 'brilliant'. Smallish library is welcoming and well stocked, there's a library lesson once a week and, according to our guides, 'always lots of new books'. Around 30 pupils with SEN, mainly mild to moderate dyslexia, dyspraxia etc. School approach focuses on developing necessary skills and self-confidence via one-to-one lessons with specialist staff (extra charge).

Extensive games fields plus astroturf for hockey and three tennis/hockey pitches. As at 'the big O', sport, above all rugby, is central with local and national successes. More than one parent commented to the effect that a non-sporty child would not get the most out of the place. Creditably, we heard no grumbles that girls' sport comes second, nor that the keen but less good were overlooked. The rather swish 25m swimming pool plus separate learners' pool is a real bonus. Decent sports hall but boys' locker rooms must be bit of a bear garden at peak times – our guides thought they ought to go on head's improvement list. Seven music practice rooms plus a recording studio; large numbers of singers and instrumentalists have gained grade 5 or above by the time they depart. Serious choir (for mass) plus orchestras, ensembles etc – we were treated to a blast from the excellent jazz band as they rehearsed for forthcoming annual trip to Torquay.

Enthusiastic and knowledgeable debate on arms escalation in the First World War – serious stuff enlivened by role playing

The children we met were polite and sociable. Four houses, named after the school's previous locations, compete for the usual glory and silverware. What about bullying, we asked, in front of a notice board showing work done during recent anti-bullying week. Our guides were confident: 'You can tell any teacher and if you tell them it will stop.' School's extremely useful parents' handbook covers policies about this and pretty much everything else.

Compulsory Saturday school has been replaced with an optional Saturday enrichment programme for pupils in years 6, 7 and 8 which includes talks from visiting speakers and a range of modules that pupils can join including geology, acting, debating, orienteering, life skills, philosophy and more.

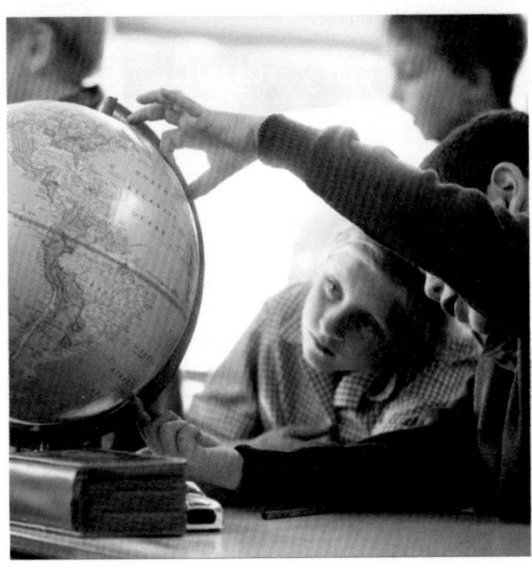

Our visit coincided with CE results day and was punctuated by relieved, happy year 8s clutching mark sheets and being warmly congratulated by their teachers. Some concerns expressed that smaller numbers of girls in years 7 and 8 meant that fallings out were harder to weather, but on the plus side there are plentiful opportunities for positions of leadership and responsibility. And, as a parent observed, girls who stay on don't seem to grow up quite as fast.

Boarding described by one parent as 'fantastic'. Lovely quirky dorms at top of main building, various size rooms with maximum 10 beds. Boarding (flexi from year 3, full and weekly from year 6) most popular in the last year with pupils keen to gain experience for senior school. Regular influx of Spanish boarders who stay for a few terms.

Jolly common rooms with properly comfortable sofas and cushions for film nights, quizzes and meetings. Nurse on site. Matron, houseparents and family live in, staff augmented by gappies. Flexi and occasional boarding possible if there's room and school will always 'scoop up anyone' in emergency. Working parents praise 'huge support' from matrons who will, for instance, review and acquire necessary uniform items and kit on their behalf. Likewise weekly newsletter that keeps all informed about what's going on.

Day pupils come from within a 30 minute drive: Henley, Reading, Watlington, Didcot and closer villages, vast majority are white British. Families, 60 per cent of whom are not practising Catholics, choose school for its strong faith based values. Overseas boarders mainly from Spain. Active parents' association (FOPS) organises coffee mornings, fundraisers and class reps.

Pre-prep housed in delightful chalet style, wooden buildings (were old stables) with verandas and bright hanging baskets. Top of the range outdoor facilities include a good size kitchen garden, 'jungle' (wooded) and covered play areas and athletics track. Majority of staff female, balance redressed somewhat by gap chaps who looked as enthusiastic about the games set up for a pretend fête as the excited children. Yellow curtained classrooms are plastered in colourful posters and children's work.

Multi-sensory approach to learning includes lots of work outdoors and exploring in adjoining fields and ponds. Weekly baking, art and all other messy stuff happen in a stand alone room so no need to clear up ongoing projects. In core subjects (maths and English at this stage), a teacher plus a TA cover one topic but pupils (max 18) divided according to learning style and ability to tackle the work in different ways. RE (Catholic syllabus) once a week, pre prep mass once a term. Lovely old barn for assemblies and after-school clubs (include Mandarin, music, dance, lego) that run from 4-6pm starting with tea. Small charge for activities goes towards buying new equipment – head of pre-prep ensures after school toys and equipment are 'not the same as those used during lessons'.

New Little Oaks nursery now open. One or two parents commented that they hoped there would also be investment at the top end.

The Oratory Prep is a vibrant, welcoming community, just the place for your sporty all rounder – boy or girl – and now the 'little O' experience is available to their younger siblings. We were told that someone described the school as a 'sleeping giant', and while we're not sure about the slightly scary part of that simile, we agree that it has been a little under the radar – undeservedly so in our opinion.

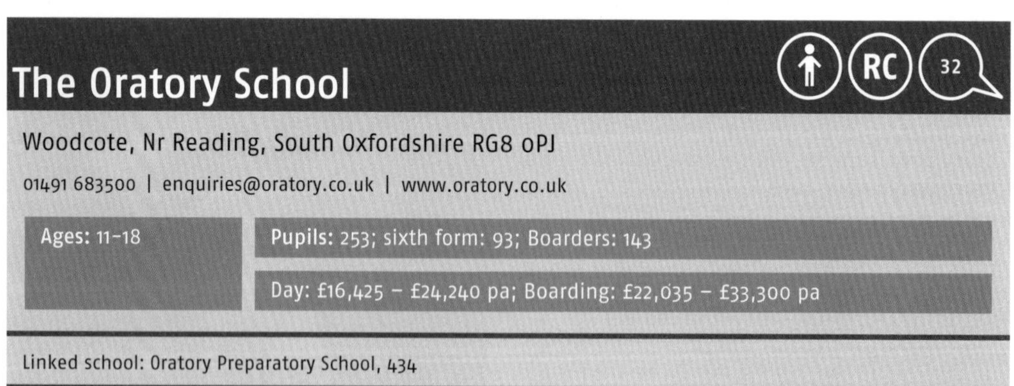

The Oratory School

RC 32

Woodcote, Nr Reading, South Oxfordshire RG8 oPJ

01491 683500 | enquiries@oratory.co.uk | www.oratory.co.uk

Ages: 11–18

Pupils: 253; sixth form: 93; Boarders: 143

Day: £16,425 – £24,240 pa; Boarding: £22,035 – £33,300 pa

Linked school: Oratory Preparatory School, 434

Head Master: Since September 2016, Joe Smith BA PGCE MEd (40s), formerly head of Oratory Prep since 2010. Was 'invited' to take up current position following departure of Adrian Wyles who was in post for one year having taken over from the 'very charismatic' long term head, Clive Dytor. Educated at Catholic primary school and the local comp in King's Lynn, then Liverpool University where he got

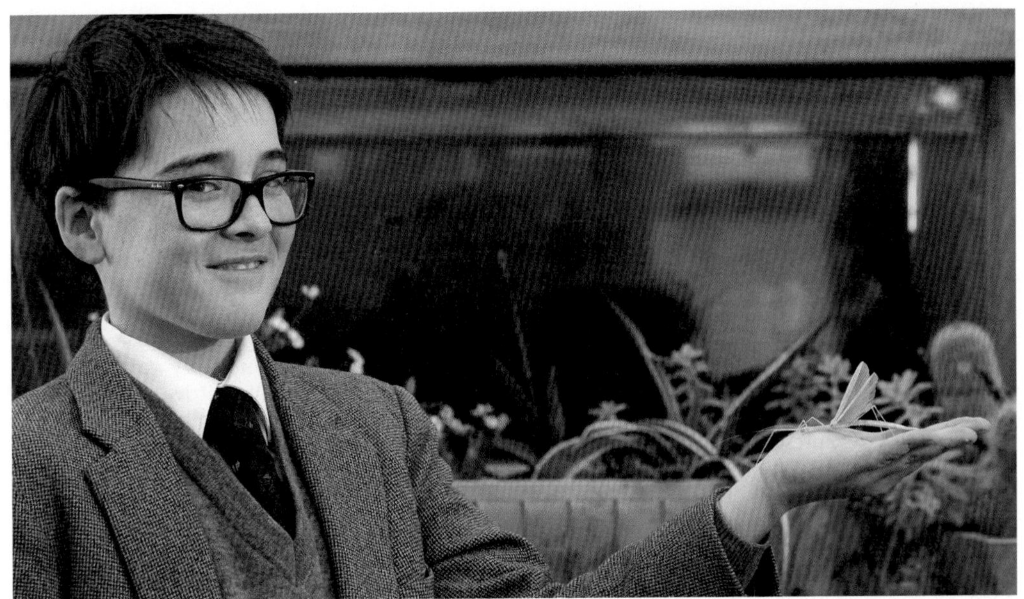

a first in English. PGCE at Brunel, followed by his first teaching post at Colfe's School then 12 years at Monkton Combe, Bath where he became head of English and housemaster.

Sees his role as 'a huge honour and privilege' and, armed with intimate knowledge of the perception of the so called 'Big O' (thanks to candid parents at the prep), has set about pruning dead wood ('who you put in front of boys in the classroom is crucial') and surrounding himself with a (mainly) young and dynamic senior leadership team – some existing staff, some newly appointed – with a strong focus on the senior part of the school, particularly the sixth form. First job was to shorten the school day by an hour to finish at 6pm to allow day boys an extra hour of family time. The second was to double the broadband speed 'to allow boys the same access to social media as they would get at home' – he knows his audience.

Youthful, extremely personable – we'd happily spend an hour or two with him chewing the educational cud in the pub – and popular with parents and boys, who parents say 'hugely respect' him. Apologised when we arrived for the smell of bacon in his office – he'd just finished breakfast with a group of pupils, a weekly event ('getting to know them is incredibly rewarding'). Always 'out talking to everyone', say parents – and even occasionally serves coffee at school events. Lives on site with wife Debbie, his three children, two boys at the school (one at the OS; one at OPS) and a girl at nearby St Helen and St Katharine, and two dogs.

Devoted foodie, wannabe chef and has recently and reluctantly retired from village cricket.

Academic matters: Unashamedly gentler on the grey matter than the local competition and results are a bit of a mixed bag – not surprising given the mixed ability intake. Head acknowledges middle ground school status ('we know our niche') but keen to up the academic ante and has appointed new academic deputy to make it happen, and some new young staff who, according to parents are 'spicing things up'. He remains insistent, however, that he won't alienate the less academic all-rounder and will continue to accept some boys achieving 40 per cent at CE (50 is the usual requirement) provided they have 'something else to offer.' Pupils now sit the more challenging IGCSE in English language and lit, French, Spanish and sciences. Most take 10 GCSES, and although in 2017, 36 per cent of these were graded A*-A/9-7, this stat is heavily skewed by stellar performance in art department, with B the most prominent grade across the board of subjects and a fair number of Cs and Ds in the mix – particularly, and somewhat bizarrely, in RS.

Parents, however, praise teaching staff – in some cases for helping their son pull a C grade in maths out of the bag when they never thought he would – and, uniquely for this most academic of geographical enclaves, are fully accepting of the mixed bag of innate ability. We even heard of one parent who turned down a place at Magdalen in favour of The Oratory, confident that their high-flying son would do equally well here, on the basis of its 'relaxed atmosphere'. The bright and focused, however, are not an endangered species and we spotted one or two boys who had achieved seven or more A*s (identified by their special striped blazers, known as 'deckchairs') during our tour. Head explains ethos thus: 'Boys in our top leagues would be average elsewhere – but we believe that to be a big fish in a small pond can be incredibly beneficial for many children's confidence.' Also: 'We do really well with boys who need a bit more time to mature'.

Trad curriculum with French, Spanish and Italian in the languages department (no German but parents report boys picking it up from their international schoolfriends), plus ancient Greek and philosophy to A level for those so inclined. New for 2018 is computer science GCSE, on offer to lower sixth formers. RS (Catholic syllabus) compulsory at GCSE and into sixth form, when boys do not have to work towards an A level but have 'a carefully designed scheme of work on theology taught by Fr David and other members of staff'. A level results, as with GCSE, are representative of the mixed ability cohort: 37 per cent were graded A*/A in 2016 (although only 18 per cent broke the A* barrier and, again, almost all of these in art) and 58 per cent at A*/B. No significant change to trends in results over the years – we'll watch with interest to see how, as head 'raises expectations of staff and boys', things ramp up. Just one or two take the EPQ each year.

No makeshift former broom cupboard for the learning support department here – it actually is, well, a department. And one that means business too – with 29 per cent of boys on the SEN register it needs to be. A full time SENCo, supported by eight subject-specific part timers, who use a combination of in-class and one-to-one support strategies – and where appropriate a reduced timetable – to bring boys with mild to moderate learning difficulties, dyslexia or ASD up to speed. Super EAL teaching for international pupils – we met several (one who had just achieved an A* in his English GCSE having arrived from Germany with 'school English' in year 9) who could pass as natives.

Get any member of staff talking on the subject and take your seat for a comprehensive education, all the way back to Henry VIII

One UK born boy joked about his international friend 'speaking better English than me'.

Games, options, the arts: Historically synonymous with rugby of the 'guts and glory' variety (is there any other kind?), but look a little closer and you'll find that there are plenty of alternatives for boys less inclined to 'drive for the line' (their words not ours). Nestled amongst pitches and fields galore that fall away into glorious woodland, plus 90 minutes of sport at the end of the day four days a week (the fifth day is CCF – compulsory to year 10), any boy would find it hard not to throw himself into the plenitude of games on offer. There's everything you would expect (rugby, football and cricket are major sports) plus seriously competitive shooting, rowing, badminton and tennis (played not only on hard courts but also grass in a heavenly walled garden), plus activities including basketball (coached by head), swimming (in super modern indoor pool complex) and golf (school has its own 9-hole course, natch). A separate mention for real tennis: Oratory has one of only five courts in UK schools and has hosted the national championships – get any member of staff talking on the subject and take your seat for a comprehensive education, all the way back to Henry VIII. All abilities represent school in fixtures: 'We're great for the keen but average as well as the superstars', says head; 'our size means we need everyone to play to make up team numbers.' There's that big fish/small pond advantage again. Head says that past marketing focusing heavily on sport 'is a problem' and assures us that school has 'loads of gentle, arty types' but it seems to us that even those boys tend to enjoy casting the paint brush aside and getting stuck into something physical – and if they really don't then this probably isn't the school for them.

Whilst on the subject of paint brushes, we were welcomed to the creative oasis (the words 'art department' simply don't do justice) by the positively effusive head of art with the words: 'Why give a boy a paintbrush when you could give him a powertool...or a mop?' And why indeed, when with such tools and alternative techniques such as collage, printing presses, 3D photography, ceramics and modelling can deliver such masterpieces as those by the swathes of boys who choose to take art GCSE, A level and Pre-U? 'We take students much wider than mere draughtsmanship – if they can't handle representation, we get them into abstraction and really engaging with the materials – it's very much a boys' course'. And not a still life in sight. With this ethos in place, results unsurprisingly outstanding. Around half the sixth form cohort take the Cambridge Pre-U rather than A level, with the vast majority achieving D3 or A*/A. Several each year to art college or degree courses – most skipping the foundation stage having surpassed the standard in school. DT adjoins art and is similarly impressive both in terms of facilities and teaching – 'another of our crown jewels' according to our pupil guide. 'Gone are the days of making a coffee table', we were assured. Using industry standard software and equipment, boys are encouraged not to merely design products but to make and, crucially, sell them too, with entrepreneurship encouraged to the extent that more than one boy has a business running on the side outside of school. As with art, exam results are superb and the half dozen or so who choose to pursue the subject after school are typically given very low offers from colleges and universities keen to snap them up.

Dramatic productions performed in very smart recently renovated studio, complete with soundproofed prop room and swish sound and lighting suite. Recent annual junior, middle and senior school productions have included A Midsummer Night's Dream, Oklahoma and Amadeus, with female roles played by girls from nearby Queen Anne's School. Lots of music too: the inclusive Schola Cantorum sings at masses, vespers and school functions (plus, recently, a tour to Hong Kong) and all the usual bands, orchestras and ensembles are present and correct. Plus one for bagpipes. Nothing out of the ordinary on the extracurricular activities list – although we love the sound of the very popular ballroom dancing class for sixth formers in conjunction with Queen Anne's which culminates in a ball.

Boarding: Junior boys (years 7 and 8) housed in St Philip House which has its own recreation, social and teaching areas. Boys join one of four senior boarding houses in year 9: Faber in the main building is 'more like a family' with its smaller numbers, according to our guide; Norris, FitzAlan and St John are purpose built, the former two modern, well kitted out (table football, table tennis and darts) and spacious (if a little soulless) with younger boys four to a room, doubles for GCSE students and singles for the sixth form. Housemasters deliberately mix nationalities, and boys' rooms are moved every term. Boys in senior boarding houses expected to manage their own laundry – even the ironing (taken particularly seriously before a social, apparently). We approve. Quality and quantity of food a common grumble by parents and pupils and the pizza delivery scooter is not an uncommon sight – tuck box required.

Boarders and day pupils take part in a full schedule of evening activities on week nights: sports, public speaking, debating or academic societies. Wednesday is house night with trips out to cinema, go-karting or trampolining. Weekend activity schedules for the hundred or so who stay are kept deliberately light, although some parents would like to see more on offer. As all boys finish their week after Saturday fixtures, on Sundays there's mass (compulsory for all) followed by brunch and then they are free to do their own thing – either relaxing in school or taking a bus into Reading.

Boarding is full or weekly, no flexi, although school has recently introduced occasional boarding – a maximum of 10 nights per half term.

Background and atmosphere: Founded 1859 by Cardinal John Henry Newman, Christian thinker and educational pioneer (beatified in 2010) to create a Catholic boarding school along the lines of the major English public schools ('Eton minus its wickedness') to serve the Catholic community. He provided the school with its motto: 'cor ad cor loquitur' (heart speaking to heart). School remains proudly Catholic ('Catholicism is central and fundamental to our identity – it affects our pastoral and moral side', says head) although there are none of the ostentatious shrines or symbolism so often found in Catholic schools on show (we were actually surprised and delighted by lack of austerity) and pupils from all faiths and none are equally welcomed. Head too refutes any trace of a formerly austere reputation and institutionalisation: 'I want school to be joyful – formality's really not my style.'

Twenty minutes from Reading and situated just off a main road, and yet the setting is the quintessential best of Britain: rolling hills, woodland and playing fields tipping off into farmland. The 400 acres of grounds are spectacularly well maintained and atop it all is the Queen Anne style manor house which has homed the school since 1942. Beyond the rather severe marble foyer and 'black room' used for concerts and teas, corridors and classrooms rather wash over you – remarkable only in their ordinariness – and for a school so prolific in producing outstanding art work, the main buildings are somewhat bereft of displays of creativity ('the art department probably wants to keep it all', said one of our guides). Safe as houses for any parent concerned about errant sons tripping off to the local – there's not so much as a shop for miles around and school and overall feel is of a slightly other-worldly, idyllic and wholesome bubble – we wonder whether this is at the expense of preparation for real life, though.

Pastoral care, well-being and discipline: School 'really excels' in pastoral care according to parents, to the point of staff supporting not only the child but the parents and visiting family homes in extreme cases. The four senior houses engender 'incredibly strong house affiliation', says head, to the point that sixth formers recently rejected the idea of their own separate house, although a sixth form centre is in the planning. The Rose Bowl competition – the annual house competition comprising everything from drama and music to sport and debating – is fiercely fought and the most common reason for day boys to take up the occasional boarding beds. Relationships between pupils and staff 'really strong,' say parents – we lunched with a number of senior staff members and can concur we would be happy to entrust our male offspring to their care on the grounds of inspiration, enthusiasm and humour. The resident priests are praised as approachable sounding boards for both parents and boys in need of a chat.

Daily masses and other services in St Joseph's Chapel. Daily prayers in houses, Sunday masses with RC and non-RC boys welcome to serve at the altar.

Few sanctions required, according to head, and traditional methods when they are: head's detention on a Saturday night pretty much as bad as it gets, and there's 'not a huge amount of drinking or smoking' but occasional suspensions for eg violence or repeated defiance. All sixth formers given the honour of prefecture 'unless they have seriously blotted their copybook'. Very little in the way of bullying: 'we are such a small community, the bully themselves would be ostracised', one pupil assured us and boys said that diversity in terms of race or sexuality was well tolerated, although head admitted to school being 'a bit behind the times' when it came to supporting any LGBT pupils.

School has 'loads of gentle, arty types' but it seems to us that even those boys tend to enjoy casting the paint brush aside and getting stuck into something physical

New appointment of girls' school co-ordinator aims to build strong and meaningful links with the likes of Downe House, Queen Anne's and Rye St Antony. Events include language dinners, guest speakers and rowing competitions (oars not arguments) as well as 'good old socials', where the boys get to showcase those ballroom dancing skills.

Pupils and parents: Traditional with the proverbial capital T is the order of the day here with not a shaggy head, thin tie or pointy shoe in sight. If you like your boys clean cut and preppy then look no further. We are told that quirky boys do exist here but failed to spot any. Established, professional parents in the main with fewer first time buyers than many other schools. Twenty-five per cent of boarding cohort is international, with boys from European Catholic countries, Russia, Nigeria and Asia. Locals come from around Reading and south Oxfordshire villages – a radius of up to one hour.

Entrance: Entry not very academically selective. Around 15 to 20 places at 11+ with boys tested in English, maths and VR/NVR plus informal interview. Applicants largely from state maintained sector at this point, plus 11+ preps like St Piran's, Chandlings and St Edward's in Reading. ISEB pretest introduced for entry in 2018 and beyond with around 50 per cent CE pass required at 13+ plus prep head's report and interview. Around 25 out of 35 boys move up from the Oratory Prep school each year, accounting for about one third of year 9 cohort (head aiming to up the numbers to half). Other feeders are Moulsford, Woodcote House, St Andrew's Pangbourne, St John's Beaumont and Papplewick.

Scholarships at 11+ and 13+ for academic, music, sport, art and all-rounder.

Exit: Between six and 10 leave after GCSE, mainly in search of a co-educational existence, with nearby Henley College a big draw: 'They are attracted by the lack of uniform and co-ed culture, but it's a battle we'll win,' says head, and parents in the know say the boys in question often miss the 'roundedness' of The Oratory.

Not vast numbers to Russell Group universities (around 25 per cent) and only the occasional one to Oxbridge (one in 2017). Popular destinations over past few years include Bath, Exeter, Oxford Brookes, Royal Holloway, Swansea and West of England. All manner of subjects with a strong bias towards vocational over academic.

Money matters: Full boarding fees in line with top public schools, now topping £30K. Generous scholarships and exhibitions up to half fees, plus means-tested bursaries.

Remarks: Somewhat overlooked by local people in recent years but now's the time to look again. Still not the obvious destination for a single-minded scholar, but for the arty, the sporty, late developers and just those who prefer a lower temperature environment, definitely one for the list.

d'Overbroeck's

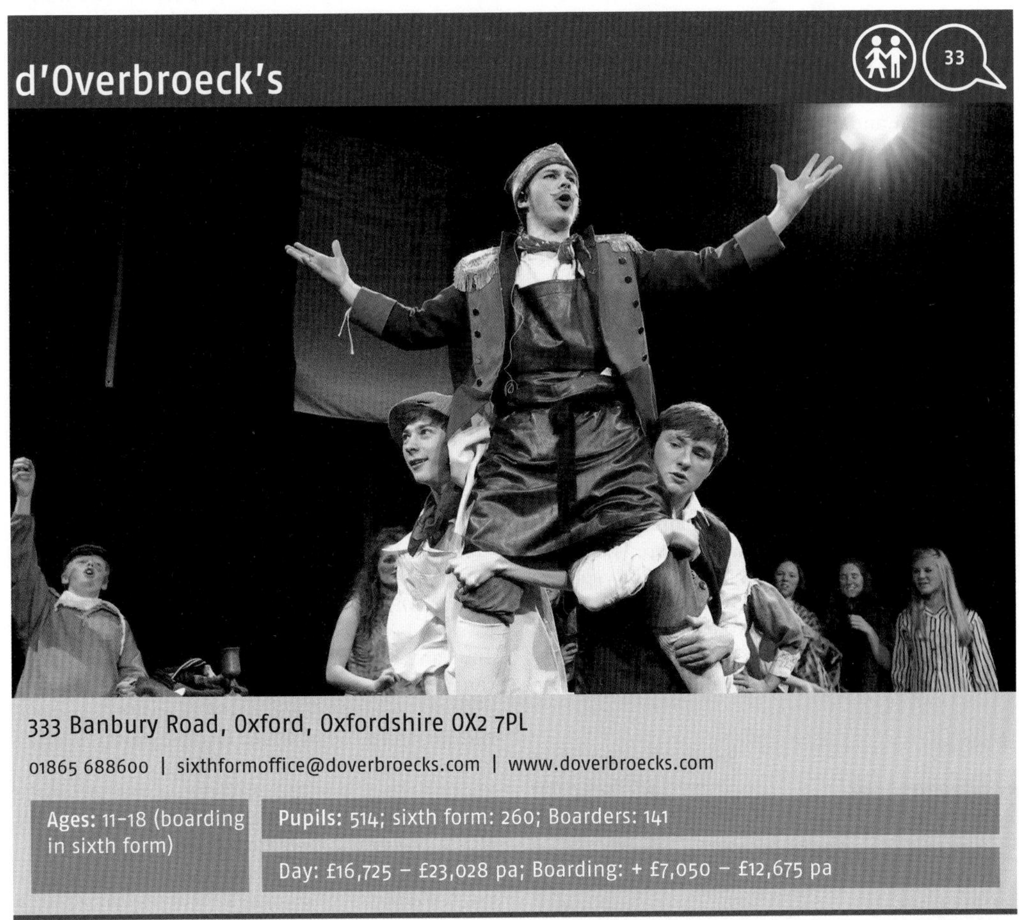

333 Banbury Road, Oxford, Oxfordshire OX2 7PL

01865 688600 | sixthformoffice@doverbroecks.com | www.doverbroecks.com

Ages: 11-18 (boarding in sixth form)

Pupils: 514; sixth form: 260; Boarders: 141

Day: £16,725 – £23,028 pa; Boarding: + £7,050 – £12,675 pa

Principal: Since September 2017, Emma-Kate Henry, previously principal of Hampshire Collegiate School. Read English literature and African & Caribbean studies at Kent after a gap year teaching in Jamaica, which inspired her to do a PGCE at the Institute of Education after a year in IT recruitment. She has taught in state and private schools, including Surbiton High and St Christopher, where she was deputy head. She is married to Tony, a qualified athletics coach, and they have a young son.

Academic matters: Sixth form offers 35 subjects at A level (all the usual, plus others like film studies, history of art, philosophy, sociology and photography). Unlike some schools (and thanks to nifty timetabling) students can choose virtually any mix of A levels. 'The key to students' success is getting the subjects right,' says the school, which encourages students to choose the subjects they'll enjoy and do well at. 'There is no subject combination that we rule out,' says the head of sixth form. Alongside their A levels some sixth formers do an

Extended Project Qualification (EPQ). In 2017, 88 per cent A*-B and 62 per cent A*/A grades.

The principal says the school appoints teachers 'who know their subjects inside out,' are enthusiastic and care deeply about teaching. Lessons are relatively informal, while being highly engaging and interactive, with teachers constantly checking that everyone has 'got it' before moving on. The students we met were unanimous in singing their teachers' praises. 'You won't find better teaching anywhere,' one girl told us appreciatively. 'I switched to economics quite late and my teacher stayed behind for an hour every week to help me catch up, from the day I started till the week my exams began. I've never found teachers who care this much.' Another said: 'The teachers want the best for you and it makes you want the best for yourself.'

GCSE results are good too. In 2017, 54 per cent A*-A/9-7 grades; 18 students achieved grade 8/9 in maths and 14 in English. Successes in biology, chemistry, physics and art are also particularly notable. Most students take 10 GCSEs, including three separate sciences and at least one language. French, Spanish, Latin and classical civilisation are on offer but school can organise German, Italian, Japanese, Mandarin and Russian if required (the benefits of having the dreaming spires of Oxford close by).

Academic ethos is the same in both sections of the school. 'We are an academic school,' Mark Olejnik, the genial head of years 7-11, told us, 'but we want children to enjoy their learning. Happiness is the very essence of what we do here.' Learning support offered for mild dyslexia and dyspraxia at no additional charge. Sixth form teachers have been known to spot issues that have been missed by previous schools and target appropriate help for students. Class sizes are small – no more than 15 up to GCSE and up to 10 at A level. There's an emphasis on discussion and confidence-building throughout, with pupils encouraged to offer their views.

Games, options, the arts: The school has worked hard to offer a broad range of sports and activities. Sport isn't compulsory for sixth formers but students are expected to do at least one extracurricular activity in the lower sixth – everything from hockey, rugby and netball to film club, yoga and first aid, plus Young Enterprise and D of E. Lower sixth students also have a compulsory enrichment programme – a variety of outside speakers, from university professors and admissions tutors to writers, scientists and entrepreneurs.

d'Overbroeck's doesn't have its own playing fields but makes the most of the extensive facilities across Oxford. This seems to work well, with students being ferried by minibus to a number of excellent sporting venues including Oxford Brookes (which has an Astroturf, fully equipped sports hall, fitness gym, squash, badminton and basketball courts, climbing wall and more). Year 7 and 8 pupils get three hours of games a week while those in years 9, 10 and 11 have two hours and 20 minutes of timetabled sport.

Drama is a delight, with younger pupils teaming up with sixth formers to stage major productions like Les Misérables and Peter Pan. In years 7, 8 and 9 pupils have a double lesson of art and a double lesson of music each week. When we visited, a group of year 8s were studying 'impossible architecture,' designing fantastical creations that would give our most eminent architects a run for their money. Many go on to study art in the sixth form and one parent told us: 'I am an artist myself and can say that my daughter has been brilliantly taught.' Eighty students take individual music lessons – all levels (beginners to grade 8) and everything from the violin to electric guitar. Recitals by pupils are often held at the Jacqueline du Pré auditorium at St Hilda's College, as well as regular concerts for students of all ages in the school hall. Music and music tech are popular at A level too.

Debating and public speaking are hugely popular. A couple of years ago, a team of year 9 pupils reached the national final of the Youth Speaks public speaking event. 'Opportunities are thrust on you here,' one of the team told us. 'It really makes you want to participate.' Loads of school trips, including recent summer expeditions to Namibia, Iceland and China for year 10 to 13 youngsters, annual ski trips and visits to theatre productions in London and Stratford-upon-Avon, science visits to the Rutherford Appleton Laboratory, one of the UK's national scientific research centres, and much else besides.

Boarding: Most lower sixth boarders live in one of two co-ed boarding houses close by (60 places at new

Islip House, opposite the new sixth form building, and 18 places at Hayfield House). Double rooms with en-suite bathrooms at Islip, singles with shared bathrooms at Hayfield. Girls and boys live in separate 'zones', but meet up in communal areas for meals and socialising. Houseparents cook supper, lend a friendly ear to boarders, oversee the 7pm to 9pm study periods and make sure everyone is in by the 10.30pm curfew (11.30pm on Fridays and Saturdays). There's also a small girls' boarding house – Benson's.

Most upper sixth boarders live with host families, all carefully vetted and regularly inspected, though they may live in a boarding house if space allows.

Background and atmosphere: d'Overbroeck's is 'a mushroom-shaped school' – the place gets bigger as it progresses up the age range. It started out as a sixth form college, founded in 1977 by French and Spanish teacher Malcolm van Biervliet, who was head of languages till he retired in 2007. Invited to speak about the school's ethos he said: 'Friendship is a cornerstone in the d'Overbroeck's structure, contributing to the happiness of staff and students alike, and thus making the process of teaching and learning a more enjoyable and symbiotic experience.' Staff and students agree that his vision still holds true today. Was purchased in 2014 by the Oxford International Education Group.

'We don't stand on ceremony but there are clear boundaries and we have high expectations of the students.' Youngsters heartily approve. 'It's not stuffy here at all'

Brand new sixth form centre on Banbury Road brings all facilities onto one site including science labs, a 180 seater auditorium, performing arts suites, library and common rooms.

There's a real buzz everywhere you turn – lots of lively chatter, teachers and pupils on first name terms and an informal and energetic atmosphere throughout. New caterers based in the sixth form centre provide meals for students throughout the school, including dinners for boarders. Some students stroll up to M&S or Taylors in Summertown to buy lunch – they're spoiled for choice. 'This is a relatively informal environment. We don't stand on ceremony but there are clear boundaries and we have high expectations of the students.' Youngsters heartily approve. 'It's not stuffy here at all,' a girl told us.

d'Overbroeck's opened its lower school in 2005, snapping up a Victorian building in nearby Leckford Road previously occupied by Phil and

Jim's, a local state primary. A 10-minute walk from the sixth form, the years 7-11 site is compact but makes the most of every inch of space. The lower school now boasts an ingeniously designed main building, with a galleried library resembling the upper deck of a ship, light and airy classrooms and a social area with a vivid pink wall, café tables and glossy blue lockers. The original school hall next door is used for lunch, assemblies and theatrical productions. Numbers in years 7-11 are now pretty much on capacity at around 175, with two forms in years 7 and 8 and three from year 9.

No uniform for sixth form but year 7 to 11 pupils wear smart navy polo shirt or jumper with school logo. 'Apart from that they can wear their own clothes,' says the head of years 7-11. 'As long as they are reasonable. No purple hair, hoodies, hats or nose piercings.' He admits that being called by his first name took a bit of getting used to though the school and students reckon it enables everyone to be themselves.

Pastoral care, well-being and discipline: Pastoral care is widely praised. Sixth form students are assigned their own director of studies (universally known as a DoS) – usually one of their subject teachers. Youngsters talk to them about academic and pastoral matters, with academic progress, attendance, punctuality, work rate and general well-being closely monitored. 'I see my DoS every day,' one boy told us. Parents get a progress report by email every six weeks. Pupils can also talk to a trained school counsellor if they prefer and many turn to the school's dynamic young social organiser – a huge asset to the school, who organises everything from film nights to barbecues. 'We are strict about the things that we need to be strict on,' says the school, and students and parents agree.

Firm rules on alcohol, drugs and smoking. No drugs tolerated – offenders asked to leave immediately. Students say bullying 'just doesn't happen here' and that unlike many other schools 'there is no sense of being considered cool or not cool.' 'Everyone is included,' a sixth former told us. 'It's a really friendly place.'

Sixth formers say that d'Overbroeck's has got its priorities right and appreciate the fact that it doesn't impose pointless rules and regulations. 'If you want a school that makes you go to chapel and has an army of prefects this probably isn't the right school for you,' one boy remarked. The school is firm about pupils being prompt for lessons and handing work in on time. Students who are 10 minutes late aren't allowed into the class at all and an email is immediately sent to their parents. The only gripe we heard from sixth formers was the lack of lockers – a perennial whinge.

A galleried library resembling the upper deck of a ship, light and airy classrooms and a social area with a vivid pink wall, café tables and glossy blue lockers

Form teachers are the first port of call in years 7-11, with tutor groups meeting every day and staff holding a meeting every week to discuss pastoral issues. The head of years 7-11 stands at the school gate every morning to greet pupils – 'even in the pouring rain,' said one girl. 'It makes you feel really welcome.' Younger pupils we spoke to praised everything about the school, from the small class sizes, 'fair' rules and chocolate cake ('it's not overcooked') to being able to email teachers for help and getting answers back in double-quick time. 'You rarely have anyone in a bad mood here,' said another pupil. 'And I'm not just saying that.' The school has its own car-themed house system – Cooper, Morris and Austin – but unlike more traditional establishments, these focus on environmental matters and fundraising for charity as well as competitions and sport.

Pupils and parents: Pupils are an eclectic mix of high achievers and grafters. Year 7 pupils generally arrive from local primary schools while year 9 entrants tend to come from Oxford preps like Christ Church, the Dragon and New College. No boarding at 11-16 – most live in Oxford and surrounding villages, but some travel from as far afield as Wantage, Faringdon, Swindon and even Warwick. More boys than girls in lower years, but a few more girls than boys in the sixth form. Post-16, equal numbers of day pupils and boarders. UK students come from a vast range of schools (both state and independent) while international students fly in from more than 30 different countries, including Italy, Spain, Russia and China. A handful of very clever Thai government scholars every year too.

The school makes a big effort to keep parents in the loop. Parents we spoke to appreciated its 'modern, unstuffy approach,' 'family atmosphere' and 'emphasis on the important things.' 'My son never enjoyed school until he came to d'Overbroeck's,' one mother told us. 'But he has thrived and been happy here right from the start. He'll be very sad to leave.'

Entrance: The school is selective but emphasises that pupils should have 'a reasonably wide range of abilities.' Alongside the academic requirements staff are looking for students 'who will enjoy the environment and make the most of it.'

Main entry points are year 7, year 9 and sixth form. At 11 and 13 applicants take internal assessment tests in English, maths and non-verbal reasoning, plus a short interview and reference from current school. 'We are looking for potential,' says the head.

At 16 prospective students have an informal interview (they can also sit in on a few lessons if they wish) and need the equivalent of eight A*-C grades at GCSE, including maths and English. The school also stipulates that pupils need at least a B/6 in subjects being taken at A level while those doing maths need at least aa A/7 at GCSE (further maths needs an 8/9 or A*). International students sit written English language test (and maths test, where appropriate) and their level of English must be strong enough for the courses they want to do.

Exit: At 16, around two-thirds of year 11 pupils progress through to the sixth form (a few head to local state schools like Cherwell and Cheney and in recent years a few girls have moved to Magdalen College School's co-ed sixth form). At 18, virtually all go to university – five to Oxbridge in 2017, plus three medics; Leeds, Birmingham, Bristol and Manchester all popular, with some to eg Imperial, King's College, LSE and Queen Mary's.

Money matters: A range of academic, art and performing arts scholarships for pupils entering years 7 and 9 (up to 20 per cent of tuition fees). Academic, art and performing arts scholarships available at sixth form level (up to 40 per cent of fees).

Remarks: d'Overbroeck's has made its mark in Oxford as an exciting and forward-thinking place to be, with a lively, happy environment that fizzes with energy and ideas. Along with top-notch teaching and rigorous academic standards the school helps students to achieve impressive results and make lifelong friends along the way.

Pangbourne College

34

Pangbourne, Reading, Berkshire RG8 8LA

01189 842101 | registrar@pangbourne.com | www.pangbourne.com

Ages: 11-19

Pupils: 426; sixth form: 137; Boarders: 93 full, 144 part

Day: £17,055 – £24,036 pa; Boarding: £21,408 – £33,996 pa

Headmaster: Since 2005, Thomas Garnier BSc PGCE (40s). Educated at Sandroyd and Radley, read physics at Bristol and was a seaman officer in the Royal Navy for seven years. He left the Navy 'for love' after meeting his wife Alexandra and trained as a teacher. Did PGCE at Oxford, followed by first teaching job at King Alfred's, high performing state school in Wantage, Oxfordshire. Spent 10 years at Abingdon School, where he progressed to housemaster and then head of boarding.

Dedicated, energetic and keen to listen to pupils' views, he still manages to fit in some physics teaching and runs the naval section of Pangbourne's CCF. He describes Pangbourne pupils as 'good, solid citizens who are prepared to work hard and willing to participate.' Makes a point of being out and about in school and meets the two chief cadet captains (head boy and head girl) for 10 minutes every morning. 'We suit active children who like being busy,' he says.

Head's wife is very involved in school life and they have two sons. Headmaster's office in the main school building has panoramic views stretching 20 miles across the Berkshire countryside. In his spare time (not that there's much of it) he enjoys rowing, running and music. A firm believer in 'lifelong learning,' he recently took up the flute again after a 25 year gap, passed his grade 8 with ease and plays in the school orchestra. He is keen to start piano lessons too. 'Someone said to me "you can always find 15 minutes a day and if you do that it adds up to 90 hours a year".'

Academic matters: School takes children across a broad range of ability. Head agrees that Pangbourne is sometimes perceived as being 'for the less able' but says they do a very good job for academic children (there's a gifted and talented programme for the most able). In 2017, 51 per cent of A level grades were A*/B and 27 per cent A*/A. The school told us: 'While the top students gained their straight A grades, some of the most heartening performances were to be found in the middle ground, among those who worked tremendously hard to secure Bs and Cs. We take real pride in these.' Some sixth formers, particularly those considering careers in the Forces, take public service BTec as well as their A levels. BTecs are also offered in DT, music, performing arts and sport.

Most pupils take nine GCSEs, including IGCSE English language, English literature and maths. Pupils choose between combined science and two or three separate sciences. Other subjects offered include French, German, Spanish, history, geography, art, business, computing, drama, design technology, music, PE short course RS. Latin is also offered as an additional extra. Pupils are set for maths, English, science and French. In 2017, 36 A*/A grades.

Pupils told us that the parades 'bring us together'; parents are hugely supportive. 'It seems to give them great pride in what they do'

Teaching staff (two-thirds male and a third female) are a healthy mix of experienced and newly qualified teachers (school has links with teacher training departments at universities of Buckingham, Reading and Oxford Brookes). Half the teachers live on site. Staff hold regular academic clinics for youngsters who need help (pupils can also email their teachers). Learning support available for pupils with minor learning difficulties – individual lessons on offer at extra cost. Tutor system – in senior school pupils stay with same tutor for year 9, then change for years 10 and 11 and again for the sixth form.

Games, options, the arts: A very sporty school. Teachers and pupils alike told us that 'Pangbourne punches above its weight' when it comes to sport, and its impressive results bear this out. School regularly beats far larger schools, particularly at rugby and rowing. Pangbourne boathouse is a mile from the school, on the scenic banks of the Thames, and school has won the Princess Elizabeth Challenge Cup at Henley four times.

Unlike some schools, where pupils drop sport in the sixth form, everyone does sport here. School's size means that virtually all get the chance to represent Pangbourne. Main boys' sports are rugby, hockey, rowing and cricket while girls do netball, hockey, rugby, rowing and tennis. Open-air pool (keen swimmers get bussed to indoor pools at Bradfield, Reading and Newbury). Lots of equestrian enthusiasts – riding and polo are popular.

Stunning new music school houses recital hall, recording suite and 10 practice and teaching rooms, as well as four prized Steinway grand pianos. Around a third of pupils take individual music lessons, with brass, drums, guitar and singing leading the pack. Loads of musical groups to join, including orchestra, jazz band, choirs and a marching band. Art and DT departments thriving, with healthy numbers taking subjects at GCSE and A level. Performing arts are on the up with a variety of college productions, theatre trips and drama workshops. Three drama studios and pupils encouraged to take LAMDA exams. Everyone does CCF for at least a year and D of E is compulsory in year 9.

Boarding: Four boys' houses and two (ultra-modern) girls' houses. Just over half of the pupils board – more than 100 are full boarders while the others ('part boarders') board four nights a week (Monday, Tuesday, Thursday and Friday). Boarding grows in popularity as the pupils move up the school – by sixth form 75 per cent are boarders. 'We don't actively push boarding,' one teacher told us. 'It's a natural phenomenon.' No flexi-boarding, although school offers parents chance to buy 15 extra boarding nights a year per pupil. Girls' houses are stylish and bright – 'I want to make it like home from home,' a housemistress told us. Pupils eat breakfast, lunch and supper in the central mess hall.

The youngest pupils (years 7 and 8) are housed in Dunbar, a detached red-brick house with its own garden (loads of space to play football, jump about on the trampoline and catch up with friends). Lower school lessons take place in the main school, but the rest of the time pupils make their way back to the cosy environs of Dunbar. The new housemaster of Dunbar brings a wealth of experience

One boy told us that wearing the distinctive uniform had given him 'a sense of discipline' and that most pupils see it as 'really cool'

to the role, having been a head of science and pastoral tutor for many years. New additions on offer to the pupils in Dunbar this year include baking and drumming (not at the same time). Dunbar pupils have their own head boy and head girl and all pupils are divided into four 'watches,' (Port, Starboard, Forward and Aft), each with their own 'watch captain'. Broadly similar numbers of boys and girls, with slightly more boys than girls at present, although the numbers vary from year to year.

Background and atmosphere: School is set in 230 acres, in an area of outstanding natural beauty. Founded in 1917, Pangbourne's aim was to prepare boys for service in the Merchant Navy and Royal Navy. In 1969, however, the school was established as a charity, with a similar curriculum to other schools, and these days only two or three leavers a year join the Forces. Even so, Pangbourne prides itself on maintaining many of its original traditions and is the only school in the UK where pupils wear Royal Navy officer cadet uniform every day.

Pupils parade in their number one (ceremonial) uniforms eight times per year. Uniforms have to be immaculate and shoes polished. A guest of honour inspects the whole school on the vast parade ground and takes the salute as pupils march past. Head says Pangbourne's parades are an integral part of school life and help to develop self-discipline (pupils have to stand still for 15 to 20 minutes, often with a biting wind whistling across the parade ground), confidence, teamwork, leadership and a community spirit as well as attention to detail. When we visited pupils told us that the parades 'bring us together' as a school, while parents are hugely supportive (many turn up to watch every parade). 'It is very impressive,' a mother told us. 'It seems to give them great pride in what they do.' But despite the emphasis on teamwork, the school encourages youngsters to be individuals. 'We certainly aren't trying to put everyone in a mould,' one teacher told us.

Pangbourne has its own distinctive vocabulary, much of it nautical. Study bedrooms are cabins, house common rooms are gunrooms, the dining hall is the mess hall and casual clothes are always referred to as scruff. When the head arrived he introduced 'flag values' – kindness, integrity, industry, moral courage, selflessness, resilience and initiative. He sees these as the school's core values and pupils are urged to display them throughout their time at the school. Firm Christian ethos. Chapel is a key part of Pangbourne life, from 'congers' (congregational practice) to Saturday evensong for boarders. Many services are held in the Falkland Islands Memorial Chapel, opened by the Queen.

School has been fully co-ed since 1996 (it's now two-thirds boys and a third girls).

School is keen on student voice and pupils sit on food committee and pastoral welfare committee. Very inclusive 'Team Pangbourne' feel to the place and pupils are fiercely loyal to their school. Sixth formers can apply to train as peer mentors, helping others to cope with everything from time management and exam preparation to friendship issues and internet safety. Raft of prefects – called cadet captains – chosen by head and senior staff. Lower sixth pupils take leadership course in readiness for their responsibilities in the upper sixth and head reckons this has reaped dividends.

Pastoral care, well-being and discipline: Head says school's policies on drugs, alcohol, cigarettes and knives are 'crystal clear.' Any pupil caught using, selling or possessing drugs 'can expect to be expelled,' he says, though 'every case is treated on its merits.' School devotes a lot of time to PHSCE and is strict about boy-girl relationships – PDAs banned. Sixth formers have their own bar (Medway), which is open for soft drinks on Thursday evenings and pizzas and beer/lager (strictly limited) on Saturday nights. In 2017, the college's mobile phone policy was reviewed and updated by pupils, and 'ensures appropriate use in free times and in specific areas of school'.

A firm believer in 'lifelong learning,' he recently took up the flute again after a 25 year gap, passed his grade 8 with ease and plays in the school orchestra

Staff believe that the school's strict uniform policy is a 'great leveller.' Pupils must need hefty trunks to pack all their kit though – list includes number one uniform (jacket, trousers/shirt and cap with badge for Sundays and ceremonies), number two uniform for every day (trousers/skirt, navy jersey, epaulettes, beret and Dr Martens shoes), and recreational rig (known as 'rec rig') for social occasions and away matches. And that's before they even think of throwing in games kit and weekend clothes.

Pupils say that Pangbourne is 'a caring, friendly school' and that it's easy to settle in. One boy told us that wearing the distinctive uniform had given him 'a sense of discipline' and that most pupils see it as 'really cool.' Asked whether it's a snooty school, sixth formers said 'definitely not.' Other pupil comments during our visit included 'people come out of their shells here,' 'it makes you really independent' and 'it prepares you for life outside.'

Pupils and parents: Fleet of minibuses brings day pupils in from as far afield as Basingstoke, Newbury and Highclere. New bus routes in 2018 will come from Henley-On-Thames, Wargrave and Twyford. Majority of boarders live within an hour's drive. Around eight per cent from overseas (including the Far East and Germany). Despite school's naval associations, only 20 youngsters from Forces families. Former pupils include the late film director Ken Russell, Olympic gold and silver medallist sailor Andrew (Bart) Simpson (a sailing foundation was set up in his name after he drowned whilst training for the America's Cup), motorcycle racer Mike Hailwood, hedge fund founder David Harding, former Second Sea Lord Admiral Sir Michael Layard and Dazed & Confused founder and journalist Jefferson Hack.

Pangbourne prides itself on taking pupils 'from a broad spectrum of ability.' A parent told us: 'Pangbourne isn't known for being an academic school but the opportunities are there for academic children and they do really well. At the same time the school brings out the best in those for whom studying isn't so easy. Every child seems to have their chance in the sun.' School says it selects as much on character and suitability as academic criteria and is looking for youngsters who will throw themselves into Pangbourne life and make a difference. The only children the school might turn away, says the head, are those whose learning difficulties are 'too profound for us to cope with' or youngsters with 'behaviour issues.'

Entrance: Pupils come from a host of state and prep schools, including Brockhurst, Moulsford, Thorngrove, St Andrew's, Pangbourne and many more. Main entry points are at 11, 13 and 16. At 11 and 13, admission is by school's own entrance exam or CE (interview and head's report taken into account too). Pupils joining sixth form (up to 20 a year) must have at least five GCSE passes, including English and maths.

Exit: A small number leave after GCSEs, mainly to do subjects not offered by Pangbourne, or as one pupil told us wryly, 'because they want more free time'. Around 90 per cent go on to university and are encouraged to be aspirational when they apply, with a high proportion getting their 'firm choice' and sometimes one or two a year to Oxbridge. Popular destinations in 2017 included Bristol, Exeter, Birmingham and Leeds. The rest start full-time work (one boy recently went straight to aviation college to do his commercial pilot's training), with a handful going into the Forces.

Money matters: 'We're not a rich school,' the bursar told us, although in preparation for its centenary in 2017, many buildings were upgraded. Means-tested bursaries available (from 10 per cent to 100 per cent) and a variety of scholarships (including academic, music and sport) at each entry point.

Remarks: A small and distinctive school that puts huge emphasis on self-discipline, teamwork and leadership. Caring and supportive, Pangbourne buzzes with activity and encourages every pupil to have a go and get involved.

Papplewick School

35

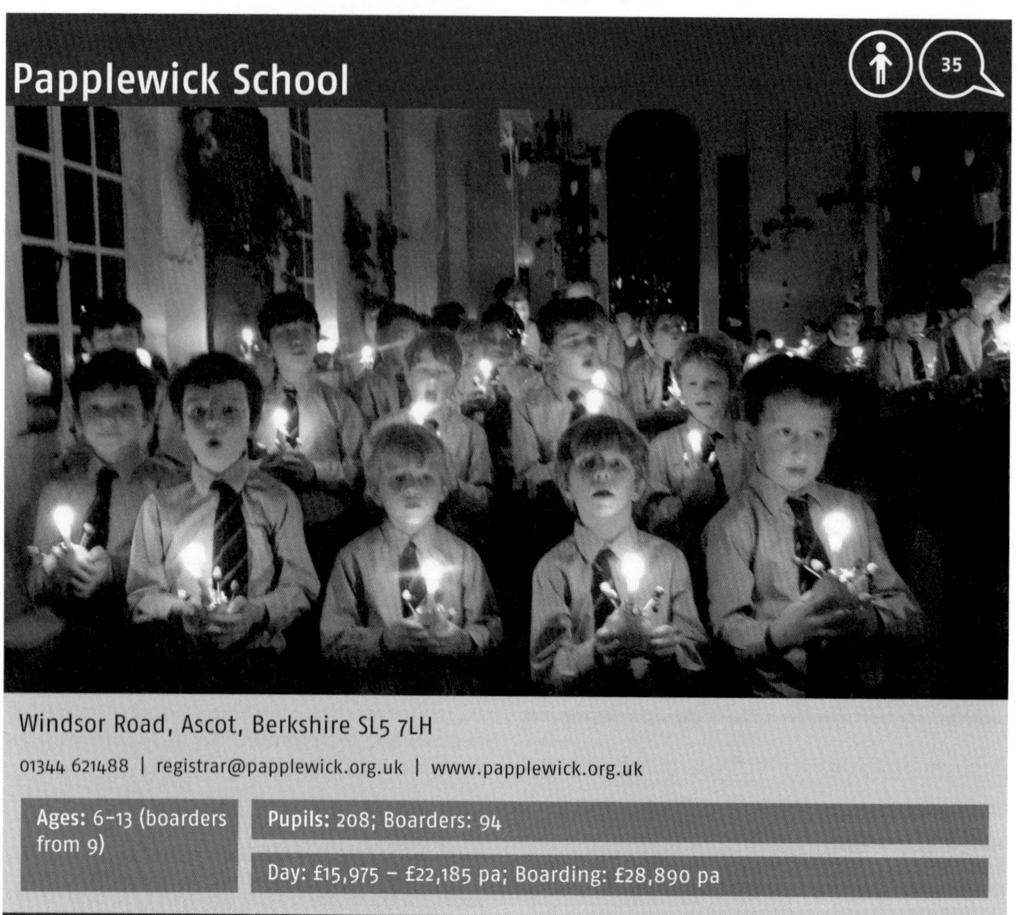

Windsor Road, Ascot, Berkshire SL5 7LH

01344 621488 | registrar@papplewick.org.uk | www.papplewick.org.uk

Ages: 6–13 (boarders from 9)

Pupils: 208; Boarders: 94

Day: £15,975 – £22,185 pa; Boarding: £28,890 pa

Headmaster: Since 2004 Tom Bunbury BA PGCE (50s). Educated at Woodcote House Prep and Millfield before heading to read law at Durham and ultimately returning to Woodcote to try his hand at teaching. Landed at Papplewick in 1993 after completing PGCE at Homerton College Cambridge, and has remained ever since. Route to headship included spells as head of maths, housemaster and deputy head.

Quite the most genuinely charming head teacher we have ever met. Jolly (we were reliably informed by a pupil that 'head's detentions are actually fun') yet utterly sincere; a wry smile never far from his face. At heart an educator in the most holistic sense: he speaks of the 'luxury of inculcating the values required to be a really good human being' upon his young proteges and turning them into 'leaders...but compassionate ones'. 'Kindness' is also a buzz word around here. We don't doubt that under his influence they emerge with such attributes in spades. Firm believer that 'prep school should be fun – but with some really high standards.' Parents say that he 'knows every boy' and is 'headmaster first, businessman second'. Sounds like a winning formula to us. During his tenure has made enormous investment in the staff team (evidenced by eyewatering fees) – says 'there's genuinely not a weak link'.

Lives on site with (equally delightful) wife Sallie and their four children – two girls who attend The Marist School in Ascot, one boy at Bradfield College and another still at Papplewick. Escapes in the holidays to bolt-hole on the Isle of Wight.

Entrance: School 'passionately non-selective – but character counts', says head, as do reports from former schools, and no offer will be forthcoming 'if there are any worries on a behavioural front'. School structure is an 'inverse pyramid'. Up to 16 boys join year 2 from a mixture of local pre-preps (Upton House, Coworth, Lambrook) and state primaries. Class splits into two smaller forms in year 3 when more come from the surrounding areas and there's another significant intake into year 4 when the London boys start to appear, transported by the Papplewick Express that whisks them away from the academic pressure-cookers of west London (stops are in Brook Green and Chiswick) in a mere 40 minutes. A good handful, public school places already in hand, join in years 7 and 8 and, with the help of friendly peer mentors who get in touch over the summer, often arranging to get together before school starts, 'integrate seamlessly,' according to parents. Greater emphasis on total size of school ('it's a conscious decision to remain just 200 strong so everyone knows one another,' says head) than on individual form sizes.

Exit: Feeds all the biggies – Eton takes the largest number then Harrow, Charterhouse, Winchester and Wellington as well as all the other great and good in smaller numbers. Between 10 and 15 scholarships most years (11 in 2017), across the board from academic to sport and art, with a King's Scholarship to Eton not considered an anomaly (there were two, in fact, in 2017). Anyone ever sufficiently unconvinced by the boarding experience that they head to day school? Rarely. Occasional 11+ exits to eg Hampton, Merchant Taylors', RGS Guildford or the odd grammar school are 'driven mainly by parents,' says head.

Remarks: We're trying not to think of Papplewick as the Prince Harry of the school world but if it were human you'd definitely be attracted to its quirkiness, sense of humour, wit and kindness (may we add slightly dishevelled appearance?) rather than any trace of flawless beauty. A surprisingly urban campus directly opposite Ascot racecourse, with 'the square' – a concrete playground littered with lethal looking ripsticks and scooters (anyone for 'ripstick wars' at break?) at its heart, surrounded by a jumble of buildings of various architectural styles. None of the dreaming spires, endlessly rolling playing fields or pristine topiary boasted by some of the local competition, but things are getting smarter with the addition of a new, purpose built year 8 boarding house atop two year 5 classrooms (opening September 2018) and the airy newish entrance hall: part entertainment space, part art gallery to showcase boys' masterpieces. And anyway, Papplewick parents say they value 'culture and staff above new facilities'.

If the school were human you'd definitely be attracted to its quirkiness, sense of humour, wit and kindness (may we add slightly dishevelled appearance?)

Despite the rather ramshackle – and in some parts shabby – school fabric, all mod cons are incongruously present and correct: a gleaming fleet of Macs; music technology suite and high-tech language labs; large sports hall; on site pool with retractable cover; and music practice rooms galore. But it's the innately confident buzz at Papplewick that blows any comparison with more self-consciously pristine schools out of the water. Boys whizzing past on scooters? Check. Teachers nonchalantly strolling around in fancy dress for a themed language day (the first time we've ever been introduced to a teacher as 'the school dragon')? Yup. Seven year-olds casually sporting living, breathing

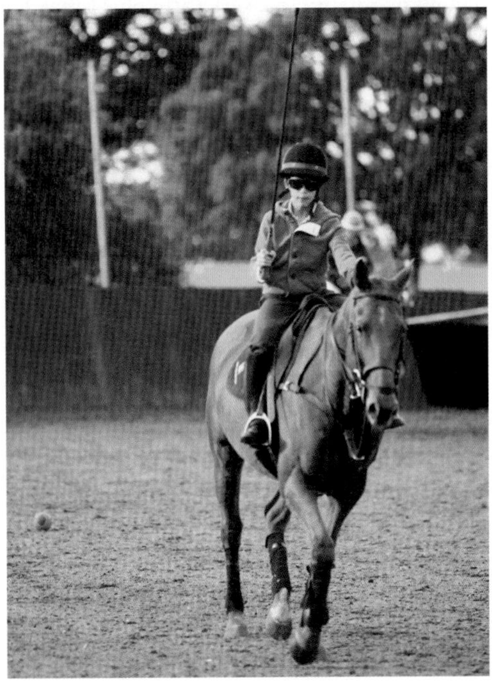

royal pythons around their necks? Well, yes – and more of that later. 'Infused with kindness and understanding,' said one happy parent. Another: 'Teaching is just a small part of what Papplewick is all about'.

Parents 'a pretty jolly interesting bunch,' according to head. Plenty of first time buyers take away any sense of old school stuffiness, with a healthy mix of entrepreneurs, professionals and dual income families thrown in with the more trad boarding prep sort. Boys unassumingly charming and totally down to earth – not a plum in mouth to be found. It's been a while since we've been asked over lunch whether we have any brothers and sisters or pets, but ask they did with a disarming innocence and then told us all about theirs. No script or message, just good old fashioned small talk, and parents love the way their children's eccentricities and individual character traits are embraced.

'We genuinely don't want to be known for anything in particular', says head and whereas some boys' preps scream sporting machismo from the moment you arrive, Papplewick has the nonchalant air of an all-rounder about it ('we are absolutely a boys' school to our core – but not macho,' says head). Up to 16 pupils per class, with year 2 almost exclusively class taught, specialist teaching introduced in years 3 to 5, and years 6 to 8 benefiting from a tutor (matched to boy according to shared interests) to guide them through their last three years in school from both academic and pastoral perspectives. 'Deliberately' trad curriculum ('it's evolution not revolution here') including French (taught by a native speaker), Latin plus Greek for scholarship candidates. It's a six day a week timetable with Saturday school, followed by assembly, chapel and sports fixtures. Never fear that you'll barely see your boy at weekends, though – parents, siblings and even grandmas and grandads are invited to join for proceedings from chapel onwards, including lunch which 'makes for a big family feel,' says head.

With such an elite list of destination schools, surely there must be some sneaky outside tutoring afoot? Not much, apparently, and it's 'actively discouraged', according to school. Parents say 'they just don't feel that pressure'. Preparation for the pre-test is covered in English and maths and 'thinking skills', including verbal and non-verbal reasoning, is on curriculum in year 5. 'What we do in school is sufficient,' says head. 'There are many layers of preparation for common entrance and above all you need to be interesting to get into Eton or Winchester. You can't tutor that.' Well said. Parents concur that 'there's real intellectual rigour' in the upper years. Former prep school headmaster comes in to brush up boys' interview skills just to be on the safe side, though.

There are 'lots of fun and games' right up until bedtime, when tutors scoop up their charges for hot chocolate and a chat about the day

Not an obvious choice of school for a child with anything above mild to very moderate SEN. All pupils screened for dyslexia with a small number benefiting from two additional support lessons per week (charged as extra). 'We don't write anyone off', director of studies told us – 'there's no sense of not being able to do it and our potential scholars pull up the 50 per cent CE candidates'.

Boarding compulsory – absolutely no exceptions – from the summer term of year 6, with a few full, part-time or occasional boarders beforehand in years 5 and 6. Official visiting is Wednesday afternoon but it's a 'modern, family friendly model of boarding' these days according to head and 'parents can drop in whenever – we make sure they know they're not being a pain'. A compulsory, non-stop merry-go-round of activities in the first two weeks of boarding life wards off homesickness and boarding parents report that thereafter, although allowed mobile phones in the evenings, their offspring are 'too busy to call home'. There are 'lots of fun and games' right up until bedtime, when tutors scoop up their charges for hot chocolate and a chat about the day. On top of that, 'babies and puppies help,' says head, and with two-thirds of staff living on site, there are plenty of each. Photos of matches and other activities emailed to parents unable to make it in person. Colourful, cheery dorms, walls adorned with murals of snowboarders and surfers, are reached via a narrow staircase in the main school building. Unusually for boys, it seems to be cool here to have plenty of personal effects around your bed, although that might just be because storage is minimal – just a few hooks behind the bed, with 'home clothes' kept in a separate location and handed out by matron as needed. Importantly, boys know exactly who to call if they need an 'outside listener' – posters are prominently positioned in each dorm. Full boarders are treated to outings eg Thorpe Park, Gravity Force or the cinema on Sundays, or are just able to 'chill out'. Socials with Heathfield, St Mary's and Godstowe are termly highlights.

'Very good' drama, according to pupils and parents, with recent productions including A Christmas Carol and Macbeth and all parts covered by boys (our guide was apparently 'terrifying' as Lady Macbeth). New director of music (Classic FM's 2017 Music Teacher of the Year, no less) is breathing new life into the department. All year

4s now learn whole class recorder and year 5s a brass instrument. African drumming's another new addition to the music curriculum, inspired by music director's recent past teaching in an inner London school. Music technology on curriculum for all in years 7 and 8. On top of all the funky stuff that's going on there are three choirs – non-selective for the younger pupils, and the first of which sings in chapel every morning. Wind and brass bands plus a string ensemble give the 70 per cent of pupils taking peripatetic music lessons the chance to brush up their performance skills.

Over 600 fixtures a year on the sporting calendar with 'opportunities for all' and A to D or sometimes E teams fielded most weeks. 'Being in the A team is really played down', said one parent, 'to encourage kindness'. A legacy of a former ex-pro director of sport, it's football rather than rugby in the long Michaelmas term ('it plays to our international strengths', says director of sport – 'our Spanish boys, for example, have never picked up a cricket bat before they come here') followed by rugby then cricket, but there's also croquet (including fixtures), golf and basketball. Boys say 'it's quite important for us to win', but school feels that its 60 per cent win/draw hit rate is just the ticket to teach boys how to lose with humility too.

And so to extracurricular. In true Papplewick style this is stuff boys' dreams are made on. There are, of course, other schools that can match the karate, fencing, chess, Airfix and Lego activities on offer here. Perhaps a few can also offer shooting and polo (played off site). But we are yet to find another that can boast herpetology – known to Papplewickians as 'snake club.' Less of a club and more of a school obsession, herpetology takes place in a science lab with wall-to-wall cages homing reptiles of all shapes and sizes, plus the crickets and new born chicks needed to feed them. When we visited, the club was in the ongoing process of breeding 'the most orange' snakes (and bearded dragons, of which they hatch around 40 per year) possible. Breaks and lunch times see boys in their droves head off to handle and care for their reptiles – 'these are the eco warriors of the future,' we were told. True enthusiasts are presented with the covetable 'herpetology colours' – a tie featuring a serpent coiling one of its stripes. Well if that doesn't make a boy interesting enough to nail the Eton interview, we're not sure what will.

The Pilgrims' School

C of E 36

3 The Close, Winchester, Hampshire SO23 9LT

01962 854189 | admissions@pilgrims-school.co.uk | www.thepilgrims-school.co.uk

Ages: 4-13 (boarders from year 4)

Pupils: 260; Boarders: 90 full

Day: £10,740 – £18,690 pa; Boarding: £23,580 pa; Choral scholar £14,148 pa

Head: Since 2015, Tom Burden (40s), previously head of Hereward House in London. Originating from the Isle of Wight, he won a scholarship to Oxford to study theology. Teaching after graduating while considering careers, he realised that education was for him and so stayed for five years at Alleyn Court in Southend. He followed this with five years at Lockers Park boarding prep in Hertfordshire, as head of English, in charge of scholarships and doing lots of sports coaching. He 'loved every minute', realising 'that boys should be boys, enjoy their precious childhood and grow through being trusted with responsibilities'. A sportsman and fanatic about Southampton FC, fascinated by ecclesiastical gothic architecture, his passion is nonetheless for education. He believes that Pilgrims' is first and foremost an all round academic prep school with strong sport, music and other activities, which happens to have two professional choirs. There is no hierarchy in the school even though the choristers – who sing in Winchester Cathedral – and quiristers – who sing in Winchester College Chapel – rank among the best in the country. He is adamant that these years, which will give boys the memories and foundations for their whole lives, should inspiring and enjoyable as well as industrious for every boy in the school.

Entrance: Boys are assessed in individual taster days, designed as much to gauge whether the boy will take to Pilgrims' life as to establish educational ability. Pilgrims' is selective but interested in boys who will do well there rather than just academia alone. Entry to the pre-prep is by fun activity mornings, and there are 10 or so places available at 7+and 8+, and a few at 11+ for preparation for senior school entry at 13+. Boarding is from 8 and boys can come in for trial stays.

Applicants for the choral scholarships are auditioned in November and voice trials include a prepared piece, aural tests designed for those who may not have musical experience and academic assessment. Most choristers and quiristers join in years 4 and 5. Boys come from far and wide, including abroad, as well as from local nurseries, primaries and independent schools.

Exit: Pilgrims is not the prep school for Winchester but enough families see it as a route for there to be a separate form in year 8. Winchester exams are earlier and different from common entrance, which accounts for another form, as well a third group for scholarship candidates. Prepares scholarship boys are very specifically and successfully for the academic requirements of Eton, Winchester, Radley, Charterhouse, Sherborne and other major schools, as well as the local King Edward VI and Portsmouth Grammar. Unsurprisingly, music awards and exhibitions are also plentiful.

Remarks: Strong academically with Latin as well as French, which is started from reception and later benefits from trips to France. Science in impressive labs, with some serious scholars on our visit assiduously absorbed writing down observations on an experiment. Teaching looked to be fun and boys clearly enjoyed an English lesson while a maths group we saw was involved in establishing the purpose behind algebraic calculations and definitely getting the point. The head says he has struck lucky in having remarkable teachers. Art, including some pottery, computing and CDT all well equipped too. Parents report pupils work conscientiously and one commented that the school is right for all of her boys although they are widely different in abilities and inclinations. SEN stepped up recently with screening from the beginning with plenty of expert support on hand, with the occasional pupil needing one-to-one but more benefiting from in class support. Plenty of prep but boys taught not to exceed allotted time for it, one parent gratefully explained. The pre-prep has its own new purpose built centre tucked lovingly in between the school and the deanery garden, which is generously open to them as a forest school, clearly much enjoyed by the muddy group we saw. Though pre-prep is a separate unit, it feels cosily within the main school and its staff value sharing the common room above it, which definitely facilitates coordination of curriculum and info.

Dormitories must be the nicest anywhere. Cunningly themed rooms amazingly decorated – the Beano room even has comic strips revealed when the blinds go down

Music is central to the curriculum with pretty distinguished senior and junior choirs and chamber choir, as well as the two professional choirs. A huge orchestra was successfully tackling Beethoven 'on sight' in the medieval Pilgrims' Hall (also used for assemblies) when we visited, while the Big Band was swinging away in the music department. Nearly everyone learns an instrument and the boys said that both music and games are 'cool' here. Lots of opportunities for small groups and supervised practice for boarders. Music school in the converted stables bulging with pianos (even one tucked into

a practice cupboard under the stairs), rehearsal space and equipment apart from designated chorister rehearsal room. The high musical standard enhances productions such as the Mikado. Drama is on the curriculum, but there are masses of events like the Christmas cabaret as well. Other activities range from Latin and Greek speaking workshops and trips abroad to wetter pursuits such as wakeboarding and angling.

For a smallish school Pilgrims' fields an astonishing number of teams. Sport is cleverly timetabled so that choristers do not miss main sports for rehearsal, though sometimes musical team players have to bow out for a professional engagement. Football boasts 20 and rugby 18 teams for the various different age groups while cricket has nine, though not all play very frequently. Lots of sporting activities, sailing, hockey, water polo, though as yet listed building planning has prevented cover for the outdoor pool. Boys also get plenty of supervised kick about time on games pitches where, one pointed out, Henry VIII might have watched events from Wolvesey Castle, which forms a stunning backdrop.

Being in the middle of the close in largely medieval buildings, Pilgrims' has managed to expand into three attractive courtyards, one grassed with a pretty little pepper pot venue for small performances, one Astroturfed for play with a climbing wall, and one tarmac, where parents collect day boys and mingle with boarders up to all sorts of intriguing after-school pastimes. Lovely light and spacious purpose built classrooms and library cleverly harmonise on the outside with the medieval and Georgian close.

Pastoral care is mainly through form teachers until the last three years, when boys are in tutor groups of up to nine. Fortnightly progress bulletins to parents now 'thankfully online', said one parent, no longer drowning in paper. Very prompt action on behavioural and other issues with parents kept in the loop.

Boarding, 90 strong but expanding by parental demand, is available from year 4. The two houses originate from the choristers' and quiristers' needs, which form the core of boarding life. The increased number of main school boarders means that activities, which can sometimes be a little denuded by choral demands in the lower years, will become more viable. Dormitories must be the nicest anywhere. Six or eight on bunk beds with cunningly themed rooms amazingly decorated – the Beano room even has comic strips revealed when the blinds go down. Pristine decoration, though the head feels they should not be too unnaturally tidy. Teaching houseparents, with their own boys in school, make it seem like a family, and three professional nurses are all approachable, parents say, and happy to keep in touch over the smallest thing. Particular concern given to supporting troubled or

anxious pupils to the extent of appointing a new director of well-being, available to all. Parents can visit whenever and apart from the demands of the choirs and overseas boarders it is all pretty flexible. Wrap-round care from breakfast with boarders and supervised prep until 8pm for families that need it for a 'small fee'. Choristers who have to stay on over Christmas and Easter for choir weeks get a pretty good time as well as working hard and one mother told me her son couldn't wait for his first Christmas.

Uniform is informal and comfortable with jerseys, red for choristers and blue for quiristers, while year 8s wear hairy tweed jackets. Food ok with formal dining and grace before meals as well as a much-loved new tuck shop. Parents from all walks though still pretty well to do, with a good sprinkling of musical families. Boarders from abroad (10 per cent), Hong Kong etc plus some expats. Past pupils include Patrick Gale, Jack Dee, Jon Snow and four BBC choirboys of the year since 2000, with at least one finalist almost every year.

Choral scholars get 40 per cent off fees and free tuition on one instrument. Bursaries and music awards means-tested up to 100 per cent, with first school uniform free to holders.

Altogether a stunning and distinctive school, gracefully combining an up-to-date outlook with ancient traditions, now becoming more cohesive and adventurous under Mr Burden's guidance. There's something special here for almost every boy.

Queen Anne's School

37

6 Henley Road, Caversham, Reading, Berkshire RG4 6DX

01189 187300 | admissions@qas.org.uk | www.qas.org.uk

Ages: 11–18

Pupils: 459; sixth form: 128; Boarders: 134

Day: £23,205 pa; Boarding: £34,215 pa

Headmistress: Since 2006, Julia Harrington BA, NPQH (50s), previously deputy head at Prior's Field School. Mrs H comes from a family of teachers, was educated at a grammar school in Lydney and studied history and politics at Exeter. Worked in the media and then decided to train as a teacher and psychodynamic counsellor. As a child she 'wanted to be a vet' but was told that 'girls didn't do jobs like that'. You don't need a qualification in counselling to see that this experience might have shaped her as an adult.

Mrs Harrington is a head who doesn't just sit back and let the same old tried and trusted methods do their best. She keeps up with the latest neuroscience research into how people learn, working with university psychology departments at Reading and Oxford. It's certainly heady stuff; never before have we heard the word 'amygdala' used so many times in one conversation. She stresses the importance of environment and mindset, 'Instead of saying, "I can't do this", we want girls to say, "Why not me?"' To this end she is working with preps so that girls don't come into senior school already thinking, for instance, that they're 'rubbish at maths.'

Let us say with admiration that the teenage brain is, apparently, not a mystery to this head. 'I tell the girls, the reason you want to keep checking your phones or Facebook is for the dopamine hit. If you understand the brain then you can give a reason for behaviour. Girls on the social front are hardwired to conform and it's this that can lead to behaviour like saving seats or being unkind. We challenge this by making girls aware of what they're doing and why.' Mrs H has the zeal of the convert and her enthusiasm is infectious, but before we got too carried away on the crest of a cortex we wanted to know whether she was in danger of treating her school like a laboratory. 'Not at all. I always ask, so what? How can this research help our girls?'

Mrs Harrington enjoys running but 'doesn't find it easy', and is learning Mandarin at Saturday morning classes alongside QA parents. Lives on site with her husband, who works in IT for a cancer research charity, and has three adult children (doctor, barrister, nuclear scientist. Yes, really). Favourite book would be, we assumed, some weighty work of neuroscience. It's not, well not quite. The Little Book of Thunks is a compendium of brain challenging questions that she likes to use in assembly. Favourite childhood read is good old Enid B's Five at Finneston Farm.

Academic matters: In 2017, 54 per cent A*-A/9-7 at GCSE. Very good results in individual sciences and IGCSE maths but languages are trailing a bit. At A level, 36 per cent A*/A, 66 per cent A*-B, and again the sciences and maths are strongest with French still in dernier place. New head of modern foreign languages appointed.

Teaching methods are developed through the school's Life and Learning programme and staff are encouraged to apply their knowledge of the teenage brain to develop 'brain friendly lessons'. Such educational initiatives notwithstanding, teaching we observed was reassuringly similar to what we see in good schools everywhere – small classes, attentive pupils, smartboards, plenty of Q and A. The World Cup based maths lesson we witnessed was described by the teacher as 'light relief' after summer exams and looked like a lot of fun. As Mrs Harrington explained, 'by providing a complex real world mathematical challenge but framing it as an ethical conundrum,' girls are 'encouraged to take risks suggesting competing solutions to find the most ethical outcome.' In the smart and very well equipped biology lab we were impressed by the lack of squeamish squeaking as scalpel wielding as pupils prepared to dissect hearts. Girls are set in core subjects following the first half term in year 7. Lessons are 40 minutes long, doubles for eg languages, maths and science.

Our year 9 guides had obviously been paying attention to the head and were keen to tell us that 'striving' was very important at their school. 'We're not put under pressure but teachers help us strive to achieve our very best.' One or two parents mutter that they would like their daughters to be pushed to strive a bit harder, but general consensus is that school has balance about right.

Heaps of praise for excellent individual attention, subject support and UCAS advice in the sixth form but we hear that girls who don't want to go to university feel rather sidelined. School says that recent pupils who haven't gone on to university have taken up places at RADA, Central St Martins and the Deliotte Undergraduate Training Programme.

SEN support mostly provided in class; individual sessions also available if necessary. EAL taught in place of modern foreign languages or Latin; all international pupils take English language and literature GCSE.

Games, options, the arts: At the time of our visit, the performing arts centre was being fitted out for the lower school production of Peter Pan (flying scenes to be done with puppets) and we enjoyed chatting to some very excited cast members. What would they do with a million pounds to spend on their school, we asked? 'We'd build a theatre like the one in Glee!' they cried. These young actors felt the school would benefit from bigger, better performing arts facilities but, though smallish, their current theatre lacked for nothing as far as we could see.

International students love to cook up a taste of home, and Ocado delivers esoteric ingredients not to be had in Caversham

Plenty of options for the musical – choirs, ensembles, swing band and orchestras plus an exciting programme of visiting professionals, not only from the world of the arts but also science and business, all part of a programme called World Class in Class. The head is keen for girls to 'see and know excellence' and also to demystify it. 'They meet these talented people and discover that they are also ordinary human beings who work very hard.'

Sloping games field is apparently a bit of an uphill struggle in lacrosse matches (it's the C team that gets to play on the steepest bit) but such hardships are obviously character building since QA lax is pretty fierce and successful. Main rival is Downe House. Excellent sports facilities, including 25m pool, fitness suite, dance studio, climbing wall plus loads of tennis and netball courts mean that there's something for everyone – even ballroom dancing with The Oratory boys. Plenty of horsey stuff, too, including riding and polo clubs and the annual

Queen Anne's Grass Roots and Inter-Schools' Show Jumping Competition.

Boarding: All seven boarding houses are tip top – these are the bases for day girls as well – and quite the smartest we've seen. Purpose built, modern and (very) brightly furnished (pink and blue chenille sofas and bucket chairs) and carpeted in house colours. Student artworks decorate the walls and common rooms, as does an abundance of bunting. No poky kitchenettes here; huge kitchens with all the kit are a great social hub. The large fridges are filled with Waitrose bags – older girls may go down the road to this and other local emporia in groups. International students love to cook up a taste of home, and luckily Ocado delivers any esoteric ingredients not to be had for ready money in Caversham. Girls are challenged to produce meals on a budget, they bake cakes for charity sales and teach each other favourite dishes. They also host dinner parties and invite chaps from nearby schools.

Regular socials with nearby schools – mainly The Oratory and Shiplake. Parents say that there's not much to persuade older girls to stay at the weekend and most prefer to head for home.

Upper sixth day and boarding girls are based in Michell, a house that is separate from the main cluster of buildings, affording privacy and a degree of independence. Many older day girls drive in and can park on site.

Background and atmosphere: Built on 34 acres of primest Caversham (or 'Caversham actually,' as it's known by residents. It may be just over the bridge from Reading but mix the two up at your peril). Handsome Victorian brick pile set in immaculate lawns with, at the time of our visit, groups of girls dotted decoratively about, reading in the sunshine. Reception hall and offices are elegant, rather in the smart country hotel style; vibrant contemporary stained glass panels in the front door are the first hint that this school may be traditional, but with a modern twist.

Atmospheric galleried chapel now only accommodates everyone when upper years are on study leave. Chapel services for lower and upper school several times a week and regular hymn practice; female chaplain recently appointed. Brand new sixth form centre, The Space, also includes a digital library, a restaurant for staff and pupils and Kirstoff's at Café 6. Meal times are staggered and those who need to be at clubs and activities get packed lunches or can collect a deli-style lunchbox, and the food got a moderate thumbs up. Apparently breakfasts are fantastic and fish and chips on Friday is top lunch. Sixth formers have their own rather cool café in an old hall (former gymnasium); other years can get lunch there on Saturdays – much friendlier than having to eat in a half empty dining room.

Queen Anne's is part of the Grey Coat Hospital Foundation (other schools include Grey Coat Hospital, Emanuel, Sutton Valence and Westminster City School) and was established on its current site in 1894. Historic links with Westminster and the Abbey remain.

The World Cup based maths lesson we witnessed was described by the teacher as 'light relief' after summer exams and looked like a lot of fun

Website and marketing material are big on warm and fuzzy but rather low on boring old facts such as exam results by subject. We don't want to come over all Gradgrind but sometimes facts are necessary. Especially when parents or grandparents are making expensive decisions. The prospectus declares that the school is 'full of bubbly, smiley and enthusiastic people'. While we can't argue with that (actually, we might pick a fight with 'bubbly': it's usually an adjective of last resort and rarely applied to an intellectual equal), one can't help pondering whether all the buzz words – resilience; empowerment; brain plasticity; synthesis – might put off those who just want to know exactly what you get for boarding fees of over 10 grand a term. Stick with it, we say, it's all here and a bit more too.

Pastoral care, well-being and discipline: Day girls have a desk and often a bed and can stay over at short notice – flexi and weekly boarding options much appreciated by parents. It's a long day (home at 6.30pm) but prep is done under supervision in houses and tea is provided. After 4.30pm it's clubs and, if necessary, subject clinics; girls choose a minimum of three clubs from an enticing range of sporting and cultural options.

Parents told us that pastoral care is excellent, and our guides loved the strong inter-year group relations; the older girls 'are like big sisters'. Girls told us that there are no cliques and that everybody gets a chance to shine in drama, sport and music. Sixth formers have smart single en-suite study bedrooms. As we observed and several parents confirmed, university accommodation is sometimes a let down after this.

Recent drive to spruce up uniform not entirely popular with older pupils but has gone down well with younger pupils and parents. Sleeveless red V neck pullovers, white shirts, blazers and, according to our guides, socks, not tights, even in winter, 'In the snow!' Perhaps there was a bit of dramatic licence here, since school says it isn't the case. Staff are 'very' vigilant about skirt lengths, apparently. Sixth formers wear the dreaded 'smart business' mufti. Distinctive red hooded cloaks are no longer mandatory but still used at biennial service of thanksgiving at Westminster Abbey, carol services and other special occasions. They're also rather photogenic, especially in the snow, and as a result are more frequently seen in marketing material than in real life. Girls we spoke to thought the school rules were 'strict but fair. Apart from the socks.'

Pupils and parents: Generally rather well-heeled. Majority local, boarders mostly live around an hour away. Increasing numbers from London who see it as a positive and also convenient (only 25 mins to Paddington) alternative to metropolitan school rat race. International students from over 15 countries seem to integrate well and UK girls get invitations to plenty of exotic sleepovers. Famous old girls include Posy Simmonds, Jenny Seagrove and the real Joan Hunter Dunn, immortalised by John Betjeman.

Entrance: Prospective pupils (from wide range of local preps and state primaries) are encouraged to attend a taster day and overnight stay. Assessment for entry at 11+ consists of tests in maths, English, verbal and non-verbal reasoning and a group interview. For entry to the sixth form students sit an exam and will need a minimum of six GCSEs at grade C/4 or above (including English and maths) and B/6 in subjects to be studied at A level

Exit: Some 30 per cent depart after GCSEs to local colleges or co-ed sixth forms. Those who stay for A levels go on to respectable universities including Bristol, St Andrews, Nottingham and Leeds. Wide range of subjects (law, medicine, engineering, art and drama) testament to strengths in all areas. Two medics in 2017 and two to apprenticeships, at Ernst & Young and Coca-Cola.

Money matters: Boarding fees broadly in line with home counties compatriots. Day fees are good value considering girls get extended school day and thus some of the boarding perks. Art, music, drama, sports and all-rounder scholarships at 11+ and 13+. Will help in cases of hardship.

Remarks: A welcoming, dynamic and forward-thinking school. Delivers academically but there's much more than that to an education at Queen Anne's. Who would it suit? We leave the answer to Mrs Harrington: 'When parents ask what kind of girl is a Queen Anne's girl, I answer that I hope there never is one, they are all individuals.'

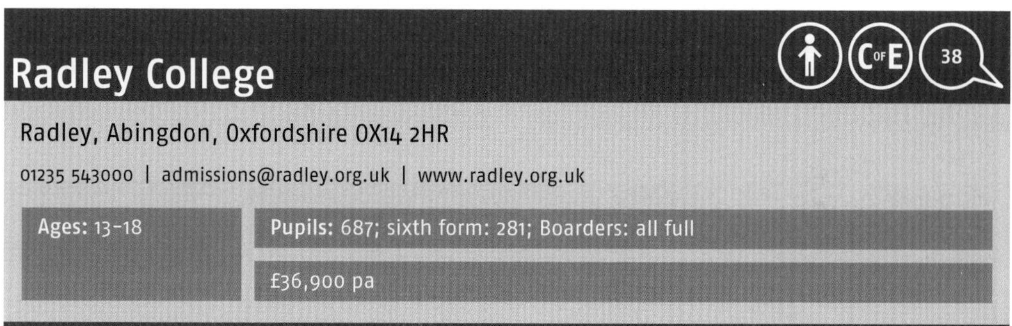

Radley College
C of E
38
Radley, Abingdon, Oxfordshire OX14 2HR
01235 543000 | admissions@radley.org.uk | www.radley.org.uk
Ages: 13-18
Pupils: 687; sixth form: 281; Boarders: all full
£36,900 pa

Warden: Since 2014, John Moule MA (40s), previously head of Bedford School. Educated at a Telford comprehensive and sixth form college, he won a history scholarship to Lady Margaret Hall, Oxford and left with a first. Refreshingly atypical background for a post like this. Taught history and politics at Dean Close, Cheltenham, moved to Stowe as head of history and became housemaster, then senior housemaster. Perhaps it's Radley's proximity to Oxford but we thought Mr Moule had a little of Laurence Fox's (aka Sgt Hathaway in Lewis) lean, pale intensity. This impression only somewhat dampened when we learnt that pallor was a result of his 'feeling under the weather'.

He seems to have made a very favourable impression and was described to us as a 'brilliant' speaker, able to hold an audience of parents and boys simultaneously. 'He's very visible and really involved' one mother told us, 'He drops into Socials (Radley-speak for boarding house) and plays chess with the boys.'

Married with three children, his eldest daughter is a veterinary student, his son is finishing A levels at Bedford School and the youngest is at a girls' day school nearby. Having worked in medical research his wife completed a second degree in maths and now divides her time between the many and varied duties of a head's spouse and teaching at a school in Oxford.

Like so many heads Mr Moule claims to have 'fallen' into teaching. (Watch out, there must be a huge and cunningly disguised hole somewhere designed for just this purpose.) It goes like this. He was all set to study for a PhD in 16th century English theological history but the grant-awarding bodies had other plans and chose this moment to withdraw the financial support that had hitherto been awarded to arts students with first class degrees, 'You could say that I was saved by lack of funds'. At a loose end in Oxford, someone inevitably suggested he try teaching. 'I'd never set foot in an independent school but after two weeks I knew it was right.'

Of course Mr Moule is convinced of the benefits of a full boarding school. 'It fosters strength of character and independence'. He goes on, 'The 24 hour culture is hugely creative, it allows teachers to develop boys' genuine interests beyond the classroom.' He describes the 'powerful' triangle formed by the school, the parents and the boy, 'all have to buy into it', he says. For fee paying parents that is both metaphorically and literally the case.

Since becoming warden Mr Moule has done a great deal of observing. Not only has he dropped unannounced into lessons and watched every don (Radley-speak) teach, he also shadowed pupils throughout their day (including late afternoon and evening) to learn more about their experience as well as the school's 'flow'. And what were his conclusions? He was seriously impressed by the variety he found but felt some lessons were rather too teacher led. We imagine it can be hard to avoid in a school full of bright boys who for the most part will arrive having had eight or more years' listening and learning in prep school. We saw some young hopefuls during our visit, serious little chaps wearing polished brogues and tweed jackets – just like the fathers accompanying them.

He wants to do more to raise boys' awareness of the world beyond Radley's 800 prime Oxfordshire acres and has also told parents, and boys, that he intends to 'wage war on teenage apathy'. While acknowledging that every day should still contain a little time for creative boredom, he says boys have a tendency to do 'just enough' and feels this should be challenged. When he's sorted that one out perhaps he could let us know.

His plans for the school itself are well underway. The website has already been improved beyond recognition – it's now (fanfare) welcoming and informative – and the college's famously esoteric ('mystical' was how the warden described it) entry procedure has been revised. It used to be the case that if you had to ask Radley how to apply then you were probably too late. The process is now more open, in line with other, similar schools, though the 'List' remains and is an advantage for those who want to sign up early. Increased bursarial support is another target, as is 'careful' recruitment of applicants from beyond (even far beyond) the home counties.

Mr Moule's strong Christian faith means Radley's timeless tradition of whole school chapel four times a week is in safe hands. Boys 'love' chapel he told us, 'especially as they get older', and indeed this was borne out by those we spoke to. Of course it's important to the 'sincerely spiritual' but it's also valued by chaps who just want a bit of peace and quiet, or 'separated space' as the warden puts

Radley's timeless tradition of whole school chapel four times a week is in safe hands. Boys 'love' chapel, he told us

it. It may not be as fashionable, but perhaps this is mindfulness, Radley style.

When not wardening Mr Moule says he is an 'avid' armchair sportsman and enjoys a spot of golf or real tennis. Reading is, naturally, another recreation and favourite books include Wilkie Collins' The Woman in White and P G Wodehouse's classic, The Mating Season. Box sets are also high up on this warden's list, especially The West Wing and the US version of The Office. And if he hadn't so carelessly 'fallen' into teaching? Journalism, the law and the church are all the poorer for his stumble.

Academic matters: Even with the recent changes to its entrance procedure Radley is not a school that selects solely on academic ability; excellent GCSE and A level results stem from fine teaching and staff who don't think their job is done when the lesson finishes. Recent reintroduction of the linear, two year A level has proved that Radley wasn't so maverick after all when it held out against AS levels being taken at the end of the first year sixth. We did detect a certain quiet satisfaction that the rest of the country has finally come into line. Sixth formers sit three or four A levels, a fourth subject is generally one that contrasts with the other three. All will also do an extended project.

In 2017, 84 per cent A*-A/9-7 at IGCSE/GCSE; particularly strong results in, well everything, but also some Cs, Ds, even a few Es. At A level 63 per cent A*/A, most popular subjects history, maths and English literature followed by sciences. Notable proportion of A* in art and English lit. Nice to see decent numbers taking classics, languages and geology too. While maths and further maths are very popular, Radley has always stood apart from the overwhelming science/maths dominance so commonly found in boys' schools and we're glad to see this remains the case.

Teaching in the lessons we observed was of the tried and tested sort – a fast pace and lots of quick fire questions kept everyone on their toes. Very clearly exam focused. However, despite adding a distinctly scholarly air, gowns didn't seem to make Radleians any more elevated or less prone to muttering at the back than their non-gowned counterparts at other schools.

Latest ISI report called learning support 'exceptional' and parents are in agreement. All boys have to meet the entrance criteria to get into the school but once there SEN support is extensive and lacks stigma. Individual and small group sessions are arranged according to need. Some take place during what is known as 'central hour' (1.30-2.30 daily), time set aside for relaxing, working, music lessons, extracurricular activities etc.

We met some really amusing and inspiring dons who just seemed to love their jobs (less jobs, more way of life, we thought) and the very stones of the place. Good mix of ages and lots of women among teaching staff. Dogs seemed to be part of the package too – that explained the water bowls we'd wondered about in some of the classrooms. All dons and their families live on site.

Much talk of efforts to 'learn from other schools and widen diversity'. Strong links with local primaries and a Maidenhead secondary school; some exchange of teaching staff but latter a little too far away for frequent activities. Closer to home the warden hopes to further develop joint academic extension activities for A level subjects such as music, English and geography with Headington School. There are links for the scholars with St Helen and St Katharine's and plans for 'ambitious extension days' with Oxford High School. Lest we get too carried away by all this talk of diversity, at Radley take your dog to work day is unlikely to be joined by enrol your daughter day any time soon.

Games, options, the arts: All rather civilised. Manages to maintain a creditable sporting reputation without the ruthlessly competitive atmosphere than can prevail at boys' schools. We got the impression that the disinclined to run are not regarded as also rans. Rugby is main game of Michaelmas term – around 20 separate teams do battle every Saturday.

When it warms up the 'wet bobs' row; 'dry bobs' play hockey, fives, cricket or tennis in the summer term. Boat house on the Thames is 10 minutes away and those wet bobs are usually up there with near neighbours Abingdon and rivals Eton and St Edward's during the Henley Regatta and head of the river competitions.

Twice weekly so-called 'minor sports' include swimming, golf (there's a course on site), fives, squash, real tennis, cross-country, rackets, tennis, badminton. Those who wish to can do a spot of beagling. Alternative sports programme (ASP), is a circus of different sports for boys (remove upwards) who don't take to rugby. Sixth formers can choose which sport they want to play.

Art school, complete with rather cool gallery space, is in Clocktower Court. Pupils' work, paintings, ceramics and photography, not confined to here, it's all over the school – eerily lifelike papier mâché boys peer down from beams in the library. Ambitious projects undertaken in DT include surfboards and a rather spectacular trebuchet. Once again, facilities lack for nothing and are open late into the evening and at weekends. Nine or 10 boys take art or DT at A2 with creditable results.

Large chapel choir with trebles from local primary schools and preps sings at services and evensong in chapel and elsewhere, including Oxford colleges. Weekly concerts in the school coffee shop, house and college concerts give boys as many solo and ensemble performing opportunities as possible. The music school is open until 10.15pm and boys are expected to organise their own practice although a member of staff is on hand to help. Just one or two doing music at A level despite high profile of music in the school – theatre studies more popular option.

Inter-house competitions and endowed prizes are great motivators and boys take to the stage for such keenly fought contests as the part song competition, debating, declaiming, battle of the bands, piano and percussion trophies. The legendary Piano Extravaganza featured, most recently, 91 players from age 6 upwards (under 13s are dons' children) playing on eight pianos. The Silk Hall is school's premier music venue and next door is the theatre where college and year group plays are performed as well as A2 drama devised pieces. Parents rave about the drama at Radley; even shy boys take to the stage. No reluctance from boys to take on female roles but every so often school puts a 'Girls wanted' advert in the local paper if the production requires the genuine article. Warden told us he directed several plays at his former school and might be tempted again.

CCF compulsory for removes, fifth form do community service and sixth formers can choose enrichment activities such as opera, film or cooking. Couple of parents thought a few more 'life skills' wouldn't go amiss at this stage. Seriously

In the quartet of boys' full boarding schools (first violin Eton, second violin Winchester, cello Harrow), Radley would be the viola

impressive calendar of visiting speakers including WW2 RAF hero, Auschwitz survivor, scientists, authors, journalists, MPs and members of the clergy. Vast array of trips – theatre in London, art in Florence and music tours (singers and instrumentalists) to America. Energetic fundraising for variety of good causes including partner school in Tanzania and Christian Aid.

Boarding: Boarding houses at Radley are known as 'Socials' and Socials are distinguished by letters of the alphabet (A Social, B Social and so on). First years ('shell') have curtained 'cubs' or cubicles with a sink and cabin bed. Apparently Radley was the instigator of this arrangement that affords pupils some degree of privacy within a dormitory. It caught on and can still be seen in many prep and senior boarding schools. From removes (second year) on it's single study bedrooms. In typical boarding boy fashion these were all rather tidy, noticeboards generally unadorned by photos, posters and the like. Our guides told us they liked the busy, structured days at school and appreciated the relative freedom of home life all the more for it. 'We probably take Radley for granted,' one added.

Boys may buy uniform, stationery, tuck etc in school's shop (known, wait for it, as 'Shop'). Card system for purchases in Shop or coffee shop; 'jam account' (upper limit of £60 per term) for tuck. One parent thought it was a shame there was no opportunity to buy secondhand uniform, sports kit etc.

'Oxford leave' allows boys (mostly sixth formers) to travel into Oxford (by bus or taxi). Upper sixth chaps may spend Saturday evenings there as long as they're back in Social by 10.30pm. Quite a restricted regime for boys of this age, although exeats and privis allow a few slightly longer Saturday nights out elsewhere.

Background and atmosphere: In the quartet of boys' full boarding schools (first violin Eton, second violin Winchester, cello Harrow), Radley would be the viola – less frequently played ('mystical' entrance requirements), smallish solo repertoire (690 boys), confident, necessary, but unflashy (low profile) and so on. It's also the newcomer, having been founded by Oxford movement devotees, The Revs Sewell and Singleton, in 1847 to 'provide a public school education on the principles of the Church of England.'

The founding Revs organised their school along the lines of colleges at the University of Oxford, hence some of the nomenclature: warden, dons etc. Indeed, Radley still has that slightly separate feel of an Oxford college, enhanced by the sight of boys rushing to and fro, gowns billowing behind. Last vote saw proposal to do away with gowns defeated by 95 per cent. Daily choral services were, and remain, a key aspect of the school.

It was believed boys' minds and souls would be improved by learning in a beautiful rural setting and well-designed environment. Shades of William Morris perhaps. School motto is the succinct, Sicut Serpentes, Sicut Columbae ('Be ye wise as serpents, and harmless as doves'), and these creatures appear on the coat of arms – with the cross keys of St Peter, to whom the college is dedicated, safely between them.

Radley College is neither overwhelmingly grand nor intimidating. Reception is small and unpretentious, seating would indicate that they do not expect more than three people to arrive at any one time. Reception staff friendly, but appeared to be fighting a losing battle to stop the office becoming overwhelmed by online delivery packages. 'Radley boys keep Amazon in business,' said a long-suffering voice from behind a pile of boxes.

School originally occupied the Mansion, an 18th century house that belonged to the Stonehouse, then Bowyer families. This rather elegant building with grand panelled reception rooms is now home to admin and the warden's offices. Other parts are usual mix of charming and slightly less charming additions. Wide vistas, generous lawns and paths are another great advantage of a large, rural site. The grounds were by laid out by Capability Brown and some features of his design remain visible. Many trees, looking especially lovely on the golden autumn day of our visit. Immaculate pitches (delightful cricket pavilion) stretch into the distance.

'Most people find out about us through word of mouth. They've met and liked a Radleian at work or university and think of us as a possible school for their own son'

Queen's Court (aka the Doughnut), opened by Her Majesty in 1997, may dominate aerial views of the college but we were rather taken with the inside, which seems to have stood the test of time. It's home to maths, economics, biology, geography and geology and the communal space outside the classrooms is full of fascinating natural history specimens and large tanks containing turtles, scorpions and cockroaches. Members of the animal society come here to get up close with reptiles and snakes, if not doves.

Pastoral care, well-being and discipline: The tutor (housemaster) is the key figure in a boy's life at Radley. He oversees the boys in his Social along with sub-tutors and pastoral housemistresses (PHMs) – the latter come in for particular praise from mothers of younger boys. Form masters monitor academic progress. Boys in the first two years also have a lower sixth mentor. Cocoa at 9pm every night is a chance for all the boys in a Social to meet up and chat about the day; this and other activities help blur year group hierarchies. Boys are expected to help with the running of their Social: shell do chores such as collecting post; sixth form house prefects supervise prep and bedtimes. Parents all praise dedication of Social staff and say that any enquiries are dealt with 'by return', they also like the regular progress reports.

Two exeat weekends per term and boys earn 'privis' or privilege weekends for good behaviour, work etc. On 'Sunday outs' boys can go out with parents or a friend after chapel for the day. One mother lamented, 'My son doesn't take his privis, there's too much going on at school to miss.' Rather sweet little handbook sent to boys before they join includes useful advice such as, 'Bring more tuck. Most don't bring enough,' and, 'If you are lost, confused or unhappy don't be afraid to ask for help.' Information about who to ask (both in and outside college) and how to do this is also included.

School places great emphasis on tolerance, kindness and manners. Biggest crime, according to new boys' handbook is, 'to be rude to a cleaner, a member of catering staff, the ladies who help you in Shop or any other member of the College staff.'

This is not intended in a de haut en bas way – as the Warden says, 'we discourage any sense of entitlement or arrogance.'

School is keen to enhance the quality of social activities with girls' schools. Shell still get the chance to disco with the likes of Wycombe Abbey, but older boys now join girls from St Mary's Calne, Tudor Hall, Headington and St Helen and Katharine for dinner and discussion or joint theatre trips.

Pupils and parents: The warden describes a Radleian as 'civilised, friendly and engaging, in short, good company' and all the boys we met lived up to his definition. He also debunks a commonly held myth (that may stem from former entrance procedure) that most boys are sons of former pupils. 'It's 15 per cent', he told us. Seems that the lower sixth drama group we had spoken to where all but a couple were second or third generation Radleians was just a blip. 'Most people find out about us through word of mouth,' continued the warden. 'They've met and liked a Radleian at work or university and think of us as a possible school for their own son.'

No reluctance from boys to take on female roles but every so often school puts a 'Girls wanted' advert in the local paper if a production requires the genuine article

Even so the hour has arrived to tweak what school describes carefully as its 'cultural variety'. Don't expect a revolution, or a rainbow nation – it'll be a while before the grain of truth packs its bags and departs from school's nickname, 'Ra Ra' Radley. Change will happen, carefully, in Radley's own time, and it will most certainly be for the (even) better.

Former pupils (ORs) include Andrew Motion, poet; Sir Clive Stafford Smith, human rights lawyer; Lord Wilson of Dinton, former cabinet secretary; Peter Cook, comedian; Sandy Nairne, former director of the National Portrait Gallery; Christopher Hibbert, Historian; Ted Dexter, Andrew Strauss and Jamie Dalrymple, England cricketers; Sir Charlie Mayfield, chairman of John Lewis; Lord Wolfson, CEO of Next. And many other actors, writers, lawyers, engineers, sportsmen, clergymen and public servants of all kinds.

Entrance: Still the forward planner's choice. Radley remains loyal to those who register early and 'conditional' offers are made three years in advance to boys on 'Provisional' and waiting lists. Subject to interview and ISEB common pre-test results, they will get firm offers on 1 March of year 6. No open days, individually arranged visits all through the year. Friendly and approachable admissions staff will explain system.

Admissions procedure is changing but up until 2018 boys not already registered may apply for one of around 40 'Warden's List' places. Radley puts 'much emphasis' on candidate's performance at interview and head's report when assessing applicants for these. From 2019 onwards, after offers are made to boys on the 'Provisional' list, there is an open entry system whereby all interested candidates are first asked to sit the ISEB common pre-test in year 6 and send a school report; interviews will be offered to shortlisted candidates and offers made in June of year 6.

Few (around eight) places at 16 + but on the whole this is a settled community and there's not much movement.

Exit: Bristol, Durham, Edinburgh, Exeter, Leeds, Manchester, Newcastle and UCL hoover up most of Radley's leavers. Regular 15–20 boys to Oxbridge every year (18 in 2017, plus one medic) – mock interview exchange scheme with nearby Abingdon School seems to benefit both sides. School's university entrance team recently expanded to integrate expertise in applying to universities in North America, Europe and beyond.

Money matters: Cheapest of the quartet (no viola jokes please) but there's barely a gnat's crotchet between them. Uniform requirements less painful on the purse – parents told us that suits, shirts etc can be bought from high street. Gowns aren't expensive and, look on the bright side, might save on jacket dry cleaning bills (and they cover books if it's raining, boys told us). Sports kit will cost you, but then it does everywhere. Lack of coffee shops (or indeed any shops) in immediate vicinity looks promising but remember the Amazon overwhelmed reception desk ...

Scholarships of up to 10 per cent off fees awarded annually at 13+ and can be topped up to 100 per cent with means-tested bursaries. Foundation awards enable boys from state system to attend a prep school for two years before admission. Armed Forces Fund provides assistance to boys from Forces families. All very clearly explained on school website.

Remarks: In our last review we said that Radley was the connoisseurs' choice; this remains the case. Yes, it's traditional, but it's utterly unstuffy. Like the serpent and the dove in the coat of arms, respect for tradition lives harmoniously with tolerance, intellectual curiosity, humour and humanity. Radley provides boys with an immersive education of the highest quality and a strong moral and spiritual core.

Ryde School with Upper Chine

39

Queen's Road, Ryde, Isle of Wight PO33 3BE

01983 562229 | school.office@rydeschool.net | www.rydeschool.org.uk

Ages: 11-18

Pupils: 497; sixth form: 130; Boarders: 55 full, 1 weekly, 2 flexi

Day: £12,810 pa; Boarding: £22,215 – £28,215 pa

Headmaster: Since 2013, Mark Waldron. Previously head of the English College in Prague, deputy head of Sherborne, and taught at The Leys School and Radley College. Eager for a new challenge, returned from Prague to run Ryde – and for the joys of Waitrose. Mr Waldron's experience in Prague has given him a different perspective and he feels well placed to make a difference at Ryde: he emphasises the importance of preparing pupils to compete internationally, and has shaken up language provision to support this. Parents find the head approachable, are impressed by his change in priorities, and say the school is friendlier now he's in residence.

The head encourages his teachers to think about the potential for creative and independent thought when planning their lessons: could the lesson take place without the pupils? Mr Waldron teaches maths – always the bottom set, so he knows the lowest common denominator. Regularly turns cakes into fractions; and what are the chances of getting that elusive blue in a tube of smarties?

He is learning to sail, and currently classes himself as incompetent crew; is a politics junkie and devotee of the races. Just finished reading Solar by Ian McEwan, and is about to embark on a book about Gordon Brown's spin doctor – feels a bit guilty when reading fiction. Likes pub quizzes. You can see how he might.

Academic matters: Good solid academic results for a non-selective school. In 2017, over a third A*/A at A level. At GCSE, 47 per cent A*/A /7-9. IGCSE also available, and the head has introduced the vocational IB (IBCP) alongside the IB. In 2017, average 34 IB points. Ryde is chosen by some parents for its consistently good results, which give a 'degree of assurance': it is in the privileged position of being virtually the only independent mainstream school on the Island (the other is very small), and it is fair to say that Island state secondary schools do not rank highly in the league tables. One parent said that he feels his children 'have the chance to excel and achieve their full potential'.

Class sizes at A level 8-14, a maximum of 22 at GCSE. Lessons are now 55 mins instead of 35 mins – an improvement, pupils and parents agree.

There's a five min break between lesson times to ensure that no one is late – or 'that's the intention,' said one pupil, cautiously. There is a strong work ethic at Ryde – the classes we saw were almost universally heads down, working hard, the concentrated effort almost palpable. Pupils who have come from other schools comment on the fact that it is ok to work hard at Ryde – 'It's not something that you get teased for: it's actually cool to be clever.'

Maths and science are popular – due in part, says the head, to the large number of doctor parents; and illustrated by year 10 turning the whole periodic table into cupcakes in the school bake off. Victoria sponge...or periodic table...They must like it.

The head has come from a school where students were studying in their third or fourth language, and firmly subscribes to the saying 'if you only speak one language then you can only live one life': he is determined that everyone shall learn at least one other language. Spanish is the new second language at Ryde – it's also easier for dyslexics to learn. Mandarin and Latin are also finding a place in the curriculum.

With Mr Waldron has come a new emphasis on the sixth form, which now blossoms in a new sixth form block on the main campus. The sixth are pleased that the previous nod towards career planning, apparently only really useful if you wanted to be an engineer, has been replaced by something really helpful; and lifelong learning has been introduced in a personal development lesson every Monday. It's about destinations, says Mr Waldron: pupils needs to understand where they want to go, and how to get there. IB students know what they are doing and why; not always the case for those studying A levels. So at Ryde even A level pupils will do the theory of knowledge core of the IB, so they 'get an idea of what it means to think.'

The sixth formers we met were polite and articulate, although they didn't quite have the spit and polish you might encounter in some mainland independent schools: perhaps this is because the Island and school constitute a secure and rather more laid back environment. Mr Waldron is well aware that his domestic pupils might lack some of the edge which is evident in his international students, particularly those from the eastern block, who are well aware of the privilege of attending Ryde and of the international stage on which they will be competing. This is something he is clearly determined to address.

Parents receive mini monthly report cards detailing effort and progress, until GCSE, when this turns into attainment, and predicted and target grades – to flag up any problems with work. Focus on praising effort: merit badges worn on blazers, like awards for courage under fire, are awarded entirely for effort. When the school as a whole has achieved 2,000 efforts there's a mufti day.

Site shared with an activity centre, so there are plenty of outdoor facilities for boarders to enjoy – anyone for after-school caving?

Strong SEN provision: around 15 per cent of pupils here have special needs, and the school makes provision for up to moderate dyslexia. Aim for SEN pupils: to make all capable of independent learning.

Games, options, the arts: Music is super here – our tour guides, neither of whom were taking music A level, said their happiest hours at school were spent in the music block. The teaching inspires a real love of music, and as well as junior, chamber and concert orchestras, there is a student-led ukulele orchestra. Pupils relish the joys of the annual Global Rock – an international dance competition. Students put together routines and costumes themselves: parents describe the results as 'incredible'. The summer musical and winter production are popular with parents and locals alike, and lots of pupils are keen to take part.

Not a school, says the head, for a top sportsman or woman: two pupils left at 16 to attend schools with more focus on hockey and rugby. The provision is decent; but a parent commented that it's difficult to get good mainland schools to come and play on the Island because of the travel expenses involved; another said that although sports teaching and facilities are good, Ryde is a small school, so there's a limited choice of pupils for teams. But the compensation is that those good at sport get to be a big fish in a small pond and can become team captains – positions they might not occupy at larger schools.

Pupils say there is not sufficient emphasis on sport: because their standard is much higher than that of the other schools on the Island, they easily win local matches, but can struggle with matches against schools on the mainland, who tend to play at a higher level – 'we don't lose all our matches,' said one sixth former (actually, this is a bit harsh – most sports have a respectable showing). But sailing, recently started at the school, is thriving (as might be expected at an island school where so many children sail regularly with their parents). More alternative options for sixth formers include yoga and mindfulness.

Grand DT room in the predominantly glass block built three years ago to house art and DT. 'If I get them in year 7, they stay,' said the DT teacher with a smile; and indeed both our guides expressed huge enthusiasm for the subject, and remembered with affection their first task of designing an insect in year 7. Roof terrace with lovely view out over the sea – it's made full use of for parties – and a few beds of weeds which apparently have an eco purpose. The art rooms have the hushed atmosphere of a cathedral: any talking is done is whispers, pupils concentrate hard. Here, clearly, there is no sense that art is a light option: it is afforded proper respect. Pupils commented on the dedication of those taking art A level; and GCSE students are apparently rarely out of the art department, spending all their lunch times perfecting work. The new building contains a large IT suite just for DT and art – apparently the other IT space can get crowded, and it isn't quiet enough for the artists here. Lower sixth reached the regional finals of a young enterprise competition last year selling luxury gift items, cards and gift wrap and such, and won a Kenko competition for designing a logo. Design is clearly a thriving area.

Both CCF and D of E are popular here; a parent commented that it is the good provision for music, arts and extracurricular that give children here such a good level of confidence.

Boarding: The boarding campus is some 10 miles from the school, but there's a daily bus service and the school pass can also be used to obtain free travel on public transport on the Island. The boarding houses are beautiful arts and crafts buildings, sensitively restored and converted. Admiring the lower gallery, a long elegant sitting room with squashy sofas, packed bookshelves and piano, you might think you are being shown around a rather lovely National Trust property. Then you would spot the drum kit and TV and know you're not. The upper gallery above has been turned into double bedrooms surrounding a living area for year 10 girls – an idyllic set up, flooded with light from the long windows. Sixth formers get single rooms, unless they request to share. Others are usually in rooms for two. Two house parents resident overnight so pupils have someone who they can contact if ill. There's also a sixth form boarding house in Ryde within walking distance of the school for those who want to live more independently.

Ryde chosen by one parent for the strong sense of family in the boarding houses, compared to other schools where boarding provision seemed like 'housing for battery chickens.' His children are happy; any minor issues arising have been dealt with successfully, and he has 'absolute confidence in the boarding set up'. Some boarders' parents fall in love with the Island when they visit their children here: one Tunisian mum even decided she would rather retire to the Island than to the south of France.

The large site is shared with an activity centre, so there are plenty of outdoor facilities for boarders to enjoy – anyone for after-school caving? Indoors there's a room with pool, table tennis and table football. Pupils say the boarding experience is sold on the basis of lots of activities, but really some of them rarely happen: quad biking, for instance, only happens during the first week of term. (There is, perhaps, a particular push on special activities at the beginning of terms to help new kids to bond.)

Boarders can roam the 100 acre grounds more or less as they please, providing they sign out first. Must keep in sight of the drive on dark winter days, and need to seek permission to go the beach, which is off campus. The youngest boarder is currently year 6 – there isn't an age restriction, but the head of boarding likes there to be boarders of a similar age to keep each other company.

Pupils comment that the food in the boarding house is 'awful' (in comparison, food at the school is 'gourmet'). School is well aware of the problem, which is tricky to rectify since the catering facilities at the boarding house are shared with the activity centre. But there is a gorgeous mural in the dining room of animals waiting to board Noah's ark, a pair of black cats, tails held jauntily high, leading the way. The mural remains unfinished: the painter pupil didn't return from the First World War to finish it off; but it must be lovely to look at while wading through the substandard grub.

Roof terrace with lovely view out over the sea – it's made full use of for parties. The art rooms have the hushed atmosphere of a cathedral: no sense that art is a light option

Boarders set up their own clubs – cheesy Tuesdays (the cheese on toast club) and the Coco Pops club – foodie clubs popular for obvious reasons. They make good use of the kitchen facilities, and can cook as they please – there's plenty of fruit and cereal available at all times, and a Tesco run every Friday night (no Red Bull allowed).

Boarders have plenty of opportunities to make their views heard, with a suggestion box, weekly house meetings and an open door policy for the head of boarding (and yes, they have mentioned the food).

Background and atmosphere: A school surrounded by stunning scenery – how lovely to sit in the library and stare out at the picture postcard view over the sea. Venerable main building with nondescript (but well cared for) adjuncts; swish new glass DT and art centre.

The advantages of attending school on the Island are clear: it is safe, secure and beautiful. The counter to this is perhaps an element of complacency born of isolation: the head is keen for pupils to look beyond the Solent – pupils must not be limited by the stretch of water: they will need to be able to compete nationally and internationally. Mr Waldron intends to ensure they can.

Pupils are friendly and polite (although this is not a leap to your feet place) and pupils clearly enjoy being at school – a pupil who transferred to Ryde from a local school commented how good it is to be at a school where he actually wants to stay and do activities; just because it's nice to be there. One parent said the best thing about Ryde are its pupils: 'grounded, mature; and nice kids to be around.'

Feels like a traditional environment – although surprisingly pupils are allowed to use mobile phones in class for task-related research: one parent commented that he is not happy with a rule so open to abuse. C of E but with a light touch – prayers at the end of assembly, because that's just what happens; much like a full stop at the end of a sentence. But Mr Waldron is keen for religion to play a larger part, and has introduced compulsory church as a fortnightly event. Sixth formers are unimpressed: they've been told that this is reflection time, but don't quite see why it should have to take place in church.

Parents are happy with communication levels, and reaction to complaints (which are rare): when one did have a problem and raised the issue with the head, it was dealt with swiftly and well.

School council of pupil representatives who have been feeling a bit disenchanted with the slow reaction to their views and requests: for instance, the school council requested a shelter outside the canteen, so that pupils waiting in the lunch queue on rainy days didn't get wet. A sensible request – but it took a couple of years to happen. The head says this has been addressed: democracy has come to Ryde, and the school council is operating under a new pupil-run system.

End of year trip to somewhere theme parkish has been replaced by an activity week focusing on life skills. This has not been uniformly welcomed by pupils, the majority lingering on the side of 'not fair.' Lower sixth, in particular, felt they might have had more fun on a roller coaster than learning to tidy and clean – although there must have been a number of grateful parents, and those changing a tyre skills may well come in handy. Year 7 spent their week building a secret garden, which some love; another year group were camping on the games field with team building exercises – apparently a bit too local to be considered fun.

Uniform is the usual fare, but some parents, apparently, are obsessed with wanting a 'trendy exclusive uniform' – think black blazers with yellow trim; although one parent we spoke to observed dryly that 'Ryde kids don't actually want to stand out on the bus.' Quite.

Head muses on whether the Norland nanny in last year's batch of sixth formers will be happier than the Cambridge mathematician

Pastoral care, well-being and discipline: Parents view the pastoral care at Ryde as exceptional – 'they do a terrific job' – and describe the advantages of a small school where staff know all the pupils and their families. Parents like the strong community atmosphere at school, and comment on the extraordinary level of support and counselling from the school following the tragic death of a pupil, both to the immediate family, and to other pupils; another parent was similarly appreciative of how supportive the school were after a family death: 'wonderful' and 'very caring'.

The head is keen for his pupils to achieve a balance in life, and there is new emphasis on life skills and mindfulness to emphasis the importance of enjoying and experiencing the present (involves controlled breathing – even those who were sceptical beforehand were happy to admit that this was super – one admitted to taking relaxation as far as sleep). This does not feel like the sort of school where grades will be achieved at the expense of well-being; indeed the head muses on whether the Norland nanny in last year's batch of sixth formers, who worked hard to achieve her two A levels, will be happier than the Cambridge mathematician.

Disciplinary system of minus points and detentions run on Friday and Saturday mornings (Saturdays are relatively rare). Drug taking can and has led to expulsion.

Pupils confident that there would be a teacher or form tutor they could talk to if they had a problem. There is a move to involve sixth formers more with younger years, and prefects now wear listener badges, so kids have an obvious person to go to if they want to talk to someone other than a teacher. Any bullying occurs is dealt with properly – 'sensitively and appropriately' said a parent.

Pupils and parents: Large number of parents scrimp and save to get their kids to Ryde – the state schools on the Island are famously poor. Around 80 per cent of boarders are international; also pupils from all over the Island, DFLs, and those from Portsmouth who commute over on the ferry. More pupils arriving across years 9/10/11 since Island middle school closure. Parents range from fish and chip shop owners to medics. Not a snobby school, although one parent commented that 'a few parents are'.

Former pupils include: Seb Clover (sailor), Donald Gordon (cricketer), Philip Norman (author), Lucy Emmerson (academic), Arthur Venables (cyclist) and the second sea lord vice admiral Jonathan Woodcock OBE.

Entrance: Interview with head for all prospective pupils. Most pupils stay through to the sixth form.

Exit: The majority of sixth formers to a range of universities, particularly King's College London, Southampton and Loughborough. Two to Oxbridge in 2017 and two medics; others to eg design engineering at Bristol, film and television at Edinburgh and sport rehabilitation at Bath.

Money matters: Wants to keep fees affordable for Islanders. Scholarships open up means-tested bursaries. Academic scholarships are available for entry into years 5, 7, 9 and the sixth form with sailing, music and sports scholarships also available for entry into years 7, 9 and the sixth form. McIsaac scholarships also available and some HMC scholars are placed at Ryde.

Remarks: A school distinguished by its strong community, set in beautiful surroundings with solid academic provision. Not somewhere you are likely to encounter much unscheduled exuberance, but vitality is likely to increase with Mr Waldron at the helm. Clearly the best option for many Islanders.

Rye St Antony School

RC 40

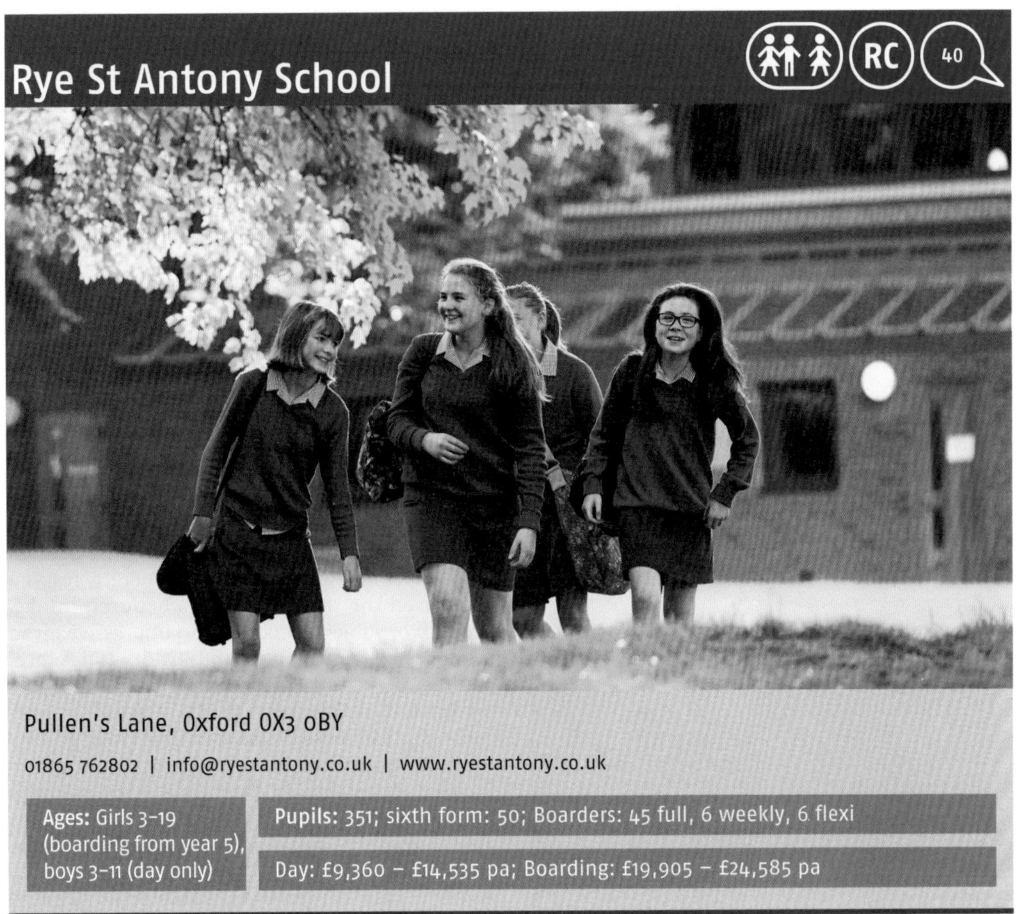

Pullen's Lane, Oxford OX3 0BY

01865 762802 | info@ryestantony.co.uk | www.ryestantony.co.uk

Ages: Girls 3-19 (boarding from year 5), boys 3-11 (day only)

Pupils: 351; sixth form: 50; Boarders: 45 full, 6 weekly, 6 flexi

Day: £9,360 – £14,535 pa; Boarding: £19,905 – £24,585 pa

Headmistress: Since 1990, Alison Jones BA (apparently early 60s although her skin says 20 years younger). Read English at York followed by PGCE from Oxford from whence she cut her teeth teaching English at St Mary's School, Cambridge, ultimately rising to head of sixth form. More chairperson than CEO, a figurehead and embodiment of Rye's value system, ably supported by a dynamic senior management team comprising some impressive young blood. Which is not to say Miss Jones is old fashioned – quite the contrary. Despite her tenure and the fact that she is only the fourth headmistress since Rye's foundation in 1930 she comes across as open minded and progressive ('very straight talking', according to parents), speaks with passion about overturning gender stereotypes and is bang up to speed when it comes to modern day issues affecting young people. 'Confiscate all technology?' she scoffs, 'No! Teach them how to keep themselves and their friends safe. And educate the parents.' Right you are.

Reportedly the only head in the area that speaks directly to the girls rather than their parents when she meets families. Acts as conduit between old girls past and present who may be able to help each other, or simply just get along well. Trusted and revered by girls, perhaps because she consults with them about, well, everything. It's not just about the school council at Rye – girls are appointed to committees aplenty covering site development, scholarships and plain old disciplinary issues which, according to head, fills them with an all-important 'sense of duty and community.' Knows every pupil and family by name and pays no heed to league tables or competing in the uber Oxford education scene: 'rank and order in league tables doesn't mirror rank in real life', she quips.

Retiring in July 2018. Her successor will be Sarah Ryan, currently deputy head of Mayfield School in Sussex. She is married to Paul, also a teacher, and they have a daughter.

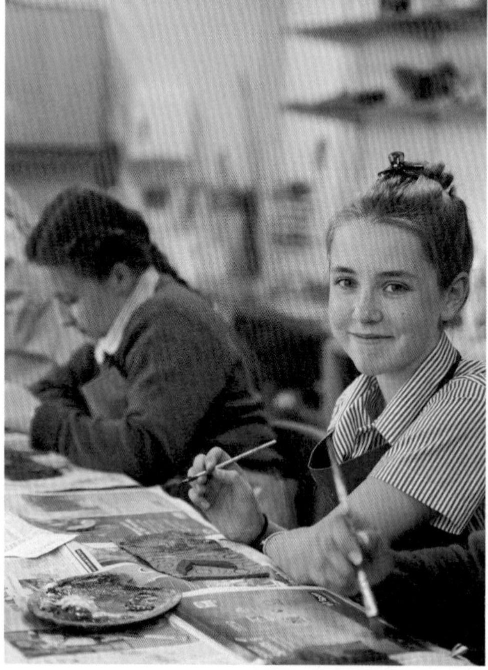

The pre-prep and prep departments are headed by Mrs Emma Coode, a relative newcomer who joined the school in 2012. The inclusive philosophy of Rye starts from the get-go: 'everyone here is valued for who they are', she says.

Academic matters: You won't see Rye hovering around the top of the league tables alongside the plethora of academic superpowers that populate the local school scene – but that's just fine with them. And with their pupils' families, for that matter. 'We value the mix of ability', said one earnest sixth former; 'it's not judgmental and we all help each other'. 'Very nurturing', say parents. 'What you see is what you get and it's all about what's good for the pupils not about what they can do for the school.' Head steadfastly allows school to steer its own course – 'we are unique in a different way', she says. As focused on instilling 'a sense of duty and community' in its pupils as sending them off in the right direction when it comes to higher education – which incidentally covers anything from Oxbridge to secretarial college in any given year group. 'Parents want a school that can look after all their girls, whatever their academic aptitude', says head. To this end, school is constantly seeking ways to enhance and expand opportunities with options such as a BTec in business option for sixth formers or the Leiths Food and Wine course, on curriculum for years 12 and 13. Parents (many of them academics) of the brightest girls 'choose Rye with every confidence it can deliver on the academic front' but are also attracted by the unique quality of 'valuing the idea that happy people are the most successful.'

Public examination results bear out the soundness of this approach with some consistently solid outcomes; in 2017, 33 per cent of A levels were graded A*/A with 55 per cent grade A*/B. At GCSE in 2017, 28 per cent were graded A*-A/9-7. Pretty respectable given the thoroughly broad church intake. Breadth of subjects on offer also impressive given school's size, with maths and history top A level choices. All the usual suspects on offer at GCSE, plus food and nutrition, drama and Latin. At A level, girls can include Chinese, classical civilisation or government and politics in their choices should they be so inclined. Timetable almost entirely – and uniquely – flexible, again a benefit of school's size, with girls able to combine any mix of subjects without the restrictions of fixed 'blocks'. A level classes tend to be tiny – just four girls were studying French and two religious studies when we visited – and it's no sweat if just one wants to take any given subject at A level – 'we just make it work', says head.

Class sizes in the senior school up to GCSE average 16 and with a pupil to teacher ratio of 1:5 there's little chance of any strugglers slipping

'When it comes to games, we're never going to win all the trophies. But we're enthusiastic and inclusive and that's what counts'

through the net. When it comes to SEN, 'we have catered for the needs of the extreme and the mainstream', says head. Those needing the most support are given the flexibility to complete their schooling in the most appropriate way and emerge with a skill set that equips them for life. Learning support (charged as extra) is available to any pupil who needs it but outside of formal intervention little touches such as the fact that there are four maths sets help iron out any minor issues without a fuss. Strong links with several European countries – as well as boarding pupils joining from eg China and Russia – means that specialist teachers support a significant number of pupils with EAL, with outstanding results: 'sometimes after a couple of terms you can't tell they're not English', enthused one pupil of her international peers.

Games, options, the arts: 'When it comes to games, we're never going to win all the trophies', says head, 'But we're enthusiastic and inclusive and that's what counts'. It's a traditional roster of netball, hockey and athletics at Rye plus a super range of clubs including badminton, fitness and rounders in the senior school. An outdoor heated pool provides a popular summer term lunch time club for pupils from year 3 up. Some success in fixtures – occasionally against much larger schools – but winning at any cost is not Rye's raison d'etre, which is better described as by one pupil as 'competitive and fun'. Parents say girls are always – charmingly – a bit surprised when they win a fixture. School has grounds rather than acres of showy playing fields, but as with everything here, it does the trick and a large, multi-purpose sports centre, well-equipped gym and respectable tennis courts provide ample facilities for pupils to get sporty. School boasts 'serious' rowers and horsewomen amongst its cohort and celebrates victories won outside of school in assemblies. In fact, parents say school 'celebrates everything'.

Punches way above its weight when it comes to extracurricular activities with a good array on offer for all ages. Books feature widely, with A Book A Month and Carnegie Medal Shadowing Club building on the fantastic foundations laid in the junior school by Rye's devoted librarian (when we visited she was outside with some of the youngest children drinking pumpkin soup and reading Halloween stories). For prep pupils there's forest school, indoor climbing, small animal care and even a festive decorations club (Christmas is huge at Rye, but more of that later). Seniors throw themselves into everything from dissection, mindfulness and Minecraft to psychology, Duke of Edinburgh and Young Enterprise. There are choirs aplenty (happily, almost all non-selective) as well as an orchestra and chamber music group. Additional optional activities for boarders cover baking, power walking and climbing and there are further opportunities to join external clubs such as the Oxford Fencing Club and Oxford Isis Korfball Club. No wonder school feels the need to produce such a beautiful booklet to showcase its plethora of activities.

Arts taken seriously and 'very strong' according to head. Drama on curriculum from reception, LAMDA and ABRSM results alike are very good and there's no shortage of opportunities for pupils to flex their performing muscles. From termly teatime concerts for novices to drama festivals (when we visited the sixth formers were preparing to perform a musical with script and score both written by pupils), the halls of Rye are certainly alive with the sound of music. And it's not just local performances on the agenda – notice boards in the smart music block advertise past and future musical tours to far flung regions including Paris and Venice.

Lovely drama studio gives girls all the space they need for performances with the light and bright art studio, festooned with high quality paintings, 3D work and textiles, the cherry on top of the arts offering.

Boarding: Boarding officially available for girls from year 5, although when we visited the youngest were in year 7. The idyllic Croft, boarding house for girls up to year 10, is straight out of Enid Blyton with its parquet floors, sweeping staircase and spacious dorms. Communal areas are vast and beautifully furnished, years 7 to 9 are in mixed age dorms and the eldest girls aspire to quirky attic rooms, up endless flights of stairs, sleeping just two or three and with panoramic views of the grounds. Years 11 and up are housed in The Cottage – also home to the sixth form centre – in single study bedrooms with a halls of residence feel, perfect preparation for uni. Maximum 65 boarders at any one time and there's full, flexi or weekly boarding on offer – even occasional nights if beds are available. Good chunk (70 per cent) of boarders are from overseas – lots of South East Asian names on study doors, particularly in the upper year groups, but also a few Europeans (mainly Spanish) – three or four per year. Girls really value the opportunity to build international relationships: 'it makes for the best friendships', they told us. Breakfast and lunch are taken in houses, with dinner for all boarders in the main school dining hall. On top of special boarders' after-school clubs, which include anything from pumpkin carving to climbing, good provision over weekends with school making the most of proximity to London and Oxford, plus sports, art and drama, film or cinema nights. Each year kicks off with a team-building weekend away and girls can venture into Oxford in groups from year 10 upwards.

Background and atmosphere: One parent told us 'there's a little bit of magic at Rye', and we definitely sensed a special and unique 'girls own' atmosphere – an inexplicable feeling of sisterhood that can clearly be traced back to the founder and very first headmistress, Elizabeth Rendall, of whom a wonderfully atmospheric photographic portrait (complete with packet of cigarettes in foreground) presides over the entrance hall. She and Ivy King started the school in a house on the Woodstock Road in 1930, moving to its current site, a house formerly owned by Henry, curator of the Pitt Rivers Museum, in 1939. King's mother and sister moved into the new school and many saw out the war here, growing fruit and veg in the gardens and taking fire warden duties at night. Girls learned to scull on the Cherwell and swimming was taught at Dame's Delight (ladies' counterpart to Parson's Pleasure). Miss King took over the helm on Miss Rendall's retirement, succeeded by Miss Sumpter, from whom Miss Jones took the reins in 1990. It is from these formidable females that the school still takes its lead and the bravery and progressiveness of the founders – who were as competent in site maintenance as teaching Latin, all whilst persuading parents to allow their daughters to go to university – lives on. It's no wonder that Old Ryes are so dedicated to their alma mater to the point that there are, at time of writing, five on staff.

One parent told us 'there's a little bit of magic at Rye', and we definitely sensed a special and unique 'girls' own' atmosphere – an inexplicable feeling of sisterhood

Oft described as a 'hidden gem', you stumble across the school at the end of a residential cul-de-sac just off London Road. Very different to the first impressions made by the heavy hitting schools in the area, and initially it feels a bit like entering via the tradesman's entrance, but this is where books by covers should never be judged, as past this little car park with its modern attachments lies a charming, leafy – albeit bijoux – campus. The main school building is a fine example of late Victorian splendour with immaculate modern additions nestled amongst beautifully tended gardens and ancient trees. Signs of investment and updates abound. A lovely new reception area provides a warm welcome to the main school building with its tall ceilings and wide, light corridors, bedecked with works of art and colourful notices. The modern library, among the most inviting we've seen, is well stocked and furnished with a mix of cosy beanbags and more formal tables and, presided over by a dedicated (and dare we say dynamic) librarian, is hub to the many literary activities (author visits, creative writing workshops, book clubs, trips to Oxfordshire Author Awards) on offer. Plus the views across the lawns are to die for. Other new additions such as the sports hall and stunning sixth form centre, with its own dining room and boarding quarters for most senior pupils, have been skilfully integrated, delivering the necessary facilities without ruining the quaint original architecture. There's a super new food tech centre too. Hopefully next up for some attention are the rather basic science labs.

School has a genuine 'all-through' feel, with juniors and seniors taught in a collection of equally charming buildings separated by just a winding path. The nursery is housed in King House, in quirky, rambling classrooms up in the eaves that can't help but inspire young imaginations. Nursery open from 7.30am to 6.30pm – useful for the working parents that largely make up the Rye cohort. Juniors housed in Langley Lodge, part of the original collection of school buildings that retains its Victorian charm with winding staircases (complete with colourful giant papier mâché giraffe at the bottom), giant sash windows, fireplaces and high ceilings, yet with all the requisite classroom technology present and correct. Prep now a member of IAPS.

Pastoral care, well-being and discipline: School has a lay Catholic ethos, meaning that while Catholicism is integral, it is outward looking and inclusive of all religions (or none) and cultures, and focused on spirituality rather than doctrine. Indeed, staff reported one Muslim girl 'gaining the confidence to wear the full hijab' in sixth form, thanks to her supportive experience at Rye. In this vein, pupils are expected to understand and observe certain principles of tolerance and consideration to prepare them for adult life. There are no frocked clergy or nuns on the teaching staff and the lovely little chapel is an understated stand-alone building open throughout the week and used in particular for the weekly Sunday mass.

A more contented cohort you couldn't hope to find. Absent are signs of pressure, stress and ferocious competition, and instead smiles abound. There's a genuine feeling of girls looking after each other, but the support infrastructure is built upon a friendly and down to earth (largely, from what we saw young-ish) staff room: 'the support we get from teachers is amazing', said one pupil.

Patricians (senior prefects) are trained in basic child protection and advise staff and governors as well as organising a mentoring system for all new pupils which involves each girl being allocated a 'house-mother' – an older pupil – to help her to adapt to school life and answer any questions or concerns. And for when things do go wrong, there's an 'independent listener' – a retired teacher at the end of the phone – to help put things in perspective.

Girls say they know every other pupil at least by sight, if not name, and talk about the school's 'family atmosphere'. 'We love it when the whole school comes together', they say. Which, as promised, brings us on to Christmas. As with any family, it's the unrivalled highlight of the calendar, and even on a dull day in early November, enthusiasm effuses from staff and pupils at the mere mention. Girls say they're 'hoarse by the end of term' with all the singing that goes on, from the staff panto (male teachers in drag an apparent highlight), the Christmas lunch, classroom décor competition, traditional 'tangerine party' and carol service. Much enthusiasm too for the house system ('house points really matter,' according to one earnest year 7) with its many year-round competitions from charities day to sports day with the top house winning a house barbecue.

Discipline takes a magnanimous approach with head often consulting with offenders' peers to 'get an insight into family matters' and 'steadily unpick the issues to find the reason'. Open discussions are key and resolution rarely involves suspension or harsh sanctions. Even detentions are unheard of.

Pupils and parents: 'Representative of local fluid population', says head. Happy mix of locals and overseas pupils with many parents working at nearby BMW, the university or John Radcliffe Hospital. Largely down to earth, dual income – plenty of first time buyers mixed in with old farming money and the children of old girls. Strong links with European countries (Italy, Spain, France and Germany), with pupils visiting from these countries for part of the summer term most years.

Entrance: For entry into all year groups, parents and prospective pupils are interviewed together by head who always tries 'not to turn girls away'. It would be 'hypocritical and silly' not to admit all girls from the prep school. So parents can happily buy into Rye safe in the knowledge that it is a genuine all-through offering. About two-thirds of girls of the 30 or so moving into year 7 join from a mix of local state and independent schools – no particular feeder. Parents and prospective pupils are interviewed together by head who always tries 'not to turn girls away'. Candidates asked to bring a portfolio of their work and attend an assessment day which is 'diagnostic rather than selective'.

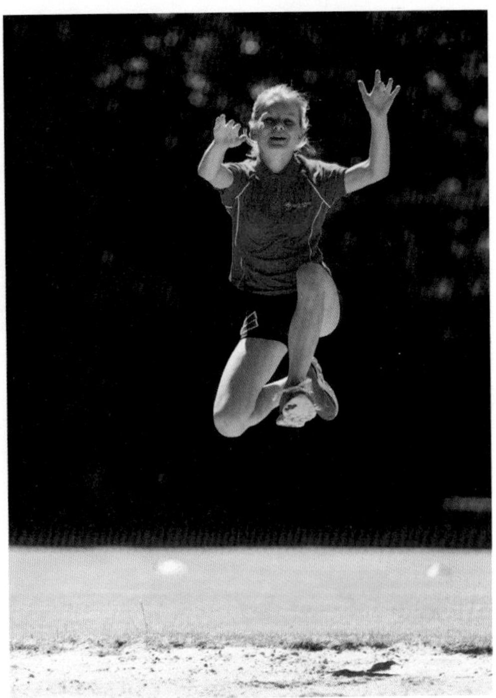

Exit: Boys now peel off at 11 (rather than 8 – a recent change made due to parental demand) to a variety of local preps and secondary schools with almost all junior girls moving seamlessly up to the senior school. Up to half leave post-GCSE and, due to the broadest church of intakes, impossible to identify trends when it comes to higher education which runs the gauntlet from Oxbridge (two in 2017, plus one medic) and other Russell Group universities to secretarial college, art schools or performing arts colleges.

Money matters: Fees comparative with nearby 'league table' girls' schools with all their gleaming facilities might raise eyebrows from some. Scholarships and some means-tested bursaries available at 11+, 13+ and 16+. Pupils can apply for a King Award for up to £300 to enable them to further an interest or learn a new skill.

Remarks: Above all, a most civilised and humane school which achieves good individual outcomes for its girls wherever they sit on the academic spectrum. Although not an obvious choice if your girls are all high academic flyers, parents select Rye for all the girls in their family, safe in the knowledge that their daughters will have their individual potential developed whatever their ability. In the words of one happy sixth former: 'Rye accommodates everybody. We all have a chance to shine.'

St Andrew's School

41

Buckhold, Pangbourne, Reading, Berkshire RG8 8QA

0118 974 4276 | registrar@standrewspangbourne.co.uk | www.standrewspangbourne.co.uk

Ages: 3–13

Pupils: 294; Boarders: up to 30 flexi

Day: £10,500 – £17,490 pa; Flexi boarding: + £3,240 pa

Headmaster: Since 2015, Jonathan Bartlett (40s), previously head of Moor Park School in Shropshire for seven years. Read PE and history at Brunel University. The youngest of seven children, he grew up on a pig farm but also 'loved' his time at a boys' boarding school in Wiltshire, so much so that his first job after university was at Papplewick, one of the boysiest of boys' boarding preps. Took off on a round the world trip which included setting up an online education company in America, where he also met his wife. All very entrepreneurial and exciting but he still missed Papplewick, eventually returning there and becoming deputy head.

When we met he was beaming with pride at pupils' CE results ('I can take very little credit for these'). Given school's size and non-selective admissions policy, the scholarship haul was certainly worth smiling about. Says he was drawn to St Andrew's because of its 'country prep values' and 'relaxed, informal feel'. He has plans, of course, but there's no revolution on the cards (and none necessary). Somewhat overdue improvements to sport and drama facilities are underway and longer term he's keen to 'build boarding'. On the academic front he has appointed a new head of learning and reintroduced Latin (year 6 upwards).

Mr Bartlett, who says he 'hates being behind a desk,' takes year 8 scholars for problem solving and reasoning. His wife, a linguist with a masters in health education, also teaches. Favourite books? Animal Farm (unsurprisingly) and A Prayer for Owen Meany.

He describes the school's demographic as 'quite diverse' (emphasis on 'quite', we think) and definitely 'not stuffy'. And what do parents think about the Bartletts? 'It's so exciting, they're absolutely fantastic for the school,' said one. 'Mrs Bartlett is really involved and easy to talk to,' said another, who thought Mrs B's being American was a 'breath of fresh air'. Several others commented that they felt the head was genuinely listening to parents' ideas and had a clear vision of what needs to be done. Children were won over almost at once by the zip wire and new climbing frame that were installed at the same time as their new head.

The Bartletts live on site and have three children (one at Moor Park, one at Malvern and one at St Andrew's) plus two of the obligatory prep school head labradors – 'heads have them because they're bombproof,' countered Mr B. Down time is for sport (cricket and golf) and family bolthole in Pembrokeshire.

Entrance: Mainly from local nurseries and primary schools or families relocating from London. Admissions ethos couldn't be simpler: St Andrew's is 'a family school which offers places to children who will be happy and thrive academically'. That all sounds lovely but remember, it's also a popular school that receives many more applications than it has places. Main points of entry are at ages 3, 4 and 7 although places may become available in other years. Younger children invited to spend a day or half day in the school; older children sit 'short' tests and year 7 candidates are assessed formally. Priority given to siblings and children of former pupils.

Exit: Mainly all over (the home counties). Co-eds Bradfield College and Pangbourne scoop up the majority; one or two each year to Wellington and Marlborough. Fair few boys head to Abingdon, Magdalen College School and Radley; girls to Downe House, Tudor Hall and Queen Anne's Caversham. Head says they lose 'a few' girls to day schools at age 11 but can sometimes arrange 'deferred places.' Good spread of academic, sport and music scholarships – an impressive 15 in 2016.

Remarks: St Andrew's motto is Altiora Petimus ('we seek higher things') and this is certainly the case as one ascends the steep hills of the Thames valley in search of the small village of Buckhold. School occupies a rather delicious gothic revival pile designed for Herbert Watney (of the brewing family) by Alfred Waterhouse, better known as architect of the National History Museum. Not all parts of the school building are by him – no prizes for guessing those in which he didn't have a hand. Lawns roll down to meadows and woodland, in total 54 acres of greenest Berkshire, where Buckhold birds do their best to drown out the persistent hum of the M4 – a reminder that less pastoral regions (Reading and Newbury) are close by.

Not a school with ancient lineage, it opened in 1934 under joint heads. Two heads may be better than one but this was somewhat over specified considering the inaugural page of the register runs to eight boys. First girls were admitted in 1971. At just over 290 pupils it's comfortably full and while head acknowledges it 'could expand', he says there are no plans to stretch numbers beyond 300. Parents will be relieved; several told us that they chose the school for its size. 'We looked at bigger preps but felt that our child might get lost.'

Our visit started with a walk through the dining room, worth a visit if Royal Doulton tiled panels are your thing (they are ours). Then it was out and over to the cluster of modern buildings housing nursery and pre-prep. Up to year 2 children are taught by stage, not age, we were told as we tiptoed past a group working hard on their phonics. Adaptable multi-purpose conservatory with small cookery area was lovely and bright (though we wondered if it didn't get a little warm in summer). Specialist teachers for French, music, PE and swimming. Parents told us that pre-prep was 'on top' of the basics such as reading, spelling and times tables and aimed to get these 'out of the way' before move to prep.

What did they like about their school? 'We have two breaks every day and you can climb trees, it's just amazing.' 'Everyone can be in a team; no one is left out'

Some parts of the pre-prep looked in need of a revamp – outside areas in particular were a bit scruffy and didn't appear to make best use of extensive space available. Staff acknowledged things could do with 'sprucing up' and told us that future plans include opening up the reception class and extending the indoor/outdoor space with a canopy.

Some of the forest schools we've seen are a challenge to the conventional meaning of the word 'forest', but with 50 bosky acres St Andrew's isn't one of them. Actually it isn't officially a forest school yet, but staff are being trained. Accredited

status may be pending but outdoor activities, rain or shine, have always been a big part of the school day – whether it's collecting bundles of 10 sticks for maths or going on a 'shape hunt'. Each child plants a tree on arrival and sees it grow as they move through the school. All-in-one waterproofs and wellies hang in the cloakroom and get a lot of use. 'We love the fact that children can play and explore in the grounds. They're encouraged to be bold and enjoy the freedom.'

Independence is the aim and even the youngest are expected to dress themselves, use knives and forks and pour their own milk or juice at break; some parents take a little convincing, especially if they have to wash the aftermath. We loved the noticeboard in the nursery cloakroom which had a filthy shirt pinned to it with labels pointing to each stain reading, 'I'm sorry that my uniform got dirty today but this shows that I have been learning x.'

After-school provision has been beefed up for all age groups. Equestrian skills are honed at the next door stables. The summer bike ride club has been a huge success: 'We weren't sure if parents would want to bring their children's bikes into school, but they love it.' (Preponderance of 4x4s may be a factor.) Pupils learn cycling safety via the 'bikeability' scheme and the course culminates in an Enid Blyton style group ride and picnic.

We came across a group of pupils (according to our notes they were all called Daisy, Harriet or Freddie, but surely that can't be right) enjoying their morning break 'squash and bs (biscuits)' outside and conducted a quick vox pop. What did they like about their school? 'We have two breaks every day and you can climb trees, it's just amazing.' 'Everyone can be in a team; no one is left out. And everybody cheers.' And what about their new head? 'He's SO nice and really friendly. He chats to

One mother said, 'I don't really want to tell my friends about St Andrew's; it won't be so unique and special.' Er, sorry about that

us about football during supper.' 'He's strict, but not mean strict. He's only strict to keep us in order.' 'We've got more freedom to climb trees, as long as you do it in threes so that if someone hurts themselves there's one person to tell the teacher and one person to calm them down if they're upset.' So, all good – especially on the tree climbing front.

Next stop was year 5 history and pupils arrived, sorted out their seats and were ready to work in double quick time. It was an enjoyable, pacey lesson based around interpreting portraits and every pupil got to contribute their ideas. Teaching style seems to be fun – hands on with lots of activities and trips – but also rigorous. None of the parents we spoke to thought it was an academically pushy school, instead they used words like 'intense' and 'thorough.' Science labs are pretty trad, with specimens in glass cases and stuffed alligators; pupils told us that they really enjoyed all the practical work.

Learning skills (no longer known as learning support, 'everybody decided on the name change') steps in quickly if necessary, whether for short-term confidence building or extended help for pupils with mild SEN such as dyslexia. Focus is on individual, rather than group, work and the approach is holistic – children are taught relaxation techniques and staff are vigilant for signs of stress. Parents say homework 'not excessive, just a bit of reading or spelling until year 6, unless there's a test coming up'.

'We're quite sporty,' a pupil told us, modestly. In fact St Andrew's, though small, is a big player. Hockey was described to us by one parent as 'phenomenal' – recent achievements include girls' team getting to the national finals and boys' team winning the county championships. School orienteering team are also national champions. Swimming, tennis, lacrosse and equestrian also enthusiastically and successfully pursued. One of our guides was glad she could now play cricket instead of rounders but thought that girls should also get a chance to play rugby (not yet on the cards). Fantastic new sports centre with swimming pool and climbing wall.

Drama lessons take place in the rather small studio – lots of lighting equipment but no actual stage. After-school drama club is popular and there are regular productions (performed in sports hall) but head and parents acknowledge that the subject has been something of a Cinderella. New specialist teaching has already improved matters and plans for a proper stage and better facilities are afoot. Pupils may work towards the LAMDA grades and several have won drama scholarships to senior school.

While drama may be playing catch up, music at St Andrews is in a class (in fact a music block) of its own. Head told us he was 'blown away' by the high standard. A quick look at the noticeboards revealed three recent grade 8s and even a diploma, not to mention a range of individual instrumental lessons that started with bagpipes and, for all we know, ends with xylophone. Three choirs (plus one in pre-prep), a full orchestra, a string orchestra, big band, jazz band and concert band and any number of ensembles. Parents of musical children are delighted with the provision but we did hear one or two mutterings about (almost inevitable) music/sport timetable clashes. The sporty and musical child might be stretched rather thin here, given the predominance of both.

Boarding (Mondays to Thursdays) increasingly popular. Accommodation is up in the eaves of the main house (boys at one end, girls at the other and a sensor alarm between) and preponderance of beams and wood give the space rather an alpine feel. Small numbers make for comfortable and homely arrangements, dorms spotless but not at all institutional. Boarders love the experience – hot chocolate and toast in the common room, summer evenings playing tennis, swimming or 'just lying on the grass talking'.

No house system; school has 'sections' distinguished by colour (red, blue, green etc). 'It's a bit boring but that's the way it's been since the beginning', we were told. Parents confident that pastoral care system would pick up any problems early on and also praised home-school communication, 'Teachers respond very quickly'. Chapel (can just about seat whole school) three times a week; 'it's a buzz when everyone is singing,' said our guide; Christmas carol service is held at Bradfield College. When asked about food the pupils were very keen to share: curry Mondays and chicken in barbecue sauce are firm favourites; rocky road and chocolate brownies are top puddings. Opinion sharply divided as to whether macaroni cheese was best or worst.

Families live within 45 minutes' drive and are mostly long-term local or London escapees. Parents, many both working, appreciate the improved after-school care. Very active parents' association, FOSA (Friends of St Andrew's) arranges social events such as pub nights and charity fundraisers. 'It's not a cliquey school,' we were told, 'there's a really good mix'. While this is undoubtedly true, it's worth bearing in mind that the 'mix' doesn't have that many different ingredients ... Former pupils include author David Cornwell (aka John le Carré); broadcaster Adam Hart Davis; artist Sir Howard Hodgkin; actress Emily Bevan and, wait for it, James and Pippa Middleton and their sister, Catherine, Duchess of Cambridge. Apparently it was at a hockey match on the fields of St Andrew's that Prince William, then a pupil at Ludgrove, first saw his future wife. All credit to the school for not overplaying this particular connection.

Many of the parents we spoke to had looked at larger or better-known schools before choosing St Andrew's. 'It's a little gem,' was a phrase we kept on hearing. The fact that it has been below the radar appeals to some, rather like that favourite, 'unspoilt' holiday destination. One mother said, 'I don't really want to tell my friends [about St Andrew's]; it won't be so unique and special.' Er, sorry about that. School's relative youth means that some founding old boys from the 1930s are still on the mailing list. The registrar told us of one chap who, at nearly 90, loves to come back and visit. And his verdict? 'Yes, it's changed, but the magic is still here'.

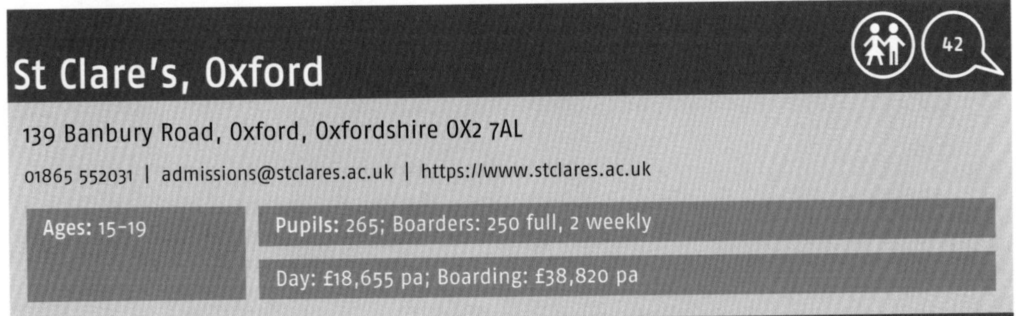

42
St Clare's, Oxford
139 Banbury Road, Oxford, Oxfordshire OX2 7AL
01865 552031 | admissions@stclares.ac.uk | https://www.stclares.ac.uk
Ages: 15-19
Pupils: 265; Boarders: 250 full, 2 weekly
Day: £18,655 pa; Boarding: £38,820 pa

Principal: Since January 2017, Andrew Rattue MA PGCE, previously head of King's College, the British School of Madrid and before that head of RGS Worcester. English degree from Oxford and PGCE from King's College London; taught at Mill Hill and Haberdashers' Aske's, head of English at Highgate, second master at RGS Guildford. He was a Fulbright Exchange Teacher in Dallas, Texas and also worked in Thailand after leaving university so internationalism is very much in his blood. Four children; his interests include drama, music, film, all sports, the Victorians (he has a masters in Victorian studies from Birkbeck) and other cultures and languages.

Academic matters: They come from the four corners of the globe to study here for the two-year IB diploma. The school was a proud pioneer in offering the IB, now has over 40 years' experience, and achieves consistently high results. IB is no walk in the park, six subjects: three at standard level, three at higher, including home language and English, a humanities subject, science, and maths, not forgetting the compulsory theory of knowledge course; extended essay and community, activity and service (CAS) programme. School describes it as an 'outstanding qualification in terms of the breadth and depth it offers'. Parents happy with the diversity of subjects: 'My daughter had no clear idea of what to do, therefore keeping it broad in range of topics rather than specialising too early was one of the things that attracted us to the IB'. Others with children who had attended a range of different schools abroad felt the IB was the only option: 'It would have been difficult for him to settle into a traditional English school, with uniform and rules'. St Clare's claims that it has the edge over other IB schools in that it doesn't attempt to teach A levels at the same time. Average score of 36 in 2017, with nearly a quarter of students getting 40+ points.

Students too young to sit the IB course, or whose English needs practice, take the Pre-IB course. This is flexible in length (up to one year) and can be joined at any time, to prepare English and core subjects for diploma level.

All tuition is in English and class sizes average nine, some even smaller. All students study the literature of their home language so individual tutors are often recruited from the university for more exotic tongues, anything from Ukrainian to Farsi. Classrooms, dining room, Sugar House café, hall and activities are based on a campus in elegant Summertown. There is free Wifi throughout the campus and in houses – students encouraged to bring their own laptops. Informal teaching style from a multi-lingual staff; 'if you can't enjoy teaching at St Clare's, I don't know where you will enjoy teaching'. Parents are impressed by calibre of staff: 'They simply ooze experience' said one. 'None of this fluffy "your son is such a nice boy" stuff'. A new teaching block, with four new science labs and classrooms, coordinates with local architecture. Cosmopolitan lab technicians and librarians can juggle Dostoyevsky in English or Harry Potter in Cyrillic. Art takes place in a new, purpose designed art studio with optimal, north facing light. There's a dark room, complete with leering skeleton, for photography.

Apart from the display of retro propaganda posters from various nations, the classroom was more like a modern boardroom, throbbing with discussion about European current affairs; 'It brings history and economics to life,' said a student. Watching these 16 year olds unpick global economics certainly gave us hope for the Euro crisis.

There is no SEN department. Profound learning difficulties are not provided for, but the college has had students with dyslexia, ADHD and hearing impairment.

Games, options, the arts: As a mandatory part of the IB programme, students take CAS (Creativity, Activity and Service) over the two years to develop personal skills of planning, team work and conscientious thinking. A minimum number of points is needed in these areas, preventing any of the students becoming too bookish. In reality, the plethora of activities from art to zumba make up the social life of the school and run into the weekends and evenings. A mass of notices about clubs, classes and overseas projects draws students to the 'covered way', a busy corridor between classes and café. One family chose the school for the efforts it made to accommodate their son's ice hockey talents; 'I didn't want to go to a school where everybody rowed or played rugby'. The creative part involves a wide range of arts, music, writing, debating, Model United Nations, dance and drama. Behind the guitars, drums and piano in the music room is a full-time music teacher, and Sibelius music software is available for the budding composer. Concerts take place throughout the year, but the hot ticket is the international day concert in which students and some staff stage their own gig, with singing, dancing and jokes. Theatre productions by each year group were remembered fondly by senior staff, even if they had a senior moment remembering the titles.

All students study the literature of their home language so tutors are often recruited from the university for more exotic tongues, anything from Ukrainian to Farsi

The school has no playing fields. All students are given membership of the local sports centre and swimming pool; other facilities are a short minibus ride away at local schools or at Oxford Brookes University. Football and rugby teams use Astroturf pitches at Oxford City grounds. Parents forgive the lack of facilities: 'St Clare's does a great deal with very little'. Girls' volleyball and football are a particular strength. The CAS programme also involves community service (not the punitive kind), which takes the form of charity work in local shops, visiting the elderly, wildlife conservation projects or helping at local schools. A personal tutor is on hand every week to monitor progress and offer advice. The programme is open to Pre-IB and IB students and changes every term.

Students make full use of the cultural life of Oxford University, as well as the local shops and cafés of nearby Summerstown. There are organised excursions to places of interest in half terms, plus working towards the Duke of Edinburgh Gold Award. Students are encouraged to go home in the holidays to recharge, but foreign excursions and tours to more remote parts of the British Isles are arranged for those who want them. Each year's leavers celebrate on an exclusive cruise on the River Thames in London.

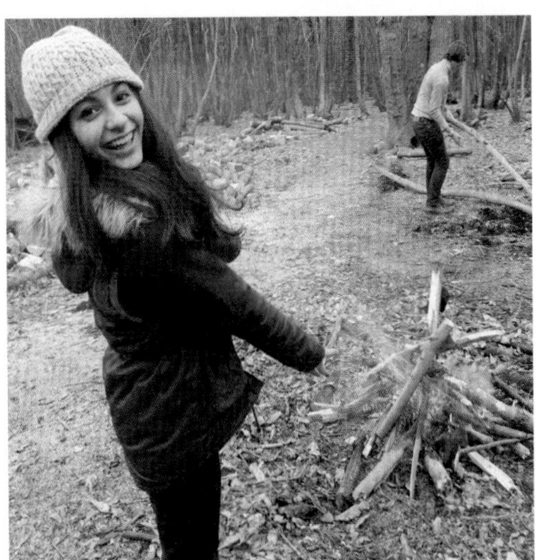

Boarding: St Clare's boarding houses are all within a five-minute stroll. First years share rooms with someone of a different nationality; 'arguments are rare,' we are told, and language learning rapid. 'Suddenly he had a massive range of friends from other backgrounds,' chimed a dad. Second years can have a single room or join with a friend in a double. All are comfortably furnished, most with own shower, hairdryer, strongbox and Wifi. Fraternising takes place in the common room, over the TV and kitchen area. A warden, in loco parentis, handles general well-being of the youngsters and counts them all in before the strict curfew. Day students are allocated a house and can stop over one night a week. Our impression when stepping out into the raked gravel drive was less of having visited a typical teenager's bedroom and more of a comfortable hotel.

Background and atmosphere: The school motto, 'To advance international education and understanding', stems from the principles of the visionary founder, Anne Dreydel, who despite being confined to a wheelchair by a bomb during the blitz, established exchange programmes for German students in her drawing room. Recognised with an OBE and the German equivalent, her cultural olive branch towards international peace has grown into a thriving sixth form for 265 students. A collection of fine Victorian villas (27 buildings in total) along the cherry blossomed streets of genteel north Oxford provides boarding accommodation and classrooms. 'The buildings do not look as smart and luxurious as those of most boarding schools', commented one parent. To the rear, gardens dotted with the quirky addition of red telephone boxes have been joined and landscaped to allow the students some green space to eat, work or chill, but no loud music, smoking or ball games allowed.

Students can take three meals a day in the canteen, which serves up a suitably international menu. Predictably, none of the students rated the dish from their own country but were positive about the others. Stylish refectory tables encourage mingling and English chat out of the classroom. The Sugar House (refreshingly un PC name) offering a continuous temptation of snacks, pizzas and lattes, was doing good business when we visited.

Pastoral care, well-being and discipline: With so many youngsters far away from home discipline could be a problem, but isn't, thanks to the school's clear code of actions and 'consequences' – a portentous term that is famously effective at deflecting trouble, we are told. A strict 11pm curfew is respected. Alcohol is not tolerated, drugs result in an immediate suspension and we couldn't see any bike sheds for the usual teenage experiments: smoking and sex. The system works on trust; 'It's a very powerful glue,' says the school. The students are given a reasonable degree of freedom in return for responsible behaviour. 'When my son transgressed (in a very minor fashion), they were immediately on to him', said a parent. Lateness or poor behaviour results in loss of free time, confinement to the library or the house for varying spells, at worst for a term. 'It's rare someone will transgress twice', smiles the vice principal, eloquently.

We couldn't see any bike sheds for the usual teenage experiments: smoking and sex. System works on trust; 'It's a very powerful glue'

A weekly session with a personal tutor, on first name terms, covers pastoral and academic issues. Rather than homesickness, the students complained that home life now seemed quiet; 'I miss people around me'. Student council, elected democratically, is first experience of democracy for some of these youngsters. Councillors hold office from January to December so as not to interfere with serious study, and meet with senior staff once a week to pow-wow: coffee machines, laundry problems and swivel chairs were the order of the day when we visited. 'It's easier to deal with a small problem than let it grow', says the school pragmatically. Parents have email addresses of teachers and tutors as well as official parents' days at the beginning and end of terms. 'There isn't the tradition of parents' evenings as in a normal school', said a parent, but in practice, there is an open invitation to visit whenever in the UK. Reports and test results can be viewed electronically via the parent portal, explained a parent, and 'we can see when he's been late!'

The students grow noticeably in confidence over the first term, and parents report that after seven weeks a different person has come home – 'the levels of motivation are astonishing' – confident in English and more self-reliant. 'At the start of the year people looked for comfort in their own national group, but not now', chorused a bunch of students. 'The more you get to know about each other, the more relaxed you are'. Despite the school's name, there was no sight of any religious bias, rather an emphasis on internationalism, learning about culture and diversity from each other. 'People think differently here...you learn a lot of stuff about the world. It's eye-opening', said one student. 'Awesome,' said another.

Pupils and parents: Forty-six different nationalities with almost as many different languages; biggest groups are German and Italian, but Russian is also common. Some 85 per cent of boarders are from overseas. Students criticised the size of some of the national groups. Eight per cent are British, who join from international schools abroad or are UK youngsters with an interest in the IB. Ten per cent are day children, with parents working in Oxford at the university, BMW or similar businesses. Round a table, they are an impressively mature, articulate and dynamic bunch, redolent of a UN delegation. School says, 'students bring each other on'. Perhaps they were hiding the mumbling, moody teenagers, but we didn't meet any. Instead, the break time discussion was open-minded and lively, peppered with a dose of multi-cultural joshing. Hugely purposeful about the work; 'Studying in the UK gives international prestige and broadens your interests', said one girl. The standard of English was astounding – rivalling many native schools – and the dress sense a positive improvement.

Entrance: Students are drawn to St Clare's by word of mouth or siblings' experience. No entrance test (except for scholarships), but highly dependent on two years of reports and references from previous school. The 'personal and intense' selection process won over one family who had initially looked for a public school. Interview in UK is compulsory, at which students are sized up for their enthusiasm for the IB programme. 'This is not a place for people to try to escape from their existing school'; St Clare's is full to capacity. Test for maths at interview determines which IB maths course students can tackle. There is a four day induction programme for newcomers, supported by senior students.

Exit: Majority go to university, 75 per cent to UK (LSE, Bath, Exeter and UCL are recurring choices) some to US or European universities and business schools eg Sciences Po, McGill, Bocconi, Medical University of Warsaw. Six to Oxbridge in 2017. Popular courses are engineering, medicine (two in 2017), law, economics and, not surprisingly, international relations. Staff proud that St Clare's has equipped them well for it; 'our students do not drop out of university'. An award-winning careers adviser offers one-to-one advice on applications and CV with seminars to prepare for UK and USA applications in the final year. 'Within a month...he was suddenly seriously considering his future and deciding what he should do', revealed a shocked mum. An education day of visiting speakers from business was under way when we visited, with groups of students carrying out Alan Sugar-style challenges, the kind of thing most of us first experienced at job interviews. These global citizens are ahead of the game; 'they are more willing to look abroad for opportunities in education and for work', says the careers adviser.

Money matters: Fifteen students each year receive scholarships or means-tested bursaries based on previous academic performance and scholarship exam; February deadline. Registrar called the fees 'reassuringly expensive, good value for Oxford'.

Remarks: Academically and pastorally mid way between school and university: 'University life with safety nets'. St Clare's attracts ambitious students from around the world, with an eye to a global career via a UK, US or European university. 'In some ways St Clare's is not a boarding school', said one mum, 'but rather a pre-university college'. The diverse student population is savvy; already aware that the world is a shrinking place and that the motivation to do well comes from within. Restores your faith in world peace.

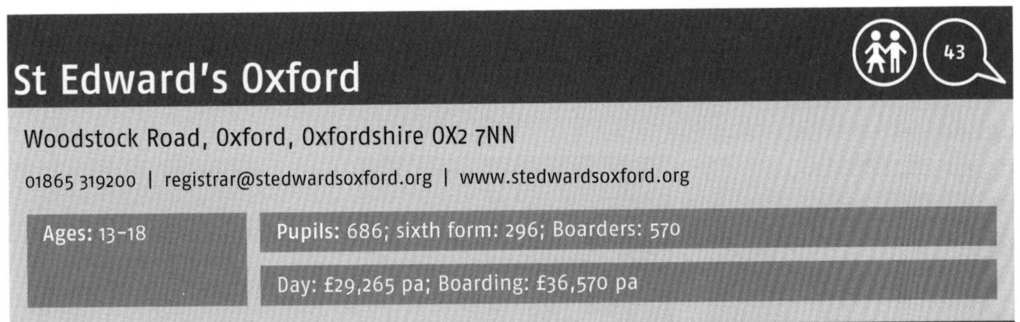

St Edward's Oxford

Woodstock Road, Oxford, Oxfordshire OX2 7NN

01865 319200 | registrar@stedwardsoxford.org | www.stedwardsoxford.org

Ages: 13-18

Pupils: 686; sixth form: 296; Boarders: 570

Day: £29,265 pa; Boarding: £36,570 pa

Warden: Since 2011, Mr Stephen Jones MSc MLitt (50s), previously head of Dover College. Educated at both Hurstpierpoint and Lord Wandsworth Colleges. Erudite, a man of many degrees, went to Durham to read maths and physics but graduated with a rare first in philosophy, then read maths before embarking on research in philosophy of maths. Was an assistant housemaster at Cheltenham College, head of maths at Berkhamsted School and a social tutor at Radley before his appointment at Dover. Married to the delightful Katie, who has her own successful career in the church – no mean feat alongside being a headmaster's wife. They have three children, two of whom have flown the nest.

We're told he is a good sportsman, keen on staying in shape, enjoys fives and sailing and has a keen sense of humour; 'His student house was dubbed Front, so he could talk about going back to Front'. An accomplished mathematician, he loves poring over the figures and has a brain that specialises in pure logic, in whatever discipline. Parents say, 'Youngsters respect him, he is easy to talk to.' When we meet he is chatty, relaxed, enthusiastic – 'I don't have all the answers, what head does?' – but stresses that 'I want to engender a culture of academic excitement, sharpen things, raise expectations tempered with understanding of what the world is really like'. He is realistic, too, and under no illusion that keeping St Edward's on top of its game and rubbing shoulders with competitors will demand toughness and vision.

Academic matters: Most take nine or 10 subjects at IGCSE/GCSE, all the usual plus Latin or classical civilisation and Greek alongside PE, DT and drama. In 2017, 61 per cent of GCSE papers were graded A*-A/7-9. Philosophy/ethics/political literacy courses for lower school pupils and all sixth formers study for an EPQ or equivalent: 'Great preparation for independent study at university and beyond,' says warden. In 2017, 77 per cent of A level grades were A*/B (47 per cent A*/A) and the IB average was a creditable 35. Scholars' societies – OX2 for lower school and The Woodstock Group for seniors – stretch the able. Parents say science teaching is variable: 'Joint offering of IB and A level has resulted in good teachers being stretched too thinly' – school says IB/A level combination 'is now a fundamental part of school life and timetabling, and has impressed the IB Schools and Colleges Association. I don't think parents would see it this way now.' At A level, biology and art & design popular and successful.

Good for self-esteem: 'Those who can, will, those who can't will be encouraged to be independent, guarding against learned helplessness. We are an inclusive school so classroom teaching is at the forefront of supporting all pupils. All pupils have learning challenges at some point; learning development staff can monitor, assess and advise on the best way forward.'

Warden wants children to develop intellect, to reason. 'Some arrive browbeaten through CE; we have to rebuild their confidence'

Has a reputation for being gentler on the old grey matter – both entry and exit – than many of its near competitors yet, in these league table propelled days, parents may seek a school that is 'forgiving' on entry but don't want an apology on exit – nor do they get one. Teddies (as it is affectionately known) has been shimmying up the league tables: not via hothousing – 'There are enough schools in the locality doing that,' says school – nor by upping the entry ante (though scholarships have been expanded and a new girls' house, Jubilee, helpfully nudges boy-girl ratio close to 3-2); rather the main thrust has been to eke more out of everyone, think good breezy airing, rather than squeezed through the wringer. Pupils write A* and keep in their pockets; IGCSEs introduced; IB now taken by around half the sixth form. A levels remain, though no Pre-U, the tougher alternative to A levels; 'Not really the thing for our cohort', said warden.

However the biggest buzz (and buzz-word) is meta cognition ('know about knowing,' said our young informant). Warden wanted children to develop intellect, to reason, question and enquire. 'Some children arrive browbeaten through CE; we have to rebuild their confidence, inspire and invigorate them'. Working on the youngsters meant developing staff. 'I appointed a new academic director who encourages staff to share good practice, go off-piste, explore and enjoy their subject,' says warden. A move that appears to be working:

'Teachers love the curve ball question but some had lost their nerve, teaching only to pass an exam rather than exploring their subject,' says academic director. 'That is changing'. Dead Poets Society this isn't, there is still a generous nod to the syllabus and ticking boxes – plenty of routine revision, past papers, chalk and talk during our spring visit, but our guides said they're treated to discussion-based, interactive, active lessons. Parents approve: 'It's a happy, friendly common room with a great vibe that rubs off on kids'. Academic push still a work in progress but generally all things learned are looking up and bucking up.

Games, options, the arts: Fabulous facilities – 100 acres of prime north Oxford; outdoor courts, cricket pitches, a new cricket pavilion (Gloucestershire Cricket Club runs a satellite academy at the school for pupils and local juniors), a nine hole golf course, boathouse. Indoors there is a superbly equipped, sparkly leisure centre – the hub of middle class Oxford mummies working off their lunches – shared with, and leased from, the school, providing a fantastic gym, indoor and outdoor pools, indoor tennis courts and fitness and dance studios. Pupils win accolades – cricket team undefeated, have their fastest first eight ever, runners up at National Schools' and Henley; several GB junior oarsmen and county cricketers; girls' hockey teams particularly successful. Rugby less robust: 'We take a few hits,' confess boys, though tide is turning. New director of sport is working hard to tempt talent of tomorrow to Teddies – with an array of special events. Not that those who wince at the thought of catching a ball should worry: 'They will find a sport you can not only do but do so proficiently; it's all about building confidence. Staff get involved too – it's lovely to see their commitment – it rubs off on the youngsters.' Only moan is expense of sports kit: 'Always something else on the bill; they must be in-league with the supplier,' joked one parent.

Art good with results to match, especially at A level with facilities for jewellery making, ceramics, sculpture and large fine art displays. The North Wall Arts Centre (enjoyed by the local community – hosts visiting artists and theatre groups) boasts exhibition galleries, drama studios and a cosy 250 seat theatre. Parents say dance has come on in 'leaps and bounds' and music is on the up (new music school features, inter alia, recital and rock rooms plus a recording studio), with something for everyone regardless of where you sit in the talent pool. 'Kids try hard, there's a huge number of bands, plus excellent choirs including one for parents and the community.' Excellent extracurricular provision including ever popular Duke of Edinburgh and CCF.

Boarding: Boarding houses have own identity – quad or field side: choose quad for a disorganised

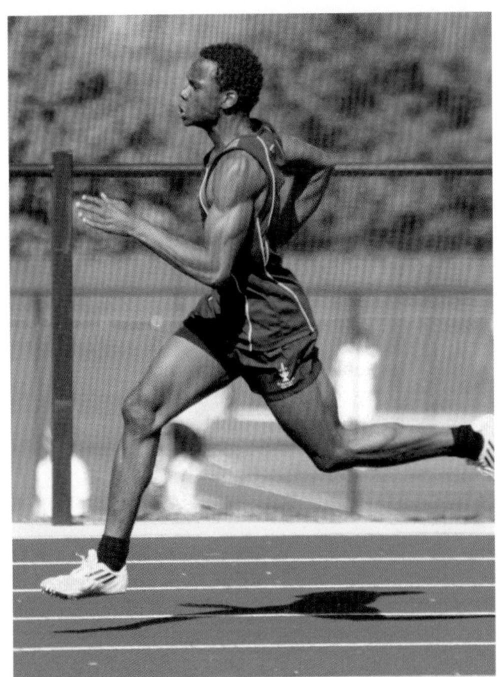

child, field for those who relish open space. New girls' house, Jubilee, is, according to warden, 'more like an upmarket hotel than a traditional school house'. For most of the rest, including odd Cinderella house ('about to improve,' say school) it is standard, homely rooms – shared save for the older years, with an assortment of communal facilities.

Cohesive boarding houses provide welcome support and foster inter-year friendships. Good food, all dine centrally, pupils say it's fun to mix with friends from other houses, parents rue table manners: 'They're noticeably very much "bolt-food" variety.' Safari suppers, ice-skating and discos are a sample of the many weekend jollies.

Boarders may go home on Saturday evenings after sport or other commitments, or stay for Saturday night activities and to explore the local attractions. 'Lots of boarders go home on Sunday after chapel, leaving school feeling somewhat empty and unloved for those forced to stay in,' said one parent, but another added, 'I like that they can come home on Sundays; we relish the family time.'

Background and atmosphere: Situated in leafy north Oxford, the setting is privileged indeed. Much akin to an Oxford college, the main buildings surround a lawned quad. Recent additions include an eco-inspired life sciences building – solar powered with 'more technology than you could wish for'. School isn't the grandest we've seen, it may lack the edge of some of its established upper-crusty rivals, but it has enough of everything, is polished and looks good. Simple peaceful chapel, compulsory on Sundays for boarders, C of E but all faiths welcome. Day pupils may go home at 6.30pm, but the majority stay until 9pm to do prep and extracurricular activities with their friends; all can have a bed in the boarding houses and sleep over if they're too spent to go home.

Pastoral care, well-being and discipline: Parents say pastoral care is excellent, only caveat, 'We'd love our child to have the same tutor throughout, someone who can help and support when pressure builds or child overloaded, overwhelmed or overwrought'; school counters, 'structured tutor system for continuity of tutoring in lower school and in sixth form is ideal for a boarding school'. Still has its fair share of rich kids, some with arguably too much pocket money at their disposal.

Tough on drugs; warden says, 'If we suspect, we test; if positive, save the most exceptional circumstances and I can't think of any of those, they're out.' Punishments for smoking, parents say booze handled brilliantly for the child. 'Quite a number drink and smoke in younger years (same everywhere?), they push boundaries but school pushes back.' Local pubs policed, those aged 18 get a pub pass but other savvy sixth formers sneak off to Summertown for their Saturday night tipple. 'If they get caught they get bust but it doesn't stop them,' said our mole, adding, 'You must be able to say a lucid goodnight to your HM, otherwise it's a night in the san and the ignominy of being woken every 30 minutes.' School adds, 'All have cheese and biscuits and spend an hour with HM when they return; it's great fun for HM and means we get to keep a friendly eye.' Despite tolerance, some parents feel school needs to be more trusting, offer more privileges to older ones, with a long rein tugged hard for those who rail against.

Pupils and parents: Parents a mix of academics, professionals and business. Fifteen per cent of boarders from overseas, from a huge variety of countries. Most of rest from Oxford or the home counties. Has a local reputation of privilege and at times pushing the boundaries – Teddies' girls in particular – yet the pupils we met were grounded, down to earth and friendly, a view shared by others we spoke to. 'They're clubbable, they've had to live with people in close confinement, they learn how to get the most out of others,' says warden, with a student adding, 'My parents gave me The Good Schools Guide and I chose Teddies; it has lived up to all in the review but especially on the friendship and friendliness front.' Notable former pupils include Kenneth Grahame, Laurence Olivier, Douglas Bader, Guy Gibson, Jon Snow, Emilia Clarke and Sam Waley-Cohen.

Entrance: From a range of prep schools, majority of day from Dragon. Skype interviews possible for those based overseas. Gently academic 55 per cent at CE, non CE candidates take the school's own exam. A handful sit an exam at 11+ to guarantee a place. Runs an academic challenge day for local year 6 pupils, with diet of philosophy, Arabic, economics, architecture and politics, to spot scholarship potential and encourage applications.

It holds its own, taps on elbows and keeps them on their toes. All-round broad education with plenty of nurturing, raising expectations

Exit: Handful (some 10 per cent) leave post-16 to pursue courses not offered here or to save on fees. Seven to Oxbridge in 2017, rest to eg London, Exeter, Bristol, Edinburgh, Newcastle, Durham, the US (UCLA, Northeastern, Brown, Dartmouth), Canada and Europe. Two medics in 2017; other popular subjects include geography, biomedical sciences, engineering, maths, modern languages and history. Inspiringly, St Edward's doesn't view the path to university as job well done: 'We look to the bigger picture, the young employable 25-year-old making strides in business, commerce, enterprise and academia. Understanding the cut and thrust of the world beyond university is paramount.'

Money matters: New scholarships introduced – academic, music, sport and all-rounder can be means-tested to a maximum of 100 per cent. Sizeable number on bursaries: 'Often the most able,' says warden. 'Attracting bright pupils is good for the school, good for the teachers and good for results.' All are considered annually for an honorary scholarship. Minor scholarships available for drama, art and dance.

Remarks: For those uncomfortable with ultra prestige, the trappings of the old and bold, or the sheen of highly-polished academia, St Edward's offers an established, acceptable, dependable alternative. Those who seek out Teddies will either be judging it against day school rivals or other co-ed boarding schools; it doesn't sit at the top of either pile but it holds its own, taps on elbows and keeps them on their toes. All-round broad education with plenty of nurturing, perceptibly raising expectations and results while maintaining its discernible cheer and friendliness. A busy school with a rosy outlook, ideal for a broad range of academic abilities, the late bloomer, the all-rounder and the high-flyer who doesn't wish to be a mere pebble, fighting for survival, in the tidal wave of Oxford's academic powerhouses.

St George's School (Ascot)

44

Wells Lane, Ascot, Berkshire SL5 7DZ

01344 629920 | admissions@stgeorges-ascot.org.uk | www.stgeorges-ascot.org.uk

Ages: 11–18

Pupils: 261; sixth form: 75; Boarders: 92

Day: £21,900 pa; Boarding: £32,460 – £34,350 pa

Headmistress: Since 2016, Liz Hewer (only just 40s), two children, one dog. Destined for pointer and whiteboard from the cradle; her mother taught special needs. A brief flirtation with the financial world before and during her Cambridge career but back there for her PGCE. Relaxed, friendly, very sporty, captained the women's hockey team at Cambridge and won two half-blues for cricket. She comes here from literally just down the road as she did seven years as deputy head at St Mary's Ascot, but plenty of other top schools on her CV, including Marlborough.

Supporters are vocal and enthusiastic; she has taken time to understand the workings of the school ('she turns up for everything' and 'meets questions head on') before she makes too many changes. There's obviously much more going on inside both her head and the school, but the hot topic now is the introduction of traffic lights on the way to the car park, not ground-breaking but a jolly sensible step. She lives happily on site, finding 'going home to be mum helps me switch off'.

Academic matters: LH is confident that the balance of teachers – average age early 40s – is correct, and there was no mass exodus at the end of her first year in office. Our impression was plenty of younger faces amongst the staff, and the girls said they liked the variety of teaching styles. A new academic deputy head has been brought in to ensure that all levels of ability are catered for, as there had been some intimation from parents that the most able were not being stretched enough. Small classes in the first years, a maximum of 20, but more usually 15 or 16 are reduced to 10 for GCSE courses and often single figures at A level.

Setting starts from day one in maths, followed by Latin, French, science and Spanish in the third year and English at GCSE. Monitored twice a term, pupils say they are happy with the flexibility, confident that the staff are on it. One pupil told us that she had moved from the bottom to the top set at exactly the right speed.

You have to get your beauty sleep here because there is a deliberately long day; starting at 8.15am, it's pretty full on until the end of prep, which varies from 6.15pm for the younger ones to 6.45pm for the sixth form. If they add in other activities or clubs it can often be a 12 hour stretch before the day girls get home. Despite the long hours, the format appeals to both boarders and day girls because it means that they can chill when the school day ends with homework out of the way.

At present, but undergoing review, the lessons are only 35 minutes, which elicits the odd grumble but means they fit in nine lessons and slot in one more for A level students. The average number of entries for each girl at GCSE is nine or 10 with the occasional super-bright spark taking 11. The majority of students in the sixth form take three A levels plus an EPQ in the lower sixth. Some of this year's entry were not entirely convinced that they had sufficient time to do the extra work needed for an EPQ, although LH contends that it is becoming a valuable source of content for UCAS personal statements and interviews.

The 10 per cent or so of the school who have special educational needs, mainly dyslexia, speak highly of the SEND provision. One pupil told us that her problems had been so well dealt with that they no longer existed, and another that her only gripe was that she was limited to 25 per cent extra time in exams. Equally, a mother said that they had 'bent over backwards' to make her dyslexic daughter's life as easy as possible. Any girls who want or need that little bit extra can attend clinics, often with one-to-one teaching at no extra charge, which were described as 'brilliant' by one parent.

You have to get your beauty sleep here because there is a long day; starting at 8.15am, it's pretty full on until the end of prep

After consultations with parents they also have the option of calling in the nearby Helen Arkell Institute, one of the UK's leading dyslexia centres.

We left feeling that there was a high level of satisfaction with the teaching although there does not appear to be one particularly outstanding academic area. A more accurate evaluation might be the across-the-board added value (GCSEs average a grade higher than expected at entry level). The impression is that they are trying hard to raise the academic bar and their results are very consistent. In 2017, 42 per cent A*-A/9-7, 74 per cent A*-B/9-6 at GCSE, and 42 per cent A*/A, 72 per cent A*-B at A level; and LH is rightly proud that the A*s at A level were gained across 13 subjects.

Games, options, the arts: The new head certainly has all the right sporty qualifications and seldom misses turning out to cheer them on.

In the summer the outside lacrosse pitches turn into tracks for athletics and the six netball courts magically grow into eight tennis courts. You can play everything from badminton to squash in the sports centre, which incorporates a viewing balcony for fans. Lower down everyone gets a chance to be in a team, but further up participation becomes more focussed and the teams more competitive, with one parent commenting that 'the coaching was second to none'. One of the results of all the hard training has seen them crowned Small Schools Lacrosse Champions two years in a row, but they don't just cater for sporting heroines. On top of the daily offerings they can provide private coaching for everybody from wannabe ballerinas to polo players.

There is a mass of popular options when it comes to out-of-school activities, including a surprisingly oversubscribed ukulele club. The older girls are fully involved and often run clubs for the younger lot. The only negative was a mention from a boarding parent that there was 'too much knitting club'.

The arts are another example of how this school refuses to be limited by the small number of pupils. There may have only been two sixth formers in the art room but their work was colourful and accomplished. An indication of how seriously they treat the subject was the presence of the artist-in-residence as well as a new young art teacher who has taken over from a Georgian legend.

The music department is headed up by a long-term, much praised contributor who twinkles at the new enthusiasm for the flute amongst the possibly less talented pupils but also helps the very able to move on to specialist establishments, such as the Royal Northern College of Music. The choir is 'so good', according to parents, that they regularly sing in public, including in the Albert Hall and with the BBC Symphony Orchestra.

Drama and music for all is the guiding principle and serious time and effort goes into carrying this out through inter-house drama and music competitions, LAMDA exams, the opportunity to take drama at GCSE and A level and even a theatre director in residence. This year they are going to stage a production of Cats involving over 80 girls.

Boarding: The balance tips more towards boarding as they move up the school with only 20 per cent full-time boarders in the first two years but increasing to nearly 50 per cent in the sixth form.

The formal stairs out of the main hall lead up to cheerfully decorated, cosy dormitories for the first two years, 'deceptively spacious' in estate agent speak; we liked the look of them and believed the assurance that they were 'always that tidy' was down to a daily vetting. Sensibly, they mix up the first and second years so that there is an experienced old hand around if it all seems daunting to begin with. The number sharing diminishes as you go up the school with the upper sixth having their own room in a separate house. This is a bit dingy at the moment with strange 80s wallpaper in the passage and rather depressing ex-bedrooms used as studies by day girls. Staggered improvement here is next on the list and due to start soon.

One parent felt that full-boarders were quite often left to their own devices and that it was more a school for free spirits than girls who needed a lot of TLC; having said which there was strong confidence in the house system and that the older girls looked out for the new intakes. Parents speak highly of the flexibility on offer: 'if she wants to stay for dinner, she can stay for dinner'.

The food is win, win all round, being both gastronomic and healthy; one parent said it was so good that she was moved to write a thank you letter. The only eating problem might be avoiding the temptation to want seconds of everything. Day and boarding pupils all muck in together, which is another way that the school avoids barriers springing up.

Background and atmosphere: Originally a boys' prep, until it went bust in 1904 despite having Winston Churchill as a pupil. After a sex-change into a girls only establishment it continued on surprisingly strongly through two world wars, thanks to an air raid shelter enterprisingly built at the start of the second.

This tiny kingdom lies down a lane only a short canter from the finishing post at Royal Ascot. The main circle of buildings crowns the top of a steep hill, guarding the green lawns and well-tended playing fields below from the encroaching hordes of modern houses. The original Victorian house grew over the years with the most obvious additions of more classrooms, a chapel, labs, music rooms and a sixth form house, all built in the 1980s. Later buildings include a technology block, a sports complex, a performing arts centre (no prizes for guessing that it was opened by the Duke of York) and, most recently, an imaginative, light new library complete with a feisty librarian: 'she was part of the package'. Next on the list is to be a swanky new swimming pool tucked under the hill.

As with their equine counterparts on the racecourse across the road, careful attention is paid to each well-bred individual, persuading them to give of their best

Once past the intercom and the keypad, the modern sentries of scholastic establishments, you find yourself in a large entrance hall, bedecked with trophies, cups and futuristic fashion. The centrepiece is a splendid flower arrangement distracting your attention from the friendly ladies on reception (not there at weekends) sitting beneath a board listing the names of the school's head girls, past and present. As in almost all buildings that have evolved over time, the rest of the layout is slightly confusing to the outsider but poses no problems to its inhabitants who all talk of its 'homely atmosphere'.

Pastoral care, well-being and discipline: LH's ease with social media means lots of communication with parents, which goes down well. She is quick to tweet praise and encouragement and parents feel they are kept in touch with their children's progress on all fronts. The school has a pastoral deputy who deals with petty disciplinary problems quickly and efficiently and there is no evidence of serious issues. This is a school that takes modern dangers seriously, and he also oversees the successful blocking of social and streaming media for older girls during lessons; younger girls having zero access.

The pupils now have a clear structure of authority, with the head girl supported by a team including a group of peer mentors; girls in the lower sixth who choose to undergo formal training with the school counsellor so that they can offer a friendly shoulder to lean on or even cry on if necessary. This format works really well, according to parents, with the inevitable odd grouse being sorted out so discreetly that the original sufferer is only aware that the problem is no longer there. Members from all years are elected to take part in a school council where they can air their ideas or their moans, and the sixth form has its own separate version.

Pupils and parents: As with so many similar schools, the evolution from the days of old school parents – who dropped their children off at the beginning of term and picked them up at the end – to present day parents – who prefer them to sleep in their own beds – is almost complete. High earning, mainly very local parents of both sexes drop their children off before they go to work for the rest of the day, thankful that they can arrange for sleepovers if they are still chained to their desks or stuck on an aeroplane.

A large number of pupils live locally but some are bussed in from as far away as Chalfont St Giles and a smaller number come from west London, often on a school bus that operates at weekends. Some 10 per cent come from international families spanning the globe from Mexico to China with the occasional Russian or European.

Entrance: Described by one parent as 'pretty much non-selective', intakes are at 11+, 13+ and into the sixth form. At 11+ admission is by exam, interview and report from current school. Pre-assessment operates for 13+ entry with exams in maths, English and verbal reasoning plus an interview. Access to the sixth form requires a minimum of six A*-C/9-5 grades at GCSE and at least a B/6 in any subject to be taken at A level. There is a wide variety of feeder schools including local preps such as Lambrook, Upton House, Godstowe and Coworth Flexlands and local primaries. Some also come from west London schools including Thomas' schools, Knightsbridge, Broomwood Hall and Garden House.

Exit: Around 15 per cent leave after GCSEs, girls tempted by the lure of co-ed and parents by the savings made if the move is to a sixth form college. Leavers after A level in 2017 went on to a variety of destinations: one to Cambridge to read veterinary medicine, 24 to Russell Group universities, 14 to other universities and a number to study art or into the world of work, with only four taking a gap year.

Money matters: Academic, music, art, sports, performing arts and all-rounder scholarships available at 11+, 13+ and 16+, all offering up to 10 per cent off the fees. In addition they offer a limited number of means-tested bursaries.

Remarks: As with their equine counterparts on the racecourse across the road, careful attention is paid to each well-bred individual, persuading them to give of their best. However, it is done in a spirit of camaraderie and they are actively discouraged from being academic know-alls, bullies on the games pitch or divas on the boards. Old-school tradition meets 21st century sensibilities to turn out intelligent, civilised, young women proving that the Georgian formula continues to work.

St Hugh's School, Oxfordshire

45

Carswell Manor, Faringdon, Oxfordshire SN7 8PT

01367 870700 | registrar@st-hughs.co.uk | www.st-hughs.co.uk

Ages: 3-13 (boarders from 7)

Pupils: 355; Boarders: 8 weekly, 97 flexi

Day: £11,220 – £19,320 pa; Weekly boarding: + £3,780 pa

Headmaster: Since 2006, Mr Andrew Nott BA (early 50s). Son of a bishop, educated at The Beacon Prep and King's, Taunton. Studied history at the University of Wales, PGCE Westminster College, Oxford. Worked for the Church Commissioners where he met his wife, Sarah. First teaching post at St Andrew's School, Eastbourne, rose to deputy head. Thence to Davenies for his first headship prior to St Hugh's. Parents describe him as 'amazing' (adjective also frequently applied to Sarah) on a personal level; one or two said they found him a little shy on more public occasions.

Mr Nott is proud of his scholars' achievements but he is also a true champion of the strugglers and late bloomers who are inevitably part of the cohort of a non selective school. He told us that he had thoroughly enjoyed his time at prep and it is this 'carefree' existence that he wants children

at St Hugh's to experience. He loves sport, especially cricket (he is a member of MCC and had a bookcase dedicated to copies of Wisden) and is determined that all the children at St Hugh's get a match, including the E and F teams. He vividly remembers 'the boys who weren't in the A team picking daisies on the boundary' during his prep school cricket matches, and though St Hugh's may be a traditional school in many ways, this is one bit of history Mr Nott does not want to repeat. His mantra is 'excellence and inclusion' and he's also a big champion of kindness, a 'hugely important virtue' that he believes is undervalued these days.

School has acquired five acres of adjoining land for additional games fields, but although the roll is full there are no plans to increase numbers of pupils significantly. Mr Nott says, 'We could be a lot bigger but I want to keep the character of the school, to know every child.' Sounds pretty definite to us but a few parents expressed worries about the school getting bigger. Development on this beautiful rural site is no doubt a planning nightmare, but the newish Cannon Building – named like other parts of the school after a former head – is a superb facility housing science, art and DT. The heads of these departments worked with architects to design their ideal rooms and are still purring contentedly.

Mr Nott and his wife Sarah have five children; four attended St Hugh's and the youngest is still there. Sarah is responsible, among many other things, for the tastefully low key marketing and excellent newsletter. The Notts live just over the lane from school; it's not much of a boundary but just far enough to allow time to switch off and enable the head to enjoy planning the family's next trip abroad and practising creative cookery. Though usually pretty competent, he admits to a recent disaster courtesy of Heston Blumenthal (who doesn't?). He's also fascinated by the academic side of leadership. Favourite childhood reads? Tintin and the Willard Price series of adventure stories.

Entrance: Non selective, non competitive, it's first come, first served. Mr Nott likes to meet parents as well as children. Prospective pupils spend a day; those entering year 3 or above have assessments in English and maths. Main entry is into reception (up to 26 places), year 3 (up to six places), year 5 (up to eight places). Nursery takes up to 25 a year.

Exit: To schools all over home counties; most popular destinations in 2017: Abingdon, Cheltenham College, Marlborough, St Edward's, Radley and St Mary's Calne.

Over 95 per cent of girls stay on until age 13; apparently this is very popular with parents – perhaps because their girls stay children for that little bit longer.

Remarks: We arrived on a perfect English summer's day and Carswell Manor, which looks like a bijou country house hotel, seemed to glow with the golden warmth of Cotswold stone. On closer inspection much of façade is pebbledashed but somehow still pretty classy. The Manor was once home to the Niven family and it seems fitting that David Niven, the quintessential English gentleman, was born here – the old place even gets a mention in his autobiography. St Hugh's is without doubt the tidiest school we've ever visited and it's not just the buildings and grounds that are polished and groomed, the teachers too were quite remarkably elegant – not a baggy cardigan or tatty sandal in sight.

Founded 1906 in Chislehurst with three pupils and co-ed since 1977, St Hugh's is now very much a family school – nursery was established in response to parent demand and the minute it opened was 'immediately full with younger siblings.' Mothers walk their dogs in the grounds after morning drop off. Indeed dogs are a bit of a feature: they kept trotting by or popping out from under tables during our visit – all glossy coated and impeccably behaved, of course. Though we saw no ponies we hear that they also loom large here – jodhpurs (very much not pyjamas) are what the busy St Hugh's mother wears first thing in the morning.

Small classes (average 13), spacious modern facilities and glorious surroundings are enough to inspire any child to reach their full potential, and while not all will be scholars and high flyers, everyone is encouraged to find their talent. Much is expected of these children and sometimes Mr Nott's role is to manage expectations; by their second or third child old hands know they can relax and put their trust in the school. Parents we spoke to felt that Mr Nott's advice about senior schools was excellent and absolutely right for their child; the broad spectrum of schools St Hugh's sends to bears this out.

Maths and English set from year 3, French from year 6; rest of subjects taught in mixed ability groups but this can and does vary from year to year according to cohort. French and Latin for all, optional extracurricular Spanish and Mandarin. Greek for scholars. Middle school pupils (years 3 and 4) have their own teaching block and activities such as drama, choir, sports day etc – a nice way to let the youngest take centre stage. Low turnover of staff apart from gappies (usually old boys and girls) who stay for a year. In lessons we observed pupils were quiet, engaged, working hard individually and in pairs. Small class sizes mean teacher can tailor tasks according to ability; they also make it hard to mess around at the back (not that there seemed to be any such tendency). Parents describe SEN support as 'brilliant'; the head of the service told us that the aim is for it to be 'flexible and fluid', to give pupils a boost when needed and then 'launch them back, even if they need to be picked up again later.' Support is either individual or in booster groups and is not charged as an extra. Pastoral care also came in for high praise – merest whiff of bullying is dealt with at lightning speed.

Dogs are a bit of a feature: they kept trotting by or popping out from under tables during our visit – all glossy coated and impeccably behaved, of course

A school tradition and one of the highlights of year 8 is a week's post exam adventure trip to Wales, during which Mr Nott gives the children their CE results over fish and chips on the beach. Once back in Oxfordshire as part of an extensive leavers' programme, pupils are initiated into important life skills such as how to tie a bow tie, polish shoes and iron shirts; they also create and stage a fashion show for a local children's charity.

Excellent sporting facilities both inside and out host sport for all, every day. All main ones plus squash, basketball, tennis and introduction to lacrosse. Head confirms that every child gets to represent the school in matches. Notable recent success in riding, tennis (and real tennis) and cross country. Large number of sports scholarships awarded to St Hugh's pupils every year. Music and drama are also inclusive with enough plays, choirs, bands and ensembles to accommodate the full range of abilities and a new music block. Outdoor production of A Midsummer Night's Dream staged around atmospheric ivy clad 'temple' in the grounds. St Hugh's seems to produce thinkers and listeners (as opposed to shouters) and recognition for this comes in the form of a clutch of top awards for debating and public speaking. Art and DT thriving in their new building – art room boasts a large walk-in kiln, ready to receive the most ambitious ceramic creations and electric windows that can be controlled to provide optimum natural light conditions.

Pre-prep is housed in the old stable block with classrooms round a flexible central space that can be divided up and used for small group work. Rooms are carefully decorated with colourful posters and children's work and, as in the main school, the atmosphere seemed to be one of gently restrained exuberance. Or so we thought until we came across a monsieur from the big school delighting the pre-prep pupils with his all-singing and dancing weekly French lesson. Literacy taught via Read Write Inc phonics programme and for this children are grouped by their stage of development, not age. Official forest school: pupils from nursery to year 6 get to do lots of messy learning in the woods (last two years have bushcraft). As one member of staff remarked, 'Some children come to life outside, and it's not just the boys.' Parents promised us that pupils really are allowed to get muddy.

Youngest (age 3 upwards) start in The Cottage nursery, a charming house that originally belonged to the groundsman (he is happily accommodated elsewhere). On our visit we saw determined excavation in the large sandpit that is, fortunately, six feet deep. Children sign in for their sessions on the interactive whiteboard and there is an ICT suite upstairs along with a rest room for pupils who still need a nap. Same phonics programme as pre-prep used to introduce letter sounds etc. Specialist teaching for music, dance, ICT. Introduction to French is via croissants and chocolat chaud.

Flexi and weekly boarding – parents pre-select boarding options at the start of term. Those wanting a full week get priority, those who want a couple of days are most likely to get them if they are consecutive. As a rule can't do sleepover style occasional boarding but will work something out in an emergency. Boarding is very often 'children driven', it's the parents who need persuading. Comfortable, characterful dorms up in the eaves (the boarding house has recently been refurbished), all very civilised – common room with original John Piper on wall (sigh). Matrons inspect every morning to ensure that boarders live up to the St Hugh's standard of tidiness. Day pupils can stay until 7.30pm for prep and supper (no extra charge) and about a third do. No Saturday school. Wednesday evenings are reserved for 'fun' things and there's no prep. Parents pre-select home time but emergencies and late changes accommodated. Sensible uniform and termly bill low on the dreaded 'extras'. Fees include all trips (including trips abroad) and SEN support. Means tested bursaries of up to full fees available.

So, what's the demographic? Put on your deerstalker and consider these clues: nearly all the pupils are children of privately educated parents; a school bus scheme was discontinued after a couple of terms because no one used it (private lift sharing arrangements more popular); mussels are a favourite on the scrumptious lunch menu. So far, so county, but though the social profile be small, parents say it's neither snobbish nor exclusive and the children we met were down to earth, funny, normal kids.

St Hugh's is seemingly a school with nothing to prove. It doesn't advertise and prospective parents are not bombarded with glossy anythings. For a flavour of the place, ask to see a copy of the beautifully produced half-termly magazine, St Hugh's News. Such understatement, coupled with fees that are higher than local average (but are all-inclusive and considered 'good value' by the parents we spoke to), might seem counter intuitive in an area that is not under served with preps, but St Hugh's is always full, courtesy of the low tech marketing marvel money can't buy: word of mouth. Happy parents, happy children, happy dogs – what could be better?

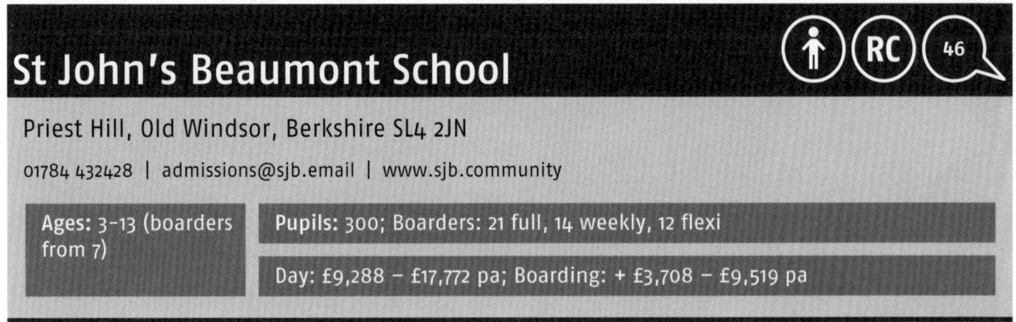

St John's Beaumont School

RC 46

Priest Hill, Old Windsor, Berkshire SL4 2JN

01784 432428 | admissions@sjb.email | www.sjb.community

Ages: 3–13 (boarders from 7)

Pupils: 300; Boarders: 21 full, 14 weekly, 12 flexi

Day: £9,288 – £17,772 pa; Boarding: + £3,708 – £9,519 pa

Headmaster: Since 2006, Mr Giles Delaney (40s). Educated at Hereford Cathedral School, studied music and psychology at Cardiff (instruments are the not-at-all-easy French horn and organ). PGCE at Cambridge and thence to St John's Beaumont. Became deputy head three years later before being catapulted at a very young age to headship on sudden death of his predecessor. He seems so at one with the school, staff and boys that we wonder if it was always his plan to stay at the old place for so long; his answer is a wry smile.

St John's Beaumont, like other RC schools, has a reputation for being pretty disciplined, although Mr Delaney is anything but a martinet. He sees no reason why boys can't be expected to give their very best in a caring and nurturing environment. He's extremely interested in research on how boys learn, especially the importance of pupils' relations with staff: 'boys don't learn subjects, they learn teachers.' In a boys' school 'everyone will have a go at orchestra, choir, dance. They will give everything a shot and smile if it doesn't work.' Certainly when it comes to the importance of context, relating academic subjects to the real world, it seems that Jesuit schools were there long before the educationalists.

Mr Delaney, who looks a bit like a young Colin Firth, is modest and charming. He told us that he had taught 'most stuff', still teaches year 5 ('getting them ready for pre-tests surreptitiously') and is looking forward to a new challenge: introducing the pre-prep boys to music. We weren't taken in by his self-deprecating answers. Boys and parents say his teaching is 'absolutely brilliant', 'fantastic', 'the best'. Loves preparing assemblies and shares a keen interest in medieval history with his wife, Katie, who teaches in a school in north London. He is currently studying for an MSc in education at Oxford. They have four daughters – must be something of an antidote to life at SJB. And if he hadn't gone into teaching? A conductor, he thinks, or a graphic designer, 'something not in an office.' Favourite book? Solzhenitsyn's One day in the life of Ivan Denisovich: 'It's about endurance, valuing the smallest things.'

Entrance: There's a waiting list so plan ahead. Most boys enter at age 4 after attending a taster session (no formal entry test) to assess suitability – looking for boys who will 'thrive' here and 'play an active and positive part' in school life. Parents and children interviewed by the head. Further small intake at year 3 (dependent on performance in school's own assessment and reference from current head). Priority given to practising Roman Catholic families, siblings and applicants with connections to St John's or a Jesuit education

Exit: To all the big beasts and all the more impressive given non-selective intake: Eton, Harrow, Tonbridge, Winchester, Wellington, Charterhouse, Ampleforth, Downside, Stonyhurst, Hampton. Notable record of academic, sport and all-rounder scholarships.

Remarks: St John's Beaumont sits in red-brick gothic grandeur on a hill overlooking Old Windsor, surrounded by 70 acres of grounds and playing fields next door to Windsor Great Park. Designed by John Francis Bentley (also responsible for Westminster Cathedral) and opened in 1888, it was the first purpose-built prep school in England. Tucked behind the Victorian edifice are recent additions: a fine sports centre with vertigo-inducing climbing wall, music, science and art departments, a theatre and the pre-prep block, all on a rather more human scale. The huge reception hall, hung with portraits of old boys and next door neighbour Her Majesty the Queen, sets a rather formal tone. Classical music playing discreetly in the background only just takes the edge off what could be an intimidating first impression for some prospective parents and their boys.

Our visit started in one of the original high ceilinged classrooms with a year 8 maths lesson. Considering it was nearly the end of term and these boys had done CE (many had won scholarships), their quiet concentration was remarkable. Working in pairs, they applied themselves to bisecting a line so that they would 'impress maths teachers at their next schools'. In accordance with the principles of Jesuit education, they then discussed context, suggesting where this technique could be applied in real life. Maths is a particular strength of SJB and the best take part in national competitions and maths challenges, winning medals at all levels. Three finalists recently gained distinctions in Junior Maths Olympiad. Science very hands-on; boys told us that a highlight was 'setting custard powder on fire' and went on to explain the theory behind the conflagration. Latin from year 6, Greek for scholars.

Having learnt (and swiftly forgotten) how to bisect a line it was off to year 6 history in a slightly less lofty Portakabin. After the maturity of the mathematicians we were relieved to find a sparky class tackling the causes of the First World War. Their presentation skills may have been a work in progress but there was no doubting their enthusiasm and depth of knowledge. Here, context was relating 1914 alliances to the current situation in Afghanistan. Distracting them from the task in hand, we asked what one thing would improve their school. The answer was unanimous: girls! Apparently girls would 'make the place tidier' and 'help with questions'. Dream on, chaps.

Golf, cycling, climbing, sailing, skiing – SJB boys pursue and excel at all kinds of sport, but rugby rules. They regularly field 16 teams and successfully play David to some much bigger Goliaths. Most recently the 1st XV was undefeated in all but one match. Usual parental grumbles that it's not much fun in the lesser teams who don't get any of the specialist coaching. Football gets a proper look in, too. There's an impressive swimming pool and a climbing wall in addition to all the usual facilities. Proximity to the Thames doesn't always guarantee a commitment to rowing but in this case it does and there are 50 boys in the squad netting a haul of medals in regional and national championships. For years 6, 7 and 8 it's sport every day plus matches on Saturday. It's a long day too: years 4 and 5 finish at 5pm, for older boys it's 6pm or later if they're doing extra activities (wraparound care available for younger boys). One of our guides said he thought parents should know that 'it's quite tiring'. Music, art and drama don't seem to be overshadowed by the sports behemoth; that long day means there's time for both.

Fifty or so boys board (one junior and one senior dorm). Full weekend programme of activities, many chosen by boys on the boarding committee, includes paintballing, tank driving and trips to Windsor Castle and the Science Museum. Weekly boarding also an option. Interesting animal themed house system engenders keen rivalry for 'TYE' points (Tiger, Yak and Emu). Junior uniform (navy blue Bermudas until year 6) looks smart but several parents still reeling from eye-watering cost of anything crested, including jumpers and shirts.

We weren't taken in by his self-deprecating answers. Boys and parents say his teaching is 'absolutely brilliant', 'fantastic', 'the best'. Loves preparing assemblies

Approximately 60 per cent of boys come from RC families but don't imagine this leads to monoculture – a peek into any classroom will dispel doubts on that score. Parents unanimously praised the pastoral care and the way the school welcomed diversity. One who was not Catholic said that religion was 'not an issue' but described the RE curriculum as 'very truly Catholic, up to and including creationism', so SJB unlikely to be destination of choice for Dawkins minor. School's view is that they welcome boys of any faith or none but those who join, 'join a community', and must play their part, including attendance at mass. Admissions process wise to parents who are only interested in the school for its CE results. The scholarship boards provide a record of the school's evolution. Thirty years ago practically all went on to Catholic schools such as Stonyhurst, The Oratory, Ampleforth; today's scholars are just as likely to be bound for Eton, Winchester and Wellington.

Mr Bentley the architect obviously believed in giving boys lots of space and air, hence the wide corridors and high ceilinged classrooms, and the generosity of his design, while unmistakably Victorian, stands up pretty well to the demands of the 21st century. His intimate and beautifully decorated chapel, bearing the scars of wartime bombs, only seats 60, and at Christmas there are several services so that all parents can enjoy the special atmosphere and 'magical music'. Whole school events take place in the somewhat less atmospheric sports hall. Part of the Jesuit educational ethos is that a child should be 'well rounded and worldly wise' and to that end SJB boys go far and wide; not only history and sports trips to France and Italy but also swimming the Midmar Mile in South Africa to raise money for charity. They're also stretched by the school's impressive Magis programme; senior boys have weekly lectures from visiting speakers, parents and members of staff and are also encouraged to present talks themselves. Recent subjects include deafness and language acquisition, Battersea Dogs' Home and space exploration. Lots of fundraising to support a sister school, St Rupert's, in Zimbawe.

Day boys come in from a 10 mile radius (bus service operates from Chiswick and Maidenhead); about 40 per cent of boarders from overseas. Parents a mix of trad Windsor and glossy Middletonshire (or as someone put it, those who have Wentworth membership and those who don't). Their sons are commendably oblivious to such pigeonholing and there's a great sense of camaraderie; boys are proud of their school and its traditions. Mr Delaney describes St John's Beaumont as a community that asks its members, 'What can you give?' It expects the very best but also give boys the confidence to try new things and learn from mistakes. As a parent remarked, 'It can appear prescriptive but the boys don't see it like that, they thrive on structure and clear rules. My son loves going to school.'

St Mary's School Ascot

RC 47

St Mary's Road, Ascot, Berkshire SL5 9JF

01344 296600 | admissions@st-marys-ascot.co.uk | www.st-marys-ascot.co.uk

Ages: 11-18

Pupils: 391; sixth form: 127; Boarders: 368

Day: £26,190 pa; Boarding: £36,780 pa

Headmistress: Since 1999, Mrs Mary Breen BSc MSc (40s). Married, no children. Previously spent seven-year stint at Eton, where she ended up as head of physics. Before that, taught science at The Abbey School Reading.

Her career was kick-started by head at Wellington who, having appointed her husband to a teaching post, saw Mrs Breen's useful physics degree lying fallow and suggested putting it to practical use. 'A few months later, my first class was 22 Wellingtonians. I discovered I could do it and loved it,' she says. The rest, as they say, is history or, in her case, science.

The school's first lay head, she has commendably piloted St Mary's through the choppy waters of changing educational fashions without once changing course. The result is a school that has remained totally true to itself – and unapologetically so. 'We're not trying to be all things to all people', she says, 'but we've got a coherence that works'.

Smart, with a hint of va va voom (and no doubt requiring every ounce of it at times), she relishes the job and is reassuringly in control without anything of the martinet about her. Her genuine and purposeful charm is particularly effective when directed at parents. 'I say "we're Catholic. We're all girls. We're full boarding. We're a good medium size, with just under 400 and no plans to get any bigger or smaller. And we're very proud of our academic reputation. If that's a match for your daughters, let's take it further".' Most do.

Head is no slouch when it comes to heading off potential defection higher up the school. 'Having seen them grow up as teenagers, you want them as your gorgeous sixth form', she says. Plenty of official endorsement too. School recently breezed through visits from Ofsted and ISI (who decided to pop in at the same time) and scored glowing reviews from both.

Parents are universally full of praise, highlighting head's professionalism and nous. One father told us she should have a 'sainthood'. 'All you could ask for in a head', said another parent. 'She's the right person at the top to build the right team round her'. Admiration extends to 'excellent'

communication following a one-off resignation of a member of staff found with inappropriate images on computer in an incident which was, the head is at pains to point out, 'unrelated to school'. Equal enthusiasm from pupils. 'She knows everyone's name and is personable, efficient and approachable', said one. Felt to be particularly good with family-related issues requiring delicate handling.

Wears regular questions about whether she's thinking of moving on with slight (and understandable) weariness. Her answer? Until she wakes up thinking she doesn't want to do this job, she has no intention of moving on, though she wouldn't be averse to a bit of industry-spokesperson duties on the side were the opportunities to come her way. Our advice to suitable bodies? Snap her up while stocks last. A natural in front of a crowd, she'd be jolly good at it too.

Academic matters: All round excellence, helped by well-stocked staff room (overall pupil-teacher ratio of six to one). Class sizes average 16 up to year 9, 15 for GCSE years and seven at A level. Three in a class not uncommon for more rarefied subjects such as further maths.

At A level, 76 per cent A*/A grades and 92 per cent A*/B in 2017. IGCSE results similarly classy – 91 per cent A*/A grades. Head is keen to dispel the suggestion that results are easily come by or a foregone conclusion. While they may suggest highly academic intake at 11+, with the vast majority at the top end of spectrum, behind the scenes number crunching (school uses MIDYIS) tells a very different story. Pupils span just about everything from the mid-range and below to the giddy super-bright heights.

A well-managed process steers a careful line between encouragement and pressure. The universally cheerful and confident demeanour of sixth formers about to enter final preparation for final A level exams indicated that it was working. Pupils rated supportive ethos – 'It's cool to work', said one – and extensive out of hours access to staff. 'So many of the teachers stay late that it's easy to meet up with them', confirmed another. Well-structured lessons where peers, as well as staff, assist with problem areas are a boon, too, say pupils.

Head is no slouch when it comes to heading off potential defection higher up. 'Having seen them grow up as teenagers, you want them as your gorgeous sixth form'

Transformation of geese to high-flying swans isn't lost on parents, who talk of being 'staggered' by strings of GCSE top grades achieved. It's something that the head, to her credit, doesn't care to over-stress, given that it's unlikely to do much in the way of improving pupil confidence.

Subject range, though not vast, is well chosen and augmented only after considerable deliberation. Religious studies a non-negotiable core subject at GCSE. Latin (taught like French from year 7) taken by around half the year group at GCSE, well ahead of Spanish, German, Italian (added year 8) and Greek (year 9).

Three cheers for science, a particular strength, with five well-equipped labs and surging physics numbers post-16 (head takes some classes) on a par with biology and chemistry. Around 20 per cent take science subject to A level.

Maths also has consistent numbers of fans, though broad sweep of subject popularity (English literature, politics and French all make an appearance in the top five most years) means most tastes are well catered for. 'There's no subject that's a no-go area. When people ask me, I'm really proud to say what I'm doing,' said a further maths and science star.

Games, options, the arts: 'We're academic but with lots of extracurricular activities', a pupil told us. 'The school encourages you to thrive'. And how. Being not just good but 'brilliant' at everything, including sport, drama and music, is the goal, though not easy in such a small school stresses the head. If anything holds them back, it won't be resources, with sports facilities positively glistening with new honed and toned additions. In addition to swimming pool, the Orchard Centre has a big sports hall, two squash courts and a dance studio. One of few girls' schools to have own 400-metre running track, green instead of customary red. Polo available, courtesy of local stables.

While there's a steady crop of outstanding individuals and teams at county level and above (tennis a particular strength), any lingering perception that the keen but hopeless are left to languish is out of date, says the head. All shall have matches (if not prizes). Team sport ceases to be compulsory post 16 but there's enough to inspire even the most sedentary-minded to stay happily active. Body conditioning, universally (though to official disapproval) known by girls as LBT (legs, bums and tums), particularly popular.

As with sport, the arts boast range of spaces that would be outstanding in a school with double the numbers. With its studio, full-size theatre, enormous green room (partitioned for girl/boy casts), bar and extensive costume room, the Rose Theatre is a budding thespian's dream. Many work towards LAMDA exams, gaining the full set by the time they leave. Productions every term, some girls-only, others involving other schools. Production of The History Boys featured an all-girl cast, apart from the French mistress, who was played by an Etonian. A sixth form group took its own play to Edinburgh Festival, gaining good reviews into the bargain.

Mercy dashes aren't unknown. 'Only this school would put a damaged pigeon in a taxi and send it to the only vet open on a Sunday,' said a member of staff

Art, housed with textiles (DT, though not a GCSE option, is taught as a carousel subject in years 8 and 9) is terrific. In some schools, head of department's hand often all too visible in strikingly similar interpretations of GCSE/A level coursework theme: here, variety (including burqa-clad, slogan adorned figures in entrance) suggests pupils really do think for themselves. Quality is so impressive that you almost forget where you are and start peering for red spots. Portraiture wonderful – not surprising as school, in one of many go-ahead moments, offers life drawing. Here as elsewhere, school's decision to go its own way has left it ahead of the game. 'We stick to traditions worth sticking to', a senior teacher told us.

Music is a high-profile affair. Well-equipped recital room, numerous practice rooms (including one, doubly soundproofed, for drums), concerts also in the chapel to capitalise on 'wonderful' acoustics. Head of music who grows her own compositions is now inundated with requests for new works following première of spine-tingling Easter Story and also plans to up numbers taking subject at GCSE and A level (scant handful currently).

Activities provide outlet for girl power in every form. For younger pupils, few delights trump pet club housed in mish-mash of cages and runs. Hamsters and rabbits dominate, with talent shows featuring animals in natty little homemade outfits. Animal friendliness is a big thing generally and mercy dashes aren't unknown. 'Only this school would put a damaged pigeon in a taxi and send it to the only vet open on a Sunday,' said a member of staff.

Wide range of clubs and societies, from the mind-expanding (human rights, music appreciation, current affairs) to D of E, London theatre trips and upscale wine-tasting (upper sixth only). Born movers and shakers (and there are many) can hone their organising skills in assorted forums, from influential school council ('what we recommend gets done', say girls) to range of committees. Old girls regularly pop up to widen careers horizons as part of a programme that kicks in from year 9.

Boarding: Modernising elsewhere in the school has seen large-scale abolition of big dorms (mostly no more than five to a room). Top favourite, however, was blast from the past curtain-partitioned 'cubies' in year 8 dorm, voted the best fun, with last night of term midnight feasts.

Sixth form privileges include no uniform (pupils were delighted by this, some parents less so), permission to queue-barge at meal times and annual ball. Biggest perk is separate living quarters, away from main school hurly burly, circle of little homes corralled around own courtyard. Decent kitchens are well used (fruit and veg high on request list, adding to menu staples of toast, pasta – and chocolate crispie cakes). Entertaining is encouraged, with guests treated to more elaborate fare (visiting Etonians haven't thus far reciprocated in kind. 'They don't have the same facilities,' say the girls).

Multitude of house-organised weekend activities helps to dispel any boarding blues. Staples include mass pizza ordering as well as rare forays into deepest girly territory (nail decoration a favourite) and specials like St Patrick's Day marked with cookery (Irish potato scones) and crafts (shamrock felt jewellery).

Background and atmosphere: School was founded in 1885 by the Institute of the Blessed Virgin Mary (IBVM), a religious order begun by Mary Ward (1585-1645). Her dreams of founding a Jesuit-inspired apostolic women's order (she even crossed the Alps on foot to put her case to the Pope) came to nothing in her lifetime. Undaunted, followers continued to plead her cause, though it was 2009 before her 'heroic virtue' was recognised by Rome.

Catholicism defines the school, sweeping in the committed and the less so. Morning chapel compulsory for all while regular weekday masses are optional, attracting anything from a dozen to 60 just before exams. Houses take it in turns to organise mass and pick the hymns, the more rousing the better. The election of the current Pontiff greeted with huge excitement. 'Someone started screaming "white smoke!" – I had coursework to do but the Pope comes first', a sixth former told us.

School makes the most of its 55-acre site. Main buildings, some on gothic revival lines, go up rather

than out, with long but not unfriendly corridors, helped by warm terracotta and mosaic tiles and a riot of gleaming staircases (some now adorned with essential if unattractive anti-slip edging).

We were the first outsiders to experience the gorgeousness of school's former concert hall, now transformed into a terrific new senior library (juniors separately and snazzily catered for). Nicer than many universities, say pupils. No wonder, with its curvy window seats, acres of bookcases and wonderful first floor curved ceiling. Café, complete with morning papers. No learning resource centre faffage here. Pupils can take in iPads and laptops but the printed word is definitely the star of the show. 'Books betoken silence', says head firmly.

Pastoral care, well-being and discipline: A little light rule-bending aside, few serious offences on this head's watch. Sanctions, when they do occur, are now consistent from house to house (just about the only minor imperfection found after recent inspections). Internet misuse would lead to merit-cancelling red ticket. Drink and smoking, almost unheard of, would result in suspension and 'you'd be out' for drugs.

Day to day, six heads of house have the biggest pastoral responsibility. They're considered mainly excellent. Praise too, for boarding. Inevitable beginner homesickness well handled with the help of older buddies and kindly boarding staff, vast majority of whom don't teach. 'They're lovely and very sympathetic if you say you have too much work,' said sixth former. Residential chaplain is mentioned by almost everyone as inspirational force for good and a multi-tasker to boot.

There's a fair bit of moving around which stems from a sensible desire to head off anything that could lead to cliques forming. Sleeping arrangements changed at least once a term and occasionally twice to mix and match the personalities. As a result, happiness tends to rule, and on the rare occasions it doesn't, there's a swift resolution of problems. Sixth form exceptionally strong, with friendships that often endure for life.

Pupils and parents: Around a third from London, a third within an hour's travel, a fifth from overseas (half non British) and the remainder from elsewhere in the UK.

Before head's arrival, vibe was a bit Frost in May, with slight sense that the very grandest of old Catholic families had a more exalted cachet than others. Now, though they're still represented, and anyone paying full fees needs to be 'mega rich' to afford them, there's a more egalitarian spirit abroad.

Increasing numbers are funded by bursaries, and though there's lots of emphasis on socialising with other top notch schools (Eton the top favourite) there's careful control of the trappings of excess. Nickames, amongst them Biggles, Squeaky and Booey, are plentiful and once bestowed are generally there for life.

Parents are a happy bunch. Not hard to see why, given the St Mary's effect, resulting in girls who emerge ready to subdue the world with charm, intelligence, confidence and poise. 'I think anyone in my year could stand up quite happily in front of 500 people and speak,' one former pupil told us.

Entrance: Selective but not awesomely so. Siblings, while favourably viewed, need good dose of what it takes to secure a place. School gives preference to girls who are Roman Catholic (nearly all pupils are). Many from bilingual backgrounds, though no formal support offered. Special educational needs geared towards those with 'generally mild' dyslexia, with learning support lessons and workshops.

Main entrance points are 11 (English, maths and general knowledge/intelligence tests) and 13 (English, maths, science, religious studies, history or geography, MFL, Latin). Feeder schools many and various (300 preps and maintained primaries); so oversubscribed that inevitably there will be some disappointments.

For the unsuccessful, there's another chance in the sixth form (test in proposed A level subjects plus general paper). Chances of success are diminutive though. The maximum new intake is just five, though in reality often fewer.

Exit: Virtually no fall-out after GCSEs. Four to Oxbridge in 2017, plus five off to the US/Canada, and one medic. Bristol, Edinburgh and Exeter also popular. Subjects range from sciences to languages, law to art. Numbers going into performing arts are increasing – one old girl is currently working with Steven Spielberg.

Money matters: Standard range of scholarships at 11, 13 and 16 on offer (five per cent reduction on the fees). Music scholarships include free tuition on up to two instruments.

Remarks: Catholic education at its best. So popular that when it comes to getting a place, faith may not be enough.

St Swithun's School

48

Alresford Road, Winchester, Hampshire SO21 1HA

01962 835700 | admissions@stswithuns.com | www.stswithuns.com

Ages: 11–18

Pupils: 518; sixth form: 136; Boarders: 118 full, 111 weekly

Day: £20,163 pa; Boarding: £32,310 pa

Headmistress: Since 2010, the contained and cogent Ms Jane Gandee MA (40s). Read French and Spanish at Girton College, Cambridge, then a local government accountant until she went into teaching (OU PGSE) at Lord Wandsworth College, Oakham, Queenswood and finally director of studies at City of London School for Girls. The stamina and thoughtful tactics that make her a successful athlete (represented Cambridge at athletics and cross-country, captained the women's football team) are combined with a rigorous passion in her stewardship of the girls here. She teaches Spanish

in the lead up to GCSEs and speaks at two out of the five assemblies each week, finding raw material in books ranging from Freakanomics to Daphne du Maurier novels.

Proud of the expanded co-curricular and sport options ('she's got the place buzzing'), determined to open the pupils' eyes to a real range of issues via external speakers – John Humphries, Michael Portillo, Sir Ralph Fiennes, Laura Bates (Everyday Sexism) – so they can make their own decisions. Committed to developing girls' resilience and confidence – they once took the mickey out of her for her frequent championing of feminism, but now they join in.

Academic matters: Brilliant exam results, up in the dizzying thin air at the top of the league tables. How a relatively unselective school like this one manages it is mysterious and must drive the London hothouses – with their exacting entry testing of pupils from the age of 4 – around the bend. Parents say, 'They don't cream off the top of their applicants; they help girls reach their potential'. Famed for hotshot sciences (three floors of dedicated labs) and maths; English is just as impressive, even if pursued by fewer girls – pupils say teachers are great, 'no duffs'.

Psychology, politics and art history offered at A level (with art history lessons also on offer for parents). Compulsory GCSE subjects are English, maths, plus a foreign language and at least two sciences. Setting in maths and modern languages – with support (one full-time SENCo, part time assistants and outside support if necessary) an SEN child can still access the curriculum. French and German both studied to the end of year 8 when Spanish enters as an option. Most take (only) 10 GCSEs, and just French taken early – a strategy that produces few results below a B. In 2017, 85 per cent A*-A/9-7 grades at GCSE. At A level, 63 per cent A*/A.

Parents report that teachers expect a lot and the girls push themselves, which means that confidence must be built elsewhere if not academically strong. The whole of the lower school enters the Maths Challenge, which encourages different ways of thinking. The Stretch programme helps put academia in perspective – a compulsory hour per week of a loosely cerebral activity for every pupil eg film clubs, music composition, chess, Amnesty international.

The timetable is in half hour units but most lessons are an hour; each A level choice has an hour of each subject per day for balance and to mitigate risk when missing a day. The light and warm library is used for study periods mostly by the sixth form, although whole classes can book out the IT area. In the upper sixth both day and boarding girls can return to their one dedicated house to study and hang out.

Careers fair annually in Harvey Hall with parents and old girls and speakers ranging from architects to philosophy teachers. Families report that careers advice strong on well-trodden paths such as medicine and Russell Group universities, yet quirky directions need more research initiative from home.

Games, options, the arts: Lacrosse is the strongest sport with a fixture every Saturday in both the two terms it is played, attendance at the nationals and amazing international tour a highlight. Conscious effort to broaden the range of sports – netball and tennis are on the up in terms of competition; also swimming, archery, golf, fencing, squash, scuba diving, badminton, cheerleading, football, polo, skiing, pilates. Some of these are only on offer as one of the 30 or so co-curricular choices, others have emerged into the fixture list. The pool is 25m with an Olympic standard diving board (Winchester residents use it too), stables are 10 minutes away and the sailing squad heads off most Sundays. Location in South Downs National Park means limited permanent floodlighting for sports pitches but play continues regardless through temporary arrangements. Early morning swimming popular until studying gets really serious in sixth form, and equipment has been recently updated so apparently girls watch The Big Bang Theory while running.

In the lower years there is an hour of art, drama and food tech each week. Very enthusiastic art team with a regular life model, Rosa Verloop inspired sculptures (stuffed tights), nominated desks and eventually cubby holes for A level students – DT floor just as sparky with electronics, laser cutter and Green Power car (has to be fast, green and involve good team) racing every year at Goodwood, but no A level take up at present. Amazing aromas sandwiched on the floor between the other choices, cooked up in the professional tech kitchen. Textiles popular too with A level newly on offer.

Performing arts centre provides a lively hub for music and drama in the school (and doubles as the venue for morning assembly). Drama studio backs on to the main stage and is used for lessons (no A level at present). Girls do plays on their own initiative too, inviting Winchester boys in for male parts (and vice versa) eg Alan Ayckbourn's Bedroom Farce. Recent joint performance of Oliver! with Winchester College, and more planned. Parents would like more academic links to Winchester College, but it plays quite hard to get; lots of local girls' schools would like to be partnered with it more closely.

School wide and term long game of tag has everyone searching for their targets, who in turn dye their hair, swap uniforms

Great range of orchestras, bands, ensembles and choirs – chamber, gospel and a capella – some open to all, others more selective. Music school houses practice rooms and an IT suite with Sibelius for composition, basic Cubase skills for recording performances. Around 75 per cent of pupils learn a musical instrument and some 215 candidates are entered for external music exams each year. Senior choir sings evensong each term in the cathedral and tours overseas every other year.

Boarding: Separate boarding and day houses until a single combined one for upper sixth; the latter are the only ones allowed to go back to their house to work during the day. The seniors do prep duty for the younger ones and there are clusters with a 'mother' in the sixth form and younger 'sisters' or 'cousins' in other years, a 'family' that looks out for each other. A race back to day houses for a hot chocolate made for the girls at break – and letter delivery for the boarding girls; day and boarding girls become less separate as they move up the school. Different nationalities are more likely to hang out with their own at the weekend – the balance is well set between cultural comfort and integration.

Initially Toblerone shaped dorms with equal sections under Velux windows, flexible boarding and school bed linen for the youngest, a single room for most from 12+ with a hand basin, useful essay quotes and posters on the wall. Each house has thoughtful inclusive touches that soften the necessary (safeguarding) communality – word of the week board for little ones, movie night, pool table, Wii, piano – as well as the vital drudge of learning to do laundry. Everyone sits around the breakfast bar at the weekend in their pyjamas and the houseparents make sure that full boarders keep busy with three activities during week nights and three at weekends eg a trip to the zoo, decorating your mobile phone cover, making gingerbread men, skating or music practice.

Background and atmosphere: Founded as Winchester High School in 1884 by Anna Bramston, daughter of the Dean of Winchester, who remained as school secretary for over 40 years – the dean, the headmaster of Winchester College and the mayor are still part of the governing body. Changed its name to St Swithun's in 1927 and moved to the present 45 acre site in 1931. Vast, intimidating, red-brick, Queen Anne style building with blonde parquet flooring, large windows and long corridors – girls learn to look up and smile as they pass each other rather than hold/avoid gaze as they approach from either end.

A tight community of supportive girls with a culture of 'go for it' rather than 'too cool' to join in eg minority of girls remain in normal clothes on dress up days. Flip side of this is the pressure for good results that they can exert on each other. Boarders and day pupils retreat to different houses for break but all eat together at lunch, and head girl team runs the school forum and instigates a school wide and term long game of tag. This has everyone searching for their targets, who in turn dye their hair, swap uniforms and even hide in cupboards – all for glory, chocolate and side effect of integration. Pupils give regular assemblies and topics range from Beyoncé to the Khmer Rouge, while the school forum has input to subjects as disparate as the air con in the gym and more tenor timbre in the hymns. Fundraising Friday is another equaliser, as money is raised for the voted annual charities, and some girls do EdClub, a worldwide initiative that uses Skype to encourage disadvantaged children (many in slums) to learn using broadband.

Winchester the town is important for the freedom it offers only 15 minutes' walk away – and usually a cab ride back up hill. Provides an opportunity to meet up with Winchester boys; the seniors can eat out or go to a play. The outgoing ones say it is very relaxed, no-one puts on make-up, they are all just a group of friends with about 20 per cent in relationships and many of the day girls knowing the boys from local life; the less confident ones mention a pressure to add the boys as friends on Facebook as soon as they return – yet all monitored (some girls reckon too closely) by the housemistresses and house assistants. Both have a reduced teaching timetable so that they can concentrate on the emotional temperature in each house – there is a health centre on site and a clinical psychologist offers discrete appointments in the old chapel; the whole school benefits from her years of experience of the lives and issues of teenage girls. The leavers' ball is usually just for the girls alone (their choice, no Winchester boys); that, and the singing of Jerusalem, is guaranteed to cause some tears to be shed.

Pastoral care, well-being and discipline: Houseparents are first point of contact for issues from homesickness through bullying to A level choices – although a form tutor is vital for the latter too. Parents feel everything is dealt with swiftly and sensibly; avoiding a before bed phone call can give both parent and child a less weepy night. Phones are used for email nowadays, particularly useful for older girls looking at timetables and emailing essays, restricted for the younger ones.

An art project of smiles photographed around the school has found a permanent home on the wall of the modern (2013) chapel – all full boarders and staff attend every Sunday, optional for the upper sixth. Over-indulging in alcohol the most common serious disciplinary issue – and that not very, if girls' shock at relaxed attitude observed in their visits to boys' or co-ed schools is anything to go by.

Girls sit around the breakfast bar at the weekend in their pyjamas and houseparents make sure that full boarders keep busy with eg skating, making gingerbread men

New Thrive programme for all years 'aims to inculcate the habits of good mental and physical health, and to prepare students for the world outside the school gates'. Lessons designed around 'real world' experiences have included year 7s trying out setting up a new community after a plane crash on a desert island, year 10s practising empathetic listening through role-play and year 13s taking part in a student survival programme including cooking and cycling.

Pupils and parents: Down to earth parents who value education; armed forces, businesspeople, diplomats, lawyers, doctors and bright children with parents working in less lucrative professions; four wheel drives rather than Bentleys. Over half are day pupils – school bus services are getting better after unflattering comparison with King Edward. Twenty (and rising) per cent of boarders from London, often with more local weekend houses – weekly boarders make up 20 per cent of the school. Heathrow is less than an hour away and Southampton airport only 20 minutes, so 16 per cent of boarders from overseas, range of 17 countries. Occasional international guest pupils come for a term from France, Germany, Spain, Czechoslovakia – must be fluent in English. Alumni range from actor Emma Chambers (Alice in the Vicar of Dibley) to journalist and radio presenter Fi Glover and Emma Walmsley, CEO of GlaxoSmith Kline.

Entrance: Main intake by pre-test, January 11+ and CE. Places offered on pre-test and reference from current head – no longer in order of registration. Everyone must pass CE, whether from state, private, or school's own junior school. The latter provides about a third of the intake, others from London day schools and local preps. About 20 more enter at age 13 with a pre-test 18 months before (can be taken overseas) and then a firm offer; if there is a crisis and they don't make the necessary 60 per cent at common entrance then there is leeway – occasional places further up the school. About 20 join the sixth form with own entry and test in November; a summer year 10 report is necessary before registration – very competitive.

Exit: Around 30 per cent leave after GCSEs, bound for the local sixth form college or for other co-ed sixth forms. Almost all the others go on to university, mostly the old-established ones, with Oxbridge (five in 2017), London, Edinburgh, Bristol and Durham being favourite destinations, sciences unsurprisingly popular (three medics in 2017, plus one vet and some biomedics and neuroscientists).

Money matters: One in six pupils has a means-tested bursary, an academic scholarship, sports scholarship or a music award (available at 11, 13 and 16). All scholarships are for up to 20 per cent of fees and based on the calibre of the applicant, rather than need. Bursaries are means-tested and available for 50 to 100 per cent of the fees. Music awards include free music lessons.

Remarks: Academic powerhouse with bluestocking reputation now widened into great co-curricular and sports options; pupil assemblies range from the Beyoncé to the Khmer Rouge. Girls egg each other on to great results and fun too.

Shiplake College

49

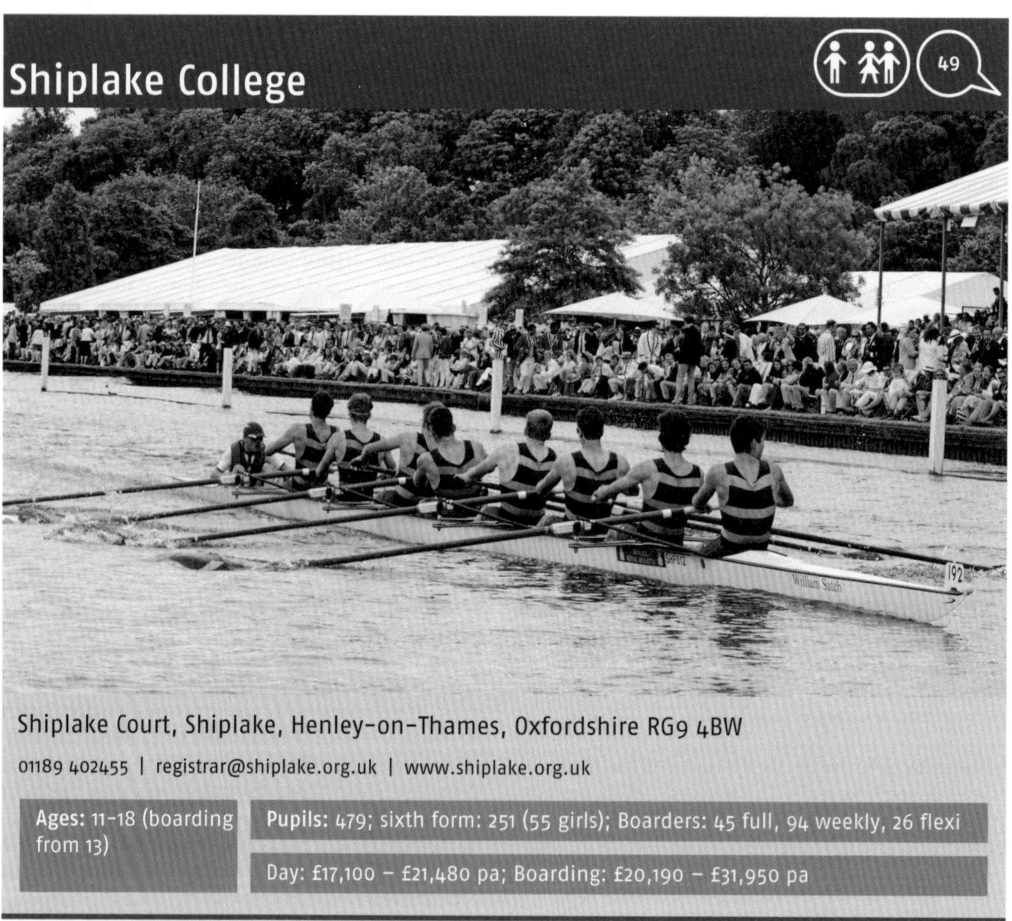

Shiplake Court, Shiplake, Henley-on-Thames, Oxfordshire RG9 4BW

01189 402455 | registrar@shiplake.org.uk | www.shiplake.org.uk

Ages: 11-18 (boarding from 13)

Pupils: 479; sixth form: 251 (55 girls); Boarders: 45 full, 94 weekly, 26 flexi

Day: £17,100 – £21,480 pa; Boarding: £20,190 – £31,950 pa

Headmaster: Since 2004, Gregg Davies BSc Cert Mgmt (mid 50s). Married to Alison, who works in learning development here, and to whom he frequently refers in conversation. They have a daughter, who is an Old Viking (former deputy head of college), now at university. Mr Davies, a reporting inspector for ISI ('the best CPD I do') is, at once, intimidating and benign, humorous and serious, mischievous and earnest. His luxury is the speedboat he keeps moored just below the front lawn. He is direct, looks you straight in the eye, but has a light touch. Immediately likeable, he not only has a twinkle and warmth, but is the kind of man you would be pleased for your son (and daughter) to have as a role model.

Passionate about 'growth mindset' – 'I grew up dreaming of playing rugby for Wales or Scotland and at 36 I played for Scottish veterans – that's an example of growth mindset.' He coins words/phrases for the year. Last year it was 'yet', this term it's 'just try'. Mr Davies, with his two great bearded collies that share his office, is a man you could work with in a crisis. Parents describe him as 'very extrovert', 'going the extra mile', refer to his 'refreshing, individual approach' and a noticeably 'thoughtful, non-judgmental attitude but unafraid to say what he thinks.'

He started his career at Haberdashers' Aske's boys where he taught biology (his degree was in physiology), and moved on to Fettes where he relished the role of housemaster. As a young boy at a local comprehensive, he was spotted by one of the masters at Shrewsbury school, who recognised his commitment and potential. Mr Davies still regards Eric Anderson, his headmaster at Shrewsbury at the time, as a mentor.

While proud of the 'all ability' nature of Shiplake – 'students here go into people jobs,' he says – he is still keen to impress upon us the steady improvement of results. 2016 was the first year that they achieved 100 per cent pass rate at A level. Pupils perform outstandingly in BTec too. He is determined that no one leaves the sixth form feeling they've failed.

Davies is a headmaster who genuinely knows his pupils. By name, sight as well as by their dreams and fears. He enjoys randomly summoning them, whether to talk to us, to discuss their state of dress or praise a recent achievement. The same applies to his staff. No-one escapes any encounter without some sort of remark, observation or comment. They in turn appear to feel great affection for him. He succeeds in treading the delicate line between being everyone's friend and confidante and that of esteemed and highly respected headmaster.

Academic matters: Very small class sizes, maximum 16, allowing each child to get individual attention and creating strong value added scores. Boys take eight or nine GCSEs, enabling them to concentrate on maths, English and sciences. Maths offered as an IGCSE now as well as a GCSE; English, French and Spanish are all IGCSEs too. For science it's either double or triple science award (even when small numbers choose the triple option, the school will support it) and exceptions will be made if a boy arrives late and wants to continue with his, say, two chosen science subjects. The modern language options are French and Spanish (but will facilitate the teaching of other languages such as Mandarin for an additional fee). No Latin, Greek or Arabic. Successful in performing arts and solid but not quite so glowing in ICT, music and PE. In 2017, 31 per cent A*-A/9-7s at GCSE

New sixth formers have a weekly lecture series and complete either an EPQ or a CoPE (Certificate of Personal Effectiveness). BTecs in business, travel/tourism, music and sports studies, the two latter available as A levels too. Proving to be popular as well as successful – particularly business. Computing, ICT, media studies, drama, philosophy, photography and psychology are also options. Results have improved enormously over the past few years; 52 per cent A*/A grades at A level in 2017, 72 per cent A*-B.

His luxury is the speedboat he keeps moored just below the front lawn. He is direct, looks you straight in the eye, but has a light touch. Immediately likeable

A school that celebrates its 'all ability' intake, Shiplake is creative and innovative in how it instils a healthy learning attitude in it pupils. The Shiplake Seven is a mantra engraved in the breast pocket of every maroon, black and gold striped blazer (curious, open-minded, motivated, reflective, determined, creative, independent). This is enforced and reinforced throughout the academic, as well as the co-curricula. In addition there is a highly developed programme of 'flipped learning'. Students are expected to have researched a topic before a lesson – frequently teachers will have created video presentations for the pupils to watch before the lesson begins – so that the lesson itself can be used for more in-depth exploration of the issues and themes. Mindfulness is an option as an activity, but if you want your child to be educated in Happiness this is not the school for you. 'My aim is to create an environment where happiness is not taught but a by-product,' says Mr Davies.

The Thinking Space – what we would usually call the library – is modern and high-tech, but only two small neon shelves with books – this library is online. Brightly painted telephone boxes contain periodicals and store laptops. A canary yellow pod filled with cushions is where, one imagines, you might find a student or two curled up with a book (if there were many to choose from). Moving seamlessly through to The Quiet Space or Flow Room, a cool blue and white area, designed to represent the Henley regatta and the Thames. This is where students can tap away at their essays in silence and calm tranquillity.

Shiplake has long had a strong reputation for excellent provision for those with special educational needs, a reputation that Mr Davies regards with wry scepticism. Quite apart from the fact that he likes to regard each child as having a special educational need, with their own unique learning style, he feels that reputation was undeserved when he arrived here over 10 years ago. Now, however, the support provided by the learning development department is exceptional. There is a definite drive, nonetheless, to diminish the understanding that SEN is Shiplake's strength. No one in years 7 or 8 will be offered support from the learning development department. Anyone who needs that kind of support applying in those years will be told that this is not the right school. The story is different from year 9 upwards. Parents pay extra, but their sons can receive up to four 50 minute lessons per week (always replacing a modern language lesson). Seven dedicated teachers as well as two support workers give a wide range of support from small seminar subject tutoring to one-to-one help as well as assisting with organisation and study skills. We witnessed years 12 and 13 benefitting from 'guided study', given help with structuring essays and proof reading. On average about 15 per cent of pupils have access to the LDD, with a range of conditions – most commonly dyslexia and dyspraxia but also a smattering of ADD as well as Asperger's and ASD.

Games, options, the arts: The focus on sport here is evident from the number of teachers who have some kind of physical education qualification and/or interest. There is tremendous enthusiasm for sport throughout the school and this is the arena where many of the students grow their confidence and self-esteem.

Rowing is excellent. The boathouse nestles below the main building and grassy slope right on the bank of a bend in the river Thames. The Lynch, the island beyond owned by the school, makes this area ideal for adventure, rafting and camping exercises. This isn't a large school, and yet the boys who row, do very well, and it is a growing sport for girls. Three Vikings represented Great Britain in the European and World Championships last summer, winning four gold medals. A lot of enthusiastic rugby, football, cricket, netball, hockey and tennis players too. Games sessions are timetabled and there is an emphasis on inclusivity. Students who might not get a chance to play in matches in some schools will definitely get a chance if they're keen here. Plenty of pitches as well as an Astroturf, a well-equipped gym (especially for the rowers), with squash courts, charming outside pool and refreshed sports hall. Enthusiastic and popular D of E, community service and CCF.

Art housed in spacious beamed roof space in the eaves at the top of one of the modern buildings. Photography in the adjoining space. Lots on display around the school. About 11 pupils do art A level each year. Busy ceramics department, a stunning life-size ram made out of chicken wire and fur ushered us there. Large DT space, four rooms with capacious work stations. DT compulsory in years 7, 8 and 9 about 28 choose it as a GCSE. Large lecture theatre where the full orchestra practises and performs. Chamber choir and auditioned-for First VIII a capella group, as well as an HM choir for those who can't sing but want to, although it sounds pretty painful. Another example of Mr Davies' natural ability to muck in. One parent cringed at the idea of performing badly on stage – the headmaster's choir embrace it and work on the motto 'choice, risk, consequence' that permeates so much of life here. Plenty of jazz groups and string groups. Winter, spring and summer concerts give them a chance to perform. Music technology with all the gear – Macs and keyboards – takes place in the comfortable, new John Turner building. Lots of individual practice rooms and all overseen by an energetic and inspiring head of music. Recent drama productions include Curious Incident of the Dog in the Nighttime (years 9 to 11) and The Jungle Book (years 7-9). Atmospheric theatre in the Old Tithe Barn area. Painted black, with black wooden floorboards and black stone walls, complete with old wood smell. We witnessed a red nosed group of year 8 boys bringing colour and humour to the place with their improvisations about the Olympics.

'One of the exceptional things about the school,' observed a parent, 'is the ability to find something in which a boy or girl can shine.' Singers emerge who never knew they could sing, and the same applies to drama, dance and all areas of school life. 'A lot of this is down to Mr Davies's influence,' commented a father. 'He knows the children so well and he learns what their needs are, how they can be motivated and inspired.'

Boarding: Five core houses from years 9-12, mixing day and boarders (though full boarders predominately live in Burr House). In addition there is a sixth form girls' house (Gilson), as well as a house dedicated to the year 13 boys (College House). Years 7 and 8 join Olympians or Titans, and attend the majority of their lessons in their house group. Some senior girls lucky enough to have ensuite bathrooms. Younger boys normally share their room with two or three others.

Boarding comes in all varieties here and is tailor made to meet the demands of the families. Far more weekly than full boarding pupils. 'We haven't done a full marketing push to attract overseas families,' says the school's communications director. The school feels relatively local. Flexi-boarding is popular and attractive to busy families where both parents work but can have quality time with their children at weekends.

The boathouse nestles right on the bank of a bend in the river Thames. The Lynch, the island beyond owned by the school, makes this area ideal for adventure

Not a lot of pupils stay at school at the weekends, but a dedicated team of housemasters and teachers as well as matrons make sure that there is plenty to do for the few who are in. We were told of a particularly popular trip to Liquid Leisure in Slough, as well as enjoyable nights out at the local curry house. Each house is comfortably (and remarkably tastefully) equipped with sofas, kitchens and games rooms with, when we visited, a delicious smell of clean laundry, and the lubricated sense of being well run.

Background and atmosphere: Situated in the luxurious Oxfordshire countryside, on the banks of the Thames only a couple of miles from Henley, but far enough from the bustle of Reading to feel secluded and remote, Shiplake Court began its existence in 1895 as family home and farm. In 1959 it became a boarding school, and it has always been smaller and a more nurturing environment than many schools of similar ilk. The site has been very tastefully developed through the years, modern buildings and windows, blending with the old, and the red brick and flint atmosphere here is calm and well kempt. Church services are a short walk away in St Peter and St Paul. Daily services are short but an important part of the routine in keeping students focused, on message, and well clad – Mr Davies will pull anyone up for scruffy attire, let alone poorly polished shoes.

Mr Davies runs a tight ship. Staff are wholly committed and everyone rows together to achieve the best possible outcome for each student. He has recently bravely tackled the modern bane – mobile phones. Now every student has to hand their phone in at the beginning the day, to be returned in the evening. Reluctant to do this initially as he regards technology as an important element in their learning, he was driven to do it after observing that young people 'rarely talk to each other any more'. The benefit has been palpable as chattering can be heard again over break and while walking down the numerous pathways.

Parents praise the communication. It's frequent, inclusive and inescapable, from everyone – the receptionist to the head – and covering everything from discipline to rewards and merits. Not a school for a fire-and-forget parent.

Sports fixtures happen on a Saturday morning – if Jack isn't in a team then he can find another programme to keep him busy (art club, LAMDA, for example). There are no Saturday lessons, allowing more family time at the weekend for day pupils and weekly boarders.

Pastoral care, well-being and discipline: Shiplake's reputation as having an exceptional standard of pastoral care is justified (we couldn't find anyone to disagree). This is founded on high teacher to pupil ratio (roughly 1:6), a highly effective school chaplain, the Rev, who doesn't teach but is the pivot of the pastoral system. Parents even go to him with their troubles ('He is your Rev too, I tell them,' says Davies). A strong system of tutors (primarily assigned to individual pupils for academic support and normally house-based, but sometimes work across houses for older students), as well as house-parent, matron and various support staff within the house. Parents warmly praise the extent to which the staff get to know their students and understand any difficulties. The school GP is excellent and is proactive about communicating with any external specialists. There is cross communication throughout the departments and houses and through to the head, and in turn excellent communication with parents. Pupils feel safe here. The structures are there to keep them so.

Quite apart from the structures, however, there is also a strong set of principles running from the top downwards. From growth mindset, the Shiplake Seven and the annual key words and phrases to mindfulness clubs and good old-fashioned exercise and fresh air, constant care and attention is given to the well-being of the students. The food is delicious – and there is plenty of it (one parent was delighted that her son eats six sausages for breakfast) with properly cooked meals, and a wide choice in the wood panelled gothic great hall plus piles of toasts back at the house. Mentoring – responsibility taken by the sixth formers for the new year 9s – is both popular with the students, and an effective way to break down hierarchies. Bad behaviour not tolerated – from drugs to bullying – and the school will not accept children with behavioural difficulties. However, Mr Davies is remarkably open minded about young boys who come to him with a chequered past, always prepared to recognise potential and give people a second chance.

Pupils and parents: Set in the heart of shiny Range Rover well-heeled territory with sky high property prices, Shiplake has plenty of parents who live up to their environment. Most parents work, a lot are in business. Some are demanding and discerning, some completely hands off, and school prefers the former. Most parents share a balanced view about exam results, and while they want their children to flourish are not obsessively competitive about how they are performing academically. Not a smart or fashionable school ('no fancy airs and graces,' said one former pupil), parents here are grounded and practical, with sound middle class values and concerned more about the right fit for their children than brand. A few Forces children, but mostly local families (the majority live close enough to be day or flexi boarders). Only five per cent of families from overseas, school looking to increase that number. Most of the catchment is east of Reading (navigating Reading during rush hour puts a lot of people off).

Pupils here are allowed to be individuals. They are taught to be practical and hands on. Encouraged

The food is delicious – and there is plenty of it (one parent was delighted that her son eats six sausages for breakfast)

to roll up their sleeves and get a Sunday job. Work experience ideally is work in a builders' yard (no holding onto to mummy and daddy's coat tails in a law firm here). The broadness of selection helps to contribute a colourful mix of ability and personality. They come in all shapes and sizes with a range of skills, from the uber rower, to a committed oboist, with no doubt some future actors, designers and entrepreneurs in between. We were pleased to meet Will Satch, Olympic gold and bronze medallist and old Viking, who was visiting his old school. Mr Davies, clearly proud of Will's rowing achievements, was equally full of praise for his communication skills (Will is regularly wheeled out to deal with the media). Other notable alumni include Nick Jones, Soho house proprietor, Alex Pettyfer, actor, Chris Standring, jazz musician and Jonty Hearnden, antiques expert.

Entrance: Assessment is thorough, takes a day and enables school to see 'the whole picture'. A maximum of 20 pupils are assessed on any one day. Numeracy and literacy is just one part of the jigsaw. Candidates participate in a group activity during the afternoon, they are interviewed by the house-parent and deputy and finish the day with a sports activity. The question staff ask themselves is would this child be happy here – the long days, the exercise (even for day pupils there is a strong boarding ethos) – and what will they contribute to school life? A mix of 11+ prep and state primary pupils enter at year 7; the main intake, however, is at year 9. The number of girls in the sixth form has doubled, now at 55. Incomers require 5+ GCSEs (with at least a C/5 in English and maths) though they make exceptions for those they feel will fit in. 'We will let our own boys stay on if we can find something useful and enjoyable for them to do.' Will rescue those burnt out from (or shot out of) Thames valley swot-houses.

Exit: Nearly all to first or second choice university. 'We got the pupils onto the right courses,' says head, 'played to their strengths.' A huge range of universities. Two to Oxbridge in 2017; others to eg Exeter, Oxford Brookes, Nottingham, Bristol and UWE. Applications are starting to be made to US universities. Equally wide range of courses from law and mathematics to sports development, television production and maritime business and logistics. Around 25 per cent leave after GCSE but are replaced.

Money matters: Art, drama, music and sports scholarships awarded but more for prestige than pounds. Sixth form schols depend on general aptitude test, plus test results in two subjects to be studied at A level. Means-tested bursaries awarded at the school's discretion with small pot to assist existing pupils, should financial hiccups occur.

Remarks: Perhaps the only child Shiplake would not suit is the super clever nerd. Possibly the only parents not suited are those for whom brand comes before substance. In Gregg Davies, Shiplake has found a head who perfectly reflects and holds dear those values that have made it stand out as a uniquely nurturing school for half a century and more. It is highly unlikely that anyone will leave here with a feeling of having failed; some will shine more than others but no one will be made to feel less valued. The key to success, however, is a wholehearted commitment to contributing to the community – in whatever way suits.

Sibford School

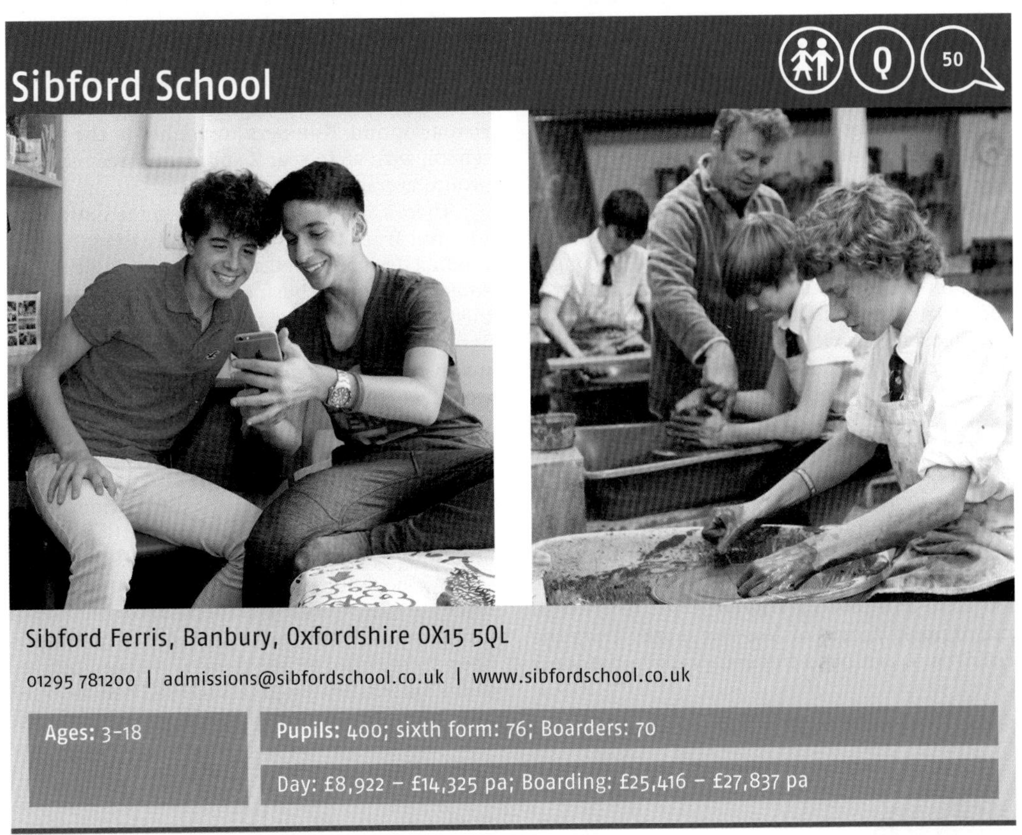

Sibford Ferris, Banbury, Oxfordshire OX15 5QL

01295 781200 | admissions@sibfordschool.co.uk | www.sibfordschool.co.uk

Ages: 3–18

Pupils: 400; sixth form: 76; Boarders: 70

Day: £8,922 – £14,325 pa; Boarding: £25,416 – £27,837 pa

Head: Since September 2016, Toby Spence. Joined from Greensteds, a British curriculum boarding school in Kenya. A Quaker by upbringing, his career has included a five year stint as head of history at another Quaker school, Bootham in York: 'I'm a late medievalist and it was a joy to see York Minster out of the window'. He also had the delicious experience of returning to his old school – King's School in Tynemouth – as deputy head, and as the boss of a teacher who had disliked him in his schooldays. 'We got on better as colleagues,' he says.

Toby is married to Jill and they have three young children, all providing proof of the pudding by being at Sibford School. They are a super sporty family, and Toby is something of an action man, with swashbuckling tales of paddling a sea-kayak with killer whales off Vancouver Island, making a number of first ascents of mountains in South America, and sailing Tall Ships around the coast of Australia. He has brought a fervour for triathlons to the school, with much excited chatter about one held earlier in the week when we visited.

A new emphasis on sport is at his instigation, as is a greater emphasis on the academics, although not to the detriment of those requiring learning support, he assured us robustly. His watch is bringing not quite a new broom – not the Quaker way – but rather a dustpan and brush to some dusty corners.

Has a habit of referring to himself in the third person, which along with the Quaker way of all staff including the head going by their first name, takes a little tuning into.

Parents told us he is 'inspiring to students and parents' and they felt confident Sibford was in good hands for the future. 'He's open to opinion and change,' said one. Others appreciated his deep involvement in helping sixth formers to secure university places.

Academic matters: Sibford has a long held reputation as the go-to school for the child who needs a little extra nurturing and support. Toby insists it will remain that way; but that he also wants to develop its academic offer. 'Sibford has an unfair reputation as warm and cosy, but not particularly strong academically. For me they are not mutually exclusive,' he says. Work is underway on what he terms as 'rebalancing'. There's a newly appointed director of learning and teaching, and a fresh tracking and monitoring system. There are working groups led by the heads of English, maths, and science, looking to build on good practice, and to deliver improved added value results. 'My expectation would be 0.5 on value added, so if you are predicted four Bs you would get two As and two Bs,' he says.

In 2017, 51 per cent of A level grades were at A*-B, a third A*/A. At GCSE, 23 per cent of grades were A*-A/9-7.

The junior school is small – 90 pupils – with the majority joining the school at year 4 or above. Year 1 and 2 are in a joint class. Subjects are mainly class taught, with specialist subject teaching for music and PE. There is setting for English and maths. We looked in on a year 5 maths class, and received an unprompted chorus of 'We love maths' from the children. Learning is frequently taken outdoors

'Our role is to find the talents and qualities in each individual to develop and celebrate. You don't have to be one type of person'

– we saw a troop of little ones coming through the mist in their orange boiler suits, looking like a tiny chain gang. Reception parents spoke fondly of welly walks and forest school.

In the senior school there is setting for English, maths and science. Pupils can choose the dual award or separate sciences. The language choice is French or Spanish, with German as an extracurricular option. Numbers are higher in the senior school, with 46 in year 7, split into three teaching groups averaging 14 to 16 pupils.

There's a choice of 28 courses in the sixth form, ranging from traditional A levels to textiles or product design, as well as BTecs at levels 2 and 3 in subjects including business studies, sport, ICT and media. Courses will be laid on for small numbers, as one parent said: 'My daughter's French class has just two pupils. I had worried about whether this would work, but it does and the teachers respond well to any class size.'

Sixth form is 'led by an outstanding head who knows all the pupils well. The sixth formers are encouraged to be young adults and provide leadership to younger pupils and amongst themselves,' according to a parent.

'We have lived in three different countries since my daughters began their education, and so far the teaching staff and experience at Sibford has been far superior to anywhere we've been before,' said a parent. 'My daughters have all had an excellent connection with their teachers, and I have felt that they quickly understand their learning styles, strengths and weaknesses, and work with them individually in the ways that motivate them best. The teachers at the junior school make it fun and engaging to learn, and they have been quick to see where they can 'stretch' and encourage them to push themselves to work harder and excel.'

Around 20 per cent of pupils receive learning support for any combination of literacy, numeracy, fine motor, attention and focus, and speech and language needs. Children will typically come out of language lessons for support, and in years 7, 8 and 9 will receive three hours per week. For years 10 and 11, it's two hours, and sixth formers have one-to-one for an hour or two. It's possible to have additional one-to-one on top.

The learning support department is well regarded – one parent said it had given her child 'confidence and belief in her abilities'. And it is not restricted to those timetabled sessions out of class. 'My mantra is we are all in the support for learning department,' Toby says.

There's also extension work for more able children – one parent told us her child was in a small group having additional English to stretch them further.

Games, options, the arts: 'We tend to do better in the younger rugby teams,' said our honest guide, when asked about sporting wins. 'Sport is not all about winning, culturally we are more into full participation and giving our best,' is the head's take.

As a small school, and one with a contingent of children there for gentle nurturing, it wouldn't be the place if league-leading teams and dazzling matches are top of your requirements. But you can expect it to claw its way up the fixture lists under this sports-mad head – we did notice his eyes straying out of his office window to the rugby pitch conveniently in view when the 1st XI were playing.

And it can be a joy for pupils shunted to the sidelines at previous schools. 'I'm now in the 1st XI rugby team when I wasn't in a team at my other school,' one boy told us proudly. A parent concurred: 'At her previous school our daughter wasn't great at sport, didn't get into any of the school teams, and felt left out of sport generally. At Sibford the school finds sports that everyone can participate in, and everyone gets a chance to be on school teams. She has been much more sporty, doing swimming, hockey and netball, and representing the school in enthusiastic teams.'

From year 7 there is a sports carousel so if competitive sport is not your bag you can do other things. On our visit we watched a mixed sex group having a ballet masterclass with two male dancers. A new climbing wall adds to the options, and there's a newly formed equestrian team. Triathlon, swimming, hockey and cross country are the strongest sports.

Plenty of bands, orchestras and ensembles, and an egalitarian approach to performance opportunities. There's a dedicated drama studio, and the school gets a strong showing in LAMDA exams. The head of drama is RSC trained, and a number of sixth form leavers have gone on to production and acting careers.

Boarding: Boarding pupils number around 70, with slightly more than half from overseas (predominantly Asia, a few from Europe). There are three boarding houses – one each for 11-16 year-old boys and girls, plus a co-ed sixth form house – all with games rooms and quiet areas. Sixth formers have one or two to a room, in the younger houses it may be up to four to a room. Rooms are standard boarding fare.

There is plenty of flex – some pupils will board only one night a week, to tie in with after-school clubs or early morning swimming, or as a chance to sleep over with friends. 'There are always things to do,' one boarder said, and the sixth form girls assured us the presence of their friends meant that they often got more studying done than they might at home alone.

Boarding is for seniors only, but occasionally they will take a year 6 when an older sibling boards.

Background and atmosphere: It's a long wind through tractor muddied lanes to a bigger campus than you'd expect for the number of pupils. It sits in 50 acre grounds with an orchard, woodland and pond. The original manor was sold off, and the campus is now a hotchpotch of purpose-built blocks including the more recently added music and art blocks and a sixth form centre.

It was founded as a co-ed boarding school by the Quakers in 1842, with an ethos to find that of god in everyone. 'The way I interpret that today is finding the good in everyone,' Toby says. 'Our role is to find the talents and qualities in each individual and develop and celebrate it. At this school you don't have to be one type of person, or one particular fit. We talk about the three Rs but for us that means respect, resilience, and relationships.'

You can expect it to claw its way up the fixture lists under this sports-mad head – we did notice his eyes straying out of his office window to the rugby pitch

There are meetings for worship twice a week, where the community sit in silence, but anyone can speak or give a reading. Fewer than five per cent of families are Quakers, but the rest are drawn here for the values, and many more parents attend the meetings. 'No parent should be put off Sibford for a moment because it is a Quaker school – it is an entirely positive and largely benign influence,' one parent said. Our pupil guides told us that meetings were a nice time to reflect. 'Like walking into another world, it's beautiful,' said learning support head Catherine Stockdale.

The use of Christian names for all children and adults, and the meetings, result in excellent relationships across the school, parents said. Another commented that the sense of community means that teachers often stay for many years, giving tremendous continuity and commitment.

Pastoral care, well-being and discipline: 'Always believe you might be mistaken,' is Toby's starting point, meaning errant pupils always have an opportunity to speak in their defence. 'Let's hear, listen and understand. We look for the good in anyone; however bad has it been, we ask, where's the good in here?' Discipline mainly comes in the form of positive reinforcement and praise, but there are 'full sanctions if need be' which has included pupils being asked to leave.

This approach means they will consider pupils who may have gone off track in other schools. 'We are open to discussion, and we say if you want to come in these are our expectations. We have some real success stories.'

A parent commented: 'On the rare occasion, I have felt that sometimes the staff are not quite as strict on certain children who might require more discipline. They work very hard to support children through kindness and patience (living the Quaker values demonstrably), working with the broader classroom to encourage support that will lead to the necessary behaviour change in the particular child. I think this is mainly the case in the junior school, which is understandable as the children are young and need support to work out rough edges. The senior school is more firm, which we recognise and appreciate.'

Two well-being counsellors are on site two days a week, and the school offers training for parents in identifying and supporting mental health problems. For children with autism or other needs requiring emotional support throughout the day, they will put together a timetable of key people who are free at every point throughout the day. 'It needs as immediate a response as possible; after the event isn't good enough,' says Catherine. Where children have social communication difficulties, they will sometimes be coached during their learning support sessions on strategies they can use in class.

'Always believe you might be mistaken' is Toby's starting point, meaning errant pupils always have a chance to speak in their defence

The school has also supported a few pupils who are transgender or gender questioning. 'Our senior leadership team is reviewing what we need to do to get it right. Our school community understands why this school is at the vanguard here – equality, tolerance, and liberal values are very important to us.'

A key ethos of the school is that children should grow into what they are, not try to be like everyone else. 'Peer relationships are very accepting,' parents said.

Pupils and parents: The school is set among the mellow Cotswold stone of the Cameron-Clarkson brigade, but pushy parents are a rare breed here, we're told. Those choosing it are like-minded, in putting equal store by the values a child will gain to the certificates they leave with. 'Not a yummy mummy brigade, you don't have to dress up for the school run,' said one mother.

Others love the mutual support, and lack of jostling over which set or which team your child is in. 'There's a big fan club if a match is on, and they'll be shouting for all the year groups, not just their own child's,' one parent said.

Another praised 'the inclusive manner of the school, where all ages mix frequently, and there are no groups of girls who exclude others from their circle. Everyone gets on very well, regardless of age, ability, background, etc.'

Entrance: Will Sibford's changing focus alter its intake? 'Early days,' says Toby. 'But the numbers coming to see us doubled last year.' There is now a formal assessment day in January for year 7 entry (before it was come when you like). However, he says, 'There is no bar to jump, no Sats, no 11+. Pupils take CATS tests, do some outdoor learning and ceramics. We are a non-selective mainstream school, so as long as the child can cope and thrive in that environment they will be offered a place. It might be more tricky where we feel we might not be able to meet needs.'

Progression from the junior to senior school is as good as automatic. Last year all were offered a place, and all but two took it up. For more academic sixth form courses they ask for five or six B/6s at GCSE for externals taking up A level courses – for vocational courses that would be more flexible.

Sibford is looking to small scale expansion, so it's a good time to enquire about places. And they might literally go the extra mile for you. 'We were very impressed that the school altered a minibus route to pick up our daughter,' said a parent.

Exit: About 60 per cent of pupils stay on into the sixth form. Leavers include those who may move on to something more vocational; a few who want a more rigid academic focus; and a few who are seeking a bigger sporting offer.

The majority of sixth form leavers go on to university, and to a wide variety including King's College London, Warwick, Cardiff, Oxford Brookes, Royal Northern College of Music, Birmingham Conservatoire and Royal Agricultural University.

Money matters: There are academic, sports, music, drama and arts scholarships worth 5-10 per cent of fees, and means tested bursaries covering up to 80 per cent of fees.

Remarks: One of the few schools which is genuinely all ability, in every meaning of the word. There's a place here for those who need learning support, and those who might apply to Oxbridge; for those who want to perform on stage, and for those who want to quietly contemplate; for those who've made teenage errors of judgement, and those who need cosseting. It's a great option if your brood all need different handling.

You won't come here if a slick and shiny public school is what you are after; despite having an international contingent, the feel is more of a local school. But if competitive parents and league table chasing turn your stomach, you will find your ilk here.

Stowe School

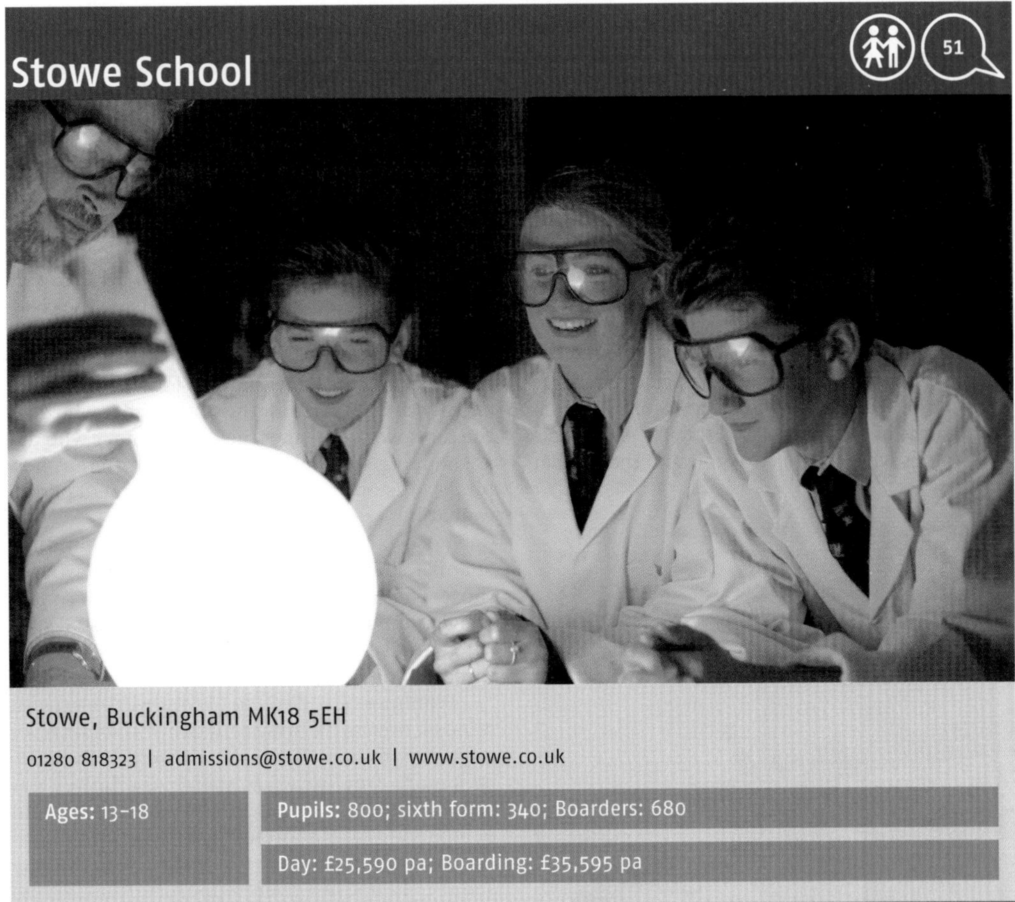

Stowe, Buckingham MK18 5EH

01280 818323 | admissions@stowe.co.uk | www.stowe.co.uk

Ages: 13-18

Pupils: 800; sixth form: 340; Boarders: 680

Day: £25,590 pa; Boarding: £35,595 pa

Headmaster: Since 2003, Dr Anthony Wallersteiner MA PhD (50s), Cambridge history scholar and art historian, married to Valerie, three children. Previously at the academic powerhouses of St Paul's and Tonbridge, but in Stowe he has discovered his nirvana, and certainly seems a perfect fit for this unique school with his erudite and maverick charm and the very fact that he doesn't have a watertight educational track record. Indeed, his prep school report told of a time waster, a lazy boy who would never amount to anything, yet his final school report raved about a cerebral scholar off to Cambridge. 'Children need to find their passion and drive, to be inspired and to inspire, to appreciate the beauty of life, to be creative, to find their utopia. And that's what we do at Stowe, awakening pupils' enthusiasm and excitement and igniting the spark.'

A man with presence but also fun, we found him unstoppably talkative and have rarely come across such name-dropping (old Stoics and other famous visitors to the school; he even showed us a video on his phone of Supertramp's Roger Hodgson playing in the school's recording studio). Parents enthuse that he has done wonders for the school improving facilities through fundraising; but some feel that he glorifies the benefactors at the expense of ordinary parents 'who struggle to pay the extortionate fees.' Other praise him for 'talking our language' and 'epitomising what education should be about.' 'Ah headmaster!' bellow staff with a smile as he approaches (he does 'the walk of the school' once a day), while students are in awe. 'He knows us all by name and what our latest achievements are.'

Stowe was in the doldrums when he joined. It needed lifeblood and direction and he's made it his mission to return it to its glory days, but with a 21st century twist. 'We used to stand shoulder to shoulder with Eton, Rugby and Harrow and we were renowned for being idiosyncratic, for looking after the individual, encouraging them to pursue interests with enthusiasm, allowing characters to emerge – Leonard Cheshire, David Niven – Stoics with an innate sense of confidence. Branson in the 60s probably typifies what it is to be a Stoic and that's what I wanted to inject into the place. Old Stoics have set the world alight; I want that to continue.'

Academic matters: Tasked with raising academic standards at both the point of entry and departure, Dr Wallersteiner has made the school more selective ('We lost the bottom 10 per cent') and moved academic rigour centre stage, with a particular emphasis on value added, with story after story of pupils who were predicted Cs or Ds, but wound up with As. 'At St Paul's and Tonbridge, pupils both came in and left as thoroughbreds. But, sticking with the racing analogy, how much more interesting to come in as an outsider and win the race?'

A level results on the up – 36 per cent A*/A in 2017; 47 per cent A*-A/9-7 at GCSE. Maths, sciences, languages and history strongest subjects at GCSE; Latin, Greek, English and chemistry at A level (unbroken 25 years of Stoics becoming chemistry Oxbridge graduates). Head insists once flakier departments have strengthened, but pupils told us maths, English and biology are still weaker than others and a couple of parents said year 9 teaching could be more rigorous overall ('they have a tendency to go over the same things the children learned in their previous school'). Teachers also a mixed bag, say pupils and parents, with excellent pockets of interactive, engaging teaching, 'but a few old-timers that seem to stamp out fresh ideas that the newer teacher come in with.' Subject clinics and extra tutorials for those who fall behind, plus a firm mantra that what goes on outside the classroom is just as important, hence encouragement to join and start up clubs, get outside speakers in, visit relevant museums and do a lot of work experience (with £100 prize for the sixth former who does the most work – we met the latest winner who did a whopping seven weeks across five different hospitals). 'It's one of the reasons our students do so well at interviews,' a teacher told us.

Sets (six) in most subjects, 'but with fluidity.' Spanish, French and German (plus Mandarin for those who want it) from year 9; one modern language compulsory at GCSE. Most take 10 GCSEs; 50 per cent take four A levels, while the other half do three and an EPQ.

Prominence is given to Carol Dweck's growth mindset theory, building confidence and marginal gains ('go to sleep 10 minutes earlier; do five minutes more exercise a day; spend 20 minutes less on social media a day' etc). SEN provision for mild to moderate cases thorough and 'second-to-none,' according to parents, with dyslexics enthusing about help not just from support staff but across the board. 'If anyone told me they have a child who is dyslexic but who is bright and determined, I'd recommend Stowe any time. They have been exceptional,' one parent told us.

Games, options, the arts: Whether running or reading, beagling or bugling, singing or shooting, there's something for everyone – and probably a lot you've never even considered. Sport up there with the best of them, with national representation in rowing, running, golf, cricket, rugby, fencing and equestrian events. Teams draped in accolades too – top of the national schools' league table for cricket, first division lacrosse champions, with similar levels of success for polo, hockey and rugby. Facilities outstanding, including playing fields, assault course, a new golf course, courts, sports hall, climbing wall, fencing salle, fives courts and pool. Latest offerings include a scrambling track (shiny motor bikes), athletics track (opened by Sebastian Coe – there's that name dropping again) and new equestrian centre with 20 stables. Bring your own horse or ride one of the rescue ones. Key winter sports of rugby, hockey and lacrosse cede to summer offerings of leather on willow, athletics and tennis, with polo, rowing, sailing, clay pigeon shooting and golf just some of the country club offerings. 'The school has given our daughter confidence on the sports field even though she's not that co-ordinated,' said one parent. 'Gym is pretty poor, though,' say pupils.

'Children need to find their passion and drive, to be inspired and to inspire, to appreciate the beauty of life, to be creative, to find their utopia. And that's what we do'

Strong in art – several to art school. Some terrific work on display and in the making during our visit, in the now sun-drenched studios (mezzanine level removed to let in more light). Emphasis on cross-curricular, with examples of architectural drawings and geography-based paintings reminding pupils how art isn't an add-on. Art eclectic too – in a single lesson, you can go from post-conceptual abstract expressionism to figurative to neo-classism.

Music popular, plentiful, oft polished with weekly, summer al-fresco performances the perfect backdrop for picnicking parents. New music school, with high quality performances coming from every nook and cranny, from the piano room with two Steinway grands to the swish recording studio. Every year 9 pupil tries out a musical instrument and over half of all pupils learn with a peripatetic teacher. High number of music diploma students. Everything from bagpipes to violinists – 'The range is unbelievable,' said a student. Resident DJ nights in the weekend nightclub (kitted out from the remnants of Crazy Larry's in London).

Drama performances 'as good as the West End – just extraordinary,' say parents. Whole school production of 1984 in the making during our visit – 'but with a modern take to reflect the Trump era.' Annual arts festival encompasses science, sport, dance, music, art, drama.

All do CCF or D of E with push towards community work, plus endless charity involvement. You'd be hard pushed to find a corner of the globe Stowe pupils haven't had a chance to visit over the years on tours and trips; but although there are clubs, including student-led, some parents felt extracurricular provision could be more plentiful, 'particularly in the younger years.'

Boarding: Ninety per cent board across 13 boarding houses, all comfortable with kitchens and communal rooms. Some boys envious of newer, purpose-built accommodation for the girls (one of them opened by the Queen, 'although I'm not sure she actually approved of the architecture,' says head), which boasts in-house gym, pool room, en-suite etc; others perfectly happy – and there's a new boys' boarding house opening in 2018. 'The girls' accommodation is more like a hotel, whereas ours is really cosy,' one boy shrugged. Dorms of up to 10 for boys (although most much smaller); and up to four for girls; by sixth form, most in twos or singles. Colourful and comfortable common rooms and study areas throughout.

Care delivered in abundance with everyone from cleaners and caretakers, housemistresses and academic staff on hand to help, plus close liaison with parents, as befits a proper full boarding school. Buddy system ('which can feel forced') replaced by a new house family system, in which two pupils from each year group 'look after each other.' School strict on which weekends are for exeats; pupils would like more floater weekends. Also strict on routines – bedtime at 9.30pm (for sleep at 9.45pm) for year 9s, moving up in 15 minute increments.

Each house has its own identity, say pupils – arty, sporty, academic, horsey etc. 'Although friendships are not confined to your house, there is a great loyalty towards it,' they told us, with house competitions (singing, debating etc) major calendar events.

Day pupils (some 120, but rising) insist they aren't left out and are free to roam the boarding houses (including having their own desk), with plans to build two day houses.

Background and atmosphere: To say the physical environment is breathtaking feels like the understatement of the century. The 750 acres of parkland and sublime landscape gardens are widely regarded as most significant in Europe and the embodiment of 18th century enlightenment. They include exquisite woods and waters, temples and gardens. Youngsters adore the place: 'Once you get here you never want to leave; when it snows, it looks more magical than Narnia.' Members of the public can get a slice of it too – in 1989 gardens passed to the National Trust and opened to visitors.

The main building – 'the mansion' – is a splendid, neo-classical palace, largely modelled by Robert Adam in the mid-18th century and benefiting from the respective geniuses of Sir Johns Vanbrugh and Soane, William Kent and Capability Brown among others, and became a school only in 1923. The stone-flagged, below-stairs administrative centre includes the head's breathtaking study – 'Sir John Soane in gothic fantasy mode' – a mini replica of Henry VII's chapel in Westminster Abbey with fabulous fan vaulting, lead canopies, brass screens and tracery.

Other buildings on the surprisingly compact campus have nearly all had facelifts, so few blots remain. You can't help but be in awe of the library with its magnificent ceiling, while the most recent renovations and additions include the theatre, music school, science block with sixth form study centre and new art school. 'We have many generous alumni who feel warmly disposed to the school and I make no apology for inviting them to invest in our projects,' says head. He laughs that he'll probably be remembered as 'the king of stucco', such is his desire to ensure all buildings blend in architecturally – even the gardener's cottage now has columns.

Purposeful atmosphere with boredom-busting teaching injecting a good dose of fun. Practical teaching where possible – 'The upper sixth told me they were a bit rusty on a particular area, so I thought we'd do a quick demo to sort that out,' a chemistry teacher told us as we watched them create bubbling pink liquids. Pupils encouraged to be go-getting and they seem to think nothing of writing to the likes of Richard Branson and head

The stone flagged, below-stairs administrative centre includes the head's breathtaking study – 'Sir John Soane in gothic fantasy mode'

of chemistry at Cambridge to help them with their EPQ – and why not?; they get answers (usually the ones they want) back. Nice to see a public school uniform that doesn't look scratchy, as well as unusual haircuts that suggest young people are able to express themselves – but head is so fanatical about length of girls' skirts that 'I've introduced a new one that goes to below-the-knee.' Pupils attend chapel twice a week (three times for boarders), but atheist views are accepted, say pupils.

Girls first admitted into year 9 in 2007 to expand numbers (previously it was only co-ed in sixth form), now up to 40 per cent and rising.

Pastoral care, well-being and discipline: Houseparents, in-house tutors, matron, counsellors and sixth formers who have been trained on the peer support group programme make up the strong pastoral team at this nurturing school, which parents say is less strictly regimented than other schools ('no petty rules'). Head sees every child on their birthday 'to have a general chat and find out what's working and what isn't.' We quizzed the pupils on vices and sins: drink and drugs? 'Testing random and compulsory. Second chances may be possible but never a given'. Bar for sixth form but random breathalyser catches those who transgress. Eating disorders? 'PSHE lessons, external talkers and close monitoring is good at preventing this.' Cyber bullying? 'Zero tolerance, discussed openly and frankly in both assemblies.' In the past, pupil transgressions at Stowe made regular headlines; less so these days and there are fewer exclusions too, says head – five suspensions and two permanent exclusions in previous 12 months to our visit, mostly for sexually related misdemeanours. For lesser offences, it's a sanction (early morning detention) or Saturday night grounding.

Pupils and parents: 'Accepting' and 'diverse,' according to pupils, although not many non-white faces (school doesn't have an ethnicity breakdown). Attracts the solid and traditional types plus oddballs and those who might be overlooked elsewhere. Pupils, formal in approach, are charming, polite, grounded, confident and entertaining. Parents a mix of entrepreneurs, academics, old money (lots), new money (rising numbers), country and creative (plus a few celebrities). 'Stowe may look posh but most of us aren't,' say pupils; parents concur. 'Yes, you get the hugely wealthy backgrounds, but not all of us are millionaires.'

Entrance: More selective than in the past, the school is no longer the 'back up plan' but a conscious first destination, particularly for girls ('they are nearly there with boys, but not quite,' believe some parents). Pre-tests in year 6 or 7; looking for 55 per cent plus at CE. But, true to its founding principles, high grades aren't the be-all-and-end-all. 'They are welcome, but more important is a spark, something we can ignite – evidence of effort more than natural ability. The imagined destination is less important than the drive and journey,' explains head.

A handful from state schools, rest from a range of preps, including Winchester House, The Dragon, Summer Fields, Ashdown House, Papplewick, Sunningdale and Windlesham. Around 50 additional pupils enter at sixth form (100-120 apply), for which entrance criteria (and this goes for existing pupils too) is minimum of six Bs (or numerical equivalents), including As in subjects to be studied.

Around 10 per cent international students, with the school caught up in a 'cash for places' scandal in 2016 in which the registrar told an undercover journalist if there was a 'marginal decision' over whether to admit an overseas student, a six-figure donation from their family could help secure the place. Needless to say the registrar has now resigned, although head at pains to point out no money actually passed hands and seemingly more incensed by the underhand journalist than the registrar 'whose career has now been unnecessarily ruined.'

Exit: Around 10 leave after GCSE, mostly to day schools, performing arts school or occasionally because they underperform academically. Of those who leave after sixth form, nearly all to university – three-quarters to Russell Group, especially Bristol, Edinburgh, Exeter, Newcastle, Warwick, Manchester, York, Kings and UCL. Usually a few to Oxbridge (two in 2017) and one or two to US. Business-related courses popular. A considerable number to good art schools, with some going to highly-acclaimed music or drama schools.

Money matters: Eight per cent of income goes back into scholarships and bursaries – means-tested options for both, with a small number of fully-funded places for exceptional candidates with proven financial need. Additionally, Roxburgh schols (named after Stowe's revered founding headmaster) awarded to outstanding all-rounders nominated by the heads of their previous schools. Stephan schols available for bright day pupils from the state sector – worth up to 25 per cent of fees, with further support from means-tested bursaries as with other scholarships.

Remarks: What makes your child get out of bed in the mornings? What really interests them? What do they want to be good at? These are the questions Stowe gets to the heart of in its quest to nurture the individual and, as such, gives young people space to grow into their identities. 'Stowe is the catalytic converter of education,' says head – and although it's a bold claim, it's not entirely unfair. Captivating, with something for everyone, this is a school that mixes the erudite with the sporty and studious, and in which the eccentric can shine. And it all takes place in stunning surroundings. A privileged education for those for whom more conventional schools might feel too much like a straitjacket, although if your sights are firmly set on league tables and academic brags, Stowe is ready for you but you're probably not ready for Stowe.

Summer Fields

52

Mayfield Road, Oxford, Oxfordshire OX2 7EN

01865 454433 | admissions@summerfields.com | www.summerfields.com

Ages: 8-13 (4-13 from September 2018)

Pupils: 250; Boarders: 200

Day: £22,608 pa; Boarding: £29,193 pa

Headmaster: Since 2010, Mr David Faber MA Oxon (50s); came to Summer Fields as old boy; former parent and governor, as well as grandson of illustrious alumnus, Harold Macmillan PM. After Eton and Balliol, became a Conservative MP from 1992-2001, including Opposition spokesman foreign affairs (recently secured schools minister as a speaker for a meeting of prep and public school heads). A keen cricketer (sits on MCC committee) and has introduced new cricket nets to the fields; also referees boys' football matches.

Interesting appointment as not originally from a teaching background. Urbane and reserved in manner until on the subject of the boys' achievements – fond collector of past medals; 'sporting caps' and historical mementoes of the school. Uses his experience as a historian and author (two books on modern history) in teaching history to the older years and lecturing on 'Appeasement and the Munich Crisis' to public school history societies. Popular with parents ('dream headmaster'), who have seen him institute 'a lot of changes for the better, one thing at a time'. Makes himself available to the parents and appears to know the boys by name and character. Married to Sophie, not on school staff, with two school aged daughters and a son at Oxford University.

Head of the new pre-prep that opens in September 2018 will be Joanna Chapman, currently head of junior school and pastoral lead at Knightsbridge School, with degrees from Exeter and Winchester.

Entrance: Boys are selected by assessment day, which includes written tasks (English, maths and non verbal reasoning) and informal interview, along with an all-important report from current school. Early registration necessary, but occasional late entry places and mid-year starters also accepted. Special assessment day for the Maclaren Scholarship – up to 100 per cent bursary for a year 6/7 boarder given to a high-flyer, usually from a state primary. Academic and music scholarships at 8. Head refers to it as a 'national' prep school, with most coming from within an hour's drive of Oxford; some overseas and regular group of Old Summerfieldian sons. Previously thought of as upper crust, and hasn't entirely shaken off the image. Head disagrees, but one parent regretted the narrow social compass. No plans to take girls. A new pre-prep opening on site in September 2018 for 4-7 year olds.

Remarkably neat dorms, with effective incentives for boys to change own sheets, polish shoes and tidy up. A parent commented, 'What I like is that Summer Fields doesn't smell like a school'

Exit: About 60 per cent to Eton, Harrow, Radley and Winchester. Lots of scholarships in recent years offered by Eton, Harrow, Bedales, Wellington, Radley, Harrow and Oundle. They covered academic, art, sports and outstanding talent. Head maintains, 'Proof of the pudding is that the less academically able boys still get into public schools'. Parents like the fact that it doesn't feel like a 'feeder' but still gets great results.

Remarks: Set in over 70 acres of stunning grounds in the heart of North Oxford, the school is unremarkable from the front, but boasts a stately bow fronted building with fields, woods and river at the rear. Founded by Victorian educationalist husband and wife team, Maclarens, in 1864 and still conscious of its Christian traditions with Victorian chapel and oak paneled hall. However, there are more modern additions of several smaller houses

along adjoining road; two pools (indoor and outdoor); a sports complex, Eton fives courts, a climbing wall, new all-weather tennis and astroturf courts, as well as 9-hole golf course and cricket nets and relatively recent very large sports pavilion.

Very long day for both boarders and day boys, starts with whole school convening for chapel or assembly. Lessons in small classes (10-17) and early setting promote strong academic results at CE. Scholarship class in last two years given Greek, and Latin and French learnt by all. New DT and ICT suite and science labs, where boys encouraged to 'design your own experiments and make things pop', as well as large, busy library. Boys genuinely motivated by trips to Oxford museums and field trips, including to France. Teaching staff visible round school, as most live in, some of long standing (30+ years); 'most staff leave to become a headmaster somewhere else'. Academic success earns boys personal and house points which can be enjoyed by tangible rewards in the school shop ('Buzzer') and a house feast. A staff of six for learning support, with some experience in EP support and statements. One parent felt that it was particularly good for boys who aren't particularly socially confident and so may experience difficulties elsewhere.

Lodges (boarding houses) for boys of same year group; run by husband and wife team and kept apart from the teaching rooms (no homework or dining in lodge). Remarkably neat dorms, sleep four to six boys, with effective in-house incentives for boys to change own sheets, polish shoes and tidy up. One parent commented, 'What I like is that Summer Fields doesn't smell like a school'. Weekend leave for boarders regularly throughout the year. Pastoral care is managed with a three tier 'belt and braces' approach. Lodge parent claims, 'Homesickness is more of a problem for the mums' than the boys, who are kept busy in the evenings with board games, computers and giant chess sets. Parent of a young boarder was hugely relieved how easily the youngest were settled in. Discipline maintained by healthy competition and withdrawing privileges rather than anything more gruelling. Boys appear to appreciate this.

Music is a strength, with a dedicated music block and theatre. Three choirs, one with adult voices, sing in Oxford colleges and on tour (Rome recently). Specialist music staff allow boys to take up to three instruments (we heard of a 10 year old playing four), ranging from conventional to electric guitar, even quirky. They recently hunted down a Marimba (eastern xylophone) teacher in Oxford for a lad from the Far East. Drama productions for different year groups from Twelve Angry Men to We Will Rock You, open to all those who risk taking time from their scholarship clubs. Sport is plentiful and all-inclusive; parents like the fact that all boys make the teams, which play twice a week. Football has recently had its best season since 1937; rugby and hockey also strong, with some players in county cricket and rugby teams. Prolific art and ceramics studio, obviously not PC – fantasy coats of arms and big game trophies made from papier mâché adorn the walls.

Boys emerge from lessons brightly but quietly. They are articulate and confident, although suspiciously neat and clean in brightly coloured shirts and sweaters. Parental niggle that boys were 'a bit too polished'. However, children appear kind and supportive – 'when you are in the third year you know everyone's names' – and a nice touch that both staff and children refer to the school as 'We...'. Boys don't seem fazed by formality or overt competition – academic progress bulletins are posted on the board every two weeks for all to read – but seem to enjoy it as 'healthy rivalry'. There is a wealth of extra mural activities, spanning spiritual (Time for God group), sporting (fencing, shooting, polo) and more earthy interests (cookery and Adventure Quest – bushcraft-style camps – for handy skills in lighting the campfire and skinning a rabbit).

Boys emerge from lessons brightly but quietly. They are articulate and confident, although suspiciously neat and clean in brightly coloured shirts and sweaters. They appear kind and supportive – staff and children refer to the school as 'We...'

An appreciation of the school's history is encouraged with scholars' boards lining the walls of the hall; and a moving remembrance day service, when choral speakers read out names of the fallen alumnae. Boys follow this up with a trip to the Somme. Old Summerfieldians include generous helpings of baronets, colonial civil servants and military leaders as well as Dick Francis, who set one of his detective novels at the school. Active old boy links suggest happy memories.

A small and cosy school, in a serene and beautiful setting, successfully eases a boy in to a boarding career. It provides a breathtaking array of sports and music facilities as well as being reliable in placing boys in top public schools. Sense that boys work hard/play hard and turn out to be happy, considerate and polite, if slightly formal. Not for Just Williams.

Sunningdale School

53

Dry Arch Road, Sunningdale, Ascot, Berkshire SL5 9PY

01344 620159 | headmaster@sunningdaleschool.co.uk | www.sunningdaleschool.co.uk

Ages: 7-13

Pupils: 110; Boarders: 100

Day: £18,180 pa; Boarding: £23,400 pa

Headmaster: Since 2005, Mr Tom Dawson MA PGCE – and recent distinction in grade 1 piano (40s). Previously taught at Harrow before taking over the shop (school is fully owned by the Dawson family) inheriting headship 'because I'm the boy,' he jokes (slightly).

Family-run is understatement and a half. Wife Elisabeth, fellow modern languages graduate, is highly organised director of studies, garnering almost as much praise as husband. 'Lovely' 'kind' and their ilk crop up in conversation with parents with Swiss railway regularity.

Amy, a jolly Dawson sister, one of three (others educationally occupied elsewhere) runs high quality art department and masterminds school productions, more fulfilling than previous career as mural painter (only so many David Beckhams you can glorify on child's bedroom wall without spot of existentialist angst).

Also living and working on site are Mr Dawson's own parents and uncle, who acquired school as going concern in 1960s and are a genial background presence, mother putting final touch to colossal flower arrangements, father waving from ride-on roller. 'Keeps them going,' says their son.

We wondered about sotto voce presence of school parents, who don't, currently, have own association. 'Don't need one,' says Mr Dawson, who points to numerous 'meet the Dawsons' opportunities at well-attended matches, concerts and exhibitions. Parents, professing ardent faith in his leadership, fall over themselves to deliver several carillons' worth of ringing endorsement apiece. 'Exudes incredible values,' 'outstanding personality' two among many.

Mr Dawson, while amiable, is reckoned to miss nothing and parents felt that wouldn't shirk from tough decisions. 'If there's one super naughty boy in the school then I guess somebody has to be expelled, as in all schools,' thought one. Impressive networking skills don't go amiss either. 'I know a lot of people,' he says, and what a useful crowd they are. Barnaby Lenon, former Harrow head, extols virtues of pupils and school at length on school website. Mr D cultivates contacts through cricket – a predictable passion. Another – repairing pre-digital Roberts radios (impressive range neatly arranged in his study) – possibly less of an obvious social asset.

Entrance: Register at birth for one of 22 places, waiting list if full (as, increasingly, it is). Mr Dawson understandably hates putting up 'no vacancies' sign – 'don't want to be known for it,' – but is currently 'turning down a lot. It's a cosy, happy place and I don't want to get any bigger.'

While has plenty of high flyers, entrance requirements aren't stratospheric. School expects fluent reading and writing and grasp of basic arithmetic. May ask for report from current school and very occasional pupil is directed elsewhere.

Prospective pupils spend day at the school year before they join when sit short papers in maths, English and VR. Also attend music, art and sport workshops. Main purpose is to work out forms ('we don't really operate in year groups,' says school). Some scholarships available as well as means-tested bursaries. Weekly boarding available for the first three years. Also takes maximum of 10 day boys through the school, all locals, inherited by Mr Dawson who has 'just stuck with them.'

If you miss the boat, there's a diminutive chance of place or two in year 7 – 'incredibly rare for anyone to leave,' says Mr Dawson – offered after cognitive ability tests (though non-academic strengths also taken into account).

No linked feeders; elite London mob – Garden House, Thomas's, Eaton House – increasingly feature, as do old boys' offspring – at 10 per cent and rising, says school, which stresses that fees 'are kept as low as possible.' School buses to London at exeat weekends, long leaves and end of terms.

Gaps increasingly filled by international families – one boy we met saw family only three times a year – though school has recently started live feeds for concerts. Otherwise, pupils come from all over the country 'except Cornwall'. We were hoping for some ancient West Country vs home counties blood feud. Disappointingly, down merely to poor transport links.

Exit: Mr Dawson not a fan of serial entrance exams and suggests maximum of three senior schools, two aspirational, one 'a safer bet'. To most of major, trad names in south-east. Harrow often features prominently. Other usual (and desirable) suspects include Winchester, Eton, Harrow, Charterhouse, Uppingham, Oundle, Radley, Stowe, Tonbridge and Marlborough.

Remarks: Long the place where old money arrived as small change. Cricket commentator Henry Blofeld, Duke of Westminster, horse trainer Sir Henry Cecil – list of old boys says it all. All it takes is names of first two heads – Girdlestone and Crabtree – to know you're in the presence of Tradition, with capital (and gold-embossed, gothic-lettered) T. Would make a fine detective series title as well. Additional helpful pointers come by way of slightly fly-blown pictures of Victorian worthies in visitors' loos – OBs Duke of Marlborough 1893; Lieutenant the Honorable FHS Roberts VC, killed Colence SA 1899,

Bright, super-engaged staff include several of distinctly young fogey-ish disposition and bouffant charm – Boris Johnston recast with auburn and brunette tresses ...

Scratch the surface and you'll find...more tradition, bookcase packed with Biggles, Worrals and even a Henty or two (remnants of old library) adorning the morning room – or, more prosaically to those of less gentle birth, the school office. Makes statement architecture of curved library – first building visitors see and the newest – the more startling by comparison. Accoutrements – refectory table and two sternly positioned sofas – are set off by glow-in-the-dark bright blue carpet (also a dormitory feature), bare walls crying out for some splendiferously mustachioed OBs, picture windows giving vistas not of bosky woods or slumbrous streams but cars approaching up the drive.

Shelves reassuringly weighted in favour of fiction, wooden blocks with school number marking borrowings, one per boy. And if you want to borrow two books? 'Two?' asked Mr Dawson, experiencing mild Beadle-like moment. 'Why would anyone want

to read more than one at a time?' It's the hallmark of a school with a strong sense of its own place in the world, conventional yet not in thrall to crowd mentality. Summer half term, for example, happens a week later than normal. Trade off, with school taking strain of final revision for CE exams, worth hassle of arranging two sets of holiday activities for offspring elsewhere, reckoned parents.

Class structure, average size 12, also takes a bit of getting used to. Ability rather than age-based, so while nobody is ever moved down, brighter boys will go up a year, sometimes two, never more. In top years, carefully planned scholarship work ensures there's no 'here's one I made earlier' duplication.

From animated debate on how to stop extinction of coral reef in science – 'tries to make it as visual as possible,' said star pupil – to year 6 pupils reading (beautifully) extracts from end of year English exam, a 'do-able' past CE paper, impression was of willing learners enthusiastically taught. Bright, super-engaged staff, majority male and with average age of 39, includes several of distinctly young fogey-ish disposition and bouffant charm – Boris Johnston recast with auburn and brunette tresses.

Impressive commitment to pupils with SEN. One, with ASD, initially reluctant to attend lessons, supported with one-to-one help, funded by parents, 'fully integrated,' says Mr Dawson. More usual needs (mild dyslexia) respond – miraculously so, thought one parent – to small classes and skilled teaching without intervention. Head 'isn't a big believer in throwing tons of time and money at extra tuition,'

Many cheering examples of mild reprobates transformed by gift for singing (there's a queue to join the choir, say parents)

said one parent. 'Because the classes are so small, and teaching so good, you don't really need it.'

Staff praised not just for ability to inspire love of learning – 'never did we expect such commitment,' said mother – but for reinforcing universally wonderful manners and behaviour. One parent thrilled when master told son to 'stand up and show the way for your mother.' Compliments, convertible to house points, awarded for the dutiful, complaints doled out for the untidy or overly chatty lead to writing out code of conduct.

Had been very slight relaxation in discipline, now checked, thought one pupil (like peers, a charming lunchtime host) and all to the corporate benefit. 'Wasn't working so well before – now good for the school but bad for the individual.'

Minor transgressors write out school code of conduct; serial offenders lose 'privs' for a week, part of plentiful school jargon that includes 'going across' (signals need for comfort break rather than deepening interest in spiritualism), 'grub' (sweets) and 'lemonade' (a generic term covering hot chocolate, juice and even cake).

Parents universally thrilled by restricted presence of i-anythings out of lessons, and tactical use within. Rather than mass breaktime retreat into solitary cyber universe, pupils here whizz energetically about in real time with friends. 'Really important because children become so addicted to these games that they don't interact with their peers,' said relieved mother.

Plenty for them to enjoy, from lovingly tended plots with courgette flowers and tomatoes to three Gloucester Old Spots, sensibly not named, bees ditto – though for logistical rather than emotional reasons. Other tucked away treats include shaded mini-adventure playground for first years and personable wood-paneled and about to be extended colonial-style chapel, consecrated 1880 after arriving in kit form (so many identical labradors on site that you start to wonder if assembled in similar way).

While academic success is all well and good (and often very well and very good), school also does best to find ubiquitous spark. Music a strength, with 80 boys learning at least one instrument, variety of ensembles to play them. Many cheering examples of mild reprobates transformed by gift for singing (there's a queue to join the choir, say parents).

But whichever formerly dark area of the curriculum light of budding talent might illuminate, helps to have at least nascent interest in sport. Not for everyone, one OB recently describing it as 'an acquired taste', but for most, it's a way of inculcating right values, particularly as school size ensures participation by all. 'Perfect because even the boys who are mediocre at sports all get to make the teams – nobody gets left out,' said parent. Year to year results vary considerably – inevitable consequence of small size. One cricket and rugby team had been undefeated all season; others with less enthusiastic cohort won't do half as well.

In addition to big three (football, rugby, cricket), tennis, Eton fives (since 1892), golf and swimming are all provided on site. Five pitches (four multi-use) appear to stretch away into far distance, courtesy of clever landscaping that makes the most of stand out planting, including massed rhododendrons (Mr Dawson has sole pruning rights over favourite). Provides effective masking of more functional buildings including vast sports hall (for basketball, fencing, air rifle shooting and much more) and gives 25-acre grounds feel of something much bigger.

Sport, inevitably, dominates the summer term after school activities list, replaced in winter by idiosyncratic range that currently includes Warhammer and fly-tying (teachers, all required to take at least one sport or activity, encouraged to indulge own enthusiasms). All adds to the fun, as do the 'endless' activities (now that's what we call organisation). Being on the go essential (particularly for new boys) in helping to acclimatise to full boarding lifestyle – weekly an option in the first three years, though 'half full board from the word go,' says school.

In addition to two long weekends (Friday to Monday evening), a couple of bonus Sundays and half term, there's much anticipated treat of year group excursions to school/family-owned house in France. Icing on the cake (almost literally) is first class food prepared by Mrs Dawson Snr. One boy 'asked why I can't cook like that,' said mother.

School points out that boarding for all hurts parents far more than the boys – 'always rather sad for the mother,' agreed one, 'but we just knew they'd be so happy.' Also ensures a full house at weekends for Saturday film nights (no lonely minority waiting for life to start again on Sunday evenings) when all but first years, who have own small scale version, pile into theatre with pillows and duvets.

All happens within or next to main building, dorms six to eight-bedders, comfortable rather than haut couture ('they're nice, cute, small, humble,' said parent), possessions neatly arranged, pinboards sometimes rather sparsely filled. Bathrooms and loos clean, fragrant and hygienic – bar single cracked tile surround in need of repair. Most pupils in top two years enjoy additional privacy of individual cubicles (new arrivals will start off in dorm). Buddies take settling in duties seriously – 'boys were all waiting and had his bed made,' said parent, leaving son for taster weekend.

For the very youngest there are separate quarters with common room (reassuringly compact) and playroom (ditto – Hide and Seek games a non-starter) and own live-in matron, one of five, three full time, notable for reassuring names (Miss Turnball and Miss Foynes – yet another detective team, surely?) and a guaranteed presence on the touchline at matches.

Education here is all about bestowing resilience, self-awareness, realism and courage (fairy godmothers might blench). 'Finally and most importantly, pupils must learn to love life...' says website. If they don't while they're here, won't be for want of trying.

Parents are in no doubt they succeed. 'We put our trust in Mr Dawson,' says mother. 'We've been so incredibly impressed with the results.'

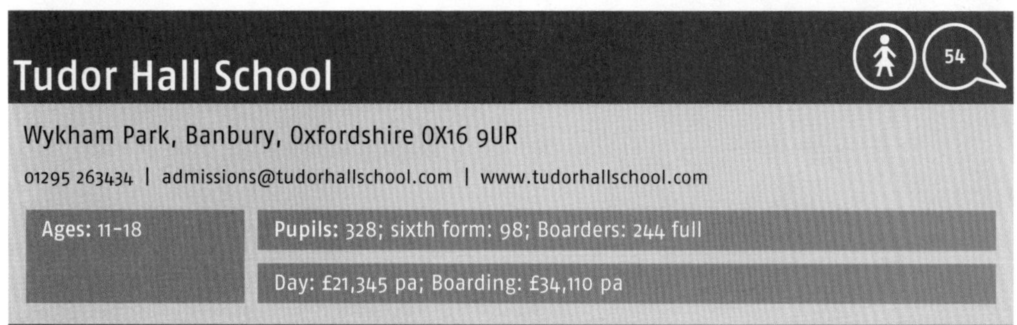

Tudor Hall School

54

Wykham Park, Banbury, Oxfordshire OX16 9UR

01295 263434 | admissions@tudorhallschool.com | www.tudorhallschool.com

Ages: 11-18

Pupils: 328; sixth form: 98; Boarders: 244 full

Day: £21,345 pa; Boarding: £34,110 pa

Headmistress: Since 2004, Miss Wendy Griffiths, BSc PGCE (50s). Educated at Queen Elizabeth Grammar School, Carmarthen, read zoology at University of Wales – still a trace of her Welsh accent. Previously head of sixth form at Tormead School, then director of studies at St Catherine's, Bramley.

Before our meeting we'd already been entertained by the sight of Miss Griffiths dancing and lip synching to Chic's We are Family in a film made by the girls of Todd (year 7 house). There aren't many heads we can call to mind who would even consider doing this, let alone be able to pull it off with such groovy aplomb. The video was playing on a wall-mounted screen, somewhat at odds with the restrained décor of the entrance hall. It's also on the school website, along with others – they like making films at Tudor Hall.

As a student she had plans to become a doctor, but while teaching in a Portsmouth comprehensive Miss Griffiths had an epiphany. After seeing how excited her class became during an 'ambitious' practical lesson she succumbed to pedagogy and has never looked back.

With her sleek bob and leather skirt, Miss G is poised and highly professional (albeit with a twinkle). She was described to us as someone who 'never slows down', which may account for the fact that in addition to the responsibilities of headship she is also just coming to the end of a stint as chair of the Boarding Schools Association in its 50th anniversary year. What about boarding schools then, we asked, are they still necessary? 'Almost more than ever', was the not unexpected reply. A boarding school is able to inculcate so much more than narrow academics: 'Instead of sitting at home glued to social media, at boarding school children have to be be social, they learn how to get on with everyone'.

Miss Griffiths still interviews prospective pupils and teaches a GCSE biology class – that's four lessons a week, very unusual for a senior school head. She lives on site with her husband, who teaches history at Sibford School; they have one daughter. Spare time, should there be such a thing, is for dog walking – plenty of Cotswolds on the doorstep for that.

To conclude, here's a little list of the the words parents used to describe Miss Griffiths: 'Outstanding', 'astonishing', 'highly professional', 'diplomatic', 'inspiring' and (we heard this one repeatedly), 'a great role model'. 'She just gets it', said one.

Academic matters: Gradual upward trajectory of academic results is testament to small classes (average 15), plenty of individual attention and by all accounts, dedicated and inspirational teaching. In 2017, 61 per cent A*/A at GCSE and 78 per cent A*-B at A level (44 per cent A*/A). Top performers at A level are geography, economics and maths. That maths is one of the most popular A levels speaks volumes for the teaching – head told us with regret how girls continue to arrive from prep schools saying they 'can't do' it.

Innovative work to inspire girls to stay engaged not just with maths but also science subjects. Super new labs for exploding jelly babies as well as more serious experiments. We saw girls in smart red lab coats investigating their own cheek cells under the microscope. Lively programme of extracurricular science clubs, visits to science fairs and National Space Centre etc.

We shared a delicious lunch with girls who had very different and exciting plans for their future – lots of gap years followed by courses from criminology to drama. No sense that sixth formers are all expected to board the non-stop university express – one told us how much support she'd had for her

decision to go straight into interior design rather than take a degree in the subject.

Visiting speakers widen horizons as does head's initiative, 'Tudor in three continents', which includes travel scholarships for girls to participate in projects in India, Bolivia and South Africa; has recently become 'Tudor in four continents'. School has added a project that doesn't involve epic amounts of air travel: mentoring children at the Bolton Lads and Girls (sic) Club. Meeting less fortunate children in their own country, rather than thousands of miles away, has been a very profound experience.

Parents told us staff keep an eagle eye on each girl's progress and are quick to intervene if she appears to be lagging. 'Teachers work so hard to get the right results; if there's a problem they really drill down to find the root cause'. Girls love the fact that teachers are so accessible: 'there's always a subject teacher who can help if you're stuck on homework or revision'. What parents love is the individual attention given to their daughters' academic progress; all those we spoke to said they were confident no child would be allowed to struggle or fall behind.

We'd already been entertained by the sight of Miss Griffiths dancing and lip synching to Chic's We are Family in a film made by the girls of Todd (year 7 house)

SEN or EAL support provided individually or in classes but head says this is not the place for a girl with serious needs; 'we want all pupils to be able to participate fully in the curriculum'. Dynamic learning support team uses variety of approaches including latest educational technology such as iPad apps.

Games, options, the arts: School has put considerable efforts into improving sports provision and parents say that it's much better. Facilities are all present and correct including glass roofed outdoor swimming pool (not used in the winter) and plenty of pitches. Girls told us that a 'bigger gym' and a 'pavilion on the top pitch' would be great. Larger schools' A teams are likely to have the advantage so notable and sustained recent successes at county level in hockey and cross-country are all the more creditable. Individual talents in tennis (lovely courts in former walled garden), skiing and riding are well supported and a wider range of non-competitive options such as swim fit and zumba are offered in the sixth form. Girls also work with Carrdus School (Oxfordshire prep owned by Tudor

Hall) and local primary schools to provide pupils with coaching and taster sessions in eg lacrosse.

Drama is offered at GCSE and A level but TH girls love to perform, whether or not they are pursing it as a subject option. Great results in LAMDA speech and drama exams too. Regular participation in Shakespeare Schools' Festival, plenty of theatre trips and a choice of stages – new (2015) studio theatre has eye-catching neon sign. Dance is accorded greater status here than at other schools and can be taken as a GCSE. Reaction, the audition-only school dance group, has been going for over 20 years; the house dance title is as keenly fought as house singing and drama competitions. Music, too, offers girls of all abilities the chance to perform – whether at school concerts, carol singing at care homes or carrying off trophies at Banbury Young Musician of the Year competitions.

The quality of the art, both in the studios and (perhaps a little infrequently) displayed throughout the school, fair took our breath away. Quite the best we can remember seeing anywhere. Likewise textiles and photography. Style and subject matter went from traditional to unexpectedly edgy and challenging. The textile and art rooms stay open into the evening and at weekends and girls love the freedom this gives them to work on their projects outside lessons. Textiles currently housed in Portakabin but purpose built studios are in the offing. Leavers regularly go on to art foundation and fashion design courses.

Extracurricular options encompass just about everything from Model United Nations to the very popular dissection club. It seems not only can a Tudor Hall girl address a crowd and whip up a soufflé (if she's done the Leith's course), she can also eviscerate a frog. Parents approve of the way girls are kept very busy lower down the school, gradually developing independent study skills as they approach the relative freedom of the sixth form.

Boarding: The full Monty – two exeats per term and no flexi or weekly. Saturday school with lessons until 1pm and games in the afternoon, trips, activities and down time thereafter. Boarding is arranged horizontally – ie by year group – meaning that everything (activities, bed times etc) can be tailored to the age group. Works especially well at exam times – much easier if everyone around you is revising.

A great summer treat for the older girls is, we were told, to walk to the nearby farm shop, buy a picnic and eat it in a field. Wouldn't suit a committed urbanite

Year 7 boarders and day girls are based in Todd (named after the school's founders), a charming house with a large peaceful garden on the edge of the school grounds. It's as uninstitutional as possible with a large family kitchen, colourful soft furnishings and lots of toys and games. And, when we visited, a body on the sitting room floor. 'Just step over it, we're doing first aid,' the housemistress told us. Todd girls love putting on plays and concerts for their captive audience, they also enjoy 'special breakfasts', baking and Sunday excursions (day girls can go too). Todd girls have lower sixth buddies, described to us as a 'big sister support system'.

Dorms vary from two to six cabin beds; bathrooms are clean but on the functional side.

Apparently they're 'due for a refurb'. Personal technology at this end of the school limited to mobile phones for 10 minutes a day. Skype etc always available, 'we never stop a child speaking to their parents'. Glad to hear it. Housemistress has set up a Facebook page for Todd parents who get daily photos and updates on their girls' activities.

Other houses (known as The 11s, The 111s and so on) are spacious and well equipped. Girls need no encouragement to personalise their space; walls were papered with photos, letters, bunting and many, many rosettes – plenty of keen horsewomen here.

Each boarding house has its own character and traditions so there's a real sense of progression through the school. Sixth form accommodation is designed as a halfway house to prepare girls for living independently. They can cook, are responsible for their own laundry and organise trips and activities. One such is the Christmas shopping trip to Paris (plus Disneyland Paris); no shortage of teachers signing up to chaperone that one, we imagine.

Background and atmosphere: One of the oldest girls' boarding schools in England, Tudor Hall was founded in 1850 by Rev T W Todd and his wife. In 1908 the school moved from London to rural Kent and on the outbreak of the Second World War it decamped to Burnt Norton, a small Cotswold manor house, to escape the air raids. Pupils, teachers and parents stayed here, even during the holidays, and old girls remember those times with great affection. It was a visit to the gardens at Burnt Norton that inspired T S Eliot to write his eponymous poem, a meditation on time, memory and original sin. Perhaps he would have penned something a little jollier than 'Garlic and sapphires in the mud clot the bedded axle-tree' if he'd visited a few years later when the Tudor Hall girls were in residence.

Surrounding area predominantly rural – grazing cows more common than passing traffic – but access to Oxford, London, Stratford etc pretty easy. Nearest town is Banbury. A great summer treat for the older girls is, we were told, to walk to the nearby farm shop, buy a picnic and eat it in a field. Wouldn't suit a committed urbanite, but that's not really the demographic which is, we suspect, one that is accustomed to town and country living and has the right shoes for both.

First time visitors may be surprised to find no busy reception desk; the entrance hall, with its bergere furniture, beautiful flowers and polished wood, is rather reminiscent of an exclusive hotel – but the welcome is warm and personal. Usual mix of buildings – not everywhere is country house gracious – but all well tended. School magazine and publicity material are similar – high production values but nothing boasty or brash. Come to think of it, that probably sums up the Tudor Hall pupil.

Pastoral care, well-being and discipline: Tudor Hall has long had a reputation for the highest standards of pastoral care, but don't confuse caring with soft. Yes, it's a nurturing environment, as all the best small schools are, but within that environment girls are encouraged and tested; challenged to over-reach their own boundaries and try new things.

All the parents we spoke to felt that their daughters were in the safest of hands and cited many examples of occasions when tutors or other members of staff had gone above and beyond to help or advise them. Day and boarding parents get a weekly update from tutors about what's been going on and home school communication in general receives nothing but praise.

A couple of people we spoke to thought the downside of year group boarding was that it contributed to a somewhat stratified hierarchical atmosphere, but we didn't feel this was the case. Vertical house system, not to mention the mix of different clubs and sporting activities, must go a long way to defuse this.

They can cook, are responsible for their own laundry and organise trips and activities. One such is the Christmas shopping trip to Paris; no shortage of teachers signing up

Day girls are very well integrated and can join their boarding friends for trips and weekend activities, but it's a long day and, with Saturday school, a long week. Even year 7 day pupils don't finish until 6.45pm or later, although they will have had an hour or so's break, a snack and done their homework.

Regular socials with chaps from Radley, Eton and Harrow. The young gentlemen from Harrow are current favourites, but apparently this changes from year to year.

What do you gain from boarding, we asked a group of sixth formers? They all cited strong and lasting friendships; others valued the 'accessibility' of teaching staff and the fact that there's always someone around to help with academic work. 'It helps you become responsible and independent – and it stops you taking home for granted.' We like that last one but doubt it survives the summer holidays.

Pupils and parents: Most recent ISI report described Tudor Hall pupils as 'overwhelmingly positive in outlook' which sounds rather alarming – a posse of Pollyannas, perhaps. It would be so easy to fall back on the old stereotype of Tudor Hall girls as darling daughters of the home counties, what with Leiths, polo, doing the ski season, etc – but that wouldn't be fair or accurate.

The girls we met were friendly, thoughtful, comfortable in their own skins and definitely not the identikit result of an educational production line. There's no arrogance or sense of entitlement and definitely no hair flicking. Girls know they are fortunate and are very aware that the world beyond Banbury is considerably less shiny; it certainly won't be any the worse for having Tudor Hall alumnae in it.

Pride in one's school is not usually compatible with the teenage psyche, but Tudor Hall girls aren't too cool for that. Lots of daughters of old girls – always a good sign. Other old Tudorians include Katherine Hooker, tailor to Duchess of Cambridge; Cleo Barbour, shoe designer; Julia Peyton-Jones, director of Serpentine Gallery.

Entrance: Candidates for 11+ and 13+ invited for 'taster day' (or day and night for prospective 11+ boarders) and assessment days with tests in maths, English and verbal reasoning. The tests are to 'ensure girls are compatible with academic pace' of school. Girls applying for entry at 13+ offered conditional places dependent on outcome of CE. All candidates are interviewed by the head who told us she is looking for 'character.' She believes that girls who are 'sparky about something' succeed because the school can channel their enthusiasm into other areas.

Exit: Art foundation seems to be a popular post A level choice and Oxford Brookes attracts quite a few. Bristol, Birmingham, Edinburgh, Exeter, Leeds, Newcastle, Nottingham are current Russell Group favourites; also one to Parsons fashion, art and design school in New York and one to the Academy of Contemporary Music. Occasional one or two to Oxbridge. One to study in the US in 2017 and one to do medicine.

Money matters: Fees at the slightly less eye watering end of the boarding range; day fees look like good value considering time spent in school. Academic, music, art, drama and sport scholarships (up to £1,000 pa) available at 11+, 13+ and 16+. Also textiles and dance at 16+. Means-tested bursaries to support new and current parents in financial need.

Remarks: Leave your preconceptions at the door and prepare to be bowled over. Whether your daughter is headed for fashion design or Oxbridge, under Miss Griffiths' dynamic stewardship Tudor Hall deserves a place on everyone's short list.

Twyford School

55

High Street, Twyford, Winchester, Hampshire SO21 1NW

01962 712269 | registrar@twyfordschool.com | www.twyfordschool.com

Ages: 3-13 (boarding from year 4)

Pupils: 408; Boarders: 8 weekly, 111 flexi

Day: £9,246 – £18,942 pa; Weekly boarding: £23,838 pa

Headmaster: Since 2010, Dr Steve Bailey BEd PhD FRSA; educated at Kent College, Canterbury, Southampton University and St Paul's College of Education (50s). Born and raised bilingually in Hong Kong before teaching history (all levels) at Winchester College for 30 years; housemaster for the last 12. A Fellow of the Royal Society for the Arts, research fellow of the International Olympic Committee, author of six books and with an international reputation as a historian of sport and the Olympic Games, it's no surprise that he has shaken things up a bit at Twyford.

Dr Bailey began by curtailing lessons to 45 minutes and encouraged teachers to deliver lessons beyond narrow CE requirements. Regularly observes teaching and makes no secret of his ambition for more creativity in the classroom; is keen to avoid 'death by worksheet.' Banished formal exams in the first two years of prep school and introduced extension lessons, known as Apprenticeships, in the timetable. 'Children are capable of far more than we sometimes offer.' Intellectual and erudite, is also a keen sportsman. Played hockey at county and regional levels and enjoys tennis, water polo and surfing. Wife Paula MSc (health psychology) has taught ICT as well as tutoring children with specific learning difficulties. They have three children, all in full-time education.

Entrance: Main entry points are nursery and year 3, although places are occasionally available in other years. Nursery places allocated according to date of registration; siblings have priority on waiting lists at other times. Short half-day assessment in November for those joining prep school the following academic year, which school says is 'not a rigorous hurdle.' Most pupils live within 30 mile radius, some weekly boarders further afield.

Exit: Nearly one third of boys leave for Winchester College, a steady few with music and academic awards. Other boys and girls scatter far and wide, but most popular destinations are Bradfield, Bryanston, Canford, Charterhouse, Cheltenham Ladies', Downe House, Eton, Godolphin, King Edward VI, Marlborough, St Swithun's, and

Sherborne boys' and girls' schools. Tally of scholarships is on the up under Dr Bailey's stewardship; boys and girls gain a more diverse range of awards including academic, music, sport, all-rounder, art and DT scholarships and exhibitions.

Remarks: Main school building, a beautiful Queen Anne house, is set in over six acres of playing fields and surrounded by the South Downs. Moved to its present location in 1809 from premises in nearby Twyford and can probably trace its origins back to the mid-17th century. (A Latin grammar book has turned up bearing the inscription 'Twyford School, 1775'.) Boarders still live in original house, which has a pretty Victorian chapel, oak-panelled library, atmospheric old school hall and large modernised refectory. Teaching takes place in a collection of modern buildings dotted around quadrangles.

Lots of hard work going on for CE when we visited; most pupils aim to sit level 3 in subjects across the board (some level 2 if appropriate). 'Dr Bailey has increased the aims and aspirations of the children.' Maths set from year 4 and all subjects by year 6. French from reception, Latin from year 5 and study skills as a separate subject from year 7, otherwise all subjects taught as usual. 'Learning qualities programme' encourages children to think more independently and take responsibility for their own learning (praised in an ISI school inspection). Classrooms are modern, bright and spacious; science labs are immaculate (including snakes!). Class sizes average 16-18. Children are divided up into three sets in the last two years, depending on their 'next school'. Boys aiming for Winchester and all other scholarship candidates join 'W set' in year 7, the rest are divided into two common entrance sets. ICT provision is well planned, with fixed terminals for younger ones and laptops for year 5. Year 6 up have tablets to enable independent research in geography, history and science lessons. Five SEN specialists help with (mild) learning difficulties and around 70 one-to-one sessions (including pre-prep) were timetabled when we visited. These are free, but school doesn't take children who need more than one session a week.

Traditional prep school sports for boys and girls, with matches on Wednesday and Saturday afternoons. First and second teams have an excellent sporting record in fixtures against other schools. School tells us it 'has addressed girls' sport' by drawing up C and D teams and organising more fixtures, and everyone gets on a team the majority of times. Pupils also compete in swimming, water polo, athletics, tennis, lacrosse and girls' tag rugby. School is a 'centre of excellence' for girls' cricket in Hampshire. Large gym and indoor 25m swimming pool sit side-by-side, with 25m traversing wall outside. Has several all-weather courts for tennis and netball, plus astroturf for hockey and football.

'Sports day is fabulous.' Netball teams have had success at regional and national IAPS tournaments (with the U12 team recently winning the nationals) and individual footballers at national schools' level. Other pupils perform at county level in cricket, cross-country running, hockey, rugby and swimming. 'Court Cricket', invented at Twyford and played here for at least a century, is still in robust health at break times.

Painting and ceramics excellent. Artist in residence paints school scenes on site so children can observe brushwork – no surprise that art scholarships on the rise

Outstanding art and DT departments, probably the best we've seen for quality of work. Small, permanent gallery at the side of two storey art block displays pupils' work throughout the year; standard of painting and ceramics is excellent. Artist in residence paints school scenes on site so children can observe brushwork – no surprise that number of art scholars is on the rise. DT is also very good with some really imaginative work (high level of design) on show, eg insect 'hotel'.

Music block sits in unusual amphitheatre setting overlooking tennis courts. Bright, airy performance space upstairs with several practice rooms on lower floor; more pianos are dotted around elsewhere in the school. More than 80 per cent of children learn at least one instrument, including the less usual, eg harp, drums and bagpipes. Lessons are fixed for older children and rotate for younger ones. School is a centre for ABRSM and Trinity College music exams and many pupils pass these at higher grades. Three school choirs, including a show choir, school orchestra and various ensembles give occasional concerts. Drama is improving, with a weekly lesson for all taught by specialist teachers and more performance space in Mulberry Pavilion, but 'dramatic aspirations could be higher ... we need a whole-school musical once a year.' Dance (ballet, modern and tap) is on offer as a lunch time club. Regular Shakespeare workshop for year 8 takes place after CE.

'Court Cricket', invented at Twyford and played here for at least a century, is still in robust health at break times

Apprenticeships (Saturday activities) are compulsory for all children from year 4. Activities become increasingly academic further up the school, and include ancient Greek, Arabic, critical thinking, debating, fencing, Mandarin, music theory, philosophy, photography and horse riding. Everyone chooses a different apprenticeship each term, and 'children often get their first choice.' Staff run weekday clubs after school, eg art, cookery, judo, water polo and yoga. Outdoor education programme, eg navigation, orienteering, shelter building and survival techniques, 'encourages children to solve practical and physical problems.' One residential course away for each year group every year; in school there is a treehouse complex with outdoor classroom and advanced adventure playground.

No longer offers full boarding, but can arrange for long-distance boarders to stay with local guardians on Saturday and Sunday nights (on average, there are 15 weekly boarders every term). Otherwise, most children board a few nights per week (68 stay one night a week, 38 for two nights and just three for three nights) from year 6 in preparation for going away to senior school and around 20 from Monday to Friday. Dorms for younger children; cosy two-man (or girl) cubicles for year 8s allow more privacy and the chance to room with a friend. We noted clean, well-appointed bathrooms, a comfortable common room and plenty of storage space for belongings. Boarders have limited use of mobile phones (matron keeps phones at all other times). Parents full of praise for boarding houseparent, also head of sport.

Excellent meals are served cafeteria-style and atmosphere is informal; children can sit where they like (we didn't notice staff on each table). Perhaps (enviably) this isn't needed, as school works hard to instill a broad set of values in its pupils. Regular services in chapel throughout the term are reinforced by anti-bullying PSHE lessons and constant vigilance by boarding and teaching staff (often around in the evenings running clubs or supervising prep). Everyone belongs to one of four houses and is assigned a house tutor from year 6. End-of-term team feast for house with the highest house point scores; individual high scorers are 'sent up good' on Fridays for lemon sherbet from the head (a Twyford tradition). Still has a friendly atmosphere, although parents say times are now more formal. Nevertheless they add, 'It still feels like you're part of a big family and [that] requires family involvement.'

Pre-prep is going from strength to strength with over 126 on the register when we visited. 'The nursery is outstanding.' Two classes in reception and year 1 grow to three in year 2, which is located in the recently built Forest Lodge. Nestling in the trees, Forest Lodge provides three spacious, bright and airy classrooms for year 2 – windows at child height is a nice touch. Children grouped for phonics and spelling ability; reading is taught both individually and in groups. French and music learned from an early age. Homework is limited to spelling, reading and topic work, eg Knights and Castles. 'It's a really full-on day.' Has small SEN room and ICT suite. Lots of outdoor play; recent additions include an all weather sports games' area, a wooden covered outdoor classroom, giant connect 4 games, a wooden train and outdoor musical instruments, a theatre stage and an outdoor adventure play area. All attend chapel services and use the pool and library. Puts on annual show for 'grandparents' week', where little ones can show off their music, ballet and ESB exam preparation. Clubs include gardening, hand bells, ukulele and recorder ensemble. Most go on to join prep school in year 3, causing prep school numbers to rise. Universal feeling from parents is that school is at capacity; would like to see new pupil numbers capped.

A relatively wide mix of families, but it's safe to assume that most are comfortably off. Two 100 per cent bursaries (means tested) for new children joining as weekly boarders in year 7; sibling discounts are limited to five per cent for third and subsequent children. Boys and girls are polite, confident and increasingly aspire to top schools. Old Twyfordians include Alexander Pope, Douglas Hurd, Hubert Parry, Mark Tully, Thomas Hughes and, more recently, The Apprentice winner Tom Pellereau. Very active Twyford Society keeps ex-pupils in touch.

Although well into the process of changing from 'a slightly scruffy, not very ambitious place' to one with a much greater focus on academic success, Twyford is still a friendly school where parents enjoy being part of the 'family'. Will continue to send a good number of boys to Winchester College, but is clearly aiming just as high for girls and boys going on to other schools.

Walhampton School

56

Walhampton, Lymington, Hampshire SO41 5ZG

01590 613300 | registrar@walhampton.com | www.walhampton.com

Ages: 2–13 (boarders from 7)

Pupils: 370; Boarders: 20 full, 13 weekly, 27 flexi

Day: £8,775 – £17,100 pa; Boarding: + £6,300 pa

Headmaster: Since 2012, Mr Titus Mills (Eton, University of East Anglia and Oxford). Has taught across the spectrum, latterly as head of The Paragon, an independent school in Bath, and prior to that as head of St George's International Junior school in Rome and deputy head of St Mark's C of E school in Lambeth. Named Titus after the family donkey. The kids from St Mark's sang Oh Happy Day at his wedding to Jemima, who is involved in many aspects of school life, from meeting parents to arts and crafts. They have three young sons at the school.

Head is charming, his ease of manner no doubt stemming from his Eton roots; he is also warm, penetrating, and very enthusiastic. Mr Mills relishes a challenge: he has turned around schools in the past, and has a remit to do something similar for Walhampton. Not that it was failing, but he is there to make it fly – 'he's brimming with positivity,' said a parent.

Since taking up his post, head has swept through the school like a brisk wind, removing all dusty elements and making significant changes to staff, uniform, even the school emblem (the sticking out tongue has been lopped off the stag). There was 'lots of debris,' commented a parent. Another enthusiastic parent said that the head works 'at the speed of light' and will respond to an email request within half an hour with an action plan. Happy constituents indeed.

Entrance: Non selective. Tests for placing purposes.

Exit: To more than 20 senior schools. Canford and Bryanston most popular, followed by Sherborne, Marlborough and Radley.

Remarks: Walhampton is exceptionally lovely, with glorious buildings and grounds. But there's something more than that: a feeling that your favourite childhood fiction might come to life in this place. The prospectus dust jacket (no, we've never seen a dust jacket on one before either) is just like the map in the front of Swallows and Amazons – there's Portmere pond for sailing, Sandwalk pond for fishing; even a Curly Wurly mountain. For Enid Blyton lovers there's the Faraway Tree and a Wishing Seat. Beehives sit in a wildflower meadow and there are stables, camps and bluebell woods.

Thoughtfully arranged library – books reserved for years 7 and 8 on one side, so the librarian can see if a crafty year 3 nips across to pick a book that is not age appropriate, although 'We don't really do [books full of teenage] angst here.' Library sessions each week, but library evidently used at all times: a jigsaw is always on the go – a child stressed out by a lesson apparently calms down after five minutes with a jigsaw. New librarian intent on creating a welcoming and accessible space.

This place's stately past is not completely diluted by its school present. Standing on the terrace during break, watching the children at play, it is extraordinary to think this is a school and not a home. The family feel is underscored by the fact that many teachers live on site with their families.

Children are a lively, happy bunch and properly young: they all play at break time, including the enormous 13 year old boys, who looked as though they should already be at a senior school, but raced around, twisting each other on a tree swing. There are the usual number of screens here, but children are equally likely to enthuse about an outside activity – riding, flags or the tremendously popular 'escape from Colditz': children have to escape from an area of the grounds, in the dark, and get up to the headmaster's study and ring the bell. Staff, equipped with miner's lamps as headgear, try to spot and stop them. 'Wet, windy and wild,' says the school mag, The Mercury. This is a school where they are not afraid to get dirty; or take risks.

Manners well to the fore: children leapt to their feet as we went around and held open doors, one small child moved out of our way, saying decidedly 'good evening,' (just after lunch). With much fanfare, Mr Mills introduced new comprehensible school rules and a merits/sanctions so kids understand what they've done right and wrong. Beach huts in house colours collect stag tokens, handed out for behaviour, effort and achievement – very popular with kids who love posting their tokens. Each half term the school, pupils and teachers alike, aims to develop a particular learning characteristic – perseverance at the time of our visit: clearly taken very much to heart by the children, and the determined cross-country runner who came in last, but persevered to the end.

The head is keen to take learning outside as much as possible and as a result this was one of the most deserted schools we have toured. 'Mud is part of the curriculum'

Children feel that their views are listened to: school council got the water fountains it requested and also managed to secure something more yummy than banana chips at break. Food much improved since regime chance – it was certainly delicious on the day of our visit.

Head's main focus has been on increasing academic standards, and for the first time in the school's history two boys were awarded academic scholarships to Winchester recently. Subjects are traditional (Latin is compulsory), but learning comes alive here: the Battle of Trafalgar takes place on one of the ponds, and ditches are currently doubling as trenches for WW2 enactments. History, understandably, is a tremendously popular subject. The head is keen to take learning outside as much as possible and as a result this was one of the most deserted schools we have ever toured. 'Mud is part of the curriculum,' said one member of staff. New outdoor classroom in the woods with firepit for winter warmth and canopy for summer shade. Class sizes range from 15-20.

In the pre-prep the little ones have wet weather red dungarees, coats and wellies and recently enjoyed operations in a mud kitchen with wok and watering can. Ella and Daisy, the pre-prep hens, potter around happily. There's a outside area, Owl corner, with bushes to hide in, a wooden stag to climb on, and a rope to pull yourself up a steep slope.

Learning support provided across the spectrum. Although most fit mild to moderate categories, there are a few children here with severe dyslexia. Whether or not children with severe learning difficulties are accepted depends partly on assessment and the balance of children in that year. Support charged as an extra, but 'not expensive,' said a parent. LSU provides 'exceptional support,' said parent of a child with dyslexia. 'No stigma,' and kids likely to help each other with difficulties. EAL support expanded.

Mixed age tutor groups for years 6 to 8. Pupils have some say in which tutor group they wish to be in and good relationships develop across the age groups, with pupils often helping each other out with academic or other difficulties.

Pupils know who to go to with problems and bullying is dealt with promptly. Parents feel that pastoral care here is very strong. 'The time and energy which goes into each child is remarkable,' said one. Most parents attend chapel on Friday nights – 'a lovely way to round off the week.' Kids say what they want to pray for – there's usually a rabbit or a finger shut in a car door (although the school is 'not deeply religious,' the mum added).

Head of sports sees those who claim they don't enjoy sport as a challenge and does his best to find an activity that a child will take to, archery or golf for instance. Great to see the girls learning rugby. Good sports hall and Astroturf, and funding for two new netball courts. Six Oppies (sailing boats to the rest of us) recently purchased. Riding is extremely popular and many boys ride although they tend to prefer games – anyone for buzkashi? (a Mongolian game played with the stuffed hide of a goat). Even if it's not your turn to ride, you can always go down to the stable and fling your arms around a pony.

Well-equipped music rooms in new music block and over half of pupils learn an instrument. Pop bands – The Stags and The Does – as well as a selection of choirs and orchestra. Joseph was in its final rehearsals, and sounded good – a hefty show for a prep school.

There are around 20 full boarders, with numbers increasing to 60 during the week with lots of flexi-boarding arrangements, the latter very popular with busy parents. New handmade 'bespoke' bunks aim to 'create a dream bedroom where children feel relaxed and at home'. For those who suddenly find themselves stuck in a late meeting, emergency boarding is a bargain. The Walhampton express runs weekly from London down to the school, one of the houseparents travelling backwards and forwards to escort weekly boarders. Accommodation has been renovated and redecoration has been sensitive, younger girls having pink and frills, the older girls a more restrained version. Things are kept very neat – posters are carefully framed – no bluetac and tatty edges. Nice little kitchens with cereals for any time (Dorset muesli included, naturally), and tempting hampers of healthy snacks. All kids come into school on Saturday for activities and boarders have special trips out on Sundays.

Parents are well heeled, lots of professionals and businesspeople. Apparently it used to be a school where grandparents paid the fees but this is no longer the case. Most pupils are from the surrounding area, including the Isle of Wight, but some also from London and overseas. Academic scholarships awarded to internal or external applicants from year 2 upward; sports scholarships of up to half fees from year 3 upwards aimed at those talented in a range of sporting disciplines who would not otherwise be able to afford to come to Walhampton.

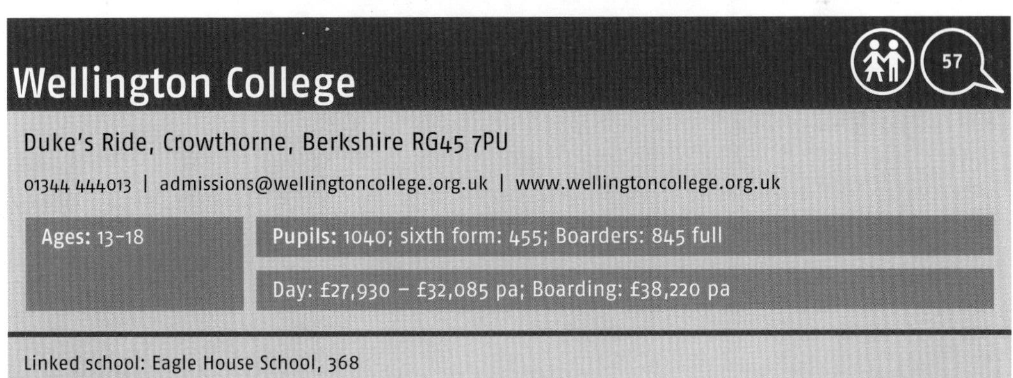

Wellington College

57

Duke's Ride, Crowthorne, Berkshire RG45 7PU

01344 444013 | admissions@wellingtoncollege.org.uk | www.wellingtoncollege.org.uk

Ages: 13-18

Pupils: 1040; sixth form: 455; Boarders: 845 full

Day: £27,930 – £32,085 pa; Boarding: £38,220 pa

Linked school: Eagle House School, 368

Master: Since 2015, Julian Thomas BSc MBA FRSA (apparently 50s, though looks about 27). Read computer science at King's College, London – not a common headmagisterial start. After launching into banking, light dawned and he took a Cambridge PGCE, winning a half-blue in rugby league. Taught maths at St Dunstan's College and Forest School, co-authoring several text books. Thence, as director of studies, to Portsmouth Grammar and on to Hampton School as second master for four years during which he took an MBA in educational leadership (international). Prior to

Wellington, was head of Caterham School for eight years doing great things. Engagingly, he tweets as @Welly_Master.

Instantly likeable. Relaxed, open, friendly and clearly capable, Mr Thomas relishes everything about the college and his centrality to it. Taking over a school so publicly identified with a predecessor isn't easy. However, he was clearly in sympathy with the Seldon ethos and values and, to a considerable extent, maintains them, though his emphasis is less on generally desirable lists of values and aptitudes than on each individual pupil. Remarkably, while we spoke to numerous staff, parents and pupils who evidently deeply revered his predecessor, no-one regretted the move into the post-Seldon-era – a tremendous tribute to Julian Thomas and his sensitive and sensible handling of the transition. In fact, as some parents suggested, 'Everybody was feeling a tad exhausted – it's a wee bit calmer now.' Pupils feel known and engaged with. 'He'll just stop us and say, "What do you think of this?" about some idea or other. He really wants to know what we think.' And, 'He knows stuff about you. He'll just ask, "How did it go?" It's amazing.'

'Exciting,' was the word Mr Thomas used most often to us. And we heard it often from parents and pupils too. An astute appointment. Wellington will grow greater and richer in his care.

Academic matters: A place in which learning matters. We loved what one parent told us: 'It's cool to do well there – it's embarrassing if you don't.' College offers both A levels and the IB in the sixth form – 45 per cent currently opting for the IB. The IB middle years programme was dropped due to

'A school like Wellington has a duty to do what's right in education,' he says. 'The things that really matter can't be measured by league tables'

lack of uptake – a disappointing but hardly surprising decision. A level results are impressive overall. Maths and economics by far the most popular options; history and Latin get impressive results. Ninety per cent of history candidates achieved A*/As – remarkable. Likewise, the seven Latin candidates all got A*/As. Minority subjects, eg some languages and art history, also outstanding though a less starry showing in eg English, business and photography. Overall, 66 per cent A*/A grades. IB diploma results similarly impressive though a bit more of a mixed bag, perhaps. The average score of IB diploma candidates in 2017 was 39. 'Our teachers seem to like teaching the IB more than A levels,' one sixth former thought.

Mainstream range of GCSE subjects offered and results in maths and all three sciences are excellent. Of the options, history, geography and Latin are especially popular – Latin with spectacular results; Spanish and Greek also sparkle. Good choice of languages but German no more buoyant here than anywhere else, sadly. Alongside the core GCSE subjects (which include one ancient or modern language), everyone takes two or three electives from a range eg computer science, dance

and photography. Year 10/11s also take a level 2 EPQ. Overall, 81 per cent A*-A grades in 2017.

But Julian Thomas no longer publishes examination results for national league tables. This is a part of the college's shift from raw results to a focus on value added. 'A school like Wellington has a duty to do what's right in education,' he says. 'The things that really matter can't be measured by league tables.' We agree. We approve. This approach is supported by eg Harkness tables – large oval seminar-style tables to facilitate the sharing rather than the imparting of knowledge. And, as independent learners, the pupils do much of the preparation for lessons. Every kind of modern IT device and programme abounds but most designed, again, to allow for the sharing of learning. Mobiles allowed for eg messages re assignments and catch-up sessions and Microsoft Surface is embedded so that class participants can all contribute to the same piece of work at once.

Two-weekly cycle of lessons – each one hour long. Regular monitoring, reports and 'interims'. Staff:pupil ratio of just over 1:6 which is remarkably low, although actual class sizes are not smaller than average. Some parental grumbles about the high turnover of staff: 'They do go. They like to have Wellington on their cv and then they get promoted.' But many long-serving staff, very few of whom have lost the light in the eyes.

Everyone is assessed on entry for baseline skills. Remarkably high number of mild or other deficits picked up at this stage – sometimes coming as a surprise to parents. Good support for the 10 per cent of pupils on the SEN register. Emphasis here as throughout on independent learning. Help delivered individually or in groups. Some forego a second modern language for individual support and maybe take one or two fewer GCSEs. One-off subject help sessions abound.

Games, options, the arts: 'If I stayed here for twice as many years, I still wouldn't get round to trying everything,' is a cry we heard over and over. 'You have to sign up for everything you like the sound of in College Carnival [freshers' week to you and me] try it all out, then make a longlist, then a shortlist and then try and do what you really want to. But it's still difficult.. and there is class work too..'

Sports, clubs and enrichment activities galore and any teacher or pupil with an enthusiasm is encouraged to start a club of their own. So – a tea drinking club when we visited where the members. er, drink tea. And a ukelele orchestra was in full swing. And our concert band is the biggest in the country.' 'Service' is central to the ethos, providing numerous initiatives to work here and abroad with the less privileged or less physically/cognitively able. They walk the talk.

Rugby rules – this is a quintessential rugby school. However, girls' sports are now firmly on the agenda and the new arena, due in 2018, will up both the provision and the profile of girls' sports to more of a parity. Though rugby will still rule! The third form can take dance as a curriculum option. We saw a class of excellent textile work but, sadly, not a boy in sight. WTV is an institution and produces professional quality broadcasting. New performing arts centre – a vast building site when we visited – will transform the provision in 2018. The auditorium will seat 1,300 and will be complemented by TV editing suite, recording studios, concert rooms etc. Drama and music pretty spectacular anyway – with high performance values in all media. Visits by professional companies of the highest order too, especially for the occasional Welly Arts Fests. Art in many media, DT and general creativity busting out all over. Trips, exhibition, visitors – it's all just too much.

Boarding: Seventeen boarding houses – 'inhouses' close to the main building, and 'outhouses' nestling in the grounds, some with their own dining rooms – each with its own character, provision, facilities, traditions, lore and argot and each seemingly inspiring loyalty and affection: even when, in the case of one, 'it's been on the upgrade list for the last five years'. Houses bar one are single sex. We were impressed by some small, high-ceilinged, rooms in which the clever use of stairs and a little mezzanine transformed the space into study bedrooms. High standard of bathrooms, showers etc. Lots of honours boards – new and old. Feeling that the character of a house much depends on the character of the sixth form boarders in a given year – some being more inviting and less exclusive than others.

Saturdays are full school days with lessons in the mornings and sports in the afternoons but most go home after that until Sunday evening. Around 150-200 boarders in school most weekends – obviously mostly those with families abroad – and a full programme of activities is on offer if you want it. Wisely, overseas boarders are distributed between the houses so everyone meets everyone. Four weekends annually everyone is required to stay in school. Occasional grouses about the disparity between the houses in terms of upkeep, facilities – and sofas. It's clearly happening, but too slowly for some. More water dispensers around the site would be popular and also the introduction of bikes on which to get around – even if only for the older students.

Careful and thorough induction and acclimatisation activities to help newbies settle in – and to support their jittery parents. Masterclasses give parents a chance to take on eg social media, teenage eating and coaching. Countless events offer parents opportunities to feel part of the wider Wellington community – embraced enthusiastically by many but, of course, not all.

Background and atmosphere: By top English public school standards Wellington, which opened in 1859, is an upstart newbie. It was built as a monument to the first Duke of Wellington (the vanquisher of Bonaparte) by a grateful nation and Queen Victoria laid the foundation stone. But it stands proudly with our most illustrious schools and, when you visit – and even more when you become part of the school – you cannot ignore the pride, the history, the tradition and the splendour of the place. Third form history is largely based on the college's own past and the extensive archives are a rich resource.

Four hundred acres – around half of which are playing fields, lakes (five of them), forest and gardens – embrace the college's main building – a surprising (given the essential Englishness of the place) exercise in low-rise, Rococo-chateau-red-brick designed by John Shaw Jnr (Prince Albert's choice). A very attractive frontage and the interior still boasts some attractive features. Chapel designed by G Gilbert Scott. Rarely for a school chapel of this size and capacity, this one has a warmth and genuine consolatory ambiance. 'It's one of the things you never forget,' a wise alumnus told us. 'Maybe because Wellington is so modern and progressive, we love the chapel because you can think over the college history and what it was like here before.' Numerous later buildings – mostly in red brick – are in sympathy – even the newest glassy additions – and we saw nothing here which was unpleasing to the eye. The Mandarin Centre – complete with gold Chinese dragons, lake, bridge and traditional gateway – comes as a bit of a surprise. Quads – especially the Combermere with terrific central huge bronze of The Iron Duke's horse, Copenhagen – are simply stunning and the upkeep of everywhere is impressive. The V & A is the hip modern café and meeting place – we felt quite at home. Excellent signage too, though a speed bump more or two might be an idea to discourage some over-eager visiting parents.

The Mandarin Centre – complete with gold Chinese dragons, lake, bridge and traditional gateway – comes as a bit of a surprise

The forest and lakes abut the centre. The darkness of the close-growing trees add a welcome touch of the less-formal and structured and people do take themselves for walks there, especially when – as they will – closer relationships develop in the sixth form or when a breathing space and solitude are needed. But the school life provides little time for such things – even in the sixth, there are only 45 minutes of free time, between 9.00-9.45pm.

The atmosphere is orderly, friendly, purposeful and relaxed. The light in the eyes when you stop to talk to anyone – and everyone – is immediate. An air of engagement, quiet busyness and enthusiasm pervades the place plus a sense of privilege but not entitlement, and a focus on learning of all kinds. Parents seem universally thrilled: 'They generate a culture where it's all about having a go – nothing is impossible – there's such a buzz about the place.' 'It wouldn't suit everyone – you need a lot of energy and independence,' Interestingly, the word 'whacky' crops up a lot – meant warmly and kindly.

Wellington is now at the heart of a major global and national educational business. It has a portfolio of schools, several in China, and two academies here. This informs aspects of life on the home front – partnerships and exchanges and there is Dukebox – an online sharing platform for the entire family of schools.

Pastoral care, well-being and discipline: Famous for it – well-being, mindfulness, restorative justice, coaching, leadership, counselling etc; they explore and practise it all. 'Our children – who are all so different – are equally happy,' said one parent. 'I'd give it 10 out of 10 on the pastoral side,' said another. Carefully structured pastoral care system – every teacher is also a tutor and attached to a boarding house. But self-discipline is the norm. A school with rewards and punishments but punishments are rare and exclusions far rarer. Repeated bullying will see you out but isolated episodes seen as an opportunity for learning. Virtually all staff have training in coaching and this, alongside the school's Basic Courtesies, Core Values, and Mr Thomas's Five 'I's – 'Inspired, Intellectual, Independent, Individual, Inclusive' – underpin the tangible moral purpose of the place. 'The Stiff Upper Lip is long gone,' we were told. Nonetheless, some of the most forbidding uniform rules we have encountered (especially for girls) – seemingly at odds with the school's ethos in other ways, but this is not something the master has got round to looking at yet. 'But I like them to look smart.' It's a Christian foundation but now pretty ecumenical, though with a 'gently Anglican' bent, we were told. Health centre operates 24/7. Vast dining hall (former school hall?) with excellent menus on a four-weekly cycle. We snaffled a memorable flapjack.

Pupils and parents: Majority of UK pupils come from west London and the home counties. School's weekly boarding policy adds to its attraction in the south east. Around 13 per cent come from state and non-prep schools; around 12 per cent from overseas – from 41 countries at time of our visit. Around a third of pupils based overseas are British expats. Interestingly, a good proportion of the Uk based boarders are from non-British or dual citizenship homes. A genuinely inclusive and cosmopolitan constituency and a feature that is fostered by its schools overseas. Very few overseas boarders need EAL support – but those that do get individual help for which the college does not charge. Parents feel welcome here – 'I've never felt I shouldn't be on site. They are brilliant at involving us.'

Entrance: Around 190 pupils enter year 9 – some 110 boys, 80 girls. Around 900 apply. All candidates sit the ISEB common pre-test in the autumn term of year 6. References from present schools also sought. Long-listed candidates visit the college in January/February for an assessment day – a mix of collaborative problem-solving activities plus interview. Offers made in March – at least 65 per cent expected across all subjects at CE.

Around 25 boys and 20 girls join after GCSEs. Sixteen-plus candidates submit recent school reports and a personal statement about a year before entry. Applicants outnumber places 10 to one. Long-listed candidates attend an assessment day in November of year 11 and sit three papers in the subjects they mean to study in the sixth form, plus a maths skills test and an interview plus group discussion. References too, of course. Offers made on December 1 – A*s and As (9-7s) expected in all subjects – A*/8-9s in subjects to be pursued in the sixth. Internal pupils also expected to produce 6+ A/7s but there is always 'leeway if they are good citizens'. Attention paid at all levels to characteristics such as independence, inclusivity, grit plus the college's Virtues.

Wellington has led the way in sending its leavers to good universities across the pond. Runs the best conferences on this as on many other subjects

Exit: Penny numbers leave after GCSEs. Good proportion of Oxbridge places – 18 in 2017, plus six medics. High numbers also to, especially, Bristol, Durham, Edinburgh and Exeter but Mr Thomas plans to expand the breadth of destinations and wants to provide 'tip-top advice on all options' – including the modern, high calibre, degree apprenticeships path. Also a good number to the US and Canada (more than 20 off overseas in 2017) – Wellington has led the way in sending its leavers to good universities across the pond. Runs the best conferences on this as on many other subjects. Tremendous list of notable alumni includes: Christopher Ewart-Biggs, British ambassador assassinated by the IRA, current politicos Crispin Blunt, Michael Spicer and Edward Garnier; Harold Nicolson, numerous sports jocks including James Hunt and Max and Thom Evans; arts and entertainment types eg Robert Morley, Nikolai Tolstoy, Rory Bremner, Sebastian Faulks, Christopher Lee, Will Young and Elize du Toit; the Beeb's Peter Snow and Robin Oakley; practically the entire British military including 15 holders of the Victoria Cross and hosts of other worthies in many fields.

Money matters: The international schools help to fund the school's burgeoning bursary fund – scholarships no longer carry any financial benefit, with funds now routed into bursaries. However, without meriting a scholarship no-one is eligible for a bursary. Bursaries means-tested as elsewhere and worth anything from 10 to 95 per cent of school fees. Some £1.7m and rising annually available. Prince Albert Bursary Fund offers life-changing bursaries up to full fees to entrants who would otherwise have no chance of such an education. Ten holders at time of our visit. Also the Jimmy Higham sports' bursary and the Sir Anthony Seldon arts bursary. Well worth checking out. Foundation supports the children of deceased military officers up to full fees.

Remarks: Hard to imagine it done better. A site and campus to dream about. A school with mind, heart, guts and a constant fizz.

Winchester College

C of E 58

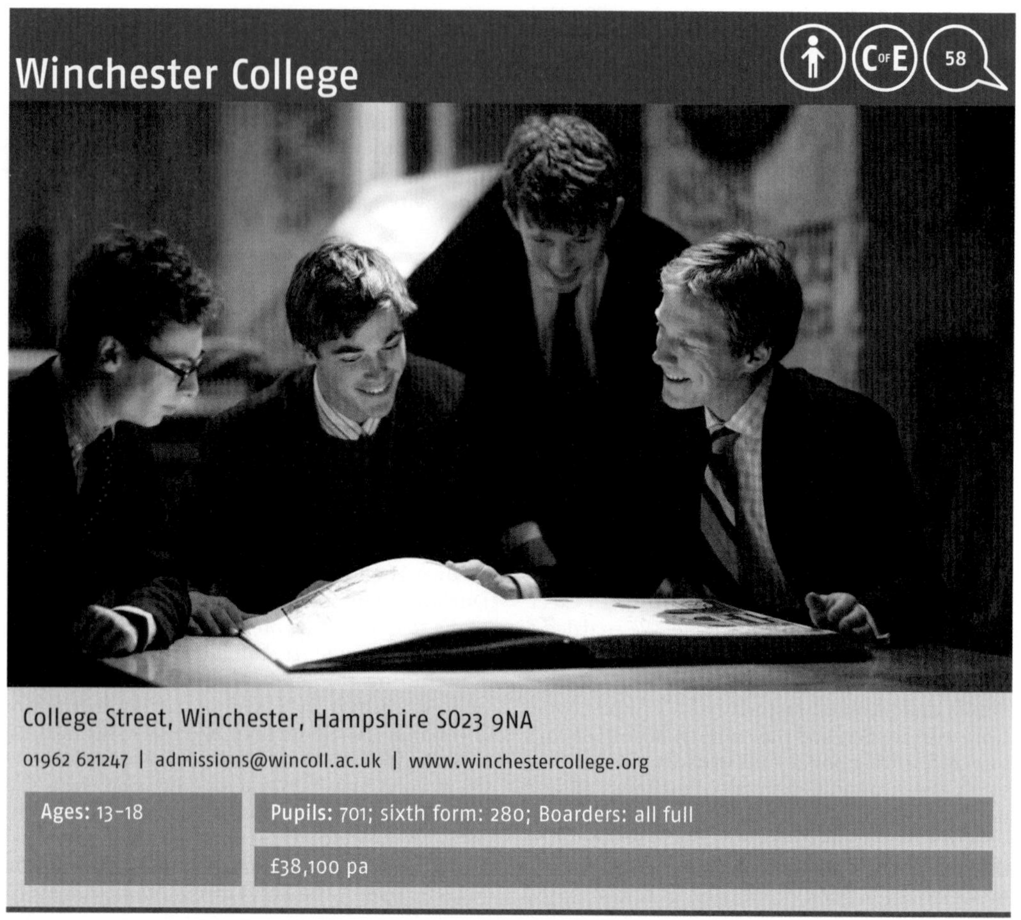

College Street, Winchester, Hampshire SO23 9NA

01962 621247 | admissions@wincoll.ac.uk | www.winchestercollege.org

Ages: 13–18

Pupils: 701; sixth form: 280; Boarders: all full

£38,100 pa

Headman: Since 2016, Dr Timothy Hands, previously master of Magdalen College School. A state school pupil turned down by Cambridge ('I was told by the careers adviser at my grammar school that I wouldn't get to university at all'), he studied violin at the Guildhall before reading English at King's College, London, then went on to St Catherine's, Oxford, followed by Oriel, where he ended up as a lecturer. He became housemaster at King's Canterbury, then second master at Whitgift School, then head of Portsmouth Grammar. He comes from a long line of teachers, including both parents and an ancestor who was schoolmaster on HMS Victory. Likes sport and music – was co-leader of the London Schools Symphony Orchestra and conductor of the Oxford University chamber choir, Schola Cantorum. The author of several books about Victorian literature and teaches English A level.

Married to Jane, a solicitor who read classics at Oxford; two sons.

Academic matters: Winchester offers Cambridge Pre-U examinations as a replacement for A levels in all subjects, finding them more flexible and academically challenging. The school takes a dim view of A levels, especially in modern languages which have been 'vandalised' ('you can now take an A level in French without reading a book!'). The Pre-U opens up sixth form study as a serious two-year programme, studying three subjects in depth, with examinations at the end – a format now copied by revised A levels. Most pupils take three subjects, but some, mainly mathematicians, take four (or even five) Pre-U exams.

Results always outstanding (nearly 48 per cent D1-2 – A* equivalent, and 73 per cent D1-3 – A*-A equivalent, in 2017), and the school continues to offer the shortest list of exam subjects of any reputable sixth form in England. Forget film studies and froth – here you will not find sociology, classical civilisation, politics, business studies, PE or psychology. Maths, chemistry, physics and economics the most popular Pre-U subjects, followed robustly by history and English lit. Philosophy and theology on a roll at the minute. No great cornucopia of GCSE choices either: all boys sit nine IGCSEs in two or three sciences, maths, English, Latin, French or German, plus other subjects which can include history, geography, music, art, design or more languages. In 2017, 90 per cent A*-A/9-7 grades at IGCSE.

'Div' is the unique and highly-prized complementary programme at the heart of the Winchester ethos. It aims to instill a knowledge and understanding of British, European and world history and culture and, as such, is a true, liberal education. 'The boys and dons love it. It's the one bit of this over-structured world in which they can pursue their own intellectual interests.' It's a holistic approach that we expect to find in Montessori education and schools on the alternative end of the spectrum. 'It means the staff have to be of the highest calibre so that they can lead this cross-subject, cross-cultural tutorial,' a parent explained. Average age of teachers has come down significantly in recent years, and is now a youthful 38.

Now fully embracing IT, with introduction of Firefly (learning platform) and Surface laptops for all from Y9 entry in 2018. Offers learning support for around 100 boys, mainly for mild dyslexia, dyspraxia and information processing.

IT not cutting any edges, reflecting an institutional reserve about the digital world. Little, if any, work done on computers in a boy's first year (or two) here. Offers learning support for around 100 boys, mainly for mild dyslexia, dyspraxia and information processing.

Games, options, the arts: Sport is 'brilliantly flexible', a parent told us. Enthusiasts can play as much as they want. 'My son went from the 4th team at his prep school to the A team here', chuckled one mum. 'There's a great spirit in the school sport', another told us, 'very unpressurised.' 'If you are determined to do no games, it's possible' (refreshing, and probably unique, to hear this said in a British public school). But some sort of physical exercise ('ekker') is compulsory. Main sports are soccer (coach is ex-Southampton FC captain Jason Dodd), Winchester College football (read the rules) and cricket (huge here – the cricket coach also runs the Hampshire U16s) but these are supplemented by everything from aikido to water polo. Fabulous playing fields and sports facilities of all kinds. Recent national competition wins in fives, fencing and sailing.

'The boys and dons love it. It's the one bit of this over-structured world in which they can pursue their own intellectual interests.' 'The staff have to be of the highest calibre'

Music very important, very strong and very classical. James Blunt, Genesis and Mumford and Sons may have attended public schools but they would not have been Wykehamists. Two-thirds of boys learn a musical instrument; many learn two or three, taught by a long list of specialist teachers. Pipe organ very strong here (one Winchester boy we know was making a tidy sum playing weddings while still in sixth form). Music school includes 50(!) practice rooms, a music tech classroom, recording studio and editing suite. Vast range of musical ensembles and performance opportunities – weekly Tuesday concert and many more throughout the year – many open to the public.

Art and drama lively and of quality, though they do not quite enjoy the accolade of music. CCF compulsory in year 10, after which it can be replaced with community service.

Boarding: All boys board. First year boys are generally in rooms of four to six. By IGCSEs they're in rooms of two or four. All sixth formers have single rooms, except the scholars. A boy's life here begins and ends with his house. Houses, while still more autonomous than at any other school in the UK, have been brought some distance into dreary conformity in this era of health and safety, school inspections and the like (school says: 'have greater consistency of practice than before'). There is now a lot more consistency of discipline, food (all meals are eaten in house) and day to day routine and less competition between houses (and housemasters). Current crop of housemasters praised by the parents we spoke to. Accommodation and food improving but still seen as of secondary importance, both to the school and to (British) parents.

'There are some very studious individuals here – yes, but there are also normal, clever but lazy boys who like their sport and are not averse to sunshine'

Saturdays consist of lessons until lunch, then sport, then reading, then prep. Many boys go out after chapel on Sundays – to lunch at home or out with parents, and older ones can go into town. The school's inflexible attitude towards Sunday boarding is a source of contention for a few boys who have to pass up outside sports fixtures.

Background and atmosphere: Founded in the 14th century by William of Wykeham, Bishop of Winchester, Chancellor to Richard II, and the sage behind the school's motto: Manners makyth man. Began in 1387 with a warden, 10 fellows, two schoolmasters, three chaplains, 70 scholars and 16 quiristers – the Winchester version of choristers. The bishop also founded New College, Oxford, with which the college maintains strong links. The quiristers are now educated down the road at the Pilgrims' School but continue to board at Winchester College and sing in chapel. So this is a quiet land of flinty walls, leafy quads, a venerable chapel, many other buildings of ancient date and visible history (the school was used as Cosette's Paris convent in the film version of Les Mis). Later foundations, eg Eton College, seem like modern upstarts by comparison. Not that the college hasn't kept building and acquiring. There are 10 boarding houses in adjacent streets, and buildings for all major disciplines. The college has built a new museum in a converted stable to display its trove of treasures – paintings, porcelain, silver, scientific instruments, books etc.

The atmosphere is donnish – the masters are called dons here and the college has a language of its own (called Notions) for almost every aspect of daily life. The lack of girls, together with the school's academically elitist ethos, gives the boys the gift of unselfconsciousness rarely seen elsewhere. The school considered admitting girls under previous head – 'I started off thinking we'd do it', he remembered. In the end, they decided against: 'Girls dominate academically, especially in the lower years. To introduce that here would change the intellectual ethos of the school. What we do is distinctive – we do not have a wide ability range. It is the high quality of the boys' ability at the "bottom" that is key here.'

Surprisingly, the school has no formal relationship with Winchester Cathedral – who needs it when you've got such a superb school chapel (built 1392)? The cathedral is used for school choir concerts. 'It casts an ecclesiastical aura.' Has a 5+ year relationship with Midhurst Rother College (academy) and some pupils from the academy come to Winchester for a Saturday morning programme of classes.

Pastoral care, well-being and discipline: School rules cover 10 tightly spaced typed pages and make a terrifically good read. You will find a complex list of warnings about alcohol (depending whether wine, beer or spirits and where purchased) and learn that the possession of firearms or explosives is forbidden (with the exception of 'shotguns brought into school with parent permission'). Boys are also reminded not to wear 'T-shirts bearing slogans which are anagrammatical' (what harm is an anagram, we ask?). No hats. And before you ask, no earrings.

Mobiles allowed so long as they are 'inaudible and invisible'. School takes a hard line on drugs. Unusually, for a school of this vintage, there is no sixth form bar. Housemasters run most aspects of a boy's life – pastoral and academic – but serious matters end up with the head.

Pupils and parents: Some 87 per cent of boys come from the UK. All pupils speak English as it if were their first language; around 20 pupils are bilingual. Quite a lot of Hong Kong Chinese families – who tend to coalesce at the academic hothouses of this land. 'Russians haven't found us yet,' commented one of the admissions staff (more likely, they shun it because it's single sex). Boys come from a large assortment of preps mostly in the southern half of the UK, with Pilgrims' School, Horris Hill, Twyford, The Dragon, Summer Fields and Sussex House leading the field. The school does not break its back to court parents – neither current nor prospective: there is one rather sober open day each year.

Parents we spoke to were keen to emphasise that though boys must be clever and academic to be happy here, they need not be geeks: 'There's a view that Winchester boys are anaemic swots. There are some very studious individuals here – yes, but there are also normal, clever but lazy boys who like their sport and are not averse to sunshine.' Not the place for hovering parents – signing on here takes a leap of faith and the school is set in its ways ('clear about what it wants and expects,' says the school). List of well-known old boys is long, but curiously unexciting. Lots of politicians, academics, cricketers, journalists, pillars of The Establishment.. and Tim Brooke-Taylor.

Entrance: You'll need to be on your toes. The school asks parents to register their sons after they've turned 8 but 'well before the end of year 5'. No need for early registration for those attempting scholarships – winning an award carries with it the automatic right to a place. Admissions for Commoners are via the housemasters who see 25 to 30 sets of parents when the boys are 10-11, interview and test them (a short verbal and numerical reasoning test), get reports from existing schools and offer places to around half. A deposit is then requested and the place is firm, barring (rare) failure of the college's entrance exam which is taken two years later in May of the year of entry in all usual CE subjects (with Greek and German as additional options, but not Spanish). It helps to have an idea of which houses you are interested in – parents may arrange meetings with up to three housemasters. 'If parents are still unsettled after seeing three houses, this may not be the school for them', said the admissions department with customary directness.

Scholars and exhibitioners selected by exams in English, maths, science and a multiple choice 'general reasoning' test. Candidates must also choose three optional papers from among: Latin, French, Classical Greek/German/Spanish, history, geography, maths II or general paper II. Scholars live in College – a separate house pulsating with hyperactive brain cells. The life of a scholar here is not for all, and we know of families turning down an academic scholarship (especially now that they bring no automatic fee remission). A half dozen boys come fresh into the sixth form via exam and a minimum of six GCSE A*-A/9-7 grades (ie mainly A*s but the odd A won't rule you out).

Exit: In 2017, 37 to Oxbridge, and seven medics. The rest to a predictable spread of the best redbricks. Increasing numbers (around 20 lately) to a distinguished list of top North American universities. Although the six As/7s at GCSE for sixth form entrance is a low hurdle for most boys here, the college is said to be 'ruthless' (school says 'firm') about enforcing this rule. A handful of unfortunate boys receive 'the letter' each year.

Money matters: Since 2011, all scholarships – given for academic and musical ability (and from 2018 for sporting ability); no sports, art or drama frippery here (though candidates with those talents may bring along a portfolio of their work) – bring zero fee remittance. However means-tested bursaries can be awarded up to 100 per cent of the fee where necessary. Music scholars, of which there are 10 (usually grade 8 by age 13), receive free tuition on up to two instruments and singing; music exhibitioners (closer to grade 6) get free tuition on one instrument. NB Charges an inexplicable £500 'entrance fee' (in addition to a registration fee and deposit).

Remarks: A very special place for intellectually curious boys and their teachers. Unique.

Wychwood School

59

74 Banbury Road, Oxford, Oxfordshire OX2 6JR

01865 557976 | admissions@wychwoodschool.org | www.wychwoodschool.org

Ages: 11-18

Pupils: 110; sixth form: 20; Boarders: 20 full, 10 weekly, 4 flexi

Day: £15,225 pa; Boarding: £22,950 – £24,300 pa

Headmistress: Since 2012, Mrs Andrea Johnson BSc (50s). Comes from a family of teachers and doctors and intended 'never to do either'. She read chemistry at Durham, did a PGCE 'because it might be useful' and unexpectedly fell in love with teaching. Formerly assistant head at Tudor Hall where she worked for 20 years, she is the first head of Wychwood not to be an old girl. Teaches chemistry to year 7 and 11. Married to a retired scientist, two adult children, at least one intends to continue the family tradition and is training to be a teacher.

Mrs Johnson is energetic, genuine and very friendly – her presence is reassuring, rather like a wise owl, and one feels she could cope with anything (parents tell us that she does). Just as well really, since that's what you need to be able to do when you run a small school. And as far as Mrs J is concerned, when it comes to education, small really is beautiful. She sees Wychwood as a place that can be responsive to the needs of the individual, to educate girls who 'want to think and achieve but would sink in the hurly burly of a bigger school.' The school gets its fair share of 'burn out' refugees from some of Oxfordshire's super-heated girls' independents, but is equally a positive choice for many families from the word go. 'We enable any child who comes here to get the best possible exam results.'

Parents we spoke to were extremely supportive of Mrs J and tell us that they welcome her sensitive moves towards modernisation and determination to raise the school's profile.

Academic matters: With only 110 pupils in total, results would benefit from micro, rather than macro analysis, but they're respectable: in 2017, 50 per cent A*-A/9-7 at GCSE and 62 per cent A*-B, 37 per cent A*/A at A level. Small class sizes mean teaching staff can give every girl individual attention and customise their approach. We watched year 8s getting to grips with evaluating historical sources and you could almost touch the intense concentration in the room. In fact quiet and studious pretty much sums up the atmosphere of Wychwood. A display of beautifully produced project work showed Jane Eyre's end of term report, as well as prospectuses and other material from

The school will ('within reason') run a course for just one student; GCSE astronomy was taught to a single stargazing girl

Lowood (somewhere that definitely wouldn't make it into the Good Schools Guide).

In a smart and well-equipped lab we came across the head teaching year 7 chemistry and yet more rapt attention and eager answers. The biology lab was festooned with a long, pink papier mâché tube; 'That's a life-size model of the large intestine,' we were told. Length, not girth, we hope.

One thing we kept hearing about Wychwood was that 'teachers have time for you' and that 'they encourage us to follow our own interests'. The school will ('within reason') run a course for just one student; for instance, GCSE astronomy was taught for the benefit of a single stargazing girl. In the sixth form, some A level classes might just be two or three strong – more like the tutorial teaching that goes on at the university down the road. Individual tuition in particular subjects can also be arranged and in some cases girls may repeat a year.

Girls take maximum of nine-and-a-half GCSEs and different strengths and interests are accommodated: double or triple science; both Englishes or just English language; psychology; art, textiles and, unusually, photography. Most do French and Spanish, German offered privately, as are GCSEs in, for example, Chinese, Japanese, Persian, for native

speakers. Exchange trips to Spain and France in alternate years. All do short courses in RS and ECDL in ICT. At A level most popular subjects are maths, the sciences, photography and history of art.

Games, options, the arts: Textiles, art and photography each enjoy their own light and modern studios in a converted stable block decorated with impressive examples of students' work. As one pupil commented, 'for our size we have so many resources.' It was in the textile studio that we had a sneak preview of the new uniform 'unshortenable' skirt, designed by the textiles teacher. If it's successful she should patent it and make her fortune, but since it doesn't feature something that padlocks it to below the knee we fear that girls will always find a way. Newish uniform design has not been received joyfully, but is it ever? In fact, as far as we could see, Wychwood pupils seemed rather modest in their skirt minimising aspirations, compared to other schools we've visited.

Few mutters that Mrs Johnson isn't as supportive of the arts as former heads have been. School says that girls may opt for more than one GCSE out of art, textiles and photography but since they only take nine-and-a-half in total they often only choose one. At A level girls can do all three if they so choose.

There's a school orchestra and choir, a chamber choir and music lessons are offered in any instrument – harp seems to be a favourite. House plays, written, designed and directed by the girls, are performed competitively; LAMDA exams popular. D of E up to gold offered and Model UN.

If your daughter is sports mad and keen to play for the winning side then, with heavy heart, we suggest you look elsewhere. On the plus side, as a parent pointed out, 'you always get picked for the team.' Not that Wychwood is a complete stranger to victory: our guide was still buzzing from a recent and unexpected rounders success. As the head says, 'Girls learn to lose with grace, but when they win ...' On-site facilities include tennis, basketball and badminton courts, and fitness suite (in a rather gloomy basement room). Nearby off-site are an athletics field, Astro, and more tennis courts. Main opponents are Oxford High and St Helen's; years 7 and 8 play against The Dragon. School does all it can to support girls competing at high levels (county and national) in particular sports by adapting individual timetables etc. Rather surprisingly we discovered that there is a Wychwood equestrian team. No sign of horses trotting down the Banbury Road, rather girls with their own steeds compete on behalf of the school. Recent 'uproar' when timetabled sport was reduced to an hour a week during GCSEs. Schools say that this was to accommodate girls doing 12 GCSEs at the time. Timetabled sport will increase once option choices are rationalised. Quite right too.

Until the 1960s swimming took place in the nearby River Cherwell. Girls used to cycle down to a muddy pool called (for reasons lost in history) the Rhea, where non-swimmers were initiated by being dragged through the water on the end of a pole. Punting was also on the curriculum. There are delightfully nostalgic accounts of the Rhea and its rather whiffy mud in the school's centenary history book. Today's Wychwood swimmers use the Kidlington pool, undoubtedly safer but much less to reminisce about in future years.

Boarding: About a third of pupils board, a fairly even split between full and weekly or flexi. Parents book flexi boarding (usually 1-3 nights per week) at the start of term but school can, and does, accommodate pupils at short notice. Day girls can stay after evening activities such as trips to London or the theatre – bunk beds (only for occasional boarders) add to the sleepover excitement. We were told that news of major road works caused a spike in boarding applications – even fairly local parents appreciate the benefits when gridlock threatens Oxford's already notorious traffic.

When we describe the boarding as 'homely' it's a compliment as well as a reality check. Years 7-9 have large first floor rooms – sash windows and high ceilings – with three to four beds in each. School says mixing the age group helps foster sisterly ethos; colourful curtains and duvets, bedside clutter and lots of family photos and posters add to the family feel. There's wardrobe and under bed storage but no desks – homework takes place elsewhere under supervision.

Sixth formers have characterful single study bedrooms, mostly up in the eaves. Rooms have names such as North Pole, Elysium and Valhalla – harking back to earlier and less centrally heated times. What would their former occupants think about today's duvets and power showers?

During the week there's a table plan for supper – another way of making sure everyone knows each other – but things are more relaxed at weekends. Girls can make themselves snacks – they just go down to the kitchen and ask for supplies. Activities include film nights, Oxford-based bowling, ice skating and trips to Port Meadow along with regular forays to Camden and Bicester Village for shopping. Boarders also take part in community activities – most recently litter picking for Oxclean (voluntary but apparently rather popular). There's a big trip once a year to somewhere like Thorpe Park that's funded by old girls – day pupils can go too but they have to pay.

Background and atmosphere: The school was founded by a Miss Lee and Miss Batty in 1897 and has always been on Oxford's busy Banbury Road. Miss Lee, the younger of the two, was a pioneer, obtaining a first-class degree in English at St Hugh's and going on to lecture and become vice principal. She funded the school from her earnings and continued to lecture in both Oxford and London. The school was named after Oxfordshire's Wychwood forest in 1918, having formerly been known unofficially as the Battery or Battery Lees, and a uniform of forest green was adopted. One of the early teachers, the redoubtable Miss Rendall, went on to found another Oxford school, Rye St Antony.

Today's Wychwood is still domestic in scale, the original brass plaque on the door (featured heavily in promotional literature) modestly announcing its presence in an area where a Latin primer, carefully launched, is bound to hit a venerable educational establishment. There's nothing flash here, no plate glass or modern architecture, but everything is well loved and cared for. Head of boarding is from the hotel industry – what a good idea – and facilities have been upgraded accordingly, although The Randolph it isn't. This was Mrs Johnson's first undertaking on arrival, strongly backed by the 'brilliant' governors, the chair of whom is a former pupil.

Pastoral care, well-being and discipline: Mrs Johnson says, 'a child can't learn if she is unhappy.' Parents say that pastoral care is outstanding: girls who need it are given time and space but this doesn't mean that the school can't be tough when called for. In a small community one person's actions can significantly affect all and Mrs Johnson will ask a girl to leave if she feels that the school can't accommodate her needs. As one parent put it, 'Yes, your daughter is an individual, but she is also part of a respectful community.' Some grumbles that pupils arriving at odd times eg half way through a term can make things a little disjointed.

Famously democratic, girls are genuinely involved in decision making – much to the horror of the Daily Mail in the 1960s (plus ça change ...). The founders' original forward-thinking structure of councillors and 'citizens' with voting rights, responsibilities and privileges still operates today (albeit with a few modern tweaks). As Mrs Johnson says, 'We're so small that everybody can be involved.'

An area where a Latin primer, carefully launched, is bound to hit a venerable educational establishment

Lower ground canteen is as nice as a lower ground canteen can be. Girls mostly complimentary about the food – favourites are the breakfasts and Friday fish and chips. There are, and have been since the school's foundation, buns at break time. Cook deserves honourable mention for skilfully adapting meals so that girls with eg dairy or gluten intolerance can eat the same as everyone else.

Some might discount a school such as Wychwood because of its small size, but consider the benefits: it's responsive, girls notice there's a play or event on down the road (this being Oxford it's more than likely) and arrangements can be made to go double quick. Parents are very involved, professionals including medics from the John Radcliffe come in to talk to pupils – this happens in other schools but it's more likely to be a lecture than a conversation. Parents told us that Wychwood was uncliquey and that foreign students integrated very well. One commented that it was very good preparation for work because you 'had to get along with everyone'.

All schools say that they nurture every child as an individual, but common sense tells us that this is easier to achieve in a school of 110 rather than an academic super tanker of 800 or more.

Pupils and parents: Used to be known as the 'Dons' school' but draws from a wider pool these days. Majority of local parents are Oxford professionals – lawyers, doctors etc. Girls we met were thoughtful, independent-minded – lacking the swagger of nearby sisters perhaps – and fiercely loyal to their school and its ways. Lots of summer-born girls, fair few refugees from schools that were too big and girls going through upheaval eg parents' divorce.

And then there are girls who visited on an open day and 'fell in love' with Wychwood.

Former pupils include Margaret Casson, architect, designer and photographer; Joan Aiken, writer; Vicky Jewson, film maker; Rebecca Stockland, opera singer; Matilda Leyser, actress and aerialist; Izzie Lawrence, comedian; Honor Fell, microbiologist.

Entrance: Girls join at age 11 from local primaries/ preps and there's another influx from preps at age 13. Prospective year 7s spend a day at the school and are tested in maths and English. External candidates for sixth form need minimum of six GCSEs at grades A*-C /9-4 and A*-A/9-7 in A level subjects. Places may be available in other years, subject to interview and assessment.

Exit: Around 30-50 per cent leaves after GCSEs. This isn't a school that unthinkingly crams sixth formers onto the non-stop university express, although most girls do go on to further study. One to Cambridge in 2017 to read natural sciences. Art and design at Oxford Brookes and elsewhere popular; other courses range from chemical engineering at Surrey to midwifery at Birmingham City to food and nutrition in Hong Kong. Girls have also gone on to be Norland nannies, Montessori educators, farriers and business entrepreneurs.

Money matters: Day fees on a par with local equivalents – OK, you're not getting the sports facilities but you are getting something pretty close to a customised education. Boarding comparatively good value. Academic, music and creative arts scholarships of approximately £1,200 pa available, as are means-tested bursaries.

Remarks: Charming pint-sized power house. Much-needed alternative to the academic overdrive of some other Oxford girls' independents (if it didn't exist someone would certainly have to invent it). A positive choice for many relieved families, one of whom described it as 'a jewel, we wouldn't want our daughter to be anywhere else.'

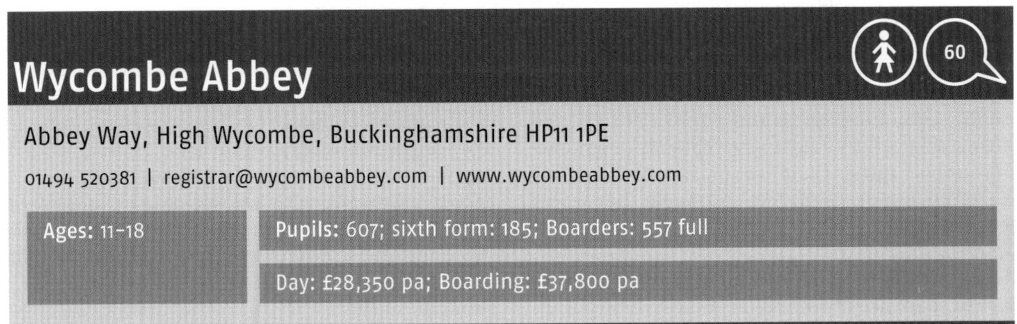

Wycombe Abbey

60

Abbey Way, High Wycombe, Buckinghamshire HP11 1PE

01494 520381 | registrar@wycombeabbey.com | www.wycombeabbey.com

Ages: 11–18

Pupils: 607; sixth form: 185; Boarders: 557 full

Day: £28,350 pa; Boarding: £37,800 pa

Headmistress: Since 2013, Mrs Rhiannon Wilkinson MA MEd (50s). Previously principal at Harrogate Ladies' College, one of many curves in perfectly rounded career that includes five years at Haileybury as director of studies and two at Cheadle Hume School where was director of pastoral system. Married with children – husband, Donald is a retired headmaster.

Choice of profession early and unwavering, thanks to family clan of fulfilled teachers (has happy memories of washing out paint pots in mother's classroom). Started in large comprehensives in Devon and south Manchester, then (sensibly ignoring relative's confident predictions of 'career suicide') spent 11 years in Hong Kong and Brunei schools where managing international and affluent families honed parent-whispering skills. Only career downside – has lived in school accommodation since age of 27. 'Probably makes me a sad person.' (Not on evidence so far.)

Far more to the post than simply ensuring all that excellence in terms of popularity and superb results carries on ad infinitum, from righting genuine wrongs – 'would always be first to admit if we make a mistake' – to curbing 'me, me, me' excesses, nicely. 'You can't run any school for an individual,' she says.

Key is transparent admissions process, ensuring name and glittering prizes don't blind families to school values. 'Want parents to choose us because truly know us, not based on the name.' Spends every Tuesday with prospective parents – 45 minutes apiece – to get message across.

Staff love her and she's getting there with parents. 'A true educationalist who is clearly passionate about the school – maybe too passionate,' commented one. 'I don't think you can be too passionate because if you weren't you would lose your enthusiasm when you face some challenging times,' counters Mrs W.

Weekend 'meet the head' lunch programme under way to increase exposure, linked to match fixtures for maximum efficiency. Has also put in the time with pupils, from individual meetings in top years to throwing jolly party at house in grounds for all 65 first years. 'By end of first half term, knew everyone by name,' says parent.

Expert knowledge extends to on-site wildlife, from nesting red kites to badgers, deer and – her favourite – Stumpy the Canada goose, named for deformed wings, tenderly cared for by school with occasional Jammy Dodger as a treat.

Girls like what they've seen of her: has achieved finely judged balance that hovers somewhere between friendliness and formality, thought parent. 'She's super, so there for them, doesn't go round being all huggy or anything – they're scared of her in a nice way and the staff are also very behind her,' said mother.

Unlike predecessor, doesn't teach – yet – and is eyeing up the timetable (shame to waste that Oxford history degree). May have work cut out with building programme – two new boarding houses on site of disused swimming pool. Also starting, in a quiet way, to build public profile – was quoted in The Times talking about the ability of boarding to rescue children from otherwise pressurised existence. Looking at results with jaundiced eye this might seem a tad kettle and pot-like but no, she insists, school does amazingly well with all-embracing support rather than 'trot on Smudgy' crack of the whip. Pupils might feel cocooned; they won't feel driven.

Academic matters: Easy to see results as inevitable consequence of admissions process – bright in, gleaming out. Results impeccable – 85 per cent of A levels and 97 per cent of GCSEs graded A*-A in 2017. 'Results are amazing,' said parent. 'Feels as if no barriers to what the girls could achieve.'

However, not quite the effort-free equation it might appear. Smaller numbers applying to come here means school has to spread admissions net just that bit wider than equivalent boys' school – and it's how they manage the talent that's their forte. Whisper it softly, but sexism is still rife in education, thought parent. Boys get the very best, but for 'the girl it doesn't matter quite as much, so a school like [this] has not got such a huge pool of clever children to draw from.'

There's also the darling daughter factor, thinks Mrs Wilkinson, where doting parents can't quite bear to part from their girls. 'They are very precious, daddy's little princess, the friends of mothers and hard to let go.'

Everyone here is bright – with compulsory Latin and attempt at classical Greek for all, wouldn't cope here if they weren't, though don't overdose on GCSEs, with 10 or 11 the goal for most, one girl insistent on 13 talked down to more manageable 12. 'Great achievement is bringing up girls who are competent but don't shine and getting them to get the really top grades,' said parent.

Not a place where learning support is rushed off feet: though 54 (around 10 per cent) are identified as having special needs, for most this translates into academic support – aka learning enhancement – to plug previous curriculum gaps, particularly for overseas pupils. Just five have help with SpLD, a further five working with EAL specialist – and every pupil in the school needs to enjoy the challenge. 'My daughter's somewhere in the middle [which means] she has a lot to strive for and works harder,' thought mother.

Key is micro monitoring. No slightly below par result is given the benefit of the doubt, no progress

chart left unplotted, communication between staff of the instant message variety. Parents, pupils and staff know exactly where every girl is in every subject (pre-GCSE tracking grades include three for A* – high, secure and low – alone). If anticipated trajectory shows any signs of premature wilting, the SWAT team is ready and waiting. 'The ones that would struggle, they just spend more time with them. Literally, the teacher's all over them,' said mother. 'Nobody's going to fail their grades by accident,' agreed another. Timetable underpins the message – Saturday kicks off with breakfast at 8.00am with lessons until 11.50am (detention, scheduled for 8.20am, isn't compulsory, we were pleased to hear).

Best teachers 'adored' by pupils for effortless ability to take scenic route through the curriculum and 'teach round the subject, which I think is really important'

Tests, predictably, are frequent but well managed and not done 'in a kind of heartrendingly tedious way,' thought parent. Inevitably, some girls find relentlessness of approach harder to bear than others, but transmogrified into gratitude when desired grades came in. 'There are times when you think "wish you would stop hounding me and accept standard" but it's worth it in the end,' said sixth former.

Parental comments acted on. Issue with one teacher relating to lesson pace 'sorted out instantly and school kept us informed on an almost daily basis [until] problem solved,' said parent. One teacher, total convert to boarding, felt it enabled tiny changes where girl 'not quite herself' to be picked up and sorted before could escalate. 'It's that swift response to a change in demeanour – remarkable, rewarding and very satisfying.'

Staff fabness is the norm, best teachers trending at top of charisma settings and 'adored' by pupils for effortless ability to take scenic route through the curriculum and 'teach round the subject, which I think is really important,' said mother. (Latest inspection report gushes agreement.)

Among many favourite subjects history teaching gets rave reviews, sharing joint honours with maths. 'School encourages you to do the subjects you love,' says pupil. 'Very foolish to take on two years in sixth form to study subjects you're not committed to,' agrees teacher.

Fairly brisk staff turnover inevitable consequence of recruiting top talent – no weights are going to hold back rise to greater things for long. Recent departure of fab director of studies to become head elsewhere par for the course. 'If you're recruiting at the top level, it's going to happen,' said parent, one of many who perceive this as price worth paying for quality teaching, while long stay figures (average age 46 with 76 staff members here for 10 years plus) do send reassuring message of stability. Only niggle is that some departures could occasionally be better timed, thought one. More quality staff accommodation – school lags behind others in this respect – would also help, feel staff and parents.

While care and attention that goes into creating the finished pupil hugely appreciated by parents, we heard more than once that aspects of culture had been a tad joy-free. 'There's a sense that growing up is a serious business,' said parent. 'We don't laugh at ourselves, we don't question ourselves that much. We know what we do, we're good at it, deal with it.'

Similarly, when rules are broken 'there's no knowing smiles, no "I've got to give you this penalty, please don't do it again but we're still friends",' said parent. 'It's "we really expect girls of your age to behave much better than this and it's not funny at all".' Occasionally po-faced? Possibly, thought staff. 'I think staff felt they needed permission to let hair down,' says head.

Staff confirm that fun, once the three letter word that dare not say its name, is now out and proud – mostly. Immediate muting of clearly very jolly (and refreshingly noisy) Latin lesson heard when this reviewer hove into view suggests not all teachers have got the message that head is, as one put it, 'in favour of jollity.'

Girls, though, stress noses are removed from grindstones on regular basis. Everyone works hard but there's 'lots of laughing and joking in the kitchen,' stressed sixth former. 'Not so serious that you shouldn't be scared to come here. We know how to have fun.'

Games, options, the arts: As with other high-achieving schools, everything you'd expect in the way of stunning stuff to play, perform or create is on show on a nearby pitch, platform or podium. Bashful won't get you places though, thought parent. 'If you're not going to do grab the opportunities, probably wouldn't suit.'

Caters for all sorts in innumerable venues, sweet-toothed first years to Cadbury's World, skiers to Whistler, budding sixth form medics to West Herts Hospital and female highflyers past and present regularly celebrated with events and talks – subsequent pupil write-ups, even by youngest, are little gems of well-observed journalism.

The 550 plus weekly instrumental lessons are also somehow fitted in, handful most years reaching diploma standard, substantial numbers hitting grades 7 and 8. Drama, equally ambitious, includes day of Shakespeare miniatures – Titus Andronicus (and others) each done and dusted in just 30 minutes.

Games widely enjoyed and lots of them, team sports 'formidable' with even tiniest slivers of talent encouraged to flourish. Teams don't straddle the alphabet – size means lacrosse, for example, only reaches C after the first year when 'have more teams so as not to make the girls feel left out.' Sure footed pretty much across the board, football, netball, tennis and squash teams among those whizzing up to quarter final stage and above in national tournaments, sailors recently taking part in world championships.

Not so sporty thrive, happy to trade games for other interests, school good at helping find inner something ('funasize' weekend activity option sounds fun, bootcamp possibly less so). Music, drama, or art, 'they'll find a way of making that come to you,' said parent.

Marvel of timetabling helps to avoid overloads – one third year had opted for piano, violin, ballet, riding and extra lacrosse. 'Very tailored. I don't know how they do it,' said parent. Sheer willpower and not letting sun set on unfinished work was pupil tip though can lead to lateish finish (10pm rare but not unheard of).

Only small bone of contention was desire to embrace the new rather than stick to tried, tested and trophy-ed – one parent thought rowing, recently introduced, could be made more of. Another, however, had nothing but praise for polo, also new to the school and thus far a galloping success.

Boarding: It's all or nothing full boarding (unless you're one of the very few day pupils). School operates non-negotiable 'closed' weekends (following hols, half terms and exeats). No choice over houses either – decision is made by school and that's that, though with posh lighting, carpet and paint upgrade programme, will be few complaints wherever you end up – fabbed-up bits of Daws Hill, for example, well worth a visit.

'Don't want them to be in a privileged little bubble,' agrees head, while pointing out that anyone who can afford the fees unlikely to be on breadline

Oldest and youngest pupils have own houses. First years get chickens for extra homeliness, upper sixth ditch poultry for first taste of independence – wear own clothes, too (sensibly point out that as universities don't insist on work wear, why should they?). Can be heady experience – school occasionally has to coax those briefly high on prospect of unlimited toast making and TV watching back into more humdrum aspects of school life.

In between (years 2 to lower sixth) girls join one of 11 mixed-age houses (two new ones just opened), each with around 45 pupils. Older girls are enlisted as mother and granny substitutes, brilliant at 'been there, done that' advice, many issues resolved without recourse to adult intervention. Also compels older girls to keep conversation within age-appropriate limits, pointed out parent. It's rounded off with formality of timetabled slots with housemistresses and elected house prefect system (one housemistress uses two vote system, one for loyalty candidate, the other 'for one they'd really like to win – they're never wrong').

Add packed programme of evening and weekend activities, from shopping trips to ice skating and even, according to website, 'vegging out' (inverted commas – theirs – probably say it all) and parental approval pretty much universal.

Background and atmosphere: Entrance via one of High Wycombe's statement roundabouts makes countrified setting a particular pleasure. 'Abbey' is a misnomer (it's a nun-free zone, name for status purposes only) but from ecclesiastic trimmings in main building – an 18th century former mansion – to performing arts centre overlooking lake, with incredible number of performance areas (one handily combining grand piano and chaise longue for artistic swooning to music), school is very easy on the eye.

Founded 1896, school was 'new experiment' by pioneering Miss – later Dame – Frances Dove.

One of Girton College's test batch of girl students and school's first headmistress, was every ounce a character, on-line portrait notable for fabulous, gravity-defying hair probably held up by principles alone.

Her aim – girls' education every bit as good as boys' through pursuit of excellence, development of talents, godliness and an understanding of the needs of others – remains top of the checklist. School's view is that even if her reaction to chicken nugget-making or 'baking with Mr Whiteley' sessions might be harder to call, Dame Frances would feel right at home with current ethos and achievements.

All happens on suitably inspirational site, originally belonging to Carringtons (current Lord Carrington is school enthusiast and regular visitor), enlarged by 1929 purchase of next door estate, Daws Hill, big enough to house a school all on its own, used for weddings and a good five minutes from main school by car (staff often drive, girls in its three boarding houses take compulsory scenic route). Has just got back World War II underground bunker, annexed after school was requisitioned as HQ for US Eighth Air Force – history department no doubt licking lips at potential for truly authentic lessons.

Little sign of world-weary London – and on and on – vibe here. Instead, children remain children – against the odds. Delightful Fairies event (you'll have to ask for details – we're sworn to secrecy) where magical beings turn every house into (tinsel) town one night in Christmas term, appears proof against teen cynicism.

Everything you'd expect in the way of stunning stuff to play, perform or create is on show on a nearby pitch, platform or podium. Bashful won't get you places, though

Was it really healthy to put so much distance between pupils and real life, wondered one older girl, worried for health of contemporaries' souls. Definitely, think parents, who appear simply relieved that school's imposition of rules, including bans on make up and travelling unaccompanied on public transport until reach 16, keeps them off the hook. 'Might be a bit ridiculous but means girls feel safe and can be scruffy and dirty when it's appropriate,' said parent.

They also love their jargon. Prefects, unofficially, are 'mons' (once monitors); booters the temporary lockers where pre-lunch gubbins is stowed. (And, oh, the relief of seeing a bit of

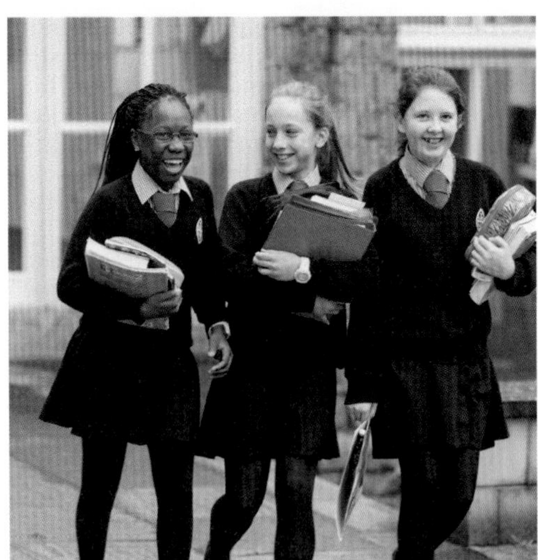

learning sprawl, with books, calculators and even the odd sock in contrast to pristine conditions elsewhere.)

There's Big School (actually the school hall – smell, instantly recognisable, of 'dust, old wood and overworked brains,' thought staff member) overlooked by bust of Frances Dove, grim as death, a martinet in marble, exiled from classrooms where was scaring the teachers (a joke, they said – though we wonder..)

Add Gym Courtyard (gym went years ago), four boarding Out Houses, inside the school grounds but 'you have to go out to them' – well, of course – and Long Corridor – the through route that thinks it's a communal room – and no wonder that even long-serving staff freely own up to being occasionally surprised by unfamiliar nooks and crannies.

Pastoral care, well-being and discipline: Housemistress as personality cult may be dead but continue to exert considerable beneficial influence, experts in even-handedness and clued-upness, matron and tutor completing house triumvirate. 'You get this impression, if something's happened in the morning, housemistress will know about it by lunchtime,' said parent.

Not always a breeze. Some girls won't get on with others in their house – and sophisticated urbanites vs the rest can make for occasional trouble. Staff antennae don't miss much, however, and one parent was pragmatic. Daughter has 'realised that she's just going to have to get on with it,' she said.

Pupils and parents: With school seen as nearest you'll get to girls' Eton equivalent in terms of ethos, location and facilities (impressive list of joint social events adds to sibling feel), it's often purchased as part of matching pair. Old girls are solidly brilliant type you'd expect (reality TV slebs aren't their thing, so far) and include Rt Hon Lady Justice Butler-Sloss, Baroness Howe, plus star journalist India Knight and actress Rachel Stirling.

You won't find idle rich featuring in the parental mix: hard-working, high-flying, well connected and dual income professionals dominate – as indeed they must to stump up hefty fees, though still find time to attend matches.

Some reservations about amounts of money sloshing about. 'Do worry that when many of her friends have their own Addison Lee account daughter might have a warped view of what is "normal",' said one mother. School asks for birthday celebrations to be limited to pizza or noodle bar excursions to avoid escalation of party politics.

'Don't want them to be in a privileged little bubble,' agrees head, while pointing out that anyone who can afford the fees unlikely to be on breadline. Fast growing bursary programme will help those who can't – new boarding houses will lead to gradual increase in numbers to 600. 'Thirty extra girls over seven years won't dilute product,' says head.

Girls may cover the gamut of characters, outer appearance occasionally au naturel as regards make up but sharing hefty degree of inner self-confidence (it's the quality most commented on by parents elsewhere) and appetite for success. 'Good with strong, silent type,' said one parent. Won't be squashed and there's 'healthy situation where girls help each other [but] if you're not the type that is striving to do well, you'll soon be left behind.'

Entrance: Potential pupils will 'like their notebooks and fluorescent pens – busy little bees who love finding out the way things fit together,' says head – which might help when it comes to working way through complex entrance procedures and deadlines. Register 18 months to two years in advance for 11+ and 13+ entry and at least 15 months ahead for sixth form hopefuls – minimum nine A and A*/9-7 GCSEs required. Pre-tests for all candidates.

Feeders include high profile preps in London and South East: Maltman's Green, Bute House, Francis Holland, Pembridge Hall, Glendower, Ken Prep and Garden House in year 7 (65 places – around 180 applicants). Godstowe and The Dragon at 13 (more competitive with 100 applicants for 25 places), separate exams for UK prep and overseas/senior school candidates). Around 25 per cent international pupils, Hong Kong, Malaysia and Nigeria most strongly represented. Thirty day places awarded to top performing locals.

Exit: Head's lightbulb moment was to stop post-16 exodus by giving fifth formers Through the Keyhole invite to previously, and pointlessly, top secret delights of upper sixth boarding house. While Westminster remains most desirable of alternative destinations (for some, lessons with b**s just too much of a lure) vast majority now stay on. With 20 Oxbridge places in 2017 and nine medics as well as Yale, Stanford and Cornell, why risk chances elsewhere, argues head?

Money matters: At five per cent off the fees, scholarships more gloss than dosh (hopefuls also need to invest six pounds in past papers); exhibitions worth £600 a year. Help for those in need via expanding bursary fund, donor generosity permitting.

Remarks: A classy, focused school, true to high-minded educational objectives of pioneering founder. Knows what it's about and makes year in, year out results look easy. Appreciative parents accept school for what it is and don't expect much in the way of radical change – except, that is, at Christmas, when the Fairies come to call. 'Encourages girls to dream big and shows them what is possible,' said one. 'We'd do it again in a heartbeat.'

London and South East

City of London
East Sussex
Greater London
Kent
Surrey
West Sussex

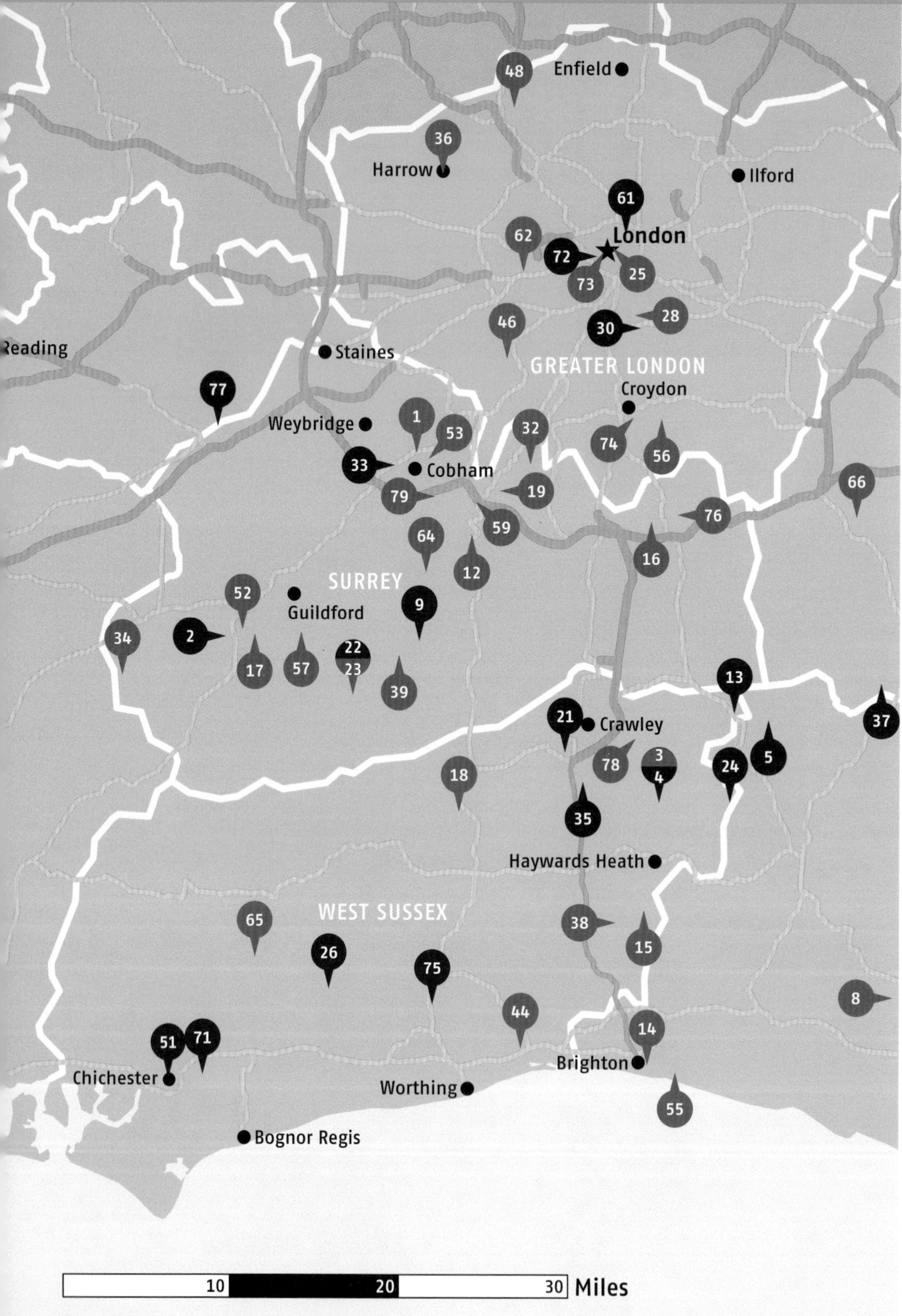

Enfield
Harrow
Ilford
London
GREATER LONDON
Reading
Staines
Croydon
Weybridge
Cobham
SURREY
Guildford
Crawley
Haywards Heath
WEST SUSSEX
Chichester
Worthing
Brighton
Bognor Regis

48 36 61 62 72 73 25 28 30 46 77 1 53 32 33 74 56 79 19 66 59 76 64 12 16 52 9 34 2 17 57 22 23 39 13 37 21 78 3 4 24 5 18 35 38 15 65 26 75 8 44 14 51 71 55

10 20 30 Miles

Basildon
Southend-on-Sea
Gravesend
20
42
Gillingham
54
70
Ramsgate
60
58
40
Canterbury
43
50
Maidstone
67
KENT
6
27
Dover
68
11
41
29
Cranbrook
Folkestone
45
10
47
63
Strait of Dover
69
EAST SUSSEX
Hastings
Bexhill
31
Eastbourne
49
7

LONDON AND SOUTH EAST

ACS Cobham International School

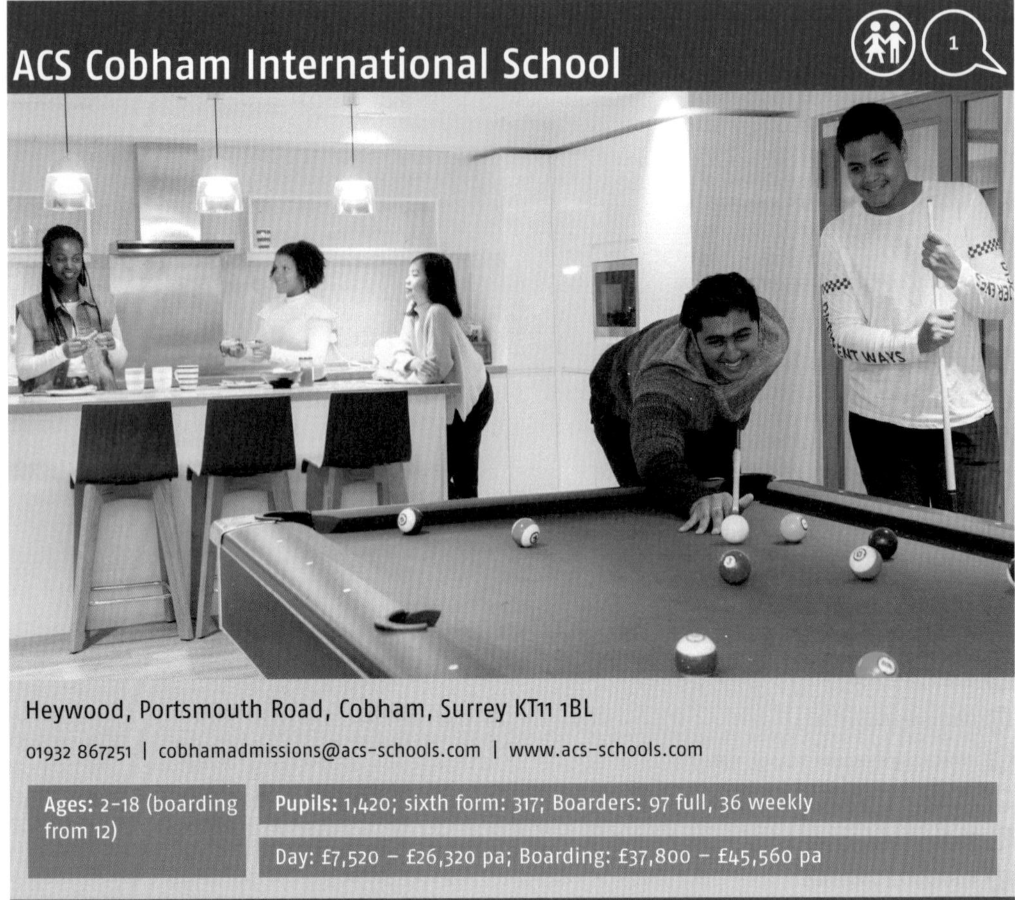

Heywood, Portsmouth Road, Cobham, Surrey KT11 1BL

01932 867251 | cobhamadmissions@acs-schools.com | www.acs-schools.com

Ages: 2-18 (boarding from 12)

Pupils: 1,420; sixth form: 317; Boarders: 97 full, 36 weekly

Day: £7,520 – £26,320 pa; Boarding: £37,800 – £45,560 pa

Headmaster: Since 2011, Tony Eysele (50s) BSc Natal University, HDE Edgewood College of Education, organisational behaviour degree Heriot Watt University. After two years in the army, started his teaching career in a South African state school before moving into, and progressing upwards in, the independent sector. Headships in Johannesburg and Harare until, in 2004, moved to the UK with his wife and sons and became foundation director at Lord Wandsworth College, Hampshire. One of his sons is now a teacher, the other is a professional athlete. His wife is admissions director at Marymount International School in Kingston-on-Thames.

Enthusiastic, approachable and popular, he says, 'Children in our school are all incredibly happy', and from what we saw as we walked round, we tend to agree with him. Parents say 'very approachable', 'quick to react to good suggestions for change' and 'really does seem to be listening to us'. Has increased the number of staff where needed. It's hard to take over from a long-standing predecessor (who spent nearly 20 years at the helm) but Tony Eysele seems to have handled the challenge well and parents, staff and pupils are all equally happy.

Leaving in July 2018.

Academic matters: Non-selective so a real mix of ability throughout. A truly international school – 72 different nationalities represented and a multitude of different languages spoken.

In the early childhood years pre-schoolers are prepared gently for the future. They build their social skills and interact with each other, developing their language and communication abilities through play. With such a large range of backgrounds, we were delighted to see them chattering away together and enjoying participating in group discussion and activity.

The lower school contains grades 1-4 and the majority of core lessons are classroom-based. They largely follow the American curriculum, but elements of the International Primary Years programme are also included. These are the preparatory years, when teachers discover strengths and weaknesses and begin to unearth any particular talents. All classes are mixed-ability. No formal exams or tests at this stage, though parents say general testing is continuous – presumably because MAP (Measure of Academic Progress) begins in grade 2.

At around 10 they move into the middle school for four years. This is when their futures begin to be mapped out. Timetables are based on the individual needs of the children, who are grouped by ability within their own age groups. Each child begins to follow a curriculum based on his known strengths and weaknesses. Classrooms are now subject-based, and it's the pupils not the teachers that move. The school is determined to provide a solid grounding and ensure that pupils can work together in teams, sharing their ideas and listening to each other. Exceptionally able children will sometimes be transferred to work with older pupils for particular subjects, thus assuring that they are being properly stimulated and working at their correct levels. Middle school children can be found studying their native language several grades higher than their ages.

At 14 it's high school, still in the same building as the middle school. They are separated by a large marble hall where these older pupils have Wifi access and the use of computers. The curriculum is wide and mixed, with 17 languages currently available. Timetables are based on each child's needs, exams are coming into the picture – decisions will soon have to be made. Some opt to study IGCSEs for a year, though they don't sit external exams in all subjects. For their final program(me), some decide to follow the International Baccalaureate, others take a variety of AP courses (18 available), and the rest work for the American High School diploma and SATs. Much depends on whether they are heading for university in the UK, the USA or continental Europe. This school prepares them for all, thus really meriting the international label. Generally around 80 per cent get 3+ AP scores – average 3.6 per exam in 2017; IB average 34 points. Not bad for a non-selective school.

Games, options, the arts: At a school sitting in 128 acres of country, with plenty of playing fields and its own a six-hole golf course, you'd expect the sports to be good. And they are. Not only outdoors, but in the all-singing, all-dancing sports centre as well. We were fascinated by the swimming pool with its computerised touch pads, enabling the raising of the pool bottom or adjustment of water temperature, at will, depending on activities of users. And as for the dance studio/gym with a professional sound system and sprung wood flooring; the fitness suite for older exercisers where the equipment is card controlled; the international-sized basket/volleyball show court and the café for spectators and participators alike – these children have no excuse for being unfit. PE is compulsory for all the whole way through the school.

From middle school up, all take part in a good mix of indoor and outdoor sports, competing against other schools and, once in high school, in the ISST (International Schools Sports Tournaments) programme Europe-wide. A varied selection of different sports each season, something for everybody. A parent said, 'Sport is a big deal. Even the less sporty children find something they enjoy doing.'

A banner in the entrance hall reads: 'Because we are all different, we are all the same'. Jolly, caring, head of boarding says, 'We are a home from home'

Theatre, drama and music are also 'a big deal'. The amazing new performing arts centre provides everything budding thespians and musicians need. Several drama studios and music practice rooms; a music technology suite and an amazing high tech theatre which some drama schools would die for – even has an automated fly-tower. Instrumental and choral groups to suit all tastes. For those who want it, it's all there. No wonder the middle school singers have won their category in the Godalming Music Festival at least twice and drama students have been selected to participate in the National Theatre Connections project. Plenty of opportunities for students studying theatre for the IB. And for the musicians, it's all there for them as well – there is even a large lift so that a grand piano can take its place on the stage for a special recital. Good

artist in residence programme when, for instance, a visiting band spends time with all instrumentalists, working with them and introducing them to new concepts.

Art on display all round, certainly appears to be plenty of talent. Imaginations run riot. Well-equipped studios enable experimentation, self-expression and developing talents to thrive.

Plenty of expeditions and field trips within UK, Europe or worldwide – exploratory, educational or languages involved. Around 100 working for the Duke of Edinburgh Award, at all levels. Recently two current students got their golds – a significant achievement given that most don't complete this till university.

Boarding: More than 100 boarders aged 12-18, most full, with equal numbers of boys and girls. About 80 per cent from overseas. Boys and girls in separate wings, but plenty of chance for social mixing. A banner in the entrance hall reads: 'Because we are all different, we are all the same'. Jolly, caring, head of boarding says, 'We are a home from home and, with children representing so many nationalities, this is a great opportunity to understand and embrace different cultures. All are well integrated, no cliques.' New boarding house with single rooms for grade 12 (year 13) students plus twin rooms for grade 11s.

Lots of expats, some in transit, some who have decided to settle here – at least while their children are at school. Truly representative of today's mobile world

Trips organised every Saturday. Supervised prep every evening between 7.00pm and 9.00pm; the younger ones in a study room, the older ones in their rooms with the door open. Rooms look clean and comfortable. Seniors given personal privacy and do their own washing.

Background and atmosphere: Originally built in the 13th century, the main house at Cobham went through a variety of owners, from the aristocracy to businessmen, until it was acquired by ACS in 1975 in order to create their first American school in England. They now have two others in Surrey and Middlesex, and one overseas in Doha. Originally aiming to provide an American education for families living and working here, they have now become 'international' and the curriculum has been broadened to include the IB programme and enable pupils to attend universities worldwide. Looking round at the huge mix of nationalities represented, 72 at present, the change is merited. And you certainly notice it as you walk round this ultra-modern, high tech school where classroom and studios are fully equipped with every possible learning aid. This is the 21st century.

A music technology suite and an amazing high tech theatre which some drama schools would die for – even has an automated fly-tower

No uniform, but a code, for both pupils and staff, and those not sticking to it are in trouble. Some parents told us they would prefer to have one, and felt staff should perhaps be stricter on the boundaries, but they also agreed that their children are perfectly happy with the way it is. We noticed no extremes: most pupils we saw looked neat, tidy and relaxed. The head says having no uniform 'means focusing on the child'.

A closed campus, surrounded by its own land, no entry without a pass; this is a safe place for children of all ages. The early childhood village cossets the very young, giving them a sense of security before they move on to the lower school building. Here floors and classrooms are colour coded, all mixed ability, light, bright and welcoming; they only move for specialist classes. Great library, where language books are plentiful and some are colour coded to lend variety to different reading levels. For the first two years children are each lent an iPad for class use; from grade 3 onwards, they are given their own to take home. Both lower school and early childhood have their own playgrounds, while the middle school has its own playing fields, and the high school pupils have their own designated areas during break times.

The technology is blinding in the middle/high school building. From the interactive learning centre in the basement where they appear to be able to reach out all over the world, to the science labs where they can work together with their iPads, to huge divisional libraries again filled with books in a multitude of different languages, you could say the atmosphere buzzes.

And as for fuelling the inner child – the new dining area is high tech. Canteen style, children collect their food, from a range of options, in coded containers, which are then scanned and a thumb scan identifies the child – no money changes hands, and parents are digitally informed what their children are eating. Or, at least, what they are taking to their tables. Big Brother is definitely watching over these children. Selections are such that no-one can get away with eating unhealthy food, and staff are watching carefully for any secret non-eaters.

Pastoral care, well-being and discipline: With such a large range of nationalities, there is a huge need for EAL support, particularly in the lower and middle schools. So, EAL numbers are capped. Children are initially assessed by EAL teachers and given as much support as they feel necessary. Depending on need, this can be in class or out of class, either in small groups or individually. IPads are used for translation and general help.

About 250 pupils have some form of mild to moderate learning difficulty or EAL need. Each one is looked at individually, 'one-to-one case management', and a programme devised for them. Learning support numbers are capped each year and children are only accepted if the school feels it can support their particular needs.

Parents report some communication problems over learning support, as teachers are not always ready to listen but, on the whole, happy with the situation. The holistic approach adds extra dimension, treating the whole child. Excellent occupational therapy room, and imaginative ways of helping. Enthusiastic, sympathetic teachers with specialists at even the youngest age groups.

Head said substance abuse problems rare and dealt with quickly and efficiently on a case by case basis. Can't realistically control what happens outside the school grounds, but does not believe anything serious. As school in own guarded grounds, cases of bringing forbidden items rare. No toleration of antisocial or unkind behaviour. Rules are there to be obeyed.

Pupils and parents: A multi-national, multi-cultural school. Around a third are American and about a third of the rest are from the UK and other English speaking countries – the remainder cover Europe and the rest of the world. Inevitably, turnover quite large in the early years. Lots of expats from various different walks of life, some in transit, some who have decided to settle here – at least while their children are at school. Truly representative of today's mobile world. Excellent bus service, covering a huge area from Godalming to Hyde Park Corner, before and after school, means that quite a few travel from London. Beware the fleet of buses at arrival and departure times.

Parental involvement huge, as you would expect from a largely American school. Also makes relocation and transition easier. Plenty of charity support, organised social gatherings and career advice given.

Students appeared relaxed and happy. We asked one what he would change about the school: 'Nothing, really but maybe lessons could be shorter?'

Entrance: Inevitably, because of the transitory national side of the school, places can crop up at different stages. So it is always worth trying. Academic records examined and references required, but no testing until 13+, when English is assessed. However, school adds the caveat: 'We will take any child at any stage providing we have space and can meet their needs academically and socially'. In the last two years, they will only take IB pupils if they are already following the programme and their courses can be matched. Any child can join the American Programme, even, occasionally, for their last year. But they do have to stay for at least one semester.

Exit: Typically 40 per cent of students to UK universities, 40 per cent to American universities and the remaining 20 per cent worldwide. Every student assigned a college counsellor at high school level. For the first two years they may just consult them, but at 11th grade it is compulsory for each student to work with them. A huge and varied exit list, with three medics in 2017 (UCL, Edinburgh and St George's), plus others to a range from Bath to Bristol to Le Cordon Bleu London. Forty off to the US; other overseas destinations included Canada, the Netherlands, France and Japan.

Money matters: Well, it's certainly not the cheapest. But just a look around will tell you why. That said, fees cover pretty well everything, including curriculum related field trips, all books and those iPads. Private corporate owners of all four ACS schools. No scholarships and limited bursaries but some financial aid occasionally available.

Remarks: If you are looking for a large, lively, international school with a multitude of opportunities and facilities to die for, or if you are in transition round the world, then this could be perfect for your child. Shy, retiring children might just get a bit lost, but then again the holistic approach could also help them. Anyone looking for a traditional, structured, English establishment, however, should probably look elsewhere. That said, this school has a huge amount to offer any child prepared to think outside the box.

Aldro

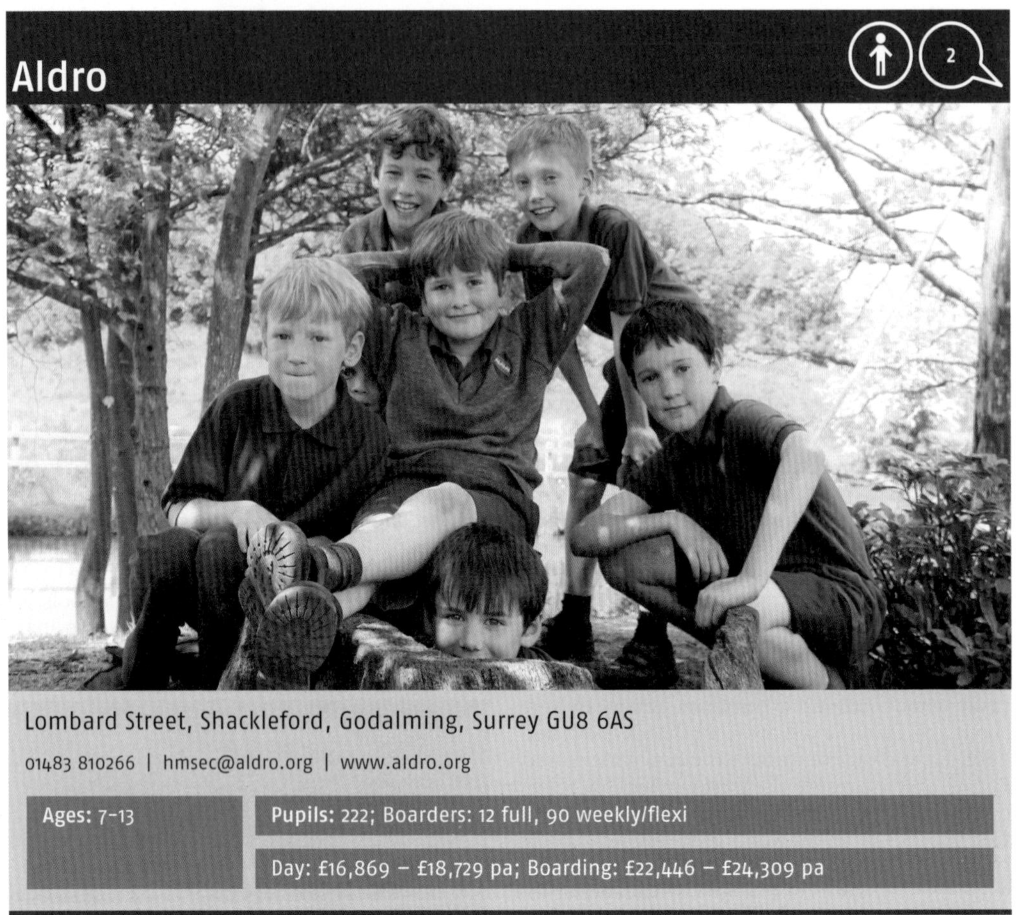

Lombard Street, Shackleford, Godalming, Surrey GU8 6AS

01483 810266 | hmsec@aldro.org | www.aldro.org

Ages: 7–13

Pupils: 222; Boarders: 12 full, 90 weekly/flexi

Day: £16,869 – £18,729 pa; Boarding: £22,446 – £24,309 pa

Headmaster: Since 2015, James Hanson MMath (Oxon) MSc (Oxon) MPhil (Brunel). Read maths and zoology at Oxford. Spent a decade at Harrow, where he was the senior maths master, deputy housemaster and head of rowing, then head of boys' senior school at the Royal School, Haslemere. Here he teaches maths to top year scholarship set and weekly lesson to year 7.

An avid follower of all sport but particular fan of rugby and rowing. Has a weakness for board games, and teaches the boys to play bridge and backgammon. Also fanatical about Lego and has mounds of it in his study for boys to play with at break time. Volunteers as a youth worker at external kids' clubs in holidays and is not averse to dressing up as Elvis when the occasion demands it. Governor of schools in state sector. Active member of local church.

Enthusiastic, approachable and welcoming. 'He is getting into his stride now,' commented one mother. Married to Jenny, with two young daughters.

Entrance: One form entry in year 3, rising to three parallel forms by the middle of the school. Parents either join an open morning or have a bespoke tour with headmaster. Once registered, boys attend an assessment day. For those entering year 3 or 4, this involves online tests in spelling, writing and maths. Boys also given a taste of school life with music, drama and sport as school tries to make the day 'as enjoyable as possible'. Older pupils sit online reasoning tests and written assessments in English and maths. Some participation in academic lessons and sport in the afternoon. School asserts that 'no preparation is necessary for the entrance tests'.

A report from pupil's current school is viewed as an important safety net in case the boy significantly underperforms on the assessment day itself – 'which can be an issue with younger candidates'. If a boy does have a wobble then a member of staff from Aldo will often visit the boy's school and watch him in action. 'We want to get a full picture and want to create opportunities,' says head.

About a dozen families turned down each year 'if the fit is not right'. School will not take overseas boys if their English is too weak to fully access the curriculum. Would also not accept a boy if he had a learning or behavioural challenge that could not be fully supported. Head explains, 'If we think the length of the day and length of the week will be too much for a child emotionally, then we won't take them. It is not fair on the child'. No sibling policy but school does what it can to take brothers.

'Family-friendly' boarding is proving popular.

Exit: Leavers' destinations include Charterhouse, Eton, Wellington, Harrow and Winchester. Some head for Royal Grammar School, Guildford at end of year 6. One mother we spoke to felt that 'some parents feel that more advice on a greater range of senior schools would be welcome.' Scholarships thick on the ground – academic, sport, music, art, DT and drama.§

Remarks: School's 20-acre grounds in prime Surrey countryside include an adventure island, complete with wooden fort, only reachable by rope bridge or rowing boat. Aldro boys have fun, whether den-making in the woods or playing with the model railway. As one pupil explained, 'The thing I love about Aldro is that there is always something to do.'

Average class size is 14 and maximum is 18. Head has introduced one hour lessons, extended from 35 minutes, to avoid time being wasted as boys move from place to place. The mathematician in him has worked out that the boys gain one whole extra week of teaching a year by this.

Compulsory Saturday morning school from year 4. Boys need stamina and resilience to cope with mega long day, stretching to 10 hours for older boys. Once home, however, they can totally chill as all homework is completed at school from year 5 upwards.

Inspiring lessons in full swing when we visited. Pupils fully engaged, whether racing through timed Latin quizzes on the interactive whiteboard or dissecting poetry by Thomas Hardy. Soothing music and soft candles created serenity in chemistry lesson, as boys worked at full capacity on the reactivity of metals.

Setting in year 4 for maths, year 5 for English and maths, and year 6 for English, maths, science, French and Latin. No separate scholarship class until final year – 'if this happens too early then you risk dividing the whole year group, including parents. Also some boys are slow developers'. Three criteria for selecting for boys for scholarship class: initiative, self-motivation and natural flair. 'We recognise their potential and we feel that the additional burden placed on them is something they can take.'

Teaches the boys to play bridge and backgammon. Also fanatical about Lego and has mounds of it in his study for boys to play with at break time. Volunteers as a youth worker

'Reading is the centre of our world,' says head and the light library is well used. Head has introduced a third language – French, Spanish and Latin (from year 5) offered. A smattering of Greek at the top end: 'Just a drip feed. We can't give everything in a prep school. I don't want to spoil all their senior school joys!' smiles head.

School prepares boys well for pre-tests, including copious amounts of online reasoning. Head relishes interview practice with older boys. No manic tutoring going on her, unlike the London scene, but if a boy needs a top up then school pushes for clear dialogue with external tutor. Numerous parents emphasised 'Aldro is not a hothouse.'

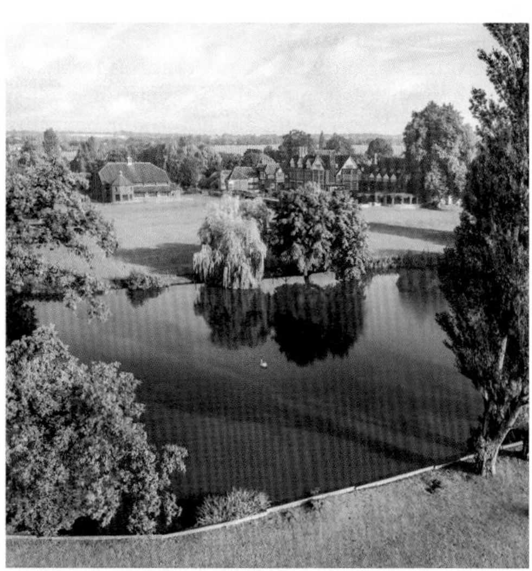

Currently 46 on SEN register. School can support pupils with mild levels of difficulty – mostly dyslexia, dyspraxia, processing and working memory. Some individual learning support lessons with three on-site teachers.

Head has recruited a cohort of lively, younger teachers to replace some of veteran members of staff. He explains, 'I'm not interested in an 'old school' master who teaches history and cricket – I want someone who is going to be brilliant in the classroom.' Would rather have excellent part-timers than a full-time jack of all trades. Head wants Aldro to be a teaching school that mentors new staff and offers placements to PGCE students. Through lesson observations, teachers share good practice so are constantly learning from each other. Roughly half teachers are female. Student masters from Harrow and Shore College in Sydney stay for a year and are put on a pedestal by boys.

Head feels 'we are a day school with a boarding house'. Boarding is racing ahead at full throttle with supremely dedicated housemaster, supported by three young matrons. Boarding grows organically as boys move on up the school. 'We don't push it and the parents don't push it. It tends to come from the boys themselves,' comments housemaster. 'We are preparatory in every sense of the word and want to prepare them for boarding if that is the route they are going down at their next school.' Big boarding weekends regularly laid on, with day boys welcome. Paintballing and laser quest activities proving quite a pull. Out of the 200 boys in the school, 150 experience boarding in some form during the year. 'It really is like a second home,' chirped one happy boarder. Housemaster explains, 'I prefer the term 'family friendly boarding' rather than 'flexi-boarding', as we are not a hotel nor a babysitting service'. Parents commit to regular nights in advance. Full boarding possible from the start, but a minimum of one night per week, and has become a hit with juniors.

Around 10 per cent of boarders are overseas. Not much homesickness but dealt with sensitively when it does occur. Very rare for any boy to stop boarding once they have started it. Numbers are going up – 'it's popular and it's working, as the statistics show. Boys feel they get so much more done when boarding. Thankfully, it is very different now to what it was 30 years ago,' says housemaster. Evening routine for boarders involves dinner, then activities such as Swedish longball or Capture the Flag. This is followed by Mars time: work (on prep or revision), rest (reading) and play (musical instrument).

Daily sport. Extraordinary facilities: rowing lake, new sports centre complete with climbing wall, all-weather tennis courts, swimming pool, croquet lawn, rifle and pistol ranges. School hosts annual regatta. Impressive range of sports offered including football, rugby, hockey, cricket, golf, athletics, cross country, basketball, badminton, fishing and polo. Matches on most Saturday afternoons from year 5. Boys we spoke to felt the school excelled at cricket and rugby. Pupils perform at a very high level, frequently winning tournaments, cups and swimming galas. 'We're quite a competitive school,' explained one boy. Every child plays in a team; no one excluded for lack of ability. The rule is that everybody who is fit plays sport. One mother commented that 'the only thing missing is Astroturf – the boys travel to Charterhouse to play on their hockey pitches'.

Big boarding weekends regularly laid on, with day boys welcome. Paintballing and laser quest activities proving quite a pull. 'It really is like a second home'

Outstanding chess, which is part of the curriculum, pupils winning over 20 national titles. Breadth of education seen as important, though some parents bemoan the fact that there are not enough school trips. 'We need to devote time to music, drama and art to let children fully develop,' comments head. Music is certainly flourishing, with over 90 per cent taking individual music lessons, ranging from beginner to grade 8. Thirteen different ensembles, including 50-strong brass ensemble. String quartet recently won the Ensemble Rose Bowl at the Godalming Festival. Choir of 40-50 described as an 'all singing, all dancing club,' which is cleverly timetabled so boys do not have to skip break. Mixture of informal and formal concerts throughout the year.

One boy we spoke to said 'the drama productions are the things I will remember most once I have left here.' Every child takes part in plays (such as Lion King and HMS Pinafore) and form assemblies; some 50 boys take LAMDA exams. Informal showcases put on so boys gain confidence before performing on the big stage. Art described by one mother as 'definitely not as high profile as sport and drama,' though some impressive work displayed around the school, including meticulously executed wooden chessboards complete with glazed pottery pieces.

'We have a strong Christian heart,' says head. Boys of all religious backgrounds or none, though all are expected to attend morning chapel most days of the week. 'Chapel needs to be fun – it is hugely participative. When you ask for a volunteer, 195 hands go up!' laughs head.

School says it wants boys who will throw themselves into everything, though insists there is room for the quiet, retiring types. Head explains that 'parents need to buy into the ethos of our school. Everyone needs to take part'. Will not take girls because 'in our area we want to stand out, to be unique. We are the only school for miles around that does what we do' ie all boys, full boarding, family-friendly boarding or day, not attached to a senior school.

School now boasts a six-strong pastoral care team, all of whom have been through mental health training. 'It's an all-boy world at Aldro and because we have sport every day, there is always competition there. We need to manage that,' explains head. School is very supportive of boys going through emotional difficulties, from bereavement to dealing with exam stress. Parents mentioned occasional bullying but say it is dealt with effectively. 'They clamp down on bullying very quickly,' one boy reassured us.

School celebrates achievement. Badges for drama, art and cookery sewn on boys' sleeves, like cub scouts, when they have done well. Pupils also rewarded with golden tickets for 'collective amounts of really good behaviour'. Can be used to get to the front of lunch queue, double rations of break or a handful of sweets from head's study. Form groups invited up to head's flat once a week for tea and cake with head and his wife, which is a big treat.

Mainly professional and business families from Surrey, 'but we have the complete spectrum'. About 10 from ethnic minorities. Some boys from Asia, Africa and mainland Europe but fewer than 10 have EAL. Head welcomes diversity as it teaches the boys to respect different cultures. Mixture of single and dual income families. Thriving parents' association. Great sense of community.

Ten to 12 full bursaries a year. Some set aside for candidates who approach the school via the Royal National Children's Foundation; and in line with the school's Christian foundation, some are earmarked for the sons of people in full-time Christian work. Head is keen on social mobility and is delighted when he can support a boy who could not otherwise afford to come here.

The pupils take huge pride in their school and in each other and the ones we met were happy, courteous and articulate. One member of staff described Aldro as 'a 100 mile an hour, Boys' Own paradise.' An outstanding prep, perfect for an energetic all-rounder.

Ardingly College

C of E | 3

College Road, Ardingly, Haywards Heath, West Sussex RH17 6SQ

01444 893000 | registrar@ardingly.com | www.ardingly.com

Ages: 13–18

Pupils: 599; sixth form: 250; Boarders: 299 weekly/full

Day: £22,650 – £23,610 pa; Boarding: £31,950 – £33,420 pa

Linked school: Ardingly College Prep School, 564

Headmaster: Since 2014, Ben Figgis MA (Cantab). Previously deputy head at Oakham, where he also taught sixth form history and theory of knowledge. Has also been history teacher, housemaster and head of boarding at Abingdon. Before taking up teaching had a life in media, which he left after concerns about the ethical compromises involved in newsgathering. Keen to provide pupils with a modern education, and a world view. Enrichment is a word which comes up a lot – an interest and excitement in subjects is as important as achieving a particular grade.

Pupils are very enthusiastic about the head and say he's 'balanced' (in comparison to his predecessor who was apparently more hard line). Described by a parent as 'approachable'; she said her children all really like him. Loves theatre, and enjoys fly fishing. Just finished Paradise Postponed by John Mortimer. Married to Joanna.

Academic matters: Record-breaking GCSE results in 2017 with 66 per cent A*-A/9-7 grades. Subjects are almost uniformly excellent, with sciences and maths being popular high performers, and humanities also doing very well.

IB points a very good 37 per pupil. A levels: 44 per cent A*/A, 83 per cent A*-B in 2017. The international nature of the sixth form means a good showing in MFLs such as Chinese, Russian and German; but performance is less strong in other areas. A reasonable list of subjects on offer, although one parent said she would like to see the inclusion of some less purely academic subjects, such as sociology.

High take up of IB in this internationally minded school (40 per cent): they're in the top 10 IB schools in the UK, and very enthusiastic about it. The IB way of learning and thinking is here viewed as so beneficial that it has been adopted for A level pupils, who also study the IB core of extended essay, theory of knowledge, and action and service. A parent described her daughter as 'a bit miffed' at the extra work, but can see the benefits of the community service and mindfulness elements. She was rather more dubious about the extra written work, feeling that A levels on their own are quite enough for some stressed teens to cope with.

There are plans to develop science and technology to enhance pupils' preparation for undergraduate study – computer science is now on the timetable, and the head is particularly keen to make sure science options, usually dominated by boys, are appealing to girls.

Ardingly is keen to promote independent learning and one of the parents we spoke to said this was one of her favourite things about the school: she praised their promotion of independent research, thinking outside the box and examining information with a critical eye. 'It sparks their interest', she said. The skills for independent learning start in year 9 with iMind – not, as you might think, a new app, but how the brain functions, mindfulness and a personal project on any chosen subject (from what makes the perfect curry to what makes people interested in the paranormal). In an eye-catching project which illustrates their innovative thinking, pupils built a solar car which was entered for 3,000 km World Solar Challenge across Australia recently. Didn't complete the course but was a first for a school in Europe.

Pupils here are lively and interested in what they're doing. We joined an English lesson on The Importance of Being Earnest, and were impressed by an energetic teacher, and pupils' interested and thoughtful approach. A parent commented that she loved the 'relaxed open relationship with teachers', and this was evidently the case.

Learning support good for those with mild disorders. We spoke to a parent whose daughter has mild dyslexia, and whose LS with maths and English helped her get the grades she needed at GCSE. But pupils need to be able to cope on their own at A level.

Games, options, the arts: Grounds are extensive and gorgeous – it is succulently green all around. One of our guides glanced with familiar affection across the fields: one of them, the scene of a recent victory, had become his favourite place at school.

Strong sports department with county and national winners in hockey, football, fencing and golf, and plenty of individual winners too. Pupils were keen to point out that the glory is not exclusively for high performers: pupils in first XI all the way down to the sixth XI go on school tours, and receive school awards, although a parent said she felt that the greatest focus was on the senior A and B teams. A bit boy-heavy in emphasis, said a mum, with the girls only really excelling in hockey; but the head points out the same resources are put into

The IB way of learning and thinking is here viewed as so beneficial that it has been adopted for A level pupils, who also study the IB core

girls' and boys' sports and girls are excelling in football as well as hockey, with national representation in both sports. A minimum two games sessions a week for all, and day pupils' kit often ends up being laundered at school.

Monday activities include minor sports such as horse riding, and sailing or rowing on the reservoir; and an ever-changing variety of other activities, from beekeeping and book binding to the interestingly named Ardinglay (it's a chicken club). D of E: lots do silver, and a few gold – in canoes and on horseback in recent years. It's not cliquey – the head relishes the fact that footballers about to play in the Boodles cup opted to spend the morning at the Ardingly national Shakespeare conference. You can choose to be very busy indeed; but pupils assured us that not everyone does, and that's fine too.

CCF is not popular here, to the chagrin of one of our guides, who clearly has a wonderful time. 'I think the parades put people off,' she said wistfully, 'but it's so much fun. There's a section attack on the headmaster's field this afternoon,' she added enthusiastically, as a cannon was wheeled into the quad. 'It just shoots blanks,' she said cheerfully, 'but it makes lots of noise.' It's difficult to argue with the evident joys of shooting a cannon. Almost worth the parades, one might think...

Large number of instrumental lessons and ensembles; in particular the 70-strong flourishing chapel choir which sings at cathedrals at home and abroad – and is a good outlet for exam stress. A vocal ensemble and the London Philharmonic visit to coach and inspire, and Ardingly hosts a concert series which stars national and international musicians.

Drama is popular, particularly with boys, to the delight of the head, who feels that creative art is too often the preserve of girls. They haven't got the posh modern theatre many independent schools boast, and one of the parents commented that the infrastructure could do with a bit of investment, but a gradual programme of modernisation is under way. Pupils perform at the Edinburgh fringe and home grown ArtsFest each year (a post-exam joy here), fun even for those not into drama, who do half day workshops on anything from making short films to mask mimes. Drama is super in the prep too, said a mum. Annual big production in a professional theatre, Oliver! the last one; anyone and everyone gets involved. Lots of singing at this school, with trips in the UK, and abroad; last year to Paris, next year to Rome.

Superb art department with a gallery packed with amazing work – we could happily have spent hours here appreciating the extraordinary creative work on view, showing that art students at Ardingly see life from all sorts of interesting angles, from butterfly dresses to a view inside a body which almost seemed to pulsate. There's a free range element to the GCSE, A level and IB art curricula, with students choosing which areas they wish to pursue; and you can see how much this freedom is appreciated by the quality of the work. Pupils can even have lessons from the sculptor in residence.

Boarding: Feels a bit like a university campus, with boarding houses reached by a path through a tranquil bluebell-lined woodland glade. Boarding houses are modern purpose-built blocks, decorated in house colours. Corridor walls covered in photos chosen by boarders, organised by year, up to lower sixth on the top floor. Very strong house feeling – all must compete in cross-country run, and apparently even reluctant runners are happy to compete for their house. A map of the world decorated with flags and photos shows where each boarder comes from in this truly cosmopolitan school; and there's a list of names of older students from whom youngsters can seek academic help. There's a teacher on duty every night too, but one boy said that older pupils can often help better – they explain things in a different way.

We could happily have spent hours here appreciating the extraordinary creative work on view, showing that art students at Ardingly see life from all sorts of interesting angles

Parents of boarders were full of praise: one said all her children wanted to board, and really enjoy it. The boarding master responds promptly to emails, and she likes the easy mix between boarders and day pupils.

Rooms for two to four younger boarders, with singles for older pupils. A housemaster admitted rooms are on the spartan side, being limited to bunks, desks and wardrobes; but said he doesn't want pupils lingering in bedrooms: they are for sleeping and studying, and the rest of time should be spent in the common room: spacious, squashy leather sofas, TV, pool, table football, the Times and Telegraph. Girls' houses recently refurbished. Brew rooms (kitchens) on each corridor, and one equipped with oven for more serious culinary matters (used under supervision). Lower sixth supervise youngsters' studying and bedtime rituals, studying supervision being much preferable, said one of our guides, with small shudder at the thought of bedtime duty (they are given advice about how to manage this).

Activities and sports on Saturday – recently a night of cowboy fun complete with hired rodeo bull; the head of boarding was moving with due care for bruises. Sundays for relaxation (gym and pool are open), with a trip out every three weeks. There's a tremendously popular Sunday shuttle to Sainsbury's, with each year group getting £50 for ingredients: serious cooking follows. No making their own breakfast though: kitchens are locked to ensure pupils go to the dining hall for a proper breakfast – 'no surviving on just toast until lunchtime.' Each floor has a disabled loo and lift access.

Around half of boarders are overseas students, including expats, so there's no dominant country and no general exodus at weekends. Every Wednesday the blog is updated to communicate boarders' latest doings to parents. Pupils use own laptops to keep in touch – letter writing is largely a thing of the past here.

Upper sixth have their own boarding house – like Premier Inn, suggested a member of staff; there is some similarity, though we've never seen a Premier Inn in such a lovely setting; or with such a nice gym. Super en suite study bedrooms, kitchens, huge common room, which is divided at 10pm between boys and girls, and opens at 7am. There's even a bar (two beers or two wines limit) but not many choose to drink. Encouraged to do own laundry– some actually do.

Background and atmosphere: Not as stiff and traditional as the cream paper in the guide for parents would suggest. One parent chose the school because the children who go there seem so 'normal', and for the strong sense of community. There's no held breath tension in the corridors here: pupils are relaxed and happy, with an outward looking politeness (pupils enquired after reviewer's journey etc – it doesn't often happen). It's not a leap to your feet school, but there was a genuine friendliness in the courtesy and smiles we encountered on our tour.

In the latest edition of Logos, the school magazine, there are articles on the Bible and feminism, and whether the Christian tradition ever treated women with respect

Charming red-brick buildings form the older parts of the school, whose atmosphere lacks the rarefied feel which often goes with the presence of quads. Modern and rather nondescript buildings house the music and boarding houses; but the green surrounds offer ample distracting beauty. One of the favourite places of our guides was the terrace, with its stunning views over the Sussex countryside; just below lies the head's garden, viewed longingly by both pupils and the head of prep – it's clearly Eden here.

This Woodard school was originally for the children of clergy; and it is no surprise that there is a clear religious structure here, with a weekly communion service in the chapel for all (including non-believers and other faiths). High church with bells and smells, and what one parent called 'some obscure hymns'. The parents we spoke to liked the weekly service, one saying she felt it was important for children to develop the ability to sit still, be silent and respectful: 'you can hear a pin drop,' she said approvingly. Another, while liking it herself, admitted her children thought it was boring, and said the head is revisiting the ethos of chapel with pupils. The head believes there's a value in exposing pupils to chapel, but there is no expectation of them adopting Christianity –'pupils need to feel comfortable and welcome.' Notably, divinity is joined by philosophy in the curriculum, and in the latest edition of Logos, the school magazine, there are articles on the Bible and feminism, and whether the Christian tradition ever treated women with respect. The Sophos philosophical debating club regularly debates pupil chosen topics such as life after death. This is not a school for unquestioning acceptance, and this critical eye extends to its founding Christian ethos.

Pastoral care, well-being and discipline: Pastoral care is 'outstanding,' said one parent; 'paramount,' said another, who said the ability to cater well for each child's individual needs is the best thing about the school. What's more, 'they take on difficult kids from other schools and bring them into line.'

Eudaimonia, not a rare disease, but 'human flourishing' al la Aristotle (PHSE to the rest of us) is part of the curriculum throughout senior school. Encompasses the usual sex, drugs and internet warnings; but also friendship, positive thinking and the wonder of every individual.

Firm line on bullying: pupils are encouraged to whistleblow, and expulsions will follow if the situation's unresolvable, say pupils, who also commented on some expulsions a few years ago for smoking dope, which they completely supported – 'we wouldn't have wanted them here,' they said in shocked voices.

The head is clearly just as principled as his predecessor, and has expelled a pupil for being rude and disrespectful to a member of the catering staff. But he seems more likely to understand that children experiment and less likely to damn them for doing so: those who come clean about offences and promise not to reoffend are likely to have a second chance.

Pupils meet their personal tutor fortnightly to ensure individual needs are being met – for example in timetables or teaching methods. However, the head also has a strong belief in the values of service and community, and is wary of growing expectations from customer parents to have school life flexed to suit their children. Some requests are reasonable, but there is some danger that children who always having things adjusted to their needs feel everything will always revolve around them: the values of living in and adapting to a community need to be understood.

One of the favourite places of our guides was the terrace, with its stunning views over the Sussex countryside

There's an on campus chaplain and independent listener for those who need to talk through problems confidentially.

The community here is very strong, say parents, which is reflected in the reward structure: the usual system for effort and attainment, but with extra emphasis on becoming a good citizen: ACES (Ardingly Citizenship Exemplary Student award) is given to pupils whose good behaviour models the justice and compassion desired for all pupils at Ardingly. Good citizenship is the avenue for year 8 pupils to achieve monitor and prefect status.

Pupils and parents: Thirty different nationalities in the school, with some 30 per cent of pupils coming from overseas. The head deliberately manages the numbers of overseas students, from around 18 per cent in Shell (year 9), up to a third in upper sixth, increasing diversity and international thought as students get stuck into the IB.

Parents include many London professionals, expats and foreign office. 'There is wealth in the school, but it has a down to earth quality.' There's someone topping up fees by working in Sainsbury's; and then there's a few more who buy their new four wheel drive every February when it's bonus time. Not a posh school, said a parent, although some are incredibly wealthy. The Russian pupil who required an armed guard was refused a place.

The head's introduced a weekly email telling parents what's going on, which is much appreciated. Parents are confident they could approach a form tutor or head of house with a problem.

Old Ardinians include racing driver Mike Hawthorn, Ian Hislop, composer Stephen Oliver, actors Terry-Thomas and Alan Howard.

Entrance: Pre-test in summer of year 6, with common entrance used for setting purposes only. For those not in a prep school, written assessments in English, maths and verbal reasoning. Overseas students need to have fluent English, and pass the same assessments as English counterparts.

Entrance to the sixth requires six or more grade B/6 passes at GCSE, including at least a C/5 in English and maths.

Exit: Some 30 per cent leave after GCSEs, mostly for local sixth form colleges. Lots of sixth form leavers to Russell group universities eg UCL, Exeter,

Manchester; two to Oxford in 2017 and one medic, with one off to McGill and another to IE Segovia.

Money matters: Over a third of pupils on some sort of support or bursary. Once a prospective pupil gets a scholarship, the level of support depends on need, and is not restricted by the numbers already in receipt of scholarships.

Remarks: A strong and caring community which finds a balance between excellent pastoral care and academic achievement. This modern school with its focus on independent thought would suit those with a broad outlook and interests.

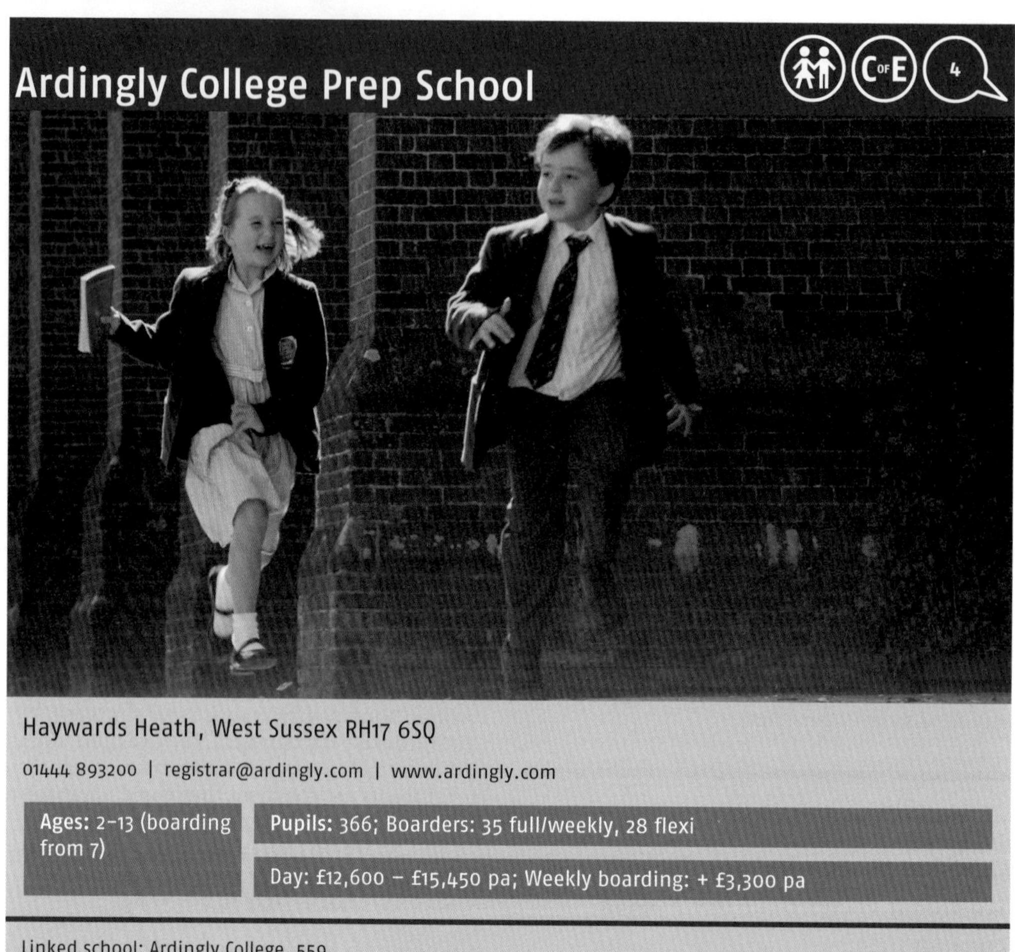

Ardingly College Prep School

Haywards Heath, West Sussex RH17 6SQ

01444 893200 | registrar@ardingly.com | www.ardingly.com

Ages: 2–13 (boarding from 7)

Pupils: 366; Boarders: 35 full/weekly, 28 flexi

Day: £12,600 – £15,450 pa; Weekly boarding: + £3,300 pa

Linked school: Ardingly College, 559

Headmaster: Since January 2018, Harry Hastings, previously head of Brighton College Prep. His introduction to teaching was through gapping at his old prep, and his path to this second headship has led him through Exeter and Oxford Universities, a prep in Devon, Peponi House in Kenya, the Dragon School and eight years as assistant head at Cumnor House Sussex.

Entrance: Most join in nursery (pre-nursery from age 2), year 3 and year 7, with a scattering across the other year groups. Taster day with assessment of reading, spelling, vocab and maths. Doesn't accept those performing below their age in all tests, and below the standardised performance in maths. For year 7 and 8, entrance exams in English, maths, verbal reasoning and reading, and an interview with the head.

Exit: Majority (90 per cent) move on to Ardingly College, up to five departing to Bede's, one or two to Eastbourne, Brighton College and Hurst or state secondary schools. Common entrance in all subjects except humanities. Need to pass core subjects to move up.

Remarks: The all-round ethos appealed, said a mum. '[Ardingly] don't expect everyone to get straight As...they cater for the super bright and the not too bright at all ...[they] find out what you're good at and celebrate it, which gives the children huge self-confidence.'

Independent learning and thought is the great strength here. Children get as much choice as possible, younger children deciding the term's topic – year 2 chose circuses, and all subjects were taught through the circus medium, children learning their tables through juggling; year 3 chose chocolate and for their stunning starter a parcel from Willy Wonka arrived during assembly.

Older children are more constrained by the CE, but year 8s choose the books to study in English – and read many more books when they've made the choice, says the school. Parents like the removal of history, geography and RS from the CE – fewer exams mean less stress and hoop jumping for kids, who instead choose a topic which encompasses these subjects – one child chose the Mafia, another picked Vietnam, and parents are delighted as their children become absorbed and fascinated by their chosen topics.

They're always thinking and arguing, said one mum, not just downloading information off the net: the weekly thunk, on the school website, is often a moral question, such as would you like always to be happy? Pupils are encouraged to write a response, the emphasis on there being no right answer, but forming arguments to support your view.

One parent described her un-history minded child coming home enthusing about Thomas Becket and keen for a trip to Canterbury Cathedral

The mindfulness teaching which is prevalent in the senior school is also present here: in year 3 the children learn to massage each other. It's a moment to pause and respect each other; and you can see how most people's day could be improved by the cat grip or ice skater moves. 'Would now be a good time for a massage, mummy?' one child asked mum after a stressful phone conversation. Older prep children also learn Paws b mindfulness – about breathing, pausing, and making calm choices in moments of stress.

Teaching here can be really exciting, and one parent described her un-history minded child coming home enthusing about Thomas Becket and keen for a trip to Canterbury Cathedral, after dressing up as a monk and acting the 'will no one rid me of this troublesome priest?' part out on the playing fields.

There's a large new computer suite (year 4s are already programming apps),and iPads are in regular use. Two-thirds take their own, though iPads are available at school. A grateful parent commented on the help at parents' evening from sixth formers, who were available to help parents with the foreign lands of privacy settings and Instagram. iPad use is carefully policed – a 'poor comment' made by a boy about a girl in a class email chatroom was down within two hours, and she received a written apology from the boy.

Not much prep lower down in the school: years 3 and 4 just have reading, spelling and tables (much emphasis on reading here – the children write reviews of children's books for the local Waterstones, and have a super new library with colourful lava lamp style bubbly water containers alongside the books – to underline the joy of being in the library.) Year 6 has two prep sessions a week; years 7 and 8 have three, which are completed at school, to parents' delight.

One shell-shocked London prep parent, whose children were skilled at reasoning and maths but could do little else, glowed about the balanced curriculum and pastoral care at Ardingly: 'I could see them blossom before my eyes'. She admitted it was a jolt for her children, who were used to being spoon-fed in London, but commended the dedication shown by the staff in providing extra classes for her daughter to catch up.

Children are set from year 5, and class sizes usually around 16. Two form entry from reception to year 4; three forms from years 5–8.

Learning support is available for mild special needs. A child may have two half hour support sessions in English and maths each week; more than that is not really do-able, says the school. A couple of children depart each year to find a school capable of providing more specialist support.

'They're huge on sport,' said a pleased parent: there are all the usual ones, and sailing, water polo and riding as well. Second all weather Astro pitch recently added. The prep has use of the superb college facilities for games. Three games lessons a week and a PE lesson, which might be swimming, dance, or gym.

Ardingly achieves excellence in football, hockey, cricket and swimming, but rugby is not perhaps their most prominent sport: one parent commented on the brutality in matches against 'rugby schools'. When the queues outside matron's room of those suddenly struck down by illness before matches became regular, it was decided to make participation in rugby matches optional.

Lots of clubs, including Lego, knitting, massage, Ardingly adventurers (own version of scouts for boys and girls) and tag rugby for the girls.

Drama is super, said a mum. Annual big production in a professional theatre, Oliver! the last one; anyone and everyone gets involved. Lots of singing at this school, with trips in the UK, and abroad; last year to Paris, next year to Rome. New art studio.

There is a feeling of child ownership about these dormitories – it is very much their domain, and it would be easy to feel at home here. Comfy common rooms

Children may board from year 3. All prep boarders go home for weekends, but may return on Sunday night (almost all return on Monday, though). Boarding accommodation is immediately above the prep school, rooms varying in size: there's a huge barn-like bedroom for 10 – very popular, with a few letters remaining of the big notice telling boys not to stand up on the top bunks – to smaller rooms for two or four. Houseparents (who are 'lovely', said a parent) are situated in between the boys and girls. Girls' rooms are rather pinker, and (whimsically) named by the girls: Narnia, Pandora and Fantasia (the boys inherited their rather more feisty dormitory names – Hogsmeade, Camelot and Helmsdeep). Showers and basins are all modern and spotless – the kids take good care of them.

There is a feeling of child ownership about these dormitories – it is very much their domain, and it would be easy to feel at home here. Comfy common rooms with squashy sofas and bean bags, and more upright rooms with tables and chairs for working. The girls and boys run their own small tuckshop with mini versions of sweets, where they are allowed to spend their pocket money. The strong community is evident – parents say older pupils look out for the younger ones, and some volunteer for community service, which involves getting up an hour early to help make breakfast or pick up litter. Children generally keep in touch with home by email. They can phone (from the school phone), but there's no point in taking mobiles because there's no reception anyway, said a mum diplomatically.

Celebration assembly every Friday – the entire prep and the least 100 parents assemble to watch those who had received an HMI describe their achievement – 'my handwriting used to be like a spider on the page.'

Bullying is taken seriously, and may result in exclusion. A mum whose son was bullied confirmed that the school resolved the matter thoroughly and quickly, and there was no recurrence. Her son received a written apology from the perpetrators by morning break on the day she complained.

Children may also be excluded for continuously naughty and disruptive behaviour, but the school tries to avoid using the label exclusion – 'these children just need more support than we can give them,' says the head.

One parent, who loves the feeling of community at the school, said her favourite memory was of the taking of the school photo, 700 children, squeezing onto a stand. Nursery children were last up, crying and upset by the whole exercise. The older children spontaneously started singing nursery rhythms, and within a few rhymes the little ones were laughing and clapping along.

A religious school with weekly chapel – 'my son hates it, but it's good training to sit still and be taught respect', and it's not 'shoved down your throat.'

A variety of parents, but mostly professionals living locally and working in London. Not a posh school, said a parent, although some are incredibly wealthy. The Russian pupil who required an armed guard was refused a place.

Communication is excellent – if anything they over-communicate, said a parent. Easy access to teacher or head with problems. Parents receive reports five times a year which detail effort and attainment. Reports issued in the middle of terms please parents, who can then talk about the contents with teachers –'it makes such a difference.'

Pre-prep, headed by Hilary Nawrocka since 2010, is down the lane in the old Ardingly farmhouse. Low-slung farm buildings with beamed ceilings on three sides of the farmyard, a long broad corridor library running the length of one building, so children are always moving past books. Reception dozed peacefully to music at rest time, a lively year 2 were in a circle on the floor: huge excitement as they took it in turns to pull an item from the bag to identify a story. Nursery class occupies the old pigsty, and takes pre-nursery tinies who have just turned 2. Free flow inside and out for nursery and reception. Lots of outside equipment, and a magical place to sit in the felled tree carved into seats and badgers. Weekly forest school lessons for nursery to year 3; forest club for the rest of prep.

Ashdown House School

5

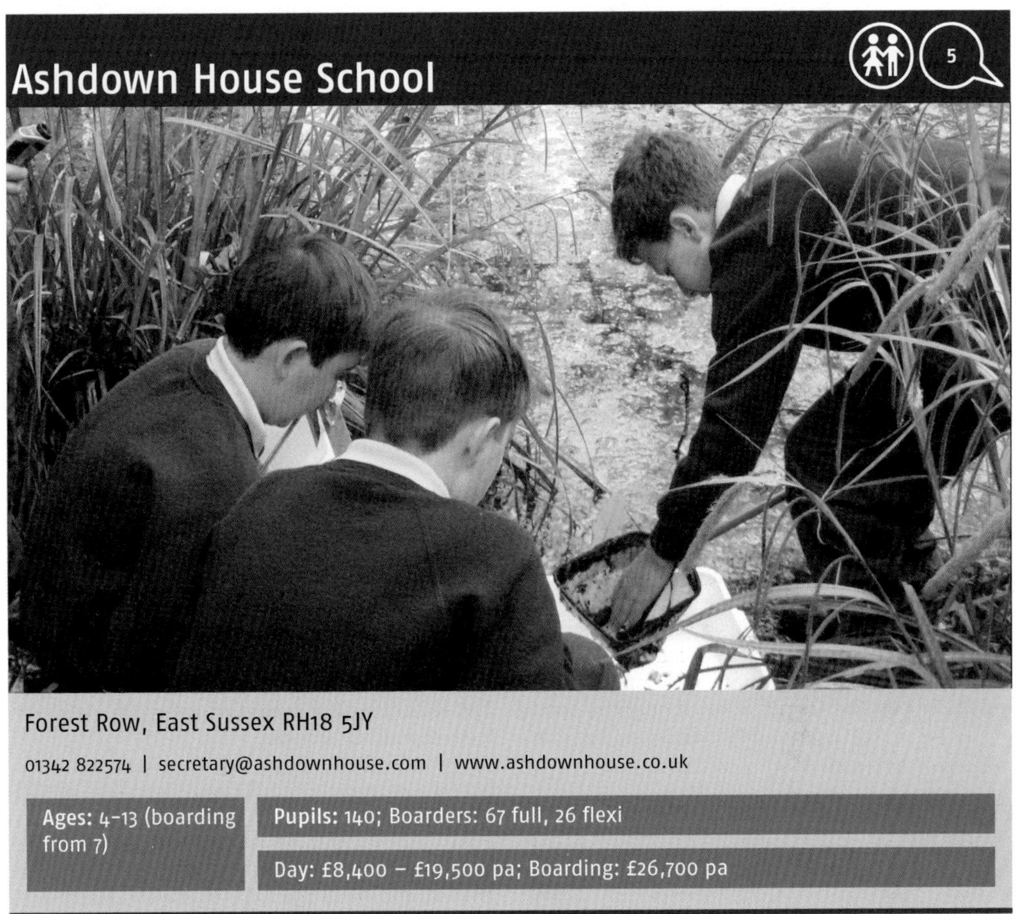

Forest Row, East Sussex RH18 5JY

01342 822574 | secretary@ashdownhouse.com | www.ashdownhouse.co.uk

Ages: 4-13 (boarding from 7)

Pupils: 140; Boarders: 67 full, 26 flexi

Day: £8,400 – £19,500 pa; Boarding: £26,700 pa

Headmaster: Since 2012, Haydon Moore, married to Annie, with three children, all of whom attend or attended Ashdown House. Mr Moore has had a long relationship with Ashdown House, teaching here since 2002. The head's aim is for pupils to leave with an appreciation of the real world: they are privileged, but need to have their feet firmly on the ground, and show it in a well mannered respect for all those around them, from the head to the school cleaners.

Much liked by pupils, who evidently take his words to heart: he says a joke is only funny if everyone is laughing, one pupil told us seriously. 'He's nice'; 'he listens'; 'I could talk to him about anything'. Parents say: 'The head is very empowering... encourages children to do something that frightens them – love him'; 'very approachable, great relationship with children'.

Entrance: Steady intake all the way through, many coming from local big preps where they are unhappy and 'not flourishing', and others who are relocating from London. Foreign nationals only if English is up to scratch.

Entrance by interview with head and ed psychologist report if necessary. Not selective.

Exit: Parents want a 'named' school, says the head. Some feeling of an expert matchmaking service in the way in which this head matches up pupils with senior schools: 'the biggest and best thing we do,' said the head, who knows the public schools at an individual house level, so he knows where each pupil would fit best and flourish. A subtle art.

Eton, Rugby, Harrow, Benenden et al.

Remarks: 'Slow – free range children and animals', says a sign on the drive, and this is quickly proved by wellied children noisily playing amongst the rhododendrons, Charles and Camilla (turkeys) strolling amongst them. 'There's a lovely feeling of coming home', said a parent.

The rather splendid main house, with its elegant columns, was designed by the Yorkshireman who went on to design the White House; but here the oval office is a lobby full of wellies and ceramics. 'If they're a long way from home', said a parent in the Cayman Islands, 'you want small school with nice homey feel about it', and this school certainly has that.

'Not a school who focus on petty things', said a parent, 'like top buttons, ties and shiny shoes. It concentrates on the important things, like kindness and being able to talk to grown ups and hold open doors'. Another parent told us that when they were shown around the school, their pupil guides disappeared. The head came out to look for them, and pointed up a tree, where the guides' legs dangled, finished in scuffed shoes. 'Perfect'.

'It is structured – but doesn't look like it. When you walk in, kids are running around everywhere', a parent commented, and the kids say the best thing about school is the freedom. 'In your free time you can go anywhere', said one, including the woods: they're not allowed near the pond or the pit of death (a muddy sink hole), but can climb trees, 'even if you break your arm'. Pupils hone their skills in the Larva Tree and the Spaghetti Tree, progressing to the Love Tree (pupils scratch name of their beloved into the top of the trunk). Not the Welly (Wellingtonia), 100ft+, out of bounds since a pupil, aptly named Everest, made it to the top a few years ago. 'Not cotton wool and cosset', said a parent approvingly. 'They let children take risks and explore their environment'.

Freedom extends to access: there are keypads everywhere, but all the doors are left open during the working day – 'we trust the children', said the head. 'You can wander in, but I don't think anyone ever does', said a parent.

Pupils hone their skills in the Larva Tree and the Spaghetti Tree, progressing to the Love Tree (pupils scratch the name of their beloved into the top of the trunk)

C of E, but it's more about kindness, willingness and helpfulness, say parents; they welcome pupils of any or no faith, and explore many. A parent described arriving at school the other day to see the head sitting barefoot on the lawn with some pupils humming – 'it was a Buddhist thing I think...'

'Academically strong – all sorts of different types thrive there', said a parent. Pupils are streamed from year 6 upwards. Not a frenzied approach to work, and homework pressure is not excessive – year 8, an hour a day, year 7, 45 minutes. And with this calm measured approach, Ashdown feeds top public schools.

Lessons are generally fun, say pupils: not Latin, but DT is extremely popular, and geography and science also got a mention as really enjoyable subjects. Pupils enjoy a half a term at Château Sauveterre to improve their French, and science, geography and outdoor pursuits trips to the Old Malthouse in Dorset.

There's not the usual emphasis on IT – 'not the driving force', said the head firmly; though iPads are available as an enabling tool in lessons. Only year 3 has an interactive board – the rest of the school does very well with whiteboards and projectors. 'Get lost in a book, not a computer game', exhorts the head. For pupils who like playing computer games, they can – but only if have programmed it themselves first.

Class sizes 10, max 15. If numbers reach 18, a class will be split in two. Saturday school is optional for year 3, and compulsory thereafter: lessons until 11, then clubs and matches. The weekend is just a couple more working days for staff, which parents feel is fantastic – 'staff are the school's biggest asset'; 'they're dedicated, like spending time with the kids'; 'they make lessons exciting and interesting'.

Learning support – learning enhancement here – is accessible to all. Wouldn't suit those with severe special needs, but prides itself on helping those with mild dyslexia extremely well, and has successfully helped a profoundly deaf pupil. Learning support is charged as an extra.

Classrooms vary from modern, light and smart in the Jungle block to old and bit shabby, but perfectly functional. Pre-prep (14 pupils) has recently moved into a refurbished bungalow – light and colourful, with trainers in a scruffy tumble on the floor and laminated poppy handprints in flower bed.

Drama is described by a parent as 'an absolute dream', explaining that they don't take it too seriously: lines are handed out the week before, so if you fluff up, no one minds – but it's very good. Everyone's involved – backstage and lighting, if not performing. Farce is popular, as is the annual Mock Trial.

Clubs for evenings and weekends include gardening, cookery, poker and a gentleman's club for the first XV (they learn how to iron a shirt). Strolling through the dance studio (also used for discos and exams), we saw something that resembled a mangled skateboard – apparently the head was rip sticking with kids the evening before.

Art is everywhere – not just the best stuff – with the artist's name dangling on a luggage label from the picture. One pupil said her favourite place in school is the art room: 'cosy... you're not forced to be hard working...it feels free'.

Several pupils said they were attracted to school for the sports; it's odd when you consider this is a small school which is rarely able to field winning teams against big schools. '[You're] not allowed to be a bad loser', said a parent. They play sport every afternoon here, seriously and with much enthusiasm, polo and golf featuring amongst the usual, with the girls also playing football, and cricket (as a club). 'As long as enough pupils to put together a netball team, it doesn't matter there aren't ABC teams – purpose and dedication are installed...', said a parent.

'It's a traditional school', said the head, 'but very, very supportive'. Parents commented happily on his partnership with wife Annie who they say has a leading role in pastoral care, and knows every child.

A parent described the 'extraordinary care' of their son while his brother had heart surgery, and the school's amazing care of both boys subsequently: 'they were willing to take our son... who was a walking time bomb. Ashdown goes out of its way to keep children safe'.

Both pupils and parents told us how good Ashdown is at helping problem children: 'Children who have had a terrible time at other places and

been bullied or expelled are turned around by Ashdown', said a parent; 'They don't give up on anyone', confirmed a pupil.

They're very supportive of mental health here, particularly aware of the anxiety that kids can suffer near CE. Children are divided into groups with a supportive mentor and learning support will provide extra help to anyone who needs it, with extra tutoring available in maths and English – 'fantastic', said a grateful parent. For those who are really worried, there is an art therapist and a baking counsellor – 'because no child wants to just sit and talk to someone about their problems', said the head. A CBT counsellor helps pupils by Skype, giving them practical exercises to help them cope with exam stress.

Clubs for evenings and weekends include gardening, cookery, poker and a gentlemen's club for the first XV (they learn how to iron a shirt)

Parents told us incidences of bullying are dealt with by the school 'quickly and efficiently'. 'They don't put up with any nonsense at all'. Pupils say if you behave really badly, you get sent to Mr Moore – 'he doesn't shout', said one boy appreciably. Punishment is a 'pause for thought' (detention). Parents said children could go to anyone with a problem – teacher, form tutor, matron – would get immediate responses from all. Can and will speak to the head if needed – 'very flexible'.

Communication is good, and parents appreciate the school office being open on Saturday, though views vary on school administration, from 'brilliant' to 'a bit dodgy', and another thought that a greater use of social media could make a more efficient school – 'if matches are cancelled, I would like to know'.

'A true boarding school', said one parent, 'with a seven days a week presence'. Nearly 70 full time boarders, flexi-boarders on regular nights, with designated beds. Boarding is a 'way of life,' says the head, in tones of deep dedication; the boarding community takes priority here, and half the staff live on site. A parent thought that it would have been a shock to go directly to boarding senior school, and Ashdown is a 'cosy [first] experience of boarding...' Two fixed exeats a term, and two floating, 'but the children never want to take them', said a parent; 'there are so many things on at the weekend'.

'No rules for rules sake', says the head, who accommodates parents who want irregular contact with their children; for instance, when Foreign Office parents are on tour, Ashdown will care for their kids full time, but when parents are home they can pop in and take the kids out for pizza.

Rules do have their place in the day-to-day mechanics of boarding, which is very structured – much like having strict but kind parents who know the importance of a good night's sleep. 'Not a sleepover atmosphere...', says head. Homesickness is addressed with a mixture of comforting and keeping you busy.

Boarding accommodation is comfortable, though not plush: dorms for 6-12 in bunks and singles with duvets from home, decent bathrooms and friendly common rooms with TV, water cooler, ample supply of fruit and books. Matron can make toast for those who ask. Photos all over corridors – 'I adore this', enthused one parent.

Pupils write a proper letter home every week – 'quite sweet,' said a parent – and parents can phone in to the landings between 7-8pm. The head keeps all devices in his study, but pupils can ask for their mobiles to call parents or use the phone room. Contact home for overseas pupils is arranged taking into account time differences – one pupil leaves morning lessons to Skype her parents each week.

'Get lost in a book, not a computer game', exhorts the head. If pupils like playing computer games, they can – but only if have programmed it themselves first

Everyone agrees that the food is delicious and it is no surprise that the chef also runs a restaurant. He has reduced the salt and sugar in food, and bottles of ketchup, used to happy excess by pupils, have been replaced by a one sachet policy. Pupils would like a tuck shop: it's just one chocolate bar on Sundays at this health conscious school. 'There are no fat children here', said a parent bluntly.

Would suit pretty much anyone, think parents, from the over-assertive (whom the school will mellow) to the quiet and shy ('If you can play one note on the oboe, you'll still be in the concert'). 'A sadistic bully would probably be asked to leave though', said one parent, on further consideration. Pupils thought this school would not suit someone who doesn't try hard. But it's not, they say, a school which expels people – 'they give people a chance'.

Ashdown families are generally traditional, wealthy and established. Not many new Porches here. Some 30 per cent from overseas. No scholarships, but can support families if things go wrong.

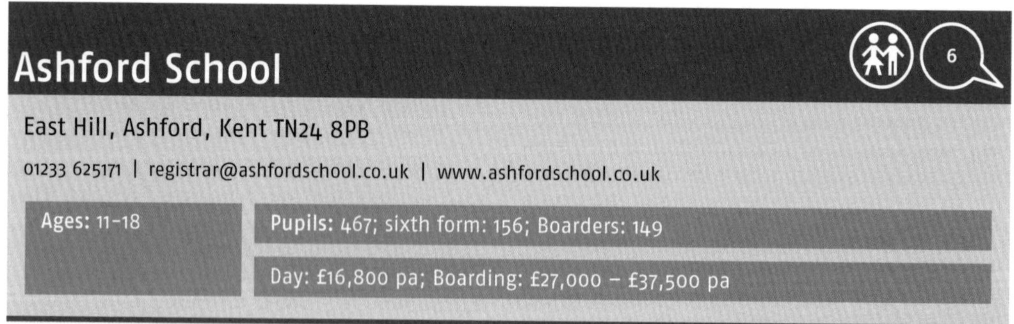

Ashford School

East Hill, Ashford, Kent TN24 8PB

01233 625171 | registrar@ashfordschool.co.uk | www.ashfordschool.co.uk

Ages: 11-18

Pupils: 467; sixth form: 156; Boarders: 149

Day: £16,800 pa; Boarding: £27,000 – £37,500 pa

Headmaster: Since 2005, Michael Buchanan (50s) BSc PGCE NPQH. Educated at Downside and King's College London, where he read physics and trained as a teacher. Previously spent 10 years at Highgate School in north London, where he left as principal deputy head. Part of his brief there was to bring in co-education, and he has done a similar job at Ashford with great success. Previously head of sixth

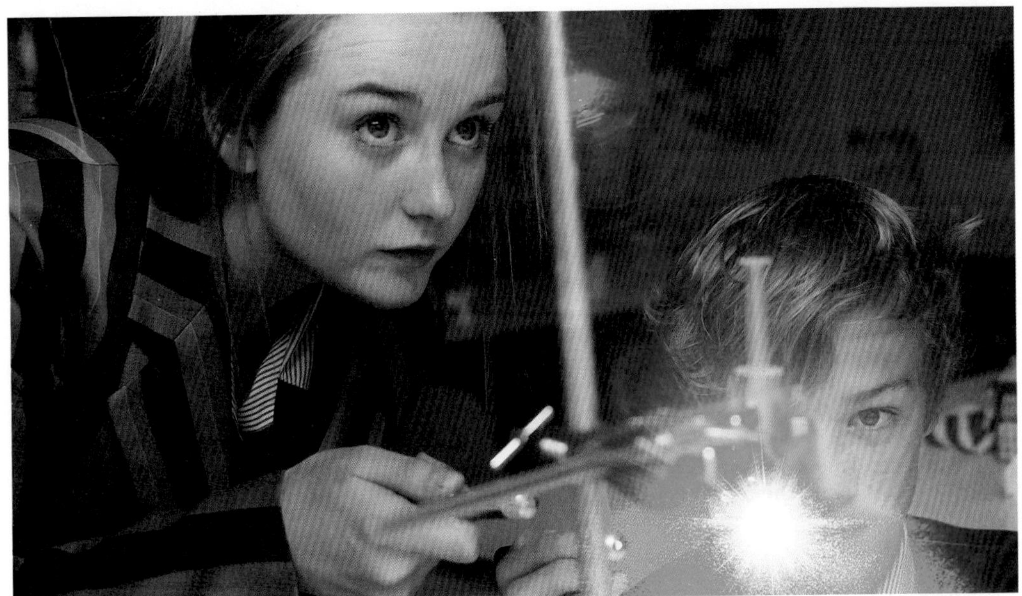

form at Royal Grammar School, Guildford. Businesslike and charming, he has a passion for physics, sport and choral music – he is a highly experienced, lead ISI inspector. 'Very approachable and a good communicator and you know who is in charge', according to one parent. Still teaches and referees sport when he can. Married with two daughters who attended the school; his wife works for a bank in London. He says the whole family felt welcomed from the moment they arrived at Ashford.

He is a 'very good motivator', according to one former pupil, and has introduced the Adventurous Learning programme that is all about taking people – staff and children alike – out of their comfort zone and challenging in all areas, personal as well as academic. It might be trying something new like speaking in front of the whole class and then the whole school. He 'wants children to develop as self reliant all-rounders who have a sense of responsibility, compassion and teamwork and the resilience to cope with adversity'. He also wants pupils to take responsibility for their own learning and to feel able to make mistakes. Likes every sort of success to be rewarded and feels that learning should be fun. Head and staff lead by example: Mr Buchanan has taken up the euphonium and 40 teachers have taken up other musical instruments to remind themselves what it feels like to be a pupil.

The school has grown by over 150 since he arrived, helped by the massive building boom in Ashford and the fast rail link to St Pancras. He is gradually replacing the ageing school buildings at the same time as driving the rise in academic standards.

Retiring in 2018.

Academic matters: Broad intake, results improving year on year. In 2017, 73 per cent A*/B and 49 per cent A*/A at A level; at GCSE, 43 per cent A*-A/9-7. Particularly good results in science and maths. Everyone takes separate sciences from Year 7. All students learn two languages chosen from Spanish, German and French; German most popular. Pupils from abroad also encouraged to take GCSE in their first language eg Chinese or Dutch. Good range of subjects at A level including Chinese, business studies, psychology, textiles, sports studies and drama. In sixth form Russian, German and Spanish offered

Biology teacher won a UK top teacher award and also organises the school's rock festival, AshBash

as a business language (basic language skills, mostly conversation). Very accommodating timetable and school willing to offer a subject to only a handful of students. Digital literacy programme for year 7. A very tech savvy school – radio voting handsets have proved popular and effective – children text answers to the screen anonymously, useful for shy children but also means there is no chance of a snooze at the back of the class as everyone has to participate. Pupils set by ability in core subjects but there is plenty of flexibility and children can be moved up or down mid term if appropriate. No plans to introduce the IB.

Loyal team of teachers who love the challenge and freedom to innovate and are encouraged to use their initiative. Headmaster likes to recruit those with outside experience who can offer something different. Good mix of old hands and NQTs – school runs a leading and innovative graduate teacher training programme. Biology teacher won a UK top teacher award and also organises the school's rock festival, AshBash. A new higher education advisor has recently joined the team to help with UCAS forms and beyond – he was previously a university admissions tutor. The Oxbridge Club provides extra coaching in problem solving and analytical and critical thinking. Lots of language exchanges and trips that help bring learning to life and 'take school work into the real world,' according to one happy father. A level physicists visit CERN.

Some 35 pupils with SEN ranging from organisation skills to severe dyslexia, dyspraxia, dyscalculia and school can support children with physical disabilities, 'The teachers really go the extra mile for a child who struggles – nothing is too much trouble'.

International Centre for 11-16 year olds offers a one-year intensive English language course.

Games, options, the arts: Good sports facilities also include two gyms as well as a fitness centre and dance suite, indoor swimming pool and all weather basketball court. Cricket played at the local club a few minutes' walk away and a new sports centre opened in 2013 with Sport England specification. Boys' sport now fully developed and there are senior first teams in rugby, hockey and cricket, but fixtures still a bit sparse as other schools are a 'bit slow to twig that Ashford boys are actually rather good at games'. Teams maintained into sixth form and everyone has to take part in a physical activity at least once a week. Yoga and exercise classes popular, especially with the senior girls, along with

Head and staff lead by example: Mr Buchanan has taken up the euphonium and 40 teachers have taken up other musical instruments to remind themselves what it feels like to be a pupil

street and jazz dance and personal survival. Strong house loyalty and everyone expected to take part in house events.

Lots going on in the drama department from house plays and speech and drama recitals, lower school productions and the spectacular whole school summer musical. Active junior drama club as well as technical drama club for those who prefer to keep out of the spotlight. Drama a popular option at GCSE and also offered at A level and school prepares pupils for speech and drama and LAMDA exams. Vibrant music and art departments: head of music is a colourful character who has transformed the musical life of the school; numbers participating have shot up, as has the standard. Tuition on most instruments available from the bassoon to the organ and school has two Steinway pianos as part of the Steinway schools programme. Lots going on: concert band, chamber music groups, string quartet, rock bands, string ensembles, community orchestra. Concerts every three to four weeks. Head wants music to be 'about performance and enjoyment' with plenty of opportunities for showmanship from 'teatime tootles' in the atrium to singing in Westminster Abbey.

Fabulous textiles and 'big and bold' approach to art; several go on to art foundation courses each year. A group of pupils recently designed a stained glass window for a church in the Holy Land and were then invited to install their work in situ. Another group made some wall hangings for the local hospice. 'We do random and different things and let it all come out', says one pupil.

Huge range of clubs and activities, from Lego robotics to cooking and debating – something for everyone and all have to take part until sixth form. Strong debating team has represented the school at the Oxford and Cambridge Unions' competitions and taken part in the European Youth Parliament at the Foreign Office. Amnesty group won an award for 'Best Fundraising Event in UK Schools' with their 'Dare to be Different Day'. CCF popular and about 12 pupils complete their D of E Gold each year.

Boarding: Boarding from year 6 (bussed over to junior school) but very few in this age group.

Boarders well supported and cared for; they are also allocated a house and are not allowed back into their boarding houses during the day, which means plenty of interaction with day children. Lots of boarders' activities and birthdays always celebrated. Houses recently refurbished; sixth formers have en suite bathrooms. Six houses, each led by a head of house, a teacher who oversees academic progress and personal development of each child. Children from abroad spend the first weekend of term with a day pupil – helps integration. Close liaison with parents and tutor and regular progress reviews. Lots of leadership opportunities running house events and activities, from community work to the house play. No lessons on Saturday mornings but time devoted to sport, rehearsals and activities – day children always happy to come in and it means the boarders are kept busy.

Background and atmosphere: Founded in 1898 with the aim that the pupils should play an active role in the life of the town and with an emphasis on 'training and development of character', the school moved to its present site in 1913 and became part of United Learning in 1999 (a group of 31 schools). This brought a welcome injection of cash resulting in new buildings springing up all over the place. Senior school is at the foot of the High Street, approached by a narrow lane and enclosed by high red-brick walls with lawns and greenery stretching down the hill. It's a green oasis in the middle of busy Ashford and quite difficult to find if you don't know where to look. Extensive rugby and cricket pitches are a short walk away. It's an international and friendly community – pupils are expected to engage with school life, and head says he 'does not want passengers on board and expects everyone to take part'. Good food, cafeteria style, lots of choice and healthy salad options. Brightly painted Atrium café a popular meeting place, also open to parents at pick up and drop off time.

Pastoral care, well-being and discipline: Strong pastoral care via house system; everyone is allocated a house on arrival as well as a specialist tutor; new joiners in year 7 also have a sixth form mentor.

Pupils and parents: About 70 per cent day children from as far afield as Maidstone, Sittingbourne and Cranbrook (minibus service). Very few weekly boarders so room for growth here. Families from a broad social spectrum; parents have high expectations and are encouraged to get involved and be part of the community. Twenty per cent foreign nationals, over 24 nationalities and particularly popular with Chinese, Germans, Eastern Europeans and Nigerians – school takes care that no nationality dominates. 'Ashford is very good at taking kids of any type and getting the best out of them', says a parent, 'and I like the way the school takes trouble to develop the kids' characters as well as the academic side.'

Entrance: About 60 per cent come up from the prep school, others from local primaries and prep schools eg Sutton Valence, Dulwich and Spring Grove. Wide ability range – some very bright, others who struggle, but all must have the ability to pass at least six GCSEs. Almost automatic entry from prep school but must be within the academic range. Children joining from other schools sit assessment tests in English, maths, science and non-verbal reasoning and take part in a team building exercise. Preference given to siblings where possible. A further 15 or so join at 13+ via school's own tests. Sixth form entry tested in proposed AS subjects and must have six GCSEs A*-B or equivalent, plus English proficiency test if appropriate. Lots of foreign nationals come for sixth form as well as several each year from local state schools.

'Big and bold' approach to art; several go on to art foundation courses each year. A group of pupils recently designed a stained glass window for a church in the Holy Land and were then invited to install their work in situ

Exit: A few leave at 13+ – no coaching for CE but good relationships with other local schools; around a third depart after GCSEs. Sixth formers to a huge range of different institutions from Russell Group (over half) to modern, including a smattering to Oxbridge over the last few years (two in 2017): broad minded higher education and careers advisor takes huge trouble to guide right student to right course.

Money matters: Academic, music, art, drama and sports scholarships offered – usually 10-30 per cent of day fee. Means-tested bursaries for children of clergy, mostly Anglican but will consider other Christian denominations. Twenty per cent discount for Forces families, discounts for siblings. Church Schools Foundation Assisted Places assessed on a combination of academic ability and financial need, worth up to 85 per cent of fees – offered to those entering in year 7, 9 or sixth form. Short-term emergency bursaries available.

Remarks: A forward-looking school with a strong international contingent which is going from strength to strength, benefitting in part from the huge growth of Ashford town. The school has 'changed beyond belief in the last eight years' and appeals to a wide range of families with its strong pastoral care and adventurous learning programme.

Bede's Preparatory School

Duke's Drive, Eastbourne, East Sussex BN20 7XL

01323 734222 | prep.admissions@bedes.org | www.bedes.org

Ages: 3 months–13 years (boarding from year 4)

Pupils: 388; Boarders: 13 full, 14 weekly

Day: £9,930 – £16,875 pa; Boarding: Supplement £7,845 pa

Linked school: Bede's School, 576

Headmaster: Since 2013, Mr Giles Entwisle BA (French, politics and economics at Loughborough) PGCE (late 40s). He came from a deputy headship at Highfield, prior to which he was head of year, housemaster and head of MFL at Holmewood House, near Tunbridge Wells. An enthusiastic, ambitious and engaging, career prep school man. A keen skier – so, clear sighted, focused and energetic – he has a palpable commitment to getting the best out of everyone – pupils and staff alike. Married to a Spaniard and school fosters many links with Spain. Oh – and he is an expert juggler, always useful for a headmaster.

Parents are delighted: 'He's lovely with the children – he knows everyone by name and is getting an excellent new team around him.' 'His door is always open.'

Entrance: Not yet oversubscribed by much but this is likely to change so get in early. Around twice as many boys as girls – as elsewhere.

Exit: Vast majority to the senior school (you need to see it and feel it to understand why) though a few to other local and less local senior schools.

Remarks: You can't beat it for location. At the upmarket end of the grassy Eastbourne seafront where the land curves and rises to the great cliff of Beachy Head, perches an attractive five storey, mock-Tudorbethan pile, its long windows facing

Married to a Spaniard and school fosters many links with Spain. Oh – and he is an expert juggler, always useful for a headmaster

the sea. Surrounded by fields on all but its southern aspect, with a cluster of smaller buildings round about, it sits like a benign hen comfortably supervising its offspring, assured that all can run about safely in a healthy, beautiful, open space.

Space is a key asset and to anyone used to, for example, an urban prep or primary, Bede's is a revelation. There are more fields five minutes up the hill and another five minutes inland – all facilitate the range of sports available to these lucky children, who have the look of relaxed freedom that inhabiting such openness gives. Space also in, for example, the dining hall, one wall of which is just large windows fully open on warm, sunny days, so that the outside and the inside blend.

Two main buildings. Holywell Mount – a large Edwardian house to the right of the main building if you face the sea – houses the pre-prep and nursery. We visited at the end of a long day and were astonished by the bright eyed vitality of the teachers. They told us of the new topic with which each term is launched in each classroom: 'It's so exciting – they can't wait to come in and see what we're going to do!' And on offer in just some rooms were: Under the Sea World, Ice World, Out of the Egg (and you should have seen the egg!) and Knock Knock – imaginative stuff, inviting exploration and discovery of all kinds.

Sports are exceptional – and not just because of facilities – at both ends of the spectrum. Says Mr Entwisle: 'We're the best cricketing prep in the country' and, as parents told us, 'even the non sporty get enthused – and they have elite schemes for the really talented'. 'They do wonderful trips, especially for sports and languages.' Children concur: 'We went to Portugal and got trained by Benfica.' Senior school fields also used. Several teams in most sports for all years so that all but the child with thumbs glued to his iPad get a look-in, though some sense that more could be done for the less than athletic. Dance is serious – remember that Bede's is home to The Legat Dance School – so all do dance up to year 5 and many continue. Teachers seen as 'brill!'. Music has a relatively new director and is set to sparkle; art and drama well on the way.

Parents enthuse: 'The teachers are wonderful – so imaginative and approachable!' – and especially about individual needs and pastoral care: 'superb – any problems or hint of bullying are dealt with at speed' and 'they answer emails practically before you've sent them'. Weekly staff meeting to discuss and act on academic or pastoral concerns with head of learning support on hand if needed. Pupil praise too – 'They push you to your potential and we are only 10 in some groups so they can really help you'. Small group specialist work in eg fine motor skills, writing, reading, phonics for tots who seem to be falling behind. All lower classes have a TA to support individuals but some feel this should continue into upper years, 'where they need it just as much if they are struggling with a subject'. As a pupil told us, 'When I'm stuck, if they take time to explain it to me, I really get it!' Individual support – and around 25 per cent on the SEND register here – described as 'good but pricey'.

'Health and safety are taken very seriously,' parents tell us, as are efforts to integrate newcomers, especially into year 7 when there is a fairly substantial intake. And there is masses to do. 'My daughter was very shy but there are so many performances and so on – her confidence has grown unbelievably.' No shortage of facilities, inside and out – big sports hall, 18m pool, climbing walls, decent library – 'they'll get books you want if you ask' – good theatre and lovely, light rooms with the downside that 'if I'm facing the sea I just go into a daydream,' as one youngster confessed.

Dance is serious – remember that Bede's is home to The Legat Dance School – so all do dance up to year 5 and many continue. Teachers seen as 'brill!'

Most are local, though word is spreading and pupils now bus or car in from a wider range of villages. School runs its own bus service on eight routes. Boarding – small but growing here, unlike elsewhere, with 13 full and 14 weekly boarders – currently starts at year 5 (nearly half of boarders from overseas) and is found in two attractive houses over the road from the main buildings, staffed by warm and cheery houseparents with their own children on site and lively Aussie gappies. Plans afoot to develop this provision and school set to become a significant player in prep boarding on the south coast.

A happy school – 'It's good at turning out all-rounders,' said several. 'It's pretty unsophisticated and relaxed – you don't get awful pushy parents there – they trust the school to know what it's doing.' And, in the words of a pupil, 'My parents wish they could have come here.'

Bede's School

The Dicker, Upper Dicker, Hailsham, East Sussex BN27 3QH

01323 843252 | admissions@bedes.org | www.bedes.org/

Ages: 13-19

Pupils: 765; sixth form: 347; Boarders: 189 full, 99 weekly

Day: £21,450 pa; Boarding: £32,070 – £34,095 pa

Linked school: Bede's Preparatory School, 574

Headmaster: Since September 2016, Peter Goodyer, previously deputy head at Colston's School in Bristol. Educated at Rhodes University in South Africa (BA in psychology, postgrad diploma in international relations and PGCE in secondary education) with an MBA in education from Keele, he started his career as a history teacher and sports coach at St Andrew's College in Grahamstown, South Africa. He moved on to St John's Leatherhead (head of psychology and housemaster) before joining Colston's, where he has been interim as well as deputy head. He is married to Laura, also a teacher, and they have a young son.

Academic matters: Unusually large range of GCSE options includes two popular business courses, Mandarin, dance and PE alongside all the more predictable options. Also popular are art, history and geography. Impressive results in art and the sciences in particular. BTecs on offer in nine subjects – including animal management, music performance and business studies. Similarly impressive list of A level subjects includes accounting and computer science. Pre-U rather than A levels offered now in English and music – wise choices. EPQ added recently. Art, again, the standout subject in terms of results, but this is not – thankfully – a results-driven school. The point here is to be 'better' – school unfussed about league tables save those which measure value added – and Bede's scores very highly here. 'We prove you can have great results with inspired, holistic teaching.' Parents agree. One – a parent of three – told us: 'It's ridiculous to say it's not academic. My exceptionally bright son is brilliantly taught and is flying. And my other two, who are very different, are well-supported and are equally happy and successful.' In 2017, 42 per cent A*/A at GCSE, and 80 per cent A*-B, 53 per cent A*/A at A level.

Learning enhancement in its own block and central to the ethos of the school. Lots of screening. Years 9-11 have effective revision technique classes, and 'anyone can have learning support in individual subjects or just help with learning in general' – a useful approach. Year 9s also have 'prep project' to learn study techniques. Some 25 per cent of entrants to the earlier years and 12-15 per cent of sixth form entrants come with some kind of, usually mild, SEN. So, additional help is normal here and, as several grateful parents told us, with 'absolutely no stigma'. One parent typified the rest. 'My son has mild SEN problems – I looked at 25 schools and then made a shortlist. They all promised everything but there were cracks in what they said. Bede's learning support finds what they're good at – the teaching is multi-sensory, the classes are alive, the teachers are passionate. My son has grown in independence. He doesn't need support any more.' Others agree: 'They find ways to ensure you don't fail though, on occasions, some more constructive criticism wouldn't be bad,' we heard. Separate EAL dept.

Super art – as good as anywhere we know. No strait-jacketing here but evidence everywhere of imaginations encouraged to flow and flourish

Library not the most impressive aspect of school's provision, though modern fiction stock is good. But why a whole set of Hugh Walpole and no Thackeray? Or were Barry Lyndon and The Newcomes etc out on loan?

Games, options, the arts: Dance is big. Bede's is home to the Legat School of Dance and dance attracts much young talent to the school. One large and two smaller studios – the large one is light and lined with photos from the school's history. For some, dance increases in importance and they leave to pursue careers in this area. For others, academics or other pursuits take over and dance becomes a passionate hobby. Teaching is dedicated and inspirational. Dancers work. 'It has been hard at times but it's so convenient having everything in the same place,' one young hopeful explained. 'Dance can be stressful but the pastoral care here is amazing.' Very good drama, led by lively staff in excellent theatre and studio, encompasses the conventional to the experimental. And not just musicals. Technicians from Glyndebourne help and guide, and major productions shown in Eastbourne theatres.

Let us know if you find more inspired, better equipped or more varied ceramics anywhere. It's a real feature of the school, led by veteran potter in the Old Kennels, with three kilns, a spray glazer, electric wheels and a kick wheel dating from 1945 which he found on eBay. Graduates of this A level go on to product design, architecture, fashion, photography, interior design and textiles – a fabulous hand and eye education. Good music, super art – as good as anywhere we know. Photography, mixed media – all impress. No strait-jacketing here but evidence everywhere of imaginations encouraged to flow and flourish. Endless other activities from beekeeping to the breeding of small animals in the unique Animal Management Centre, where we met some of the 500 inhabitants including a common plec, a sun beetle and a lesser hedgehog tenrec. Links with several zoos. All go to support pupils' studies in the practicalities of animal care.

And then there's the sport. Cricket on glorious pitches – now embellished by the Martin-Jenkins Pavilion celebrating the family's links with the school. Elite sportsmen and women on the staff; many a young sports star in the making stays on here rather than joining some club programme or other, 'because it's just as good and I can do my academics too'. They do anything from athletics to water polo – huge range and super facilities. They don't necessarily win everything but some sports, eg boys' U18 tennis and football, are hard to beat. Everything done with verve and energy.

Boarding: Just under half of the senior school board of whom 18 per cent are from overseas. Majority are full boarders, about 100 weekly. The five boarding houses, are, of course, mostly recent and cleverly designed with large, light and airy atria which act as common rooms and off which rooms radiate. This system 'produces community right away – no long corridors in which people can get lost or hide away.' No mixed houses. Younger years in rooms with four beds, later in twos or singles. Good shared bathrooms, no en-suites. Houses staffed mostly by

couples/families, their cats and dogs being house pets adored by all but asthmatics. Everyone 'patriotic' about their houses.

Background and atmosphere: Unusually, Bede's Senior grew out of a prep. The prep, founded in 1895, was thriving and, in the 1970s, its then head was urged by parents to provide continuation and the search for premises was on. Could they have done better? They found a house – The Dicker – around 12 miles inland – which had belonged to the extraordinary Horatio Bottomley (well worth looking up if you don't know) – a splendid, early 20th century, arts and crafts-cum-mock-medieval-Tudor extravaganza with a splendid landscaped park surrounded by stunning countryside. Head's own 'salon' is an exquisite blend of the Victorian at its best and the ultra modern. Gorgeous 'old' dining room.

Large, light and airy atria which act as common rooms and off which rooms radiate. This system 'produces community right away'

The school opened in 1979 and has, since then, spawned around 40 lesser buildings – everything from prefabs to a building described as a Kenyan Safari Lodge, atop which, in an improbable eyrie, sits the school library. Huge MPH houses gym, pool, vast assembly space etc. Sussex flint, free-standing chapel used for talks by chaplain but no heavy-duty religion practised here. Biomass boilers and solar panels – school runs almost entirely on sustainable energy. Plans to lose several lesser buildings and construct a major, multi-flexible, classroom block – pupils are involved in the planning of the project and school pays tribute to their insights and ideas. All nestles in the park – extensive fields, meadows, gardens, plus a large, lilied lake and all, seemingly, in terrific nick. All this and train connections to London are close and quick.

Pastoral care, well-being and discipline: Pupils consulted at each stage. 'We're a real believer in pupil leadership. They make real decisions and decide on their legacy to the school.' Tartan skirt and blouse for girls, who wear suits in the sixth; boys wear dark suits but can move into chinos in the sixth. Most enthuse about the food and all like the range of choice.

Parents testify to the absence of bullying and say that anything more than light banter between pupils is handled sensitively. 'And they don't force you to do things you're uncomfortable with,' a parent averred. 'They allow you to be who you are without mortifying you as other schools do.' Tutors, houseparents and a thoroughly understood system of rules and sanctions maintain the school's tangible peace. Few serious misdemeanours – those few handled 'both formally and personally', according to pupils. Permanent exclusions a rarity. School well up on 'safe' internet use: 'We have a group of kids advising us on what we need to know.'

A happy school – 'It's good at turning out all-rounders,' said several. 'It's pretty unsophisticated and relaxed – you don't get awful pushy parents there – they trust the school to know what it's doing.' And, in the words of a pupil, 'My parents wish they could have come here.'

Pupils and parents: From an ever-widening arc – Bognor to Hastings. The vast majority are local or local-ish. Boarders from hither and yon and likely to grow in number. Everyone from wealthy Sussex farmers to London refusniks, to looked-after children in care of the LA – seamlessly and sensitively integrated. United in being smiley, fulfilled and grateful.

Entrance: Oversubscribed at all points but not by much. This is set to change and far-sighted parents need to get down and register. For year 9 entry, applicants invited to a Bede's Experience Day, which includes a group task and discussion, interview, verbal and non-verbal reasoning assessment and a co-curricular activity. Currently, for sixth form, at least five B/6 grades for A levels, depending on subjects.

Exit: Far fewer now leave after GCSE (some 20 per cent) and most who do go locally to sixth form colleges. Post-sixth leavers to a great range of places and courses. Lots to vocational courses eg sports management, advertising, accounting but also eg maths, medicine, English at Russell group universities and a few most years to Oxbridge. In 2017, two to Oxbridge and three medics. Plus seven off abroad, including maths in Lausanne, film in New York, mechanical engineering in Connecticut, photography in Rotterdam.

Alumni of either the prep and/or the senior branch include Eddie Izzard, Nicky Henson, Jamie Lloyd, footballers Dan Harding and Solomon March and a growing stream of cricketers including Ollie Rayner, Luke Wells and, newbie, Shai Hope.

Money matters: Scholarships of up to 25 per cent and a good and growing bursary fund. But – being a newish school – without massive endowments etc, of course.

Remarks: School says, 'What we want parents to know is that their children will be bloody well taught and we are doing great things with them.' Parent says, 'Look at it seriously – whoever your child is'. Pupil says, 'I am so lucky to be here.'

Belmont Preparatory School (Dorking)

9

Feldemore, Holmbury St Mary, Dorking, Surrey RH5 6LQ

01306 730852 | schooloffice@belmont-school.org | www.belmont-school.org

Ages: 2–13 (boarding from 7)

Pupils: 212; Boarders: 5 weekly, 35 flexi

Day: £9,060 – £15,390 pa; Boarding: + £1,575 – £6,540 pa

Headmistress: Since 2006, Mrs Helen Skrine BA. Following a music degree at Exeter, she took up posts teaching music, English and Latin at Wrekin College, Greenacre School, and Chinthurst Prep and was deputy head at Highfield School, Liphook.

A sound business head comes across when she describes how she has steered the school through the challenges of the recession, but there's also a strong maternal streak. On our tour we came across a boy with a bloodied knee being helped in by his friends. 'Oh my darling boy,' she exclaimed. 'Let's get that knee up. Matron is coming with her blue light on.'

Described by parents as 'very hands on and responsive' and 'a strong but caring leader.' Much praised for pastoral care. 'She has even offered support to our son whilst he struggles to adjust to secondary school,' said one mother. Another said: 'She is completely honest and open when it comes to issues with bullying. We were approached by her regarding our daughter being upset in school, something we found most refreshing.'

Two sons now at university. Her home is next door to the school building, not even a stone's throw away. She's not remotely tempted to move off site for a more private off duty life, as some heads are. 'Last evening the children were all outside here playing,' she said. 'Some boys came to borrow the dog. I love it. It's a life, not a job.'

Entrance: 'First and foremost I look at the parents,' says the head. Yikes. No need to brush up on algebra though – she means she wants to be sure that they are buying into the school's ethos, which is not of the all-stations-to-Oxbridge variety. 'We want parents who understand what the ethos of this school is,' she says. 'We do a really good job academically but we are also interested in developing the co-curriculum areas and developing the children as people. I really believe school should be fun, not weighed down in endless testing, stress and strain.'

Who wouldn't it suit? 'Some of the tiger mums I met in my daughter's previous school,' says one mother. Another parent concurs, telling us: 'I haven't met any overly pushy parents at Belmont but I imagine that they would struggle to fit in.'

Next on the head's selection list is: 'Does the child have a spring in his/her step, will they throw themselves into everything and will they fit academically in the range of the year group?' Assessment is through reasoning tests and classroom observation. 'We won't take children outside the average range, but we will take low average pupils – sometimes it's just that they're not thriving in their current school,' the head says. Once in, the children are guaranteed a place until 13, unless any serious learning difficulties arise.

Key points of entry are at 2, reception, year 3 – and some come from other preps at 11. Entrance mid-school is well catered for. A mother told us: 'The parents in my daughter's year have been extremely welcoming. A barbecue and trip to Legoland were organised by the class rep before the start of the academic year so the new children could meet everyone before their first day. Mothers were quick to give me tips and advice about matters such as games kit.'

There's a two form entry per year, and that's the limit. 'I won't go to more than 32 to a year group,' says the head. 'I don't believe big is beautiful.'

Exit: Most parents are buying into private education for the duration – it's rare for a child to leave at 11 for local state secondaries. The head is a big fan of boarding and the children spread their wings far and wide. St John's, Hurstpierpoint College, Box Hill, Dunottar, Seaford College, Lancing, Claremont Fan and Manor House all popular recently.

'Last evening the children were all outside here playing,' she said. 'Some boys came to borrow the dog. I love it. It's a life, not a job'

Remarks: The campus is a glorious 65 acres, with children's playtime roaming through nooks and glades – only constrained by dots on the trees, which indicate when they are out of hearing range of the bell. The main school building is based around the one time home of Edwin Waterhouse (of the Price Waterhouse Cooper accountancy firm), and although the original 1880 house was rebuilt after a fire, it retains its grandeur, with high corniced ceilings, lots of wood paneling and deep window seats. Classrooms for the older children are based here, while years 2 to 4 are accommodated in a modern building, and early years children – two reception and two year 1 classes – have their own buildings arranged around a courtyard, patrolled by three cats.

Specialist subject teaching kicks in from year 5, and children are split into two sets for all CE or scholarship subjects in years 5 to 8. This is flexible, with lots of movement between the sets, and pupils feel it's no big deal to be in a lower set. 'It's exactly the same work – they just slow it down to your speed,' they explained to us.

Parents are overjoyed by the fact there is no homework until year 7 (even then it's not an arduous load, with two preps of half an hour each). Up until then prep is timetabled in a daytime session. 'This is where Belmont differs from most prep schools,' a parent told us. 'They actively keep the pressure off the children and parents right up until year 7. The work handed in is theirs alone, and not the parents'. In addition, the school never sets time consuming projects for the children where the parents end up spending endless hours making models of Egyptian vases or the like. 'It's such a relief, as a working parent.'

Feedback to parents comes in the form of half termly grades, full written reports twice a year and parents' evenings. There's lots of informal reporting. 'Every parent has the email address of every teacher,' says the head. 'I encourage email and we have a policy of getting back within 24 hours.' There's also afternoon tea with the head on a Friday afternoon, which parents say is a great way to meet other parents and have an informal chat with the head and teachers.

The head is passionate about ensuring that it's not just academic achievement that carries kudos here. 'We get lots of awards for things such as work of the week, good manners, boarder of the week,' said the children. During our visit the head's table was strewn with rosettes and certificates – all being sorted ready for prize giving at the weekly assembly. 'Winning a commendation certificate from the headmistress is a most sought after prize,' said one parent.

An array of clubs. These can be mixed and matched, most having no requirement to commit for a term – no battles then to haul a recalcitrant child along to a club which he didn't like by week two. Invitation clubs for the most talented run alongside general access clubs.

Sport is very much an all-inclusive affair. The commitment to involve everyone, combined with small year groups, mean that if a prestigious A team is high on your list, it may not be the place for you. 'Some may feel it does not have enough children to pick teams of excellence,' said one parent. 'We feel our daughter plays her major sports externally, at county level, so for us she is learning to be a team player, to lose sometimes, and to enjoy sport.'

Another told us: 'Small class sizes and year group numbers do limit sports team ability levels at times since the teams often have to mix in different year groups. The benefit of this, however, is that every child, however good or bad at sport, gets to play sport for the school.'

Head points out that the school fields U13, U11 and U9 teams that are selected on ability, and says they 'win many more games than they lose.' Parents praise the school's willingness to embrace individual needs – timetabling cricket and tennis sessions with the boys' teams for a very sporty girl, for example.

On the arts side, the head says 'every child is on stage in front of the parents at least once a year.' Bands, choirs and string groups, with teaching from a professional opera singer and a director of drama. The school has its own biannual festival, Bel Artis, where visiting professionals lead workshops for children, culminating with an evening of performance.

The school shares the site with Moon Hall, a specialist school for dyslexia. The two have separate governing bodies and are separate companies, but there's much crossover outside academic lessons. The Moon Hall children wear Belmont uniform and join Belmont for playtime, assembly, lunches and extracurricular activities. They can be in a school play and board alongside the Belmont pupils. Superb option if you have a dyslexic in the family.

Children can be dropped for breakfast from 7.30am and parents have a broad range of pick up times to choose from – at the end of the school day at 4.30pm, after clubs at 5.45pm, after supper at 6.30pm, after prep at 7.45pm, or children can board for an occasional night or any number up to five nights per week. All of this can be done on an ad hoc basis, so there is great flexibility for the working parent. Nearly 100 pupils board in some form, mostly flexi. 'Our daughter begs to board as often as we will let her,' a mother told us. 'It is a wonderfully warm and friendly environment with the boarders doing lots of interesting activities and going on trips.

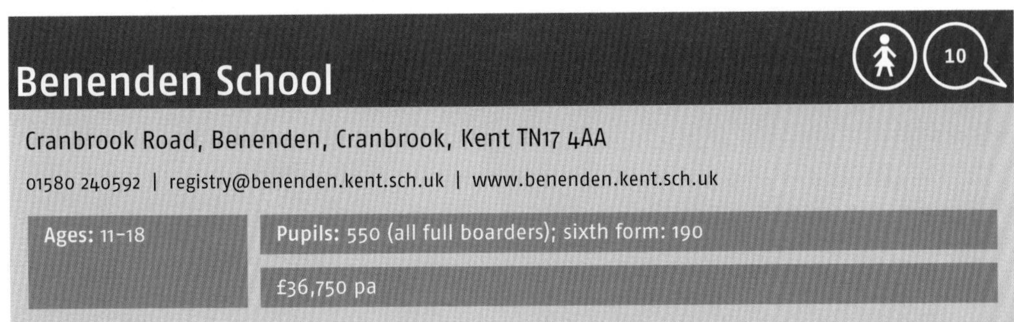

Benenden School

10

Cranbrook Road, Benenden, Cranbrook, Kent TN17 4AA

01580 240592 | registry@benenden.kent.sch.uk | www.benenden.kent.sch.uk

Ages: 11–18

Pupils: 550 (all full boarders); sixth form: 190

£36,750 pa

Headmistress: Since 2014, Samantha Price, 40s. Attended Malvern Girls' College (now Malvern St James), so knows about life at a girls' boarding school from both sides. Read history of art at Edinburgh University and began her career in the Tate Britain marketing department, but soon felt office-bound and switched to teaching. Worked at Reading Blue Coat School, King's Canterbury and Hereford Cathedral School before taking up her first headship at Godolphin School in Salisbury, from whence she was headhunted for her present post. Leaving was a very difficult decision, she says, but she has no regrets: 'Benenden is my dream school, and full boarding is in my DNA.' Married to Iori, an army chaplain, with a young daughter and son.

A passionate devotee of girls' education, and a powerhouse of ideas and energy underneath a warm and civilised exterior. 'I'm very proud of this school. It's a wonderful place to be.'

Academic matters: In 2017, 81 per cent A*-A/9-7 at GCSE and 60 per cent A*/A at A level (A*-B 81 per cent). Pretty much always in the top 50 independent schools nationally. Everything you'd expect on offer, with breadth prized as much as depth: girls study a good range of languages, both modern and classical, and DT, art, music and drama are compulsory throughout the lower school. Science very popular, and is taught in truly amazing science block, all glass and blond wood: a floor per science, and at least three laboratories per floor, plus designated experiment rooms just for sixth formers, and a 150-seater lecture theatre which hosts a rolling programme of visiting speakers. 'My daughter's teachers have inspired her to be really passionate about science,' wrote one happy father, 'and she has really enjoyed science club.' Classrooms are large, modern and well-equipped, and superb library offers space and quiet.

No plans to introduce the IB: A levels are taught as part of a refreshingly commonsense yet innovative approach which makes any such change unnecessary. Girls can almost always study the combination of subjects they want, and the EPQ is offered to all girls to provide additional academic challenge. Lots of skills and vocational courses on offer which sound genuinely appealing rather than drearily functional. For instance, 'I don't think we'll do a food technology A level,' says head, 'but we might run Cordon Bleu courses, and I'd like to run the Leiths Diploma. Being realistic and practical will be increasingly what gets you ahead.' No danger of gender bias in this forward-looking school, however: DT is one of the most popular options, taught in an excellently-resourced technology block which even sports its own ICT suite. The school has introduced a Professional Skills Programme for the sixth form, which enables girls to work alongside professionals in a variety of fields and develop real-life experience of eg reading balance sheets, developing ideas into business proposals. For younger pupils there's the Benenden Diploma (years 7 and 8) and real life problem solving linked to different aspects of service for year 9s.

The effect is gorgeous. We found ourselves thinking of Daisy Pulls It Off, and apparently most newcomers cry 'Hogwarts!' as soon as they get through the front door

The tutor system allows for a lot of contact time, and parents and students alike praise the caring and friendly approach. SEN department supports those girls diagnosed with dyslexia and dyspraxia, and students can have weekly individual lessons if needed (as with most independent schools, these are chargeable). That said, the school acknowledges that this probably isn't the school for those with more than mild difficulties. Extension programme for gifted and talented throughout the school.

Wherever we looked we saw girls relishing the curricular opportunities on offer. As one put it, 'At a school like this, you get to try everything!' A parent added, 'Academically, my daughter has come on amazingly since she joined the school.'

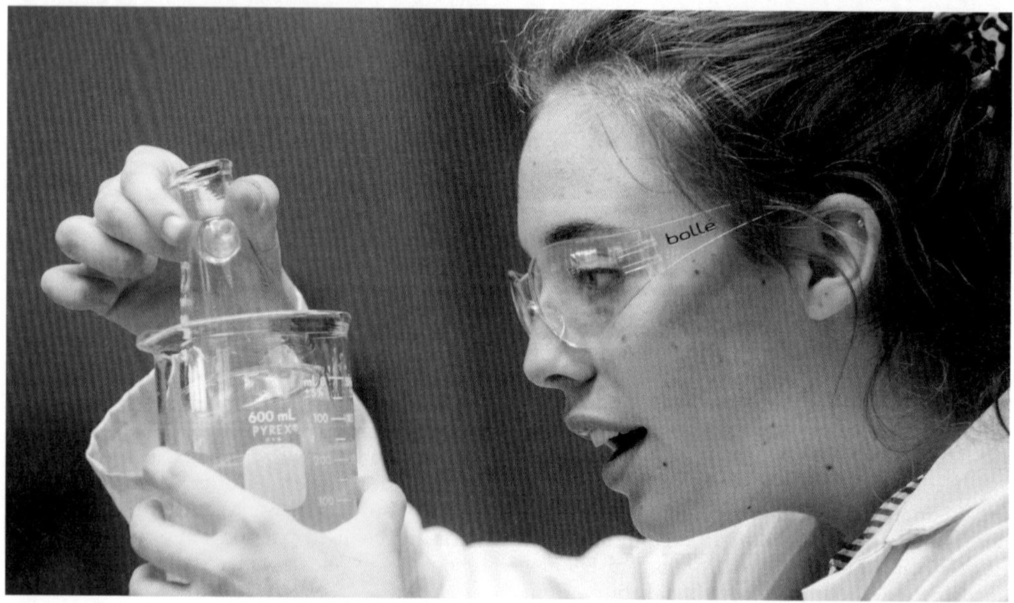

Games, options, the arts: 'You've got to involve yourself,' observed our tour guide, and there's so much to do here that it really would be crazy not to. Loads of traditional girls' sports, with lacrosse, netball and tennis topping the list; but more niche activities such as scuba diving and pool also popular. Dance is big here: there's a lovely dance studio where girls can learn tap, ballet and contemporary dance, plus a rather ace fitness suite for those wishing to acquire the body beautiful (or just keep fit). Newish all-weather sports pitch and pavilion.

Fabulous theatre was opened by Helena Bonham Carter, staffed by two full-time technicians from whom the girls can learn lighting, sound and set construction. Professionals would kill to have facilities this good. Drama is concomitantly lively with at least two major productions a year and lots of student-led performances. LAMDA also flourishing. Music block was built in the 1960s and in another school would be something to boast about, but here looks down-at-heel and in fact is due to be rebuilt soon. Masses of music going on notwithstanding – instrumental lessons, ensembles, orchestra, choir, the works. Art and design is particularly impressive, with wonderful work on display: etching, lino printing and some whacky sculpture rubbed shoulders with really beautiful embroidery. How refreshing to find a school where girls can still learn such things if they wish to.

Lots of trips both home and abroad. Good range of weekend activities appreciated by students and parents alike. 'My daughter has thoroughly enjoyed the weekend programme,' said one grateful mother.

Boarding: All students here are full boarders. School is relaxed about letting girls go home at weekends. Boarding rooms are colourful, light and homely – perhaps a little crowded for some tastes, with up to five girls in a room for the lower school, but all the girls we spoke to insisted they liked it that way. Older girls can choose to have smaller rooms and fewer room-mates, and all sixth formers have their own room in a deluxe modern block built especially for them, designed to be a halfway house between school and university. Fully equipped and spotlessly clean, we couldn't help thinking that most university accommodation would be a bit of a come-down afterwards.

Background and atmosphere: Started in 1923 by Miss Sheldon, Miss Hindle and Miss Bird, three teachers from Wycombe Abbey, the school moved to its present site in 1924 and has flourished ever since. Held in immensely high esteem by its alumna, many of whom had gathered to pay it affectionate respect when we happened to visit. Many girls here whose mothers – even grandmothers – attended the school.

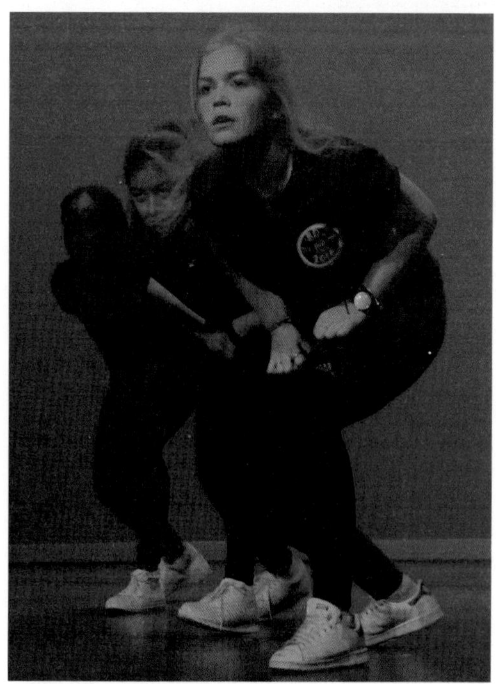

The original house, Hemsted, still serves as the school's main building, and must be everyone's idea of what an English boarding school looks like. The magnificent wood-panelled entrance hall and staircase are hung with portraits of the Earl of Cranbrook's family, and coats of arms are etched upon the stained glass. It was actually built in the 19th century, but was designed to look much older, and the effect is frankly gorgeous. We found ourselves thinking of Daisy Pulls It Off, and apparently most newcomers cry 'Hogwarts!' as soon as they get through the front door. It's still possible to board in Hemsted, and the girls that do told us they absolutely love it.

'I love it!' confirmed a cheerful sixth former, adding in proper Benenden patois, 'and you can walk into vill whenever you like'

However, a massive programme of refurbishment over the past 20 years has ensured that Benenden can more than hold its own in the 21st century. All the facilities here are stunningly good, and the whole is set in 240 acres of exquisitely landscaped grounds: beyond the playing fields, where we saw girls desporting themselves at lacrosse, are lawns, roses, woods, water features, flower beds, a walled garden, lime tree avenue, all overlooking miles of hills and greenery beyond. 'I love it!' confirmed a cheerful sixth former, adding in proper Benenden patois, 'and you can walk into vill whenever you like.'

Excellent school shop, where students can buy everything needful from shampoo to study aids, and an air of unfussy practicality throughout. Food universally praised (we can confirm the chocolate brownies were to die for), and girls say that their suggestions for the menu are listened to. Impressive building programme has added eight new staff houses to overcome issue of local property prices deterring many good teachers from applying. Construction about to start on new school hall and music school. This is a school that takes people's everyday comfort seriously, and puts its money where its mouth is.

Pastoral care, well-being and discipline: No real behaviour issues – this is a happy ship, and the care and support given to the girls were praised everywhere. 'It was a big move to the UK for my daughter,' wrote an overseas mother, 'and the house staff looked after her as if she were their own, giving cuddles and love whenever she needed it. They still do so now.' And everyone we contacted said something similar. In addition to her tutor and housemistress, each girl is allocated an older girl or 'big sister' to look after her, and girls spoke to us with fondness about the friends they'd made across the different year groups.

Girls can work alongside professionals in a variety of fields and develop real-life experience of eg reading balance sheets, developing business proposals

Rules are enforced with a light touch. One mother commented, 'I like the fact that they teach the girls the right thing to do rather than impose really strict rules, eg they don't ban access to the internet – even for the younger girls; they spend time teaching them about internet safety instead.' Girls said again and again that they felt able to be themselves, and mothers frequently commented that their daughters hadn't felt pressured into growing up too quickly.

Considerable privileges and latitude given to sixth formers, who really value the increased independence and are consequently less likely to switch to co-ed at this stage. The school has opened a new café bar where sixth formers can buy a glass of wine on a Saturday night (with parental permission). All the girls wear uniform, even the sixth, but it's an unfussy uniform and the girls honestly didn't seem to mind – it's a community that fosters a sensible and pragmatic attitude to life's challenges. As one parent enthused, 'Everything at Benenden is done so smoothly and efficiently. Our daughter loves it and so do we. We are struggling to find a school as good as this for our son!' Another wrote, 'My daughter speaks of being school-sick during the holidays, the opposite of homesick, because she loves everything about the school so much – she is very, very happy at Benenden.'

Pupils and parents: Fees are high, and Princess Anne may be Benenden's most famous alumna, but this is not a school for snobs. About 12 per cent from abroad, many of them expats. Otherwise, families are solid professional London and home counties people who want the best for their children and 'work their socks off to send their girls here,' according to head. Bursary assistance ensures at least some social diversity: one girl on a 110 per cent bursary spoke movingly to us about her own experience: 'The school has helped in every possible way. I've never felt out of place, and I owe them so much.'

Entrance: Forty girls join at 11 and 50 girls at 13. Both intakes oversubscribed, but not dauntingly so. Plan ahead, though: the lists can close a year or more in advance. Early offers programme means 13+ entrants can be offered a firm place in year 7. Girls have to achieve at least 55 per cent at common entrance, but in practice many applicants will, so the school also uses pre-tests and interviews and works closely with local prep schools to be sure they're getting it right. 'We're looking for sound academic competence and potential. We're a broad church.' Occasional places for other years – the school operates a waiting list. Entry to sixth form dependent on exam, interview and current head's report, but fantastic sixth form opportunities mean that very few existing students leave, so not many additional places available.

Exit: At 16, hardly anyone leaves: occasionally girls may opt for a co-ed experience at schools such as Charterhouse. At 18, four to Oxbridge in 2017, the rest mostly to Russell group universities (half places are in UK top 10) to read a broad range of subjects – six medics in 2017, engineering and physics currently enjoying a surge in numbers. London, Durham, Bristol and Exeter all popular destinations. Four to the US and one to Canada in 2017, with another off to Switzerland to study international hospitality management.

Money matters: Scholarships of up to 10 per cent for academics, music, art, DT, sports and drama. Those who've been awarded a scholarship can apply to the generous bursary fund: a number of girls here benefit from means-tested assistance of up to 80 per cent. The Benenden School Trust also offers up to three 110 per cent bursaries each year to girls coming from local state schools.

Remarks: Traditional girls' boarding brought radiantly up to date, jettisoning what was bad, retaining everything good and adding a huge amount more. An exciting and appealing place: if we were young again, we'd be clamouring to go there.

Bethany School

C of E | 11

Curtisden Green, Goudhurst, Cranbrook, Kent TN17 1LB

01580 211273 | registrar@bethanyschool.org.uk | www.bethanyschool.org.uk

Ages: 11–18

Pupils: 327; sixth form: 104; Boarders: 80 full, 30 weekly

Day: £16,245 – £17,925 pa; Boarding: £25,185 – £30,585 pa

Head: Since 2010, Mr Francie Healy. A graduate of Trinity College, Dublin, he began his teaching career at an inner city school in Dublin, before taking up a post as maths teacher at Bethany in 1989. He's never wanted to leave the place, and grew his role to head up the IT department, then through director of studies, academic deputy and deputy headship. He doesn't, however, plan to stay quite as permanently as two previous heads, who are buried in the grounds.

'Genuinely held in high regard by the students. He is also very funny,' commented one parent. Not many heads would go to the lengths he did in a charity raffle which resulted in him changing places with a pupil for the day. He rang the school's uniform supplier to ensure he could be properly kitted out for the day, and queued up with his tuck money at break.

Known for his friendliness to both parents and pupils, it's hard to imagine any stern reprimands delivered in his County Clare burr. As we wandered through the sixth form common room and the boarding houses where pupils were converging at lunchtime, we noticed how relaxed the children remained in the head's presence – there was no straightening up or jumping to attention.

'Loves those children with a passion,' a parent told us.

Academic matters: Bethany is characterised as a mainstream school with a specialist learning support department; around one-third of pupils receive support for specific learning difficulties, and 45 foreign nationals have English language support. Its day intake is also skewed by the density of grammar schools in the region, which tend to cream off the top achieving pupils at 11. Given its broad ability range, it produced a very decent 25 per cent A*/A grades (54 per cent A*-B) at A level and 27 per cent A*-A/9-7 at GCSE in 2017.

As a small secondary it also appeals to those not suited to the rough and tumble of bigger schools. 'The small class sizes and, therefore, closer relationships with the staff have really helped her find her feet,' commented one parent. One boy who moved here from another secondary told us, 'The difference here is the teachers spend more time with you'.

The broad ability range is catered for through setting and an individualised approach. 'Get to know and understand the child, then you appreciate how that child learns and thinks. Then you set targets, and as soon as those are reached, raise them,' is Healy's approach.

Those on full learning support are not expected to study a language. Others who don't have an aptitude for languages are free to choose an alternative subject for GCSE (dance recently introduced). Only those in the top two sets study English literature in addition to English language. 'Bethany treats its pupils as individuals and is really flexible, it will change the timetable to suit the pupils, not the other way round like most schools,' said a parent.

Setting begins in English, maths and science from year 7. We saw this at work in English classes, where one group was tasked with finding unfamiliar words in the dictionary, and composing a sentence with them. All were working on laptops. Another group were looking at how sound and visual effects were conveyed in a piece of writing. The EAL group meanwhile were working separately on language skills.

Science is moving to the three individual subjects (previously all pupils took the dual award), enabling the strong scientists to do all three, and those who are less keen to opt for one or two science subjects. There are two well-equipped labs each for biology, physics and chemistry. Pupils were working on decomposition – looking at bread under what they told us were the optimum 'wet and warm' lab conditions, as well as a dead bird they had handily found outside.

School now teaches computing instead of ICT, which focuses more on coding.

Those who like to tread the boards are well catered for. Ex-pupils include the Brit award winning music producer Charlie Andrew, who pops back to cheer on pupils

Mandarin is introduced from year 7, and the school has an exchange programme with Taiwan. This, says the head, is because 28 per cent of the world's economy will be Chinese by 2050.

Food tech is compulsory for years 7 to 9 (split for half of the year with design technology), and in the sixth form, where they do a 'university gourmet for life course' to prepare them for living away from home.

DT has a good following to A level, and the workshops are well equipped with all the kit to cut, stick and mould. A level students were hard at work on their final exam pieces, the range clearly indicating their own interests – a golf cart, electric guitar, go-kart, a desk with a built in fish tank, and a dog house.

The work on display in the art rooms is a joy to behold – some catwalk-worthy costumes on mannequins produced by the A level textile students, and tremendous portraits by the art students. Others working on installation pieces were allowed to take over whole areas of the art room – one based on the birth of a lamb, complete with sound effects, straw bales strewn with lambswool, and film footage.

There is no requirement at sixth form to stick to the traditional/academic subjects. Those wishing to take three creative subjects are free to do so, and the school also offers two BTecs, in sport and business. 'They truly do find what you are good at and therefore make the things you aren't so good at much less important,' said a parent.

Learning support is given either as full support (10 per cent of timetable) or part-time support (three per cent). This is all timetabled with no sessions outside of school hours; as Healy says, 'pupils with learning support work harder in lessons, therefore they are the last pupils who should be getting extra lessons'. So the support is given instead of French in years 7 to 9, and in place of one GCSE in years 10 and 11.

Support for external exams is reportedly excellent, and we saw a small group in the learning support room being coached in revision techniques. In year 9, the learning support team sifts through the whole year group to establish who should apply for exam concessions, and who might need to get an educational psychologist's report.

All of the pupils have a laptop or iPad, so use of these in lessons is no big deal, and the school uses Dragon speech recognition and Read & Write Gold dyslexia software.

All children receiving support will have an IEP (individual education plan) which identifies strengths, weaknesses, strategies, and targets. Subject teachers can look up the strategies for that individual child – which might be asking short questions; looking at the resources they are giving out and ensuring key words are highlighted; using coloured overlays; using cards so the child doesn't blurt out the answer; and advising where they should sit in the classroom.

The school's specialism is dyslexia, so this is the area of need where you will find the best support, but parents suggest it is not as focused and effective for other areas of special need.

Parents commented on the stability of the teaching staff – that the same people were there as the child reached the top of the school as when they joined. 'On the very odd occasion that teachers have not been up to scratch, issues have either been dealt with, or the teacher has been replaced,' said one parent.

Games, options, the arts: There are compulsory activities four afternoons per week. Teaching finishes at 3.40pm, and after a 20 minute break, children go to activities which finish at 5pm. The wide range of options includes the likes of chef's school, bushcraft, horse riding, sailing, model making, symphony orchestra, lifesaving and pilates.

Bethany is a very creative school, and those who like to tread the boards are well catered for. Ex-pupils include the Brit award winning music producer Charlie Andrew, who pops back to cheer on the pupils. Music productions are reportedly terrific – one father's voice was breaking with emotion as he recalled a performance from the previous evening. Music teacher 'turns them into gold', he said.

Everyone does sport all afternoon on Wednesday – alongside the traditional team sports there's options to suit all including clay pigeon shooting, tennis, basketball, badminton and table

tennis. School is increasing outdoor learning and high ropes provision.

Sport is an inclusive affair, with fixtures matched to schools of similar standard – one or two parental grumbles that standards in sport are not demanding enough. But Bethany also caters for hotshots, with current pupils including a boy ranked third on the European golf circuit, and a pupil placed 16th in the world for sailing. Arrangements are made for the sporting stars to catch up if they need time out of school to attend key competitions. As they were for a boy who had acting commitments, and was allowed to take his A levels over three years.

A level students were hard at work on their final exam pieces, the range clearly indicating their own interests – a golf cart, electric guitar, go-kart, dog house

Sixth formers have a Young Enterprise Company – they sell shares in it, with the aim to give a dividend back. They choose a different product to sell each year, and outside advisers come in to give timetabled sessions on business strategy. Pupils learned an important lesson when they tried to sell scented candles at a Christmas ice rink at the wrong price point.

Boarding: Around one-third of the pupils board, and around 40 per cent of the boarders are international students. One weekend in each half term is designated as a 'home' weekend, but full boarders and overseas students can remain in school for these weekends.

Most weekends will find about 80 students in residence. There's no Saturday school, but Saturday activities – trips to Brighton, London, Thorpe Park, shopping trips, sporting activities – are compulsory. Sunday activities are optional.

There are three boys' boarding houses, one for girls, and a co-ed one for the sixth form. In the sixth form block all rooms are singles with ensuite bathrooms, modern, and a reasonable size. Some sixth formers stay in the houses for younger pupils if they want a leadership role, or prefer to live in the sixth form house – this has smaller rooms, which are not ensuite. Younger pupils' dorms vary from twin to five bed rooms.

The last ISI inspection report relayed pupils' complaints about the food – this has been addressed by a supper boarding committee, and greater sensitivity to the preferences of international students.

Background and atmosphere: None of the usual eau de cabbage, trainers and pencil shavings smells greet you here – instead you catch wafts of strategically placed aromatherapy diffusers.

The school is a mixture of the glitzy and homely. Classroom blocks are utilitarian – you could be inside a comprehensive school. 'We don't do posh,' says the head. You might beg to differ when it comes to the facilities – a swanky £1.7m swimming pool; a fitness room groaning with running machines ('five grand each'), rowing machines, weights and exercise bikes; the cricket pitch and pavilion, tennis and squash courts. A digital performing arts centre with a performance space, practice space, concert space, and the digital equipment to film, edit and make music is in planning.

The school has a strong Christian ethos, and chapel twice a week is compulsory. But head says the sermons have a moral rather than religious bent.

Pastoral care, well-being and discipline: 'Seem to have them on a long flexi-lead which they will let out quite far, but they know when to pull it in,' said a parent.

There's no pussy-footing around on the serious issues, though – boarders are checked for drug-taking by random mouth swabs and the occasional appearance of sniffer dogs.

Pupils are made aware of their relative privilege, and duty to those less fortunate. The head reeled off a series of recent charitable events, including a tour to South Africa where pupils helped to build a school in a township. 'They can bring an idea and know they will be listened to,' says Healy, relating how the school celebrated the Indian Festival of Colour at the behest of three year 8 pupils, who successfully convinced him that its tradition of dousing each other in coloured dyes would be a great post-exam stress reliever. They raised funds for Unicef in the process.

There's no shoehorning into option blocks, or diktats about studying certain loathed subjects. If they want to do three art A levels, fine, if that's what they're good at. Dyslexic? No need for a language

'Bethany has the knack of bringing out the best in each and every child, not only academically, but by drawing out hidden talents, and recognising the gifts and abilities children have that are not measured by grades or traditional accolades,' summed up one parent.

Parents are given email addresses for all staff, including the head, and there's a policy to respond within 24 hours. Healy's first step as head was to make all his correspondences on first name terms. Parents agree this helps to build relationships, and that any issues are dealt with quickly.

Pupils and parents: The school is set in the middle of nowhere but a fleet of buses bring the day pupils in routes from Tunbridge Wells, Sevenoaks, Tenterden, Kings Hill and Frant.

About 15 per cent of pupils are international students, hailing from Russia, Ukraine, Europe, China, Hong Kong, USA, Nigeria, South Africa, Cambodia and South Korea. The biggest group – around one-third of the total – comes from Hong Kong and China, but the school keeps numbers in any particular year group small to encourage them to converse in English.

Its dyslexia provision is a lure, but its small and nurturing ethos also attracts those pupils who would find the hurly-burly of a large comprehensive too much to cope with, and the parents who want something more holistic, and to avoid the treadmill of the highly competitive schools. The head's own three children have been through the school. His daughter got 10 A*/As at GCSE, proof indeed that they cater for the high fliers.

There's a preponderance of boys, owing perhaps to its one-time legacy as a boys' school, or the fact that boys tend to be diagnosed with dyslexia more readily than girls. 'I would tell prospective parents of girls to check that there are enough girls in the year group, as some year groups have literally a handful of girls which would have made our experience of the school very different,' advised one parent.

However we also heard repeatedly of the friendships that form between different year groups, perhaps making the girl issue less of a thing than it might be in schools where friendships stick rigidly within year groups.

The parent community is also warm and supportive, we were told – to the extent that 'a number of parents choose to remain involved with Bethany once their children have left,' according to one parent.

Entrance: Pupils wishing to join in years 7 to 9 take the school's own entrance assessments. Sixth form applicants need to be predicted at least four C/4-5 grades at GCSE level, although for some subjects a grade B/6 is preferable. Overseas students can take assessments at their current school, and have their headmaster's interview via Skype.

Where a student has additional learning needs, the staff will, if necessary, go and see them in their current school, consider school and educational psychologist reports, and sometimes suggest that the prospective pupil spends some time at Bethany. They will usually be looking for standardised scores no lower than 90 (where 100 is average), but this can be flexible where a child has a particular ability in some areas. Autistic students are considered if high functioning, and if they can manage appropriately in the school environment (one former autistic pupil is expected to get a first in her university degree). The school promises that if the pupil is not best suited to Bethany, they would always recommend an alternative school to approach.

Exit: Two-thirds to three-quarters of pupils stay on into sixth form, and at this point leaver numbers are matched with new entrants. Those leaving at the end of year 11 are usually those not best suited to an A level curriculum, and they go into higher level apprenticeships or further education courses. Joiners come from overseas, or for the curriculum choice. One girl came because her school wouldn't let her do three art A levels – at Bethany she achieved A* in each of art, photography and textiles.

At the end of sixth form more than 90 per cent go to university (in 2017, included Durham, Loughborough, Heriot-Watt, Portsmouth, Oxford Brookes, Sussex and Nottingham Trent), and the school's creative bent sees high numbers achieving places at the top art and design colleges – one recently grabbing one of only 30 places in the country on an automotive design course.

Money matters: Scholarships (10 to 20 per cent of the fees) are offered for entry into year 7, year 9 and the sixth form in art, dance, drama, music, technology and sport. Academic scholarships are also offered to a maximum value of 40 per cent of fees. Two special scholarships called Christopher Jackson Scholarships can pay up to 100 per cent of fees, and bursarial awards are available covering 30-50 per cent.

Remarks: What we loved here was the sense of letting children be free to be who they want to be. There's no shoehorning into option blocks, or diktats about studying certain loathed subjects. If they want to do three art A levels, fine, if that's what they're good at. Dyslexic? Then no need to do a language. The result: happy children, free to do what interests them, and all the more successful for it. 'We let the children excel at what they are good at,' says the head. We wish a few more schools would follow Bethany's lead.

If you have a creative, goes against the mould child; or the deep thinker who can't bear the hustle and hassle of a huge school; or a bright dyslexic; or you just can't stand the competitive treadmill of some schools – then you have found your place.

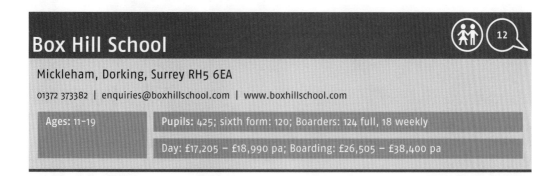

Box Hill School

12

Mickleham, Dorking, Surrey RH5 6EA

01372 373382 | enquiries@boxhillschool.com | www.boxhillschool.com

Ages: 11-19

Pupils: 425; sixth form: 120; Boarders: 124 full, 18 weekly

Day: £17,205 – £18,990 pa; Boarding: £26,505 – £38,400 pa

Headmaster: Since 2014, Mr Corydon Lowde BSc MEd NPQH (40s), previously school's deputy head who took over following sudden departure of predecessor. Before that, nearly three years' handy overseas experience in similar role at British International School of Boston, preceded by seven-year stint at Hampshire Collegiate School, starting career at large state comprehensive.

'Has a vision he wants to share' and 'never tires of talking about what we're doing.' Hours he's putting in (lots of them) paying off, thought insider. 'School is going up.' Was 'gutted' that had to speak on the phone (in hospital having wonky knee put right on day of visit) as meeting best way of 'understanding where all that energy is coming from and where the school is going.'

Felt to be doing as good a job as anyone could manage in difficult circumstances, style reserved but friendly, reviews cautious but generally positive. 'It's new thing but I feel that Cory is on the right track,' thought one parent, speaking for pretty much everyone. Overwhelming desire is that he keeps school atmosphere just the way it is. Nobody is hungry for change.

A teacher from the off (management, part of his degree, was the career that got away), he comes across as quiet, mild-mannered and slightly quirky with self-deprecating Brit humour (honed, no doubt, during own schooldays at Dragon and Frensham Heights) that must make international parents want to take him home gift-wrapped in a Burberry bag. (Should really be Duchamp, says Mr Lowde, a loyal fan of their ties, socks and, indeed, 'pochettes'.)

Goal is school that reflects the world when it comes to nationalities (they have around 30 but no monocultures) and ability range. Would like more Brits – 'who wouldn't?' he says – and is hoping rising tide of Londoners is high enough to lap against admissions desk.

When not headmastering, follows sport. Was British Karate Champion in the 1990s (not an Olympic sport – down to international wrangling). We had visions of desk being reduced to matchwood after one emphatic gesture too many but, no, it's all neat and splinter-free.

Karate, he says firmly, is all about 'turning search for perfection into your own personal journey – not about aggressive confrontation,' – a nothing-to-prove message that's not million miles away from how would like school to see itself.

Academic matters: That increasingly rare sighting in them thar Surrey hills – senior school that has continued to welcome the all and sundries who, these hard-nosed, results-driven days, wouldn't necessarily gain a place elsewhere. In circumstances, 60 per cent A*-C at A level in 2017; IB diploma average of 32; and 26 per cent A*-A/9-7 at GCSE a tribute to quality of teaching.

Every tool's home marked by pencilled outline on wall behind – very Patrick Caulfield

While near neighbours have sought solid A grade glory, here they've carried on with broader ability range (many are around the national average). But school's frequent self-referencing as 'non-selective' needs grain of salt. Minimally selective, yes, but everyone accepted as 'greenies' (blazer colour worn to year 11) needs to be capable of passing eight or nine GCSEs.

Able pupils who do deliver top grades (parents pinching themselves at children's better than

predicted results aren't hard to come by) won't, however, be held up as only aspirational model worth pursuing. 'Am great believer that competition crushes one's self-esteem,' says head (though not when it comes to sport, where all-out drive to win is 'about character'...).

Academically, it's about 'my growth, learning and success [being] made greater by your learning,' sentiments that do him credit, as does desire for kind, empathetic colleagues. They're well up to the job, say pupils, and palpably keen to get everyone involved. Maths department gets X Factor squared award for pupil recruitment, department head 'a genius.'

Similar stories elsewhere. Even visitors may find themselves dredging up rusty French and Spanish greetings, courtesy of bustling, friendly language teachers who won't take non for an answer, while we assume whiteboard spelling of 'clergimen' [sic] in otherwise pacey English lesson was designed to test pupils' eye for detail.

Ethos derives in part from membership of Round Square group of schools, linked to ideals of eccentric but hugely influential educationalist Kurt Hahn, who stressed compassion coupled with 'just do it' mentality. (We quizzed tour guides who, impressively, were able to cite every one of key principles – and swore they hadn't mugged up in advance...).

Extreme cleverness catered for but also support 150 pupils with SEN, from mild dyslexia to school refusers – 'though we're not special school,' says head and pupils must be able to access curriculum. Helped by lowish pupil to teacher ratio (nine to one) and small class sizes (average 15 to 18 up to year 11, as few as two pupils in EAL and ISC lessons). Support includes one-to-one specialist help (normal maximum of an hour a week, mostly maths or literacy focused) and multi-sensory teaching. Will also try to help those (often with high functioning Asperger's) struggling with social communication.

About 70 of 110 EAL pupils follow mainstream syllabus, 50 in sixth form, English studied at range of levels, from IB diploma level to IGCSE, ESOL and IELTS. Others are found among 40 plus pupils at International Study Centre who can chose from four courses aimed at 14-16ish age range, most popular the one-year intensive GCSE programme (also marketed as pre-IB).

Some ISC pupils start a year or so behind peers, about half eventually joining 'mainstream' pupils (school's words, not ours). All 'fully integrated into school life...' says glossy literature (repeated several times for added emphasis) though some national groups stick together and school pupils can feel onus is on them to make first contact and bridge the cultural gap.

School's best recent curriculum decision has been reintroduction of A levels, reducing at a stroke post-16 departures of the IB-averse who 'want to stay but don't want to take six subjects,' says head, though they're encouraged to opt for extras such as IB theory of knowledge, extra maths and creativity, action and service – and some do (one keen A level student was even doing IB Spanish module out of love for the subject, though skipping the exam). Staff, insouciant about extra workload involved, see dual system as best way of boosting numbers studying top subjects at top unis, particularly maths and straight sciences.

Games, options, the arts: With practice rooms open all hours (7 in the morning till 9 at night) and free instrumental taster lessons, no shortage of opportunities for 100 or so budding musicians who hone skills, some to diploma level – one so impressive that visiting top musician offered tuition on the spot.

Karate, he says firmly, is all about 'turning search for perfection into your own personal journey – not about aggressive confrontation' – a nothing-to-prove message

Other hands-on subjects housed in range of (mainly original) buildings including small, cobble-paved stables minimally converted to create atmospheric and fitting home for DT, every tool's home marked by penciled outline on wall behind – very Patrick Caulfield. Visual arts headed by practising artist, who, paintbrush in hand, was adding final touches to own masterpiece as pupils worked around him, inspiring similarly accomplished work (our favourite among many featuring off-duty angels enjoying an off-duty cig).

Sport key to 'holistic' approach, though girls enjoy pinker-shaded version – holassism, perhaps? – and do netball and rounders (rugby and cricket for boys) with hockey and football in common, though pupils confident that if school would happily accommodate changes if demand was there. Frank acknowledgement that team sports 'not for all'; new sports hall construction pencilled in to finish in mid-2018. Room to improve, thought parent, as not viewed as top priority, perceptions rubbing off on potential staff recruits (lure not yet sufficiently great to attract top talent). Results, which tend to align with levels of each intake's innate talent, can fluctuate fairly widely from year to year. That said, manifest advantages for the keen who, with minimal numbers of school teams, can get their fill of matches, though accepted that anyone requiring high quality sporting fix and nothing but will probably end up elsewhere.

Sensible decision to offer individual fitness from year 10 when 'almost anything is possible,' says school, the more so as sport happens twice a week, Tuesdays and Thursdays being reserved for school activities including magic club, sign language and – a rare treat – corsetry and dressmaking class which teaches traditional panelling and boning skills and is run by passionate devotee, enthusiasm largely responsible, as with fashion and textiles GCSE, for bringing in impressive numbers of boys.

Boarding: With large numbers of full boarders (around two-thirds boys), spending priority is six boarding houses, four in the grounds, two across the (quiet) village road. House names, though full of meaning to school, have certain random quality for outsiders, Constantine named after eponymous Greek king – school patron; Ralph apparently commemorating past VIP (though sounds like rakish English take on IKEA furniture policy).

Plenty to help boarders take mind off décor difficulties. After prep on Saturdays, seniors can travel into London. Must be back by '2230' [sic] (time rather than century, we assume), shopping trumping culture every time. Excellent range of trips including 'experiences' (Jamie Oliver and Harry Potter). One houseparent (male) runs regular pizza making sessions ('leave dough to rise during the day, cook in the evening.') 'Never a dull moment,' insists school, firmly. Boarders agree. 'Can be almost too much going on,' said one.

Background and atmosphere: Word du jour, judged to pack a punch in terms of punter appeal, is 'inspiring', writ large throughout new school video, overlaying jolly images of suitably fired up pupils fencing on the school lawn (a summer term reality, not just camera-friendly set up) or putting up tents at summit of Box Hill, buffeted by gale force winds.

There's also much talk of holistic approach, though 'mindfulness', other all-purpose buzz word of choice, appears to be the meme that got away – so far. 'Not sure why aren't using it,' says member of staff.

'Stunning' is other obvious candidate, given village setting in Mickleham, between Dorking and Leatherhead and about 20 miles from London. As pretty as they come, main building once private gothic revival Victorian house with aspirations to grandeur, full of delightful stained glass biblical scenes and window seat epidemic (even modern boarding houses are rotten with them). Newer wings tacked on at the back sufficiently sympathetic to keep the charm intact though some more elderly stand-alones have their work cut out. 'Has the smell of an experienced building,' says one of tour guides of modern languages block.

Original grandeur belies school's relative youth, founded only in 1959 by Gordonstoun housemaster on principles inspired by inspirational educationalist Kurt Hahn, with much emphasis on whole pupil development (and plenty of non-Hahn inspired beatings for those failing to progress along right lines, according to one rueful 1970s-vintage OB). Now, pupils 'will all excel at something,' reckons school, while extending talent range to include high profile qualities such as friendship and general good egg-dom, which are 'acknowledged though not in OTT way,' says member of staff.

School activities include magic club, sign language and – a rare treat – corsetry and dressmaking, run by a passionate devotee

In any case, it's Hahn-lite (don't set them loose in all weathers on high seas: land-locked setting on Surrey Downs is against them) but ticks off must-dos: democracy, environment, adventure, leadership and service – with whole school activity week in September with camping, canoeing and rock climbing for all in Wales or New Forest. D of E – closely linked in ethos – from year 9 and just about everyone takes bronze. 'No reason not to,' says school, though silver and gold recruited on opt-in basis. Star attraction is trip to Philippolis, South Africa, where pupils have helped add new buildings including crèche and classrooms. 'Proof of faith in school,' said mother, whose son, just turned 13, had spent a month there.

Luxury goods on offer to counteract struggle with elements – 90 inch TV in new sixth form common room used for films and for pupils to 'enjoy live streams from the Royal Shakespeare Company,' trumpets prospectus. We're sure they do little else (sotto voce giggling when we asked undoubtedly down to recollection of Bard's many bon mots...). And when Titus Andronicus palls, there's always fun of watching vast tame rodents (gerbils not rats, despite unnerving tails) rolling around in exercise balls.

Overall impression is of well-tended school with little evidence of slight messiness reported by a couple of visiting parents – nothing to do, we're sure, with sign reading 'GSG visit [today]. Rooms have to be very tidy...' And so what if it's not immaculate? 'Don't send son to school for the décor,' commented mother.

Grounds undiluted gorgeousness (impressive mown stripes of grass that continued either side of small pond on back lawn giving unnerving impression that Jerry – the groundsman, and noted duck whisperer; pupils say he's followed by family of mallards each year – can walk, or at least ride, on water).

Golden glow set to spread as governor-sanctioned spending spree continues, aided by canny bursar who 'always has six months of staff salaries in the bank,' and is clearly a dab hand at curbing any headmasterly dash over cash tendencies. 'We're strong and robust – though hate that word, makes me sound like politician,' says head.

Now well on the way to transforming slightly dismal befores to far nicer afters. Rooms where clutter of tables and beds currently fight yellowing paint for supremacy slowly but surely transformed by attractive furniture, much of it custom created 'by our own maintenance team' and essential as most non-standard alcoves aren't compatible with off the peg designs.

'Work in progress,' says head. Will be followed by new sports hall (biggest current absence) – local council currently dragging heels – and more space for creative arts ('absolutely not forgotten,' says head). Some Portakabins – some exteriors slightly shabby, interiors as well as can be expected and could be far worse – will remain.

Pastoral care, well-being and discipline: 'Willing to cherish the children for what they are – don't treat them as a commodity,' thought feeder school registrar. 'Very open and honest, don't sweep things under the carpet,' agreed parent. Example is alcohol policy. If over 18, boarders can purchase but 'carefully monitored' – to ensure any headaches are admin, not consumption, related.

Quality of communications only widespread complaint, described with single-word pithiness by several parents fed up with night-before notifications of matches and recent music event. (Though full marks to music staff for re-running one child's performance so late arriving mother didn't miss out).

Other parents, however, reckoned that greater attention to termly calendars and school website would iron out most of the difficulties. Fortnightly newsletter from head also generally going down well, while more text alerts and email updates should take uncertainty out of nitty gritty-ness of who is doing what and when.

After prep on Saturdays, seniors can travel into London. Must be back by '2230' (time rather than century, we assume), shopping trumping culture every time

Nurturing element otherwise practically perfect, attended to with care and sensitivity. One pupil, bullied elsewhere and finding settling in hard, was cajoled out of foyer into class by head of year, now thriving. 'Helped him become accustomed to school until he was able to let go of that helping hand for a day or two.' Unpleasantness does happen but quickly and effectively dealt with, think parents whose children have been on receiving end. School's 'expose and eradicate,' approach includes ambassadors – 'our eyes and ears,' says head – who report any hint of transgression, backed up by anonymous online whistleblowing.

Boarders send two reps from each of the six houses to discuss issues – often food related, with school headed by 13-strong syndicate who supervise breaks, administer tellings off for minor uniform infringements and are led by head boy and girl, known as Guardians, superhero connotations a highly successful recruitment tool. Handover speech to successors an annual tear jerker, with one post-holder 'talking to her parents through the speech and saying how grateful she was,' said mother, welling up all over again at the memory.

Unlike other top dogs we've encountered, not shy about using superpowers and will impose detentions, though not often and mainly for repeated rudeness. 'Know when someone's just being cheeky.' Given incumbents' nicknames (President Nice and Madame Fuhrer), we thought they showed commendable forbearance, though all pupil behaviour witnessed, in and out of lessons, was universally immaculate.

Pupils and parents: Parents range from diverse international community to ecstatic locals, often first time buyers, thrilled about what school has done for their children. All aware that school still seen as second choice. 'Wrong postcode for some Reigate mums,' said one. General sense that won't last, though nobody's in a hurry to add more competitive feel to a place felt to run on happiness. Boy numbers (outnumber girls two to one) and international element (around 84 per cent of boarders) also put others off, though seeing real life consequences of world events played out – one parent cited falling out of former best friends from different war zones – provides 'amazing' insights.

Parents range from diverse international community to ecstatic locals, often first time buyers, thrilled about what school has done for their children

Monthly Friday teas for parents when school provides the cakes but 'doesn't overpower with teachers,' said mum. Later life reunions all over the place – Hong Kong the latest when checked bustling Facebook page (as well-tended as the grounds), though plenty of alumni stay don't move far away, careers covering eclectic range from surveyors to musicians and authors.

Entrance: Officially take into years 7 (40 places), 9 (20 places) and 12 (variable) but if there's space, will take at other times.

Warm-hearted, encouraging school. 'Not right for families who want everything in neat and tidy boxes,' thought mother

Majority of pupils from 10-mile radius though extending, Kingston and Horsham (as well as thriving metropolis of Nork) all now within reach thanks to extensive bus network (6.45am start for furthest flung locations). Micklefield, Downsend, Reigate St Mary's, Chinthurst, Aberdour, Priory Prep and Kingswood House among preps sending pupils, though no official feeders. Local primaries also well represented.

Exit: Many schools have much-trumpeted cohort who leave post-16, recognise error of ways and stage tearful prodigal son (and daughter) return, accepted with nary a 'we told you so'. Here, parent confirms it's the real McCoy with mother phoning Mr Lowde to ask if could have place back. 'Missed it so much.'

Other post-16 losses, often to local sixth form colleges, partially staunched but trickle will continue, think parents, as pupils cast off 360 degree care for grittier experiences elsewhere. 'Not a criticism of the school but tribute to confidence-building,' pointed out mother.

Of the 40 or so percent who stay on, university entrance for most, over 80 per cent to first choice, no Oxbridge currently (though one medic in 2017) but aiming for one or two a year – no special department as 'we're small enough to personalise timetable where needed.'

University of Arts, Westminster, Exeter, Bristol and Royal Holloway currently popular. Subjects include business, management and economics, regular contingent each year to art and music colleges including Central St Martins and Northern Royal College. In 2017, students off to Amsterdam, Navarra and Beijing.

Money matters: Generous support for deserving families whose income range isn't cosily clustered at top end of £ dial. Warmth of welcome and matter-of-fact help with bursary application process felt to speak volumes about school's ethos.

Remarks: Warm-hearted, encouraging school that's easily overlooked in favour of guarantees of undiluted top grades elsewhere. 'Not right for families who want everything in neat and tidy boxes,' thought mother. 'It's not draconian here. You're doing it because it's what you need to succeed.'

Brambletye School

13

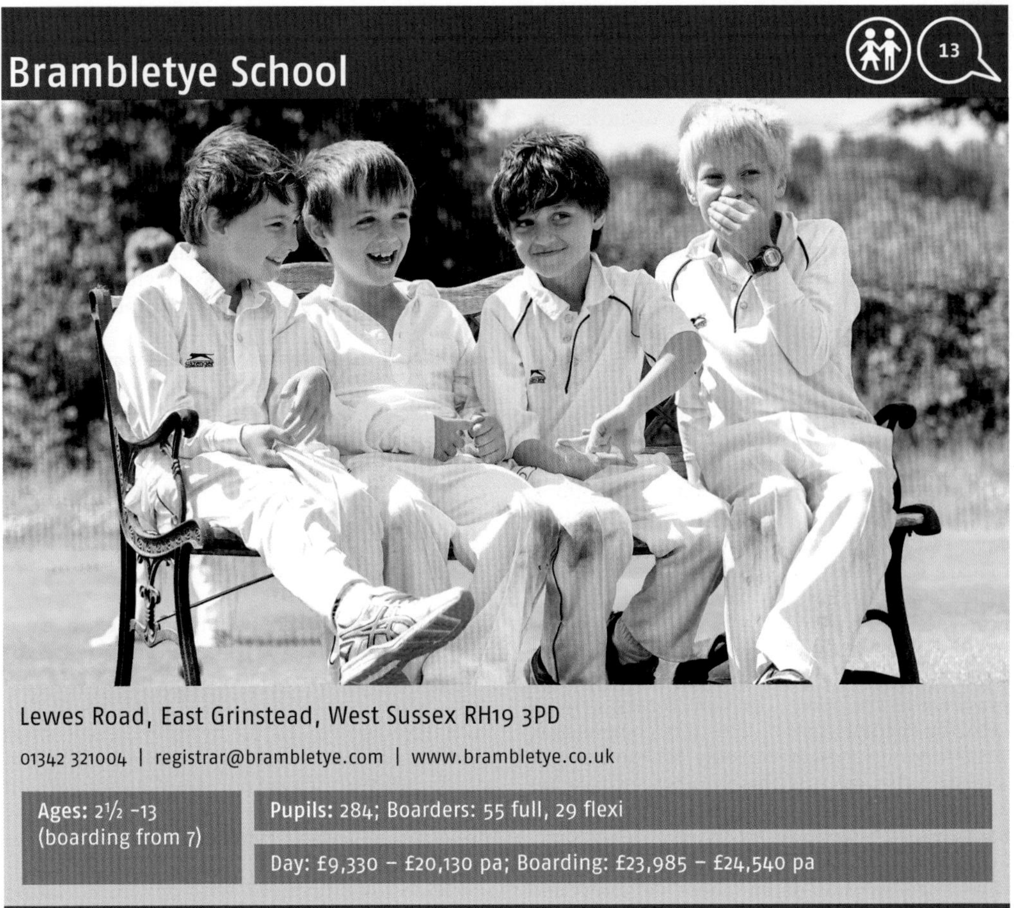

Lewes Road, East Grinstead, West Sussex RH19 3PD

01342 321004 | registrar@brambletye.com | www.brambletye.co.uk

Ages: 2½ -13 (boarding from 7)

Pupils: 284; Boarders: 55 full, 29 flexi

Day: £9,330 – £20,130 pa; Boarding: £23,985 – £24,540 pa

Headmaster: Since 2015, Will Brooks BA (Durham), in tweed and pink (Brambletye's colour). Started by teaching maths and English at Bruern Abbey, where he was promoted to deputy head, followed by two more deputy posts at Sunningdale and Port Regis; glad now to be in a cosy family school and determined to keep it that way: knows all the names, addresses groups with 'Hello rascals', and wants to extend childhood for as long as possible; encourages children to build dens in the woods, and when a child knocked on his door to say – 'come and see our den, we've just finished the second floor...', did so with alacrity...('children need make mistakes... but we're not reckless...').

Parents gush about Will and his wife Amelia: 'great having a younger team with loads of energy and ideas'; '[they've brought] new vitality to school...[they] really encourage the children'; Will and Amelia are 'extraordinary. Love their enthusiasm...endless energy...so passionate about what they do' and 'lots of time for us'.

Pupils approve too: 'nice and fun'; 'easy to talk to' and 'always involving us in his problems', said one to general hilarity of the rest, clarified to 'he wants our opinions about things' (and indeed has changed homework in response to criticism from pupils).

Entrance: Light touch assessment and interview.

Exit: Twenty-five scholarships in 2017. Children depart for a wide range of destinations, from Eton and King's Canterbury to Ardingly, Brighton College and Worth. Head emphasises the importance of children flying into the right senior school in the middle or top of the cohort.

Remarks: An old country retreat in the Sussex countryside with views over Ashdown Forest that stretch out into forever. Described by one parent who chose it over a place at a desirable London prep as a 'school in the woods' – 'how could any child not love it...[there are] trees to play in...' Inside, panelled walls, wood fires, a strolling sausage dog (Hercules) and comfy sofas. A stately home with pupils lounging happily by the fire, as if they were at home;

which, of course, they are, pupils telling us it feels like a 'big family'.

Academically 'a real mix of kids,' said a parent at the this lightly selective school. 'High expectations', said the head, 'but plenty of support if necessary'.

A pupil told us, 'it's different to other schools because the teachers help you so much', another saying, 'you can give your opinion... a different opinion is not wrong'. Special praise for the maths teacher who 'makes it really clear', and for IT, a parent commenting, 'it could be desperate, but it's fun and creative...' The Latin teacher rewards full marks with a turn on the zipwire – an effective incentive for most. Scholars learn Greek, all learn French, and the head has introduced Spanish for years 7 and 8, which will trickle down to lower years.

'No one slacks in year 8', said a pupil, 'you're too scared', but the head makes no assumptions; he has introduced 'how to revise' for pupils to engage with what they know, don't know, and how to learn most effectively: 'they won't all be up all night before their finals when they're 21', says the head ruefully.

Smart new labs following a recent refurbishment, with the academic space to one side, practical to the other. The new library, art and debating chamber space is due to be completed in 2019 (fundraising started in May 2017 and they're already half way), and the old library space has already been turned into classrooms with stray books hosted in English classrooms.

Communication is 'excellent', say parents, with a new website, parent zone, and effort and attainment grades fortnightly. 'If a child gets a C3, a member of staff will call to discuss'.

A flexible approach to those with different needs – 'excellent to all its students', said a parent, describing how her fidgety son in pre-prep was allowed sit under his desk provided he would listen. 'Beautifully managed, no-one bats an eyelid'. A pupil of high ability with poor writing skills and a need to move around sits on a movement cushion (as do several others), has pencil toppers and wrist things on which to chew, is being taught touch typing, has a scribe in the meantime and is, said his mum, treated as an individual. Bored with history, he has been given a special project on WW1 propaganda and time to discuss it with the head of history. '[They] accept pupils as they are...'.

Described by one parent who chose it over a place at a desirable London prep as a 'school in the woods' – 'how could any child not love it... trees to play in...'

Around 20 per cent of pupils have extra learning needs, and most learning support is free of charge, provided in small groups or in class support. Where one-to-one support is necessary, this is charged as an extra. The head says it's all about communication, and an appreciative parent told us that the learning support team have drawn up a learning passport for her son, which details how he works and feels and has been communicated to all teaching staff.

It's a long day here, with day pupils being dropped off at 8am, and picked up at 6pm, or 7.10pm if they have activities, but all work is completed at school (very popular with parents). Saturday school on alternate weekends, lessons in the morning, matches in the afternoon – 'allows it to be a proper boarding school...keeps it alive at weekends...', said a parent.

'Strong, nurturing care – confidence building', said a parent, describing how her nervous son has gained a natural sense of confidence through drama, music and giving presentations; another told us her children's senior schools have said children from Brambletye are 'not daunted'.

Changes to pastoral care under the current head. The traffic light system moves pupils with pastoral needs to an amber light, which kickstarts a process with their tutor, and gets parents involved. Tutors are 'very, very vigilant and know of children's niggles', said a parent, but children can also speak to a school listener, or a counsellor (the school even found a Chinese counsellor for a Chinese pupil who needed help).

Generally 'children respect each other and are kind', said a parent, fresh from helping with school trip to Lords, but when there are problems between children ('not really bullying, but unkindness', said a pupil), parents say they are dealt with quickly and throughly, one telling us her daughter's problems were dealt with 'sensitively and discreetly'. The school's approach, said a parent earnestly, is that the bully needs as much attention as the victim – they address the problem, rather than handing out punishments. 'You're always given a second chance', said a pupil.

Amelia is always standing outside to greet the children in the morning, notepad and pen in hand to jot down any concerns. 'I feel I can really trust the school – and thank God we're not in this alone as parents'.

Pupils take real pride in the house system with discipline minuses and credit pluses contributing to the inter-house contest – 'it really works, they take responsibility', said a parent. Pupils get to know everyone in their house – 'younger pupils do talk to us about upsets...or just anything,' said a year 8.

Children are not allowed phones, and are not bothered – 'we manage time better without them', said a pupil, but older children would like more daytime access to computers and email (windows and iPads are lesson specific). The head works hard to help pupils understand their digital footprint, recommending that if they wouldn't be happy to show their grandparents, they shouldn't post it.

A domestic and international boarding community includes pupils from Russia, France and Thailand. 'Many don't like the idea of boarding when they start, but come around to it', said a parent. 'It gives them a unique experience of comradery'. Flexi-boarding is available from year 3, and is used by many local parents, who like to be able to just pop in to school. Years 7 and 8 have to choose between weekly boarding (opting in or out of weekends as they wish) or day; most board, with just three of year 8 remaining day pupils.

Dormitories for up to nine with bunk beds, old and quirky rooms for boys, a modern wing for girls, but all recently refurbished to a high standard. The most extraordinary views to wake up to. All dorms named after flowers and trees, and thank goodness for a school that doesn't think it detracts from boys' masculinity to sleep in Tulip. Showers not baths. Boarders can use telephones and bank of iPads to Skype parents whenever they want. Houseparents or matron are close to all rooms for night problems – 'very nurturing...' said a parent. Bedtime for years 7 and 8 (8.50pm) was the cause of some disgruntled discussion – they really want that extra t10 minutes, the girls particularly telling us they need more time for ablutions.

Between 50-90 pupils stay at weekends, and enjoy trips out, such as go-karting or trampolining, or mucking around at school – a slope outside turns into a water slide in summer and snow slide on rugby tackle pads in winter.

No one goes hungry here – fruit is always available in the dining room, and 'grub' is available every evening until 8.30pm: toast, cereal, fruit, sandwiches. A parent told us how hard the school worked to help her fussy child to eat normally, emailing the parent every day with progress.

'Music and drama are exceptional', said a parent, describing the musicals in the school theatre as 'like West End productions' and an 'enormous pleasure'; another saying her child who didn't want to do a play was 'nearly jumping off the stage with enthusiasm'.

The standard of art here is exceptionally high for a prep school – 'amazing', said a parent, and they've had 180 art scholarships to senior schools in the last 20 years. 'Second to none, the teacher cares so much', said a parent whose unartistic son is slowly developing confidence and enjoyment.

Sport every day for an hour, and activities on top of this, although an extremely musical child who wanted more practice time for a music scholarship was allowed time off games – no rules for rules sake at this flexible school.

The ample grounds include a golf course, and pupils are very excited by the new Astro. The current swimming pool is not very large, but has full length glass doors which open onto the countryside – the new model will be bigger and have a concertina glass door.

'Not so many to pick from [for teams] but we punch above our weight', said a pupil, another adding, 'If you're good at sport it earns you enormous respect'.

Pupils get to know everyone in their house – 'younger pupils do talk to us about upsets...or just anything,' said a year 8

Girls have been in both cricket and football teams, and the first girl on the rugby team has apparently 'played a blinder' – but there's 'not been a boy in the rounders team', said a parent thoughtfully (although all pupils play in inter-house rounders). Hockey is now included on the curriculum for boys, who will soon play their first fixtures.

Pre-prep is described by a parent as 'so nurturing...a really safe space to hold the children as they grow'. Pupils have a great affection for their exceptional head – 'Mrs Atkinson, I love you a lot...' said a child, arms flung around her knees, and it's the first head we've seen invited on a sleepover.

Golden leaves for kindness fill a tree in the entrance hall and jewels are handed out for good work. Lots of time outside, pupils wearing their all weather muddy puddles. Growing boxes for each year (for outdoor maths), plants in wellies, two enormous rabbits (Moonbeam and Paddington) and a proper hobbit hole. A jolly nursery filled with happy busy tinies – 'George cries on the day he doesn't go to nursery', sighed a parent.

The head says Brambletye wouldn't suit a child with a flat learning curve, or one who never gives anything back – they need to engage with what's on offer. Parents thought reserved children might struggle, but pupils said that shy children will develop confidence, one year 8 telling us she was 'quite timid' in year 4, but 'it's small, everyone is welcoming and you get used to school quickly'.

Brighton College

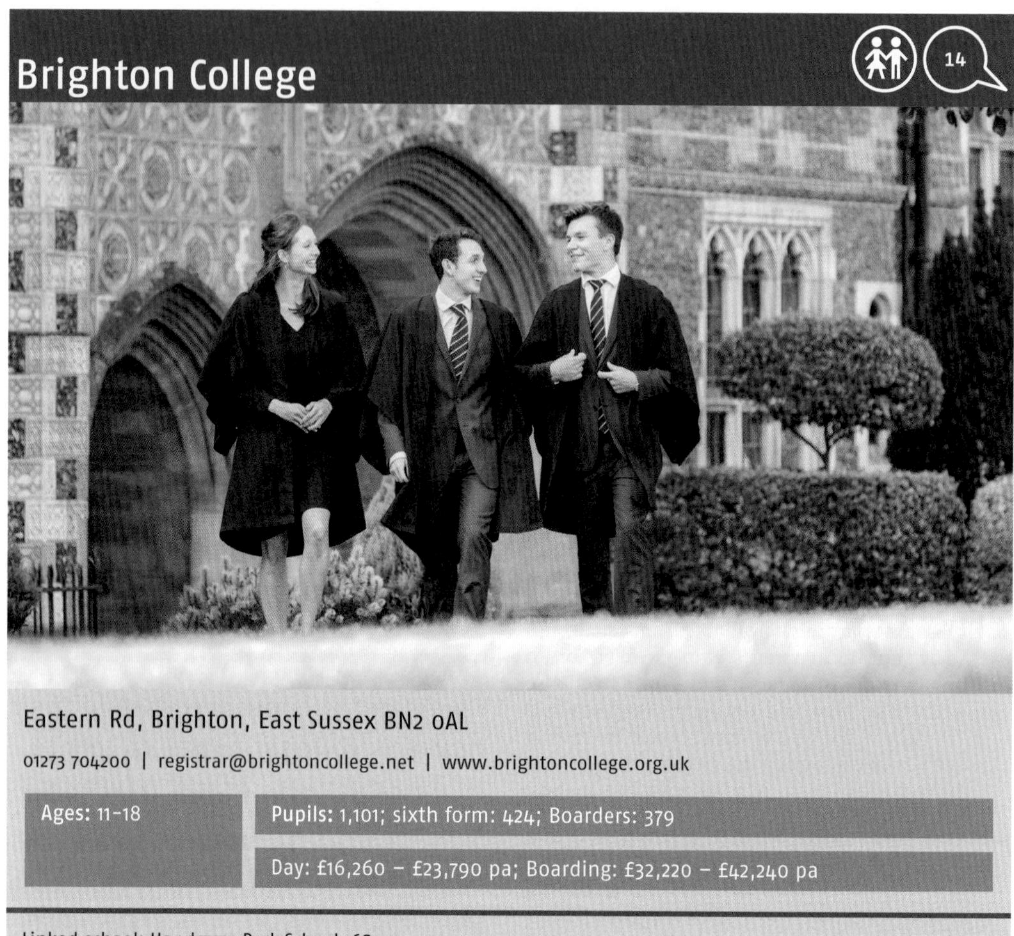

Eastern Rd, Brighton, East Sussex BN2 0AL

01273 704200 | registrar@brightoncollege.net | www.brightoncollege.org.uk

Ages: 11–18

Pupils: 1,101; sixth form: 424; Boarders: 379

Day: £16,260 – £23,790 pa; Boarding: £32,220 – £42,240 pa

Linked school: Handcross Park School, 680

Head master: Since 2006, Mr Richard Cairns MA (40s). Oxford history first. His path to Brighton was via a law firm in Australia, a Palestinian refugee camp, Stewart's Melville in Edinburgh, The Oratory in Reading and the deputy headship of Magdalen College School, Oxford. Staggering list of achievements/accolades includes the opening of Brighton College, Abu Dhabi; a rise from 147th to top 20 in the UK academic rankings; doubling boarding numbers; trebling applications; a huge new building programme; the acquisition of Roedean Junior and Handcross Park Prep Schools; ISI inspection report with outstanding in every category; The Sunday Times Independent School of the Year.

Keen not to take sole credit for this, he has built a teaching and management structure to ensure that ideas and initiatives can be sparked and grown – inside and outside the student body. This attitude is magnetic – for pupils, parents and staff. He sees himself and the college as a mix of tradition and modern – that was the design brief for the decorating team that were part of the recent revamp but it goes much deeper than the furnishings. 'I want every pupil to be who they want to be – as I say to them in assembly [pupils agree he does, and they remember it ...] "If I try to be him, who will be me?".'

Plenty of other schools try to tempt him away – the governors recently agreed a 10 week international trip, he says, 'to give me thinking time for the next seven years'. It was a global reconnaissance mission, visiting universities in the US and Canada as well as potential twin schools in Finland, Sweden, Singapore, Ontario and Hungary. Such symbiotic connections are characteristic of this head – and they appear to stem from a dedication to improving education wherever he can use his influence or initiative. He kicked off his tenure with compulsory Mandarin lessons but also connected with Kingsford, an East London school that was doing the same. Out of this link grew the London Academy of Excellence (LAE) in Stratford, East London, the first new sixth form free school academy in the country, helping children from disadvantaged backgrounds to get into university by making sure they pass the right A levels – with a powerful independent school sponsoring one of each of the major subjects eg Brighton College sponsors economics, Eton does English, Highgate does maths etc.

Has high expectations for his pupils, wanting them to be excited in the classroom. Teaches history to the fourth form. They report creative punishments from him for inattention eg writing a whole story about a turtle, or a poem about the girl the note was being passed to. Less formally, he has breakfast with the prefects and invites sixth formers to dinner. The pupils love getting to know the head in this way (one of seven children, he certainly knows how to cope with a large dinner table) and they discuss everything from divorce to cricket. He's not shy of involving the pupils in practicalities – from how much the new boarding developments cost to how much he would need to be sponsored to run the Big Balls relay for charity.

Academic matters: Shining results: in 2017, 87 per cent A*-A/9-7 at GCSE, 96 per cent A*-B and 76 per cent A*/A at A level; this is up with the best in London too. One of top value-added schools. Twenty-six subjects offered at A level. A 60/40 split arts/science at A level; biology, chemistry, economics and maths are particularly popular (the latter taken by about two-thirds of the pupils). About a quarter take four A levels. Outside speakers (John Major, Boris Johnson, Viv Richards, David Dimbleby, David Starkey, Jeremy Paxman, Michael Gove, Matt Prior..) visit in a Wednesday afternoon slot. Each department runs both a course-specific and a general Oxbridge activity, which obviously pays off, with a record number of pupils heading up to Oxford or Cambridge.

Staff are sparky and motivated – attracted by the charms of 'London by the sea' and being part of a school that's going up and up. An appraisal system is at the heart of the classroom: pupils fill in an online questionnaire on each teacher which gets fed back to the head of department, who in turn gives a summary to the director of studies. Quirky and effective teaching is respected by the pupils – whether it is their Mandarin teacher throat singing on YouTube or a video of a worked through past paper available for maths A level revision. The Story of Our Land course combines history, geography, philosophy and religion for the third form who, when talking about an invasion force coming over the cliff, study the geography of that cliff or debate the merits of the Muslim or Christian standpoint while looking at the Crusades.

No Saturday morning school means that everyone has a full weekend and the chance to be part of the town instead of just being educated within it

Languages popular, not just through the Mandarin innovation – compulsory in the pre-prep since 2007 and now a GCSE option (mostly A* grades so far), with graduate students from Chinese universities to assist – but also Latin, French, Spanish, Russian, Italian, German and Greek. The burgeoning Mandarin option is a USP, with the school being awarded Confucius Institute status by the Chinese Government as a centre of excellence for the teaching of the language – the first such honour for a UK school. The school-wide recommendation of only nine academic GCSEs (with at least one other being artistic or creative) encourages a good balance between academic and extracurricular – as does lesson time between 8.30am and 4pm being sacrosanct, enabling an extra five hours a week for music, sport or dance.

All new pupils attend a literacy class and the dyslexia centre is nationally famous, specifically helping around five per cent of pupils. English is taught within the centre (instead of a second modern language) for years 7-11 in small groups, individual help available in sixth form. Taking complete control of English makes a huge difference, removing embarrassment and stress. School actively seeks out and welcomes the bright child with dyslexia, dyspraxia or dyscalculia. Entry based on recent education plan report, CE assessment morning (observed in groups) and interviews by head and excellent head of centre. Approximately 50 taught in centre, also supports the prep school students. Group work means that children become fantastically supportive of one another, concentration on remediation with younger ones and study skills with older. Time to finish tasks is not an issue – a good end product motivates students.

The bright library has a mezzanine level used for quiet working space for the sixth form frees. Dedicated sixth form centre also has computers but is generally more social. Comprehensive intranet with update alerts sent by email and text. Saturday morning revision classes on offer in the holidays, mostly to boost confidence before exams. Class sizes average 18 up to GCSE; after GCSE, the average is eight.

Games, options, the arts: Year groups of 150 and everyone has to do dance, PE and drama. House drama, house song and up to 15 different productions a year (including visiting companies, A level and GCSE performances and Commedia dell'Arte). Dance achieves nearly 100 per cent A*/A at A level and at GCSE happens in performing arts studio completed in 2000 (outside classes offered to the community). Six-strong faculty teaches over 70 dance classes a week. Examinations in ballet, modern, tap and jazz, and the school boasts boys' street dance, modern and tap groups from junior to senior level. The Montague studio is two minutes' walk away.

New music school. Half of the pupils have individual music lessons, from more than 40 visiting music teachers; 22 music groups: choirs, orchestra, rock groups, concert band and various chamber groups, with participation in the National Chamber Music Competition as well as tours to Prague and Moscow. Ex-parents miss going to the performances.

Two hugely popular and innovative sixth form house competitions stem from the entrepreneurship programme and Strictly Come Dancing. The former gets academics and creatives developing a business plan together, each team competing to win £3,000 to commercialise their idea – previous winners have been a parking app and a device to stop babies knocking hot tea over. Strictly ensures boys are valued for more than just sport – the biggest applause in Monday morning assemblies goes to most unconventional achievements.

Cricket for both sexes a great strength – three former pupils have gone on to play for England women's team

Purpose-built spaces for art, photography and DT make for beautiful art and design – there are still some lessons when the pupils watch a video for low maintenance inspiration but the proof of the art is hanging on walls around the campus.

Sport is enormously important here, all pupils taking part in games twice a week – rounders, netball, tennis, cricket, swimming and rugby possible on campus, otherwise it's a minibus to the college's Jubilee Ground, with six rugby pitches or two cricket grounds, further floodlit netball courts, a pavilion and three hockey Astroturfs nearby. Withdean's athletics stadium also hosts fixtures; each weekend sees some 300-400 children involved in competitive matches. National trophies in rugby (1st XV has particularly strong record of victories in Sussex) and netball (Sussex champions and national finalists), and leads the county in athletics. Cricket for both sexes a great strength – three former pupils have gone on to play for England women's team.

Community service a vital part of school life: pupils visit elderly people and help disabled children or teach pensioners how to use a computer; Make a Difference Day (MADD) sees every member of the college serving the community in more than 100 different activities, from cleaning beaches and clearing scrub to sorting clothes for charity. School raises money for local charities (including Whitehawk Inn, Rockinghorse, Chestnut Tree House) and those further afield (Romania, Kenya, Sri Lanka, India).

Boarding: Weekly boarding extremely popular – no Saturday school; many go straight home after Saturday morning matches. Full-time boarders can avoid the school curfew at the weekend if they stay with local families who take responsibility. Pupils can return from home by 9.30pm on a Sunday night or on a Monday morning – buses from outlying towns.

Five boarding houses for years 9-13 – two for girls and three for boys – plus a junior boarding house for 11-13 year olds at Handcross Prep and a new co-ed sixth form boarding house. Plenty of inter-house competitions, plus lectures, debates, music evenings, quizzes etc, and the after-school use of all facilities eg swimming pool and art department.

Background and atmosphere: Compact campus in Kemp Town, just four blocks from the sea front. Imposing buildings purpose-built in 1840s by Gilbert Scott (designer of St Pancras Station and the Albert Memorial). The school has spent £35 million in the past five years on an award-winning School of Design and Technology and teaching block for English, language suites, two boarding houses, two sports pavilions and an award winning Smith Café, where boarders can meet in the evening, health centre and staff common room. The most popular part of this are the places where the boys and girls get to hang out casually together instead of signing in and out of each other's boarding houses.

Sited to the east of the landmark pier and pavilion, the school succeeds in being fashionable, practical and innovative – no Saturday morning school means that everyone has a full weekend and the chance to be part of the town instead of just being educated within it. This could put some parents off, since Brighton and Hove, like many seaside cities, has its fair share of addicts, drunks and loons. However, we've heard no disturbing reports and most sensible local parents realise that their children are going to come to Brighton at the weekend anyway and it is far better that they feel comfortable in their favourite cafés, bars and shops rather than loitering round Churchill Square.. Officially, there is a square patch of Kemp Town streets where pupils can stroll for 20 minutes of an afternoon, in a group, as long as they sign out. However, some definitely sneak a walk to the beach – they feel it's their right considering the prospectus proudly features pupils enjoying this out of bounds place.

Pupils are thoughtful and articulate – we visited on the day of Margaret Thatcher's funeral and got into a discussion with a group of 13 year olds about whether people would dislike her so much if she had been a man who had implemented the same policies. The head picks an individual each Monday to share a random act of kindness in assembly – this type of awareness is at root of the school's ethos which goes a fair way to balancing the social mix here. As in all schools, cliques could be found if you looked for them but the most popular are not necessarily the richest or prettiest; difference is respected and often admired. The pupils are aware that they are privileged. Has now scrapped its uniform code for 11-16 year olds in favour of a 'skirt uniform' and 'trouser uniform', with either sex able to wear either. The sixth form wear smart business-like clothes with some restrictions that are flouted when girls fancy tottering on high heels. They can drive themselves into school but must use street parking – high council charges are unpopular, with parents driving to attend chapel as well.

School benefits from a sense of the outside world, whether through exchanges with schools in Russia, Africa, America and Australia, the perspective offered by pupils from an inner-city school or the opportunity to twist their tongues round a year's worth of Mandarin Chinese. Link with Kingsford Community School in Newham, East London, beginning with heads' shared desire to make Mandarin mandatory, has grown into an HSBC sponsorship of three Newham pupils' education in Brighton for a year. Sixth formers buddy up with pupils at the London Academy of Excellence and share study tips via Facebook (boarders allowed 10 minute slots) and email.

Brilliant enrichment days for Gifted and Talented at local primaries – practical lessons in science labs, language work and unique experience of a senior school

The chapel, just big enough for the whole school, used three or four times a week for secular and multi-faith assemblies as well as Christian ones. Tradition still holds firm here (the oldest public school in Sussex) with the heads of school taking it in turns to sit alone in a pew, yet the chaplain is entertaining and eccentric – a new hymnal was an opportunity to get each house to prepare a song and belt it out in competition.

Pastoral care, well-being and discipline: As the head comments, this is 'a town school that is part of the real world, not apart from it'. At the beginning of every term he reiterates the ground rules on theft, bullying and beyond: expulsion and no second chances is the line on drugs and the security at the school gates is tight, yet cheery.

Report emailed home every three weeks and there are parent meetings – although some parents report not much time for parent feedback. Those needing the most help definitely get it – those who are motivated enough to dance between options will attract it too.

Head of lower school and the headmaster meet every registered pupil in their own school before they enter Brighton College. This reduces the fear of attending a new school and gives the pastoral staff a heads-up on what house and friendship group might suit a newbie. The little ones arrive three days before the rest of school and go on a treasure hunt to help them get their bearings. The transition to the upper school is another focus point for the empathetic head of lower school – moving from being one of 40 to one of 150 under the shared care of tutors and houseparents.

Food available in the Smith Café and Café de Paris below the dance studio – and the houses all have kitchens for an emergency stack of toast for a starving teenage boy

One lower school house and 13 others when the post-common entrance cohort enter, 325 boarding and 650 day – about 70 children in each so a good chance to develop cross year relationships. All of the youngest year in each senior school house share a tutor – as pupils grow they are matched with another for GCSEs and then A levels. Majority of housemasters and housemistresses are married and parents report incredible empathy for the fall-out from tricky family and financial situations. Pupils learn how to iron a shirt, sew on a button and hold their own at a dinner party through house activities – really useful preparation for university admission and beyond.

Any bullying is dealt with speedily and with emotional intelligence – no homophobia or racism, some teasing but real respect for individuality. Two options at meals and dishes containing wheat are labelled, the school is nut free. Food is also available in the Smith Café and Café de Paris below the dance studio – and the houses all have kitchens for an emergency stack of toast for a starving teenage boy.

Pupils and parents: A great social mix from the children of butchers to highbrow TV presenters, successful entrepreneurs and a smattering of Conservative MPs; 33 per cent boarding, most weekly but seven per cent overseas (five per cent Asian). Lower school just under 50 per cent from Brighton state schools, also many from London schools that stop at 11. Head ensures that useful parent contacts are wound into life of school in way that benefits both – from Leon providing soup recipes for sidelines at matches to a stylist helping with a fashion show. No Saturday school (weekly boarders can leave Friday 4pm, return Monday am) is popular with parents. School buses from towns ranging from Crowborough to Eastbourne with express services for weekly boarders Friday evening and Monday morning from Tunbridge Wells and Chichester. Pupils are cheerful, enthusiastic, friendly and polite and have an easy, relaxed relationship with teachers – at the top end of the school they feel part of a wider community; again, good preparation for life outside.

Entrance: Eleven plus entry via maths, English and verbal reasoning tests. Dynamic head of lower school has worked hard to build brilliant enrichment days for Gifted and Talented at local primaries – practical lessons in science labs, language work and unique experience of a senior school. All of this very attractive alternative to Brighton state school ballots.

Pre-test assessment for 13+ entry; CE pass mark now 60 per cent – whether from coming from prep school or externally – with a minimum of 55 per cent in English and maths. Emotional intelligence used in assessment of intake for Brighton College Prep so a maximum of five out of 60 each year do not go through to the college – they must be the bright side of average or they will not be happy here – and those who disrupt the learning of others won't fit in either. Around 45 from the prep join 40 already in the lower school. Seventy more from 54 other preps including St Christopher's, Hove and Handcross (now run by Brighton College).

Around 70 new pupils at sixth form (at least B/6 grades at GCSE are essential), mostly from Burgess Hill, Brighton and Hove High School, Eastbourne, Hurst and Lancing.

Exit: A handful after GCSEs to local sixth form colleges, almost always for financial reasons. One hundred per cent of A level leavers to university. Twenty-five to Oxbridge in 2017, and 13 medics; UCL, KCL, Bristol, Imperial, Durham, Manchester, Exeter and Leeds all popular. Five off to the US in 2017, one to Hong Kong (medicine) and one to Canada. Famous Old Brightonians, including Peter Mayle (writer), Lord Alexander of Weedon (lawyer and banker), Lord Skidelsky (historian and politician), Laurie Penny (writer), David Nash (sculptor), Matt Prior and Holly Colvin (cricketers), Sir John Chilcot (chairman of the Iraq Inquiry), Sir Michael Hordern (actor) and Jonathan Palmer (racing driver), testify to range of successful careers which may ensue.

Money matters: At a recent open morning, parents were wondering about what extras Brighton College might offer to justify its fees being higher than rival local schools' despite its limited campus space – half an hour later they were totally sold, having been treated to a Commedia dell'Arte take on the drama, a taste of Strictly Come Dancing by sixth formers and the heads of schools speaking about the high quality lessons. Many parents struggle to pay the fees but bursaries and up to

20 academic awards (5-50 per cent off basic fees), five music scholarships (up to 30 per cent off), art, drama, dance, sport, chess and all-rounder awards (up to 25 per cent off) and a DT scholarship (up to 15 per cent off) are available.

Registration fee and hefty deposits for accepting an offered place, into five figures for overseas boarders. Only refundable if pupils don't pass the entrance exam. Deposits retained to cover extras charged in arrears, balance refunded on exit from the school.

Extras include dyslexia support and EAL tuition.

Remarks: Happy, broad-minded town school for children and families who are keen on learning – producing fantastic results and sparkling individual success stories. Pupils are encouraged to achieve as much as they can, so you'd never be bored, but you could end up with too much on. Bold ideas fostered in student, staff and parent body, all the while anchoring the opportunities enabled by the fees in real world experience. Detractors of the school (often parents of ex-pupils at the prep or pre-prep) see it as too results focused, with some families turning to outside tutoring to enable their children to get into the college. Raising of CE pass mark to 60 per cent fuel for the fire of those who judge the school to be top-slicing to climb the results ladder, explained transparently by the school as a tool to manage the high volume of applications.

Burgess Hill Girls

15

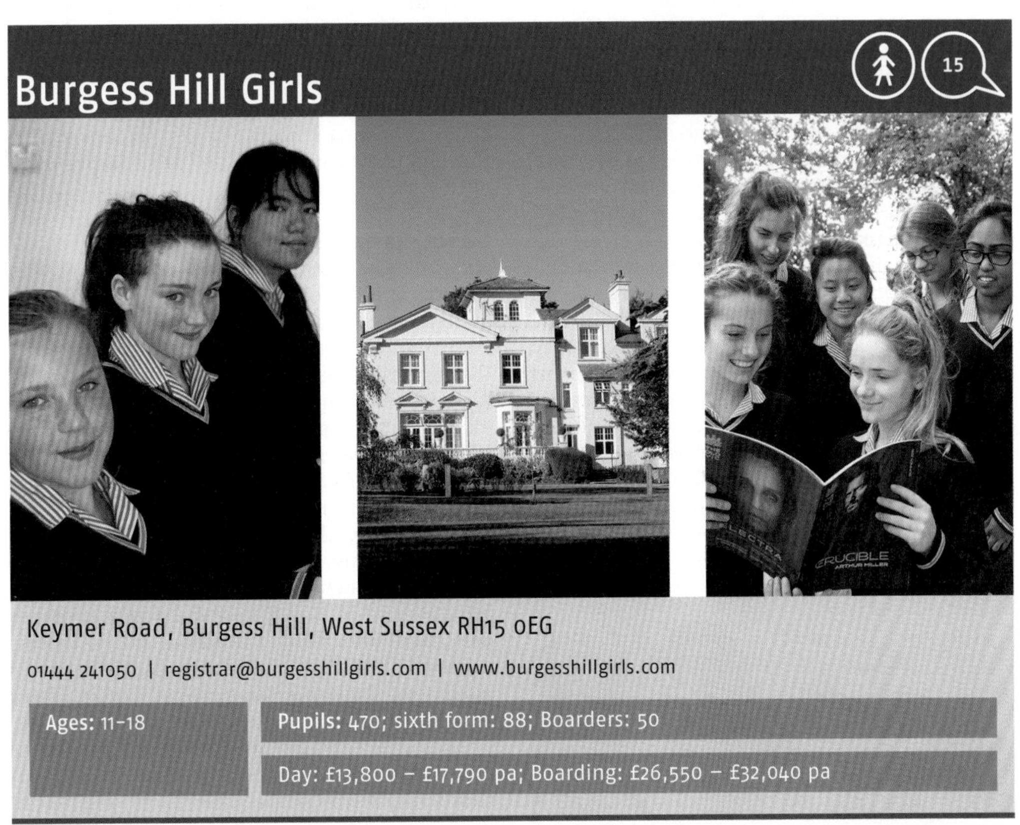

Keymer Road, Burgess Hill, West Sussex RH15 0EG

01444 241050 | registrar@burgesshillgirls.com | www.burgesshillgirls.com

Ages: 11–18

Pupils: 470; sixth form: 88; Boarders: 50

Day: £13,800 – £17,790 pa; Boarding: £26,550 – £32,040 pa

Head: Since 2017, Liz Laybourn BEd, previously interim head after the retirement of the previous head due to ill health. BEd in physical education and maths and masters in educational leadership. She joined the school as a newly qualified teacher in 1986 and became deputy head in 2006.

Academic matters: Generally excellent results; 42 per cent A*/A at A level in 2017. Parents are very satisfied with their children's progress. Consistent achievement at GCSE, with 64 per cent A*-A/9-7 in 2017.

GCSE maths and IGCSE science are high performers, alongside success in English, humanities and the arts. A good variety of mostly traditional subjects, with plenty of languages, both ancient and modern. Lovely language suite built in 2013, with laptops which rise from the desk lid when required. A pupil was awarded a gold medal at the International Linguistics Olympiad, which included a four hour challenge translating the Universal Declaration of Human Rights from Armenian into English.

Small class sizes in sixth form (3-12) mean the girls have plenty of attention in class. Around 40 per cent of entries at A level are in science, maths and technology, and girls achieve excellent results in these subjects, with plenty of experience in using them: 'engineering experience day made me realise that engineering is not just about fixing things but about being creative and making a difference'. There's also an engineering education scheme, in which lower sixth pupils have a seven month project working alongside a company.

Good results in many other areas, including PE, media studies and textiles, and although one parent commented that the range of subjects on offer at A level is not extensive, she was satisfied that the it was best for her daughter to concentrate on 'bread and butter' subjects now: she could always specialise at university. 'Traditional values and methods here,' she added. Traditional values clearly do matter here; but this school comes across as modern and engaged. Value added is carefully monitored using CEM, which shows that GCSE performance is on average one grade higher than of children of a similar ability: girls certainly thrive academically here.

There's a good mix of male and female staff, and the dedication of these teachers is, parents say, extraordinary. Extra clinics and one-on-one support means no one falls behind – one parent described how her daughter received extra help in science, running over things whilst others were at registration. Pupils say it's easy to ask for help.

There's a new focus on SEND, until recently ad hoc in different rooms, but now in a dedicated

Creative arts events for all to enjoy – 'they don't choose the in-your-face confident girls to do everything here', said a parent approvingly

room. Parents who have used the SEND provision say it very good, and are pleased that the support in small group sessions (in English, maths and science) is free of charge. (One-one is charged as an extra, as it uses outside support.)

A beguilingly named head of futures advises on A levels, university and careers, and will go over personal statements umpteen times until just right. There's lots of careers advice, and parents are encouraged to participate in 'take your daughter to work day' – all part of the head's drive to get the girls out there.

Decent size library, open 8.30am-6.05pm. Super computers sunk into the desks, screens visible through transparent desk top, key boards pulled out for use as required.

Games, options, the arts: Both curriculum sports and clubs available to all, regardless of ability, with fixtures at all levels. There's one field on site for athletics and rounders, lovely pavilion, five floodlit hard netball courts, also used for tennis, and floodlit Astroturf. The gym is old, but light and well kept. Facilities are not quite as extensive as parents might like, but on site expansion limited by site. Size of facilitates is no predictor of success: teams here do very well, girls saying being a small school means that they get more time from coaches. The girls excel at netball, hockey, athletics, rounders and horse riding.

Girls enthuse about extracurricular sports for all ethos at lunchtime, with clubs in badminton, ultimate frisbee, and fitness and dance. If there's demand of an activity, the school will do its best to provide: polo club started recently. School buses pupils to Ardingly reservoir for water sports and uses excellent local facilities for swimming and hockey.

Rare weekend fixtures means girls have the time to join local clubs, and girls like the fact that those busy with competitions have ring-fenced time to catch up with their academic work.

Creative arts events for all to enjoy – 'they don't chose the in-your-face confident girls to do everything here', said a parent approvingly. Busy drama and music departments, with regular productions ranging from Euripedes to Playhouse Creatures (a play about the struggles of actresses in a men's world). A big musical every year, last year The Shot Heard Round the World – written, composed and directed by three girls in upper sixth (one of the girls is now at Berkeley USA studying music and song writing). Croft II Drama was built onto the hall in 2013, a circular soundproof room with good acoustics which serves as a drama studio, recital room and place for parents to mingle during the interval of events held in the hall. The hall was refurbished at the same time, the (underused) stage removed and replaced with removal flooring, and stadium seating for 300 installed, which can fold back into a huge wooden wall.

Art is housed in a prefab block with a flat roof (bane of the bursar's life), surprisingly light around the edges, with a dedicated room for sixth formers, who can leave work undisturbed. The darker, but well lit space towards the centre of the building houses the exhibition of excellent A level and GCSE work.

Textiles are taken seriously here, and it's a very successful department. Material here is used for anything and everything, from the practical making of device cases for laptops, to a handbag styled like a pocket watch, with an opening clock face (the maker winning national handbag designer of the year aged just 15).

Plenty of extracurricular, from law society and public speaking to D of E and Young Enterprise. But, the girls say, if don't want to be busy, that's fine. OMG here (not the expletive – Only Motivated Girls), but 'in our own particular little ways'.

Boarding: Boarders live in one of the two elegant Edwardian boarding houses, which house girls of mixed ages. Alongside full and weekly boarding, there are two flexi boarding spaces. Boarding available from year 7 upwards, occasionally year 6 depending on the maturity of the child.

Most boarders are from overseas (Hong Kong and China), with around eight nationalities in total (no wish to increase overseas numbers, says the school). One parent told us he would prefer boarding to be less of an overseas service; but it has meant his daughter has a best friend from Madrid and a desire to learn Mandarin.

Describes as a day school with boarding, and this felt like the case. The boarding house we visited felt quiet: the girls don't return to houses during the day, so there's not the busy to and through evident in many big boarding schools. But boarders are very happy here, and call the houses home. One parent told us, 'The care and attention from the staff is exemplary. I feel my daughter is extremely well looked after'; another, that 'boarding has had a huge and positive effect'.

Inviting trellis covers the entrance to a boarding house; inside, a comfortable common room with TV, table football, books and games; kitchen with fruit and cereal always available. Games room, with a church pew to perch on – makes lingering games seem unlikely – and large screen in front, also used for dancing with the Wii. One of the messiest rooms we have ever seen, but we are told this is unusual, and a reward scheme is in place to encourage tidiness. Fresh decoration, with bathrooms recently redecorated and deep cleaned.

If parents are late picking up day girls, they simply go over to the boarding house. Burgess Hill Girls is well situated in town, so if boarders haven't got a club, they may go into town in small groups after school. Supervised prep, then down time in the boarding house until bedtime, with years 7-9 handing in electronic devices before lights out at 10pm. Wifi is turned off at midnight and comes back on at 6am. Boarders contact home via Skype or internet phone, with the office phone or computer available as back up.

An immediate sense of safety and seclusion. But the girls here are not cosseted; school feels it is important to 'get the girls out there' – and they are out there a lot

Activities organised for each weekend, both trips and on site activities, compulsory for year 7-10. Ideas for activities come from the girls. There is a suggestion box, a weekly discussion between pupils and catering; and although parents told us the quality of evening meals is not the same as lunches, the school say suggestions for changes to food are acted on immediately.

Background and atmosphere: Set back from the road in a leafy suburb of large houses and big old trees; we had to peer up driveway to be sure it was the right place – planning permission is being sought for an 'illuminated totem' (a bright sign you can see from the road) and new entrance railing. Buildings are a mixture of old Victorian villas and modern, with a slightly colonial feel; beautifully kept grounds, encircled by trees gives an immediate sense of safety and seclusion. But the girls here are not cosseted; school feels the most important thing is to 'get the girls out there' – and they are out there a lot.

Entry through glass doors, a large navy sign fronted with gold chairs, and a vertical radiator. Everything about the entrance says up to date. Parents describe the buildings as 'clean, crisp and fresh.' Decor inside varies from swish purpose built to elderly, with recently refurbished areas in blue and gold; a blue stripy carpet that makes you feel as if you are in a mathematical game with lines which sway and lift your path. Traditional moments though: portraits of heads decorate an old staircase, much like 10 Downing St.

The food is tasty, agree the girls, and the chef takes on board suggestions from the box in the dining hall. There are old fashioned school desks filled with fruit (described in several languages), a spoon and fork clock, and a good selection of food, to which soup is added midway through the autumn term. In the annual poverty lunch, pupils lunch on soup, with one piece of bread and a piece of fruit: a reminder of how fortunate they are.

The lower sixth set off at sunset to walk across the downs to reach Beachy Head by sunrise, dressed up for the occasion as nuns, football players and pirates

Most of the parents we spoke to were not specifically looking for a single sex school, but chose Burgess Hill Girls because it was school they liked most –'it felt the most authentic', said one; 'plain speaking', said another. The school believes being away from boys allows girls room to develop, to be themselves – and the necessary strength, resilience and broad shoulders to cope and be the best in a male dominated world. The girls we spoke to agreed; one girl who came from a mixed sex school said she was not afraid to shine here – 'boys interrupt,' she added. Parents feel girls here don't get shouted down or belittled by boys; and although one admitted her daughter did find life at university a bit of a shock, she added that the sixth formers are well prepared, and have workshops on everything...including boys.

Girls here are encouraged to step out of their comfort zones: on Roche days, twice a year, pupils spend a day pushing their boundaries – we saw a group learning to plaster, patiently working their way up four columns planted in the lawn (no chance of contamination, with hooded plastic space suits and plastic goggles). Roche day ends listening to motivational businesswomen, encouraging the girls to take risks to succeed.

Other activities are designed to practise business rapport, and networking breakfasts are organised by the girls. There are plenty of trips out, from Greece to the Old Bailey; and the lower sixth annual challenge to race the sun, setting off at sunset to walk across the downs to reach Beachy Head by sunrise, dressed up for the occasion as nuns, football players and pirates; the nuns, appropriately, treating everyone to highlights from the Sound of Music on the way.

Kilt and pinstripe uniform, with sixth formers in suits.

'I am, I can, I ought, I will' are the words of the school motto, and they pop up all over the place. There is a strong moral tone about this non-denominational school, with a focused time to reflect on moral messages during a period of silence on arrival and departure from assembly, and healthy links with the local community. This is one of the few schools we have visited which views community service as an essential part of life balance, alongside academic work and play, rather than an optional extra, and it appears in many areas of life at Burgess Hill: from raising money for local charities, to holding an annual pamper day for local carers, and helping children with their reading at a local primary school. Sixth formers raised money for a local nursery and helped set up its Facebook page, while year 10 held a workshop to make bags for hospice patients to hold medication. The whole school takes part in the Sports Relief Mile, and on an international level, the school supports Plan – a charity to raise the profile of girls across the world who do not have access to education.

Pastoral care, well-being and discipline: Parents say the staff work 24/7 for the girls 'above and beyond the call of duty'. 'If you send an email saying you're worried about something, you'll be at school at 8am the next morning chatting about it'. The school is excellent at keeping in touch, and parents emphasis the all round care – one described how she was chatting to a teacher about her worries about her daughter's anxiety, and the next day received a handwritten card through the post suggesting websites that might help. Girls agreed that they all knew who they would go to with a problem, from the head to favourite teachers, or the nurse (much loved by all). Sixth form mentors help younger girls, and all girls meet their teacher mentor every fortnight, to discuss work and anything else.

Bullying is dealt with straight on, and rapidly, said a parent. Both parties received counselling, and, most importantly to the parent, her daughter was taught strategies for dealing with bullies.

The honesty of this school is much appreciated by parents, who feel that problems here are dealt with head on: they are very engaged with the problems that can assail girls, and often make their appearance in years 9 and 10 – for example, obsession with image and being skinny, and rare instances of self harm. 'They are right on it', said a parent. A comprehensive drugs policy exists, with every girl treated as an individual and every situation independently assessed before decisions are made.

This feels like a place where a high standard of behaviour is expected, and by and large adhered to by the girls. Parents felt that poor conduct is very unlikely and would be much more of an issue here than poor performance.

A lively house system; though a little strange, you might think, for a modern girls' school to name its houses after dead male poets. A little bit of left over tradition, says the head. Lots of inter-house competition throughout the year, from public speaking, chess and sports, to performing arts day.

Pupils and parents: Parents are a mix of wealthy and not: city professionals, businesspeople, and working several jobs to keep their girls at Burgess Hill. Some are competitive – 'keen to ensure their daughters are achieving and being seen to achieve'.

Parents receive a grade sheet for attainment and attitude to learning every half term. Year 10s upwards receive working at and working towards grades as well. Two parents' evenings and one full report per year.

The school bus service is popular – a year 6 girl described her bus driver as one of the nicest things about school. It covers eight routes around Sussex every morning, children coming from as far afield as Horsham, Crawley and Uckfield. Each route is offered in the morning and twice after school, with an early bus at 4.00pm and a late bus at 6.15pm. Drop off is a bit tricky; cars can drive in, through, and out, but it gets congested, and many parents drop off at the road outside. School is three minutes walk from Burgess Hill station, and just 45 minutes by train from London.

Communication with parents is excellent, and there's no prolonged email back and forth with parents: the school encourages teachers to invite parents with a concern or issue to come in, or pick up the phone.

Notable former pupils include Holly Willoughby, television presenter, Kim Sears (Mrs Andy Murray) and Caroline Atkins, former international cricketer.

Entrance: Most senior school entrants (80 per cent last year) come from the junior school, though this is not automatic. A good number also from local state primaries and preps in the south east and London. Skype interviews for overseas students.

Exit: No one has had to leave in the last few years due to poor GCSE results. This school emphasises personalised education, and will create a programme to suit the needs of a pupil who got weak grades at GCSE, to include resitting key GCSEs, and close monitoring of progress.

To a range of destinations in 2017 from history at LSE to game art at De Montfort to marine biology at Exeter to economics at British Columbia. One vet (Sussex).

Money matters: No charge for pre and after-school care, from 8am-6pm, including breakfast. Academic, music, art, sport and drama scholarships, up to 40 per cent of fees, awarded at 11+,13+ and 16+. A number of significant bursaries (which do not take account of academic standard). Great value for money, say parents. 'The John Lewis of education,' says the school.

Remarks: This nurturing school puts time and thought into finding the best in each girl. Its excellent academic standards do not make it intellectually exclusive – parents felt it would suit all sorts, one saying that it suited both her very academic daughter, and the one whose talents were more middle of the road.

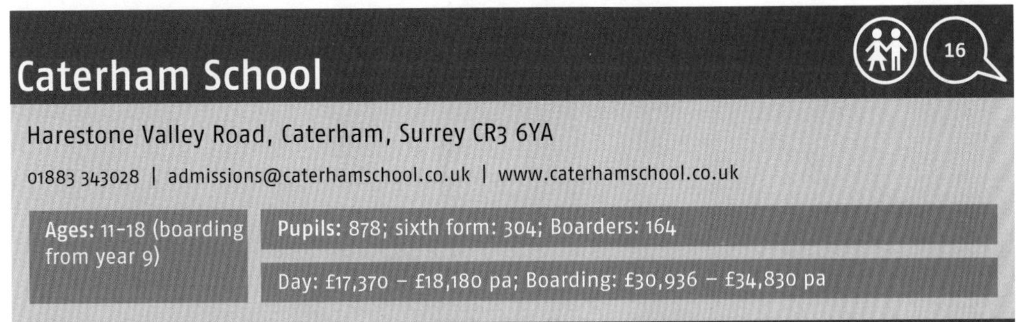

Caterham School

16

Harestone Valley Road, Caterham, Surrey CR3 6YA

01883 343028 | admissions@caterhamschool.co.uk | www.caterhamschool.co.uk

Ages: 11–18 (boarding from year 9)

Pupils: 878; sixth form: 304; Boarders: 164

Day: £17,370 – £18,180 pa; Boarding: £30,936 – £34,830 pa

Headmaster: Since 2015, Mr Ceri Jones (40s). Attended Nab Wood Grammar (now the Samuel Lister Academy) in Bradford, which had already turned comprehensive by the time he started, then read history at Fitzwilliam College Cambridge. Went into teaching straightaway because he loved his subject. Began his career at Godolpin & Latymer, then Bancroft's, then joined Caterham as head of history. Left to take up post as housemaster at Tonbridge, where he stayed for 11 years. During that time he rose to become deputy head, and was seconded to run the Marsh Academy in the Romney Marshes. Returned to Caterham because he liked the quiet confidence of the students – 'they were all very different, very assured, but not arrogant.' Married to Kay Moxon, head of politics at Tonbridge, and they have two daughters.

Unlike many heads we meet with similarly glittering credentials (he has a masters in educational leadership), Mr Jones impresses as a very human headteacher with his feet firmly on the ground. With his kindly energy and soft-spoken manner, he is clearly popular with parents. 'An excellent head, and a very clear and intelligent thinker,' said one; 'he is definitely a doer, and we can all see positive changes and improvements.' 'We really appreciate that he's passionate about education being holistic, and not all about academic achievement,' said another. Manages to fit in some football in his spare time (he played for Cambridge), still teaches A level history. Runs the Accelerate and Access Foundation, a charity which helps bright children from disadvantaged backgrounds in the south east.

Has no wish to change the ethos and values of the school, but is a skilled moderniser – he introduced the policy of issuing all Caterham students with iPads.

Academic matters: Impressive. In 2017 85 per cent A*-A/9-7 at GCSE, and at A level 90 per cent A*/B and two-thirds A*/A, putting it comfortably in the top 100 independent schools in the country.

Class sizes in first three years around 20-24, dropping to 15-20 for GCSE teaching and usually 8-12 for sixth form. Broad curriculum, with core subjects supplemented by Latin, philosophy & theology, computer science, 3D design, all the usual creative arts, and a good modern languages offering: French, German, Spanish, and, from year 9, Italian.

The Wildcats Adventure area, a woodland paradise of treehouses, ropes and zipwires, looked like every child's dream

We particularly liked the Davey Building, home to the science departments, which had a real buzz about it. A biology teacher clad in brilliant pink lab coat and blue trainers saluted us with great good cheer, thoughtfully cradling the departmental mascot, Buffy the bearded dragon, as jazz drifted out overhead. The skeletons in the labs wore Jack Sparrow headscarves, and it really did seem refreshingly unstuffy.

Lessons universally praised as lively and interactive. 'My daughter has been inspired by the teachers' love of their subjects,' wrote a mother. 'The teaching standard is of the highest quality at Caterham,' wrote another; 'our son has blossomed in all subjects, making his choices for GCSEs even harder.'

The key note here seems to be approachability. One sixth former thought the best thing about Caterham was 'the relationship between staff and students – I've never seen anything like it. They're incredibly supportive and happy to give up their free time.' School introduced iPads for all its students in 2015, and is formally accredited as an Apple Distinguished School. Parents approve. 'The

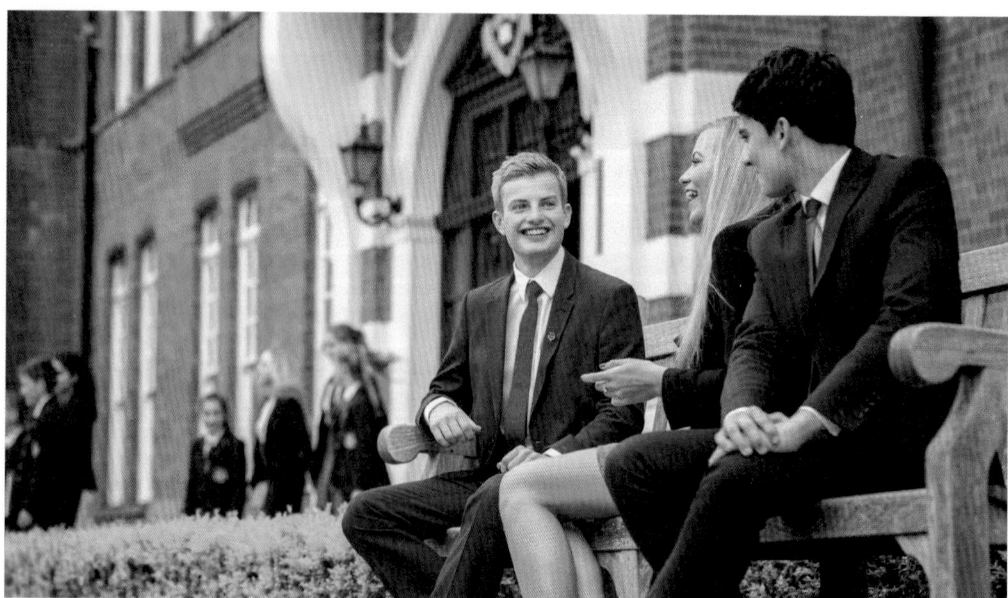

iPad use for school communication for the children is excellent, both for homework and for keeping in touch with what is going on in school,' observed one parent. 'I was sceptical at first, but have been proven wrong,' a father was happy to admit. 'I've seen how it allows the students to embrace technology as a great medium for learning.'

Full-time SENCo (here called the assistant director of learning and teaching), aided by two teaching assistants, offers support to the 15 per cent or so of pupils who need it – dyslexia, processing difficulties, the occasional high-functioning autistic student – mostly in a classroom setting. 'There is one-to-one support, but it's not the bulk of what we do. Otherwise I'd become a crutch, and we want them to be independent,' commented the SENCo, whose office was decorated with reassuring posters of celebrities with SEN – Daniel Radcliffe, David Beckham and the like. This is an academically selective school, however, and they were keen to stress that it's unlikely to be suitable for pupils with more than mild difficulties.

Games, options, the arts: Strong on all fronts, and superbly well-resourced: almost the first thing visitors see as they approach the school is what impresses as a Wembley-sized brand new Astroturf. Dual approach to sport: elite athletes go onto the Caterham Programme, where top-class coaching pushes them to their limits. But everyone is encouraged to have a go, and the school works to ensure that no one is left out. Rugby, hockey and cricket are the main sports for the boys, lacrosse, netball and tennis for the girls, and school has invested heavily in the coaching and facilities for these. It struck us as a rather traditional delineation, but the girls we spoke to liked it, praising the 'community feel' of lacrosse – something we couldn't remember about the game, frankly, so it's good that times change. There's also sixth form girls' rugby, synchronised swimming in the school's own magnificent pool, and a myriad of other exciting things to try, from horse-riding (the school has its own equestrian team) to judo, archery, golf, fencing – etc. Splendid sports hall the size of an aircraft hanger is open to the public, and the English hockey regional training team uses the facilities here. The Wildcats Adventure area, a woodland paradise of treehouses, ropes and zipwires, looked like every child's dream.

Performing arts has its own thriving centre. Drama has upped its game, with the opening of a new dedicated studio theatre in 2016 supported by full-time theatre technician – who also runs the Humphries Theatre, the large multi-purpose space across the foyer – with a strong team of tech enthusiasts drawn from the students. Annual shows for both senior and lower school pupils – 'I don't think I can count the number of things I've done in the

drama department!' beamed a stage-struck sixth former. Recent productions include Grease, Les Misérables and Our Day Out. Lots of other things going on, including a trip to Edinburgh in summer 2017. Fabulous new air-conditioned dance studio – 'Dance is big here,' confirmed a male student, who praised the way the school encouraged both boys and girls to get involved. Annual MADLive dance performance showcases the students' achievements. Music department is lively and busy: orchestras, ensembles, concerts, choirs, and lessons on almost any instrument you can think of.

A biology teacher clad in brilliant pink lab coat and blue trainers saluted us with great good cheer, cradling the departmental mascot, Buffy the bearded dragon

As you'd expect, visual arts are well-resourced, and we liked the textiles area – a pleasure to see sewing machines in a school in this day and age. However, the work on display, whilst stylish, didn't strike us as particularly inspired or visionary – perhaps there just isn't much creative angst at this down-to-earth, affluent school – and it's probably no coincidence that the only negative feedback we received concerned this part of the school's provision: 'I would pick out art as an area of weakness,' wrote one parent, bluntly.

D of E and CCF are flourishing, and there are dozens of extracurricular societies catering for every taste. Of particular note is the Innovations Centre, where pupils can play and experiment with all things digital and robotic, and home also to the film club, where pupils have access to their own Green Screen room and Mac editing suite for creating special effects.

Boarding: We thought the boarding pretty special. Houses are comfortable, spotlessly clean, light, modern in feel and attractive. In addition to everything you'd expect, girls' boarding house boasts a beautiful dining room with oak panelling and a rather lovely Positive Message Tree in the corner, which could have been tacky but simply wasn't. The boys are housed in equal comfort, and are about to get their own kitchen. Bedrooms are for four or two students in the lower years, then single rooms for lower sixth formers and single with ensuite for those in their final years. Good number of live-in staff, and a team of matrons are on site from 7.30am until 10pm.

Nearly 90 per cent are full boarders, mostly international students who do the IELTS (English language learning) programme on Saturdays. Weekly boarding introduced in 2016, and is attracting UK families – numbers small at present, but school hopes to grow them. However, now offers boarding from year 9 only (previously from year 7). Lots of trips and things to do – and a nice leisurely 10am breakfast on Sundays. The boarders we met struck us as a thoroughly happy and well-adjusted lot, and, as a student confirmed, 'the boarder and day pupil relationship is really good.'

Background and atmosphere: Founded in 1811 to provide a boarding education for the sons of Congregational ministers – William Wilberforce was one of the school's first governors. Moved to its present lovely site in the wooded Surrey North Downs in 1884. Even then the school was a forward-looking place. The main building, a beautiful late Victorian red-brick and terracotta affair, was the height of modernity for its time, with the heating being provided by circulating warm air through the Hare Stone Tower, now long gone. The school maintains its links with the United Reform Church – bursaries are available for children of URC clergy – but now describes itself as 'multi-faith' and welcomes children of all faiths and of none.

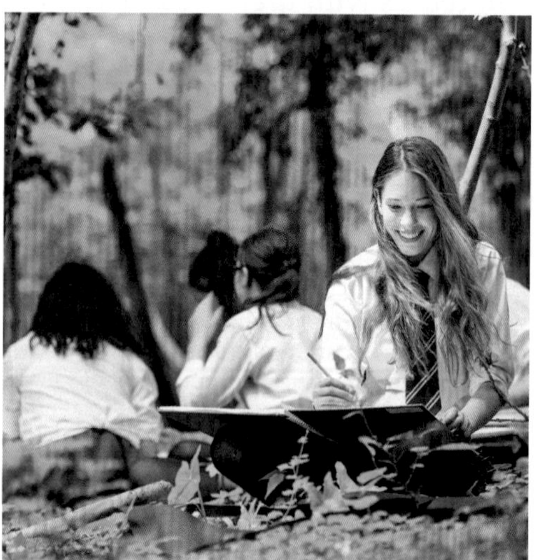

Of particular note is the Innovations Centre, where pupils can play and experiment with all things digital and robotic, and home also to the film club

Lots of new buildings, all of them practical and most of them tasteful, and astonishingly well-equipped and extensive outdoor areas – playing fields, woods, bridle path, you name it. With 200 acres to play with, space is not an issue, and the students move about with an air of confident purpose, smartly dressed in their businesslike uniform. Co-ed really works here. The boys aren't loutish, and the girls aren't cliquey. More than anything, they're just themselves. 'For me, it's the most natural environment,' observes the head, and everyone we spoke to agreed. Students work hard, but are encouraged to play hard too and take advantage of the many opportunities on offer. 'Both my children find the school environment positive,' wrote a mother, 'and it's been a place where we've seen them develop. We cannot ask more from a school as we watch our children grow into young adults.'

Pastoral care, well-being and discipline: Universally praised for being a caring place that nurtures the whole child, and this is shown in lots of small ways rather than anything obvious. One such that impressed us was that boarding house prefects are there simply to support the younger students, not to discipline them – the house staff do the latter, so relationships between older and younger pupils remain friendly. Students appear confident without being arrogant, ready to have a go at anything, and really did come across as keen to serve the wider community. Behaviour throughout is lively but courteous.

Across the school, the words that kept coming up were 'approachable' and 'welcoming'. 'An unstuffy, happy school where the children do really well without being highly pressurised,' was one parent's verdict. Another wrote, 'There have been a couple of occasions when our circumstances have meant that the children needed some extra care and I found the school and staff incredibly helpful, and very swift and ready to offer and provide sensitive and genuine care for them.'

Form the top down, the school seems to have got the work-life balance right, and the result is a sane and kindly place where people have room to look about them. 'The school leadership at all levels seems genuinely to be on the watch for pupils in need of support and then deliver this in a sympathetic manner,' wrote a parent. A member of staff commented, 'People are nice to each other, because we're given the time to be nice to each other. We're valued by both leadership and parents. It's busy here, but we're not pushed to the limit.'

Pupils and parents: Parents are a grounded lot, mostly dual-income and working hard to give their children a Caterham education. Supportive of the school, and very much involved, turning out in great numbers for sporting fixtures and other school events. School works hard to include them, running a lively programme of talks – Revise Like A Champion was aimed at parents wanting to help their children – and putting at their disposal an amazing hospitality suite complete with terrace overlooking the playing fields. Pupils are level-headed, proud of their school, very happy to be here.

Entrance: Around 90 places at year 7, a third of which go to children coming up from the junior school. Others come from a range of local schools, both state and independent: The Hawthorns, Hazelwood, Oakhyrst Grange, St Mary's C of E Junior School, Sevenoaks Prep, New Beacon School, Copthorne School, etc. Fifty additional places in year 9 to pupils coming from preps, either via year 6 deferred entry or standard year 8 route. Some additional places available in the sixth form, but almost everyone stays on, and, very commendably, the school doesn't weed out: the threshold of six B/6s at GCSE is 'a discussion point, not an ultimatum'.

Exit: A very small number after GCSEs, mostly for financial reasons. After A levels, the overwhelming majority to university; eight to Oxbridge in 2017, plus four medics and a vet. Nottingham currently top choice, followed by UCL, Bath, Exeter, Birmingham, Bristol, King's College and York. A Study Abroad evening was recently offered for students looking to go overseas (including the USA). Vocational courses also becoming increasingly popular, and the head is currently in discussion with at least one high-profile financial company about apprenticeships (three on KPMG and Deloitte apprenticeship degrees).

Money matters: About a third of pupils on some form of financial assistance. Bursaries of up to 100 per cent available for pupils from low income families. Academic scholarships at 11+, 13+ and 16+ can be worth up to 50 per cent of fees. Broad range of 25 per cent scholarships offered in specific areas: sport, music, drama, science, art and design, all rounder and boarding.

Remarks: A traditional yet innovative school offering all that's best in modern independent education, both day and boarding, without putting its students through the mill. 'Caterham's one of the best schools in the country already,' the head told us proudly at our meeting. We're inclined to agree.

Charterhouse

17

Admissions Office, Godalming, Surrey GU7 2DX

01483 291501 | admissions@charterhouse.org.uk | www.charterhouse.org.uk

Ages: 13–18

Pupils: 818; sixth form: 431 (150 girls); Boarders: 647 boys, 147 girls

Day: £31,449 pa; Boarding: £38,061 pa

Headmaster: Since January 2018, Dr Alex Peterken BA MA DEd (30s), previously head of Cheltenham College and returning to his roots. Before joining Cheltenham in 2008 as deputy head he spent 12 years at Charterhouse, as head of higher education and careers and latterly housemaster of Saunderites. Educated at The Prebendal School, Chichester where he was head boy and head chorister, thence to Eton College as a music exhibitioner. BA in theology from Durham, MA in educational management from London and a doctorate in education from Surrey. Six children; he enjoys choral singing (bass) and walking.

Dr Peterken replaces Richard Pleming MA, who joined in January 2014. We took to him at once. However, others didn't. There was a campaign against him from the outset and things have run less than smoothly since, in some respects. He stood down as head in December 2016.

Academic matters: Most take either the Cambridge Pre-U or the IB diploma. A levels survive in four subjects, the most popular of which is government & politics. The Pre-U still seen as controversial among parents, who worry unnecessarily that universities are bemused by it. IGCSEs taken in preference to GCSEs in most subjects. But Mr Pleming – who was new to the Pre-U – was a convert and made no plans to change the current arrangements while, as he said, A levels are 'in flux'. Whether his successor agrees, remains to be seen.

The mix of curricula here make judgements about exceptional performance in specific subjects difficult. Maths, history and economics are the stand-outs in terms of sixth form popularity. Art does well and many minority subjects shine. IGCSEs sparkle and demonstrate the value added by good teaching and individual attention. 2017 results saw 80 per cent of IGCSEs A*/A; 93 per cent of Pre-U/A level exams achieved distinction or merit (or A*-C) in 2017 and 56 per cent distinction (or A*/A) in 2017. Average IB point score 36. This has to be impressive for a school which requires only 60 per cent at CE.

'Not frighteningly academic if you've come from a pushy London day school,' we were told by one parent, while another said, 'It's far more academically rigorous than we'd expected.' A third felt that, 'A lot of the seriously bright chaps are the international students.' However, 'There's a culture of trying hard and achieving,' another observed. Previous head introduced an 'academic tie' ('It's a rather attractive apple green,' he avered) for under school boys, to match the one for senior school boys and girls. We deeply approve of the first year's geography and history syllabus being largely focused on the rich history of the school. Not here do you meet pupils with no idea of the key figures and moments in the story of their alma mater. Careers provision and university preparation, having been described as 'needing a kick' by several parents, now rapidly improving, and school is building on Old Carthusian networks and willingness to support current leavers.

System of 'Calling Over' – boys get praised for effort or pulled up for lack of it publicly in class four times a term – is controversial. 'It's brutal,' complained one parent while acknowledging that 'it does mean they are doing something if a boy isn't pulling his weight.' Previous head admitted he was uncertain about it at first but then saw it as a useful tool to help monitor progress, and assured us that 'the more difficult conversations are held one-to-one'.

Very few with recognised or serious SEN of any kind. No withdrawal from classes for individual support. 'We subscribe to the idea enshrined in current legislation that all teachers must be teachers of special educational needs. The best person to support a pupil's needs is his or her subject teacher. All teachers receive regular training in supporting pupils' individual needs. We individualise learning as much as we can.'

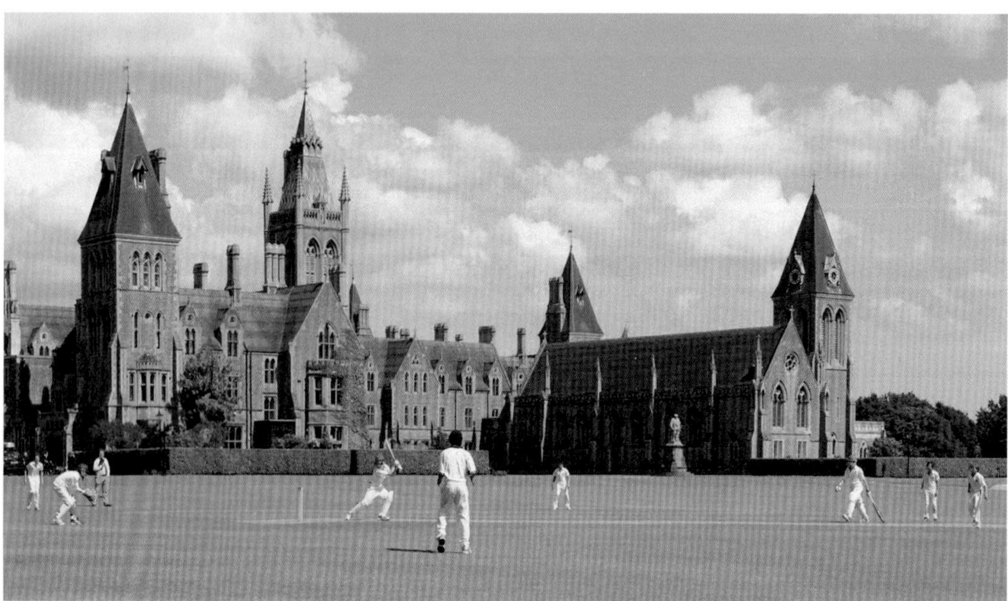

Super library – subdued lighting, comfortable sofas, tables with laptop points and exemplary stock; it has been nurtured and loved

Games, options, the arts: Everything done with vigour, dedication and enthusiasm. Ben Travers Theatre – opened by the great farceur himself in 1980 (at 93) – now looking a little tired, but still an excellent performing space with a cosy foyer. Lots of productions. Surprisingly small proportion learn an instrument – only 280 of the 800 pupils – but the standard of those who do, and the intensity of participation in multiple performance opportunities of all kinds, is exemplary. Very lively and creative art and DT ('someone made a motorbike') – each sixth form artist has their own space and we admired the flair and scope of work. Super ceramics, collage and painting, especially. Two new 3D printers.

Enormous sports complex with everything you'd expect and used, out of lesson time, by the general public. All-weather pitches, courts, fields and tracks in all directions plus a nine hole golf course. A famous football school – Spurs 'Legend' directs the game – with seven teams in each year and masses of matches for all. Sporting opportunities and achievements here of all kinds and hard to better. 'And if there's something you want to do which they don't offer they will try and set it up for you,' we were told. Also a famous CCF and formidable pioneering expeditions to all kinds of high up and far away places.

Boarding: Old houses and new houses and everyone has an opinion on each and on the system as a whole. The new houses – 'architecturally weird and further away from everything' – are preferred by some as more functional, better resourced and nearer to sports facilities. Eating in the new houses is communal, so 'You can't go down in your pyjamas – such a shame,' thought one parent. Four girls' 'hostels' but they study in the boys' houses until 10pm when they trot demurely home. Boys not allowed anywhere near girls' hostels – ever. Sixth form facilities being extended at time of our visit to add a further 30 or so boarding places.

Girls' hostels felt to be better – all rooms have en-suite bathrooms, are very cosy and their rooms are only for sleeping. Accommodation in the older houses is not up to that offered in many top schools these days. En suites are scarce, some rooms are tiny, though no-one shares a room with more than one other. Arcane systems of swapping rooms and girls changing hostels every term – we won't try to explain here; you need to ask – but all is aimed at integrating people and fostering community.

Background and atmosphere: Lincolnshire man, Thomas Sutton (1532–1611), discovered coal on two estates he had leased near Newcastle-on-Tyne and made his fortune. He endowed a hospital on the site of the London Charterhouse and left a legacy to maintain a chapel, almshouse and school. After much legal wrangling, a foundation was set up to run a home for 80 pensioners (gentlemen by descent and in poverty, soldiers that have borne arms by sea or land, merchants decayed by piracy or shipwreck, or servants in household to the King or Queens Majesty), and to educate 40 boys.

The school moved to its present home in stockbroker-Surrey in 1872. The main school building, a substantial gothic statement of purpose, cannot fail to awe. Its post-WW1 chapel – the largest war memorial in the country – is vast, stark and sombre; no mistaking the genuine horror and grief at the nearly 700 lost Carthusians which inspired it. Many more buildings – some of less obvious architectural merit – have since accrued, some having been opened by impressive visitors eg HM the Queen and – the MFL building – by Javier Perez de Cuellar in 2007. Super library – subdued lighting, comfortable sofas, tables with laptop points and exemplary stock; a library that has been nurtured and loved.

Parents comment on that old-fashioned thing, the school 'spirit'. 'There's a strong sense of loyalty. They engender it very quickly. Loyalty to both house and school'

The site has grown to 250 acres with fields and pitches stretching away into the landscape. Trees, little gardens and courtyards humanise it and pathways meander about to give the impression of a sizeable and complex school 'village'. And some people definitely drive too fast down the main thoroughfares!

The advent of sixth form girls into what many still feel is a very male establishment is a source of joy for most. 'The boys love it when the girls arrive,' one seasoned father of boys told us. 'It gives them the best of both worlds.' One sixth form lad told us the only thing that would make the school better would be more girls. Others concur, though stress, 'it takes a certain type of girl – they have to be confident and not stand any nonsense.' Sporty girls go down particularly well, it seems. And, inevitably, 'They do rank us on prettiness so you have to be robust'. School getting better at integrating the girls. A two-day get-to-know-you pre-term event introduced in previous head's first year has done much.

A Christian school and a school in which this is still overt – for all its inclusiveness. A school with its own argot – yes, teachers are 'beaks' here. Parents comment on that old-fashioned thing, the school 'spirit'. 'There's a strong sense of loyalty. They engender it very quickly. Loyalty to both house and school.' A seriousness about the place reflected in its publications, its sending of expert teachers to support the teaching of individual subjects in local state schools and in the appointment of a likeable 'director of social responsibility'. We like this.

Most weekends, pupils may go home after sports fixtures on Saturday afternoons and return for chapel on Sunday evening. For those pupils who remain in school overnight on Saturday (around 20 per cent), a full programme of weekend activities. This was a Pleming innovation – 'There used to be absolutely nothing to do at weekends,' a sixth former told us. 'Now there's loads.' So not, as some parents fear, a lure to keep boys from going home – though it might work that way with some. Most staff live on site – many in a strange tower, nine floors of a highly eccentric 1970s folly – and all live within a mile of school. Some school officers allowed bikes to get around. We wonder whether this privilege could, without imperilling safety or hierarchy, be extended to others on such a large campus?

Going fully co-ed and will take first girls into year 9 in 2021, with school roll gradually increasing to 1,000 to accommodate them.

Pastoral care, well-being and discipline: Vertical tutor system described as 'brilliant!' – one tutor for two boys from each year. Tutor sees each tutee at least once weekly and parents feel 'My son's tutor is

'It doesn't suffer from being too fashionable,' one wise parent ventured. 'It is good at choosing the boys who will suit it'

on his side – we can't fault the system'. Very much a school for joiners-in. 'They do their best to make them try out everything. So even lazy boys get really pushed to try things.' Pupils are polite and charming and discipline is good, though parents tell us of the odd drink smuggling escapade. 'It's really not a problem here' though, affirm sixth formers. Junior boys wear tweedy jackets, older boys wear blue blazers and girls seem uniformly to have long hair and short black skirts. No pushing at boundaries to be seen anywhere.

Most housemasters accorded warm praise, though one or two houses described by parents as 'out of control'. School assures us this is being tackled – and we gather there have been several recent changes in the pastoral team. Boarders are 'very well supervised,' in their leisure time and 'the school is very sensible about absences and so on,' assert parents. Matron is especially highly praised. Most teachers described as 'incredibly kind' and as being a good mix of 'nice young ones – sharp-witted and impressive – and safer, older pairs of hands'. 'Kindness' was a word we heard a lot from parents – this being valued highly in the school community as a whole. School seen by almost all as collaborative and encouraging mutual respect between staff and pupils.

Pupils and parents: About 80 per cent from London or the home counties, and currently many go home after Saturday sports at weekends. Vast majority boards and all boarders have to be back for Sunday night chapel. Twenty per cent made up of around 37 nationalities – a few have some EAL support but this is not the norm. Presence of overseas pupils is not new: Charterhouse has a relationship with Hong Kong going back 200 years and has long valued its international reach and reputation. The IB seen as reflecting the school's long-held international perspective. Some sense that being sporty is valued more highly than being arty, and some creative but left-footed types take a while to feel at home.

Immense list of notable Old Carthusians includes poets Richards Crashaw and Lovelace, writers Joseph Addison, Richard Steele, WM Thackeray, Max Beerbohm, Ben Travers, Robert Graves, Simon Raven, Frederick Raphael, publisher John Murray, classicist Henry Liddell, actor-manager Johnston Forbes-Robertson, founder of the scouts, Robert

Baden-Powell, cartoonist and wit Osbert Lancaster, composer Ralph Vaughan-Williams, historian Hugh Trevor-Roper, sculptor Anthony Caro, politicos and journalists James Prior, William Rees-Mogg, Dick Taverne, the Dimblebys, Jeremy Hunt, Duncan Carswell, philosopher Don Cupitt, pop impresario Jonathan King, the rock group Genesis, composer Rachel Portman and innumerable venerable ecclesiasts (among them, John Wesley) and redoubtable military men of high renown.

Entrance: About 125 places in year 9. Register early. School very popular and lists can close three years before entry, so don't hang about. Houses matter here. Parents and boys visit two or three houses, meet housemaster and staff and boys and have a good poke about. All are interviewed in the first house they visit – a record is kept for other housemasters to see if necessary. Parents then choose their preferred house – but they don't always get it.

Candidates now sit the ISEB common pre-test in the autumn of year 6 at their current school. Boys (and, in future, girls) invited for interview and activity afternoon in spring term and close contact maintained with prep schools. Some consternation among parents who wish that the school had 'stuck to its guns'. School insists it will continue to take note of any major discrepancies between the pre-test results and the picture created of an individual by the interview and school report and consult prep heads where necessary. A few places not dependent on pre-testing will remain for late applicants and exceptional cases.

Sporting opportunities and achievements here hard to better; also famous CCF and formidable pioneering expeditions to all kinds of high up and far away places

Most are offered conditional places at end of year 6 spring term plus places in their first or second choice house. Parents pay an initial deposit to confirm place and are asked whether Charterhouse is their first choice. Those not offered house places are placed on the general list, as are those who are accepted after general list interviews. They are invited to choose a house after meeting housemasters during the spring of year 8. In the autumn of year 8, preps send updated reports – this can result in some boys being asked to withdraw. CE pass mark of 60 per cent expected. They don't over-offer, which is refreshing.

At sixth form, 75 girls and 30 boys come, most as boarders and a few as day pupils. Admission by competitive examination, school reports and interview. Offers of places are unconditional but high proportion of GCSE A*s and As (or numerical equivalent) are expected. Little choice of houses.

A few places reserved in years 9 and 12 for overseas candidates. Quite diverse admissions systems, depending on where you are from. 'It doesn't suffer from being too fashionable,' one wise parent ventured. 'It is good at choosing the boys who will suit it.' And from, 2021, year 9 girls.

Exit: Twenty-one to Oxbridge in 2017. Large numbers to Bristol, Edinburgh, Durham, Exeter, Manchester, Nottingham, Newcastle, London unis and, increasingly, to prestigious colleges in the US – Columbia, Cornell, Stanford, University of Pennsylvania, UCLA. No narrow range of subjects studied but a bent towards economics, politics, business and management perhaps. No silly subjects pursued by anyone.

Money matters: Not a rich school. Most fee assistance now in the form of bursarial help rather than scholarships. Scholarships – whether at 13+ or 16+, exhibitions, academic, art and music scholarships – more for glory than dosh. However, can be topped up by mean-tested bursaries up to the value of full fees in cases of proven need.

Remarks: An all-round impressive school – confident of what it does and doing it well. Pupils genuinely value what they are given here. As one, thoughtfully, expressed it, 'You feel you're part of something that should continue'. Obviously, now experiencing a bump and a hiccup and hoping for stability in the form of the new head.

Christ's Hospital

C of E 18

Horsham, West Sussex RH13 0LJ

01403 211293 | enquiries@christs-hospital.org.uk | www.christs-hospital.org.uk

Ages: 11–18

Pupils: 900; sixth form: 280; Boarders: 830

Day: £16,950 – £21,330 pa; Boarding: £32,790 pa

Headmaster: Since September 2017, Simon Reid BA (50s), previously principal of Gordonstoun, who was housemaster here for six years earlier in his career. A South African who read English at the University of Witwatersrand. Came to Britain in 1985 because he 'wanted to teach English literature in the country where it was written'. Has also been deputy head of Worksop College, having started his UK teaching career at Brentwood School, thence Stowe. His wife, Michele, is French, the family bilingual. Two grown up young.

Academic matters: Junior class sizes up to 25, 20 in core subjects at GCSE and fewer in option groups, 10 or 11 for A level or IB. Latin compulsory for first two years, second foreign language for one. GCSE subjects chosen at end of year 8 – one modern language and one humanities subject must be included in the four options outside the core curriculum. Pupils say staff try exceptionally hard to incorporate exams in unusual first languages. IB becoming established. Take up was slow initially (28 in first year but now rising), partly because pupils are very concerned about getting it right (most have no family money to fall back on if exams don't work out). In 2017, 63 per cent A*-A/9-7 grades at GCSE, 63 per cent A*/A at A level; IB average 36 points.

Campus arranged by subject blocks, all with high ceilings and plenty of space and equipment, including science and language labs. The ugly sister IT department (was known as Grange Hill by the students), replaced with a new classroom block, library and resource centre. A new sixth form centre was opened in 2016 with a focus on careers and vocations – the thinking is that Old Blues can provide enough mentoring and connections for some pupils to enter a profession in the City without going to university. Art and humanities have their own specialised libraries (open for evening work, as are all academic departments, providing support).

The SEN unit has one part-time and two full-time SENCos – support ranges from mild to a tailored IEP if SEN is profound. Everyone with SEND gets a laptop. The whole campus has Wifi and all the IB pupils and upper sixth are offered a laptop too – these can be taken home. Parents appreciate 'equality of provision and equality of access to provision.'

Weekly chapel and tutorial periods; upper sixth get weekly lectures on topics ranging from photo-journalism, through medicine, dentistry and accountancy to Tom Avery's experience as a polar explorer. New sixth form and careers centre sees weekly careers events. There is a huge amount on offer here and as pupils grow older they tend towards the management of their own studies, as they would at university, an enormously important piece of preparation for life after CH. Houseparents and staff who supervise prep periods play a great role in advising children on study choices as well as pastoral issues.

Games, options, the arts: Main sports are hockey, netball, football, rugby, cricket and tennis, with a decent fixture list against local co-ed schools, winning about 60 per cent. Blue Coats sports centre – 25m pool, double-sized sports hall, six squash courts, spin bikes, split-level fitness suite, vending machines and a café – is used by the public 60 per cent of the time, although the school has its own changing rooms. More esoteric sports such as fives also on offer. D of E and CCF very popular. Scout hut now converted to a multifunction theatre seating 200.

A 500-seat theatre, modelled on Shakespeare's Globe, with padded red benches instead of the standing yard, is used by travelling drama companies too (contemporary dance as well as curriculum-relevant plays). Open access attitude for these performances endears the school still more to Horsham residents. The debating society and the Model United Nations give student speakers more confidence in competition in and outside school.

The music department is a popular target for donations such as harps, bassoons, French horns. Listen to, play or sing in any one of the 43 ensembles, inside or outside the school, and the joyful noise is gorgeous. Chapel choir is now restricted to a maximum of 150, the gospel choir has around 80 members as does the Big (jazz) Band, the junior choir 50, 150 in the symphony. Most pupils love to sing and the cathartic feeling of their voices joined together, soaring past the frescoes in the chapel, is one of the moments they squirrel away in their hearts – the BBC was hugely impressed that it could record them in just one take. Lots of Macs enable bedroom producers to hone their skills with music technology at A level.

Energetic art department, successful and focused on working on pupils' own ideas, which produces an enormous range of work – exhibiting at the train station and a theatre in Horsham grants a wider audience. Three floors of bright and naturally-lit space, an artist in residence, art historian, two full-time staff, sewing room, computer suite (although the primary source of each project is drawing, digital images are always involved) and a library full of glossy books – all open from 7.15am to 10pm. DT department occupies almost as large a space and is just as well equipped with computers, AutoCAD, laser cutter, graphics area etc and admirable focus on SMART objectives for each project. One pupil not only achieved the top Pre-U art mark nationally recently, but also won the sculpture category of the new HMC schools' art competition with his remarkable recreation of a Brazilian favella.

Boarding: Eighteen boarding houses – 16 single sex ones along The Avenue and two upper sixth co-eds built in 2000. Nearly all are looked after by a married couple (most of the 110 staff live on site, often with their own families), so every child gets a taste of parental and sibling relationships that may well be lacking in their own home. A recent revamp has left these boarding facilities sparkling – no junior shares a room with more than three others, big common rooms with ping-pong and snooker, bright kitchens, a phone room (for the first two years everyone hands in their mobile until 2pm). Every new arrival gets a nursemaid in the year above – they write letters to the new students the summer before they arrive – and this relationship produces a family tree stretching across year groups. Ingenious support where need arises – matrons giving hugs, cleaning staff joshing the dedicated student and the head of learning support teaching a tai chi course, an innovative balance to the busyness of student days.

Upper sixth get weekly lectures on topics ranging from photo-journalism through medicine and accountancy to Tom Avery's experience as a polar explorer

The two Senior Grecian houses (the nomenclature comes from the sixth form historically having to study classics) would be the envy of any university student. Often more space than the children might have to themselves at home – big windows, a sink in each (senior's) room, double-height communal spaces, bowls of fruit, kitchens shared between eight, a BBQ on the deck, a little library area with a piano and students' art displayed. A quarter of the Grecians might be in long-term (more than a year) relationships with each other but no peer pressure to do this. The proximity of co-ed living space means that sex could be a problem, but the co-ed nature of the full school normalises boy/girl relationships. Lovely story of a Valentine's Day charity fundraiser, pay a penny for a snuggle – really inclusive.

Matches on Saturday afternoons while Saturday evenings feel good with discos, theme nights or just a fun time in each house – watching football, a film or playing a game devised by the seniors with a slapstick pie in the face for those who mess up.

CH runs in three-week blocks before a leave weekend – some children don't want to or can't go home; they can stay in or get matched with a friend and spend the weekend with their family. 'There's no one way to be a CH pupil,' we were told. This diversity is the school's strength – whatever obstacles or advantages your home life might present, everyone is equal as soon as they tie on the bands of their uniform. The new 'deps' (deputy Grecians, lower sixth) probably find the acclimatisation most difficult. Pupils learn within the first year to live with a huge range of personalities, which stands them in good stead in later life.

Background and atmosphere: School was given its Royal Charter by Edward VI in 1553 to help orphan children of London. In 1902 the boys moved to the current purpose-built campus in Horsham (designed by Sir Aston Webb, also responsible for the façade of Buckingham Palace and King's College, Cambridge). The girls, who had stayed at a site in Hertford, joined in 1985 to make it co-ed once again. Nowadays the demographic is much more mixed, but the uniform is still resolutely Tudor – mustard coloured socks and long blue coats. The pupils love the warm Houseys and although the younger ones choose their 'civvies' carefully after lessons are over, the older ones default to school tracksuits – a refreshing lack of emphasis on trainers as a signifier of social tribe.

Progress supports the heritage showcased by the plaque-studded cloisters – from the plasma screen with BBC news and current school photos in the reception to the skylight-lit food hall. Six days a week, barring rain, the entire school marches to lunch from the quadrangle, house by house, to the accompaniment of the parade band. Parents and pupils say 'butterflies in the tummy' are caused by this sharing of 'music, ambience, exhilaration, aesthetic, ceremony, tradition and spirit' on a daily basis.

The food (delicious and varied) is cooked by team headed by a chef who has turned down offers from Michelin starred restaurants, and is eaten under the longest oil on canvas in Christendom. This mingling of tradition and technology is characteristic of the school. It may appear incongruous yet, in truth, it is inspirational.

Ingenious support where need arises – matrons giving hugs, cleaning staff joshing the dedicated student and the head of learning support teaching a tai chi course

The pupils are proud of their uniform, don't mind being taunted as Harry Potter lookalikes on trains (they prefer references to The Matrix), are delighted to be recognised by Old Blues on the tube and smile wryly when confessing to smelling like wet dogs after marching in a rainy Lord Mayor's Show. They pour through the cloisters between their lessons, some holding the lead of a master's dog for a treat. One of the best bits of the school is reported to be the spread at breakfast. They need that as fuel to get them around the huge campus – by the upper sixth you earn the privilege of a bike.

The whole school meets in the chapel on Sunday morning – seats 1,000, 140 in the gallery. Stained glass windows (some Victorian and a couple of 14th century Flemish) came from the earlier campuses, but the Sir Frank Brangwyn frescos were commissioned for the Horsham site. Whole school assembly is conducted every week by the head in Big School, under the largest unsupported wooden ceiling in the country.

Pastoral care, well-being and discipline: Chapel services are important, not least because it is a space big enough for all the pupils to gather on Tuesdays and Sundays. The school was founded partly in response to a sermon preached by the Bishop of London and sermons are still powerful today; even if every pupil is not touched, they definitely pay attention. Lots of children here whose parents or carers are ill or struggling, so faith can be a real touchstone. School council is very thoughtful, student-run although spearheaded by an English teacher. Recent topics include racism, considering the effect close groups of international students (Hong Kong Chinese) can have in a community – empathetic research came up with how tiring it was to speak in your second language all day long, therefore what a retreat your own culture could be.

Minor misdemeanours mean getting up for 7.15am and a dress parade. Mini-detentions on Sunday am, the big one is on Saturday night, and a card system which restricts free time by having to sign in (for smoking, bullying, drinking alcohol.)

Internet access is not restricted very much (you often can't get onto useful sites with blanket bans) but it is monitored – a 14-year-old looking at porn will lose his/her laptop and school email account. 'Swearing at the staff is unacceptable' (suspension) and continued difficulties will result in a behaviour contract between the pupil, parents and school – a line drawn in the sand. Drugs – class A or supplying – mean immediate expulsion with the involvement of the police; for cannabis there will be one chance, after which the ongoing drug testing policy is implemented. Family circumstances are always taken into account. Parents really appreciate consistent and accessible staff. Email conversations may continue long after they have been sparked during parents' evenings.

Pupils and parents: The pupils know they're lucky to be here. For every student who gets in, four or five are turned away. Accepts pupils from all over the UK, in reality about 30 per cent from London (Hackney, Tower Hamlets, Islington, Acton), 30 per cent from Sussex, 30 per cent south west and home counties, rest from Scotland, Wales, north of England (most from further afield enter at sixth form, but only if they have some extended family in the south east). Historical links with Richmond, Newbury, Reading and Twickenham – the towns on the route of John and Francis West (17th-century scriveners) to Christ's Hospital.

Eleven per cent international pupils – mostly Europe (three and a half per cent) or the Far East (five per cent). Lots of second and third generation Nigerians and Gambians, Hong Kong Chinese are particularly attracted by CH's status as The Royal Mathematical School and German anglophiles love the school's excellence and tradition while valuing the fact that it is not an enclave of privilege. Since 2011, five per cent each from the UK, Europe and the rest of the world pay full fees – these are families who have made a conscious choice to pay for an egalitarian ethos. It has not been easy to change the pupil profile. A small number of international pupils were admitted initially with great care taken to see what they and their families needed. Now students appreciate the still wider diversity. It's easier to chat in German with a friend who is a native speaker or swipe some Asian cooking tips in the house kitchen.

German Anglophiles love the school's excellence and tradition while valuing the fact that it is not an enclave of privilege

Only 42 per cent of pupils have both parents resident at home and lots of aspiring middle class and freelancers. Houseparents encourage communication between parents when new pupils arrive (forums and blogs online help this). Pupils are drawn from all walks of life and the majority enjoy some form of means-tested bursary. If CH does its job, then former pupils will be ineligible to send their children to their alma mater, unless they pay the full fees.

Notable Old Blues (the dead ones have boarding houses named after them) include Coleridge, Middleton, Peele, Barnes Wallis, the cricketer John Snow, comedians Mark Thomas and Holly Walsh, the academic Alan Ryan, conductor Sir Colin Davis, Martin Linton MP, England Rugby Union second row Joe Launchbury, Baroness Ruth Deech, Lord Simon, former Chairman of BP, and General Sir Garry Johnson MC, strategic adviser to the MOD.

Entrance: Most at 11+, 25 to 30 at 13+ and 45 to 50 after GCSE. No feeder schools, but a very good relationship with south of England primaries and preps. Fifty heads came to a recent open day so they can see what type of child will thrive at CH.

Not on the public school radar, so not much cachet on the dinner party circuit. The initial application form elicits lots of information about family circumstances and finances – from previous school, local church, social services. The staff in the admissions office are at the end of the phone to answer questions and baffled or swamped parents really value this.

Exit: Some 10 per cent leave after GCSE for vocational courses. More than 90 per cent of sixth formers to university – the Upper Grecian houses are a real stepping-stone to life there. In 2017, five to Oxbridge and four medics. King's College, Nottingham, Bristol, Cardiff and Exeter popular; engineering, archaeology, classics, law, music, maths degrees. Artists seem to take it in turns to go in posses to Camberwell, Falmouth and Central St Martins.

Money matters: Currently 14 per cent pay nothing, 34 per cent pay less than 10 per cent of full fees, 72 per cent per cent receive some level of bursary support and 19 per cent pay the full boarding fee. Of the £301 million allocated to means-tested bursaries by ISC schools last year, £15.5 million of that was at Christ's Hospital alone.

Parental contributions are assessed on the total family income of the home in which the child resides, interest and dividend payments plus a percentage of any financial and other assets above £25,000. Most DSS benefits are included, but not housing benefit, disability allowance and carer's allowance. Reviewed each year. Discounts for siblings within school. Tudor-style uniform is free. Extras include £20 pocket money per term, music contributions (means-tested again), a dictionary and a bible. CH has a big endowment but, like every other school, lives beyond its means.

Curriculum-based trips are partially funded by the foundation (means testing applies). Old Blues provide travel grants for gap years etc.

Remarks: Well-adjusted, confident and accepting children who look forward to coming to school. This is the only independent school that escapes the state school prejudice when attracting principled teachers. The Old Blues are incredibly loyal and you can see why – with 75 per cent of them in the top quartile of income in their later life, CH turns many lives around in an unpretentious and joyful manner. Admirable work.

City of London Freemen's School

19

Ashtead Park, Ashtead, Surrey KT21 1ET

01372 277933 | admissions@freemens.org | www.freemens.org

Ages: 13–18

Pupils: 526; sixth form: 229; Boarders: 57

Day: £17,541 pa; Boarding: £26,079 – £29,259 pa

Headmaster: Since 2015, Mr Roland Martin (40s), cheerful, communicative, intellectual, and thoroughly likeable. Grew up in a council house and won a Foundation scholarship to Rendcomb College in Gloucestershire, where he was a boarder, got involved with everything and had a wonderful time. Read English at York and was about to embark on a PGCE when he was offered a job at Newcastle-under-Lyme School and decided to learn on the job instead. Six years there were followed by 13 years at Eton, where he taught English and drama, and was also head of year 11 and a housemaster. Returned to his alma mater Rendcomb in 2011 as headmaster, so well versed in the demands of the role before moving to Freemen's four years later. Married to Kerri, who works at the school as outreach officer, with two children.

Thinks that if he hadn't become a teacher he might have chosen to be ordained as a minister ('And I still might be!' he adds), and certainly feels that teaching is a vocation. Delighted to be at Freemen's – 'This school gets under your skin really, really quickly.' A theatre lover and true scholar, whose passion for all things 18th century was so infectious that we wanted to join his sixth form classes on tomb sculpture ourselves. Popular with students, who describe him as 'humble', 'down-to-earth' and 'involved'. Parents concur, grateful for improved communication and commenting that he is 'quietly confident and very approachable, with a clear vision of where he wants to take the school,' and 'incredibly kind'.

Academic matters: Extremely good results year on year at both GCSE and A level – in 2017, 88 per cent A*-A/9-7 for the former, with 64 per cent A*/A and 90 per cent A*/B for the latter.

Viewed by parents as pretty much the best in the locality, and students say that the school 'feels very academic'. No feel of being a pressure-cooker, however, and parents and pupils alike praised the way that academic performance was achieved without undue stress. 'You don't feel that you're lacking if you're not in the top set. The teachers always encourage you to do well.' Independent study skills a priority: 'They give you the tools you need to work with, but they don't spoon-feed you,' was a typical comment. 'My history teacher is so interested in everything about history, and is always up for a chat – it led to my choosing history,' enthused one sixth former. 'The opportunities for my son to challenge himself academically both in school hours and in terms of extracurricular provision are excellent,' wrote a mother, 'for example maths challenges, literary society, science and technology seminars. The small classes and tutorial group system work well and the children are all very motivated.'

Curriculum is traditional but broad, with all the usual subjects taught and enjoyed. School offers French, Spanish, German and Latin, and is looking at introducing Mandarin ('We're behind the curve on that one,' admitted head). The lessons we attended were sound and solid, with all students keen to participate. Head not especially a fan of giving out iPads, but felt that the school was behind the times on the ICT front when he arrived and has worked to modernise the provision.

At sixth form the school offers A levels, plus the Free Minds programme, a kind of internal baccalaureate introduced by the head and aimed at helping students to go off-piste intellectually. 'It has helped my children to broaden their interests and thinking,' wrote one mother. Unless they're taking double maths, all sixth formers have to do the EPQ.

A theatre lover and true scholar, whose passion for all things 18th century was so infectious that we wanted to join his sixth form classes on tomb sculpture

A smattering of students with mild SEN are supported by a team of three SEN teachers across the junior and senior school. Support is 'done quite subtly' – at breakfast and lunchtime clubs, for instance – and students with dyslexia may do one foreign language rather than two. However, this isn't the place for more than a minor level of need.

Games, options, the arts: Sport is very strong here and the facilities are stunning – huge hockey Astro is very impressive – but the emphasis is on inclusion, with a number of grateful parents praising the participation and enjoyment fostered by the school's culture. 'My son chose to play down a team in rugby because he was frightened of tackling and the school was happy to accommodate this, as the focus is on building the boys'confidence and enjoyment of the game,' wrote one mother. Boys do rugby, football and cricket, girls do hockey, netball, tennis and rounders. A very traditional divide, and one mother, who was effusive in her praise of the school, did comment, 'My only gripe is that the boys have no choice in the lower school other than to do football, then rugby, then cricket and don't have the opportunity to experience tennis or hockey – which would suit some of them far better.' Swimming suffered a bit of a setback when the pool burnt down in 2014, but there's a new six-lane replacment. Varied programme of extracurricular sports eg fencing, squash, pilates, kickboxing, archery, and coaching for these described by parents as 'outstanding'. Ski trips highly rated by students. Cracking gym and fitness suite, where perspiring young men were pumping iron under the guidance of a trainer when we passed by.

Music taught in excellent purpose-built block, complete with recording studio, Live Room for pupils' own band practices, Mac suite and all the practice rooms you could desire. Orchestras, choirs, ensembles – always plenty going on, including collaborations with the other City of London schools and the chance to play at venues such as Milton Court and St John's Smith Square. 'The music at Freemen's is excellent, with very high standards of concerts and individual music teachers,' wrote one parent, adding, 'It is a shame they don't offer a music tour abroad as other schools do.'

Drama is accommodated in the Ferndale Theatre, which is an odd shape but very well-equipped and staffed. Lots of scope for getting involved. School plays are 'amazing!' according to pupils – previous productions have included Phantom of the Opera, Evita, Romeo & Juliet and Laura Wade's Alice set in a prop cupboard. School has just appointed a dramatist-in-residence to help extend the clubs and activities on offer. School scores regular successes in the Shakespeare For Schools Festival.

The main house, built in the 17th century and given the Bonomi treatment in the 18th, is flanked by Palladian balustrade, topiary, manicured lawns and is gorgeous

Art is flourishing, although the work we saw struck us as enjoyable rather than particularly inventive. CCF and Duke of Edinburgh offered from year 9. Generally, both parents and students were full of praise for the enrichment here, although a couple hinted that some of the opportunities on offer looked better on paper than in actuality.

Boarding: New and spruce boarding house opened in 2014 and can accommodate up to 30 boys and 30 girls in years 9 to 13. Attractive floor-to-ceiling etched glass entrance doors give immediately onto a big open plan common room, light and airy, although not, one imagines, particularly private. Students share two to a room until the sixth form, when they can have a room to themselves. Two kitchens for boarders' use, plus very nice laundry facilities. There are plans to extend the provision to include a dedicated sixth form boarding house. Full, weekly and flexi-boarding are all offered.

The school was founded to care for orphans, so boarding is part of the original statute and must be provided. However, it's fair to say that the current residents are rather different to those in 1854. Almost all today's boarders are paying full fees and hail from overseas eg China, Hong Kong, Malaysia, Kazakhstan. They have to have good English to start with, and a specialist EAL teacher visits three times a week, ensuring they make rapid progress. A very small number of weekly boarders, and these are usually from the UK.

Only two live-in staff, supported by a day matron and other assistants. This is a small community, and reading between the lines, a quiet one. We didn't get to meet or talk to any boarders, and couldn't detect the kind of buzz so palpable in other boarding houses we've visited.

Background and atmosphere: The second of the three City of London schools to be created, Freemen's opened its doors in 1854 with a remit to educate 'orphans of the Freemen of the City of London'. Housed originally in Brixton, it could accommodate up to 65 boys and 35 girls – applicants had to be aged between 7 and 10 and could stay until they were 15. So whereas many schools have added on boarders, girls and junior-aged children in order to survive economically, Freemen's took them all from the off. In 1924, the school relocated to the 57-acre Ashtead Park estate in Surrey; fee-paying boys were now also admitted, with fee-paying girls joining them in 1933.

Oddly higgledy-piggledy entrance – the grandly named Gatehouse is just a modern Portakabin-style extension – gives little indication of the beauty and space that awaits just around the corner. The main house, built in the 17th century and given the Bonomi treatment in the 18th, is flanked by Palladian balustrade, topiary, manicured lawns and is simply gorgeous. 'It's a very nice place to be,' agreed our tour guide, as we paused to admire the wonderful wood-panelled entrance hall. Despite this, the campus has a modern feel to it: lots of new buildings – the Haywood Centre is the hub of the school and bang up to date. Even more is planned: a huge overhaul of facilities is set to take place over the next 8-10 years. No danger of anyone feeling cramped, though: there are space and green fields in abundance, stretching far away into the distance. We walked about at lunchtime and saw both girls and boys charging hither and yon in what seemed like a civilised pastoral idyll, laughing, shouting, playing, generally being active, healthy and noisy.

House system helps to build positive relationships across the school. A pupil told us, 'I absolutely love it here. It's really friendly and welcoming,' and another added, 'Everyone's really open-minded. It's a happy school.' A parent wrote, 'There is none of the razzamatazz and sales manner of some other schools.' We agree – if anything, the school was a little too unconcerned about showing us its best side, with the result that it came across as successful and contented, rather than dynamic and self-searching.

Pastoral care, well-being and discipline: Universally praised as a kind, non-judgmental place where children can flourish. 'I am a single mother and the school has been nothing other than supportive to myself and my sons, who have had a massive adjustment period over the last year,' was a particularly heartfelt testament we received. This is all the more praiseworthy given that it runs alongside the school's longstanding emphasis – commented upon by many – on students thinking for themselves. 'Freemen's children are expected to be independent from arrival in year 3 onwards and as a result in the main the school produces very confident, organised individuals and we feel that our children have benefitted from this,' wrote a parent, adding, 'There is little hand holding though, and the onus is on the child to seek out help.' Students agreed: 'There's a lot of support in place if you ask for it.'

Behaviour is like the uniform: sensible and smart. Tutor system ensures that everyone is known and supported, rules are clear, and children say they know what's expected of them. Pupils can bring their own lunch, but most choose the school meals, which are very good ('much better than they used to be,' confided a sixth former), and served in the main house dining room under the beneficent painted gaze of former school dignitaries.

Free Minds internal baccalaureate programme aimed at helping students go off-piste intellectually

Head has open door on two mornings a week for staff and two mornings a week for pupils. A delegation of girls came to talk about their concerns for PSHE – they'd felt the school was stuffy on topics such as sex and sexuality. Head listened and acted – 'We've worked a lot on pupil voice.' No issues with transition from junior to senior – Freemen's operates as one all-through school, and the younger children are familiar and comfortable with the site and senior staff well before they move up at 13.

Students say: 'The balance is good here. It's academic, but they let you get on with it. The homework load is manageable. Most people do stuff outside school and the teachers are aware of this.' 'My children have thrived since joining the school and are very happy there,' was a typical parent comment.

Pupils and parents: This is classic commuter country, and Freemen's families are mostly professional but from a range of backgrounds nonetheless; some affluent, some making large sacrifices to pay the fees. Parents Association is proactive and supportive of the school. Pupils predominantly from surrounding Surrey towns of Ashtead, Epsom, Banstead, Leatherhead, Esher and Cobham, and school offers a return coach service to these areas and more. Shuttle bus to and from Ashtead station also a great help, particularly to those travelling from further afield.

Freemen's students are able, cheerful, polite and grounded. Very little ethnic diversity, reflecting the area's demographic, but all the children we saw were mixing happily together regardless of difference.

Entrance: At 13+, the overwhelming majority come up from the junior school. There is absolutely no academic barrier between junior and senior school, something which is a huge draw for parents: entry from year 8 to year 9 really is automatic. 'Once you're in, you're in,' confirmed the head, 'The children arrive at age 7, and our expectation is that they'll still be here 10 years later.' An additional 20 places for outsiders, all keenly competed for – applicants mostly come from local preps eg Downsend, Danes Hill, Cranmore and Lanesborough. At sixth form around another 20 join, including overseas boarders. Sixth form places for UK students are offered on current academic performance (applicants must be sitting at least eight GCSEs), school report and interview, although offers are conditional upon GCSE grades achieved. International students sit papers in January in English, maths, non-verbal reasoning and the A level subjects they wish to study.

Exit: A small number at 16+, either for financial reasons or because they fancy a change. At 18+ the majority to Russell Group unis. In 2017 the most popular destinations included Oxbridge (eight places), UCL, Exeter, Birmingham, Warwick, Bristol and Durham.

Money matters: Fees are competitive alongside other comparable schools in the area. Academic and music awards at 13+ and sixth form available to current pupils and incomers. Means-tested bursary awards, sponsored by the City Livery Companies and often tied to certain professions. A very small number of children of Freemen who have lost one 'family breadwinner' parent attend completely free as Foundationers, whether they are day pupils or boarders.

Remarks: A school that produces confident, motivated, happy young achievers. A blessing to parents looking for a high-quality stress-free educational route that will take their academically able sons and daughters from age 7 right through to 18. Almost unique in this neck of the woods.

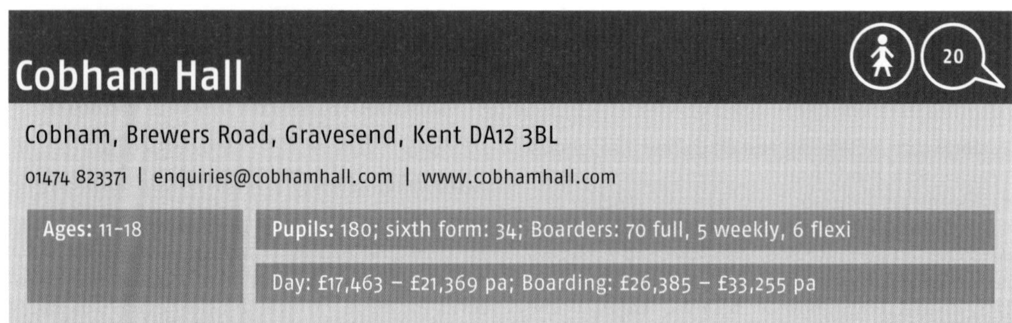

Cobham Hall

20

Cobham, Brewers Road, Gravesend, Kent DA12 3BL

01474 823371 | enquiries@cobhamhall.com | www.cobhamhall.com

Ages: 11–18

Pupils: 180; sixth form: 34; Boarders: 70 full, 5 weekly, 6 flexi

Day: £17,463 – £21,369 pa; Boarding: £26,385 – £33,255 pa

Acting Headmistress: Dr Sandra Coates-Smith BSc PhD is holding the fort during the 2017/18 school year. Chemistry degree from King's College London and completed her PhD in physics whilst being sponsored by BP. She teaches physics and chemistry to sixth form level and is keen on encouraging girls to think of science as a career. She has worked in the Girlguiding movement and the D of E scheme, and counts finishing her old own gold award as one of her major achievements. Once a kayak instructor, she now crews for her husband on their boat.

Academic matters: The IB was introduced in 2009 and A levels phased out at the same time: however, this is going into reverse from 2018 with the IB being replaced by A levels. The results reflect the wide range of abilities within the school. The average diploma points in 2017 was 35; 42 per

cent of GCSEs were A*-A/9-7. All girls take at least eight GCSEs and most do 10. Girls setted in maths, English and science from year 7 and sometimes in other subjects depending on the size of the year group. Sixth form curriculum tailored to each girl and some take IB certificates rather than the full diploma. 'Girls generally do better than expected,' says the school. Class sizes up to 20 in the lower years with an average of 12 and no more than 12 per class (and some much smaller) in sixth form. One parent said that she was concerned about the small classes before her daughter started but added: 'the brightest girls are stretched and encouraged'. The teachers are a 'good combination of the homely and the vibrant and dynamic' – about half are male.

French, Spanish and Latin offered at GCSE and at standard and higher level in the IB. German offered as a first language to native speakers in IB. Chinese offered as first or second language in the IB and can be taken ab initio at standard level – taught by a native speaker. Science is popular and most take three separate sciences at GCSE although dual award is available – 'girls are braver about sciences in a single sex school.' Good range of subjects offered in the IB including theatre, psychology, music and computing science at the higher level and sport and exercise science and health and environmental systems and societies at standard level. The small size of the school means that they can be 'reactive to demand and flexible with the timetable'.

Cobham offers a pre-IB/A level course and girls joining this for the year have the option of sitting up to five GCSEs. Many join for only one or two terms to brush up their English or as preparation for the sixth form at Cobham. They are taught separately in most subjects but may join the school's GCSE students for sport. They live in Main Hall with the other GCSE students.

About 60 girls need help with English and the EFL programme is tailored for each girl. Girls joining in years 10 and 12 need good English and will generally study the English B qualification (English for non-native speakers). The school is a registered centre for ESOL exams but not IELTS.

Sport has come on by leaps and bounds in recent years. 'It was at the egg and spoon race stage when I arrived. Now we have girls trialling for the England hockey team'

The school is CReSTeD registered – about 20 need some sort of learning support. Much emphasis on inclusivity; girls offered one-to-one support to develop strategies and there is good support for teachers in the classroom to enable them to get the best out of students. Occasionally have to turn a girl away if the school feels they cannot meet her needs.

Girls offered careers advice from early on: via PSHE in the lower years and are then help with interview technique before work experience in year 10. They take part in the Big Business Pitch, a two day event where girls learn about starting and marketing their own business. Year 12s attend a higher education fair and an Oxbridge conference. Plenty of help with personal statement and university choices. The school also belongs to the ISCO which, for a fee, offers girls individual interviews and career profiling until the age of 23 – most sign up to this.

Games, options, the arts: Sport has come on by leaps and bounds in recent years; 'it was at the egg and spoon race stage when I arrived,' said the previous head. 'Now we have girls trialling for the England U18 hockey team, the Kent County Schools show jumping champion, a girl in the South of England eventing team, finalists in the National Biathlon Championships and an Elder (old girl) headed for Rio with the modern pentathlon team.' Good links with local hockey club – some county hockey and netball players and a girl training with the girls' U16 West Ham football team. All girls up until year 11 have to take part in team sports two or three times a week and sixth form have to take some exercise – zumba and yoga are popular. Indoor heated swimming pool with swimming coaching twice a week. Duke of Edinburgh compulsory in year 9 – most do bronze and a good number do silver, some start gold at school but complete it at university.

Impressive artwork displayed around the school reflects the internationalism of the pupils. Photography popular and school has its own darkroom as well as a suite of Apple Macs for digital work. One photography student invited to exhibit at the Royal Academy. Ceramics and sculpture particularly dynamic under the tutelage of the 'legendary clay man'.

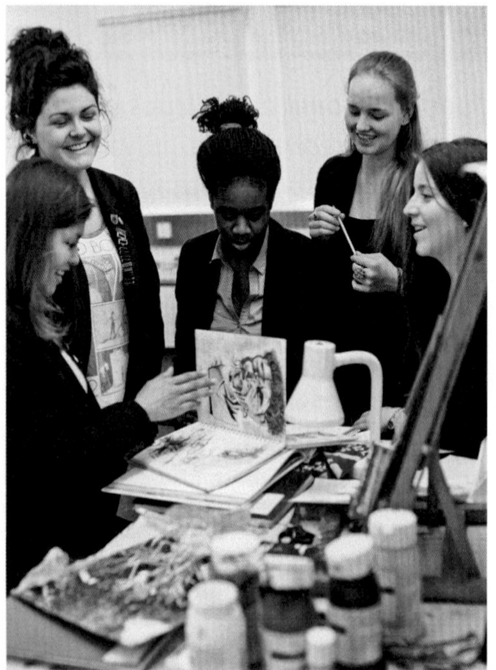

Ambitious head of music who previously worked in Barbados 'pushes the boundaries and has got the choirs going'

The school has a fully-equipped drama studio, but the magnificent Gilt Hall is often used for productions and everyone has to take part in the inter-house drama competitions. One whole school play a year and girls do well in LAMDA exams.

The school fosters a spirit of adventure and leadership – girls encouraged to take assemblies and stand up in public, and about 20-30 attend the Model United Nations each year. Trips and expeditions all over the world as part of the Round Square – conferences and exchanges, usually for three to four weeks but sometimes for a whole term, and involvement in international projects working with students from other Round Square schools.

Ambitious head of music who previously worked in Barbados 'pushes the boundaries and has got the choirs going'. The school has links with Rochester Choral Society and the chamber choir has recently returned from a trip to Poland. About half the school takes individual music lessons in the music wing with nine practice rooms, a recording studio and digital music suite. 'It's a small, lively department – not that many do music, but those who do are very good and into it,' according to one girl.

Boarding: About 50 per cent board, mostly full with a few weekly and flexi-boarders – school is very accommodating but likes 24 hours' notice unless there is an emergency, and charges accordingly. The younger girls sleep in Main Hall in bright light dorms of two to five. Two sixth form houses – Bligh and Brooke – with single and double rooms, many ensuite. All boarding houses have kitchens and common rooms with large televisions.

Sixth form boarders can eat breakfast and cook supper in their houses – they have a weekly visit to supermarket and are taught about food hygiene. 'We have a lot of fun in the boarding houses and boarding makes you learn how to rub along with people,' said one girl. Girls have genuine friends in different year groups and it really does seem to be a 'home from home'.

No Saturday school, but day girls have to come in on some Saturdays for activities, project work, and some school trips. 'My daughter sometimes asks to stay in for the weekend as the boarders have such fun, especially if there is a tip to Bluewater shopping centre,' said a mother. Cookery club runs on Saturdays: girls cook a meal and eat together in the evening

Background and atmosphere: The school is housed in a grade 1 listed Tudor mansion complete with turrets and chimneys and set in 150 acres of parkland between Gravesend and Rochester, about 30 miles from London and 10 minutes from Ebbsfleet station, with Eurostar connections to mainland Europe. Built for the 10th Baron Cobham in the 16th century and sold to the earls of Darnley in the 18th, it remained their family home until 1957. Often used as a film set, including for the Hetty Feather BBC series by Jacqueline Wilson and feature film Tulip Fever, as well as weddings and conferences. The school was opened in 1962 by Mrs Bee Mansell as an international boarding school for girls where they could enjoy the same education as boys. Cobham joined the Round Square in the early 1970s and was the first girls' school to do so. The name comes from the Round Square building at Gordonstoun, one of the original member schools where the first RS conference took place in 1967. Everyone given a map on arrival but girls quickly get used to their stunning surroundings – the ornate fireplaces and plasterwork ceilings and the glorious Gilt Hall complete with an 18th century organ soon get taken for granted.

Pastoral care, well-being and discipline: The Round Square philosophy 'there is more to you than you think' and 'education through experience' underpins everything the school does. 'It is only when girls step out of their comfort zone that they truly discover themselves.' Girls given a lot of autonomy and encouraged to use opportunities and 'they seem genuinely to care about the Round Square programme,' said one mother. 'Girls want to do well and we put so much pressure on ourselves – it is important to make time for yourself,' said our guide. Girls are trained and expected to take part in the running of the school and all staff and girls vote for the Guardian (head girl).

Older girls very supportive of younger ones and everyone is given a 'big sister' when they arrive; the mixed aged tutor groups in each house means there is good mixing between year groups. 'Everyone is very kind and my daughter and I both felt part of the Cobham family from the start,' said a mother. Years 7-11 have their own common rooms with kitchens, which encourages mixing between day girls and boarders. Weekly 'family lunch' when girls sit in tutor groups and practise their conversation skills. Bullying rare but nipped in the bud and restorative justice applied. Automatic suspension for drugs or alcohol – not that it is an issue here – and repeat offenders would be asked to leave.

The CAS (community, action, service) element of the IB has been extended to the middle school and there is a dedicated member of staff who gives half her time to this – anything from visiting old people's homes and collecting food for food banks to helping out in local primary schools and youth clubs. There is a Christian Union group within the school and those of other faiths are encouraged to worship locally – there is a Sikh temple, mosque and synagogue nearby. Good communication between staff means any problems are picked up quickly

Pupils and parents: About 40 per cent of pupils are foreign nationals, rising to about 60 per cent in the sixth form, with increasing numbers of Europeans. No one nationality dominates; 'girls really do mix' and integration taken seriously – no two girls of the same nationality are allowed to share a bedroom and there are 'small sanctions, like kitchen duty, if you are caught speaking your native language during the day,' said our guide. Day girls come from as far afield as south east London. The school turns out girls who are 'confident and worldly-wise, who are keen to get involved and tend to be quite adventurous. The girls don't grow up too quickly and there is no need to yank up your skirt or slap on the make up as no one is going to see..They are more likely to be seen chatting in Lady Darnley's garden or swinging on "the branch".' 'Turns out confident and beautifully eloquent girls,' said one mother. The girls all see themselves as global citizens and have no fear of travel – 'the Round Square network means they have friends all over the world,' said a parent.

'We have a lot of fun and boarding makes you learn how to rub along with people,' said one girl. Girls have genuine friends in different year groups

Elders, as the old girls are known at Cobham, are hugely loyal to the school and include Mishal Husain, news presenter, Olivia Graham, archdeacon of Berkshire, journalist Alex Crawford, Francesca Amfitiahtrof, creative director at Tiffany's, Princess Antonia, Duchess of Wellington and Kate French, who was part of the modern pentathlon team at Rio.

Entrance: Entry into years 7, 8, 9, 10 and sixth form via tests in English and maths and an interview with the headteacher in the autumn before entry. International students can either take the school's own tests or apply via UKiset. A taster afternoon and sleepover can be arranged at any time and parents are also given the opportunity to get to know each other. Main feeder schools are Steephill and St Joseph's at Gravesend, Pointers in Blackheath and south east London preps and local state primaries – the school runs a minibus service as far as Sevenoaks.

Some 10-20 join from abroad for the increasingly popular one year pre-A level course.

Exit: Around half leave after GCSEs, mainly to larger co-ed schools, local grammars and sixth form colleges. For those who stay on for the sixth form, great trouble is taken to choose a course and university that is right for each girl. Around a fifth to Russell Group universities (one to Cambridge and one medic in 2017); art foundation and business courses popular as are eg criminology and biomedical sciences. One to study fashion design in Milan and one to the royal Conservatoire of Scotland in 2017. Growing expertise in helping girls with the process of applying to foreign universities including Australia and the US – the school is able to help with SATs.

Money matters: Art, drama, music, sport and Round Square scholarships by application, and general (academic) scholarship by invitation only – identified through the entrance assessments. Means-tested bursaries are available for up to 100 per cent of fees.

Remarks: A small, truly international school which turns out compassionate and adventurous global citizens.

Cottesmore School

21

Buchan Hill, Pease Pottage, West Sussex RH11 9AU

01293 520648 | office@cottesmoreschool.com | www.cottesmoreschool.com

Ages: 4-13 (boarding from 8)

Pupils: 175; Boarders: 120 full

Day: £9,363 – £17,535 pa; Boarding: £26,899 pa

Headmaster: Since 2008, Tom Rogerson, married to Lottie, with two small sons, Wilf and Bear. Cottesmore runs in the family (grandad and dad were heads before him) – 'I've been quietly planning to take over since I was 17', said the head. Routed via other schools (Ludgrove, Eaton House and Broomwood); his dad wouldn't let him take the headship too early. Quite right, dad.

Articulate and thoughtful, focuses on each pupil and knows them all – they chatter away happily with him. A strong team with Lottie, who provides ballast for the head's lively energy.

Parents like him – 'He's a warm guy, easy to talk to, and always there when I pick up and drop off from exeats'. Another: 'A school derives its culture from the head – and I like its culture. It places emphasis on traditional Christian values: kindness, courtesy, honour and fair play.'

Entrance: Pre-prep: taster day, during which prospective pupils will do a piece of work assessing English and maths. Prep: English and maths tests, interview (children need to be 'interested and interesting') and head's report from previous school. UKiset test for non-English speakers.

Exit: To many of the more magnificent public schools: Eton, Harrow, Cheltenham Ladies' College, Benenden, Downe House, Winchester, Radley

Remarks: Approach the school past towering rhododendrons, lawns mowed to velvety smoothness, golf flags, the fragrance of flowers and hedges. Cottesmore is a stately Victorian pile – enter through the heavy wooden door carved with mischievous sprites. Wood panelled walls, stately hall with minstrels' gallery; fishing rods leaning casually against the wall in a corridor. Things here are orderly, but it's not an institutional tidiness: there's a feeling of a home, where places for things arise organically and become established through habit.

Grounds which beg to be played in: climbable trees everywhere, from 'the monkeys' – a cave of under rhododendron/tree branches – to the hollow oak: climb its ancient trunk in a circular direction (teacher present, and only up to a certain height). Bamboo for forts and den making – so popular here that it occasionally has official activity status. A parent described his son, who had fallen out of a tree, limping towards his wife on the last exeat – 'he's having a childhood and that's wonderful.'

Children here are bubbling, confident and eager, so keen to tell us about their school that we hardly needed to ask questions. They happily fill their own skin: we've rarely met a group of children so content to be themselves. Some bounced up to say hello and give their views; easily said, in front of their head, what they didn't like about school (the chairs are too low and they want new showers).

We met too, quieter introverts, busy with the library and their model railway in the basement. They've started their own after-supper library lecture series ('tea' was exceedingly popular). Not so likely to bubble eagerly about the things they love; but no hesitation in expressing their views, and total confidence in their value. Geekiness is certainly not frowned upon – 'they're lauded for loving the library', said Lottie.

The head said, 'we're a family school', then chuckled; whether this is a good thing clearly depends on how dysfunctional the family. Certainly the warmth and care seen here must exceed what many families experience at Christmas. Home to 150 pupils ('beautifully small', said a mum).

Broad church here – which means chapel isn't optional. Cultural Christianity, whose values informally underpin the community, but 'we go about it quietly'.

Runs in the family (grandad and dad were heads here before him) – 'I've been quietly planning to take over since I was 17'

An academically rigorous school – 'rigour balanced with fun', said the head. A flamboyant fashion designer to be is celebrated; but 'he has to be good at maths by the time he leaves'. Lack of endeavour here would be a problem – 'that's not an option'.

'Not a pressure cooker', said a parent who has experienced the hothouse of London preps, '[and] notches up in balanced and useful lives'. Relative to other preps in the area, it's doing extremely well: another parent we spoke to was very happy with the academic side, describing it as 'pretty strong and rigorous', with parents getting regular feedback – every three weeks. (His son had just got a place at Harrow – he was an extremely happy dad.)

Small classes, no bigger than 14. Single form entry until year 4, then double form entry, finally splitting in three in the final year. Pupils are streamed (but not labelled) and set within those streams. Academic subjects take place around the quad, the fountain in the middle providing restful accompaniment to those getting their heads down. Lively walls showing work, but order and method evident – displays are exceedingly neat. This school does extremely well at enthusing its pupils: they showed a keen interest in Latin, eagerly pointing out Latin in the roots of words, and telling us their favourite myths.

Children talked with great joy of a trip to Brighton Pier, when older pupils were allowed to go off in groups of four, and told us how much they love the independence – 'at my last school they never stopped watching us'

Maths lessons have been transformed by new IT (iPads, Chromebooks and a Raspberry Pis). Pupils were whizzing through tables on iPads – less time marking means more time teaching; or 'connecting', as the head likes to say. Excelling at maths is something this school particularly prides itself on: the head has increased the number of maths teachers and seen CE scores soar.

A geography teacher was enthusiastically making geography pertinent to the real world: 'What are the pros and cons of building a Tesco in the Cottesmore grounds?' (The head's smile became a little fixed at this point...) Making ant homes was cited by one excited little girl as the best geography lesson ever. Parents are happy that the computer room is well policed: no chatrooms or other elicit YouTube pleasures; no own devices in school (other than for travelling).

Achievement is celebrated through stars (house points), show ups and stay ups. Show ups for extremely good work or behaviour; stay up for a jolly if you come top in an assessment or effort, or when teams have an unbeaten day – popcorn, movie and games. A popular treat.

Learning support helps students who have mild dyslexia, dyspraxia and dyscalculia, also those with speech and language difficulties. Ten to 20 per cent of pupils receive one-to-one help, and in-class assistance (charged as an extra). The fact a child has SEN doesn't make any difference to attainment here, says the head.

Behind a glass panelled door is pre-prep, the colour and liveliness evident through the glass panels. Coloured cellophane hung from the ceiling in strips – 'we're doing under the sea at the moment'. Single form entry, around 10 per class, children seated at round tables, doors in each class opening onto the lawn: a much more relaxed, crazy colour atmosphere than on the other side of the door, but a similarly high standard evident from the written work in displays. The rather extraordinary cubed times tables produced by a boy in year 1 caused adults in the area to look at each other blankly, each hoping one of the others might know if he'd got them right. A parent told us that Cottesmore was the only school they visited which was more interested in the child than the parents: Lottie got right down to her daughter's level – 'so, do you like spiders?' And off they went to find one.

A large array of sports on offer: 33, including all the usual major sports, as well as the less usual: archery, shooting and billiards. Pupils of all abilities play in matches, and even the C and D teams play a good number of fixtures. They win plenty of matches (the Colts As and Bs recently unbeaten in any sport for seven months) and get plenty of support – Danish housekeeping team take great joy in waving their pompoms in support of the third X1.'It is competitive – they care a lot for sport, but they know they have all types, and encourage and get the best out of everyone.'

Houses here are called sets, and there's plenty of friendly inter-set competition. A parent, commenting on the set dash, said 'The whole school cheer each other, particularly the useless ones...To be very kind is to be very Cottesmore', he added.

Indoor heated pool and Astroturf large enough for three tennis courts; three grass courts too, with some boys racing in from playing tennis at break. The 'gravel' – an open sided, covered Astroturf – is so popular that ripping it down was out of the question: the roof has been replaced.

Plenty of clubs, from real tennis to fishing for carp in the pond – 'the film club is just the best', said one girl. Chess compulsory for two years – it's taken very seriously here (under 11 girls champs).

Music is strong, with 80-90 per cent learning instruments; there are three choirs, including the chapel choir, which often tours abroad. The head of music is also head of drama, so every play tends to be a musical, said a parent: Oliver! the last, described by another parent as 'excellent – my quite shy son volunteered for it...'

Everyone in the prep has a bed and boards to some extent: 80 per cent full time, everyone else up to four nights a week (must stick to chosen nights). In this small school, there are no separate boarding houses: everyone just troops upstairs to bed, the matron's flat situated between the boys' and girls' dorms.

Large dormitories for 8, three per room for older pupils, the usual is six. Pupils wake to music – the latest charts.

'Palatial since my day', said a parent; but actually they're mid renovation – decoration of some rooms is a bit tired. Some new loos, one landing with a squidgy new carpet, and couple of lovely lampshades, one in white feathers, another rose shape (both in response to pupil request). Pine bunk beds, well used. Showers and basins clean, but a bit elderly – nice old taps though; 'it's all going', said the head briskly; although the parents we spoke to were happy with it as it is.

Matrons and nurse (who is an angel, we were repeatedly told) reside in nearby rooms on every corridor: if pupils are poorly in the night, they wake the dormitory monitor who gets matron. Lovely bright sick bay, complete with bears and TV.

Year groups take it in turn to occupy the drawing room in evenings (music, piano, chess, Wii dance), other year groups spilling out into hall, library and ICT room, playing ping pong or snooker. Children here flow everywhere – no feeling of being penned into a particular area.

Lots of activities at the weekends: Saturday morning school, then matches; trips on Sundays – children talked with great joy of a trip to Brighton Pier, when older pupils were allowed to go off in groups of four, and told us how much they love the independence – 'at my last school they never stopped watching us', said one, impatiently. 'Here, they trust us'.

Children keep in touch by email 'asking for things', Sunday letter writing, Skype and can phone if they want to.

Each class sends a rep to the school council and food committee – a food committee board in a class room simply stated 'BETTER BURGER'; but they don't have much to complain about: they've won awards for their food, which a parent described as 'brilliant' – the custard (with stewed apple) was clearly not just tipped from a tin of Ambrosia.

The children's happiness is testament to how well they are cared for – and indeed the school Happiness Charter is on the wall of every room. A parent described the school as 'gentle'; they chose Cottesmore for its rounded, happy pupils, and nurturing environment. Easy for pupils to speak to staff here – they're all out in the hall at break time, accompanied by their coffee trolley.

Certainly the best mannered children we've met at a prep, leaping to their feet if we so much as glanced over, opening doors, shaking hands. Watching the children, it seemed evident that the respectful environment influences how they treat each other.

Time out area on a wooden chest in front of the study – pupils who've been a bit rowdy perch there until they've calmed down. A clear bullying policy: pupils and staff are expected to bring forward if they see it. The one incident a parent described to us was 'clamped down on quickly'.

Pupils from London, home counties, and abroad, including expats and diplomats (about a third of boarders from overseas). Lots of London parents, but not the competitive ones (school reckons that leavers' list suggests some parents are competitive). A parent from London told us he looked at 20 prep schools, and Cottesmore had the best combination of options one could get: 'A* in all the things that really matter in life'.

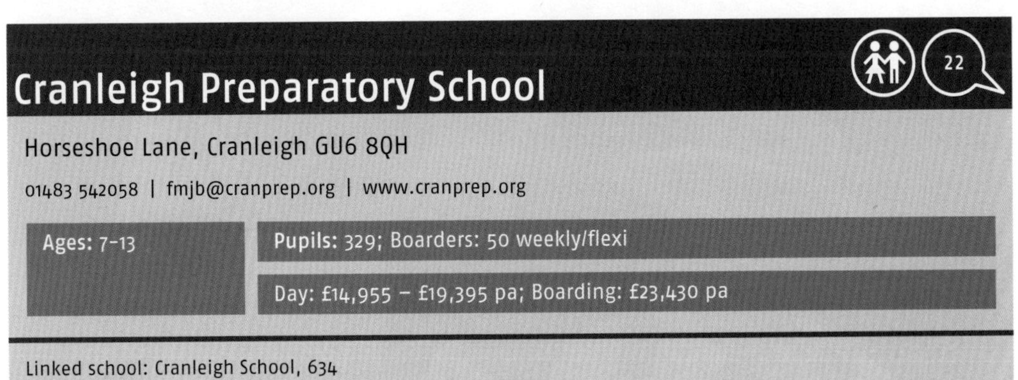

Cranleigh Preparatory School

22

Horseshoe Lane, Cranleigh GU6 8QH

01483 542058 | fmjb@cranprep.org | www.cranprep.org

Ages: 7-13

Pupils: 329; Boarders: 50 weekly/flexi

Day: £14,955 – £19,395 pa; Boarding: £23,430 pa

Linked school: Cranleigh School, 634

Headmaster: Since 2008, Mr Michael Wilson BSc (50s). Raised in Africa, educated in Kenya and at Sherborne then Keele University. He started his teaching career in the early '80s at Cranleigh as a chemistry teacher and sports coach in the senior school. After a few years he returned to Africa, held teaching posts at a couple of schools in Nairobi and was a national and Davis Cup team tennis coach.

The draw of Cranleigh pulled him back and over the next seven years he worked through deputy house master, head of sixth form girls and girls' housemaster. After short-lived posts in Thailand and at Bradfield he was back at Cranleigh as housemaster in the senior school again, 'brought back to help sort out boarding,' he tells us. Then in 2002 he became head at Edge Grove Prep and finally moved back to Cranleigh Prep as head in 2008.

His own 'uncluttered' Kenyan childhood forms the core of his beliefs about how childhood is best conducted and is a recurring theme in his conversation. He likes old-fashioned values, letter writing, good manners and the freedom to play unfettered outdoors; he doesn't like materialism, selfishness and moaning. He believes daily chapel is important for reflecting on shared values and the Christian ethos of the school.

The school has a family theme for the Wilsons; Mrs Wilson heads up the prep's learning support department and their three children have all been educated at least in part at Cranleigh. Mr Wilson's long-term on-off career here means he has taught the parents of many of his current pupils.

Mr Wilson tells us that he sees all parents at school social events or parent briefings and reminds them to 'buy into the whole school', meaning they should celebrate and support all the teams whether their children are in them or not. 'They may get their chance in the future but not everyone can play for the firsts and it's a lesson in life'.

Moving on in July 2018 to head Cranleigh Abu Dhabi. Successor will be Neil Brooks, currently principal of Fulham Prep Schools.

Parents describe it as 'busy, robust and challenging' and those children who enjoy life here are energetic and sporty

Entrance: The main entry point is at 7+, with another chunk of pupils wanting to join at 11+, enough to add one or two more classes. During the assessment day for entry at 7, children complete comprehension, maths, spelling and reasoning on computer, plus a handwritten piece of creative writing; they also take part in art and PE sessions. Quite a day for a 6-year-old, although the school does 'try to make it as relaxed as possible'. For entry at 11 children come to an 'activity morning' for an interview plus art, sports, problem solving and team building sessions. They then return a few months later for computer based maths, reasoning, spelling and reading plus handwritten comprehension and creative writing. At this stage children are being assessed on whether or not they would thrive academically and socially at the Cranleigh School across the road. However, this is not a pre-test for the senior school; pupils still need to take common entrance and go through the formal admissions process at Cranleigh School. Crucially, Mr Wilson ensures he meets the parents, usually twice, and talks to feeder heads. He tells us he uses his 'gut feeling' about which children will cope with and contribute to Cranleigh.

Exit: Around 85 per cent move 'across the road' (an oft used phrase here) to Cranleigh School. The links between prep and senior schools are increasingly strong and up to a third win Cranleigh scholarships. However, it is quite accepted that others will want to move elsewhere and they are given equal support and advice. Those who do move go on to a wide range of public schools including Wellington College, Charterhouse, Millfield, St Catherine's Bramley, Prior's Field

There were recently 47 scholarships garnered, 10 of which were academic (9 of the latter were to Cranleigh School). Outside of the Cranleigh School scholarships, there were also scholarships to Brighton College (including an academic one), Charterhouse, Millfield, Prior's Field, Reigate Grammar and Wellington College.

Remarks: A traditional prep school with an outdoorsy, sporty feel. Whilst it's co-ed, the boyish culture seems to dominate somewhat. Parents describe it as 'busy, robust and challenging' and those children who enjoy life here are energetic, sporty and have a sense of humour about 'banter' from other pupils and younger staff. Families are generally well-heeled, some extremely so, mostly from the surrounding countryside and villages. They pitch up to school events and matches, often more dads making an appearance than at other schools, and describe themselves as a pretty vocal and often demanding lot. Mr Wilson tells us he spends plenty of time seeing parents one to one, managing expectations.

Academically inclusive with the range of abilities catered for by extensive setting within classes and, in the top two years, streaming into one scholarship and three or four common entrance forms depending on numbers. 'Academics have been upped, which is no bad thing,' reported a parent of long standing; another told us her scholarship form daughter gains confidence from being at the top here academically. Learning support, co-ordinated by Mrs Wilson and her specialist team, is 'at the centre rather than a satellite' with dyscalculia, dyspraxia and dyslexia all catered for and just under a fifth of pupils receiving some level of support. Needs are spotted early on and thoroughly addressed with classroom assistants and interventions in small groups or one-to-one. All pupils' progress is closely monitored via a thorough record system with inputs from all staff.

Art is of an amazingly high standard. The head of art is confident and enthusiastic about children's abilities and she seems to get fantastic work out of everyone. The art room is stuffed full of current projects by pupils of all ages, including some really unusual ceramics, textiles and sculptures alongside more expected drawing and painting. Talented artists could find the perfect niche here.

Drama and music are also well covered; both are part of the curriculum for all ages with numerous performances each year. Individual instrumental or singing lessons are held in the music school, recently enlarged with the addition of a practice room for ensembles and choirs. Talented musicians benefit from a programme called Cranleigh Music 7-18 in which music teachers work at both Cranleigh Prep and Cranleigh School and the most able musicians play in ensembles across the age range.

Sport is a major focus of school life, whether you ask pupils, parents or staff; it's timetabled every day with matches mid-week and on alternate Saturdays. Rugby and hockey are big, but there are less usual options including riding over at the senior school's on-site stables. The Cranleigh Sport 7-18 programme brings sports staff over from the senior school to spot talent and coach at all levels. Parents expect their children to be able to represent the school in matches and teams are fielded from A to D to give everyone a good chance. Of course pupils know who will be in the As but they say, 'it's possible to get places in other teams'. Non-sporty or quiet bookish children may well find this whole active vibe just too much; as one parent says, 'it's horses for courses'.

Pastoral care is the remit of the deputy head; she has been at Cranleigh Prep for 21 years and is familiar with the ups and downs of life here. Incidents are tracked and dealt with pragmatically, parents are phoned, high jinks are recognised,

punishments are taken and pupils move on. An annual anti-bullying questionnaire identifies any new issues – such as the ever-present Facebook, which has been addressed using a visiting outside agency to talk to children and parents. A few parents have told us about persistent unkindness from other children which has left their own feeling upset and unsupported; the deputy head responds that bullying and unkindness are taken seriously, efforts are focused on changing unsociable behaviour and pupils have been suspended in the past. She points out that she recently asked staff to send her any notes from parents praising their children's care and her file of these is much thicker than her file of dissatisfied and problematic correspondence.

Her scholarship form daughter gains confidence from being at the top here academically

The great outdoors is what defines Cranleigh: acres of grassy pitches, an astro pitch, tennis courts and netball courts. The senior school across the road dominates the views, keeping that future option ever in mind. The buildings are a mix of Edwardian and a hotch-potch of newer, including a recent one providing three more classrooms and a common room. Some are a bit disappointing inside, a few rather poky classrooms and a sports and performance hall which felt like a cavernous shed; others are good, the well-stocked library, a couple of IT suites with brand new desks and integral computers and the welcoming, very comfortable reception area. The school is currently having a further new development built which will house classrooms, three science labs, design & technology, food technology and a veranda to boot, overlooking the cricket pitch.

Boarding houses are traditional, or somewhat old-fashioned depending on your view. The girls' boarding house we visited (18 girls board compared with 28 boys) had dorms for four or six boarders, high windows, firm mattresses and lots of Justin Bieber and 1-Direction posters. In the bathroom, rows of wash basins, four or five showers and a bath. Two matrons are always on hand to keep an eye on things for boarders and day pupils; they offer TLC in their cosy room or the next door sick bay or in the brightly furnished sitting room cheerfully labelled the Ikea Room. Boarding is weekly or flexi with a minimum of two nights a week; there are no weekend boarders. Although day pupils hugely outnumber boarders, the daily routine of late finishing, prep at school and Saturday school on alternate weeks feels rather more like a boarding school.

A few scholarship awards are given to exceptional candidates at 11, nothing earlier. Sibling discounts are available for third and subsequent siblings at any stage in Cranleigh Prep or senior school.

In short, a sporty co-ed school run on traditional lines in a glorious rural setting with strong links to its senior school. A good choice for a broad education, less academically pressured than many others and with plenty of learning support for those who need it. Robust and energetic pupils preferred.

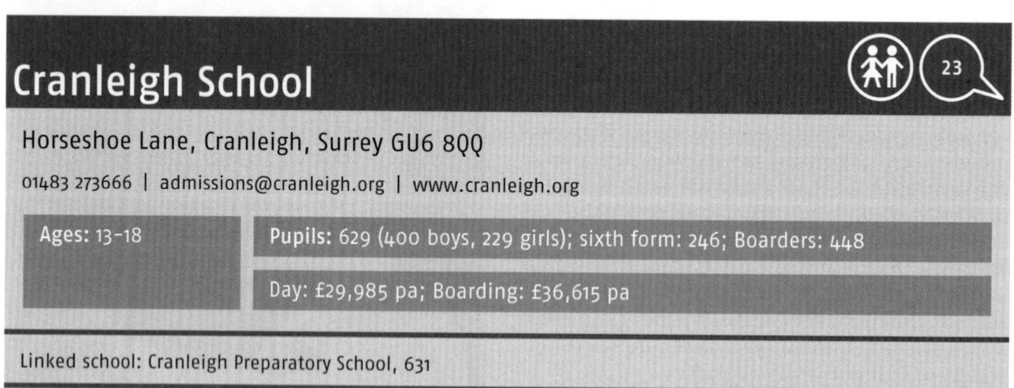

Cranleigh School

23

Horseshoe Lane, Cranleigh, Surrey GU6 8QQ

01483 273666 | admissions@cranleigh.org | www.cranleigh.org

Ages: 13–18

Pupils: 629 (400 boys, 229 girls); sixth form: 246; Boarders: 448

Day: £29,985 pa; Boarding: £36,615 pa

Linked school: Cranleigh Preparatory School, 631

Headmaster: Since 2014, Mr Martin Reader (40s). Brought up in Orpington and attended St Olave's Grammar School, which he describes as 'an academic school that also offered breadth of sport, art and music.' Thence to University College, Oxford where he read English, played lots of rugby and stayed on for an MPhil (his dissertation was on an 'anonymous early Scottish poem'). Also has an MBA in school leadership. Harboured early ambition to be a television presenter and has the look – think twinkly but unimpeachable silver fox.

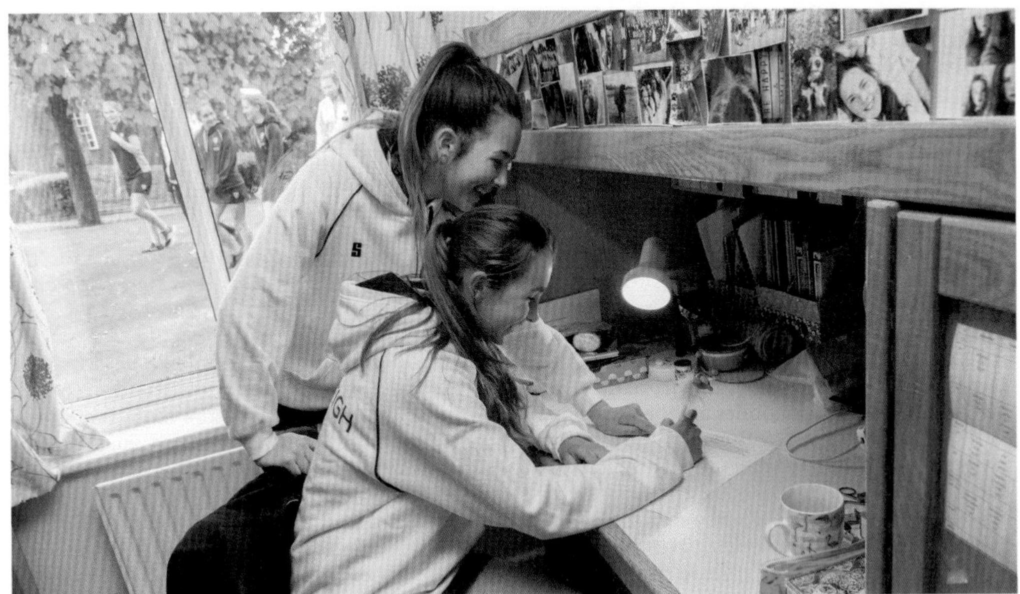

First teaching post and first experience of a boarding school was at St Edward's Oxford, from there he went to Oundle and then to Reigate Grammar where he was senior deputy head before taking up headship of Wellington School in Somerset, where he spent eight years. Loves the boarding ethos, 'Boarding gives us time to develop deeper trust and partnership. Nothing is more rewarding than having time to talk to children.'

He describes his headship as 'coming home' and says he has found Cranleigh parents to be 'very grounded.' They in turn describe Mr Reader as 'a very good fit', 'approachable', 'diplomatic' and 'visionary'. Changes he's made have been generally well received: lessons are now 50 minutes instead of 35 ('gives pupils more time to think and encourages problem solving', he says) and there's a drive to get pupils going with independent learning skills from the prep school up. His mission to 'ensure we are current' has lead to the appointment of a head of contemporary music to support 'non-traditional' musicians. Art provision has had a makeover and the new head of DT is a robotics specialist. What makes Mr R's heart sink is 'constant measuring'. He fears 'the enriching cultural experience' that lies at the heart of a good education is in danger of being sacrificed on the academic altar. 'It is possible to do both and be successful,' he says.

Head feels school needs to 'burst the Surrey bubble' and to that end has encouraged the Beyond Cranleigh programme. Pupils help the local community, litter picking, working in local schools and staging joint concerts. He is developing an exchange with a Chinese school and building on longstanding links with a community primary school in Zambia. His wife, Amanda, who is head of careers, is also very involved with this project. The Readers have a son at the prep and a daughter in the senior school.

Might it all be too much for some, we asked one mother? She thought not: 'Yes, it's full-on but the children are so happy and if they're happy, they perform better'

Outside school Mr Reader enjoys cooking and he also preaches in the local church. He's a trustee of the Hawk and Owl Trust and hopes to encourage barn owls to nest on campus (maybe he should offer a barn owl bursary...). Favourite book? 'Crime and Punishment. It's got everything – violence, love, tragedy, morality.' No owls though. When asked to sum up the Cranleigh ethos he says, 'It's a competitive school. We love to compete but we play for the shirt, not individual glory.'

Academic matters: One competition school doesn't enter is the race for exam league table glory – the Cranleigh way is educational breadth rather than narrow academic focus. Nevertheless, the healthy spread of exam grades from A* to Cs and Ds, not to mention a good handful of Oxbridge places every year, confirms that teaching covers the spectrum of ability. In 2017, very creditable 68 per cent A*-A/9-7 at GCSE; at A level it was 41 per cent A*/A (72 per cent A*-B). General feeling is that Mr Reader will tighten academics where necessary. The newly-appointed director of teaching, learning and innovation (who also teaches physics) told us about plans to build up the EPQ and a school-wide drive to embed independent learning and thinking skills.

We sat in on a fourth year art lesson where not everybody was as engaged as they might have been, but it was just before lunch. Fair to say this is not a school where you will find silent concentration behind every classroom door – we got the feeling that while most eyes were on the board, more hearts were outside on the pitch. A level options pretty standard but also include geology and Greek (as two-year AS courses) and, unsurprisingly, PE. English, history and economics are the most popular subjects at A level, followed by maths and sciences. Very small numbers for music and languages – as elsewhere. Pre-U so far only for maths and further maths. Cranleigh also runs its own specially designed EPQ courses with everyone taking perspectives on science or culture and humanity course.

Around 100 pupils with SEN, mostly mild dyslexia etc. Some receive one-to-one tuition (extra cost) but most are supported in class. Parents were keen to tell us how well their very different children have done, 'Pupils are treated as individuals academically,' and 'There are lots of subject clinics and if a child needs some hand-holding they'll get it.' One mother said that the teaching at Cranleigh had 'absolutely been the making' of her daughter.

Golf mainly played for relaxation, pupils told us, but that doesn't stop the golf team winning inter-school tournaments

Longer lesson times took a while to bed in, 'My children complained at first but they appreciate them now.'

Games, options, the arts: Cranleigh has 31 sports pitches and appears to be outstanding on all of them. This success is all the more impressive considering that the school is half the size of its closest rivals, 'We have to play big schools to get all our teams matches,' the deputy head told us. He added, 'Sport here is about participation, not just about the elite. Everyone is expected to be involved, staff as well as pupils.' Recent silverware includes National Rugby 7s schoolboy champions, Finegold Cup (riding), under 16 girls' indoor and outdoor hockey champions and Devizes to Westminster (international kayaking challenge) title holders. There will undoubtedly have been more wins since so best see school website for latest. Average of 29 teams playing on match Saturdays which doesn't leave many to cheer from the sidelines. More than 20 sports are on offer, there's a nine hole golf course – golf mainly played for relaxation pupils told us, but that doesn't stop the golf team winning inter-school tournaments – several Astros and a conditioning room. Two physios, a sports doctor and strength and conditioning coaches on hand to tailor individual fitness and nutrition programmes. Equestrian centre has two all-weather arenas and 60 acres of grazing and riding land. Pupils may bring their own ponies; those without learn on the school ponies.

Music and drama are tackled with typical gusto. According to the school's handy infographic, Cranleigh in Numbers, there are nine plays and 70 concerts (home-grown and visiting talent) a year. The arts certainly aren't a competition-free zone with keenly fought contests for house dance, singing and drama. Strings and woodwind also compete (separately), as do poets and creative writers. Speech Hall is the largest performance venue, seating up to 500 and there are two smaller studio theatres. When we visited one of these was being very creatively fitted out for a junior production of Treasure Island. The Merriman Music School (named after first headmaster) has a 100 seat auditorium and 14 practice rooms. School bands can practice in the fully soundproofed 'rock room'. New head of contemporary music adds another, possibly louder, string to school's bow. 'Spine-tingling' congregational singing is more than fully supported by splendid three manual-pipe Mander organ in chapel. Organist in residence gives lunchtime recitals and organ lessons are available. Much participation at all levels, but as elsewhere, small uptake for music and drama A levels.

Plenty of extracurricular options, including visiting speakers and lecture programme for A level students. Timetabling genius ensures CCF and D of E don't clash. There's so much going on it's hard to see how pupils fit everything in; little wonder day pupils stay until 9pm several nights a week. Might it all be too much for some, we asked one mother. She thought not: 'Yes, it's full-on but the children are so happy and if they're happy, they perform better.'

To conclude, Cranleigh is a very sporty school but, as parents and staff were at pains to tell us, it's not just a sporty school. Message received. Even so, perhaps not the confirmed ball dodger's first choice.

Boarding: Four boys' and three girls' houses; a new girls' house opened in September 2017. No flexi boarding, day pupils are fully part of boarding houses and have a cabin desk in boarders' rooms – it's their 'centre of gravity' within the school where they do prep, get changed for sport, make toast and drinks and take part in house activities. Day pupils can sleep over occasionally if activities such as school plays or trips finish very late and 'we will always scoop up in an emergency.' All do prep in their rooms 'with doors open and prefects in corridors.' 'We expect proper, disciplined work,' said housemaster. Tutors are on hand to inspect and any slackers can expect a short sharp spell at one of the 'naughty boy desks'.

Head of contemporary music adds another, possibly louder, string to school's bow. 'Spine-tingling' congregational singing supported by splendid Mander organ

Boys' houses are, inevitably, older and, though clean and bright, looked pretty worn out. Grubby polystyrene ceiling tiles rarely enhance a room and walls looked as though they'd been crashed into by generations of schoolboys – probably because they have. Common areas very lived in; walls decorated with team photos and vintage style black and white shots of heroes: Mohammed Ali, Steve McQueen, James Dean. Dorms of up to four for first years, single study bedrooms for sixth formers. Very few personal touches (artistic arrangements of massive shoes don't count), but that's boys' boarding for you. Sixth formers' single study bedrooms looked better – more in the way of photos and posters. Matron's room is the focal point on the ground floor from where she keeps an eye on comings and goings. Nice big garden for kickabouts and barbecues. All upper sixth formers are prefects – 'they're positive role models' – and year groups are mixed (not segregated by corridor). The housemaster stressed how 'integrated' the year groups were and how seriously his sixth form prefects took their house responsibilities. 'We have a beer and a chat with the prefects, they're quick to notice if things are getting a bit scratchy.'

All in all one feels that the concept of gender fluidity has yet to find a foothold in Surrey. Girls' houses are modern, done out in pinks and purples and considerably better provided for on the soft furnishing front. Perhaps they could loan a few beanbags or pom-poms to the boys? Matron ('She knows everything,' our guides said) resides in a room just like a family kitchen, with sofas, throws and lots of photos. Girls can make drinks and snacks and talk over the day's events in comfort. Study bedrooms (most are doubles, some ensuite) are tidy and colourful, bedecked with bunting and fairy lights. Girls are 'affiliated' to boys' houses – 'it fosters co-ed spirit', we were told – and join them for activities such as plays, music and themed socials (wine and cheese, jazz).

Staff reassured us that houses are competitive 'but not tribal' and that the school works very hard to mix pupils up, especially important when so many come from the prep across the road.

Background and atmosphere: Founded in 1865 by George Cubitt, MP for West Surrey, and Rev John Sapte, who decided that what Victorian Surrey needed was 'a public school for the education of the middle classes.' The school was to 'provide a sound and plain education ... for the sons of farmers and others engaged in commercial pursuits.' The Surrey County School, funded by public appeals, was built on eight acres at the top of a hill just outside the village of Cranleigh. As the school grew to its present 280 acres, neighbouring farms were gradually acquired, remembered only in names such as The Butts (a sixth form café). If the original red-brick buildings embody the school's founding ideals: 'sound and plain', their elevated position at the top of a short avenue lends a certain aspirational grandeur. Most recent addition, the Emms Centre, houses modern foreign languages, science labs and IT, its double height atrium, flooded with natural light, was being well used by pupils revising for exams when we visited. A new humanities teaching block with dedicated business and careers centre is next, but definitely not last, in line.

Transition to co-ed, which started in the 1970s, was finally realised in 1999, but numerical equality of boys and girls is not on the cards. A ratio of 60:40 in favour of the chaps is the desired aim and the third girls' boarding house should help achieve it. No plans for significant increase in pupil numbers and parents certainly think school is 'just the right size'.

Parents told us they felt Cranleigh's reputation as a school that was just good for sport was always unfair and has, finally, been laid to rest. 'The school itself hasn't changed but the mindset of some people has', one told us. In our last review we noted that Cranleigh had become 'fashionable'. The school is undoubtedly still fashionable but its enduring popularity owes more to highly satisfied pupils and parents than any transient modishness. A 'sister' school, Cranleigh Abu Dhabi, was opened in 2014.

Pastoral care, well-being and discipline: 'Houses are everything' at Cranleigh, both academically and pastorally. 'Returning to your house should be like coming through a family door,' we were told. Each is almost like a mini-school but they 'aren't empires' and are run on consistent lines. Houseparents have a detailed overview of every aspect of a pupil's school career and tutors, teachers and prefects form 'layers' to catch problems. The parents we spoke to were very positive about all aspects of pastoral care, several commented on how well the school had dealt with 'difficult' teenage moments. 'They're so supportive, whatever the problem,' said one parent. Another told us, 'they expect the pupils to be independent but they know exactly when to step in.' Tutors are very quick to pick up on and let parents know about missed homework deadlines – whether the child is a boarder or day pupil, 'they want to work with parents'.

All in all one feels that the concept of gender fluidity has yet to find a foothold in Surrey. Girls' houses are done out in pinks and purples

Pupils told us that their opinions were listened to although the democratic triumphs we heard about were small and mainly food based: Weetabix is now served every morning, spaghetti hoops are on the Wednesday menu and pepper is back on the tables (we couldn't find out why it disappeared). More significantly, after some wrangling, a termly teaching feedback survey will be implemented. 'It will improve communication', our guides said. Teachers weren't available for comment.

We heard several observations to the effect that expectations were higher for girls and that it was possibly a bit easier being a boy at Cranleigh. These weren't criticisms, consensus is that school is right to make allowances for chaps' 'rough and tumble', although the interior décor of their boarding houses might disagree. Relationships between pupils are 'few' but 'managed extremely well'; the rules are crystal clear and it's not the Cranleigh way to break them – apparently 'you just wouldn't do that.'

Pupils and parents: Very much a local (home counties and London) boarding school – nearly all parents live within a two hour drive and matches, plays and concerts are very well supported as a consequence. 'I love the fact that my children get a great education and also have local friends', a mother told us. While school didn't seem to us as high end as its popular reputation suggests, a quick count of the Range Rovers doing Sunday night drop off will give you the superficial demographic. That 'Surrey bubble' may be in Mr Reader's sights but perhaps he's going to need a bigger pin.

Pupils are relaxed, confident and friendly, 'not overly sophisticated', said one mother, approvingly. There appears to be some leeway when it comes to hair and uniform (especially skirts below the knee rule) and many of the boys looked like they'd be much more comfortable in sports gear than suits. Very small number of international students, mainly from Russia and Poland. Former pupils include numbers of successful sportspeople, fair few military types plus Patrick Marber (actor, director, screenwriter); actors Julia Ormond, Laurence Naismith and Michael Cochrane; historian Andrew Roberts and former editor of the Guardian, Alan Rusbridger.

Entrance: About half come at 13+ from Cranleigh prep. Also Feltonfleet, Aldro, Danes Hill, Godstowe, Amesbury and Windlesham House. From 2019 the majority of places will be offered at 11+ for a 13+ start. Applicants are invited for an assessment day with a short test in English and maths and an interview to make 'an informal assessment of their interests and abilities.' Conditional offers made on the basis of this and reference from current school. Offer dependent on performance in CE or other assessments. School says it is looking for children who will thrive academically but also those who will make the most of the many opportunities on offer. All schools say this but oversubscribed Cranleigh means it and can afford to be choosy.

A few places are available at 16+ but competition is strong. Candidates should be predicted A*-A/9-7 grades at I/GCSE and must sit verbal and non-verbal reasoning papers and submit an essay. Interview and reference also required.

Exit: A few leave post-GCSE, mostly to pursue courses not offered at school. University destinations and courses of those who stay on are as diverse as one might imagine. Lots to Bath, Birmingham, Bristol, Exeter, Durham, Newcastle and York. Handful to Europe and North America. One to Oxbridge in 2017.

Money matters: Fees broadly in line with similar schools. Day fees towards the upper end of the scale but you are paying for six long days a week. Variety of scholarships on offer (music, sports, all-rounder) and these can be supplemented by means-tested bursaries.

Remarks: Cranleigh's motto, 'Ex cultu robur' (From culture comes strength), is a potent and timely reminder that education is about so much more than just exam results. This is a school where the team is defined as much by its fellowship as its success, although it helps that team Cranleigh does win quite a lot of the time. Mr Reader has distilled the famous Cranleigh ethos into five words: wholeness, time, family, love and hope. We think he's got it about right.

Cumnor House Sussex
24
Danehill, Haywards Heath, West Sussex RH17 7HT
01825 790347 | registrar@cumnor.co.uk | www.cumnor.co.uk
Ages: 2-13 (boarding from 7)
Pupils: 394; Boarders: 80 full and flexi
Day: £10,140 – £19,155 pa; Boarding: £22,800 pa

Headmaster: Since 2001, Christian Heinrich BA PGCE (40s). Degrees from Kent and Oxford. Previously housemaster, then deputy head, at Summer Fields. ISI Inspector, IAPS appraiser of fellow heads, and chairman of the Boarding Schools Association in 2013, so plenty of insight into schools at all levels. Confident, and very sure of his approach to childhood and education: 'If a child is happy, education takes care of itself.' Described by pupils as fair, fun and someone who 'doesn't get unreasonably cross.' Most important quality for pupils to achieve in their time at Cumnor House: consideration. Loves films, skiing and wine; takes great joy in picking the bottles for post-parents' evening jollies.

Parents are very enthusiastic about him: 'Incredibly kind and supportive of kids – particularly those who struggle'; 'Easy to see when you want to'. 'Radical and brave...in that he works for the kids and not the parents,' added one parent thoughtfully, giving the example of his support for strong story lines in year 8 film making: a recent film told of a child desperate to win a swimming gala who practises all night and drowns. It was felt parents might not be able to stomach this ending, and a parent version was filmed in which the child comes up for a breath. Parents might find it difficult to accept the extraordinary level of pressure to succeed that can be absorbed by children – but the head and pupils here are fully cognisant, and the head does what he can to relieve the pressure.

Married to Belinda, who teaches French in the pre-prep; they have four children.

Entrance: Non-selective in early years; thereafter selection of those most likely to be fully involved in school life. Prospective pupils join in for a day to be observed for fit, with interviews for the occasional candidate for year 6 or above. Most join in nursery or year 3, but there's a healthy smattering in other years up to year 5. No waiting list as such; but they'll only show you around if there's a space. Two full bursaries for talented (academic and/or sport and creative arts) pupils joining year 4, covering 100 per cent of fees up to 18 at one of the partner schools (these are Ardingly, Benenden, Eastbourne College, Hurstpierpoint College, King's Canterbury, Lancing College, Mayfield, Radley, Roedean, St Mary's Ascot, Sevenoaks, Tonbridge and Worth) – apply by April to join in September.

Exit: To a large variety of senior schools (30+), with Hurstpierpoint most popular recently, then Cranleigh and Brighton College, Ardingly and Charterhouse. In directing children towards schools, considers not just whether they can meet the academic requirements, but also whether they're sufficiently emotionally robust to cope with life at the school in question.

Remarks: Beautiful setting in the Sussex countryside overlooking the downs. Buildings range from the charming to the unremarkable, in a village-like cluster. The core of the school was once a farmhouse, and some feel of this remains, with the carcass of a barn, formerly a splendid all-weather outdoor area, recently revamped into 'music HQ', and a new science, technology, engineering and maths centre called The Peake. Lush green grounds, and large pond to row over in the Cumnor boat, or swing over on a rope (it's drained and cleaned and carefully tested for any virulent bacteria first, assured the head's wife).

Main entrance is slightly scuffed country house hotel – parquet floor and log fire, and a few Famous Five books on a window sill by a sofa. Lego table and 70s sweets jigsaw on the go. 'Another genius from Cumnor' cushions – to reassure existing parents, or perhaps tempt prospective ones?

Common room with a log fire, couple of pool tables and newspapers (including Times and Independent) – not read at the time of our tour, but perhaps flicking through the papers comes later in the day. Award-winning art work on the walls, and a long piece of paper where pupils had drawn self-portraits in the style of Quentin Blake to celebrate World Book Day. A new library area provides a welcome space for peace and calm.

Sport is for awareness, commitment and health – and everyone: a poor, enthusiastic player will be in teams all the way through, playing matches

Pre-prep is a cosy separate entity that particularly attracted one mum, who remembers fondly the special mothers' day celebration in reception, children presenting mums with handpicked flowers wrapped in foil, then escorting them into school for special cakes and poems – 'very simple and lovely.'

'Academic, but not pushy academic,' says the head. Certainly a school which achieves a goodly number of scholarships, but not, in atmosphere or method, like a prep with an eye on the prize for

the duration. Many parents fresh from pressurised London preps may struggle initially with the comparatively relaxed Cumnor environment – 'you don't know at what level everyone else's child is reading,' said one startled mum. Take a deep breath, parents: your kids are not going to be constantly tested, so you won't receive that reassuring stream of test results as evidence that they are progressing nicely towards the senior school of choice. I have to tell them to trust us, says the head – 'children are meant to be enjoying themselves and having fun.'

So things don't get really serious until years 7 and 8, when a scholarship set comes into being. The focus shifts somewhat towards achieving the desirable scholarships, and others start preparing for common entrance.

Usual range of subjects, with children being put into sets from year 5. Just French and Latin on the languages front – Latin is the basis of European languages, says the head, and teaches logic which can apply to other subjects, giving a derisive snort in passing to other schools' cosmetic glance at Mandarin. Careful consideration of the timetable, which is broken up so kids are not using their brains in the same way for long periods of time – pre-prep dance outside before each maths lesson. No one model fits all – so if there is good reason for the usual school curriculum not to apply to a child, then an exception will be made.

Not much prep until year 7: just vocab and spelling, which could be learnt in the bath or around the dinner table, and reading, occasionally left undone – 'I don't read on Friday nights as mummy and daddy have gin and tonic,' said a child in year 1.

Year 7 and 8s all have iPads for use during lessons, purchased by parents in an optional scheme ('you didn't have to sign up, but if everyone else was going to have one...'). No social media or unsuitable apps.

Learning support is excellent, and not only provides support to (around 30) pupils with special needs, but also to those who just need a bit of extra help now and then. There's an educational psychologist on the staff, who observes classes, and deals with any emotional problems suffered by pupils which may be exacerbated by school, from separation anxiety to bereavement. No extra charge for counselling or one-to-one learning support. Additional charges for extras such as speech therapy.

Saturday school on alternate weekends, which children seem happy with (though some parents would prefer a lie in, and more family time).

School motto – 'be kind' permeates everything, said one parent: apparently the head boy's job is to make sure everyone is happy at break time, and no one is being left out; so it comes as no surprise that the pastoral care is very thorough: regular full staff

pastoral care meetings where every child's name is read out, and their welfare considered, and a new well-being curriculum programme. Form teachers are the first port of call for difficulties until year 5, after which each child has a tutor whom they meet twice once a week to talk about everything and anything. School policy on bullying is to make sure children understand what bullying behaviour is, and ask them to blow the whistle: senior children attend the ABC committee (Anti-Bullying Committee) every week to report on anyone they are worried about. One parent whose child experienced bullying behaviour said it was dealt with quickly and efficiently, and also praised the presence of 'gappers' (gap year students), who she said could pick up on things teachers might not get to hear.

Take a deep breath, parents: your kids are not going to be constantly tested, so you won't receive that reassuring stream of results

C of E, but not evangelically so. Exposure to the most valuable tenets of faith with a bohemian touch: daily prayers described by head as also a school silence – a time for a loud school to be silent and consider things (there is a cheery noise as kids move around here, but children are friendly and well mannered).

The school shares facilities in the local community, and links with a local primary each year. The head is setting up the Cumnor certificate (own brand D of E), which will involve years 7 and

8 working in the local community, and being part of drama workshops with younger pupils from local primaries.

Food is 'amazing' say kids – apparently there are no adjectives which can do justice to the wraps. In-house custard creams and jammy dodgers bulge with cream and jam and were startlingly yummy to those of us used to the pedestrian version (they've got an award winning pastry chef). Well, if the cushions didn't do it for you...

Occupations, as clubs are called at Cumnor, range from boules to calligraphy, and vary each term. Cinematography described in detail by enthusiastic kids – 'it makes you look at films in a completely different way.' There's a waiting list for cooking, but everyone gets a turn eventually. Year 8 learn to cook a three course meal as a post-exam treat.

The 'co-curriculum' (sports and arts) is given equal rather than ornamental value here ('they find out what every child has going for them,' said a parent).

Sport is for awareness, commitment and health – and everyone: a poor, enthusiastic player will be in teams all the way through, playing matches most weeks. 'It's nice to win,' said a pupil; but it's not the only or main purpose of sport here. No A, B or C teams until year 7: teams change from week to week, and the make-up of teams depends on whom they are playing. Lots of it – up to seven sessions a week, including swimming. Ample playing fields and courts with views over the rolling downs, and a new Olympic size Astroturf. Swish indoor swimming pool, old chilly outdoor version.

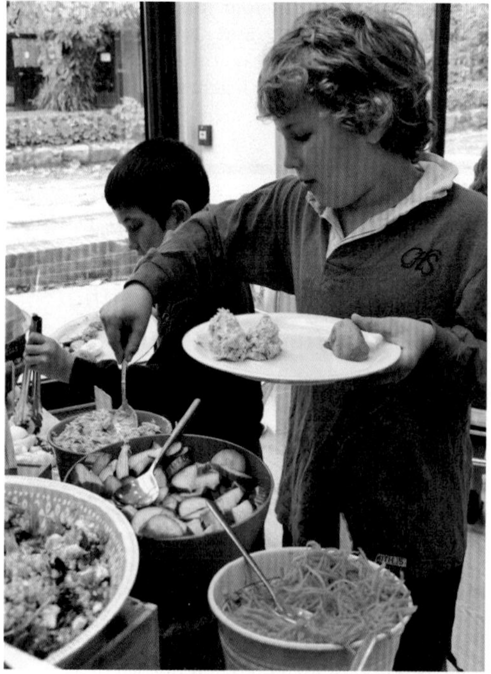

Art is 'exceptional,' said one parent. Housed in a barn-like room with high beams, glass doors and space to hang strange colourful objects. Secured the two top prizes in the Royal College of Art Young Art Exhibition last year.

School motto – 'be kind' – permeates everything, said one parent: apparently the head boy's job is to make sure everyone is happy at break time

All learn a musical instrument – it can be dropped in year 7 to make way for the demands of common entrance and scholarships, though many continue. Eight instrumental groups, from orchestra to the sort-of-samba group.

Each year from year 3 upwards does an annual production, Shakespeare being the year 8 remit (one heavyweight, one adapted comedy for those with less Olivier inclinations) to be performed in the mossy green outdoor theatre. Everything from Snow White to Oh! What a Lovely War in the years below.

The uniform and sports kit is good quality but expensive – one parent complained indignantly at the cost of school sweatshirts; but there's some second hand provision in the uniform shop. Sports kit is laundered by the school, much to the joy of parents.

Boarding is possible from year 7: 3+ full timers (although all go home every other weekend), and up to 50 flexi boarders, who spend a few nights every week at school. 'They are completely flexible,' said one grateful parent. Tremendously popular with pupils, several of whom commented on their difficulty persuading their mums they were old enough – 'but it's so fun.' Lots of activities: preparations for Dragons' Den were under way, not to mention Marlborough Murders, Friday night is magic night and day trips at the weekends. So much going on that on just one night in the summer term did boarders watch anything on TV. Gappers help make the boarding experience really fun, said one parent: they're always there to play a game and provide an injection of energy and enthusiasm.

Rooms are for five, and cosy: four beds at ground level, and one bunk. Bathrooms are clean and up to date. Parents like the proximity of houseparents (described by parents as 'warm and welcoming' and 'extremely efficient'), and the easy access pupils have to gappers, who have rooms on each corridor, and are the first point of call in the night.

Fruit is always available, and there's a pantry where boarders can make tea, toast and hot drinks (with gappers' help). Obligatory weekly letter writing, and phones available for making calls in the evening or at break time – parents and pupils were happy this was sufficient. No Skype, iPads or mobiles allowed ('they get technology soon enough,' said one parent). Useful experience for those who move onto boarding senior schools. Currently no overseas boarders.

Parents around 30 per cent London, the rest local, mostly professionals or city types. Not cliquey, said one parent, outgoing and sociable, inclusive of newcomers, with an imminent buddy system to match new parents with old. Parents are encouraged to use the swimming pool and join the zumba class – 'not a drop and go school.' Indeed coffee and croissants are available every morning in the dining room after drop off. 'Parents should certainly not worry about being lonely in the country.'

New nursery open 7am-7pm 50 weeks a year, available to the whole community. Pyjama-clad children can be delivered in time to have breakfast alongside the older boarders and then picked up ready for bed at night.

DLD College London

25

199 Westminster Bridge Road, London SE1 7FX

020 7935 8411 | dld@dld.org | www.dldcollege.co.uk

Ages: 14–20

Pupils: 494; sixth form: 343; Boarders: 195 full

£22,000 – £28,000 pa

Principal: Since January 2018, Irfan Latif BSc, previously head of Sexey's School in Somerset (40s). Read chemistry at King's College London followed by a PGCE. First teaching post was at Kidbrooke School in Greenwich, then taught at several independent schools, including Haberdashers' Aske's Boys, Whitgift and St Benedict's in Ealing, where he was head of chemistry and director of science. Before joining Sexey's he was deputy head at Bedford School. He and his teacher wife Jocelyn have two daughters.

Academic matters: College offers a two-year GCSE programme aimed at international students with intensive English tuition in the first term; a minority (usually those who are older or who have transferred from other schools where they started their GSCEs) do a one-year GCSE course. Most take seven subjects, from a list of 12 options including the basics, plus French, religious studies, art, graphics and drama. Russian, Chinese, Spanish, Italian, German and Arabic are available via individual tuition. Commendable results from a mixed ability intake. In 2017, 26 per cent A*-A/7-9.

A level students get a choice of 33 subjects, including music technology, photography, film and media studies, sociology, psychology and languages, in more or less any combination. Art, economics, religious studies and philosophy are consistently popular, alongside English and maths. In 2017, 70 per cent A*-B grades and 41 per cent A*/A. BTecs also available in media production and business.

Some students are disaffected when they arrive, but it's rare for them to be anti-education after a few weeks. 'Because of the small class sizes – on average, 12 – they get lots of individual feedback and huge amounts of encouragement, and most start making progress very quickly,' says the college, attributing their academic success to their focus on fitting the right course to the right student.

Parents can't praise the system enough. 'The small class sizes, and the extra attention that provides each child with, have been the absolute making of my daughter,' one parent told us. Another, who has had two children at DLD, said, 'DLD has a record of helping children who felt they weren't going to achieve anything in a regular school to really do well. There's something about the small class sizes, easy-going environment and quality of teaching that gives them a chance to break out of set patterns of underachieving and underperforming. It really shows, more than anywhere I've seen.'

The college can cope with a wide range of special needs, generally picking up several previously undiagnosed cases each year, including dyslexia, ADHD and autism. Thirty-four per cent SEN when we visited and those benefit from support with study and essay writing skills; individual help is also available at extra cost. 'Our SEN students get more or less the same level of results as the others, due to the amount of input from SEN department, which is run by a two-strong team. This extra help is critical.' Accredited by CReSTeD, whose most recent report speaks of it as a unique school.

'I love my room,' one student told us. 'And because it's soundproofed, I can be as loud as I want and study in peace regardless of how loud anyone else is'

Very bright students also well catered for, with parents confirming that their children feel stretched and challenged in a positive way. Others point to the personalised approach of monitoring, feedback and target setting ensuring that students continue maximising their full potential at all times.

Indeed, educational expectations are high for all, with patchy work not accepted by staff. 'We believe in helping students believe they can move up to the next level.' Many staff are from Oxbridge and some come from non-teaching backgrounds – the theatre, the City, the BBC. 'This means our tutors know exactly what employers really want from graduates and it also means they have great connections,' said one student. 'My music teacher, for instance, has invited in songwriters, a music lawyer and others to talk to us, as well as sending out our coursework from people in the industry to get feedback.'

Teachers only employed if they are accessible to students outside classes, with many not only being available on email, but on a live chat system. Students say they are treated as adults and for many of them, it's that mutual respect that gets them back on track with their education. The most recent ISI report states that students like being at the college and are very happy with the personal support that they receive.

Extended Project Qualification increasingly popular, with 12 students doing it when we visited, although college admits some drop off in first few weeks. 'It's a tough programme.'

Games, options, the arts: A level art and photography are two of the most popular and successful subjects here, and the artwork we saw on display in the large and well-equipped art rooms was striking, with a notable creative energy among the students while they were working. 'I can honestly say every photography lesson is fun,' said one student. LAMDA examinations on offer and the DLD youth theatre puts on two performances a year.

All GCSE students play curricular sport at local centres on Wednesday afternoons, including football, basketball, tennis, netball, dance, rock-climbing and aerobics. Sports clubs and matches after school too, including cricket and yoga. On-site sporting facilities include a swimming pool and gym in the basement. 'But although sport is accessible and enjoyed by many students, DLD is probably not the best place for your child if they're really, really sporty,' one parent told us.

Music popular, with facilities including a recording studio and various practice areas, all of which are soundproofed. There's a vocal group, ukulele group, recording studio club and 59 students do private music lessons, including classical and jazz piano tuition, rock guitar, pop singing, singing and drum kit.

Extracurricular offering has improved in recent years, including Duke of Edinburgh Award, EPQ, debating and art clubs. Located in the heart of Westminster, it's no wonder the school takes full advantage of the galleries, museums and theatres practically on its doorstep, with overseas trips to the likes of Barcelona and Paris.

Boarding: The new site includes over 214 student beds (195 of which were being used when we visited) over 15 floors, with views over the Thames. More to be converted in the future. The areas are gender split, with younger ones on the lower floors. Strict curfews in the week from 9.30-10.30pm and, which are extended on Fridays and Saturdays until 10.30-11.30pm (depending on age). All full boarders, although some do visit home during weekends and half term and the school is very flexible when it comes to students wanting to visit friends and families. Boarders will often arrange their own activities for the weekend, but there are always free activities going on in the boarding house, including movie nights, quiz nights, zumba, birthday parties etc, along with visits to local museums, galleries and places like Harry Potter World.

Mostly single rooms, of different shapes and sizes, all ensuite. Some twin rooms share a bathroom. These rooms have a partition between beds that can be extended along the whole length of the room if required. 'It's the twin ones that are the most popular,' a staff member told us. Rooms are hi-spec, contemporary and minimalist, with a clear wow factor. 'I love my room,' one student told us. 'And because it's soundproofed, I can be as loud as I want and study in peace regardless of how loud anyone else is.' Weekly inspections mean they are kept reasonably tidy, although lots of unmade beds when we visited. Light, airy and spacious communal kitchen on each floor, complete with comfortable seating areas, fridge, freezer, microwave, kettle and toaster, but no hob or oven, with students expected to eat main meals in the refectory. 'It's a really sociable area,' one student told us.

Pastoral care for boarders includes a strong team of house parents, who are fully residential, run by a director of boarding and his assistant – who in turn is overseen by the vice president of principal welfare.

Background and atmosphere: Now one of 16 schools and five colleges owned by the Alpha Plus Group, founded in 1931 to provide tutoring for Oxbridge and Colonial Service entrance exams. After World War II it began to specialise in A and O level teaching. In 2004 it moved from Notting Hill to light, airy, refurbished premises in Marylebone; in 2015 moved again, amalgamating with Abbey College in a new, purpose built site on Westminster Bridge Road.

On first sight, this shiny new building looks more like swanky corporate offices than any school, both outside and in, but a closer look reveals that education is very much at the heart of the design. A large open space – with huge projector screens on the wall, and which doubles up as a 350-seat performance area when required – forms the central atrium. Then the teaching and study areas – all arranged in colour co-ordinated zones so students can't get lost – sit around the edges. These facilities include six high-spec labs, a creative arts and media faculty, 40 tutorial rooms and an open plan library, study and ICT facilities.

'There's something about the small classes, easy-going environment and quality of teaching that gives them a chance to break out of patterns of underachieving'

Informal atmosphere, more akin to a college than a school, with staff and students on a first name basis and no uniform. But there's no room for slacking, with students engaged, inquisitive and busy in the classes when we visited. 'Academically, it's tough, but people want to learn,' said one student. Helping students keep up is a vast array of break-out areas dotted around the different floors – some with individual booths for private study, whilst others have small or large tables for group study.

Active student council, which meets twice a month and organises plenty of charity events (breast cancer awareness day when we visited), as well as bringing about changes such the reintroduction of table football, although one parent told us she'd like to see 'more of a student voice overall.'

Fresh food available in the cashless refectory, which is reviewed by a food committee comprised of students and staff. Starbucks also on site. The day begins for students at 8.50am and finishes at 4.40pm, with enrichment extending that until around 6.30pm.

Pastoral care, well-being and discipline: Very strong pastoral system, which had recently been restructured when we visited, so that there are separate staff for pastoral and academic care. 'This is important because we do attract some needy students, including school phobics and SEN,' says college. 'There's no stigma if you need help,' said one student. 'Staff really care about you here,' said another. Parents we spoke to were very moved by what the school had achieved for their children pastorally. 'Staff are so kind and supportive that I'm welling up thinking about what they've done for my daughter,' one told us.

Electronic register is taken in every lesson and parents are texted or emailed if attendance becomes a problem. Each student has a weekly meeting with their personal tutor to talk about progress and future plans; three directors of studies and three directors of welfare work closely with the personal tutors. Expectations, rather than rules, are the norm here. 'My son kicked back about things like strict uniform and not being allowed to go out at lunchtime at his last school, and he's much happier here, where you're expected to turn up and do your work and be respectful, but without lots of petty rules and an authoritarian environment.'

Students engaged, inquisitive and busy in the classes when we visited. 'Academically, it's tough, but people want to learn'

Significant proportion of pupils smoke (nurse runs a stop smoking programme), but there's tough penalties for misusing drink and drugs – those under suspicion are sent for drugs tests, to general parental approval. Most students, even the most troubled ones, buckle down eventually, although occasionally things don't go to plan, with around two exclusions every academic year.

Sanctions include supervised study; also a system of verbal and written warnings based on employment law. Bullying is taken very seriously, although students told us the atmosphere is so relaxed and accepting that it's exceptionally rare. 'Nobody judges you here,' said one student.

Peer mentoring had around 60 students involved when we visited. 'It's improving my interpersonal skills,' said one student.

Pupils and parents: Students aged between 14-18 (with the odd exception up to 20), most of whom have come from private schools. Some have been ill; some have had mental health or other problems; some have found their previous school too rigid or too stressful. Others come from peripatetic diplomatic families. Some lack confidence and need to learn good working habits. Most thrive in the informal but structured atmosphere. Around 30 per cent from UK, with others mostly from Germany, Latvia, Ukraine, Malaysia, China, Burma, Vietnam, Italy, Kazakhstan and Russia. Little, if any, sense of community among parents, which one said is 'disappointing, but hardly surprising.'

Entrance: Everyone is interviewed and previous schools are asked for references and reports. Those going into the sixth form need a minimum of five grade Cs at GCSE (or numerical equivalents); if they haven't passed maths or English they will need to retake these, alongside their A levels. No student who has been disruptive elsewhere is accepted without a discussion about the need for a change in behaviour. School is registered for 725 students, although only 500 when we visited. 'Our vision was always to open the new facility with 500 and build it up.'

Exit: Quite a few students move on after GCSEs – perhaps to state sixth form colleges – but more than half go through to the sixth form. Those aiming at Oxbridge (one place in 2017) are given an intensive course including lectures, seminars, mock interviews and individual tuition. Popular destinations include UCL, Goldsmith's, King's College, LSE, Imperial, Cass Business School and Bristol. Wide range of degree courses, with business studies, economics and specialist art areas being the most popular. Extra help also for potential vets, doctors and dentists, via a bespoke medical programme, with three or four a year going onto study these at university.

Money matters: Several scholarships available, worth 10-100 per cent of fees, on the basis on academic attainment, plus means-tested bursaries. 'We're fortunate to have free rein to be sympathetic to the individual.' Indeed, one local boy supported 100 per cent financially when we visited.

Remarks: This unique educational environment seems to capture all the best things about a college environment, combining them with the pastoral care and motivational structures that are more typical of school provision. All this takes place in small classes, with one-to-one help when required, in a state-of-the-art, purpose-built building in the heart of London, where students have the option to board on-site. The result is an informal atmosphere with an underlying structured regime where everyone is kept up to scratch. A fantastic place for the very bright, as well as re-motivating the disaffected, although not for young people who want a more traditional boarding school experience.

Dorset House School

26

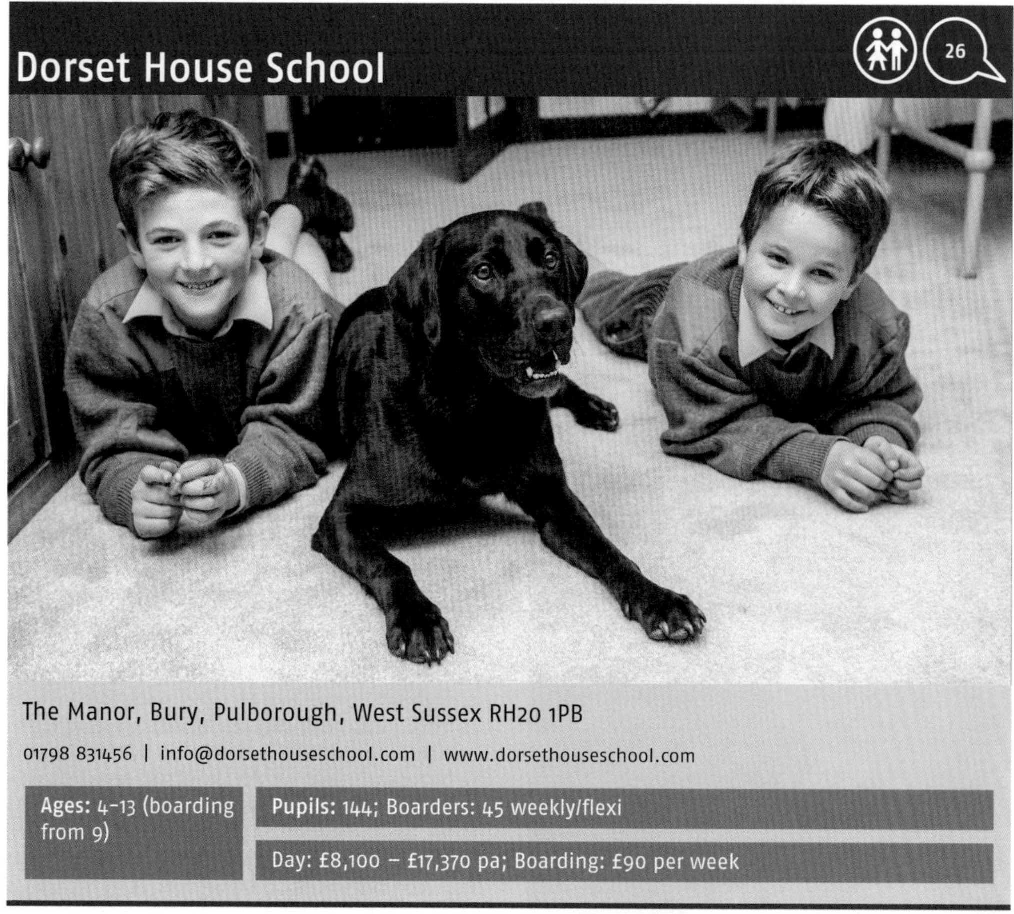

The Manor, Bury, Pulborough, West Sussex RH20 1PB

01798 831456 | info@dorsethouseschool.com | www.dorsethouseschool.com

Ages: 4-13 (boarding from 9)

Pupils: 144; Boarders: 45 weekly/flexi

Day: £8,100 – £17,370 pa; Boarding: £90 per week

Headmaster: Since September 2016, Mr Matt Thomas, previously deputy head (academic) at Moulsford Prep. Degree in PE, geography and education studies from St Luke's Exeter; recently completed a master's in educational leadership. Has had a wide variety of roles including teaching

GCSE and A level at state schools, being a lead teacher for two education authorities and various positions in independent schools. A fellow of the Royal Geographical Society, he likes to attend Monday evening lectures there. Enjoys trekking in the Himalayas and has climbed Kilimanjaro; runs marathons and ultra-marathons. Married to Julie and they have two children, both at the school.

Entrance: Children can join at any time so long as spaces, subject to informal tests in English and maths, a report from their current school and, ideally, a taster day. Parents are made aware of what the school is able to offer and that the ultimate goal is CE.

Exit: To a wide range of senior schools, including Hurst, Brighton College, Seaford, Lancing, Ardingly, Christ's Hospital, Winchester, Marlborough and Shrewsbury. Most children stay until CE at 13+, but will prepare for 11+ entry to senior schools and also for pre-selection tests. Scholarships won every year for the past few years – mixture of academic, music, sport and all-rounder.

Remarks: Founded in 1784 as Totteridge Park School in Hertfordshire. After various incarnations it became Dorset House in 1905 and moved to its present site in 1964. Housed in a 12th century manor house, with medieval great barn, modern teaching blocks and separate junior school building. Set in 16 acres of grounds at the end of a quiet country lane, next door to the church and with magnificent views in all directions. Children allowed to build camps and dens in the woods and play in the adventure playground. 'No one minds about mud – you just fling on your wellies,' said one boy. Children spend as much time as possible outside – pre-prep has two hour forest school session each week – and some of the younger children often drink their break-time hot chocolate on a log in the woods. Small amphitheatre in the garden used for speech day and house drama competition.

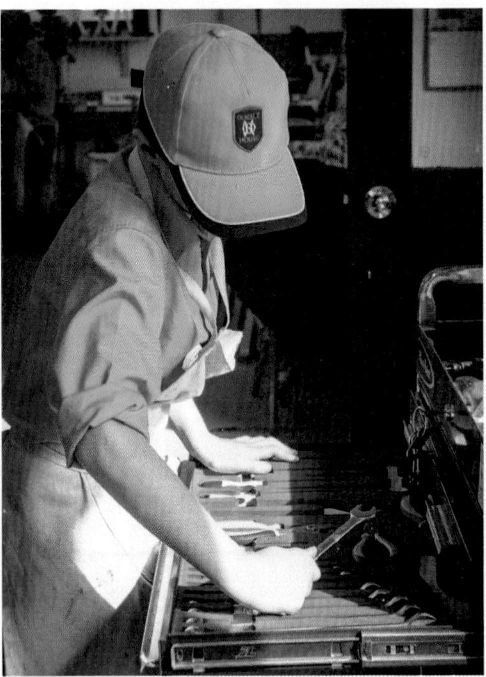

Dorms under the eaves, reached by a spiral stone staircase, are warm and cosy, with iron bedsteads and lots of teddies

One-form entry, with a maximum of 20 per year group – nearly full in years 4 to 8 and waiting lists further down. Numbers have now reached 140 (maximum capacity of 160). The 45 boarding places for flexi and weekly boarders are now over-subscribed on some nights – often suits families who live in London and have a weekend cottage nearby. Warren of dorms under the eaves reached by a spiral stone staircase are warm and cosy, with old fashioned iron bedsteads and lots of teddies. Real family atmosphere – feels more like someone's elegant country house than a school – the children take their breakfast and tea on the terrace during the summer. Everything immaculate with not a weed in sight and fresh paint everywhere. School sees itself as 'traditional but forward looking.'

Streaming for maths, English and science from year 5, depending on the class size and the ability range within the group. Scholarship children kept within their year group and offered extension classes at break and lunchtimes.

A dynamic team of staff with a good mix of age and experience. Charismatic science teacher who brings the subject to life – he teaches through experimentation and investigation like testing the efficacy of indigestion remedies. Bright, light and airy science lab where 'we love blowing up jelly babies in the fume cupboard,' says one budding young scientist. Recently won Green Link award which funded the boardwalk around the pond. Children do particularly well in science at CE, often achieving top grades, and many go on to study it at university. Very enthusiastic young geography teacher is also the director of sport – geography trips to the Isle of Wight and the Jurassic Coast; the flood plain of the river Arun just beyond the garden makes a wonderful outdoor classroom. French taught by a native speaker. Latin or classical civilisation introduced in year 5; Greek taught to bright year 8s.

Light, cosy library with comfortable sofas where children can curl up with a book. Prep done at school and supervised by members of staff. Three full-time SEN teachers, mainly for mild dyslexia and dyspraxia. Bright yellow room for the junior SENCo where the motto is 'learning with laughter.' Children not routinely tested but any problems picked up quickly in such a small environment.

Magnificent medieval barn acts as the school hall and is big enough to fit everyone in – also doubles up as the sports hall and is hired out for weddings. Inner barn is used for plays and assemblies. New head of art has revitalised the art department. Art and DT are linked and the kit car club built a car and raced it at Goodwood as part of the Greenpower project. Photography very popular – each child is given their own memory card from year 3 to take photographs around the school and taught to use Photoshop. Photographs of the children displayed around the school and dining room doubles as an art gallery. Brightly coloured totem poles made from recycled materials dotted around the garden.

Young director of music (Dorset House old boy) also acts as a houseparent with his wife (who also teaches reception) and dog Mylo – has made music 'cool and fun' and now lots of informal concerts, ensembles and whole school concerts. The choir sings at services in the church next door and at the Christmas carol service at Arundel. Music timetabled from the early years and every child learns to read music through learning the recorder – about 60 per cent learn a musical instrument. Is apparently the first prep school in the country to have JamClassHD system which is linked by JamPod technology (no, we don't know what that means either). Senior play each year, plus one or two for juniors as well as the house drama competition. Annual poetry reciting competition and children have to read out match reports and prayers – all great for building self-confidence.

Heavyweight sporting success: under-9 rugby team recently unbeaten in Sussex. Almost all the boys and girls in a year group are required to make up a team and often children who did not consider themselves sporty step up to the plate. All children in years 3 to 8 play in at least three matches a term – everyone has a go. Now enough girls to put together netball and hockey teams to play other schools. Ballet and gymnastics particularly popular and girls can take exams in these. Riding a popular extra and team takes part in regional competitions.

Other extras include drama, pottery, Mandarin, cookery and football coaching (with pros from Chelsea). Chess taught by outside specialists. Recently formed cub group with children from local primaries and some from Dorset House meets in the barn every week during term time.

Leadership and taking responsibility promoted from a young age through leadership programme – 'Children learn how to work together as a team and to listen to one another.' Leadership training once a week before school for year 8s – they take part in the decision making of the school as elected representatives of the school council and act as positive role models. More opportunities to take a position of responsibility in a small school – children start as lunch helpers and book monitors and progress through outdoor adventures and camping trip (including one to the top of Mount Snowdon). Grand finale is an adventure training week in north Devon after CE.

Small nurturing school with a family atmosphere produces open, chatty children where everyone knows everyone and each child is given the chance to find their niche. 'It's a lovely, friendly school where children have a proper country childhood and don't grow up before their time,' one happy mother told us. School is run on Christian principles and the parish church next door is central to the life of the school – Monday morning assembles in the church and parents often come to the special Friday service. The vicar is a part time member of staff and teaches RE. New pre-school for 2+ on site.

Charismatic science teacher; bright, light and airy science lab where 'we love blowing up jelly babies in the fume cupboard,' said one budding young scientist

Recently introduced house system means lots of crossover between year groups and as one parent said, 'The older children are sweet to the younger ones'. Firm policy on bullying. Many young members of staff live on site and in the manor house, which contributes to the family feel. Board games round the library fire in the evenings for boarders and a dedicated games room.

Most children live within a 20-mile radius and the school is increasingly popular with families moving out of London – 'a good antidote to the pushy London day schools,' according to one new arrival. Active parents' association raised £25,000 at the summer ball for an Astroturf (in a school with 140 pupils). Also organizes bonfire night party, quiz and welcomes new parents to the school. A fathers' cricket team meets regularly. Famous old boys include former Gordonstoun head Mark Pyper, comedian Harry Enfield and actor Ed Speleers (of Eragon fame).

If you are looking for an all-singing, all-dancing school with facilities galore, this school might not be for you, but if you are looking for somewhere that achieves good academic results, is small and nurturing and where every child gets a chance and is expected to do their bit – take a closer look.

Dover College

Effingham Crescent, Dover, Kent CT17 9RH

01304 205969 | admin@dovercollege.org.uk | www.dovercollege.org.uk

Ages: 3–18 (boarding from 11)

Pupils: 279; sixth form: 66; Boarders: 86 full, 12 weekly/flexi

Day: £7,500 – £15,600 pa; Boarding: £20,250 – £30,000 pa

Headmaster: Since 2015, Gareth Doodes, previously (briefly) head of George Heriot's School in Edinburgh, and before that head of Milton Abbey School in Dorset. Read history at St Andrews; PGCE from Cambridge; worked at Taunton school then at Oakham for seven years, two as master of scholars and five as a housemaster, before joining Milton Abbey.

Academic matters: One class per year group in the junior school and class sizes limited by the size of the classrooms – usually 10 to 12 but up to 16 at key stage 2. Non-selective so a wide range of abilities. Spanish taught from year 1 and French from year 3. Pupils take annual NFER tests in maths and English, with CATs (cognitive ability tests) from year 4. Optional Sats from year 2 onwards.

Specialist junior school teachers for sport, music and languages. Juniors have their own laptop room but also use the senior school's ICT facilities – ICT taught across the curriculum by ICT savvy staff and early years children have touch screen computers. All classrooms have either an interactive whiteboard or projector.

A broad ability range – 44 per cent A*/B and 34 per cent A*/A grades at A level; 15 per cent A*-A/9-7 at GCSE in 2017. Sciences taught separately for the dual award. Good range of subjects offered in sixth form. The introduction of BTecs in sport and PE, travel and tourism and health and social care has meant that more are staying on for sixth form. Apart from the usual subjects, GCSEs offered in health and social care, PE and business studies.

About 12 per cent need some sort of SEN – lots of help available, from help with study skills to more intensive one-to-one help. All pupils screened for dyslexia and other potential problems every year. Two individual needs teachers in senior school and one part time in junior – sometimes children go over to senior school or teachers come to them, either one-to-one or in small groups and mainly help with maths and reading. A very dedicated team of teachers who 'go the extra mile' for the children and focus on individual learning styles. 'I could not believe how much trouble the teachers took with my son,' said one mother. Small classes – 12 to 14 for GCSE and sometimes only six for A level.

Has welcomed international students since 1957 and the International Study Centre opened in 2001 – total immersion in English plus lessons with peer group in maths, ICT, DT and sport. Depending on the level of English, pupils prepared for Cambridge Preliminary English Test (PET), IGCSE or IELTS. All international pupils are integrated into the main school. Some start in International Study Centre and move over when ready. Others join the main school on arrival. About 50 pupils need some sort of EAL support.

Games, options, the arts: The usual sports – football, hockey, netball etc. Cross-country popular and successful (Dover College hosts a big inter-school event each year). Aerobics, basketball, sailing with Dover Sailing Club, swimming at a local pool. Everyone given a chance to shine and 'teachers are always trying out new people for sports and giving people a chance to showcase their talents'. Some matches for under 9s and lots for under 11s, with most children getting a chance to play in a team. Strong swimming team – two inter-school swimming galas a year held at a nearby leisure centre as well as a junior school gala. Sport compulsory up to sixth form and most carry on after that. Most girls continue with sport but fitness classes, dance and yoga also popular. Not a school with acres of rolling fields but has its own pitches as well as an Astroturf, sports hall, dance and fitness suites and a basketball court. 'Some of the sports facilities could do with a bit of a makeover,' say some parents. Link with Canterbury Christ Church University's sports department ensures a steady supply of recently qualified sports teachers who 'refresh the department and bring new ideas'.

Strong family atmosphere and parents invited to Friday chapel, a highlight of the week when children's achievements and birthdays are celebrated

Lots of music, including chamber orchestra and ensembles. Members of the local community often play in the orchestra and the choir sometimes sings evensong in Canterbury Cathedral. Tallis Music School has been relocated and refurbished and now provides soundproof pods, a recital room and teaching rooms. Informal junior concerts twice a term in the Tallis Music School as well as a summer concert, carol concert and junior school Christmas play. School also takes part in Young Voices concert at the O2.

Strong arts. Textiles, art and photography offered at A level. Particularly good photography – annual photographic competition also open to parents and fabulous photos displayed around the school.

Huge range of activities – from belly dancing and debating to madrigals and horse-riding. Leadership activities, including D of E Award (up to eight gold awards a year) and Young Enterprise, all designed to build self-confidence. Junior school has listened to parents and worked on the outdoor curriculum – a discovery garden recently opened and street dance and taekwondo added to the long list of clubs.

Strong emphasis on community and charity work. Senior pupils can get involved in the Ukraine project. A group raises money for the charity and then spends two weeks in the Ukraine refurbishing an old people's home, running a sports camp for disadvantaged children and chopping logs for the elderly. One parent described it as 'a life changing experience for my son, who realised for the first time what true hardship is'.

Boarding: Vast majority (86) are full boarders, with just a few weekly and flexi. Roughly two-thirds are boys. Year 7 and 8 day pupils are housed separately in Priory House, which ensures a gentle introduction to the senior school. All the other houses mix day and boarding so everyone gets to know everyone. 'It's nice to mix with different years because then you get to make more friends', a pupil told us, although another said 'some nationalities still stick together and keep themselves to themselves'. There is 'major house loyalty' and lots of inter-house events – music, sport, drama and the keenly fought house conker competition. All boarders have supper together at the weekends. Entertainment, theatre and shopping trips organised although many are happy 'just chilling with their friends' and catching up with schoolwork.

Background and atmosphere: Founded in 1871 by a group of local businessmen who wanted Dover to have its own public school. Housed in the grounds of the 12th century Benedictine St Martin's Priory, an oasis of green in the middle of Dover with wonderful views of Dover Castle and nestling behind the famous white cliffs. Went co-ed in 1974 (one of the first boys' schools to do so) and now almost 50:50. Although much of the original priory was destroyed by Henry VIII, there is still a feeling of history. This is despite the hotchpotch of buildings added over the years, from late Victorian houses to the uninspiring modern. The school has the only Norman refectory in Britain – still used for its original purpose and doubles as a concert hall and theatre too. Junior school opened in 2001 and occupies two houses in the grounds. Light and airy classrooms decorated with cheerful artwork.

Dover College is a small local school with an international dimension and a strong sense of community 'where everyone knows everyone'. We heard comments like 'it's not overly posh but perfect for where it is' and 'it's a local school with a kind and caring environment which understands the kids' needs and gets the best out of each pupil'.

Christian foundation. Chapel is physically and spiritually at the heart of the college but all faiths and none are made to feel welcome. Three services a week, including Friday afternoon chapel.

Pastoral care, well-being and discipline: 'Think differently' is the motto of the school and huge emphasis is placed on personal development and building pupils' confidence, wherever their talents may lie. 'I am confident that the school has the control of my children's well-being and promotes good social skills and ethics,' a parent told us. 'I am very proud when people comment on how well-mannered my children are'. Well-developed tutorial system, and house staff and prefects have finely tuned antennae for drugs and alcohol. School likes to bring together the students and the non-teaching staff. For example, the kitchen chef is also linesman for the first XI football team, a minibus driver is the referee and the estates manager runs D of E.

Strong family atmosphere and parents invited to Friday chapel, a highlight of the week when children's achievements and birthdays are celebrated and house points awarded. Heads of senior school hand out awards in their flowing red St Andrew's gowns. Parents like to feel involved. One mother told us that her children 'are treated in a caring and understanding way and I can talk to the teachers whenever I want'. School has worked hard to develop lines of communication with parents and sees the relationship as a partnership overseeing the children's education. Parents kept up to date with events via parent portal and social media sites.

Pupils and parents: Day children tend to be fairly local and many are ferried to school via a network of minibuses. About 30 per cent from abroad (30 nationalities). About 10 per cent of local children choose to board 'because it's fun'.

Everyone given a chance to shine and 'teachers are always trying out new people for sports and giving people a chance to showcase their talents'

Huge range of abilities – some children very bright whilst others struggle to get five good GCSEs. 'A lot of the pupils are not that academic but the school brings out the best in them', said a parent. The emphasis on building confidence produces comfortable, well-adjusted children who are happy to strike up a conversation with anyone. Life is full on here and as one pupil said, 'sometimes we are just too busy as every teacher wants you to do their thing'. Even so, they seem to love every minute of it.

Prefects given lots of responsibility and say that 'it is important to act as role models to the rest of the school'. They apply in writing and are then interviewed by a panel chaired by the head. Lower sixth enrichment week takes the pupils well out of their comfort zone and often a few previously hidden talents come to the fore. Pupils have to stage a senior management meeting, role play a crisis, take part in an Apprentice-style marketing project and film a debate – all in one day.

No typical Old Dovorian, although many are entrepreneurs who have made their own way in the world. They tend to keep in touch. Former pupils include composer Dai Fujikura, choreographer Sir Frederick Ashton, X Factor supremo Simon Cowell, film producer Guy East and various ambassadors and military figures.

Entrance: School takes children from 3 and most start in the nursery. Some join in year 6 and then move up to the senior school. Non-selective and will only reject a child if school feels that it can't meet a child's needs. Happy to take children who might fail elsewhere and build their confidence. All children strongly encouraged to attend a taster day before they join. Will take children who might fail elsewhere and give them the confidence to succeed. Only turns children away if they won't be able to cope. Most join at 11+ from the junior school and local primaries. A few come in at 13+ from prep schools like Northbourne Park, Spring Grove and Wellesley House. About 25 students join the sixth form – mainly from abroad. Pupils can join at any time if there are spaces, except into year 11.

Exit: Most juniors progress to the senior school, but numbers vary from year to year. Good record in the Kent Test – mainly to Dover Grammar and the Folkestone grammars. School helps children with practice tests but parents sometimes get outside tutoring as well. No entrance exam as such for senior school. Smooth transition.

About 25 per cent leave after GCSEs, mostly to the state system. Sixth formers head to a range of universities for a wide variety of courses – recent choices include business at City University, sports science at Canterbury Christ Church, pharmacology at Bristol, business at Surrey, engineering at Nottingham, computer technology at Portsmouth. Some to universities in Europe and USA. Lots of help with UCAS – careers adviser knows pupils well and 'keeps expectations realistic'. Not many take a gap year.

Money matters: Range of awards offered, including11+ scholarships in English and maths, 13+ scholarship awarded on strength of CE and 16+ scholarship on strength of GCSEs. Academic, art, drama, DT, music, sport and all rounder scholarships on offer. About a third of local pupils on some sort of scholarship or bursary. Not a rich school and bursaries come from fee income but school does what it can for those who encounter unexpected financial difficulties whilst at the school.

Remarks: Not hugely academic and nor does it pretend to be, but this is a happy, relaxed place where the building of self confidence underpins everything the school does. It's high praise indeed when a sixth form pupil said, 'I have been very happy here and can't fault it'.

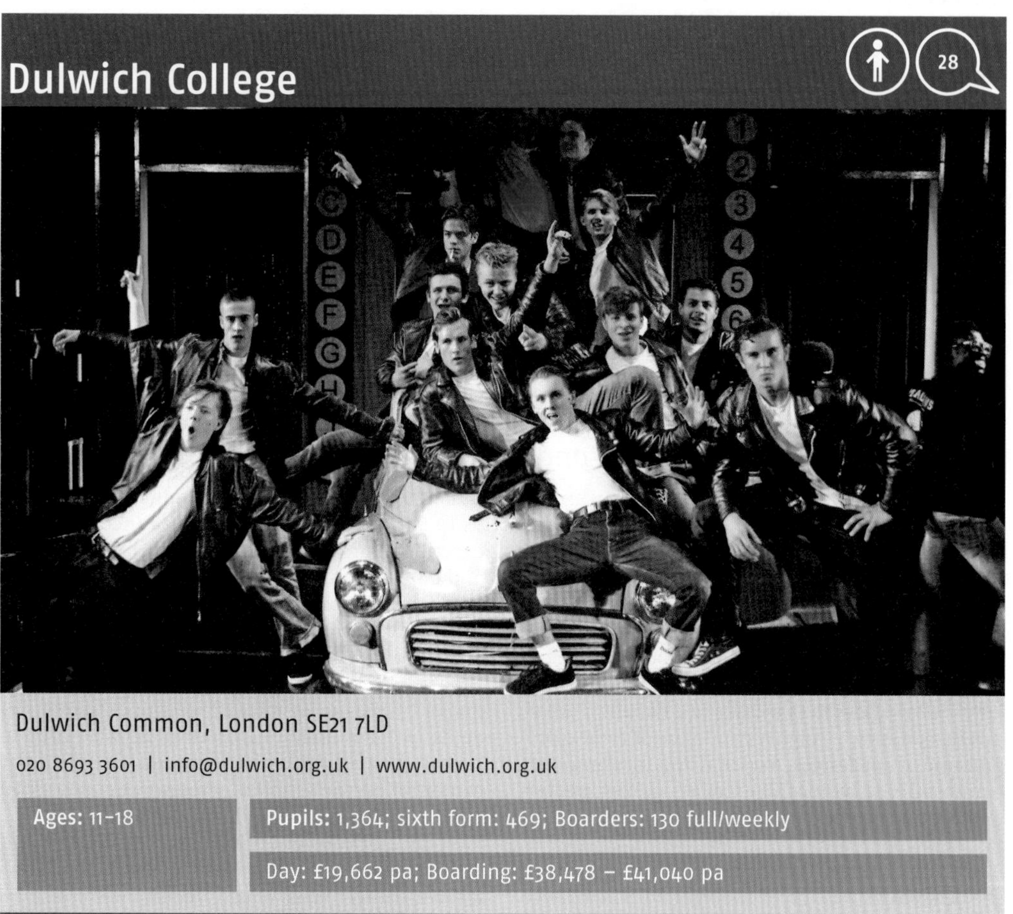

Dulwich College

28

Dulwich Common, London SE21 7LD

020 8693 3601 | info@dulwich.org.uk | www.dulwich.org.uk

Ages: 11–18

Pupils: 1,364; sixth form: 469; Boarders: 130 full/weekly

Day: £19,662 pa; Boarding: £38,478 – £41,040 pa

Master: Since 2009, Dr Joseph (Joe) Spence BA PhD (50s), a graduate in modern history and politics; the Irish histories and literature of his postgrad line his study walls. Previously headmaster of Oakham School and for 10 years until 2002 held the prestigious position of master in college at Eton, housemaster to the King's scholars, 'surrounded by the brightest'; it was here he found his vocation.

His first decade at Dulwich College will coincide with the college's 400th anniversary, entwining their legacies.

Grammar school educated, he describes his career path as the 'story of accident', a happy one. The turning point was a friend's encouragement that one 'no longer has to be behind a desk as headmaster'. Immensely warm and charming, putting one at ease, the embodiment of the oft repeated 'Dulwich boys can talk to anyone'. He brings a sense of fun to those around him, appearing to wear his responsibilities lightly, preparing to ad lib a speech to a grand assembly as he says goodbye.

He is married to a lawyer, with two sons and daughter. He still finds time to write, recently penning a new libretto for a concert at King's College Cambridge, turning a poem written by PG Wodehouse's brother into a song. He wants these sustaining passions for the boys: 'My duty is to make sure that every Alleynian leaves with something intellectual... a passion which will be with him for the rest of his life'.

Parents, seeming to have adopted the Ofsted phraseology, unanimously declare him to be outstanding. They enthuse: 'a good orator, a great listener'; 'as fiercely passionate about the arts as academics'; 'a great presence and a motivational leader'; 'excellent, effective and innovative'.

Boys laughingly said the only thing they didn't like was swimming as there was no point trying to keep up with the Olympic swimmers and water-polo players

His vision for the transformations in progress – physical and philosophical – start with 'get the classroom right, then everything else', but quickly go beyond with the desire to create a generation of original thinkers. You don't have to be a scientist or an artist here – 'learning that is free from the syllabus' allows boys to take risks in a dazzling (we've rarely seen such a weighty catalogue of riches) programme of challenges, national and international competitions, symposia, external prizes, performances and physical adventures.

Academic matters: It's well known that improving the academics was top of the agenda. The college is now in the top eight per cent for value added nationally and the master is confident that the best is still to come. In 2017, 87 per cent of I/GCSE grades were A*-A/7-9. Plenty of A*s in sciences, English literature, maths, French and Spanish. At A level/Pre-U, 62 per cent A*/A, and (again including Pre-U) 86 per cent A*-B. Maths is most popular by far, followed by physics, history, economics and chemistry. High percentage of A*/As in physics, plus history of art, English, further maths, history and art. A levels remain as the core upper school offer but individual heads of subject have the flexibility to offer Pre-U.

Academic teaching is described by parents as solid lower down the college but inspirational higher up. Thirty-five per cent of teachers in residence for over 10 years. The master says candidly that now only a handful are perhaps not on message, and he won't see boys stuck with them, which chimes with parents, who say, 'very good standard of teaching, noticeable improvement' and 'incompetence would not be tolerated'. They also describe staff as 'hugely committed'; 'they understand a boy's potential'; 'they set the bar high academically' and 'the daily report system is excellent'.

The master drives innovation. A key recent appointment is the director of science, formerly at lauded Brighton College, plus two new deputy heads. Turning things on their head, 'flip' lessons might give boys homework first, then the boys come in and discuss how they found it, or mini-whiteboards may enable a teacher to see at a glance whether boys have 'got it'. Boys were initially consulted on their view of assessments, and came back saying they actually felt there was grade inflation – pupil voice has been used in every key decision since. Staff share with each other a 'speciality dish' ie what is working for them in the classroom.

Curriculum is largely as one might expect; choosing options is quite complex. Languages have a particularly strong focus throughout. French, Spanish, Chinese and Latin are taught in the lower school, later on there is the addition of German, Italian and Greek. Appealing language trips: year 9s to Salamanca, year 11s to Florence. The boys describe them as holistic, taking in both language and culture, raising their passion for the subject up a notch. Exchanges take place too, but with boys considerately settled in host families in pairs.

The only setting is for maths. All pupils study separate sciences up to IGCSE and the college doesn't necessarily encourage the collection of an excessive number. Intellectual boys wishing to stretch themselves further between years 7 and 11 can enrol on the scholars' programme, described by one as 'the highlight of my week'.

Quirkier A level options include critical and contextual studies and ancient history. Liberal studies in the upper sixth in conjunction with the girls at JAGS allows boys to try something new: modern poetry, yoga, book-binding, Italian cinema and even ballroom dancing.

Also for sixth formers, the Dulwich Diploma, which looks to offer the depth of A level with the breadth of the IB: the three components comprise academic study, including an extended essay or research topic of their choice – recent examples Who Killed Sylvia Plath? and Is Medical Research the New Imperialism? – engagement beyond the classroom and preparation for life after Dulwich.

Whilst all of this adds up to a very full plate, parents say there are 'high expectations with excellent support through study skills sessions' and 'it's pretty intensive in terms of workload but not too high pressure'.

A team of four well-qualified learning support teachers are shared with the junior school, and provide support to individual boys with a diagnosed learning difficulty – 20 per cent. Eight per cent of middle and upper school boys receive EAL support.

Games, options, the arts: In year 7, whilst skills are built and some sports tried for the first time, rugby, football, hockey and cricket are all compulsory. By year 8 choices emerge, one being dropping rugby for fencing. Tennis currently squeezed for space with only three courts. No single sport is compulsory in the middle school but a plethora of teams make it tempting to get involved – skiing, rowing, fives, squash, cross-country and basketball, to name but a few. Years 10 and 11 may try golf, rock-climbing, self-defence, taekwondo and rugby 7s, whilst upper school choices aim to involve boys in sport however that may be, perhaps officiating or coaching as well as trying gentlemanly pursuits such as croquet, horse-riding and sailing. The school has responded to the national appetite for competitive cycling and boys are able to use the superb facilities at nearby Herne Hill velodrome.

Seventy acres of playing fields recently reseeded, and rugby is the triumphant sport with 1st XV recently winning the NatWest Schools cup for the third consecutive year. Success, too, for the under 14s rowers, who are national champions, and the school supplies four members of the under 15 GB water-polo team. Boys we had lunch with laughingly said the only thing they didn't like was swimming as there was no point trying to keep up with the Olympic swimmers and water-polo players.

Dr Spence continues to ponder how one achieves balance amidst such rich opportunities: '50 boys will have played at Twickenham, that's a once in a lifetime experience', but are there 'boys who might have done better academically if they had not done so much?'

'Arts, music and co-curricular are outstanding'. We arrived just in time to be treated to a sensitive rendition of W H Auden's Stop All of The Clocks as part of that day's house poetry competition. The school has a rich theatrical tradition, a flexible theatre space, Chewetel Ejiofor and Rupert Penry-Jones are OAs, makes the very most of the London theatre scene, and each year produces three drama festivals and 24 performance pieces.

A parent said, 'What I really like is the drive to go beyond the curriculum and inspire'. This term's Dulwich Creative week was produced with all of the finesse and confidence of a national arts organisation gone guerrillan and saw art hijacks where every pupil – astonishingly even the babies in the kindergarten – produce a clay self-portrait, which then came together into one installation. A surreal note remains overlooking the cricket pitches, giant polyurethane mushrooms by international street artist Christian Nagel. A new 'found' space, The Store, chills to the bone, but provides an edgy, white-washed, informal rehearsal space which boys can call their own, which also houses art exhibits.

Art and DT facilities are light and bright, and where we found some of the most exuberant classes in full flow. We admired Grayson Perry-ish vases produced in ceramics classes, and groovy dog kennels in DT.

Numbers learning instruments peak in the lower school at 45 per cent of boys, falling naturally enough to 25 per cent by the upper school. Standard of musicianship varies from enthusiastic beginners to boys who are leaders of section in the National Youth Orchestra or principals at Glyndebourne and the ENO. The music department is in the process of upgrading: there is a shiny new Mac suite for music technology, a new acoustic percussion suite, and small and large practice areas. Another funky new facility is the electric 'shed', fully sound-insulated, a great place to let rip with the electric guitar.

World class performances from a formidable debating team, who recently trounced the competition at the Oxford and Cambridge Unions. Where next for the boy currently ranked number one in the world?

Long lunch hours ensure even the senior boys feel they have time for clubs and societies, which continue after school. For the lower school these might include fencing, card games, woodwork and Scouts. For the middle and upper school a sophisticated list offers Japanese culture, alternative thinking, finance, Norse and Germanic, ultimate frisbee and rocketry. Poultry society boasts its own hens; whether they are ever eaten is set to be a college myth. Our curiosity was piqued as to what goes on at the Gentlemen's Club (no-one seemed to know); presumably no cigars.

The careers office has a 2,000 strong network of former parents and corporate contacts: a recent event invited 40 such to the Dulwich Picture Gallery. Boys were instructed to read up on everyone's biographies then were sent off to network fiercely.

Boarding: There are 130 boarders, two-thirds in the sixth form, majority from China and Hong Kong but also Eastern Europe. The boarding houses are on the campus, modernised period houses decorated with OA sporting team photos: quite basic in our view, small-ish rooms with less than luxurious en suite bathrooms, but unlikely to worry most boys intent on studying and playing hard surrounded by friends. Common rooms with large screen for movie nights, table football and all-important toasters.

Background and atmosphere: Founded in 1619 by the wealthy actor and businessman, Edward Alleyn. He set up and endowed the Foundation, which distributes its surplus profits to a group of schools including Dulwich College, JAGS and Alleyn's. The college moved to its present site in the 1870s. The main buildings are stunning Italianate red brick designed by the son of the architect of the Houses of Parliament. Inside, the panelled Great Hall lined with the names of Oxford and Cambridge scholars – up until the wall space ran out in the 1960s – has featured in a Hollywood film or two, more often the site of Old Alleynian dinners, the master's library and the Wodehouse library (PG is an Old Alleynian), with a significant theatrical archive including a Shakespeare First Folio.

'If your child is gifted in one area, they will soar here. If they are a good all-rounder they will be encouraged to be a great one'

Sitting amidst vast manicured pitches, the college is a gracious and intriguing south London landmark. Closer up, the collection of modern buildings forming a large part of the teaching spaces, particularly in the lower school, are plain and nothing more than functional, quite possibly a bit depressing. The buildings housing the upper school feel fresher – Ned's place looks like a commercial café, and there is a huge common room, whilst a second one was sacrificed to create a popular 'work room' with banks of computers. Ironically for a school that appears so stunning to the passer-by, it's the fabric of the school which could currently disappoint parents if not boys.

However, we donned hard hat and work boots to inspect the then almost complete Laboratory, costing over £21m, which is now open and should put the college's science offer ever more firmly on the map. Led by prestigious Grimshaw Architects – Cutty Sark, The Eden Project – It literally removes the divide between arts and sciences, including a 240 seat auditorium, as well as five IT suites and 18 glassy labs looking over the beautiful trees of Dulwich.

At its centre is displayed Shackleton's boat, a treasured college possession previously residing appropriately enough with a stuffed penguin in a chilly cloister. Conrad Shawcross RA, with a committed team of 10 boys, worked on an installation. Naturally it leads the way environmentally too. The finishing touch, which may transform the feel of the college as much as anything, is the bright idea of removing the central car park, replacing it with landscaped recreational and thinking spaces.

The Dulwich College partnership schools overseas thrive, the latest in Yangon, Myanmar, but the master is clear that Dulwich is his absolute focus: he has delegated all but top level sign-off. Similarly, although he has championed outreach and partnership with a London academy group, a pie-chart of time devoted would see this account for only 10 per cent.

Sartorial traditions define the college – 'colours' blazers are boldly striped affairs awarded in recognition of achievement. 'Buy a big size,' advises the school captain – they will be de rigueur come OA reunions. You need a spotters' guide to identify old school ties, there are so many for every society and event. The master sees the Christmas fair attracting 3,000 local residents as a way to prove that the school isn't 'stuck up'. He is aware that the uniform gives off mixed messages, but wants the boys to wear it with pride. Believes the school is and should be 'class, creed and colour-blind'.

School lunches seem due for a make-over, but boys won't starve. Students we spoke to in the lower school were amusing, boisterous; those higher up articulate, but not at all arrogant, and all with different interests. A regular visitor to the school said, 'The boys appear relaxed and happy, there's always plenty of banter and camaraderie in evidence'.

Pastoral care, well-being and discipline: A senior prefect told us he's a rarity, having been at the school all the way from year 1, but has relished meeting new boys – 'each intake year interests and friends shift' – and although the school is large, boys feel they know each other within their year. The transition points are handled thoughtfully, ensuring boys get to bond with each other, for instance on a Welsh adventure when joining the lower school.

Houses are named after great Englishmen, and wooden boards throughout the school see Drake, Spenser et al jostling for position – house competitions facilitate new friendships as well as much rivalry.

We were on the look-out for indifferent pastoral care, but found no evidence for it whatsoever, instead much praise. A parent – 'Boys know where they stand with the master, and whilst he's friendly and approachable, boys know he won't tolerate certain misdemeanours...hard line on bullying'. Another, 'He strikes the right note on being nurturing but also seeing that the boys get on with being independent'. 'A caring atmosphere which celebrates the individual,' said a parent of a child diagnosed with ASD. One noted realistically that 'pastoral care is good, but the biggest problem is to get the boys to overcome male pride and admit they need help.' Gross misconducts such as possession of drugs or bullying would result in consideration for exclusion, whether fixed term or permanent, rather than an automatic exclusion.

Pupils and parents: The college is academically selective and socially inclusive, with a very culturally and ethnically diverse population, augmented by the boarders. Lots of multilingual children who might speak Chinese, Russian, Spanish or French at home. Boys mentioned pupil-led assemblies: recent topics include homosexuality and discrimination. The school captain said: 'There is no Dulwich way. You don't have to conform.'

A parent: 'It takes boys who are sporty, academic, musical, artistic and a mixture of all those things. If your child is gifted in one area, they will soar here. If they are a good all-rounder they will be encouraged to be a great all-rounder.' And it may come as a surprise to find that parents describe each other typically as 'a good bunch of mixed, non-stuffy parents', 'un-snobbish and not cliquey.'

Alumni include Chiwetel Ejiofor, Bob Monkhouse, Raymond Chandler, P G Wodehouse, Nigel Farage, Lionel Barber, Sir Ernest Shackleton.

Entrance: Not the ultra-elite intake of a few London schools, but still a top 15 per cent ability profile. At 11+, half of the 75 boys arrive from Dulwich College Junior School and half from a variety of local primary and prep schools including Hornsby House, Blackheath Prep, Rosemead, Dolphin School, Oakfield, Honeywell, Belleville, Corpus Christi, Dulwich Hamlet, St John's and St Clements. Parents are asked to send a letter from a registered professional regarding SEN needs to ensure appropriate assistance with the entrance exam. At 13 + the main feeders are Dulwich Prep London, Northcote Lodge and Fulham Prep. Non-refundable registration fee of £100 for Brits and £200 for overseas candidates.

At its centre is displayed Shackleton's boat, a treasured college possession previously residing appropriately enough with a stuffed penguin in a chilly cloister

A good number come from the immediate vicinity of Dulwich, but Foundation coaches brings pupils from as far away as Notting Hill, Canary Wharf, Wimbledon and Chislehurst.

Exit: Recent leavers to over 47 universities including Bristol, Durham, Edinburgh, Exeter, Imperial, KCL, LSE, UCL, Warwick and York; 18 to Oxbridge in 2017. Increasing focus on global destinations, particularly Ivy League – 10 to US in 2017 including Stanford, Berkeley, Princeton. Also Dutch universities and Chinese University of Hong Kong.

Money matters: Nearly a third of boys have some financial assistance: two-thirds of these from scholarships (from a third of fees to 105 per cent), a third from bursaries (up to 100 per cent of fees). Dr Spence has stated his ambition for for college to provide financial support to up to 50 per cent of its pupils in year 7 and above. 'Superb value for money,' said one parent of three privately educated children. 'Quite simply, Dulwich College far outstrips the rest in terms of communication, professionalism and results'.

Perhaps most exciting of all in terms of evolution is the college returning to its early 20th century past in launching a New Dulwich Experiment, championed by the master, which will see up to 50 per cent of pupils coming from families who cannot afford to pay full fees, opening up admissions to some of the brightest pupils from all backgrounds. In some ways it is a protective measure against becoming a school for the global super-rich, and the master freely admits it is 'enlightened self-interest', but partly funded by OAs keen to give something back, it sits very well in this already socially enlightened place.

Remarks: A school with a long tradition, with all of the prestige that comes with it, but now with a thrilling new dynamism which is raising the academic ante in every way, creating glittering new learning spaces and delivering a stunning co-curricular vision. Far more inclusive than one might imagine, the new bursary scheme needs to be trumpeted far and wide to ensure the school is on the radar of the brightest from all backgrounds.

Dulwich Prep Cranbrook

29

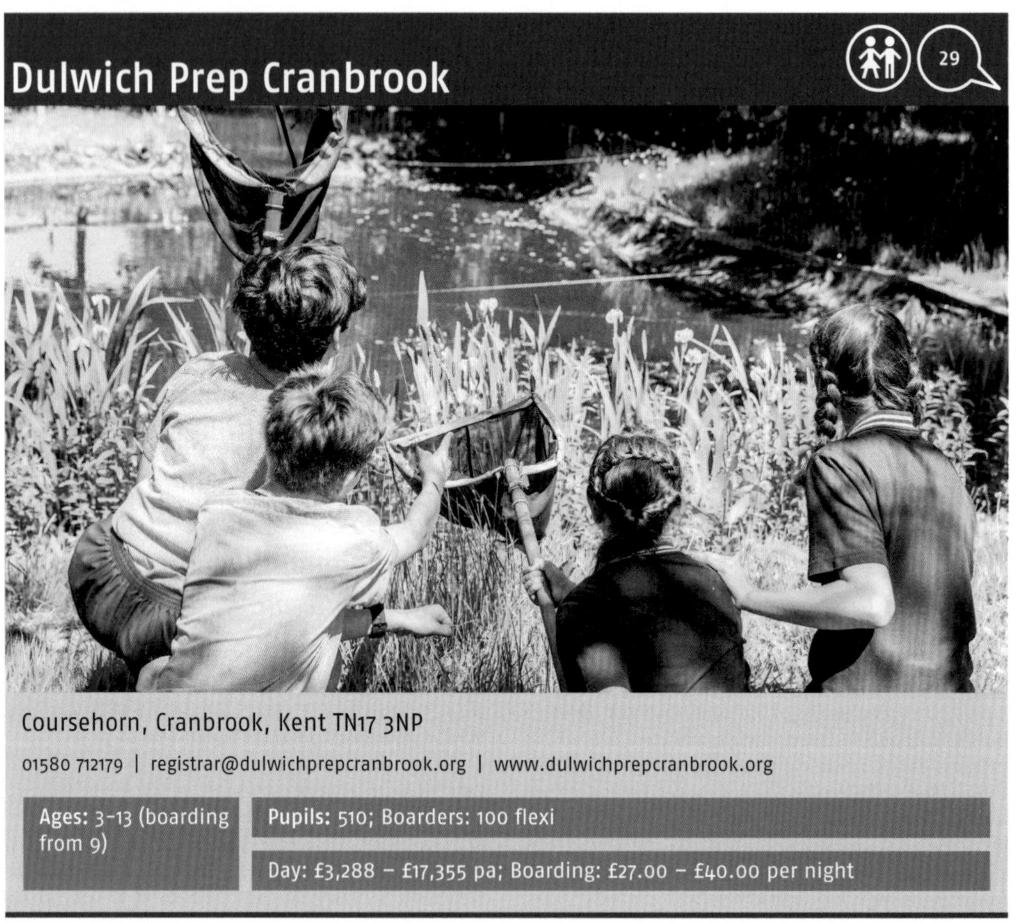

Coursehorn, Cranbrook, Kent TN17 3NP

01580 712179 | registrar@dulwichprepcranbrook.org | www.dulwichprepcranbrook.org

Ages: 3–13 (boarding from 9)

Pupils: 510; Boarders: 100 flexi

Day: £3,288 – £17,355 pa; Boarding: £27.00 – £40.00 per night

Headmaster: Since 2010, Paul David (50s) with a BEd in maths and PE from St Luke's, University of Exeter (he grew up in Cornwall). He taught at the City of London Freemen's School in Surrey, where he was housemaster, prior to becoming deputy head of St Paul's Juniors. He also taught maths at St Paul's. He was appointed headmaster of Eaton Square School in 2002. We meet in his comfortable panelled office in The Manor and find him to be very well turned out and easy to talk to but are most impressed with his ease with the younger children.

He is a keen sportsman, and whilst his rugby playing days are behind him, he's now a keen skier and tennis player. He is married to Nicky, a prep school teacher, and they have two children. Parents describe him as an excellent leader, appreciating his dedication: 'he's very visible – gets involved with school life – playing in charity hockey matches, school panto, coffee mornings, and I think I've even seen him playing the trumpet...' Yes indeed, Mr David is a trumpet player.

Perhaps his biggest challenge is the changing nature of exits with pre-testing and more 11+ leavers (especially to the now 11+ Cranbrook School) meaning the final years will need to be restructured. Mr David sees this as an opportunity and is already planning to introduce the Dulwich Diploma to augment common entrance and scholarship preparation. The school's shape may change ultimately so that it will have a 'slimmer top and fatter middle'.

Entrance: Unconditional offers for children joining nursery to year 2. Main entry points 4+ and 7+. Not oversubscribed. In years 3 to 8, children sit an assessment and spend a day at school. Most live within 15 miles but families come from all over the Weald of Kent and as far away as Maidstone and Ashford.

Exit: Around a quarter of pupils exit at 11+, but this will inevitably rise now that local state grammar Cranbrook School has a year 7, and 11+ entrance is on the rise everywhere. A couple to Sevenoaks most years, a handful to Sutton Valence and Tonbridge and others to a wide spread across Kent and Sussex: Benenden, Bethany, King's Canterbury, Eastbourne College, Roedean and others of the Kent grammars. Some 34 scholarships gained in 2017, with the top academic scholarships in three of the last four years to Tonbridge and Benenden.

Remarks: Nash House is for 3 to 5 year olds, Little Stream for those aged 5 to 9 years and the Upper School for pupils in their final years of the school.

The only aspect of the school which did not garner 'excellent' from the latest ISI report was the teaching, graded as 'good', much to Mr David's disappointment, but he has wasted no time making the minor adjustments needed to the staff room and points to the scholarships indicating that 'it's clear there is differentiation and stretching going on'. One father felt: 'Maths has a reputation amongst some parents for being less strong, particularly at the lower end.' Otherwise, we hear nothing but praise. One long-standing parent told us: 'The quality of teaching has been excellent across the curriculum and in many areas exceptional.' Recent migrators say: 'outstanding' and 'the standard is high'.

Nineteen teachers have been at the school for longer than 10 years. Standard curriculum. There is a new head of modern languages. Latin commences in year 6 and is led by a passionate new recruit. French is taught from Little Stream with

Spanish added in years 7 and 8. Late joiners may play catch up with languages not encountered before. Personal tutors monitor progress of children in years 7 and 8 as well as acting as mentors.

IT is well integrated within the school. Each pupil in years 7 and 8 has personal ownership of an iPad which just become part of their pencil case – the head describes a textiles project which students used their iPads to record from start to finish with time-lapse photography. The library is large with a full-time librarian and boasts some 7,000 titles.

Evacuated its 300 boys by train to Cranbrook at the start of World War II, setting up in huts in the headmaster's orchard

Plenty of dressing up days in Little Stream and Nash House: on Egyptian day they mummified a member of staff. As well as form teachers, subject specialists for maths and science. Very ordered, bright and inviting classrooms with tortoises in the science room. Children seem smiley and chatty and teachers are thrilled with the new building they had input into designing. Plenty of individual attention. A mother having observed her children learning through play in the initial years: 'It is obvious great care has been given by the teaching staff to establish a curriculum which suits the children both academically and emotionally.'

This is a school which places an emphasis on 'oracy' – standing up and speaking well is all part of the school's effort in developing socially confident individuals. Several parents credit their children's flourishing independence to the school. Some testing lower down the school, then more of an emphasis on twice yearly exams from year 5 – the children we met about to sit them said they were used to testing and it was no big deal.

'The kids at Dulwich are so fit,' enthused a parent and the first thing one notices about the school are the extensive, manicured acres. Every child plays sport and everyone in year 3 and above plays in a match against other schools. From year 4 children must be available to play in Saturday matches. A mother whose daughter is a talented sportswoman said: 'the opportunity given to her to excel at any of the sports really is hugely impressive.' There are also Tribe (house) fixtures for each age group. Girls play netball, hockey, lacrosse, rounders and tennis, also taking part in cross-country, track and field events, triathlon and swimming. Boys take part in these too and play football, rugby, hockey and cricket. The pool is outdoor and the children tell us it's warm, but we witnessed boys clutching towels and shivering. There are additional options such as badminton and orienteering for the non-rugby devotees.

A parent said, 'Sports coaching, particularly for those not in the first team, needs to be improved', but Mr David seems particularly hot on inclusivity and says that every child in years 5, 6, 7 and 8 plays a match, they do 'bottom up' house sports tournaments and the specialist coaches and gap students are shared around teams of all abilities. As if anticipating our question, the school plans to start a girls' cricket tournament and aims to find more matches across the board. The school has hosted IAPS and national cross-country competitions, the under-13 lacrosse team were the only one from a prep school to reach the last 16 of the national championships and the schools boasts handy table tennis players too.

Sixty per cent take instrumental lessons.Taster music lessons are available to children in year 3 on a wide range of instruments from the kinderhorn to the ukulele. Some attend the Junior Royal College of Music on Saturdays. Children play at regional festivals such as the Hastings Music Festival and musical ensembles have toured Prague and Italy. The Tribe music competition, performed in front of the whole school is a highlight: last year pupils chose to perform One Direction songs. There is a string orchestra in Little Stream and a senior orchestra, percussion groups, woodwind ensemble, Stringcredibles, jazz band and choirs.

Drama is timetabled. Each year group performs annually, whether straight plays or musicals such as Grease or The Sound of Music. Performances, musical and dramatic, are spectacular according to parents, who if they appear windswept it's because they all report being so frequently 'blown away'.

We're pretty sure that every school we now visit will have its art compared to the benchmark of Dulwich Prep Cranbrook: truly stunning from the earliest beginnings in Little Stream to the beautiful scholarship work that to our eyes easily compared to GCSE projects elsewhere. Leavers were working on a sculpture project making a flock of porcelain Matisse inspired doves (there are two kilns) holding bundles. The head of art conceives of new projects every year, so year 4 does not always do X and year 5 Y but says much is child-led.

Plenty of dressing up. On Egyptian day they mummified a member of staff. Children smiley and chatty

There are trips relating to every subject, ranging from visiting Lullingstone Roman villa, to trips to the West End for drama and a residential geography trip to Felixstowe. In Nash House all classrooms have an outdoor learning area (under a retractable roof) leading onto the playground. Little Stream enjoy forest school activities and from year 5 start there camping in the grounds progressing to a full week in Snowdonia by year 8. Teachers with a passion run clubs, most included in the fees. New this year is on-trend coding and Mandarin. Clubs that caught our eye: rock club, mah-jong club, water polo and DT jewellery.

An hour from London by train, rather more by car, the school resides in 50 beautiful acres of Kent countryside. The school has a charming history – Dulwich Prep London (DPL) evacuated its 300 boys by train to Cranbrook at the start of World War II, setting up in huts in the headmaster's orchard, and after the war remained as a separate school. The two schools are still linked and are run by The Dulwich Preparatory Schools Trust. It became fully co-educational in 1975.

The school buildings are so nondescript we barely noticed them. However, the pre-prep resides in a stylish new-build, with the same architect as DPL – a wooden exterior, fabulous in and out spaces and a large soft surface playground. Classrooms are vast by metropolitan standards and every inch looks fun. Little Stream also has use of a heated swimming pool.

Parents praised the pastoral care as 'excellent', 'impressive' and 'thoughtful' and there has been a move towards developing the softer, pastoral side. The head places an emphasis on nurturing self-confidence but says 'you don't need to be "robust" to do well here'. All new children have buddies. Children have been given more responsibility. The Head attends all of the pastoral meetings and says he's never before worked with 'staff who are so attuned to children'. Everyone is delighted with the recent partnership with Place2Be for one-to-one counselling and group sessions.

In addition, the school provides learning support for approximately 170 pupils, including children with dyslexia and dyspraxia. A wide range of other needs such as maths, sensory processing, or speech and language difficulties; hearing or visual impairment and complex medical conditions are also catered for. The school has its own medical centre. SEN provision in small groups and occasionally one-to-one. Some withdrawal, some in class. All learning support is included, not always the case elsewhere.

New, more extended day care options – a choice of breakfast and after-school clubs. Day boarding is available until 8.00 pm for year 5 and above and year 4 siblings: includes tea, supervised prep and an activity. Then there is flexi-boarding from one night to full weekly boarding. The girls' boarding house is The Manor with beams aplenty, fresh new carpet in the common room, flags and fairy lights in the lovely high ceilinged bedrooms and standard issue pine bunk beds. Everything very ship-shape. The boys' boarding is housed at Lodge, a modern building set in the grounds. Recently refurbished with a red, white and blue theme. Dorms of six sleep in year groups and all bring their teddies. Lobby full of tennis racquets and cricket bats, overflowing bike shed, boarders' fire pit.

British, no overseas pupils. No EAL. One mother: 'It is a real mix from the creative industries, doctors, finance, and farming.' Not all bankers, lots of business owners,' said another. Lots of events, a real community, friendly to newcomers and highly caffeinated (plenty of coffee mornings). 'There's a real sense of goodwill and warmth,' said a new mother. One parent concluded: 'it definitely feels like great value for money'.

Dulwich Prep London

30

42 Alleyn Park, London SE21 8AT

020 8670 3217 | registrar@dulwichpreplondon.org | www.dulwichpreplondon.org

Ages: 3-13 (co-ed nursery); (boarding from year 4)

Pupils: 850; Boarders: 20 flexi

Day: £12,570 – £18,570 pa; Boarding: + £1,440 – £4,648 pa

Headmaster: Since 2009, Michael Roulston MBE MEd (50s). Married with three children, educated in Ulster, he is warm and friendly, zipping about and offering to 'play mother' with the Darjeeling on our visit. First impressions aside, one senses his combination of vision, drive and no nonsense was forged during his first headship in the 1980s at The Model School – an informally religiously integrated school in Northern Ireland. His contribution to conflict resolution in the field of education was recognised by the BP Gulbenkian Citizenship Award in 1994.

After a stint in Japan as headmaster of The British School in Tokyo, earning him an MBE for services to education, he returned to the UK as head of Cranleigh Prep in Surrey. This is a man who clearly thrives on challenge and change, with his eye on the prizes – his and the boys'. We see him as a definite moderniser, sprucing up the old traditions, delivering a slickly presented school with a few fashionable nods – boules, allotments – without straying from his brief of happy parents and pupils at common entrance. Prior to our visit we had heard him described by parents as being 'rather like a successful CEO'. We found him to be businesslike certainly, but not stiffly corporate. Yes, very 'on message', but sincere too.

He says of the school, 'It's fun, full of energy from the earliest years all the way though...every day you cannot but be inspired by what the boys do. They are valued, recognised and well-loved'.

Head of the pre-prep since 2011, Mrs Ruth Burtonshaw BSc Phd PGCE Dip dyslexia and learning, is an early years specialist.

Entrance: Admission is selective. Multiple points of entry but majority start in the nursery at 3+ (girls and boys), at 4+ (boys only) or at 7+ (boys only). Limited number of means-tested bursaries to new applicants in years 3 and 4, determined by academic assessment.

Exit: Don't think that entrance to DPL is a do-not-pass-go ticket straight to Dulwich College, but a large proportion of pupils do gain entrance – with others heading in a variety of directions, foremost Westminster, Alleyn's and Tonbridge. Recent leavers exited to 28 different schools. Conversation regarding choice of senior school starts as early as year 4, and headmaster claims that every boy achieves his first (guided) choice of destination. Good tally of academic, sport, art and all-rounder scholarships or exhibitions, with many scholarships offered to Dulwich College. Only two or three boys a year choose to leave at 11+.

Remarks: The main curriculum is fairly traditional. French from year 1 and everyone tries their hand at Latin. Spanish offered as alternative to French. We found the lack of fashionable forward-thinking options such as Chinese or Russian surprising when even the local state primaries are giving them a go. The head says Mandarin has been offered as a club in the past, but there was little interest.

Setting in maths from year 4, extended to all examined subjects by year 7. This really works, with parents confirming there is sufficient flexibility for boys to move within the year to find the right level for them, and to be encouraged by their ability in different subjects. In each of the classes we visited, young male teachers were particularly noticeable, in amongst the boys or sitting on desks, easily relating to the boys in lessons ranging from European history, via maths to music technology. Energy fairly resounds and parents of pupils at the lower school, particularly, describe it as 'buzzing'.

Almost 20 per cent of boys are identified with a learning difference, mainly mild to moderate dyslexia. The head says that the school will do its best by all, but any with significant difficulties may find themselves guided to a more specialist school such as Fairley House. Highly-trained specialists lead a good number of staff in the learning support department. We saw great learning integration in the older years with dyslexic boys using laptops alongside their peers; parents confirm that boys don't feel singled out in any way if they need extra help. Nonetheless, some comment with feeling on just how tough it can be and wish for a little more two-way communication with teachers.

Sport is well resourced, with fixtures both after school and on Saturdays. Seven full-time PE teachers, specialist coaching from year 4, more than 70 teams, and achievements at national level, particularly in rugby and swimming. Every boy has an opportunity to play. Parents say coaching is less good at the lower levels, and whilst clubs offer

We hear that there is a healthy mix from the scarily ambitious to the more laid back, so there is a good chance of finding like-minded souls

exciting opportunities from rock-climbing to kayaking, 'alternatives to the obvious sporting options are very limited in the younger years'.

Homework is as ever controversial. One mother comments that whilst the boys love the varied topic work, parents find it 'never-ending' at weekends.

Drama varies from year to year. There is a year 6 play and an upper school play each year. Year 7 classes have drama and each year 8 class is off timetable for two weeks to produce an original production. Art continues to year 8 with clearly inspiring teaching, new facilities and technologies. We were wowed by the boys' 3D acrylic sculpture after Jackson Pollock, and the excitement in the room as the boys made sophisticated digital animations.

Music is rich, appealing and widely pursued, with over 20 ensembles and choirs, concerts of every type at venues in and out of the school, such as the Royal Hospital, Chelsea and Southwark Cathedral. Ninety per cent of the boys from year 2 upwards study an instrument, many achieving grade 8 before they leave.

Clubs (only a few additional charges) and activities run at lunch-time for boys from years 1-4, but also 4-5 pm from year 5. Current options include Lego, Warhammer, movie-making, beekeeping, street dance, juggling, Greek, golf and gymnastics. Wide array of trips – no stone unturned on the London museum circuit; further afield during school holidays (often built into the fees) eg Pompeii and Normandy. All this plus a thought-provoking lecture series – featuring recently a holocaust survivor, notable writers, broadcasters and adventurers.

The school was founded as Dulwich College Prep School (DCPS) in 1885. Despite the confusion arising from its name, the school is completely independent from Dulwich College and is an educational trust with its own governing body. This has been clarified with the school now styled as Dulwich Prep London (DPL). Situated in a wide, quiet West Dulwich street a few minutes from the train station, the buildings, mostly fairly modern, crowd around the playground.

With just over 800 pupils the school is large, but we saw how the division of the school into four distinct sections, each with its own library and classrooms, really works – 'the boys are quite protected from feeling lost in a huge place, and they're fully prepared for moving on,' said a parent.

Parents from the nursery year to higher up the school all comment on the benefit of a single sex school where teachers are free to focus on knights, dinosaurs, bloody battles etc. If there's one thing this school seems to do brilliantly it's the ability to really 'get' boys and how they learn and put this into practice. There is wiggle time (dancing around between lessons), marble parties or even a pool table as a whole class reward – 'the motivation and excitement are huge'.

The school motto is 'one for all and all for one' and the houses are named after North American Indian tribes from Chippeway to Objiwas. The winning tribe raises their flag weekly up the pole in the playground and if this is all sounds incredibly macho, we hear the boys sometimes choose to sing ABBA as their victory song. Meanwhile others, who choose the calmer activities from book club to weaving and needlework, do so without fear of ridicule. Some parents transfer from a co-ed environment for exactly this reason.

While the head's emphasis on character and kindness rings true – right on cue we witnessed children relating the story of the Good Samaritan to their day – a couple of parents commented that it can take a good while to find your niche. 'If you're not good at sport, you're not popular in the playground.' This is a school which aims to develop 'resilience'. When asked which kinds of boys would be happiest here, parents suggest: 'the bright and the best', 'a self-starter, bright and athletic', 'you've got to be robust'.

There is wiggle time (dancing around between lessons), marble parties, even a pool table as a whole class reward – 'motivation and excitement are huge'

No surprises that the majority of parents are highly affluent, most living within an expanding 10 mile radius of the school. However, we hear that there is a healthy mix from the scarily ambitious to the more laid back, so there is a good chance of finding like-minded souls.

School has one boarding house called (not so aptly in our opinion) Brightlands; this can accommodate 25 weekly or flexi-boarders from year 4. Rather a sombre looking house with a garden next to the pre-prep, it's been recently redecorated, and though the housemaster and his family are young and welcoming and boys rush around busily, we spied scary paint colours downstairs and 1950s style curtains in the dining hall. We wondered how this rated as a home from home compared to the boys' weekend surroundings. Definite fun, though, is one week a year when years 5, 6 and 7 stay from Sunday to Thursday; they experiment with life away from home and gain the Tomahawk Award for life skills such as button-sewing and bed-making.

The pre-prep early years department is a stunningly designed new-build – all wide open flowing spaces, blending indoor/outdoor, the classrooms give way to a huge covered sandpit for wet days. It has a delightfully green outlook surrounded only by playing fields, woodland and the grounds of Dulwich Picture Gallery. Nothing locally compares to the rural feel of this setting, a great comfort for any parent who didn't expect to raise their children in one of the world's biggest cities.

Girls are the minority but are carefully selected and more than hold their own. Parents of girls have little need for concern – except getting them in: applications are oversubscribed. Rainbow Club, staffed by regular teaching staff, offers care and activities pre and post school, from 8am to 4.45pm.

The head assists in girls' applications to local private and state schools. Almost all the boys move up to the prep.

Eastbourne College

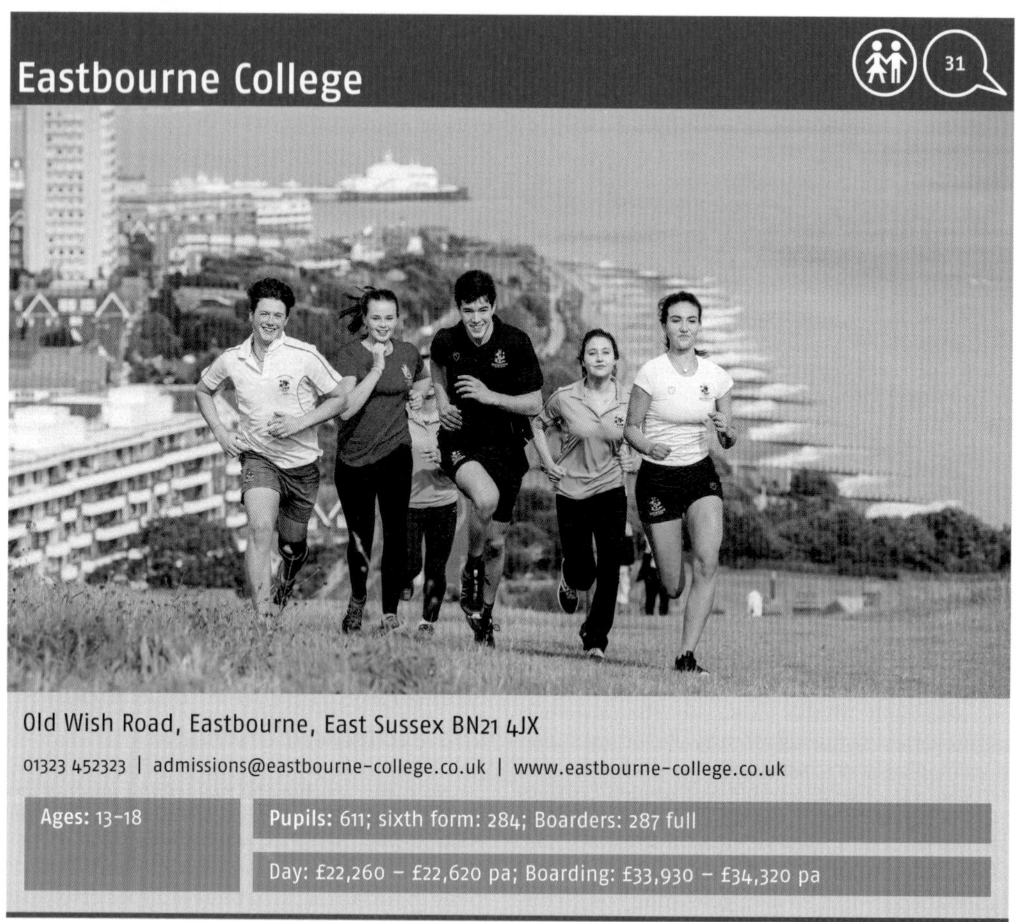

Old Wish Road, Eastbourne, East Sussex BN21 4JX

01323 452323 | admissions@eastbourne-college.co.uk | www.eastbourne-college.co.uk

Ages: 13–18

Pupils: 611; sixth form: 284; Boarders: 287 full

Day: £22,260 – £22,620 pa; Boarding: £33,930 – £34,320 pa

Head: Since September 2016, Thomas Lawson (40s), previously deputy head at Christ's Hospital. PPE degree from Oxford; taught economics and humanities at Winchester for 15 years, where he was also a housemaster, and under master for two years. His wife, Jessica, is also a teacher, and they have two young children.

Academic matters: Everyone starts with a wide sweep of subjects, tasting everything until they settle down to GCSE choices; can take a selection of French, German, Spanish, Latin and Greek. Parents say not the place for the brightest of the bright but meets the needs of the very smart ones (and stretches – one ex-London prep pupil went up a set in most subjects after first year) while the value added in the classroom and out is excellent

– as the school says, 'what really counts is how you work with people'. Lovely large science labs, six ICT suites, fibre optic network, three theatres, library with silent, chatty and headphone screen-watching areas – also an amazing three floor design technology centre.

Four assistant heads, one dedicated solely to the curriculum, mean that each pupil can have a bespoke timetable according to their choices. Mind boggling yet liberating, since 'you only get children achieving their best if they are doing what they want to do'. And they do – whether sciences and languages or textiles, woodwork and product design: in 2017, 57 per cent of GCSE grades were A*-A/9-7. School day from 8am to 8pm means that parents have their day children home with no homework when they finally arrive – there is a 6pm bus for those who have nailed all their commitments for the day and commute from further afield (Rye or Tunbridge Wells). Houseparents and the co-curricular assistant head juggling sports, clubs and preps help synchronise multi-talented kids and single-minded staff and ensure 'whatever happens, the kids don't feel the pressure'.

Not a huge breadth of A level subjects – no psychology, sociology, politics. If demand is timely then senior management team will make it happen – RS has become an examination subject with intelligent wide-ranging debate. Maths, science and humanities most popular; EPQ and scholarship/leadership courses now offered. In 2017, 39 per cent A*/A grades overall.

Parents are relieved by challenge grades rather than predictive ones (much more motivational)

Entire jigsaw is monitored with the slick electronic report card which culminates in the tutor sitting down with the pupil and focusing on the past, present and what needs to be done. Input far more supportive than reflective as the houseparent adds their comments before a pdf report is emailed home at least twice a term. Parents are relieved by challenge grades rather than predictive ones (much more motivational). Continuous opportunities for parent or staff to monitor and add input when the issues arise and overseas parents particularly enjoy this access (10 per cent of pupil body). Ramps up staff's accountability to parents and Duke of Edinburgh, Oxbridge or scholar reports can be added for those interested. This transparent system was created by a full-time software developer, who continues to mine the data and present it to the staff via web-based platform, winding in pastoral incidents and academic progress, enabling a holistic view of the pupil when considering discipline or going up or down a set. Parents appreciate standardised teaching that makes it easy for a pupil to move between sets even mid-term.

Plenty of Macs for digital editing and two kilns for firing experimentally glazed ceramics – all anchored by visits from artists making a living in the outside world

Informative 'white book' provides a structure that the new pupils follow, empowering them to such an effect that a parent recently just sat back and observed as the parents' evening went on between the pupil and their tutor. School aims to include all SEN pupils where possible, but specific provision for mild dyslexia, G&T and EAL. One full-time and one busy part-time teacher. All children are screened on entry. Individual SEN lessons are charged for. No separate cost for the G&T provision, however, which is department specific.

A group of sixth formers meets up with year 11s from Willingdon Community College every Monday afternoon to go over GCSE subjects with them – a session known as Roy's Homework Club, after the head's dog.

Games, options, the arts: Activities and sport sandwiched between morning and afternoon of classroom learning suits the youngest ones especially. Myriad teams so that 95 per cent of the pupils take their turn to win or lose together against another school, and with elite talent emerging, there are Olympic or international professionals coaching in tennis, hockey, netball, rugby and cricket; major sports tours for these too. The manicured rugby pitch dominates the front of the school but the main sports fields are a five minute drive away – the girls in particular enjoy the walk for the warm up and catch up it provides. The range of sports currently on offer stretches from basketball to equestrian events (a bit more parental input) and there's zumba classes if team sport really doesn't appeal, or space to chat and listen to music. All full-time sports staff teach academic subjects and are tutors as well, meaning that badminton, table tennis and jujitsu have emerged from clubs to potential fixtures by encouraging children's initiatives.

Ongoing development on one and a half acres in the centre of the site includes sports centre and swimming pool (due to open in spring 2018). Sharing resources and experiences with the wider Eastbourne community important: the school's creative arts centre (next to the Towner Art Gallery and Congress Theatre) is a part of the town's artistic centre, with musicians from the school busking to raise money for St Wilfred's Hospice, professional artists coming in to run masterclasses in creative barter for the foyer exhibition space and a resident from the Rambert Dance company running courses for local state and private schools and the rugby team. Pupils are involved in all of these initiatives, as well as working with adults with learning needs and teaching pensioners to surf the internet.

Interlocking array of different sized lockers and muted practice rooms is testament to the orchestral music tuition (three choirs, a concert band and two orchestras) while Battle of the Bands is a highlight of the musical year, with a recording studio enabling music technology as an A level option. The art studios are light and bright with examples of excellent student work dotted around the school (routinely 100 per cent A*/A at A level and over 92 per cent at GCSE), plenty of Macs for digital editing and two kilns for firing experimentally glazed ceramics – all anchored by visits from artists making a living in the outside world. Paths to the commercial acting world also well trodden, a whole school production annually, while all year 9 put on a play in their first term and house concerts are really enjoyed – sometimes end up on YouTube.

Boarding: Separate day and boarding houses, so no day pupils feel they miss out on dorm time horsing about, and 6pm and 8pm buses give them the chance to 'organise their work, co-curricular activities and family life most effectively for them and their families'. All pupils are registered in the common room of their house, assemblies, announcements here too; good facilities, each with their own garden; junior boarders share three to

This is their home from home, but they can invite others to come and knock about between preps. In the lower years this means mostly single sex hanging out when not in lessons or activities (whether on comfy sofas or around a pool table)

five to a dorm, reducing up to the sixth form, where they have large single rooms – the more modern girls' ones with en suite bathrooms. Real retreats, managed by the houseparents and matrons, with touches that appeal, whether a pupil-run tuck shop with entrepreneurial offers or a mirrored dance studio, girls plaiting each other's hair and boys kicking about on floodlit Astroturf. New development promises more open social space for boys and girls to mix (now mostly the atmospheric cloisters), with no dark corners and the staff common room next door. Majority of sixth form don't have boy or girlfriends at school; boarders get town leave on Saturday night; they hang out with each other in the holidays too. Younger boarders explore restaurants in Eastbourne too and petition their parents to come and take them (and all their friends) out for lunch.

Background and atmosphere: Founded in 1867 with the seventh Duke of Devonshire allotting 12 acres to the new enterprise, the current Duke is president of the Eastbourne College council along with influential Eastbourne residents. Main school is an imposing red-brick building, amid an aesthetically pleasing mix of others, old and sympathetically new and ensconced in the heart of Eastbourne, with five-storey Victorian houses, retirement homes and boarding and day houses all cheek by jowl. Parents see three main communities in this part of Eastbourne, the old people, the young people and those who serve those two communities – many staff live on site or very near; 'kids walk around old people with respect and the old people are safe in the knowledge they won't be mugged!'

Close to the railway and next to Devonshire Park, home to the pre-Wimbledon men's and ladies' tennis tournament; constant traffic of hearty pupils hurrying to lessons; friendly, happy and confident teenagers, who all belong to a single sex day or boarding house. This is their home from home, but they can invite others to come and knock about between preps. In the lower years this means mostly single sex hanging out when not in lessons or activities (whether on comfy sofas or around a pool table). Everyone eats as a school (new dining hall on the horizon); good food with an excellent range of choices.

New sixth formers are welcomed, those from local state schools make new friends and keep their old ones too, broadening the sixth form across all backgrounds and outside the college. Some drive themselves in from more rural homes, others keep younger ones company on the train commute. Chapel every Sunday for boarders and visitors, otherwise one weekly service – with alternative arrangements possible for other faiths – a spiritual basis but nowadays more about a collective act, with thoughts about the wider community.

Pastoral care, well-being and discipline: Very, very strong indeed, with excellent and insightful communication; the first thing all happy parents say is 'they really know our kids'. Probably why it is so successful at reaching all abilities and improving the confidence of many. Housemasters and housemistresses are first point of contact, for day pupil parents on drop off or pick up, for those further afield on email and phone. Often issues have a plan to sort or are sorted before a parent even learns about them, within a school day. 'Families' in girls' houses, with a mother in the sixth form, a cousin in year 10 and peer listeners. Support in boys' houses is organised less metaphorically but the same relationships develop – older ones sit in on prep; not a chore to help with studies, this opens conduit for buddy support and cross-year friendships. A recent charity bike-a-thon had girls and tutors staying up and eating pizza and supporting the 24 hours of pedalling.

New sixth formers are welcomed, those from local state schools make new friends and keep their old ones too, broadening the sixth form across all backgrounds

We heard concrete examples of issues dealt with empathetically, tactfully and effectively, whether they stemmed from a staff or a pupil incident, with the children's welfare held at the centre. House and school prefects are in the upper sixth; head says, 'not a position for privilege but for service'. Drinking and drugs stamped on hard (although supportive testing if drug use happens out of term), deputy and assistant head of pastoral are fully aware of the range of misdemeanours, from shaving a head, roughing up playing football, through to sexting – and the electronic system enables rapid staff communication on spotting patterns or a change of routine.

Pupils and parents: Varied social mix, with children that are spread across all four quartiles. On one side you have the Sussex Downs and the rolling Sussex countryside, the other side the deep blue sea. Fifty-fifty day to (no flexible or weekly) boarding, farming families who have been coming for generations, more recent locals who also have horses, London boarders and the international contingent (10 per cent) of Chinese, German, Russian, Italian, Spanish and Nigerian. Only 90 minutes by train from London; boarders have exeats every three weeks but Saturday school does cut the weekend short. Parents don't mix much away from the touchline or horse events, unless they know each other from prep schools, although more social functions are being organised.

Entrance: Overseas pupils are accepted provided their level of English is proficient. Candidates for year 9 entry sit CE or the college's scholarship papers. The hurdle for sixth form is B grades or better at GCSE. About 35 pupils enter for sixth form from surrounding state or private schools.

Exit: Up to a third leave after GCSEs. At 18, mainly to a mix of redbrick, Russell group and vocational colleges; three to Oxbridge in 2017, and one medic; some 25 per cent take a gap year; Durham, Exeter, Leeds, Manchester, Newcastle and Nottingham popular over the last few years. Old Eastbournians come back to talk about being a pilot, farmer, doctor or graphic designer at the careers fair, just one of over 50 events organised by The Eastbournian Society for alumni, parents, staff and current pupils.

Money matters: Scholarships available for most subject areas (five to 20 per cent) and means-tested bursaries for up to 60 per cent of the fees. The registrar is very switched on, candid and efficient – his practical approach much appreciated by parents, especially if their financial circumstances change. Foundation director oversees the fundraising and bursary fund. He is aiming to build a pot by contributions from parents and staff to allow financial help to the struggling. All staff contribute the price of a pint per week to the fund. This equates to approx £250 a week and thus £15,000 a year. This philanthropic pint fund consequently translates to a) a full bursary for a fortunate and worthy pupil and b) a thirsty staffroom.

Remarks: A school for families who take joy in what their kids become rather than pride in what they've made of them. Bespoke timetables backed up by outstanding pastoral care make for happy and stimulated kids who work and play hard.

Epsom College

32

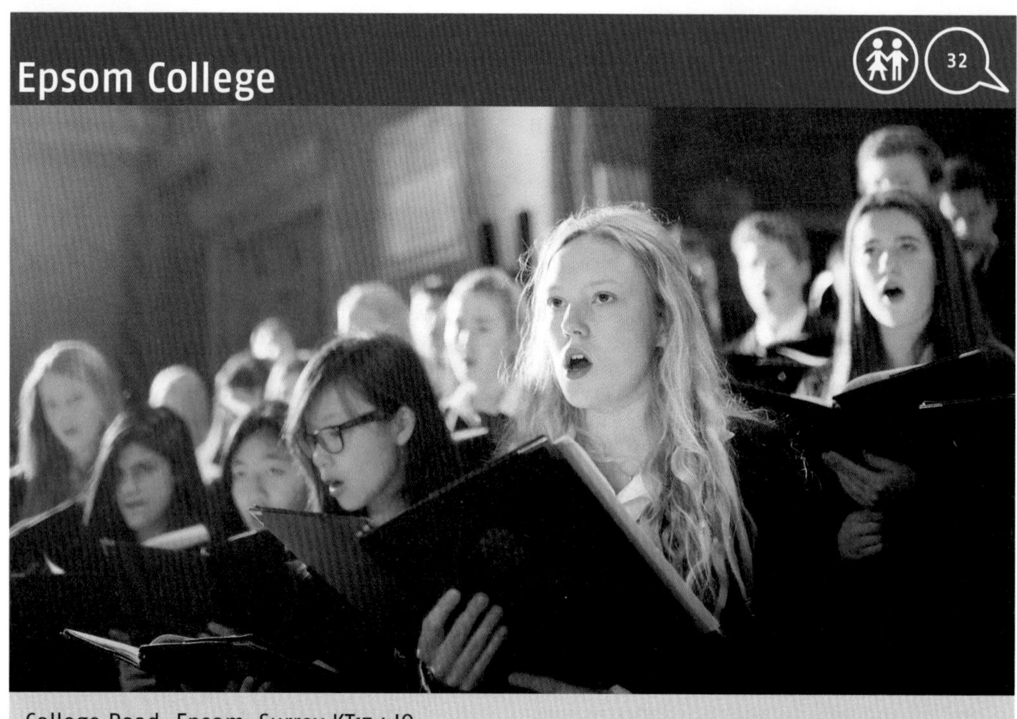

College Road, Epsom, Surrey KT17 4JQ

01372 821234 | admissions@epsomcollege.org.uk | www.epsomcollege.org.uk

Ages: 11–18

Pupils: 883; sixth form: 343; Boarders: 160 full, 208 weekly

Day: 24,177 pa; Boarding: £32,391 – £35,658 pa

Headmaster: Since 2012, Mr Jay Piggot BA MA PGCE (50s). Previously headmaster at alma mater Campbell College, Belfast between 2006 and 2012, and, before that, put in 17 years at Eton (clearly a hard place to leave) starting as assistant master in 1989 and becoming housemaster 10 years later. Not bad going given that it was only his second teaching job: his first, immediately after completing his MA in English Renaissance literature at Liverpool, was at Millfield, where he taught A level/Oxbridge English.

Career success undoubtedly assisted by personality and appearance – quietly dashing, though doesn't overdo the leading man business. Gimlet vision, too – noticed and swiftly dealt with errant piece of rubbish, a very small plastic wrapper, only one in otherwise immaculate grounds.

Lordy, lordy, what a popular man he is. Pupils – 'a joy,' he says – say he makes an effort to know names, comes to matches and makes with the social chit chat. Biggest vote winner, however, are the birthday cards – otherwise sophisticated international pupil clearly thrilled with his, particularly handwritten signature – cynic had checked authenticity with damp finger just to be sure. Parents also like what they see. Innovations all welcomed. 'Very proactive behind the scenes and has pushed through some sensible changes,' said one. Definitely a step up from predecessor. 'School ran well but didn't have the personality.'

College was already known to him before the headhunters came a-callling, and found vision, ethos and commitment very much to his taste. Younger son, a keen golfer, moved with him (older brother is going great guns at Eton).

'Would love' to teach again and might when has got through current to-do list, which is lengthy. Getting shorter by the minute, though. 'Some heads would take a while to work out what they were going to do,' says teacher. 'He's made lots of changes already.' Popular changes include axing of seasonal timetables, originally to make most of winter light, but cause of mega all-round confusion to all.

High profile reintroduction of matrons into the houses was an Eton-inspired development that's brought a caring, maternal touch (thus far, all women) to details such as tracking down missing shirts and sewing as well as control of rowdy element. Of even greater significance has been academic shake up, still ongoing, starting with observation of every member of staff since he arrived, followed with ISI-style feedback. 'A privilege,' he says. (We're sure they feel the same). Many stay for years. No wonder, with perks headed (for many, though not all) by housing either on-site or within a few minutes' walk. 'My wife told me we're not going to move,' said one. Given Epsom property prices, you can't blame her.

In addition to the introduction of heads of year, designed to add missing link identified in recent inspection, he's also not going to stand in path of old-timers who could be moving on to greater things elsewhere, while rejigging weak spots including A level languages and biology and GCSE English literature. Dynamic incomers, including former Uppingham head of modern foreign languages – similar developments in science – are being brought in together with fledgling new generation of bright young things adding oomph to lessons (occasional dullness one of few inferred criticisms in last inspection report).

Still more shaking up to come, however, essential given school's previous sleepiness and 'red-hot' competition – Wellington, Cranleigh and Charterhouse as well as St John's Leatherhead and Reed's School. Bumping up interior life of school is part of the process, with Eton's dawn to dusk (and beyond) intellect-boosting programme the inspiration for mind-expanding programme – expect more pupil-organised drama, musical and debating activities (medical, history and politics societies are already on the go) sparking impassioned discussions that ramp up the intellectual temperature from tepid to mercury-busting.

Mark of success? Would like popularity of places to increase to the point where competition for boarding places as strong as for day hopefuls.

Academic matters: One of formerly mid-ranking schools to have substantially upped game in recent years. Fun lessons got pupils on the go, literally so, with movement minus the music, A level students standing up for miracles (theology) and marginal cost (economics) – everything, in fact, but their rights.

Parents, while agreeing with head that some teachers are 'past their best', think generally offset by vast majority who are 'engaging, personable and, most importantly, able to motivate. They appear to love their subjects and to enjoy teaching and the company of the children – none of these are a given, in my experience.' Megawatt enthusiasm often a game-changer, especially at sixth form level. Sciences score particularly high conversion rates. 'Was my dream to be a translator – now it's chemistry,' said pupil.

Ability to devote time to all (an impressive 55 hours contact time a week) means that 'there are no lost causes,' says head. Plentiful tracking and feedback means pupils know where they are and how they can improve, feedback seamlessly integrated in lessons. 'We put down our comments when we've had a test and it gives teachers a good idea of where we are,' said sixth former.

Though class sizes aren't teeny tiny – average 20 for GCSE (maximum 23) and between 10 and 12 at A level (15 max), with pupil to full time teacher ratio of 8:4 – school is consistently good when it comes to added value, setting in maths, banding in languages and sciences (where small group of less able students might do GCSE dual sciences rather than IGCSE triple). No-one takes 'silly' numbers of GCSEs, says senior teacher – aim is to ensure good grades in manageable quantities.

Lordy, lordy, what a popular man he is. Pupils – 'a joy,' he says – say he makes an effort to know names, comes to matches and makes with the social chit chat

Currently, results generally very good given relatively mixed intake, with 78 per cent A*-A/9-7 grades at GCSE; 86 per cent of A level entries graded A*/B and 53 per cent A*/A in 2017.

Good, largely traditional subject range, almost ology-free – 'nothing against psychology but it just isn't us,' says teacher – though language options now include GCSE Mandarin, originally for overseas students but now open to all. However, MFLs not the strongest suit, with few takers at A level – maths and economics much the most popular.

Hugely dynamic head of DT is also bumping up recruitment, particularly amongst girls, by ensuring that environment, full of technological marvels – though it's pupils' superb mortice and tenon joints and chamfering skills that help pull in the A* grades – is also tidy ('was grubby and fragmented') with plenty of wood-turning (apparently the secret of cross-gender appeal).

Big feature is Extended Project Qualification (EPQ), a mini-dissertation that, at best, combines originality and staying power (recent topics include carcinogens in food and madness in Henry VIII's court – separately). Worth the effort. One pupil, down an A level grade and out of university course, called department head and used hers to talk her way back in again. No doubt that attracts the very able – one pupil, exile from leading girls' school, delighted to be somewhere that praised good work rather than training spotlight on pupils only when failed to deliver top grades – though one parent queried its suitability for the truly brilliant. 'Might be a bit too comfortable,' she thought. 'It's a broad church and some kids are too bright [and] shouldn't be there.'

Extra scaffolding where needed, with clinics all the way through the school in all key subjects and teachers not just present (many live in) but in many cases 'always available.' That said, school isn't geared up to cope with anyone with more than mild learning difficulties. Of the 100 or so pupils with SEN, none is currently statemented, SpLD the overwhelmingly dominant need, though have coped with (mild) ADHD as well.

Plenty of emails home and 'progress reports every three weeks,' ensure that everyone knows what's going on, while lengthy school day (finishing 6.00pm) incorporates sufficient free periods for the organised to sock it to the homework.

And though initially gentle pace startling to alumni of non-stop pushy preps, school gets praise for stress-appropriate levels of pushing tailored to each child. 'They know which way to push,' said mum of recent leaver. 'The teacher told my child that she "might get an A in biology GCSE, but I don't think so".' Nettled, daughter was spurred on to do just that.

Games, options, the arts: Sport success plentiful – boys' and girls' rugby VIIs regular regional winners, lots of post-school success, too (five OEs play for Harlequins), ditto hockey (mixed seniors won Surrey U18 competition), as do minors with recent captain of golf driving his way to Stanford golf scholarship (first European for over 10 years, says school) and shooting. Facilities generous – including swimming pool – and, in case of one of two sports halls, close to giant-size (even better with new sports pavilion up and running), two cracking sports halls, one giant sized, six squash courts, a swimming pool and a fencing salle. No partridge in pear tree (but would undoubtedly be doing a few press ups if there were).

Everybody gets out a lot, DT excursions to real factories (Brompton bikes to Henry vacuum cleaners) so popular that school staff sign their Saturdays away

Outside, timetable pushes variety – first years will have both outdoor and inside sports in an afternoon and, further up the school, non-standard sports can be done off site – riding, for example and climbing, though school now has its own climbing wall. Range ensures that 'you're not penalised if you're not sporty,' thought a mother, with matches for all. 'Sport is very important, whether you're A team or D/E/F team material,' agreed another parent. Sports captains, rated by the rank and file – 'positions are well earned,' thought one – have a real say in team structure. 'You can discuss team composition with the coach and that's good,' thought pupils. Termly activity sheet encourages pupils to experiences shock of the new. One boy, initially dreading jive dance, discovered instead that he was 'that sort of person' – and loved it.

Plenty head for D of E, room for all (can add more staff if demand is high). CCF feather in school cap – one of oldest and biggest in country, teeming with facilities (we liked esteem-heavy 'confidence' rather than assault course). Wears success lightly – numerous impressive sports cups casually behind bars with the guns).

Arts also attacked with relish. Music felt to be 'on the ascendant,' thought teacher, with lots of instrumental lessons – drums, singing, electric guitar and piano the biggest sellers, some reaching diploma level; challenging, performance opportunities ranging from low stress impromptu recitals to high quality productions including The Cunning Little Vixen and excellent chapel choir, masses lining up to audition – a macho-free area, reckoned year 9 and 10 pupils. Those not making the grade can 'let voices develop' in non-selective Glee Club instead.

Visual arts, recently upgraded, feature confident, instantly recognisable year 9 pictures of Kew Gardens – one of many trips. Everybody gets out a lot, DT excursions to real factories (Brompton bikes to Henry vacuum cleaners) so popular that school staff sign their Sundays away, too, school chef enjoying outing to Cadbury's as much as pupils.

Boarding: Similar numbers for full boarding and weekly. Boarding houses, dotted round the site, now all done up to the nines – matching up to head's aspirations to equal best in Britain – with decking and glass snazzy-ness. Sensible trouble-preventing measures include half-termly dorm swaps and plenty of weekend activities for full boarders, from trips to Thorpe Park to house evenings and bowling. 'Never lonely because lots going on,' said sixth former.

Buddy system helps combat homesickness (most reckoned that worst was over within first week), one house even creating own surrogate family, one year group per generation and organising popular old fashioned sports day as an ice-breaker. Here, too, matrons, add much appreciated extra tea and sympathy layer (housemistresses – always academic staff – can 'sometimes be more of figure of authority,' thought sixth formers).

Background and atmosphere: Altogether a civilised place to be, starting with laid-back parking regime, permitted along one side of the one way road that winds round the lush green campus (new upper sixth drivers are vetted by the head), imposing chapel at its heart. Though patron is HM the Queen, not a high-society institution. Started life as the Royal Medical Benevolent College, a charitable Good Thing, helping the relics of deceased impoverished medics. Strongly Victorian in spirit and execution – most buildings completed between 1850s and 1920s. School wasn't welcomed by all, overt charitable status 'distasteful' to recipients, reckoned contemporary letter to Lancet.

Took only boys for the first 120 years or so (sisters presumably expected to marry their way to economic success); girls added 1996 largely as emergency recession-busting tactic (local area had suffered heavily and pupil numbers had plummeted). Now, of course, school wouldn't be without them and they're on almost equal terms in the sixth form, though minority partners in other years. Desired ratio is 60:40 is, thinks head, about right, ensuring girls have the same options as boys, particularly when it comes to games. 'All get the chance to contribute,' he adds, firmly. No complaints from girls themselves, or parents, so seems to be working. Added a lower school – years 7 and 8 – in 2016.

Though it's all 19th and early 20th century authenticity from the front with 'real wow factor,' thought parent, sold on first visit, tasteful modern extensions stretch back a considerable distance to the rear (current bursar, a woman, was a former architect, and it shows). Behind public face is 'pupil world', the second sweep of buildings where most of the teaching takes place. Modern additions – humanities building particularly palatable – don't jar (though some areas, like maths and theology blocks, could be nicer, and almost certainly will be when funds permit).

When it comes to décor, different departments exhibit endearing idiosyncrasies – from pot plants in chemistry lab (and sign announcing 'nudisme interdite au delà de cette limite') to blue-painted English rooms (also notable for friendly clutter of framed posters and attractive display boards already filling up nicely in second week of term) while modern languages is all-purple (even down to lampshades). Black wall in one of physics labs, however, is for sensitive experiments and 'not because we're pandering to goths,' explains larger than life department head.

Technology warmly embraced with Wifi throughout (and 'extreme' internet safety settings triggered by word Middlesex) and the Hub, new high tech room where lessons can be recorded for posterity. Tradition equally enjoyed but not pointlessly so – most of original medical artefacts and stuffed animals that once dominated science rooms have gone. 'Antiques dealer took the rest,' says teacher, cheerfully.

Big plans include new careers centre, lecture rooms, art gallery/café and social areas for sixth formers.

Pastoral care, well-being and discipline: Seniors a strong force (and will be even more so once head succeeds in replacing current sixth form block with something altogether spiffier). Take turns to lead assemblies that are so far removed from commonplace fare that we had to double check that searingly articulate reflections on 9/11 were being delivered by sixth form girls. It appears effortless.

No wonder – it's been in rehearsal since June, points out the friendly chaplain. Older pupils keen to stress that 'hierarchical system associated with traditional English boarding school, pitting year group against year group' is 'a terrible idea' and will pitch in to take sides if older boys show signs of picking on younger ones. 'It's part of our role and it works.'

Little in the way of serious misbehaviour, however, with just two pupils 'withdrawn by parents' (expulsion by face-saving euphemism) in senior teacher's 15 years. Drugs issues in both cases, though it's very rarely the end, behind the scenes second chances often possible. Day to day, class silliness and late homework the main issues, reckoned pupils, with escalating sanctions – lines, notification of tutors, warnings, departmental then school detentions – rattled off by all.

Endearing idiosyncrasies – from pot plants in chemistry lab (and sign announcing 'nudisme interdite au delà de cette limite') to blue-painted English rooms

Lots of rewards, too – from pizza or chocolate for work-related merits and distinctions to privileges of seniority – sixth form day girls cited joy of leaving sports kit on shelves in study rooms instead of trekking, when younger, to go to separate storage area.

And though house system (separate for day and boarding pupils) engenders ferocious sense of competition (choir contest in particular), it isn't carried over into lessons, 'which stops it becoming tribal,' reckoned parent.

Pupils and parents: Predominantly local intake with vast majority of pupils, including 95 per cent of UK boarders, living within 10 to 15 miles. School keen to expand the range but, meantimes, results in happy fusion of streetwise Londoner with leafy Surrey-ite, reckoned teacher – cool without the ennui.

Many staff have own children here (has peaked at 40 or so). One parent we spoke to who'd opted for local alternative thought numbers were excessive – though appeared to be a lone voice. Working mums – far more these days – were something of a feature to the point where socialising tends to feature nights out to ensure 'you don't feel out of the loop,' thought career-driven mother.

Cosmopolitan feel added by international component (largeish at 20 per cent) drawn from Hong Kong, Malaysia, Russia and Korea, though many more from western Europe. For the 10 per cent who are non-native English speakers there is a structured EAL programme in place, but they're fully integrated into the curriculum says the school, 'right from day one'.

Malaysian numbers probably not affected by opening of sister school in Kuala Lumpur in 2014 – first foray into pastures new, as 'there will always be pupils who want a UK education,' reckons school.

Entrance: School is after all-rounders with several strings to their bow and 'fair share of the bright pupils'. Once a second choice regular, increasingly a bill-topper, recruiting from over 40 preps and state schools, likely to increase as it extends reach (Danes Hill and Downsend, Shrewsbury House, Aberdour and Feltonfleet feature prominently though no official feeders). Full-on charm offensive attracting south west London schools.

New 11+ intake via maths, English and VR tests plus interview in January of year 6. Second intake into year 9, with January pre-test in year 6 (VR – scores of around 118-120 the norm – NVR, English and numerical skill plus interview), same again (minus NVR) for non-prep candidates in January of year 8. Once 'day pupils were brighter and more studious' than boarding pupils, thought one insider. No longer the case.

If no joy at 13+, small number of places at 14+ (three to five only, English, maths and NVR tests). Second biggest influx is post-GCSE with 45 to 50 joining the sixth form, following VR, NVR and numerical skills tests plus interview. Push to up state school numbers (currently around 20 per cent of the total) as a way of 'supplementing the ratios'. Some haggling after year 12 for a handful of pupils whose progress gives cause for concern. Repeating year not an option, dropping a subject can be the solution.

Exit: No shortage of ambition, most achieving first choice unis; Exeter, Bristol, LSE, Loughborough, Nottingham, Warwick, Durham, Edinburgh, SOAS, Manchester, Oxford Brookes and Queen's Belfast are top 10 university destinations; one to Oxford in 2017, plus five medics and one vet. Economics and finance followed by business, geography and sociology popular; one student, garlanded with an A* in art, off to an art foundation course in 2017.

Money matters: Annual bursary spend close to £750,000 on up to 100 per cent of fees. Possible additional financial support for families with medical connections through the Royal Medical Foundation, based at the school, though since 2000 a separate legal entity. Lots of scholarships on offer, academic and headmaster's (for 'a wide range of disciplines' from drama to chess) at 11+ and 13+, sports and music at 16+ too.

Remarks: With demographics and parent power going his way, head's boarding aspirations could well be realised. 'A brilliant school for my son,' said mother. Another commented that school had got 'everything there was to get' out of her child. 'You really can't ask much more than that'.

Feltonfleet School

33

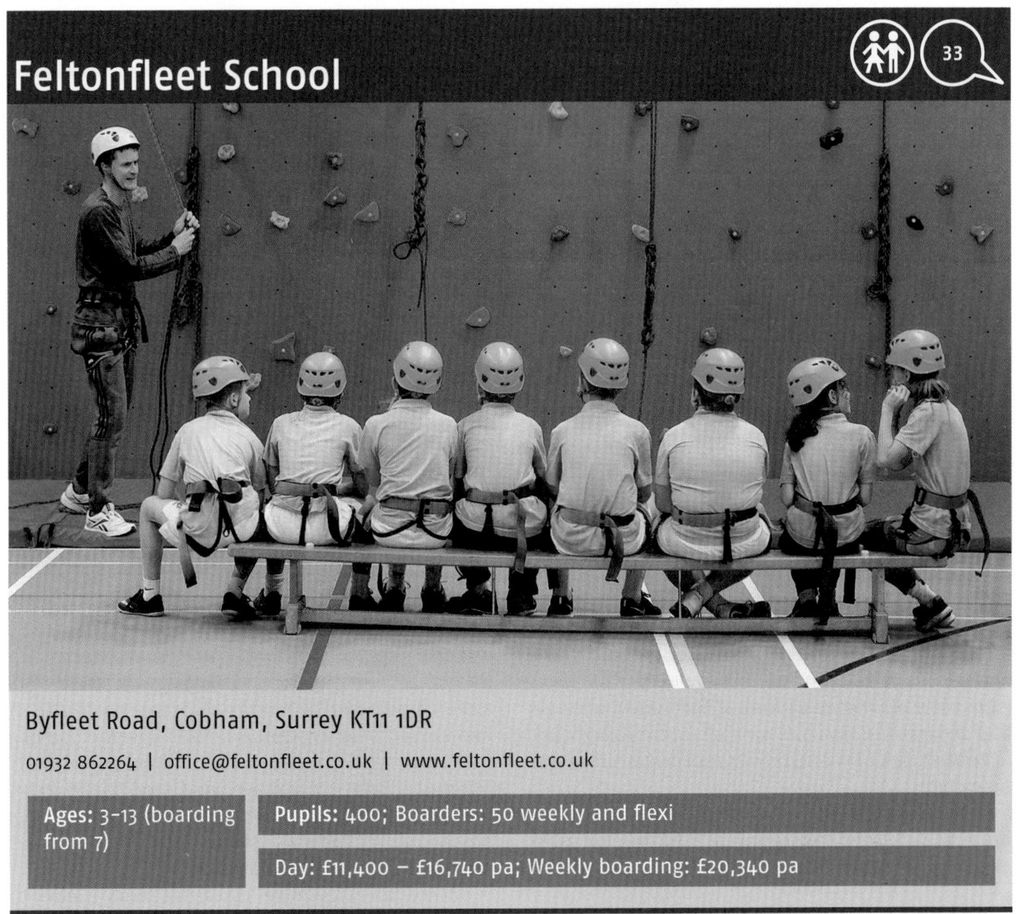

Byfleet Road, Cobham, Surrey KT11 1DR

01932 862264 | office@feltonfleet.co.uk | www.feltonfleet.co.uk

Ages: 3-13 (boarding from 7)

Pupils: 400; Boarders: 50 weekly and flexi

Day: £11,400 – £16,740 pa; Weekly boarding: £20,340 pa

Headmistress: Since January 2018, Shelley Lance, previously deputy head. Theology degree from King's College London; began her teaching career at Alleyn's, then taught at Whitgift, where she was head of lower school and responsible for the school's pastoral care provision. She joined Feltonfleet in 2010. She is married to Ed, head of lower school at Epsom College. They have a young son, Henry.

Entrance: Though no longer as non-selective as it used to be, exam success still 'not the be all and end all,' thought one mother.

First come, first served nursery entry means, says the school, that 'broad range of ability inevitably comes through.' Parents well advised to be fleet of foot, successful bagging one of just 20 places achieved by registering at (or possibly during) birth.

Competition for 35 external year 3 places less of an extreme sport, though popularity growing so fast that border controls in form of maths and English assessment plus interview 'to search out character and enthusiasm for learning' are now in place. (Own year 2 children aren't tested.) No official feeders, though The Rowans, Wimbledon College Prep, Lion House, The Merlin, Weston Green and Glenesk all feature on suppliers' list.

Lots of behind the scenes liaison to ensure smooth transition to prep, extra support formalised in year 5 (English and maths), setting introduced for most subjects in year 7 – in class and one-to-one support for 11 EAL and 80 or so SEN pupils a fixture on the menu, head's desire to ensure barriers posed by learning difficulties are surmounted tempered with realities of what can be achieved. While classroom disruption, if severe, is the point at which school says no, parents praise thoroughness of approach. 'They did assessments and have been all over it – definitely worth it,' said one whose child has mild difficulties.

Occasional places also crop up, year 7 next biggest entry point following some post 11+ departures at end of year 6.

Judging by children we met, school's character-judging abilities are first rate, pupils to a boy or girl displaying a maturity, vivacity and sense of fun that made them outstanding tour guides (and some of the hottest – blazer-clad, through choice, on boiling June day).

Exit: Good guidance on future schools. Epsom currently most popular followed by Reed's, St John's and Bradfield College. Also Charterhouse, Wellington College, Worth and Cranleigh. One or two to Box Hill, Sherborne, Bryanston, St Edward's, St George's and Tring.

School has right connections, reckon parents; 21 scholarships, mostly for sport, but also art, drama, DT, music, academic.

Some year 6 departures inevitable, says school, 'mainly those who parents perceive would struggle with CE.' Makes equal boy/girl split in each year group commendable, though with year 7 places easily filled, virtue pays off.

Remarks: 'Really lovely,' say parents, who warn against being over-influenced by either location (side turn off fast road makes for 'hairy' arrivals and departures, says one mother) or building work (a performing arts centre was recently built and is now open).

Occasional cement mixing aside, charm is order of day. Calvi, the separate building for nursery to year 2 pupils, winningly equipped, from own hall to shaded play areas (trees a feature everywhere) with big sandpit and marked out scooter track, library that doubles as ICT room (now rechristened Digital Learning Facility – good tinies' tongue-twister, we'd have thought), double-banked computers forming orderly row down the middle.

Idyllically bounded by woods, dipping pond much used by all year groups, boarders given exclusive romping rights once day children have gone home

Sensible child and parent-friendly touches, from box packed with named bottles of sun cream by door on sunny days to big, smiley puppets adding comforting touch to office. Plentiful wildlife, too, some real (popular guinea pigs, available for cuddles, and tadpoles, who aren't) others artistic creations (we liked jellyfish hung at optimum viewing height for the under-7s; adults compelled to peer through forest of dangling paper fronds, Sir David Attenborough-fashion).

Homely domesticity extends to main prep building (mid-19th century Victorian gothic), which opens out into sweep of green, stretching away down gentle slope towards grass pitch, idyllically bounded by woods, dipping pond much used by all year groups, boarders given exclusive romping rights once day children have gone home. 'Wouldn't even guess space was there,' said parent. 'Like a little hidden pocket.' Weekly and flexi plus day boarding options – latter can include a full boarding day without the sleepover.

Here, as elsewhere, essential to shut ears to competing clamour of A3 that borders one side of site, though pupils oblivious.

Head's study, essay in dignified blues, gets best of panoramic views, where life 'is all happening in front of you,' said parent, from matches to pleasant end of day tradition of biscuit distribution, children flocking in from all over grounds in response to telepathic signal beamed out by biggest box of bourbons we've ever seen, like navy-clad pigeons.

Plenty of idiosyncratic charm throughout, from recently revamped junior block (years 3 and 4) classrooms with winning cosiness, colour and light to seniors' French classroom with miniature shop and restaurant, complete with groceries and chalk 'specials' board, much used for role play.

We'd also recommend viewing astonishing Latin room, folders block-banked by colour like giant rubik cube, walls ringed with sturdy supermarket bags – one per child – for instant decluttering before tests, and even back-office,

Perspex towers of meticulously labelled stationary boxes soaring to the ceiling, the whole like prayer to Roman god of organisation (if one existed).

Teaching styles similarly varied, shock and awe a science speciality. Most staff are 'lovely', said pupil. 'My son randomly said, "Mummy, I've got the best teacher in the whole world, because she's really kind",' confirmed pre-prep parent.

Best, judging by quick-fire exchange with prep pupils in English lesson to tease out clues in short story, are also brilliant, though zeal not yet universal, thought parents. 'Some are not as motivated as I think they should be,' reckoned a mum.

Years 1 and 2 stick broadly to national curriculum (as was) with specialist teaching for French, PE, swimming and music and get shot at DT, too – as well as input from grand-sounding and popular director of digital learning who sweeps in to 'enhance use of computer' – visits nursery and reception, too. Options grow with age, array of tempting additions bulked up in prep, judo to trampolining all good, food tech so sought after that canniest book up in winter, the longest term.

Surprise subject addition all way through from year 1 is positive living, new(ish) big hitter on PSHE timetable, stopping in year 7 (when perhaps pupils are so positive expectations need to be hoicked down slightly). 'Love it,' said pupil. 'It's about living a happy and good life.' Useful antidote to emphasis on emotional resilience made much of elsewhere.

Maximum class sizes of 18, optimum size for lively classroom atmosphere, reckons school, and overall teacher ratio is around half that (one to just over nine) ensuring help for any waifs and strays (almost universally true, save for one child whiling away whole class reading session by reconfiguring contents of pencil case, apparently unobserved).

Parents generally delighted with academic running, bar desire for a little more in the way of help both with exam preparation – 'Child didn't even know how to revise,' thought one – and additional feedback outside formal parent teacher meetings. 'Have to assume no news is good news,' said prep parent. The school is on the case with 'eye on the reporting structure,' also stressing staff responsiveness to parental concerns whenever and however expressed.

A few will relate to sport. Strong range on offer (netball, hockey, rounders and lacrosse basic range for girls, football, rugby, hockey and cricket for boys, swimming, cross-country and athletics for both). Fab facilities, too, indoor swimming pool, Astroturf and 'suite' of cricket nets most recent to be added to 25-acre site which already accommodates yodelling-quality sports hall, hard surface tennis courts and two rifle ranges (air and.22) on top of scenic sports fields. All tucked in neatly, consistency of design making additions easy on the eye.

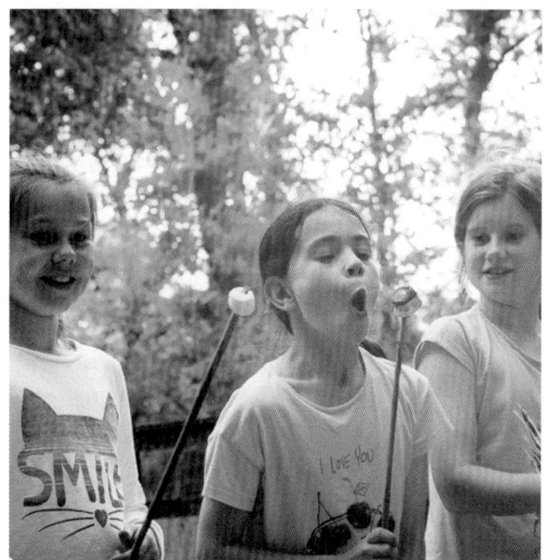

School recognises not just talent but wholesome attitudes by awarding internal sports scholarships to year 7 pupils (does same with drama and music). Strategy is to seek out challenge, everyone representing the school regardless of talent, plenty of tolerance for the rugby-averse – not the case elsewhere. 'Often the nicest boys who do hockey,' said year 7 pupil.

Pleasant end of day tradition of biscuit distribution, children flocking in from all over grounds in response to telepathic signal

Mega results in shooting – teams beat everyone everywhere, including older siblings in senior schools (Wellington and Epsom College). Coach, who travels here from Wales 'because he likes us', secret weapon. Success not always replicated elsewhere, felt parent. Enviably good sportsmanship comes at a price – teams losing when 'I know that if they had wanted it a bit more, they could have done it.' Delicate balancing act, thinks parent, who reckons top layer of loveliness needs to be scraped away and long-buried competitive instincts excavated so sport can take off. 'Winning matters, that's how life is, you get the job or you don't get the job. School needs to teach pupils that should love to win but that it's OK to lose.'

Performing arts popular and wide-ranging, one year 3 boy renowned for tap dancing, budding actor in year 6 making West End début. Drama high in pupil approval ratings for raising serious issues (bullying, gender wars) but not neglecting humour.

'Emotional but funny – what you'd find in everyday life,' said year 7 pupil of recent production.

Music draws in many, courtesy of good peripatetics ('nicest school I work in,' said one) almost half learning instruments, talented hitting grade 5 and up, occasional prodigy whistling through to diploma stage, orchestra supplemented by different single-instrument ensembles (flute and wind) as well as choirs (junior and senior), rotating timetables made easy with yellow badge reminders distributed daily. 'You're not going to forget with this hanging off you,' said pupil.

Something of a sanctuary for with those arriving from nearby little prince (and princess) establishments, often breathing big sigh of relief at low tiara factor (or gender neutral equivalent). That said, parental attitudes, though NFS (Normal For Surrey) can prove unwelcoming for incomers. Fine for those in at the start – 'joined in nursery and our friends will be friends for life,' said one mother – but can translate to 'cliques and queen bees,' according to parent who joined further up the school and felt the school might usefully beam 'be kind' message into minds of some adults, too. 'Am hoping influence will trickle down.'

Ditto consideration. Some irritation over parking habits of minority who cope with what one parent described as 'wholly inadequate' spaces by routinely usurping slots reserved for minibus. 'Seem to feel that so special or busy those normal rules don't apply,' said another parent. Other (minor) niggles include lost property black hole which can suck in objects for months, then mysteriously spit them out again – whereabouts in the meantime a mystery. Recruitment of year 8 prefects to scan changing rooms reducing the problem, reckoned pupils, though excessive spoon-feeding should be curbed, thought mother. 'Kids have to learn the responsibility for keeping their own things in check.'

Strategy is to seek out challenge, everyone representing the school regardless of talent, plenty of tolerance for the rugby-averse

Amongst all parents we spoke to, biggest gripe was reserved for uniform. Tons of it, some sensible or suitably traditional (woolly blazers, nice looking and sufficiently robust to stand repeated use as ad hoc goalposts, a case in point), others tending towards overkill/slightly bonkers, headed by summer only fleece. And don't get parents started on the ankle socks, dark blue with – go faster? – stripes. Justifiable in summer, with khaki shorts, less so in winter with long trousers 'when can't see them anyway.' 'Needs a cull, or at least a rethink,' thought parent. Good news, it's getting one. Watch this space.

This atmospheric school seems set for still better things to come in years ahead. As long as the kindness that really does emanate from delightful pupils remains, it's a gem heading for disco ball sparkle (but without corresponding tackiness). Expect more bullseyes – and not just in shooting.

Frensham Heights

34

Rowledge, Farnham, Surrey GU10 4EA

01252 792561 | admissions@frensham-heights.org.uk | www.frensham.org/school

Ages: 11–18

Pupils: 392; sixth form: 90; Boarders: 93 full, weekly/flexi

Day: £17,790 – £19,830 pa; Boarding: £25,470 – £29,790 pa

Headmaster: Since 2004, Mr Andrew Fisher BA MA DipEd (50s). A relaxed, breezy and natural educator. It's in the genes – his grandfather headed Repton and became a bishop, his father was head of Geelong Grammar, a brother heads an international school in Belgium and other relations have run schools both here and in Australia. Mr Fisher – 'Andrew' (everyone is on first name terms at Frensham) – still sounds Aussie, despite 20 years in the UK – the first 10 spent at Wrekin College, where he became head of English and, finally, deputy head (pastoral), and you can immediately see why – the pastoral aspect, that is.

This is a practical, hands-on head and one of the roundest pegs in the most circular hole we've met. He's a motivator and a believer in people. Parents pay tribute to, especially, his skills as a communicator: 'He is a complete star and inspiring,'

'he can speak equally well to parents and children,' 'extremely human and talks to everyone as individuals,' 'he keeps you in touch, even on minor matters' and so on. Wife, Catherine, is deputy head at one of the local large sixth form colleges attended by one of his daughters, the other a pupil at a local comprehensive at time of our visit. A likeable, unpretentious head – we queued for lunch along with everyone else – no way he'd jump to the head of the queue – and he clearly values highly his relationships with the pupils: 'They treat me with great respect but it's not based on traditional school values. I can laugh at myself.'

Academic matters: Not 'selective' as normally understood – this school is more concerned that you join them for the right reasons than because you will help them soar to league-table-topping prominence. A smallish school, so not the hugest range of subject options at GCSE or A level. Very high pupil:teacher ratio makes for lots of small group and one-one support. Impressive results in Eng Lit; the three sciences, when taken separately, also impress though most take IGCSE double award. Blissfully small classes for eg RE, ICT (computing GCSE, computer science A level). No Latin, no Greek. Photography taken – spectacularly – as an extracurricular GCSE with huge numbers and great success – see below. All A level subjects taught in small groups – much appreciated by students. English, maths, geography, history, art most popular. Only a few take langs, including some native speakers. Sixth form seen by some as being less rigorous academically than it might but the newish head of sixth is 'driving up standards,' we were assured. And 'we are upping our game in stretching the gifted and talented'. Parents concur. 'Not hothousing doesn't mean they can't achieve highly,' affirmed one. In 2017, 42 per cent A*-A/9-7 at GCSE and 45 per cent A*/A grades at A level (56 per cent A*-B). Disappointing library which doubles as café and place to sprawl in breaks with little evidence of its books being used. Recent expansion of science block to create six separate labs.

Newer buildings nestle in trees and witty sculptures sprawl on the lawns and in foyers – we loved the slumbrous wire rabbit ('the little kids curl up in its ears')

Loads of support – eg maths clinic each lunchtime. Not great for wheelchair users as the site is huge, bumpy and has steps. Main House not wheelchair-friendly at all. But school will try to take anyone they feel will benefit – mild SEN are catered for with enthusiasm and dedication and some families shared between Frensham and nearby More House for those with greater needs. 'My daughter had one-to-one for her reading and her reading age jumped two years in a term.'

Games, options, the arts: Think, Create, Explore is inscribed around the school and the vast menu of extracurricular options should tempt the most sluggish teenager to do just that. Bike maintenance,

American football, boules, tap dancing, barbershop and various dance forms – before, during and after school and at weekends. Excellent new music block; around half learn at least one musical instrument in school – 'Frensham bends over backwards to find teachers if you want to learn some different instrument,' a budding soloist enthused. Masses of bands, orchestras, ensembles, choirs and performance courses through the veins of the school. Dance much praised and popular. Drama is well-provided for and central to the school. The theatre is a wonderful asset – it has everything and does everything – and is well used, as are the two drama studios and the little wooden outdoor theatre on the front lawn. Performance values are high with a healthy, pervasive culture of it being OK to perform. Creative drama team under innovative long-serving head of dept.

Outstanding photography under even longer-serving, inspirational leadership and now with unique facilities for techniques old and new. Brilliant, diverse and poly-faceted artwork – we were truly struck by the rigour and values underpinning the skills and the freedom pupils were given to develop as they needed. Witty ceramics, clever textiles, wood and resistant materials productions with mind-opening themes explored with structure and solidity. 'Art and drama must challenge me,' says Andrew. Arguably, the most impressively led art dept in the country.

Sports are enthusiastic, various and 'improving', according to parents, though some feel they could and should be better. School points out that they are now competing against much bigger schools and taking part in various national cup competitions. 'Outdoor education' is important – there is forest school, the outdoor Terrace Theatre, the swimming pool in the walled garden and loads

Think, Create, Explore is inscribed around the school and the vast menu of extracurricular options should tempt the most sluggish teenager to do just that

of activities to develop outdoor skills – D of E gold award taken here and the whole school breathes in its own glorious 'outdoors'. Facilities – indoor and out – are certainly conducive to performance but one senses that real energies go into creativity rather than goal-scoring.

Boarding: Boarding arrangements changed in 2014 to become co-ed throughout the school. Hamilton House accommodates the 11-13 year-old boarders – boys and girls housed on different floors. They share a breakfast room/kitchen and a large garden. Main House houses the older boarders – girls and boys in opposite wings and with entry codes. Roberts House, the sixth form centre – co-educational from its inception – is unchanged and is everyone's base all day: day pupils share studies and workspace. We knocked at a random door and found two lads in hoodies actually working and blinking at the disturbance. Whole school on fibre-optic broadband and Facebook etc blocked till tea-time. Boarding is good – decent sized rooms in the main though some singles are tightish; nice bright shower rooms and good kitchens. Exceptionally welcoming sitting rooms – especially The Sit, which looks like home. Food – very good, we tried it – served in big dining room with tables and banquettes and everyone eats ensemble. Around a third stay in at weekend and are busy – see note about extracurricular above. Powerful cleaning fluid smells almost knocked us over in several buildings.

Background and atmosphere: Charles Charrington, the brewer, acquired Fir Grove House on the edge of Rowledge village, overlooking a panorama of Surrey woods and hills and transformed it into Frensham Heights – an imposing gothic red-brick residence with turrets, leaded lights and stained glass, splendid Georgian-style interiors, cornices, architraves, fireplaces – the lot – in 1902, as a would-be ancestral pile. Alas, the First World War intervened and the house became a military hospital and, as the old order changed, was reinvented as a school by three redoubtable women – Edith Douglas-Hamilton and joint headmistresses, Beatrice Ensor and Isabel King. Ensor, an early proponent of Montessori education, was a theosophist, a vegetarian and an anti-vivisectionist. Fascinatingly, one of the teachers at the school in those early years was Krishna

Menon. But the school's progressive credentials, being coeducational and liberal, were integral to its ethos from the first. Strangely, every head since its pioneers has been male.

Set in extensive woodlands and the older children trail 10 minutes through the woods to the village with its supermarket and sweetshop. Immense and meticulously kept grounds – Andrew pays tribute to the excellence of the financial management and, indeed, it is admirable that the place is so well maintained with so small a population of fee-payers. Newer buildings nestle in trees and witty sculptures sprawl on the lawns and in foyers – we loved the slumbrous wire rabbit ('the little kids curl up in its ears') and the jokey wax mushrooms, as well as the huge black panther.

No uniform – so everyone bar a few in uniform of hoody, leggings/jeans, sweatshirts, boots/ trainers. It looks relaxed and sane – enhanced by the amount of linked arms and hugging we saw – more like a bunch of French children, we thought. Central to the ethos is personal maturity: 'They are given real responsibility,' one parent told us, 'and can take the initiative – the school's approach to that is excellent.' This extends to falling in and out of love, which, of course, they do, but we were impressed by the compassion and mutual respect with which this is handled. 'It does happen but anything more than a hug or kiss in public is frowned on and people are respectful of what others want to see.. if people break up, we look after each other,' a wise mid-teen averred. 'It's not for everyone,' said another. 'If you need real structure and routine it's not for you.' 'Conventional parents need to look beyond the informality and recognise that the pupils respect the teachers because of the way they treat them rather than because of the rules,' a less conventional parent asserted.

Pastoral care, well-being and discipline: Everyone agrees about the staff: 'It's almost personal tutoring – they know how I learn so they explain it to me how they know I can understand,' a bright sixth former told us. 'They encourage pupils to excel in music, art, sport – whatever they're good at,' said a parent. Also a sense of a recent tightening of discipline – especially on illicit fags and booze. 'Some people were getting cocky – they've cracked down on it now,' we were advised. But pastoral care universally praised: 'They're not heavy-handed over minor transgressions – they see them in a learning context but if you cross a line you'll be suspended.' And another parent: 'If you've got that much freedom you need the support to go with it.' A strong sense that mutual respect and mutual support is central to the ethos of the place.

Pupils and parents: Around 75 per cent day pupils who come from a radius of about 40 miles – Petersfield, Goldalming, Farnham. Boarders are weekly eg from London or from overseas and school has wise policy of not taking more than four pupils who speak any one language into any senior year. So penny nos from eg Russia, Germany, Croatia, Spain. Intensive EAL available though needed by very few. Notable Old Frenshamians include performers Bill and Jon Pertwee, Jamie Glover, David Berglas, Rufus Hound, Hattie Morahan; also Sir Claus Moser, Noah Bulkin (Merrill Lynch, Lazard, now entrepreneur) and Uber-fraudster, Edward Davenport.

'Conventional parents need to look beyond the informality and recognise that the pupils respect the teachers because of the way they treat them'

Entrance: All candidates for years 7-9 are interviewed. Exams a week or so later – 11+ take tests in reading, writing, spelling, maths and non-verbal reasoning. Same plus a science test for 13+ candidates. Similar for occasional places which do occur. Sixth form places require six GCSEs at A*-C, ideally with Bs in A level subjects, 'but we're flexible,' says Andrew. School also sets its own papers for sixth form entry. Oversubscribed by 4:1 at this stage.

Exit: Around 50 per cent leave at 16 – mostly to the several large state (free) sixth form colleges round about, some few for the IB or for subjects not on offer here. Nearly all who stay get to their first choice university which suggests good guidance and realistic applications. To one of the widest range of tertiary education establishments we have seen. Many to creative courses – arts, design, music – but also the odd Oxbridge entrant (one in 2017) and others to study everything from architecture at Nottingham to geography at King's, London. Different, diverse, distinctive.

Money matters: Sibling discounts for third and subsequent children of 10 per cent. Scholarships and exhibitions in academics, performing arts, creative arts and sport up to £750 pa – so glory rather than gold. Means-tested bursaries in case of need but school has no endowments so not plentiful.

Remarks: A place to grow up in. Every kind of opportunity to become the person you are meant to be and to learn about others while you're at it. Civilised, liberal values with wraparound care and support. We loved it.

Handcross Park School

35

Handcross, Haywards Heath, West Sussex RH17 6HF

01444 400526 | registrar@handxpark.com | www.handcrossparkschool.co.uk

Ages: 2–13 (boarding from 7)

Pupils: 371; Boarders: 36 full, 14 weekly

Day: £9,420 – £18,570 pa; Boarding: £15,660 – £23,730 pa

Linked school: Brighton College, 598

Headmaster: Since September 2016, Richard Brown MA, who lives on site with his sons. Previously head of Dorset House School, with a stint before that as housemaster at Pangbourne College. Five years in the army are not immediately apparent in this head, who likes best to spend his free time writing or walking. Was a 'tennis parent' and understands parents getting a bit twitchy about teams. His most important qualities to inspire in pupils: love of learning and kindness.

'Bent over backwards to help us', said parent seeking urgent places for her four children mid year, '...transition was incredibly easy'; another said 'one step ahead and always thinking about what needs to be done' (passing places appeared on the drive as if by magic...). A bit more traditional than his predecessor, thought another, explaining that he has introduced grace before meals, and increased the emphasis on manners. Parents appreciate the well attended surgeries the head has introduced for the parents of each year group, and say he is at his best one-to-one.

Following an adored predecessor has its challenges, but most appreciate the new head's ideas: 'The...leadership programme is brilliant,' say pupils, with its command tasks and collaborative creativity – the usual helping each other across shark infested water; his busy programme upgrading facilities – new arts building and science lab – is very popular. He's good at focusing on children's abilities, said a parent – '[he] makes a point of telling a child if they're doing well'.

'I like his different approach – more focused on academics', said a year 8 pupil thoughtfully; '...his assemblies [are] very enthusiastic...' said another. A boarder told us, 'he's really friendly; comes and chats at lunchtime and visits boarding houses.... helps with maths'.

Entrance: By one or two-day taster experience including English, maths and reasoning assessments and interview, plus reports and references from previous school. Remote assessments and

Skype interviews possible for overseas applicants. Pupils come from local nurseries and preps, but with expansion of boarding the catchment area is widening to Brighton, Crawley, Haywards Heath and London. Boarders mainly from London, Forces families, a few from Europe.

Exit: Pupils move to a variety of schools, including Brighton College (30 per cent in 2017), plus Wellington, Hurst College, Ardingly, Charterhouse, Worth, Epsom College, Eton, Harrow, Marlborough, Winchester, Dulwich, Cranleigh, Caterham, Bryanston, Oundle, Roedean and Woldingham.

Remarks: A parent told us 'the culture [of this school] is to do with the magic of childhood'; or perhaps the magic of how we think childhood should be, with acres of green on which to run around, ancient trees to climb, and teachers who say, how about doing this lesson outside in the sun? There are even moving pictures on Harry Potter day. Children seem young here compared to city schools, and the head aims to extend childhood for as long as possible (whilst of course preparing pupils for senior schools). It's impossible to resist the happiness of this place, and this reviewer received more random smiles in corridors from children here than at any other school; a tribute not just to their politeness, but to the genuine warmth and friendliness which seems to fill this school.

It's not selective, but parents say it's an academically challenging school: 'we joined the school for more academic stretch', said one; 'the bright are well challenged', said another. Parents say teachers are as the best thing about Handcross, and feel that its small size means they know teaching staff well: 'phenomenal'; 'energetic and engaged'; 'commitment beyond what you expect'. 'The teachers are very inspiring – particularly...in English and science', said a parent, relaying her surprise when her son, enthused by science for the first time, and talked about time and black holes the whole way home.

'Teachers are kind', agree pupils, one commenting that English has become less scary because the teacher uses her own stories and experience; a year 3 pupil said of the history teacher, 'he tells wonderful stories...and they're all true!'

Handcross is a Google reference school, and a lot of academic learning here is through this medium. Pupils start using Chromebooks in pre-prep, and have their own from year 5 of prep school (although not to the exclusion of using a pen). Parents and pupils are enthusiastic: revision notes and homework are all detailed there (no more problems with forgetting that scruffy handout) and pupils can email the teacher if they're not sure about a topic.

In Spanish, Chromebooks mean that each table can be doing something different; in the class we saw one group answered questions on a video, others were translating, others practised conversation. Pupils here all learn Spanish and Mandarin. French and Latin are available in upper years for the adventurous.

Learning support has been transformed here in the last year, with parents and pupils bubbling over with enthusiasm for the wonderful staff

'[Google Chrome] works across so many different things', say pupils, who particularly love the multiple choice Caboodle. Google expeditions mean pupils can travel the world in geography and history – 'so amazing', said a pupil, enthusiastically recalling a virtual trip to the theatre to see Lincoln die. GoGuardian means teachers can see whatever pupils are doing on screens – 'so they know if you sometimes look at the football scores...', said a pupil feelingly.

Learning support has been transformed here in the last year, with parents and pupils bubbling over with enthusiasm for the wonderful staff in the 'dairy'; '[My son's] self confidence has soared...', said a parent. Innovative thinking in this unit: there are no desks, but beanbags, a ball to lounge over and wobble boards; a teacher may well say, 'let's do our half an hour of English walking among the trees': they understand here that dyslexic children need to move while they learn. Dyslexic pupils were

using tweezers to move dinosaurs from bowl to bowl to increase their dexterity – a fun way to improve handwriting; a pupil struggling with maths was using a toy horse rider and jumps to learn his four times table (four faults every time you knock down a fence).

Around 20 pupils receive regular support (one-to-one charged as an extra), but this is a department with school wide relevancy, a parent telling us that any pupil who feels 'flaky' about exams can do them in the dairy instead of the school hall, and in this friendly environment feel more confident and do better. Dyslexic pupils become Nessy ambassadors, and go down to pre-prep to explain the programme; instead of the indignity of handwriting club, there is the supremacy of Scribe masters. '[Learning support has] gained heart with the new headmaster', said a parent. '[My son] doesn't feel embarrassed any more'.

There's a scholarship set, but they are aware that strengths can be subject specific; teachers will focus and encourage particular strengths, and exhibitions can be in one area. There's detailed monitoring of value added, and IEPs for all pupils.

Handcross is part of the Brighton College family, but is no back entrance to the college; pupils must hit same standards as other applicants. The link provides a quality standard, and staff throughout the family share best practice. Around 30 per cent go to Brighton College; others to schools which range from Eton to Seaford College.

Pastoral care is a particular strength at Handcross. The head is keenly aware of the mental health issues which can assail young children, and is keen to increase pupils' resilience to life's knocks. If pupils have a problem they will talk to their tutor or the deputy head (pastoral), loved by pupils and parents alike, and pupils can also talk to an independent listener.

Random acts of kindness rewarded with kindness bands, on the day of our visit for handing in money, helping a younger pupil find their parents and for lending someone shin pads.

Not a school to leap for a punishment: time is taken to reflect, discuss and decide on action to address the problem. Parents say that complaints of unkindness or bullying are dealt with quickly – '...same day, took seriously, dealt with it discreetly. School investigates misdeeds, doesn't jump to conclusions'. No exclusions in the last year, one suspension.

Parents particularly appreciate that this school is upfront when things go wrong: an incident was dealt with 'head on...in a mature manner...and avoided the school gate gossip', said a parent; 'they allowed children to make a mistake and be helped rather than punished. Their way of dealing with the situation made me feel we're at the right school'.

Clubs include pig care; the field to plate scheme didn't work out, and the pigs look set for a long and happy life at Handcross

The usual sports, and gorgeous grounds to play them in, with an indoor pool too. Chances for all in A-E matches every week, and a celebration of the less able in the 'Be Trewe festival' where the D and E teams play other schools. Girls play football as part of the curriculum, and cricket as a club – although one girl has made it on to the cricket team. Cricket is due to be included in the curriculum for girls next summer, as is rounders for boys, which gives every player a chance to play – unlike cricket, which favours the strong few.

Most pupils here learn instruments, and music lessons are an energetic business: shoes were in a scruffy pile at the entrance, pupils were sitting on the floor, drums and other instruments between legs, singing and playing with gusto. It's a traditional set up musically, which one parent thought could benefit from some street dance and hip hop. More than 70 pupils do LAMDA exams, with drama lessons and annual productions for all year groups.

The swish new art and design centre houses art of all sorts, including pottery, textiles and photography. Music played as pupils practised watercolour techniques; next door in woodwork, pupils were turning recycled wood into flags and making plastic coffee containers into Christmas bells.

The lavish range of clubs includes pig care; despite calling them Thing One and Thing Two, the field to plate scheme didn't work out, and the pigs look set for a long and happy life at Handcross.

Around a quarter of years 5-8 do some sort of boarding, with full, weekly and flexi available. An international presence, with boarders from Spain, China, India and more. The varied activity schedule at the weekend always includes a trip; Thorpe park, laser quest and the shopping centre are all popular. Day pupils can join boarders for breakfast at 7.15am for small extra fee, and can stay for supper until 6.30pm. 'Takes the pressure off if you're both working', said a parent (pre-prep also provides wrap around care for 50 weeks of the year).

Boarding facilities are of a very high standard, and 'sensible bedtimes,' said a parent approvingly. Food is equally good, and pupils enjoy food from around the world on Tuesdays – a taste from home for overseas boarders.

The best things about boarding is the freedom they get compared to home, pupils agree. Phones were banned a few years ago, and for a few days, boarders didn't know what to do with themselves.

Now they're up and out, or involved in sport or drama or watching a movie. 'We can interact with friends more'.

It's easy to contact parents, by phone or Skype, and parents here are welcome to pop up to the school any time. 'My child loved his trial [of boarding]. He felt safe and secure'.

Pre-prep is headed by Mr Gayler – 'a big kid at heart; throws himself into everything', said a parent. It's set in what would once have been the walled vegetable garden, now a magical place of willow arches, cherry trees and every sort of adventure equipment. The children make full use of the surrounding woods in their forest school lessons, and on the day of our visit, reception, all in pjs, were about to take a magic trip on a bed to a jungle.

Communication is good ('to the point of saturation', said a parent), by email and text; not just if matches are cancelled, but even if a road is closed that might be a problem on the school run. Parents are confident of quick response when they contact the school.

One means-tested bursary, virtually 100 per cent, and one free place in nursery.

No average family, say parents, but it wouldn't suit 'someone overly aggressive or full of their own importance and abilities', said a parent crisply.

'Believe the advertising,' said one parent earnestly. 'Its very welcoming, very kind'. 'Scatter kindness' is a sign which appears all over the place at Handcross, and it seems that everyone here has taken this to heart.

Harrow School

36

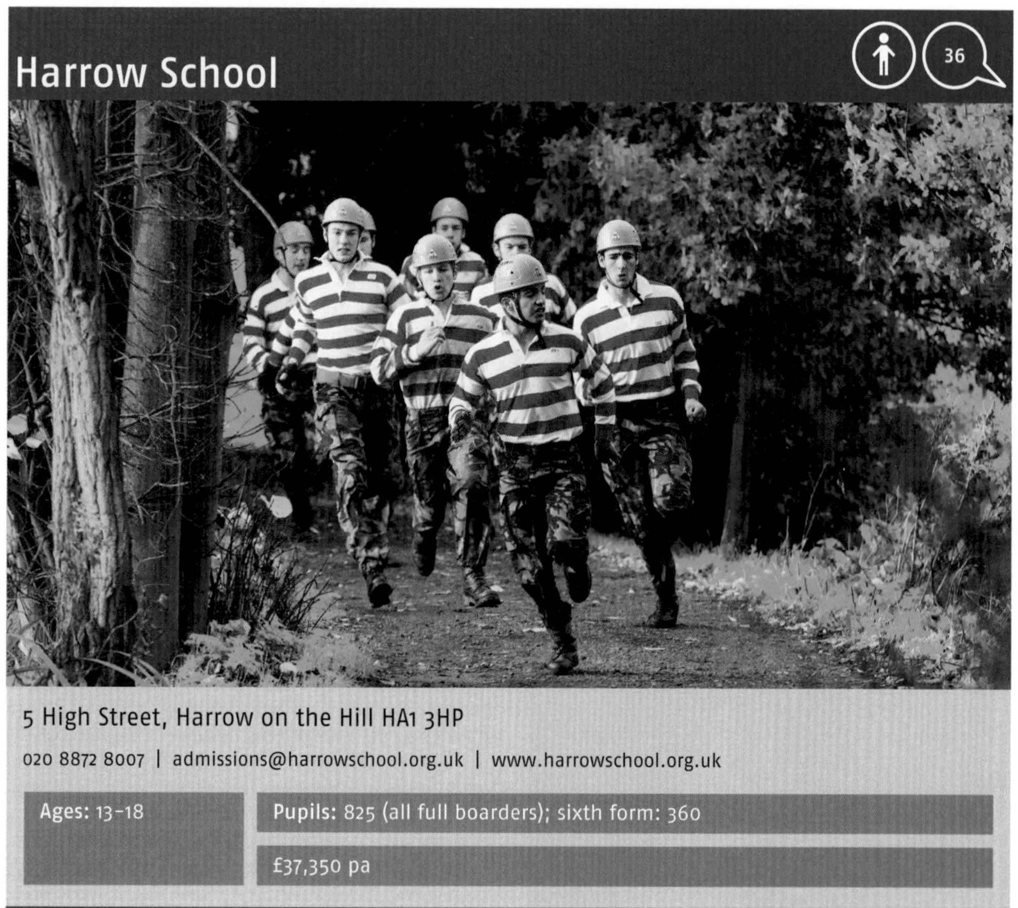

5 High Street, Harrow on the Hill HA1 3HP

020 8872 8007 | admissions@harrowschool.org.uk | www.harrowschool.org.uk

Ages: 13–18

Pupils: 825 (all full boarders); sixth form: 360

£37,350 pa

Head master: Since 2011, Jim Hawkins MA (40s). Educated at King Edward VI Camp Hill School for Boys in Birmingham and read maths at Brasenose College, Oxford (he was a year above David Cameron and knew the PM slightly). Did PGCE at Oxford before first teaching job at Radley – perfect combination of teaching maths and coaching rugby and rowing. Head of maths at Forest School in Walthamstow, then deputy head at Chigwell School. Prior to Harrow he was head of Norwich

School for nine years – 'a fantastic school in a beautiful city.' Norwich went co-ed during during his headship but there are 'no plans' whatsoever to follow suit at Harrow. 'We are very happy as we are,' he says firmly.

Proud of the fact that Harrow enables boys to enjoy being boys. With a plethora of activities from dawn till dusk, he reckons the school suits 'the kind of boy who wants to take the opportunities we offer and throw himself into things.' He says education at Harrow goes 'way beyond the exam syllabus' and that there's 'no better place for the really bright boy with a strong attitude towards life and learning, the sort of boy who is going to contribute and soak everything up.' School sends loads of boys to Oxbridge but head is equally proud of those who 'work jolly hard to get their As and Bs. They are some of our great successes.' When we asked who the school wouldn't suit he was unequivocal. 'It wouldn't suit someone who wanted a sixth form college sort of experience. Harrow is a highly organised, very busy school and it's very clear what the demands are.'

Dynamic, focused and urbane, with dashing good looks. Still keeps his hand in at the chalkface by teaching 'a bit of maths' to the youngest boys at the start of the academic year. 'It's really nice to have 40 minutes when you are focusing on something entirely educational,' he says. 'The key thing as a head is to find ways of interacting with the boys. Without that you lose touch with reality.' He makes a point of having lunch with boys and in the 'beaks' dining room' when he can. Very sporty – he rowed for Oxford's lightweight crew and was captain of Brasenose rowing. Ran the 10-mile Long Ducker, school's annual charity race from Hyde Park to Harrow, in 90 minutes, though laughingly admits that the director of studies did a faster time.

Last year lots of their fathers had played and there was even one grandfather in the side – 'but we were very careful with him'

Loves his job, although he admits 'the highs are very high and the lows are quite challenging'. Says there are three main educational areas he wants to develop. First is the 'super curriculum' to encourage academic scholarship above and beyond the timetabled curriculum, research, independent thinking and university-style learning. Second is to look at preparing boys even better for university – he's appointed a five-strong universities team with specific knowledge of Oxbridge, medicine and the US universities – and third is to concentrate on 'leadership and service'. School is already very active in local community (links with primary schools, tea parties for elderly, projects with Mothers Against Gangs charity etc) but head would like to do more. 'We want the boys to understand that leadership and service go hand in hand,' he says.

Wife Zoe is an artist and they have a young daughter. They live right in the heart of the school (along with their cocker spaniel) and regularly invite boys for breakfast – 'bacon butties and croissants.' Enjoys music, sport, reading and the theatre.

Leaving in July 2018 'to take up a senior management role in a global education initiative that will develop 30 new schools in major cities around the world'.

Academic matters: Teachers, parents and the boys themselves describe Harrow as an 'academic' school. Harrow's results don't appear in league tables – head says he's fed up with the 'one-dimensional snapshot' they deliver – but results are impressive. At A level in 2017, 70 per cent A*/A grades, 91 per cent A*/B and 83 per cent A*/A at IGCSE. IGCSEs taken in English, French, German, Spanish, history, geography, maths, as well as biology, chemistry and physics. Drama and PE introduced at GCSE recently.

Thirty-one subjects on offer at A level – all the usual, plus business studies, government and politics, history of art, music technology, photography and theatre studies, with a range of languages. Maths is the most popular subject at A level, with nearly two-thirds taking it. Half the boys do four subjects at A level rather than the usual three (one boy recently did nine). Sixth form electives are a recent innovation for sixth form pupils – a chance for boys to experience university-style teaching in specialist areas and have increased from five to eight periods a fortnight, with boys taking three one-term courses – the last relating to their chosen university course. Cerebral subjects on offer include programming, the history of western art, the greats of European philosophy, psychoanalysis and its impact on European culture, conflict and creativity in creation, post-genocide Rwanda and financial mathematics. Now offers EPQ.

Dazzling array of languages on offer – French, German, Spanish, Italian, Russian, Turkish, Polish, Japanese, Arabic and Chinese. All three sciences are compulsory at IGCSE. School has its own observatory with three telescopes and astronomy offered as a GCSE. Timetabled reading periods and new seminar programme for years 10 and 11. At GCSE classes range between 14 and 20 pupils while at A level the average is eight and none are greater than 12.

Embracing technology: all new joiners asked to purchase a (subsidised) laptop to be used in all lessons.

School caters for mild dyspraxia and dyslexia. One-to-one help given off-timetable, at no additional cost. Dedicated band of teachers (or 'beaks' as they are known at Harrow) includes many writers of scholarly books. Women make up 19 per cent of staff.

Games, options, the arts: There's no doubt about it, Harrow is a very sporty school, with hordes of teams regularly trouncing their opponents. Sport played five afternoons a week, 32 sports on offer and director of sport encourages even the less enthusiastic to 'have a go' at something. Main sports are rugby, soccer, cricket and Harrow football. The latter is played with a pork-pie shaped ball which absorbs the wet and can be propelled by any part of the body. Even though it's played in the depths of winter and is a very muddy affair the boys love it and only wish more schools played it (Harrow is the only one). When we visited pupils were counting the days till their Harrow football match against an OH team. Last year lots of their fathers had played and there was even one grandfather in the side – 'but we were very careful with him.'

Vast expanse of playing fields, sports centre with indoor climbing wall, weights room, 25m pool and sports hall, courts for tennis, rackets and squash, nine-hole golf course and Olympic-sized running track. School boasts national champions in rackets, fencing, fives and judo, two boys playing rugby for England and number of cricketers playing at national and county level. The mother of a gifted sportsman was full of admiration for the way the school nurtured her son's sporting talent whilst keeping him focused on his academic studies and helping him achieve stellar grades. 'The school sees each boy as an individual and were very supportive and flexible,' she told us.

Head of music admits that when he arrived there was a perception among rival directors of music that Harrow was 'an old-fashioned school where little value was placed on music and the arts.' To his delight he found the reverse was true and there's a 'wealth of musical talent.' Half the boys learn musical instruments and 50 per cent of these achieve grade 8 or better by the time they leave. Practice sessions timetabled for younger boys. Loads of orchestras, choirs and strong tradition of singing. More than 100 concerts a year, with recent performances at the Royal Albert Hall and Royal Festival Hall. Steady stream of boys to top universities and conservatoires to read music too.

Excellent Ryan Theatre seats 400 and is used for school and professional productions but annual Shakespeare productions take place in the beautiful arts and crafts Speech Room. A huge, wood-panelled half-moon, it boasts authentic Globe-style staging and seats the entire school. Wonderful art and, befittingly for a school where photography pioneer William Fox Talbot was a pupil, photography. DT, sculpture, art and photography now in a new state-of-the-art facility that also includes a new digital design suite. There's no lounging around with nothing to do at weekends either – scores of extra-curricular activities to choose from, everything from the Alexander Society for boys interested in military history to the Turf Club for horse racing fans.

Boarding: All pupils board at Harrow. We visited two very different houses – Druries, which dates back to the 1790s and is a maze of charming nooks and crannies, and the ultra-modern Lyon's, or the Holiday Inn, as a few wags have nicknamed it. 'It's the best piece of real estate around here,' joked one boy, hugely appreciative of its light, airy, five-star rooms. 'There's room for us to move around and not cause too much havoc.'

Annual Shakespeare productions take place in the beautiful arts and crafts Speech Room. A huge, wood-panelled half-moon, it boasts authentic Globe-style staging

Each house has common rooms, games rooms (kitted out with plasma TV, pool and table tennis tables), garden and 'yarder,' an area where boys can run off steam and kick a ball about. Two boys sharing is the norm in the first year but by year 11 (or even earlier) they get their own room, complete with desk, shelving, computer and, occasionally, en-suite shower. All pupils' names etched on wooden house boards, with head of house's name picked out in gold. Boys can make toast and heat up soup in their houses – 'and the more ambitious make Pot Noodles,' said one boy. We trust he was joking. Meals are eaten centrally and food gets a firm thumbs-up – from us too, if the lunch we had with sixth formers was anything to go by. Boys are allowed to go out for a meal with their parents on Sundays but there's no weekly or flexi-boarding. Two weekend exeats in the autumn and spring terms and one in the summer.

Background and atmosphere: Harrow is one of only four all-boys, full-boarding schools left in the UK (along with Eton, Winchester and Radley). Boys have been educated here since the 13th century, but the school was founded in 1572 under a royal charter granted to local farmer John Lyon by Elizabeth I (Lyon's, the newest boarding house, is named after him). The aim was for the school to provide free education for 30 local scholars, a number later increased to 40 by the governors. School sits in picturesque Harrow on the Hill, surrounded by 400 acres and with panoramic views across London – of it, yet remote from it, as we said last time. On a clear day you can see Canary Wharf from the head's study and it's just 25 minutes by tube to Green Park. Visitors to the undulating school site take note – flat shoes are a must.

School is steeped in tradition and history. The 17th century Old Schools contain the beautiful Fourth Form room, with names carved into every inch of panelling, from Byron to Robert Peel. It's also where Professor Flitwick's charm classes were shot in the first Harry Potter film (lots of tourists gazing admiringly when we visited). The stunning Vaughan Library, designed by architect Gilbert Scott (he also created London's St Pancras Station) has chess sets on tables and stays open late during exam periods. War Memorial Building commemorates the 633 OHs who died in the First World War. You can't help but be profoundly moved by the Alex Fitch Room, an Elizabethan wood panelled room with stained glass windows and a Cromwellian table, given by a grieving mother in honour of her 19-year-old son after he died in the First World War. She asked that it should be used for the purpose of boys meeting their mothers and that a light should always be left on over her son's portrait. Plaques and memorials commemorating quirky events are everywhere. Charles I rested here while preparing to surrender and little inclines have memorable names like Obadiah Slope, wittily named after Trollope's unctuous Barchester Towers character.

Harrow Songs are legendary. No Harrovian, either past or present, fails to mention the strength of feeling they engender and the lump in the throat they provoke. Songs have been an important part of the school since 1864, when the head of music wrote the first song, and they are considered to be 'a unifying force.' In November each year the whole school assembles in Speech Room in honour of its most famous alumni, Sir Winston Churchill, for the Churchill Songs. Like rival Eton, school has its own jargon. 'Skew' is a punishment, 'tosh' is a shower, 'tolley up' is permission to work late and so on.

Pastoral care, well-being and discipline: Pastoral care is meticulous, with highly structured system of resident housemasters, assistant housemasters and matrons. Harrow's 12 houses are integral to the school and boys are fiercely loyal to their own house. Some houses are regarded as stricter than others and parents we spoke to said it's important 'to pick and choose carefully.' One of the houses – West Acre – was recently the subject of an ITN documentary series, following the life of the school for a whole year. Housemasters in post for 12 years and as well as doing most of the admissions assessments each gives their house its character and reputation. They also work round the clock – 'at the beginning of every term I say to my wife "see you at the end of term",' one housemaster told us with a grin.

Harrow takes a pragmatic approach to technology and social media but the boys are so busy there isn't much time to sit around and play computer games. Pupils understand that bullying is 'completely unacceptable' and head says that it has plummeted, 'not down to zero, but pretty close.' School does a bullying survey every winter and housemasters, year group tutors, matrons, two school chaplains, health education tutors and school psychologist pick up on most things. Discipline is clear and firm but the place feels pretty relaxed, with boys knowing exactly where they stand. 'You are given freedom but if you abuse the freedom you would be punished,' one boy told us. Zero tolerance on drugs and use or supply in term-time or holidays means expulsion. Anyone found with spirits suspended and warned while smoking is handled through 'escalating sequence of sanctions imposed by housemasters.'

We said last time that it's the sort of place where a Yorkshire farmer's son will be sharing a room with the offspring of a City banker – and it still holds true

Smart uniform of dark blue jackets (bluers), grey flannels (greyers), white shirts and ties, plus, of course, Harrow's infamous boaters. Boys wear them or carry them and either love them or loathe them. They're allowed to write their names and draw pictures on the inner rim and spray them with varnish to protect them. Members of Philathletic Club (school's top sportsmen) get to wear bow ties. Sunday wear is black tailcoat and the whole kit and caboodle.

Pupils and parents: Pupils come from all over and school is proud of its 'broad and varied intake.' We said last time that it's the sort of place where a Yorkshire farmer's son will be sharing a room with the offspring of a City banker – and it still holds true. Between 10 and 15 per cent are progeny of OHs, while 20 per cent are from overseas (some expat, others from vast range of countries – 40 at last count). Twenty-five with EAL requirements. Most boys are C of E but there's a 'significant' RC community. Small numbers of all other main faiths or none.

The boys we met were engaging, appreciative of the fine education they get and very proud of their school. 'It doesn't give you a sense of entitlement, just a great responsibility to give something back,' one boy told us, while a sixth former who'd joined from a state school at 16 said that he'd been 'pushed and challenged' and that there was 'a lot more opportunity for debate' than at his previous school.

Parents reckon the school suits all-rounders who work hard and like sport. 'It's very disciplined and the boys are busy all the time so they have to be organised,' one mother said. 'There isn't any time to get up to any mischief and the boys are really tired by the end of term. There's a real camaraderie about the place and the boys make life-long friends. I can't fault it.' Another reckoned that even though it's 'strict,' any boy would thrive at Harrow, as long as they can cope with being in a large school where they won't necessarily be 'king pin.'

Long and distinguished list of former pupils – seven former prime ministers (including Sir Robert Peel, Lord Palmerston, Stanley Baldwin and Sir Winston Churchill), 19th century philanthropist Lord Shaftesbury ('a towering figure – we refer to him a lot,' says the head), Jawaharlal Nehru, King Hussein of Jordon, Lord Cardigan (who led the Charge of the Light Brigade), General Sir Peter de la Billière, plus countless other men of military renown (20 holders of the Victoria Cross and one George Cross holder). The arts and sciences are equally well represented, with a dazzling list of luminaries including Lord Byron, Richard Brinsley Sheridan, Anthony Trollope, Terence Rattigan, John Galsworthy, Cecil Beaton, Edward and William Fox, Richard Curtis, Benedict Cumberbatch and James Blunt, plus Crispin Odey (one of the UK's most successful hedge fund managers), Julian Metcalfe (founder of Pret à Manger), cricketer Nick Compton and Tim Bentinck (better known as David Archer).

Entrance: Very competitive. Around 600 apply for the 160 places on offer at 13. Prospective pupils supply school reference and sit pre-test in year 6; most are expected to be invited for assessment at the start of year 7, through tests and interviews. Offers are made – subject to CE or scholarship exams 18 months later. Sixty-five per cent expected at CE. 'Some weight' given to sons of OHs and boys' siblings – 'but brothers don't automatically get in,' said a parent. Boys arrive from more than 100 regular feeder schools. All-boys' boarding preps like Caldicott and Cothill top the pack but others from a myriad of co-ed and day schools.

Total of 24 new pupils a year into the 340-strong sixth form. Candidates need at least seven or eight A*/As at GCSE but many will have straight A*s (or numerical equivalents). Candidates write a CV, plus letter to the head explaining why they want to come to Harrow, and take tests in their proposed A level subjects. The best attend a day of interviews and assessments.

Exit: Very few leave after GCSEs and nearly all sixth formers off to university, with 26 boys off to Oxbridge or Ivy League colleges in 2017. Other top destinations include Exeter, Bristol, Edinburgh and UCL.

Money matters: School has given franchises to Harrow Beijing, Harrow Bangkok and Harrow Hong Kong, with a fourth likely to follow in the next few years. These are all successful enterprises carefully monitored by Harrow and also fund generous bursary schemes at home.

Wide range of scholarships and bursaries at 13 or 16. School offers means-tested bursaries of up to 100 per cent of fees to pupils who win a scholarship of any sort. Up to 30 scholarships a year for academic excellence, music, art or talent in a particular area (normally worth five per cent of fees).

There are also Peter Beckwith scholarships for gifted and talented boys whose parents can't afford to send them to Harrow. Two awarded each year to boys aged between 10 and 13 – these can cover fees at a private school from the age of 11 and Harrow fees from 13.

Remarks: Parents looking for a top notch, blue chip, full boarding, all boys' school will be hard-pressed to beat Harrow. This is a school on top of its game.

Holmewood House School

37

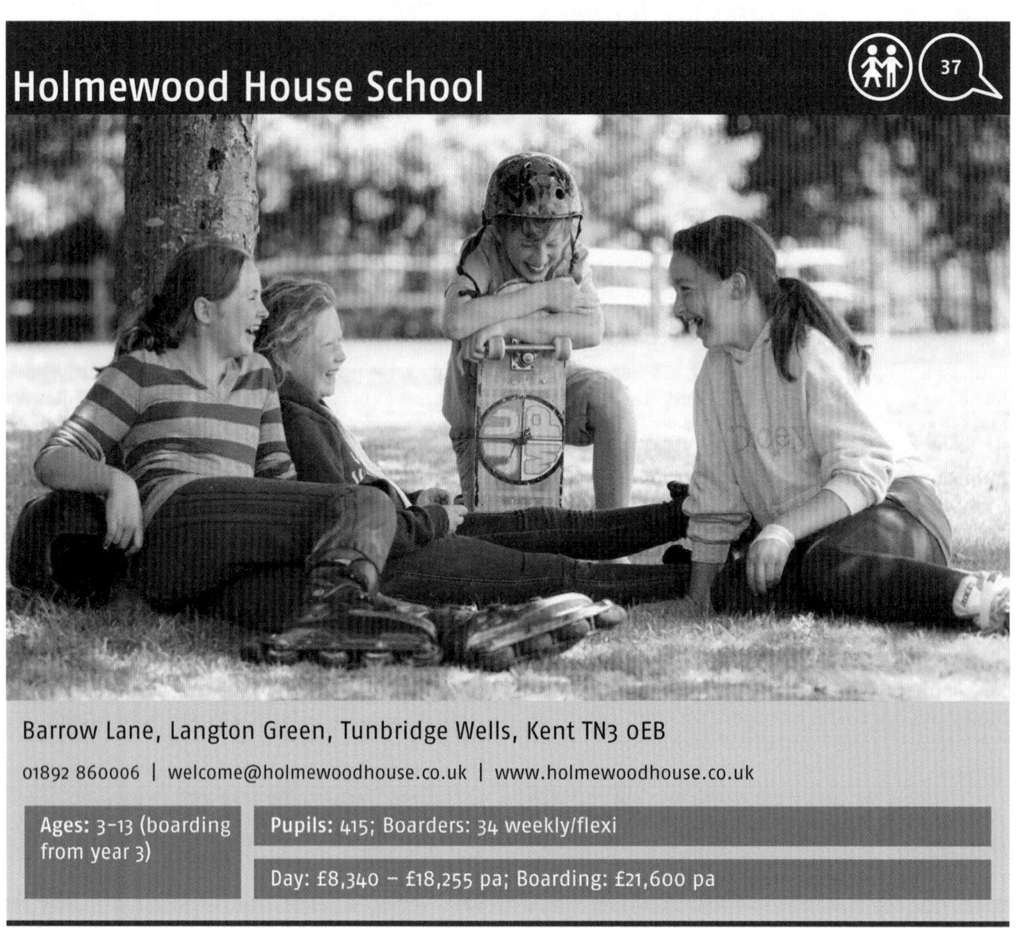

Barrow Lane, Langton Green, Tunbridge Wells, Kent TN3 0EB

01892 860006 | welcome@holmewoodhouse.co.uk | www.holmewoodhouse.co.uk

Ages: 3–13 (boarding from year 3)

Pupils: 415; Boarders: 34 weekly/flexi

Day: £8,340 – £18,255 pa; Boarding: £21,600 pa

Headmaster: Since September 2017, Scott Carnochan, previously head of Sedbergh Prep in Cumbria. Degree from Heriot-Watt University and postgrad from Nottingham. Has taught at Hillcrest Prep in Nairobi, been housemaster at St John's College School, Cambridge and head of boarding at Repton Prep. He played 1st XI cricket at school, was captain of rugby at school and county level and played international rugby, representing Scotland at U18 and student level.

He and his wife Kate have two young children. Kate is also the new head of marketing for the school.

Entrance: For nursery and reception it's first come first served, and entry into the pre-prep is non-selective, although informal assessments will ensure the child can keep up. Around 15 children join at year 3, and for this stage onwards prospective pupils take tests in maths, reading and spelling, plus there's an interview, and reports from the previous school are considered. Academic scholarships, which can be topped up with bursaries, are available from year 3.

Exit: Has previously had a reputation for not supporting children aiming to take the 11+ and for frowning on departures before 13. (A thorny issue indeed in the grammar school hotbed of Tunbridge

Wells, and that policy has now changed). School now says it welcomes children intending to leave at 11, and although it does not provide bespoke 11+ tuition, the preparation all children receive for secondary school entrance and common entrance pre-tests will be relevant. It's likely to take a while for this change of heart to filter through both in local reputation, and through a cohort which entered before this policy was in place. Not that it was ever impossible to move to a grammar – parents have previously organised their own tuition, and the last few years have seen many pupils move on to grammars.

At 13+ the school has a reputation for harvesting a good crop of scholarships. The range of schools children go on to has broadened – Tonbridge, Sevenoaks, Eastbourne College, Brighton College, Mayfield, Walthamstow Hall, Cranbrook and other local grammar schools. Music, sport and drama scholarships.

A roadshow with 20 senior schools is held every two years to help families decide schools.

Remarks: No doubt about it, the facilities are fantastic with £4.5 million building project adding among other goodies new classrooms, science labs, learning hub, digital library, enrichment centre as well as a modern cloister.

It's one of very few prep schools with its own 20 metre rifle range – and the pupils are champion shooters among English schools. There's also a 25m indoor pool, squash courts, a climbing wall, and a snazzy sports hall. Lots of sporting success at county and national level. But we like the fact that the non-sporty don't get it rammed down their throats as much as in some other prep schools – there are two afternoons of compulsory team games, but on the other three they can choose drama, music or craft activities, or individual sports instead.

There's a 350 seat theatre and lots of big productions – and treading these boards launched the careers of old boys actors Dan Stevens of Downton Abbey and Tristan Gemmell (Casualty and Coronation Street). More remarkably, perhaps, Shane McGowan of The Pogues was also here.

All this, alongside what the school claims is a high staff to pupil ratio (1:9), and the number of specialist teachers, comes at a cost. You know what you're in for when one of the FAQs on the website is 'Why are your fees relatively high?' School has deliberately narrowed the fee gap with neighbouring preps, but it's still about £1,000 a term higher than others in the locality. We heard talk of school gate grumbles about fees funding large numbers of bursaries; whether you applaud that or not will be a matter of personal conviction.

They do a great deal to ease the way for working parents. There are minibuses at 4.30pm and 6pm to accommodate different finishing times through the school, and children can be looked after until 7pm. There is also a health centre staffed by nurses between 8am and 7pm every day. It means they can manage complicated medical regimes, but also look after a child who just needs to rest for half an hour before bouncing back, rather than having to call parents to collect them. Saturday morning school has been abolished.

There are two afternoons of compulsory team games, but on the other three they can choose drama, music or craft activities, or individual sports instead

Full-on timetable with the aim to be the top academic prep school, and to ensure that children in common entrance forms (year 6 to 8 have two of these and one scholarship form) are well prepared enough to get into their chosen school without any doubt. 'The last thing we want is them sitting the common entrance exam with everything crossed.'

Has put back creating the scholarship class to the start of year 6, believing they can better identify the children suited to this class after they have had a year working with subject specialist teachers, which begins in year 5. 'It's not a designer accessory. It's hard work and the last thing we want is a child in there who is struggling. Parents perceived that they got the best teachers, but we have deconstructed the idea that you get a better deal in the scholarship class. Now we get children or parents who turn it down because they don't want to be put under increased pressure, and scholarships are not worth much financially these days.'

From year 5 there are two periods a week of Latin, and scholars can also do ancient Greek. There's also Mandarin philosophy in year 8, a Spanish option from year 6, and French from nursery.

The seniors get Christmas and summer term exams in every subject, although for year 5 this has now been cut down to just English, maths and science exams in the Christmas term. Teaching is generally very good; the children learn a lot and are pushed quite hard, parents told us.

There are two full-time specialists and three part-time learning support assistants, and parents reported being very impressed with this input. It was highly visible on our visit, when a number of children were receiving individual or small group tuition.

In the junior school, years 3 and 4 are classroom-based with a form teacher, although they go to music, art, DT and science in dedicated classrooms. There are three proper science labs, complete with a skeleton, and the art department has specialist equipment for etching and a kiln for pottery work. Interesting work on display included flint knapping and cave art.

The pre-prep curriculum includes timetabled IT, and everyone starts an instrument in year 1. This, along with a specialist music teacher just for the pre-prep, enables them amazingly to have a pre-prep orchestra. Reception, year 1 and year 2 have a separate block with their own dining room. Posters around the building ask: 'Do you have good manners?' They're big here, even illness isn't an excuse, as another poster in the health centre asks children whether they have said please and thank you.

Boarding is available to children from year 3. Currently majority of boarders are flexi, but school aims to bring the weekly ratio up to half; some 50 per cent of boarders are from overseas. Boarding accommodation underwent a recent refurbishment, and there is scope to increase the places to 50. Dorms are six-bedded and there's a combined games room. It's loved by the children – the two houseparents are 'really kind', they say, and they enjoy activities such as playing It, having a pizza party, or playing outside on skateboards.

There's a new energy about the place as reforms are working their way through. 'We have deconstructed the atmosphere of elitism generated by a very competitive scholarship stream and attitude to sport; it is wholly inclusive and there is no-one outside looking in.' Whether your child is a scholar or needs extra support, a sporting whizz or an arty type, they'll find their place here.

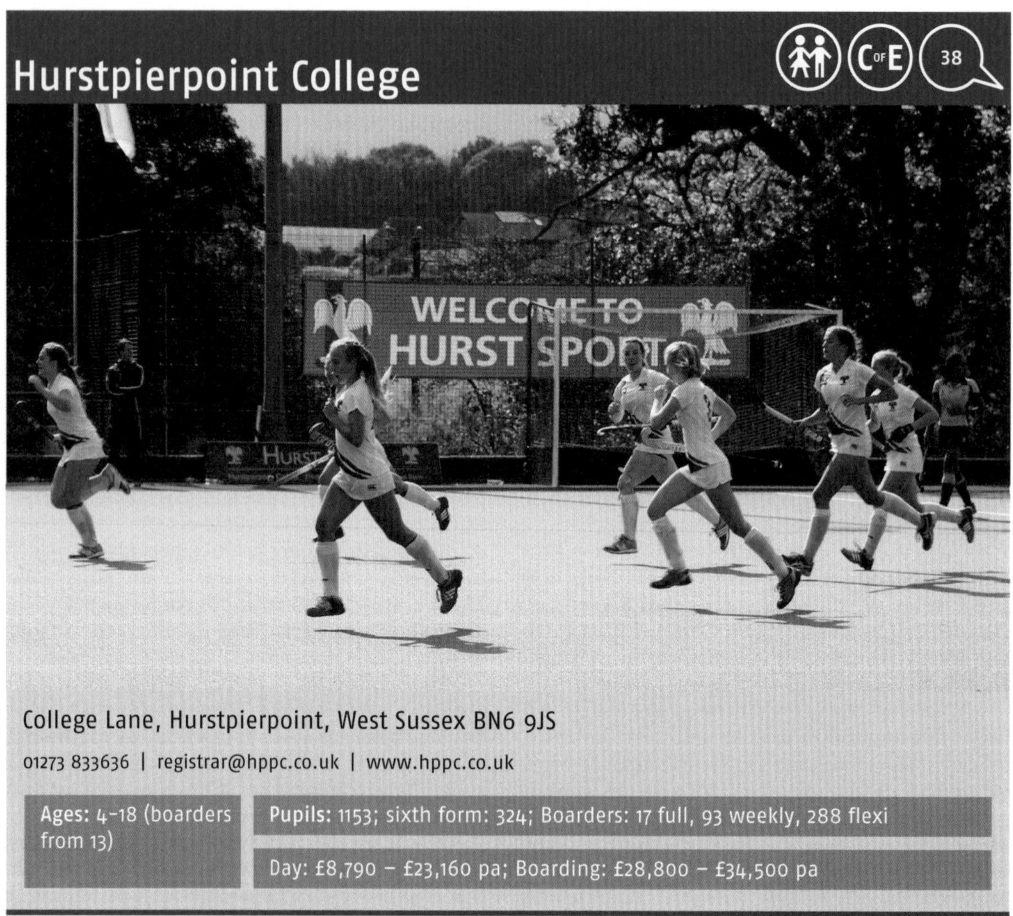

Hurstpierpoint College

C of E | 38

College Lane, Hurstpierpoint, West Sussex BN6 9JS

01273 833636 | registrar@hppc.co.uk | www.hppc.co.uk

Ages: 4–18 (boarders from 13)

Pupils: 1153; sixth form: 324; Boarders: 17 full, 93 weekly, 288 flexi

Day: £8,790 – £23,160 pa; Boarding: £28,800 – £34,500 pa

Headmaster: Since 2005, Tim Manly (Oxford, LSE and Cambridge), married to Henny with four children, all of whom attend or have attended Hurst. Abandoned a career in commerce to teach, first at Sevenoaks, then as deputy head at Oakham School before joining Hurst. The only head we've come across where pupils gave an audible 'aaaah...' when asked for their views: 'the best head'; 'respectful of us as pupils....makes the effort and knows all names'; 'not scary...you can have a conversation with him'; 'really proud of us' (the Amazon vouchers for achieving good grades are much appreciated). A parent told us how much her daughter liked the head on first meeting – 'he looked her in the eye, talked to her like a person. She was the focus'. The head likes to keep teenagers busy and expectations of pupils are high, said another, who described the head as 'a man of boundless energy; always there, always visible... who is very engaging as an individual. [He] takes every opportunity to include parents in what the school is thinking and intending'.

Head of prep and pre-prep: Since 2013, Ian Pattison (chemistry, Southampton), married to Janina with one son at the prep. Joined Hurst as a chemistry teacher in 1997, and became a housemaster in 2006. This warm, enthusiastic head loves hockey and cycling up mountains; no surprise, then, that he wants his pupils to be ready to take on the world. 'Not a place for children who just want to turn up to do lessons and go home,' he says, seeing promoting independent thought and action as one of the main points of the educational experience at Hurst. A head pupils can go and talk to about anything.

Academic matters: 'Pupils are well taught and achieve their academic potential', said a parent. '[It] does its core purpose brilliantly'. In 2017, 47 per cent A*/A at A level, 78 per cent A*/B. At GCSE, 73 per cent A*-A/9-7. Sciences and maths are popular high performers.

No IB takers in the current cohort, but the door isn't closed to those keen to take the IB in future years. A good range of subjects available, including BTec in business and sport, though pupils felt media studies was a noticeable omission from the list. The head initiated dropping from four A levels to three, with all pupils doing the EPQ.

Results have gone up in the last four years: parents speculate that this is partly due to a more selective intake, partly due to a change of staff – 'it's a very quality staffroom now', say staff. Parents approve greatly of the new young staff – 'happy and willing to work incredibly long hours', said one appreciatively.

Hurst has a challenge grade system, which means that each child's performance is assessed according to the challenge set for them: tick is on target, +1 exceeding target, -1 falling short. There are no comparisons between pupils, and a parent commented that she likes the fact that a very academic child can get minus marks because they're not achieving their potential. 'If it was an absolute system, rather than a relative system, it wouldn't have this subtlety'. There are frequent reviews under the challenge grade system, and teacher comments are 'thoughtful, personal and helpful' said a parent. Pupils say the system 'helps you get to where you want to be', and it certainly works for pupils, with Hurst in the top 10 per cent nationally for value added. 'Academic performance is not the be all and end all', said a parent, but her child 'achieved more than she thought she would achieve'.

'If pupils don't engage academically, there will be more and more supervision to ensure they do engage and get the grades they are capable of getting'

One hour lessons and a longer school day means there is a steady pace, said a parent – not that you can slack ('slacking won't get you anywhere', a pupil told us crisply), but expectations are in accordance with your abilities: 'you are recognised and supported as a person'. Parents describe great support from staff – a history teacher encouraging pupils to go in at the weekend and go through things; extra time devoted to helping a pupil who was struggling; and 'they make it easy to catch up if you fall behind,' said a pupil.

Parents told us that the school has always had a focus on academics, but things cranked up a gear recently, with a tightening up of standards and new process of detentions for work not completed on time, instead of 'a clearing' (wiping up after lunch). 'If pupils don't engage academically, there will be more and more supervision to ensure they do engage and get the grades they are capable of getting', said parent. Some 'disquiet at new rules', with a few parents expressing concern that Hurst might be edging into the territory of the local high flying competitor (described by a parent as 'stretched and fast paced and anxious about everything'): 'They were pushing too hard, and Hurst is not like that'. But things have settled down – 'softened a bit'; and parents are delighted by the new regime for Oxbridge, with eight places in 2017.

There's the usual odd incident of disquiet over setting, but importantly a parent reported a school who listened to her views, and asked whether being in the wrong set would affect her daughter's enjoyment and performance in the subject. Hearing that it would, they changed the set.

iPhones are allowed in the senior school: the school is strict about usage, and pupils generally keep them switched off when they're meant to be. Pupils in years 9-11 have MacBooks, and iPads are frequently used in the prep, which one parent said has made a 'huge difference [to her son's] learning and confidence'.

Hurst is described by the head of prep as 'a genuine through school', and it works hard to ensure continuity between prep and senior school: a single deputy head academic covers both schools, and any change to the college curriculum will result in changes all the way down; for example, the introduction of Spanish GCSE means that this is now taught in years 7 and 8 of prep.

Year 8s take exams before leaving prep; it's not the CE, but there is a ritualistic formality about them, and all the frisson of results in envelopes. Pupils want to do well, though not through fear of failure: all progress to the college (the few whom it is felt would not thrive there are told in good time). The absence of CE frees up the curriculum – year 8s spend time doing a presentation and essay on a topic of their choice.

The learning support department provides mostly one-to-one support for pupils with mild learning difficulties. A parent described how their unconfident dyspraxic son turned into a different child at Hurst – 'he didn't feel a misfit anymore'. He was assessed straightaway, and the parent was asked how her child learned and what worked for him; her advice was forwarded to all her son's teachers and has been every year since.

Games, options, the arts: One parent said what she liked best about Hurst was 'the sheer level of opportunity and encouragement. Everyone has a go and gives everything they've got. Whether you're good at something or not doesn't matter – everyone will support you. That's what you're paying for...'

The wide range of co-curricular activities here includes dissection, mechanics, environmental conservation, CCF and D of E (silver for all). There is an element of compulsion in years 9 and 10 (until the power of peers is watered down with age, says the head), but older pupils can choose their activities.

There is no feeling of piety at this school, but weekly chapel evidently plays its part in drawing the community together

'They encourage anything which enthuses the kids', said a mum, describing how her chamber music loving daughter was encouraged to create a group.

At music A level, her daughter was 'totally inspired' by her teacher. Numbers taking A level are few, but music is a popular pastime, and every taste is catered for, from classical, to jazz and contemporary; there's a huge non-audition choir of 160, and a selective one too. Hymn practice on Monday mornings makes singing fun – 'everyone who is the eldest in their family sing verse 2...' A lively outreach programme sees Hurst musicians entertaining the local community: the Big Band playing for village pensioners at Cake at the College, and the brass group playing festive music for the WI in the village.

There are a great number of dramatic performances every term, from Cabaret to Titus Andronicus and Lord of the Flies (by the prep). 'It's better to do lots, than one Barbican level performance a year', says the head, and this means that performers include both the experienced and novice at this school which champions 'give it a go', regardless of ability. 'It's the only way to learn about themselves and other people', says the head. Drama is enormously popular at the prep school, 120 of the 140 pupils in year 7 and 8 signing up to take part in Lion King, and even the year 5/6 productions benefiting from the luxury of college technicians and facilities.

A rugby school in the main, with just a couple of teams giving a nod to football. Netball is strong for girls, and both girls and boys play hockey and cricket. '...[there are] isolated moments when rugby comes first, netball second...but girls' sport has come on tremendously and does extremely well', said a parent. Pupils from pre-prep to senior school enjoy the indoor pool. A school with an inclusive sports ethic: a parent said her son is in a D team, but still enjoys matches every other weekend. 'You can't tell which team they're in on the basis of enthusiasm', says the head of prep.

A flexible approach to sixth form games – you can do what you want three times a week, and games haters can do yoga instead. Even lower down in the school, there is a humane quality to games here – a parent told us how her son, rugby hater, joined

Hurst prep, and was immediately allowed to do kayaking, rock climbing and orienteering instead.

Art is displayed throughout the school, in beautifully mounted neat and tidy style. Standards are high, and facilities have recently expanded to include a printing press and textiles room, in which pupils used wax and sewing to produce a mixed media hanging exploring man's impact on the environment. Only a handful take A level, but GCSE is more popular, with most pupils achieving high grades.

Boarding: A strong house system here with separate houses for day pupils and boarders. A parent described their child's house as 'a refuge, not just a place to leave books': there are homely common rooms, cosy bedrooms with bunkbeds or studies for day pupils, and kitchens ('for cookie baking', said a parent).

Pupils can flexi board for three nights a week, weekly board for five nights a week or board full time (only available to sixth form pupils whose parents work away from home). 'Care is extremely good', said a parent, who added that on the odd occasion her daughters had had problems with girls they roomed with, the housemistress had listened, and switched the girls' rooms.

Pupils are together with 10 or so others in their year group, and form a really strong bond: their 'own clan', said a parent. 'It's the main way you make friends', said a pupil, and they evidently enjoy much lively inter-house competition, including house water polo.

St John's is the sixth form boarding house, and popular with parents and pupils alike. 'St John's is brilliant', said a parent, 'a good step up towards university...but still well monitored and controlled'. One parent described the increase in her daughter's confidence at St John's, the pleasure of making friends across the year group, and the joys of bar night (pupils have drinks tokens to use, so 'no sneaking off', said a parent approvingly). Individual rooms at St John's mean pupils can sleep during the day if they want to; the head is evidently not speaking lightly when he says 'it's a busy place, pacy – pupils need some stamina'. There is a very small number of international students in the sixth form (most of whom do not stay on site at weekends, although activities are provided for any that do).

Currently no prep school boarding, but plans to introduce this soon for years 7 and 8.

Background and atmosphere: Parents choose Hurst because they feel it provides something more than an academic education: 'We want [them] to do well academically but not as an expression of everything else... we want them to be brought on as people...'; 'we wanted the children to be themselves'. Seen, then, as a holistic educational experience by parents, it is no surprise to hear the head say, 'I don't want to win everything, it's not healthy...'. Learning here comes from many different angles, and the school is loyal to its pupils – 'Anyone who is in the school can stay. We will back them. We always take siblings if we can...'

There are, of course, gorgeous grounds here – 140 acres of them, but they are not the main pull for pupils. 'I fell in love with Hurst', said a pupil. 'It was the atmosphere, everyone was involved'. In this strong community, staff know who all the pupils are ('[I] wouldn't want the school any bigger – would like staff to be able to retain that knowledge of every pupil', said a parent). Pupils have friends across the year groups, a sixth former proudly telling us 'younger pupils are often disregarded in other schools, but not here; younger pupils can have leading parts in plays'.

School buildings mostly with grand old Sussex flint walls, and Grimm's fairytale windows. Draughty cloisters surround a courtyard where pupils perform Shakespeare in the summer, pupils pitter-pattering fingers on the glass, so the audience felt for their coats, convinced it was starting to rain.

Prep buildings sit alongside the college, surrounded by play areas, including a wooden adventure climbing course, and woodland school for outdoor education. They have their own library, computer room and classrooms, but share the college's science labs, DT workshops, and music and sports facilities.

Chapel – 'the still place', was named as a favourite place of many (dining hall, with its delicious food, and the rugby pitch also figuring). 'Chapel', said a pupil, 'is where we consolidate the week. The whole schools gathers'. The head gives a thought for the week, pupils are recollected – there is no feeling of piety at this school, but weekly chapel evidently plays its part in drawing the community together.

Uniform: smart navy for boys, and a lovely tartan skirt for girls (though ending at a troubling mid-calf length). Once pupils reach year 7, they get college blazers – quite a milestone. Sixth form must wear suits, can choose the colour and must look smart – 'to match the work ethic', said a pupil gravely.

Pastoral care, well-being and discipline: The head is well aware of the whitewater nature of adolescence – 'it's all about the speed of turnaround after a dip', and whilst this school works hard to try and keep children from vulnerable situations, there are good support networks in place to support pupils: houseparents, tutors, staff and school counsellors. 'It really is a fantastic community', said a parent. '[A] strong culture, and out of this, children support each other. Problems are addressed and dealt with swiftly'.

A parent described their child's house as 'a refuge, not just a place to leave books': there are homely common rooms, cosy bedrooms and kitchens ('for cookie baking')

A parent described the effective support given to her child, whose friend suffered serious trauma: counsellors provided 'what she needed'. They are very aware that some pupils might suffer from anxiety, said another, and are 'right on' in their support of pupils. Counsellors give advice and talks to pupils on mental health issues, and although one parent felt that there is not enough work done with pupils about knotty life issues such as consent, others felt this was dealt with adequately.

Tutors are the first ports of call for pupils with difficulties in prep, but they are happy to extend support to whatever is necessary, including family therapy or a life coach.

House guardians (pupils) regularly meet to discuss anyone who might be in distress, at both the prep and senior school. Bullying is discussed a lot – 'the school have a firm grip on it...and my son is ripe for it...' said a parent. Pupils were very clear that incidences of bullying could result in suspension or expulsion: not harming others or self is evidently a mantra they have absorbed.

There's careful education about what constitutes bullying and how to form positive relationships with each other (boys, in particular, sometimes don't even realise they've upset someone, says the head) and creating an environment where children feel they can talk about problems. The head has, and will, suspend or expel pupils for being unpleasant to others.

The head, said a parent, is 'almost Victorian' in his laying down of the rules: the Big 12. Parents say everyone knows what they are, and the disciplinary consequences of breaching them. 'It's strict', said a parent, 'which is a good thing...'

'Not a school for second chances', said another, 'though punishment is about trying to educate and improve'. This very thorough head even gives out best practice on parties – timing and adult supervision etc. This is, a parent told us, entirely consistent with his character. 'What you do at the weekend does matter', say pupils. 'Particularly if there might be photographic evidence', one added feelingly.

Pupils and parents: Hurst feels like a local school in its intake, said a parent who likes this, and the typical Hurst family consists of the upper middle class white professionals who live in the area. One parent said the only downside of Hurst is that you can't get to school by public transport; although she added that if both parents get stuck in London, they know the school will look after the children. The school buses serve the local area, and are due to expand to Chichester and London.

A parent told us this is not a school for those who want to fly under the radar and just get to the end of their school days: 'the thing you do at this school is engage – it can be anything, there are endless opportunities'. They agreed that rowdy pupils would have a bumpy ride but 'the school welcomes exuberance – within boundaries'.

There are lots of parenting workshops, and the views of parents on teaching and pastoral care are sought regularly: 'The level of engagement with parents is excellent', said one. 'I feel totally a part of the school'. School 'goes out of their way to explain what they are doing so they can incur support', said another.

Day-to-day communication is good, confirm parents, and school will email or text if matches are cancelled.

It's a long school day with a six o'clock finish, which can be tricky for parents collecting day pupils – 'we moved to be close to the school', said one. Prep school day finishes at 4.20pm, but with after-school care (included in fees), can run until 6.00pm to match the college day.

Entrance: Not aggressively selective, but recruits better than average. Those joining from outside take ISEB pre-test in year 6 for year 9 entry and need to get over 55 per cent in maths, science and English, 50 per cent in other subjects at CE. Hurst prep year 8s make up less than half of year 9: there is a big intake from outside at this stage which 'avoids stagnation', says the head of prep.

At prep, most pupils join in reception, year 3 and year 7 (which, like year 9, is oversubscribed).

Exit: Most depart to Russell Group universities, London, Bristol and Exeter are popular choices. Eight to Oxbridge in 2017, and three medics, including one off to Poland; another to Leiden.

A handful leaves the prep school for other local senior schools.

Money matters: Academic bursaries from 11+.

Remarks: Parents are clear why they chose Hurst: '[It has the] right balance... the right direction, the right balance of pastoral and academic. Our four very different children have thrived there. [There's] lots going on and it's very inclusive'. 'It's a good time to have kids here', said another. 'It's hitting a high – and Tim Manly is inspiring for kids'.

Hurtwood House School

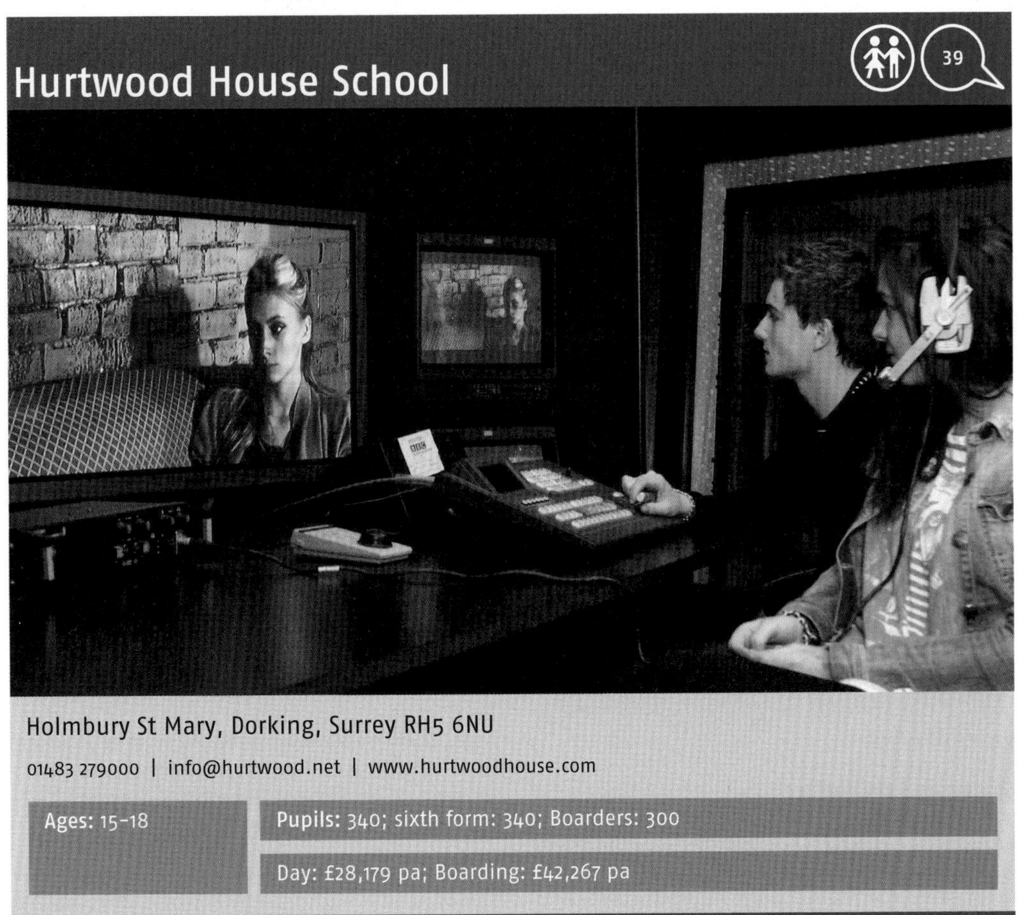

Holmbury St Mary, Dorking, Surrey RH5 6NU

01483 279000 | info@hurtwood.net | www.hurtwoodhouse.com

Ages: 15–18

Pupils: 340; sixth form: 340; Boarders: 300

Day: £28,179 pa; Boarding: £42,267 pa

Joint headmasters: Mr Richard Jackson MA (70s), originally an English teacher, is the founding head. Richard's (we are all on first name terms here) soft-spoken and understated manner belies the weighty and imposing presence of a man who has lived and is still living a remarkable dream, a dream he and his team bring about daily for their privileged students.

Mr Cosmo Jackson BEd (40s) and son of Richard was appointed 2004 to do the main day-to-day running of the school. An alumnus of Charterhouse, Cosmo spent two years at Bristol University not enjoying economics and thence to the University of the West of England to do his – perhaps inevitable – BEd. He was, in all senses, to the manner born, as were the majority of his siblings, their spouses and, quite possibly, ultimately, their offspring as Hurtwood is, triumphantly, a family concern and four other Jacksons are on the staff. Parents seem a little bemused. 'He's very charming but the students don't see much of him once they're in. He doesn't teach anyone.' A pity as he is easy to talk to, smilingly enthusiastic and loves his job.

Academic matters: Contrary to popular opinion, this is not just a school for arty/media types. Sciences are strong and the results across the whole range of subjects are uniformly starry. A levels offered include all three sciences, economics and sociology. Some students yearn for more eg philosophy. Most popular are, unsurprisingly, drama, media, English, maths and psychology. Fine art and textiles an astonishing stand-out success.

Average class size is between eight and 12, often smaller. Teaching is, according to parents, 'pretty excellent' and the students we spoke to were extravagant in their praise, admiration and, in some cases, hero-worship of teachers. The Jackson philosophy is all about bringing in the best and assiduously monitoring both staff and students to ensure that no slacking, laurel-resting or coasting occur. Parents know what they are paying for: 'They're spoon-fed to a terrible degree,' said one, 'but that's why the fees are so enormous.'

According to the Jacksons, success depends on kindness and monitoring. 'Socially and pastorally we are the friendliest school in the world but we're strict when it comes to work.' Cosmo says, 'We have the cosy feel and intimacy of a prep with the academic rigour and maturity of a university.' Weekly staff meetings to check on anyone whose performance causes concern. Everyone graded A1-U5 and staff swift to pick up on anyone not meeting expectations. In 2017, nearly 84 per cent A*-B and 58 per cent A*/A at A level.

No SEN dept – Richard talks of 'enthusiastic amateur support' and acknowledges that among such creative people, the 'dyses' are bound to be common. But, he feels, 'they should, by now, have learned the strategies and techniques to manage their difficulties'.

Games, options, the arts: The glory of Hurtwood and at the heart of its ethos. Arts and media all to professional standards – largely because the teachers are West End/media pros absolutely on top of their game and all the latest in production. And this is the great attraction. We spoke to numerous academically-minded students who had come to Hurtwood because their previous schools offered the chance of one or two productions each year in which they might, or might not, get a part. Here, productions, films, videos of all kinds and sizes roll off the blocks constantly and, if you are of a mind to, you can be constantly engaged in them. Acting 'company', a film 'academy' and a dance 'company' are elite groups restricted to a dozen or so devotees.

No glitzy performing arts centre such as are now routinely found in 'top' schools. The theatre is good, of professional quality and seats 180 though with little backstage or flyroom/wing space. The students learn the design and building of sets not by doing, but by seeing it done by the pros, very expensively, brought in. This a positive policy decision of the Jacksons. They do learn lighting though, again, lighting pros brought in to do the actual biz in the 'jaw-droppingly good' concerts and shows, as parents concur. 'They walk out of here and could manage a BBC studio,' one thought, 'and those who go on to media courses find they know pretty much everything they do in the first year, at least.' New TV studio complex and edit suite the envy of many strapped production companies.

Around a quarter learn an instrument. A further quarter take singing lessons and a sixth take dance. Music tech is, inevitably, a big deal here with two tech rooms plus recording studio. Art is rich and varied – impressive and imaginative portfolios emerge from the small studio down the track through the woods. Costume design makes practical use of textiles skills and the results are stunning. Monthly newsletter produced in-house and largely by students is a slick, cool number.

'They walk out of here and could manage a BBC studio,' one thought, 'and those who go on to media courses find they know pretty much everything'

Games an also-ran. It's just not why you come. 'If you want to do a sport, you're pretty much in the team,' we were told by an enthusiast who gave up his place in his elite's school's elite first XI to come here. There's a football pitch, all weather-hockey/basketball pitches, two tennis courts, a new sports pavilion, so it's there if you want it. Pool and table tennis around the place as well.

Boarding: Around 50 boarders live in the upper floors of the main building. Not over-roomy or over-appointed but perfectly adequate and with inspiring views. The rest in houses within a short bus ride – school keeps a fleet of buses which shuttle to and fro. All boarding houses are attractive and interesting architecturally though the loveliness of the interiors varies according, as much as anything, to taste. But most parents agree, 'it doesn't worry the pupils,' and 'the house staff are lovely.' Assuredly, here are not the dinky study bedrooms with en suites and all mod cons found elsewhere. As one parent opined, 'They haven't

'There is,' a clear-eyed student told us, 'an ever-present sense of being part of an elite, but most people are very grounded'

chucked money at the accommodation, but I'd rather have good teaching than smart bedrooms.'

Background and atmosphere: Richard Jackson conceived his school way back in the late 1960s and it bears the stamp of those idealistic, anything-is-possible, heady and experimental days. Hurtwood's first incarnation was in a building rented from the National Trust and he looked for three years until he lighted on this lovely house in its perfect spot. It was always to be a 16-19 school, GCSEs being, for Richard, 'the absolute natural breaking point.' And so it has proved.

Set in 25 acres of stunning Surrey rural idyll, the house is a 1900s late arts and crafts, genteel mock Tudor fantasy, beautifully sited on the hills overlooking the North Downs. Getting here is a challenge as the road darkens and narrows, winding though and over the wooded hillsides – reminding one just how rural Surrey can still be, though each bend has a gated entrance with entryphone – this ain't your hill-farming sticks. The place is beautifully kept and the car park must have one of the most privileged views in the country. Downstairs is lovely – a huge and inviting drawing room with coffered ceiling, grand fireplace, sink-into sofas and lots of warm limed oak. Similarly, the library has a wondrous ceiling and, when you look down, a jolly good stock of books, periodicals etc. Dead posh loos too. Less artistically pleasing outbuildings house various subjects and classes, common rooms etc.

Food is 'out of this world'. One parent marvelled at 'the amount they must invest in the kitchen. It's all cooked there – nothing is brought in.' Another enthused, 'I turned up one day out of the blue and there was a dressed salmon!' Breakfasts apparently so good, superlatives fail. Much-loved ice cream machine and barbeque bar.

Pastoral care, well-being and discipline: Pupils and staff on first name terms – works fine although those who come from stiff public schools never quite get used to not saying 'Sir'. Parents praise the 'very secure environment'. Residential 24/7 but students are free to go home at the weekends with permission and around 75 per cent do. No rich programme of activities over the weekends as elsewhere because those who do remain – or come in especially – have rehearsals, projects etc they just can't put down. Occasional weekend activities include hiking, camping in Snowdonia, paragliding, powerboating, high ropes courses and paintballing. School runs buses into Guildford and Cranleigh for shopping etc.

Very strict regs on smoking, drink and drugs. On our trail down to the arts block we met the 'smoking teacher' ready to ambush those having a sneaky drag but, although some parents sighed over these perennial problems, most felt it happened at weekends out of school and school is absolutely resolute against all such folly. Lots of counselling given when needed; random testing for drugs. Mixed boarding houses though sexes on separate floors or wings and 'very-strict no-go areas'. Girls wear black leggings, ankle boots and hoodies and boys wear skinny jeans, trainers and hoodies. Very little self-expression via 'see-me' garb. Sensible attitudes seemed pervasive. If there are any worried parents, we did not find them.

Pupils and parents: Approximately two-thirds are British, mostly from London and the home counties. Rest from, well, everywhere – nationals from 33 countries at the time of our visit. Sixty with EAL needs supported by specialist department. We did hear knots of students talking Chinese but mixing is better than at many schools – largely because productions bring people together. No distinction made or felt between day and boarding students, those who drip wealth and those on scholarships. 'There is,' a clear-eyed student told us, 'an ever-present sense of being part of an elite, but most people are very grounded and it's only with some of those from overseas where you really sense loadsamoney.' Everyone says how well everyone mixes.

Parents also a good mix – many in the arts. School/home links not touchy-feely. One parent said, 'They don't do parents' evenings – such a

relief as we're not hands-on parents.' On the other hand, another said that they'd like the teachers to be around when they pick up on Friday evenings and a third echoed the feeling that she didn't get a chance to know her son's teachers.

Notable former pupils include Nikki Amuka-Bird, Emily Beecham, Phoebe Boswell, Emily Blunt, Amelia Brightman, Ben Chaplin, Amelia Curtis, William El-Gardi, Edward Fox, Aidan Gillen, Sam Harrison, Jack Huston, Tom Mison, Leah Wood, Hans Zimmer, Hannah Herzsprung.

Entrance: There are 150-170 vacancies each year (55 per cent girls and 45 per cent boys). No open days, it's much more personal here. School says, 'We are looking for students who are going to make a positive contribution to our community. Character, personality, willingness, cheerfulness, liveliness, helpfulness, maturity, a sense of responsibility and a strong sense of purpose are all qualities that we are looking for.' Admissions criteria like these – in all their triumphantly civilised vagueness – are not found everywhere.

Parents and prospective pupil are seen by the head and the interview usually lasts over an hour. Then, if you are still keen, you register and apply. What matters is whether you will fit in and make the most of the opportunities on offer. Some turned down at that point, a few, obviously outstanding, applicants are offered an immediate place, subject to reference, at that stage; the rest are put in a 'pool' for selection later in the year. Oversubscribed and currently a waiting list of around 50-60, entirely acceptable, hopeful would-bes. Places not dependent on GCSE results (except for eg the sciences and maths).

Exit: To a surprisingly mixed bunch of courses at a very wide range of unis from Oxbridge (two in 2017) to California eg LSE, Durham, Bristol, King's College London, Warwick, Imperial. Music, art, drama and film courses, as you'd expect but maybe fewer than you'd expect. Quite a few engineering and business management degrees. School runs its own agency, now headed by Emily Blunt.

Money matters: Famously and unashamedly expensive. Until you get here and sense the quality it's hard to gauge quite why. Two performing arts scholarships on offer annually worth 50 per cent of fees; two more at 25 per cent. Jacksons use their discretion to support those who deserve it and need it. Definitely worth trying, especially if you are local and utterly determined to succeed.

Remarks: Unique and impossible to label or compare. If you're talented, hard-working, collaborative, appreciative of opportunities and in love with performance and production, you'll have a stunning time.

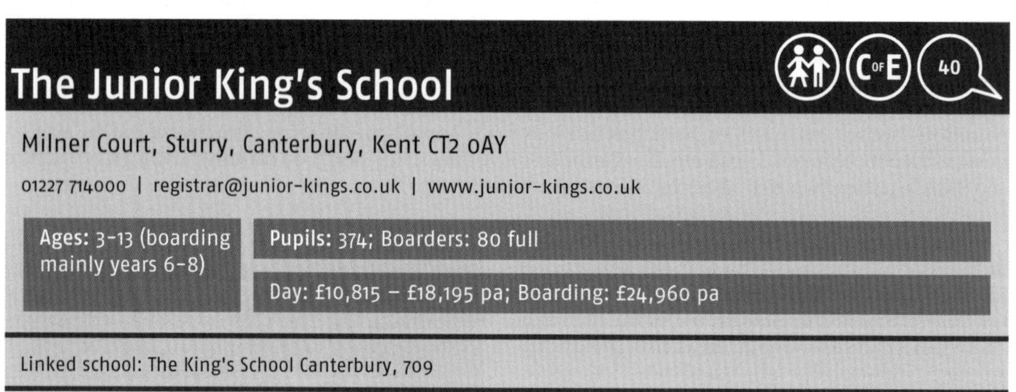

The Junior King's School

Milner Court, Sturry, Canterbury, Kent CT2 0AY

01227 714000 | registrar@junior-kings.co.uk | www.junior-kings.co.uk

Ages: 3-13 (boarding mainly years 6-8)

Pupils: 374; Boarders: 80 full

Day: £10,815 – £18,195 pa; Boarding: £24,960 pa

Linked school: The King's School Canterbury, 709

Head: Since September 2017, Emma Károlyi, previously deputy head and director of studies at Loretto. She has a degree in classical studies and ancient history from St Andrews, is married to Julian, also a teacher, and they have two children. A keen viola player, she hopes to get involved in music and orchestras in Canterbury.

Entrance: Most join in nursery and reception but major intakes into year 5 and year 7 when extra classes are added and occasionally into year 8 for common entrance if going on to King's. Younger children have a taster day and informal assessments and from year 5 children tested in English, maths and non-verbal reasoning.

Means-tested bursaries available from year 7 for up to 100 per cent of the boarding fee. Academic scholarships offered at 11+ for new joiners and children already in the school – worth a max of five per cent of fees. Additional bursary support available.

Exit: About 75 per cent go on to King's Canterbury. Others to destinations including Benenden and St Edmunds. A few leave for the grammar schools at 11+ – some after-school coaching provided but parents usually get their own as well. Scholarships to King's Canterbury every year. Those considered borderline for King's required to sit a pre-test and parents are given plenty of advice if it is thought a child might not pass common entrance to their chosen school.

Remarks: Founded in 1879 as the prep school for The King's School, Canterbury and spent its first 50 years in the precincts of the cathedral. Boys were known as 'parrots' because of the noise they made and houses are still named after parrots. Moved to current site in 1929 when Lady Milner gave Sturry Court, an Elizabethan manor house, together with the Tithe Barn, in memory of her husband. It was opened by their friend Rudyard Kipling. Two miles from the centre of Canterbury, it is set in 80 acres of grounds and playing fields with the River Stour running through the middle. Along with King's, it is part of the Canterbury Cathedral Foundation, shares a governing body with King's and has a committee of four governors closely linked to the junior school.

School has a reputation for being quite competitive and according to the prospectus 'endeavour and success are held in the highest regard'; however, the number one golden rule is 'Do be kind, gentle, helpful, respectful and polite' and there is great emphasis on good manners, tolerance and friendliness. Parents full of praise for the school: 'My children are all very different and have all been happy – you don't have to be very sporty to have fun here'. 'The competitive environment has brought my daughter out of herself and given her confidence.' All agree that this school is 'best for children who are good at something' and that 'there is a very nice balance between academia and other things so children can build confidence in different areas'.

One mother commented slightly wistfully, 'My daughter wants to be at school more than she wants to be at home'

Strong Christian tradition with weekday and Sunday services at the village church and confirmation and carol services in the cathedral but all faiths made to feel welcome. Full-time and weekly boarders (mainly from year 6+) cared for in two immaculate houses: Kipling (boys) and Juckes (girls). Local children often ask to board for the last year and one mother commented slightly wistfully, 'my daughter wants to be at school more than she wants to be at home'. Lots of evening and weekend activities plus Saturday school with lessons in the morning and sport in the afternoon means there is no time to get bored or homesick. Around 45 per cent boarders are from overseas.

Relationships with staff relaxed but respectful and there is always someone to talk to – year 5 onwards have two class teachers, one male, one female. 'The teachers seem interested in developing my child as a human being not just on an academic level,' said one happy parent. Bullying rare and dealt with swiftly via detailed anti-bullying policy. Good healthy food with lots of choice and staff make sure children eat a balanced meal.

School supports a variety of charitable causes and all children expected to be involved at some stage during the year – sponsored walks, donations to Salvation Army, the school fête, visiting old peoples' homes etc. They share their sports facilities and theatre with local groups; school is keen be part of the local community. Junior King's provides funds for a school in Malawi and children are encouraged to take an interest.

Average class size 15-16, max 18. Three parallel forms with setting in maths from year 5, English, maths and languages from year 6 and science in year 8 – very flexible and all about challenge and support. Separate scholarship class in year 8. Children start learning French in reception and Spanish and Latin taught from year 5. Greek offered to scholars. Special provision for French, Spanish and Chinese bilingual children. Separate sciences taught in specialist laboratories from year 7. ICT incorporated into most subjects and also taught as a specialist subject from year 1 and children learn programming skills eg making computer games as well as spread sheets, presentations and website design. 'Everyone is expected to participate in class and it is a fast-paced academic school which does not suit everyone'. Very occasionally, it is suggested tactfully that a child might do better elsewhere.

Bright, sunny library central to main school with 14,000 books and run by a part-time librarian – the most widely-read children are appointed to The Most Honourable Order of the Book. Pre-prep and year 3 have their own libraries. Experienced staff of 'inspiring and dedicated teachers' as well as talented young graduate assistants who come to work for a year before going to train as teachers. Much more attention given to SEN in recent years, about 10 per cent with some sort of learning support, either withdrawal or in-class help – system of monitoring and referrals means problems picked up early. Two dyslexia teachers, one full-time, one part-time plus a graphologist. EAL support if required.

Forest school in the grounds where children learn about nature and risk-taking in a safe environment – they were making nettle pancakes over a camp fire when we visited

Sport taken seriously and the school likes to win; pupils consistently encouraged to make the most of everything. Superb facilities and children can go to King's for anything not available at Junior King's. Rowing an option from year 7 in conjunction with senior King's plus a cricket pro and winter coaching and squash offered at King's. Floodlit Astro (funded by a parent) means hockey now a major sport for boys and girls. Girls have been IAPS champions three times in recent years. Huge galleried sports hall and 14 tennis courts. LTA tennis coach recently appointed and school usually sends a team to the national IAPS tournament at Queenswood. Heated outdoor pool for fun but serious swimming taught at the King's recreation centre. Fencing particularly strong and a number of international fencers started at Junior King's. Few parental grumbles about children not getting picked for teams or getting into school plays but school aware of this and tries to address it. Inter-house competitions give everyone a chance to take part and new talents often emerge at the summer sports day when a huge variety of sports are contested.

Performing arts take place in the Tithe Barn, recently insulated and refurbished thanks to another very generous parent. Music is central to the life of the school with class music from reception upwards, over 60 per cent learn at least one instrument and the choir is a special part of school life. New purpose-built music school opened in 2016. Range of bands, choirs and ensembles cater for every age and ability and with at least one big concert each term, 'music is never far from your ears.' Advent carol service and sung evensong at the end of the summer term are held in the cathedral and there are music scholarships to King's senior most years. Drama part of the curriculum from year 3 and just about everyone has a chance to get up on stage at least once a year.

Busy art department – photography, film making, art history, graphic design, pottery, textiles – the sort of opportunities you would expect to find at a senior school and children can use the facilities at King's as well. DT from year 3 includes racing car design when children build and race a car in the Kent championships, jewellery making and T shirt design and a Dragons' Den type competition when children form teams to solve problems.

Annual Spanish exchange, skiing, weekend in Normandy, post-scholarship trip to Greece, the much looked forward to post-CE jaunt to Cornwall, rugby to Paris, hockey to Holland, cricket and choir tours to Brussels – European destinations which do not put too much strain on parental pockets.

Activities most afternoons and evenings, dozens to choose from (some charged for), everything from animation, circus skills and bushcraft to debating, gardening, jazz dance, riding and photography (digital and dark room).

Day children from a radius of about 40 minutes via minibus service plus accompanied train from Ashford. Most from professional families – doctors, medics, lawyers and City and creative types. About 45 per cent of boarders are foreign nationals from a variety of countries; strong links with Brussels and the Foreign Office – many parents choose the school for its global outlook. Active Friends' Association has weekly breakfasts and organises social events such as hog roast and Christmas bazaar to raise money eg funded the new adventure playground.

Alumni include: former Olympics minister Hugh Robertson, actor Orlando Bloom, Commonwealth Games president Tunku Imran Ja'affar, ceramicist Edmund de Waal and cricketer Freddie Kemp.

Pre-prep housed in the Oast House with own hall and library. Seven classrooms with up-to-date ICT provide a colourful and stimulating environment. Children learn PE, French, dance and music from reception onwards and use the prep school facilities – sports hall, Tithe Barn, sports fields and dining hall. Accredited forest school in the grounds where children learn about nature and risk-taking in a safe environment – they were making nettle pancakes over a camp fire on the day we visited. Nursery now housed in newly built Swiss-style chalet known as Little Barn with all the mod cons and under floor heating – a busy happy place with guinea pigs and fish tanks.

Kent College

41

Old Church Road, Pembury, Tunbridge Wells, Kent TN2 4AX

01892 822006 | admissions@kentcollege.kent.sch.uk | www.kent-college.co.uk

Ages: 11-18 (junior boarding from year 4)

Pupils: 402; sixth form: 118; Boarders: 85

Day: £19,875 – £21,375 pa; Boarding: £24,840 – £31,671 pa

Headmistress: Since 2016 Julie Lodrick BA (music, Chichester), MA (educational leadership, OU). Previously principal of the The Mount, the Quaker school in York, deputy head at Farlington school, house mistress at Queenswood school, and director of music at St Margaret's in West Sussex. Abandoned a career as a singer to teach – 'there was always something missing'. Loves being head of Kent College (KC) – 'I don't feel like I've got a job... it's a fantastic way of being'. Married to Andrew with two grown up stepchildren.

Believes that appearances matter, as well as substance: parents think the head wants to 'produce nice young ladies who can present themselves to the world', not a million miles from the 19th century KC aim: to educate girls 'having regard to the cultivation of a Christian and ladylike deportment...'.Tips from Debrett's appear at assembly, and startled pupils are learning the importance of good posture, etiquette, and looking your best – and when to use a mobile phone on a train (don't, in case you were wondering); though the head points out that this is all about being dressed and behaving appropriately for the environment you are in. The parents we spoke to, impressed by the head, were quite enthusiastic ('great to prepare the girls for the outside world'); not all the girls were so keen – 'it doesn't matter how you look', said one indignant child to mother; but with many skirts hitched far above the knee, parents feel the head does have a point. (Girls with too short skirts will now issued with a blue slip to remind them that skirts need to be knee length.)

On a practical level, parents say that when you ask for things to be done, the head listens, responds quickly and sorts the problem out. Less popular is the perception that she is trying to make the academic profile 'sharper', though we were assured that she has no intention of creating a hothouse, believing it is far more important to focus on the good mental health of pupils, and the potential each child has to develop their abilities. Mindfulness is also important to the head, who emphasises the need for moments of stillness and silence: girls are trying meditation, and mindful eating, concentrating on the mindful consumption of chocolate and raisins.

The girls we spoke to described the head as 'very optimistic', and someone who has made, and will make changes: the promised land Astro has finally been built, and there's a new catering company on board too: 'how many schools have quinoa at lunch?', said a pupil proudly. Well, actually...

Academic matters: 'Not a hothouse', said a parent, 'but they will make the most of your child's talents, and get the best out of them academically'.

Results are consistently good: in 2017, 70 per cent A*/B grades, 32 per cent A*/A grades at A level; GCSEs: 50 per cent A*-A/9-7 grades. English is popular, with most pupils receiving top grades (it makes a difference having published authors on the staff, says the deputy head), and geography, with its 'fantastic teachers' is one of the most popular GCSEs. RS is compulsory at GCSE; parents could opt their kids out, but none do.

Plenty of traditional subjects here (options include classical civilisation, Latin, ancient Greek and history of art), but psychology, the new kid on the block, is very popular with pupils, and heeding pupil suggestions, and sociology is now available.

The head of sport 'completely understands that some hate it, but her enthusiastic approach makes even haters optimistic...'

This school prides itself on making any combination of subjects work – the deputy head here is a timetable mastermind.

Teaching is good, say parents and 'what a nice bunch of teachers...it's not so long since they were young'; ' [They're] in touch with kids' lives, very committed, hard working...know my child... I'm very pleased'.

Maths is the one area of concern, parents worrying about staff turnover and inflexible teaching styles of new teachers, high levels of tutoring, and the best teachers teaching the top sets – 'they should be good all through', said one indignantly. KC points out that pupils achieve good results in maths, and a new head of maths will be starting soon.

This school emphasises that ability is not fixed, and all have the potential to grow, which is evident in their superb value added: MidYIS data shows that KC adds at least a whole grade per GCSE; and, more remarkably, a further grade at A level: BBB to ABB can often make the difference between Russell group and non-Russell group, points out the deputy head. KC achieves this by placing girls in small classes with focused teaching, and constructing classes around individuals: this is not a

school which unquestionably follows the same pattern year after year.

ICT is under review, and developing: the VLE will be live in 2018, and there's Wifi throughout site. There are six dedicated computer rooms, and laptop suites.

The SEN unit supports mild difficulties, in one-to-one and group sessions (extra charge for one-to-one). One parent described excellent support from the unit for her daughter's problems with processing, and the 'amazing change in [her] grades'. The unit will support any pupils who need extra help, from those with gaps in knowledge to those struggling to engage with lessons.

Parents describe a school which is very attentive to learning styles: one said her daughter was upset because she seemed to make no progress; the school suggested a mentor: 'Now she has a learning support journal; can see the progress she is making, and is learning to organise herself'.

Sixth form can feel like relentless pressure, and parents feel KC is a listening school on this: one who emailed the school to report a daughter in meltdown over the amount of homework said it all eased up the following week. Pupils say the deputy head has an open door so you can 'just go and vent' when it gets too much.

Study support sessions are available both in holidays and term time: 'It's easy to get a revision session with teachers', said a sixth former. '[There's] no one who doesn't want the best out of you. Twenty people tell you you can do something: you believe in your own ability'.

There's lots of support with UCAS, although a parent suggested there could be more interview practice for university and jobs. The head's push on developing a global mindset means more visits from inspirational speakers, talks ranging from apprenticeships to Cambridge.

Games, options, the arts: Games at KC was what drew one parent to the school: she described visiting as the parent of a child on an opposing team and noticing the rapport of the girls with their sports teacher; a pupil challenging the teacher to a race, and 'the joy they both experienced'. The humane quality which runs through KC penetrates even sports, pupils commenting that the head of sport is 'so endearing, completely understands that some [pupils] hate it, but her enthusiastic approach makes even haters optimistic...'

The sports department has grown in the last four years: there are more teams, more matches and more specialist coaching. The school has two large sports halls, a new fitness suite with music and screens, so girls in it are virtually outside, and an indoor heated pool. The new Astro is enormous and impresses even those who have no desire to run across it, and a confidence course (assault style)

runs through the woods: only to be used under supervision, but seniors can walk in the woods during break times between bluebell time and October. KC runs specialist academies in gymnastics and swimming, and gymnastics is a particular strength here, with national and individual team successes.

Startled pupils are learning the importance of good posture, etiquette and looking your best – and when to use a mobile phone on a train (don't)

Everyone who turns up to training gets included in matches, and pupils told us the school doesn't get miffed if you want to play out of school – '[they're] really flexible with everything'.

KC excels at drama: they have a 300 seat theatre in which they run a theatre academy, and drama is often one of the most popular options, with pupils achieving top grades (its popularity waxing and waning with the choice of production). The latest production was Ghetto, hard hitting stuff about a Jewish ghetto in Lithuania in 1942, with school dancers, jagged and staccato, emphasising the unsettling nature of the play.

Parents told us of the magic effect drama has had on their shy offspring – '[she's] always laughing and confident now' – one pupil telling us that she had been painfully shy when she arrived at the school, and probably still would be but for the enthusiastic support of the drama teacher: one word well uttered felt like an achievement.

Music is housed in a purpose built centre, complete with drum studio and Apple Mac suite. Musicians play a crucial role in the success of the school annual productions, and recently performed the Marriage of Figaro, complete with guest professionals.

Activities are compulsory until year 11, and the girls have a fine array to choose from, including beekeeping and fencing. Sixth formers can choose between community service, EPQ, Model UN, Young Enterprise and the school newspaper for their enrichment option block.

A popular option in lower sixth is the Leiths course: 'you get a knife set and a chef's uniform', said a pupil with enthusiasm, 'and two times a week you can forget all about work'. It's also rather nice having children who can come home and cook a good supper...

Chocolate club, run by the learning support team, gives pupils who struggle socially practical help, for instance suggesting ways to open a conversation

Textiles is big here: KC hosts and often wins prizes in the Young Fashion Designer of the year. Photography now a full A level, and is now more popular than fine art.

Boarding: 'It's very important for the girls to feel cherished', said the head of boarding, '[the boarding] house needs to feel like home'. Boarding staff are also teaching staff, so pastoral and academic staff cross the whole school day. A parent told us: 'My girls loved boarding; they made it fun for them. [The girls were] very much at home [and staff were] very attentive to their needs'.

There are 85 boarders, including flexi boarders – on regular nights, just during exams or when parents have a last minute work crisis: popular with parents and pupils alike. Around a quarter from overseas (China, Hong Kong, Europe, Africa). No real divide between day pupils and boarders, say the girls, though the Chinese/HK pupils do form strong friendships within their community. UK boarders tend to go home on weekends, but there's a full programme of activity for stay behinds.

Around 35 of the boarders are juniors (years 4-9), of whom 18 are weekly boarders, and 12 full timers; but Saturday activities are so popular that some parents take home their child on Friday and drop them back on Saturday morning so they can go on the activity (trips to trampoline parks or castles) and stay Saturday night.

Juniors are in rooms of around six (which change each term); no bunkbeds, and facilities are clean and well kept. There's a comfortable common room and kitchen where they can make toast or help themselves to fruit. Juniors must hand in all tech 15 mins before lights out, and can collect it in the morning once dressed.

Seniors are in double rooms, with single study bedrooms for upper sixth who can request favourite rooms: front, back, slanting roofs etc. Rather more substantial kitchens than in the junior house, and grown up feeling common areas. Girls can keep tech at night, but Wifi turns off at 10. More freedom for seniors, who can take the 15 minute walk to the farm shop on the other side of reservoir, but no wandering around in the woods on their own. Buses into Tunbridge Wells are organised for girls in year 10-13, and weekend trips to theatres and shops might go to Bath or London.

Lots of special boarding community events, such as the boarders' international evening to celebrate every boarder's culture with food and performances, and the leavers' BBQ – 'we hire inflatable things', said head of house – an assault course last year. The leavers' bag includes university essentials: an adult colouring book, fairy lights, a mug and a rose.

Background and atmosphere: Pupils describe a school of strong family feeling – '[we're] like a bunch of sisters'. Biscuits are put out for the girls at the end of the day: 'all the girls in happy chatter', said a parent. Not cliquey, say pupils, who told us they could happily sit down to lunch with over half the year. Although one parent commented it would be nice to see someone at the front of the school to say hello in the morning, pupils here have strong relationships with teachers, one telling us it is the best thing about KC – 'I can go to [to them] with any problems or personal issues. A friend in grammar school has one teacher she can go to problems – here, there are many'.

A girls only environment is a grade enabler, says the school; a STEM subject enabler too, and no worries about fitting the box and behaving a certain way. 'They can roll over and over down [a slope in] the grass', said a teacher, 'which wouldn't be cool with boys [present]: they can be children for longer'. One pupil told us the best thing about the school was 'how comfy I feel... but not babied or hand held'.

A Methodist school, but welcomes all faiths or none; though the John Wesley prayer about doing all the good you can is part of daily conversation here. The chaplain is always available for a chat, and leaves chocolate outside his door. God is 'not forced on you,' said a pupil, who nevertheless appreciated talking about things with the chaplain – 'what is truth? Is it an optical illusion? Food for thought', she said. Indeed.

The main building is a Victorian manor house set in beautiful Kent woodland, surrounded by a miscellany of other buildings and styles: the new Walker building 'is amazing' say pupils: arts and textiles have their own space, and the new library is great (though we never quite got the bottom of the body outlined on the floor in tape...). Pupils would like more infrastructure improvements, and work is on the cards, but even the older buildings here were well cared for.

There is a house system (Celts, Danes and Saxons), with all the usual inter-house sport, drama and quizzes, but the girls weren't very engaged with it: 'it could be improved', said pupils.

The uniform is basically blue, and has been through a few changes: the plain version made the girls look like cadets at Hendon police college, said one parent, and others say the current blouse reminds them of toothpaste: we rather liked it. Sixth formers wear a suit (skirt or trousers), and are pleased to be relieved of the need to choose what to wear.

Pastoral care, well-being and discipline: One parent described KC as an 'extremely caring small community' where 'teachers genuinely care a lot what happens to girls'; it was chosen by another because she felt her daughter would get a good education in a small class environment, but be more nurtured than at a grammar school, where 'middle of the road can get a bit lost': 'Both girls came out really believing they can achieve – and having achieved academically'.

The school takes a pastoral approach to disenchanted pupils, which, the head says, is usually due to lack of confidence: 'We need to unpick the reasons why a pupil cannot engage'. They will talk to the pupil and parents and provide a huge amount of extra support to help resolve problems. A pupil said, 'No-one does anything wrong, because you don't want to disappoint the teachers. They're so lovely and caring, you don't want to upset them. [I'm] more bothered by [disappointing] teachers than mum and dad...' Although one parent thought the school 'needs to be a bit stricter' with girls who mess around and answer back, there were no problems evident on our visit.

KC has a good eye for pastoral care: a parent told us about the lovely change in her daughter, who found it difficult to make friends at her old school: chocolate club, run by the learning support team, gives pupils who struggle socially practical help, for instance suggesting ways to open a conversation; other support includes the buddy system, ensuring that nervous girls have someone to walk with to the bus stop, and to sit with at lunch time, until they are confident they can manage on their own.

Bullying is dealt with effectively, though the head is quick to point out that long targeted bullying campaigns are very rare; problems are more likely to be the small tiffs typical to childhood, which are quickly resolved by talking; and in fact a parent whose daughter received unpleasant texts from other pupils said it was dealt with within half an hour of her phone call, and there have been no further problems. The school counsellor will help both pupils and families if necessary, a service described by a parent as 'very, very subtle'.

Lots of special community events, such as the international evening to celebrate every boarder's culture with food and performances

A parent described a school that is 'good at spotting what happens', and thinks that eating disorders would not go undetected; not least because of the fingerprint system at the entrance to the dining hall, and the supervision during the meal. There are no drug checks, but the higher education programme includes advice on drugs, sex and consent. Communication is good – 'brilliant at responding to telephone/email queries'; 'oh yes, grades all the time'.

Pupils and parents: Parents range from extremely wealthy to those making sacrifices for fees. Parents agree that this is not a school for very pushy parents or children who are only interested in work (go to a grammar). Eleven different bus routes around local villages and beyond; most pupils from East Sussex or Kent.

Entrance: One hundred or above on standardised scores, leeway for those from state primaries. Feeder preps: Sevenoaks, Derwent Lodge, Dulwich, Wallyhall junior. Fifty per cent of intake from own prep.

Exit: Around half to Russell group, with Birmingham and Nottingham popular destinations, but a range from architecture at Edinburgh to events management at London Met. Occasional Oxbridge; three off to American universities in 2017 including one studying English and drama at McGill.

Money matters: Means-tested bursaries, and scholarships of up to 10 per cent of fees.

Remarks: The word parents use most to describe KC is 'happy'; next up is 'all rounder'. 'They will make the most of what your child is good at, whatever it is', said a parent.

King's Rochester

C of E 42

Satis House, Boley Hill, Rochester, Kent ME1 1TE

01634 888590 | admissions@kings-rochester.co.uk | www.kings-rochester.co.uk

Ages: 13-18

Pupils: 262; sixth form: 95; Boarders: 48

Day: £18,705 pa; Boarding: £30,390 pa

Principal of King's Rochester and head of the senior school: Since 2012, Mr Jeremy Walker MA (Oxon) (40s). Previously head of sixth form and senior manager at Berkhamsted School, Hertfordshire. Educated at Sherborne School and read theology at Oxford before taking an MA in educational leadership and management at the Institute of Education, University of London. Started his career at Bishop Stopford School, a state secondary in Kettering, and became head of department after a year. Then moved to Ardingly, where he was head of religious studies and of theory of knowledge, and housemaster. He does not have time to teach here but is involved with Oxbridge preparation and interview technique and lateral thinking skills. His main objectives have been to improve academic performance, sports and careers and he has already negotiated the acquisition of a local sports centre and had it refurbished, introduced sports scholarships and been involved in setting up an effective careers network.

He says that he has 'built on the strengths of the school but has not shied away from areas which needed attention'. He is proud of the wide ability intake and believes in a broad curriculum and personalised education and, most importantly, that school should be fun. 'You get the best of both worlds here – a day school with a boarding school ethos.' He is 'sticking with King's traditions but making them relevant' and encourages parents to come to services in the cathedral. Parents full of praise: 'He is very disciplined and hard working, and that is the message he gives to the pupils'; 'A very efficient, caring man who knows the kids well and drops into lessons and chats to them; 'Very enthusiastic and has brought new vigour to the school'; 'Kids love him'. He is tightening up on everything including the uniform and has introduced zero tolerance on alcohol.

Met his wife, Harriet, when they were both at Sherborne; they have two children in the school and she teaches in the nursery and is involved with the Friends' Committee (parents' association). The school is their home and family life is very important to them. Mr Walker sits on the Cathedral Business Guild and a local cultural partnership to promote Rochester, and has strong links with the local military – the Royal Engineers.

Academic matters: Caters for a wide range of academic ability from 'Oxbridge to average'. In 2017, 48 per cent A*-A/9-7 at GCSE and 34 per cent A*/A at A level (54 per cent A*-B). Pretty impressive for an almost non-selective school in grammar school country – in fact they often outperform grammars in exam results. Offers double and triple award science and all do RS and ICT at GCSE. PE, music, classical Greek, Russian and German are among other subjects offered. Business studies, government and politics and history of art amongst 24 A level offerings. Will run an A level class for as few as three pupils and 'will go to great lengths to tailor the timetable to suit the children'. Extended Project Qualification also offered alongside A levels – another feather in your cap for university entrance.

An extraordinarily dedicated team of teachers – a good combination of some who have been in the school for many years and bright, young, newly qualified staff, and Mr Walker has brought in some new blood since his arrival, including a dynamic new head of ICT. 'The levels of devotion are extraordinary – they even ran revision classes on Easter Monday,' said one parent. 'The teachers really seem to care how we do,' said a pupil. Dedicated careers department – 'school has beefed up advice for university and beyond,' said a parent. An old boy has set up Jobs Network to provide advice and work experience to current and former pupils and help with interview practice and technique. Current and former parents encouraged to offer help with work experience or as a mentor. All upper sixth have mock job interviews with feedback and lower sixth have cv writing clinics.

Team of qualified SEN teachers – mainly for mild dyslexia, although school happily accommodates those with greater needs where possible. Pupils assisted in class, through withdrawals and with IEPs.

Games, options, the arts: Sport on the up helped by the introduction of sports scholarships and the new facilities. School has recently taken over the Stirling Sports Centre and adjoining Holcombe Hockey Club from Medway Council, now refurbished and renamed the King's Rochester Sports Centre, a 10 minute walk or short minibus ride from the school. Olympic standard Astroturfs and new outdoor tennis and netball courts plus indoor hockey, badminton and cricket nets and a fitness suite. Free membership for King's parents and open to the general public too. Some team sports still played on the pitches within the school grounds. On site netball means the girls now get match teas – has made the 'netball mums' very happy. Rowing from the school's own boathouse on the Medway near Maidstone – 18 rowing boats and five large canoes. School very supportive of outside achievements eg national level pentathlon plus sailing and skating, and several pupils play cricket, rugby or hockey at county level. Strong tradition of fencing – fencing master was involved with organising

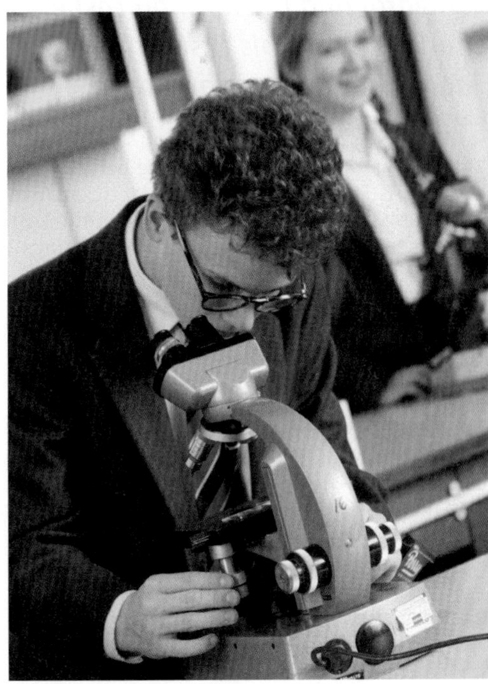

Olympic competition. Duke of Edinburgh popular and 10-15 do gold each year. CCF offered in all three services – compulsory for the first two years and many keep going. Our guide had learnt how to fly a plane with the RAF division.

Impressive music – the prep is a cathedral school so the choristers (boys only 8-13) are part of the school and the chapel is Rochester Cathedral. Choir trips all over the place and they make recordings for Radio 3. Several choirs, orchestras and ensembles, a wind and jazz group and inspirational and 'brilliant' director of music. About 50 per cent learn at least one instrument with several reaching grade 8 each year, and a number go on to study music, often with organ or choral scholarships; pupils recently won scholarships to the Royal College and Royal Academy of Music. On a lighter note, the annual house music competition and popular termly Open Mic night gives pupils an opportunity to perform in public.

Busy art department with photography, sculpture and fine art offered – product design particularly popular and pupils often go on to art college. Three major drama productions a year, numerous theatre and opera trips to London, and visiting theatre groups organise drama workshop within the school.

A great sense of history here with the buildings clustered round the cathedral and the Norman castle; Charles II spent his first night in England at Restoration House

Numerous after-school clubs and societies with 'something for everyone' including bell ringing, debating, ICT and chess. Ballet popular throughout the school: some up to grade 8, and a handful keep going into sixth form. Lots of trips and outings – choir to Vatican and China, Physics to CERN, maths to NASA and World Challenge to Northern India.

Boarding: Up to 70 boarders, about half from overseas – 14 different nationalities and school works hard on integration. Boys' boarding house for 43 and girls' for 25. Start off in small dorms, and sixth form and most of fifth form have their own room with ensuite bathroom. School sports facilities available in the evenings. Always something organised at weekends eg shopping and cinema trips and children are expected to take part.

Background and atmosphere: Part of the Foundation of Rochester Cathedral, the school was founded in 606AD at the same time as the

'A very family oriented school where there are genuine friendships across year groups and kids look after each other'

cathedral and re-founded under Henry VIII in 1541 when the monastery at Rochester was dissolved. It is the second oldest school in the UK after King's Canterbury. Prefects wear a gown and carry a cane but the school is certainly not old fashioned and inward-looking. A great sense of history here with the buildings clustered round the cathedral and next to the Norman castle; Charles II spent his first night in England at Restoration House on his return in 1660 and Queen Elizabeth I is rumoured to have stayed at Satis House (now the school administration building). A range of buildings from the medieval cathedral to Georgian, Victorian and 21st century, with Watling Street running down the high street. An unexpected and peaceful oasis in the middle of the bustling Medway towns. One of the few co-ed independent schools in Kent which offers a seamless education from 3-18 years.

Pastoral care, well-being and discipline: Strong Christian ethos; the cathedral is the centre of school life and the service held four mornings a week is a period of quiet reflection before the day begins. All faiths and backgrounds welcomed. All are expected to come to the services in the cathedral but do not have to participate. A tangible sense of community where everyone knows each other well and it is 'a very family oriented school where there are genuine friendships across year groups and kids look after each other,' said one happy mother. 'It is a close knit community that produces confident, self-reliant children who are not cocky,' said another, and 'It really does try to cater for all, and they are very personal in the way they deal with the kids'. 'My son has at last found a school where he is happy – it offers the best pastoral care I have come across. Most schools say they treat every child as an individual but King's Rochester really does,' said a father. School takes a firm line on drugs and runs a programme of drug awareness through PHSE but has not had any issues.

Pupils and parents: Big range from traditional to first time buyers and some who make genuine sacrifices to send their children here. Some come from the Medway towns and villages, some from 25 miles away and some come down on the train from SE London, Bromley and Blackheath. Extensive minibus service from as far away as Tonbridge and Sevenoaks. Children generally 'down to earth and engaging – they exude confidence and are compassionate, sociable and great fun to be with'.

Former pupils known as Old Roffensians and are hugely supportive with a great sense of loyalty to the school, and tend to keep in touch. They go on to follow a variety of careers and include surgeons, musicians, authors, artists and poets. Alumni include Prof Sir Derek Barton, who won the Nobel Prize for Chemistry, John Gummer, former Conservative cabinet minister, Pete Tong, Radio 1 DJ and Matthew Walker, professional cricketer.

Good communication with parents who say they feel involved. Moodle, a virtual learning environment where children can access classwork, homework and notes is proving popular with parents, who can keep an eye on what is going on.

Entrance: Broad ability intake but children are expected to be able to take 9/10 GCSEs and 3/4 A levels. Summer exams for those coming up from junior school are used for setting purposes and very few fail; and school will give plenty of warning if this is likely to happen. Entry from other schools at 13+ via common entrance or school's own tests. Occasionally spaces in year 10. Very few leave after GCSEs. Another 20 per cent join in sixth form and are expected to get at least five GCSEs at grade C/5 or above and As or Bs in subjects to be studied at A level.

Exit: Around a quarter leave after GCSEs. Birmingham and Loughborough universities popular in 2017, with others off to Prague (dentistry), Hong Kong (medicine, with a scholarship) and the Birmingham Conservatoire.

Money matters: Offers sports, academic and music (including organ) scholarships worth up to 30 per cent of fees which can be topped up with means-tested bursaries up to 75 per cent of fees. Choral scholarships offered in the prep school. Discounts for clergy, Forces families and siblings.

Remarks: A warm and caring family school with some of the best pastoral care around where children can grow up in the shadow of the cathedral. A wide ability range but all made to feel valued and the brightest get into the best universities. Going from strength to strength under the dynamic head.

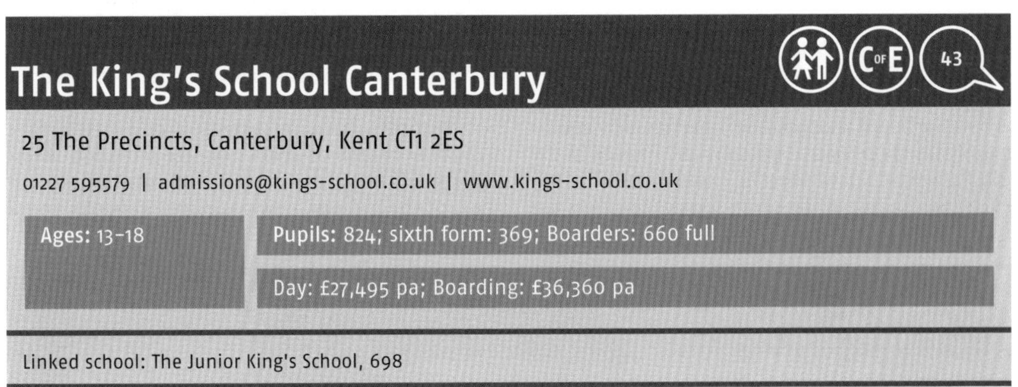

The King's School Canterbury
C of E
43
25 The Precincts, Canterbury, Kent CT1 2ES
01227 595579 | admissions@kings-school.co.uk | www.kings-school.co.uk
Ages: 13-18
Pupils: 824; sixth form: 369; Boarders: 660 full
Day: £27,495 pa; Boarding: £36,360 pa
Linked school: The Junior King's School, 698

Headmaster: Since 2011, Mr Peter Roberts MA PGCE (50s), previously head of Bradfield College for eight years. He was educated at Tiffin Boys and read history at Merton College, Oxford where he got a first, followed by a PGCE at London Institute of Education. Started teaching career at Winchester as head of history, then also as master in college. Always immaculately dressed – 'sometimes a vision in tweed and sometimes besuited'. He is super brainy and regarded as 'quirky and eccentric but with a good sense of humour and perfect for the job – we would not want anyone who was run of the mill,' said a happy parent. A thoughtful academic 'who works unbelievably hard and is always out and about with his dog.' He attends every play, recital and concert and even attends the matrons' meeting; describing his job as 'vastly enjoyable.' Teaches the Shells (year 9) 'when he can'. Five big projects now on the go, in a once in a generation opportunity to develop what are a series of World Heritage sites in the heart of historic Canterbury: a new day house in the 19th century garage where Ian Fleming set Chitty Chitty Bang Bang, an up to date science block coming out of the quirky Victorian labs, a performing arts centre in a listed Malthouse, a new dining hall and a series of refurbished classrooms in the cathedral precincts.

The headmaster describes the ethos of the school as 'interactive osmosis'. 'It is the richness, the diversity and range of our lives here that makes it distinct and special.' He feels the school 'gives a strong sense of belonging, a realisation that King's helped to make them (the pupils) what they are' and 'this creates the wish to give something back in return' and sees the atmosphere of the school as 'like a massive confidence-building machine'. Expects very high standards from the children at every level and has tightened up on discipline, manners and presentation. Each week the Robertses invite 15 different pupils, one from each house, to lunch in their private dining room. Much expected too from staff and light being shed on the few pockets of less than good teaching.

Married to Marie, an elegant and accomplished Frenchwoman who was head of department at two large state schools and, in addition to playing an active part in school life, is also a harpist. They have three daughters. They enjoy spending time in France where he sails, and they both practise calligraphy and paint watercolours – helping to uphold the renaissance ideals of what is technically the oldest school in the country.

Academic matters: The pursuit of academic excellence is at the heart of everything the school does but co-curricular activities given equal weight and pupils have a 'rich' day. The brightest take some GCSEs early, allowing a head start on A level subjects; the less academic may drop a subject at GCSE. Pupils encouraged to take a creative subject like art, drama IT or music alongside academic subjects. In 2017, 60 per cent A*/A at A level, 70 per cent A*/A at GCSE (IGCSEs for most subjects). Strong across the board and languages particularly good – mainly taught by native speakers and housed in the Old Palace. Sciences popular – female head of science and five out of the seven physics teachers are women. Most subject combinations can be accommodated even if some have to be taught outside the timetable. School always looking at ways to stretch the most able and curriculum constantly adapted. Currently 27 subjects to chose from at A level (including geology), including seven at Pre-U, and advanced extension awards in most. Astronomy offered as a GCSE along with Italian, Russian and Mandarin GCSE ab initio in sixth form. Strong work ethic and 'Children do not seem to realise how much they cram into the day, it is just normal for them,' said one mother.

Always immaculately dressed – 'sometimes a vision in tweed and sometimes besuited'. He is regarded as 'quirky and eccentric but with a good sense of humour'

Pupils encouraged to think about their broader academic profile and alongside A levels there are enrichment subjects such as critical thinking, perspectives on aesthetics, globalisation and science and the extended project. Careers advice starts in the first year on a drop-in basis and fifth form have timetabled careers periods to help with A level choices and beyond.

Stunning William Butterfield designed library (1848) is centre of academic life with a hushed and studious atmosphere and combining the best of the old and new with 30,000 books and a

range of periodicals and European newspapers as well as DVDs and online reference sources. It is a great source of pride and always staffed and open every day until 10pm and at weekends. Somerset Maugham and Sir Hugh Walpole both left their personal libraries to King's.

About six per cent need extra help, mainly for mild dyslexia, and any pupil can ask for help with study skills. Probably would not suit anyone with bigger difficulties and some parental concerns that children do not get as much support as they need. EAL for a handful of pupils but all must be fluent on arrival. No plans to introduce the IB.

Games, options, the arts: Acres of playing fields about 15 minutes' walk away as well as a modern sports centre incorporating pool, indoor courts, climbing wall, café and gym – more akin to the smartest private leisure centre than the school sports department. Huge choice of sports – girls' hockey thriving with 15 girls in the English hockey training system. Cricket and rugby going from strength to strength and several boys have been selected to play for Kent U18s; school has also produced several international fencers. Rowing on the up for boys and girls after a period in the doldrums and old boy Tom Ransley won gold at Rio 2016. Sports coaches include England cricketer Mark Ealham and Olympic hockey player Jennifer Wilson. Not everyone represents the school in matches but still play sport for 'fitness, health and fun' and most people find something they enjoy. Everyone is expected to get involved and participation is everything – 'you don't have to be brilliant but just give it a go and have fun.' Sporting trips all over the world – rugby in Argentina, cricket in Grenada and netball in South Africa.

Long tradition of excellent drama and music and anyone involved is definitely awarded 'cool status.' Fab new junior music school opened early 2016 – over half the pupils learn at least one instrument. Symphony orchestra plus numerous bands and ensembles; the pupil-run jazz club is particularly popular. Plenty of choral groups, from the Crypt Choir which tours annually, most recently to China, to the choral society which is open to anyone who enjoys singing, including parents and staff. 'Wherever you go around the school there is always music coming from somewhere'. Masses of drama both on and off the curriculum – house plays, GCSE and A level productions, drama competitions, fashion shows, full school plays – 'Wherever there is a quiet corner, you will find a rehearsal going on,' as well as regular theatre trips to London. Busy art department housed in 12th-century priory has a different artist in residence each year. New photographic studio and pottery centre opened by old boy Edmund de Waal.

Huge range of activities continues into sixth form – anything from academic societies with visiting speakers to mountain biking, cryptic crosswords, debating and the Model United Nations. CCF once again a popular option. Community work and volunteering are central to school life and are often part of Duke of Edinburgh Award and include teaching science in local primary schools, riding for the disabled and help with swimming for handicapped children.

The famous King's week at the end of the summer term is the highlight of the year for pupils and parents alike and is a festival of music, drama and dance with events being staged in all corners of the school every day for a week – parents and friends come bearing picnics and it is a major social event culminating in Commem Day and the leavers' ball. 'The quality and variety are phenomenal' and there is everything from Shakespeare, classical concerts and jazz as well as a lighter touch provided by the house harmonies. Those not involved do not feel excluded and have as much fun as those taking part.

Boarding: Six boys' and five girls' senior boarding houses (latest, Kingsdown House, for girls, opened in 2015). Half the houses clustered round the cathedral and the other half across the road on the St Augustine site where they have their own dining hall. Pupils equally happy to be in houses in either location, most popular houses booked up years in advance. Boarding houses friendly and welcoming with areas where pupils can make their own snacks and relax. Small dormitories for younger children and individual study bedrooms for sixth form. Large and popular social centre open for the whole school during the day and for sixth formers in the evening.

Background and atmosphere: Set in the shadow of Canterbury Cathedral and part of a World Heritage Site, this has to be one of the most inspiring settings for a school. Founded in 597 when St Augustine arrived in Canterbury and then refounded as The King's School during the reign of Henry VIII after the dissolution of the monasteries – not many schools can produce a list of headmasters going back to 1259. Beautiful ancient buildings and cloisters and immaculate gardens with the busy city life going on just beyond the gates. Pupils enjoy the contrast and the fact that the city with its shops and cafés is on the doorstep and say, 'it makes us feel part of the real world'. The headmaster says the combination of the cathedral and a vibrant student city 'grounds the children in a wider reality'. The school sponsors the Folkestone Academy and lends its facilities to the wider community.

Took girls into sixth form in 1970s and went fully co-ed in 1990. Boarding houses plus thee day houses and a smaller sixth form girls' house in a variety of architectural styles from the 13th century Meister Omers to 21st century Grange. A close knit community, 'it's got everything, the spiritual dimension from the cathedral and a sense of beauty and history'. Former pupil Michael Morpurgo said, 'King's is like a university designed for younger people.'

Beautiful ancient buildings and cloisters and immaculate gardens with the busy city life going on just beyond the gates

Pastoral care, well-being and discipline: Smart uniform worn throughout the school, pinstripes, wing collars and a jacket – and a brooch for the girls. All look very professional and businesslike; monitors wear purple gowns and are, unsurprisingly, known as Purples. Astonishingly busy day – one of the first lessons the children learn is how to plan their time – but there is still room for lots of fun. Strict rules and punishments regarding drugs, alcohol and parties and children know where they stand. Strong Christian tradition and moral values. The main school services held in the cathedral but different religious and cultural backgrounds recognised and valued.

Children have a healthy respect for each other and are generally self-regulating regarding bullying and other misdemeanours, and honesty and integrity are highly valued. Pastoral care comes in for particular praise from the inspectors. Big effort to address everyone's happiness with several staff/pupil committees to ensure all have their say.

Regular communication with parents especially through housemasters and house mistresses. Good interaction between year groups facilitated by mixed age tutor groups and mentoring from older pupils. New Shells have a top year mentor. Day children and boarders mix well and 'you can't tell the difference,' according to one pupil.

Pupils and parents: A good mix socially and culturally with a wide catchment area – popular with locals, London and county sets and Foreign Office families and increasing numbers from abroad. About 20 per cent foreign nationals. Doesn't really produce a type but pupils are articulate, well rounded and very supportive of each other, appearing genuinely to celebrate each other's achievements. 'The finished product is amazing,' according to one mother. 'The boys and girls are charming, personable, not shy or arrogant and have a great sense of fun but are still ambitious'.

The recently formed King's Society, a cultural, social and educational society for parents and friends, now comprises over 300 families. Members organise lectures, music recitals, tours of the cathedral with the dean and social events. Old boys and girls include potter and writer Edmund de Waal, astronaut Michael Foale, Patrick Leigh-Fermor, Christopher Marlowe and William Somerset Maugham, supermodel Jacquetta Wheeler, Olympic silver medallist and world champion rower Frances Houghton and Anthony Worrall-Thompson.

Entrance: At 13+ by common entrance. School's own exam and an interview for those who have not been prepared for CE. Occasionally spaces in year 10. About a third come from Junior King's but they still have to take the same exams as everyone else rest from a range of Kent and Sussex prep schools and London day schools. Pass mark has recently been raised to 60 per cent but school likes to keep families together and takes an enlightened view if someone is borderline. It is also possible for pupils to take an entrance exam to Junior King's at 11+ which would guarantee entry to the senior school – they would still have to take CE for setting purposes. About 30 join in the sixth form with entrance by competitive exam and interview in Nov before entry with minimum of seven Bs/6s at GCSE – also required of current pupils.

Exit: Those who leave after GCSEs (very few), usually go to local schools or London day schools. Vast majority of sixth formers depart to top universities – 12 to Oxbridge in 2017, with UCL, Exeter, Edinburgh, Durham, York, Imperial and Warwick all popular. Increasing numbers to American universities (eight in 2017, including one to Berklee College of Music). Languages, sciences and economics/business management most popular degree subjects recently. Ten medics and two dentists in 2017.

Money matters: Up to 20 King's Scholarships and exhibitions as well as music and sports and art scholarships, all with a rigorous selection process and worth up to 10 per cent of fees. Three or four sixth form scholarships awarded for outstanding performance in the sixth form entrance exam. Greater emphasis on bursaries – the King's foundation has been set up to fund both scholarships and bursaries and allocated over £1 million a year. Parents means-tested annually and can receive up to 100 per cent of full boarding fee.

Remarks: Thriving academic school with highly motivated pupils. 'The children never stop – I do not know they fit everything into their day and still have time for a busy social life,' said one parent. Not a heavily religious school but the Benedictine tradition of care for body, mind and spirit is very much in evidence.

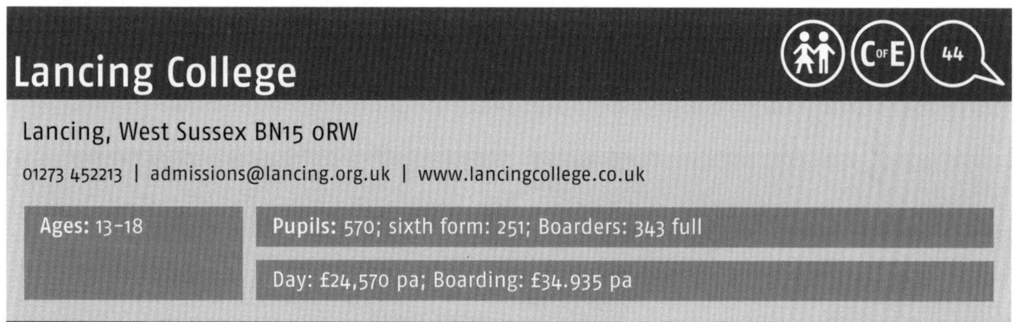

Lancing College

C of E 44

Lancing, West Sussex BN15 0RW

01273 452213 | admissions@lancing.org.uk | www.lancingcollege.co.uk

Ages: 13–18

Pupils: 570; sixth form: 251; Boarders: 343 full

Day: £24,570 pa; Boarding: £34.935 pa

Head master: Since September 2014, Dominic Oliver MPhil, who left an academic career at Oxford to teach in schools, starting out at the Royal Grammar in Worcester, then moving to head of English at Malvern College, before becoming deputy head of Bedales schools. Married to Lydia, with a child at Lancing College and another at Lancing Prep.

Clearly feels comfortably at home at Lancing, which he describes as 'recognisable public schooling with a unique combination of warmth and vigour'; more subtle than Bedales 'self consciously liberal' approach, but perhaps no less radical under its new leader. As a head who enjoys the work of old boy David Hare and other establishment rebels, he wants to hear his pupils' voices: school council will soon come into being and Mr Oliver teaches the third form debating – he enjoys provoking argument. It takes a certainty and confidence in both self and school to allow dissent and a bit of cheekiness; and quite some nerve to put a big wheel and carousel outside that grimly beautiful sinners and hellfire chapel on founder's day.

Mr Oliver brings a new culture of reflective education, with a greater emphasis on enrichment, and more students than ever doing the EPQ. They're tightening up on entrance standards – there must be evident sparks of intellect, and the very best grades will be needed for entrance and expected as outcomes (although they should be a natural outcome of the new intellectual regime).

Mr Oliver's most desirable quality for pupils is to be illuminated (a word which suggests a glowing sort of enlightenment).

Academic matters: Very good, consistent performance at GCSE and A level: 58 per cent A*-A/9-7 grades at GCSE in 2017; at A level, 51 per cent A*/A grades, 77 per cent A*/B: great results from a virtually mixed ability school. Not top grades at all costs: pupils are set a target appropriate to them, and there is celebration if the target is met; whether that target be a C or A*. 'Not an exam factory, so doesn't attract those sort of parents', and one parent commented that they opted for Lancing over a more academically pressurising competitor. Tremendous value added at Lancing – pupils achieve exam grades they wouldn't have dreamed of.

Core subjects are always streamed, others usually so (where numbers allow). Class sizes around 18 in years 9-11, down to a maximum of 15 in the sixth form. Maths is outstanding, popular with pupils and excellent results – a triple maths A level student enthused about the teaching, and useful weekly drop in sessions. Pupils give good reports of history too. Super science labs, remodelled in last few years, although science results not outstanding. Great well-stocked library with mezzanine level of computers. There are plenty of languages on offer: French, German, Spanish, Italian, Greek, Latin – pupils start with two languages in year 9, and must continue with one until GCSE. German and Chinese strong. A jolly year 9 German class showed off their iPads (now standard issue), which come into their own when teaching languages: teachers can set oral homework, and iPads will correct pronunciation; no more lost homework since pupils are emailed assignments.

Farm includes rare pigs, alpacas, llamas, geese, goats and lots of cuddly sheep – kids can get permission to stay out late and help with the lambing

Two reports during each term with grades for each subject, and a full written report at the end of term. Early remedial action if someone is falling behind – 'no one falls through the net'. A learning support department supports around 80 pupils with mild to moderate learning difficulties (mostly mild dyslexia), of whom 35 require continuous one-to-one support (at extra cost). Recent significant increase of in-class support via two full time and one part time learning support teachers who assist small groups within curriculum areas.

Games, options, the arts: School week covers six days, so four afternoon sessions for options – pupils here like to keep very busy. One afternoon a week students choose between CCF or community service. Drama is popular, even with non-actors – some of the academic hard core work backstage for light relief. Theatre seats 180, retractable seating means it's possible to play in the round, and make an

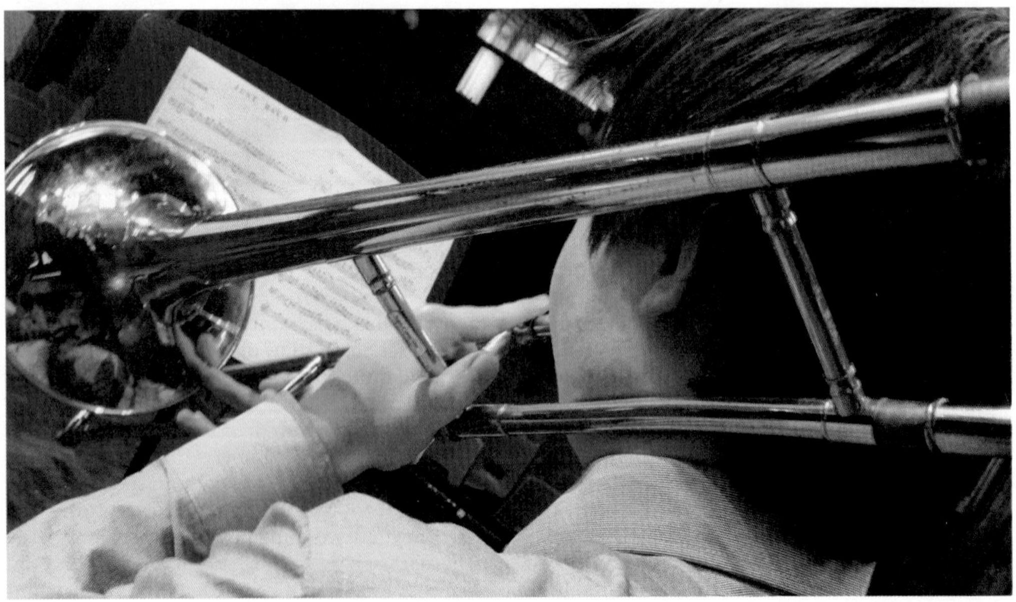

orchestra pit in part of the old swimming pool on which the theatre was built. Drama GCSE, but not enough takers for A level, though LAMDA available. About 15 productions a year – recently full-scale musical Oliver! and risque 'Tis Pity She's a Whore. Also an open air theatre.

Plenty of games sessions (down to twice a week for sixth formers), with lots of choice – focus on football, hockey, netball, cricket and tennis, but lots of other options, even for the not keen – 'I get by on yoga,' said one. One boy said he came to Lancing because it's a football school – other public schools generally favour rugby. Extensive playing fields, tennis courts, Astroturf pitch and swimming pool. And for those who love animals, farm is a sports/activities option – a sport hater/animal lover could exist blissfully at Lancing. The farm has really developed in recent years, particularly on the conservation front, and includes rare pigs, alpacas, lamas, turkeys, chickens, geese and goats, and lots of cuddly sheep – kids can get permission to stay out late and help with lambing. Meat and eggs from the farm have started feeding the school this year, and they are experimenting with a market garden with the aim of supplying veg too. Opportunities for five years' worth of vet experience as well as links with local agricultural colleges and primary schools and, via the school's Young Enterprise programme, for the marketing of college produce and wood supplies.

The music department is housed in standard 60s fare, but is staffed by teachers full of love for their subject and incredibly enthusiastic about sharing that love with pupils. Their scruffy studies overflow with sheet music; one, curiously, with a child's layout mat on the floor and a dog in the corner – who has apparently won over many recruits to music. 'They are mad,' said one pupil kindly, 'but we have a great time.' Plenty of practice rooms, which only get too busy at Associated Board exam times. Drum kit handy for those who want to pop in for a jam. Glorious choir (lovely CD – Surrexit), and numerous orchestras and bands. Lunchtime concerts most weeks, and a big concert every half term. Many continue to patronise the music block even if they don't take the subject, and around 300 learn instruments, some multiple instruments. A fine tradition of composition and of producing organ scholars to Oxbridge colleges.'It's all about joy in music making,' said one teacher – there is certainly much delight taken in music here. One parent, who encouraged her reluctant son to join the choir, says he enjoys it more than he ever (as a teenager) would admit – 'It's a very special thing to be part of.'

Art is a strong area: housed in a contemporary purpose-built centre, full of light, with eager students keen to show off their amazing work: everything from oils to an installation of hanging clingfilm, called 'Urban' – clay room and kiln, printing, etching, photography and fine art – 'Waterfront was our first topic this term, so we went to Venice' – where else? Older pupils have their own areas, so don't have to clear up paintings under way – the spacious rooms feel full of many little studios. Weekly drop-in art sessions for those who have never lifted a brush, or keen artists who just haven't got enough time to follow an art course. Art at every turn throughout the school – one house has turned the curve at the bottom of a stairwell into Venice.

Great DT centre, with examples of GCSE and A level work which wouldn't look out of place in a designer furniture store, along with a few quirky ideas – for dog owners who feel all that bend and throw is just a bit too energetic, how about an automatic dog ball launcher? Again, those who don't continue with this option can nevertheless return to pursue DT as a hobby.

Boarding: Over two-thirds of pupils at Lancing are boarders, around 330 full and 70 flexi (more boys than girls). Certainly boarders seem very happy and enjoy having a wealth of activity available on their doorsteps. Modern, comfortable accommodation, with a rolling programme of refurbishment, although you won't find the gold taps one parent was hoping for. Years 9 and 10, two to four in a room, from year 11, single study bedrooms. Shared rooms are filled to capacity with beds and desks, but the pupils don't object to cosy conditions: one sixth former told me how much she missed sharing a room with friends – 'I've been with them since I was 13 – they are like my sisters.' Day pupils can board for a night free if they are at school after 9 pm on school business, such as play rehearsals, which pleases parents.

Friends can visit house communal areas – although pupils often go and chat out on the quads after dinner. Houses have common rooms (with Sky +), squashy sofas and views over rolling countryside, and kitchens with daily deliveries of bread, spreads, and fruit for any time consumption. Each house has Wifi throughout; one house has a sweet shop open in the evenings. Sixth formers have their own common room and houses have a number of kitchens for different year groups – 'It's the best thing about the house.' School café opens at break, in the afternoons and evening for hungry pupils after prep.

Flexible boarding structure, with no differentiation between full and weekly boarders, who pay the same fees and can stay at weekends if they wish. Day pupils can pay by the night for flexi-boarding if they have evening activities.

Background and atmosphere: Grand old buildings of Sussex flint, dating from 1848, with elegant quads and huge chapel standing on the hill overlooking the rolling Downs. In this beautiful setting, it feels distinctly public school, but it's not as cut glass as all that. Clearly impresses parents – 'They're experiencing things to do with heritage and a sense of history which seep into their experience and become something they value.'

A Woodard school, it has a strong Christian tradition, still very much in evidence. No skipping weekly chapel here, for conscientious objectors or other faiths – 'It might not be something they carry on with later in life, but at least they have been exposed to it – like maths,' said a teacher. Although a Christian school, they are not out to convert you – pupils of all faiths or no faith are welcome here. It's more about the values of Christianity, and in particular caring for each other. The service is a

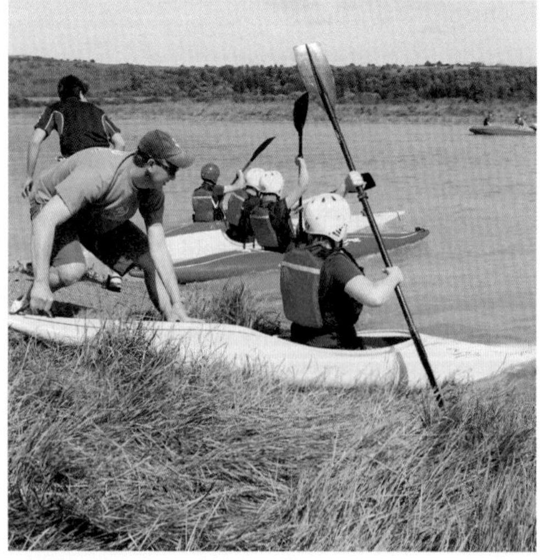

A fine tradition of composition and of producing Oxbridge organ scholars. 'It's all about joy in music making,' said one teacher

wonderful thing to experience – inside, the chapel is glorious and the voices of the choir soar – only St Paul's Cathedral has a higher ceiling. High church with plenty of bells and smells and the accompanying pageantry. Pupils seem to attend quite happily though, girls wrapped in 19th century style cloaks of house colours; boys just cold. Most troop up for communion or a blessing. Pupils assure us that a fair number attend voluntary chapel – held in the crypt daily before breakfast or in the evenings in houses. One parent said she felt doing the communal thing is very important – apparently leavers most miss their time in chapel. New television screens mean that, on high days and holidays, when the place is packed with parents and former pupils, all can see and be involved in the services.

There is a rather splendid dining hall – could almost be a back up chapel should something happen to the other one, with long wooden tables and new wooden chairs. Wide range of food available, nice, but not remarkable on the day of our visit – one pupil said it 'goes up and down a bit.' Sixth formers can skip breakfast in the dining hall and cook their own.

The sixth form is not for those who want to scruff around in jeans and tee shirts for a couple of years – smart business wear is expected here, with more responsibility as prefects or house captains, and more independence, in organising time in and out of school: year 11 and sixth formers can go into Brighton, and they're considering allowing the sixth up to London. In common with the rest of the school, some fabulous trips on offer: the travel section of the school magazine resembles a highly desirable travel brochure.

Pastoral care, well-being and discipline: Parents say it is 'like being part of a community with a strong family atmosphere.' Well-defined house system with a network of people taking care of pupils. As well as housemasters/mistresses (the first point of call for parents), there is a matron on hand, year 10 'uncles' and 'aunts' for new year 9s, and the peer support system provided by sixth formers. If all this fails, 'there is always a teacher you get on with particularly well'. Pupils admit to feeling a bit homesick for a few weeks, but say it quickly wears off. At break time, kids troop back to their house common room for squash and biscuits: some kids pop in and straight out again, others sit and chat to matron and other house staff. It is a moment away from work – like having a break with your mum. Matron – 'We are their family here.'

Parents feel discipline is 'not in your face'. Seems to work, but quite gently done. Approach 'firm but fair'. One mum says the balance must be right, because the kids are so relaxed about going to school. Bullying, drug and alcohol abuse not generally a problem, but will be dealt with severely. The one pupil who could recall an episode of bullying was clearly startled by how strictly it had been dealt with.

Communication is good where a parent has a concern – email or telephone contact will lead to a rapid and thorough response; new Parent Portal. Parents say school is very welcoming and encourages parents to feel involved; plenty of social events – plays, concerts, matches, lectures, informative talks, dinners and a healthy Parents' Association. There is some small tension between the parent who felt that parents of day pupils require more communication (than those of boarders), and the staff feeling that 'occasionally helicopter parents need to be told to buzz off in the interests of their child.' This does feel like a school where parents should be prepared to step back a bit, and let their child develop responsibility for themselves.

Pupils and parents: Fits oddballs – we met some pupils who were strongly individual but seemed very happy at Lancing. 'Not for the inert,' said one teacher, 'nor for one-dimensional academic types,' said another. Pupils from Lancing's two preps and other prep schools in the area. Parents generally middle class professionals, city types, and around 25 per cent of boarders from overseas. School runs its own buses, routes to suit need from the surrounding area, and shuttle between Lancing College and the preps.

Former pupils include playwrights Sir David Hare, Christopher Hampton and Giles Cooper, lyricist Sir Tim Rice, novelists Tom Sharpe and Evelyn Waugh, Shakespeare scholar and writer John Dover Wilson, singer Sir Peter Pears, Archbishop Trevor Huddleston, TV presenter Jamie Theakston, Sir Christopher Meyer, Charles Anson, Dr Rana Mitter, Sir Roy Calne, Stephen Green (Baron Green of Hurstpierpoint) and Alex Horne.

Entrance: Gently selective – mid 50 per cent pass rate at CE, with separate assessment for those from the state sector. For the sixth form, need good GCSEs and school reference, interviews and tests. New 'Advance Programme', allows for conditional early acceptance for year 7 students, based upon school's own admissions tests which prioritise independent thought and personality. A few places in year 10; some 30-35 places for girls at sixth form, 10-15 for boys.

Exit: Around 10 per cent leave after GCSEs. Five to Oxbridge in 2017, plus one medic. Several to North American universities. UCL, LSE and other London colleges popular alongside Exeter, Warwick and Bristol. Broad mix of subjects ranging from engineering and economics to zoology and theology.

Money matters: At 13, academic, music, art, drama, sports and all-rounder scholarships, up to half of fees, which can be augmented depending on family circumstances. Sixth form awards – academic, music and art, up to a third of fees.

Remarks: A friendly and beautiful place to grow up. Pupils are happy, and unselfconsciously themselves. This is a place where individuals will flourish, and there is evidently great care and attention to ensure this is so. Not for those who like to take things easy – a culture of keeping busy.

Marlborough House School

45

Hawkhurst, Cranbrook, Kent TN18 4PY

01580 753555 | registrar@marlboroughhouseschool.co.uk | www.marlboroughhouseschool.co.uk

Ages: 3-13 (boarders from year 4)

Pupils: 340; Boarders: 45 flexi

Day: £8,475 – £17,535 pa; Boarding: £31 per night

Headmaster: Since 2013, Martyn Ward, married with two girls at Marlborough House School (MHS). Went to Westminster College Oxford, then taught at The Hall and Cothill House, before becoming deputy, then acting head of Eastbourne College Prep.

Warm and personable, much liked by pupils – 'he's fun, and interested in us' – and parents – 'he's a breath of fresh air'; 'always around when you want to speak to him'; 'knows the children and is genuinely interested in them' (he sends birthday cards to all the children, which is much appreciated).

Entrance: 'No type it wouldn't suit', says the head. Broadly first come, first served, with taster days and soft touch testing so they know where pupils are and can monitor development. Wouldn't accept a child who would feel exposed in a year group, academically or socially, which would be unfair on the child. A parent thought that it wouldn't suit children who don't recognise discipline – pupils here need to be respectful of all ages.

'Took a long time to get in', said a parent who waited two years to get a place for her daughter, but it's evidently worth the wait. 'Our experience is overwhelmingly good at many different levels...'.

Exit: Large number to Cranbrook (which started 11+ entry in 2017, and may affect numbers at MHS); Eastbourne College, King's Canterbury, Benenden and Tonbridge are also popular. A few to Eton, Harrow et al.

Remarks: Some children really do skip between lessons here; it's a very buoyant place. Elegant buildings, beautifully kept. Gravel crunches under foot. Mature trees (no climbing); but under the rhododendrons at break time, flashes of uniform and scrambling limbs. A plastic cow peers around the edge of the bushes, a school jumper draped around its head.

One teacher blows a bugle of brilliance if he reads something fabulous in class; another gives top gun award for great work: aviator shades and a moustache

'When education looks [this] good and learning is [this] inspiring, how can you not choose it for your children?' said a parent. When the head arrived, he replaced some of the old guard with a young, lively staff which transformed the school academically – 'fun and active lessons'; 'inspiring', say the children (yes, the children). 'The staff the head brought in are utterly amazing', said a parent, 'and anything you might wince at occasionally is overwhelmed by their reinvention of lessons'. One teacher blows a bugle of brilliance if he reads something fabulous in class; another gives top gun award for great work: aviator shades and a moustache for the day. 'They enthral the children', said another parent, in awe. Dull or mediocre will not be tolerated from teaching staff here; an assistant head's role is continuous assessment and improvement of all teaching staff (360 appraisal is coming, and these articulate pupils will welcome the opportunity to make their views known).

The curriculum in year 5 starts to prepare pupils for both CE and 11+, the focus being on maths and literacy – 'this is what gets pupils into senior schools', says an assistant head. Commenting on the atmosphere, a parent said ' it's not wholly laid back; but [doing] the best you can do is perfect'. Both the very able and those towards the middle of the pack thrive here, bright pupils being stretched with extension work.

The SEN unit is open door to anyone, including those who just want a chat and some reassurance. One pupil with difficulties at home knows that they can go at any point to the unit, to sit quietly, or as a safe quiet place to work. They help those with a variety of needs, including severe dyslexia, and one parent described how her daughter's English has come on in leaps and bounds. Most support is offered in groups of up to six (the dynamic is better in small groups, they say, and it's more fun for pupils). One-to-one help is also offered, and is charged as an extra.

The school is divided into nursery, pre-prep, middle and upper school, with separate buildings for pre-prep and nursery. A jolly nursery, with children learning to care for rabbits, guinea pigs and giant snails. A quiet area behind ribbons, for snuggling down for a nap or quiet time.

MHS is often chosen by parents and children for the happy comfortable atmosphere that pervades the school, one parent adding that it is 'neither as clinical or feral as other independent options in the area'. Another was attracted by the respectful interaction between staff and children, and described the role modelling by staff as 'exceptional'. 'It does feel like a special greenhouse environment', said one parent who worries a bit that her children won't be able to cope in the real gritty world, and would like more integration into the local community – 'but they learn great values [and] they have found [my son's] areas of potential and fanned them'.

MHS promotes British values, says the ISI (tolerance and respect, in case you were wondering). Officially non-denominational with a Christian ethos; it actually feels distinctly Christian, with a sung grace (lovely chime-like responses), and chapel twice a week. One parent said, 'I like the fact that it's not afraid to have a Christian ethos: in word and genuinely in spirit it is a kind school'.

The uniform is moving from navy to grey tweed, 'curiously old fashioned', said a parent: the

A big door at the edge of the woods with Forest School across the top gives a feeling of welcome to the jungle: camp fire, mudslide

school listened to pupils and parents about the faults of the current uniform (itchy jumpers and tricky tracksuit bottom linings), but parents don't feel they were sufficiently consulted over the new design. Pupils do feed back their views on school through the class rep to the pupil forum twice a term, but these very vocal pupils were clear that they would like a greater voice, particularly to make suggestions about food: puddings are excellent, first courses variable, and some outrage that only year 8 get to visit the salad bar. More outrage that burgers and doughnuts have disappeared (quiet hurrahs from the parents), and disgust at the courgette buns and beetroot brownies which have appeared in their place. Thank goodness for much loved fishy Fridays.

Sport every afternoon from year 6 upwards (three times a week for younger pupils), with lots of pupils saying that sport is their favourite thing about MHS. They excel in many areas, often achieving national level: quite something for a small sized prep. But for a school that fields excellence, there is a pleasing emphasis on sport for all, with an approach that highlights enjoyment, inclusion and effort: coaches focus on the bottom teams, with most parents and pupils saying that everyone gets a regular chance to represent the school in matches.

Superb outdoor facilities (although one parent said the outside pool is the 'size of a pond' and 'the team is not strong as a result'. It looked a fairly standard school pool to us, and there are individual successes who supplement their training outside school at swimming clubs). Decent sized indoor sports hall.

There is the traditional sports gender divide along cricket and rounders lines, which causes a little parent discord – 'as a progressive prep, they should have girls' football'. The school is not averse to girls playing boys' sports, but it can be hard to find other preps for them to play against.

Forest school for pupils up to middle school, and it's very popular – a big door at the edge of the woods with Forest School across the top gives a feeling of welcome to the jungle: camp fire; mud slide; dragon (felled horse chestnut); tarpaulins and hides when it's raining. A magical place to learn – 'you can see the kids' shoulders going down', said a teacher.

Music is really lovely – pupils benefit from a comprehensive programme, which evidently fosters a real love for music: an ad hoc group was singing a pop song at break, accompanied by the year 5 music scholar on the piano (blimey), while pupils passing the room in the corridor outside joined in with the odd phrase as they went past. Various instrument and vocal coaches from illustrious stables such as the ENO and the Globe. Busy programme of concerts, from informal at home events, to chamber choir at the Wealden Times Fair, and Junior choir with the Cranbrook Choral society. Parents particularly like the informal concerts, one describing with pleasure one held in the local pub.

Pupils here love drama, and would just like to do more of it (a play a term in pre-prep, but only in year 6 and sometimes year 8 in the rest of the school, say parents; school insists that there are annual plays for all middle school children and more informal plays and recitations higher up).

A wealth of clubs, including philosophy in the forest and theatre make up. Must be one of the only schools with a permanent indoor maypole, children learning that the important thing is to keep smiling merrily, even if the ribbons are getting in a frightful tangle.

'Good manners cost nothing but mean a lot', says a notice on a door. 'Are you looking as smart as you could be?' says another. Respecting self and others is the theme which runs through this school from nursery to year 8, with much of the system of rewards and sanctions being tied in to this ethos. Bad marks may well land you in the reflection room to consider the impact of your behaviour and what you might do differently in the future.

Most pupils said that they would go to their form tutor if they had a problem, one shyer pupil saying he would rather use an independent listener box so he wouldn't have to talk in front of others. 'It's a very caring school', confirmed a parent whose daughter needed a lot of support after her father died: the school made sure there was a safe person to go to if she was upset, and weekly meetings at SEN to talk about her dad. A parent whose son experienced bullying at his previous school said he was 'brought back to life' by MHS. There have been one or two incidents at MHS which caused concern, but the school sat the boys down together and talked things through – 'it was dealt with thoroughly and communicated well', said the parent. 'I have the odd issue with friendship or inappropriate behaviour', said another parent, 'but it's dealt with straightaway and properly: questions, small or large, get a response the same day'.

'The best club is boarding', said one boy, who has finally persuaded his mother that he should have one night a week at school. Forty-five boarders over the course of a week, around 17 a night on Tuesdays and Wednesdays, and 26 on Thursdays (a bit of party atmosphere was suggested by one parent.) Last minute requests for boarding will be accommodated if there's a space. Pupils can board from year 4, but most are older. Some pupils drop in and out of boarding to get used to being away from home, one parent praising the support given to her nervous son who has gradually built up to boarding two nights a week, and loves it.

Comfortable common room with sofas, TV and table football. Evening activities are popular – laser guns and throwing marshmallows into a bucket are recent hits, and pupils enjoy roaming the grounds. A nice supper for boarders – 'pitta bread things, and hot chocolate or milkshakes', said one boy with enthusiasm (no kitchen for snacks at present).

Rooms with bunk beds, mostly for six; cosy, but not cramped. Ample bathroom facilities in good condition. Blue sheets for boys, pink for girls; but white provided to older girls who asked. Boys' dorms named for sport, mostly skiing, with the black run stairs (roped for safety) down from their top floor dorms; girls' dorms named after flowers and bubbles (pupils chose dormitory names a few years back). An evening matron comes in for bedtime and stays overnight, and both she and the head of boarding are available to pupils who need help during the night. Matron's rooms is conveniently situated for knocks and injuries.

Parents are diverse: city, professionals and business, old money, and 'just working hard to get them through school'. A very parent-friendly school – coffee and nibbles in school every morning after drop off, and clubs including yoga, football and bootcamp; even a special breakfast for fathers and daughters. The friendly parent group quickly scoop up newcomers.

Marymount International School

RC 46

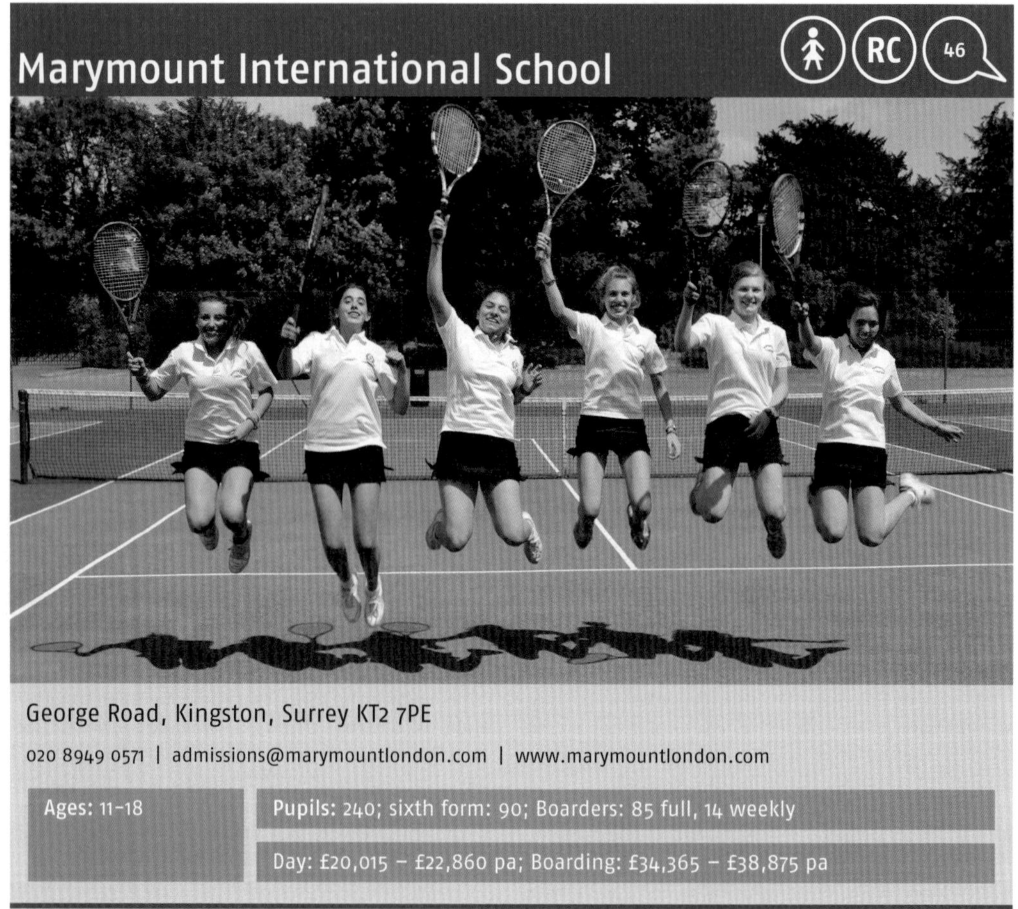

George Road, Kingston, Surrey KT2 7PE

020 8949 0571 | admissions@marymountlondon.com | www.marymountlondon.com

Ages: 11–18

Pupils: 240; sixth form: 90; Boarders: 85 full, 14 weekly

Day: £20,015 – £22,860 pa; Boarding: £34,365 – £38,875 pa

Headmistress: Since September 2017, Meg Frazier, previously head of upper school at the Stone Ridge School of the Sacred Heart for girls, Washington DC (one of 147 Sacred Heart schools in 30 countries). History degree from Dartmouth College, has over 25 years of teaching and admin experience in the Washington area in the Jesuit and Sacred Heart networks of US and international schools, plus worked with international boarders at Georgetown Prep in Maryland. Describes herself as an avid gardener and reader, a rusty golfer and a life-long sailor who enjoys cooking and travel. She and her husband have three children, one daughter studying in London and two sons both seniors in US colleges.

Academic matters: Marymount is a Catholic secondary girls school offering the IB middle years programme (MYP) and IB to an international community. The first (1979) girls' school in the UK to take up the IB in Britain, Marymount's grade 6-10 curriculum is built on solid institutional foundations. In 2017 pupils scored an average of 36, with 25 per cent earning 40+ points and 49 per cent awarded bilingual diplomas.

No resting on laurels; they've been reviewing the MYP to align it with IGCSE content, ensuring all topics are covered in the MYP context by end of grade 9. School wants parents to be assured of MYP rigour: the priority is to be learning-driven, not taught to the test. Range of IB subjects and results is excellent. Lots of sciences, 'and we do lots of field trips', say the girls. The school is offering a relatively new IB course, environmental systems and societies, which satisfies either the IB science or IB humanities requirement. 'My sister likes geography and science so it's perfect for her.' Marymount's MYP covers the broad spectrum of disciplines, with the interesting addition of philosophy to introduce the girls to 'the language of philosophy' before they embark on theory of knowledge at diploma level. Fab Lab (fabrication laboratory) full of computer controlled tools that can make 'almost anything' is used to teach computer programming, coding, robotics and design, and aiming to stimulating creativity across the arts and sciences. As would be expected, religious education is also a key part of the MYP.

School prides itself on the wide range of languages offered. Extra mother tongue support in German and French in grades 6-8 dependent on enrolment. Parents warn that languages are sometimes subject to demand and in a small school it's not always possible to satisfy all requests for second language. It seems that there are mixed messages here and prospective parents are advised to discuss this at the early stages to clarify. The school does its best to support girls in working out alternative options – as one pupil explained, 'a friend who speaks Thai is taking IB Thai mother tongue; she's self-taught with the help of a tutor'.

The school is wireless throughout; iPads now in grades 6-9 and move up the grades as pupils progress; girls were excited to show off the first new Mac TVs, and there are more to come. The library has undergone a complete refurbishment – it has 9,000 volumes and membership of London Library enhances the collection.

Classes never more than 16 and many, particularly at diploma level, only four to six, fewer still for languages. Some classrooms are designed with small seminar-style groups in mind.

The teaching faculty is an international bunch, average age 40s. Pupil-teacher ratio is six to one and all staff seem to know most of the girls, affirming parent comments about supportive and nurturing environment with a caring individualised approach. Low turnover and enough long-termers to provide a cohesive core. Plenty of support staff and school nurse on site.

Consensus is that the most fun of all is the 'international day', when everyone shares their culture and cuisine. 'The Japanese do the best, and the boarding girls are already planning even though it's still months away'

Mild/moderate learning difficulties and other issues managed collaboratively by the learning resource coordinator, teachers, parents and students themselves. Lots of individualised support throughout the school and the girls themselves were quick to talk about peer tutoring offered during free periods or after school.

The enrichment programme for able students has about 40 on the register. These students are invited to apply to programmes sponsored by Ivy Leagues (Stanford, Yale, Princeton, Johns Hopkins) and top tier UK universities. Additional provision includes extracurricular activities as well as resources which are made available to students for independent study and wider reading.

Games, options, the arts: Mix of competitive and non-competitive sporting activities available for all grades on and off site. If the school does not offer a particular sport they will help connect with local teams. Marymount is part of the International School Sports Association and they have produced an impressive record of results in soccer, badminton and tennis at championship tournaments hosted by member schools in different parts of Europe. One pupil training with the Chelsea Ladies' development squad and several play with the Richmond Volleyball Club. When girls were asked why they chose Marymount, one replied that she came for the sport and when you hear that one of their football trainers is with Chelsea, no prizes for guessing which team Marymount girls support.

Musicians have plenty of opportunities to play in ensembles and chamber groups. About 20 per cent take private instrumental or singing lessons; school boasts a 100 per cent pass rate in grade exams. Entry to the choir is by audition and choristers participate in school concerts and annual tours to European cities, performing in major churches and cathedrals. Teachers encourage girls to perform in local festivals and competitions.

Sisters no longer teach but are very much part of the fabric of the school, occasionally eating or sharing cocoa and study evenings with the girls

Drama is inclusive and the entire community builds up to a major production each year. Keen thespians can participate in ISTA (International School Theatre Association) festivals and when we visited girls were buzzing about their weekend ISTA trip to Stratford upon Avon. LAMDA examinations offered. Visual arts seem focused on painting and photography – the girls tell us that the art teacher is an inspiring photographer. Framed art by generations of pupils displayed throughout the school. Fab Lab includes a range of 3D printers, laser cutters and other digitally driven tools.

Consensus is that the most fun of all is the 'international day', when everyone shares their culture and cuisine.'The Japanese do the best, and the [boarding] girls are already planning even though it's still months away'. Zumbathon – a fundraising activity involving the whole community beeping and bopping, swinging and swaying to music – was also highly popular and yielded no casualties.

As a Catholic IB school, community service involves everyone at Marymount. Middle schoolers do environmental projects that include cleaning along the bank of the Thames. Older girls volunteer in local activities including soup kitchens and schools and further afield join other RHSM students in projects working with children in places such as Zambia. All students take part in the spiritual life of the school and attend an annual retreat. Girls of all faiths come to Marymount and this provides opportunities for students to learn about other beliefs and traditions; care is taken to ensure that everyone feels comfortable at mass and prayer. We visited on a Hindu feast day and the girls said they had started the day with a Hindu prayer; Muslim girls wear their headscarves with confidence.

Boarding: Almost one third of the pupils board and there are four halls, each with its own duo of houseparents. Boarding rooms (some bunk beds) have recently been refurbished (2016) and facilities are clean and pretty tidy. Boarding areas are kept locked during the school day unless a girl has a reason to be back in her room. Oldest boarders have the spacious shared bedrooms above and the remaining nuns living in a wing just off their hall. Sisters no longer teach but are very much part of the fabric of the school, occasionally eating or sharing cocoa and study evenings with the girls.

The school's proximity to Heathrow is an attraction for boarding parents; the girls say that the school's proximity to London is the attraction for them. The lure of London aside, boarders enjoy theatre and music trips as well as days out to the seaside (Brighton) and theme parks such as Longleat. There's plenty going on inside school too, including dance and music workshops and opportunities to explore and develop one's faith. Worth mentioning here that the school also takes weekly boarders from local (ie London) families and it is sometimes possible to arrange short-term boarding for day girls whose parents travel.

Clear procedures allow boarders off-campus freedoms to visit friends and family while ensuring their safety. One guardian who has long looked after boarders during half-term breaks told us that some older girls feel the school is too strict. She helps them, and their far-off parents who hear the grumbles, appreciate that the school is being cautious and not unreasonable. Two exclusions in the

All students take part in the spiritual life of the school and attend an annual retreat. Girls of all faiths come to Marymount and this provides opportunities for students to learn about other beliefs

last three years of boarders who, after several warnings, broke the rules about leaving campus.

Background and atmosphere: Established in Kingston in 1955 by 10 nuns from the Religious of the Sacred Heart of Mary (RSHM), sent by the Eastern American Province. Mid-19th century French founder of RSHM aspired to provide charity for all classes through schools, homes and orphanages that worked interactively across socio-economic barriers. Schools opened in France, Ireland, Portugal, England, the US and later Latin America and the rest of the world. The first sisters who came to Kingston started a 'year abroad' programme for US university women, then a school offering the US secondary school curriculum. Early 70s saw the arrival of Sister Anne Marie Hill, a determined Irish mover-and-shaker, well known in international education circles and now executive director of the network of schools. She introduced the IB, making the school more relevant to its growing international student body and reflecting RSHM's original ethos. During the noughties Marymount had a series of heads as RSHM grappled with transition to lay leadership and during that time the board of governors was created.

School works closely with the other Marymount partners under Sister Anne Marie's guidance, meeting every six to eight weeks to discuss areas such as strategic planning and communication. Increasingly involvement with the international network of RSHM schools – 19 worldwide – is now bringing more opportunities to the pupils.

The school is based in an affluent part of Surrey occupying a large Edwardian house plus various more recent additions connected by walkways. Elegant grounds with lawns, manicured flowerbeds and sculpted hedges. 'The teddy bear topiary sold me', said one dad, 'How can you not love a school that has teddy bear topiary?' (We presume he had already consulted the GSG about minor details such as teaching and pastoral care.) Main house, with original wood panelling and stained glass, is head office and reception. The nuns are loved by the girls and parents appreciate their presence. Small school chapel is used by boarders and local community alike and plans to re-develop and open the ceiling to the rafters and heavens above are under way.

Modern blocks house multi-purpose classrooms, the newly refurbished library and university and careers counselling rooms. Another block has the gym (floor replaced recently), music rooms and auditorium for assemblies, all-school mass, drama. Yet another has more dorms, new dining hall with a 'chef's theatre' – and, school tells us, much improved food from new catering company – classrooms, infirmary, student lounges. A new quasi-Scandinavian wooden structure houses more small tutorial rooms just right for the many language classes and designed with IB language examination conditions in mind. Most of the buildings surround the garden and have big windows that bring the outdoors in and give a refreshing sense of space and light.

Pastoral care, well-being and discipline: Spiritual values underpin the ethos of Marymount, rooted in the mission of the RSHM, 'that all may have life'. These values are made explicit on the website: even the most casual browser will see them on every page, running alongside photos. School welcomes girls from all faiths but we think it might not be a comfortable environment for the girl who has none. Plenty of support available at the school: academic, social, emotional and personal; more expertise called upon if necessary.

Parents' Association hosts a welcome back family barbecue during the first weekend of the school year when boarding parents are there dropping off daughters so they are able to meet day families. One parent said the school went out of its way, allowing their daughter to board temporarily so she could start at the beginning of the year, before the family transfer to London took place.

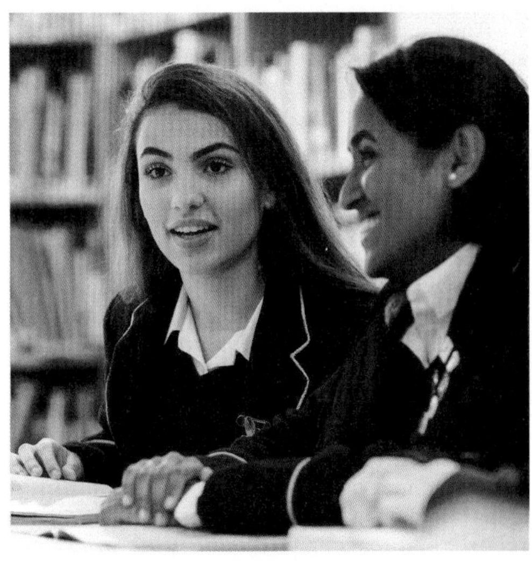

Another described how the teachers made an effort to encourage her daughter to join the orchestra for a big performance, even though her late arrival meant she had missed several rehearsals.

Pupils and parents: Marymount girls are internationally diverse, cheerful, articulate, academically motivated, quietly confident and as a bunch, quite enchanting. More aspirational than ambitious, they love their school and really enjoy having peers from all over the world. They look out for each other, especially new ones, and although one day girl said she wishes there were more ways to get closer to the boarders, everyone, including day parents, feels that the day girls and boarders are pretty integrated.

The girls are reflective about the realities of being in a single-sex environment. They feel they are able to focus more on learning, but they would like to find a partner boys' school and the student council has made some moves in this direction. Trouble is that 'all the boys' (schools) seem to be taken', but they have not given up. 'When adolescent girls become interested in boys, it can be frustrating to see how much they measure themselves against the approval of the boys in the group. Without that distraction they can develop as intellectually rigorous learners; they are their own people.'

More aspirational than ambitious, they love their school and really enjoy having peers from all over the world. They look out for each other, especially new girls

The families that choose the school value the ethos of school, its Catholicism and internationalism, but are equally attracted to the IB. There are 40 nationalities in the school, British representing just over half. Other significant groups are German, Spanish, Japanese, Chinese, US, Australian, Korean and Italian. The numbers within these groups are balanced very carefully to facilitate integration. The school bus service extends into London to Sloane Square and more routes are under consideration.

Parents' Association organises events including outings for parents which are appreciated by newly-arrived expats.

Entrance: Local families are urged to attend one of the open days. Inbound expats on 'look-see' trips to London may book appointments. Girls' admissions based on availability and a review of school reports and teacher references plus interview.

One said that she came for the sport and when you hear that one of their football trainers is with Chelsea, no prizes for guessing which team the girls support

English language fluency is required with exceptions made for younger students for whom English is a second language. Most classes have waiting lists so best to apply a year in advance, though there is some turnover so you could be lucky.

Local feeder schools include Holy Cross, The Study, Fulham Prep, St Agatha's, The Grove, The Old Vicarage, The German School (Deutsche Schule London), Garden House, Unicorn School, Cameron House, Ursuline School. Day girls come from most SW London postcodes including Richmond, Wimbledon, Putney, Chelsea, South Kensington.

Exit: Most head to university and the chart we saw on the college counsellor's wall listing every 12th grader's destinations confirms that they are applying to many countries. Counsellor stays in close contact with parents, especially boarder parents, about each girl's plan and the process they must follow depending on the country of their destination. PSAT and SATS also offered.

Of UK universities, Bristol, London, Exeter and Warwick are popular. A good few to US as well as Japan, Munich, Netherlands, Libya and Egypt. Occasional one to Oxbridge (none in 2017); four to study medicine/biomedical science and engineering.

Money matters: School has no endowment so financial stability is maintained by tuition and fundraising initiatives. 'Being an international school and in the current economic climate, we need to be sure we are guarded and forward looking – we can't rest on our laurels.' The PA also fundraises for activities that support the school and pupils.

Scholarships (academic, art, music, drama, sport, community service) for grade 6 and 8 students. Some offered for grades 10, 11 and 12. Some financial aid available for means-tested students. About 20 per cent of the pupils benefit from this.

Remarks: Successfully serves a niche market of internationally-minded families seeking a girls' school with a Catholic ethos. In the words of one parent, 'We've been over-the-top-happy. The school provides excellent support and people from all over the world fit in and are welcome there.'

Mayfield School

RC 47

The Old Palace, High Street, Mayfield, East Sussex TN20 6PH

01435 874600 | registrar@mayfieldgirls.org | www.mayfieldgirls.org

Ages: 11–18

Pupils: 367; sixth form: 109; Boarders: 154 full, 20 flexi

Day: £20,400 pa; Boarding: £32,925 pa

Headmistress: Since 2008, Miss Antonia Beary, previously deputy head here, and before that at New Hall, Ampleforth and The Leys. Read English at Cambridge. Devoted to the school and its pupils, and determined to inspire her girls to do anything: 'they don't have to be something safe or obvious [in their careers]'. Hear hear.

In assembly, challenges Britain's Got Talent as lamentably failing to model good behaviour or taste; in fact, encourages the girls to challenge lots of things on a regular basis. Parents are confident that she handles the school well, and impressed at her knowledge of every child. 'Delightful head... very professional', said one; 'slightly eccentric...has helped us so much', said another. 'Girls like her, but have a healthy respect for her', said a dad, adding that his daughter is happy to write or speak to the head if things go wrong.

Academic matters: 'Some absolutely amazing teachers', said a parent, who told us about staff who have 'engaged and enthused' her daughter in subjects she didn't like. 'I feel that teachers really know my children', added another. A good number of top end results at this gently selective school – 63 per cent A*/A at A level, 71 per cent A*/A at GCSE in 2017. Top 50 ranking in The Telegraph Independent schools A level results table 2017. The school is in the top 20 per cent of value added schools, adding at least one grade onto pupils' scores.

Maths, chemistry and biology are very popular here, determinedly bucking the trend for girls to choose more humanities. The head says it is important to create an environment where girls can make mistakes, and the approach to learning maths at Mayfield is based on this: 'Maths is brilliant', confirmed a parent. Geography is also a favourite – 'we're evangelical about geography...' A delighted group of girls were departing on a field trip to Morocco on the day of our visit. RS is 'very lively', say the girls, and a parent who described herself as a committed atheist said how much her children enjoy this subject: plenty of challenge and discussion.

Lessons of quiet, determined concentration; though an excited physics teacher showed us a burst of air pinging out of a bucket, to the slight embarrassment of our guides.

Most pupils take 11 GCSEs, which must include a language: pupils choose from French, Spanish or Latin. Class numbers in lower school are up to 15, with up to 12 in A level classes.

Pupils here happily mix subjects, splitting their time between sciences and arts, for instance, and the school prides itself on not labelling pupils and persuading them to choose options accordingly. One parent felt that that girls should be guided towards studying their strengths, though the school was very supportive when her daughter needed to change her A levels. But other parents like the open choice at A level – 'I knew the girls would struggle to choose, but it was important it was their choice'. We love the idea of the subject fair, with teachers pitching their subjects to girls. A wonderful way of keeping teachers on their toes. (As is their habit of getting girls to help interview new staff.)

One parent said she was 'worried they wouldn't push kids enough', but they have been 'brilliant at handling different levels of maths, and pushing them where necessary'. Subject clinics are open door and well attended, and pupils can email teachers direct. Pupils described teachers willing to put in extra time, one saying how her physics teacher came in early to go through work she hadn't understood. New sixth form enrichment programme with options ranging from global perspectives to farming and land management to diploma in culinary skills and the art of effective communication, plus an Erasmus research project.

The Hub (café) is the centre of the school, and many pupils' favourite place (for good reason: deluxe hot chocolate, doughnuts and blue raspberry slush)

Small library with age-appropriate books in the lower school (much liked by the younger girls, who felt that the upheaval of changing schools was much helped by having their own safe area away from the rest of the school), and a well-stocked main library for years 9 upwards (New Scientist, Psychology Review, Pharmaceutical Tech and The Tablet).

Swish new sixth form centre, complete with kitchen and 'friends' common room'. Lovely views over the countryside, study rooms with designated desks, and intimate classrooms. Own clothes for sixth formers, but no jeans or leggings. A small room overlooking the chapel with beanbags and candles for quiet moments of reflection.

Around 40 pupils receive SEN help, which in this school can be anything from assistance with a particular problem, to help for dyslexic pupils or extra work for gifted and talented. 'No extra time in the real world', says the head, and the unit aims to give pupils strategies to deal with and make the most of their talents. A parent whose friend's daughter attended the unit raved about it: 'They have a very practical way of helping with difficulties'.

'No negativity smudge', said a parent; 'so many use [the unit] one way or another'. Help is usually on a one-to-one basis out of class, although it is occasionally one-to-two, or in-class help. Help is charged as an extra. Dyslexic pupils achieve at the same rate as other pupils.

Games, options, the arts: Sports are extremely popular, and there's everything imaginable here, though some, such as football, are extracurricular options rather than mainstream. Pupils have PE three times a week, the usual compulsory sports in years 7, 8 and 9, with free choice after that (pilates, fitness room and zumba become options at this stage). Girls decided they wanted to learn kickboxing, and a couple of months later it was up and running – 'an incredibly responsive school', said a parent. Cricket now an option with coaching by a former England player. Riding is immensely popular: pupils can bring their own horse to school, or take part in a horse share. Fabulous equestrian facilities on campus include an indoor and outdoor school – pupils ride at national level. All have a chance to represent the school in matches if want they to, and netball is popular even with the girls who find it difficult. One parent described how her daughter was awarded a muffin when she scored in netball – 'her ball skills were so abysmal', she cheerfully explained, 'they didn't think it would happen again'.

Plenty of trips, an imminent one to Cambodia to teach children English – 'an extraordinary initiative', said a parent, with teachers managing to fit teaching TEFL to pupils into the school day. 'I was gobsmacked', said a parent, who said the trip has led on to so many things, such as designing a t-shirt, and a video workshop so that pupils can compile video libraries while away.

Two-thirds of pupils here learn an instrument, and many play them in the orchestra. Several choirs, the more selective ones singing at illustrious venues, such as Westminster Abbey. Regular school productions, and both LAMDA and GCSE drama are popular, though there are fewer takers at A level.

A vast range of options available, with activity sessions built into each school day – compulsory down time. There's even a farm club with livestock – though the last residents have just been eaten.

Food and nutrition is 'quite splendid,' said a parent, and compulsory in years 7-9, on the basis

Girls decided they wanted to learn kickboxing, and a couple of months later it was up and running – 'an incredibly responsive school'

that however brilliant your mind, you can't function in life without a healthy body. There's a session every Saturday morning for boarders, and it is part of the life skills course for sixth formers – how to eat well on a budget (roux sauce and making bread – no white slice at uni for Mayfield girls).

Exceptionally beautiful artwork on display around the school, with some lovely ceramics: a pot modelled on church architecture captures the feeling of a soaring church roof, and butterflies fly from the edges of a ceramic gold fish bowl. A parent said 'we've got ceramics dotted all over the house, they're fantastic, so professional...' One student recently got the highest marks in the country for Pre-U ceramics. A dress inspired by WW1 is made of teabags and luggage labels; a half decomposed shirt shows the stress and texture of the material. Shelf after shelf of coloured fabrics and shining silks: such riches would tempt even those who can't sew.

Despite these glories, these subjects are less popular as exam subjects than academic options; but really it's about pressure of time. The girls love them, but want to do other things more – and anyway can keep up an element of artistic work during activities. Often art or ceramics will complement a science or maths A level.

Boarding: Around 50 per cent of pupils are boarders, divided into four houses by age. 'The school is ultra flexible about adding extra nights', said an appreciative parent. We saw Leeds, the junior house, and St Dunstan's, the sixth form house. Leeds has comfortably sized rooms for two, three and four, with beds for anyone who boards more than two nights a week, bunkbeds for the odd night flexi boarder. All rooms have basins. Common room of colourful squashy sofas, Wii and TV; lovely to see a dressing up box.

Plenty going on: a crammed notice board includes details of a trip to the Harry Potter studios and an animal rescue centre, and Pride and Prejudice catch up night; two-thirds of boarders are around at weekends to enjoy activities. Fruit, toast and cereal are always available in the kitchen, where a map of the world – 'where do you come from?' – shows a wide spread of flags.

All girls have their own laptops, but can't access certain sites, and devices are handed in at 8.45pm, though pupils can reach parents on school phones if need to. Trusted to keep them from year 11.

'Rooms are quite nice,' said a parent, 'but it's the personalities that make [the boarding experience]', describing his daughter's slightly eccentric housemistress who enjoys extreme sport – 'a great role model', he said with enthusiasm. 'They love and respect her in equal measure'.

Sixth form boarding, in St Dunstan's, is spread across the top floor of the old school in four areas, with around 20 pupils in each. Over 60 sixth form boarders, of whom 50 or so are full time. (Anything over three nights is full time, because this encourages pupils to stay for the weekend, which makes a better atmosphere.) Good-sized individual study bedrooms. Considerable freedom and responsibility for sixth formers, who are allowed up to London at weekends, and into Tunbridge Wells by bus.

No work on Friday night – movies, popcorn and mocktails...'food is important to these girls', said the housemistress. Brunch in house on Sundays: pupils turn up in their pyjamas for waffles and eggs of all sorts.

Laundry is done for younger ones, with pupils gradually assuming more responsibility, until they are doing their own in sixth form.

An overseas parent was full of praise for the care her homesick daughter received from the housemistress: she was confident that the school would email her straight away with any problems, and they respond immediately to any emails from her. Her daughter keeps in touch by telephone and Skype (mobile signal comes and goes). Transport home is arranged well.

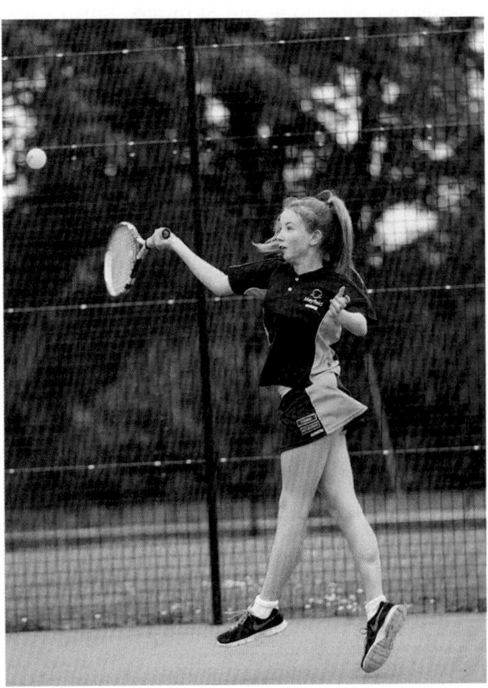

Background and atmosphere: One parent said that the moment her girls walked into the site they loved it: 'They saw the school in action and were enchanted by it'. It offered something to both her girls, the more academic and the less so. Another said that the surroundings and small size of the school attracted them – 'everyone knows each other'.

The religious backbone of this Catholic school underpins the supportive, caring atmosphere. Pupils are of any or no faith, but they do have to attend liturgy (some think it's boring; some like the space to be quiet and think), and boarders must go to mass on Sundays. But the Catholic ethos is applied gently, and often with cake – the history teacher described attending mass at a church in France on a school trip, and the delight of going to the patisserie next door for cream cakes afterwards.

Community service, in the Actions not Words programme, is scheduled into the day: 'A fundamental part of who we are', says the head. This sees girls working at a local primary school or an old people's home, and helping with riding for the disabled. 'I think they benefit more from doing it than the people they help', said a member of staff thoughtfully, explaining how important it is for girls to look beyond themselves.

Most parents are happy with the single sex environment, one saying that she felt girls don't want to appear cleverer than boys – 'I don't want them to have to bother to look after male egos...' The head says the girls value the space to be themselves, and of boys – they also have social and academic engagement with boys' schools, including nearby Tonbridge and Skinners. But it's not exclusively female here: there are male teachers in nearly every department.

Plenty of smiles and good manners from pupils. 'They develop the whole person', said a parent, who felt that girls from other schools are not as well rounded or comfortable with themselves and adults; another that 'they look after every aspect of the girls and every aspect is equally represented'. 'They are good academically, but there is not too much pressure', said another. Girls here are competitive, and there is certainly vigorous competition between the houses, but 'resilient, not bloodthirsty', said a member of staff.

Some lovely ceramics: a pot modelled on church architecture captures the feeling of a soaring church roof, and butterflies fly from the edges of a golden fish bowl

Food is good: since the new chef arrived 'they come home raving about it'. Changes are made in response to suggestions in the food comment books: the request for savoury snacks at break time resulted in the delights of cheese scones and sausage rolls.

Beautiful buildings and grounds, once a palace for an archbishop, discovered by the school's founder when she took her girls on a picnic from the school, then situated in St Leonards. The chapel is ancient, movingly plain and unadorned. At Christmas, the village cluster in for the live crib – baby, donkey and all, the angel Gabriel singing from a balcony. The Hub (café) is the centre of the school, and many pupils' favourite place (for good reason: deluxe hot chocolate, doughnuts, and blue raspberry slush, with healthy snacks besides).

The school puts itself out for parents – one parent said that when they were unable to make the last parents' day, the school gathered all the teachers for a tailor-made alternative meeting. Another confirmed that 'if we're unhappy about anything, an email or phone call gets an immediate response'; but 'occasionally they make changes to something without fully socialising the changes amongst the parents...' referring to the extension of the day from 4.30pm to 6.00pm, adding in more extracurricular. The school says there were focus groups and letters home before the change, and this certainly was a move popular amongst many parents (a fuller school for longer is also great for boarders). The overall impression is of a listening school: 'They are constantly trying to make it a better experience for parents and girls', confirmed a parent.

Pastoral care, well-being and discipline: Pastoral care is the particular responsibility of the deputy head, who is quick to point out that actually it is a responsibility of each teacher here. This works, emails shooting around between teachers, boarding mistresses and parents so that any problems are quickly picked up. There are plenty of people for pupils to talk to: tutors, the head of pastoral care, the school counsellor, the chaplain – and two members of staff additionally trained in counselling, one in CBT, the other a humanist. 'Care of pupils here gives stability. I feel teachers will listen to any problems they have', said a parent.

Tutor groups in the middle school stay the same for three years, which means the eight girls get to know each other really well. Girls are good at looking out for each other, one teacher telling us that some girls came to see her, anxious that one of their friends was skipping meals. This school is extremely aware of the various conditions which can affect teenage girls, and staff are ever vigilant.

The head is keen to teach girls coping skills – 'in the real world they are going to meet difficult and dominating people...if they're wrapped in cotton wool, they won't be able to cope'. True to this, a parent said bullying behaviour is often 'cut off at source by the girls'. But systems are also in place to capture anything untoward, from general unhappiness onwards – 'they're very vigilant', said a parent, who described a conflict between girls, efficiently sorted out by the housemistress.

Disciplinary measures are rarely needed here, though accumulated bad marks would result in detention, where you sit in silence and consider the implications of your crime. No one has been excluded in the past year, though persistent disruptive behaviour could lead to a mutual conclusion that a girl would be better placed elsewhere. Selling drugs would result in immediate exclusion; a contrite drug user would probably be given a second chance. Behaviour out of school must be as responsible as in, and things that happen out of school will have implications inside.

Pupils and parents: 'You won't find old girls on the cover of Hello', said the head. 'They will be influential, but this is not the cult of the celebrity'. The large variety of families at this school is reflected in the mixed entry, with 50 per cent from state primaries and the rest from local preps, with a small number from overseas.

Entrance: At 11+, 13+ and 16+. Gently selective, but largely on the basis of fit: pupils attend a two day assessment, which includes papers in English, maths and verbal reasoning, and fun activities. Less good performance in one area can be compensated for by excelling in others.

For sixth form entry, pupils take exams in three of the subjects they wish to study at A level, and a general paper. Pupils must get at least eight GCSEs at A*-B/9-6, with at least a B/6 in the subjects they wish to study at A level.

Exit: Around 20 per cent leave after GCSEs. One to Oxford in 2017 (music, with an organ scholarship), others to Bath, Edinburgh, Exeter, Durham and Oxford Brookes, amongst others. One medic in 2017; other subjects range from fashion to neuroscience.

Money matters: Encourages prospective pupils to do the assessment, then ask if a bursary is available. Seven full bursaries, one in each year group, and scholarships worth 10-20 per cent of fees.

Remarks: A great all-round school with high academic standards, extensive extracurricular and the outward-looking expectation that its pupils will enrich the lives of others, both at school and beyond. A parent said: 'They get so much right. Would recommend to anyone. Sheer awe...'

Mill Hill School

48

The Ridgeway, Mill Hill Village, London NW7 1QS

020 8959 1176 | registrations@millhill.org.uk | www.millhill.org.uk

Ages: 13-18

Pupils: 675; sixth form: 259; Boarders: 63 full, 39 weekly

Day: £20,625 pa; Boarding: £27,828 – £32,892 pa

Head: Since January 2016, Mrs Frances King MA PGCE MA MBA (50s), and about as experienced a head as you'll find anywhere. The first woman to head this school. Educated at Ashford School, Kent, read theology at Oxford, followed, later, by a degree in philosophy and religious ethics plus an MBA in international leadership (ie headship) in the independent sector. She taught RS at Lady Eleanor

Holles, Francis Holland (NW1), Guildford County and Tormead. Thence – as head – successively to Heathfield, Roedean and Beau Soleil in Switzerland. She's a bit of a one-woman Change Management Team, having overseen major adjustments in both her previous UK headships. This plus her recent headship in Switzerland must have made her the ideal choice, given Mill Hill's new international school, The Mount.

But she does it so well. And, despite arriving and making changes within weeks, she seems, to their great surprise, to have taken everyone – staff, parents, pupils – with her. She met all the pupils in groups of 10 and asked what could be improved. 'She won hearts and minds,' as one colleague put it. And sixth formers – not noted for embracing change – concur: 'My first reaction was, "oof! no!" – but then we realised what she had in mind and how good it was.' She is ambitious for her school, but it's not the leaping-up-the-league-tables type of ambition – 'We're not trying to be another Habs.' So she promotes eg leadership, teamwork, public speaking, inter-personal skills. 'Professional' in the best sense seems the aptest epithet. Clued-up on every educational innovation and tool, Mrs King is pre-eminently an independent-minded and creative thinker. 'The government is going backwards in so many ways. At Mill Hill, we are becoming ready for a world that is changing before our eyes. Twenty-first century employers will want personal skills because computers will be doing all the work.' Great appointment.

Founding head of The Mount, Mill Hill International School since September 2014 is Mrs Sarah Bellotti BEd (50s). Mrs Bellotti is steeped in international education, having spent 20 years teaching English in international schools in Rome and, latterly, nine years as the director of King's, Ely's International Study Centre. It has to be a dream job, this – a beautifully reimagined and refurbished school dedicated entirely to educating able children from overseas in English subjects via intensive language support to enable them to gain places at good English boarding schools – and down the road from and sharing the facilities of the main school. And she fits the bill. Intense and intensely committed to the task: 'I passionately believe in the international community – we celebrate internationalism here' – she exudes focused excitement and a determination to realise the considerable potential here. She spent her first year 'going across the world' spreading the word and recruiting pupils. At the time of our visit, there were 66, including, interestingly, 10 day pupils who find in the flexible curriculum etc something to suit their individual circumstances. Her new school is perfectly placed and equipped to make a real impact on this market.

Sixth formers concur. 'My first reaction was, "oof! no!" – but then we realised what she had in mind and how good it was'

Academic matters: Pretty trad curriculum though some interesting novelties eg an IGCSE in further

pure maths and A levels in computer science and psychology, not found everywhere. Popular A levels are English, business studies and maths – maths being the stand-out success story in terms of results here. Results, otherwise, are a spread. Not vast numbers of A*s and a range from A-C across the board (in 2017, 43 per cent A*/A grades). Popular GCSE options are geography, history, RS and French. Best results in all three sciences, art, Latin and statistics – popular and successful but replaced by further pure (see above) under exam reform. In 2017, 63 per cent A*-A/9-7 grades overall.

Lots of changes under the new regime include an Innovation Hub – a room where techie things can be tried out. If the DT workshops and the work we saw there is anything to go by (eg stunning sliding work station) great things will emerge. Another King innovation is three-weekly progress reports – 'Before, if you were really good or really bad everyone knew but no-one really noticed the in-betweeners. Now you are monitored and have targets. It is more pressure but it's helpful.' And, of course, to counter the pressure, they now have 'mindfulness' and drop-in, stress-reducing activities like colouring. It had to happen. There are masses of catch-up classes, clinics and individual support. It's all there for the taking – though some sense among parents that the extent of what's on offer isn't always made clear – 'If we'd realised, we wouldn't have had a tutor. It was there in school for us all along.'

Good trad Piper Library – impressively full shelves though some stock needs updating and the bookshelves unaccountably not labelled. Good stock of periodicals. F/t UCAS teacher can be found in sixth form centre – 'She's brilliant'.

Interestingly, 20 per cent of the school's population is on the SEN register and we were told over and again how supportive the school is of eg dyslexics. Mrs King immediately enhanced the staffing and provision in general and the effects are obvious. 'Some of them are slow developers but they can be absolutely the children we want and do well by.' Support is given by individual and small-group lessons which are timetabled not to cut across pupils' other periods, following and reinforcing aspects of the main curriculum and teaching study and organisational skills. Learning support assistants intervene in mainstream academic lessons to support particular pupils or groups. School mainly caters for pupils with mild to moderate specific learning difficulties but also accommodates some statemented pupils eg those with impaired hearing.

The majority at The Mount comes for the one-year IGSCE course, though you can stay for anything from one term to two years. No IB. Small classes with a maximum of 12 pupils. It takes children from 13-17. All teachers have EAL qualifications/

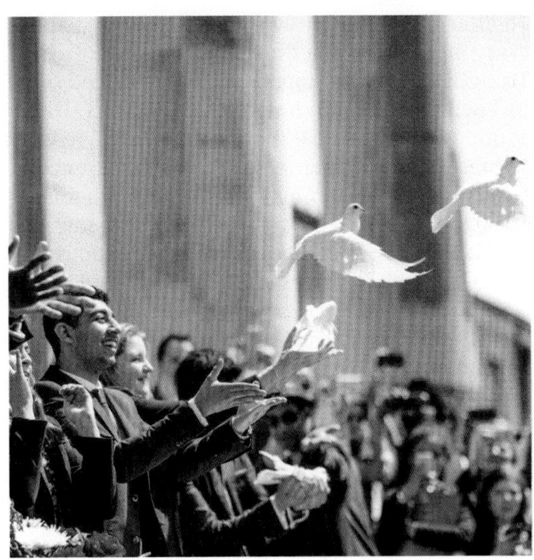

experience. Flexible courses depending on the level of English you arrive with. Pre-A level programme. We met several students on our visits – clearly a happy, stimulated and cohesive group who were enjoying a first class education.

Games, options, the arts: Long and pioneering tradition in the arts. We remember coming for an arts festival some 30 years ago and the vitality we met then has only grown.

Famously sporty and, while having fun, sports are taken seriously here – girls' sports, seemingly, as much as boys'. 'We have fields and fields and fields,' pupils enthused. Partnership with Middlesex University provides high level support for elite athletes. Good to see extension activities with sports scholars – with specialist staff to help them build and challenge themselves. Remarkable number of representatives in local and country teams across a range of sports – netball, cross-country, cricket, golf and – new to us – bouldering. Lots of teams in eg rugby and hockey so not restricted to the real jocks. School magazine reports – written with an honesty rare in such publications – attest to the earnest approach and a capacity for self-appraisal we seldom see. However, some feeling among the pupils that there was, notwithstanding, a lack of ambition and acceptance of below par performances when a bit more get-go might tilt the balance.

'You don't have to be sporty,' said one parent; 'there's so much else to get involved in.' Exceptional music dept and no lack of ambition in its vast repertoire and the 230 concerts and services annually for which it provides the ensembles, choirs, soloists etc. 'The standard varies from professional to er, well.. but they are so inclusive – everyone feels they can have a go.' House music and house drama on alternate years involve – intensely – just about everyone, as does the music competition. Patrick Troughton Theatre (capacity 150+), a rigged stage in The Large ie main hall, and a spacious drama studio with seating for a small audience. We were impressed by the range of art media: 'They encourage you to try everything,' a non-artsy sixth former enthused. We loved the variety in what we saw – no production line stuff. Impressive range of activities on offer. 'There is masses to do,' and lists and lists of clubs, outings and trips bear witness to that.

The Mount could accommodate three times the present number – it is spacious, superlatively kitted out; no expense has been spared. While some facilities are shared with the main school, there is little lacking here – own DT studio, plenty of outside space. The only shared teacher is one of the PE dept. Excellent range of weekend activities, again, shared with the main school.

Boarding: Boarders make up a fifth of the school population and most are full boarders, based overseas. They come from around 15 countries from China to Spain. However, only a third of them need EAL support, which is given individually and in groups when needed. Small number of UK-based weekly boarders. Boarding is set to grow here and not just for overseas pupils. The market for weekly boarding in the London of busy working parents is buoyant and Mill Hill is beautifully placed to supply it. Vertically-aged houses; all but one are mixed. Good bonding activities for newbies. Enticing and varied list of compulsory weekend activities includes outings eg theatre and music trips, catch-up and revision classes, sports, clubs and interest groups – lots of choice. Day pupils come in for much of it. Boarding isn't state of the art – no en-suites here yet – but most are in two-bedders of reasonable sizes and all year 13 boarders in singles. Good games rooms.

When we visited The Mount there were, among its 66 pupils, 24 home languages spoken. School will not take more than 25 per cent from any one country. Boarding takes place in the main school and The Mount's boarders are fully integrated.

Background and atmosphere: Founded by nonconformist merchants and ministers in 1807 in the then village of Mill Hill, safely located away from 'dangers both physical and moral, awaiting youth while passing through the streets of a large, crowded and corrupt city'. It's not just safe but high – ought to be called Mill Hill-on-the-Hill – and looks over the northern suburbs much as a more famous, boys only, school on a neighbouring hill does, only from a different angle. In many ways. A rare thing, a boarding school of this size – 120 acres – so close to the national hub and unique, now, in offering, as it does, coeducation from 3-18 with an in-built international school integral to its offering. In parkland with some glorious trees which still date from the planting of a former resident, the botanist Peter Collinson, the main building – colonnaded and with tall windows – makes a confident statement. Inside are some splendid rooms and many walls are lined with huge oil paintings of school worthies – again, this is a school which had, from its inception, no modest aims. Democracy rules here and even the grandest meeting room – The Crick – is open to bookings from pupils for meetings and discussions.

Countless additional buildings – many attractive, some functional – and dating from all eras. Walkways, staircases abound – 'You get used to stairs here'. We loved the rustic vernacular Winterstoke Library and were desperate to know what is housed in its little tower; we loved the McClure Music School (1912) redolent of an innocent age, and we loved the Favell Building (2007) – which houses humanities and the top floor of which is hung with huge flags from everywhere. Most recent addition: an Innovation Hub. An attractive chapel (1896) by Basil Champneys, architect of many notable scholastic buildings. The chapel – though obviously of Christian origins – is now very much an ecumenical hub, and actively celebrates all faiths and their key festivals. We visited over Harvest Festival but missed Rosh Hashanah, the week before, and heard about the preparations for Diwali on the week following. One of our guides explained about Ramadan and the difficulties of fasting. The chapel was decorated by self-portraits of the new year 9s who explain to the gathered classes why they depicted themselves as they had – an excellent way to start to get known and know others.

Away from the main corridor and atrium, some areas are pretty old-school Spartan and need

Democracy rules here and even the grandest meeting room – The Crick – is open to pupil bookings for meetings and discussions

painting or a general refurb. Others are mint and sparkling.

Strong and popular house system and here, unlike in many other schools, houses you belong to are actually physical houses – or, at least, parts of buildings. They are defined by a house colour scheme – you can't miss it in upper areas of the main building where the overhead light is retina-bendingly harsh. Parents praise the heads of houses: 'They deal with everything and they always phone you back'.

New sixth form centre is making staying on more attractive and the King revamp is upping the profile and quality of what Mill Hill sixth form has to offer in general.

Outstanding food – we can't remember seeing – or scenting – better. The home-made cookies made us want to curl up and stay for the day.

The Mount – formerly The Mount Girls' School – has been beautifully refurbished. It has lovely grounds, good-sized classrooms and a happy collaborative atmosphere. The pupils – from everywhere – mix well with each other and the boarders they share houses with in the main school.

Pastoral care, well-being and discipline: Universal praise for pastoral care – both when you need it and when you only need to know it's there eg on arrival in the sixth form. 'It was so welcoming!' 'It's not a school where people act up much,' we were told, 'and if you do hit trouble it doesn't define the rest of your time in the school. They try to help you and find out why.' Very rare chuck-outs, mainly for drugs and nothing recent. House structure is the bedrock of the overall care and support and much praise for house staff in general.

Pupils and parents: Boys vastly outnumber girls, especially in the sixth form. This is true in pretty much all co-eds but is markedly noticeable here, partly due to the number of local, first rate, girls' schools. However, again, Mrs King is working on redressing this and, in any case, girls, evidently don't feel outnumbered and no-one complains that provision for them is second-class. We did note an activity called 'programming for girls' and wondered.. Parents praise the inclusiveness – 'My three are all completely different and the school is brilliant for all of them'. Most day pupils live locally and are the, mostly, comfortably-off, ethnically mixed, professional families you'd expect in this prosperous part of north west London. Mrs King speaks, knowledgeably, of the local 'ambitious clientele'. Active Parents' Association – clearly very popular.

Most Mount students based abroad but it could also be an option for recently relocated families, for local or other UK pupils whose education has, for any reason, been interrupted eg by sports prowess, filming, illness etc because of the flexibility and the intensive courses it offers.

Entrance: At 13+, 80 come up each year from linked prep Belmont, which means 70 places available for outsiders. However, places now offered in years 6 and 7 at Belmont – the prep school is expanding, particularly in hopes of attracting girls. Entry to the senior school from Belmont is not competitive so well worth investigating. Computer-based pre-testing in year 6 for external 13+ Mill Hill applicants in reading comprehension, verbal, non-verbal and numerical reasoning plus group activities and interview. Places also available via year 8 exams in maths, English, science, French and Latin (if learned) plus interview and report; 14+ places tested similarly.

School magazine reports – written with an honesty rare in such publications – attest to the earnest approach and a capacity for self appraisal we seldom see

At 16+, 22+ places available (40 joined in 2017) and candidates need at least two As and three Bs (grades 7 and 6) at GCSE.

Exit: Uncompromising chucking out post-GCSEs of those who didn't make the grade stopped by Mrs King on arrival. At least two As and three Bs (or numerical equivalent) expected but there is flexibility – as there should be – for those who otherwise make a strong contribution to school life. We find this so heartening – not every school should be trying only to cater for the super-bright. Most of us aren't. Post-A level, one of the most impressively diverse list of leavers' destinations – in terms both of course and university – that we've seen. This suggests a real focus on developing the individual and not turning out an identikit product – we like this. Encouraging five to Oxford in 2017 (linguists, historians, English scholars), plus four to the US and one to the Netherlands.

The list of notable Mill Hill alumni is equally multi-lateral: actors Jasper Britton, Patrick

Troughton (Dr Who mk 2), Harry Melling (Dudley Dursley); Richard Dimbleby and Simon Jenkins; Francis Crick, Norman Hartnell, Bob Marshall-Andrews, Tanika Gupta and Dennis Thatcher.

Around 50 per cent from The Mount move to Mill Hill main school after, usually, a year. Some stay at The Mount for years 10 and 11. The rest to, mostly, other boarding schools better suited to their needs.

Money matters: More than 10 per cent of pupils receive some level of fee assistance and some few are on 100 per cent fee remission. Scholarships in academics, sports, arts all worth 10 per cent of fees – but bursaries available which can contribute, in a few cases, up to 100 per cent of the remainder. Three 100 per cent sixth form bursaries. Hardship fund may see you through short-term liquidity problems. 'Thorough' and regular means-testing, of course. Numerous smaller awards bring kudos and Mars Bar money. Some interesting one-offs eg The Grinton award – a senior school scholarship for a girl boarder who wants to study art and The Donald Hall award for someone who wants to take sixth form science.

Remarks: 'My school is a place where you can express yourself and do anything,' we were told. Spot on. Set to regain its pre-eminence in this part of the world, wider still and wider.

Moira House Girls School

Upper Carlisle Road, Eastbourne, East Sussex BN20 7TE

01323 644144 | admissions@moirahouse.co.uk | www.moirahouse.co.uk

Ages: 1–18 (boarding from year 5)

Pupils: 253; sixth form: 53; Boarders: 46 full, 3 weekly

Day: £9,120 – £17,625 pa; Boarding: £21,375 – £33,420 pa

Principal: Since 2017, Elodie Vallentine, previously deputy and acting principal.

Academic matters: No setting or streaming in junior school and all classes are mixed ability – occasionally subjects are taught in mixed age groups.

French taken seriously and immediately: taught from nursery by a native speaker, and each year the hall is transformed into the French town of Moiraville where the girls are given Euros to spend at the café and market stalls and in the boulangerie, and can send postcards from the post office. Mandarin is offered as an after-school option.

Particular emphasis on reading and the pleasure it can bring – regular book weeks when the girls can read to each other and share their favourite books and dress up as fictional characters. Citizenship is taught as a separate subject and involves discussion about social justice, diversity, human rights and sustainable development.

All girls are assessed for learning difficulties on arrival and are then offered extra help as required – mainly for mild dyslexia and dyspraxia. No specialist unit, children given a mixture of help in class or in small groups or individually. All have individual learning plans, parents kept closely involved. EAL also available for those who need it.

A broad church in the senior school too, with non-selective entry and a good reputation for value added. In 2017, 41 per cent A*/A and 74 per cent A*/B at A level. Maths and the sciences popular, followed by business studies and psychology. Inspirational science teaching; trips all over the world including one to NASA. Indeed, our strong impression is that the general standard of teaching here is good. The science labs are well equipped but quite small so girls taught in very small groups.

Drama, PE and photography offered. Mandarin and Japanese as extracurricular subjects. GCSEs: 33 per cent A*-A in 2017 with IGCSEs in English, maths and science. Over 20 subjects to choose from including ICT, PE, German and Spanish. Separate sciences available. Year 7 and 8 girls are introduced to five languages within the curriculum – French, Latin, Spanish, German and Mandarin, with numerous trips and exchanges arranged.

Results generally pretty good for non-selective entry and all girls are allowed to sit exams irrespective of ability – no one is turned away because they are not expected to get the 'right' grades.

The senior school learning support department consists of one full time SENCo, mainly for mild dyslexia and dyspraxia. All those from overseas with English as a second language are given a language assessment on arrival and, if necessary, have

The school is very flexible about outside events eg training for an international eventer in the U21 Italian team

to complete a one year foundation course in intensive English and are expected to take the English IGCSE.

Good careers advice. Girls encouraged to think about their long term future from early on, and careers interviews start in year 9. Compulsory Friday afternoon lectures for sixth form – former students often come back to talk about life at university and beyond.

Welcoming, well-used library with enthusiastic librarian, assisted by student librarians. Girls encouraged to read books for pleasure and then discuss them at the MoHo Bookworms book club and book chat groups. Lots of trips and visits to bring the subjects to life – Hampton Court Palace, Imperial War Museum etc. French exchange programme, annual Spanish trip and Latin trips to Bath, St Alban's and Fishbourne.

Games, options, the arts: Vibrant music department with various ensembles, a chamber choir – 38 girls recently went to Barcelona to sing at Montserrat. Newly refurbished music studio and a recording studio. The school will go to great lengths to make it possible for a girl to learn any instrument. Drama productions every term for the senior, middle and junior schools. Biennial performing arts tour: music and drama productions at link schools around the world. In recent years they have performed in St Petersburg, San Francisco, Hong Kong and Dubai. Despite this, not heavy on or particularly successful at arts-based exams. School of music and performing arts: evening and weekend dance, drama and music workshops and lessons (at extra cost) plus trips to professional productions and the opportunity to take part in national competitions.

The usual sports – hockey, netball etc and also cricket, which is on the curriculum from year 7 – Moira House was one of the first girls' schools to introduce cricket and has several county players. Wimbledon standard grass courts and provides ballgirls for international tournament in Eastbourne. Everyone does a bit of everything each week up until year 10 and tends to keep going – it is considered quite cool to continue with sport. Extraordinary variety of minor sports, including sailing, windsurfing and canoeing in the sea. The school is very flexible about outside events eg training for an international eventer in the U21 Italian team. A number of keen and highly competent golfers, a GB archer, some county level athletes and particularly strong swimmers – girls have swimming lessons all year in the school's own indoor heated pool and keen swimmers can opt for extra training before school; many swim for local clubs and some at national level. Very fortunate to have their own playing fields across the road. Has recently opened an equestrian centre and has a partnership with local stables.

The school is keen that girls are involved at a local level and that the school works with the local community. The sports hall and swimming pool are used by pupils at neighbouring schools, and they also come in for Mandarin lessons and masterclasses as well as dance and drama. Moira House girls take part in the Eastbourne Festival of Music and Drama every February. Girls and staff play in the local netball league and girls also play in the Eastbourne Hockey Club teams. The older girls visit local old people's homes and the disabled and get involved with local charities.

Boarding: A few weekly and flexi-boarders, but mostly from overseas, from year 5 up, but majority in the sixth form. No Saturday school but plenty of matches – never a problem getting girls to come in for these.

Always something going on for the boarders at weekends – visits to art galleries, ancient buildings, bowling, ice skating, cinema etc. Boarding houses for years 5-9, 10-11 and Boston House for the sixth form, which serves as a bridge between school and university; girls are given increasing independence and are expected to manage their own time.

Background and atmosphere: Founded in 1875 by Charles Ingham and Mona Swann – pioneers of female education who were determined to give girls the chance of a good start in life. Charles Ingham's philosophy of 'Respect for self and for others and a sense of duty and responsibility' lives on in the school today.

The MoHo spirit is 'about respect and friendship with teachers when you are lower down the school, and the other way round when you are in the sixth form'

A step back in time, at least for Londoners. A jumbled, flamboyant late Victorian house complete with turrets and towers in the semi-rural outskirts of Eastbourne. Comfortably scruffy in places with a welcoming and homely atmosphere. The two head girls are known as Knights and the prefects as

Standard Bearers, others with positions of responsibility are called Pages and Squires.

Much of the teaching in 1960s blocks in the garden – not architecturally inspiring, to speak unreasonably kindly of them, but no one seems to mind. The grounds open directly onto the South Downs and there are views of the sea from the upstairs windows.

Junior school is a self-contained unit within the senior school and has the use of many of its facilities. Light and airy classrooms all recently refurbished with their own ICT suite and outdoor playground and play area. Includes a nursery, also known as Mini MoHo, for 0-5 year olds (takes boys, open for 50 weeks a year).

Pastoral care, well-being and discipline: Tutorial-based lessons with tutors acting as mentors and guides. Good relationships with teachers – very natural and relaxed. As one girl put it, the MoHo spirit is 'about respect and friendship with teachers when you are lower down the school, and the other way round when you are in the sixth form' 'A very nurturing school – not just of the girls but the parents as well,' said one happy mother.

Old girl Katie Gibbons was the first woman to win the Top Gun award at NASA and was awarded an air force flying scholarship – she flew jets for the RAF

Parents particularly struck by the 'unpressured family atmosphere and the fact that girls are given the space to think for themselves and the freedom to learn from mistakes'. Lots of involvement with the local community – girls take part in the Proms concert at Seaford and have even read extracts from their history project work on Eastbourne Youth Radio.

Pupils and parents: Boarders from a huge range of countries (27 different nationalities), the biggest proportion coming from Asia – plenty of cross-pollination between cultures. Locals generally down-to-earth businesspeople who like the small classes and the all girls environment. 'Popular with parents who want a bit more than the state can offer,' according to one mother. Most of the day children live within a 20 mile radius, with a fleet of nine minibuses bringing them in from as far away as Hastings, Battle and Brighton. The two groups of children get on well, and parents are clearly very happy with the school.

Active parents' association ensure all new parents feel welcomed, host new parents lunch as well as organise summer ball and various social and sporting events. 'It is a very nurturing school to us as well as the girls,' according to one new parent.

Pupils thoroughly nice, charming in fact. Welcoming. Entrepreneurial. Old girls include Prunella Scales, Susannah Corbett (actor Harry's daughter), author Rumer Godden, explorer Virginia Fiennes, whistleblower Katharine Gunn who founded the Truth Telling Commission. Katie Gibbons was the first girl to win the Top Gun award at NASA and was awarded an air force flying scholarship – she flew jets for the RAF and is now a pilot with Cathay Pacific. She first discovered her love of flying whilst on a school trip to NASA.

If we were to single out one quality of this school it would be the calm, not at all brassy, self-confidence of the older girls: 'I can do it', 'I'll give it a go'. Unusual, and most heart-warming to see.

Entrance: Students can and do join every term as long as there are spaces – some international students come on a short stay for perhaps a week, a term or a year – very flexible. Lots of Spanish in the autumn term and French, Germans and Italians in the summer – all integrated within their year group. Accept girls with a wide range of abilities, but they must be able to follow the GCSE course. No entrance tests – really non-selective – everyone comes for a taster day, including girls joining in years 5 and 6 from local primary schools, and those coming in at 11+ from outside are assessed by interview and on their school reports. Automatic transfer from junior to senior school, but girls can apply for academic scholarships and art, music and drama awards.

Exit: Nearly all junior girls move up to the senior school. Some two-thirds leave after GCSE – tend to go to sixth form colleges for more vocational courses. To a variety of universities, some to Russell Group and art foundation courses. Some to former polys to read everything from veterinary science, politics, history and biomedicine to product design and fashion photography. Three medics in 2017. Very few take a gap year.

Money matters: Two academic scholarships worth up to 35 per cent of fees are awarded each year. Can be topped up by means-tested bursaries. Exhibitions up to 10 to 20 per cent of fees in drama, music, art and sport, can also be topped up with a bursary.

Remarks: A traditional English girls' school with a 'cosmopolitan and international flavour and a global perspective'. Does not look for UK pupils beyond its local catchment, but for the right girl will be the perfect school wherever she comes from.

Northbourne Park School

Betteshanger, Deal, Kent CT14 0NW

01304 611215 | office@northbournepark.com | www.northbournepark.com

Ages: 3-13 (boarders from 7)

Pupils: 153; Boarders: 42 full, 2 weekly, 5 flexi

Day: £7,632 – £16,326 pa; Boarding: £20,376 – £23,673 pa

Headmaster: Since 2015, Sebastian Rees, previously head of Seaford College Prep in Sussex. He has also been assistant head at neighbouring Northbourne Primary School and director of studies at Junior King's School, Canterbury. Studied French at UCL; is also fluent in Spanish and worked in two Spanish schools earlier in his career. Coaches football, cricket and rugby.

Entrance: Taster day and tests in English and maths. The head likes to meet the whole family where possible. Almost non-selective – can adapt the curriculum to suit a child with learning difficulties as long as they are not too severe. They look for children who will be happy at Northbourne and most children are of at least average ability. Usually spaces in most year groups.

Exit: Most children go on to King's Canterbury or St Edmund's in Canterbury. One or two a year to Benenden and Kent College and one or two to Sevenoaks, Tonbridge, Dover College, Cranbrook. Occasionally a couple go further afield. Three or four each year leave at 11 to go to the grammars – the school will prepare children for the Kent Test but doesn't offer one-to-one coaching. Good range and number of scholarships each year – academic, music and sport.

Remarks: Set in 100 acres of parkland and woods on the Betteshanger Estate near Deal, formerly the home of the Northbourne family. Large, rambling Victorian house – a much-loved, happy place. Traditional values, a strong work ethic and a belief in and encouragement of service to the community. Not a grand school – great sense of informality and freedom with a cosy, family feel. Children are encouraged to climb trees, and each year group has a designated area of woodland where they are allowed to play. Some classrooms housed in very well-appointed outdoor classrooms in the garden erected by the Canadians during the war, which somehow got listed along with the rest of the house. Lord Northbourne, whose family used to live in the house, is still involved with the school and likes to take the top year to tea in the House of Lords.

A broadly Christian foundation, with great emphasis on instilling a sense of care and respect for the needs of others both within and outside the school. Boarders attend the local church in the grounds on Sundays. One class per year of about 15 children with a maximum of 19. The brighter children are extended and the less able are nurtured and encouraged. Some setting in the last two years; the scholarship children are taught within the class. Well-equipped new computer room and increasing use of ICT in curriculum. New girls' boarding house with bright airy dormitories; boys' dormitories all recently refurbished.

The French and Spanish programme is unique among prep schools. Two full-time classes of French and French-speaking Spanish children – the equivalent of an extra year 7 and 8, known as the Sixième and Cinquième. This programme is not actively marketed but is spread by word of mouth amongst families in France and Spain whose children come to learn English for one or two years. The smart French children are often from top Parisian schools. The Spanish children tend to be already attending a Lycées in France and might then opt for British or American schools abroad – tend to be very European-minded. The French and Spanish children are taught separately by French staff and follow the French national curriculum in history, geography, French and maths – the exams are ratified by the Lycée in London and monitored by the CNED in France. The deputy head is French. Children come together outside lessons for all other activities and sport (including cricket), art etc. Charming to hear echoes of French and Spanish voices along the corridors. Inevitable benefits to English children who also spend a few days with an exchange school in Lille and with families in Spain. The children interact well, lots of close friendships are forged here and there is 'much to-ing and fro-ing across the Channel during the holidays,' said one happy mother, whose daughter has been invited to France several times. 'What makes Northbourne really special is the interaction between the English, French and Spanish children. It gave my son a real head start in languages,' said another.

After-school academic societies include The Sophists, a literary discussion group open to all and held in the head's study

Excellent pastoral care – 'Happiness is at the core of everything they do,' said one mother – and much emphasis on children becoming good citizens. Active school forum for children to develop their own ideas on eg break-time rules and expectations around manners, and an increasing emphasis on the role of the prefects. Girls sometimes have special 'girls' nights in' when matron administers 'beauty treatments' and does their hair. Full time boarders about a quarter French and Spanish, with some flexi and weekly boarding. Wednesday and Saturday film nights in the old drawing room.

Good food prepared on site and served on a cafeteria system. The school regularly gains the National Heartbeat Food Award – two sittings for lunch and staff sit amongst children to supervise table manners and encourage conversation.

Dynamic director of sport, a Kent county cricket coach, has re-energised sport and breathed new life into the game, and there are now increasing fixtures against other schools – although some parents feel that there could be still more. Quite a small pool to choose from which means everyone has a chance to play in a team, and often children who might be overlooked in a bigger school find they have a sporting bent. Usual range of sports including rugby, hockey and netball, plus cross-country, triathlon, tennis, badminton, fencing, clay pigeon shooting and archery – something for everyone. Outdoor heated pool – they go to Duke of York's School or Dover Leisure Centre for triathlon training during the winter.

Gets at least two or three music scholarships each year – recently to Benenden, King's Canterbury, Kent College and St Edmund's. About 70 per cent of children learn at least one instrument, some up to grade 8. Music tech also taught and iMacs used for composition. Lots of collaboration with the local community, and a number of children play in the Betteshanger band and join the Saturday music club. The director of music is an old girl of the school. Lots of encouragement and music lessons from pre-prep upwards. Several opportunities to play in informal concerts – children are encouraged to have a go. Plenty of opportunities to stand up in public too. One junior and one senior play each year – usually a musical. Public speaking competition and occasional debates. In-school clubs include electronics, art, pottery, computers, cookery and the popular and productive gardening club in the old walled garden. After-school academic societies include The Sophists, a literary discussion group open to all and held in the head's study, bilingual society, Greek, Latin, new science, maths, geography and history societies. Senior children and especially scholars are encouraged to attend.

Busy art department – head of art works for the Canterbury Festival and produces vast three-dimensional pieces so likes big projects eg remarkable (authorised!) graffiti in the changing rooms, and won the prize for the best giant scarecrow at the Hampton Court Flower Show. The children love getting involved even if they are not very artistic. Lots of art competitions, Christmas card competition, pavement art on MDF. Local artists invited to workshops. Pottery housed in the dairy, which still has the Victorian tiles and marble slabs intact.

They are challenged to build camps in groups – they learn how to make a camp fire and are allowed to use penknives. They then spend the night in their camps

Good learning support – one full-time and two part-time teachers – mainly dyslexia, dyspraxia and ADHD. Problems identified early and support given either individually or in small groups, in or out of the classroom, each with an individual education plan reviewed by teachers and parents each term (extra charge for the support programmes). The few children in the school with mild Asperger's are carefully selected and assessed. School will take statemented/EHC plan children but not more than one per class. Wants to attract bright dyslexics.

The school day finishes at 5pm, but about half the children stay on for prep until 6pm. The pre-prep children can be looked after until their older siblings are ready to go home. School every other Saturday from year 4 – as well as lessons and games, a leadership course which has been going for years and is a particular feature of the school – like a mini Duke of Edinburgh scheme with lots of den-building and campfires in the woods. Very popular with the children – gives confidence and fosters team-building and leadership skills. Lots of gutsy stuff; children are encouraged but not made to take part. They are put into teams and challenged to build camps in groups – they learn how to make a camp fire and are allowed to use penknives. They then spend the night in their camps, are given luxury ration packs and can turn rabbit and pheasant into a stew if they choose. This often develops a life-long love of the outdoors. Year 8 children go on an adventure holiday to the Ardêche as part of their leadership programme.

The recently-introduced Lord Northbourne Award Scheme also recognises life beyond academia – sport, music, expeditions, drama; children complete this at different levels in their own time. They have to visit the Mountain of Sport, the River of Adventure, The Temple of Learning and the Forest of Beauty and complete challenges in these areas. It culminates in a overseas expedition.

Close links with the French Lycée in London, which sends a group down for a weekend each summer – sleeping outside in the camps can be a bit of a revelation for some of them. Northbourne children do a return day trip to London.

The pre-prep school is housed in the recently-refurbished Old Rectory about 10 minutes walk away, and caters for 3 to 7 year olds. They eat separately – food prepared in main school. The head takes assembly once a week and gets to know the children, who are taught French by French nationals every day from nursery upwards. Hall for assemblies and PE. Directors of music and sport come over from the prep; lots of team sports. Seamless transition to prep school with year 2 going over once per week for science, games lessons and swimming.

Parents mainly local farmers and businessmen as well as a few from London. Lots of first time buyers and working mothers – quite a cross-section of parents, many of whom have made great sacrifices to send their children here. Loyal and enthusiastic team of staff – some old hands and new young teachers including new heads of maths, science and English. Governing body reinvigorated by new chairman with a clear sense of purpose and direction. Friends of Northbourne Park a welcoming and sociable group. Lots of social and fundraising events – wine tasting, quiz, Christmas fair, a major summer event and a ball every other year.

Old boys include writer Giles Brandreth, composer Sir Richard Rodney Bennett, concert pianist Freddie Kempf and reporter Giles Dilnot.

The Prebendal School

51

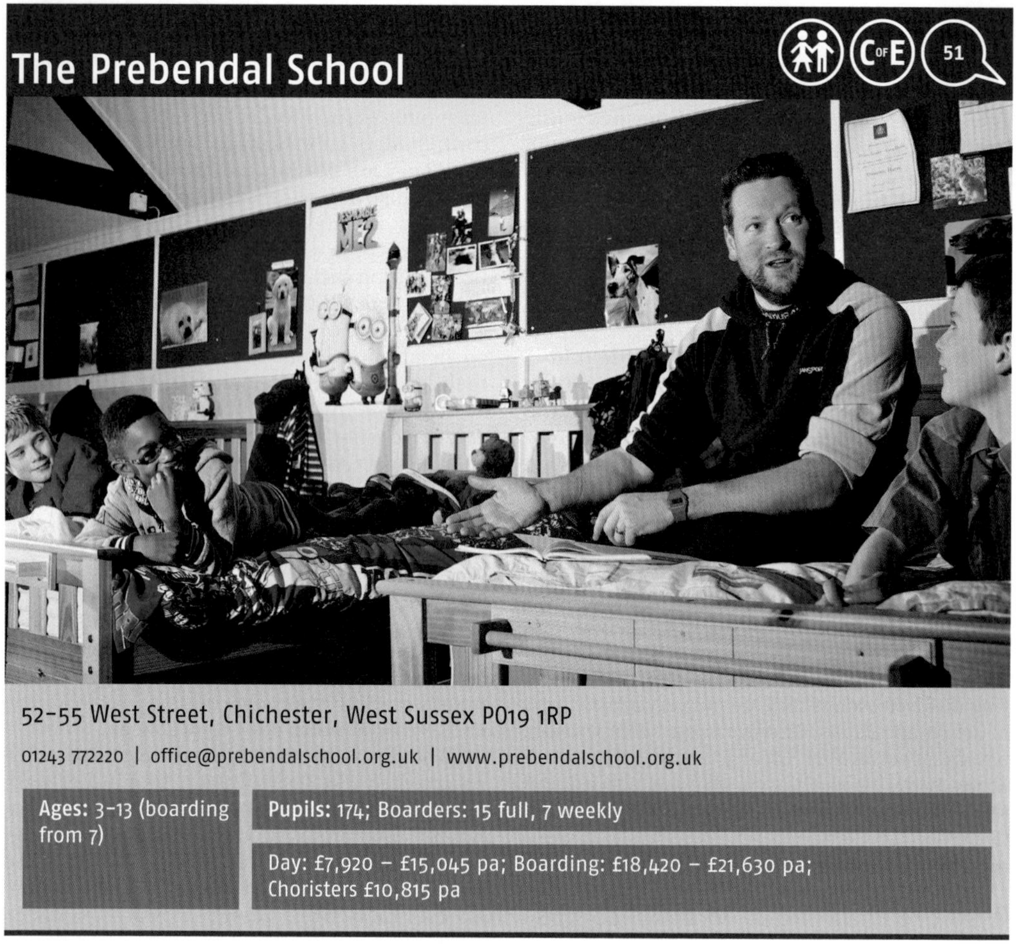

52-55 West Street, Chichester, West Sussex PO19 1RP

01243 772220 | office@prebendalschool.org.uk | www.prebendalschool.org.uk

Ages: 3-13 (boarding from 7)

Pupils: 174; Boarders: 15 full, 7 weekly

Day: £7,920 – £15,045 pa; Boarding: £18,420 – £21,630 pa; Choristers £10,815 pa

Head: Since September 2017, Louise Salmond Smith BA MMus PGCE MBA FRSA (40s), previously head of junior school at Tormead School in Guildford and the school's first female head. Read music at University of East Anglia (emphasis on performance – recorder – and electroacoustic composition) then MMus in performance and educational composition at Hull University. A PGCE from Gloucestershire soon followed, as well as an MBA from Keele. Experience in education ranges from being a gap student in a boarding school to working on large-scale educational projects for a music charity. Five years as director of music at The Grange School, Santiago; a stint in the maintained sector; then director of music at Hall Grove. Also loves teaching ICT and English, and has run photography and podcasting clubs as well as musical activities. Always a keen volunteer on school trips that are likely to involve mud, rain and jumping into lakes. Has two teenage daughters.

Entrance: Parents can register their child for entry to the nursery at 3, but otherwise at any stage; those entering up to year 2 are informally assessed, while those in year 3 up may be tested in English, reading and maths. Current school report is required from year 1. Voice trials for chorister places – boys only – take place in November and February each year, usually for entry the following September, but sometimes sooner. Choir hopefuls are also assessed in verbal reasoning, English and maths to ensure that they can cope with the extra demands of chorister life. Choral scholarships (at least 50 per cent, sometimes more) are awarded by the cathedral chapter and include free piano tuition. Bursaries and academic scholarships (both means tested) worth up to 50 per cent of school fees are awarded at head's discretion; sibling bursaries offered in increments of five per cent (10 per cent for a third child). Music scholarships (also up to 50 per cent) include free tuition on one instrument. All candidates going into year 7 may apply for two awards in three areas (sport, art, academic) worth up to 15 per cent of day fees. There's also a Forces' bursary (maximum award is 15 per cent fees remission).

Exit: Most leave at 13 to a range of senior schools, many with music, academic, all-round, sport or art scholarships. Music scholarships abound here naturally, but there is a healthy scattering of academic awards too and art scholarships are on the up. More than half of year 8 leavers have gained a scholarship for the past 10 years and the tally is rising. Parents full of praise for school's ability to steer children in the right direction. Popular destinations include Seaford College, Lancing College, Brighton College and Hurstpierpoint as well as Harrow, Bryanston and Sherborne. A few leave at the end of year 6.

Remarks: Dating back to the foundation of Chichester Cathedral in the 11th century, when it would have been a 'song school' to educate the choristers, the school is the oldest in Sussex. Re-founded as a grammar school in 1497 by the then Bishop of Chichester, it was attached to the Prebend of Highleigh, hence its name. School now occupies a range of buildings dating from the original 14th century song school to the modern Highleigh building.

Separated from the beautiful edifice that is Chichester Cathedral by a stone wall and an iron gate, there is little physical division between the two buildings and this is reflected in the spiritual ties that link church and school. The cathedral is the venue for major concerts and services, eg Founder's Day, and school assemblies take place in the nave twice a week. Next to the splendour of the cathedral, some parents remark that interior of main school building is 'dated and needs modernising ... a bit like a rabbit warren with lots of staircases', but school's expansion into the building next door provided more space for classrooms and a more user-friendly layout. The children probably don't mind their surroundings and doubtless learn their way around quickly.

Classwork is based on the national curriculum up to year 6, followed by a focus on CE and independent school scholarships in years 7 and 8. Pupils are taught as a class up to year 4 and then by subject specialist teachers from year 5. Average class size is 13, rising to a maximum of 16. School has adjusted the academic timetable, increasing lesson length to 45 minutes, 'so less time is wasted between lessons.' Outdoor learning has also started to feature on the curriculum – school also has 'beach school' status. We observed sound teaching in year 5 maths (regular revision throughout the year) and a lively French lesson, which is taught from the age of 3. CE syllabus in core subjects is completed by the summer of year 7 to allow for scholarship preparation and exam practice. Maths is set in years 7 and 8 to stretch the able. 'Prebendal really gears up for the scholars,' commented one mother, adding that leavers are usually ahead of their peers in year 9. Latin for all from year 5 is taught by a member of the cathedral clergy and set from years 6 to 8; as a result Latin scholars gain a very good grounding. School monitors the gifted and talented as well as the less able. Academic clubs support classwork after school and on Saturday mornings, eg science revision, maths and French at CE and scholarship levels, geography, history and homework clubs. 'Brilliant' learning support teacher coaches around 20 children; others with special needs are supervised by teachers and a learning support assistant.

Music is at the heart of school life, although it is by no means the sole preserve of the cathedral choristers. 'Music for all' is the school's philosophy

Good-sized art and DT studio at the top of the building (up the inevitable long flight of stairs) gets plenty of light; artists enter local school competitions (and win) and gain scholarships to senior schools. There is a well-equipped ICT suite and new science laboratory. Classrooms opening off narrow corridors aren't especially spacious, but are not overcrowded. Assembly hall doubles up as a performance space for drama and music – year 6s were reading poetry to the whole school on the day of our visit. Another large, if rather cold and damp, older room used for orchestra and ensemble rehearsals; school says a new music block is part of

the current expansion plans and will house music technology facilities and a small performance space. Modern Highleigh building, home to the nursery plus all of pre-prep, has light, airy, spacious classrooms and a small separate playground. Charming walled garden provides a quiet outdoor area close to the cathedral gate.

Main dorm has an unusual vaulted ceiling and comparisons with Hogwarts are irresistible – the likeness ends there, however, as parents speak highly of the matron

As expected, music is at the heart of school life, although it is by no means the sole preserve of the cathedral choristers. 'Music for all' is the school's philosophy and most parents and pupils buy in with enthusiasm (only six were not learning an instrument at the time of our visit). Peripatetic musicians teach some 280 instrumental lessons each week; there are also two orchestras, two concert bands and five choirs in which over 200 children sing. School choir sings evensong in the cathedral once a term. In addition to the big concerts twice each year, there are regular informal concerts, a house singing competition and a week-long music festival. At the two weekly cathedral assemblies, junior and senior pupils take turns to perform solo, one of the school choirs sings the anthem and a pupil from year 8 does the bible reading. A parent commented that she 'cannot put a price on how much the children gain from performing music and reading in the cathedral.' The pre-prep sings the last anthem of term and has its own music coordinator, orchestra, choir and recorder ensembles. Every chorister receives free piano tuition and usually plays a second instrument; many other students also learn more than one. Although some music lessons are fixed, most rotate through the timetable and parents say the system works well and appears to have little impact on academic work (there is an edict not to miss games). One parent said, 'music exams make all other aspects of life easy, like French aurals,' and results support this. A child doesn't have to be musical to thrive here, however, as 'the school is good enough at other things, like sport and academic work.'

Although school has sacrificed one weekly games session, there are still three afternoons largely devoted to games – soccer, rugby, hockey and netball in the winter terms and cricket, athletics, rounders and tennis in the summer. School has its own outdoor, heated pool for swimming lessons in the summer term. As well as the usual grass pitches and courts, there is an all-weather cricket pitch and all-weather cricket nets; the school also has access to Chichester College astroturf. Everyone is encouraged to represent the school in sport; the less sporty are rotated through the B teams so that they are able to play a match at least once a term. First hockey, cricket and netball teams regularly do well as does the girls' soccer team. Fencing and gymnastics clubs, plus cross-country running, offer alternatives to main school sports.

School has a friendly feel and children lining up for lunch looked happy (meals are provided by outside caterers and appeared reasonable). Literature states that individual happiness is important, and this was certainly evident during our visit when one young man seemed distressed during a lesson changeover. Whilst we talked to the (hugely enthusiastic) children about their work, head immediately took the time to speak with the teacher. Two heads of pastoral care (years 3 to 5 and years 6 to 8) lead a regular weekly assembly and are responsible for any serious issues. Parents confirm that discipline is fair and that school is 'very good at dealing with energetic young boys; what happens in school, stays in school' commented one. The chorister tutor sees the 18 choristers and probationers every day to sort out any issues, check prep and manage their busy lives.

The cathedral choir is the mainstay of the boarding community as boys remain in school to sing weekend services. They are joined by a small number of weekly and flexi boarders and occasionally by children attending Wednesday or Friday 'theme nights', eg LAMDA performance evening, Canadian evening – even water fights. All pupils are English speaking; a few of the school's pupils speak other languages (Romanian, Polish, Chinese, Japanese); most overseas boarders join for the summer term. Many of the local medics choose to send their children here. Main dorm has an unusual vaulted ceiling and comparisons with Hogwarts are irresistible – the likeness ends there, however, as boarder parents speak very highly of the matrons. In practice, the choristers are the only boarders in school after lunchtime on Saturday, although they have the opportunity to go home on most Wednesday and Saturday evenings (chorister parents are welcome for Sunday brunch). One mother felt that lunchtime supervision could be better to ensure that younger children are eating well; there are also no mid-morning snacks provided beyond pre-prep for day children.

Extracurricular activities take place every day after school and on Saturday mornings (no Saturday school) and are open to all. Activities range from ICT and music theory to rugby, knitting and stamp clubs. Choristers can join Saturday morning clubs after music practice, eg tennis, rugby and cricket. There are also supervised prep and revision sessions and voluntary maths coaching on Saturdays. Day pupils can come in if they wish; some clubs incur a charge (eg fencing) but most are free. School trips have included residential trips to Normandy, France, youth hostelling in North Wales and a week in Rome. Very active PTA raises funds for anything from loos on the sports field to whiteboards and car park resurfacing. 'There is a good social network here if parents want it.'

Actively sought out by local parents for its strong Christian ethos, this is a friendly, 'softer round the edges' place than some cathedral schools. It is agile enough to meet the academic, social and spiritual needs of the whole student body without sacrificing the particular requirements of a small number of choristers. The unification of the entire school on one site can only benefit pupils, improve internal communications and continue to foster a family atmosphere.

Prior's Field

52

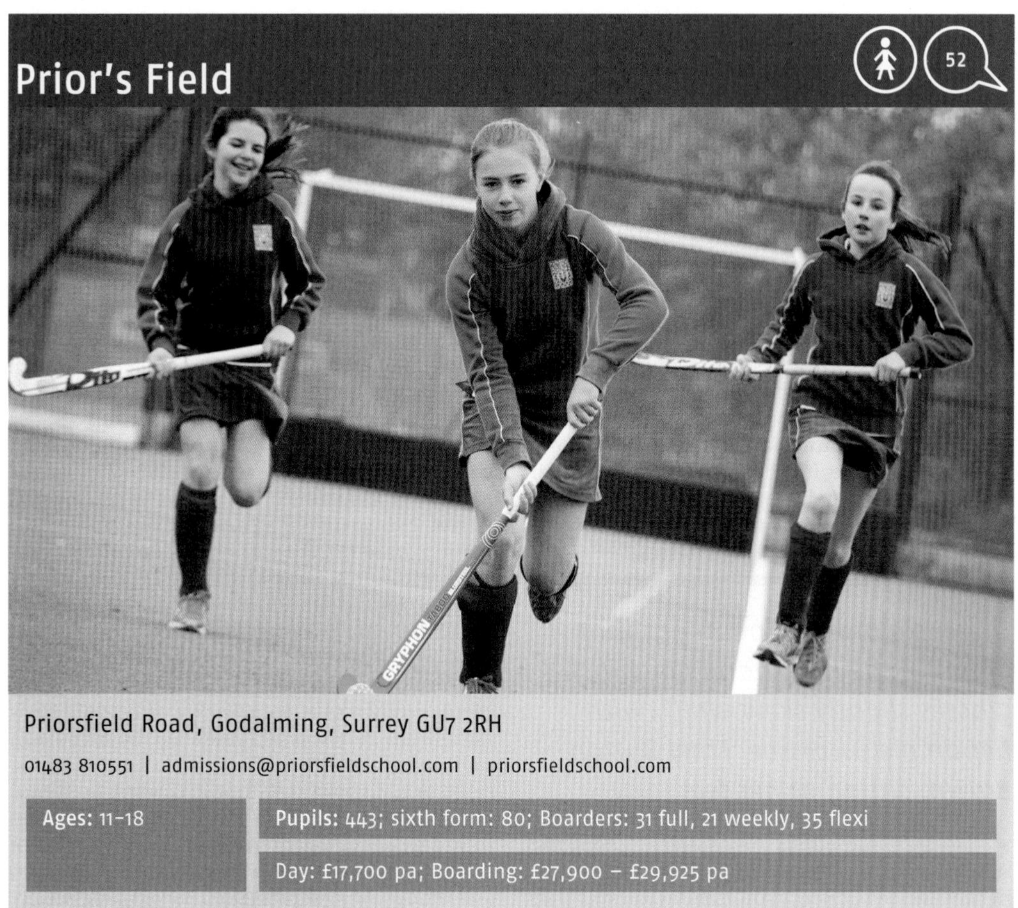

Priorsfield Road, Godalming, Surrey GU7 2RH

01483 810551 | admissions@priorsfieldschool.com | priorsfieldschool.com

Ages: 11–18

Pupils: 443; sixth form: 80; Boarders: 31 full, 21 weekly, 35 flexi

Day: £17,700 pa; Boarding: £27,900 – £29,925 pa

Head: Since 2015, Tracy Kirnig, 50s. Born and brought up in London, she ventured to university in Aberystwyth, reading RE and philosophy. Ms Kirnig was never in doubt about a teaching career and returned nearer to her roots to take a masters in education at King's London and then a PGCE at Lancaster before working in both the state and private sector. Her interests in music and travel are re-enforced by the scaling of Mount Kilimanjaro last year, particularly impressive as she admits to being a late-comer to the joys of climbing. Moving here from her last job as deputy head of co-ed Caterham school, she is noticeably happy in her own skin with a firm belief in the worth of her school and in particular of the girls in her care. Married to a geo-technological engineer with a side-line in potting.

Academic matters: An academically selective school, although not in the high-flying category; in 2017 grades at GCSE were 54 per cent A*-A/9-7 and at A level 22 per cent A*-A and 59 per cent A*-B. There has been a noticeable, recent, attempt to redress the balance away from the arts, with around half the year taking one or more maths and science subjects at A level. Languages are not an obviously strong point, but they make a great effort to find outside teachers if pupils voice sufficient interest in a language outside the fairly narrow choice on the core curriculum of French, Spanish and Latin at GCSE. Everyone takes one or two of these at this stage and recently up to 20 per cent have taken at least one language at A level.

The average class size in the early years is 18, reducing to 15 as they move up the school and six in the sixth form. Setting takes place on arrival at both 11+ and 13+ for English and maths and later in the first term for science, MFL and sport. The girls speak of flexibility and are confident that they will be moved up or down rapidly if it appears necessary.

The staff, with a ratio of one teacher to eight girls, have a relatively high average age but, as the head says, 'this brings a wealth of experience,' 22 of them having been at the school for more than 10 years. Despite this statistic, she feels that there are plenty of younger members and promotes them on the basis that 'they are old enough if they are good enough'. Certainly, on our visit, the enthusiasm and interaction with the pupils was noticeable with plenty of young faces and absolutely no stuffed shirts in evidence. It may be a smallish school but the determination to help each girl reach her academic potential is clearly evident.

There is a brilliant photograph of her in the hall, hand on chin, glasses slightly skew whiff, with her ample successor, Ethel Burton-Brown, sitting at her feet

The staff and pupils are confident about the SEND provision; it appears to be handled efficiently and sensitively, although they admit that they might dissuade a parent from sending a child with problems that would prevent her from coping fairly easily with the school's academic expectations. However, one parent told us that they were 'great about accepting my very dyslexic daughter' and that the SENCo was 'fantastic'. One-on-one help is available, if necessary, at an hourly rate.

Games, options, the arts: A surprisingly sporty school despite its size. Netball, hockey and athletics tick the most boxes and teams compete locally and nationally. Tennis is huge; they even run to a tennis academy (started in 2012 complete with a permanent coach), which paid off this year in the Surrey U15 championship and with their first tennis scholar having her pick of American universities. At a more achievable, if slightly wacky, level the inter-house cross-country competition last year had an underwater theme, with the girls sporting mermaid tails; it may not have increased their speed but it was good for a laugh.

Clubs and activities are a big deal, meriting their own brochure, and are often free, although if you're into creating Funky Food, not surprisingly, you have to pay for the ingredients as well as persuading your parents to eat the results. Rugby and cricket now available, the latter becoming popular after the success of the England women's team in 2017. In a nod to the country, you can go riding after school or if you're a home bod, you can get into knitting and crochet, of which we saw an imaginative, if eccentric, example in the making.

Completely unsurprisingly given the school's arts and crafts heritage, there is a major emphasis on art, music and drama. The art rooms are designed for people taking it seriously, with sixth formers each having their own space that fills up with imaginative work during the year. The result is that several girls go on to art college and a high proportion of alumnae make it a career. They mean what they say about encouraging talent, as one girl with a natural bent for photography persuaded them to add the course to the GCSE curriculum. New music rooms encourage even the less musical to give an instrument a go, whilst the more gifted are nurtured carefully. Drama is definitely front stage with brave large cast musical productions, entry in the Shakespeare Schools Festival and popular LAMDA and RADA classes.

Boarding: About a quarter of the girls board but increasingly this is on a weekly or flexible basis rather than full time. At weekends the school can seem a little empty lower down as only around seven to eight board full time in the first two years, but further up the school the percentage increases to 50 per cent in the fifth year and up to 60 per cent in the sixth form. One parent was a bit unhappy and thought that her daughter lacked supervision, but this was contradicted by several of the present cohort.

The younger girls are up in the attics in cosy if slightly cramped quarters of up to four in a room, but it feels cheerful and there was no griping when asked if they had enough space. You wouldn't want to be a budding fashionista with a lot of frocks as the hanging space is strictly limited, but there are lots of drawers for 'stuff' and you are encouraged to make it as personal as possible. The bathrooms looked newish and were pretty spotless, a nice cleaning lady telling us they had a 'really good go twice a week'. The sixth formers all have larger

The art rooms are designed for people taking it seriously, with sixth formers having their own space that fills up with imaginative work

rooms with good work space, the upper sixth even having their own bathrooms – a much appreciated luxury. The general consensus was that there was plenty to do out of school hours and some of the day girls would love their parents to come up with the cash so that they could board.

Background and atmosphere: Prior's Field nestles in a hidden corner of leafy Surrey, just out of sight of the London hubbub. A rather surprising unicorn-themed advertisement for the school is squished on a small roundabout off the A3, but the tree-lined road leading off it soon reveals a pebble-dashed, beetle-browed arts and crafts set of buildings. The original 1900 house, designed by CFA Voysey, has grown since through the addition of convincing fakes and the whole ensemble fits happily into its surrounding acres.

The founder, Julia Huxley, was related by blood, marriage and proximity to the intellectual and educationally passionate giants of the Edwardian age. You could not dream up someone more suitable to start a school than the granddaughter of Dr Thomas Arnold (the Rugby legend), niece of Matthew Arnold (the poet), wife of Leonard Huxley (a Charterhouse schoolmaster himself before becoming an important literary figure) and friend of Conan Doyle. Her children, Julian, a scientist and director of UNESCO, and Aldous, author of Brave New World, provide further evidence of why she was the perfect person to run a school based on moral philosophy and forward thinking. There is a brilliant photograph of her in the hall, hand on chin, glasses slightly skew whiff, with her ample successor, Ethel Burton-Brown, sitting at her feet, made more touching by the fact that she died a year later aged only 46. Conan Doyle sent his daughter here and the germ of the idea for a short story entitled The Adventure of Priory School must surely have come from his knowledge of Prior's Field, although the plot is not exactly an advertisement for pupil care.

The slightly labyrinthine layout of a turn-of-the-century house is not ideal for a modern school, but a newbie told us that despite getting lost frequently for the first two weeks she had quickly learnt the necessary shortcuts to make it everywhere on time. Again surprisingly, the interior, whilst a tad scruffy, is not as dark as you would expect and is greatly improved by art on every available wall as well as impressive displays of textile work for which the school is justifiably famous. Amongst the newer buildings, they are proudest of their pristine science, technology and music centre, which manages to be light and attractive inside despite its folksy exterior. The area at the front of the school is cramped, but the back opens up to a wide green space, a new all-purpose Astroturf pitch, several tennis courts and woodland beyond.

Pastoral care, well-being and discipline: This side of the school was high on the head's agenda when she took over and she has changed the structure so that now there is one person responsible for the emotional development of each individual, separate from the person in charge of checking whether they've got the right tights on. PSHE is not just an acronym here but built into the whole workings of the school, and the result hits you straight on, all the girls we talked to genuinely appearing to put helping each other above being competitive. The school has definitely got across their belief in moral welfare but it is not heavy handed; common sense rather than a set of rules is the order of the day. With her philosophical background, the head also wants to broaden awareness and a series of talks on mindfulness are scheduled, the first one being given by a Buddhist nun. Zero evidence of wrongdoing: the head girl sounded puzzled when we asked her if she had to discipline the younger ones.

The beautifully presented food (think huge Moroccan bowls of salad and a bread offering that would challenge a trendy London bakery) is seriously yummy, one girl giggling that it was much better than her mum's. Being allergic or just fussy is not a problem, a non-gluten pupil telling us that there was masses of choice and they were 'really helpful about it', and teachers seem very aware of any potential problems.

Not the smartest of schools in terms of uniform, but this is being remedied with major input from the pupils who, slightly to our surprise, actually want to wear blazers with badges to show off where they come from.

Pupils and parents: Majority of day girls bussed in from all points of the compass, increasingly from nearer London as parents turn away from the capital's pressure-cookers and look for an academically competent school with an individual flavour. Some 10 per cent from a wide range of foreign countries; these, when asked, said that they had settled in straight away, and certainly all had smiley faces. Parents' backgrounds are as diverse as the children's ambitions but they say that they feel fully involved with the school via personal contact and email communication as well as the PSA.

Entrance: An open morning or a pre-arranged 'Meet the head' coffee morning plus school tour are followed by a taster day in November and an exam in January. The school is oversubscribed at 11 and 13 but they don't just go on exam results. Rather, they try to find girls who are 'sparky, curious about life and learning and want to get involved with everything on offer'. A genuine effort is made to determine whether this is the right place for each individual and they're pretty good at it, judging by the great attitude of the present lot.

Exit: In this tough financial climate and due to the school's location, it is hardly surprising that a large number leave after GCSEs, a percentage of which are replaced from outside. We suspect that affordability is the major reason, but the assumption that life is more 'real' in a co-ed still attracts a proportion to either private school sixth forms or state colleges with good A level results. No Oxbridge entrants in 2017 but 11 straight to Russell Group universities, 14 to other UK universities, several to sought after direct (no foundation year) places on a fine art or fashion degree course, one to acting school, one to university in the USA and the rest onto a gap year. Grandparents will be thrilled that Enid Bagnold (National Velvet) was an old girl, watchers of Netflix will know of Victoria Hamilton (the queen mother in The Crown), and others will be encouraged that Baroness Mary Warnock was at the school.

Money matters: Plenty of scholarships and bursaries; academic, sporting, musical, artistic and dramatic abilities are recognised by an award which equates to between £250 and £1,000 per term. One or two exceptional tennis players are awarded a place in the tennis academy, with coaching costs fully funded by the school. A handful of foundation awards (100 per cent bursaries funded by parents, alumnae and friends of the school) are awarded each year and a 20 per cent discount on the fees is given to the daughters of parents in the Forces.

Remarks: A century may have passed but the aim to turn out resilient young women, capable of achieving the maximum possible in the outside world, remains the same. It is still a school where 'it is cool to try out new things', and the head is confident that the well-equipped young adults that leave are recognisable as the children that arrived five or seven years earlier. The school is also long on charm and good at detail, winning us over immediately by giving us a car parking space with our name on it.

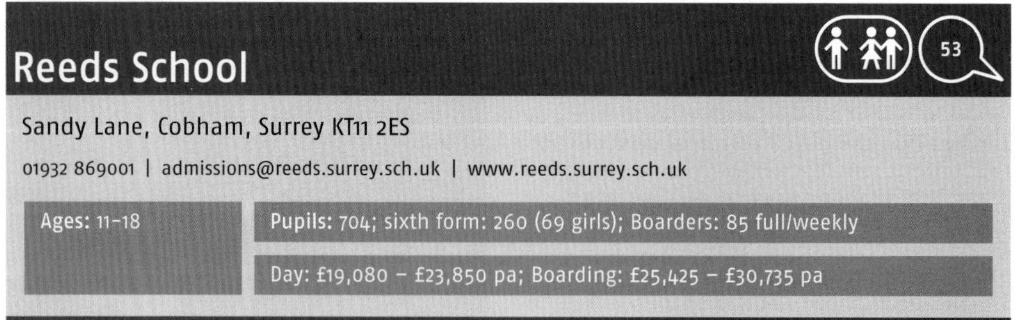

Reeds School
53
Sandy Lane, Cobham, Surrey KT11 2ES
01932 869001 | admissions@reeds.surrey.sch.uk | www.reeds.surrey.sch.uk
Ages: 11-18
Pupils: 704; sixth form: 260 (69 girls); Boarders: 85 full/weekly
Day: £19,080 – £23,850 pa; Boarding: £25,425 – £30,735 pa

Head: Since 2014, Mark Hoskins BA MA MSc (50s). Previously second master (senior deputy head in modern currency) at RGS Guildford between 2005-2014. Before that, spent eight years at Whitgift, starting as head of economics and business studies in 1997 and then becoming head of middle school. First posts were in highly regarded maintained schools – two years apiece at Rosebery (comp, girls) and Wilson's (selective grammar, boys). Mixed sixth form here first foray so far into co-education.

Praise from parents comes thick and fast. 'Impressive'; 'A lovely guy'; 'Has accelerated the

academic side without losing the breadth.' Ditto for wife Sharon, whose diligent attendance at events has been approvingly clocked. Has two children, son (at the school) and daughter (distinctly miffed she isn't as too young).

Though an able sportsman (coached soccer in US during gap years), Mr Hoskins talks down his successes – becoming modesty a given, he says, when working in schools with world-class pros on the staff. Nobody, though, likely to call him out on academic qualifications, what with two masters, a second in economics from the University of London, accomplished post-marriage with small children and combined with full-time teaching. 'When you're teaching bright pupils, they push you and so you want to push yourself.' Still fits in some teaching currently economics to upper sixth, switching effortlessly between different roles – father to head – without breaking step, with son's friends at ease within minutes.

Parents who already know (or have heard tell) of previous achievements at RGS are quickly converting others. He's taking the school by stealth (as well as charm) and doing the evolution not revolution thing. Latest inspection praises democratic, light touch management style, with teachers regularly observed but encouraged rather than censured while management structure is being reworked to give more opportunities to the talented.

He's forceful where necessary. 'Don't ever want to be on his bad side,' says pupil. Not out of fear but because 'wouldn't want him to lose his respect for you.' Not a hacker and slasher, think parents, whose perception is of new talent being grafted on to the staff team (average age early 40s) and tired areas jazzed up with a bit of extra colour – new chaplain, impressively also a maths teacher and rugby coach, a case in point. School was 'ripe for a shake up,' said one mother. Mr Hoskins seen as the person to administer it.

He's taking the school by stealth (as well as charm) and doing the evolution not revolution thing

State educated himself and with a strong moral purpose, he'd like to up numbers of foundation places for disadvantaged pupils.

Academic matters: Edging ever closer to nearby powerhouses like Hampton and RGS as locals wake up to educational excellence on their doorstep and, in small but growing numbers, start to make this their first choice. Elsewhere, pupils' brilliance polished till it shines but personalities remain unchanged. Here, parents feel pupils' characters have room to grow, too.

Pupils, particularly those living some distance away and involved in matches, clubs and events will, however, need to arrive with a few ready-to-wear sterling qualities, headed by keenness and motivation. Disorganised types can end up trailing home to face sizeable quantities of homework ('they do get quite a lot,' said mother) and a few, say parents, may not last the course. School disagrees. 'No-one has left due to being disorganised,' says Mr Hoskins.

Won't be for want of numerous helping hands from the school, reflection of high staff to pupil ratios – just over one to eight – and reasonable class sizes (17 up to year 11, 10 in sixth form). Following substantial makeover, there's more setting, regular testing and additional feedback on academic attainment with boys awarded bronze, silver and gold grades for effort as well as achievement. 'Have no worries about where son is going academically – am more than comfortable,' said parent.

School is notable for quality of support – currently offered to around 80 pupils, vast majority with assorted dys difficulties, and very small numbers with ADD, ADHD, ASD, visual or speech and language issues. Just under 20 with EAL are supported individually or in small groups.

Regardless of need, pupils must be able to thrive in relatively (but not ridiculously) fast-paced environment. 'If they need so much support that it would be difficult to access, this wouldn't be the right place because your confidence takes an absolute hammering,' says Mr Hoskins. If make the grade, progress is often exceptional, helped by well thought out support including ADR (assess, do and review) programme.

While overall pass rates remain pretty consistent (at A level, A*/A grades 40 per cent, 75 per cent A*/B in 2017, though record 74 per cent A*-A/9-7 at GCSE) subject popularity ebbs and flows. A few more girls taking A level physics would be good (numbers are very small) though those we spoke to felt were well supported whatever their interests.

Subject choices are fairly standard up to GCSE (electronics is about as outré as it gets), though there's a research project for year 9s. Post-16, there's an impressive 27 A level options include graphics, taken by around 10 each year. Will also keep subjects going for very tiny numbers (one or two year each year taking computing, for example, slightly more taking art). Most now take three A levels, plus additional courses from a range that includes music technology, general studies and further maths.

It's reinforced by boundless staff enthusiasm. Every subject gets own write up – 'It's been another bumper year in the world of physics,' burbles school mag – as well as appetite-whetting extras such as recently-formed medical society where would-be doctors justify career choice to peers. Most mentioned by parents, however, is fabulous Futuretech programme – DT reimagined to give free rein to 'what if' projects linking STEM subjects. DIY model wind turbines created by second years and visit from TESLA among the many highlights.

Games, options, the arts: In October 2017 we opened our new Indoor Cricket Centre. This impressive structure will offer world-class facilities that can be used by both pupils and the wider community for training and skills' development. Inside the main hall are five cricket nets, various bowling machine options and the PitchVision cricket system which combines motion tracking and video analysis for players, whatever their level.

Old Reedonians' website may convey message that life without sport is one wasted ('injury, marriage or the arrival of children...' quoted as distinct inconveniences) but school these days is natural home for those eager to improve pen or bow hold as well as racket grip. Head, with consummate diplomacy, felt by parents to avoid any suggestion of sports vs the rest, drama and music sharing equal place on the rostrum. Agreed, says teacher. 'You just don't win world titles for them.' (Just as well given that sports trophies take up almost enough space to host own open day.)

Ham-fisted, two-left feet or otherwise, everyone will have talent, however limited, coaxed out of them. Parents and pupils stress effectiveness of school's approach – a fine balance between compulsion and encouragement. 'Do something whether you like it or not – and you mostly do,' said sixth former. Activities – 75 plus, ranging from archery to golf and judo to silk painting – cater for dabblers as well as enthusiasts. Sixth form boys – who have fourth X1 fixtures – organise 'not very good' gentleman's hockey team just for the fun of it. 'We just want to play,' said one.

There's also popular D of E (with strong philanthropic dimension) and CCF. Don't neglect social skills either, with everything from debating club

Appetite-whetting extras such as recently-formed medical society where would-be doctors justify career choice to peers

(so can participate in discussion) to Toastmasters for older pupils (where discover how to lead it). Many new sixth formers, compelled to try previously hated activities (two a week in years 11, 12 and 13; three to year 10) converted into fans. Brilliant for bonding even if not, thought pupil.

Strength of arts, performing and visual, particularly impressive, from scale of ambition to levels of investment and numbers involved (over 200 individual music lessons each week and a fifth of all pupils taking part in recent concert). Sixth form technicians, recently rewarded with two RADA technical course places, work into small hours to put final touches to lighting for major productions (created a big top – inside – from scratch for The Impresario), while music scholar who complained about piano quality wasn't just listened to but flown to Germany to help choose brand new Steinway.

Whatever your specialist interest, facilities excellent, packed in on relatively compact site. Trees know their place – confined largely to the perimeter so space can be given over to cricket, rugby (big and little pitches), two Astros and tennis courts. Whole shebang has accolade of being accredited by Tim Henman Foundation as model primary school outreach programme for others to follow.

Inevitably, sport remains biggest selling point for some families. 'Why we chose the school,' said mother. Biggest lure for the ultra-talented are three academies (golf, tennis and skiing) offering elite coaching (every major sport comes with own professional), flexible timetable and extra training (before or after school and – in case of skiiers – sent off to the snow), plus osteo clinic and sports injury rehabilitation. Youngest sports scholars enjoy substantial perk of all day trackies to avoid frequent changes of clothes, school adamant that no wizard/muggle divisions exist. No swollen heads either – 'they've lovely boys,' said parent. Individual successes at national and county level are copious across range of age groups and sports (including 26 for hockey). Ditto stonking team triumphs (tennis – three consecutive wins in World Schools' Championship; golf – regular national finalists). New indoor cricket centre, available to outsiders as well as pupils, includes system that 'combines motion tracking and video analysis'.

System relies on, and gets, happy cooperation between academic and sports staff, particularly in sixth form with pupils allowed to devote some private study time to sport ('a privilege and must be able to invest time to catch up on work,' stresses school). Significant weapon is sizeable number of teachers so blessed with charm that can even make punishments a laugh a minute. 'If we forget our kit, coach makes us run and touch all the lines on the pitch – there are about 500,' said junior pupil, chortling at the very memory. 'Makes it so funny.' You probably had to be there.

Smaller numbers mean fewer limits, thought one mother. 'At other schools you have to make choices early on, here they can do anything.' One originally sports-centric boy was also singing and acting at every opportunity – slightly to his own surprise, as well as that of parents. 'Confidence has gone through the roof.'

Boarding: Though only 15 per cent board, juniors in The Close, seniors in School House, sixth formers upstairs in own courtyard block (currently under refurbishment to provide glassed-over study area and café) complete with lecture theatre, they're a happy clan, with a strong and oft-(very oft) mentioned sense of community. Sixth form girl boarders, a particularly minuscule group (under a handful in upper sixth), flock together and take pleasure in niche status, downstairs common room a homely oasis of papers and possessions. Offers full, weekly or occasional B&B – a boon to any child with a late finishing match or parents with work commitments. Despite low numbers, school rarely feels empty, say pupils.

Old Reedonians' website may convey message that life without sport is one wasted ('injury, marriage or the arrival of children...' quoted as distinct inconveniences)

Accommodation is spick and span, white and magnolia the prevailing signature décor, eye-catching touches headed by world's reddest kitchen in School House, neon signs and slinky bar-style seating for its 36 year 9-11 boarders. Elsewhere, communal areas are businesslike rather than breathtaking, though as long as there's space enough to pack in the crowds for must-watch TV (usually matches, we'd assume), pupils clearly don't mind.

Tempo of life is exceedingly brisk and a marvel of logistics, junior boarders showered and powered into breakfast in just 30 minutes – even faster when bacon's on the menu (food – bar some evening meals – generally excellent) – while all-action weekends for everyone are filled with (more) sport, mixed age cinema trips, shopping (in groups of three, one phone compulsory) and doughnutting (descending Sandown Park's dry ski slope in rubber ring).

Pace accounts for absence of personal touches. Some pinboards stay empty because there's just no time to unpack. 'Too much to do,' said pupil, who'd had initial reservations about absence of down time. No longer. 'Now realise that being busy is perfect.'

Cheerful matrons keep everything ticking over, washing machines permanently on spin cycle (18 loads of laundry in one day a personal best), aided and abetted by thoughtful, compassionate houseparents proffering small hours hot chocolate and DVDs when homesickness strikes and with welcome ability to tread the fine line between firmness and latitude. 'With boarding you try to make it like a family,' says one. 'When someone's done something wrong you try to think if they'd be in trouble for something similar at home and separate something that's annoying – like being too loud or watching TV too late – from something that merits a detention.'

Background and atmosphere: Founded in 1813 by Andrew Reed, social reformer, minister and serial setter upper of charitable institutions (and upsetter of fellow trustees), but the only school to survive intact, discounting change of name (originally the London Orphan Asylum), location (arrived here via Clapton, Watford and – briefly during WW2 evacuation – Totnes), and financing (fee-paying pupils first admitted 1950s, though charitable focus on foundationers has never changed).

Handy for M25 and with Gatwick and Heathrow just a 30-minute drive away, it's a cinch to get to, as long as you avoid rush hour and don't take address too literally (says Cobham but actually in Oxshott – it's a postal area thing).

Heart of the school is restored arts and crafts building, home – among other areas – to attractive chapel and library, surrounded by separate music school, labs, classrooms and airy sixth form block with lecture theatre which doubles as venue for film screenings. Packs a lot on to 40-acre site – including mysterious amounts of lost property, despite school's comprehensive naming service. 'Usually get it back but can take a very long time,' said mother. 'In my experience, much better than other schools on this,' says Mr Hoskins.

Overcoming pupil/space dilemma by corralling outside areas and roofing them over – small courtyard is now a conservatory-style dining hall extension while The Close boasts an impressive stretch reception, 100 or so tennis balls trapped on the roof a happy reminder of previous incarnation as impromptu sports pitch.

With master plan now agreed, there's plenty of development happening. Likely to be equally imaginative and ambitious, says Mr Hoskins, though won't put up buildings all over the place and ramp up pupil numbers as 'would ruin what we have.'

Pastoral care, well-being and discipline: Cordial relations between staff and pupils ensure that lines are clearly drawn, usually toed and rarely crossed, mild eccentricities tolerated while not actively encouraged. Year 11 boy, dealing with exam tension in his own way by sporting a rolled up trouser leg, was clocked by adult tour guide – 'High spirits' – then left to own (if rather more self-conscious) devices. Headmaster has flexed disciplinary muscles for serious breaches (as with other schools, drink and drugs the main culprits) – offenders likely to be asked to leave.

Everyone very much at home here, much emphasis on age-appropriate three-day induction programme. For year 7s includes on-site camping and games of chubby bunnies ('See how many marshmallows you can get in your mouth and still say "chubby bunnies",' said pupil – well, of course). Activities for new sixth form girls include rather more sophisticated (and confectionary-free) meal out in Kingston.

For first two years, The Close, a separate building, is a world in miniature. 'Opportunity to settle very well without being overwhelmed – a home away from home,' said parent. Have own houses, games, activities and responsibilities, plus quality pastoral back up from sixth form mentors, a high profile and popular presence, who dispense quiz questions and chocolate brownies, organise house drama and deal with acts of minor unkindness.

System works exceptionally well, houseparents keeping a close eye on charges, say parents, but not exclusively so. 'Everyone needs to have an idea of collective responsibilities,' said pupil. 'If they're not willing to put in the effort, they wouldn't be suitable.' For the majority who are, individual record books – an initiative from the chaplain (he's buzzing with them) – will be a chance to list golden deeds of compassion and virtue as well as mere academic success.

Pupils and parents: With just a handful of expats and around 12-15 international students, 80 per cent from Hong Kong, most families are UK-based Brits living maximum of an hour's travel time away, network of school bus routes reading like estate agent's bumper book of desirable destinations (Putney, Richmond, Wimbledon and Guildford).

Quality pastoral back up from sixth form mentors, a high profile and popular presence, who dispense quiz questions and chocolate brownies, organise house drama

Foundationers, some with traumatising early life experiences, are painlessly absorbed. 'Ensures other children don't live in a bubble,' says school. Parents agree, though one warned against excessive hikes in school fees. 'Run the risk that end up with two categories, those who can afford it and foundationers, with a gap in the middle.' Mr Hoskins points out that 'in the last two years, fee increases were less than many of our competitors.'

End product includes plenty of high-grade sportspeople (Tim Henman most glorious example), though crop of musicians, actors and entertainers is almost as substantial. One 1980s batch (they organise alumni by decade here) yielded two opera singers, an art dealer and a Jordanian prince. Plenty of somethings in the City as well.

Sports, arts or royalty, Old Reedonians stay in touch. 'Keep caring and giving to family long after graduation,' said one. 'Once a Reedonian, always a Reedonian.' Partners, we were told, like to swap notes, finding ORs nicer and gentler than the common herd.

Judging by today's happy mixed age lunchtime throng, pupils impressively (and unusually) relaxed about talking about their feelings, oldest pupils encouraging the youngest to speak, everyone giving strong impression of liking everyone else, nothing much has changed.

Entrance: At 11+ English and maths tests plus VR, all (normally) taken at school in January for entry in September. For 13+, register a good three years in advance, pre-test in year 6, CE in June if at prep school. Other candidates sit English, maths, science, modern language and VR papers. Sixth form hopefuls have observed lesson to judge teamwork and two subject-based exams – superior ability mentioned by inspectors.

Foundation pupils – some referred by own school or children's charity – have range of difficulties, from financial hardship to loss of a parent or seriously ill sibling. Need to sit entrance exams and will also have home visit.

While greater competition inevitably means more able applicants achieving well beyond pass mark, head doesn't go by grades alone. Good relationships with prep heads essential for CE so can consult 'if they bomb because of real pastoral issues,' and may still take, with academic support to fill in gaps.

Children of former pupils urged to identify themselves at registration. Won't give you edge over competition, says Mr Hoskins – but bad news is more likely to be accompanied by a phone call.

Exit: About 15 per cent exit post-16 – fewer each year – freedom offered by local sixth form colleges ('longer hair and earrings,' says Mr Hoskins) the main lure. If shy of required GCSE grades (official minimum 16 points – equates to around eight B grades) school will help if possible, though substitute subjects may be imposed (DT rather than physics, say). Also possible to repeat years.

Translates into gamut of places: Nottingham, Leeds, Southampton, Loughborough, the London lot (UCL, King's Brunel, Royal Holloway), plus hot favourites like Bristol, Exeter, Durham feature most years. Courses ditto – modelmaking to nutrition, speech and language to quantity surveying and design in every permutation. Several taking medicine (two in 2017), though geography currently having a moment in sunshine; seven off overseas in 2017, including one to Princeton.

Money matters: Bursaries for foundationers up to 110 per cent of fees. Also range of scholarships – DT and drama at 13+ and in the sixth form – also open to existing pupils, plus headmaster's award for able but not quite scholarship level candidates at 11+ and CE; additional scholarships awarded to existing pupils during school career if merited. Fees steep but include majority of extras – meals to choir tours so 'looks more expensive than it is,' said mother.

Remarks: One parent equated school to post-privatisation Jaguar – took a while for shift in quality to be recognised. 'Took years for prices to catch up, but they did.' With Mr Hoskins in the driving seat, this revamped model is definitely proving an all terrain winner.

Rochester Independent College

54

Star Hill, Rochester, Kent ME1 1XF

01634 828115 | admissions@rochester-college.org | www.rochester-college.org

Ages: 11-19 (boarding from 16)

Pupils: 281; sixth form: 182; Boarders: 60

Day: £12,300 – £17,500 pa; Boarding: + £11,400 – £13,200 pa; International Non EEA Boarding £31,700 – £35,700 pa

Principal: Alistair Brownlow MA (St Andrews) MPhil (Glasgow) in English, joined as a new graduate in 1997. He's a great communicator, bouncing with enthusiasm like Tigger, and expressing the school's beliefs and methods with an articulacy which backs up his reputation as an ace English teacher.

Academic matters: There's no uniform or dress code, and the teachers are just as likely as pupils to be wearing a hoody. Everyone goes by their first name. So far so hippy – until you walk around the building during lessons. Hush has descended, and opening a classroom door reveals silent pupils, and desks in rows. Alistair says: 'People try to place us in the progressive/alternative mould, but we're not. It's common sense; small classes, good teaching, and an informal but ordered and respectful atmosphere.'

The next surprise comes in the teaching methods. 'We teach-test-teach-test,' says Alistair. The idea that testing thwarts children gets short shrift here. 'A lot of schools don't do enough regular testing. At A level we do a test every week in each subject. If we're going to put something right we need a rigorous diagnosis of what is wrong,' Alistair says. There's no objection to this degree of testing from pupils – in fact the students seem to welcome it. 'Testing means you can't get delusions, you really know where you are at any point,' said one. Another, who was told by her grammar school that she needed to 'lower her sights', said: 'The teaching style is completely different, we are tested all the time and my grades have gone up consistently.'

There is a firm concentration on exam technique, but still the school isn't seen as an exam factory. One sixth form pupil said: 'The focus is on exams, but it is still enriching. We get a two hour lesson for everything which means the teachers can drift off topic which helps a lot with general knowledge and essay subjects.'

Teachers are 'very passionate about their subjects,' say parents, and another pupil, comparing the teaching to that at his former grammar school, said: 'The teaching is of a better quality and the teachers know their subject to a greater depth.' And a pupil at the lower end of the school said: 'You don't get to the end of one lesson without doing something fun.'

Many students transfer here after poor progress at AS or A level and the effect can be dramatic. One pupil told us he was predicted to get Ds and Es at AS; he moved from his grammar to the college in February, and in July he achieved three As at AS and an A at A level. Another student moved after getting a U at AS, and she said, 'In my first two weeks here I learned more than I had in the whole previous year.'

There are three pathways through the sixth form, mainly set in different teaching groups. There are those doing a two year A level course through the school; students who have transferred here for year 13 after a disappointing year 12; and those who have done two years elsewhere and are doing retakes. The A level programme is flexible with no option blocks, and students can do speed courses in a new subject to complement retakes. Results for 2017 A levels show 32 per cent of entries achieving A*/A and 60 per cent A*-B. Maths is the biggest A level subject. English literature and film studies are also strong departments, both having received Good Schools Guide awards in recent years.

At GCSE, biology, chemistry and physics are taught at IGCSE level for those aiming to study sciences at A level, and students also take the IGCSE in English and English literature. Languages on offer include German, French and Spanish, but it is not compulsory to take a language. Pupils can also take subjects such as astronomy, film studies and photography at GCSE. In 2017, 20 per cent of GCSEs were A*-A/9-7 and 53 per cent were A*-B/9-6.

Parents especially appreciate the efforts made to ensure each pupil gains the best possible grade. One said: 'There are a lot of extra lessons before exams, in the holidays and so on. They will do as much as they can if they think you can improve your grade.'

Another praised the fact that they don't charge for extra tuition in the evenings and holidays, adding: 'I was concerned about my son's maths and suggested getting him some tuition. They said it was their responsibility, and I should not be looking for tutors. They did some extra work with him and he got an A, so I was ecstatic.'

Now offers an apprenticeship course in boatbuilding, enabling students to gain City and Guilds qualifications up to NVQ level 3.

Games, options, the arts: Sport is growing, but the school doesn't have the infrastructure to provide serious provision. There's a newly created rugby team for year 11 to 13s, which uses the facilities of a local rugby club and is coached by a player from England's women's team. It also supports those playing at higher levels – one sixth former is training with a London football club, and the school enables him to fit lessons around his sporting commitments. Another sixth former is hoping to compete as a sprinter in the next Paralympics. But as one student points out, it is not the type of school which tends to attract the sporty, and so PE provision tends to be more activity based, like ice skating, sailing, self-defence and climbing.

Lower down the school the students play in mixed teams, so boys say games have to be less rough.

It's a place for individuals; there's a lovely air of tolerance and warmth between the pupils – many of whom seem relieved to have found a home among other square pegs

It would be hard to find better provision for an artist. GCSEs are offered in six disciplines – fine art, graphics, photography, textiles, ceramics and 3D. Some students take three of these to A level, which enables them to bypass a foundation year. There is terrific work on display. Two students have won places on the prestigious fine art degree course at UCL's The Slade School. Dominik Klimowski, former BBC online picture editor, teaches photography, and local artist Billy Childish is a visiting lecturer.

There's a rich cultural programme – a drama theatre hosts visiting theatre companies and art shows, and the school's on-site cinema regularly hosts the National Schools' Film week.

Boarding: Boarding is only available to students of 16+. Virtually all students have single rooms. Some have a very small 'pod' ensuite, otherwise it's shared bathrooms. Furnishings are basic but the Georgian high ceilings and big windows add light and space, and all rooms have a phone and internet point. There's a big common room with a pool table and comfy chairs, and a study for quiet work.

Currently 60 out of 280 students are boarders – 40 per cent of these are from the UK, 11 per cent from Europe, and the remainder from countries including Canada, USA, Thailand, China, Russia, Nigeria and South Africa.

Background and atmosphere: It started as an A level college in 1984, and extended to take pupils from year 7 in 2007. Bought by Dukes Education in 2016.

The campus is as unique as the school. It started as one terraced house, but as the school expanded, it gradually bought up 13 properties in adjoining roads, including a Georgian terrace which houses the boarding accommodation. What would once have been the back gardens to these houses now form the grounds with ancient apple trees and wild garden areas, paths to secret nooks and crannies, a viewing platform to climb – and an oversized garden shed where founder Brian (Pain) likes to hold his maths classes. Students work on garden projects such as the allotment as part of their D of E award, and the gardens have won a Kent Wildlife Trust Gold Award.

Mid-career, Brian took time out of teaching to become an architect, and the campus reflects this interest. The theatre in the grounds is known as the Womble building – the theatre space is underground, whilst over the top there's an outdoor seating area which can be used as an open-air auditorium.

An igloo-like structure in the garden is used as an outdoor classroom, shelter, and quiet space. Intended to inspire and motivate, it has a central roof opening for cloud watching.

When we visited the school was awaiting delivery of some steel sculptural musical gates – an art installation created by Henry Dagg, who plays with Icelandic pop star Bjork, and has transformed his garden fence into a glockenspiel. You will be able to play three octaves on these gates, sufficient to pass your music A level, according to Brian. Reflecting on the £100,000 price tag of these gates, Brian says, 'I'm committed to culture'.

Pastoral care, well-being and discipline: A level students have one-to-one meetings with a personal tutor every couple of weeks, more frequently if they wish, and pupils lower down the school have individual meetings every half term.

Parents receive formal reports once a month, which are 'meaningful, not full of euphemisms, and not from a software package'. Younger pupils have a parents' evening, but in the sixth form tutors deal directly with the students as young adults, and reports only go home which they have seen first. 'We promise there will be no surprises through that feedback,' says Alistair.

A number of the pupils have been labelled as bad apples or having limited prospects in previous settings, but have quickly turned things around at the college, where they are free from discipline based on minutiae. One such pupil, previously at a girls' independent, said: 'I was constantly getting picked on by teachers and getting detentions for stupid things, like going to the toilet'.

Ancient apple trees, wild garden areas, paths to secret nooks and crannies – and an oversized garden shed where founder likes to hold his maths classes

They are strict about homework and behaviour, but removing petty rules means the rapport between pupils and teachers is much better. Or, as one pupil put it, 'The only thing to rebel against here is education itself'.

Other pupils have come from grammars where they felt under too much pressure, or from large schools where they felt overwhelmed, and all say they are learning better and enjoying school more here. 'I worried a lot at my old school, here it's a better environment,' said one. 'At my old school if you improved, they didn't notice,' said another.

Parents all speak highly of the pastoral care, and the growth in confidence they have witnessed in their children. One has three children at the school and she said: 'They are all very different but they are spot on about all of their weaknesses and strengths.'

Pupils and parents: Local pupils form 70 per cent of the cohort and come from a wide catchment – there are minibuses from towns including Tonbridge, Tunbridge Wells, Maidstone, Ashford and Sevenoaks, and the train station opposite brings pupils from Bromley and London. A further 15 per cent come from elsewhere in the UK, and 15 per cent from overseas, including Thai government scholars (who tend to be very high performers, often ending up at Oxbridge).

Numbers lower down the school are small. It starts with around 10 pupils in year 7, who have deliberately opted for a small and different type of school. These are added to over the years, generally by pupils who have been disaffected or haven't thrived in other schools, to numbers in the mid-20s for GCSE years. By sixth form it grows to 50 in year 12, and 130 in Year 13/14. This is something to consider in the younger year groups, especially as currently two girls are each the only girl in their years. The flipside is it makes for more natural relationships between the boys and girls and less of the gender division that you see in big schools – they are clearly relaxed in each other's company. None of the pupils or parents we spoke to saw the small year groups as a problem – there's much more mixing between years, and pupils keep up with other friends in their neighbourhood – and many see this as a plus.

The students are a strikingly nice bunch. It's a place for individuals, and there's a lovely air of tolerance and warmth between the pupils – many of whom seem relieved to have found a home among other square pegs. 'They look after each other, and if someone does well they are pleased about this,' said a parent. Those whose strengths lie outside the traditionally alpha areas of academic or sporting have their own kudos. 'There is a lot more respect for art and creativity,' said one pupil.

Students say it is not competitive, and that there's a huge range in academic ability and ambition. 'If you work your hardest and get an E that's fine,' said one. 'Stronger people help the weaker people; no-one's struggling because everyone helps each other,' said another.

Parents love the lack of school gate competitiveness: 'That playground talk, everyone wanting their child to be in the top set, you don't have that here,' said one relieved mother.

About 50 per cent of pupils have been previously in the independent sector, but a lot of pupils come from families with no tradition of private education.

Entrance: It's non-selective in that there's no entrance exam for children joining at 11 or 13, and there's no minimum GCSE grade requirements for sixth form entry. But every prospective student is interviewed, and the principals say they do turn some away.

Direct entry into any year group at any point in the academic year is possible, and places can be secured in the short gap between exam results and the start of a new term. Around 60 students join each year, either to retake their A levels having completed two years of A levels elsewhere, or directly into year 13 after disappointing results in year 12 elsewhere.

Exit: The courses students go on to reflect the broad range of abilities and interests catered for: some go on to read law, maths, medicine or classics; others

have taken up courses in animal behaviour, film studies, marketing, photography or midwifery. Four to Oxbridge in 2017 (three of them Thai government scholars); two medics and a dentist; other destinations range from Anglia Ruskin (popular music) to Exeter (law) to Lund, Sweden (physics).

Money matters: Around £100,000 per year goes into means-tested bursaries, which are awarded not on academic ability, but 'if we think they'll make a good contribution'. Scholarships include the Ralph Steadman Art Scholarship, which offers a two year full scholarship for A levels.

The school has a policy to keep extras to the minimum – music lessons, buses and exam fees are extra, but extracurricular trips are kept deliberately modest. 'We don't take for granted that parents have bottomless pits of money,' says Alistair.

Remarks: This won't be one that sits on your shortlist and you can't make up your mind about. You'll either love or hate this place. Your money won't buy the trappings of a public school – no mahogany-rich headmaster's study, certainly no suave head in a handmade suit. No pupils with collars and lips firmly buttoned. No PTA committees or fundraising balls. For some that will be a blessed relief.

You'll get that warm buzz in your heart when you recognise your kid in the personalities here – or not. That might be one of several types we saw – the quirky one, condemned to be picked on in an average school; the fiercely intelligent, who has rubbed teachers up the wrong way by being too smart for his own good in other settings; the kid whose education got derailed by too much focus on petty rules and discipline.

It won't suit sporting jocks – facilities are meagre, and there are rarely enough pupils of the right age and inclination to make a team.

But it's a great option for the cash-strapped; many parents with only enough gold in the pot to fund a couple of years in the independent sector buy in for the last year of GCSEs, for the A level course, or for retakes. And it's a sound investment – most improve considerably on expectations at their previous school.

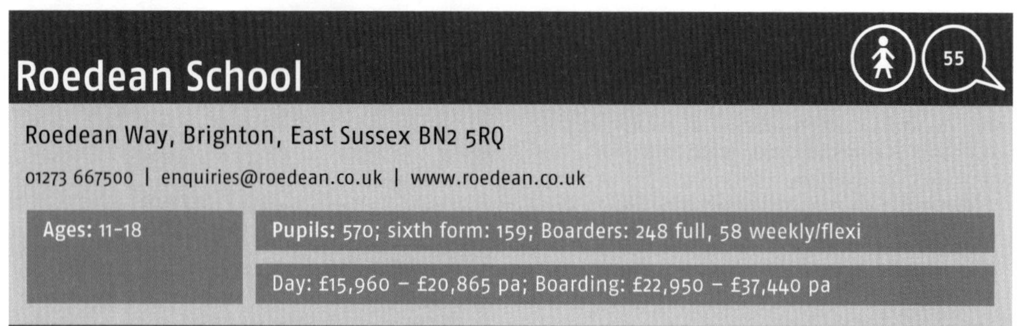

Roedean School

Roedean Way, Brighton, East Sussex BN2 5RQ

01273 667500 | enquiries@roedean.co.uk | www.roedean.co.uk

Ages: 11–18

Pupils: 570; sixth form: 159; Boarders: 248 full, 58 weekly/flexi

Day: £15,960 – £20,865 pa; Boarding: £22,950 – £37,440 pa

Headmaster: Since 2013, Mr Oliver Blond (40s). Previously head at Henrietta Barnett School, one of top selective state girls' schools in the UK, for seven year stint – perfect for seeing through a generation of pupils without starting to repeat himself, he says. Before that, deputy head, North London Collegiate, so something of an expert in all-girls education. Not certain post here was natural fit until visited, when was instantly won over by school's charisma. So far, the feeling seems to be mutual. 'Aspirational, sweet and delightful,' said old girl.

Busy, busy, busy – as well as teaching (English, drama, philosophy) also academic director of the Princes' Teaching Institute charity, as well as raising two young children with wife Helen, teacher turned successful children's author. Highly articulate (goes with the headship territory), he's also soft-voiced and a great listener (both rarer commodities). Forthright mothers, old girls and especially pupils who 'know everything that I took six months to learn': he listens to the lot.

Formerly forbidding mood amongst tight-knit school community, including a few who were a tad suspicious to find bloke in charge, now one of almost palpable relief, with rave reviews for speed with which Mr Blond has tackled perma-complacency that dominated teaching and attitudes. School is going back to roots – academic, all-round school for British girls with a smaller percentage of international students, though with many more day students and total numbers increasing to more than 500, building on an already healthy surplus.

While working on amplifying siren call to Londoners, even contemplating lowering weekly boarding prices so a closer match for day school fees in the capital, he's also ensuring locals start to see school not as impenetrable posh fortress but accessible Sussex place offering warm welcome on the cliff tops. They're coming round, brand starting to feature on trendy Brighton ravers' educational wish lists, with admissions team fielding 300 per cent increase in enquiries from locals and over 170 families attending recent open day (one of three).

Integration by stealth should help. Girls and boys from local schools now involved in co-ed go-karting to hip-hop curriculum enrichment, while sixth form Wednesday afternoon community service includes sessions in local primaries. School is also pushing bursaries for state schools in the area. And, yes, though previous attempts have been made to bring in bright but financially challenged, with slightly sporadic results, we'd back Mr Blond to make it happen.

Ensuring locals start to see school not as impenetrable posh fortress but accessible Sussex place

Longer term, would like a third of places offered to UK pupils on needs-blind basis (school already offers some support to similar proportion of existing pupils). Will only work, though, if pupils and families, with or without scholarships, have evidence of change. 'A school that's waiting to be different just isn't enough,' he says. 'That's why we've gone at it really quite quickly.'

Presciently, Mr Blond's first choice career was, apparently, Spiderman. Scaling the heights and accomplishing the impossible? No wonder he's proving so successful.

Academic matters: Formidable competition from other local independents including Brighton College and Lancing, and any number of London options, has made school necessarily self-critical about results. Things now very definitely on the up, with 76 per cent of GCSE grades coming in at A*-A/9-7 in 2017.

At A level, English, humanities (with exception of history) and languages currently minority interests, and of the star subjects, maths is outstanding year in, year out. Further maths also highly successful. Almost the cue for spot of subtle back-patting, A*/A grade percentage at A level at 54 per cent in 2017, 80 per cent A*-B.

Parents are hugely relieved that school's previous shortcomings have been addressed. The fear had been that essence and iconic status as landmark British girls' boarding school were in danger of ebbing away, with rise in international pupils and non-negotiable format – full boarding or nothing – putting off many potential customers. And while nothing wrong with cultural diversity – 'you get a huge level of tolerance for other people and ideas,' thought insider – proportion of international pupils had caused sense of alienation, numbers of OGs sending own children dropping like a stone.

One of Mr Blond's first acts was to undertake wholesale lesson observation. Though he 'didn't wave a big stick,' thought school insider, a third of staff and half the heads of department left during his first year, many taking arrival as cue to retire. Parents' perspective distinctly un-nuanced. 'About time somebody put a bomb up them,' said mother. 'If I'm paying £35,000 a year, I don't want my daughter to be told to read page 46 if she doesn't understand.'

Focus since has been to seek out 'dynamic, inspirational and energetic staff with new ideas and teaching methods,' he says. The ones we saw in action certainly lived up to their star billing, with head of drama scoring bonus marks from pupils for wearing 'Vans with a suit' (must play well in Brighton). Parents approve of youth and energy. Girls agree. 'They make you feel you can do anything,' said one.

School is also recruiting master teachers, heroic role and a half involving mentoring, studying for extra qualifications and doing a spot of original research on top of normal teaching duties – and quite possibly summoned by shining silhouette of MA gown into night sky.

More is accomplished with less, school day finishing earlier (and no longer at different time each day), some assemblies moved from afternoon to morning slots, lunch break increased and lessons shortened by five minutes. Parents approve, especially day families – under older regime many pupils were simply 'too tired,' thought one, to take advantage of the benefits of plugging into 24/7 boarding school culture.

Rethink of mixed ability teaching also under way following parental concerns about sluggish pace in English lessons. Those needing additional English help in sixth form able to take pre-A level course to bring them up to scratch, parallel streams operating in earlier years.

School also offers strong support for pupils with learning difficulties, staffing recently bumped up with appointment of new head of English with extensive experience of dyslexia. 'They push the message that dyslexic children are taken on the same basis as everybody else,' said parent. Engagement in lessons the only line that must be toed, says Mr Blond. Otherwise, school will do best to help, working with parents to put extra support – as needed – in place.

Get encouragement and self-confidence right, with school 'a platform for women to feel that anything is possible,' and good exam results will be the by-product

Million dollar question is how much can be achieved without recruiting more able pupils. Parents like current mix. 'Varied – not just full of professionals' kids who all want to go to Oxbridge,' said one. Mr Blond adamant that most important point is that 'girls at all levels will thrive here, though standard of entry is rising already with increased interest in the school.' Aspirational, yes, but 'won't become some hothouse and wasn't the case in last school.' Get encouragement and self-confidence right, with school 'a platform for women to go out and feel that anything is possible,' and good exam results will be the by-product with no need to go out and trawl for straight A grade students.

Key to success, he believes, is ensuring that pupils are listened to – he's very hot on fatalistic tendency of girls to see low grade as final judgment. Wants teachers to say less, listen more and help pupils articulate sometimes hidden ambitions so can be helped to achieve them.

Creation of more shared meeting areas – teachers' own dining hall has been sacrificed to the cause; common room with outstanding sea views is on its way out – will mean better communication. School, though, already good at 'finding people's strengths and helping them patch the weaknesses,' reckoned insider. 'Their drive is to make bring out the best in everybody, no matter what it is.' Girls all – unconsciously – smile when asked about life at school. Endorsement doesn't come much more authentic.

Games, options, the arts: A place that allows unforced blossoming amongst kindred spirits. 'Whether you're a singer, guitar player or sports player, it's very good to have social identity around the stuff you're interested in,' said mother.

No them and us divisions between sport and arts, and 'not too binary,' reckoned parent. Pupils full of praise for school's desire to cater for budding polymaths, from rescheduling some after-school events to offering subsidised or free overnight stays to ensure music or sports enthusiasts have the after-school opportunities they need, to new co-curricular programme for pupils in years 7 to 9, which offers two afternoons a week physical and intellectual stretch (car mechanics to Russian literature). Can result in unexpected blooming – only girls' team to reach national finals of programming competition, for example. Head's push for more community involvement is also building Brighton connection. 'The girls want to pitch in and go and visit old ladies in the sixth form, so there's very much a sense of community,' said OG.

'My daughter's not one who'll walk in and want to take over socially, but she's managed to have a very strong identity here'

Sports increasingly busy and competitive – 'come back in three years and we'll be winning everything,' reckoned girls, grounds at the front pitch-perfect with all the trimmings and added sea views, fixtures lists, previously on the empty side, busily being filled (and such a priority that features in new sports teacher's title), teams running to D in some sports. As elsewhere, nothing appears too much trouble for highly motivated staff, from developing tempting options for the less enthusiastic (zumba, synchronized swimming) to encouraging links with outside clubs, planning training programmes with external coaches for some of the sports scholars, even finding assessor for pupil working towards umpiring qualification.

Creativity, arts and music consistently good, even through leaner academic times. Art winds way into much of life there, with works on display as beautiful as design of original art room, partially glassed roof letting in northern light – 'the best,' says teacher – tiles with scenes of 1930s school life and, our favourite, a stove featuring heaven (gates and kettle stand), purgatory (oven) and hell (fiery flames), which broke in 1960s and hasn't (sadly) been used since.

Performing arts a particular strength, vibrant new drama team shaking things up, replacing previous worthy performance choices, all bang on syllabus but distinctly lacking in clapalong appeal, with a few more popular options. 'Was Chekhov before,' thought distinctly envious sixth form tour guides, watching infectiously toe-tapping rehearsal for open day, featuring selection from Hairspray.

Encouragement a feature of the process, with talented instrumentalists working with others who can't read music, for example. 'The degree to which they are supportive of one another is very striking. Has nice moral effect,' thought parent. Latent talent encouraged by trumpet, clarinet or violin lessons for all in first two years and around half the pupils have individual music lessons in school.

School trips extensive, masses abroad.

Boarding: Boarding – four houses each named for a colour and decorated to match – is wonderfully homely, rooms prettily proportioned and furnished, teapot lights hanging cosily down over breakfast bar to add domesticity to giant-height ceilings.

Boarders enjoy busy weekend activities such as visits to Buckingham Palace and local animal sanctuary, which day pupils can also sign up for. That said, with tunnel down to the sea (much enjoyed) and stile onto the South Downs (blank looks when mentioned to pupils, despite mention in school literature), staying put isn't half an attractive option.

Background and atmosphere: Founded by pioneering Lawrence sisters in 1885, heavy financial lifting courtesy of bunch of Midlands industrialists and friends, brilliant connections including artist Sir George Watts. Apart from brief reincarnation as HMS Vernon during the war, when was filled with Royal Navy electrical specialists while school was evacuated to Keswick, has been making stand for girls' education here for well over 100 years.

Like Eton, name has entered national consciousness as shorthand for certain type of education (school is commonly – though not uniquely – thought to be inspiration for Enid Blyton's Malory Towers series). Reality is 'consistent' finished product, thought parent: 'Articulate people who think for themselves and are conscious of the community.'

School now reacquiring spring in step, as increasing numbers of parents discount siren call of nearby co-eds whose idea of success is founded on 'noisy alpha male over-achiever,' said parent. Like others, finds this a less stressful enclave for her 'un-pushy' child. 'My daughter's not one who'll walk in and want to take over socially, but she's managed to have very strong identity here.'

Ditto school itself. 'Looking outward, aiming high,' says sixth form prospectus, with literal accuracy, dainty Oxbridge-style mini cloisters conveying – perhaps – subtle message about founders' higher education aspirations for pupils. Cosy-looking it ain't, at least from the front, with cliff top, slab-like buildings (think turreted Kendal mint cake) menacing coast road to Brighton, 45-acre site on permanent collision course with the elements, salt spray countered by special rations for plants, bracing winds the stuff of nostalgia for past pupils and, we were told by pupils, sea breezes, on one occasion, so strong that minibuses had to be used on-site to prevent accidental Mary Poppins-style departures. (Slightly overstated, thinks school, pointing out that 'we are a sunny seaside location, too.')

Odd Portakabin aside (wall of one is top party joint for local daddy long legs population), much to enjoy, including cheery dining halls (youngest two years have small scale version of their own, formerly staff area, table cloths in cupcake pinks and reds) while Horizons café, small box of lettuce aside, concentrates on essential sugar-rich snacks. Now developing a school farm (16 sheep and lambs arrived recently).

Inside, makeovers are transforming the place. Pupils have also been refurbished, with eccentric uniform policy (comfy in the week, smart only on Sundays) now reversed. Most now reconciled to house tie (initially a sticking point for a few) but all like smart, tailored blazers, badges crammed onto lapels recording sunny hours of school lives.

Pastoral care, well-being and discipline: You want it, they've got it, from excellent health centre taking range of difficulties such as diabetes in its stride to happy relationships between pupils and staff, hot chocolate and chats available for as long as needed to help boarders settle in.

School listens and responds to problems. 'Has been really easy to get help,' said parent. Bullying isn't tolerated – will expel – while effective peer listening programme, backed with proper training so sixth formers know when adult assistance should be sought, stops anyone suffering in silence. 'If someone is sitting alone in the dining hall, you'll tell them "you're going to sit with me – you're not going to be on your own",' said sixth former.

Big feature of success is open door policy that sees day girls on the premises, with school's blessing, well past advertised hours every evening and welcomed back at weekends.

'They are very clear that you are part of the school whether a day girl or boarder,' said mother. Integration something school has always done well. 'In my day, we were from very different backgrounds and just mulched along together and I'd be very surprised if there was a huge amount of perceived difference between day and boarding pupils now,' agreed OG.

Pupils and parents: 'Sweet, polite girls,' was one comment, though OG pointed out that niceness often comes with 'let's have a pop at it' attitude. 'Makes you more robust so perhaps you do a few more things you wouldn't have done.' Certainly borne out by career choice dilemmas faced by pupils, one agonising over whether to opt for being a barrister or singer, a second torn between primatology and acting...

A place that allows unforced blossoming amongst kindred spirits. 'Whether you're a singer, guitar player or sports player, it's very good to have social identity'

Pupils feel liberated by school's approach. 'When I came here I was quite a pessimistic, glass half empty person. Here, you feel you've got another chance to get things right if they go wrong, without feeling judged,' thought one.

Once part of the place, it doesn't let go easily, old girls busily spreading the word, enthusiasts one and all – and 'a mighty source of strength,' according to school literature. Old Roedeanians see school days as 'catalyst' for happiness and success in later life and very special part of lives. 'Felt I should be at the back giggling with my mates,' said one OG, who'd been back for recent visit.

Currently some 70 per cent of boarders are international. While 'it's always been quite an international school,' points out one (ample proof in OGs' website, with thriving communities all over the place), increasing recruitment of London and local families is creating a balance everyone is happy with. Mix and match in every sense 'and I like that.'

Entrance: Numbers rising, with year 7 intake now likely to be around 60. Majority from local schools, state and independent. Further 20 to 25 pupils join year 9, up to 60 admitted in sixth form.

Exit: Post-GCSE exodus now substantially slowed after massive confidence-boosting exercise to reassure pupils that school can deliver the results. 'Retentions will improve as soon as our A levels improve.'

Turns out girls with 'a bit of purpose in life,' thought OG. 'We're very good at being able to slightly reinvent ourselves and get on with just about anybody.' Strong on medicine (reflected in pupil base) – one in 2017 – and good showing in all the best places, with nearly 60 per cent off to Russell Group unis. Others off to eg Hong Kong, Melbourne, British Columbia, Chicago School of Art, Sydney International College of Management. Medicine, maths, engineering, and science-related degrees mop up around a third of degrees. History, economics, politics and business also popular.

Money matters: With £10 million foundation endowment, able to offer considerable help and scholarships worth up to 40 per cent of the fees, bright locals, in particular, should be making a beeline for the place. Brighthelm awards at 11+ and sixth form of up to 100 per cent for extremely bright girls from local state schools, who must be nominated by their current head.

Remarks: No danger of sun setting gently on past glories. This is a school that's going places. Sixth formers leaving as the tide turns would gladly do it all over again. 'Wish my daughter was starting there now,' says mother. 'It's a fabulous place.'

Royal Russell School

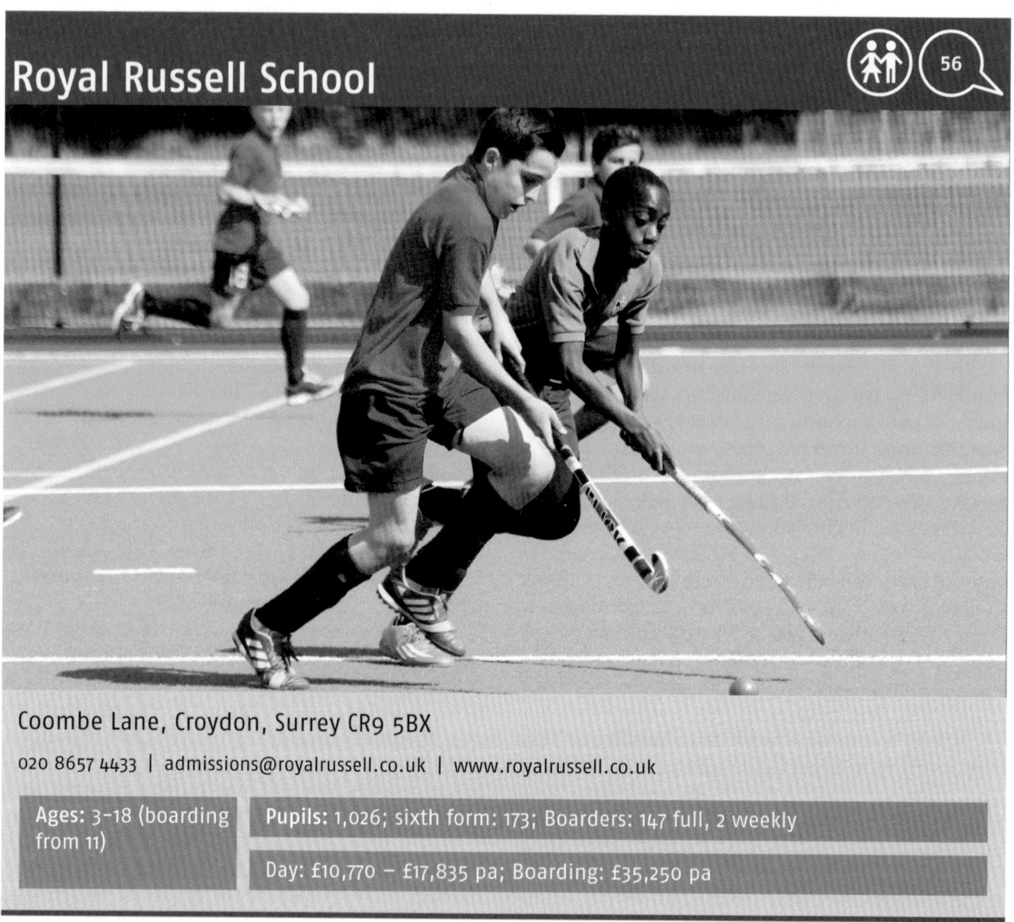

Coombe Lane, Croydon, Surrey CR9 5BX

020 8657 4433 | admissions@royalrussell.co.uk | www.royalrussell.co.uk

Ages: 3-18 (boarding from 11)

Pupils: 1,026; sixth form: 173; Boarders: 147 full, 2 weekly

Day: £10,770 – £17,835 pa; Boarding: £35,250 pa

Headmaster: Since 2011, Chris Hutchinson BMet. Second headship – first was at Newcastle School for Boys, which he joined in 2007. 'Teaching is in the blood,' he says. Brief attempt to escape destiny, opting for metallurgy degree instead of taking over family owned and run school in Wales, ended with realisation that wasn't keen enough to make a career of engineering. Worked for his father for two years, followed by formal teacher training at Cambridge and series of posts at top schools, starting with Clifton in 1990 where he met wife Alex – also a scientist. ('Some unfortunate Cliftonites were taught a lot of Hutchinson chemistry and physics.') Left as head of physics, moving to Wellington in 2000 in same role where was also a boarding housemaster.

Had completed full cycle (years 9 to 13) at Newcastle School for Boys when post here came up. Was encouraged to apply and felt instantly at home, compatible ethos of 'getting to know people well, giving them an individual opportunity to shine and supporting, rather than pushing them, on their journey' the clincher.

He fits in a bit of energetic teaching and is also notable for advanced child recognition skills. 'Knows them – every one,' said staff member in full on Tiny Tim mode (though demanded anonymity in case sounded a bit sycophantic). Pupils are equally chuffed. 'So, so good – really engages,' said one. 'Makes the effort to get to know you,'

Mrs Hutchinson has secured matching role at Woldingham (his and hers headships great as long as schools aren't rivals for same pupils – so far, only one pupil has moved between the two schools).

Mr Hutchinson finds time to indulge hobbies, including singing, gardening, Herefordshire, old Land Rovers and exercising his pets, dog Bosey (devoted Patterdale who spent considerable part of the interview comfortably curled up in his master's chair) and Linus the cat. Reflective, funny and kind, Mr Hutchinson is a major attraction for parents. Staff ditto. 'I took the job because of him,' said one, who praised mastery of details – 'Reports broken locks, picks up the rubbish' (he does, too – only gave up on stray banana skin on walk round because of its advanced stage of decomposition). 'Nothing is too trivial.' On day of visit, had just written 71 congratulatory notes to cast and backstage team of school production.

Headmaster of Royal Russell Junior School: Since 2009 is Mr James Thompson BA QTS. Previously at Ardingly College Prep School and before that at Kingswood Prep in Bath, both with linked senior schools. Dream was to be a professional sportsman, but opted for teacher training (with PE specialisation) after coaching at own prep in Kent and loving it.

If he needs a second opinion, family is riddled with teachers, while Viv, his wife, is head of a Notting Hill nursery school. Two daughters, both here – and doing best to hide whenever papa hoved into view, to giggles from friends – no doubt provide instant feedback as required.

Mr Thompson remains big on sport (cricket, hockey, golf, skiing), even writing anon column on umpiring for The Telegraph (if you need an insider's slant on the shoulder height rule in lacrosse, he's your man).

Parents approve, seeing him as genial, good at dealing with tricky types and (in the nicest possible way) typecast for the role. 'Prep school head through and through,' said one, approvingly. Approach distinctly dad-like (and all the better for it). 'Don't want to mollycoddle – better to learn the consequences,' he said, as we watched year 5s enthusiastically wielding fret saws to make moving wooden toys.

He's 'very kind, prefers being in PE kit, hates suits and wears pink trousers and odd socks,' say pupils.

We'd previously written up junior and senor school reviews separately. Now they're combined, with blessing of the school, something that tells you a lot about sense of togetherness emanating from the top.

Academic matters: Known as a gentler alternative to more selective schools in the area, though 'we do get the brightest students,' says school, which is now positioning itself as 'the family school of choice in south London,' (plays better than Croydon, 'a sell too far' for over-gentrified and easily shocked denizens of Nappy Valley and nearby sunny uplands of Wandsworth and Balham).

He fits in a bit of energetic teaching and is also notable for advanced child recognition skills. 'Knows them – every one,' said staff member in full on Tiny Tim mode

Entry requirements may not have shifted but winds of change are definitely well above zephyr level. Head doesn't need to shout it from the rooftops because, as numbers would suggest, parents are getting the message loud and clear, particularly when it comes to results. In 2017, 32 per cent of A level grades were A*/A (60 per cent A*-B) and 43 per cent GCSE grades A*-A/7-9, while government-issued value added table putting school right at the top of the country has pride of place in head's study.

Messrs Hutchinson and Thompson have trimmed, rather than hacked, their staff teams (many in any case nearing retirement age), who are now felt by parents to a strong bunch, if still a work in progress. 'You'll hear some rumblings and grumblings in the car park and it's usually about staff,' said one.

Thirty, average age close to 40, have completed first decade (one cheery and popular geography teacher on way to notching up ruby anniversary). For seniors, maximum class size is 24, average 18 to year 9, 15 for GCSE years and just eight for sixth form. Junior class average is 17 (parents make feelings known if numbers pass 20 in busy year).

New generation of vibrant staff newcomers love it here. One raved about mentoring ('have grown as a person'). Energy exemplified by new junior school librarian who has created oasis of great charm with imaginative use of lighting – Chinese lanterns, netting studded with fairy lights, even reading by torchlight sessions.

Despite school togetherness, teaching teams remain separate. Juniors have own staff temperamentally suited to this age group, with combination of specialists (music, computing, French, Spanish, sport and science) from nursery upwards, and dedicated class teachers who do the rest. Gives valuable continuity and security so pupils 'retain their childhood for as long as they can,' says Mr T. 'System works,' agreed parent. 'Always somebody to hear you out and help you.'

In senior school, star subjects include A level biology, unusually as popular with boys as girls. History, though, is the chart-topper among senior pupils, converting the marginally interested into passionately keen, helped by plenty of extras, including history society. Expect every other subject to rise to similar heights, says Mr Hutchinson.

With one day pupil speaking of new Korean and Russian friends and boarders enjoying tea with local families, horizons are impressively expanded for all

Differentiation, judging by positive feedback for teachers' willingness to explain a topic in limitless different ways until it clicked ('and if that doesn't work, will ask someone else to explain it to you') is a key part of the process. While 10 GCSEs is the norm, will adjust if necessary, provide after-school sessions and generally do what it takes. 'Always there to help,' said pupil.

Nurturing qualities appreciated by parents – 'you won't get that in some [other] schools,' said one. International pupils similarly feel exceptionally well looked after. Though around 20 per cent don't have English as a mother tongue and can arrive with large gaps in learning, expectation is that all will take GCSEs and A levels. Support provided as needed, generally at no extra cost, often yielding rapid results. One new international sixth form boarder was delighted to have passed GCSE maths in first term. Junior school similarly flexible with one pupil attending local centre part time, though with very young, 'immersion' usually does the trick.

School's reputation for supporting pupils with SEN remains undimmed. Currently, two senior students have EHCPs and between 14 to 20 per cent have ILPs. Have coped with 'very' autistic pupil, ADHD, and specific learning difficulties. Support includes additional literacy and numeracy sessions, assigned teachers who work with pupils in and out of lessons, though with just one full time member of staff in the senior school, there's a limit to the numbers they can help.

Parents also praised efforts with very able. 'School invests in children that need more time either because they're slightly behind or ahead – they have different programmes and challenges,' said mother of junior school pupil.

Games, options, the arts: A busy place with 110 acres ('all the space a child could need to run, jump and cartwheel,' says juniors' prospectus) well used by all, from nursery school pupils walking the 1.3 km cross country circuit (in a morning) to boarders taking it at a rather faster pace 'for fun' (takes all sorts). Bar an all-weather surface that, frustratingly, needs duvet day if there's a hard frost, facilities and options are top notch, including new pavilion (not picturesque but home to host of extras including gym and physio suite), and main and training swimming pools.

Little, indeed, that isn't offered, to parental (and inspectorial) approval. 'Everything is there so children don't need to spend lots of time away from education by driving to swimming,' said one. Only gripe is nagging sense that sports successes could go up a notch or two, though accepted that has smaller pool of talent to draw on, compared with single sex schools. Rugby, notable by absence, heads the parents' wishlist (and likely to remain there), hockey felt to get fair share of resources and then some. Overall, though, 'win more than we lose,' thought a pupil, quick flick through results pages revealing impressive football success (teams regularly reach semi-finals of London and national contests) but mixed fortunes in other areas.

Junior school activities range from numerous informal concerts for parents (music is timetabled from nursery) to residential trips from year 3 and over 40 activities, pupils packing in up to five activities a week, including coding club, swim squad and media club (filming and editing).

Same again for seniors – one year 10 pupil involved in choir, extra sport, Mandarin and popular CCF (night exercises the big draw, drilling 'more fun if you're organising it.'). Model United Nations is biggest we've ever seen, with school hosting annual international conference and gamely lending other local schools their placards for their own events.

Bar slight glumness from senior school pupil analysing recent production rather than doing it ('Interesting work?' we asked. 'Not particularly,' was the response) enthusiasm for the arts abounds. No wonder, given trips (West End to New York for thesps) and lavish facilities including auditorium in performing arts centre, the base for regular productions (Importance of being Earnest, Wind in the Willows). For the pianists among the 200 or so musicians there are new Bechsteins. 'I live in this practice room,' said a music college hopeful, with concerts in venues including the Royal Albert Hall for those who do make it outside.

'I live in this practice room,' said a music college hopeful, concerts in venues including the Royal Albert Hall for those who make it outside

Boarding: Of the 147 full boarders in the senior school majority, says school, stay on for weekends. Boarders have to attend at least three activities (fireworks and go-karting among them) a term. Other perks include freedom to explore fleshpots of Croydon after school as well as exclusive access to swish-looking coffee machine in dining hall. It's not always enough to ward of homesickness but 'keep talking' was advice from one boarder, and will pass. For anything more serious, school has medical centre staffed round the clock.

Girl boarders have one house that backs onto junior school (Queen's – think revenge end of social housing), boys do rather better with their two (Oxford and Cambridge). Further six houses for day pupils only; new house for 80 boy boarders and 80 day pupils now allows flexi boarding to make life easier for day pupils with longer commute who want to stay on for extra sport or rehearsals. A happy atmosphere prevails. We saw plenty of personal possessions left out rather than locked away – high levels of trust are rarely betrayed – while rooms and bathrooms are generally tidy and pleasant.

Even though the British boarders are substantially outnumbered by Chinese (majority in sixth form) and other nationalities including Russia, Armenia, Bulgaria and Ukraine, school, unlike many others, ensures that everyone mixes in multi-national social groups. With one day pupil speaking of new Korean and Russian friends and boarders enjoying tea with local families, horizons are impressively expanded for all pupils and website features overseas students (Bogdan from Romania and Yizhou from China among others) extolling the virtues of the school in their mother tongues.

Background and atmosphere: Ten minutes by tram from East Croydon, green and pleasant site, complete with own deer herd, offers antidote to crowded London senior schools.

One of the few co-ed independents in the area, owes existence to compassionate City of London clerks who set up charity to support a colleague's orphaned children in 1850s. The venture grew into a school named for its first president, former prime minister Lord John Russell. Moved from New Cross to Purley in 1866, acquired this site in 1924 and commissioned distinctly regal design from Sir Aston Webb – best known for Buckingham Palace façade. ('A Victorian guilt trip,' says head.) Added Royal to name to mark 1953 coronation and became co-ed on single site in 1961.

Since narrow brush with closure in 1970s, solved by upping numbers of fee payers (previous philanthropic desire to educate pupils FOC laudable but ruinous), has gone from strength to strength.

Buildings mainly very easy on the eye (and gradually being attended to where they're not). Oldest is modest group of 1850s cottages with surprising octagonal tower. Elsewhere, it's all rather grander, well-blended additions including two 'blue links' where mirror image staircases face each other across larger (and flashier) of two quads, marking well-managed join between original building and later additions.

'Top of agenda was to turn this into a single school journey,' say heads. So junior school pupils get to know senior school early, using theatre, chapel and swimming pool and, from year 3 up, have lunch in the attractive blue, vaulted dining hall (recently featured in TV hit show The Durrells).

There's space for all the trimmings, from 'practical' block – DT room filled with sound of merry hammering as year 7s indulging in no doubt therapeutic high volume metal beating – to traditional library. And despite lack of riches, site is immaculate, pupils smart in recently revamped uniform, high on practicality (it's largely washable) and low on crests (a white shirt is a white shirt, is the official line).

'School invests in children that need more time either because they're slightly behind or ahead – they have different programmes and challenges'

Notice boards are similarly neat and up to date and grounds tidy (bar pair of school bags languishing, Hansel and Gretel-like, in undergrowth). Even food ingredients are painstakingly handwritten on blackboard and nothing left to chance. Salad Nicoise contents – 'fish, sulphites and egg' – brilliant for pupils with allergies. 'Learn how to manage them,' said parent. Thirsty have jewel-like display of squash in every conceivable flavour to choose from (milk, also offered, is 'not that popular,' thought pupils – no surprise there).

Pastoral care, well-being and discipline: A happy place. 'It's a punishment to keep son off school,' said junior school mother. 'My child absolutely loves it,' agreed another. Teachers hugely supportive if families hit difficult patch. 'Will go above and beyond,' said parent.

Pupils similarly complimentary. 'Does take time to settle in but you do feel welcome,' said one. Tutor groups help new pupils to be subsumed into the life of the school with older senior school pupils providing informal help to younger. 'Chaplin' (religious – not Charlie) another source of support, chapel open all day for pupils for anytime prayers.

Structure spawns multi-layered friendship groups. Heart is strong house system (juniors have their own) which promotes cohesion and competition – usually at healthy rather than arms race levels. Add forms and streamed subject groups and 'you can have social groups that extend through the school – it takes some getting to grips with,' said parent.

Around one senior school pupil a year withdrawn or asked to leave (normal issues...) but it's handled in a caring way, Mr Hutchinson often making call to 'headmaster mates' with request to take on a pupil who has lost his (or her) way. It's in these situations, he reckons, that you discover just how much of an educator you are, he thinks. 'They make awful decisions but shouldn't be punished for the rest of their lives.'

Other perks include freedom to explore fleshpots of Croydon after school as well as exclusive access to swish-looking coffee machine in dining hall

For the most part, however, the focus is on rewards for the triers – 'put on a big show for effort,' pointing people in the right direction. Even the prefects, who are allowed to impose detentions, they told us (though head says otherwise) never do ('though we might remind everyone that we can,' said one).

Pupils and parents: Slightly more boys, many locals among day pupils (80 per cent from Croydon), rest from south London and into Surrey and Kent borders, lots of diversity, cultural and financial. 'Pretty much all walks of life,' said junior parent. 'And when you're doing reading at night, books aren't just about pink skinned children, which is great.'

Junior and senior parents tend to tread separate paths and organise own events. It's a homogenous mix – cars ranging from second hand specials to top of the range models, some parents dwelling in marble halls, others scraping school fees together. Increasing numbers of working couples well catered for with wraparound care. Not flash and all to the good, thought parent. 'Have quite a wide breadth of people there, and I think that gives it a nice atmosphere.'

Only mystery is where leavers end up. Not into the limelight, at least so far. 'We have a great many success stories, but nobody famous,' says school.

Entrance: Increasingly popular and currently at capacity in every year group. Sharp rise in numbers admitted after undaunting entrance process. 'Very gentle' says school. Junior school entrants, who arrive September after third birthday, are observed in small groups (no interview or formal test). 'We're looking to see if on track with development, communications and ability to interact.' More formal assessments further up the school – all joining in years 3 to 6 must be senior school shoe-ins.

Around 90 per cent go on to the senior school, some guaranteed places in years 4 and 5; they sit exams only if want to be considered for awards and get them, too, recently scooping the top scholarships, though there's no favouritism, stresses school. 'We're beginning to understand that we can produce academic excellence without driving pupils towards exams,' says Mr Thompson, in explanation.

For senior school, main entry point is year 7. External candidates sit entrance exams in maths, English and VR. Minimum score around 105, average of 111 and 128 minimum for scholarship candidates. Adds a further 20 in year 9 and varying numbers in year 12. For sixth form no entrance exam – places based on GCSE performance.

Current popularity means school could probably nudge up selectivity a notch – but won't. 'Have niche in market,' says school, 'and we want to preserve it – we've just upped the quality of what we're doing.'

Exit: Loses a few juniors to local grammars and other independents such as Alleyn's and Caterham. Seniors tend to stay on post-GCSE. One or two to Oxbridge most years (none in 2017).

Money matters: No endowment to speak of. Impressive combination of prudent management and fundraising keeps things ticking over nicely. Offer range of scholarships (academic, sport, music and drama) and bursaries of to 100 per cent (income shouldn't exceed £40,000).

Remarks: Think fab site, rising results, unified and inspirational leadership (and the odd deer) and get on that tram.

St Catherine's School

57

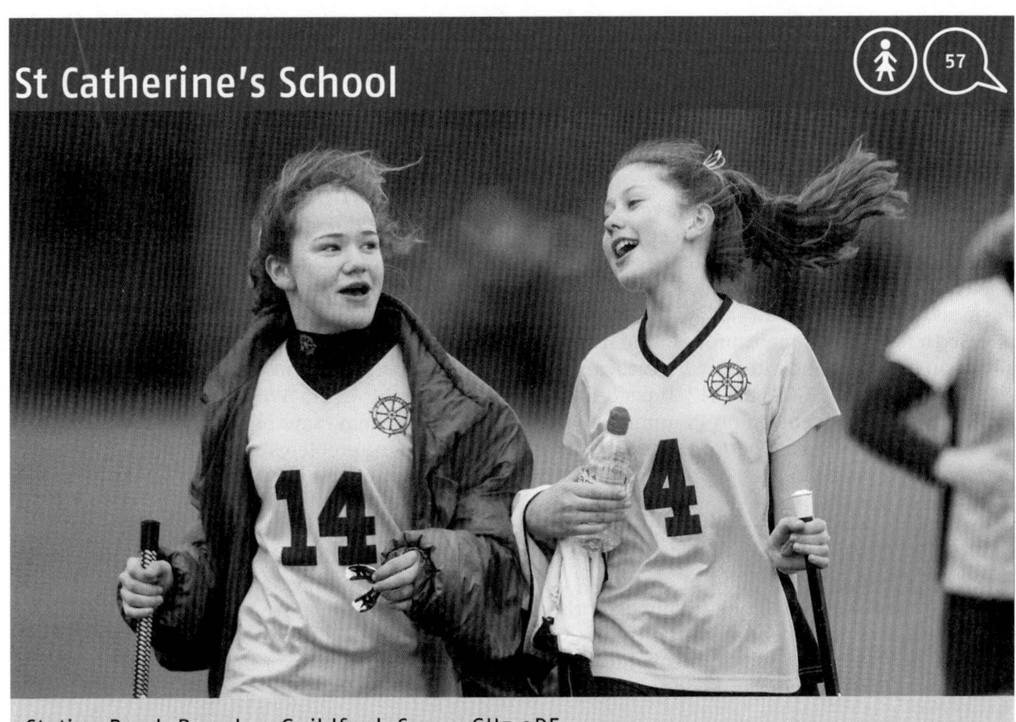

Station Road, Bramley, Guildford, Surrey GU5 0DF

01483 899609 | admissions@stcatherines.info | www.stcatherines.info

Ages: 11–18

Pupils: 653; sixth form: 169; Boarders: 89 full, 37 weekly

Day: £17,895 pa; Boarding: £29,490 pa

Headmistress: Since 2000, Mrs Alice Phillips MA Cantab (50s). First teaching post was at the Royal Masonic School, Rickmansworth, where she rose to being head of English. Thence to deputy headship at Tormead in 1993. She impresses at once as being full of brisk common sense, good humour and get-up-and go. But she is also super-bright, super-articulate and super-focused on the highest of standards for her staff, her charges and herself. 'She is utterly determined for her girls,' one mother told us. And this blazes forth in her dedication to the job of equipping girls for the future – 'girls need to be in an environment which demonstrates that there's nothing you can't do'.

Mrs Phillips relishes the process of turning her 'rough-cut GCSE diamonds into highly polished gems' – and the process needs the St Cat's sixth form to be complete. 'We hit the wall of hormones together,' she says, 'I love the wall of hormones,' which she sees as an essential stage in becoming an adult. And she is not interested in turning out demure young ladies. 'We teach them to challenge every darn thing.' Neither is she a petty disciplinarian; 'you pick your fights with teenage girls. If you pick on something trivial and make a fuss about it they will hate you forever.' Parents are universally impressed – 'Her speeches are very entertaining and she devotes her whole life to the school.' 'She is very fair and very good at sorting things out.' A few parents – and girls – can find the intensity of her commitment 'scary', but one's impression is that her uncompromising concern is for the 'whole' of each girl. When her pastoral care is praised, she responds, 'but we do also seek to get the girls into the best possible universities and to do that you have to get them to aim high and target improvements all the time'. One awe-struck mother summed her up: 'She is amazing.'

Academic matters: IGCSEs in almost all subjects now. Success relies on traditional good teaching alongside the best that modern IT can offer – so keen to keep abreast of all that is innovative and helpful. 'The apps for learning languages are fantastic,' enthuses Mrs Phillips, who tells us that her classics department has always led the way when it comes to embracing good new IT. So iPods/iPads allowed in class with an emphasis on 'learning to discriminate' between reliable web info and the rest – we applaud; in fact all girls up to year 10 now required to have iPads. We saw nothing but quiet and attentive classes and teachers who kept order by being interesting rather than via sanctions.

Results excellent across the board – no weak areas. Ninety-one per cent of subjects taken at A level in 2017 were graded A*-B, 65 per cent A*/A. Good to see Greek and German surviving alongside business, economics, history of art and photography. Sixth form enrichment programme includes advice on higher ed and interviews, heathcare and citizenship issues. At IGCSE in 2017, 91 per cent A*/A grades. Academic extension programme for years 11-13. It cometh not much better than this. Lots of options, lots of opportunities – real education takes place here.

Disquiet among some parents and girls on the subject of 'SCAGS' (St Catherine's Assessment Grades) – the St Cat's method of assessing and tracking progress. It's designed to support girls in the pursuit of improvement in their different subjects but some are confused or unconvinced. Mrs Phillips – an ardent believer – concedes, 'we are mindful that it is complex and try to inform parents as best we can.' She is lightning quick to react when we report concerns raised with us – 'It is not the St Catherine's way not to listen to parents – we will expand the explanation and make it more user friendly.' And recent results support school's contention that the scheme works – the first group of girls brought up this way achieved 17 per cent more A* grades than their predecessors.

Library open all hours and well-stocked – the only one we have so far seen with a section on 'feminism'. Sensible system of sixth form subject mentors: you're 12 and struggling with physics? – find the sixth former who understands! Overall, the best of trad with the slickest of innovative in matters academic.

'She is utterly determined for her girls,' one mother told us. And this blazes forth in her dedication to the job of equipping girls for the future

Girls with only mild dyses likely to be able to stand the heat. 'We pride ourselves on our tracking system,' says head, 'and on spotting any late-emerging problems' and monitoring, academic mentoring and clinics are more the way here than a busy special needs set-up.

Games, options, the arts: Lively art in many media – photography especially strong but ceramics, DT, life-drawing – all thrive and all run clubs for those who aren't taking them as curricular subjects. A sense of vibrant life and colour about the studios. 'The drama in the senior school is really good,' we were told and the new building has given drama and the technical side of production an immense boost. Music also lively and productive – just as you'd expect with this calibre of girls and encouragement.

Excellent sports facilities and sport now seen as more inclusive – lots of opportunities for those less than Olympian in their prowess. 'My daughter is in C and D teams', said one mother, 'and she has lots of matches.' The Olympians regularly reach the heights – county and national finals places in several sports and stellar showings in swimming, lacrosse and tennis. Range of sports on offer. Riding club run by parents. D of E thrives and everyone is productively busy all the time. Excellent outside speaker programme, sixth form lectures – and PTA lectures – and lots of stimulating trips.

Boarding: Fifty per cent of boarders from overseas. Bedrooms and dorms are spacious enough, welcoming and homely. Most in two-bedders, often with a third bed for occasional boarders. Even sixth formers mostly share: they in their own separate and much-appreciated block with common rooms – possibly the messiest we have seen – most refreshing (new sixth form block planned). Most full boarders – normally between 50 and 70 girls – remain in school each weekend and are offered a 'full and varied programme of activities'. Boarders encouraged to invite their day girl friends to board on Friday nights with them, and are invited out at weekends in return.

Background and atmosphere: Established in 1885, this is a school with a proud tradition and, unusually, has grown and developed all on the one site. Located 10 minutes south of Guildford in a quiet leafy village, it is unremarkable architecturally apart from its striking conference room plus arts 'n' crafts fireplace, its memorable gothic style chapel – splendid stained glass windows celebrating notable female saints, fabulous rose window and Willis organ. Boarding and most of the school areas are functional, a little tired in places (upgrading in process), with the emphasis on practicality rather than opulence. Useful 'chat-rooms' for one to-one sessions – a good idea but the one we nosed into was freezing.

Now boasts a 'fantastic' £15 million complex – the 125th Anniversary Halls arts and sports building with an unrivalled auditorium (seats 300 and has 'better acoustics than the Barbican') plus other studios and backed by the sports hall, gyms, dance studios etc. All carefully, thoughtfully and skilfully integrated and an exceptional new resource with which the girls are clearly thrilled. School buildings mostly abut big central area used for car parking though pitches and courts stretch away on the perimeter. Latest addition is 'university style' sixth form study centre, designed with input from the girls, plus refurbished lecture theatre that now hosts chamber music recitals, talks, presentations etc.

Unremarkable architecturally except for its memorable gothic style chapel – splendid stained glass windows celebrating notable female saints

Immensely strong house system – everything done in the six houses to which loyalty is unflinching – underpins virtually all school activities. Strong ethical dimension to energetic charity work – extends to water vending machine which supports pumping system in Africa. Food seen as improved – salads particularly praised – though 'it can get a bit monotonous for boarders,' we were told. The day we visited the choices included 'deep fried battered pangasius' and 'oven roasted pangasius'. (We had to look it up too – it's a type of catfish.)

Pastoral care, well-being and discipline: 'Lovely dedicated staff,' universally praised. A sense that all girls can fit in and do well here – whatever their aptitudes, enthusiasms, personality – something to which all parents we spoke to attested. 'It can be a bit full-on for some of them,' one parent admitted – and others agreed: 'the girls themselves push themselves to the limit – the atmosphere makes them want to be the best of the best.' 'They do the best they can,' another said, 'but they do it while looking after each other.' 'They are very supportive of each other's differences,' another agreed. School divides the girls into houses, sets, classes – lots of mixing up to encourage friendship and to discourage cliqueyness – and it works. Strong sense of an equitable and kind community. 'They don't favour the bright ones – my two very different girls feel equally welcome and valued.' 'Every single child gets a well-thought-out prize at prize giving – for best results or for kindness – everyone walks out feeling valued for what they are.'

Serious misdemeanours off the radar. Preventative and common sense approach. 'We do some very robust woman-to-woman talking with the girls about our expectations and what is and is not acceptable,' says Mrs Phillips and a sense of friendliness, mutual support is tangible. Some of the most approachable staff we know.

Pupils and parents: St Cat's Association now a 3,000 strong membership of alumnae, parents, former staff – makes a real community of the school, past and present. Head's PA one of around a dozen alumnae now on the staff. Lots of parental involvement and unquenchable enthusiasm. Mostly local-ish families. Lots of old girls' daughters. Middle class and comfortable backgrounds, in the main. Notable old girls include Francine Stock, Juliet Stevenson, Elizabeth Beresford, Zena Skinner, Davina McCall, Fay Maschler, Joan Greenwood, UA Fanthorpe, Dorothy Tutin, Elinor Goodman, two ambassadors and legions of academics and other high flyers.

Entrance: Entry by academic selection, using St Catherine's own assessment. Eleven plus candidates take papers in English, maths, science and verbal reasoning. Few places at 12+, 13+ or 14+ – papers in English, maths and reasoning. Reports from existing schools. Sixth form general paper, verbal reasoning and predicted GCSE grades – As expected in A level subjects. Interview for potential sixth formers. Roughly 1.3 applicants for each 11+ place – so not too daunting for a bright girl; for those who try for places in higher years, date of registration is important so register as early as you can. Around 70 apply for the 10 or so annual places in the sixth – they can afford to be very choosy. School flexible and helpful – happy to interview via Skype if you're abroad. Locals come from everywhere but mostly the school's own prep and from Haslemere, Midhurst, Farnham, Guildford, Godalming, Cranleigh, Woking, Esher, Oxshott, SW London. Overseas pupils predominantly English with some EU nationals. Full boarders from Turkey, Moldova, Nigeria, Japan, Hong Kong, Russia, Ukraine,

Malaysia, Korea and Singapore. Not a school for anyone with less than fluent English.

Exit: Around 20-30 per cent leaves after GCSEs – mostly to co-ed sixths or to have a change. Sixth form leavers to top unis – seven to Oxbridge in 2017 and four medics. Exeter, Cardiff, Birmingham, Leeds, Warwick and UCL popular – aeronautical engineering and chemical engineering two choices. Unusual number of geographers. All do proper subjects. Three off overseas in 2017 including one to Harvard.

Money matters: Small number of scholarships – some open and some internal – most worth up to 20 per cent of fees. Music and art awards. Bursaries for the bright broke at 11+ and sixth. Usual means-testing and disclosures required but up to 100 per cent of fees on offer.

Remarks: The 2016 inspection report was one of the most impressive we've seen. If you want convincing that girls only education is the right and modern way for your bright and motivated daughter, go and look. This is as good as it gets.

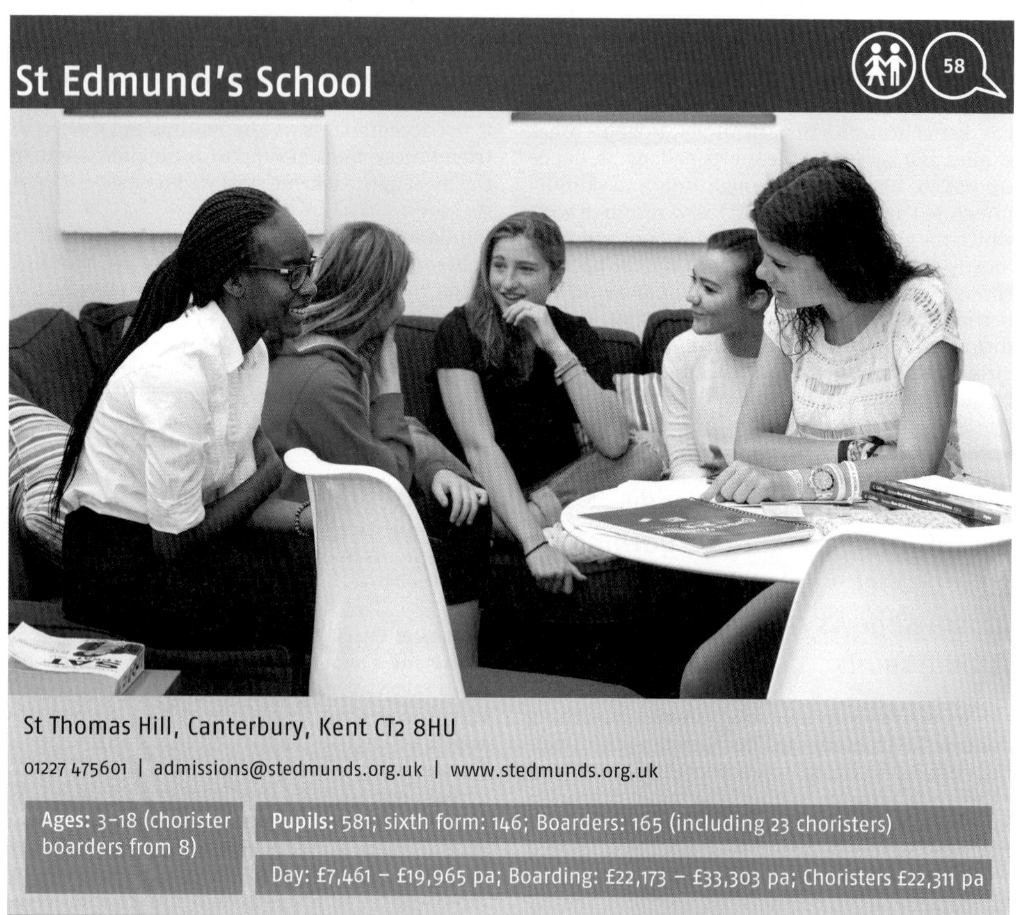

St Edmund's School

58

St Thomas Hill, Canterbury, Kent CT2 8HU

01227 475601 | admissions@stedmunds.org.uk | www.stedmunds.org.uk

Ages: 3-18 (chorister boarders from 8)

Pupils: 581; sixth form: 146; Boarders: 165 (including 23 choristers)

Day: £7,461 – £19,965 pa; Boarding: £22,173 – £33,303 pa; Choristers £22,311 pa

Head of school: Since 2011, Mrs Louise Moelwyn-Hughes (40s). Previously senior deputy head of The Perse in Cambridge, and spent 13 years in various roles from year head to housemistress at Marlborough College, following a degree in classics at Cambridge. Now immediately dismiss the picture you've formed, because she's far from the Cambridge to Perse public school head you're imagining. Still has the accent from her humble but bookish Belfast background, and says she didn't really know what Cambridge was when a teacher suggested that her schoolgirl love of ancient Greek could be a ticket there.

Utterly comfortable in her own skin, seems to enjoy being different to the pack. 'I do things my own way, I call a spade a spade,' she says. No airs, no grandstanding, just that type of quiet authority which can bring a room to silence just by sitting still. 'A quiet powerhouse,' said a parent. 'She attends many events, but never seeks to take glory from those who organise – so at a chapel service, she may be sitting in the back pew while the lovely chaplain does his bit; same at junior school concerts, there to show support and cheer them on, but lets the master give the thanks and praise. Very respectful, but she watches everything, and seems to know everything.'

She's been responsible for some record-breaking results, and a 20 per cent increase in pupil numbers in the last three years. Parents describe the school as 'better in every element', and the transformation as 'quite extreme'. 'I can't speak highly enough of her,' said one. 'She has turned the school around, and changed the whole ethos, and it's clear teachers have a lot of respect for her.'

Another said: 'It is always quite obvious to me that she knows the students individually, as is the tremendous respect both students and staff members all have for her. I have met very few people in life who display such grace and level of consciousness in their dealings with others.'

Remarkably she has also transformed her home life, with two children produced during her time in post, and these toddlers are now curbing her hobbies of squash, running, walking and reading.

Returning to Marlborough College as head in September 2018. Her successor will be Ed O'Connor, who has been deputy head here since 2013 and is currently acting head of junior school. He has a degree in history and an MEd from Cambridge and a MPhil in international relations from Oxford. He started off working in the City before joining St Albans School as head of history and politics, thence to Sutton Valence (director of sixth form and head of history) and then head of sixth form and politics and history teacher at The Perse School.

Academic matters: The strong Perse connection is bound to have an impact, and the head makes no bones about the fact that she is stepping up expectations. 'Perse is in the top 10 academically, St Edmund's will never be that, but I am looking to raise the bar so that people feel tested,' she says. Rebranding means the school is no longer marketing itself as a music and drama school, and no longer describing itself as non-selective.

But while all the families we spoke to were aware of the change, none felt that a more academic bent was at the expense of less able pupils, or non-academic activities. 'I think this is an additional benefit to the school. The music and drama department is just as excellent as it was,' said one parent. 'It's a great turn around, without losing the school's comprehensive ethos,' said another. 'There is no feeling that you can settle for what you get – if you are predicted a C you have to try to get a B or higher.' Sixth formers told us that they would be heartily congratulated for a C grade if that was the best of their ability. 'Everyone has their own target grade which they are pushed to exceed,' said one.

'It is always quite obvious to me that she knows the students individually, as is the tremendous respect both students and staff members have for her'

We heard particularly strong praise from parents of dyslexic children. 'They are very good at identifying but not labelling,' said one. Another described a child who was struggling with the GCSE curriculum, but through what was described as 'learning tailor-made to him' went on to win a place at Cambridge. Moelwyn-Hughes says she expects higher academic standards to result in more pupils with special needs, as it will encompass more students with Asperger's, many of whom are in the highest academic band nationally.

Should your child fall behind, it won't be seen as your problem. In this instance, the head says they find out what is behind it and put in a lot of pastoral and academic support. 'We don't say to parents you are going to have to supervise this, we make it our business to turn things around,' she says.

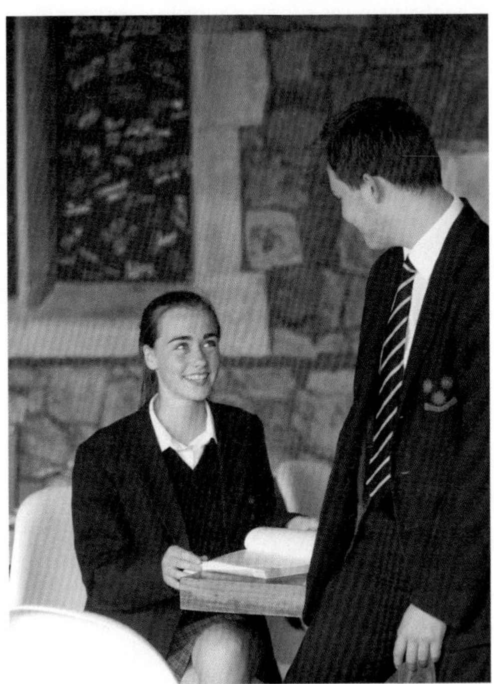

When some pupils were struggling in French, her response was 'Let's throw Arabic at it'. These pupils took a Cambridge Certificate in Arabic and Middle East studies instead. 'Four kids got distinctions. It's a Perse way to take something which looks higher end and give it to kids who are struggling, it builds confidence,' she says. It might also be testament to her teaching, as the children studied with her. She dismisses her own mastery of Arabic with an 'oh that' wave of the hand.

When some pupils were struggling in French, her response was 'Let's throw Arabic at it'

As well as Arabic other new subjects the head has introduced are economics, politics and Greek. At A level there are 26 subjects to choose from, the EPQ and an option to do the AQA Baccalaureate. The most popular A levels are biology, history and photography. Maths and theatre studies are also strong departments. In 2017, 21 per cent of A level entries achieved A*/A grades; at GCSE, 41 per cent of entries were A*-A/9-7.

There's no hiding place for teachers. 'If a parent complains about staff performance, I call the teacher in immediately and tell them and I deal with it,' the head says. Teachers are left to their own styles, as long as it works. Music teaching is said to be 'inspirational' and the head of junior school music was running a lively class investigating scores from Bond films when we visited. A sixth form economics class was studying the cement market, and the teacher was relaxed about some having earphones plugged in as they worked, as he said they were all turning in A*/B grade work.

'There are some fabulous teachers, and there have been some teachers whose tenure has been short because they just weren't up to the job. That's what we call progress. They use different techniques for different children – above all it's not a one size fits all school,' said a parent.

The junior school has its own bright and cosy classrooms, and the curriculum includes swimming, music, dance and French from the earliest years. In years 3 to 5 subjects are extended to include geography, history, IT and Latin. There is some streaming – we saw year 5 maths groups tackling number problems on paper in one set, while another was learning weights and ratios through making biscuits. The artwork on display in a variety of media is notably good.

In the upper half of the junior school – years 6, 7 and 8 – lessons are taught in a separate block in the upper school, where they can use the senior's science, art and design technology rooms, and all lessons are taught by subject specialists.

Games, options, the arts: Go in with your eyes open. It's a small school so you can't expect to have top flight teams. Some parents mourn the lack of rugby – the school plays football and hockey instead, which works better in a mixed year group of just 65. 'There's lots of sport there if you want to do it, but you have to be realistic, they are not going to beat the massive teams,' said one parent. For the top level players it can be frustrating, but a parent of one of these is pragmatic about it, saying, 'Even in big schools they are only going to get one or two county level players. And they are doing a lot to improve, such as getting in professional coaches.'

Music is strong, as you might expect in the school which educates the choristers of Canterbury Cathedral. There's a purpose-built music school with a recording studio. It's big on theatre too, with theatre studies well subscribed, and a full size theatre with five wings and a green room to perform in.

Some parents would like to see more trips, though one reeled off an impressive list her children had taken part in – skiing in Italy, drama trip to New York, music/language trip and watersports to Spain, Rua Fiola survival adventure, Christmas trip to Lille, language trip to Switzerland, and history trips to Portsmouth.

Saturday morning school is now optional. It's not charged for, pupils don't have to wear uniform, and the activities are the likes of international cuisine, technology, art, film making, sport, and music. One-third of day pupils come in for it.

Boarding: There are 160+ boarders, over half of whom are from overseas. There are flexi, weekly, and full boarding options. Junior boarders (11-14) live in School House, a newly refurbished wing of the main school building. Senior boarders live in the main school building or in the nearby Clare, Sunfield and Gorsefield Houses. Boys' dormitories have views over the fields to the cathedral, through arched mullioned windows. Girls overlook the changing rooms. Boys have ensuites, girls don't. The boarding rooms are fairly cramped, but there's a big common room/kitchen and sixth formers have separate studies shared between three or four people. After optional morning school on a Saturday, afternoons are free, and Sundays see outings to London museums, Bluewater, ice skating and so on. The 23 choristers (boys only) live separately in Choir House within the cathedral precincts, with a timetable which includes 20 hours singing, attending evensong six days a week, and recordings.

Background and atmosphere: The school is centred around a High Victorian building with its own chapel. The exterior is grand, and there are commanding views across the fields to Canterbury Cathedral. But the senior school interior has stained carpets, holes gouged out of plaster, some cramped classrooms shoved into unlikely parts of the old building, and is frankly scruffy. If you're doing the circuit its shabbiness will be evident among the more glitzy schools; but current parents don't notice it and see it as all part of the warm, family atmosphere. The head has made staffing and small class sizes a priority, and says increased pupil numbers in the last two years will now fund refurbishment: and indeed a new academic hub building is under construction.

It's a school with a smile on its face, a great sense of ease and happiness pervades. 'It's as friendly and warm as a prep school. Every single teacher knows me and you just feel welcome,' said one parent.

Will you fit in? One parent described it thus: 'It's not a competitive school. If you want to be told that your child is number one at everything, don't come here. If you get your kicks from being told you're better than everyone else, it's not for you. If you are a show off, don't come here. There's no pride in being better than someone else here – it's about being better than your own expectations and about being part of the school.'

Pastoral care, well-being and discipline: Praise for the pastoral care from parents was overwhelming. One child missed several months of school owing to health problems in his GCSE year, and he was given one-to-one teaching on his return to enable him to catch up. We also heard about a teenager who had derailed; the response, as the parent described, 'Spending days after talking, planning, resetting goals and wiping the slate clean for a new start. At all times protecting his dignity and his self-esteem. Within days all teaching staff adopted a completely different set of rules for him, and never mentioned earlier failings.' Moelwyn-Hughes says: 'I'm a big fan of meeting with parents and the pupil and deciding what we're going to do.'

Another family had to deal with bereavement, and the parent said: 'I can categorically say that had it not been for the pastoral care and time and attention Louise Moelwyn-Hughes and her housemaster provided to him, and what he gets out of the school community, his world would be a far worse place than it is today. I am eternally indebted to Louise Moelwyn-Hughes and St Edmund's School.'

And lots of parents told us that the head will always seek out children and congratulate them individually on a big achievement in their own sphere. 'It's the little touches you don't normally get in a senior school,' said a parent.

Pupils and parents: People tend to stick with the school. At transition recently, 52 out of 54 came up from the junior to senior school, and around 10 new pupils join at this point.

International students represent 28 nationalities – there are larger groups from China and Germany, but kept no bigger than 15 students, and also students from Thailand, The Congo, Kazakhstan, Russia, Nigeria, Poland, Belgium and France.

The head will always seek out children and congratulate them on a big achievement. 'It's the little touches you don't normally get in a senior school'

It's not a school where you need designer clobber for the school run. One parent described the parent body as 'trying to do the best for their children. Very mixed finances, not all necessarily finding the school fees that easy, and not doing it for the social cachet of being an old boy. Very few pushy parents, certainly not seeking advance for their own child at the expense of another.'

Another described the school gate as 'friendly, warm, no parents whinging in your ear "my child wasn't the shining star ..."'

Entrance: Usual entry points (3+, 7+, 11+, 13+ and 16+) plus other year groups when places available. Junior school entry is based on assessments on a taster day to gauge academic levels; nearly all juniors move up to the senior school with no entrance test. At 11+ entry for outsiders (a few join at this stage) there are formal entrance tests (verbal and non-verbal reasoning) and consideration is given to Kent Test results. Year 9 entry involves tests in maths and English, and a guideline requirement would be common entrance marks of around 60 per cent or above (although you don't have to pass common entrance). Sixth formers need A*-B/9-6 at GCSE in the subjects they wish to study. On top of that, head says personality and character is part of it. 'It matters the mix you have. I take the opportunity to meet every kid so they recognise that I chose them,' she says.

Exit: Nearly all juniors join the senior school. All sixth formers go to higher education including conservatoires and drama schools, and popular university destinations are Manchester, Reading, Exeter, UEA, Sussex, Durham, Bristol and Canterbury. Two medics in 2017.

Money matters: Scholarships of varying value are offset against tuition fees for both day and boarding pupils are awarded in academic, music, sport, art and drama categories. These can be topped up by means-tested bursaries for those currently at the school. Discounts offered to children of clergy, members of the armed forces, and third and subsequent children.

Remarks: Which of the effusive quotes to use? We've seldom seen such overwhelming praise for a head, and for pastoral care, from parents. Nor such a sense of a cohesive parent body without factions. Not for you if you want a school high on social cachet and entry to society by school tie, or smart teas after thrilling wins against top flight teams. But if you want a school which is going to take great care of your child, and get the best out of him/her, whether s/he's a Cambridge or C grade student, definitely one for the shortlist.

St John's School (Leatherhead)

59

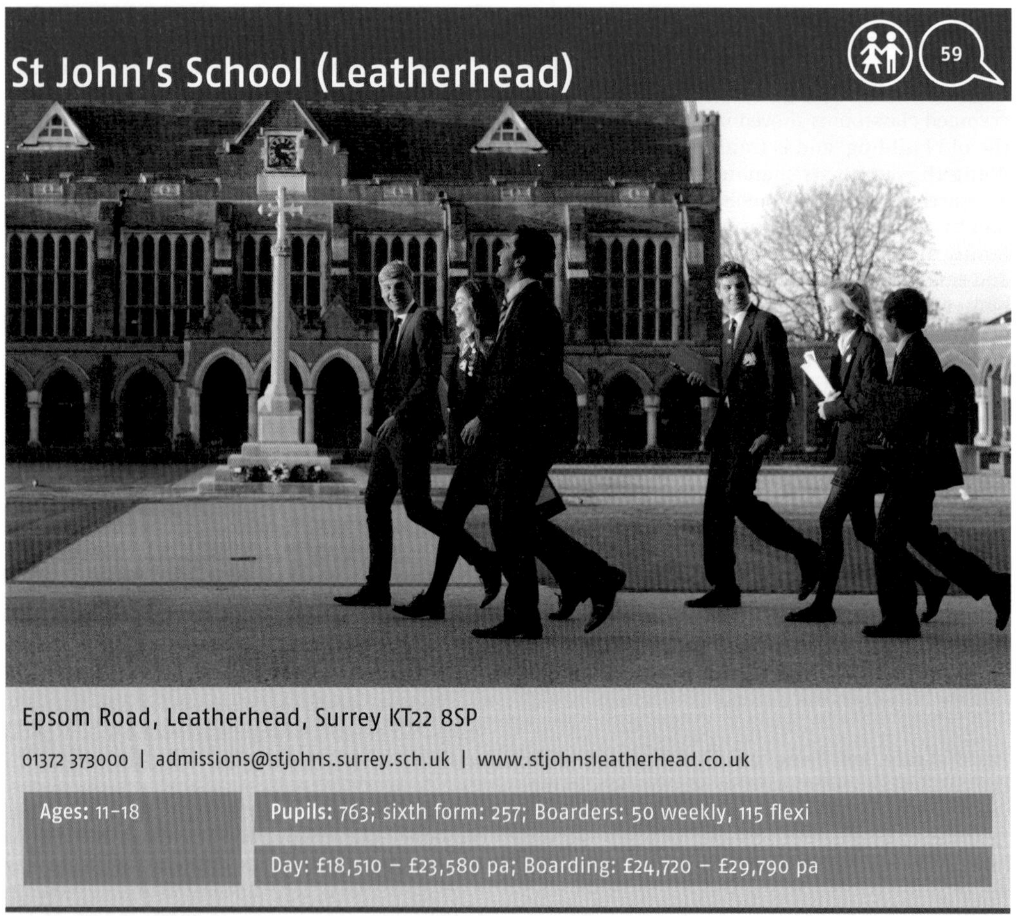

Epsom Road, Leatherhead, Surrey KT22 8SP

01372 373000 | admissions@stjohns.surrey.sch.uk | www.stjohnsleatherhead.co.uk

Ages: 11–18

Pupils: 763; sixth form: 257; Boarders: 50 weekly, 115 flexi

Day: £18,510 – £23,580 pa; Boarding: £24,720 – £29,790 pa

Head: Since September 2017, Rowena Cole BSc PGCE MBA, previously head of Dunottar School in Reigate. Biology degree from Exeter; taught biology at Howard of Effingham and City of London Freemen's before deputy headship at Guildford High. Married to Alistair; they have two young children.

Academic matters: St John's has been gradually on the up academically over the last few years and is aiming still higher. Exam results in 2017 were 74 per cent A*-A/9-7 grades at GCSE, and 45 per cent A*/A at A level. It has been considered as a school which provides a good education but not a high pressure one – a suitable place for a child who would not be happy or comfortable in a highly academic environment. Parents here certainly want their children to do as well as they can academically, but are also looking for an all-round education including social values and leadership.

School believes improving academic results goes hand in hand with improving pastoral care and, unsurprisingly, higher levels of academic selection at entry. It's not rocket science, and the effects of changes taking place now should be seen over the next few years. There has been somewhat of a range of teaching styles and standards at the school including one or two described by parents as 'rather unimpressive', but they are reassured by the and improving exam results.

This big academic push has still to filter through to all pupils; parents tell us that hard work and academic success is not universally seen as cool. Although pupils do work hard and want success, sometimes they keep it rather quiet. School notes that girls' academic work and success helps to pull the boys along, although by the sixth form they are equal. The school recognises that boys and girls have different needs and pace at different ages, their operation and processing is different, girls gain confidence and maturity earlier than boys. The range of academic ability is catered for by setting in all subjects based on the pace at which pupils learn.

All pupils are tested on entry to identify their 'learning profile', which also identifies any SEN. School tells us that learning support is available to all pupils at all ages, ranging from study skills and time management to specialist tuition for specific learning difficulties. Around 10 per cent of pupils currently have SEN and they are catered for by staff in the classroom, by extra small group sessions and, where necessary, by individual one-to-one support. Parents praise the 'excellent' SENCo. The small number of pupils with EAL have flexible, small group provision alongside support from tutors.

Games, options, the arts: All extras and additions to the academic curriculum are taken very seriously at St John's. They are well taught and valued by pupils and their families; school is very keen on leadership development and believes that sport, drama and music are of equal value to academics in developing a rounded and balanced individual.

Sport is an important part of life at St John's and is compulsory, daily and at all ages. There are lots of options and the facilities are very good, with spacious pitches and sports centre. Essentially boys play rugby, cricket and football, girls play netball and rounders and both boys and girls play hockey and tennis and do athletics, cross-country and swimming. There's also a whole array of less usual sports and activities available. Saturdays are match days and older pupils tell us they watch and support their school teams.

The brainy (and charming) sixth former who showed us round was combining maths, physics and DT at A level and heading confidently towards an engineering degree

All this sporting activity brings a deal of success: in rugby St John's boys 1st VII were crowned Rosslyn Park National School Sevens Vase Champions for 2017 and were recently Surrey U16 county VIIs champions and in football won the national independent schools league. The girls have recently won an U16 county hockey trophy and, over the last two years, have been runners up in the county netball championships. St John's has also been named in The Cricketer magazine's list of top 100 cricketing schools for two years running, and the swimming team has been winning cups.

Music is another big part of St John's life, a third of pupils learn an instrument (up to diploma standard) and several pupils are members of national orchestras and ensembles. Choral singing is also very strong – pupils win choral awards to universities and are involved in the National Youth Choir and other top external choral groups.

Drama is well represented with lots of opportunities for aspiring actors in many and varied school productions. St John's recently won a number of awards at the local Leatherhead drama festival, and several pupils are members of the National Youth Theatre.

Art and the DT facilities are superb, housed in a gleaming new classroom block and equipped with everything the most dedicated artists and design technology students could want. The standard of work is correspondingly high, with displays of impressive and inspiring art and functional DT projects. The brainy (and charming) sixth former who showed us round was combining maths, physics and DT at A level and heading confidently towards an engineering degree.

Other activities include CCF (compulsory in year 10), community service and D of E, all involving challenging activities and trips. There are also lots of school activities going on in the evenings: concerts, plays, rehearsals and talks, all of which pupils are routinely involved in. It can be very demanding of pupils' time, particularly if they are not boarders, but it suits families who are busy and those who like their children to be fully occupied with school activities.

Boarding: Although the majority are day pupils, boarding is flourishing. Parents say flexi-boarding, two or three nights a week, has been a real winner and many pupils love it. School has further long term plans for boarding: 'currently in the foothills of change; it needs to lose its old-fashioned connotations and become fluid, social and involve parents in order to thrive'. Lower school pupils can board for up to two nights a week.

Care in the boarding houses is practical and pragmatic, although the nail polish remover in the entrance hall of a girl's house had obviously been ignored by one young lady we spotted unashamedly sporting fuchsia nails. The accommodation itself varies from neat, modern twin or single rooms with a small en suite loo and shower to some larger rooms for up to six pupils.

We found the pupils to be sparky, friendly, chatty and well-mannered. On the sports field boys are competitive but very decent

Background and atmosphere: St John's is very much a local school – most pupils come from within a 15 mile radius – with a strong sense of its own community. Essentially it's a traditional environment providing a 'values based education'; school says that parents here are interested in much more than academics, they want a well rounded, emotionally intelligent education for their children so they leave school able to interact well with others.

However, there is no doubt at all that St John's is currently going through some major changes, as previously mentioned regarding academic matters. These changes are also apparent in other areas and are leading to something of a culture shift, from an ultra-trad boys' boarding school into something much more 21st century, while still holding on to the values of an all-round schooling which are popular with parents. Since 2012, girls in every year throughout the school, albeit in the minority; Saturday lessons disappeared a few years ago with the arrival of the younger girls, though St John's is very definitely a five day a week school with matches on a Saturday. Lower school for years 7 and 8 opened in 2016. Boarding is 'family-friendly' and flexible; no full time, seven days a week any more. New buildings have popped up to accommodate the 50 per cent-ish increase in pupil numbers over the last few years, entry requirements have just been hiked to a new high, lesson lengths and timetable arrangements have all been changed and a new tutor system introduced. It's not exactly a case of being dragged kicking and screaming but there's a lot happening and there may well be diehards who need to be convinced. All this change has been brought about by a consultative process, school reassures that 'everyone has had their say' – but it's early days and, like everyone else, we can only wait and see.

Some things remain the same – notably the school's structure around houses, 'important in engendering loyalty and belonging in pupils'. School life revolves around pupils' houses, the day starts and ends there, their tutor is to be found there, studying and socialising takes place there. The culture of each house differs depending on the houseparent, but they are not quirky.

The look of the place reflects its character. It comprises a splendid Victorian building with cloisters running around a central quad and an imposing panelled dining room used by everyone for all meals (and once rumoured to be a potential set for Hogwarts). Just beyond the quad are other newer buildings including the terrific classroom, art and DT block, a new science centre and a very attractive modern new boys' house plus a new boarding house for girls.

On one side of the quad is the modern chapel which is a crucially important part of the school. St John's has a Christian foundation which forms the basis of daily life. Pupils are required to attend daily chapel as well as Sunday evening services with their house around once a month. Parents also attend these house services and go on to drinks in the houses.

Pastoral care, well-being and discipline: Pastoral care is yet another aspect undergoing a revamp at St John's. The tutor system has been reorganised so that every staff member is a tutor to a small group of pupils and every pupil has their own tutor for support and monitoring. School describes the tutor as 'the pupil's champion and mentor'; the tutor's role is as the point of reference for those pupils under their care and the individual who oversees all aspects of a pupil's school life.

It can be very demanding of pupils' time, particularly if they are not boarders, but it suits families who are busy and those who like their children to be fully occupied

Discipline is much in evidence; bad behaviour in class is not tolerated with detentions for minor infringements. There are clear punishments for drinking and smoking, fines and detentions – it does happen; the housemistress pointed out that pupils are easy to spot around town and do get pulled up. Zero tolerance policy towards drugs – any offence and a pupil would be 'straight out'; the school feels education of pupils and parents is the key and more is on the cards.

Pupils and parents: Currently the gender mix is around two-thirds boys to one third girls, but the school is aiming for a 50:50 mix. School says the differing styles of boys and girls are beginning to rub off on each other; most girls here are 'outgoing and get stuck in,' and it's all about 'a values-based education, for privileged children who learn the responsibility of service'. Families here are well-heeled, middle class professionals but less flashy and more down to earth than many other parents at Surrey boarding schools.

Pupils who enjoy St John's are those who can cope with the pace – academic plus everything else, who want to get involved in school life and enjoy the long day. This all-encompassing style of full-on days, Saturday sport and Sunday chapel would be a godsend for families with two working parents who need their children to be kept busy. However, pupils wanting to run a social or sporting life outside school may find the time commitments of school demanding.

We found the pupils to be sparky, friendly, chatty and well-mannered. On the sports field boys are competitive but very decent; rugby is their number one sport and many display its characteristic discipline alongside fun laddishness. Girls are mostly boisterous, sporty, outgoing and comfortable with the boys' banter. On our visit a group of girls were snuggled up chatting on the sofas in their house, while another group in a different house were catching up on work together. Much time is spent in pupils' single sex houses, whether day or boarding, and pupils mainly socialise with others in their own house, so boys and girls tend to socialise separately; a recently opened mixed common room may help them all normalise a bit more in each other's company.

Notable OJs include the architect Lord Richard Rogers and the senior BBC broadcaster Gavin Hewitt.

Entrance: St John's is a popular local option and has around four applicants for each place. Opened a lower school at (years 7 and 8) in 2016: entry to year 7 at 11+ by maths, English and abilities assessment plus informal interview. Selection at 13+ (year 9) is on the basis of pupil's current head's recommendation and a pre-assessment taken in the January of year 6; parents report that lately some applicants are being turned away at this stage. The common entrance entry standard is now 55 per cent across the board and 'maths is the key to selection'. St John's has its own entrance assessment in maths and English for any applicants who are not taking CE. Consideration of the pupil's strengths in sport, music or drama is also important. At 13 most pupils come from a range of local preps, particularly Danes Hill and Downsend.

For entry to the sixth form, applicants sit an assessment and interview in November of year 11, plus report from current school; places are confirmed by GCSE results. 'Co-curricular strengths are taken into account.' At 16, lots of girls come from nearby Manor House, and a few boys and girls wanting a change from local state schools or other independents.

Exit: Pupils exit to a huge range of universities, no clear favourites due to the broad academic range here. One to Oxbridge in 2017; others to eg Birmingham, Nottingham, Loughborough and Exeter. Parental and pupil expectation is certainly for university and hopes are pinned on Russell Group places.

Careers and university guidance is built into the curriculum from the lower fifth (year 10) onwards and there is regular contact with army, navy and RAF careers officers.

Money matters: Scholarships available in music, drama, art, design and technology, sport, academic and all-rounder, at 11+, 13+ and sixth form entry, worth 5-10 per cent. Means-tested bursaries and grants available, including up to 100 per cent of fees for children of Anglican clergy – Foundationers, reflecting the school's foundation.

Remarks: A local, newly fully co-ed school currently undergoing quite a lot of change and expansion. Excellent facilities and a well-deserved reputation for an all-round education. Straightforward middle class pupils and parents enjoying a busy school with days full of activity.

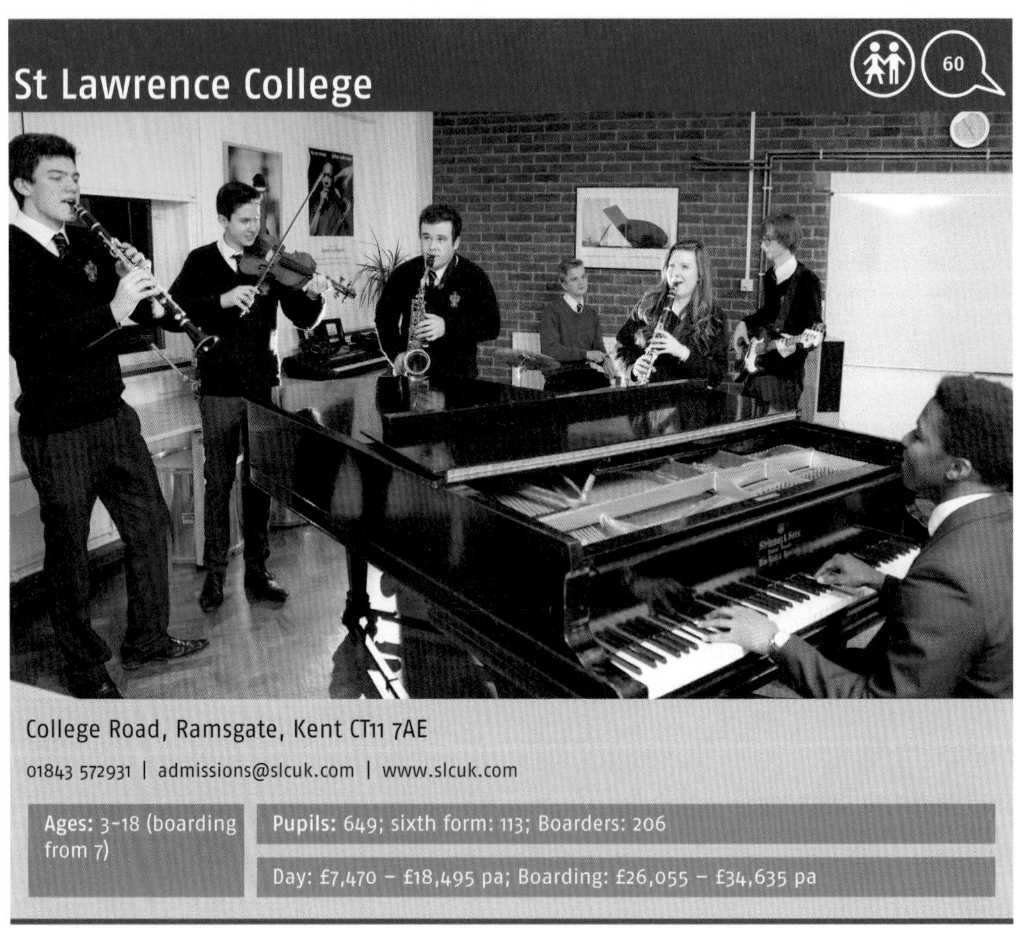

St Lawrence College

60

College Road, Ramsgate, Kent CT11 7AE

01843 572931 | admissions@slcuk.com | www.slcuk.com

Ages: 3-18 (boarding from 7)

Pupils: 649; sixth form: 113; Boarders: 206

Day: £7,470 – £18,495 pa; Boarding: £26,055 – £34,635 pa

Principal: Since April 2013 Mr Antony Spencer MA (Oxon) ACA (early 40s). Educated at Chesterfield Boys' School and Oxford, where he read PPE. Previously spent five years as academic deputy head at Clifton College and before that director of studies at Denstone College in Staffordshire. Offered numerous jobs when he left Oxford, including a place on the police graduate scheme, a place at Sandhurst and the civil service fast stream but chose to train as an accountant at Ernst and Young. The draw of teaching was always there, and after seven years in the City he answered an ad for a job at Eastbourne and has never looked back.

Enthusiastic, energetic and very chatty and easy to talk to, he 'lives and breathes the education system'. He has 'added a bit of contemporary oomph and is just what the school needed,' according to one parent, and is looking at new ways of doing things. He says he has arrived at an exciting time when the school is poised for growth, and it has grown by 10 per cent in his first year and is now nearing capacity. He is raising the profile of the school, has upped the marketing locally and internationally and redesigned the website. He feels the 'great strength of the school is its size – the optimum size for a close community', small enough to have strong links between year groups but large enough to be able to afford good facilities.

A number of recent retirements – something he knew about before he took the job – has meant that he has been able to appoint his own team, including two deputy heads and various heads of department. Well-liked by the children, who say 'he is friendly and makes us feel comfortable, and understands what we are talking about and listens to what we say'. They are particularly pleased that he has moved boarders' Sunday chapel to the evening, which means they can have brunch and a lie-in on Sunday mornings. Married to Suzanne, who he met at Oxford, they have four children who have all settled happily into the school. She previously taught history but is now training to be an EAL teacher. They live in a house in the grounds and spend much of the holidays at their house in France.

Head of junior school: Since 2016, Ellen Rowe BA PGCE, previously head of Haddon Dene Prep in Broadstairs. Geography degree from Sheffield; worked for her local authority then for Shelter before turning to teaching. Has taught at state secondary and independent prep schools, including as director of sport at Spring Grove Prep in Wye. Married to Adam; they have twins who are both at St Lawrence.

Academic matters: In 2017, 30 per cent A*/A and 53 per cent A*-B grades at A level. At GCSE 34 per cent A*-A/9-7 grades – not bad for a non-selective school with quite a few EAL pupils, and good value added. As well as the usual subjects, psychology, music and music technology, PE, ICT and theatre studies offered at A level – 24 subjects in all. AS photography proving very popular. German A level available for native speakers. Pupils do particularly well in history, maths, economics and psychology. No plans to introduce the IB. Science offered as dual or triple award at GCSE and taught by young and enthusiastic team in old-fashioned but redecorated science labs across the road, complete with small science lecture theatre. Popular science and engineering week and science lecture in conjunction with the Royal Society of Chemistry. Maths and science clinics for anyone who is struggling. Non examined RS course for all. A number of foreign trips including geographers to Iceland and physicists to CERN.

He has moved boarders' Sunday chapel to the evening, which means they can have brunch and a lie-in on Sunday mornings

About 10 per cent need some SEN help, one-to-one coaching as well as support alongside lessons and some small group teaching with focus on inclusion to make sure pupils do not feel pigeonholed. Head of department a mainstream teacher who has specialised in SEN plus two part-timers. School has CReSTeD status. About 60 pupils receive some EAL support with a determined focus upon integration; now offers intensive EAL course for lower sixth entry. Lots of support tailored to individual needs, most take English GCSE and a few do ESOL. IELTS offered for university entrance.

Careers centre open every afternoon; careers programmes for years 9 and 11 and sixth form – seminars, lectures and group sessions and one-to-one advice about higher education.

Saturday lessons and afternoon sport from year 9 upwards, with years 7 and 8 doing activities on

Saturday mornings. Years 7 and 8 taught separately in Kirby House but by senior school teachers, and can use the other specialist facilities. One lesson a week of thinking and study skills and ICT incorporated into core lessons.

Games, options, the arts: Wide range of sports offered and both boys' and girls' hockey particularly strong. Cliftonville hockey club has its home at St Lawrence and a number of old Lawrentians are in the team. The principal is a keen player and trains with the local side when possible. School brings in additional outside coaches and runs a cricket and netball academy during the winter, and several pupils train with the Kent squad – 'sports coaching is exceptional,' said a parent. The school is now the shirt sponsor for the local rugby club and the main sponsor for Kent girls' cricket. Growing sporting reputation is attracting more local families.

No-one made to take part in team sports, but everyone has to do some sort of exercise – the mirrored dance studio is popular with the less sportily inclined. Keen to encourage an ethos of sporting achievement and a healthy lifestyle beyond school. 'They like to keep you fit and active,' said one boy, and many day children stay on to exercise in the evenings. Duke of Edinburgh popular and several gain gold each year. CCF compulsory for boys and girls in year 9 and many carry on. Juniors can use the sports centre and theatre, indoor heated pool, Astroturf and games pitches and have plenty of sport and fixtures against other local schools.

Music part of the curriculum for years 7 and 8 and also offered at GCSE and A level. A number of bands and ensembles including rock, jazz, samba and concert band as well as various sixth form bands outside school, and school has its own recording studio. Regular music trips at home and abroad and school has invested in instruments for children to borrow.

'My son joined for the sixth form and felt welcome from the start – sending him there was the best thing we ever did'

Has a 500 seat multi-purpose theatre with specialist lighting and sound equipment, with seats that can be covered so it doubles as the examination hall; everyone has a chance to take part in major productions, either on stage or behind the scenes. Drama part of curriculum until year 9 and also offered at GCSE and at A level. Enthusiastic head of drama gets everyone involved.

DT taught by inspired teacher and pupils undertake projects for real clients – we saw a fine chair which had been designed and made for the local council. A number go on to study product design at university. The school has recently bought a 3D printer.

Good range of activities including maths and science club, chess, musical theatre, various minor sports and debating society. Extended school day available for juniors, from 8am to 5pm, at extra charge. After-school activities for reception to year 2, whilst years 3-6 can take part in optional Saturday morning activities – these are popular with the children and can range from scuba diving to computing to play rehearsals.

Boarding: Two boys' and one girls' boarding house all with common room, kitchen and tuck shop. House kitchens closed at lunchtimes to make sure pupils eat a proper meal. Year 7 and 8 boarders and day children live and learn in Kirby House, a light, modernist building with a glass atrium and a library which is housed in what looks like a large blue pottery chimney – inspired. All junior school boarders sleep here too. Large bright common room area with sofas, table tennis, a piano and a large television and 10 five-bed dorms with en-suite bathrooms and two flats for resident staff. Pupils allowed into Ramsgate at the weekends and some activities organised.

Background and atmosphere: Founded in 1879 as a boys' boarding school with the purpose of combining 'careful religious training with a sound, liberal education'. The college was incorporated as a public school in 1892 and went fully co-ed in 1983. It is set in 45 acres of walled grounds in the middle of Ramsgate and within walking distance of the sea. The Virginia creeper clad main building, complete with towers and turrets, is a monument to muscular Christianity. Inside it is all panelled corridors and sweeping staircases. The chapel, with its beautiful stained glass windows and fine organ, was built to commemorate the lives of over 130 Old Lawrentians who died in the First World War. Impressive 19th century dining hall decorated with portraits, shields and silverware. Major investment in building projects in recent years including the theatre and a new girls' house, Bellerby, which is light and bright with comfy sitting area, galleried atrium and en-suite bathrooms. Sports hall with fitness centre and dance studio, squash courts and climbing wall and a floodlit Astroturf.

Pastoral care, well-being and discipline: The strong Christian ethos of the school underpins its religious and spiritual life. Chapel services three or four times a week and on Sundays for boarders help maintain an ethos of consideration for others and moral values – one of the stated aims of the school is to encourage 'a sense of serving others as a source of personal satisfaction'. The popular chaplain, often with iPad in hand, 'makes the services interesting', according to the children. All major world faiths are represented within the school; Jewish pupils can attend the synagogue in Ramsgate and Muslims can observe Ramadan.

Strong house loyalty and plenty of friendly inter-house rivalry – plays, matches and singing competitions. All houses have live-in house parents and a resident tutor. School takes firm line on bullying – principal believes in restorative justice and likes to get to the root of the problem. Instant expulsion for the supply of drugs – children know where they stand.

The Virginia creeper clad main building, complete with towers and turrets, is a monument to muscular Christianity. Inside it is all panelled corridors and sweeping staircases

Good food with plenty of choice including a salad bar and can cater for special diets and allergies. Food committee made up of pupils and staff and meets regularly to make recommendations. Coffee shop open at break time, evenings and weekends – also popular with parents at drop-off time. Lots of interaction with the local community – children from nearby schools invited to watch plays and the Chemical Magic show and take part in the annual science and engineering challenge.

Pupils and parents: A big range: traditional families from local prep and primary schools, a number of first time buyers and first generation immigrants who are aspirational and ambitious for their children. Popular with the arty crowd moving down from London – new high speed railway means it is just over an hour to St Pancras. School prides itself on its internationalism and 30 per cent of pupils are foreign nationals from 27 countries including a sizeable contingent of Nepalis from the Gurkha barracks in Folkestone. Strong Nigerian connection and particularly popular with the Germans in sixth form. Children generally integrate well, although some say there could be more interaction between boarders and day pupils.

'Relaxed yet respectful' relationships between pupils and teachers. 'I love the way the children are treated like young adults,' said one parent. 'Everyone is respectful of everyone else, it is a very caring and supportive school.' 'My son joined for the sixth form and felt welcome from the start – sending him there was the best thing we ever did'. A very loyal team of former pupils – successful businesspeople and entrepreneurs who help with work experience. Pupils are 'natural and friendly and unpretentious' and very supportive of each other. Lots of mixing between year groups, helped by the house system. Parents encouraged to get involved, and are pleased with principal's improvements in communication, particularly the parent portal where they can view their children's marks, teachers' notes and homework.

Entrance: Just about non-selective but need to ascertain that a child would be able to cope with the curriculum, and international students tested in English and maths. Entry to junior school via meeting with head for parents and child plus taster day and report from child's current school, and sometimes an assessment if there is concern a child might not be able to cope. Very few take common entrance – usually just reports from a child's current school and an interview. Will take children at any stage including occasionally into year 11. About 50 per cent of senior school entrants come up from the junior school, others from a range of state and independent schools – they have a big primary school engagement programme. Some transfers from local grammars. Around 15-20 join in sixth form – assessed on GCSE performance (normally five passes) and must have adequate English.

Exit: Automatic transition from junior to senior school and some three-quarters stay on – the rest mainly to grammars and non-selective state schools. Preparation for the Kent Test is part of school life, but some parents still get outside coaching. Scholarship and a discount in fees for those who pass Kent Test but choose to stay on at St Lawrence. Around 30 per cent leave after GCSEs, either for financial reasons or to take vocational courses. Most go on to university, with Bristol, Warwick, York and London particularly popular. Others to a wide range of careers: one recently went on to train as a yachtmaster and another to join the band of the Royal Marines. Two to Oxbridge and two medics in 2017.

Money matters: All rounder, academic, sporting and music scholarships offered at 11+ and 13+ – worth up to 50 per cent of fees. Sixth form scholarships for up to 50 per cent of fees for academic, arts, music and sport. Also means-tested bursaries, and special bursaries for Forces families who qualify for the Continuity of Education Allowance. Generous sibling discounts.

Remarks: A school on the up with a new energy and buzz since our last visit, all helped by the raising of standards in all areas, especially sport, and the influx of London commuters taking advantage of property bargains. 'The school has so much potential and is just beginning to realise this,' said one parent.

St Paul's Cathedral School

C of E · 61

2 New Change, London EC4M 9AD

020 7248 5156 | admissions@spcs.london.sch.uk | www.spcslondon.com

Ages: 4-13

Pupils: 246; Boarders: 28 (boy choristers)

Day: £13,530 – £14,565 pa; Boarding: choristers £8,424 pa

Headmaster: Since September 2016, Simon Larter-Evans, previously head of boarding, housemaster and head of English at the Yehudi Menuhin School. He studied ballet at the Rambert Academy, then spent four years as principal dancer, performing in the UK and abroad. After 15 years' working in commercial management, publishing and IT industries, he gained a first class degree as a mature student in English literature, drama, theatre and performance from the University of Surrey, and a PGCE from the Institute of Education. He has been a teacher of English and head of year 9 at St Edward's School, Oxford, and a teacher of English and drama at Pangbourne College. He is married to Dawn, a director at KPMG, and they live 'over the shop' in a house within the school.

Friendly and approachable, he has quickly won over the SPCS community. 'He has a great manner with both parents, teachers and staff,' wrote one parent. 'Really lovely!' enthused another. 'Open to new ideas,' was another comment. A general feeling that the school, already good, can only get better with him at the helm. Interests include photography, gardening, cooking, cycling and writing. His study is lined with an erudite collection of books, and he is currently doing a PhD on psychological development in young musicians and dancers.

Entrance: Register early – school is massively oversubscribed. Single form entry of 20 in reception. First list is closed at 70, then reserve list of 40. After that, the school keeps names and addresses but doesn't charge a registration fee. Informal style assessment – number games, drawing pictures, telling stories, etc. Staff look for children who are able and who will get on well within the school. Preference is given to siblings as long as they're able to access the curriculum.

Year 3 entry of a further 12 pupils. School doesn't follow any kind of formal 7+ assessment programme, but children are tested on English and maths 'just to see where they are.' A few join at year 7, as others leave and places become available.

Choristers (boys only) can join at any time, including mid-year, but are unlikely to be accepted after year 5. The school takes around six per year. Auditions are held by Andrew Carwood, director of music at St Paul's Cathedral, who looks for a desire for music, an innate openness of the voice, and the ability to hold a tune.

New buildings planned which will enable two form entry to reception from 2020.

Exit: Diverse destinations, reflecting the intake: St Paul's, Westminster, Forest, City of London Boys' and Girls', Alleyn's, North Bridge House, Portland Place, Queen's College, Channing, Highgate.

Majority of girls leave after year 6 for London day schools. The few who stay on go to mixed schools with a 13+ entry eg City of London Freemen's. Excellent track record of scholarships, both academic and specialist. Choristers do very well, often winning music awards to top senior schools eg Eton, Winchester, King's Canterbury, Uppingham.

Remarks: The Choir School dates from around 1123, when eight boys in need of alms were provided with a home and education in return for singing the Cathedral Office. It wasn't a particularly child-friendly place, however, and by the early 19th century the stipend paid for the boys' upkeep was so inadequate that they were usually dismissed to roam the streets once service was over. Victorian philanthropist Maria Hackett, shocked by their predicament, campaigned tirelessly for 60 years to get them something better, and the present school was eventually founded in 1874 in Carter Lane. Threatened with demolition in the 1960s, it moved to its present brutalist modernist site in New Change. Originally for choristers only, it became a day school in the 1980s, and co-ed in the 1990s. The swimming pool that once occupied the basement is now the English department; needs must.

It is, to modern sensibilities, a very ugly building, but it's a truly lovely place to go to school, sheltering under the lofty and awe-inspiring splendour of St Paul's Cathedral, and flanked by St Paul's Cross, with its inscription that recalls 'such scenes of good and evil as make up human affairs'. The original roll of eight pupils has grown to 250, spanning reception to year 8.

The standard of work on display is extremely high – we loved the year 3 postcards from Ariadne to Theseus, complaining about being dumped on a desert island

Not a school for those seeking flashy facilities. Major building works are planned to start in 2018, which will improve both residential and teaching spaces. For now, however, the building remains a homely rabbit-warren of rooms, many of them low-ceilinged and endearingly scuffed. Pupils allude happily to the 'garden', the school's outdoor space, but it isn't very green, and the school's biggest space isn't that big. On the other hand, weekly assembly is held in the Quire of the cathedral itself, affectionately referred to as 'the school chapel', and how many schools can say that? Tell Out Your Soul was sung full-throatedly by children clustered four to a hymn book – not enough to go round, rather charmingly, in this most august of settings. Worship was friendly and child-centred but still assembly as we used to love it: a good sing, a bit of pi-jaw, a few notices, then off to the strains of the organ. Except that it's the St Paul's Grand Organ, and visiting tourists were agape.

They teach the International Primary Curriculum here; both head and staff like its theme-based approach. They're certainly doing something right. Everywhere we looked, we saw children who were confident, articulate, comfortable with wider learning. In a year 7 English lesson students had come up with their own scholarly questions about Shakespeare that they wanted to research: 'Did he copy work from Christopher Marlowe?' 'What was the political landscape when he was writing?' 'Who did Shakespeare take inspiration from?' and, bluntly, 'Are any of his plays not considered to be any good?' Year 5 maths lesson invited similarly independent thinking: children worked in pairs to 'mark' each other's (anonymous) mistakes on a recent exam paper, and embraced the task with relish, although the gleeful written comments may not have been quite what the teacher had in mind – 'What do you think you're doing?' 'You haven't put the units in, you idiot!' and, more generously, 'Don't forget to wright [sic] the answer.' The only modern language taught is French, but the children also do Latin, and Greek is offered for those who stay on to year 7. Pleasant and well-stocked library is used enthusiatically by the whole school. After a morning on the go teachers are still cordial and full of vim, and the standard of work on display is extremely high – we loved the year 3 postcards from Ariadne to Theseus, complaining about being dumped on a desert island. Science taught in dedicated science lab.

Full time qualified SENCo delivers integrated learning support in lessons, aided by team of assistants. School is able to cater for mild dyslexia, dyspraxia, etc. and doesn't see it as a barrier. At the other end of the spectrum, however, several parents contacted us to express concern about the teaching lacking stretch and challenge for the most able pupils, particularly in the middle years. 'They do differentiate in most lessons but they don't really challenge the most able with extension activities,' wrote one who seemed to speak for several. 'There are several gifted children in both maths and English for whom this is the case, and those parents are quite frustrated.' School strongly contests this. 'Extension materials are available in classrooms, and children are directed to them, or can elect to do them. The puzzle wall outside the maths room contains sums which are fiendishly difficult. But it it's true that we are not a hothouse, and we work hard not to make school a misery.'

Sport described as 'very inclusive and energetic' by parents, and boys and girls are equally encouraged to play all sports. Team games are played in nearby Coram Fields and Victoria Park, and the school has its own training playground on site. Swimming down the road in the pool at City of London Boys'.

'I think the whole chorister experience is rather magical and has probably fundamentally changed my son's life and attitude to life for the better'

Drama is 'inspirational, exciting and contemporary,' according to one parent, and recent shows have included Dr Jekyll and Mr Hyde performed by the year 8s and A Midsummer Night's Dream by the year 5s. Lots of clubs after school, and trips to all sorts of museums and galleries, both in London and further afield – the year 3 camping trip in Essex was 'the most fun ever,' according to pupils.

However, the stand-out activity, as you'd expect, is music, described by a mother as 'Superb! Very uplifting and of a fantastic standard.' Twenty visiting teachers deliver 450 individual music lessons weekly. Senior and junior orchestra, three choirs and an abundance of ensembles including early music group. Outstanding ABRSM exam results, with merits and distinctions at grade 8 common – all the more remarkable given that no child here is older than 13. Music-making here is inclusive – 'It is the norm to sing in a choir or play instruments,' confirmed one mother – but raised above the ordinary by the choristers, whose musicality pervades the entire school community.

Choristers' cathedral life happens before and after school, but their day school life is the same as the other children's. 'The school does a fabulous job of keeping the choristers integrated into the wider school,' wrote a grateful mother, 'but also manages to build a close sense of community and support amongst the boys.' For those who can cut it (for senior choristers, autumn term finishes at 4pm on Christmas Day), the musical training is unrivalled. 'I think the whole chorister experience is rather magical and has probably fundamentally changed my son's life and attitude to life for the better,' marvelled a parent. 'It has given him a love of music, a real sense of confidence, calm and an ability to slow down and relax.' 'It's busy, but in the best way, and it's become such a big part of my life,' confirmed a year 7 treble, before delivering a stunning rendition of Take O Take Those Lips Away that left us open-mouthed with admiration.

There are usually around 30 choristers and they all have to board. (They can also be of any faith – the school has no issue with this.) Boarding house is a little sparse, but welcoming: L-shaped common room offers books, board games, DVDs, sofas, a Wii, and the ever-popular Lego and K-Nex. Bedrooms were, we thought, rather cramped by modern standards, with up to eight boys to a room, but new accommodation is planned for 2020. Run by a mix of male and female staff. 'The boarding team are responsive and have endless patience for worried or slightly disorganised parents. The communication is very good and open,' wrote one mother. Parents can visit them in the evenings to help with homework, etc. There's time off on Saturday afternoons and boys can also go home on Sunday night, 'which really helps, because obviously we miss him!' according to a parent.

Behaviour is lively but generally impeccable throughout the school. House points system not unlike Hogwarts, with points won and lost for your house through good or bad behaviour. 'The sanction of removing house points is extraordinarily potent here,' remarked the head, and detentions are rare. Achievement and good behaviour rewarded through commendations, gold certificates, etc.

SPCS families are professionals from all walks of life – 'comfortable, but not super-rich,' according to school, which aims to keep its fees as low as possible. A few bursaries, funded directly out of fee income and limited to children in year 3 and above. The only scholarships available are for choristers, whose education is paid for by the cathedral. Strong international contingent – at least a dozen languages spoken here. A SPCS mother wrote, 'The school tends to attract interesting families from a wide mix of backgrounds.' Alumni include England cricket captain Alastair Cooke, Walter de la Mare, Charles Groves and Simon Russell Beale.

This is a kind, nurturing, but exciting place to learn and to grow up. 'Overall, it is a fantastic school. Caring, and academic without being too pushy,' was one parent's verdict. 'I'm delighted my children have been educated there. It's been a special time in their lives and they've all benefited from it in different ways.'

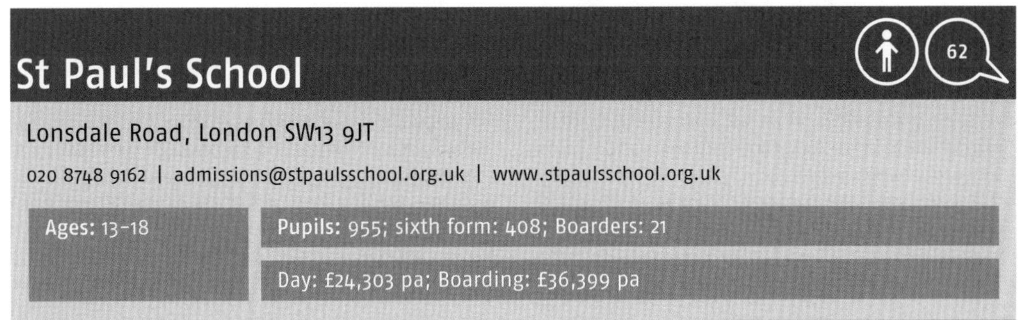

St Paul's School

62

Lonsdale Road, London SW13 9JT

020 8748 9162 | admissions@stpaulsschool.org.uk | www.stpaulsschool.org.uk

Ages: 13–18

Pupils: 955; sixth form: 408; Boarders: 21

Day: £24,303 pa; Boarding: £36,399 pa

High Master: Since 2011, Professor Mark Bailey (50s). Career has included both academia and education: former head of The Grammar School at Leeds, he has also been a fellow at Cambridge and at All Souls, and professor of late medieval history at the University of East Anglia, with whom he continues to be involved. Found time to be a rugby international (1984 to 1990) and is now president of the Cambridge University Rugby Club. A thoroughly engaging, astute, relaxed and kindly man, the complete reverse of what one might expect of the high master of such a venerable institution as St Paul's. We meet many head teachers who are fonder of their school than of the pupils in it. Professor Bailey, extremely clever himself, still cherishes the achievements of others. A people-person through and through, who likes 'reading, walking and the wines of the Rhone Valley'. Talks with a refreshing lack of jargon. Married to an HR consultant, and with a teenage son and daughter.

Self-imposed mandate on coming to St Paul's was 'Not to meddle with what this school does outstandingly well; leadership of exceptional institutions is as much about stewardship as change.' That said, he is skilfully overseeing a vast programme of refurbishment that is transforming the 1960s site into a school for the 21st century, and steering both school and students towards greater meritocracy and social responsibility.

Academic matters: The St Paul's recipe for academic stardom remains the same: cream off the very brightest, recruit the very best, light the blue touch paper and stand clear. The resulting sparks illuminate the sky. As one boy put it, 'The real pleasure about being here is going off-piste academically.' Another said, 'The quality of the teaching is beyond compare. It really pushes you further.' Parents agree. 'The teachers are brilliant at their subjects'; 'They're highly skilled at imparting their knowledge'; 'The teaching is simply superb'. A recent inspection report summed it up: 'The effectiveness of questioning in lessons, both from pupils and teachers, is outstanding.'

Broad and challenging curriculum includes ancient history, engineering and technology, and an excellent range of languages, Italian, Russian and Greek among them. Exam success is seen as a by-product of the boys' broader intellectual development; in 2017, 85 per cent of A levels/Pre-Us were A*/A or equivalent, whilst 95 per cent of GCSEs were A*/A. Amazing science building offers 18 laboratories, but such is the subject's popularity that, according to staff, 'space is still tight'. Beautiful library, silent and inviting, and facilities everywhere are excellent, although we were amused to see far fewer interactive whiteboards in the classrooms than we'd seen in a state primary school the week before. Interactivity here is still verbal and cerebral perhaps, rather than fibre-optical. Huzza! But we applauded the really intelligent decision to install air-conditioning in all teaching rooms, ensuring that minds stay alert in the muggiest of weather. (How many times have we seen pupils wilting in the heat of south-facing temporary classrooms?) Specialist support is given to those few students identified as having special needs, but this isn't the place for anything more than mild cases.

There are no plans to introduce the IB, which the high master describes as 'enforced breadth'. Various subjects eg modern languages and philosophy and theology now Pre-U. A levels now nearly all linear; boys take three or four (five if they take two maths) and can add EPQ.

You can feel the thinking going on here. Academically, a very special place.

Games, options, the arts: Superb facilities include six rugby pitches, six football pitches, five cricket pitches, swimming pool, courts for rackets, squash and fives, and its own boathouse stuffed with sophisticated rowing craft. The students wax lyrical about the sport on offer here – 'Sport for me has been the highlight here'; 'There is so much!'; 'It's a big part of my life at St Paul's'; 'Most of my friends have been the ones I play sport with' – and we saw dozens of boys throwing themselves about the playing fields in organised and impromptu games of just about everything.

An eccentric and witty geographer was padding around in Muppet-motif socks, interspersing teaching points with cheerful insults which the boys lapped up

Music and drama are both extremely strong; concerts are held in the world-class Wathen Hall, and new Samuel Pepys Theatre was recently opened. Art is taught in a magnificent suite of rooms, and the engineering and technology room is surely every young boy's dream. Clubs cater for every taste, although oddly enough we didn't see any, despite having arrived at lunchtime; even the four lads we finally came across in the 3D art room turned out to be revising their French ('I don't know why they're doing it here,' mused the art teacher). But the student-produced magazines we

read were testament to the vibrancy of this community of thinkers: page after page of exceptionally mature, sparkily written articles on cinema, sport, current events, modern architecture; a real treasure trove of ideas.

Boarding: St Paul's is a day school – one of only two to be included in the Clarendon Commission's 'nine great public schools of England' – but it does have a very small community of boarders as well, a quarter of them from overseas, who seem to exist to justify the superb round-the-clock catering which all the boys, day and boarding alike, can access if they need to. Boarding facilities have been recently upgraded, and the boarding provision was praised in a recent ISI report. Study bedrooms, common room and TV room, music practice rooms and computer suite. At least two hours' prep a night followed by supervised activities eg music or sport keep boys busy during the week. Many boarders go home at weekends, often after Saturday morning sports matches.

Background and atmosphere: Founded in 1509 by Dean John Colet, and moved four times before arriving in 1968 at its present riverside home in leafy (and very wealthy) suburbia. A £77 million ongoing redevelopment has transformed much of the site. Visitors now are presented with an exceptionally elegant, blond, modern school campus; an architectural version of the Paulines we met, really, and with the same air of informality and purpose.

Having survived the Great Plague, the Fire of London, the Civil War and the 20th century, St Paul's can afford to relax and enjoy its own success. 'Academic rigour and loose ties' was how one parent described St Paul's today, and this was echoed by the high master: 'It has the feel of an über-grammar school. It's more like a university than any other school I've known.'

It's cool to be clever here, and so, inevitably, there is peer pressure to do well. This is mostly positive, say boys and parents, and drives everyone on, although one parent added, 'If you were at the bottom of the class, SPS would be a horrible place.' But high master denies this emphatically: 'More time than ever has been put into teaching underachieving boys and providing better support.' And another parent observed, 'The bottom of this particular pile still represents an extremely high level of achievement.' We saw boys working with good humoured focus for an eccentric and witty geographer who was padding around in Muppet-motif socks, interspersing teaching points with cheerful insults which the boys lapped up and batted back, in time-honoured boys' school way. (But there was a detailed scheme of work on the board that accorded with modern practice, demonstrating that old and new styles of education can be blended successfully.)

Indeed, SPS remains an extremely masculine community, where the testosterone coming out of the circuit-gym knocks you over at 20 paces; and perhaps this shows most in the school's being unaware of just how masculine it is. The surmaster insisted that there was much 'mutuality' between the boys' school and the girls' school, but this was flatly contradicted by the Paulines we spoke to, and by one mother who felt that the school could do much more in this regard. We were ourselves surprised to find a large-scale female nude looking breastily down on us as we ascended the art department stairs, and more surprised to find another one as we went down a different way. There were no male nudes on display, and we couldn't help wondering why, out of all the subject matter that might have been on show, the school had chosen these particular canvasses. There are 'no plans whatsoever to admit girls at any stage of the school; no parents, boys or staff have ever suggested it' (high master). Which, if they want to go all Rubens-y about the stairwells, may be a good thing. But the Paulines we met were very personable young men, and the same mother who wanted more contact with SPGS also affirmed, 'Paulines are lovely, decent boys, really articulate, fun, clever and very nice.'

Pastoral care, well-being and discipline: Vertical tutoring system, ie mixing the ages of form groups so that younger and older boys are together. The concept is simple: boys will listen to their peers sooner than their parents, so utilise the more experienced boys for pastoral care and to lead extracurricular activities. It's been in place for over 10 years, and is clearly popular. As one parent commented, 'From the moment they arrive, the 13 year olds meet boys in every other year and get a sense of what they might do.' Tutors stay with the boys throughout their time at the school, and, says school, often become family friends – the advisability of which the school may be reviewing, in the light of recent events (see below). The nature of this hand-picked community means that bad behaviour is rare: 'There's an intuitive understanding of where the boundaries are,' says high master. 'I've never seen any evidence of bullying here,' was a typical student comment, and surmaster concurs: 'We have very, very few boys that would do what could be called bullying more than once, and if they do, we apply school sanctions quickly.'

Pupils and parents: One of the most expensive day schools in the UK, and compared with similar institutions, financial support for poorer families is small but increasing – see Money matters. The result is a community which is highly diverse religiously and culturally, but not socially. Parents mostly ambitious and successful professionals with sons to match, hard-working and free-thinking. Old boys list reads like a Who's Who of Influential Britons: a sample includes John Milton, Samuel Pepys, Field Marshal Montgomery, Isaiah Berlin, Oliver Sacks, George Osborne, Rory Kinnear – and Nicholas Parsons.

Entrance: State-educated parents who are starry-eyed for their children but don't know the entrance procedure should start reading it now. SPS takes about 180 13-year-old boys each year, but it's impossible to go there directly from a state school. The 13+ candidates apply either from St Paul's Juniors, whose 80-90 boys nearly all go on to the senior school, or from any other prep school – usually those in the London area. St Paul's Juniors has its own admission procedures at 7+, 8+ and 11+; see our separate entry, and don't leave it any later than September of your child's year 6 (be grateful: it used to be year 5). Prospective Paulines sit an online common entrance pre-test at their prep school, on the strength of which about 350 are invited for interview. The school then makes conditional offers: boys have to get at least 70 per cent at common entrance. The school is looking for 'intellectual curiosity and embracing of novelty'. About 20 more boys also join in the sixth form, which at SPS is called the Eighth.

An exceptionally elegant, blond, modern school campus; an architectural version of the Paulines we met, really

Exit: In 2017, 68 Oxbridge places (includes two pupils who turned down their Oxbridge places to go to Yale), the rest to Bristol, Durham, Imperial, Edinburgh, UCL and other top universities. An increasing number (31 in 2017) obtained places for USA universities such as Harvard, Yale and Princeton. Most popular courses: economics, engineering, geography, history and medicine.

Money matters: Scholarships are honorifics only – £60 pa and a silver fish in memory of John Colet. However, a more generous bursary scheme now on offer with support for families with an income of up to £120k(!) Some remission for families who send three or more children to the school.

Remarks: For very bright, confident, motivated boys who like to think for themselves, St Paul's provides a truly unrivalled education. A unique start in life.

Saint Ronan's School
63
Water Lane, Hawkhurst, Kent TN18 5DJ
01580 752271 | info@saintronans.co.uk | www.saintronans.co.uk
Ages: 3-13 (boarders from year 4)
Pupils: 457; Boarders: 45 flexi
Day: £10,170 – £17,430 pa; Boarding: £21,051 pa

Headmaster: Since 2003, Mr William Trelawny-Vernon (40s). Very much a joint enterprise with wife Emma (she's the Trelawny, he's the Vernon) – who is both registrar and head of history. Known as Mr and Mrs TV to pupils and parents alike. The couple met at Exeter, where Mr TV read biology. Previously at Stowe School for 12 years, including posts as a biology teacher and seven years as housemaster of

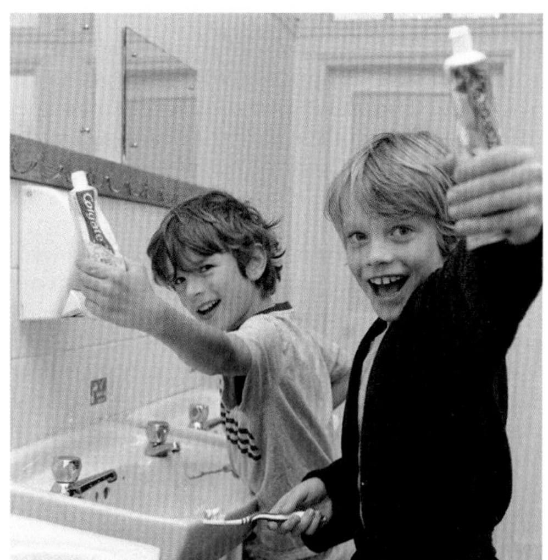

Chatham House. 'Universally loved', according to parents.

The business is in the blood – his father was head of Hordle House (now Walhampton) in Hampshire. Four children – the youngest at the prep, the other three have moved on to King's Canterbury. The family left the head's accommodation to move off site in 2005 and they eschew the parental dinner party circuit, believing it's important to maintain a distance. Parents think they get it right, as one commented: 'One of the areas in which the school excels is in managing very successfully the line between parental involvement and keeping parents distanced when necessary.'

Both grew up in a four-child family, and with their own gang of four have that deep respect for fairness and equality of treatment which comes from big families. 'Neither of us likes the concept of the alpha child,' says Mr TV.

School and family is everything to Mr TV – time off finds him socialising with the wider family, and stress relief comes by sitting on his tractor and mowing the grass, or researching the history of the two families. Both are content with home and hearth, or as Emma puts it, 'We're like labradors sitting in front of the fire'. Holidays take them to the West Country, home of Emma's ancestral seat (her brother John inherited the Salusbury-Trelawny Baronetcy).

Entrance: All children attend a taster day, and children seeking places in year 3 and above are assessed by the class teacher and take verbal and non-verbal reasoning tests. Intake covers wide-ranging abilities, but all are expected to pass common entrance or the Cranbrook grammar tests, so 'There will be a couple of children where we will have an honest dialogue with the parents and tell them that their child's needs are not going to be met here,' says Mr TV.

Scholarships are available for academic, music, art and sporting talents, and there are strictly monitored means-tested bursaries. Minibuses bring children in from Staplehurst, High Halden, Burwash, Wittersham, and the villages en route.

Exit: It's not the place to come if you have your sights on the West Kent grammars – despite these being within travelling distance, the school doesn't encourage exit at 11. Only one or two children per year sit the Kent 11+, so it'll be a lonely experience and you'll have to find a tutor.

Its quirkiness ensures there is no Saint Ronan's product – and the roll of past pupils is stuffed with the great and good

The majority of parents are buying into private education for the duration, although around 30-40 per cent of pupils have previously gone on to Cranbrook grammar at 13 (Cranbrook's new 11+ entry will no doubt affect this). Key destinations include Benenden, King's Canterbury, Battle Abbey and Sutton Valence. Others go further afield – recently to Stowe. 'Since I've been head we have fed into 63 different schools,' says Mr TV. Parents say they are very good at helping you choose the next school – the TVs visit a clutch of senior schools together each term so they are well informed, and were freshly back from visits to Sherborne, Bryanston and Milton Abbey when we visited.

Generally a good number of scholarships, and one or two parents admit to feeling some playground one-upmanship from other parents about places and scholarships secured. 'There is competition from some of the parents, which can make you feel uncomfortable if you let it, though not between the children,' said one.

Its quirkiness ensures there is no Saint Ronan's product – and the roll of past pupils is stuffed with the great and good. 'Just look at the alumni to see how successful it is in producing movers and shakers and Boy's Own heroes,' said one parent. Indeed the list reads like a fantasy dinner party guest list: BBC security correspondent Frank Gardner, spy Donald Maclean, MP Airey Neave, Olympic rower Matthew Parrish, and the late Mark Shand, travel writer (and brother of Camilla, Duchess of Cornwall) are just a small selection.

Remarks: It's a what's-not-to-love campus. Gorgeous grounds with ancient, spreading trees, inspiring views, a fishing lake, and its own 100 acre wood. And there's even a farm with pigs, alpacas, and chickens – newborn piglets greeted our visit. The emphasis is on old-fashioned, wholesome fun, making every use of this natural playground. 'It's idyllic, they get to dam streams and play with pigs and chickens,' said one parent. Everything is named for Boy's Own adventures – there's the Gulch, an area around a stream ideal for making mud pies, the Saltmines, an overgrown area with secret pathways, and even the pitches have names, such as Timbuktoo (because it's a long journey to reach it). A classroom on the edge of the woods is the Hobbit House. As one parent put it, 'If Enid Blyton was still around, Saint Ronan's would be exactly the sort of school she would be writing about. We are buying a truly magical childhood experience, not just a superb all-round education.'

The emphasis is on old-fashioned, wholesome fun, making every use of this natural playground. 'It's idyllic, they get to dam streams and play with pigs and chickens'

All this romping is made easier by probably the most relaxed and colourful uniform we've seen – corduroy trousers, skirts or pinafores in sensible colours, topped with school sweatshirts in a choice of colours – pink, green, red, purple, light blue and navy. There's a formal uniform which is worn on Fridays, key days and for trips out.

The pre-prep is in a separate bright and modern building (where a corridor poster advises on 20 things to do before leaving pre-prep, such as dam a stream, make a mud pie, and hold an animal). There's also a cosy kindergarten in the former headmaster's house.

Moving up to prep brings the grandeur of Tongswood House, a Victorian mansion built by an Oxo magnate. The original features are well-maintained – including a sprung floor ballroom, now used for performances and gatherings, where frescoes of semi-naked nymphs on the ceiling liven up assembly for the older boys.

There's wood panelling and grand staircases aplenty, and classrooms are eccentrically named, such as Old Bailey, 10 Downing Street, Lombard Street (because that's where the safe was), and Windsor Castle (once a lavatory). Children scrape to their feet as you enter – standing up for grown-ups is something the teachers are strictest about, say the pupils, along with manners, being kind, and being honest.

Kindness is the rule for staff too. 'If we heard a teacher shouting at a child, they would have to come into the office and explain why,' says Mrs TV. 'We like to treat them in the same way as our own children. I don't want to be head monster,' says Mr TV. Prefects are elected by the children in a secret ballot 'which means they go for someone who is kind and gentle, not necessarily just one of the first XV,' says Mr TV.

In reception you're greeted by a wood fire burning in the hearth – where parents come to warm up for post-match teas – and a basket of free range eggs for sale. You can also pick up school produced pork and apple juice. The head's secretary is Mrs TV's sister, known as Aunty Amanda. Parents love the reportedly eccentric ways of school admin. They talk of things being done in a Saint Ronan's way, one of 'happy chaos', which 'wouldn't suit parents who want everything done in a completely perfect planned-out way'. It looks disorganised, but it works, they say. 'We do slightly chaotic and quirky with great aplomb,' said one mother proudly.

Whilst it delivers on results (100 per cent success rate in the Cranbrook Grammar and the common entrance exam many years) it does so in a thoroughly gentle way. Prizes are given for contribution as well as achievement, and one parent said, 'although they are encouraged to achieve, this is not done in an over-competitive manner'. And pupils say that the teachers discourage any jostling for position. 'When we get exam results the teachers encourage us not to ask each other what we got, but if you get a bad mark people still always say you've done really well, or tell you what to do to improve. I once got 27 per cent but the others just said I was unlucky,' said one boy. Setting for subjects begins in year 4, with streaming in year 8. Latin is taught from year 6.

Parents praise the efforts made to find and develop talents, which may not be academic. There are 16 peripatetic music teachers, and a DT building which develops practical skills – it's equipped with laser cutters and scroll saws, and children take woodwork from year 3, making everything from working pens to cars for drag racing. 'We are so impressed that every child has something they will achieve in. For my kids it has been music for my daughter and sport for my boys,' said a mother.

Sport has developed as the school has doubled in size in the last 10 years, 'so we can now play decent schools,' says Mr TV. There's an impressive new sports hall, an Astroturf and an outdoor pool, and a great range of sports on offer – an extras programme one afternoon per week offers archery, fencing, golf, sailing and lacrosse. The school's sailing team has been prep school champions, and one girl has made the GB under-15 team for fencing. There's other options on extras afternoon for the non-sporty, such as farming, funky dance, fishing, beekeeping and touch typing.

Much is made by the head and parents about keeping the pupils children as long as possible, and they are clearly successful at cocooning them. The year 8s seem younger than their peers we meet in secondary schools – no less articulate, but definitely less worldly. Parents report no divide between age groups, saying: 'You constantly see older children encouraging and playing with the younger ones, and children in year 3 aren't scared of the year 8s.'

Parents predominantly work in the City of London; others are doctors at the nearby hospital, or farmers. 'It is very inclusive and friendly with no social divides, and parents are always ready to help one another out,' said a mother. There are fitness groups for parents to join including zumba, Nordic walking and joggy-doggy.

The only gripe you'll hear from parents – and that's a mild one – is that they find it a long day for the prep school children (8.30am to 5.15pm, with prep afterwards at home or at school from year 5 until 6.30pm). A lot of children take up the flexible boarding option – 'really fun,' the pupils agree; around one-third of children stay for up to four nights per week. Rooms are up in the eaves, and again you wouldn't be surprised to find the Famous Five up there having lashings of hot chocolate. Boarders do supervised prep for one hour, then after supper, the options include swimming, singing, and playing outside. Matron Julie is reportedly 'nice to cuddle with'.

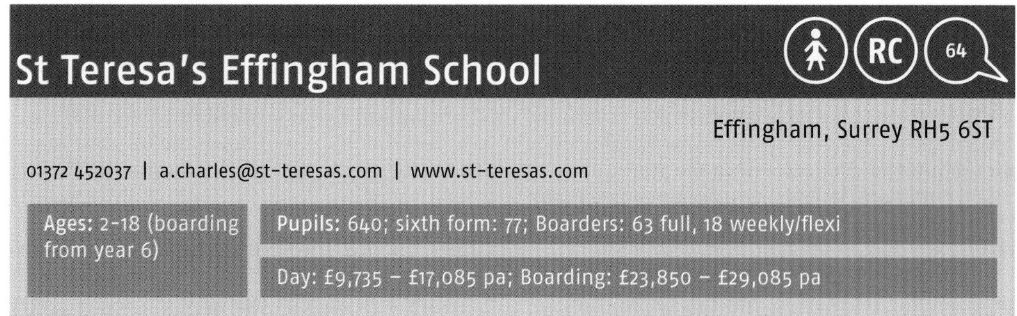

St Teresa's Effingham School

Effingham, Surrey RH5 6ST

01372 452037 | a.charles@st-teresas.com | www.st-teresas.com

Ages: 2-18 (boarding from year 6)

Pupils: 640; sixth form: 77; Boarders: 63 full, 18 weekly/flexi

Day: £9,735 – £17,085 pa; Boarding: £23,850 – £29,085 pa

Headmaster: Since 2012, Mr Mike Farmer (50s). First teaching job was as a sailing instructor, spending three years post-graduation in Greece and Turkey. He met his future wife Mary-Ann in Greece and looming marriage and family took him to a job in the real world at Godolphin School, Salisbury, where he taught economics, business and ICT. The head there, Hilary Fender, took him with her to be assistant head at Headington, Oxford in 1997. First headship was at Kilgraston in Perthshire (2003), where he achieved the gong of UK Independent School of the Year in 2011 and turned around a school that had been dubbed 'the Marie Celeste' to achieve the highest growth rate in its sector.

He has a sound business head, the confidence of his governors and a clear sight of what he needs to do to ensure the school flourishes in a wealthy and highly competitive area for independent schools. Comes across as self-effacing and unassuming but what lies beneath is steel. Has taken bold risks to finance capital projects in order to boost the roll and scythed staff where necessary. Educated at a large comprehensive himself and not at all stuffy. 'He's a very humble man – he doesn't have that ego you see in some heads,' a parent told us.

Career paths of his children show that he pays more than lip service to developing individual talents – one is a theoretical physicist, one a theatrical agent.

Head of prep: Since September 2015, Mrs Sarah Conrad, previously head of New Hall Prep School in Chelmsford. Having graduated with a BA in English, German and theology from the University of Durham and completed her PGCE, began her career in primary education teaching in a variety of schools including a four-year post in the renowned British International School, Tanglin Trust School, in Singapore. Returning to the UK, worked as director of music at top preparatory St Cedd's School in Chelmsford before moving to New Hall. Married with two daughters.

Academic matters: Prep school parents are impressed with the care and the quality of teaching. 'Our daughters bounce into school every day,' one told us. Another said: 'Our daughter had struggled at her last school. We felt she had slipped through the net and not progressed at all in years 4 and 5. We were concerned about how far behind she was when she entered in year 6. The prep school teachers were amazing. She caught up without feeling stressed or pushed at any point in the year.' Setting for English, maths and science. Pupils taught by specialists in some subjects from year 3. Science lab for the younger children within the prep and from year 5 pupils are timetabled to use the science labs in the senior school. Computer science including coding and robotics taught from year 1.

School is non-selective – head's aim is to boost its academic reputation, but not make it a hothouse. 'We have got to make sure we can stretch the top end,' he says. To this end, he has brought in a new assistant head (academic) who runs the Oxbridge enrichment society and the gifted and talented programme. She is like a glamorous Miss Jean Brodie, brainy and geeky but with spiky heels and stylish clothes. Just the job to have teenage girls hanging on her every word and parents love her weekly 'All geek to me' emails, with their suggestions of enriching books, radio programmes, exhibitions etc. She also runs academic seminar evenings, where girls present findings in front of their peers, and brings in visiting speakers – recently a talk from the Nuffield Foundation on the ethics of treating dementia.

Most popular A level subjects are English, maths and science. Head has overseen the introduction of new A levels, including classics, classical civilisation, Latin, government and politics and music technology. In 2017, 57 per cent of entries achieved A*-B and 27 per cent A*/A at A level; at GCSE, 48 per cent A*-A/9-7.

Languages include French, German, Spanish and Latin, with Mandarin and Russian as after-school options. Double and triple award science on offer and there are visiting speakers of the calibre of Sir Robert Winston. The school is considered a specialist for art, especially in the overseas market, and each year pupils progress to fashion design and art foundation courses. We saw some fantastic textiles work and sixth formers deeply engrossed in their work in the art room.

Comes across as self-effacing and unassuming but what lies beneath is steel. Has taken bold risks to finance capital projects in order to boost the roll

Pupils talk of the individualism of teaching, so there is not one particular style. We saw a key stage 4 class dissecting a poem and noted the pupils' confidence in voicing their individual interpretation; nearly all had something to say and they were unabashed in front of a visitor. Loads of praise for the English department from parents – indeed, for most of the teaching – although one told us: 'There are still a couple of old retainers who some of us feel should be sent down the hill, but generally Mr Farmer has got a grip on what he expects from his staff.'

Games, options, the arts: Lots to appeal to tennis players or riders. Newly formed St Teresa's Tennis Academy is headed by former Wimbledon player Lee Childs. Four hard courts and nine artificial grass courts. Recently opened equestrian centre stables around a dozen horses and riding is offered as an after-school option. Head says it's an unashamed way to draw in new pupils and differentiate the school from the competition.

He has performed with the most prestigious orchestras but is just as keen on bringing in local rock bands for the girls to produce

Sports hall has been redeveloped and a coach brought in to run a swimming academy. Negotiations are under way to become the Surrey hub for Pentathlon GB, which will give the school access to Olympic coaches. 'We will become a very sporty school,' says the head. Meanwhile a parent told us: 'Negative comments have been made about sport (or lack of it) by many parents but this has been addressed by Mr Farmer and a much more efficient PE timetable is now in place.'

Director of music effused enthusiasm as he showed us round the music department. A professional French horn player, he has performed with the most prestigious orchestras but is just as keen on bringing in local rock bands for the girls to produce in their own sound recording studio, or using digital technology. We saw one class composing on computers using serialism, a method often used to produce discordant film music. His contacts enable him to bring in professionals as peripatetic music teachers – cello teacher works at the Royal Opera House, flute teacher is in the BBC orchestra. Notice-boards are crammed with flyers for music events and pictures from overseas choir tours (girls have had the opportunity to perform in venues like Notre Dame Cathedral). School also hosts the Surrey Hills Music Festival, as well as numerous recitals.

Thesps can take LAMDA courses in public speaking, musical theatre and acting. Three achieved gold medals last year and some have gained up to 200 UCAS points from these qualifications. New arts centre on the way – old art rooms will be converted into an new sixth form study facility.

Week night activities for boarders range from pudding club to ice skating to picnics, with Saturday afternoon outings to theme parks, theatre, paintballing, bowling. On site activities include falconry and circus skills. Plus tennis, riding and other sports.

Boarding: Some 60 per cent of boarders are international students though school has set maximum of 10 per cent in school as a whole. Boarding accommodation recently refurbished, decorated in light neutral colours and homely touches. Rooms range from singles for the sixth form to dorms for three to six girls for the younger pupils.

Background and atmosphere: St Teresa's was founded in 1928 by the Religious Order of Christian Instruction, and the main house now forms the centre of the senior school. Other buildings have been tacked on over the years, and the former nuns' accommodation has been converted to classrooms. The prep school was newly built in 2009 (it moved here from another site) – new prep classrooms being added. There's nothing to set an architecture fan's pulse racing, but the classrooms are bright and functional. The campus is a lovely 48-acre parkland with ancient trees, set in an area of outstanding natural beauty. Very secluded – it would be nigh on impossible for girls to sneak out for a night on the town.

When the head arrived he made wide-ranging changes straight away in order to turn around the school's fortunes. Rebranding meant changing the school's name, modernising the school's newsletter and bringing in a new uniform. It was out with the old and in with the new in key staff appointments – 'there was some staff movement,' he told us diplomatically. In one year he brought in a new head of prep, head of science, head of boarding and assistant head (academic).

It's been well received by parents. As one told us: 'I have yet to hear a negative comment about Mr Farmer. I think we are all astonished at how he has managed to turn the school around and increase the numbers in such a short time.' Another said: 'He has transformed it from a good to an amazing school. The children's view of the school and their pride in it has changed a lot.'

There's a buzz about the staff – they are clearly rejuvenated by the changes. And word is spreading. 'I was at a coffee morning for new parents and the vibe was amazing. People were saying it was their number one choice and were queuing up to get in – well, that's new,' said one mother. Year 7 intake doubled to four forms.

Campus in lovely parkland, set in an area of outstanding natural beauty. Very secluded – it would be nigh on impossible for girls to sneak out for a night on the town

School's Catholicism comes in the gentlest form – as an ethos of kindness, supporting the weaker, and strong pastoral care. Around a quarter of the pupils are Catholic and there's no requirement for staff other than the head to be Catholic. Although certain feast days are celebrated, the school recently celebrated Diwali, led by an Indian member of staff. Mass on Sundays is compulsory for Catholics and all boarders attend twice a term. The chapel is modern, with some stained glass and soothing music throughout the day – a place to wander into for peaceful repose. The priest is reportedly young and trendy. There's nothing to frighten off those not of the faith, said one parent. 'The school isn't overly Catholic but it has a Christian way about it, which is a good thing. I know people are put off by it, which is a shame because it makes the school a more nurturing place to be.'

We saw a class dissecting a poem and noted the pupils' confidence in voicing their individual interpretation; nearly all had something to say and they were unabashed in front of a visitor

Pastoral care, well-being and discipline: In school, younger girls' well-being is monitored through a buddy system – sixth formers meet their charges once a week. Girls feel able to raise issues and know they will be listened to. "We can make suggestions and we will be heard and acknowledged,' said one girl. 'We weren't happy with the school food so we surveyed pupils and presented the findings and it has improved a lot since.' Head plans to introduce Big Brother style video diaries (which he previously ran at Kilgraston), where girls can raise any concerns.

Pupils and parents: Girls are wholesome looking – all pony-tails and make up-free faces. Wide range of nationalities – 15 per cent of students are international boarders from countries like China, Hong Kong, Mexico, Spain, Russia and Nigeria. Locals bus in from a radius extending to Guildford, Reigate and south London.

The chapel is modern, with some stained glass and soothing music throughout the day – a place to wander into for peaceful repose. Priest reportedly young and trendy

Most parents who choose the school haven't put academic reputation as their top priority. This means there's a blessed lack of competitive parent syndrome, we're told. Some very wealthy parents, but a mix of economic backgrounds. 'Those with limited funds will certainly not feel intimidated, although the arrival of the tennis academy and equestrian centre could change this,' said one mother. 'One prospective parent did ask me if a horse was going to be an option on the kit list.'

Entrance: Entry into the co-ed nursery is from the age of 2. Entry into the prep is by report and informal assessment during a welcome day, as well as references from previous school. The main criterion is whether the child is likely to cope in the senior school. In practice this only rules out those receiving high levels of learning support.

Senior school currently has a waiting list for the first time in many years. More top end girls have been applying, which means the academic standard for entry at 11 is now similar to an 11+ pass or level 5 in national curriculum tests. Canny parents who think their child may miss this mark are putting girls in the prep in year 5 or 6 as this gives automatic entry. However other talents can tip it. 'A girl may be very good at sport, art or music – we won't go just on the exam,' says the head. There's a big influx at senior entry – year 7 currently has 25 pupils from the prep and 35 newcomers. Virtually all year 6s progress to the senior school, many with scholarships.

When it comes to the sixth form, all current pupils are accepted 'as long as we can offer them a programme,' while incomers need six Bs and an A at GCSE.

Although the school is Catholic, there is no requirement to be Catholic. Children raised in the faith do not get priority, although it may be a deciding factor.

Exit: Vast majority of prep school girls move on to the senior school, with automatic entry, and usually several with scholarships. Recent higher education destinations include medicine at Leeds, human sciences at Oxford, accounting at Durham and Manchester, art foundation at Central St Martins and youth and community studies at Winchester. None to Oxbridge in 2017.

Money matters: Scholarships are awarded for academic excellence, art, drama, music and sport.

Remarks: Moves afoot to ramp up school's educational attainment by pushing the brightest, but not at the expense of the middling. We reckon that this is a school that truly can cater for wide ranging abilities. There's a lovely, gentle atmosphere – we saw no cliques of glossy haired alpha girls. A good fit for girls who want to take their time to grow up or those who need to know it's OK to be geeky.

Seaford College

65

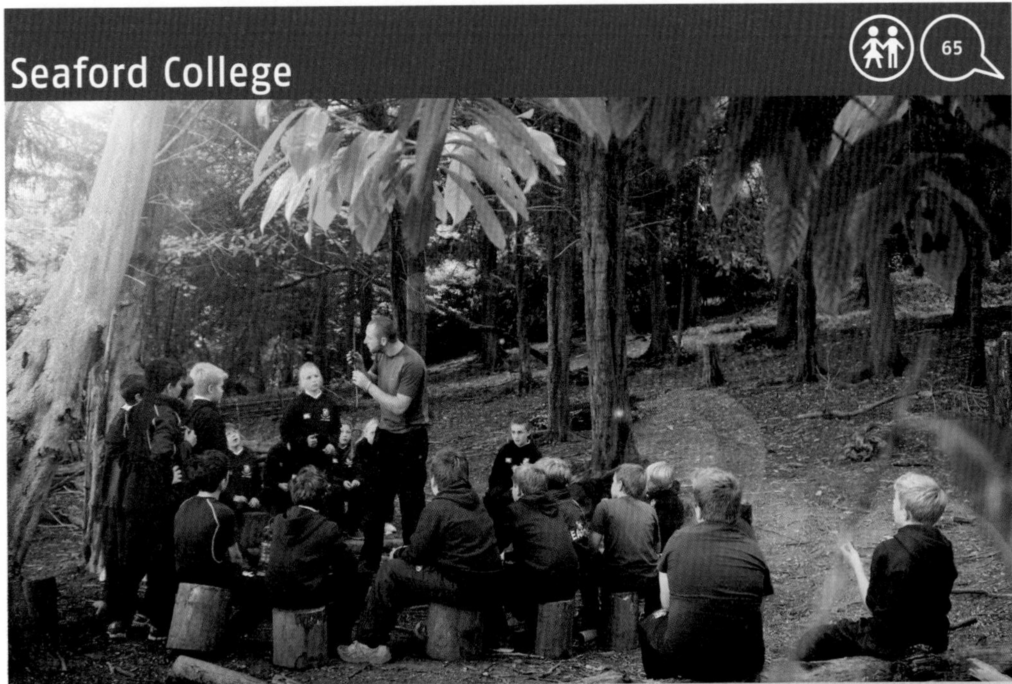

Lavington Park, Petworth, West Sussex GU28 0NB

01798 867392 | jmackay@seaford.org | www.seaford.org

Ages: 13–18

Pupils: 516; sixth form: 209 (146 boys, 63 girls); Boarders: 46 full, 98 weekly, 22 flexi

Day: £10,020 – £20,775 pa; Boarding: £20,880 – £32,130 pa

Headmaster: Since 2013, John Green. Background in professional rugby – he teaches the first team, donning wellies with suit. Taught previously at Barry Boys' School, Ardingly College and Hurstpierpoint, before becoming deputy at Seaford. Married to Sîan with three children, two of whom are still at Seaford.

Tiggerish energy, staunch and unapologetic supporter of the underdog, with a clear vision of how he wants Seaford to be. Works hard to install a sense of value and self worth in all his pupils: A* pupils at Seaford now consider Oxford; BTec pupils are told 'you could be employing those A* pupils in a few years time'. Quality he most desires for his pupils: pride in self.

Academic matters: In 2017, good solid results: 50 per cent A*-B/9-6 at GCSE; 41 per cent A*-B at A level. Judged on its place in a league table – unremarkable. But the remarkable exists within these figures at this non-selective school. The most able are achieving the high grades you would expect; but so are a good number of those of more average abilities, and as an overall picture, they are generally adding at least one grade to pupils' attainment.

New pupils at Seaford all have a data interview: a detailed meeting showing parents and the pupil their CAT scores and the national picture of attainment for someone of their abilities. 'Children in the middle can achieve highly and shouldn't put a ceiling on expectations'. For some, it makes top grades suddenly seem like something attainable: one parent told us about her son, told by his previous school that he was a no hoper. His confidence has soared at Seaford: he's predicted good grades at A level, and led Young Enterprise last year. When he went up on speech day for an academic prize, 'it was worth every penny'.

'Seaford was seen as a school for dunces,' said a parent who was initially dubious about the school, thinking it was a 'too relaxed environment.' On meeting the head, the parent quickly felt that things had changed. Rigour is now a word which could apply to Seaford. One parent described how her son did a mock paper which went wrong: 'they were all over it and him, in a supportive, but thorough way'.

There's a new focus on high flyers here: a head of enrichment now guides the Oxford application process, gently steering candidates away from inserting an academic joke into every sentence at interview. An enrichment programme is under way (in its infancy at present) which aims to select high performers in each subject and add a layer on top of syllabus stuff – masterclasses in maths this term with lectures on chaos and infinity. The aim is to develop the most able, but in true Seaford style, lecture doors will be open to anyone truly interested, while trying to exclude crafty prep dodgers.

The head has made several staff changes, to the relief of parents: 'The dead wood's gone', said one briskly. There was a lot of praise for the effort put in by teachers: 'what makes this school special is its staff'; 'the commitment of staff is extraordinary'; 'teachers go above and beyond to help failing pupils... three extra sessions a week to help my son get a pass'; 'she [a maths teacher] turns her life over to help them'.

An extremely active tutor system, with a weekly meeting of an hour, and daily catch up of five to 10 minutes every morning. Pupils are also part of vertical tutor groups spanning year groups.

A head of enrichment now guides the Oxford application process, gently steering candidates away from inserting an academic joke into every sentence

Homework is marked with comments, not grades – 'if pupils get a grade, they immediately want to know what their friend got'. Grades are only communicated to pupils in conversation with teachers. Effort grades have been abandoned – 'only pupils really know how much effort they've put in', says the head. Instead, effort and attainment have been absorbed into the Challenge Grade system: grades set are a indication of potential – what a pupil could achieve if they work hard. Different colours indicate how well they are progressing towards their challenge grades, from significantly underachieving red, through amber, green and gold to extremely high-achieving platinum. Challenge grades are set with tutors and can be upped by pupils if they feel the challenge is not sufficient (hollow laughs from the students seated next to me).

A good array of subjects on offer at both GCSE and A level, plus BTecs. Year 9 options include computing, dance, food tech and Latin. Pre-university courses, as well as EPQ. A minimum of 45 points is required to go on to sixth form for A levels (A* = 8 points, A = 7 points and so on). Most subjects have a spread of attainment in grade terms, English, history and maths with clusters towards the top end.

Learning support here is done extremely well by a staff of nine specialist teachers, five full-time, four part-time. Seaford proudly locates learning support in the centre of the campus, 'not the usual broom cupboard under the stairs', said a parent wryly. 'There's always a correlation to where the learning support department is, and how much the school embraces it', she added.

Nearly half the pupils at the school use the unit at some point, by teacher or self-referral. Parents like its size and focus, and the fact that the unit is part of a school which excels in many ways – 'you don't have to feel [your child is] attending a second rate school because they support dyslexic children'.

'I've been to a lot of schools who say they are good at SEN', said a weary mum, 'but here it isn't just a soundbite'. The unit describes an approach that involves nurturing and developing individual potential, working hard to increase confidence, by not pointing out what's wrong, but what's right, and how to improve. Even mindfulness is included for some pupils, to support a positive approach to school. High degree of joined-up thinking to enable dyslexics to access the curriculum: the unit meets with teachers monthly, and some departments regularly: someone from learning support attends the weekly English department meetings.

And their approach yields results. A parent spoke of her son's confidence soaring; another described how her severely dyslexic son 'changed overnight' here. Having been told at his prep that he wouldn't be able to sit GCSEs, he is now at the school of architecture in Oxford, having left Seaford with three A levels and an EPQ. If things weren't working, Seaford always looked for alternatives which fitted him better, she explained.

Mild to moderate dyslexic pupils in general, though the door is not closed to those at the severe end of the spectrum if they have a high IQ or good underlying ability; but they need to be able to access the mainstream curriculum with the help available. Some 220 of unit users are dyslexic, 15 of these severe, 190 moderate and 20 mild. The unit assists 44 pupils with dyspraxia and 13 with speech and language problems. Others using the unit might have slow processing speeds or memory problems which mean they would not perform up to their ability level without help. Would consider mild Asperger's, but not the place for autism. Help also given for ADHD (experienced but not specialists in this).

There is one guaranteed one-to-one session a week (which is charged as an extra). Some end up

Music at Seaford is glorious. At a year 9 lunchtime concert, treats included spine-tingling singing of a Mozart aria

with more than one session: we spoke to a parent whose son has three sessions a week. She believes he couldn't manage with less and that the level of help is an important factor in his success. Extra sessions are offered to pupils if they become available, on the basis of need. There is a little in-class support.

Challenge grades for those with dyslexia are set according to a pupil's ability, as with any other pupil. They're expected to achieve as well as anybody else, but 'it might just take them longer to get there, and they might get there in a different way', said the head of the unit diplomatically. They have had a number of high-achieving dyslexics, one achieving his eight As and one B at GCSE with the help of a scribe; another part of the current small group of high flyers trying for Oxford.

Games, options, the arts: A new focus on games with the rugby-playing head: hockey's always been strong here (county winners); now rugby's just as good. Girls were languishing behind the boys a year or so ago, but head has given girls' sport a new emphasis: more matches, and they're working hard to get them as good as the boys: hockey and netball are flourishing.

Pupils have six lessons a week (in two triple sessions). Teams for all, the best playing every week, less able around six times a term. Specialist coaching for all ability levels here; and it's not just the top performers who get the accolades: recent team of the term was the U14 hockey C team.

Cricket and tennis for both girls and boys are taking off. There's a full golf course and lots of other sports on offer, from polo to clay pigeon shooting. New sports centre includes a gym and dance studio. Swimming not currently competitive, but with a glass retractable roof soon to be built over the outside pool, this is an area about to develop.

Some notable individual success, including a national triathlete, national paddle board champion, and a player for the national first XI hockey U18s.

Music at Seaford is glorious. At a year 9 lunchtime concert, treats included spine-tingling singing of a Mozart aria. Singing is outstanding here – the head of voice is also head of voice at junior Royal Academy in London. The head soloist describes 'music coming up through my toes' – it's no surprise that she and the choir were selected to support Gary Barlow on the last night of his tour. The music block is all white paint and new wood – smooth, calm surroundings to complement the mellifluous sounds. Kids enjoy the 'incredible vibes' at Seafordstock every summer, and the head was keen to ensure that every year has a rock band.

Not as great an emphasis on drama as music ('not enough,' said one parent bluntly) – the arts calendar is dominated by music events. But drama is now part of the year 9 carousel, some pupils do LAMDA, and there's a main school production and senior production each year: Dr Faustus the last, a dyslexic pupil taking the lead part, learning his lines by drawing pictures. They don't shirk the big stuff here.

Compulsory CCF in year 10 – pupils think the parades are rather dull, but 'once you get past standing and marching for half an hour, you get to the woods and the fun stuff'. Both our guides said CCF camp was a favourite memory. D of E also available.

Art here is superb, with a big range on offer, from fine art to creative media production. Exam work was on display in room after room of glories: dresses of balloons and feathers; curvy wooden speakers and fabric stags' heads (they look so much better in tartan). Ghoulish sci-fi heads in the animation area; a fabric prawn (Shaun), life-like and eerily huge, hung casually from the ceiling. Sixth form art students almost live in the block – there's even a kitchen so they can brew – 'we look after them', said the head of art, comfortably. Students depart for art colleges across the country, including Central St Martins, Kingston and the London College of Fashion.

Boarding: It's really particularly nice here, and one of the nicest things is its lack of uniformity. The

boarding houses are all different, but each with a strong sense of home. Around 180 boarders spread between four houses: most are weekly, with the greater number of full timers being international (10 per cent of boarders are from overseas). Flexi-boarding is also available, and it's usually possible to get a room at the last minute by emailing house-parents. Prep school boarders have rooms for seven or eight in the Mansion.

Boys (years 9-12) are in a crisp new building (which parents love), run by houseparents with fluent ease. Basket drawers for shoes as soon as boys come through the door – they generally remember: it's nice to walk around in socks with underfloor heating. If they don't – hoover duty that night. Rooms for two, with temperature gauges in each room and a sofa which can turn into another bed. New wood furniture, built in above bed lights. Rooms compact, but not tight. Worth getting the big jobs – head of house gets a comfy chair and ensuite, TV and fridge (wow).

Wifi throughout (indeed, throughout the campus), and a system so house parents can see if pupils are online when they shouldn't be (after 11.30pm); younger pupils hand in tech at bedtime. Comfortable common room, kitchen for snacks, fruit and toaster. Homework is supervised, house parents pleased that their only niggle ('haven't got any homework sir') has been resolved by internet site which makes it clear what everyone's got. A house mum bakes pancakes and fudge crumpets

Ghoulish sci-fi heads in the animation area; a fabric prawn (Shaun), life-like and eerily huge, hung casually from the ceiling

for movie night. Houseparent dogs bounce into the common room in the evening. The kids love it.

Girls in years 9-12 are housed in the Mansion: rooms of all shapes and sizes for one or two, some extremely spacious – elegant windows, dreamy views. Graceful spiral staircase up to the boarding floor. In various states of paint, just done and needs doing ('needs to be modern and fresher', said a parent). Good quality wood furniture, comfortable furniture, the usual kitchen provision.

Sixth form boys housed in what parent and pupils refer to as 'the youth hostel' (aka Hedon Hall); 'but the boys are all happy in there and love the housemaster'. The fabric is old, and inside it is painted lime green (gulp); but the furniture in bedrooms and common room is smart and new, bathrooms are clean, and the common room is decorated with sports paraphernalia, donated by past and present sixth formers. Residents have a fierce affection for the house and apparently feel no deficiencies.

The pupil who randomly assumed the job of showing us around, was polite, articulate and engagingly straightforward. The usual kitchen, and not just for brews: they competed in Hedon masterchef – 'felt sorry for the people who had to try it', said our guide. Head of house is popular with the boys, and from his side, a staunch supporter of them. He enforces an hour's leisure reading every afternoon in the winter term (proper books, not magazines), having found out that dyslexic commuters do better because they read on the train.

Sixth form girls live in a bungalow, well-mown lawn with gnomes and assorted companions in front, patio with BBQ around the back. Some feeling of arriving in antipodean suburbia. Scottish giant of a house dad, casually consuming his Magnum, showed us a bright pink sitting room, golden buddha in the fire place: hippy girl power – felt like a teenage heaven. Kitchen and seated area – they can go to the dining hall for breakfast, but most prefer to eat 'healthy girly breakfasts' in house. Cosy rooms, with the usual high quality fittings. A warm friendly relationship between pupils and houseparents.

Plenty going on for boarders at weekends, with the Sainsbury's trip on Friday evening, sports and shopping trips on Saturday, and trips to places of interest on Sunday.

Background and atmosphere: A long driveway, past golf flags waving the in the breeze and ancient trees with improbably massive trunks up to the mansion house: stately home turned school. Seaford College sits at the foot of the downs, wooded hills rising immediately behind it, mists caught in the trees on the drizzly day of our visit – brewers' dubbin, said the head of English dreamily, clearly finding considerably more satisfaction in the rainy day than most of his fellows. A beautiful flint chapel nestles in the grass behind the school. Compulsory weekly service, but all beliefs welcome.

Stately elegance mixes with old cottages and swish new build. A few tatty Portakabins, due to be ripped down soon. Most parents we spoke to would like things to be a bit smarter –'there shouldn't be peeling paintwork – it needs a bit more polish'; but the head is working hard to spruce up buildings as well as pupils. Some pupils have been less than keen to polish their shoes, but most look smart: just a few shirt tails still hanging out. Manners are of the old-fashioned variety, and include standing up for visitors and handwritten letters of thanks. A taxi driver described pupils as very polite; then added, 'but they could do with mending the drive'.

There's an emphasis here on giving something back: community service activities every week, and community action day once a year, which includes activity programmes with local primary school children, or clearing beaches.

A house mum bakes pancakes and fudge crumpets for movie night. Houseparent dogs bounce into the common room in the evening. The kids love it

It would not suit a child who was full on academic with no other interests, said a parent. 'Very intelligent children will thrive there if they do other things...it could be a very lonely place for those just absorbed by maths and physics. Everyone's outside at the end of the day – you need to be able to mix and be a bit independent'.

Pastoral care, well-being and discipline: Pastoral care at Seaford is 'unbelievable,' said a parent, as she described the extraordinary level of kindness and understanding from the school when facing family tragedy. And they're very aware of the pressures of growing up. Staff in the Pink House provide a listening ear at any time – pupils can even ask to be excused in a lesson, and staff will email the Pink House to say a pupil is on the way. It's staffed by one full-time director of care and welfare, a part-time safeguarding officer, the rev, a counsellor and Poppy the dog (who is particularly busy in September helping homesick pupils). At least 10 pupils turn up at the Pink House every day, but problems can be also be picked up by phone, tutors or peer mentors. Any bullying is dealt with promptly, confirm parents. One described how her daughter would pop in to the Pink House to get some perspective on school squabbles – 'so and so's being a bit nasty, I'll go the Pink House and see what they think'.

In discipline terms, rules are firmly based on traditional good manners and strict enforcement of standards. No more easy-going Seaford: the new head is ensuring the school is up to the mark, from looking smart to the top 10 rules: break them and you risk exclusion (interestingly, dishonesty is ranked outside the top 10 as a less serious offence, alongside chewing gum...). No second chances for sex or drugs (although first time joint users might get a managed reprieve, depending on the circumstances). And to make sure no one flouts the rules, sniffer dogs (a crazy spaniel and a labrador) check the lunch queue. They're much loved by kids – and have never actually found anything. Two exclusions in the last year: for persistent disruption, and bullying. No surprise, in this caring school, that those suspended or excluded can go the Pink House for a chat with support workers 'to feel the love.'

Delicious lunch served for us in the head's study – is it always this nice? 'It doesn't look quite like this', said the head boy carefully, regarding a swirl of purée, 'but it tastes good'.

Pupils and parents: Posh, and not, here – 'I know someone with a jet, and others working three jobs to get their kids through'. Lots of weekly boarders from London, and school buses serve the surrounding area.

Fewer girls than boys (around a third), but the head is keen to attract more, and ran an everywoman conference to provide aspirational role models for girls.

Parents are happy with a good level of communication, with frequent emails from school, and teachers letting parents know if there's a problem – 'in the past we'd have had to work this out for ourselves'.

Notable former pupils include: Hugh Bentall, pioneer of open-heart surgery; Sir Louis Blom-Cooper, lawyer; Anthony Buckeridge, children's author; Val Guest, film director; David Purley, Formula One driver; Matthew Rose, opera singer; Toby Stephens, actor and Tom Odell, musician.

Entrance: Fifty per cent of year 9 from Seaford Prep, the rest from a range of preps and local primaries. ISEB Pre-test in year 6. Non-selective until GCSE; thereafter need 45 points to enter sixth form. Screening for SEN on entry.

Exit: Around 30 per cent leave to go to local sixth form colleges, usually for financial reasons. After sixth form, some 20 per cent head off to Russell group universities; Plymouth and Oxford Brookes are also popular.

Money matters: Fees good value for money, said a parent; but she wouldn't want them to be any more. Extra for SEN and counselling. Means-tested bursaries; range of scholarships available at 13+ and 16+.

Remarks: A happy, exceptionally caring school, which strive to do well by all who cross the threshold, whatever their ability.

Sevenoaks School

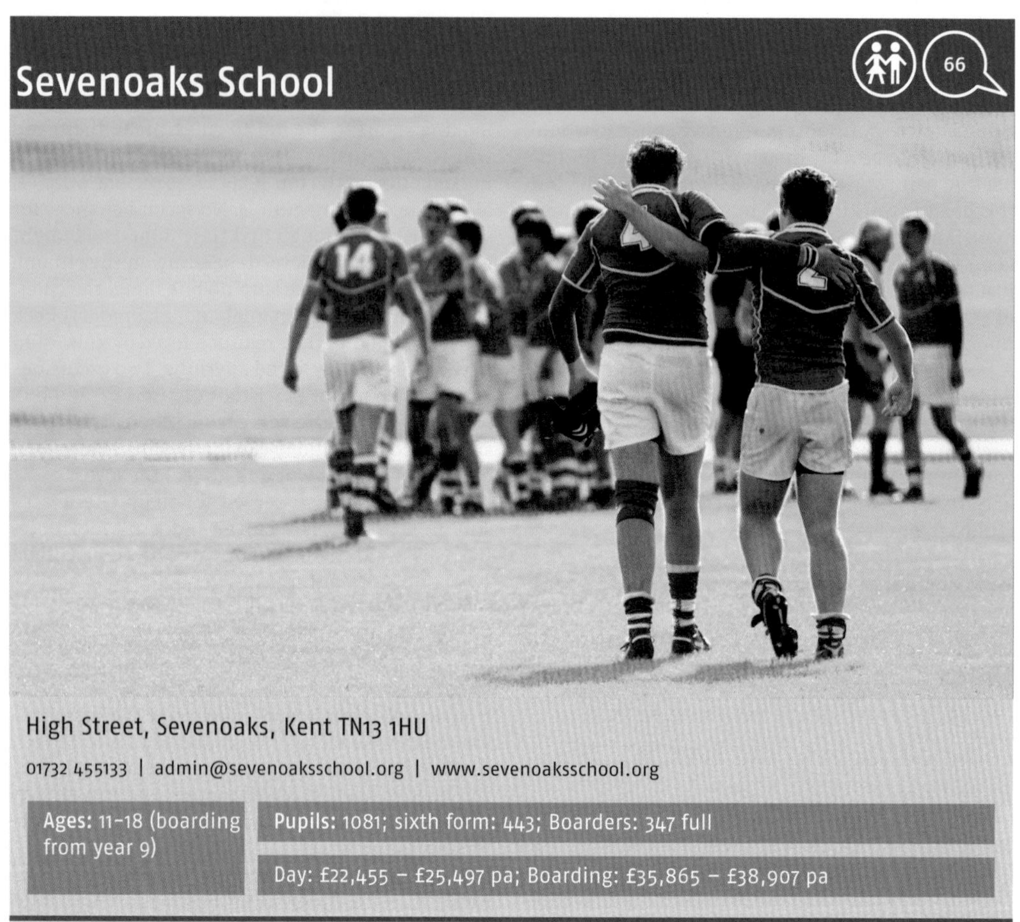

High Street, Sevenoaks, Kent TN13 1HU

01732 455133 | admin@sevenoaksschool.org | www.sevenoaksschool.org

Ages: 11-18 (boarding from year 9)

Pupils: 1081; sixth form: 443; Boarders: 347 full

Day: £22,455 – £25,497 pa; Boarding: £35,865 – £38,907 pa

Head: Since 2002, Dr Katy Ricks, 50s. Previously deputy head at Highgate School and before that posts at other top flight schools – St Edward's Oxford, where was head of English, Latymer Upper and King Edward's, Birmingham. Career choice clinched by first teaching role at St Paul's School for Girls where became clear that that 'talking to young people about literature' was going to give her more satisfaction than research.

Elegant with penchant for vivid colours, she lays claim to purple handbag, and pink and grey study described in previous review as 'minimalist' (no change there). Married to academic (at King's College London) and of course vastly intelligent (first from Balliol). Conversation is scattered with quotes – we were treated to Keats and Dr Johnson.

The first woman head in school's history has made this the place to be if you're after consistently top, top IB results (GCSEs are equally amazing). Fiercely proud of the school and bursting with ideas, she's engaging and charming – and disarmingly open about mugging up on previous Good Schools Guide's description of her 'infectious enthusiasm' and ensuring it came across just as strongly this time round. It did.

Headship is 'brilliant', biggest perk being in charge and 'making things happen,' she says. Point of education is about 'letting people feel free to be themselves in the best way that they can,' and giving them means of creating robust moral and intellectual framework for themselves – qualities enshrined in IB learner profile. Some parents see her as a CEO type rather than a hands on head but pigeonholes are unhelpful, she says. 'I'm simply myself.' They describe her as impressive, something she's aware of though feels 'completely un-terrifying'.

Pupils, particularly in senior years, say she's both inspiring and approachable. 'Barrier is still there but you feel comfortable to talk,' thought one. Another praised seamless transition from 'extremely personable' English teacher to school figurehead as required, though she's not heavy on the small talk – it's straight down to business.

Does she feel it's lonely at the top? Never. 'In fact,' she says, 'bring on the loneliness.' As to role models? 'I'm my role model.'

No plans to move – she attributes rumours of itchy feet to sabbatical taken to finish PhD. Here for the foreseeable future – 'A mover who became a lifer.' After all, why waste all that accumulated experience? 'You want to use it, that's what it's for ... and make it beneficial for everyone else.'

The school feels smiley – and she is a very smiley head. Her pride and excitement in the school permeates the place. We felt it in everyone we met.

Academic matters: Not so much a case of getting down with these kids but scrabbling up to their level. Regardless of mother tongue, notable for gift of gab and desire to avoid muscular Christianity (or contortionist's pantheism) in favour of secular education that builds curiosity, creativity and critical thinking. They leave, says school with 'enlarged capacity for independent thought' – and without, as far as we could see, acquiring swollen heads on the way out. This despite evident brightness starting early, year 7 packed with top of their year types – no surprise given school's entry criteria: grammar school level or better (possibly a bit OTT, thinks Dr Ricks). 'Other girls took five lessons to learn something; I took one,' says typically bright 11 year old. Most pupils find flocking with similar high fliers an easy transition, though brilliance of plumage can be dazzling. 'It was hard at first,' said one recent leaver.

Being on the ball essential, what with just 45 minutes for breakfast and dinner (lunch is a more leisurely 90 minutes – though you'll be packing an activity in as well) and not a place for the vague, thought parents: something that this reviewer, who'd never been whistled round a school with such friendly but single-minded efficiency, or written notes faster, can confirm. Unquenchable sense of purpose the norm. 'A lot of people had very strong opinions about where they'd be in life in the next five or 10 years time,' said ex-pupil. (And you can probably assume they aren't thinking middle rank pootling with safe pension in Basildon.)

But while spreading a little zappiness throughout, school doesn't ramp it up to mind-blowing levels. Don't sit exams early – why spoil the pleasure of discovery? Staff lay on homework with a light touch rather than trowel – if not necessary, won't set. While around 10 per cent of pupils have some form of learning need, it's mild only for dyslexia, dyspraxia, dysgraphia, ADHD, Asperger's Syndrome and visual impairment. Only exception is hearing impairment.

Stand out staff quality she's after? Personable brilliance. 'If child was on a bus with this person for two hours, would they enjoy their company and be sparked by it?'

Curriculum – naturally – is robust. Three sciences from the off, second language added in year 8. Most teaching is mixed ability – maths and languages the exceptions – sometimes adjusted instead for gender balance. For years 10 and 11, formulaic in the sense that these very bright children have only to be shown the way to strings of A*-A/9-7 grades at GCSE and it happens (94 per cent in 2017). Norm is 10, school teaching own English lit course to avoid dreary staples. ('Nobody wants to do Lord of the Flies,' said mother.) Ditto for art, music, drama, history of art and technology and critical perspectives course. New Middle School Diploma for years 9-11 records co-curricular and skills based learning.

By sixth form, IB is natural extension of school's way of thinking, most pupils revelling in mind-stretching approach that's been their lot so far. It's about 'developing brain muscle so can frame an argument,' said upper sixth English teacher leading typically lively, interactive lesson. Intellectual weightlifting produced 40 point IB average in 2017.

Maximum class sizes sound large (24 to GCSE, 15 in the sixth form), but average is far lower (16 to age 16, and between eight and 10 in final years), with overall teacher to pupil ratio of one to nine.

Credit to Dr Ricks for staff team so strong that (unusually) parents and pupils couldn't name a single weak area (inspection accolades agree). 'Can go away and think about it,' offered recent leaver. Stable core of middle management reflected in average staff age of 41, with 55 notching up 10 years plus. Inevitable turnover of younger mob to more senior positions elsewhere (around 10 to headships in recent years). Not an issue, think parents, as quality replacements are lining up to take their places (final year Oxbridge undergrad sitting bolt upright in waiting room on day of visit).

Dr Ricks shortlists all staff applications herself, exercising football manager's eye for talent. Down to being 'a curious, observant person if you put it nicely or, if you put it nastily, a nosey parker.' Stand out staff quality she's after? Personable brilliance. 'If child was on a bus with this person for two hours, would they enjoy their company and be sparked by it?'

Games, options, the arts: Visitors might find numbers of events and activities almost overwhelming. Not so pupils, busily adding more, from coding to Middle Eastern Society, at a rate of knots. Others enter – and win – high profile competitions, one group snaffling £15,000 prize after developing app for autistic children. Overdoing things isn't an issue, they say. Can mean hard choices – some pupils (reluctantly) give up drama in the sixth form, and school keeps watchful eye on the ultra-active, though approach, ladling on the encouragement rather than activating the brakes, is distinctly hands off. 'If you feel you can cope, you probably will,' says pupil. Latest initiatives are three institutes – teaching and learning, service and entrepreneurship and higher education and professional insight.

'About compromise,' says warm houseparent, who teaches ironing and cooking as university preparation, though washing happens, magically, off stage

Lavish facilities the norm. For sporty, substantial outside spaces supplemented by great indoors of Sennocke Centre – just lapping its three tennis courts, pool and giant sports hall probably enough to meet daily exercise requirements. With some international pupils completely new to team sports, hasn't been high profile area in the past, though recent successes – U14 hockey and U16 netball teams making national finals – could signal a change, achievements recognised by must-read authority, School Sport Magazine. Individual sports generally more popular – sailing especially so. However, numerous parents and pupils testified to star ratings for CCF, available from year 10, khaki-clad mob milling prior to drilling, rugged in tee shirts despite below zero temperatures on day of visit.

Performing arts impressively housed in The Space, with vast, acoustically advanced theatre that takes staging challenges in stride (pop up orchestra pit for Les Mis a doddle) and umpteen practice rooms for 750 weekly individual lessons. Very talented flourish (conductor Andrew Gourlay is a former pupil) with symphony orchestra, jazz band, gospel choir and song writing groups among many ensembles on offer, though 'have a go' spirit sees all abilities from virtuoso to enthusiast rapturously received when take to the stage.

Boarding: Until seventh and eighth boarding houses finished in 2019, sensible to book your place early – not easy to change to boarding later on and even sixth formers (house captains excepted) share rooms. Not that pupils mind, enjoying companionship and, according to one sixth former, preferring in any case to study in three-level, attractively nook-filled library, which like Sennocke Centre and practice rooms is open late. 'Less distraction as you don't have your stuff round you.'

Cleanliness comes as standard (a spot of stuffiness in one bedroom was nothing that open window or two wouldn't solve), ditto entertainment (TV/DVD, Sky, snooker or table tennis, Wifi) and bulk deliveries of bread, fruit and milk (sensible refrigerated dispensers).

Considerable variation otherwise. Sixth formers have International Centre (boys) and International House (girls). Then there's gorgeous Johnson's, one of six houses for year 9 to upper sixths, all early 20th century Agatha Christie-whodunnit-style fixtures and fittings. No longer offers boarding to years 7 and 8.

Some non-negotiables. No solo travel to more distant boarding houses regardless of age and, if late, with accompanying teacher. Youngest pupils have phones removed at night to begin with – and at any age if used after lights out (parents predictably thrilled that off this particular hook).

Otherwise, trust and flexibility dominate, from lockers (unlocked) to negotiated later bedtimes for older pupils if vital world events like US election intervene. 'About compromise,' says warm houseparent, who teaches ironing and cooking as university preparation, though washing happens, magically, off stage. House rivalry low key to point of invisibility – 'Children have to compete with the outside world, they don't need to compete with each other,' is parent's take on school's philosophy.

No them and us between day and boarder, local or international pupils – 'seamless,' said pupil of integration between the two (national groups split up, factions/combatants eg Russia/Ukraine brought together). House events include Valentine's meal (partners can be blind date, same sex, day or boarding pupils – one boy invited his best friend).

Around three-quarters of sixth form boarders stay on at weekends (it's half or so in other years). Home clothes allowed though if inappropriate will be 'sent home at the boarder's own expense...' (not a regular occurrence).

Sunday excursions enjoyable if not cutting edge (a liking for Lazer Quest definitely useful), but a welcome change from frantic pace of life in the week. School prefers parties for younger pupils when hosted out of school to be alcohol-free – and provides useful hints and tips including checking water bottles for vodka – though sensibly stops short of laying down law (impossible to enforce, we'd have thought).

Background and atmosphere: Given awe-inspiring prospectus – fabulously well written, slightly tongue in cheek self praise in vignette form – school could have work cut out just living up to it. For the most part, succeeds – triumphantly, even if tiny imperfections (like smeary bin in visitor's loo) are the more jarring by comparison. And though it comes with over 500 years of history – was one of the earliest secular school foundations in the country – and literary references in works by everyone from Daniel Defoe to Charlie Higson, isn't weighed down by it, with plenty of space, physical and philosophical, to let in plenty of fresh thinking and the odd bit of quirkiness.

'Wonderfully happy location,' thought pupil. Good for the area, too – Sevenoaks's biggest employer, owning substantial chunks of the high street (all pupils must use underpass – severe sanctions if they don't). Waitrose – appropriately – marks the boundary line. Most of 100-acre site, which backs on to Knole House, isn't visible from the road, though year 7s and 8s initially operate on a smaller scale for registration and break while are finding their way round the school's '...30 buildings, 107 classrooms, 14 sports pitches, 12 lawns, six ponds and thousands of trees.' Latest planned additions to bump up the numbers will be science and technology and IB global study centre (due 2018).

Each modern language merits own room off long corridor, the world in miniature, while English scores paved courtyard with baby olive trees and silver birch – a grove in the making – just needs own Muse. In the meantime, plenty of inspiration from works of art dotted around, many by teachers and former pupils. One orange sculpture is featured in nuts and bolts parent handbook, together with similarly toned handbag. Possible reimagining of lost property cupboard? 'Probably to give sense of scale,' thought sensible guide.

'Have a go' spirit sees all abilities from virtuoso to enthusiast rapturously received when they take to the stage

All well worth a look given that one talented sixth form artist (product of satisfyingly messy art room, complete with artist in residence and pile of larger than life-size clay busts) recently flogged one of own works for £1,000...

Pastoral care, well-being and discipline: Copers will thrive. 'You shape up pretty quickly,' said parent. Big on nurture in year 7 but given pace of life here, in other years best to get with the programme pronto. Plenty of help around. Daily meetings with tutors reckoned to be a good safety net, staff normally quick to respond to parent queries. Counsellor also well used – sometimes making appointments difficult but school is planning more.

Robust but not unkind sanctions for eg alcohol misuse. For drug use, possible that might be allowed back but would have to agree to random testing for remainder of school career.

Commonsense advice issued on everything from pocket money allowance (keep it sensibly low to avoid 'over-reliance on material goods' – nice thought, though we can't help wondering if that boat has already sailed – even recent lower school cake sales raised over £1,000) – to cases of bullying: rare, according to school surveys, but acknowledged to rear head now and again.

School sensibly quotes examples of nastiness: 'You've got no friends, you're fat/gay...' and urges telling at all times. One parent agreed that unkindness happens but room to escape the tormentors helps. 'You can breathe here,' thought pupil. Minor problems tend to work themselves out, school on the whole reserving its energies for coping with more serious problems – has fair share of mental illness including eating disorders and self-harm. 'Very on the ball,' thought mother.

Parents are also expected to behave. Don't expect leave to remove children in term time without a very good reason (weddings or funerals might just about hack it but little else). And as for taking unilateral decisions to run holiday of lifetime into first few days of term? No way. 'School holidays are fixed at the absolute maximum consistent with good learning,' says school. In contrast, an empty school is the goal at exeat weekends though pupils 'in real need' can stay.

Isn't weighed down by 500 years of history, with plenty of space, physical and philosophical, to let in plenty of fresh thinking and the odd bit of quirkiness

One parent felt that a bit more approachability 'would make it a better place for parents and allow better communications.' Emails felt by several to be a bit too abundant (about 10 a week, more at start of term, thought parent) and hard to prioritise. Rethink is underway, says school.

Pupils and parents: Has always been cosmopolitan, first international pupil arriving in the 18th century. Currently international 175 pupils from Australia to Azerbaijan, Serbia to Singapore, Malaysia to Moldova – greater proportion further up the school, plus 70 expat families. Walls of vast dining hall serving quality food that even Italian tour guide, initially sceptical, was happy to endorse, decorated in a sea of flags representing every pupil nationality.

House events include Valentine's meal (partners can be blind date, same sex, day or boarding pupils – one boy invited his best friend)

Sizeable numbers of local-ish families (Kent, Sussex and accessible bits of Surrey plus some Londoners). Can join popular parents' choir. Friends' organisation, recent innovation, going great guns with monthly drinks and cultural excursions.

Some parents reckon that small proportion of pupils – Londoners in particular – afflicted by sense of entitlement. Absolutely not, we were told, indignantly. 'We're grounded, also there's so much cultural diversity.' School's down-to-earth outreach programme (two pupils diligently sorting stock in local charity shop, medics putting in time at local school for the disabled) doubtless helps.

Entrance: At 11+, 80 places, same number again at 13+. For year 7 place, entrance tests in maths, English and VR, references, interviews and reports. Numerous local prep feeders. Rumour that state school entrants may be favoured if tie break for a place.

Applicants for 13+ entry take maths, English and VR tests in year 7, plus 40 minute group interview and reference. Unconditional offers made in June of year 7; high-fliers invited to take scholarship exam in May of year 8. Those at prep schools asked to aim for 70 per cent at common entrance (used for setting purposes). For sixth form entrance, when another 75-80 pupils taken in, tested in three proposed IB higher level subjects plus maths and English if not native language (high levels of fluency essential though can offer a session a week to 10 pupils needing short term boosters).

Exit: Vast majority (over 95 per cent) stay on into sixth form. Count down to UCAS form completion handled extremely well with teachers pitching their own degree subjects. Also 'how to' personal statement talks, coaching for US SAT tests and support if predicted grades don't work out quite as planned – school has talked near misses on to foundation places at desired uni.

Many offers from highly prestigious unis here, there and everywhere – many to US, Canada currently very popular, few to anything other than Russell Group or top international equivalents. 'Work really hard to support them, in the end it's what you pay them for,' said parent. As a result, destination list tends to resemble a global best of higher education list, 49 Oxbridge places in 2017 plus two to Yale and five to Stanford (25 to US in all); 46 medical offers (some received three).

Money matters: At least five full bursaries at 11+ (may trickle up to year 9 if funds permit), some partial bursaries and offer of temporary support if difficult times strike existing pupils. Scholarships of up to 10 per cent.

Remarks: Exhilarating, immersive education that's ideal for intellectually voracious, organised, go-getting types. Less so for those in search of a more gentle voyage of self-discovery.

Sutton Valence School

North Street, Sutton Valence, Kent ME17 3HL

01622 845200 | enquiries@svs.org.uk | www.svs.org.uk

Ages: 11-18

Pupils: 579; sixth form: 146; Boarders: 50 full, 120 part time

Day: £20,685 pa; Boarding: £26,685 – £32,220 pa

Headmaster: Since 2009, Mr Bruce Grindlay MA (Cantab) MusB FRCO (50ish). His family emigrated to Canada when he was 14 and he returned to England to take up an organ scholarship at Emmanuel College, Cambridge. He started his teaching career at Bedford School, where he was head of chapel music and housemaster, before taking up the post of director of music at Christ's Hospital in 2001. He is married to Elizabeth (Lilla), whom he met at Cambridge. She has a PhD in English from UCL, where she lectures, teaches some A level English and is in charge of the academic scholars. They have two children at the school, one of whom has been offered a place at Oxford.

They live in a house in the grounds, go to the theatre and opera whenever they can, and spend the holidays at their cottage on the north Norfolk coast or sailing in Cephalonia. Mr Grindlay is a keen cook and a Freeman of The Worshipful Company of Cooks (he doesn't like to do things by halves), and is never happier than when cooking a big dinner party. He also cooks the Christmas dinner for the 100 or so support staff at the school. Rumour has it that he is also rather good at golf. He is tall and immaculately dressed and is 'good looking and lovely,' say several mothers; 'he sets the bar high but he doesn't frighten you with his intelligence

– if anyone comes to see him with a problem, he always looks into it.'

He describes the school as 'a community where individuality is cherished and where pupils have the opportunity to make better versions of themselves'. 'Education is about improving outcomes – all have different starting points but it is the length of the journey they travel that matters – the community is the most important thing and all bring something to the table'. 'A brilliant headmaster,' said a pupil. 'You see him every day and he always says hello and is easy to talk to.' He has tightened up all areas of the school and it has grown by 20 per cent since he arrived and now operates a waiting list.

Academic matters: Twenty-seven per cent A*/A and 57 per cent A*-B at A level in 2017, and 45 per cent of GCSEs A*-A/9-7. Some 25 subjects offered at A level with geography and business studies being the most popular. A wide range to suit different abilities including economics, psychology, media and film studies, sport and photography and can also offer Chinese and Russian. EPQ available. As well as the usual subjects, the school offers media studies, computing, photography, drama and sport at GCSE.

Impressive value added, coming within the top two per cent of participating schools according to Durham University's Centre for Evaluation and Monitoring, and pupils improve by half an A level grade on predicted results – something that the headmaster is particularly proud of. The improved results are partly due to pupils being made to realise they can do it and keeping them engaged. The top 30 per cent can be stretched and achieve A* and A grades, for others a C is a brilliant achievement – staff know the pupils well and so know what they should be aiming for; attainment and effort levels are reviewed half termly. Class sizes up to 18 in the junior years and as few as four in some A level classes.

The headmaster has replaced about 60 per cent of the staff since he arrived and now has a good mix of age and experience – he takes on one new young teacher each year for on the job training: they bring academic passion and energy and reinvigorate the staff room.

He is tall and immaculately dressed and is 'good looking and lovely,' say several mothers; 'he sets the bar high but he doesn't frighten you with his intelligence'

CV writing and interview skills part of the curriculum from age 11. Annual careers convention in lower years and all year 11s have individual interviews about their career aspirations – the head librarian has a masters in careers education. Plenty of help with UCAS forms – sixth formers attend a higher education convention at the University of Kent and lectures are offered on degree subject choices and extra support available for prospective vets and medical students. The few not going to university are given help with job applications and interview technique.

Full time SENCo plus two full and two part time teachers. Pupils either given in class support or withdrawn from lessons for small group or individual tuition and are helped to develop their own learning styles and coping strategies. About 190 on the register for concern but not many need extra help. All juniors take part in a study skills programme and all are offered help with stress, resilience and exam technique.

About 40 need help with EAL and have 2-3 lessons a week instead of languages, unless close to native fluency, and can take an IGCSE in ESL and IELTS for entry to British universities.

Numerous opportunities for academic enrichment: the school has close links with the local section of the Royal Society of Chemistry. Debating and public speaking are particular strengths of the school, pupils can take part in the Model United Nations, take courses in financial services and personal effectiveness and leadership, and join the philosophy club.

Games, options, the arts: Excellence, endeavour and discipline are the buzzwords of the Sutton Valence sports department and everyone expected to aim for their personal best. Some join the talented athletes' programme and go on to be elite players and others play for the fun and the exercise. Sport for all in major and minor sports and about two-thirds play in weekend matches. School does well in competitions against much larger schools and wins many matches. No-one made to play team sports higher up the school but must take some form of exercise; PE is compulsory until year 11 and all are encouraged to try something new. Dance, aerobics and badminton popular among the less team minded. Pupils also encouraged to train as umpires and coaches. The main sports for boys are rugby, hockey, cricket and tennis and for the girls netball, hockey, rounders, tennis and cricket, and there are a number of ex-pros among the sports staff. The school also has an equestrian team but you have to provide your own horse and transport.

All do bronze D of E in year 9 and about a quarter achieve gold before they leave. CCF is part of the curriculum in year 9 – all three services but army by far the most popular; can learn to fly in the RAF and take a BTec in leadership as part of the course, and the shooting team does well at Bisley. About 10 per year take part in the Young Enterprise scheme.

Not surprisingly, given the headmaster's musical talents, music has gone from strength to strength under his leadership. About 200 learn an instrument and there are a number of formal and informal concerts throughout the year. Productions every term with open auditions to bring on new talent. The chapel choir is a central part of the school community and has sung evensong at Canterbury, Cologne and Winchester cathedrals and performed at the Pantheon and St Peter's in Rome, and top singers can attend a masterclass at the Royal Academy of Music. Large variety of musical groups including the chamber orchestra and string ensembles and quartets, several pupil-run rock groups and there is a suite of computers for composition. The band has accompanied Jools Holland, toured Paris and Disneyland and played in concerts with the Gurkhas and several pupils are in the Kent county youth orchestra. Music is offered at GCSE and A level.

Surrounded by immaculate lawns and acres of playing fields stretch out on top of the hill – it can be pretty windy watching winter matches

Drama at GCSE and theatre studies at A level, and several achieve gold in the LAMDA exams each year. A junior and a senior play each year – either a big musical or something more serious.

Art housed in a beautiful old church in the village. Everyone introduced to a range of different

styles when they arrive and 'you are given the freedom to create what you want in DT,' say the pupils.

Numerous trips and visits throughout the year have included sports tours to South Africa and Canada, a camping and trekking expedition to Morocco, a ski trip to Italy and a visit to the Neeja Modi School in Jaipur, Rajasthan as well as CCF trips to Belize, Brunei and Malaysia and D of E expeditions.

Boarding: Boarding for three or four nights a week is popular and a godsend to working parents. 'You always have the same bed and can change nights,' said a pupil. Four boarding houses: junior boys and girls live in a large residential house a few minutes away and are housed in five small dorms, all with ensuite bathrooms, and there's a small five-a-side football pitch. 'It's like a large family,' said a pupil – 'we all eat supper together in the kitchen and then have to do supervised prep before free time'.

Two senior boys' boarding houses of about 55 each and a girls' house of 44. Younger pupils share, whilst upper sixth have their own study bedrooms and all can use the school's facilities at evenings and weekends. The girls' house is below the main teaching blocks and must have one of the best views in Kent.

Saturday morning lessons and afternoon sport for all, and movie nights, pizza evenings and kitchen cook ups are organised for the full boarders. All houses have a houseparent and a team of tutors and house prefects and new arrivals are teamed up with a buddy so there is always someone to talk to and 'matron is like a second mum,' said one girl.

Background and atmosphere: The school was founded by William Lambe, a London clothworker, in 1576 and the Worshipful Company of

Clothworkers ran it until 1910, when it was transferred to the Westminster School Foundation (which also includes Queen Anne's Caversham, Grey Coats, Emmanuel and Westminster City School). Girls were admitted in 1983 and it is now fully co-ed. They have recently opened a prep school in China.

Built into the hill just above the village of Sutton Valence and with wonderful views over the Weald of Kent, the Virginia creeper clad main buildings, including a lead clock tower, dominate the skyline. Surrounded by immaculate lawns and flower beds and the acres of playing fields stretch out on top of the hill – it can be pretty windy watching winter matches. The Lambe's library, formerly the school dining hall, contains 11,000 books ranging from first editions to kindles and DVDs. Four day houses alongside the boarding houses, and the co-ed junior house for years 7 and 8 where children can find their feet before moving into the senior school at 13+.

'It's like a large family,' said a pupil – 'we all eat supper together in the kitchen and then do prep'

House based charity work is overseen by the chaplain. The school has close links with Maidstone's Gurkha community and in 2016 raised £60,000 to singlehandedly rebuild a school in Nepal flattened by an earthquake.

Strong sense of community with whole school chapel service every Monday and a weekly headmaster's assembly where sports results are read out and achievements celebrated. Leadership opportunities in all year groups and younger pupils take part in a leadership course and help out in prep school and in village community projects, whilst lower sixth take part in a community service programme. Positions of responsibility are keenly fought over and lower sixth have to write a letter of application for prefect positions and are interviewed by the headmaster. The prefects wear gowns and the Sutton Valence Blue – a dark blue gown – is awarded to those who make a major contribution to school life.

All meals cooked on site and served in the enormous dining hall – good variety and choice so everyone should find something they like.

Pastoral care, well-being and discipline: The school is small enough for everyone to know everyone else and prides itself on picking up any problems quickly. Each house has a houseparent and house-based tutor groups which meet daily. These are arranged vertically so that year groups get to know each other and sixth formers can act as mentors and role models, and tutors are the first point of contact for parents. Needle sharp inter-house competitions, plays and quizzes, as well as celebrations, generate house loyalty.

Zero tolerance on drugs and pupils sometimes put on a contract (including random testing) if drug use suspected outside school. Vaping not allowed. School promotes the philosophy of growth mindset which encourages pupils to believe that they do not have a fixed ability and therefore create glass ceilings for themselves, but that with perseverance and encouragement they can improve. 'Once confidence comes, children achieve more than they ever thought they could,' says the headmaster.

School is very aware of mental health issues and pupils can talk to the two counsellors or the school chaplain, who is kind and down to earth, and school has set up a new mental health strategy 'can I have 10 (minutes)'. Pupils can choose a member of staff they feel comfortable with and talk to them at any time. The usual cyber problems – social media issues generally happen outside school but parents are given guidance on how to manage them.

Pupils and parents: A 60:40 boy girl ratio – would like to be 50:50 but lose a lot of girls to the single sex grammars. A stable nine per cent from abroad. Others from a 20 mile radius including a number of Gurkhas. A network of school buses bring children from Ashford, Hurst Green, Hawkhurst, Kings Hill, Sevenoaks, Tenterden and the edge of Tunbridge Wells.

Eclectic bunch of parents – lots of City workers and entrepreneurs, first time buyers and local farmers – generally down to earth, hard-working types. Some struggle to pay the fees and others are very rich – it is not unknown for a pupil to be given a sports car for their 18th birthday. The headmaster describes the pupils as 'charmingly confident but not arrogant, self-disciplined with a desire to please,' and his prefects as a 'ministry of talents'.

A very sociable school with an active PTA and 'there always seems to be something going on for the parents – which is great if you have just moved to the area', said a parent. Busy Old Suttonian Society with 4,500 members worldwide who hold regular reunions and an annual dinner, and offer advice and mentoring to current pupils. Well known Old Suttonians include: journalist Robert Fisk; GB hockey player and gold medal winner at Rio 2016 Susannah Townsend; BBC journalist Ben Brown; England cricketer Mark Benson; actor Peter Polycarpou; and painter Terence Cuneo.

Entrance: Main entry points are 11+, 13+ and sixth form but will take pupils into other years if there are spaces. For 11+ tests in English, maths, verbal and non-verbal reasoning in the November before entry (practice papers available). Children at prep schools are expected to take common entrance; others, including those from abroad, can take school's own tests at an agreed time and venue. Those entering the sixth form will need a minimum of five GCSEs at B/6 plus an interview. Foreign students have to pass an English exam. The school is on the radar of heads of local preps and is a first choice school from eg Wellesley House, St Ronan's, Marlborough House, Dulwich Prep, St Michael's Otford, Sevenoaks Prep and the New Beacon

Exit: Most sixth formers go on to higher education to study a huge range of courses from sports development at Southampton Solent to computer science at Royal Holloway to archaeology at York. One to Oxford in 2017 (maths and philosophy) and others to Canada, the US, the Netherlands and France. About 15 or so leave after GCSEs either to go to state schools or because they are not A level types and want to take BTecs and NVQs elsewhere.

Money matters: Academic, music, drama, art, sport and DT scholarships – those who do well in the entrance tests are invited to sit the scholarship exams and prep schools can put pupils forward for 13+ scholarship. The Westminster Scholarship available for sixth form. Bursaries are at the discretion of the headmaster and can be applied for via the bursary committee.

Remarks: Now very much a first choice school which has grown in size and reputation under its inspirational headmaster. Can accommodate a wide range of abilities from the very bright to the less so and all are tolerant of each other's strengths and weaknesses. 'It embraces all types', said a mother, 'and you can try everything, don't have to be pigeonholed and the school is determined not to be a sausage factory.'

Tonbridge School

68

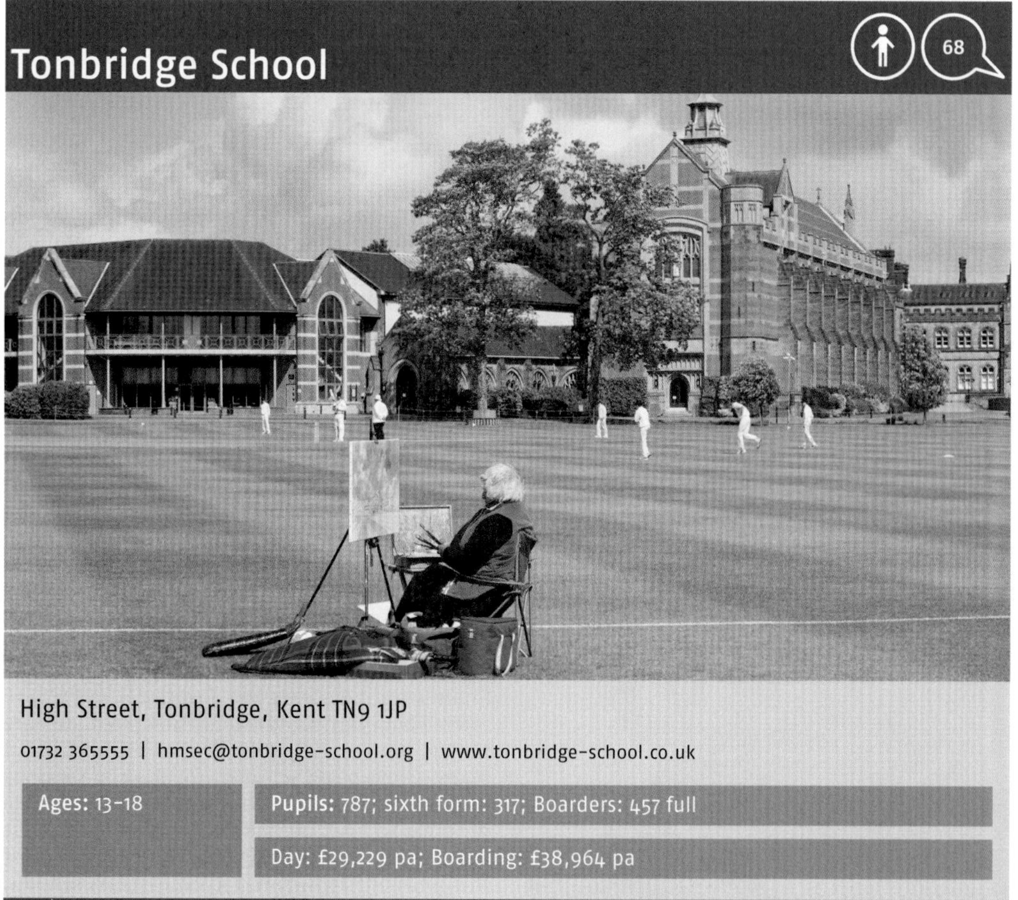

High Street, Tonbridge, Kent TN9 1JP

01732 365555 | hmsec@tonbridge-school.org | www.tonbridge-school.co.uk

Ages: 13–18

Pupils: 787; sixth form: 317; Boarders: 457 full

Day: £29,229 pa; Boarding: £38,964 pa

Headmaster: Since 2005, Mr Tim Haynes BA PGCE (50s). Educated at Shrewsbury, where he is now a governor, he read history at Reading University and after a couple of years as a stockbroker in the City, he took his PGCE at Pembroke College, Cambridge and began his teaching career at Hampton School where he taught history. He then spent 13 years at St Paul's in London leaving as surmaster (deputy head) and 10 years as headmaster of Monmouth School before taking over the post at Tonbridge. He lives in a house on the edge of the grounds and has two sons.

He is a great enthusiast and is considered very approachable. 'You can always see him in an emergency, and he is measured and helpful.' 'He talks to everyone and is not a headmaster in a gilded tower.' 'The sort of person you would like to sit next to at a dinner party.' He can always be seen bicycling round the pitches during matches on Saturdays. Highly regarded by the boys, he knows the names of all the novis (new boys) within the first few weeks. He describes Tonbridge as a 'high octane, high achieving school on so many levels. There is real ambition amongst the boys and a co-curricular breadth and a special quality of relations between boys and their teachers – informal, relaxed, respectful and purposeful'. He describes Tonbridge as a school where 'respect for tradition and an openness to innovation are equally valued'. He meets all prospective families – 300-400 per year.

Leaving in July 2018. His successor will be James Priory, currently head of Portsmouth Grammar School (PGS). Read English at Oxford, before his first teaching post at Bradford Grammar School, moving on to PGS in 2000 as head of English. Remained loyal to PGS since, taking on posts as head of English, senior teacher, and assistant head of the sixth form before becoming head. Three children; loves the poetry of Edward Thomas, the downs and choral music.

Academic matters: Very impressive. In 2017, 68 per cent A*/A at A level. Twenty-four subjects offered at A level and, apart from the usual, include Mandarin, PE, theatre studies, business studies and government and politics. Most popular are maths, economics and history, followed by physics and English – particularly good results in maths, English and economics. Boys still find time for further academic work – three presented their scientific research to an international conference in China and another has published a GCSE French text book.

The headmaster describes the typical Tonbridge parent as 'understated and low-key' and the boys as having a quiet self-assurance – 'great team players'

Most take 10 GCSEs (mostly the more rigorous IGCSEs). In 2017, 87 per cent A*/A – among the best results in the country. Science offered as dual award or individually – particularly good showing in individual sciences. All have to take a language at GCSE and a good range offered including French, Spanish, Chinese, Italian and German. Our guide singled out history and French for being especially well taught – 'the head of French is inspired'. Art GCSE offered as fine art or photography. All do non-examined course in divinity, which is largely discussion based and includes critical thinking. Everyone takes digital creativity (ICT) in three fab digital creativity labs. Voluntary Extended Project offered in upper sixth year.

Good liaison between teaching departments – very dedicated team of teachers 'who really seem to care and will go the extra mile for us,' say the boys. 'Bright young teachers [mostly male although there are now 15 female teachers] who are great role models for the boys.' Academic staff also involved with coaching sport and are 'passionate about opportunities available to the boys'.

Boys need to be organised and there is an emphasis on independence from the start, with all encouraged to find their own learning style. All boys screened for learning difficulties on arrival (mainly mild dyslexia and dyspraxia) and all are offered help with study and revision skills and note taking, essay writing, memory and organisational skills – boys often self-refer for drop in sessions or targeted help. Learning mentor training programme so boys can help each other. Novi (first year) dyslexic pupils trained as dyslexic specialist mentors and can help in partner primary schools. Two part-time EAL teachers mainly offer help with technical and scientific language.

Games, options, the arts: Huge range of opportunities help develop self-reliance and leadership skills.

Long tradition of sporting excellence but ethos of participation by all, and everyone has the chance to play in a team. Truly superb sports facilities, and was a training venue for the London 2012 Olympics. A hundred acres of playing fields, all immaculately groomed, three Astroturfs, clay tennis courts and an all-weather athletics pitch. Sports centre with cricket nets, 25 metre swimming pool and climbing wall and a fitness suite to rival the swankiest of London health clubs. Membership open to general public. School has hockey, rugby and cricket academies, has produced county and international cricketers and has one of the best rugby sides in south east; recent leavers play for Harlequins and Saracens. Every imaginable sport including fives, ultimate frisbee, fencing and water polo and sailing – novi encouraged to try lots of sports so every boy should find something he enjoys. Weekly house leagues sports for those not in the top teams.

Increasing numbers involved in music, with about five boys taking music A level each year and over 50 per cent of all boys learning one of a huge range of instruments, including the Marcussen chapel organ, one of the best in the country. All Steinway status means top quality pianos in every practice room. Director of music a professional conductor. Wide range of orchestras, bands and ensemble groups for all musical styles including flourishing jazz and pop groups and thriving choral music. Numerous concerts and recitals, including the Octagon concerts, which feature a different instrument each week. Excellent facilities include two recital halls, a suite of teaching practice rooms, music library, soundproof room for jazz and percussion, and a state of the art recording studio. Often team up with musicians outside school eg a concert with Benenden at St Martin in the Fields and South Bank Sinfonia at the Royal Festival Hall; and choir has sung at St George's Chapel, Windsor and Chichester Cathedral, and deputised at St Paul's when the cathedral choir was away.

Three boys presented their scientific research to an international conference in China

Drama also thriving, with about eight major productions a year in 400 seat EM Forster theatre (complete with orchestra pit and studio theatre), including three major school plays, with girls from local schools taking part in most productions. Boys get involved with all aspects of production including set design, stage management and lighting. Regular drama competitions and house plays, which are put together by the boys with drama staff acting as mentors, as well as other small scale productions and plays in Spanish, French and German.

Arts workshops by visiting professionals include street dance, masks, puppetry and film making and upper sixth boys invited to take a play to Edinburgh Fringe via the Hogshead Theatre Company. Boys also take part in the National Theatre's play writing competition. Varied programme of lectures by visiting speakers, and boys can choose from a huge range of societies: cultural, political, scientific and sporting, anything from bee-keeping, astronomy and wine appreciation to sub aqua and robotics.

Seminar programme in GCSE and lower sixth years encourages boys to questions their assumptions and see things from a different perspective – eg sustainability in business or organ transplants. About 200 boys take part in CCF across all three services. Duke of Edinburgh Award also popular with about 20 achieving gold each year. Not forgetting numerous foreign visits and exchange trips during the holidays.

Boarding: There are seven boarding houses and younger boys start in small dorms of up to six. Older boys have their own rooms. Strong system of pastoral care. Housemasters seen as 'father figures' who get to know boys and their families very well. Aided by assistant housemaster and five tutors per house – boys have regular meetings with their tutors. During the week all boys eat in their houses but at weekends boarders eat together in the

Orchard Centre. Most boys go home after games on Saturday, but have to be back in time for Sunday evening chapel. Although trips and outings are organised, it can be quite lonely for those who stay in.

Background and atmosphere: Founded by Sir Andrew Judde in 1553, the school still has close links with the Worshipful Company of Skinners, and Skinners' Day is celebrated each year at the end of the summer term. The school grew rapidly in the 19th century and has been rebuilt twice on the original site. Dominated by the fine rebuilt Edwardian chapel (it was gutted by fire in 1988), the school is set in 150 acres of immaculately kept grounds behind the not-so-glamorous Tonbridge High Street on the northern edge of the town, stretching down to the river and the railway line. The imposing Victorian buildings with tasteful, modern additions manage to combine a respect for tradition with the most up-to-date facilities. The Vere Lodge Centre for DT and art, with its spiral staircase and light-filled space for private views and exhibitions, is particularly impressive. Well-used library – built in 1962 and recently extended and refurbished – with 23,000 books, a number of which date from the 17th century, as well as the 1479 Jensen Bible – although boys seem to get most of their information online, and there's plenty of digital technology here too. New science centre under construction.

Pastoral care, well-being and discipline: Seven boarding and five day houses situated on the edge of the playing fields and along the high street (most recently refurbished), each with about 60 boys. Strong sense of belonging in houses helped by range of inter-house competitions in art, music, film, sport plus house plays and concerts, and close friendships are formed. School aims for as wide a mix as possible in each house and tries to split up boys from the same prep school to stop cliques forming. Good food – all eat in their houses, with grace before lunch.

Boys 'very driven – it's cool to work and there are not many problems on the behaviour front – the boys know they are there to work and are expected to work hard – the pace can be quite challenging for some,' said a parent. Mindfulness meditation is taught as part of PSHE to all boys in year 10 and is increasingly popular as an activity. Boys are taught to focus on the present and not worry about the past or the future – a skill for life which helps them cope with stress. There is an emotional literacy programme for senior boys and an on-site school counsellor.

All boys are expected to attend weekday chapel services four mornings a week, and other faiths encouraged to attend their own places of worship

Boys are taught to focus on the present and not worry about the past or the future – a skill for life which helps them cope with stress

for special religious festivals. School is increasingly connected with the local community and there is a growing sense of social responsibility, with large numbers of boys involved with Tonbridge Community Action – boys help in local primary schools and hospitals and develop the skills and confidence to do things which make a difference. Local primary school children come to use the labs on Wednesday afternoons and hold inter-school sports days at Tonbridge. Recently, 150 boys spent the night under cardboard boxes and raised £5,000 for a homeless charity. Tonbridge has close links with The Marsh Academy at New Romney and is one of its sponsors – Tonbridge boys act as e-mentors and provide help and support to Marsh students, and Marsh students come to Tonbridge for practical science work in the labs. Gap year boys can also work at Marsh Academy for a term.

Pupils and parents: Most boys live within about an hour and a half of the school and it is becoming increasingly popular with London families. The headmaster describes the typical Tonbridge parent as 'understated and low-key' and the boys as having a quiet self-assurance – 'great team players who get on in all settings'. Alpha males thrive here and sport still dominant, but boys also admired for other things and music and culture increasingly important; it is 'a much more tolerant and a kinder place than it was some years ago'.

About 10 per cent foreign nationals from 33 countries, who are generally well integrated. Each house twinned with a house at Benenden for socials, restaurant outings and quizzes. Parents encouraged to get involved, and there is always strong support for Saturday matches. Most parents are members of the Parents' Arts Society, which organises cultural and social events each term, everything from private views at art galleries, theatre trips, wine tastings and lectures to weekend trips to Europe. 'It is such a fun way to get to know the other parents,' said one mother. There doesn't seem to be a typical Tonbridgian – some sporty, some less so, some musical, some not – but all seem to enjoy themselves, and the key seems to be to take part in everything. They have a keen sense of fun, demonstrated at the annual Pink Day when all boys dress up in pink in support of breast cancer charities with some very imaginative and outrageous outfits.

A long list of famous old boys includes EM Forster, Frederick Forsyth, all members of the band Keane, Vikram Seth, Patrick Mayhew, several generations of the Cowdrey cricketing dynasty, Dan Stevens of Downton Abbey fame, Tim Waterstone and Kit Hesketh-Harvey.

Entrance: Most join at 13+ from 50-60 prep schools. Computer based pre-assessment and interview in year 6 followed by common entrance (pass mark about 65 per cent) or the school's own exams in English and maths. School operates a reserve list and keeps in close contact with prep schools. A handful joins in year 10 and about 20 join in lower sixth. Sixth form entry via tests in subjects to be studied at A level.

Exit: In 2017, 27 to Oxbridge. Other popular destinations are the usual suspects: Durham, Bristol, Exeter, Bath, London unis and Nottingham, mostly to read hard academic subjects, but not all follow the herd – other destinations include film production at Bournemouth, golf management at Birmingham, land management at Cirencester and popular music performance at the Royal Northern College of Music. Full-time university and careers advisor widely praised, plus guidance and support from housemasters and other specialist staff. University and careers offices open all day – careers and higher education programme starts at end of first year. Good relationships with European and American universities and provide on-site training for SAT exams. Boys have recently gone to Harvard, Berkeley, New York, Queen's University Canada, Trinity College Dublin and Maastricht.

Money matters: A well-endowed school which offers numerous awards. Up to 45 scholarships offered at 13+ – academic, music, art, drama, technology and sport. Academic and music scholarships offered in sixth form. Top academic scholarship worth 50 per cent and all others 10 per cent, which can be topped up with a means-tested bursary. About 15 boys on full fee remission and a further 15 on 80 per cent fee remission. Means-tested foundation awards given to boys to help fund years 7 and 8 at prep school followed by a guaranteed place at Tonbridge.

Remarks: The prospectus says that 'Tonbridge seeks to excel in everything it does' and it certainly lives up to its aim. 'We have been delighted with the school and our boys have been happy and done well here, but you sometimes wonder if the next stage of their lives can live up to this amazing start', said one parent.

Vinehall School

69

Mountfield, Robertsbridge, East Sussex TN32 5JL

01580 880413 | admissions@vinehallschool.com | www.vinehallschool.com

Ages: 2-13 (boarders from 7)

Pupils: 258; Boarders: 25 full, 3 weekly, 7 flexi

Day: £9,375 – £17,490 pa; Boarding: £20,535 – £22,785 pa

Headmaster: Since September 2017 Jonathan 'Joff' Powis, previously deputy head and head of geography at Papplewick. Geography degree from Leeds; also has a TEFL qualification and is an ISI boarding inspector. An all-rounder, his interests range from coaching rugby, cricket and football to directing school musicals and singing tenor in the school choir. He also plays the trumpet and piano, and counts skiing, sailing, canoeing and mountain-biking amongst his hobbies.

Entrance: There's an element of selection because all students are expected to take common entrance or the Cranbrook Grammar exam. Prospective pupils attend a taster day, and not all will be accepted. Those seeking places in year 3 upwards do a maths, English and verbal reasoning test. There are a small number of pupils with dyslexia and dyspraxia, but none with autism. This is more to do with geography than the school's attitude – the specialist Frewen College which caters for these conditions is just five miles away.

Exit: Most popular destinations in the independent sector are Eastbourne College, Tonbridge, Sevenoaks, King's Canterbury, Benenden, Battle Abbey and Bede's, but pupils go on to about 16 senior schools. Around 15 per cent have gone to Cranbrook Grammar at 13 each year, but this is likely to change with Cranbrook's new 11+ entry.

Remarks: If a pig could talk, should you eat it? Does a dog know it's a dog? These are lessons with which children here wrestle. Philosophy is big on the curriculum at Vinehall as a way of broadening education. 'Common entrance is quite prescriptive, it's rigorous and there's a great volume of knowledge required, but we're concerned that we teach children to jump through hoops. But do they think for themselves?' A lunchtime philosophy club has now extended to lessons in critical thinking in years 7 and 8, and 'puzzle it out' sessions for the pre-prep. It's highly popular with parents and 'sold the school to me,' according to one. Others mention 'a lot of self-directed learning, which really lights the fire'.

Staff are also working hard on turning around the school's previous reputation as academically elitist – one mother admits that local talk almost put her off viewing the school. 'If they are a potential scholar they will get a scholarship, but we want every child to be happy. Not every child is going to get a scholarship, it's the minority, not the norm. Some schools put huge pressure on the children, they are driven by fear of not getting into the next school. We want to be academically excellent, but not for children to feel a failure if they find certain aspects difficult.'

The pre-prep comprises a nursery (from age 2) and kindergarten (from age 3) all housed under the same roof as reception to year 2 to enable easy transition. It's a modern, bright building with its own hall and library and a woodland play area.

One parent with children in both parts of the school feels that the pre-prep is more traditional. 'The two environments are very different, pre-prep is very formal and structured, and I'd like to see more freedom,' she said. But the school says there has been a continuation of new innovations in pre-prep teaching, including the use of iPads, a Mandarin club, and higher-order thinking skills sessions.

'Some schools put huge pressure on the children. We want to be academically excellent, but not for children to feel a failure if they find certain aspects difficult'

The prep is situated in a Victorian mansion built by banker Tilden Smith as his family home – the head's study has glorious views over 47 acres of school grounds and miles beyond. Corridors and staircases are lined with shields, each one representing a past pupil and his or her achievements.

There's a separate Millennium building – with subject classrooms arranged around a hub with a library at its centre; also a computer suite, science block, music building, and art, design and technology centre. Subject specific classrooms are used from year 5. Years 7 and 8 have a scholarship form and two mixed ability common entrance forms, with setting for maths.

Reporting back to parents is thorough. There's an 'industry card' each half-term, which reports on how hard a child is working only, with full reports at the end of term. A system called 'classroom monitor' breaks subjects into component parts so that

parents and teachers can be better informed about specifics to work on – in maths it might say, for example, that a child is good at co-ordinates, but finds algebra difficult.

One third of the pupils receive some form of learning support, which can range from work on posture using Swiss balls, because it can help concentration, to one-to-one support in lessons.

'The calibre of staff in the prep is outstanding,' said a parent. And all the parents praise the prompt attention to any worries. 'I had an issue this morning, they emailed back half an hour later, and it was done and dusted in an hour,' said one.

Everyone studies drama, and productions are staged in a theatre which could grace a small town – it has all the professional equipment and a 250 seat auditorium.

Sports facilities include an indoor swimming pool and a nine hole golf course. School is now 'very sporty', say parents.There are rugby tours, and teams take part in the National Schools Indoor Rowing League. Girls' provision has been revitalised, and they're now winning more matches.

No more Saturday morning school for year 7 and 8s – a previous bugbear for some children and parents. Instead, there is an optional enrichment programme for years 3 to 8 – including sports, crafts, and subjects such as astronomy, media and philosophy.

School day now shortened – lessons finish at 4.30pm with optional activity programme including supervised prep (whoopee, say parents) until the school buses leave at 5.25pm.

The school attracts a number of international boarders (around 45 per cent). Full boarding is available from year 3, but junior boarders (years 3 to 6) have the option to board for four nights a week, while year 7 and 8 can opt for full or weekly boarding. There's also temporary boarding for occasional nights. 'I like it that they don't push boarding too much and you aren't deemed second class if you're not a boarder,' one mother commented.

Minibuses bring local children in from all points of the compass including Hastings, Eastbourne, Lamberhurst, Mayfield, Heathfield and Cranbrook. Some parents work in the City but there are also families who find it more of a financial struggle, and they say there is no snobbery. Those who have transferred from the state sector say it's been seamless and they've felt welcome.

Wellesley House
70
114 Ramsgate Road, Broadstairs, Kent CT10 2DG
01843 862991 | hmsecretary@wellesleyhouse.net | www.wellesleyhouse.org
Ages: 7-13
Pupils: 135; Boarders: 45 full, 30 weekly, 10 flexi
Day: £11,961 – £19,479 pa; Boarding: £25,752 pa

Headmaster: Since September 2017 Gavin Franklin, previously a housemaster at Wellington College. Sport degree from Durham; represented British Universities at cricket and went on to play for Staffordshire and Warwickshire. Spent five years at the Oval, as performance manager in charge of elite player development, becoming a level 4 cricket coach, before moving to Wellington as assistant director of sport and English teacher. His wife Claire is also a Durham graduate and a teacher with an interest in sport; they have two young sons.

Entrance: Children can join at any time from 7 upwards – many from local day schools join at this age, with major intakes in years 5 and 6 particularly for boarders. Very occasionally children join for the last year but it can be difficult getting up to speed for common entrance. Girls' boarding places always oversubscribed. Non-selective but entry via interview and reports and examples of work from the child's current school. Would only test if there were concerns about learning support or that a child might not thrive.

Surprisingly large catchment area with many coming from west Kent and East Sussex. About 15-20 from London with an accompanied minibus to Battersea at half term and exeats – school keeps in close touch with London pre-prep heads. Scholarships and bursaries available. Discounts for army families.

There are around 40 per cent overseas boarders. Pupils are able to board from year 3 onwards

Exit: To a huge range of senior schools all over the country with King's Canterbury the most popular, others to Harrow, Charterhouse, Eastbourne,

Benenden, Downe House, St Edward's Oxford, Sutton Valence, Cranbrook and Epsom College. Great trouble is taken to pick the right school for each child and the headmaster tries to visit at least two public schools a term. Over a third have won scholarships in recent years. Children hardly ever leave at 11+ and the school does not offer coaching for the Kent Test.

Old Welleslians often end up sharing flats and there are usually a couple of Wellesley weddings announced in the school magazine

Remarks: Wellesley was founded in 1869 in Ramsgate and moved to its current purpose-built site in 1898, a light and airy red-brick building which has been added to over the years and which is surrounded by flower beds and playing fields. It merged with St Peter's Court in 1969 and went co-ed in 1977. It does not have the rolling acres of some prep schools but everything is immaculate and every inch of the grounds is used – there is plenty of room for den-making, a pond, vegetable plots and even some igloos when it snows. The playing fields are divided by an elegant avenue of trees which has been colonised by a group of noisy, bright green parrots. Lots of refurbishment recently and the squash courts, shooting range and the sunny indoor heated swimming pool and barbecue area are all looking like new. The walls of the new games room were decorated by the children. Sunny, comfortable, well-used library with lots of space to sit and read and where children can curl up with a book. Each year group has its own common room – recently redecorated thanks to the fundraising efforts of the Friends of Wellesley.

Photographs of children past and present line the corridors and there are four rolling news boards around the school showing BBC headlines, birthday announcements, notices and photos of recent events.

Avert your eyes as you drive through the cabbage patches and retail parks of Thanet – it is worth it. Many parents drive miles to send their children here, passing other good prep schools en route. It is a school which embraces the whole family and where friends are made for life: 'My daughter's best friends are still the ones she made at Wellesley,' said one mother. Parents, too, make great friends here – many a mother has been known to weep copiously during the leavers' chapel service. Old Welleslians often end up sharing flats together and there are usually a couple of Wellesley weddings announced in the school magazine. It is a busy, happy school where there is great emphasis on fairness and giving everyone a chance. Academic success is highly valued but good manners, tolerance and consideration for others are equally important. At the annual prize giving each summer, there are not only prizes for academic and sporting achievements but also the headmaster's prize which can be for anything from attitude and effort to just being a thoroughly nice person.

Younger boys live in Boddington House which is joined on to the main school and where they

do most of their lessons and are cared for by a housemaster and a team of matrons, which gives them a very gentle introduction to boarding. They move over to the main school aged 10 where they are equally well cared for in large, light, airy and extremely tidy dormitories.

The girls live at the Orchard, set in its own grounds and surrounded by apple trees on the far side of the playing fields. The Orchard is run by Mr Nichol, who teaches geography and is in charge of the Thanet weather station, and his very elegant and bubbly Spanish wife, Elena, and it is very much a home from home. The Nichols have been in charge here for over 20 years and give the girls an exceptional start in life. There is only space for 43 girls so it feels like a large happy family and is always oversubscribed. Bright, light dorms, all named after Kentish apples, with an abundance of pink and teddy bears on all the beds. One mother who was reluctant to let her daughter board said, 'I cannot deprive my daughter of the Orchard experience, it's truly unique'.

The school motto is 'Open up a world of possibilities' and this is exactly what Wellesley does. There is great emphasis on the individual and 'children get noticed in a smaller school and get opportunities they would not get elsewhere', says the school. Everyone has 'a chance to shine' and with so many activities on offer virtually everyone finds something they are good at. Everything from photography and art, board games and chess, boys' hockey and girls' football, judo, fencing, riding at the local riding school, archery, cooking, needlework for boys and girls, ICT where children can create their own computer programmes and even scuba diving, with the 'shrimp' course taking place in the school swimming pool – the list goes on. Golf is popular – there is a putting green in the grounds and the lucky few are allowed to play at Royal St George's nearby – this can lead to a certain amount of envy amongst the parents. The school is always open to new ideas and the girls have recently set up their own cricket club. Rifle shooting is a popular activity culminating in the annual parents v children shooting match – not just fathers and sons but mothers and daughters as well.

The average class size of 12 means that the school can support children at both ends of the learning spectrum. Children streamed from year 5 and setted in maths and languages – French (taught by a native speaker) and Latin are taught as part of the curriculum and Spanish can be taught by private arrangement. Very bright children can be stretched and academic scholars are either taught in a separate, accelerated class for the last two years or within the top stream – depends on the number of scholars from year to year.

A good team of teachers, with a healthy balance of age and experience. The children are 'pushed and stretched with full support, and the school has pushed our son to be the best that he can be,' said one happy mother. New computers, and two lessons of touch-typing a week as well programming and website design. High praise from the inspectors who judged that 'The curriculum is excellent, well balanced, stimulating and structured', lessons are 'challenging and interesting' and 'effective anti-bullying procedures include development of awareness of cyber-bullying through PSHE and ICT lessons'.

It feels like a large, happy family and is always oversubscribed. Bright, light dorms, all named after Kentish apples, with an abundance of pink and teddy bears

The school is quick to spot problems and about 20 per cent have some sort of learning support. There are specialist English, maths and language teachers – some children taught within the class and some withdrawn but lessons rotated so they do not fall behind in any subject; close liaison between learning support and class teachers. Will go the extra mile for children with bigger difficulties. An occupational therapist has designed a programme for dyspraxics. A small number of children work with laptops. In class EAL support available for those who need it.

The school has recently been awarded International School status by the British Council which means that all lessons must have an international dimension to encourage children to have a more global outlook – it recently took part in a

European day of languages and is already twinned with a school in India.

'The school achieves things it shouldn't for its size,' and it certainly punches above its weight on the sports fields. School puts this down partly to the close bonds that develop in a small boarding community and partly to the support and encouragement from staff. They are frequent winners of the JET cricket and rounders national competitions, much to the envy and astonishment of much larger and apparently sportier schools, and are always represented at the annual national athletics championships in Birmingham. One girl has recently been selected for the England athletics squad and a boy for England cricket training. There is a long tradition of cricketing excellence and alumni include England captains Mann and Cowdrey as well as the Loudon brothers and Sam Northeast, plus three day eventers and Olympic medal winners William Fox-Pitt and Georgina Harland.

Music is part of the curriculum throughout the school with all year 3 learning the recorder and all year 4 the violin, and about 70 per cent continue with at least one instrument; they will find a teacher for any instrument – one child is currently learning the harp. There are instrumental groups and an orchestra and the choir sings in local churches and at weddings; a recent highlight was a trip to Venice to sing in St Mark's on Palm Sunday. Two school plays a year as well as smaller form productions at Christmas mean everyone has a chance to get up on stage. There are also poetry and musical recitals and children are prepared for the LAMDA exams.

Vibrant colourful artwork displayed all over the school with 'six of the best' selected to hang in the head's study. Masses of outings and trips; most year groups visit France and year 7 has an outdoor pursuits trip to the Lake District for an 'educational adventure'. Various charity fundraising events throughout the year from cake sales to sponsored swims and fancy dress days – when children can put their sewing skills to good use. Burns Night is celebrated each year with haggis and reeling and there is a programme of lectures from parents and visiting speakers.

Lots of traditional boarding school parents as well as local professional families. Arrangements can be made for children of other faiths, but most are happy to attend chapel twice a week and the full choral service on Sundays. Children not overly sophisticated and do not grow up too quickly but they are still self-assured and confident and are very comfortable talking to adults. Usually about 60 children in at weekends with plenty going on and outings planned – ice skating, clay pigeon shooting, bowling or just going to play on the beach. The top year is allowed 'down town' into Broadstairs on Sundays where they can spend their pocket money – a much looked forward to privilege, and many opt to stay in for the weekends just for this.

The Friends of Wellesley House organises social events and fundraising activities including lunches for new parents, quiz nights, the bonfire night and other parties including the recent Wellesley Fest.

A small and extraordinarily caring prep school with traditional values which produces self-assured and considerate children who go on to schools all over the country.

Westbourne House School

71

Shopwyke, Chichester, West Sussex PO20 2BH

01243 782739 | office@westbournehouse.org | www.westbournehouse.org

Ages: 3-13 (boarding from 7)

Pupils: 404; Boarders: 28

Day: £10,440 – £17,985 pa; Boarding: £16,545 – £27,105 pa

Headmaster: Since 2011, Martin Barker BEd Exeter (40s), four years as deputy before – previously at Papplewick in Ascot. Married to Helen – she teaches, masterminds special projects for the scholarship forms and organises charitable initiatives and donations. They met at university where she concentrated on primary, he on science and PE. Daughter and a son both went on from Westbourne House to Canford; they have a place near the Everglades for what little non-Westbourne time they have. He's tall and approachable (kids agree), passionate about good teaching having been burnt by the opposite at a grammar school (in the 80s...). His initial brief was on the academic side (brought a database for recording marks to the school) and an impressive scholarship rate backs up the governors'

appointment. He's also applied this talent for rationalising systems to the school day, delegation within the teaching staff and boarding options – the result is a more formal structure but parents say a more relaxed atmosphere, 'fewer meetings, the ones that happen count'. Reassuringly, he is most proud of the pastoral improvement – 'reduction in unkindness with the shorter break in the afternoon' – and that the kids are 'rounded and grounded – and so in demand for senior schools'.

Entrance: Local school – biggest commute 40 minutes away, 50 per cent of families London migrants. Also local farmers, entrepreneurs (some semi-retired), medics (St Richard's Chichester nearby) and Rolls Royce. Diverse lot – double incomes, single parents and the wealthy. Reputation locally for pushy parents. Non-selective – SEN would have to be seriously limiting to be turned away; support both in class or with a small group extracted. Entrance is increasingly flexible, with one pupil recently joining the school within a few weeks of the initial parent enquiry; currently no waiting lists. Music and academic scholarships available at year 3 entry. Means-tested bursaries available, five per cent off for siblings.

Exit: Brighton and Seaford currently top destinations. Portsmouth Grammar is a popular day school but the train journey puts some parents off. Others to eg Canford, Bryanston, Benenden, Eton and Marlborough. In 2017, 19 scholarships, including seven to Brighton. Eminent outgoers include R4's Marcus Brigstocke (funny) and the late Nick Clarke (news); Monarch of the Glen, Alastair McKenzie; England women's cricketer Holly Colvin.

Remarks: Founded as a family school and the atmosphere remains – the original owners, now in their 80s, still live on site (just beyond some wire lions as you enter the beautiful grounds) and continue to be part of school life. Early Victorian main house, sandwiched between beach and the Downs, pupils here stay kids for longer than those in more urban schools and staff make sure they are ready for entry to secondary schools by the time they leave. Complete refurbishment of pre-prep in 2015 following roof fire.

Children love it here: picnics after Saturday morning lessons, BBQ night – the astounding attraction of a sausage in a bun

School ethos grew out of scouting – the fleur-de-lys logo is sprinkled about and patrol leaders are voted in (panther, tiger, otter and owl) each term. In the summer the mothers of troop leaders (heads of school) present the prizes – this family involvement is characteristic, whether it is houseparents with children at the school, the parental barometer on teaching standards, support on the games pitches or siblings in different years. A parent could pick up at three different times each day – from nursery, pre-prep and prep; the hanging around can be frustrating but also means relationships are built and social events are surprisingly well attended. A new minibus offering is a parent pleaser.

Children love it here – their favourite parts are the communal ones: form rooms, chapel, the millennium hall, picnics after Saturday morning lessons, BBQ night in the summer – the astounding attraction of a sausage in a bun! They respond to the humanity of teachers and understand the thinking behind structures in the school eg how cleaning works in dining room; that playing in bases (dens) in the boundaries (woods) is organised by rota now – to avoid any tussles or rivalries between age groups. Long breaks during the day for playing in the woods, swinging on the monkey bars, playing football, cricket, netball and tennis.

Boarding is popular (one of houses was doubled in size recently). Boarders from year 3 (though this is rare) must board a minimum of one night in years 3 and 4, two nights in years 5 and 6, building up to minimum three nights in year 7 and full week (five nights) in year 8 – vital preparation for the 60 per cent who go on to secondary boarding schools. Six family style boarding houses in total, presided over by houseparents, caring matrons and fun gappers. Most boarders go home at weekends, often after Saturday matches, though full boarding available.

ICT is omnipresent to free up staff and pupil time for learning and playing – ideally, as in the world outside. Four trolleys of Apple Macs, Wifi – no issues with gaming, kids say they save that for home if they are into it. Smartboards in every classroom – yet, as ever, only some teachers use them to the pupils' best advantage. Landlines on wall for calling home – no need or time for mobile phones or Angry Birds apparently. Newspapers as well as screens in the library (due to be revamped).

Breadth in the curriculum, backed up by good facilities. New food tech and science labs, French vocab on doors in main school, ceramics studio a popular retreat (sometimes there's hot chocolate and often CDs playing), stunning art, sparky technology projects, drama opportunities both on, back and above stage, a lake for kayaking (sailing soon), indoor pool and Astroturf. The purpose-built music school fosters a full range – harpists to advert theme tune composers, 80 per cent of children learn an instrument. Peripatetic music teachers mean a catch up period is vital for missed academic lessons.

The long prep at the end of the day is a crowd-pleaser since no homework – the disadvantage is that parents don't see books when they come home.

The proof is in the pudding – really happy families.

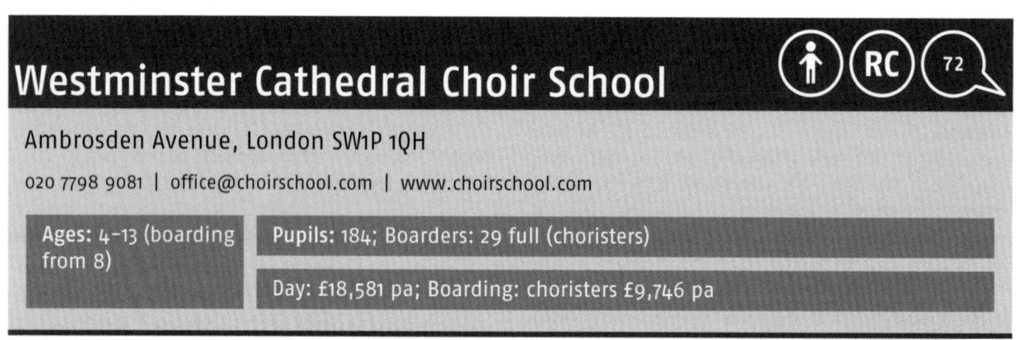

Westminster Cathedral Choir School

Ambrosden Avenue, London SW1P 1QH

020 7798 9081 | office@choirschool.com | www.choirschool.com

Ages: 4-13 (boarding from 8)

Pupils: 184; Boarders: 29 full (choristers)

Day: £18,581 pa; Boarding: choristers £9,746 pa

Headmaster: Since 2007, Mr Neil McLaughlan (40s). Married with a young son and daughter, and a man who radiates humour, decency and charm in equal measure. Read philosophy and politics at Durham and spent a few years with Andersen Consulting in London before embarking on a teaching career in 1997. After spells at Stonyhurst and Worth, he took up a post as head of English and director of development at Downside School, before joining WCCS as headmaster. He hopes to be there 'for the duration.' Parents hope so too. 'Lovely guy!' said one. 'So easy to approach!' said another. 'An extremely dedicated head and a great promoter of the school,' said a third. Typically modest, he hopes to do 'lots and lots of small things right.' We think he's doing lots of big things right too. Under his visionary yet kindly leadership, this has become an inspiring school that is going from strength to strength.

Entrance: New pre-prep takes boys at 4+. Entry by assessment, but the school is looking for potential rather than attainment. Most are expected to continue on to the prep school after English and maths tests. Thirty places available; priority to siblings. Other main entry points are at 7+, where 16 places are available, and 8+ (a further 10 places for day boys and six places for choristers). Applicants sit tests in English, maths and non-verbal reasoning in

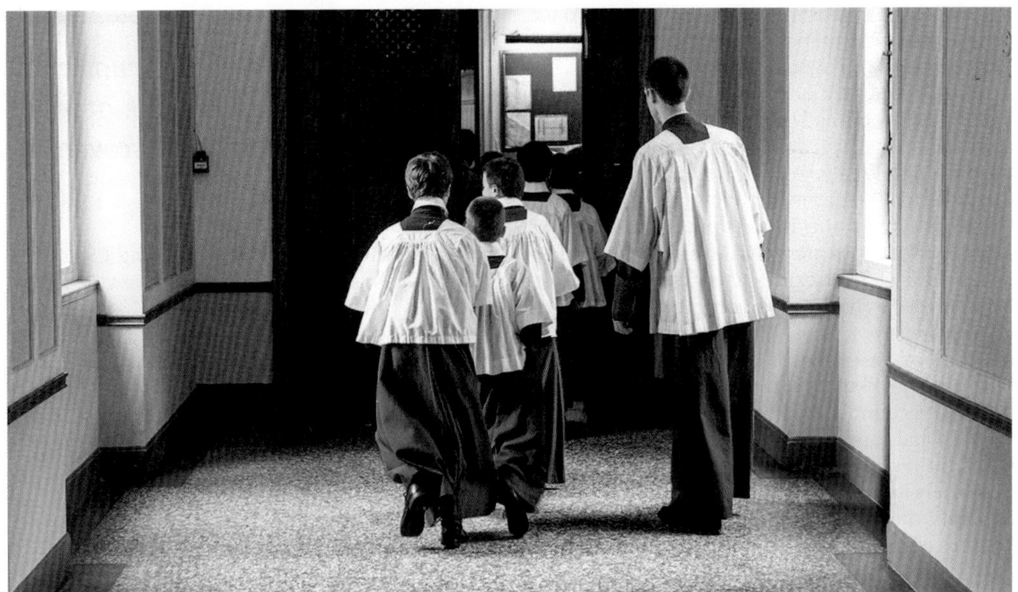

January of the year before entry. Occasional places in other year groups, notably at 11+. The school is always oversubscribed and, once boys have met the required academic standard, will give preference where possible to practising Roman Catholics and to boys with a brother at the school.

Choristers, who must be Catholic and boarders, join at 8+. Would-be probationers have to pass informal and formal tests with the cathedral's master of music, as well as succeeding at the academic assessment; and if they manage all that, they spend two nights at the school to see whether chorister life will suit them. Only then will they be offered one of the six available places. As the school's popularity grows, so inevitably does the competition; there are now half a dozen serious candidates for each choristership, and for the first time in over a decade, the school has not had to go recruiting for them.

Up to full fees assistance for choristers; none for day pupils, whose families just have to fork out. As a result, there is more cultural than social diversity here. Boys come from a wide range of nationalities, among them France, Spain, Italy, Russia, Ghana and Korea, making this a truly international school. With some 80 per cent of the boys now from Catholic families, the school is less religiously diverse than it was, but remains open to day boys of all faiths provided their families are happy to support the school's Catholic ethos.

Exit: The head has worked tirelessly to raise the school's profile, and WCCS's exit record is superb. Boys regularly leave for boarding schools like Eton, Harrow, Winchester, Radley, Downside, Charterhouse and King's Canterbury, and for a raft of top London schools, including Westminster, St Paul's, UCS, City of London, KCS Wimbledon, Latymer Upper, Dulwich College and Wetherby senior school, often with music scholarships. Others to Cardinal Vaughan and the London Oratory. 'The school is much more linked into the senior schools than it was a few years ago,' reported one satisfied parent. 'Oh yes, the head's always going on about schools,' confirmed one of the boys, equably.

Remarks: The school was endearingly shabby once, but not any more. A five-year programme of refurbishment has just finished, and everything is now bang up to date. Visitors are welcomed in the beautiful glass-fronted foyer, where handwritten Music for Mass schedules from 1905 are hung beside huge photos of current pupils radiating health and cheeriness. Throughout the building, ceilings, floors and lighting are all new, and all the classrooms are gleaming and well-resourced, with interactive whiteboards in each one. Large and much-loved playground, covered with Astroturf, where boys play 'crazy games' on the climbing apparatus. 'That was a real selling point for me,' said one parent. 'The boys have a chance to be boys.' 'The way to the heart of little boys is good food and football at playtime, and WCCS excels in both,' confirmed another. We didn't try the football, but we can confirm that the food is splendid, a delicious combination of tasty and healthy.

Boarding facilities have also been upgraded. We can't comment on the refurbished boarders' common room, because a curmudgeonly old trumpet teacher therein told us we were interrupting his lesson and to get out, but we did manage to see the sleeping accommodation, which was cheerful, light and airy. The rigours of chorister life notwithstanding, feedback on the boarding experience from both parents and boys was uniformly positive. 'The key thing,' says head, 'is to have good, kind people around the boys, good accommodation and excellent food. An army marches on its stomach.'

Years ago, parents had disquiets about aspects of WCCS. Nowadays, they cannot find enough superlatives with which to express their delight. 'We have been thrilled by both the teaching and pastoral care provided by the school.' 'The staff generate a wonderfully positive energy.' 'It's an amazing school, the teachers are so kind!' 'You couldn't choose a better school, I recommend it to everyone.' 'A wonderful warmth and care is present everywhere.'

A father of a new chorister told us, 'My son absolutely loves it. He's thrilled to pieces. The first weekend they were eligible to go home, he didn't want to come.' (Poor mum!) And a mother of two day pupils wrote, 'Happiness is guaranteed at this school; it is such a nurturing, caring and stimulating environment. I can honestly say that the only problem I have ever had is to find a way to drag my boys out of the playground and back home at the end of the day.' What's behind this remarkable success? 'The one ingredient a Catholic school should have is joy,' said the head, simply and without any side, when we asked him,.

There is joy in the teaching here, that's for sure. A quiet revolution is taking place in the WCCS curriculum that made this reviewer go all excited and wobbly at the knees. Schemes of work have been painstakingly redesigned, with scholarship and a genuine love of learning at their heart. 'The idea is to present knowledge as a unified whole,' explained the head, 'so for instance, whilst they're studying

'If the boys are doing the human body in science, they'll look at what the Greeks and Romans discovered about it in history'

Adam and Eve in RS, they'll be doing CS Lewis's The Magician's Nephew in English. Likewise, we use geometry and graph-plotting in maths to support map skills in geography, and they'll draw antique maps in art at the same time. If the boys are doing the human body in science, they'll look at what the Greeks and Romans discovered about it in history.' The boys we spoke to praised the lessons as 'really good fun,' adding, 'The work's challenging, but in a good way'.

Much emphasis on poetry, with poems studied every week, as well as learnt by heart and declaimed. 'We want them to know the great poets of the English language,' said the deputy head, and to further this, the school has produced its own wonderful anthologies, where the selection is 'unashamedly classic.' In addition to regular English lessons, boys receive two lessons a week on formal grammar and punctuation, and Latin is compulsory from the off – 'Latin is crucial for grammar, it's not an academic luxury,' insisted the deputy head. 'As an international school, the story of the world's great civilisations interests us. But children of this age also need connections, and they need the basics.' All those who have wrung their hands at the disjointed, shallow content of so many modern lessons, lift up your hearts and hope.

This is clearly a scholarly yet joyful environment, and the quality of student work we saw reflected that. We read, misty-eyed, a set of poems by the year 7s about Westminster Bridge (inspired by Wordsworth's sonnet) that were outstandingly creative and well-written; likewise, a history essay on Thomas Becket was not only mature and insightful, but skilful and lucid in its use of language. But mightn't this approach favour only the brightest? WCCS's SENCo emphatically denied it, asserting that boys at the school with SEN benefited from understanding how language works. We were impressed with the support the school gives to those with dyslexia and dyspraxia, as well as to ESL students, such as the two grave and courteous Russian boys we saw having extra English tutorials. And all the staff we met were purposeful, well-bred (curmudgeon excepted), cultivated, devoted to what they do and, according to parents, 'incredibly dedicated.'

As you'd expect, the standard of music here is outstanding. The choristers are completely immersed in music-making at the highest level (listen to the downloads on the website, and marvel), and the day boys, swimming in the same element, also achieve great things. We saw year 8 boys composing their entries for the school's Christmas carol competition, and heard much excellent instrumental playing as we went round the school. 'The music programme is amazing,' enthused one parent. 'My son's piano playing has come on by leaps and bounds in just a few weeks.' Many pupils achieve grades 7 or 8 in their chosen instrument(s) by the time they leave.

Football, rugby and cricket are the main sports here, played at local pitches, and swimming and PE are held at the nearby Queen Mother Sports Centre. Lots of extracurricular activities, including debating, philosophy, chess, scrabble, code-breaking, the Airfix model club, current affairs, and cross-country running. 'But where do you run?' we asked, glancing with some surprise at the surrounding streets. 'Oh!' said our tour guide, 'Green Park, Hyde Park, St James's..'

Lucky lads, you might think. And they are, of course. But what struck us most about this lovely little school was how considerate, well-mannered and sanguine about life its pupils seemed to be. They are achieving great things, while remaining likeable and happy boys. As one mother wrote, 'My son is neither Catholic nor musical, but has been recognised for other things he has to contribute to the school. They're grounded children with good values. It's a perfect place for my son to grow into a confident young man.' We agree with her. For boys fortunate enough to come here, this is as near perfect as it gets.

Westminster School

73

17 Dean's Yard, London SW1P 3PB

020 7963 1003 | registrar@westminster.org.uk | www.westminster.org.uk

Ages: 13–18

Pupils: 747; sixth form: 399 (131 girls); Boarders: 184 (48 girls)

Day: £26,130 – £28,566 pa; Boarding: £37,740 pa

Head Master: Since 2014, Patrick Derham MA (50s), previously head of Rugby School. At 12, he was sent to live and study on the naval training ship Arethusa, run by the children's charity Shaftesbury Homes to prepare young men for the navy. Two years later the ship was abruptly sold due to financial difficulties and, with a day's notice and little idea what a public school was, he arrived at Pangbourne College on a bursary. He eventually became head of school and read history at Cambridge (first class degree), and feels 'my life was transformed by education.'

Taught at Cheam School and then Radley, where he was head of history and a housemaster for '12 very happy years' before being advised by the warden there to go straight for a headship. Five years as head of Solihull were followed by 13 at Rugby, before landing the headship of 'the home of liberal education – the perfect culmination of my career.'

His background ('my mum still lives in a council house in Scotland') has clearly been a powerful motivating force in his commitment to widening access to a good education – as he points out, 'all the great schools were founded with that intention.' At Rugby, he set up the Arnold Foundation to provide bursaries for children who need the stability of a boarding education ('we didn't just cream off the brightest middle class kids'). He is a trustee of the SpringBoard Bursary Foundation, a national charity modelled on the same lines, and vice chair of IntoUniversity, which gives disadvantaged children academic support and mentoring to raise their aspirations.

'He did an amazing job here and will be brilliant at Westminster,' said a Rugby insider. Very down to earth, personable, fantastic speaker, say Westminster parents. 'You feel like you can trust him'... 'He really cares about getting to know everyone'... 'I like it that he already knows who I am and who my children are'... 'Very responsive to comments'... 'My daughter thinks he's great'.

Clearly no ivory tower head, he loves interaction with pupils and teaches A level history. Parents watching their sons compete in the recent National Schools Rowing Regatta were delighted to see Derham there cheering on the teams (they won the championship eights' title for the first time in the school's history).

'My son had no artistic ambition when he arrived, but is now doing art A level. They have totally inspired him,' said a parent

Married to Alison, a teacher, with two grown up children. Westminster seems to be in very steady, to say nothing of inspiring, hands.

Academic matters: With these very bright pupils, 'you can teach for the love of the subject and focus on the exam when need be,' says the head. 'It's a breath of fresh air,' said a parent. 'Intellectual risk taking is encouraged. They're never not challenged.' 'It's incredibly inspiring,' said another. Many of the teachers are experts in their fields, encouraged to follow their interests. 'I cannot believe there is a more stimulating place to teach in the country,' said a teacher. 'It is so much more liberal than at my previous school,' said a sixth form student. 'It's not constrained by the syllabus – it's learning for the sake of learning. It really allows you to get a proper understanding outside the exam baselines.' Pupils tend to internalise that love of learning. 'They read and they question and they challenge,' says the head. 'In my first lesson one asked me, "Where is the evidence?" I'd never been asked that before.'

Everyone encouraged to include a practical subject, eg art, electronics, drama, music, at GCSE. Huge range of languages includes Dutch, Arabic and Portuguese. Several parents commented that inspirational teachers had sparked their sons' interest in subjects they had previously hated. 'He'd always been a bit of a maths boy but now he is flying at English and languages too. They've understood how to teach in a way that suits him and developed all these new interests.'

Top exam results are, nonetheless, part of the package, with 98 per cent A*-A/9-7 at GCSE in 2017. At A level/Pre-U, the results were 87 per cent A*/A grades and 96 per cent A*/B. New thinking skills course – designed as a more challenging alternative to critical thinking A level – introduces sixth formers to the elements of informal logic, and helps prepare for university entrance skills tests such as the Oxbridge Thinking Skills Assessment.

High academic ability is obviously a prerequisite, but study skills coordinator works with all those who need support for eg mild dyslexia, dyspraxia or Asperger's, or just lack of organisation, helping them with the skills needed to cope with learning at different levels as they move up the school.

Links with local state schools Grey Coat Hospital and Harris Westminster Sixth Form – the latter sponsored by Westminster School – see sixth formers from these schools joining in German, Latin, art history and drama lessons with Westminster students. 'They've done a really good job at integrating us,' said a Westminster sixth former. 'I'm as good friends with students from outside as anyone else in the class.' Joint senior management meetings with Harris Westminster staff: 'We are going to learn from each other.'

Games, options, the arts: An almost overwhelming range of extracurricular opportunities. Societies often stem from the particular passions of both staff and students, ranging from feminist to secular to geography. English society may see Simon Russell Beale answering questions on playing King Lear at the National, whilst Piyush Goyal, national treasurer of the Indian Bharatiya Janata Party (BJP) party, tells the political society about Indian public affairs. 'I set up a society and had an ambassador from Panama come to talk,' said one student. 'Staff are really supportive when you want to set up new things.' Huge range of journalists and politicians, scientists and thinkers drop in to give talks; poet in residence inspires creativity. Trips everywhere: climbing in Cataluña, Beijing exchange, art history in Venice. Years 9-11 go off for a week's climbing, sailing, hill walking or camping at home or abroad.

'Phenomenal' music, with professional standard orchestral concerts at St John's Smith Square and the Barbican, carol service in Westminster Abbey, masterclasses, eminent musicians from Nicola Benedetti to Ian Bostridge giving evening concerts. One parent felt that 'unless you are excellent you won't get a look in,' whilst staff point out there are house concerts and ensembles for the less stratospherically talented. 'We like to think there is room for everyone.' Drama equally high performing – Guys and Dolls a recent sell-out but much cerebral fare too, plus house drama and GCSE/A level pieces – and again huge talent required to bag a role in the large scale school productions.

Art, too, 'wonderful', with much emphasis on traditional drawing and painting skills, life classes, film making facilities and a darkroom. Plus, of course, easy access to all of London's galleries and museums. 'My son had no artistic ambition when he arrived, but is now doing art A level. They have totally inspired him,' said one parent, whilst another commented: 'They let these academic boys be so creative – they feel free to explore.'

Sports – known as 'Station' – take place on Tuesday and Thursday afternoons, mostly on the enviably large playing fields in nearby St Vincent Square plus adjacent sports centre (in a previous life one of the Royal Horticultural Halls). In Westminster liberal fashion, no particular sport is compulsory, with a huge range of choices from sailing to judo to golf to girls' football. 'You wouldn't send a very sporty boy to Westminster,' thought a parent, who was grateful that her keen but not-particularly-athletic son had been in teams which he would have been unlikely to make at a more overtly sporty school. However, particularly successful at rowing (and was basking in the glow of recent success at National Schools' Regatta when we visited), fields nine football teams with 'at least respectable' results, and 'we do very well at niche sports such as rock climbing [third in the Independent Schools' Championships] and fencing [bronze medal in U15 Foil]'. Often dominates the London School Cross-Country Championships and the Westminster Secondary Schools Swimming Gala, with pupils representing Westminster in the London Youth Games, and is successful at fives and real tennis. 'You are encouraged to try lots of things and find something you are passionate about,' said a student.

Westminster is an integral but discrete part of central London, largely located in the walled precincts of the former medieval monastery of Westminster Abbey

Volunteering taking on increasing importance with head's passion for outreach, with nearly all Westminsters teaching music or setting up debating societies in local primary schools, working on Hampstead Heath or learning sign language to communicate with deaf children. 'People are really involved and really making a difference,' said a student. 'Staff have the time, passion and faith in us to let us get on with things.' Phab week – where year 12 Westminster students host young people with physical and/or mental challenges, taking part in creative activities and seeing London together – is a 'life changing experience'. 'With privilege comes enormous responsibility to give back,' says the head.

Boarding: The last Anglican monastery in London now houses Purcell's, a girls' boarding and boys' day house with attached chapel. Five other boarding houses, all in or near Little Dean's Yard and all of which include some day pupils. Many rooms surprisingly spacious; younger boys in College, scholars' house, in dorms of up to eight, whilst upper years have their own rooms and those in between may share with one other. 'Because these are all old buildings, the room arrangements can be random, and sometimes we have to improvise.' All boarders are cared for in relaxed fashion by housemaster (male or female), some with own family; resident tutor and matron also on site. Breakfast and supper in College Hall, the medieval dining room of Westminster Abbey, which day pupils may also join.

The only full boarders are sixth formers, and Saturday evenings tend to be quiet, though school is increasing organised weekend activities, particularly for the 10 per cent or so of overseas sixth form boarders.

Boarders have supervised prep sessions, and there are evening activities in the sports and music centres after prep, but those after a full-on boarding experience jammed full of organised activities may want to look elsewhere. 'He likes it for the independence and to be with his mates,' said a boarder parent, whilst another said, 'It feels like a convenient b&b. Much better than having to pick him up at late after a rehearsal or lecture.' However, a sixth form boarder commented on the 'serious sense of community you can only get from living with others. The people in your own house become quite special to you.'

Background and atmosphere: Whilst some other great public schools overshadow their environs, Westminster is an integral but discreet part of central London, largely located in the walled precincts of the former medieval monastery of Westminster Abbey. Its main buildings surround the square of Little Dean's Yard, known as Yard, where pupils spill out after lessons to chat or kick a football or practise basketball. The Abbey, next door and with its own private entrance, serves as the school chapel, used for twice weekly services plus carol and other concerts.

Westminster had become a school by 1179, with pupils taught by monks of the Abbey at Westminster. It survived Henry VIII's dissolution of the monasteries in 1540 and has been in continuous existence since the 14th century, with Elizabeth I celebrated as the school's official founder.

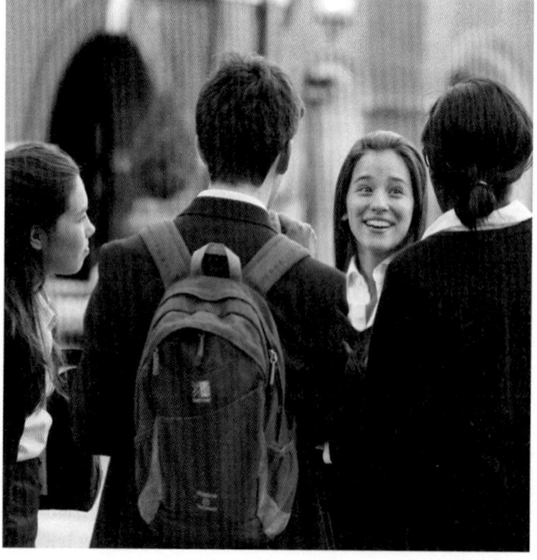

'It is an incredibly tolerant and civilised atmosphere,' said a parent. 'Unlike other schools, they don't try to mould pupils into a particular product. They are quite laissez-faire.' Parents of quirky students are relieved to find a school that is very kind and accepting of eccentricities. 'If he was at any other school he'd be toast,' said one. 'Some schools can be so unforgiving: Westminster is the complete opposite.' Another reported that it has 'catered brilliantly' for each of her very different children. 'It's so wonderful to see these kids spark off each other.'

Has signed an agreement with Hong Kong education company HKMETG to set up a six bilingual 3-18 schools in China by 2028, with 10 per cent of places free to less affluent families, and consultancy fees contributing to the Westminster bursary fund.

Pastoral care, well-being and discipline: Tutors attached to each house oversee the academic side, whilst housemasters look after all else. One parent felt that both have too many charges to know her son well. 'I feel his well-being is my responsibility, not the school's. I don't think anyone there knows him well in the round.' Others, however, described the pastoral care as 'exceptional', and a student said, 'I have always found the school really responsive. Your housemaster is always there and will take care of everything from not feeling well to having too much work.'

Pupils expected to be proactive, motivated and organised, with very full timetables but no compulsion to take part in organised activities. 'But anything you want to try, there's some way of doing it,' said a student.

Pupils and parents: 'Lots of people said I wouldn't like Westminster,' reports the head. 'They told me the pupils were arrogant, staff unmanageable, parents difficult. None of this is true.' Westminster families undoubtedly tend to be wealthy, intellectual, metropolitan, cosmopolitan and no doubt demanding, but most parents are extremely supportive of the school. 'It is very hard to withstand this full on praise and delight.' 'I am a real believer.' 'Fantastic on every front.' And from an initial sceptic: 'I am increasingly fond of it.'

Girls entering the sixth form report a much easier ride than they might have expected. 'I had heard rumours about the boys being awful and arrogant – but they weren't,' said one. 'Some would show off in lessons to begin with, but they calmed down pretty quickly.' 'I suspect they look for a certain confidence,' said another. 'If you were insecure you might find it intimidating.' 'It was quite a shock to the system at first,' said a third, 'but we can hold our own.'

'Westminster imbues in you a sense that it is fine to talk to anyone on equal terms,' said an ex-student. 'You have a real feeling of being special.'

Parents – nearly all are Londoners, with even boarders mostly coming from within the M25 – offered a cornucopia of outings to Dulwich Picture Gallery, tours of Westminster Abbey and the Houses of Parliament, plus quiz nights, drinks parties, concerts in the Abbey, and the opportunity to attend expert lectures with their children. 'Parents very friendly and there's a good sense of community and involvement,' said one.

'Westminster imbues in you a sense that it is fine to talk to anyone on equal terms,' said an ex-student. 'You have a real feeling of being special'

Old Westminsters span the centuries and the professions: the massive list ranges from Ben Jonson, John Dryden, Robert Hooke, Lord Lucan, Kim Philby, AA Milne, John Gielgud, Tony Benn, Corin Redgrave, Helena Bonham-Carter and Imogen Stubbs to Dido and Mika.

Entrance: Register by the end of year 5 for 13+ entry (boys at state primary and other schools that finish at 11 may apply to Westminster Under School). Computer pre-tests in English, maths and reasoning in year 6; high performers who also have a good report from current school called for interview, which includes short maths and English tests. Those with conditional places sit either the Challenge scholarship exam or CE (pass mark 70 per cent) in year 8.

For 16+ places, register between summer and October of the year before entry. Applicants – boys and girls – take exams in their four most likely A level subjects, and are interviewed.

Exit: Excellent and detailed preparation not only for Oxbridge but for American university entrance, with school trips to visit east coast universities. 'The school has been very supportive from an early age,' said a student, 'keeping us up to date with when to take subject tests and when to visit colleges.' Good preparation too for medicine, which is amongst the most popular degree subjects alongside liberal arts.

Up to half of sixth formers do, indeed, go to Oxbridge (78 in 2017, with 10 medics and others off to the US and Hong Kong), most of the rest to London universities, Edinburgh, Durham or Bristol.

Money matters: A number of means-tested bursaries of up to 100 per cent of fees available at 13+ and 16+; applicants must live in London. Bursaries also available at 11+; boys spend two years at the Under School before moving on automatically to the Great School. Eight Queen's Scholarships awarded at 13+; recipients must board, and the scholarship covers half the boarding fee. This can be topped up by a bursary in case of need. Five exhibitions at this level. Up to six music scholarships at 13+ worth 25 per cent of day or boarding fee, plus free instrumental tuition. Four 16+ Queen's Scholarships now available for girls.

Remarks: One ex-student commented that Old Westminsters of her acquaintance have gone into a far wider range of careers than those from other schools. 'They seem to be following their passion. Westminster instils a belief that you can do whatever you want to do.'

Whitgift School

74

Haling Park, South Croydon, Surrey CR2 6YT

020 8688 9222 | admissions@whitgift.co.uk | www.whitgift.co.uk

Ages: 10-18 (boarding from 13)

Pupils: 1,466; sixth form: 352; Boarders: 56 full, 53 weekly

Day: £19,362 pa; Boarding: £30,447 – £36,411 pa

Head: Since September 2017, Christopher Ramsay, previously head of The King's School, Chester. MA from Cambridge in modern and medieval languages; PGCE from Durham. Has also headed King's College Taunton and been deputy head at Cranleigh and head of languages at Wellington

College. Mr Ramsey is the HMC spokesman on university matters as well as a trustee of the University of Chester Academies Trust. Quick thinking, fast talking, intensely communicative. Three children in school from the juniors to the sixth form.

Academic matters: The full English but with continental option – A levels, IB (bilingual option for most advanced French speakers), BTecs and even the occasional Pre-U (occasional top ups for those requiring extra stretch). Extended essay qualifications and the like just about the only no-goes – IB covers the ground, feels head.

Results consistently good. In 2017, 55 per cent of A levels graded A*/A, 86 per cent A*/B. IB marks impressive at average 40. Maths leads subject popularity by a mile, sciences follow, English and humanities put in good showing. Rest – PE, computing and music among them – lag in single figures at the rear.

GCSEs (IGCSEs in English, maths, science, languages) similarly healthy with 84 per cent graded A*-A/7-9 in 2017. Ten sat by most. Options chosen from relatively compact range bar terrific languages (three rather than two studied) with Japanese and Mandarin already on offer and Arabic and Sanskrit possible future additions. DT hugely popular (we were shown wide range of delightful projects ranging from solar-powered beeswax storage unit to hockey stick unit).

One outsider wondered how staff can cover the range effectively, especially with same teachers for A levels and IB. Teachers, a level-headed bunch, averaging late 30s with a quarter into second decade, agree that it was their idea. Benefits of pupil choice outweigh double preparation time, said dedicated scientist, while some subjects with low A level numbers (such as DT) positively gagging to have a second go at IB now previously dreary syllabus is getting a makeover.

No shortage of teacher talent – former senior bods have gone on to headships everywhere from Magdalen College School to RGS Worcester. School has been academic non pareil in the area and 'the crème de la crème in every respect,' says local and could 'be in the top 10 [nationally] again,' says school.

Classrooms have trad feel (admittedly hard to compete with new build excitement elsewhere), pupil numbers around 18 per class, 10 in sixth form. Behaviour immaculate – all rise for adults. Fun year 7 maths class working out probability by throwing dice, sixth form biologists fighting coursework deadline (easy listening music in background to counter tension).

Well on the way to building an education that ensures those focused on academic excellence get their fill, but will customise for those with exceptional sports, musical or other talents – fistful of scholars desirable but making A*s the priority for exceptionally gifted violinist headed for music college is pointless, thinks head.

Good reports for most subjects. More experienced teachers tend to be kept for best, thought a parent, focused on GCSE years and above, though any problems raised (including those with individual teachers) are quickly sorted at whatever stage. Increasing provision for the 10 per cent of pupils with SEN (largely dyslexia though also ADHD, ASD, three statemented), team about to increase to six,

including two full time teachers. Currently around 30 EAL pupils from 20 different nationalities.

Homework sensibly organised and, though workload is ramped up from around year 8, staff stick to allocated days and good at helping absentees catch up on missed sessions while 'emails fly back all the time for boys who can't quite manage it.' Felt that would be useful to have drop in clinics and clubs in key subjects focusing more on lesson content exam technique – and we heard of parent being 'actively encouraged' to seek private tuition when child fell behind.

Head librarian in senior library (cosier separate version for juniors – some subjects also have their own areas) talked enthusiastically of ways and means to boost reading interest, from book clubs to brunch events. With many boys glued to laptops at break, blind to lure of enticingly packed shelves, looked like an heroic endeavour.

While the academically capable flourish, parents warn that while school 'does what it says on the tin,' pays to be on the ball, proactive parents getting in touch the second a report shows unexpected (downwards) grade movement. Former coasters are in for a shock. 'They do expect you to work to your optimum and you always need to be performing.'

For the natural joiner, undoubtedly paradise, and starts early with all new pupils getting free golf and instrumental lessons (though not simultaneously)

Practical teacher input praised – one boy, struggling with twin demands of homework and role in musical, had rehearsal time halved so able to catch up. 'We can't speak highly enough [of the school],' said mother. 'Their expectations of the boys really surprised us, that everything was possible.'

Games, options, the arts: 'We allow pupils to follow their passion. We're only really interested on what we can do for the individual child.' Means pupils don't have to go to university to find out who they are, they reckon (though we worry about all that existential angst forced to find other outlets...). Finding niche can require strong-mindedness, however. One up-and-coming rugby star – Harlequins hopeful – had given it all up for love of singing.

For the natural joiner, undoubtedly paradise, and starts early with all new pupils getting free golf and instrumental lessons (though not simultaneously). Much of massive co-curricular programme included in the fees (100 or so options, from animal to Islamic

club). 'So many activities that by the time you leave, you'll have other interests,' thought sixth former.

One mother felt that sporty, academic or artistic groups of boys tend to follow separate paths. Once, perhaps, said pupils, but no longer the case. 'Have friends with very different interests,' said one.

Sports facilities terrific, luring in outsiders from Surrey cricketers to Olympic hopefuls – approving quotes dot prospectus. Goodies include assorted pitches where seriously rugged hone skills to sports centre with squash courts, fencing salle and fitness suite, as well as swimming pool (different depths fit all, from armband armies to water polo teams). There's even a Transformers-style sports hall (now you see it, now it's a 1800-seat conference centre).

While talent levels mean pupils who would have made top teams elsewhere may not do so here, even C and D teams often win against other schools' As and Bs, while starry coaches including Colin Pates (Chelsea) and Steve Kember (Crystal Palace) are doing for football what is already the norm for rugby, hockey and the rest. Almost easier, in fact, to list sports that don't feature amongst over 100 national titles secured in past five years.

Performing arts also getting substantial injection of resources with International Music Competition for string players, inaugurated 2013, soloist opportunities and fees the prize, and attracting talent from Eastern Europe. Six full scholarship boarders now in residence with more to follow; all potential soloists, reckons head.

With sell-out musicals, some outstanding actors (one has already written and starred in own play) and 380 learning an instrument, some to diploma level, performing arts already in good shape, spaces indoors and out, from Founder's Garden to old swimming pool, all imaginatively used for everything from Shakespeare to sell-out musicals (West Side Story was in rehearsal when we visited), concerts ranging from beginner strings to Mahler at Royal Festival Hall.

If there's a corporate refrain, it's 'best anywhere'. Only parental niggle would be more access to facilities. Pool, for example, is 'amazing' but opportunities to use it outside the timetabled six weeks a year would be appreciated – tricky, admittedly, given extensive use by outside groups. Bottom line, though, is that 'if you're good at something, they've got all the facilities in the world,' thought mother.

Boarding: They've upped ante with boarding (house catering for 100 13-18 year olds opened 2013). Bright and beautiful, partially powered by solar (though water 'too grey' to recycle, says boarding housemaster – one of the many staff with rugby-fuelled handshake).

Features super common rooms, welcoming but airy, uncluttered feel, upmarketing furnishing (new Yamaha piano) and Subbuteo for juniors, snooker (and superior view over greenery) for seniors next door. Beds specially ordered for seven footers and, amazingly, every fragile-looking wall-mounted loo so far intact (must be made from same makers as indestructible cushions).

Highly successful, it's reckoned and, with 40+ full boarders at weekends, no forlorn few testing the echoes. While activities generally good they sounded a little low-key when majority are off on voluntary exeats. Actively not trying to create traditions (can be where problems begin, is view of school, which numbers consecutive year groups 1, 3 and 5...).

Background and atmosphere: Ancient name, lovely and unusual site – cross between wildlife park and landscaped RHS outpost. Whipsley, perhaps? Don't expect acres of Tudor panelling, however. Though school was founded in 1600 and current site was owned by Henry VIII (and home to Lord Howard of Effingham, son a very early old boy), most is vintage 20th rather than 17th century (well worth seeing fascinating archive) and pleasant rather than grand in feel, despite commanding hilltop view over south Croydon.

Deep community roots, however, not only endure but extend each year, involvement ranging from extensive financial help for families of pupils in need to vast year-round outreach programme costing around £100,000 and involving 55 local schools, each spending a week at the school with dedicated classrooms and seconded staff with sessions covering sport, arts, science and languages.

Audition-entry weekend arts academy, for local children as well as school's pupils, runs wildly popular courses incorporating drama, dance and musical theatre.

Numbers standing up well to scrutiny and, as the biggest leading independent boys only in the area, as well as highly academically successful, so you'd hope. Theoretically a matching pair with Old Palace, the girls only school also in the Whitgift Foundation, though not an exclusive relationship – joint drama and music productions with Croydon High and St Andrew's C of E High School, too.

Trinity the big rival – 'You have to say 'T' word,' counsels pupil, though others would like more contact. School says tricky logistically and for now, schools likely to keep dancing to individual tunes.

In unlikely event that new buildings don't deliver wow factor, outside loveliness certainly will, from Founder's Garden, created for 400th anniversary and graced with very own new rose, to Whitgift water gardens, tape cut by Sir David Attenborough, who was bowled over by visions of loveliness before him, rare emerald starling adding final touch of enchantment.

'We were blown away when we saw it,' said mother. Doesn't stop, either, planned science biodomes each featuring slice of life (flora and fauna) from round the world. Like the Eden Project, says school, only better (from educational perspective at least – though does win on location). Butterflies soon on order. Giant tortoise being debated.

Pastoral care, well-being and discipline: Big on nurturing from day one with older boys mentoring younger ones (a few blank looks from mentorees-in-waiting) on top of formal tutor system. Older pupils often turn to subject teachers for 'excellent' ad hoc support.

Fab induction trip to Lake Garda for year 6s (heavily subsidised) within first few weeks works wonders even for the very shy. Great care taken to create school within a school, 10+ and 11+ intake in own very pleasant building and, with the obvious exceptions such as art, music and games, form-based for lessons, and even a separate house system. Only question mark was over slightly bleak asphalt-covered junior playground, bins the only ornament. When quizzed, pupils and head unanimous in stressing year-round use for ball games (surrounding windows correspondingly battle-weary), rendering any embellishment undesirable.

Well on the way to building an education that ensures those focused on academic excellence get their fill, but will customise for those with exceptional sports, musical or other talents

Masses of boys can mean occasional testosterone overload, though any low level disruptive behaviour is effectively sorted out as pupils move up through the school. Fisticuffs rare but not unheard of, though parents tend to take this calmly. 'Typical of boys' schools,' said a mother. Ditto pupils. 'It happens. It's better just to deal with it,' said pupil.

Though corridor supervision appeared low key, boys reckoned teachers were never far away – even super sixth form common room has head of year's office in corner, though clearly gaze is benign, judging by relaxed crowd sprawled on easy chairs, one minus shoes. Hot on effective sanctions, too, reckoned a parent, with school services – times spent doing something useful, such as lunchtime litter clearance or cloakroom tidying, cordially loathed and thus highly effective deterrents.

Pupils and parents: Many Croydon-based, or close; nearby grammars and Trinity the main alternative senior schools, with around 60 per cent of intake from state primaries. Increasingly attracts those from further afield – into deeper Surrey and even north London with boarding opening it up to the world (Taiwan the latest country expressing desire to forge links).

With old boys numbering TV illusionist Derren Brown, actor Martin Jarvis and Premier League star Victor Moses amongst ranks, average career hard to define, though being a reasonably tough personality to make a success of life here and later on probably helps. 'I think if you can't hold your own then you're going to sink,' felt mum.

For the right child, however, approach works wonders. 'If he'd gone to one of the state schools I don't think he'd be the confident young man he is now,' reckoned mother. 'He's much more able to walk into a room full of strangers and hold a conversation.'

Easy-going parents can come as a relief to newcomers. 'Thought they would be very highbrow and stuffy but not at all.' Terrific socialising, too. 'We have the best time...we went to a quiz night, there's a summer ball, it's everyone mucking in,' said one.

Entrance: Entrance exam early Jan, day at school. Majority sit 10+, 11+ or 13+ exams (maths, English, VR). Fewer at 12+ and 14+ (maths, English and science). Likelies invited back to interview. Sixth form candidates need seven GCSE passes with A*/As in A level subjects (similar for IB), though possible to enter to take BTec sport, in which case five A*/C passes (or numerical equivalents) will suffice. Interesting advent of dual sixth form streams, second for less academic but highly sporty.

Exit: Little fall-out – around 20 per cent leave after GCSEs; those with below par year 12 results often redo a year or retake modules. Occasionally pupils 'advised' to look elsewhere. 'Nobody is ever directly asked to leave,' said senior pupil. Vast majority who sail on reach splendid destinations. Offers from all the big beasts (Warwick, Southampton, Bristol, UCL, Edinburgh etc) and pupils clearly well thought of – one had received Oxford IB offer of 38, high but not stratospheric. Big range of subjects from geography to performing arts and professional sport. Seven to Oxbridge in 2017 plus four medics. 'What you're paying for,' said parent.

Money matters: Scholarships are one of Whitgift's huge strengths; the number of bursaries and amount of financial help makes school a possibility for those from most deprived of backgrounds. Sensitively handled, too, with those in need of extra funding for school trips given subtle means of applying so need never miss out. Aim is for one in three boarders (mainly music but possibly sports as well) to be on full scholarships.

Remarks: 'Happy and high achieving,' thought a parent, with traditional virtues pushed but never a dull place to be, even though Zoological Society of London has declined request for elephant. Natural home for academically inclined, sportsmen and performers and ideal not just for wallabies and flamingos but also for confident joiners who may not yet have settled on their passion in life but relish process of discovery.

Windlesham House School

Washington, Pulborough, West Sussex RH20 4AY

01903 874700 | whsadmissions@windlesham.com | www.windlesham.com

Ages: 4–13 (boarding from 8)

Pupils: 342; Boarders: 177 full

Day: £8,985 – £25,830 pa; Boarding: £20,775 – £29,745 pa

Headmaster: Since 2007, Mr Richard Foster, head at Pembroke House School in Kenya, then at St Anselm's in Derbyshire for 14 years. Thoughtful, warm, much liked by parents and pupils. Incredibly busy wife Rachel is in charge of everything pastoral – parents give Rachel a ring and she races around the school to find the relevant child and tend to it. Three grown up children. Both Fosters refer slightly wistfully to Kenya as home and enthuse pupils with love for the region. Windlesham is the most child centred school Mr Foster has ever taught at – though he is careful to point out (perhaps with the more conservative parents in mind) that 'children [here are] liberated – not liberal.' In his 50s and will stay at Windlesham until retirement. Still teaches, and randomly covers all classes over the course of the year.

Entrance: Non-selective. Academic assessment from year 1 upwards for setting purposes plus night's stay from year 3 upwards. Houses have different personalities, and tester night helps school decide in which house the potential pupils would flourish. Waiting list for many years. No scholarships, but means-tested bursaries available.

Exit: Pupils move on to over 30 different schools, including Marlborough, Seaford, Hurstpierpoint, Oundle, Lancing, Millfield, King's Canterbury, Bryanston, Canford and Rugby.

Remarks: Gorgeous grounds, movingly beautiful even on the miserable day of our visit, with the elegant Queen Anne house standing at the end of a long drive past a mixture of woods, playing fields and golf course. Game rambling around (they don't shoot it here – just clay pigeons). Beautiful entrance hall with roaring fire adds to the impression of arriving at a country house hotel; one specialising in modern art – it's everywhere, and extremely good.

Feels happy and free – described by one parent as a 'tree climbing education centre.' There is a distinct feel of Famous Five here. The amazing grounds are fully used by the children; one parent described how the matrons have to drag them in to bed during the summer months, and how kids are out playing golf and cricket before breakfast – 'kids have the freedom to be children' (children with a nine hole golf course).

Parents and children all comment on the strong community at Windlesham – 'it's an incredibly kind place' – which aims to be a family home away from home. No uniform promotes the homey feel, although the strict dress code prevents a grungy look. There's no label competition here

– 'they ruin clothes at school, so don't send them in anything good,' said one parent wryly. Birthday parties for boarders in the Fosters' flat – cake, treat food and all. Huge amount of energy devoted to pastoral care. Many staff live on site: one parent said 'they never clock off'. Another: 'teachers go over and beyond what they need to do; nothing is too much effort.' One parent described the 'brilliant support' from the learning centre and houseparents after a family death – they have a 'genuine love of children [here].'

Kids love the autonomy of deciding what to do every evening: tag rugby, fencing, art, just hanging out with friends – and can always get help if there's a problem with prep

High level of responsibility and support shown between children. Peer listeners appointed from the top class, peer mediators in each year – described lavishly by one of our guides as 'unpaid spies', but a peer mediator calmly countered with an example of a love/hate triangle successfully resolved by her and her counterpart. Any help from adults? 'No, of course not – confidentiality,' she said in a shocked tones. For prep age children, they are astonishingly responsible and outward-looking. This is one of the school's aims, with the head's mantra firmly in mind – be kind, be kind, be kind. Any bullying nipped it in the bud early. 'There's not a great deal of it,' said a parent, whose daughter experienced bullying which was dealt very efficiently.

No prefect or monitor system. All pupils in the top year sign up for responsibilities, and at the end of the year it is announced who will have been head girl and boy on the basis of performance.

Huge emphasis on good manners here: children pay good heed to the head's warning – 'get your greeting in before I do.' Good evidence of this on our tour: all pupils held open doors, flattened themselves against walls as we passed and leapt up in classrooms. Children are very aware of rules set down in the code of conduct, and there's open discussion of rules in school council (top year). 'Fatigues if you're really bad' – jobs such as cleaning the dining room.

Pupils can board from the age of 8 and around half are full boarders, 18 per cent from overseas. 'Boarding provision is exceptionally good,' said a mum, whose kids started as day pupils, and all ended up boarding at their request. Pupils agree – 'it's a sleepover that doesn't stop.' Homely girls' dorms, with posters, cushions, bears; spartan boys' fare, with coloured duvets the most cosy touch (despite the school's best efforts). 'It's the girls who need One Direction posters,' said one of our guides loftily. Girls also get bedside tables and lights – boys don't because of their tendency to play cricket in the dorms. At the end of the term, children give in a list of people they like, and are guaranteed to find at least one in their dorm the next term. Twelve is the biggest boys' dorm, six the smallest, nine-three for the girls. A little unfortunate that the girls' dorms are named after colours – 'azure,' 'saffron' etc – to suit their delicate natures? – whereas boys' dorms are sturdily named after senior schools – 'Wellington' et al. Unfortunate indeed, but no other whiff of sex discrimination here.

There are two boarding houses, each of which has a male and female houseparent, a permanent matron, and a battalion of evening matrons who come in from the surrounding community to assist at bedtime, and make sure kids are clean with clothes sorted for tomorrow. Nightly showers, although boarders can relax in a birthday bath. Bathroom facilities extremely clean, but not all that new. Each year has a comfy room, reduced to cheerful bedlam for the boys, ordered comfort for the girls. No mobile phones or own computers, but phones all over the place for speaking to parents, Skype phones in the comfy rooms for those with parents abroad, and dormitory phones for good night calls to parents (time restricted to give everyone a chance).

Parents say school is just not the same for day pupils, who don't have the same access to activities or teachers as boarders. Kids love the autonomy of deciding what to do every evening: tag rugby, fencing, art, just hanging out with friends – and can always get help if there's problem with prep. Boarding is particularly useful as work steps up in preparation for common entrance, parents say

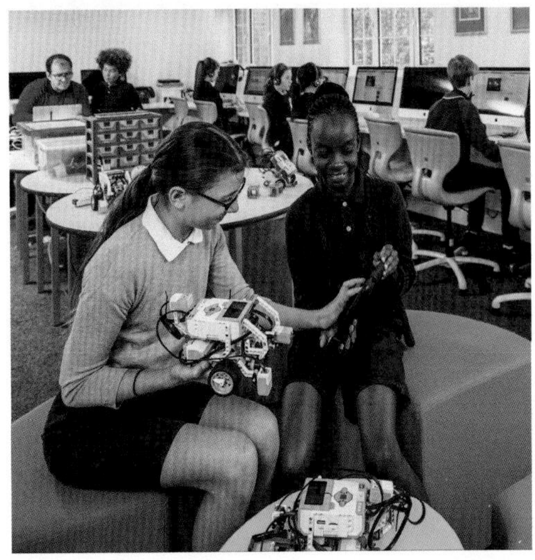

– early bird lessons start at 7.15am, and work ends at 6.30pm, so it's a long day for commuters.

No pocket money. On school trips pupils are given a set amount to spend, which goes on the school bill as an extra. Boarders get tuck at weekend – not enough to rot their teeth (a chocolate bar, a can and packet of crisps). Can earn various treats, which are usually of an edible nature. Kids talk a lot about grub, one way or another. One pupil earnestly reported that someone actually stopped boarding for lack of crisps (although it should be pointed out that the food here is plenteous and good). Academically, parents and pupils are happy with most subjects, exceptionally so in some areas though French is 'not that popular,' say the kids and parents agree, citing a reliance on work sheets. School says it has taken on new teachers since our visit.

Another parent suggested maths is also a key subject that could be taught better, although the children we spoke to gave maths teachers a glowing report – 'if you listen carefully they're really funny – very sarcastic.' One teacher apparently tells stories of his life in mathematical fantasy (difficult to imagine how this might go...). Those fiddling with their calculator may find it deposited on the outside of the window sill, so that if someone opens the window it would smash – 'really cool,' said a pupil. The head says they are about to appoint an additional maths specialist – an acknowledgement this is an area with which some children struggle.

Head says English and science are exceptionally strong. Pupils agree about science – 'one of the finest lessons.' The kids enjoy the interactive classes – 'we always do an experiment, and if you work hard, you can fit in two or three. We are doing chemical reactions, so I'm seeing things explode,' said one of our guides with relish. One science room just updated, others to be done soon.

Huge emphasis on good manners here: children pay good heed to the head's warning – 'get your greeting in before I do'

Set for core common entrance subjects from year 5. French and Spanish to all, Latin from year 6 (can be dropped by those with learning difficulties to concentrate on more core subjects). Provision for Greek, Mandarin, Italian, Russian, Norwegian and Dutch. Basically if a child arrives speaking a language, they will be encouraged to keep it up, whatever it is. Equally if a child has a burning desire to learn a particular language, school will attempt to accommodate the urge.

Forms usually no more than 18, occasionally up to 20. Starts spotting potential scholars in year 6, and a formal academic scholars' group is established in year 7. Two academic scholarship groups at the moment containing 40 children. Some strong feelings about the scholars' group (where offspring have been both included and excluded from the elite), with the suggestion that scholars are more profiled and get more support than others – and have more chances to go on the fabulous biannual charity trips. 'Opportunities should be more evenly spread,' said a parent (although the forthcoming trip to Nairobi is open to anyone in year 8).

Year 8s do have some preparation for independent learning, but one parent thought kids are hand held a bit too long, and could do with a little more independence in personal care, and organising prep.

Rigorous reporting for parents: progress report monthly with attainment and effort, both child and parents get a copy, and a full report at the end of each term. Annual parents' evening (termly for juniors). 'Amazing level of communication,' say parents: written letters from kids every week, emails and phone calls. 'School responds promptly to any query, over and above what you would expect.' Another parent commented how welcome she felt at weekends – you can attend Saturday chapel, watch a play rehearsal or recital. '[You] never feel excluded as a parent – always welcomed.' Parental portal has live stream of events, also available for catch up, ideal for parents who aren't local.

Three computer rooms, one reserved specially for junior use. Dell laptops and iPads to book out, also available to assist those with mild learning difficulties (about 15 per cent of children here). Learning development unit with head and team of assistants. Bright, well-stocked library, open from before breakfast until bedtime, news with a Tory bent – Telegraph and Times, with the honourable exception of the i.

Feels quite hunting, shooting, fishing, but manages not to feel exclusive. Sports are the usual public school fare. Parents are delighted that sports kit left hanging around at school is returned washed and pristine. Some criticism of sports facilities by parents, who feel that the swimming pool and equipment is rather tired – pupils too are keen for a new pool, and complain the Astroturf is rather worn – but new sports complex and swimming pool just completed. Changing rooms on the scruffy side. One parent felt that sports could be improved, and those in teams in the lower echelons should be playing more matches.

Most boarders are around at weekends (though it's possible to go home four weekends a term). Everyone's around on Saturdays: morning school, matches in the afternoon. Plenty of activities available – Capture the Flag is extremely popular at the moment; but also debates, mountain biking, gardening in the walled garden, shows and games – pupils can keep extremely busy if they want to (though some kids just want to live in the woods, and that's ok too.) Chess club is thriving, though the outdoor chess set is largely unused – 'but we do use a couple of the pieces for goalposts.' All love cooking club – you have to run fast if you want to sign up.

All have drama lessons, three productions each year, everyone who auditions is included in some way. Own theatre – the Malden Family Theatre – with visiting productions every term. Some rumblings from parents who are a bit tired of seeing the super-duper children starring again. Music compulsory all the way, but popular even with those who are not musical because of the inspirational director. Over 80 per cent play an instrument. Vast array of music groups of all complexions, from Miremba to rock choir.

Early years housed separately at Little Windlesham (reception – year 2). Relaxed setting, emphasis on flow and play. Tapestry method of contacting parents, who receive a video stream of their children in class directly to their email at work, which parents love. Described by a parent as being 'part of [the] big school – but very gentle, with a lot of time [spent] in their special oasis.'

The head says Windlesham would suit most types of kids, providing they join in and have a go at things. One parent suggested it would not suit a child who needs to be totally organised by others; nor is it a place for shrinking violets; although conversations with shy pupils suggested they could find their feet and flourish here. One parent emphasised that those who want their children to be day pupils should avoid Windlesham – all kids here will want to board eventually.

Parents from the Foreign Office, business, Forces, professions, and lots of expats. Some 20 different nationalities in the school, around 12 per cent non British. Assesses language skills on entry, but will give special assistance to learn English as a foreign language. Some 50 per cent of kids local, 50 per cent from abroad or other parts of the country. Parents like the mix of children from different countries, and to a degree, backgrounds – a few means-tested bursaries and no judgement, say parents; although four wheel drive likely to be parent vehicle of choice.

Several parents of leavers said their children are homesick for Windlesham: the move from this caring environment to senior school can be quite tough; but as a parent said, no one would want Windlesham to be less fabulous.

Woldingham School

RC 76

Marden Park, Woldingham, Surrey CR3 7YA

01883 349431 | registrar@woldinghamschool.co.uk | www.woldinghamschool.co.uk

Ages: 11–18

Pupils: 540; sixth form: 149; Boarders: 290 full, 30 flexi

Day: £20,085 – £21,891 pa; Boarding: £32,430 – £35,307 pa

Headmistress: Since 2016, Mrs Alex Hutchinson (40s) MA (Oxon), PGCE (Bristol); took on the headship after a year or so as deputy. Her first degree was in chemistry and she continues to teach once a week. Ever since her first post at Clifton College she has gained her experience in girls' schools. Head of science at St Mary's School, Ascot, another Catholic boarding school, she then moved north becoming head of sixth form at Central Newcastle High and chaired the HMC/GSA independent schools' heads of sixth form conference for good measure. Add to this her experience as head of sixth form at 'out and out London day school' Wimbledon High before joining Woldingham and she presents a very solid proposition in particular to the London parents looking to take their daughters out of the city.

Quick to pay tribute to her predecessor in terms of the school's solid academic reputation, the school is nonetheless enjoying a popularity surge. The winning combination of a 50/50 day/boarding school a mere 28 minutes commute from the parenting capital of south London – the school has its own station in the grounds just like Hogwarts – and a value added score that suggests that wherever your child's ability the school will help them attain the results they are capable of, without that being the entire raison d'être of the school, is revitalising its appeal.

Mrs Hutchinson feels this lies in being 'comfortable and clear about who we are: we're very confident that we deliver an excellent education across all levels. Girls here are not just the academic stars but those who have different things to offer'. Still, she's convincing that a girl destined for A*s will achieve those just as well here as anywhere – 'we're never going to take the foot off the pedal in the classroom.'

We meet in her parent-friendly office with plump soft furnishings, beautiful full-length windows and student artwork. We find her to be very friendly, engaging, carefully prepared with an attractive delivery that could see her a broadcaster in another life. In common with many pupils, her mother attended the school. She grew up in Wisbech, and lives within sight of her office with her husband, also a head of a local independent school, dog and cat. She plays hockey twice a week. Somewhere amongst the rose pergola walk and lawns there must be a veg patch too as she likes to grow her own. The students feel warmly towards her and love the fact that she lives 'just there' and find her accessible in other ways: 'she's not like one of those heads where you walk past and just smile'. Parents tell us: 'like a breath of fresh air, her enthusiasm for the school and the girls knows no bounds.' Another: 'fantastic, young, enthusiastic and very approachable.'

As the head says, 'we're good at relaxing – staff v girls "Would I lie to you?", pancake race, inter-house go-karting...'

Academic matters: In 2017, 66 per cent A*-A/9-7 grades at GCSE. Highlights include Latin and all of the sciences, with consistently good results across English and maths. Meanwhile at A level, 48 per cent of grades were A*/A. Popular subjects include English literature, maths, biology and history whilst the artists in particular shine.

All the usuals curriculum-wise, but theology is compulsory at GCSE. Girls are also expected to study a language (not necessarily modern, could be Latin)

and dual or triple science to GCSE/IGCSE. Mandarin is a club. Drama and theatre studies are offered at GCSE and A level. Most sixth formers take three. Further specialism in the sixth form introduces A levels in textiles, psychology, media studies, government and politics and classical civilisation.

Oxbridge support starts in the lower sixth with girls assigned a teacher to support their applications one-to-one. Eighteen applied in 2017 with 15 interviews. There is no fear of being made to feel like a 'geek' for being good at something is a comment we hear more than once from parents. Girls interact with their subjects outside of the grounds: a lower sixth student was joint winner of the 2017 Vellacott History Prize, awarded by Peterhouse College, Cambridge; a team of year 8 students won the 2016 teen tech awards and two teams were finalists in 2017, and a lower sixth student won third prize in the 2017 tower poetry competition, organised by Christ Church, Oxford.

The science block is newly refurbished with shiny new labs and a greenhouse on the roof to aid with botany. Whilst a new learning resource centre will make more of the library – currently such a grand but under-utilised backwater that the librarian seemed shocked we wanted to take a look.

Almost 60 per cent of staff have been working at the school for more than 10 years. A parent commented: 'the teaching staff vary in ages and sex and they complement one another. The girls seem to relate well to both the male and female teachers. They respect them and feel that they can easily approach them if they need further explanation with a subject that they find tricky.' A girl we met thought: 'They are here to support you as a person, as you grow into yourself'. We watch an upper sixth economics class where the teacher sits inside the circle of desks giving detailed essay feedback.

*She's convincing that a girl destined for A*s will achieve those just as well here as anywhere – 'we're never going to take the foot off the pedal in the classroom'*

Maximum class size is 22 up to GCSE then 14 in the sixth form. Lower sets have smaller numbers so that students can receive more support. One mother said: 'During the first three years they do not believe in setting pointless holiday homework, they believe the girls work hard enough during term time'. Hurrah.

An experienced learning enhancement department provides support for standard numbers of girls with SPLDs such as dyslexia but also small

numbers with ADHD and autism spectrum disorder. All are screened on entry. The majority receive 'light touch' support, only a few receive direct support and a reduced curriculum.

There is a significant programme of carefully thought through support for girls with EAL needs. Unusually, some one-year GCSE students (usually girls from Spain and Mexico) are prepared for the Cambridge English ESOL examinations.

Games, options, the arts: With the reality acknowledged by the head that 'these girls are not going to retire until they are in their 70s...' the school looks to create life-long interests and the 'more than' that employers are looking for beyond a university degree.

Sports facilities are not lavish given the space, and a parent's view that 'sport is average, but music and drama are outstanding' does seem to fit with the picture of the school on view today, although plans are afoot.

However, lots of timetabled sport every week, particularly in the lower school: years 7 to 9 have three lessons per week. Main sports are hockey, netball, swimming, tennis and athletics. Two students have just been selected for the Surrey county hockey squad and the 1st XI hockey team recently won the Surrey U18 trophy, whilst the 1st VII netball won the senior district cup. Further up the school choices expand to include aerobics, lacrosse, table tennis and squash. There is a dance studio and an indoor tennis dome. The school is notable in supporting its elite athletes, currently in cross-country, skiing for the GB alpine team, lacrosse, modern pentathlon, carriage driving and others – enabling them to take part in term time without falling behind. No timetabled football but soccer club is popular and cricket is coming.

Slightly less than half the school learns musical instruments, including singing, with grades from 1 to diploma level. Some stand out performers have places in national orchestras. Musicians gave two concerts on a tour of Prague earlier this year.

The most recent ISI report commented on 'the quality of writing not as fluent as speaking, particularly in the sixth form' – which the head finds incomprehensible, given the number of poets and writers the school produces. We saw the work of one published poet, also an artist, in the stunning art studio, quite the biggest we've ever seen, allowing each upper sixth student to have their own 'nest'. Fascinating projects in progress include one from a student developing her own religion and researching curses and another who is building a 'city to the lost creativity of children' in wax. Naturally, several are heading to art school.

With Carey Mulligan a notable former pupil, it's not altogether surprising to find drama facilities of such a high standard: the 550 seat theatre is stunning, with a flexible stage and space for a full orchestra. Helping girls to settle into year 7, everyone takes part in a production, most recently Roald Dahl's The Twits and The Witches. Very professional-looking production posters from former years line the staircase. Higher up the school the number of shows is limited but there are opportunities to take part in backstage work.

Pupils are far from just sequestered away in their valley. Computer science students have recently returned from a trip to Silicon Valley; year 11s and sixth formers spent four days in Berlin; year 9s visit the battlefields of Ypres and geography students enjoy an annual trip to Iceland. Eighty clubs on offer: Mandarin, archery, tap dancing, coding, dark room photography, rock-climbing and dissection caught our eye. Day girls are encouraged to stay for extracurricular activities but are free to go home from 4.30pm. Sports matches and supervised study with friends until 6.30pm. Transport is provided to facilitate this and many stay. On Saturday mornings, Saturday Active for year 7 to 10 boarders provides a range of activities.

With Carey Mulligan a notable former pupil, it's not altogether surprising to find drama facilities of such a high standard: the 550 seat theatre is stunning, with a flexible stage and space for a full orchestra

Boarding: Boarding facilities are tucked in and around the school. Years 7 and 8 have a separate block. It's tidy but plain, plentifully kitted out with sofas. Décor-wise, if we had been told the over-50s lived here we would have believed it, but what does that matter when the sun pours in across the grounds and you have all of your friends here to crowd around I'm A Celebrity and share in the odd yoga class? The upper sixth block is next door and they've recently initiated a year 7 movie night so that the older girls don't seem in any ways remote or intimidating. Years 7, 8 and 9 share a room, from year 10 girls have their own, with sixth formers getting en-suites: compact, but modern, fresh and functional, perfect for studying. Boarders are free to go home at weekends from 4.30pm on Friday. There are often boarding house pets, whether that be elderly Doris or a new, highly anticipated puppy. Flexi-boarding on hand: simply sign up for one to two nights a week a term in advance.

Background and atmosphere: Founded in 1842 by the Society of the Sacred Heart, 100 or so years later at the end of the Second World War the school of 100 pupils pupils moved to Woldingham from Roehampton. Main House is all highly decorative Victorian red-brick without and dark panelling within. Plainer 20th century additions and conversions form a courtyard and then a Millennium building smartly houses arts.

The grounds, complete with cattle, horses and the odd deer, extend to a staggering 700 acres, not particularly swooping, but more of a secluded wooded valley on the edge of the North Downs. Drive along the two mile drive and you're likely to encounter only the odd rider. This location could be rather Marmite: it does feel quite isolated, even if in reality it is not. Sixth formers are allowed to take the train into London at weekends (with planning) and clearly relish the privilege.

In part it no doubt adds to the family feel that the girls we meet are emphatic about. When the head tells us about a year 7 pyjama day we imagine the whole school wearing pyjamas to lessons every day – who would know? As for snow days, we can't think of anywhere better. As the head says, 'we're good at relaxing – staff v girls "Would I lie to you?", pancake race, inter-house go-karting...' A mother confirmed: 'There is a charming sense of fun about the school – even amongst sixth formers if they think no-one is looking.'

Pastoral care, well-being and discipline: 'We are absolutely a Catholic school', says the head – just the odd statue and religious painting on view. One third of girls are Catholics, but almost more integral to the school are the values of the sacred heart: faith, intellect, community, personal growth and social justice – 'it's very tangible for us, it's how we make decisions,' says the head. Girls no longer wear uniform to mass on Sunday but all faiths attend, even if it is just a moment of quiet reflection.

Houses are taken up enthusiastically. Day and boarding pupils are allocated to one of four houses and tutor groups are also arranged by house. The first Saturday of the autumn term is a house festival of dance, music and costume making.

The health centre is staffed by qualified nurses and a counsellor is available. With gender in the news we quiz the head on gendered vocabulary: 'I say "girls", but I would say that I'm aware of this every time I use it, which was perhaps not the case a year ago'. The head girl said at a recent presentation: 'I'm proud and happy to be the person that I have become at Woldingham'. Each parent mentions the relative lack of pressure their daughters find here. Marden, the year 7 and 8 boarding house, has an adventure playground and the head agrees girls may be able to 'stay younger for longer'.

Parents are all praise for the pastoral care: 'Excellent. If there is an issue the problem is dealt with kindness and discretion. Invaluable,' is typical. Little need for sanctions. Digital matters are the greatest challenge now, with posting something inappropriate online warranting an immediate suspension. In years 7 and 8 the school takes away devices, from year 9 girls are allowed to self-monitor, and boarders in years 7-10 hand in their devices at night. Sixth formers enjoy some uniform privileges such as their own suits, shirts and jumpers as well as taking on responsibilities as 'ribbons', one of the most charming traditions of the school, where they wear sashes and take on house or school leadership roles.

Pupils and parents: Who might the school suit? 'Not one stereotype of girl', says the head. Parents agree upon 'girls who respond to encouragement rather than pressure.' More than 100 from overseas, predominantly from Hong Kong and China but comprising 30 nationalities. 'A complete mix of backgrounds, ethnicity and relative wealth, from the daughters of Russian oligarchs downwards but all part of the school community,' said a parent.

A perusal of old girl careers throws up a number of mum-preneurs as well as a varied clutch of famous names. Interior designers including Neisha Crosland, also Louise Mensch, Vivien Leigh and Clarissa Dickson-Wright. And Carey Mulligan. Old girls may get married in the school chapel and come in for business breakfasts to share their experiences.

Entrance: There are 60 places available at 11+, 30 at 13+ and 20 at 16+. As you might expect, slightly tougher to obtain a place at 11+, around three to one, when the majority of day pupils are looking for a senior school. Occasional places at 12 and 14+ may arise. Candidates for 13+ joining in year 9 may apply for either standard entry (year 8) or deferred entry (year 6). Usual testing; the school is looking for pupils with interests beyond the academic, reasonable adjustments for SEND. Sixth form candidates are examined in two of their chosen A level subjects and a general paper.

Students love the fact that she lives 'just there' and find her accessible in other ways: 'she's not like one of those heads where you walk past and just smile'

A predominance of west Londoners and those from nearby Surrey and Kent. Established feeders include plenty of Clapham names as well as others: Granville, Hawthorns, Thomas's, Finton House, Parkgate, Broomwood Hall, Eaton House the Manor, Hornsby House, Belleville and Honeywell.

Exit: An incredibly broad range of university courses, which speaks of inspiration well beyond the purely academic – quite a few budding criminologists, digital media specialists, vets, anthropologists, electrical engineers, land economists and art historians. Over the past three years the most popular destinations have been UCL and Bristol with Cambridge, Manchester and Durham tying for third place. By our calculations 52 per cent to Russell Group and other interesting and choice UK destinations including Central Saint Martins, LSE, the Courtauld Institute, SOAS and a few in the US too.

Money matters: Not prodigiously well endowed so bursaries and scholarships unlikely to play a major role. Academic and co-curricular scholarships are offered at 11+, 13+ and sixth form, designed to recognise exceptional achievement, intellectual curiosity and persistence. Awards typically cover five to 20 per cent of day fees. No need to be stratospherically accomplished for music scholarships as potential also recognised. One scholarship to a local girl each year and two in science. Bursaries are intended for girls who demonstrate strong academic potential and where the financial circumstances of the family will make attending Woldingham impossible. Forty students are in receipt of a bursary, a few up to a life-changing 100 per cent of fees.

Remarks: Girls are sure to find a home from home in this Catholic school which welcomes all and promises fun, fabulous dramatic and artistic opportunties, strong academics and the chance to be young for a little longer.

Woodcote House School

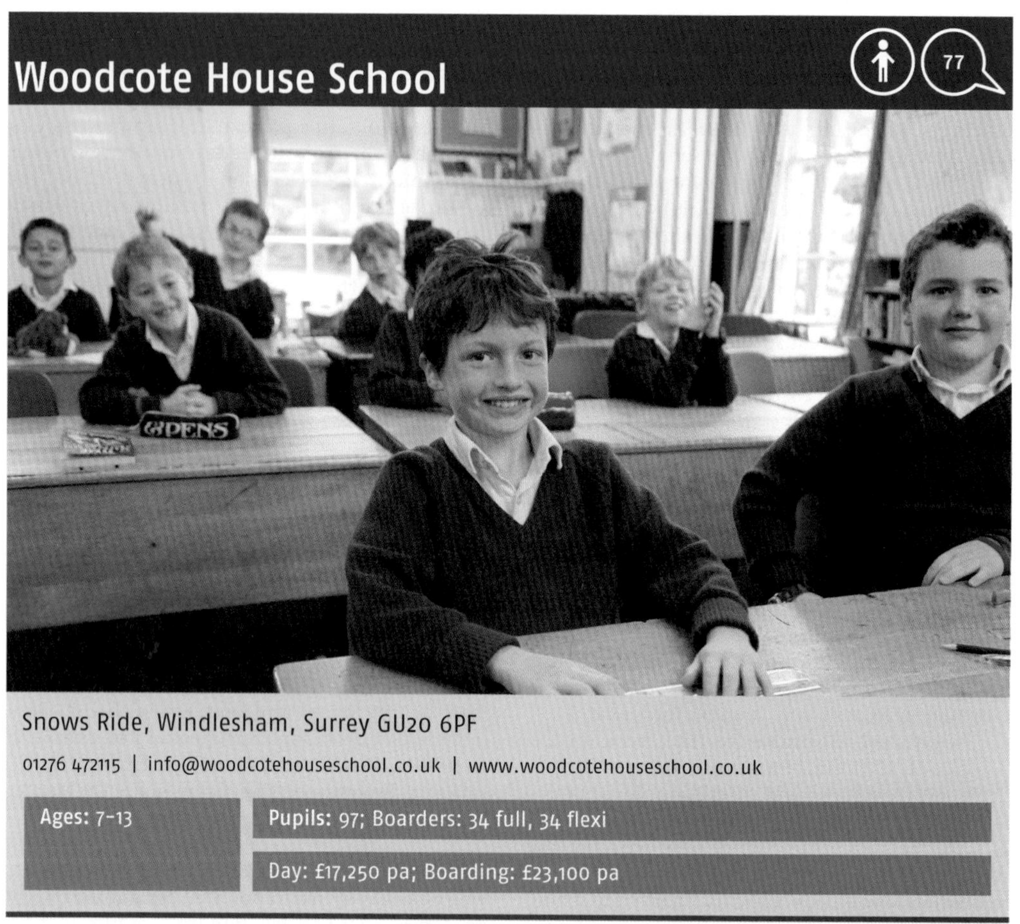

Snows Ride, Windlesham, Surrey GU20 6PF

01276 472115 | info@woodcotehouseschool.co.uk | www.woodcotehouseschool.co.uk

Ages: 7–13

Pupils: 97; **Boarders:** 34 full, 34 flexi

Day: £17,250 pa; **Boarding:** £23,100 pa

Headmaster: Since September 2016, David Paterson, brother of proprietor and ex-head Nick, and previously deputy head. Born and educated at Woodcote he returned in 1992 with his young family after a career in the City. Joined as head of mathematics and became deputy head to his brother Nick Paterson in 2000. Woodcote is a real family affair with Nick Paterson still teaching English and Spanish, and Nick's son Oliver Paterson teaching maths and Spanish.

Entrance: Places offered following internal assessment test in VR and NVR and interview with the headmaster. No linked schools or significant feeders. ('Wish there was a pre-prep,' said one mother). All quite laid back. Non-selective but applicants are invited to a taster day and assessed by the teacher during the day. Some boys will have been on a list since birth, others rock up mid-term somewhere along the line. Most families are from London and home counties. Boys may board from year 3. In essence, the school is looking for boys who will put something into the school. Will take the odd hard luck story, a boy who has been bullied elsewhere or got lost in a larger set up. Head has a 'conversation' with prospective pupils and their parents, and will suggest a chat with the SENCo if it seems appropriate – nothing more formal than that. 'We are not going to say, in effect, "you are not clever enough for our school", but you have to be robust enough to cope. We want boys who don't mind getting their knees dirty. I wouldn't say we don't want sissies or prissies, but we want boys who want to be boys.'

There is a scholarship morning each March prior to September entry for boys joining the school as day pupils or boarders. The owning Paterson family put up the equivalent of two sets of boarding fees (introduced to mark school's 150th anniversary) and divide as they deem fit – five boys could get 20 per cent of the available cash, or two boys get the lot, or sometimes nobody gets anything – school does not give them away for the sake of it. Must spot a spark or talent, academic, musical or sporting.

There are 18 per cent of boarders from overseas.

Exit: At 13 to all the top-notch public schools, from Ampleforth to Winchester, with clutches of academic, music and all round scholarships won. Lots to Sherborne of late, plus of course Eton, Harrow, Wellington. Parents given lots of guidance on future schools – evidently a strength of this place. WH parents are not always chasing Eton and down the list schools. It's all about what is best for the child, and plenty of other factors are considered. 'So the list of schools WH boys go on to does not always reflect the actual academic achievement,' said one parent. And any leaver will not have heard the last of Woodcote. Legend has it that popular long-serving master Colin Holman – a modern day Mr Chips – has been known to drop a note to many of the boy's new senior school housemasters when he remembers a nugget of useful information about them, to the effect of 'If he's like this, try this'.

Remarks: Superb example of that dying breed – the thriving family-owned school. Idiosyncratic – you will either 'get' this school or you won't. Sceptics ask where the owls are kept, but its parents and boys are so glowing in their praise it's unreal. Feels like a proper country prep, although it's just 40 minutes from London. Combines top notch teaching with tons of outside activities so that the boys are both mentally and physically challenged every day. But also makes time for them to do their own thing, so they are happy and flourish. Nice balance of nurture and push.

Unapologetically focused on doing its own thing – even the unusual brown and yellow school uniform seems a manifestation of a school confident in its own skin. Several parents mentioned how their sons had blossomed at this school, developing their personalities and interests. 'We aim to turn out a young man with good manners who is well-rounded, honest, trustworthy and friendly.'

You will see at a glance that this school isn't splashing your cash on fancy facilities, though new theatre recently completed – the place is delightfully worn at the edges. It really does look as if 100 boys have the run of the place. There's a relaxed feel, plenty of rough and tumble, all part of its charm. Not precious, but quite a cocooned existence. Known to sort out an odd bod or two.

'The Paterson family is very strong and not swayed by fashion. They know what they want to provide and are very good at doing it,' explained one parent

Set in its own 30 acres, including some attractive woods, the main building is Regency and hits you with a real sense of tradition and history – ask about 18th century highwayman, Captain Snow, when you visit. But school has been in its present incarnation since 1931 when it was bought by the Paterson family. Old boys would definitely recognise the place – and that's the idea. 'The Paterson family is very strong and not swayed by fashion. They know what they want to provide and are very good at doing it,' explained one parent. Healthy sprinkling of old boys have their sons here.

Pictures of former pupils line the walls, and many of them were clearly recalled by Paterson matriarch Angela (Nick's mother) when we bumped

into her during our visit. And the main thoroughfare, Red Lane, is a literally well-trodden path of black and red tiling, pitted and undulated from the patter of boys' feet over the years. Then the dining hall, where whole school, pupils, staff, visitors, all eat together, is decorated by the honours board and pictures of school founders. As they sit chatting together boys are clearly in a stable, traditional environment and confident about talking to adults.

Lessons are relaxed, but industrious. None of the staff 'just teach', they all wear a number of other hats so the boys see their teachers all the time, as much outside the classroom as inside it. Hence no forced formality about the classroom setting, but all is most respectful – staff exude an air of relaxed authority. Still boys scramble to their feet when visitors enter the classroom and to walk through the grounds with a staff member is to be met with a cacophony of 'Morning sir, morning sir'. Very small class sizes, average 10, never more than 14 and just four in the scholarship class we visited – having fun with the Kubla Khan. Fairly holistic approach to teaching as staff tie in topics across subject areas, so that talk of battlefields in history will link to their locations in geography. Staff more like synchronised swimmers, rather than everyone ploughing up and down their own subject lane. Parents full of praise for an enthusiastic staff always pushing for excellence.

Long day (8.20am to 6.10pm) for day boys, furthest of whom travel around 20 miles to school. First thing every morning is prep – sensible move as boys are nice and fresh and aren't able to get help from parents. Not a whiff of an interactive whiteboard around the place and school is currently rather conflicted about the role of ICT – never a huge deal here, where teachers largely prefer projectors and coloured pens. 'Many schools will find their fancy

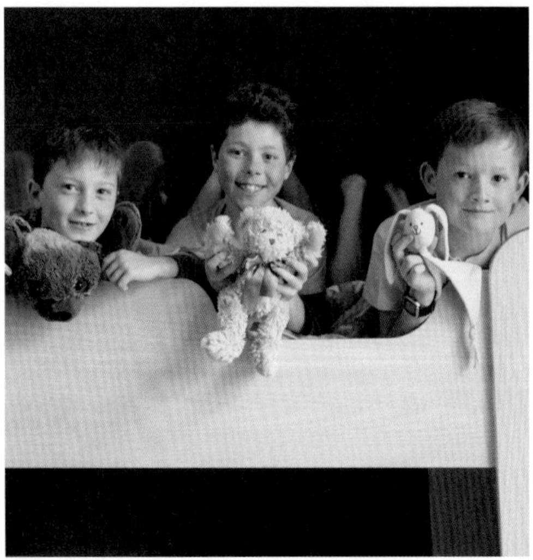

Very welcoming of parents – none of this waving them off at Waterloo in September and not seeing them till Christmas. Parents swing by if they are in the area and teachers happy to respond

ICT suites defunct as everyone clutches hand-held devices like iPads now.' (Not that school has those either.) 'ICT is certainly a subject in transition and we need to decide what stance we will take'.

Nothing state-of-the-art about other facilities either, though the boys we met described them as 'good' – 'we've got everything', said one. It's a bit scruffy and ramshackle in places, but not because nobody cares, rather it's just rather battered in places as a result of hundreds of boys kicking around the place – it's clearly a home from home for them.

Woodcote is able to accommodate some special needs and has a dedicated SENCo to handle boys on the autistic spectrum, dyslexia and EAL. About 20 boys (but a fifth of the school, remember) have some type of learning support, for which their parents pay extra. Languages taught are French and Spanish – a significant Spanish entourage among the pupils and Nick Paterson is a fluent Spanish speaker. A few boys from Thailand and Russia and some 15 per cent of Forces families, who particularly appreciate that the place is properly focused on boarding, so that weekends are busy and boys are far more than simply 'minded'. School keen to get the UK/overseas balance right. Very good relationships between the boys themselves and then between themselves and their teachers. The overseas boys tend to spend exeats with their more local friends, leading to an informal exchange programme.

Years 3 and 4 are housed in a separate juniors' building to facilitate a slow integration into main school life. Lots of praise for junior head Mrs Woodall; 'She is so very kind to my sons,' said one mother. Similarly, year 8s are given a taste of teenage life when they spend a term during their final year living in Dominies House – within the grounds, but away from the main school and set up to give year 8s some preparation for their life to come at public school – not least a taste of going to and from school each day.

Parents struggle to put their finger on a standout subject – 'It's all fantastic', said one mother. 'Whatever the talent, they will bring it out' – but music and art mentioned several times. A Woodcote boy beat 13,000 entries to come second in The Sunday Telegraph/Saatchi Gallery prize. And if your son plays an instrument, however badly, he will perform – this place is big on performance opportunities. 'My heart was in my mouth as I saw my son approach the piano, knowing that he'd only been learning for a couple of weeks,' recalled one parent. Not much timetabled drama, but usually a production per term. Staff write the plays – they seem to enjoy it, though it's probably also a necessity to find parts for so many small boys.

The philosophy here is that it is good to be a big fish in this small pool. One mother with several boys at the school felt strongly that each of her sons had found an inner confidence at Woodcote. 'I don't mean they are cocky, in fact they are more polite now, but simply that they've all formed quite distinct personalities and developed a love of study that definitely wasn't there before'.

While things are rather cosy inside, outside the school the boys are spoiled for space, with 35 acres of grounds to run about in, and are encouraged to try out a huge range of outdoor activities. Boys are even kicking about on Rip Stiks during break. From the usual cricket, football and rugby, to the more unusual CCF, bushcraft and even clay pigeon shooting (for older boys) there is masses on offer. School takes its sport seriously and reckons to punch above its weight when taking on other (almost always larger) schools – has only lost 20 per cent of its fixtures over the last five years.

Keen on outdoor education, school considering a 'very small' smallholding, and an outdoor pizza oven is also on wish list. Shame more use not made of on site swimming pool – but boys seem too busy with other things to be very bothered about this.

And fears that a non sporty boy might flounder in this place are apparently unfounded as more indoor types can make the teas and help the parents park their cars on match days. 'In fact my incredibly non sporty son even got a few games with the B team – all the rubbish players do,' said one mother. Other activities for the less physically inclined include archery and golf and plenty of indoor pursuits, even a turf club.

School has a refreshing 'let children be children' attitude and is happy for them to cook outdoors sitting around a campfire – not in a cavalier way, but just acknowledging that they will enjoy a few safe risks. Think Just William updated for 21st century. So not surprising to hear that these happy, busy boys sleep like logs. And of course with 75 per cent of pupils boarding, they sleep at school in clean and cheerful accommodation – small dorms with sea blue walls, punchy primary coloured duvet covers. Largely settled for the night by 8pm (9pm for older ones), older boys three to a room, more as you go down the year groups, but even larger dorms divided into little 'pods' to give a homelier feel. All tidy. A fairly basic common room full of bean bags for when they want to collapse.

Sky Sports available along with controlled access to TV, phones, play stations and associated electrical detritus of modern life, but school would far rather they were outside or generally more gainfully employed – and they usually are. Lovely old-fashioned insistence that, Skype and emails notwithstanding, boys will write a proper letter home once a week. Weekends (starting after Saturday morning school) typically include sports matches against other schools, an outing and a service in the school's own chapel (a charming building – apparently an early flat-pack of the type originally destined to be shipped out to missionaries in the 1800s).

Parents are welcome to attend matches and chapel and lots do. In fact we were surprised to see quite a number of parents at a predominantly boarding school – even though several of them were actually parents of day boys dropping books in or sorting out for their sons to stay on for some or other evening activity. There's a full programme of popular Friday night entertainments including visiting speakers – recently a sports commentator and a seven peaks climber. Many day boys do ask to board in the end, so that there are more day boys in the lower school and only one or two by year 8. 'My son doesn't even always want to come home for exeats, he is so happy at school,' said a parent. School offers a graduated approach to boarding, three nights as well as seven, but this is aimed to be an introduction to boarding rather than a babysitting service, although it would be flexible about the odd night here and there.

They particularly appreciate that the place is properly focused on boarding, so that weekends are busy and boys are far more than simply 'minded'

Staff all casually dressed when we visited – no airs and graces here. You won't get a fresh paint-type royal tour, but will see the place warts and all – the showers, the worst dorm (the last awaiting refurbishment) and maybe even the popular Warhammer dungeon.

Very accessible and welcoming of parents – none of this waving them off at Waterloo in September and not seeing them till Christmas. Parents swing by if they are in the area and teachers happy to respond to 'Can I have a quick word' during a match afternoon in favour of any formally structured pastoral system. 'Pastoral care is fabulous', said one parent. 'You drop the boys off without a worry'.

Not flash or fancy; old fashioned in the best sense of the world; 'Traditional with a modern twist?' offered one mother. Warm and inclusive, quite a gem. A school with a heart and soul where boys will definitely be boys.

Worth School

RC 78

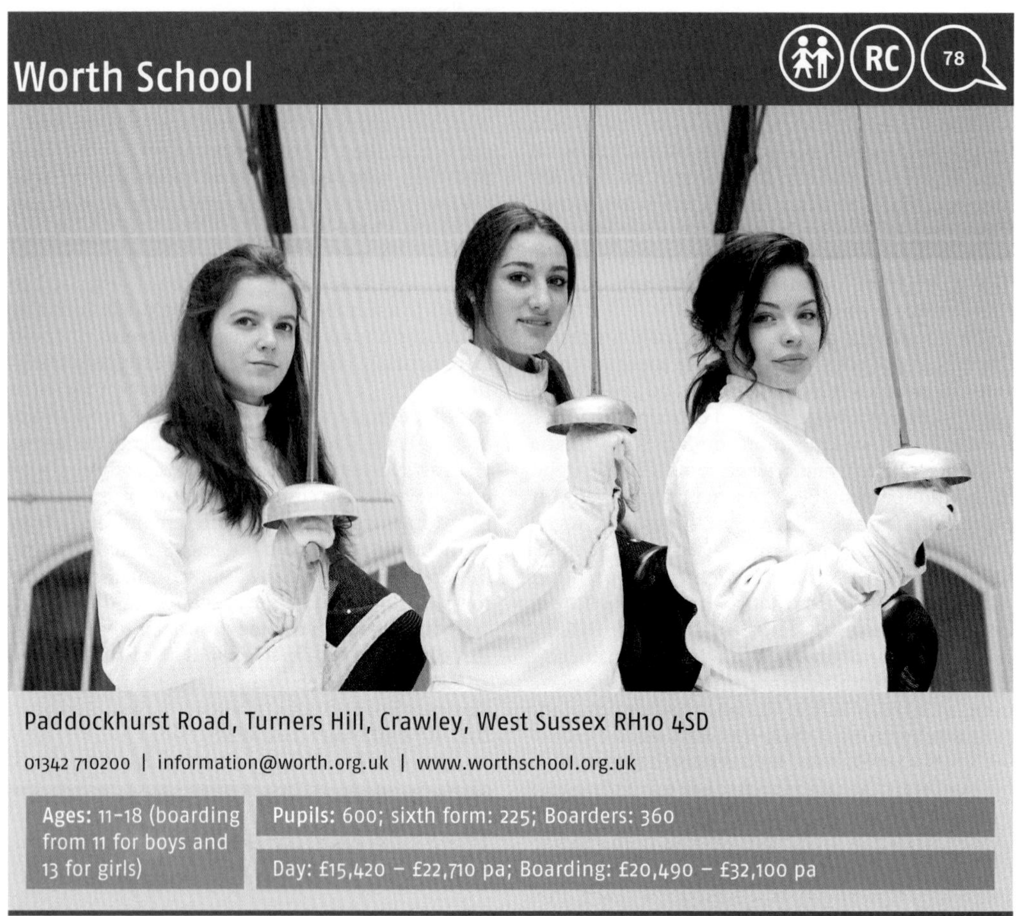

Paddockhurst Road, Turners Hill, Crawley, West Sussex RH10 4SD

01342 710200 | information@worth.org.uk | www.worthschool.org.uk

Ages: 11–18 (boarding from 11 for boys and 13 for girls)

Pupils: 600; sixth form: 225; Boarders: 360

Day: £15,420 – £22,710 pa; Boarding: £20,490 – £32,100 pa

Head master: Since 2015, Stuart McPherson MA (40s). Educated at the University of Western Australia and took an MA in literature and religion at Newcastle. He had not planned to be a teacher but joined Sydney Grammar for a year, ended staying for 10 and did his teacher training on the job. He came over to the UK on a short term teacher exchange with Eton and spent 15 years there, where he taught English and coached rugby and cricket and was a housemaster for the final five years. He is married to Johneen, who is deputy head academic at St Mary's Ascot, and they have four children. He says it might sound like a cliché but he spends any spare time reading and enjoys walking and camping – but definitely for no longer than 24 hours.

He has a strong Catholic faith and says the 'key aims of the school are rooted within the Benedictine tradition – it's about the formation of character and values and not just jumping through GCSE hoops. There is something special about the place; the ethos is tangible'. He is the third lay head and also, by coincidence, the third Australian head. 'He is a good communicator,' said a pupil, is willing to listen and is very approachable – 'he always has his door open in the morning and you can drop in'. 'He looks over our personal statements and is not a scary figure and you see him a lot around the school'. 'He hasn't raced in and changed lots but he has improved the general ambition of the school – and the food is much better,' said a parent.

A lot has been going on behind the scenes – he has reorganised the senior leadership team and now has a team of nine, some new recruits and some from within the school, and in his second year, about 20 per cent of staff are new. He has appointed a deputy head (academic) and introduced a system of target minimum grades which, once set, are not allowed to go down, as well as peer reviews and lots of scrutiny. He says this gave teachers a shock to start with but he has encountered surprisingly little resistance, and teachers say that they feel listened to. He will walk into lessons unannounced and feels it is important to be seen to be interested, and there is a sense of co-operation between teaching staff and the senior management team. He is raising the profile of the school and has upped the marketing, and says that 'while humility is important, it does not have to apply to the way we market the school'. 'He is spreading the net a lot wider,' said a parent. 'Previously the school used to rely on word of mouth'. 'The school is much more efficient and there is more of a buzz about the place,' said another.

Academic matters: The school has a fairly broad intake reflected in the results with 36 per cent A*/A at A level (75 per cent A*/B), an IB average of 37 points and 50 per cent A*-A/9-7 at GCSE in 2017. The headmaster insists that the school is not becoming more selective, but as more clever children apply there are more to choose from. About 25 per cent do the IB, which is popular with the Europeans. The school does not push it but would like to see more British children take the IB: 'The rigour is equal to A levels but with different demands,' says the headmaster. Most teachers teach both. Good range of subjects offered at IB including German and Italian at A1, psychology, philosophy, music, theatre and visual arts. Offers 24 subjects at A level, including business studies, psychology, politics, DT (new centre) and photography. Those doing A levels also take the EPQ (Extended Project Qualification). There can be as few as three pupils in the IB classes and about 19 in the average English GCSE class.

All juniors learn Latin, which can be dropped in year 9, all year 9 pupils have lessons in Christian living, and all have to take an RS GCSE. French, Spanish and German offered as part of the curriculum and Italian, Polish, Russian and Mandarin may be available via private tuition, but depends on the availability of a tutor. Native or near native speakers of French and Spanish can take the GCSE at end of year 10.

Plenty to keep the more academic on their toes with a range of academic societies including medical, philosophy and debating as well as challenge workshops and lectures. Careers advice much improved but still a 'work in progress'. Well stocked careers library and useful 'how to apply to university' guide and annual careers fair. Old Worthians very helpful with work experience and shadowing and offer careers lectures and talks. Year 13 pupils offered a course in interview technique.

Library with a large study area and IT suite is open seven days a week and before and after school. Librarian and assistant on hand to help with research skills. Learning support provided by a small team of specialist teachers, mainly for mild difficulties and study skills, and taught either in small groups or one-to-one including in the sixth form if needed. EAL provision for about 40 pupils either in group or individual lessons, some only for technical language. Intensive tuition sometimes a condition of entry. EAL pupils also taught British traditions, life and culture. All those without a recognised English qualification have to take IELTS exam required for entry to British universities. Pre-IB course available for overseas students not ready for the full diploma.

Games, options, the arts: Sport compulsory in lower years with most continuing into sixth form – sixth formers have to do four hours exercise a week as well as activities. Lots of new talent among the sports staff including new directors of sport for both girls' and boys' games and many of the coaches have played at professional level including the head of cricket who was a first class player. Huge investment in girls' games which, until recently, were considered the poor relation – hockey now coached by a women's premier league player (who also teaches biology) and girls often train with the East Grinstead hockey club. Rugby still the major winter sport for the boys and school fields 12 teams, which means keen players of varying talents can play in matches. Boys' hockey has also been introduced. Huge range of facilities including squash courts, a golf course, floodlit Astro, two fitness suites, a couple of gyms and a fencing sale but no swimming pool – keen swimmers train at the local sports centre. The school still basking in the glory of Tom Mitchell's silver medal at Rio as captain of the GB rugby VIIs.

Huge investment in girls' games which, until recently, were considered the poor relation – hockey now coached by a women's premier league player

Very busy music department based in the performing arts centre with a recital room, teaching room and practice rooms and a suite of Mac computers – about half learn an instrument or have singing lessons and the abbey choir performs at Thursday worship and Sunday mass. 'There is always something musical going on,' said a pupil – regular instrumental and choral concerts and the very noisy and keenly contested annual house music competition as well as Battle for the Bands and Worth Unplugged. Students encouraged to form their own groups and soundproof rock room is available for band practice. Two former pupils currently reading music at Oxford, one with an organ scholarship and another, who is in the Sistine Chapel choir, arranged for the Worth choir to sing alongside them at a papal mass.

Lively drama in superbly equipped theatre and other venues around the school. Every year group has the opportunity to be part of a play, either acting or behind the scenes, and pupils can learn the technical aspects from the full-time theatre technician as well as costumes and make-up as well. One pupil has won a place at the National Youth Theatre.

New art school opened in 2016 – spread over two floors with junior and senior art rooms, photography studios and dark room, ICT and research facilities and a stunning gallery and light-filled exhibition space with some pretty impressive artwork on show – drawing a particular strength as well as sculpture and large scale installations. Open door policy so students can come in whenever they want. All year 9s have to have a go at DT and photography, and both are available at A level.

Huge array of afternoon and evening activities, ranging from the usual cooking, drama and sport to Minecraft and code breaking, scuba diving, pedal cart design and street and modern dance. Polo offered at a local club and riding, as part of the equestrian club, at a nearby yard, where you can also keep your own horse. About 10 pupils per year take part Model United Nations and Young Enterprise. The Wednesday community service programme can be linked to the CAS element of the IB and to the D of E – about 30 achieve gold each year. 'The headmaster has encouraged more uptake in activities so children have much less time for hanging around,' said a parent.

Boarding: About 55 per cent of pupils are boarders. They are allowed home most Saturday nights, but about half the boarders are in most weekends. 'I am surprised how many stay in,' said a parent. 'We only live 10 minutes from the school but the children like to board as they have so much more fun.' Flexi-boarding an option for boys in the first two years only; girls board from year 9 upwards. Seven boarding houses with space for 60 boarders each – all have their own character and each is a home from home within the school. Many of the houseparents have young children which adds to the family atmosphere. The younger pupils share rooms but most sixth formers have their own study bedrooms and the lucky ones have ensuite bathrooms. Increasing number of girl boarders: they have moved to a larger house where everyone in years 11-13 has their own room with ensuite bathroom, whilst the younger ones share. The upper sixth have traditionally had their own house, but will now stay in the same mixed age house all the way through.

Cinema and theatre trips as well as in-house socials and film nights held on Saturday evenings and an outing offered every Sunday, anything from paintballing, bowling or a shopping trip to a visit to the Tower of London, and there is supervised access to the school sporting facilities and fitness suite.

Background and atmosphere: The school was founded in the 1930s when Downside Abbey bought the Paddockhurst estate from Lord Cowdray and founded Worth Abbey and an adjoining prep school. Worth broke away from Downside in 1959 and by the mid-1960s the prep school had morphed into a senior school. The first day pupils arrived in the 1990s and the first girls were admitted into the sixth form in 2008 with the school becoming co-ed throughout in 2012. Although the Abbey still owns the buildings, the school is now a separate charity with an independent board of governors and a lay chairman. The original sandstone Victorian house, together with a mock Tudor model farm and whimsical clock tower, was built for Robert Whitehead, the developer of the first rocket-propelled torpedo. Set in 500 acres of farm and parkland and approached via ornate iron gates and a long sweeping drive, it must be one of the most impressive approaches to a school – and it is only seven miles from Gatwick Airport and 30 from London. It still has the feeling of a grand country house with wood panelling and a faint scent of beeswax polish.

Ten houses, some in the main house, some in the old farm buildings and the more modern ones dotted around the grounds. All have a common room for each year group, a small kitchen, a computer room and library. Recently opened sixth form social centre with café. The remarkable flying saucer shaped chapel designed by Francis Pollen and opened in 1974, with new pews designed by the Thomas Heatherwick Studios, is central to the school: whole school worship held once a week and a mass every Sunday.

About 60 per cent of the children are Catholic and 'there is quite a lot of religion', said a mother, 'but the ethos is very inclusive and the children accept it as part of the school. It makes them think of other people and that there is more to life than who has the best mobile phone.'

'There are a lot of social events and the school is generous with its hospitality, which can lead to the development of a Worth Girth,' said one parent

Younger pupils wear uniform, sixth form boys and girls a matching suit and academic staff wear gowns.

Very much a boarding school which takes day pupils, and despite there being more than 40 per cent day pupils, the headmaster is determined to keep it this way – the day pupils are involved in all aspects of school life and activities and have to attend Saturday morning lessons and play in matches if they are in a team. A network of school buses brings pupils from as far afield as Guildford and Tunbridge Wells.

Strong ethos of service and everyone expected to undertake some community work, culminating in Worth in the Community Day at the end of the summer term – anything from helping in primary schools, gardening for old people and work in local homeless hostel to drama productions and concerts in local care homes. Pupils encouraged to take on challenges and each year a small group attempts the cross-Channel swim; five have made it so far.

Pastoral care, well-being and discipline: 'Pupils are very well cared for here,' says the headmaster. 'We don't tolerate drugs, alcohol or bullying', and the school runs a programme of lectures and seminars on the dangers of drug and alcohol abuse. Every house has a houseparent and deputy, there are house-based tutor groups which meet at least twice a week and every house has a chaplain. The school is small enough for everyone to know each other, and tutors and houseparents know pupils well and spot problems early on – it is hard to slip through the net here. Counsellor in three days a week – busy but manageable. The chaplaincy sits at the centre of the school and has a mixed team of monks, teachers and young Catholics known as the Forerunners, plus a part time Anglican chaplain – each house is allocated a chaplain. 'The monks are very special; they are always around but quite low key,' said a pupil, 'and you can call in at the chaplaincy whenever you want – and they often have cake'. The chaplaincy promotes pilgrimage and service and organises trips to Lourdes, Camino de Santiago, and the Taize community in France during the holidays, and everyone is expected to go on a retreat. Annual trip to Worth Abbey's charitable outpost in Peru which runs children's homes in the Andes.

House and school prefects act as mentors to younger pupils. 'The seniors are so nice to the juniors and there is good mixing between year groups, especially through the societies,' said a parent. Everything you need to know can be found in the school magazine Worth Knowing; 'I could not resist the pun,' says the headmaster.

Pupils and parents: Most day children live within an hour of the school and boarders mostly from London and the home counties. About 20 per cent from abroad, mainly from Catholic countries of Europe and South America with a dozen or so from Asia. The school is improving integration between IB (mainly foreign) and A level students, who now have mixed tutorial groups. Quite a broad spectrum of parents but a large number of prosperous City workers, often with both parents commuting. Strong Catholic ethos, but families from many different religions who like the sense of community and responsibility to the wider world, and don't feel religion is being imposed on their children.

Active friends' group gives parents a sense of belonging: 'You can get as involved as you want – there are a lot of social events and the school is generous with its hospitality, which can lead to the development of a Worth Girth,' said one parent.

The school likes to involve the whole family via annual parents' meetings and seminars and family mass as well as the parent portal. Although only about a third of the pupils are girls – 40 per cent in some years, and school plans to achieve this throughout – they more than make up for it in energy and ambition and 'keep the boys on their toes,' said a parent. We were pleased to hear that International Women's Day is celebrated.

Former pupils tend to stay in touch and the strong sense of being part of a community carries on afterwards – a blend of confidence and humility without the public school swagger. Well-known old Worthians include actor Robert Bathurst, art dealer Philip Mould, comedian/actor Harry Enfield, England rugby player Nick Walshe, racing driver Henry Surtees, after whom the pupils' café is named, and Tom Mitchell, who captained the silver medal winning GB rugby 7s team at Rio. As the girls come through, we expect to see their names up in lights as well.

Entrance: Pupils come from a range of prep schools including Hazelwood, Handcross Park, Great Walstead, Copthorne, Cumnor House and the Hawthorns in Surrey as well as Catholic prep schools in London. Most join in years 7 or 9 or for sixth form with a few places available in years 8 and 10. Eleven plus assessment tests at Worth in January year of entry – online English, maths and non-verbal reasoning – and informal interviews and small group tasks plus report from current school. Overseas pupils can sit the tests in their home country.

Thirteen plus entry via the common pre-test plus assessment day with informal interview and group tasks in the spring of year 7. Common entrance is for setting purposes only.

Some international pupils join in year 11 for one year pre-IB course leading on to full IB diploma in sixth form. About 25 join sixth form – reports, references and interviews plus at least six GCSEs at A*-B or grade 6+.

Exit: Most popular universities are Bristol, Warwick, Manchester, King's College London, St Andrews and Edinburgh with a fairly predictable range of subjects: economics, history, geography, languages, philosophy and music being the most popular. Four to Oxbridge, plus three medics and a vet in 2017. A handful to art and drama school each year. A small number to US universities – school can help ith applications but pupils often get outside tuition for SATS exams. In 2017, students off to Brown (political science), NYU (computer science), Toronto (communications and IT), Italy and Lithuania (dentistry). Happy to look at alternatives if pupils not keen on university. A handful leaves after GCSEs, usually to go to sixth form colleges.

Money matters: Academic, art, drama, music and sports scholarships offered. Max award of 40 per cent goes to the top scholar in each category and other scholars may receive 20-30 per cent – additional means-tested bursary can take this up to 50 per cent of fees. St Benedict's scholarship of up to 100 per cent of fees for local children from families who are in full communion with local church but can't afford fees – a child must be capable of achieving a scholarship in one of the categories.

Remarks: This school has everything going for it – beautiful setting and only 30 miles from London, good sport, music and art and improving academic performance, and an ambitious and energetic newish headmaster.

Yehudi Menuhin School

79

Stoke d'Abernon, Cobham, Surrey KT11 3QQ

01932 864739 | reception@yehudimenuhinschool.co.uk | www.yehudimenuhinschool.co.uk

Ages: 8–19

Pupils: 78; sixth form: 24; Boarders: 63

Day: £41,397 pa; Boarding: £42,492 pa for those not on music and dance scheme

Head: Since January 2018, Kate Clanchy, previously senior master at Westminster School. Degree in modern and medieval languages from Cambridge, masters from the Institute of Education and an MBA. Initially head of marketing for a French water company; French teacher at Dulwich College, head of modern langs at JAGS, deputy head at St Paul's Girls before joining Westminster in 2013. She's also

a governor of Oak Lodge School for pupils with hearing difficulties.

Academic matters: 'It's not the best, but it's OK,' was how one student described the academic provision. Results are certainly OK. In 2017, 60 per cent A*-A/9-7s at GCSE. A levels were 55 per cent at A*/A and 81 per cent at A*-B. This information isn't readily available on the website, giving the impression that the school doesn't think it of much interest; no one is here for the academics, after all. That said, the ability profile here is above the national average, and students want to do well on all fronts.

Most students take seven GCSEs from a narrow range of subjects: music of course, then maths, English, single or double science, history and German, the school's main language because conservatoires in Germany and Austria are popular leavers' destinations here. Other languages are also taught when the need is there, and Russian, Japanese, Turkish, Mandarin have all been offered. (French used to be very big at the school, but no longer, which we thought a shame.) At A level everyone takes music, and then chooses one or two further options from English, history, biology, chemistry, maths, further maths and German. No physics, because the low demand makes it hard to justify employing someone to teach it. 'That's a tricky one for us, and we'd love to be able to offer it.' Art taught throughout the school and some lovely work on show, but not usually taken as an examined subject. 'I wish there were more options,' was a concern voiced by one student and echoed by others. But the school's academic music programme, a longstanding jewel in the YMS crown, was highly praised by everyone. 'It's incredible!' 'Amazing!' 'Inspiring!' 'Harder than at Juilliard!' were typical comments.

Impossible to build year groups as such, because of very small numbers. Instead, learning is organised in four groups based on key stages. D group is made up of pupils in years 3-6, C group of those in years 7-9, B group years 10-11, and A group years 12-14. Classes are very small, and all students get a high degree of individual attention. No SEN teacher, but the school's few dyslexic pupils receive ongoing support from the regular staff and teaching assistants; one-to-one tutorials where necessary. Strong EAL support, with students who need it given regular lessons with dedicated EAL teacher. 'I couldn't speak English very well when I came,' one student told us, 'and the school has really helped me.'

Games, options, the arts: Music is, of course, the school's raison d'etre, and at least half of each day is devoted to it. Everyone has a daily practice target to meet, and it's perfectly usual for the older students to do four or more hours a day. Younger students do less and their practice sessions are supervised. Pupils receive two one-hour lessons per week on their principal instrument, and half an hour on their second study, and everyone learns composition. There are also courses in classical improvisation, choral singing, aural training and general music studies. The result is a landscape of really stellar music-making in which the students live and grow. The orchestra is stunning, and chamber music is wonderful. Huge programme of concerts, including twice-weekly ones at the school given in the beautiful Yehudi Menuhin Hall, all blond wood and gleaming Steinways, and dozens across the UK and abroad. The three pupils we saw in concert had excellent posture, were compellingly confident on the platform, and gave virtuoso performances of great beauty and taste.

Sports and physical training are provided for in a delightfully esoteric way. Pupils have two hours of timetabled sport per week, chosen from a range of swimming (in the school's own indoor pool), football, PE, badminton, tennis, cross-country running and dance. Yoga is optional but encouraged, and an Alexander technique teacher is always available for those who want or need to see her. Annual football fixture with the Purcell School for Young Musicians in Hertfordshire. The latter usually win, it has to be said, perhaps because they number brass players and percussionists among them who tend to come up beefier.

Art is much-loved and drama has always flourished at the school: shows are staged in the Square Room, and a recent production of The Tempest was set quirkily in a boarding school. Plenty of trips to concerts, theatres, art galleries, museums, etc. D of E scheme.

Boarding: Boarding has been intrinsic to the school's ethos since its inception. 'We run a boarding day and a boarding week.' There are a tiny number of 'day boarders', but they're in school from 8am until 6.30pm and are regarded as boarding pupils who sleep at home. The youngest students are weekly boarders and can go home at 4pm on Fridays. The rest stay on for Saturday morning school, after which they can go home if they choose, although many of them come from too far away for this to be possible.

Two boarding houses, both maintained to a high standard. The girls, and the youngest boys, live in Music House in quarters that we thought well-appointed and attractive. Students are grouped in 'pods' of broadly similar ages; same-age room mates can't be guaranteed because numbers are so small. Younger pupils share two or three to a room, older ones may get an ensuite to themselves: a new storey has recently been added to provide this kind of accommodation. Pianos everywhere – Debussy's L'Isle Joyeuse drifted out dreamily from under the door of one room as we passed – and practice sessions are timetabled throughout the day. Until they're aged 11, pupils can practise until 8pm; thereafter they can go on until 9pm. We'd heard reports of students practising themselves into a decline, but the house staff and students we spoke to denied this. 'We patrol the corridors and we do stop students over-practising,' said the housemistress, 'but they learn common sense.' 'It's very busy here during the day, and we want to sleep,' agreed a soignée young violinist.

The boys live in Harris House, which has a brand spanking new extension providing seven ensuite rooms and a kitchen for student use. Like Music House, it was clean, orderly, cosy and dotted with pianos. We liked the wall of clocks showing the current time in different countries around the world – 'We have pupils from every time-zone and it was a way of making them feel at home,' explained the housemaster.

As a rule, boarders have to be at least 9, but the school conceded that this wasn't rigid, and they have taken children as young as 8; we heard from one mother for whom this hadn't worked, possibly because children of that age are the exception here rather than the rule.

Students enthused about the improvement in the food over the past two years. We thought it pretty good too: a healthy and appetizing range from which even the fussiest eater could find something. Servery and eating area has been handsomely refurbished, and ranks as probably the most civilised school dining hall we've ever sat down in.

Background and atmosphere: Founded in 1963 by Yehudi Menuhin to give musically gifted children the chance to develop their potential to the full through a sympathetic curriculum, enhanced practice opportunities and superlative teaching in an immersive environment. Initially only for pianists, violinists and cellists, the portfolio has since been expanded to include double bass players and guitarists. The YMS approach has had its detractors and historically the school has known darker times, but some truly world-class musicians have come out of the place, although, 'it's not the purpose of this school to produce lots of little Yehudi Menuhins'. Tiger mums please take note.

Beautiful Victorian mansion setting in Surrey village suggests peace and harmony. Once inside, the feel is a curious mix of very relaxed and rigidly controlling. There's no uniform, the dress code is informal, and staff and pupils are on first name terms. But as a seasoned schools' reviewer, it was clear to us as we went round that this school doesn't like criticism, or what it perceives as criticism, and that it keeps a tighter grip on the way its pupils make music than the other specialist music schools. On joining the YMS students can't choose to continue on programmes at Saturday junior conservatoires, for instance, whereas at Purcell, Chetham's and Wells this isn't a problem. (Indeed, the school's Saturday morning programme would make this impossible.) The only exception to this is made for the double-bass players, whose teacher also teaches at RCM junior department and takes her YMS students there each week for the additional orchestral experience. And despite a packed calendar of performance opportunities, the system by which pupils are chosen for the most sought-after of these is a closed one (at other music schools it's often done by audition), and several pupils told us that they felt consistently excluded. 'They choose the students who are a safe bet,' said one, a remark which had everyone nodding vigorously, and others said, surprisingly, that in the time they'd been at the school they'd had hardly any chance to perform chamber music. 'We have to give pupils the opportunities that are right for them,' was the school's response. 'If you have a high-profile concert, you have to put the people in who will pull it off. It's not always easy to be fair on paper.'

However, students were adamant that the atmosphere between them all was supportive, and not destructively competitive. 'There's actually not much competition; I've never felt it here,' was a comment that everyone agreed with, and their relish for the musical experience here was unstinting. 'It's the best you can get for the age we're at'; 'It really prepares you for music college'; 'They are such good teachers!'; 'My violin teacher is like a mother to me'; 'For practice, it's so much easier to be here, everything is so close' – etc.

No parents' association. School's reason for this is that parents come from too huge a radius for such a thing to work. Ex-parents told us that they had felt kept at arms' length, with one even telling us that they never felt welcome. But the only current parents to contact us wrote, 'Headteacher and indeed other teachers are approachable and welcoming even though they must be under pressure also.'

Pastoral care, well-being and discipline: Yehudi Menuhin believed in the importance of a homely, family atmosphere in his school, and as we walked about, we saw children playing contentedly in the school's leafy grounds, cheering on their friends in the lunchtime concert, and generally appearing happy and at ease. Students attested to the kindness of the staff. 'The school's been really patient with me,' said one, philosophically. 'When I first came, I wasn't a well-behaved child. Anywhere else would have asked me to leave.' In this small, artistically-driven community, the kind of misbehaviour most schools have to deal with is rare. Pupils have worked hard for their place here and want to keep it.

We liked the wall of clocks showing the time in different countries around the world – 'We have pupils from every time-zone and it is a way of making them feel at home'

Staff to student ratio is low, and there are regular weekly meetings about pastoral issues. 'If someone's falling through the gaps, it's picked up,' affirmed housemaster. However, all the staff we spoke to put much emphasis on pupils 'self-managing': 'There's a lot of autonomy here'; 'They just get on with it'; 'They're surprisingly mature'; and we did wonder if this sometimes meant pupils were left to flounder. The school emphatically denied this – 'I have never taught in a school which discusses, and, yes, cares for pupils at this level'. The students themselves offered slightly ambiguous observations, such as 'We do a lot of our stuff on our own in this kind of school'; 'The older ones usually take care of the younger ones'; 'The boarding staff are doing the best job they can.' However, inspection reports have consistently rated the school's pastoral care as excellent, and the only parents to respond to our appeal for feedback wrote, 'Pastoral care is very important to us since we live far away but have been happy with the attention so far in that area.' Despite several attempts on our part, we could not find any other parents of current students who wanted to talk to us, although we were contacted by parents whose experience of the school had been negative and who had taken their children away.

Pupils and parents: With nearly 80 pupils on the roll, the school is the biggest it's ever been, and there are no plans to expand further. Just over half are from the UK (although this figure includes a few international families who have relocated so that their child can attend the school), the rest from overseas. Very broad range of backgrounds and nationalities makes for a truly cosmopolitan school community: students currently hail from the UK, Ireland, France, Germany, Switzerland, Spain, Poland, Bulgaria, Bosnia-Herzegovina, Serbia, Turkey, Morocco, Tunisia, China, Taiwan, South Korea, Singapore, Japan, Thailand, Brazil and Mexico. The common ground they all share is music: students have chosen to come here for the outstanding teaching, the support with practice, and 'being surrounded by musicians of this calibre,' as a student put it. It's a musical hothouse and has its fair share of eccentrics, but it's impossible not to be won over by the results. The young people we met were all really lovely: articulate, thoughtful, intelligent, personable, good-mannered and good fun.

Alumni include Nigel Kennedy, Tasmin Little, Nicola Benedetti, Kathryn Stott, Melvyn Tan and Colin Carr.

Entrance: Aspiring young musicians from all over the world apply from age 8 – there is no set entry point. The process is long and thorough: preliminary audition, then main audition, and if applicants get through both those hurdles, a three-day residential assessment during which they take part in all aspects of school life including instrumental lessons, academic lessons and boarding. Children have to be robust. A recent candidate played incredibly but wasn't ready socially, and no place was offered. Applicants' academic ability is not used to determine entry.

Unusually, students who join the school in the sixth form have to commit to doing three years. Year 14 is spent continuing with their instrumental tuition plus academic music and possibly another AS. This could be seen as another example of the school's determination to control its end product, but the year 14 students we met were positive about the experience, and felt it to be of benefit to their musical development.

We saw children playing contentedly in the school's leafy grounds, cheering on their friends in the lunchtime concert

A child must join before their 17th birthday, but otherwise a student's age isn't taken into account and the year groups aren't even. School won't admit into year 11, but happy for students to repeat a year and go into year 10. Students can join at any point in the year if there's space.

Exit: The overwhelming majority to music conservatoires around the world: at this rarified level, they choose the teacher with whom they want to study and apply to the institution where that teacher is based. 2017 destinations included Royal Academy of Music, Royal College of Music, Guildhall School of Music and Drama, New England Conservatory, Boston, The Juilliard School, New York, Hochschule für Musik Hanns Eisler, Berlin. Rarely, to university: previous students have gone to Oxford to read English and to Imperial to read biochemistry. Occasionally a student wishing to pursue broader academic options will leave at 16.

Money matters: Inevitably one of the most expensive boarding schools in the country, given all the top-calibre specialist tuition, but hardly anyone pays full fees. Families who have been continually resident in the UK for at least two years receive means-tested funding from the government's Music and Dance Scheme: the YMS is one of only eight schools in the UK to be so supported. For those ineligible for the scheme, the school has its own bursary fund: it has a good endowment, and fundraising is ongoing. Where they can, they match what the

Remarks: This is as unusual a school experience as it's possible to get, and one that parents need to choose with their eyes wide open. Don't send your highly academic teen here and then complain that they can't do triple science. Don't put your 8-year-old here if you want them to have lots of friends the same age. Try not to send your child here in the secret hope that they'll be the next Fritz Kreisler. But if the music offered here is what your child wants with all their being, and you believe that they couldn't be as happy anywhere else as they could be here, go for it.

East of England

Bedfordshire
Cambridgeshire
Essex
Herfordshire
Norfolk
Suffolk

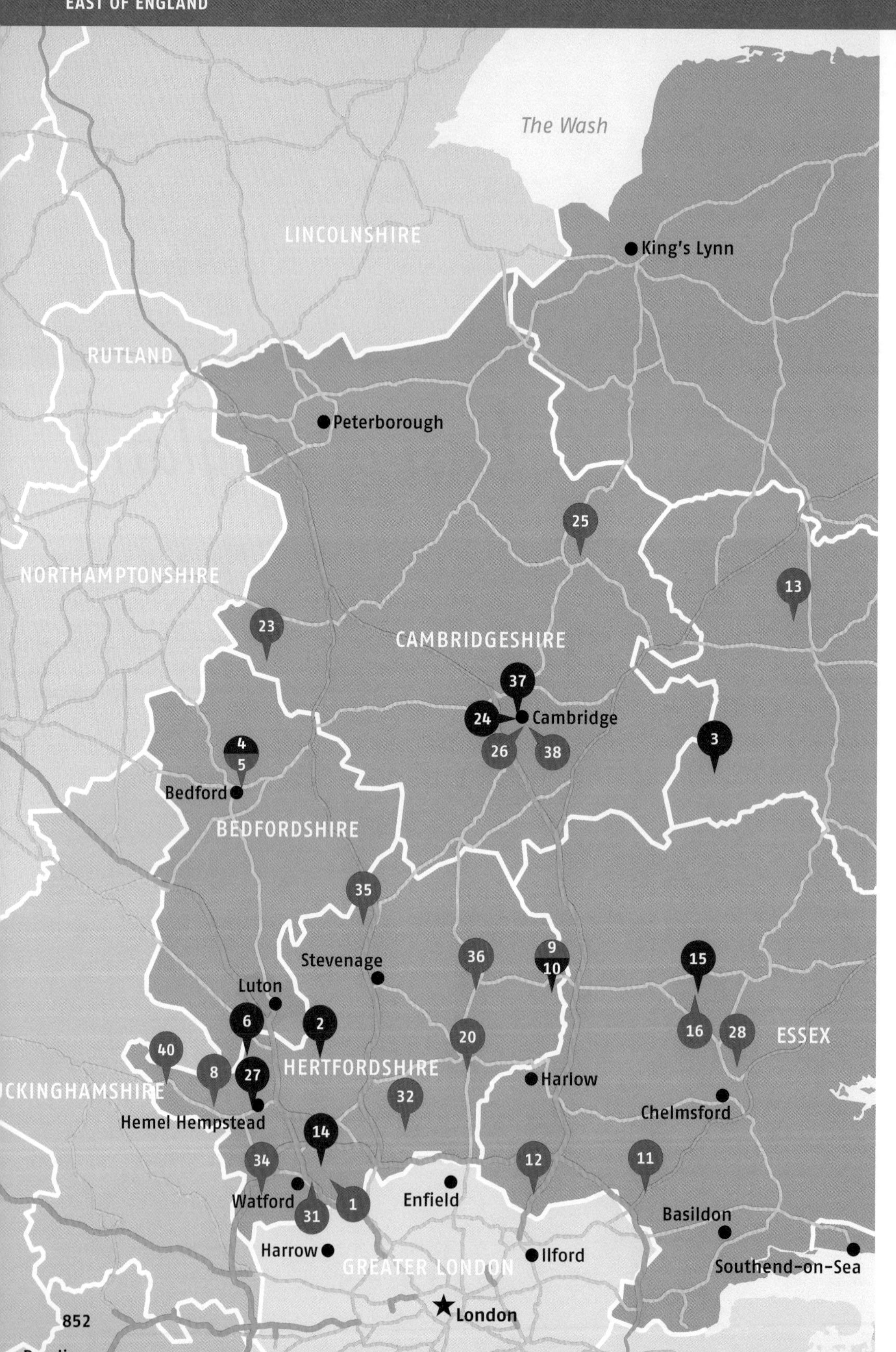
The Wash
LINCOLNSHIRE
King's Lynn
RUTLAND
Peterborough
NORTHAMPTONSHIRE
CAMBRIDGESHIRE
Cambridge
Bedford
BEDFORDSHIRE
Stevenage
Luton
HERTFORDSHIRE
Harlow
ESSEX
Chelmsford
CKINGHAMSHIRE
Hemel Hempstead
Watford
Enfield
Basildon
Harrow
Ilford
GREATER LONDON
Southend-on-Sea
London
Reading
25
13
23
37
24
26
38
3
4
5
35
36
9
10
15
6
2
20
16
28
40
8
27
32
14
34
12
11
31
1

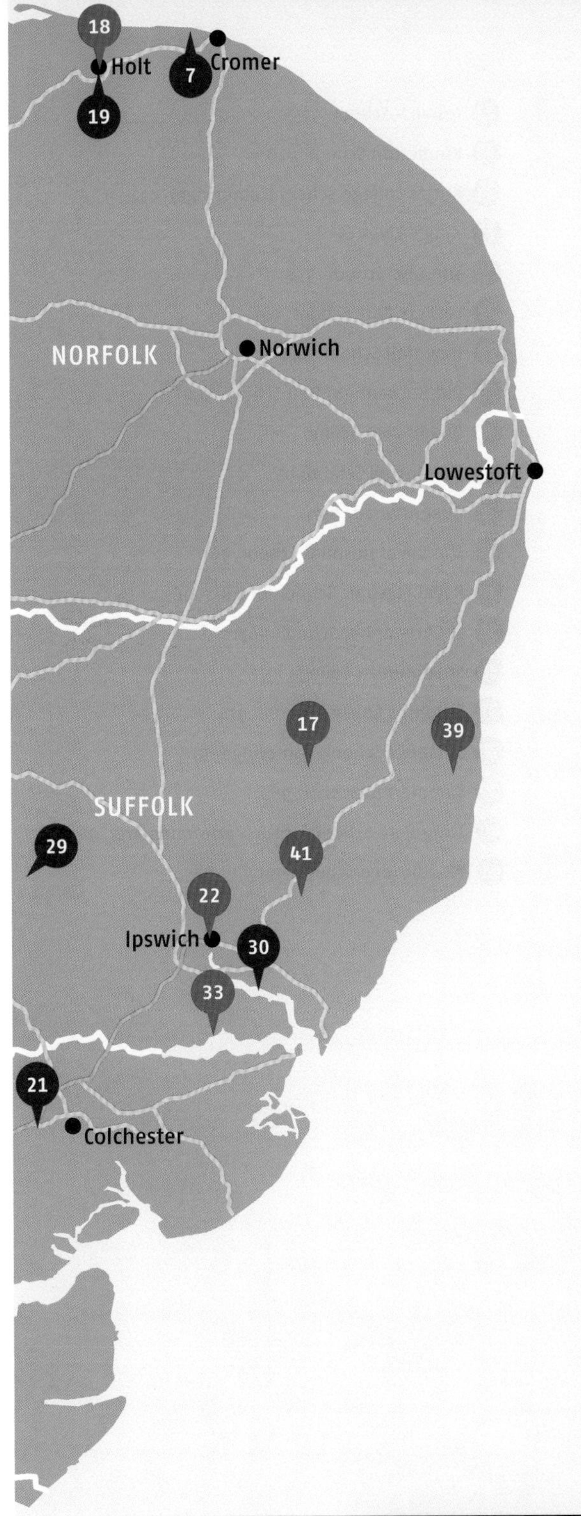
18
Holt
7
Cromer
19
NORFOLK
Norwich
Lowestoft
17
39
SUFFOLK
29
41
22
Ipswich
30
33
21
Colchester
20
40
60 Miles

EAST OF ENGLAND

Aldenham School

Elstree, Borehamwood, Hertfordshire WD6 3AJ

01923 858122 | admissions@aldenham.com | www.aldenham.com

Ages: 11–18

Pupils: 571; sixth form: 167; Boarders: 29 full, 40 weekly, 112 flexi

Day: £15,891 – £22,014 pa; Boarding: £21,966 – £32,481 pa

Headmaster: Since 2006, Mr James Fowler MA PGCE (50s). Educated at Merchant Taylors' School, Northwood and New College, Oxford where he was a choral scholar. Previously head of sixth form at Brentwood School and deputy head at Highgate. Permeates every facet of school with his relaxed charisma and understanding of what makes parents and pupils tick. Unusually, interviews every candidate with their parents before admission. Is he interviewing the parents as well as the child, we asked? 'Of course,' he says. 'I spend a lot of time helping people understand what we are and are not.' And it's to this level of mutual soul searching that he attributes the happy, enthusiastic nature of his cohort in evidence all over the school, almost all of whom he knows by name and who claim that their voice is 'genuinely heard' by him. It's not just the children who are happy with their leader, either. Parents describe head as 'always available', and 'very good at resolving issues in the right way,' adding that 'his attitude filters down to all the staff.'

Definitely not a head chasing glory in the league tables – and one totally at ease with this status; a breath of fresh air in the ferociously competitive north London landscape. Keen to provide a totally different experience to his urban competitors as applications from London families increase, and determined that his charges feel 'secure and safe'. Single-mindedly focused on school providing 'the best possible pathways' for each student, regardless of academic prowess. 'We celebrate successful entry to art school in the same way as entry to Oxbridge,' he says.

Lives on site with wife and two sons.

Academic matters: Situated in the heart of UK's spiritual home of secondary academia (Habs, Merchant Taylors', North London Collegiate et al), Aldenham stands apart with its unpressurised vibe and mixed ability cohort. Perhaps not a destination for the single minded scholar, although pupils say they are strongly encouraged to hit their own personal best; 'the natural spread of ability makes for breadth and roundedness,' according to head. Although those bright enough to get to Russell Group universities – and occasionally Oxbridge – will do, it's immediately evident that it's the journey that defines Aldenham rather than the destination.

A respectable 27 per cent of A*/A grades at A level in 2017 with 44 per cent of GCSE examinations at A*-A/7-9 grades. Many subjects have now moved to IGCSE to stretch brighter students, who are also recruited into small study and discussion groups such as Les Philosophes with visiting speakers, including Anthony Grayling, enabling them to exchange ideas and broaden horizons. 'Parents trust us with children of all abilities,' says head.

Small class sizes of maximum 22 and often down to 10 in sixth form, with setting from year 7 in maths and science. Eleven GCSEs the norm with a broad range of subjects available, from the traditional ('the brighter students tend to gravitate towards sciences,' says head) to dance, textiles and DT. French, Spanish and Latin on offer in the languages department. Non-traditional subjects on offer at A level include psychology, media studies, government and politics and computing. Parents and pupils appreciate extra revision lessons at lunch times, after school and even on Saturdays laid on in the run up to public exams. University conversations start in year 12, with a series of events including visiting professionals brought in to 'give insights' into the world of work. Pupils feel well supported and guided through uni application process, although one or two parents felt that school could secure more top level places for the brightest if things were slightly slicker.

Good provision for SEN run in dedicated area by full time SENCo, with around 10 per cent on the register – mainly catering for mild dyslexia or dyscalculia although can deal with mild Asperger's and recently sent one such child to Cambridge. One-to-one teaching rooms well used by overseas pupils requiring EAL support.

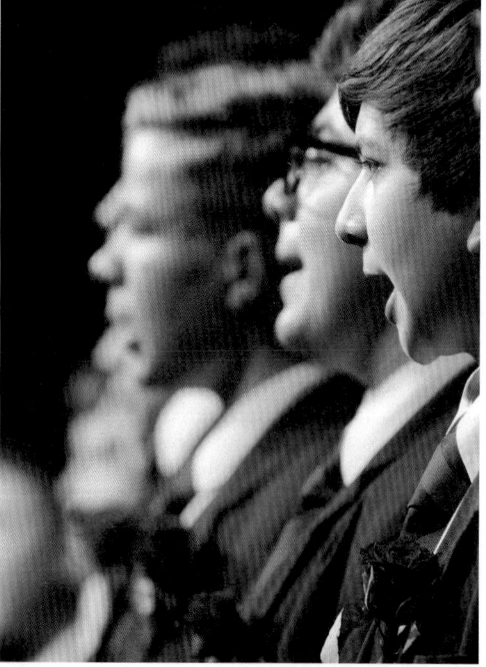

Games, options, the arts: In a setting that needs to be seen to be believed – over 110 acres encompassing woodland, playing fields plus full-sized Astro hockey pitch, tennis courts, dance studio, well-utilised weights room and an enormous sports hall (recently resurfaced) plus manicured cricket pitch that lies literally at the heart of the school ('the pavilion is one of my favourite spots,' says head) – sport is integral to life at Aldenham and thrives at all levels, from the most elite to the 'just for fun'. It's football, hockey and cricket for the boys, no rugby, while girls focus on netball, hockey and rounders. School known for its footie prowess, with a handful of boys training with top academies, and also embryonic links with Southgate Hockey Club, but parents say it suits students less inclined towards team pursuits well too. Options include zumba, archery, sailing, tennis, athletics, Eton fives, judo and climbing on its climbing wall – in the words of one parent: 'all that's missing is a swimming pool.'

Two compulsory activities a week, ranging from bell ringing, horse riding and film club to a very popular CCF, make for a long school day which for most ends at 5.30pm. This gives school a unique boarding atmosphere, even for those who do not take advantage of the marvellously flexible boarding on offer. Aldenham is 'synonymous with trips,' according to pupils, who enthuse about the 'amazing experiences' they have had on CCF trips to Holland, language trips including a Spanish trip to Cuba, cricket tour to Barbados, geography to Iceland, choir to Rome and a three week charity volunteering trip to Malawi.

Outstanding art department, unanimously acclaimed by everyone from head to parents and pupils, and so popular that school recently built a superb new art cabin to accommodate the large numbers electing to pursue art A level. Fabulous work on display: huge canvasses, three dimensional installations and sculpture with as much rigorous preparation and development of concepts on show as final works. Pupils say that head of art won't accept anything less than excellence and parents report offspring joining school 'unable to draw' and emerging with A grades. Dedicated textiles room also displays high quality fashion design and DT labs are hives of industry, complete with 3D printers in motion.

Music thrives, with bands, orchestras and choirs galore, run by 'fantastic' and 'passionate' musicians, according to pupils. As with sport, there are opportunities for musicians of all levels to participate, with pupils enthusing that the fiercely

Fabulous sixth form centre – all white walls, squidgy sofas and sliding glass doors offering panoramic view of cricket pitch

competitive annual house music event (compulsory participation for all) is one of the highlights of the year. All year 7s offered opportunity of one term's free music lessons on the orchestral instrument of their choice, leading to many taking it up more seriously. Futuristic music technology equipment puts department very much in the 21st century.

'Really strong' drama on and off curriculum, headed by 'inspirational' head of department who clearly drives excellence and pushes boundaries. 'We're into serious drama,' she says – school refreshingly veers away from the usual hackneyed shows and rarely produces musicals, mainly delivering productions of the Sophocles and Brechtian variety, oft performed in the purpose built 150 seat theatre, but sometimes out in the grounds or as a promenade, which are 'just fantastic,' according to parents. A handful of students are members of the National Youth Theatre, some take part in the Edinburgh Fringe and it's not unusual for one or two each year to head off to destinations including Central School of Speech and Drama or LAMDA, and these applications are taken seriously – head says that in the year school sent three students off to drama school and three to med school, both were supported and celebrated in equal measure.

Boarding: Around 30 per cent of the school community (some two-thirds boys) participates in boarding life at some level – enough to lend it a 'proper' boarding ethos without any trace of 'them and us' between boarders and day pupils. Boarding starts in year 7 in a small co-educational junior boarding house with 25 beds. No full boarding at this stage, meaning that cohort tends to be exclusively UK based with vast majority never having boarded before. Pupils enjoy a 'home from home' environment here – but still relish having a 'lot more freedom' when they move into one of the four main single sex boarding houses (three for boys and one for girls), each with its own strong identity, that shape the school.

Head keen that students 'experience boarding as part of their overall education,' hence provides excellent flexibility with boarders able to stay from just one night to, for a minority of mainly older, overseas students (some 25 per cent of boarders), full time. Up to sixth form, majority are reasonably local though, with boarders heading home at weekends to homes in north London, Herts and Bucks. 'Terrific' live-in houseparents supervise their charges in spacious houses – not the most luxurious we've seen, but functional (well-equipped kitchens and study spaces) and welcoming with plenty of nooks and crannies for down time and socialising. Boys dorm in fours until year 11 when they double up, with girls mostly in twos and threes then single rooms in sixth form. An ongoing programme of renovations is brightening things up.

Evenings see boarders participate in the clubs or activities of their choice, or gather in the art block, library, media suite or gym. Most popular nights to board in sixth form are Tuesdays and Thursdays when the bar opens and pizza is served in the wonderful sixth form centre. Sunday brunch is 'the best meal of the week', attended by most staff who live on site, plus their families as well as weekend boarders, and whilst there are weekend outings, trips and activities on offer, quite often students, having had a long week and sports fixtures on Saturdays, just 'want to chill.'

Background and atmosphere: Founded by brewer, Richard Platt, in 1597 after Queen Elizabeth I granted him letters patent to build 'the Free Grammar School and Almshouses' at Aldenham for elementary children. The Brewers' Company then had a controlling interest in the school and links remain strong. Original Tudor buildings demolished in the 19th century to make place for two new schools – one providing an elementary education for the local population, the second a grammar school for fee-paying boarders. School now occupies a prime position in protected green belt, attracting pupils from affluent local villages like Radlett and Sarratt, London suburbs such as Edgware and Stanmore and increasingly north London, with parents attracted by the fabulous country campus, handy coach services and inclusive ethos.

There's an annual run on the last day of term from Eros in Piccadilly to the school's statue, just one of the many traditions that pupils say are 'a huge part of the school'

Main school building is Hogwarts-esque Victorian gothic with gables, tower and turrets, with additions – some more appealing than others – from subsequent decades. Most notable new facility is fabulous sixth form centre – all white walls, squidgy sofas and sliding glass doors offering panoramic view of cricket pitch – complete with its own coffee shop and bar where years 12 and 13 can socialise, study and generally commune outside of school hours. A few tatty corners in other areas, but plenty of up to date Mac technology and a luxurious feeling of abundant space.

An extraordinary chapel (the largest consecrated building in Hertfordshire after St Albans Abbey) which can host entire school – and frequently does – lies across the road that bisects the school. Surprisingly welcoming, the Stanley Spencer altar pieces of yesteryear are but a part of school history now (sold to raise funds during the desperate 1990s) and an attractive ironwork cross and dove now dominates the altar. Despite the diverse religions of the school community (about 60 per cent Christian, 20 per cent Jewish and all other main religions represented) all attend chapel twice weekly to underscore the 'feeling of one community' that's so integral to the school. Beautiful panelled library complete with mezzanine level, spiral staircase and view of cricket pitch and miniature replica statue of old boy Alfred Gilbert's Eros. There's an annual run on the last day of term for those brave enough, from Eros in Piccadilly to the school's statue, just one of the many traditions that pupils say are 'a huge part of the school'.

Break times see pupils congregate en masse on the field with cross year group socialising in evidence everywhere ('we're like a family – everyone knows everyone,' said one happy pupil). Although not the most polished cohort we've ever seen, pupils without exception seem totally at ease with the school and are arguably one of the most sociable and understatedly confident bunches we've met. Quite possibly one of the happiest too. Girls now make up around one-third of the school – many join in sixth form – and school is content with this balance – 'we'd ideally like 35 to 40 per cent,' says head.

Pastoral care, well-being and discipline: Parents report excellent pastoral care, thanks mainly to the system that places all children in a boarding house, even if they don't board, so staff have a close eye on everyone's well-being. Good sign that many boarders we spoke to live locally and board 'because we love it.' Food has been a small bone of contention although pupils say it is 'getting better'.

Lots of busy, professional commuters attracted by the flexible boarding uniquely on offer

The usual disciplinary issues but in the main very few incidents. Suspensions for major breaches of rules (eg boarders driving off campus) but in the main little need to transgress as students given sufficient freedom to spread their wings.

Pupils and parents: Majority of pupils from a 20 mile radius. Lots of busy, professional commuters and London parents attracted by the flexible boarding uniquely on offer here – as well as the atmosphere that they say gives their children 'space to breathe', both literally and metaphorically. Mixed financial demographic – plenty of first time buyers and parents stretching themselves to afford Aldenham – with these children fitting comfortably in with those who can easily cover the fees.

Overseas boarders tend to be in higher year groups. Of these, around 30 per cent from Germany, then handfuls from China, Hong Kong and ones and twos from elsewhere. All are well respected and well integrated – boarding pupils embrace and relish the diversity of their peers. Around 40 boarders stay in school at weekends.

Entrance: Around 60 places in year 7 with between 15 and 20 of these taken by children coming up from on-site prep school and the rest made up of children joining from the state sector (40 per cent) and local 11+ preps. About 30 per cent of year 7 are girls. Another 25 to 30 join in year 9 from a vast array of preps, notably Lochinver House, Orley Farm, Northwood Prep, St Martin's and St John's and further afield The Beacon, The Hall and Davenies. Applicants at 11+ take papers in maths, English and reasoning with the addition of science and a language at 13+. Scholars are interviewed away from their parents.

Late arrivals come from other, more pressured, local schools – not always because they can't cut the mustard but mainly because they are looking for a school that's about more than exam results. And that, here, is what they find. Around 30 places available in sixth form.

Exit: Approximately 30 per cent leave after GCSE to follow vocational courses or A levels elsewhere (mainly state schools or colleges) or to employment. A broad spectrum of destination universities reflects mixed academic intake, with about 20 per cent to Russell Group, a couple each year to art schools (often Central St Martins) and regular success with applications to top drama schools. Other degree courses tend to veer towards the vocational, many with a business/management focus. One or two to Oxbridge some years.

Money matters: Scholarships at 11+ and 13+ in music, art, sport, DT as well as academic, with a maximum of 15 per cent off fees awarded. Means-tested bursaries available.

Remarks: Head describes Aldenham as 'an extraordinary school for ordinary children' and we concur. An unpressurised environment such as this makes for some of the most contented pupils we have met, and self-motivated children can fare well academically too. Tread carefully if scholarly accolades are top of your wish list or if your offspring need stick rather than carrot, but if it's a rounded and happy child you're after, then Aldenham's definitely one to consider.

Aldwickbury School

2

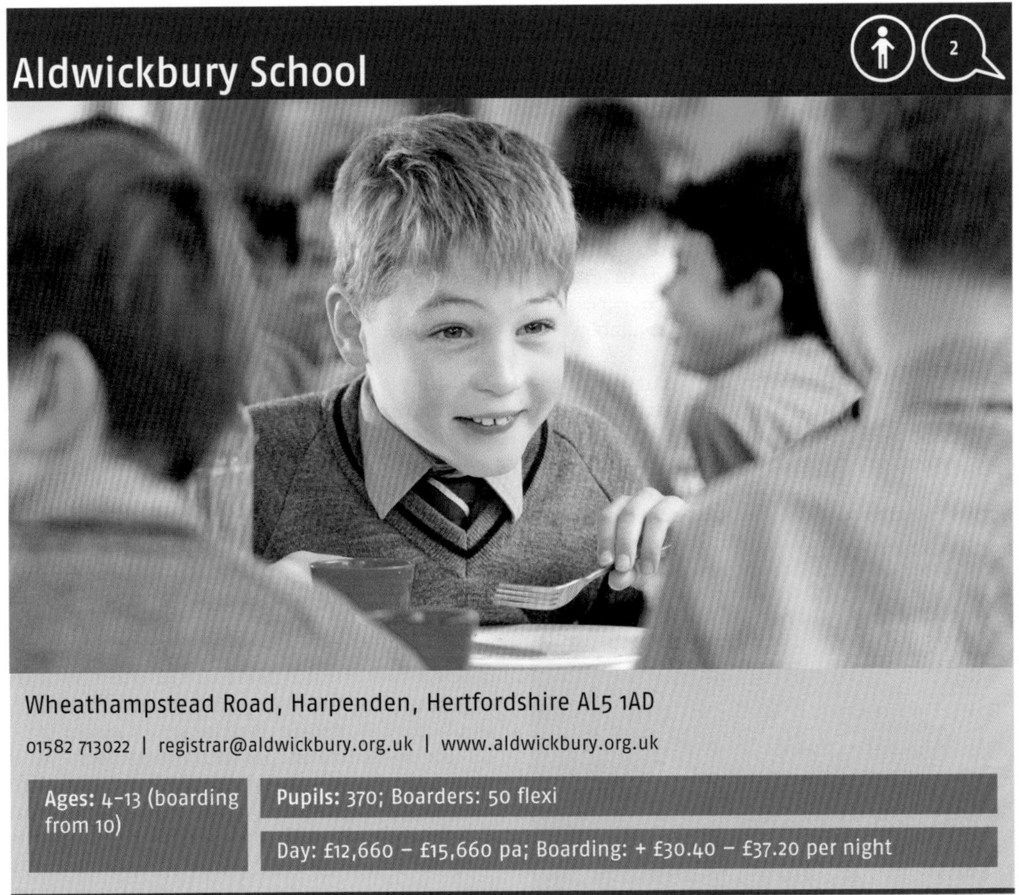

Wheathampstead Road, Harpenden, Hertfordshire AL5 1AD

01582 713022 | registrar@aldwickbury.org.uk | www.aldwickbury.org.uk

Ages: 4–13 (boarding from 10)

Pupils: 370; Boarders: 50 flexi

Day: £12,660 – £15,660 pa; Boarding: + £30.40 – £37.20 per night

Headmaster: Since 2003 Mr Vernon Hales BEd (50s). Educated at Langley Park Grammar School and Exeter University, where his education degree majored in PE. After a year in the state system, he started his prep school career at Papplewick ('great fun') before heading off to New Zealand, becoming deputy head in its then largest boarding prep school. Returned as deputy head and boarding housemaster at Elstree School, then joined Aldwickbury as the school's fourth head. Partnered through entire professional journey by wife Claire, also a trained teacher and now head of marketing at school and 'traditional head's spouse'. Educated his two sons, now late teens, at Aldwickbury and The Leys, where they are full boarders.

Relaxed, warm and jovial with the boys, and 'very visible around the school', according to parents, he recently 'came out of retirement' to resurrect his passion for club cricket and harbours personal ambitions to become a good golfer (must be the stunning course surrounding the school grounds calling). Lives in the main school building and is proud of its unique local offering as a boys' (mainly) day school, based on a boarding school model. Recognises that although sport is very important to boys, he wants Aldwickbury to be an 'all round' school. He speaks with conviction about understanding the distinctive needs of boys in their formative years, describing Aldwickbury as 'philosophically a boys school.' Would like to increase school numbers very slightly 'without losing our small school feel'.

Entrance: Non-selective at 4, the school works with local feeder nurseries to ensure smooth transition for its youngest pupils as they join reception. Recently became three-form entry at the bottom of the school, with 15 to a class, due to increased demand for places. Maximum class size in pre-prep fixed at 18. Boys joining higher up the school are invited in for an informal session with their relevant year group head, where they are encouraged to talk about themselves and take tests in reading, maths and spelling to ensure they can access the curriculum. Means-tested bursaries available.

Exit: Vast majority stay at Aldwickbury until the end of year 8. School loses just a few each year at the end of year 6, 'for either financial or academic reasons', according to head. Feeds about half its boys into year 9 at St Albans School, 'a handful' each year with scholarships. Remainder to schools including St Columba's, Bedford and Haileybury. One or two recently to Eton, Harrow and Shrewsbury and Berkhamstead. 'The key is getting parents to choose the right school for the boy', says head. Parents confirm that he gives them a strong steer in the right direction. Nine scholarships in 2017.

Remarks: Situated a stone's throw up the hill from Harpenden's second (less chi-chi) high street in Southdown, Aldwickbury Mansion, which dates back to 1871 and is full of Victorian character (albeit with a few tired corners), became home to the school in 1948. It makes excellent use of its leafy 20-acre site and has sympathetically incorporated a number of modern buildings to create an appealing and well-functioning school campus. Main school building sits atop grassy terraces and playing fields, affording the head and his boarders a panoramic view of the school grounds. A separate purpose-built pre-prep department was built in 2001, providing the school's youngest pupils with a bright and cheerful base, where they can ease their way into school life without the rough and tumble of bigger boys.

Reception has its own safe haven outside with a small adventure playground area, plus trikes, bikes and a sand table – 'very therapeutic if they've had a tricky morning in the classroom', says head of pre-prep. School places a large emphasis on outside learning at this stage – 'we're not a forest school but we do take on elements of that ethos'. On our visit, reception boys were enthusiastically doing Victorian-style laundry outside. The pre-prep building is festooned with topic-related art and written work and has its own hall for assemblies, activities and performances.

Junior department houses years 3 and 4, when the school starts to 'encourage independence in a gentle way', including the introduction of a more formal uniform. Even maths classrooms are creatively themed and staff overall exude energy and enthusiasm, reinforcing the school's ethos of 'really getting boys'. One year 1 teacher quietly plays classical music CDs when she wants her class to concentrate, and – try it at home – it seems to work. Boys in years 5 to 8 move around classrooms for specialist teaching to prepare them for senior school life.

Lovely heated indoor swimming pool – well used, with weekly lessons for all from reception, plus early morning and after-school swim clubs. Coach house now home to ever-popular DT workshop ('we really look forward to coming in here', say boys) with feel of a real man space where industrious pupils turn out quality projects from wind chimes to fruit bowls. Art room (also in coach house) is a showcase for the boys' enthusiasm. The gym is in dire need of some TLC, but school now has an 'all singing, all dancing' £3.2m hall and music department, plus several new classrooms including science rooms, 'to provide flexibility and accommodate growth'. Also boasts a gleaming modernised dining hall (food to be recommended) and library.

Parents and pupils alike describe Aldwickbury as 'very friendly and welcoming', and the nurturing feel pervades the fabric of the school. 'Definitely not pushy', say parents uniformly, suggesting that league table watchers may want to look elsewhere. Boys have the knack of knowing when to be quiet (quite a feat in a dining hall of rumbling tummies waiting for someone to say grace) and when to let off steam. Confidence and manners, without arrogance, in evidence in all age groups.

Once the plethora of after-school clubs has finished, there's more fun, with 'non-stop activities,' say boys, followed by weekly film nights in the cosy boarders' lounge

A true 4 to 13 school. 'All year 8 boys have jobs' and are given responsibilities around the school, such as helping teachers get younger boys organised in the mornings and listening to year 5 boys read at lunchtimes. With around half the teachers male, the overall vibe is of a school where boys really can be boys. Year groups encouraged to mix at meal times, with lunch taken as 'sections' (that's houses to the rest of us). Boys compete throughout the year for the section cup, not just in their academic lives and on the sports fields, but also with competitions and challenges, including section Scrabble and top autumn favourite, the 'conker-tition'.

Majority of pupils from the immediate environs, with 50 per cent 'sharing the AL5 postcode,' according to head. Remainder from surrounding towns and villages. Very few from further afield. Overwhelmingly Caucasian majority reflects the local community. Most parents in the professions, many dual income, but a by all accounts a pretty grounded bunch and a number 'stretching themselves' to pay school fees. A parents' association set up recently to bring together parents, staff and boys and foster the school/community relationship. Events so far have included discos with local girls' school, monthly tuck shops with home-baked cakes and a dads vs masters cricket match.

French with a specialist teacher from year 1, with Spanish and German added to the mix in year 5 and Latin from year 6. Specialist teaching from year 3 for ICT, art, music and drama. Mixed ability classes 'by ethos' to end of year 5, although head admits to some 'subtle setting' from year 3 and parents of able children report extra work being given to ensure the brightest are stretched. Classes mixed at end of years 2 and 4 which some parents grumble they find 'stressful', although they admit the school 'normally gets it right'. Streaming introduced from year 6, with two or three classes and a scholarship class in year 8. This, however, is not always uniform in its structure – head is determined to 'start from the point of what's best for the boys'. SEN all in a day's work and good provision in place to deal with minor blips rather than more serious problems.

Music taught by male teachers from pre-prep onwards, which really 'turns boys on to learning an instrument', according to head. Around 160 boys from year 1 upwards take music lessons in a wide range of instruments. Abundance of musical groups to join, from choir to guitar groups, including the popular Aldwickbury Strings group, a collaborative effort between staff (including the bursar, a talented violinist) and boys. Drama is 'really important', says head, with participation in plays compulsory up to year 5 to 'build confidence'. Main school play, most recently A Christmas Carol, performed in the round, is optional in years 7 and 8 but most choose to take part, if not on stage, then in lighting or costume, with the occasional rugby player taking charge of make-up.

Sport is the lifeblood of the school, with specialist teaching twice weekly from year 1 and boys from year 3 up having a daily games lesson. Competitive football, swimming and skiing are 'excellent', says head, and boys regularly compete at national level. Team fixtures for all from A-E teams, so everyone gets a ride on the school minibus and a shot at sporting glory. Colours awards on offer for stars of rugby, football cricket et al, but also for drama, music and citizenship, proving that heroes are not only found on the sports fields here. In the words of one boy, 'all things here are valued the same'.

Boarding almost exclusively flexi, with the occasional weekly boarder, but no provision for boys at weekends. The majority of those who board from year 6 are at their 'second home' (as they call it) two or three nights a week, with provision for 33 boarders at any one time. Once the plethora of after-school clubs has finished, there's more fun, with 'non-stop activities,' say boys, followed by weekly film nights in the cosy boarders' lounge and occasional events such as the popular 'chippy night' (one benefit of being so close to the high street). Functional dormitories sleep up to nine year 6 boys, with numbers dropping to four or five in the upper years. No phones with SIMs are allowed but, with all that's on offer, boys have got better things to do than phone home. With the majority of boys living so locally, most are here purely for the fun of it and speak wisely of their new found 'independence' and how boarding has changed them.

Day boys able to join boarders for breakfast from 7.40am and supper for a small cost – handy for commuting parents. All boys from year 5 up stay for prep until between 5.10pm and 5.45pm and there is an after-school club which can take pupils of any age up to supper time at 5.50pm.

Broad range of extracurricular activities to cater for all tastes, from chess, Lego or general knowledge club for the cerebral crowd to skiing, fencing or martial arts for those wanting to try their hand at something more physical. Loads of opportunities to get out and about, with trips aplenty. School makes full use of being on the capital's doorstep, with trips to art galleries and theatres and also ventures further afield (expeditions to France, Iceland and the much anticipated leavers' trip to Dartmoor). A schedule of evening seminars on topics such as 'the history of the Ashes' ('much more interesting than it sounds', says head) is in place for older boys and their parents, and a number of external learning sources are brought in throughout the year. When we visited, boys were buzzing after a visit from a 'mathemagician,' part of the maths week itinerary.

Barnardiston Hall Preparatory School

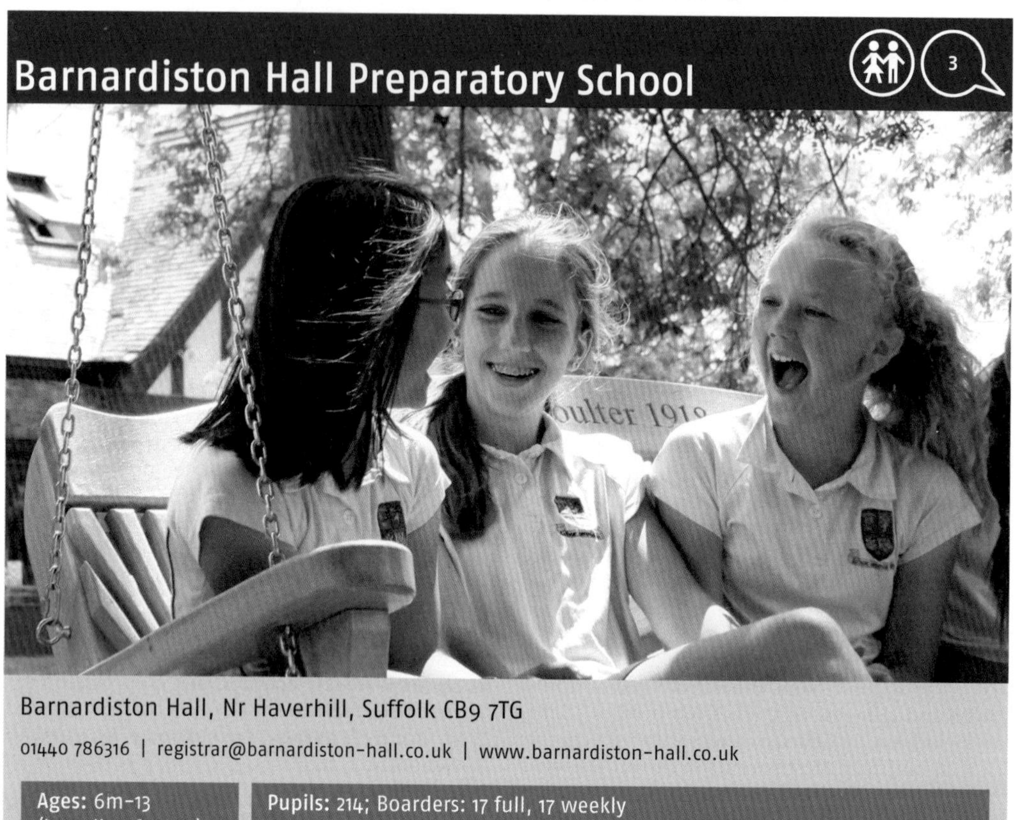

Barnardiston Hall, Nr Haverhill, Suffolk CB9 7TG

01440 786316 | registrar@barnardiston-hall.co.uk | www.barnardiston-hall.co.uk

Ages: 6m–13 (boarding from 6)

Pupils: 214; Boarders: 17 full, 17 weekly

Day: £8,040 – £13,395 pa; Boarding: £18,510 – £20,085 pa

Headmaster: Since 2017, Colonel Keith Boulter, Cambridge theology graduate and hockey blue (60s) and the owner of the school. Barnardiston is one of several schools and institutions run as a family business.

He was, in fact, headmaster several years ago, from 1990-2012, before stepping into the role of principal and passing the reins of day-to-day management over to the previous headmaster (Tim Dodgson who, while no longer head, remains at the school as a history teacher).

The Colonel has always been a force within the school, teaching mathematics, helping with games and choir work and followed everywhere by children, like the Pied Piper. He retains a certain bluff, military manner with great geniality and is greeted with wild enthusiasm and respect wherever he goes in the school. 'Who has camped in the garden with their teacher?' he asks. A forest of hands goes up. 'Who acted in the play?' – hands up again (slightly different lot). 'Who wants more homework?' groans and shouts of 'Not me!' His early career in the Royal Army Educational Corps and, later, administering

Gurkha schools, has helped shape the school's philosophy. Married, with a grown-up family, and lives in the grounds of Barnardiston. His daughter is head of the pre-prep department and his three grandchildren all attend the school.

Entrance: Non-selective. Pupils accepted at all stages through the school. A number come up from the nursery (six months-three years) to pre-prep. No formal exam but previous school reports are looked at and the children meet the head. Taster days are arranged for older children who attend classes, whilst particular needs are noted, and referrals/advice given to parents. The school has provision for educational support and few children are not accepted. Limited bursarial help for overseas pupils and siblings.

Exit: Most go on to a range of local independents at 13 – the Leys, the Perse, King's Ely, Felsted, Framlingham, Rugby, a sprinkling further afield (Gordonstoun recently). One or two leave at 11 for local state schools. Good guidance is given to parents. 'We suggest they visit three schools, two likely ones plus a wild card,' says the head. Pupils all get to where they want to go – a few scholarships each year.

Remarks: A country prep with a strong, slightly quirky character, very much the creation of its owner, Colonel Boulter. With a rural setting, agricultural rather than chocolate box picturesque, it has a splendid indifference to the customary marketing gloss. Boarders live in the main building, an Edwardian villa, alongside the headmaster and his family.

Subject teaching takes place in the converted stables which surround the courtyard, and the purpose built pre-prep department. A series of Portakabins are still in use, though no one appears bothered; in fact, the pupils see the strengths; as one pointed out in the 'temporary' science lab, 'We never have to worry about dropping liquids on the benches – they are so old!' The decorative theme throughout is inspired by the Colonel's travels including elephants and giraffes, displays from Tutankhamen's tomb, wooden carvings, ornamental ponds and, unexpectedly, two full suits of armour standing guard at the end of a passage.

Indoor sports and ballet take place in a marquee (heated), supposedly temporary but no plans to change this. School has a small theatre with raked seating and facilities for sound and lighting – 'We all learn to do it as well as act' – and productions are all-out efforts of the whole school rather than an elite group. Music, a particular interest of the Colonel, is well taught and popular; around 50 per cent learn an instrument.

No formal gardens or prefects' lawns here; the grounds resemble an adventure playground. Approached by a drive full of potholes ('We know the fees aren't wasted on tarmac,' said a parent, approvingly), skateboarding is allowed, as are tree climbing and den building, there is a miniature railway, a bouncy castle – all tastes catered for. Announcements are made over a PA system, known as the 'bing-bong', that operates all over the school; slightly disconcerting at first, rather like a tube station, but pupils like it and think it is sensible.

'We camped with our teacher in the garden when I was 6!' said one pupil, and this spirit continues up the school. Orienteering very popular, camping expeditions

A lot of parents are commuters and chose the school 'because the pupils seem so happy and relaxed, very different from London schools,' said one. 'Mine have all made tons of friends and have a crack at anything going,' said another, though also warning that 'it's not a place for namby-pambys.' (We think that remark is directed more at parents than pupils.) Adventure and independence encouraged from the outset with form sleepovers. 'We camped with our teacher in the garden when I was 6!' said one pupil, and this spirit continues up the school. Orienteering very popular (Prep National Champions), camping expeditions, and all team sports played with gusto. Long-awaited Astroturf is now installed. Parents welcome the unfussy attitude but warn: 'If you like things just so and organised months in advance then it might not suit'.

Classes are small, average 14, and setting begins early in the key subjects. Latin and French from early on, though Latin is dropped in the top three years by some. Those who might struggle in other schools find areas where they can shine. 'The staff are brilliant at building confidence,' say parents, who approve of the less stressful approach. Educational learning support is provided in the special needs department (known as The Bridge). Needs range from an extra boost to cases at the mild end of the autism spectrum, dyslexia and dyspraxia. There is also EFL and support for gifted children. A few children have statements and are LEA funded but the school won't take pupils they cannot help.

Boarding facilities are on the top two floors of the main building. Though approached by a slightly depressing staircase, the facilities themselves are comfortable and homelike. Boys and girls occupy separate floors. Bedrooms, mostly four bedded, are light, well-decorated and some have en suite bathrooms. Rather posh bathrooms in fact – think department store loos – good lighting, warm and clean. Friendly matrons, who remain on duty until the younger boarders, at least, are in bed and asleep. Boys, who form some two-thirds of the boarders, also have a common room on their boarding floor with an enormous screen for weekend viewing. The girls have one in their bedroom but, I was assured, there is no signal so can only be used for DVD watching. Mobiles, for all pupils, are looked after by the school during the day and boarders are allowed to use them for only limited periods. 'Can be hard for some, at first, especially those from abroad, but we want them to join in real life here,' said the headmaster. Weekend outings to local towns/places of interest are arranged for those, largely from overseas, who stay in school. With notice, it is possible to remain through the half term holidays also. Occasional boarding is popular and encouraged towards the top end of the school, especially for those moving on to board at senior schools.

This is a tremendously jolly school where a sense of adventure is encouraged. Most pupils thrive and go on to do well at senior schools. 'We often hear of former pupils becoming prefects or house heads,' we were told. Perhaps not suitable for those with hearts set on scholarships to the top flight schools, but definitely worth looking at for those who appreciate a less stressful, unstuffy, purposeful atmosphere and a staff dedicated to the needs of its pupils.

Bedford Preparatory School

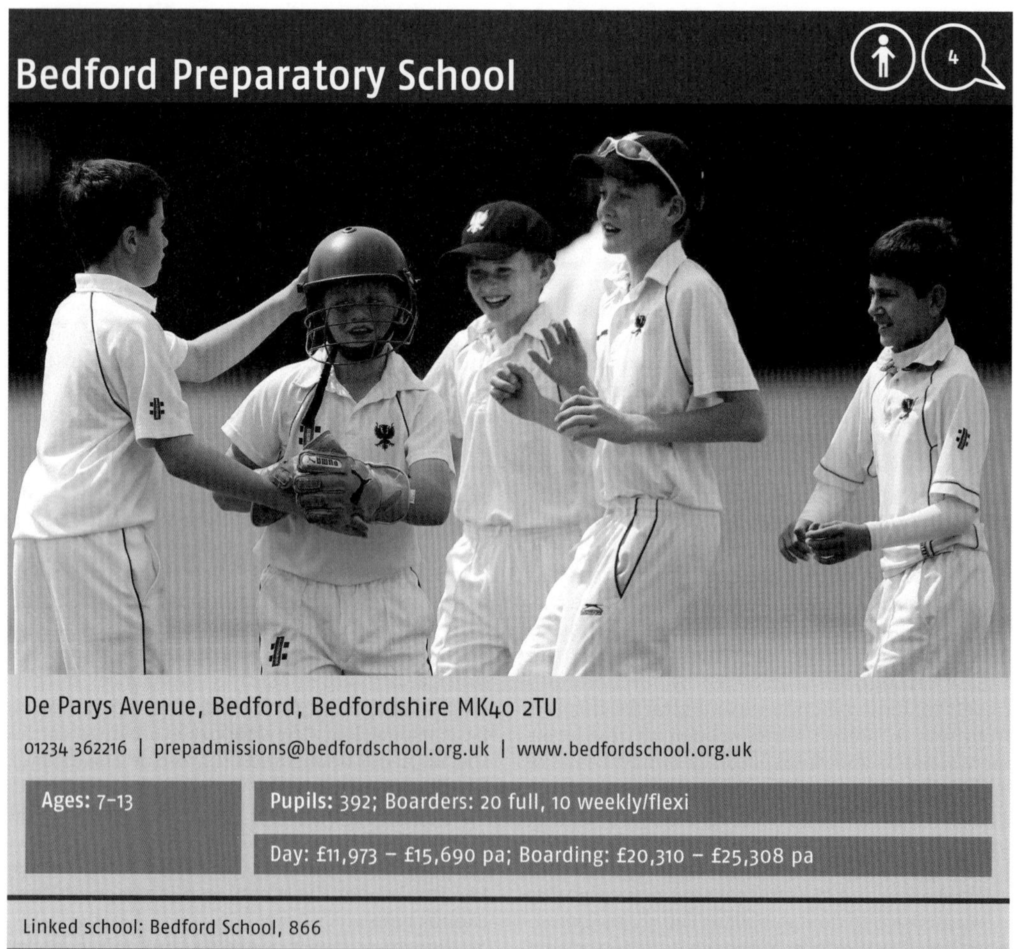

De Parys Avenue, Bedford, Bedfordshire MK40 2TU

01234 362216 | prepadmissions@bedfordschool.org.uk | www.bedfordschool.org.uk

Ages: 7–13

Pupils: 392; Boarders: 20 full, 10 weekly/flexi

Day: £11,973 – £15,690 pa; Boarding: £20,310 – £25,308 pa

Linked school: Bedford School, 866

Headmaster: Since 2013, Ian Silk (40s), previously deputy head of Bishops Stortford Junior School and former housemaster at Ardingly College. An English and drama specialist, brims with enthusiasm about all aspects of the school – most particularly the spectacular new theatre (2015) shared with the upper school and the town. Married to Sarah, with two sons both at the school

– 'they are chalk and cheese,' he told us, 'but the school is brilliant for both of them.' Knows most boys by name – lots of heads do but this is a large prep – and has lunch with all new joiners in small groups.

Entrance: Mainly at 7+, 8+ and 11+. Not heavily over-subscribed but looking for the right fit, ability to keep up and fully participate in school life. 'At 7 some boys might not be there yet,' says head, 'but we encourage them to try again later.' Assessments in English, maths, NVR, creative writing, an in-school day – and that all-important report from current head. Large contingent from nearby pre-prep and fellow Harpur Trust member Pilgrims and around 30 per cent from local state schools. Buses from Luton, Milton Keynes and Hitchin broaden catchment.

Exit: Almost all (99 per cent) transfer to Bedford School with the odd exception departing for the state sector or, for international boarders, their mother country. No prep for CE or formal advice on other destination schools, but existing pupils sit the same test as external candidates for setting purposes. Parents report a seamless transition to upper school, with boys better prepared for workload than those joining from other preps.

Remarks: A boys' own paradise which simultaneously feels separate from and integral to the upper school and offers everything young boys could hope for, whatever their interests. In the space of one lunch time we watched boys hunting for creepy crawlies in bug hotels, singing with gusto in the junior choir, planing chess boards in the DT suite, creating games in the ICT suite, building sets for the school play, having a good old fashioned kick about – and of course, in time honoured tradition for a Friday, tucking into fish and chips in the school dining hall ('really good,' we were assured). Never a dull moment.

'Nicely contained' in a corner of the vast Bedford School campus, one of the main benefits of prep is that it enjoys unfettered access to the wealth of facilities of the upper school – as well as a fair few of its own. Classrooms ranging from the antiquated 'Inky' (incubator for fledgling Bedfordians) to more modern purpose-built additions sit around a central Astro play area where boys let off steam at break times. A separate adventure playground adds to the fun – although there's so much else going on, we're not sure when pupils would get the chance to use it. Classrooms feel cosy in comparison to the overwhelming sense of space elsewhere. Science labs are well-equipped and art and DT outstanding. Super work of exceptional quality, themed to ignite passionate creativity amongst the all-male cohort by their inspiring male head of art (who doubles up as games teacher), festoons the interiors. We loved the Viking shields crafted in DT and the fabulous gargoyle masks produced in year 8 art. Not a still life in sight.

A separate adventure playground adds to the fun – although there's so much else going on, we're not sure when pupils would get the chance to use it

It's rugby, hockey and cricket ('huge' according to head) on the sporting agenda, with a fully inclusive approach and school putting out as many as 18 competitive teams for fixtures, so everyone gets a ride on the bus and a post-match tea at least once a term, whatever their ability. Tons of music and drama to temper the testosterone. Hugely popular (and, crucially, non-selective) junior choir, plus chapel choir for years 5 and up, as well as instrumental lessons on curriculum for years 3 and 4. Great excitement on the dramatic front too, as all major performances now take place in what must be the most stunning school theatre in England – a brand new £7 million structure built (thanks to a legacy donation) on the grounds of a neighbouring Moravian church – altar, stained glass and tablets sympathetically incorporated.

Dedicated SENCo with two supporting specialists and strong emphasis on training whole staff to support individual needs (mild dyslexia and dyspraxia; a few with mild Asperger's). Around 20 boys receiving support. Close communication with upper school a great strength: 'we hand parents and children over individually so nothing falls between the gaps,' SENCo assured. Strong ESOL team caters for overseas students.

Boarding in purpose-built Eagle House for up to 32 boys from year 3 and up, although most start after year 5 as either flexi, full or weekly boarders. A real home from home feel, thanks in no small part to super houseparent couple, as well as plenty of nicely furnished, comfy spaces with lots of personal touches for boys to hang out after school hours. Spacious dorms sleep between four and eight boys, who make them their own with pictures, posters and duvet covers from home. When prep's finished (supervised, in dedicated room for all bar the year 8s), there's a homely common room equipped with computers, a kitchen for snacking and a basement games room with table football and pool on offer. Where boys find the time to use these facilities, though, is anyone's guess, as there's also a full programme of after-school activities each day to take advantage of. Mobiles and other gadgets allowed but must be put on charge in the prep room overnight.

Around half the boarders overseas (from mainly Russia, China and Spain), good Forces quota as well, so there are plenty around at weekends once Saturday school (compulsory for all from year 6) and Sunday chapel are out of the way, to enjoy outings ranging from go karting or high ropes to bowling or the cinema, often followed by a takeaway or one of the housemaster's legendary barbecues.

'Zero tolerance' anti-bullying policy with clear protocol in place for inevitable – albeit rare – lapses. 'We show as much understanding to both sides as possible,' says housemaster. School counsellor available for boys to use for anything from home sickness to help with social skills.

All in all, a really super option for those looking for top notch day or boarding – as long as your sights are firmly set on an all-through education at Bedford. A kind, happy and successful school with the added bonus of a smooth transition to the thriving and successful upper school without the weighty stress of the 11+ or CE.

Bedford School

5

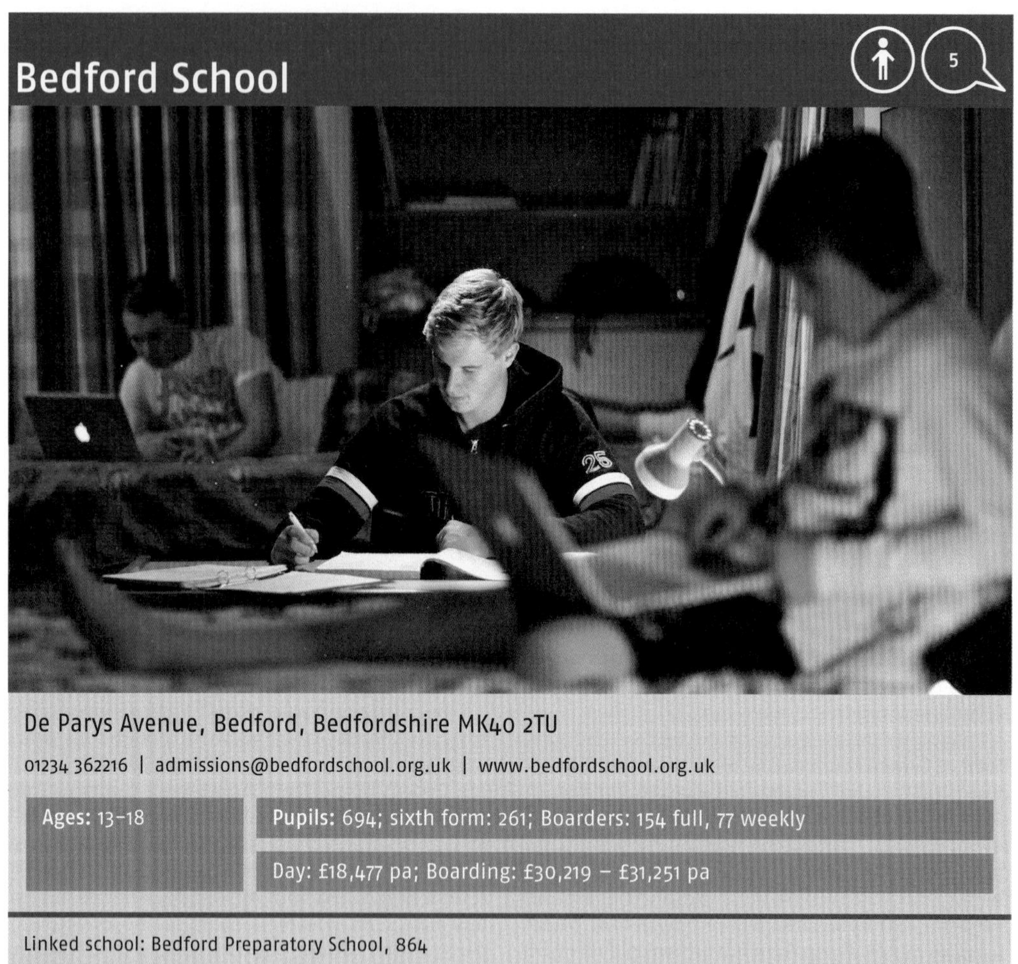

De Parys Avenue, Bedford, Bedfordshire MK40 2TU

01234 362216 | admissions@bedfordschool.org.uk | www.bedfordschool.org.uk

Ages: 13–18

Pupils: 694; sixth form: 261; Boarders: 154 full, 77 weekly

Day: £18,477 pa; Boarding: £30,219 – £31,251 pa

Linked school: Bedford Preparatory School, 864

Head master: Since 2014, Mr James Hodgson (40s), educated at Wellington College and Durham (classics) before being scooped up on the milk round by Ernst and Young and spending a couple of years as a trainee accountant. In his 20s a cricketer hovering around the fringes of the professional game – and uninspired by the world of finance – wrote to Cambridge on the off-chance of a late place on its PGCE course and turned up trumps, meaning he could pursue his long term ambition of running a boarding house as well as playing regular top class cricket, ultimately earning a blue.

Spent six years teaching in Sydney before joining Tonbridge School as boarding housemaster and director of admissions. Latterly senior deputy head of Magdalen College School, Oxford. Impressed on joining Bedford by the boys 'completely at ease' with the staff and each other – 'presenting awards in my first assembly, every single boy shook my hand, looked me in the eye, smiled and said thank you – quite something for a large group of teenagers,' he says. At peace with Bedford not quite hitting the dizzy academic heights of Magdalen but plans to up the ante a little 'for pastoral reasons – results are just a passport to the next level'. Passionate about boarding ('it develops the whole person') and ready to take on the challenge of keeping it thriving at Bedford. Parents feeling the effect of this already with the recent introduction of a full schedule of celebrations for leavers, including their own speech day followed by house events and a leavers' ball – 'a fitting end to a super education,' in the words of one.

Youthful, energetic and 'really personable,' according to parents – not just a safe pair of hands for parents to hand their sons to, but dynamic, likeable and inspiring. Accessible to pupils – has open door for a period each morning where pupils can come to discuss anything. Presence at matches and performances (with the occasional personal note of congratulations to performers afterwards) noted and appreciated by all. Married to Rachel, with four teenage children.

Academic matters: Solid academics, especially given broad church intake and large proportion who joined at 7+. 2017 saw 61 per cent of GCSEs graded A*-A/9-7; 54 per cent A*/A at A level and 82 per cent A*-B, with an average IB score of 37 out of a possible 45 (a score achieved by two boys in 2017) – testament to a focused and dynamic teaching staff ('second to none,' said one happy parent).

English and maths set from outset but rejigged along the way. Class sizes capped at 24, shrinking to a pleasing eight or nine for many A level subjects. All take 10 GCSEs, with around 30 per cent taking four full A levels in year 13 (mostly including further maths). Boys opt for either A levels or IB in sixth form. IB numbers 'a bit low' according to head with just over 15 per cent currently opting to take this route. School aims to boost numbers to around a third of the cohort.

Well thought out curriculum with separate sciences and all boys learning at least two languages. Maths and sciences extremely popular options at A level as well as good take up in geography ('a very good department,' says head) and economics. German, Spanish, French and Latin on offer in the languages department, with Mandarin available as a twilight option, but rather low take up of these at A level. PPE an interesting offer in year 10 and parents praised standard of 'inspirational' RS teaching.

Boys with SEN (mainly mild dyslexia or dyscalculia) given bespoke care with the department tailoring help according to each boy's individual needs. Strong ESOL team caters for overseas students, who are offered extra English language sessions in place of another language and about half of them take IGCSE ESL instead of English.

Head acknowledges lack of strong articulation of sixth form – super facilities abound at Bedford yet no dedicated centre for years 12 and 13. Parents identified career support as an area in need of improvement – 'so much more that they could do'. The school's recent appointment of dedicated UCAS and careers specialist has raised the school's game in this area, which is demonstrated through the award of the highly regarded 'Career Mark' (only seven other independent schools hold this award) and a Gold Education to Employment (E2E) award. UCAS application process highly praised, with parents barely needing to get involved in the process: 'exactly as it should be', although head hopes to up future Oxbridge numbers.

Games, options, the arts: Sport is the lifeblood of Bedford and although the list of recent accolades is too long to list (in all sports from rugby and cricket to swimming and golf), school maintains it's not just for the elite and says it offers all boys 'the same time on task' when it comes to training – the input and expertise from the directors of all major sports filtering down to even the lowliest of teams.

Music centre apparently positioned opposite the pavilion so that the director of music can keep one eye on the cricket scoreboard whilst conducting the school orchestra

Are less gifted boys afforded the same kudos as the macho sporty crowd, we asked one sixth former? Apparently yes, since the introduction in recent years of colours for art, drama and academia in addition to sport – a welcome addition signified by a colourful array of scarves – and special striped blazers for those awarded cricket colours. Parents, too, concur that school 'absolutely allows boys to be all-rounders'. It's a rugby, hockey, cricket school – with strong rowing too (how many schools have their own boat house on a beautiful stretch of the river Ouse?) but plenty of other options to choose from: you name it and Bedford offers it, from archery or rifle shooting to pilates and fencing. National and international honours in all main sports plus golf and fencing, and boys have gone on to play for their universities and even their country in most sports played at Bedford, where the main challenge for staff is finding competitor schools strong enough to give them a good game.

Music of a 'fantastic calibre,' according to parents, with a state of the art, super modern music centre – designed by award-winning architect Eric Parry and apparently positioned opposite the pavilion so that the director of music can keep one eye on the cricket scoreboard whilst conducting the school orchestra. Choirs, orchestras and bands a-plenty, a brand new music technology suite, gleaming new fleet of iMacs, a recording studio (Desert Island Disks with the head a recent highlight), rock room and inspirational recital hall – used for weekly performances by pupils and recitals from visiting professionals. Something for everyone and parents say even the most reluctant musician is inspired to join in. School's enthusiasm for making music illustrated by wild enthusiasm (parents and boys) for the annual house music, 'the best competition of the year,' by all accounts, which sounds like a cross between 20/20 cricket with boys, faces painted and fancy dressed, raucously chanting and cheering on their housemates, and young musician of the year ('as soon as the singing starts, everyone is silent,' explained our guide).

Possibly the most stunning theatre we've seen in any school opened in 2015, built on the site of a former Moravian Church, with original features sympathetically included to complement the modern architecture – all exposed brick and floor to ceiling glass. Shared with the town, and able to seat over 280, the theatre not only hosts school productions (recently Shakespeare's The Comedy of Errors by the prep and Henry V by the upper), often in conjunction with Bedford Girls' School, but also productions by visiting companies. A full-time technical director takes care of special effects and shows boys the ropes with lighting and scenery.

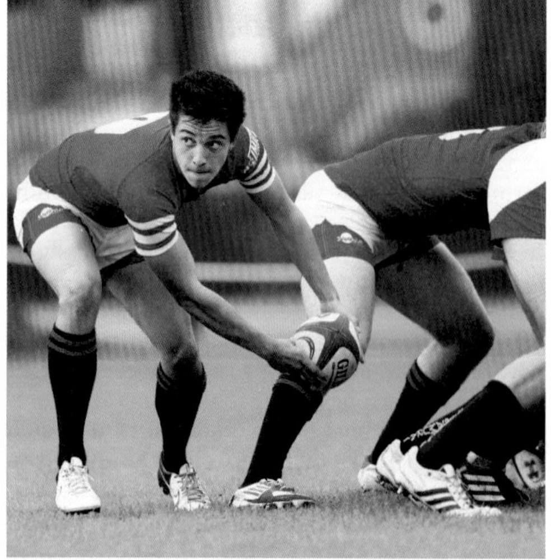

Outstanding work on show in the art and DT departments, with some mind-blowing projects on display in the year 13 workshop – no wonder so many move on to study engineering at university.

Strong rowing (how many schools have their own boathouse on a beautiful stretch of the river Ouse?) but plenty of other options

A non-stop merry-go-round of extracurricular activities keeps boys busy outside of the classroom. Options range from public speaking to a very popular CCF in all three branches, run in conjunction with Bedford Girls'. Trips and tours galore for all manner of interests from sports tours to choir trips, academic excursions and – occasionally – just for fun.

Boarding: Six senior boarding houses – four on site and two just a short walk away – offer intimate and cosy homes from home for the boys who board here. Charming in that none are purpose built, the houses are adapted Victorian villas, each with its own character – all with a fraternity house feel. Described as 'an extension of the housemaster's home', the houses are bright and spacious, with reassuringly untidy dorms (we secretly approve – boys must feel at home to be quite so slovenly) and the kinds of communal spaces day boys would probably die for (Xboxes, pinball machines, pool tables, chess tables – you name it). In keeping with rest of the school, modern facilities are juxtaposed with traditional artefacts (shiny fleets of computers beneath panelled honours boards) and boys have the freedom to come and go during the course of the day. Masters describe the boys as 'like brothers', one commenting that 'there's nothing better than seeing a huge sixth former strolling to breakfast chatting to one of the year 9s'. Many boarders are former day boys fed up with the daily commute – parents love the fact that boys can 'grow with the school'. Over 65 per cent of boarders are there full time so plenty of buzz at weekends, with regular trips and outings as well as free run of sports facilities and time for valuable R&R. Compulsory Saturday school for all.

Background and atmosphere: Don't be put off if you approach Bedford from the M1 via a somewhat grotty suburban high street, at the end of which you catch first glimpse of the school like an oasis in the architectural desert. School takes great pains to remind us of 'the other half' of Bedford which lies behind it – smart rows of Victorian villas (two boarding houses among them) leading down to a beautiful river bank. The school itself has the feel of a university campus about it – the buildings, a delightful mix of old and new, surround the manicured playing fields. The main building is all turrets, spires and a bell tower, with a magnificent hall as the central point and classrooms on four levels.

Impossible to choose a stand-out feature or department as each and every addition to the school has been made with care and deliberation to fuse function and form effectively. From the professional-looking cricket pavilion to the super modern glazed music school (who could fail to be inspired in here?), stunning library full of gleaming new books – but with the antique ones carefully displayed – and the cottage-like art building, set in its own sculpture garden, the whole campus gives the aura of a school offering roundedness in the purest sense of the word. The word chapel doesn't quite do justice to the glorious building where weekly services are held – the school accommodated amongst panelled walls inscribed with war memorials of fallen OBs.

Sports facilities unsurprisingly top notch. Super weights room would give most private gyms a run for their money and there's a 25 metre swimming pool (reportedly 'rather chilly but nobody minds,' according to our guide). Recent refurb and renovation of tennis courts and cricket pavilion – opened by England captain and Old Bedfordian, Alastair Cook.

Pastoral care, well-being and discipline: Brotherly atmosphere helped twofold by small houses with a family feel and vertical tutor groups where boys can get to know others from all year groups, with the tutor being the first port of call in the event of a problem. Head describes school as 'a fantastic community,' with everyone pitching in to help with greater problems relating to mental health or general well-being should the need arise, and parents describe the way boys support each other through the inevitable occasional difficulty as 'magic to watch'. Teachers available to parents via email, with responses to queries and concerns flying back through the ether at great speed.

'Strong discipline makes a place happier', says head, and major transgressions are dealt with by the amusingly – and aptly – named vice master. Strict protocols followed in relation to serious misdemeanours with repeated conduct warnings leading to detentions. 'Absolutely no leniency' when it comes to dealing with drugs, either inside or out of school, says head. Timetable collapsed five times each year to focus on PSHCE with age appropriate focus on drugs, internet safety etc.

Entrance: One hundred and forty boys join year 9 with about 60 per cent of these moving up from the prep. Some 50 additional places for those coming from other preps (Aldwickbury, Beechwood Park, Kingshott, Lockers Park major feeders) and state schools. Optional ISEB pre-test in year 7 potentially leading to conditional offer, confirmed by school's own online entrance examination in year 8. A few extra places at 14+ then about 25 more into sixth form, when hopefuls will need six good GCSEs to go on to do A levels (at least Bs in the subjects to be studied; A grades in maths and sciences). Not ferociously competitive for day boys but boarding places are at more of a premium.

Masters describe the boys as 'like brothers', commenting that 'there's nothing better than seeing a huge sixth former strolling to breakfast chatting to one of the year 9s'

Overseas pupils often offered places conditional to taking ESL, billed as an extra.

Exit: About 10 per cent head to pastures new post-GCSE. Good range of destination universities for those that stay on, with a handful to Oxbridge most years (10 in 2017) and around 75 per cent to Russell Group – Warwick, Sheffield, Imperial College and Durham feature heavily, with majority going on to study heavyweight academic subjects – lots of sciences and a few to medicine each year (five medics and two dentists in 2017). Small numbers opt for creative options or languages.

Money matters: At a shade over the £30K mark for full boarding, relative value for a school of this calibre in comparison with the competition. Good clutch of scholarships and bursaries for entry into years 7, 9 and 12, with art recently added to the list and golf scholarships in conjunction with nearby Woburn Golf Club. Generous – up to 35 per cent of fees, non-means tested, up for grabs 'for boys with exceptional talent' – and buoyant reserves in the hardship fund. Just under 200 boys across the school currently hold awards, with around 10 per cent of these on 100 per cent.

Part of the Harpur Trust but financially independent and benefiting from an extremely active and benevolent OB network.

Remarks: A rare beast – an uncompromisingly single sex school offering flexible day and boarding options without losing its traditional public school appeal. Thriving and successful, with happy pupils and happy parents – a place where all boys can hit their personal best, whether it's on the sports field, in academia or in the arts. Understated confidence and purposefulness abounds. A school of established excellence ready to be taken to the next level by dynamic newish head. All in all, a really super option for those looking for top notch day or boarding – as long as your sights are firmly set on an all-through education at Bedford.

Beechwood Park School

Pickford Road, Markyate, St Albans, Hertfordshire AL3 8AW

01582 840333 | admissions@beechwoodpark.com | www.beechwoodpark.com/

Ages: 3–13 (boarding from year 5)

Pupils: 522; Boarders: 40 boys, 20 girls flexi

Day: £10,560 – £15,825 pa; Flexi boarding: + £3,750 pa

Headmaster: Since 2015, Edward Balfour (40s), Winchester born and educated at Pilgrim's Prep ('extremely strict') and King Edward VI School Southampton, followed by Cardiff University where he read English literature. After a summer as a Camp America counsellor, followed his heart into teaching at the Royal Grammar School, Worcester, then gained a PGCE at Homerton College Cambridge. Secured teaching placement as English teacher at Uppingham, followed by Whitgift, then 13 years at Bradfield ('where I was educated most'), taking over as head of drama aged just 27, before turning around an 'unruly' boarding house, transforming it into school's 'most successful and desirable' (he can fight it out with Berkhamsted's Richard Backhouse who makes the same claim). Entered prep school stratosphere with first headship at Northbourne Park School in east Kent, attracted by its strength in languages and largely bilingual (French) cohort.

A skilled marketer with soundbites to rival top politicos (but don't let that put you off), says 'fluidity and progressiveness' are key strengths of school. Self-proclaimed 'evangelist' on the modernisation of prep school education. Asks 'what does preparatory actually mean? It certainly doesn't mean pushing children.' Wants to remove 'useless formality'. We approve. As does the parent cohort who, in the main, are big fans and say he's 'exactly what the school needed.' So, what's changed since his arrival? We loved the overhauled reporting structure (unique, to our knowledge) with all reports now written to children rather than their parents: 'it makes school reports empowering not didactic', he says.

In practical terms, the pool is now covered by a dome, allowing year-round usage, and any school run veteran will understand the importance of the creation of 100 new parent parking spaces. Happy days.

Married to Emma, a Cambridge linguist, who teaches at Beechwood, with three children, the youngest of whom attends Beechwood, the others at school in Canterbury and St Albans.

Entrance: Only 'slightly' selective, according to head. Now oversubscribed at 3+ thanks to the opening in 2015 of the all singing, dancing and yoga-ing on site Woodlands Nursery, which has 40 children, all of whom typically move up to the reception class in the main school. Nursery places given on first come, first served basis. A further 20 places in reception, with a gentle assessment during the year prior to entry to ensure suitability. Small intake each year into year 7, often for those who have missed out on an 11+ place at the school of their choice, with suitability assessed from applicant's InCAS scores.

Exit: Around a third of total cohort (the majority of girls plus a handful of boys) leave at the end of year 6, heading to a broad mix of private and state schools (including some of Harpenden's excellent comprehensives, eg Sir John Lawes, St George's and Roundwood). Girls also to St Albans High and Berkhamsted in numbers and ones and twos to Queenswood, Abbot's Hill and Habs' Girls most years.

At 13+ boys move to St Albans School in droves plus small numbers to eg Bedford, Berkhamsted and Merchant Taylors' – parents report extremely favourably on preparation at this stage (a few grumbles that it could be better at 11+, although school says it has been tackling this): each child is given a study plan and, for potential scholars, extra classes are put on – sometimes even at weekends. Not an obvious choice if Eton, Harrow et al are top of your wish list (you'd be in the minority – parental aspirations tend to err on the side of quality day schools) but small numbers of pupils do head off to board at eg Millfield, Oundle, Uppingham and, occasionally, Harrow – so school can deliver the goodies for these destinations if it needs to. Decent clutch of scholarships most years – 12 for 2017 entry, including four art, three music, one sport and one drama as well as academics.

Remarks: Approached down a seemingly endless winding driveway redolent of entering a fairy tale, steeped in history, the main school building is an immaculately restored Tudor manor house nestled amongst fields and woodland as far as the eye can see. Walled gardens and wrought iron gates surround the main building as constant reminder of the grand history of the house as, most notably, the family seat of the aristocratic Sebright family. The school in its current guise was founded in 1964 by Group Captain Peter Stewart OBE who bought the house in a near derelict state, saving it from demolition. And thank goodness he did, as it now boasts a wealth of idyllic space and facilities, likely the envy of most visiting schools.

At 3, pupils enter the Woodlands Nursery, a standalone wood-clad, purpose built structure on the edge of the school's enchanting woodland. Vast space, with super indoor and outdoor play areas – we loved the mud kitchen (full waterproof jumpsuits required) and yoga room. A true haven to introduce littlies to the school world without the rough and

tumble of their older peers, and parents love the almost daily online feedback on their child's progress. From there, pupils progress to the less picturesque but heartily practical junior block where they join one of four reception classes of 15 pupils, changing to three classes of 20 in years 1 and 2. Compact and colourful with its own gardens, although mobile library in makeshift area not the most inspiring for young readers. This, however, is more than compensated for by the stunning senior school library in the main school building, with its panelled walls and seemingly endless bookshelves. We were assured by the head before our visit that we would be 'blown away' by the wealth of space and facilities – the fabulous covered pool, the enchanting forest school and woodlands where pupils are now allowed to run free at break times, vast grounds, brand new all-weather cricket nets and breathtaking buildings – we certainly couldn't fail to be.

The girls are up in the eaves in a haven of pinkness and unicorns and have their own areas to chill out and 'do hair' away from their raucous male counterparts

Teaching far from the talk and chalk variety – French taught from the get-go by a specialist teacher; reception were playing French fruit bingo when we visited and at the top of the school pupils write and perform their own French play. Parents report their Beechwood alumni children experiencing resentment by senior school peers due to their proficiency in French, with one St Albans School French teacher telling a parent that all he could do was 'paper over the cracks' with her son who was almost GCSE standard on arrival. History equally engaging: what's not to love about a year 2 class setting fire in the playground to paper houses they have made to bring the Great Fire of London to life? Pupils split into four sets for maths in year 4 and for English in year 5. From year 6 onwards, all are split into tutor groups of around 10, with whom they stay for the remainder of their time at school, and are specialist taught for all subjects. Staff mature enough to be experienced but not over the hill, and across the board seem to ooze passion for their subject; science (despite the somewhat rickety appearance of the labs) impressed on the basis of the departmental head's enthusiastic description of a recent 'dunkability of biscuits' experiment alone ('we keep it very practical; it has to be') as did the year 6 pupils rehearsing for the Latin play, Cinderella. Beats reciting verbs, that's for sure, and parents describe the Latin teaching as 'phenomenal'.

All children screened for mild specific learning difficulties and around 60 on register. Three full-time staff offer one-to-one sessions in a dedicated space (mainly either before school in the morning or during library lessons to avoid withdrawal) as well as in-class support to those that need it. Whole school monitored for progress in reading and spelling and children referred for a booster if they need it. Touch typing offered as early morning club and those who satisfy the criteria are allowed to use laptops in class and in exams from year 6. But support is very much dyslexia focused, and we've heard complaints about a lack of expertise here in autism; probably best to look elsewhere for anything other than mild SpLDs.

All the usual sports – the newish director of sport has 'transformed' the offering at Beechwood, say parents, and happily now year 3s get to play fixtures against other schools, with a match for everyone regardless of ability in years 3 and 4. Things get a bit more selective from year 5 upwards but those who don't make it onto the match day minibus can choose from a plethora of activities under the new 'sport for all' banner which encompasses sailing, table tennis, martial arts and fencing. And there are always those all-important house matches where everyone can get stuck in.

The super performance hall with its flexible seating plays host to productions such as Around the World in 80 Days and The Lion King – often cross-curricular productions – and we are assured that everyone who auditions gets a role. A whopping 80 to 90 per cent of pupils take peripatetic music lessons, with groups and ensembles galore playing everything from percussion and harp groups to rock and big band (movie theme tunes a favourite) at the weekly lunch time recitals. Choirs are non-selective to year 5, when the elite are creamed off to join the chamber choir ('we work them hard,' says the popular head of music) and taken on tour to perform in European countries, recently Belgium. Minor parental grumbles that they should jazz up the formal repertoire a little. New music technology suite, ensemble room and recording studio.

And there's no need for multi-talented pupils to have to choose between music and sport – the two departments make a point of working harmoniously together to ensure that 'there's no tussle' when it comes to commitments. Art and DT equally well resourced and a high standard of work on show. The latter is taught in a charming former stable block – and we genuinely cannot think of a better use for the former wine cellar of the main house than a pottery studio. Pupils in years 7 and 8 can claim their own space in the mezzanine area of the art block – many do and come and while away any spare time there. No surprise that there is a good handful of art scholars most years.

Fabulous covered pool, the enchanting forest school and woodlands where pupils are now allowed to run free at break times

With almost all pupils living within 10 miles of school, boarding for most is all about enhancing their overall prep school experience rather than necessity or rigid preparation for a future at public school. Pupils can choose to board for two nights from year 5 under the watchful eye of the popular houseparent couple, building up to a maximum of four nights – no remainers at weekends – and around 60 boarders take advantage of this flexible arrangement. Despite that, it is very much representative of any full boarding school, with absolutely no 'hot bedding' and all the warmth and character of any boarding prep.

A warren of spacious boys' rooms takes over the upper floor of the main school building, with between seven and 17 pupils in a room, depending on year group. The girls are up in the eaves in a haven of pinkness and unicorns and have their own areas to chill out and 'do hair' away from their raucous male counterparts, should they wish to. Communal areas, like all things Beechwood, are spacious and well resourced – we can't imagine an 11 year old who wouldn't want to give boarding a try with such a heady mix of pool, table hockey, table tennis and a tuck shop on offer – and that's on top of a full schedule of boarders' after-school activities with intriguingly named games including Colditz and Murder in the Dark. What's more, they are 'fed every hour' with fruit and veg on offer after school, tuck, tea and sandwiches and milk before bed. Special events such as the Harry Potter evening, complete with dry ice, and parent and child golf competitions and barbecues, are the icing on the boarding cake.

On the pastoral side, head says, 'we try to catch and reward good behaviour' and school definitely has an overall feel of carrot rather than stick. Pupils say they feel 'safe and at home' and can be given a house credit simply for making a staff member smile, with parents glowingly describing 'a very caring community'. Badges galore are sported proudly on lapels by a cohort of smiley, individual and thoroughly charming children. Parents optimistic that bullying will be dealt with more effectively under new head than previously. With many pupils from dual income families, a fleet of coaches brings pupils from Harpenden, St Albans, Dunstable and Redbourn.

Going places. With its dynamic new head and, in the words of one happy parent, 'feel good factor', Beechwood should definitely be on the list of parents who want the certainty of a quality end destination for their child without compromising the joy of the journey.

Beeston Hall School

7

West Runton, Cromer, Norfolk NR27 9NQ

01263 837324 | office@beestonhall.co.uk | www.beestonhall.co.uk

Ages: 4–13

Pupils: 146; Boarders: 44 full/weekly/flexi

Day: £11,955 – £17,370 pa; Boarding: £18,750 – £23,340 pa

Headmaster: Since September 2016, Mr Fred de Falbe (50s). Eton (same vintage as D Cameron), followed by theology at Manchester. Was previously head of St Richard's, a boarding prep in Herefordshire that has since closed. His varied career has taken him into the film business, property management and a spell as a 'jackaroo' in Australia as well as eight years teaching in state schools close to the family farm in North Devon, where, among other things, he carried out most of the maintenance work and raised Tamworth pigs. Was drawn back into full time teaching at Knightsbridge School, a popular day prep in London.

His style is exceedingly hands on – definitely not just a man in a suit, think parents. 'He's very visible around the school and pupils like that,' said one. Easy to talk to with understated charm, has already established good rapport with staff while pupils say he's interested in all of them, not just the stars. 'You don't have to be the best in something for him to talk to you,' said one.

Has strong views about the need to nurture confidence and self reliance. His advice to parents to, 'Give your child a broken Hoover to take apart and try and fix in the holidays,' provoked media interest and he is happy to be associated with the idea of 'directed purposelessness'. Believes children should look forward to coming to school, 'Learning takes many forms and some of the best schooling is done when children are having fun.'

'We have drop-in sessions and parties and children really do see coming here as a treat'

Is very pro 'the small country prep school where we all know each other,' and is not looking to expand the school greatly. His wife Juliet is immersed in everything going on at the school. A trained artist, she was able to fill in teaching art for half a term. Very much a partnership. Three children, now almost through school and at university stage.

Entrance: Non-selective. Now admits pupils to pre-prep department in reception, but numbers increase steadily throughout the school with year 8 the largest age group. Older pupils attend an informal assessment day. Can accommodate mild to moderate learning difficulties but all must be able to follow the curriculum. Not for those with behavioural problems.

A plethora of scholarships (up to 20 per cent of fees) offered for academic excellence, art, music, sport and general all-round ability for all ages plus some means-tested bursaries and help for parents who fall on hard times. Encouraged by former pupils, a drive to fund a greater number of bursaries is underway. The head is determined to encourage the widest possible access to the school. Sibling discounts on a sliding scale are available if two or more children are at the school at the same time.

Exit: Almost all stay to the end of year 8. Majority depart for out of county boarding schools – recently Ampleforth, Eton, Harrow, Oundle, Stowe, Tudor Hall and Uppingham. A clutch most years to Gresham's and one or two to Norwich School. Careful guidance is given and pupils all get where they want to go, many – over a third in 2017 – with awards.

Remarks: The school retains a strong boarding 'feel'; many day pupils stay on into the evening for activities and supper (no extra charge). Very often the pupils themselves want to change. 'My son began as a day pupil, saw the fun and wanted to board – it was his decision,' said one mother. 'Mine both boarded and when family circumstances changed, we asked them if they would like to become day pupils – but they refused.'

Predominance of pupils from county boarding families who know what to expect and settle quickly. 'The atmosphere is so welcoming and friendly, lots to do,' said a parent. 'Older pupils look after younger ones, it is not hierarchical at all.'

They make friends for life,' felt another. 'My daughter has done her gap year travel with old boys.' Lots stay in at weekends (30 is usual) and there are regular exeats at least once each side of half term. The recent introduction of flexi-boarding on designated nights is popular, though full boarding remains the choice of many, especially higher up the school. By year 8, virtually all are boarding full time. Parents chorus approval for the way pupils are prepared for senior schools. 'By the time my son left, he had developed the confidence to cope in a much bigger school.' Year 8s are integrated into the boarding houses with other years but have certain privileges (such as access to an all-important toaster). Mr de Falbe feels the opportunities to befriend and offer leadership to younger pupils in that final year stand pupils in good stead, besides promoting a strong community.

Children create a good impression. Respectful but 'at ease' relations with staff ('none of that giving them The Look', as one mother put it), unforced good manners – standing up for visitors and holding doors open for each other as well as adults. Mobile phones are not allowed in the school. Head feels pupils should be better occupied. 'We stick to the tried and tested phone box in the hall,' he says. Close supervision of computer use in the evenings and off duty; very aware of online risks and need to educate pupils. Traditional lunch (served at tables, Grace is said, water jug passed round) for the whole school, including staff. 'We are improving the acoustics in the dining room – the noise is unbelievable, you can't hear yourself speak at times', says the head. Daily organised games and lots of off duty playtime punctuate the day. No prep before year 6 ('developing a good reading habit matters most,' says school) then it's 20 minutes a day, increasing in year 8, especially for scholarship hopefuls. Dog-friendly with several around and about in classrooms with their owners (staff) and spectating at matches. Humans (and no doubt dogs as well) are agreed on the benefits.

Idyllic setting, close to north Norfolk coast and nearby National Trust Felbrigg Estate. Sweeping lawns and a Regency house are the centre of a mixture of newer builds. Extensive sporting, music and art facilities. Everything spick and span with notices such as 'Please walk ON the grass' and, 'Why not hold the door for someone?' Walls crammed with details of daily happenings, pupils' work, art, photographs and achievements.

Small, mixed ability classes until year 4, when there's flexible setting for English, maths, science and languages. French starts in year 3, Latin from year 6 and Greek (for some) in years 7 and 8. The year 8 scholarship form gives intensive preparation for senior school awards, focusing on individual requirements rather than hothousing a group. Staff flag any problems straightaway via emails

and parents are encouraged to have informal chats with them at pick up times, though effort grades are issued and more formal consultations can be arranged.

An educational support unit, based in an attractive suite of rooms, with excellent interactive displays and hard to resist games, is run by a sparkling and vivacious teacher who makes attending a session fun and even a privilege. 'We have drop-in sessions and parties and children really do see coming here as a treat.' Parents agree. 'My daughter only needed help for a year but kept on dropping in to see staff there as it was such a happy place,' said one. Roughly a quarter receive help of some sort, usually in English and maths.

We visited on World Book Day, taken as seriously by staff as pupils, and were greeted by Captain Haddock (the head) plus the Gruffalo (DT master)

A well designed and stocked library with wonderful squashy sofas to recline on is staffed throughout the day, including breaks and lunchtime. Pupils have timetabled library lessons for changing books and quiet reading. We visited on World Book Day, taken as seriously by staff as pupils, and were greeted by Captain Haddock (the head) plus the Gruffalo (DT master, helped by 'easy access to the materials,') as well as Matilda and Cruella de Vil – and not a single Disney princess to be seen. Art is taught in a barn style studio, mezzanine floor devoted to pupils' scholarship work, each with own desk and work area so they can come and go in their spare time and leave work in progress undisturbed. Music a school strength with 90 per cent of pupils learning an instrument in timetabled lessons, lots of space for rehearsal and practice and a host of choirs, bands, ensembles and plenty of performance experience. Focus on encouragement – all pupils join the junior choir, auditions only introduced in the higher forms.

School does all the usual team sports and one of the benefits of being a relatively small school is that 'everyone gets regular match play,' said a parent. Games every afternoon, played in 'spirit of enjoyment; competitiveness is important but should not be the last word,' says the head. Also sailing on the nearby Broads (they have their own fleet of Toppers) and shooting instruction (prep league champions). Plenty of choice for after school and weekend activities: fencing, beach picnics, fashion shows, cookery club, trips to local attractions such as Bewilderwood, theme days as well as Beeston's got Talent, a well established contest, though highlight of the week for many pupils remains 'the visit of the ice-cream cart,' in summer.

A traditional, but not hidebound, country prep with vitality and warmth and a well deserved reputation for nurturing its friendly, confident pupils who are 'willing to give things a try,' said a parent. Solid grounding ensures they go on to make the most of their senior schools.

Berkhamsted School

8

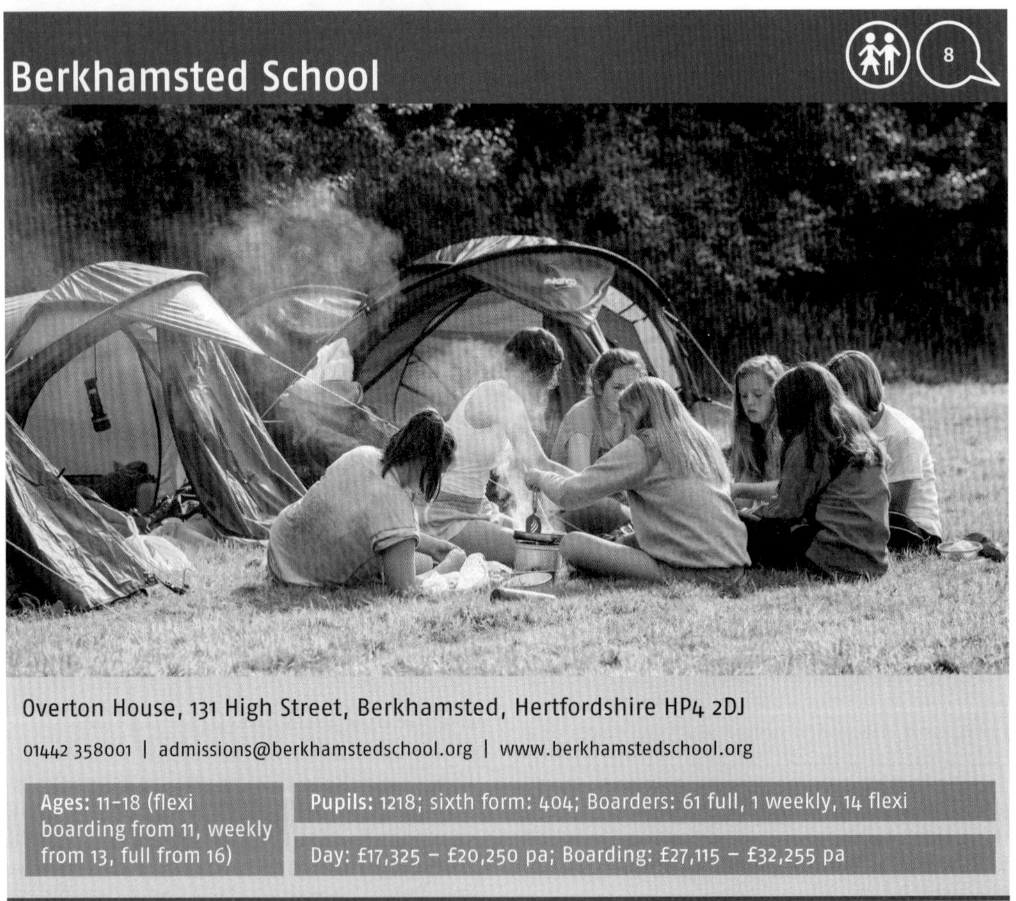

Overton House, 131 High Street, Berkhamsted, Hertfordshire HP4 2DJ

01442 358001 | admissions@berkhamstedschool.org | www.berkhamstedschool.org

Ages: 11–18 (flexi boarding from 11, weekly from 13, full from 16)

Pupils: 1218; sixth form: 404; Boarders: 61 full, 1 weekly, 14 flexi

Day: £17,325 – £20,250 pa; Boarding: £27,115 – £32,255 pa

Principal: Since January 2016, Richard Backhouse, educated at Cheam – a boarder from age 8 – and Marlborough (both parents on non-teaching staff) followed by Selwyn College Cambridge, where he read economics. From there, determined to forge a career in hard journalism, took a gap year teaching sailing in Dorset and skiing in the Alps, and was promptly bitten by the teaching bug: 'I was fizzing after my first morning with the feeling you get when you take a child from "I can't" to "I just did".' Decided at that point to teach 'just for a year or two', which led to six years at Oundle teaching economics and ultimately becoming head of year 9, followed by a stint at Bradfield as head of economics and politics, director of pastoral and extracurricular and (again, having had no aspirations to do so) head of a 'difficult' boarding house which, under his watch, became oversubscribed. From there he moved as principal to Monkton Combe School in Bath where he spent 10 years before joining Berkhamsted.

As principal overseeing both the boys' and girls' schools, is ably supported in day to day running by Liz Richardson, head of the girls' school (years 7-11) and Richard Thompson, head of the boys' school (also years 7-11). Martin Walker has been head of the mixed sixth form since September 2017. So more chief executive than managing director, days are less 'punctuated by parents' and more focused on 'getting on with strategy and innovation'. A dream job? 'My only puzzlement is why everyone didn't want it,' he quips. Despite the 'ivory tower' nature of his role, is frequently pitch side on match days, at concerts and other school events ('charming,' according to parents) and keeps finger on pulse of school life with celebratory soirées for winning sports teams and production casts at his house.

A holistic educator at heart, believes strongly in 'educating the non-cognitive areas of the brain as well as the cognitive' and wholeheartedly supports school's reasonably mixed ability cohort remaining just that: 'we want to deliver higher grades by improving teaching and learning, not by selecting brighter pupils.' Believes that 'a great school gives you the skills not just to get your first job, but to win that first promotion.' Inherited school with 'plenty of innovation and an energetic and interesting staff', but with his predecessor having acquired Heatherton House School, a girls' prep in Amersham, integrated a nearby competing prep, brought the whole lot together under a (somewhat corporate) umbrella brand, and reached a stage of considerable oversubscription at all entry levels, what comes next? 'Change for the sake of it is pointless', he says but aspires to 'continue reading the future clearly enough so that other schools continue to emulate us.'

Lives on Castle Campus with wife Debbie and has two adult children. Loves skiing, sailing, gadgets and, for his sins, Southampton FC.

Academic matters: You won't find Berko (as it's affectionately known locally) showboating at the top of independent school league tables but head and parents alike are totally fine with that, all focused on broader offering. With around 70 per cent of senior cohort joining from the mixed ability prep – many having been there since nursery – and a host of hungry grammar schools in surrounding area snapping up many of the most academic 11 year olds, plus school's determination to 'stay local', value added is king. School succeeds in delivering excellent results for pupils across the academic spectrum with parents saying it looks after both brainboxes and less stellar siblings equally well. In 2017, 68 per cent of all GCSEs graded A*/A. At A level, almost 40 per cent were graded A*/A, with 70 per cent at A*/B – that's grammar school results with a mixed ability intake; impressive. With 27 subjects to choose from at A level (all the usuals, plus sociology, media studies and photography), plus the option of either EPQ or school's own mini MBA, designed in conjunction with Ashridge Business School, it's clear to see that school is really walking the walk when it comes to providing the breadth expected by its parent cohort. The mini MBA covers not just business performance, marketing and strategy, but also places a focus on personal impact and presence, 'recognising a demand for business related education,' according to head.

Was promptly bitten by the teaching bug: 'I was fizzing after my first morning with the feeling you get when you take a child from "I can't" to "I just did"'

Consistently good results from all departments, despite a few grumbles from parents about 'patchy' teaching in one or two. IGCSEs in English, maths, sciences and RS (compulsory) ensure pupils are challenged. Setting in maths from year 7, languages from year 8 and science and English from year 9 – parents say pupils are 'assessed correctly' and moved up and down as necessary. It's a traditional offering of French, Spanish or Latin in the languages department, plus Mandarin, (replaced German in 2015), with pupils advised – although not compelled – to take at least one modern language to GCSE. Those joining in year 9 may not take up a new language. Aside from trad academic subjects, food technology popular at GCSE, thanks to outstanding facilities on both campuses, and we were thrilled on our visit not only to find eight boys diligently preparing a caramelised goats cheese and red onion tart as part of their GCSE coursework but also a male teacher in the food tech lab.

Pupils effusive about support given during university application process and familiarisation trips to universities available to some from as early as year 10. Weekly careers lunches for year 12 pupils with visiting speakers from all walks of professional life, many of them old Berkhamstedians.

School clear that SEN pupils must be sufficiently able to access curriculum but good proactive learning support department assists pupils with additional needs (mainly dyslexia or slow processing) with years 7 to 9 withdrawn from a language class to attend targeted sessions with the SENCo if required and one-to-one specialist sessions from year 10. Wheelchair access 'not an issue' with majority of campus accessible and timetables tweaked to ensure inclusivity if necessary.

Games, options, the arts: There's sport for all in the truest sense at Berko, and we're not just talking rugby, netball and lacrosse (although they play all of these – and jolly well too). Over and above the all-round excellent offering for sporty types, there exists (uniquely in the area as far as we know) a dedicated, three strong outdoor education department poised to scoop up not only the gung ho pupils who want to have a go at everything, but also those who, on arrival, purportedly 'hate' sport – and thrust them into the great outdoors. From high ropes to Nordic walking ('will they still be playing rugby when they're 50?' asks the dynamic head of outdoor ed. 'Unlikely, but they may well still be doing this') via kayaking and bushcraft, it's all here, with a genuine focus on getting absolutely everyone to find something they enjoy. Parents report 'outstanding' coaching for the traditional sports (rugby, football and cricket for boys and netball, lacrosse and tennis for girls) – although a few grumble about early morning training sessions for squads – and trophy cabinets groan with silverware, such is the competitive standard. Pupils earnestly assured us that 'if you want to get into a team, you will,' with commitment reportedly as important as talent when it comes to making it onto the team sheet.

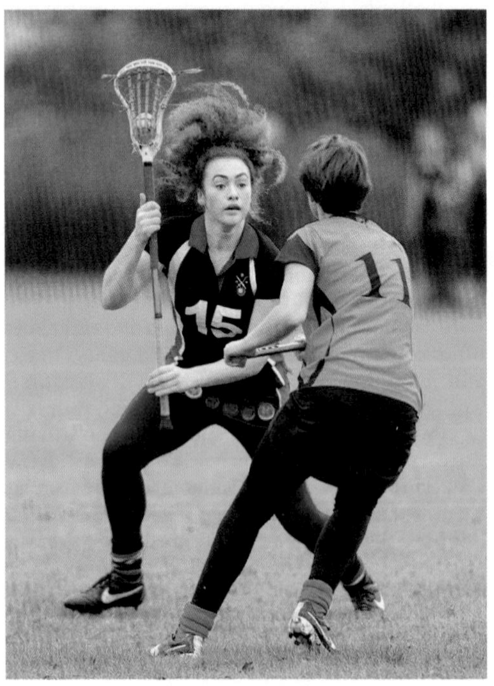

The very embodiment of leafy suburbia, school has a safe, sociable and happy feel – pupils are chatty, smiley and conventional

Flexibility offered to outstanding (county, club and national) sportsmen and women (currently footballers, gymnasts, modern pentathletes, dancers, swimmers and tennis, netball and lacrosse players) who may need time out from timetable to pursue their training – with some allowed to take fewer GCSEs. And school isn't above poaching talented girls to supplement the boys' teams where necessary. A recent former female pupil played A team and first XI cricket with the boys for the duration of her time at school (one year winning school award for most wickets taken across all teams) and is now part of the England set up. From year 10 pupils can choose from activities such as zumba or pilates to keep in shape if competition isn't their thing. Super facilities abound – a vast sports complex houses huge multi-purpose sports hall, well equipped gym and pool – sports fields that are slightly out of the way the only downside.

Strong music and drama with as many as half the cohort taking peripatetic music lessons and bands, choirs and orchestras galore (we love the idea of a barbershop choir for boys), and drama a popular GCSE option. Highlight of the performing arts year is talent show where allcomers can sing, dance or play their way to school superstardom all in the name of charity. Senior productions – recently Grease and Les Misérables – are 'amazing' and for those who prefer to stay backstage, opportunities abound in set design and backstage technology.

Endless extracurricular opportunities, with CCF and D of E, both run in house, at heart of school and strong uptake of both. D of E happily non-selective, with a 99 per cent take up for the bronze award in year 9 and one of the UK's highest number of gold awards achieved year after year. Compulsory lunch time clubs in years 7 and 8 ensure newcomers are making the most of opportunities and last period on Monday is dedicated 'clubs and societies' time. Multitudinous trips, both curriculum and enrichment based, punctuate pupils' time at school. 'Just great,' say parents. There's Greece for classics, Rome for history, language exchange trips, ski trips, and too many other expeditions to list.

Boarding: Less a boarding school and more a day school with boarding. Two large and extremely comfortable boarding houses, indistinguishable from residential houses, are situated a stone's throw from either campus. Houses boast large and beautifully furnished common rooms, mainly single rooms (lots of ensuite bathrooms in girls' house) and a well-equipped games room for the boys, plus kitchens where boarders can prepare meals at weekends. Occupied almost exclusively by international boarders (Chinese or Nigerian) who tend to join in year 12 for A levels (though can now join in year 10), often to prepare for British university. Best suited to older, independent pupils – and a good steppingstone to university life – as there is no separate schedule of activities, and organised weekend outings are sporadic, although sixth formers are allowed to venture as far afield as London on Saturdays.

Pupils can flexi or occasionally board from year 7 – the latter sometimes used by pupils staying late for an activity or rehearsal and applauded by parents for being 'flexible in the truest sense of the word – you don't even need to give 24 hours' notice'. Weekly boarding from year 9 and full time from year 12 (year 10 for international students), but at the time of our visit houses were occupied exclusively by sixth formers.

Background and atmosphere: Very much integral to the smart commuter town of Berkhamsted, the two campuses sit astride the pretty high street with its smart coffee shops and boutiques and the boarding houses and principal's office are dotted around town, yet in its entirety, school has a totally cohesive, integrated feel. The Castle Campus, which houses the boys and the sixth form, dates back to 1541 and has all the hallmarks – albeit in scaled down version – of a traditional public school. The main school building is built around a grassy quad with cloisters at the side leading to house rooms where pupils from years 7 to 11 congregate for a spot of table tennis, pool or just to chat at break times. A tour of this part of the school will also take in the beautiful, two floor vaulted library and possibly the archive room where the historic green baize door referred to by Graham Greene in his writing (Greene was a pupil and his father a former head) leads you into an archive space dedicated to all things Berkhamstedian, from old uniforms and sports kit to books. The grade 1 listed hall and 19th century Venetian-style chapel are also highlights, and indicative of the traditional roots of the school. The Kings Campus, a brisk 10-minute walk from Castle and base camp for girls from years 7 to 11, is a far more modern affair, boasting a fabulous modern double height dining room (we can vouch for the fish and chips) and sports centre. Both campuses have all-singing all-dancing classrooms and super art rooms – although it's a pity none of it is displayed on the rather sterile walls at Kings.

School follows a 'diamond' structure with a fully co-educational preparatory section, boys and girls taught separately from years 7 to 11 (although trips, productions and performances are mainly joint) and then together again in sixth form. Male and female sixth formers move freely between the two campuses and can choose to use either library (books can be withdrawn in one and returned to the other) and eat in either dining room. Coffee and tea is served at break times in a stylish and comfy sixth form common room on Castle campus with rooms for quiet study above. The very embodiment of leafy suburbia, school has a safe, sociable and happy feel – pupils are chatty, smiley and conventional and its diversity lies far more in the breadth of its academic and co-curricular offering than in the ethnicity of its pupils.

Pastoral care, well-being and discipline: Diamond structure appears to be a winning formula as boys and girls are free to concentrate on their educations 'without distractions' (their words) until sixth form and yet have sufficient exposure to the opposite sex to forge good social skills via extracurricular activities, trips, etc. Parents and pupils applaud vertical house system which brings all year groups together on a regular basis, with parents of girls in particular reporting older pupils 'scooping up' their younger peers when the going gets tough and boys saying they see the older boys in their houses as 'role models'. Pupils clear on protocol to follow should a problem arise – 'there are people on

so many levels to help you' – starting with selected year 10 peer mentors wearing smiley badges, there to support younger pupils through the highs and lows of settling in, whether it's friendship issues or not being selected for a sports team that's troubling them.

Expectations regarding behaviour are 'black and white' according to head, but 'we like to encourage a culture of acknowledging that mistakes will be made and we just have to learn from them.' Despite generally conservative feel of school – our search for hard edges was fruitless – head adamant that 'we want pupils to feel they can be who they want to be' and parents concur that quirkiness is definitely embraced and, in the main, differences in terms of sexuality, race or religion accepted as par for the course. 'There is definitely no complacency around such issues,' says head.

Pupils and parents: Pupils arrive on a fleet of coaches coming from areas mainly within a 40-minute radius of school. Healthy mix of first time buyers alongside more comfortably affluent – but has a grounded feel and is definitely in the 'private' rather than 'public' school bracket. A friendly and supportive bunch – older pupils look out for the younger ones on the coaches and around school, and there's a feeling of camaraderie between all age groups and both genders. With such a huge cohort moving up from the prep, are there cliques to worry about? Apparently not – 'even the most institutionalised mix well,' according to one happy parent.

A dedicated outdoor education department poised to scoop up not only the gung ho pupils who want to have a go at everything, but also those who purportedly 'hate' sport

Thriving OB association with regular sporting fixtures against the school, meetings with fellow professionals, reunion dinners and charitable events, and busy Friends' association, that organises well attended balls, quiz nights and Christmas bazaars.

Entrance: No longer a safe bet for those who didn't quite make the grammar school grade at 11+, school oversubscribed at both major entry points (11+ and 13+) and places sought after by bright and talented pupils from far and wide, looking for more breadth than the local grammars can offer, without the hothouse feel of some schools closer to London. Places even fewer and further between

A friendly and supportive bunch – older pupils look out for the younger ones on the coaches and around school

now there is an official year 5 intake (a whole extra class and well worth a look if you don't fancy taking your chances at 11+), with around 80 moving up from prep each year.

There are around 25 to 30 places for boys and about 40 for girls up for grabs in year 7 with a further 45 to 50 into year 9 for boys and 'just a handful' for girls. Around three applicants for every year 7 place and two for every year 9 place. Hopefuls take the school's own exam (English, maths and VR plus an interview at 11+; the same plus NVR and a language at 13+). Preps regularly feeding Berkhamsted span Herts and Bucks (The Beacon, Chesham Prep, Maltman's Green, Gayhurst, Westbrook Hay, Beechwood Park and Edge Grove to name a few) and around 30 per cent of applicants for year 7 places are from state primaries. Siblings largely accommodated provided they reach minimum academic standard. Around 45 new students admitted into sixth form (from over 100 applicants) and whilst academics remain important, school says all-round contribution is equally important.

Exit: A handful leave after GCSE. Entry requirement for sixth form is five B/6s and two C/5s and despite local coffee shop chatter, school assures us that anyone not expected to reach these grades is advised to seek alternative options 'well in advance – it should never come as a shock.' Majority leave after year 13 to higher education. A solid clutch of Oxbridge places in recent years – six in 2017, plus four medics – and a further 60 per cent of pupils to Russell Group universities. Popular destinations include Nottingham, Bath, Exeter, Leeds, Durham, Oxford Brookes and Birmingham. And one to UCLA.

Money matters: Cost of extras considered reasonable – particularly outdoor pursuits, expeditions and D of E which are startlingly good value as run in-house. Academic, drama, art, music and sports scholarships available at 11+ and 13+, usually representing a 10 per cent reduction in fees, although means-tested bursaries also available.

Remarks: In the words of one parent: 'without a doubt, 100 per cent solid and safe.' Parents send their children here hoping that not only will they thoroughly enjoy their educational journey but that the final destination will justify the fees. And in the majority of cases, that's exactly what they get.

Bishop's Stortford College

10 Maze Green Road, Bishop's Stortford, Hertfordshire CM23 2PJ

01279 838575 | general.enquiry@bishopsstortfordcollege.org | www.bishopsstortfordcollege.org

Ages: 13–18

Pupils: 600; sixth form: 250; Boarders: 160 flexi

Day: £18,915 pa; Boarding: £28,665 – £30,273 pa

Linked school: Bishop's Stortford College Prep School, 884

Headmaster: Since 2011, Jeremy Gladwin BSc MEd. Educated at The King's School, Worcester (chorister) and Whitgift School in south Croydon. Graduated from Durham in geography, taught at Shrewsbury School for 15 years, rising to become head of geography and housemaster, then deputy headmaster at the Royal Hospital School, and headmaster of St Edmund's, Canterbury. Decided to apply for second headship as 'the opportunity to lead Bishop's Stortford College was too good to miss'. Recently took a masters in education at Cambridge, focusing on 'educational leadership and school improvement', the completion of which has prompted his appointment to HMC committee for professional development. 'Heads are lonely,' he says; 'they need more support. That way we might be able to tackle the current high rate of attrition.' Also an inspector for both ISI and Ofsted (boarding). Married with grown-up son and daughter. A keen walker, enjoys watching rugby and plays tennis at club level. Loves music, especially sacred choral (weekly attendance at evensong at St John's College, Cambridge is his de-stresser) and classical. A fine pianist. Mild-mannered, considered, down-to-earth type. 'Runs a tight ship; proactive and forward-thinking,' say parents.

Academic matters: Academic results have soared in recent years – unrecognisable in comparison to the college of 10 to 15 years ago. Head attributes this to the arrival of girls when the college went fully co-ed in 1995 – not only did they bring self-motivation but they raised the academic bar. A concerted effort to improve results through academic rigour, targeting and 'working smarter' has paid off – now among top 20 UK co-ed independent schools. In 2017, 59 per cent A*/A (84 per cent A*-B) at A level. Maths, history, English literature, psychology and physics are most popular subjects, with strongest showing in theatre studies, art, and geography. Out of the running for GCSE league tables due to IGCSEs, which parents gladly accept, but a commendable 70 per cent A*-A/9-7 in 2017. Prestigious '10 club' – tie for at least 10 A*/A grades at GCSE. Language provision has broadened – on joining senior school, pupils choose two modern foreign languages (most having been introduced to French, German and Spanish in the prep, not to mention Latin). Pre-empts the changes to GCSEs which head fears will discourage language take-up.

Streams and sets for most subjects meet needs of all, including the gifted. A dedicated learning support team of three sensitively supports 30 students with specific learning needs (charged as an extra), including dyslexia and Asperger's. All international students are offered one or two EAL lessons a week and reach IGCSE level (required for university admission). However, this is not solely an academic day school – head recoils at the suggestion of a hothouse. 'We won't sacrifice the breadth that comes with a boarding school curriculum – we just want to do everything well and keep some balance.' Broad-based academic intake – 'results are due to the quality of teaching and learning,' emphasises head.

Bring Your Own Device recently introduced – Wifi all over. Pioneering use of geographical information system technology. Interactive science action centre. Solid traditional teaching facilities too.

Games, options, the arts: Successful sports: unbeaten seasons in rugby and hockey now the norm – several ex-international players offer top level coaching and inspiring role models. County hockey and district netball and swimming champions – swimming a major sport in fabulous pool; tennis and water-polo also popular. Prep pupils national finalists in pretty much everything – rugby, hockey, cricket, netball, even football, although only an after-school club. Standout individuals too, notably swimming and tennis.

Head recoils at the suggestion of a hothouse. 'We won't sacrifice the breadth that comes with a boarding school curriculum – we just want to do everything well'

Music important – around 10 per cent of pupils perform to grade 8 or beyond. Pianos in most boarding houses, plenty of airy practice rooms. Much-appreciated resident college musician supports in readiness for exams and accompanies. Orchestra and all manner of ensembles large and small. Twenty concerts a year, including choral work for pupils, parents and staff, plus a couple of ventures into the world of opera. Well-equipped theatre provides venue for some stunning musical and dramatic performances (set for recent production of Cabaret still in evidence, though slowly transforming into Scottish heathland for next epic – Macbeth). New art centre with stunningly mature GCSE and A level work on display in spacious ateliers.

Trips and tours across the globe including India, New York, Malawi, South Africa, Barbados, and a fair few closer to home too. Wide choice of extracurricular activities including D of E (the college is the leading school in east Hertfordshire) debating (standing room only for some hot topics) and community work.

Boarding: Four senior boarding houses – two for boys and two for girls. Full, weekly and flexi boarding, the latter most popular. Saturday lessons and sport mean everyone is at school till Saturday afternoon. Most go home on Saturday nights, but eg paintballing and visits to theme parks organised for those still in school. Own comfortable boarding house for prep pupils. Few full boarders but 50+ stay a minimum of two nights a week – most popular Wednesdays (sport after school) and Friday (Saturday morning lie-in for mum and dad).

Background and atmosphere: Founded in 1868 as a non-conformist boarding school, with aspirations of securing an effective and Christian education on terms that should not be beyond the reach of the middle class generally, originally sited on the outskirts of Bishop's Stortford. Once boys only, now 45 per cent girls. Full-on Saturday school for all from 8.20am until 3.40pm has its detractors, but most accept it's necessary if children are to make the most of all that's on offer.

Despite recent new developments and proximity to town, the 130 acre campus still has a rural feel. Governors canny through the economic downturn and fees have remained relatively low. Indeed, an ambitious programme of facilities upgrade ongoing and due for completion to coincide with the school's 150th anniversary in 2018. New addition to existing pretty Edwardian building under way when we visited, which provides a new girls' day house (replacing the previous one), and there will be another girls' house added. Brand new boys' day and boarding houses are next on the agenda – much more economical to design from scratch than to bring the existing original School House building up to modern living standards; instead it will be repurposed as offices for the head and administrative teams, plus 11 classrooms. By the end of the project, head predicts the college 'won't just be beautiful, it will be magnificent!'

Despite these physical changes, 'We are a large school, but we retain the small-school feel,' says head, and unabashedly goes on to describe Bishop's Stortford College as 'cuddly'. 'A really positive environment,' suggested a parent. Certainly the all-pervading ethos is one of kindness, caring and humanity – a quality the head has discovered is neatly defined by the Zulu word 'ubuntu' (which we went home and looked up – perfect). 'Pupils here are mutually supportive,' says head. 'They work hard. When asked why, they simply reply "why not?"' Head is keen to resist the spoon-feeding culture in favour of promoting independent learning in preparation for life. EPQ is popular in the sixth form as is the college's own research project programme – no UCAS points but an academic challenge and something to talk about at university interviews and mention on personal statement.

Certainly the all-pervading ethos is one of kindness, caring and humanity – a quality the head has discovered is neatly defined by the Zulu word 'ubuntu'

Superb library with two-storey bow windows, well stocked with books, DVDs (multi-lingual) and CDs. Ferguson Lecture Theatre is a cosy additional space, where assemblies can be relayed from Mem(orial) Hall, the original, atmospheric school hall. Sixth form Stars in their Eyes a sell-out. Sports hall with fitness suite in the gallery. Five all weather netball/tennis courts. Two floodlit Astro pitches.

Dining hall large and functional; food plentiful and tasty, on a three-week menu rotation (our sixth form guides tell us the pupils' request for 'chicken zinger' through the school council was provided by the catering manager and it was very tasty).

Pastoral care, well-being and discipline: Few discipline problems – head likes 'to give pupils a chance to get it right'. Strong house system offers support. 'The school expects a lot from the children and as a parent that is exactly what I want,' said one parent.

Pupils and parents: 'There really is not a type of child or parent,' said a parent. 'Plenty of commuters as London is so close, but there are farmers and scientists and just about all professions going.'

Pupils 'normal, not arrogant,' says head. 'I'm not keen on elitism.' Most from within daily travelling distance; about 65 per cent of boarders from overseas, including Europe and the Far East. Parents described by one of their number as 'friendly, sociable, aspirational, encouraging of their children'. Appreciate weekly contact by e-newsletter and the twice yearly news magazine.

Long list of distinguished former pupils includes presenter Andy Peebles, rugby player Ben Clarke, writer Dick Clement and educationalist Professor John Ferguson. The world of espionage features prominently via former heads of MI5, Sir Stephen Lander and Sir Dick White, and Peter Wright, author of Spycatcher.

Entrance: Pupils are selected via interviews, entrance tests and school references; takes a range of abilities, not just academic high-fliers. At 13 majority come from the prep school but also takes some 12-15 external entrants annually; small number join at 14, in time for GCSEs. Some 30-40 join in the sixth form – entrance is by interview and written tests; need at least five B/6 grades at GCSE with A*-B/9-6 in A level subject choices.

Exit: A handful – some 15 per cent – leaves after GCSEs to study A levels elsewhere. Nearly all sixth formers head to university. One to Oxbridge in 2017, plus one medic. Subjects range from motorsport engineering at Derby to natural sciences at Durham to theatre and performance at Leeds to social anthropology at LSE.

Money matters: Assistance for those in financial need. Academic, music, art and sport scholarships offered. 'A considerable proportion of our income goes on bursaries and scholarships,' says the head. 'If a child is talented but his or her parents can't afford us, we will do what we can to help.'

Remarks: Without five centuries of history to draw on, Bishop's Stortford College isn't widely known, but is among the generation of schools founded in the Victorian era that are quietly succeeding. Local word-of-mouth is enough to keep it oversubscribed – without needing to worry about recruiting for tomorrow, the head and governors can look further into securing the college's position well into the future.

Bishop's Stortford College Prep School

10

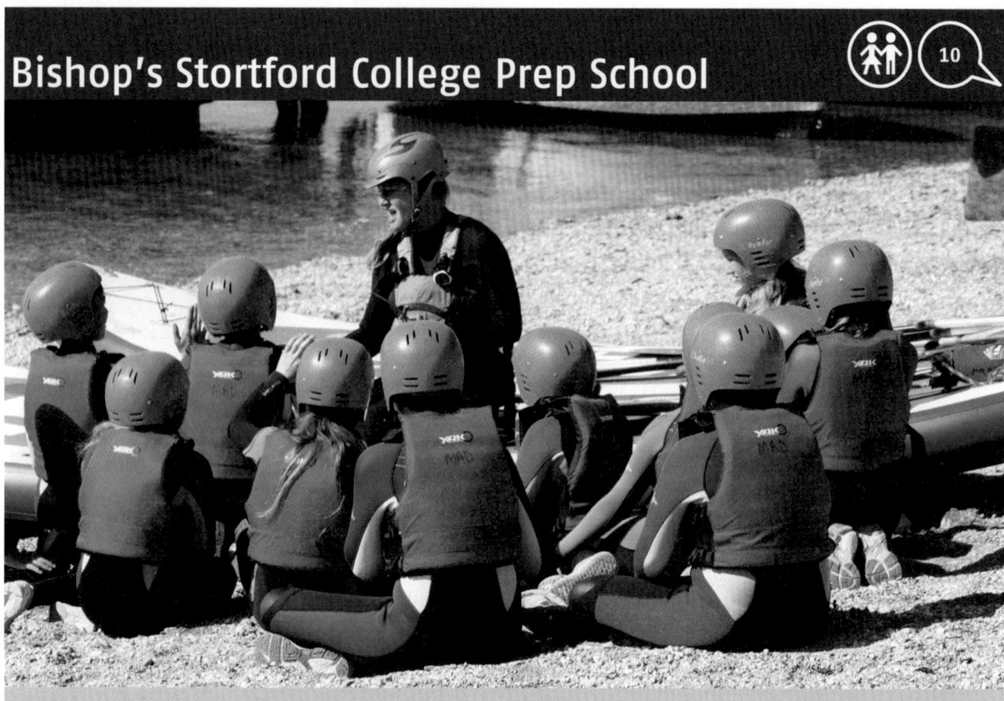

Maze Green Road, Bishop's Stortford, Hertfordshire CM23 2PH

01279 838607 | psadmissions@bishopsstortfordcollege.org | www.bishopsstortfordcollege.org

Ages: 4–13 (boarding from 9)

Pupils: 575; Boarders: 52 (mostly flexi)

Day: £8,745 – £15,132 pa; Boarding: £20,010 – £22,857 pa

Linked school: Bishop's Stortford College, 881

Headmaster: Since 2013, Bill Toleman BA MSc FRGS (40s), previously head of Yarm Prep School. Before that, deputy head at King's Worcester. Read geography at Nottingham University and has since added an MSc in educational management and leadership and fellowship of the Royal Geographical Society. Affable and so unassuming that when we ask him to describe his leadership style he calls in his PA, settles her in an armchair and closes the door on his way out. 'Approachable and informal,' she smiles, as soon as the latch clicks; adjectives bandied about by parents include 'child-centred', 'fair' and 'proactive'. Certainly in his short tenure to date he has systematically swept away all signs of stuffiness – entrance exams are now sat in a multiplicity of cosy classrooms rather than in serried rows in one huge daunting sports hall, for example, and parents and pupils alike pop in at all hours, keen for a chat. 'If people want to come and see me I'm very happy to see them,' he says, although when the queue becomes too long or other matters are too pressing his PA honours visitors with an appointment in the head's diary. 'The children love that,' she laughs. To his regret, no longer has time to teach his beloved geography, although helps out with fieldwork (most recently accompanying lower third to Walton-on-the-Naze). Enjoys surfing in North Devon and still plays occasional cricket and Sunday rugby. Married, with three grown-up sons.

Entrance: Entrance to the pre-prep is by an informal group assessment session and there is a long lead-in for tinies registered to start reception ('messy play' session in progress when we visited). External candidates for the additional 20 places made available at 7+ must sit the entrance exam to the prep school (English, maths and reading), spend a morning in school and are encouraged to meet the head with parents; no assessment required of existing pupils. A further 20 places offered at 10+ and 20 more at 11+ (academic and music scholarships available) to give a total of 100 pupils per year group by lower third (year 7). No sibling discount or preference given.

Exit: Some 95 per cent plus straight to senior school. Remaining handful to other, further-flung boarding schools (in recent years Harrow, Stowe, Millfield, Uppingham, Shrewsbury, Benenden) and a few to state at 11+. As Bishop's Stortford College is selective, prep parents are given plenty of advance warning if their child's ability to keep up after transfer is in question. Other, suitable schools, recommended. Fairly rare occurrence as school prefers to tackle underachievement to keep pupils under its wing.

Remarks: Stunning green and leafy setting right on the edge of town extending in all to 130 acres of rolling Hertfordshire. Accessed via a lane of warm, red-brick Victorian houses and school buildings, some sensitively modernised, others waiting. Nearly all with privet hedges and ancient roses. Prep and senior pupils co-exist harmoniously on the site. Main prep building now all sparkling glass and purple carpet, thanks to £3m extension and refurb. Super reception area, hall with stage and roomy classrooms. Art rooms, including kiln, plus science labs across the attractive brick courtyard (complete with happy preppies chatting on steps, idyllically). Wonderful new library with floor-to-ceiling vistas. Shares with seniors music facilities, super 50-metre indoor pool in own timber-clad edifice, sports hall and hard courts, plus pitches as far as the eye can see. No wonder prep children look relaxed, contented – and well-exercised.

'This is a purposeful, happy place to come to school – it has to be,' says head, 'because we're here for a long time.' Pre-prep for age 4 to 7, prep for 7 to 13s. While pre-prep makes use of national curriculum year group terminology, traditional names still charmingly in use in the prep – so lower and upper shell are followed by forms 1 and 2, then lower and upper third (continuing into the senior). Although less than 20 per cent of prep pupils board, school operates a boarding school week for its pupils aged over 7, with long weekdays until 5pm for the eldest and Saturday morning school for all, afternoons for form 1 and above.

'Children work hard here because they want to, not because we make them,' says head; said a parent, 'My son has been coaxed, encouraged and inspired to push himself and achieve the best he could.' Academic streaming begins in year 4, plus setting for maths. Classical civ for years 5 and 6, Latin to add to Spanish, German and French for years 7 and 8. DT and drama on the curriculum from year 3 up. Lots of visits and trips, as well as speakers in – curricular activities included in fees. Bring Your Own Device recently introduced for top two years – prep pupils say they use iPads and equivalent in 80 per cent of lessons and that they really help with self-organisation. Wifi all over.

Sport serious here and all involved. National finalists in pretty much everything – rugby, hockey, cricket, netball, even football, although only an after-school club. Standout individuals too, notably swimming and tennis. Lots of music – choirs, groups and tours.

'Have-a-go' culture is alive and well. One afternoon each week devoted to a 'wheel' of activities which changes with the term (street dance and yoga to survival skills). All pupils allocated to a house (either at random or according to family connection) – fierce competition through all manner of contests and quizzes. Highest achieving house wins supper with the headmaster. Fundraising through teddy bears' picnics, film nights, doughnut sales and auctions in aid of the annual chosen charity – £10,000 plus donated every year. Head meets prefects for 'biscuits and a chat' half-termly, and drops into lessons and activities unannounced.

Affable and so unassuming that when we ask him to describe his leadership style he calls in his PA, settles her in an armchair and closes the door on his way out

Strong pastoral care network begins with form tutor as first port of call for parents, then heads of year. Pyramid above of senior teacher (pastoral), director of studies, operations, then deputy head and head. 'Compassionate' teaching and learning support for those with mild SEN much praised by parents of children who have benefited – IEPS, one-to-ones, additional time in exams.

Own comfortable boarding house for prep pupils. Few full boarders but 50+ stay a minimum of two nights a week – most popular Wednesdays (sport after school) and Friday (Saturday morning lie-in for mum and dad). Vast majority of pupils throughout school very local and only half a dozen international students in the prep – EAL support offered.

Parents in the main professionals or city, some farmers – same as in senior as pupils grow up through the school with few additions. 'There really is not a type of child or parent,' said a parent. 'Plenty of commuters as London is so close, but there are farmers and scientists and just about all professions going.'

Prep head's relationship with college head 'mutually supportive' and clearly on the same page.

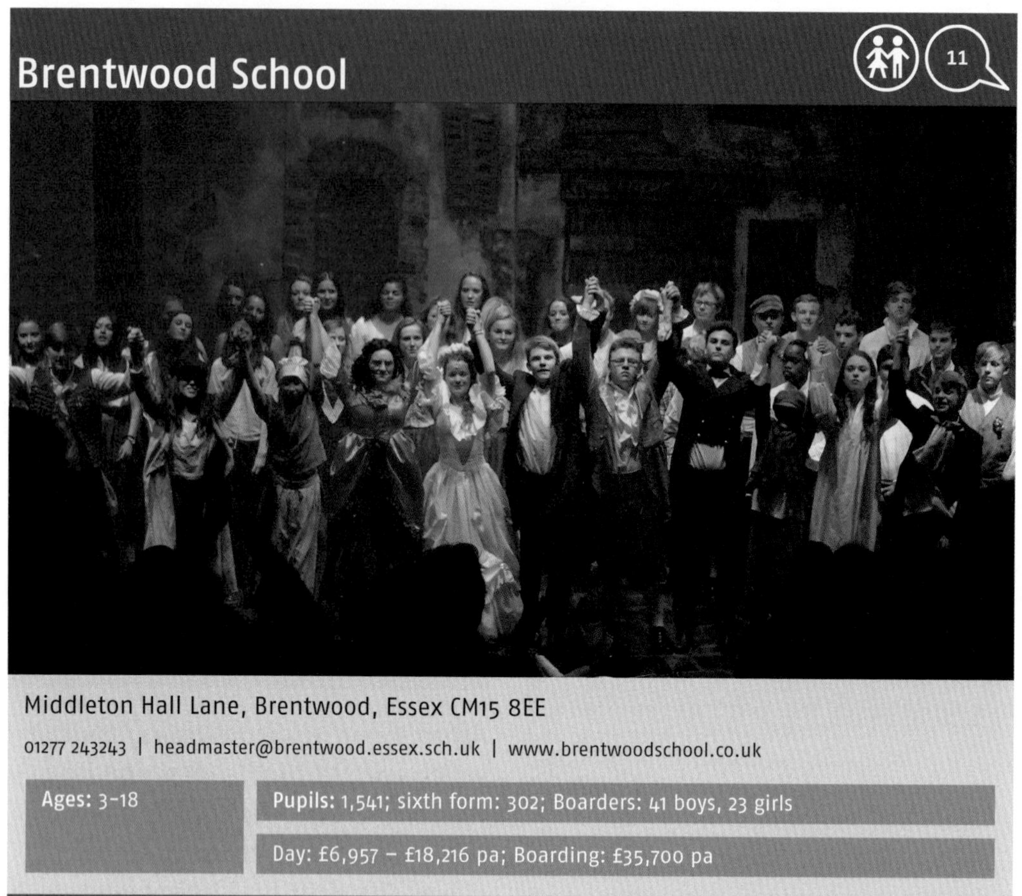

Brentwood School

11

Middleton Hall Lane, Brentwood, Essex CM15 8EE

01277 243243 | headmaster@brentwood.essex.sch.uk | www.brentwoodschool.co.uk

Ages: 3–18

Pupils: 1,541; sixth form: 302; Boarders: 41 boys, 23 girls

Day: £6,957 – £18,216 pa; Boarding: £35,700 pa

Headmaster: Since 2004, Ian Davies PGCE MA (50s), theology degrees from Oxford and Cambridge. Previously head of St Dunstan's College. Taught religious studies at Sackville School and became head of year and head of RE at The Latymer, Edmonton. An ISI inspector, member of D of E National Advisory Council, and helped select naval officers for training at Dartmouth for the Admiralty Interview Board. Very approachable – once volunteered as a guinea pig for a nitrogen experiment during science lesson where his hands were set alight. 'It didn't hurt at all, as it burnt above my hand, and the children loved it.' He sees the school as 'educationally... more sophisticated than most' thanks to its diamond structure, educating boys and girls in separate gender classes from age 11 to 16, but together at other ages. 'We all learn in different ways and I think there are gender differences and also gender stereotypes which need to be cracked.' So the school employs all 'the benefits of single sex education' while enabling pupils to 'also get the social benefits of choir, orchestra, combined cadets' and more 'as part of a co-educational environment'. He adds, 'Nothing pleases me more than having a girl who is great at maths and physics go off to university to do engineering.' Considers himself 'very lucky' in his career, having 'worked with great people all the way through' and being mentored by some 'great heads' in the past.

Preparatory school head: Since 2011, Jason Whiskerd BA PGCE. Previously head of Aldenham Preparatory School in Elstree, Hertfordshire and deputy head of the King's School (junior) in Chester. Read history and politics at Trinity College, Carmarthen (University of Wales) and serves as an ISI inspector of other preparatory schools. He is also an active member of the Independent Association of Prep Schools (IAPS).

Mr Whiskerd is a keen sportsman, having played cricket and rugby at regional level and, as testament to his Welsh roots (he attended Llandovery College as a boy), Welsh rugby and Swansea City are his passion. He is married to a junior school teacher and has three daughters attending the prep and senior school. A friendly man: extended a hearty welcome and warm handshake when we visited.

Academic matters: They start learning oral French from year 1 'since this is a time when they are most receptive to learning a new language'. Verbal reasoning is taught from year 4 and Latin from year 6. There is emphasis on 'learning habits for life' so lots of push to get children to think for themselves, ask questions and 'look at things in detail'. From year 3 they are introduced to a house system so they can build relationships with older pupils. By the time they get to year 6 pupils take on roles as prefects, house captains, council representatives and more. Plenty of preparation for the move to senior school including a Q&A session with year 7s. Able children also well catered for with plenty of challenging extension opportunities. We know of at least one boy who showed aptitude for maths and was given the chance to sit his maths GCSE at age 9. A couple of parents described similar experiences where their children had been labelled as 'slow' and 'easily distracted' at previous schools, only to move them to Brentwood and discover that the real problem was that their children had been bored, under-stimulated and capable of more.

GCSE results in 2017 were slightly down on the previous year's: 57 per cent graded A*-A/9-7. Alongside critical and creative thinking and the core subjects, they study French and Latin in year 7, and choose from German, ancient Greek or Spanish in year 8. IGCSE in several subjects; head sees it as 'a stepping stone to the IB'.

At A level in 2017, 44 per cent A*/A grades and 71 per cent A*-B. School offers 26 curriculum subjects, plus other activities such as law, cooking at university, Italian, peer mentoring training and sports leadership. IB scores averaged 37 points.

School encourages creative and critical thinking across all subjects, whether improving goal-scoring in sport, performing West Side Story in German, or applying maths in the composition of music. The school 'teaches you to think for yourself and how it is up to you to determine whether you succeed or not,' said a pupil. The syllabus is 'flexibly adapted to suit all pupils' needs' and 'able pupils do not get bored here', says the school. Parents agree with this, saying that although children are set early in year 7 in French and maths, these groups are not set in concrete and support is available if needed. 'I think it really is important that the children are not stuck with a label of being really clever or really daft,' said a parent. 'That doesn't happen at all. It is very, very flexible.'

Very approachable – once volunteered as a guinea pig for a nitrogen experiment during science lesson where his hands were set alight. 'It didn't hurt at all'

EAL support provided to 35 pupils, largely through teachers that have lived and worked abroad. The learning and development team also provides support to around 50 students with special educational needs. This includes an Individual Education Plan, one-to-one tuition, subject support and lunchtime drop in sessions. The department is very successful – some who receive additional support make such 'good and exceptional progress' that they 'sometimes outperform their peers', noted the ISI.

Games, options, the arts: There is a long sporting tradition here. This was one of three independent schools selected as an official Olympic training venue and it made world headlines when it opened up its doors to rescue an African Paralympic team

left stranded at the airport with neither host nor facilities after a funding promise failed to materialise.

Sport is one of the scholarships offered; football, cricket, hockey, rugby and netball coaches often successful sportspeople. Pupils have played at national and international level in fencing, water polo, cricket, football, squash, tennis and netball. School has won the Public Schools Fencing Competition 'more than 30 times since 1962'. Both girls' athletics teams have made it to the English schools' track and field national finals. One England U19 cricketer was offered a contract with Essex. At any one time around 400 pupils are out representing the school in a whole variety of sports. Alongside sports hall, pool, gym and dance studio, there are glass-backed squash courts, fitness suite and a fencing salle, plus extensive playing fields and a full-size running track.

Art, music and drama are also well catered for. Many pupils' works are exhibited at the annual art exhibition and school also tries to instil appreciation for art whether pupils 'consider themselves to be "arty" or not'. Various competitions include the popular water colour competition and the head's sculpting competition. DT and ICT are taught with art and food tech in the Hardy Amies Design Centre, equipped with its own library and computers. Recently a group of students scooped the top prize in an international design award with their life-saving 'glow' glove. The six, led by a student who 'a year ago wouldn't have said boo to a goose', took first prize in the annual Virtual Ventura competition against opposition from 300 teams. 'We thought about different things and narrowed it down to safety as during the dark people don't see cyclists very well.' Their winning design went on display at the Design Museum in London.

'I think it really is important that the children are not stuck with a label of being really clever or really daft,' said a parent. 'That doesn't happen. It is very flexible'

Music and drama are taught in a separate building equipped with rehearsal studios and 14 practice rooms. We witnessed one group using Sibelius to compose 'an answer in response to a melody' in preparation for their GCSE creative task: 'We have to pick the right melody chords to make it work. The answer must relate to it but not repeat it'. Many students get involved in the school symphony orchestra, big band (which creates its own CDs), choir or choral society, and the regular

Bright and lively classrooms, decorated with pupil's work, are housed in both 19th and 16th century buildings

musicals and house music concerts. A number of ex-pupils are exhibitioners at London music colleges or hold organ scholarships at university; there are two organs in the school, one in the music hall and another in the chapel. Prep school has two orchestras and a junior choir that rehearses weekly and has performed at the royal Albert Hall. On the day of our visit many of the prep school classrooms were empty – our guide seemed baffled by this and was somewhat relieved when we happened upon a very noisy music lesson where children were exploring how to synchronise sound for a silent film. They were clearly having fun with flute, cymbals, drums, voice and more, but we got the feeling that the cover teacher may have pulled the short straw.

Similar story with drama: three major annual productions covering every genre from musicals to comedy to classics. Examples include Macbeth featuring video clips showing the war in the Middle East; Antigone performed with modern ballet choreographed by a student; a third year production of Arabian Nights; and West Side Story in German, all performed in the school's 400-seat auditorium. Mainly girls, but a few boys too, take part in dance showcases including tap, jazz and street.

Too many extracurricular activities to name: Trivial Pursuits, cross-country, table tennis, chess, D of E, Cine & Literatura, a Spanish film club, public speaking. 'You have to choose at least three; it's compulsory now,' we heard a year 7 pupil tell a sixth former. The Sir Antony Browne Society invites guest speakers on a wide range of current political, financial and medical topics. One of the most popular activities at the school is the 152-year-old CCF, one of the largest in the country, which has been enlisted by the DfE to help set up branches at other schools. It really creates a buzz in the atmosphere on Fridays when its 500-odd members come to school dressed in combat gear, ready for the afternoon and weekend activities. These include map reading, camp craft, basic first aid, hill walking, canoeing, flying and skydiving. 'CCF is a big thing here,' said one pupil. 'It opens you up to a lot of things you might not have been able to do', and at very low cost. Other pupils join the community service unit and help raise thousands for charities in the local area and abroad. With so many competitions there is no excuse for not finding something you like, although one student did complain about the lack of a house dance competition.

Boarding: The two boarding houses are a 'home from home' for the small boarding community of some 23 girls and 41 boys, 60 per cent of whom are from overseas. Both are situated off campus, 'so you don't feel that you're there all day'. They are run like a 'well-oiled machine,' say the husband and wife houseparents, with regular routines (for homework, bedtimes and activities) and good links between houseparents, teachers and parents. As well as email, the 'children are Skyping every single night and we are Skyping with parents almost on a daily basis. I go into the rooms and they say, "Say hello to my mum".'

Background and atmosphere: The story behind the school's foundation is a history lesson in itself. During the English reformation a 19-year-old Protestant was burnt on order of Sir Antony Browne, then acting as a magistrate on behalf of Queen Mary. He purchased Weald Hall and land for the school in 1557 as an act of penance. The school received its motto in 1622 from the pen of John Donne, dean of St Paul's. It also has its own prayer and song. Was a boys' grammar school, principally boarding, for many years. Admitted girls into the sixth form in the mid 1970s and into the main school in 1988.

The prep school was established in 1892 and moved to its present site at Middleton Hall in 1949; became co-educational in 1999. Pre-prep (ages 3 to 7) opened in 1995 and has its own grounds and buildings. In 2013, the pre-prep and the prep were amalgamated under the one headship of Mr Whiskerd, providing a seamless progression from 3 to 11. There is a strong sense of the traditional alongside the modern – bright and lively classrooms, decorated with pupil's work, are housed in both 19th and 16th century buildings. In the gorgeous chapel (1868), pupils listen to biblical stories with a modern twist, for example, an account from one of the gospels about the danger of judging others, delivered alongside a screening of the Susan Boyle audition on Britain's Got Talent. Art and science is taught in an old stable block and Middleton Hall itself features stained glass windows and stucco ceilings. On the wall in the reception area is a large, colourful picture illustrating what it means to live by the Brentwood School motto of Virtue, Learning and Manners: 'We teach our children that the opportunities we create are best enjoyed when others benefit from them too'.

Set in the heart of the Essex town of Brentwood, across the road from the cathedral, the school stands on a 72-acre site. Not much is left of the Weald Hall save a few ruins. The Old Big School, built in 1568, still has the original front door and is

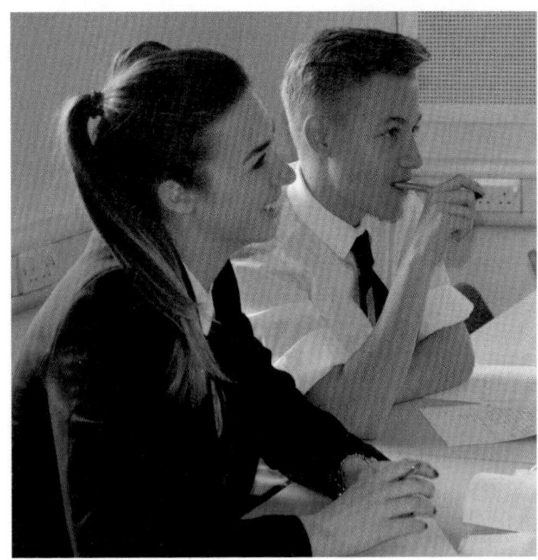

used for lectures, meetings and discussions. There is a beautiful Victorian chapel built in 1868, with arches, beams and stained glass windows detailing the narratives of Moses, Elijah and other biblical prophets, as well as patron saints of the Great War. It seats 320, so cannot contain the whole school at once, but the six year groups take it in turn to have a fortnightly service there.

More recent buildings include the science block, opened by the Queen in 1957, the 1986 Courage Hall sports centre, and the 1999 Hardy Amies design building. The refurbished sixth form block which houses the 400 seat auditorium has distinctively Victorian style arched roofs. The Bean Academic Centre, 'the intellectual heart of the school', includes a lecture theatre, café, social and study spaces. The main grounds resemble a university campus quadrangle and seem to run as far as the eye can see: beyond the rugby posts is Mill House, the girls' boarding house, Hough House, the boys' boarding house, the prep school and then the running tracks and fields.

Pastoral care, well-being and discipline: Parents say 'pastoral care here is excellent' and that 'the older pupils help the younger pupils'. They value the peer mentoring room where sixth formers make hot chocolate for younger pupils, who can sit and talk if they have a problem. Year 6 pupils are trained in peer mediation and this helps 'pupils to resolve their own problems in the playground'. Bullying is rare, and the few 'misunderstandings' that do arise are 'nipped in the bud by the school very quickly,' say parents. One, whose daughter had been home educated and found the first few weeks a little daunting, commented on how well she had been helped to settle in.

Pupils have good relationships with their form tutors and teachers – 'everyone is helpful here', said a year 7 pupil. 'The teachers do tend to treat the children as adults,' said a parent. 'They communicate openly with them, so the children are not frightened to say, "I want to speak to you about something".'

The house system fosters a sense of belonging and there is good support from a careers service, with an annual careers convention. Parents report that initial concerns are likely to involve ensuring children can cope with homework alongside the large numbers of extracurricular opportunities. 'One of the things we were told at a meeting before starting is that you've got to be organised. My son comes into school early to get homework done because he wants to do swimming and football after school.'

Plenty of contact with parents through subject, house and tutor reports and parents' evenings, but parents also appreciate in particular the introductory meeting held for parents of new year 7s. The school is 'really on the ball like that,' said a parent who has two daughters in the school, one in the sixth form and another in year 9. 'Whatever topic it might be, you get the information in time to talk about it.'

Pupils and parents: Parents are mostly professional. There is a mix of backgrounds, races and religions here, with the majority being white English. 'Although we are a Christian school we welcome pupils of all faiths,' says the school. Many pupils move from the prep to the senior, others come from local independent and state schools. The school also has a number of international students (about 60 per cent of boarders, plus a few day pupils) from the Ukraine, Russia and other Eastern European countries, Central Europe and the Far East including China.

It really creates a buzz in the atmosphere on Fridays when its 500-odd members come to school dressed in combat gear, ready for the weekend activities

A number of notable former pupils including Douglas Adams, author of the Hitchhiker's Guide to the Galaxy, Sir Hardy Amies, couturier and dressmaker (he designed the school uniform), Lord Black of Brentwood, executive director of The Telegraph, Frank Lampard, footballer, Jack Straw, former lord chancellor and secretary of state for justice, and many more.

Our guide seemed somewhat relieved when we happened upon a very noisy music lesson where children were exploring how to synchronise sound for a silent film. They were clearly having fun

Entrance: Pupils assessed on language and dexterity skills for entry into the early years (about 40 places). Twenty places are available for external year 3 entry (age 7) and candidates sit an entrance test in English and maths in January. 'They [the questions] are on the national curriculum for the child's age so I needn't have worried,' said a parent. 'They make the children feel at ease too.'

Year 7 entry by maths, English and verbal reasoning exams examination and an interview to 'assess a pupil's intellectual curiosity, potential and flair for learning'. Sixth form entrance is by interview and successful GCSE results (generally at least six B/6 grades).

Exit: Over three-quarters of prep school pupils go on to senior school. They sit the same 11+ exam as external applicants and are prepared well (parents are warned a year or so in advance if the school perceives any problems). All candidates are interviewed if they do very well (for an academic scholarship) or if they have struggled on the day (have not quite achieved the standard). A few pupils go on to local grammar schools in the Chelmsford area.

Most – about 80 per cent – of senior school pupils stay on to sixth form and most proceed to university. In 2017, seven to Oxbridge and over half to other top 20 universities such as Bristol and Exeter, or further afield to eg Harvard. Three medics. The school also helps those students who want to go straight into work through the alumni association and network of ex-pupils.

Money matters: A good variety of scholarships, of up to 50 per cent, on offer to top academic scorers in the entrance exam or those with specialist talents in art, drama, music, choral and sport. There are also means-tested bursaries of up to 100 per cent. Sixth form scholarships valued at between £500 and £1,000, offered via a two-hour critical thinking paper.

Remarks: Strong on values and has all the facilities and opportunities needed to provide a child with a rounded education. Very impressive.

Chigwell School

12

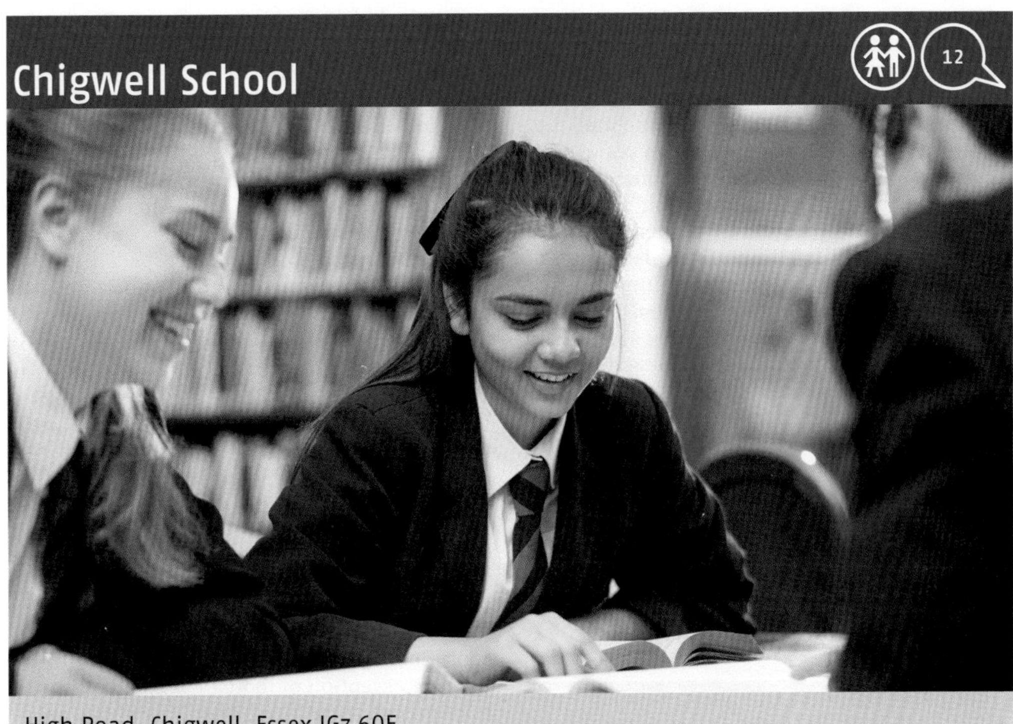

High Road, Chigwell, Essex IG7 6QF

020 8501 5700 | hm@chigwell-school.org | www.chigwell-school.org

Ages: 13–18

Pupils: 423; sixth form: 168; Boarders: 30 sixth form

Day: £16,995 pa; Boarding: £29,070 pa

Headmaster: Since 2007, Mr Michael Punt MA MSc PGCE (40s), a physicist who lives on site with his wife Gill and their three sons, all of whom attend the school – a fact that many parents say 'keeps him in tune with pupils' and parents' experiences of Chigwell.' His calm and positive influence is palpable throughout the school, with parents describing him as 'approachable,' 'well-liked' and 'respected.' In fact, many were swayed against the local competition purely on the basis of meeting him. 'He doesn't just talk at you in some grand hall – he chats with you in a relaxed way and seems to know exactly what you want to know,' said one.

Pupils also speak enthusiastically about him. 'He knows every one of us, as well as taking an interest in us,' one pupil told us. Not for him a chief executive type headship, but rather a personal touch that's helped by the size of the school and the fact that he and colleagues interview every child that comes here. Mainly, though, it seems to be down to his hands-on approach – he teaches pupils, does a lot of mock interviews and is often seen around the school. The week before our visit, he'd had all the prefects round for a meal and he eats regularly with the boarders.

Having grown up in nearby Brentwood, he did his degree at Oxford and his masters at Imperial, then worked at St Dunstan's College as a physics teacher, working his way up to head of year and head of physics, after which he did a stint at The Perse School, Cambridge, as deputy head (academic) where he continued to climb the ranks until moving to Chigwell.

Academic matters: Excellent results, which have risen steadily – 68 per cent of GCSE grades were A*-A/9-7 in 2017. Head puts this down to pupils' positive and conscientious attitude to learning and an excellent relationship with teachers, both points which the latest ISI inspection praised. 'Teachers are dedicated, both in and out of the classroom, and they very rarely shout,' one pupil told us. 'I was amazed when my son emailed teachers about his essay during half term and got detailed feedback the same day, but that's how it is here,' said a parent. The tone of the communication seems to be spot on, too. 'In many schools, it's either too matey or terribly stand-offish, but they seem to have got the balance just right here,' said one parent. Lessons interactive and busy, with plenty of IT embedded across all subjects – and a pilot of tablet-embedded learning going on in years 9 and 12 when we visited. 'We'll see how it goes and may well expand it in future,' the head told us.

Low turnover of around 6-7 per cent a year for teaching staff, with applicants for replacements of a high calibre, and they must be willing to teach beyond their subject, with the school following the somewhat old-fashioned model of all teachers getting involved in an extracurricular activity. 'It's not unusual to see maths staff getting stuck into games or English teachers helping to run chess clubs here,' says the head. 'It's the Chigwell way, this family-type approach.' Head regularly observes all teaching staff and has implemented a rigorous structure that ensures constant reflection, whilst the Teaching Skills Group means staff regularly share good practice. Tracking is big here – both pastorally and academically, with the aim of the two working closely together.

'Every aspect of music is amazing here, from the singing right through to every instrument you can think of, along with many you didn't even know existed,' said one parent

On entry, four classes of 22 maximum, although class sizes drop considerably for at GCSE level and to around a dozen at A level. Latin and French taught to all year 7s, and all try German and Spanish in year 8. In year 9, all pupils continue French and select one or more of the other three languages, with all pupils doing at least one modern language for GCSE. Mandarin also taught as extracurricular from junior school upwards. Setting in French and maths from year 7 and some in German from year 9. English and sciences setted from year 10. Regular testing means there can be movement between sets to start with, although this is uncommon later on. Homework taken seriously, although it's never set for the following day.

At GCSE, all students take one modern language and the vast majority do the three sciences. Other popular options include geography, history, RE, with a strong interest also seen in other languages, drama, DT and music. 'We don't have option blocks – we make the timetable work around the pupils' choices,' says head, who adds that there are no early GCSEs taken here, although the top maths set in year 11 take additional maths.

Wide choice of subjects at A levels. Economics, maths, sciences, geography and English are strong, but psychology, drama and DT are on the rise too, enforcing Chigwell's reputation as a place for the all-rounder. In 2017, 83 per cent A*-B and 51 per cent A*/A at A level.

Plenty of extension opportunities, including EPQ and HPQ (latter at GCSE level), essay competitions and Olympiads. Enrichment programme impressive and includes subject-specific groups, such as law groups, medics' groups, social sciences groups etc. University preparation stunningly good, with guidance for UCAS applications starting in the February of the lower sixth, with plenty of targeted guidance and support, and mock interviews aplenty.

Junior school pupils screened on entry for SEN, with further testing in the senior school. Learning support provided throughout the school as necessary either inside or outside the classroom. Not a school for severe learning disabilities, however, with only one statemented when we visited.

Games, options, the arts: Mass participation in sport does what it says on the tin here, with the possible exception of football, which one parent told us is all about the A team. Core boys' sports include football (first term), hockey (second term) and cricket and athletics (third term). For girls, it's hockey (first term), netball (send term) and rounders and athletics (third term), along with some football and cricket also in the summer term. Other sports include golf (played at nearby club), swimming, basketball and badminton. School punches above its weight in competitions, regularly getting through to regional finals, along with national finals for football and hockey.

Outdoor facilities are vast, with 100 acres of playing fields, including Astroturf, surrounding this small school, and indoor facilities are being steadily improved through an ambitious development plan. Pupils particularly keen to have an indoor pool, rather than just the small outdoor pool they currently have, and many want to see the unfancy sports centre updated – both projects under consideration.

The drama centre is an eye-catching red-brick building with impressively professional facilities – foyer big enough for pre-theatre drinks receptions; 170-seat theatre designed for use by the whole school community; green room; rehearsal and teaching spaces; and dressing rooms. All children use it for weekly drama up until the end of year 9 and it's also a popular GSCE option, with around a dozen taking drama at A level with great success. Related subject areas, such as theatre make-up and costume design, also taken seriously here, and the centre is used for public speaking, debating and LAMDA too. Numerous productions

'He doesn't just talk at you in some grand hall – he chats with you in a relaxed way and seems to know exactly what you want to know'

take place throughout the year. 'It would be rare to find a child who isn't somehow involved in drama,' says the head.

Music very inclusive, with every other pupil learning an instrument (over 300 lessons per week from 23 visiting music teachers), some of whom play to incredibly high standards (usually one a year to Oxbridge as a choral music scholar). Plenty of opportunities to perform in ensembles, with a wide range of musical tastes catered from swing bands to string bands, as well as rock and pop. The chapel choir, an elite choir for 40 odd students, performs regularly in the likes of Westminster Abbey, Canterbury Cathedral and Yorkminster, and there are plenty of other choirs too. 'Every aspect of music is amazing here, from the singing right through to every instrument you can think of, along with many you didn't even know existed,' said one parent.

Art and DT work closely together in the spacious and hi-tech facilities, with graphics offered as a GCSE option and many pupils going onto study architecture and fine art when they leave. Phenomenally good artwork displayed throughout the school, much of it in 3D.

Huge choice of extracurricular activities, from D of E and scouts to art exhibitions and the inspiring and thought-provoking talks on everything from evolution to restorative justice for schools, which are run as part of the Williams Project, named after philosopher and Chigwell alumnus, Bernard Williams. 'The amount of opportunities here is immense and you'd frankly be seen as a bit daft if you didn't utilise it,' said one student. 'I haven't had a free afternoon in the last three years – but in a good way,' laughed another. A seemingly infinite amount of trips available too, including French and Spanish homestays, hockey tour to South Africa, scout trip to Switzerland, annual ski trip to France, along with smaller scale trips including activity weekends in the likes of Wales and the Lake District. 'We are conscious that there is a broad mix of wealth and make sure we do not offer all five star trips,' says head.

Boarding: Sixth-form only boarders, of whom there are 30 living across four equal-sized boarding houses, either on the school site or just across the road. Hailing from around 16 countries – mostly central and Eastern Europe and China – the boarders are almost all international, and no two boarders who share a language share a room. Everyone agrees they bring a lot to school life, in terms of the insights they provide into other cultures and a more worldly ethos overall – all helped by the fact that they are encouraged to give talks on the issues affecting their homelands. 'The boarders help give the school a homely feel,' added one student.

Boarding houses are inviting and not the least bit institutional. Rooms mostly twin, although the odd one has three beds, and boarders told us 'there's a good balance between houseparents letting you get on with it, and providing clear boundaries.' Each houseparent, who lives in with their family, is a big part of daily life and seen as a major figure in boarders' lives. 'In our house, the parents have children aged 4 and 6 and we always love hanging out with them,' said one pupil. Curfews are 10.30pm on weekdays; 11.30pm at weekends. Daily study time between 7-9pm during weekdays – 'Even if you don't have work to do, you have to respect that others have and be quiet,' one boarder told us.

No shortage of events – the week we visited, they'd just had Divali weekend celebrations and a film night – which day pupils also join in, but boarders welcome the opportunity to be allowed to be self-reliant too. Boarders told us they'd formed close friendships with both other boarders and day pupils and already felt sad about the prospect of leaving the school.

Background and atmosphere: Founded in 1629 by the Reverend Samuel Harsnett, the local vicar, who became Archbishop of York and Chancellor of Cambridge University. Today the original red-brick schoolhouse, which is located on the approach road to the historic high street, forms the centrepiece to this pretty village of neat buildings, punctuated by gardens, blooms and trees. The surrounding playing fields stretch towards Epping Forest and give a rural aspect to the school and some lovely views from the windows of the attractive, low-rise teaching blocks. None of the facilities are more than an easy and pleasant stroll apart, with the junior and senior schools just steps away from one another and the stunning new pre-prep a few minutes' walk away. Buildings all kept up to date, with a nice combination of traditional and contemporary, and new building works always in the pipeline. In 2010, for instance, there were two new boarding houses and catering facilities, along with a sixth form coffee shop, whilst 2013 saw the new pre-prep and science labs. New sixth form centre, with a dining hall extension, new sports hall and indoor swimming pool next on the agenda.

Of particular note is the 1920s chapel, which was built in tribute to fallen alumni and is a mainstay of life here. Pupils usually attend at least once a week for a service (and another weekly service at the local church), but there's plenty of room for all the beliefs represented at this multicultural school, with speech day services including a passage from each of the six major world faiths.

All have lunch in the Harry Potter-esque dining hall (where teachers eat on the stage) and students can have tea at 4pm for no extra cost, as well as breakfast, for which they can bring parents and siblings. 'Every Thursday, our whole family has breakfast here – we love it,' said one parent. Food is plentiful and very good (we tried it ourselves), with healthy options and popular themed days. The uniform is smart and sober – kilts or plain trousers with a navy blazer, though the sixth formers wear office attire.

The boarders are almost all international, and everyone agrees they bring a lot to school life, in terms of the insights they provide into other cultures

No need for intrusive bells here to mark the change of lessons, with pupils making their way around the school in an ordered fashion, and newbies of any age wear a plain tie so they can be spotted and helped when in need. 'This is a harmonious school, with really lovely young people who, in the majority of cases, you'd be proud to have as your own children,' says the head. Indeed, 'happy' was a word used a lot by the pupils we talked to, with several referring to it as one big family. Life really does seem to just flow very smoothly, with laughter never far from earshot. Even communication systems – homework submitted electronically and an electronic noticeboard system, among them – seem to work effortlessly. No wonder old Chigwellians feel such a sense of loyalty, with growing numbers willing to come into do talks, mock interviews and offer work experience.

The school council doesn't seem to have achieved a great deal more than the usual increase in number of water fountains, although they do meet regularly. There's a strong charitable culture, with a committee consisting of staff and pupils who choose the charities to support and raise in excess of £30,000 a year. 'We want to understand the charities we support, we do a lot of promotion around that part too,' says the head, who adds that the school is very much part of the local community, which often joins in with fundraising events.

Pastoral care, well-being and discipline: The transition from junior to senior school is gentle, with parents praising the 'seamless process.' A strong four-house system, and staff who 'really know their pupils', according to the head, mean students are comfortable in the knowledge that they are being 'looked out for'. 'There are lots of personalities among the teachers here, but we all have someone we know we could speak to – a teacher that really stands out for us,' said one pupil, with many of the younger pupils talking about how friendly the older ones are. The school counsellor, employed for two days a week, is also on hand, and works with families where necessary. School promotes a society in which everyone takes responsibility for each other and the wider environment.

Discipline system highly structured, with detentions the most common sanctions, typically for late homework, missing chapel and being late. 'They're not given out willy nilly, so you take it seriously when you get one,' said one pupil. 'The pupils aren't saintly, and they've got a twinkle in their eye, but they're also hard working and really nice. We don't have many behavioural problems,' says the head. Indeed, current head has only made one permanent exclusion, although occasionally there are temporary ones, for instances such as smoking and repeated misbehaviour. Bullying rare, with pupils pointing out the 'confide' button on every school computer, where you can report issues anonymously at any time, or talk to a staff member confidentially.

Pupils and parents: This leafy suburb is spoilt for choice education-wise, with several good fee-paying schools on the doorstep and some of the best grammars in the country a short hop on the train away. Even Old Chigwellians admit to investigating the competition before signing up their offspring, but the school still wins people over with its ability to develop not just academic success, but confident, well-rounded people. 'One of the things that swung it for me was the way pupils talk to adults in a sophisticated way, but not without respect,' said one.

The parents – around two-thirds of whom are middle-class white British, with the remaining third mostly British Asian – seem to love the sense of community that the school has. 'My children have always said they felt they belong to something here – so much so that my daughter felt a real sense of loss when she left, and the same can be said for many parents,' said one. Most live within a five mile radius, although there's a growth in the number coming in from East London. Mainly affluent parents, although not exclusively. 'I was worried it would be full of rich kids and Landrover-driving parents, but although you do get that, there's a reassuring number of hard-working professional couples who make sacrifices to send their kids here,' said one parent.

There's a good 50:50 split of boys and girls, who we found to be relaxed, confident, articulate and helpful, as well as having a great sense of humour. Parents, meanwhile, particularly welcome the many opportunities to speak informally with staff about their children's progress and well-being at breakfast get-togethers and afternoon teas, as well as the programme of social events put on by the Friends of Chigwell PA which also raises significant funds for things like new canoes and stage lighting. Five school minibuses available for pupils, with others using public transport, notably the tube or bus, whilst many get dropped off by car.

The list of distinguished alumni includes William Penn, Sir Arthur Grimble, Sir Austin Bradford Hill, Sir Richard Dales, Col Bob Stewart and Sir Bernard Williams.

Entrance: Most junior school pupils move up to the senior school, forming about half of the year 7 entry, with the other half from a wide variety of local prep and primaries. 'It's very welcoming, so my children took to it like a duck to water, despite not coming from the junior school,' said one parent. Around 300 apply for these 40-odd places; assessment by interview (separate ones for pupils and parents), and English, maths and verbal reasoning papers. Small number of vacancies at 13 (English, maths and a modern foreign language exam). At 16, those moving up within the school are joined by around 10 local entrants as well as around 14 overseas boarders. Entrants to the sixth form are expected to have achieved at least four A/7s and two B/6s or in six GCSE subjects and A*-A/9-7 in their A level choices.

Exit: Hardly any post-16 leavers and 95 per cent of those who leave after sixth form move on to a degree course at university, or music and other specialist colleges. In 2017, seven to study medicine (including in Bulgaria and one in Poland) and eight to Oxbridge; some 70 per cent to Russell Group universities, notably Exeter, Nottingham, Bristol, Leeds and LSE. Others off to Switzerland, Canada, and Serbia. Popular degree subjects include economics, English and humanities.

Money matters: Academic scholarships available at 11 and 13 years; scholarships for art, drama and music offered at 16. Increasing number of means-tested bursaries available. 'I visit every family we are considering for bursaries,' says the head.

Remarks: A happy, nurturing and busy school with a genuinely family feel and an emphasis on creating caring all-rounders. Academically, pupils are put through their paces, but it all seems to be done in such a civilised and pleasant manner that you're far more likely to hear pupils talk about opportunities and prospects than pressure and stress. 'Anyone that wants to do well will do well here,' said one student, 'and I can't think of a nicer place to succeed.'

Culford School

13

Culford, Bury St Edmunds, Suffolk IP28 6TX

01284 385308 | admissions@culford.co.uk | www.culford.co.uk

Ages: 3-18 (boarding from 7)

Pupils: 729; sixth form: 147; Boarders: 281

Day: £8,700 – £18,990 pa; Boarding: £24,645 – £29,340 pa

Headmaster: Since 2004, Julian Johnson-Munday (50s). MA in English at Leicester followed by MBA at Durham. Toyed with joining the advertising industry but ended up at Cranleigh, where he became hooked on teaching. Rose through the ranks to be a housemaster, 'the best job in the world,' headed to London (Mill Hill) but decided a small rural boarding school 'where I knew all the children' was for him. Very settled at Culford and well liked by parents and pupils. Accompanied everywhere by his two dogs, 'they slow the children down,' who are greeted with enthusiasm by pupils, parents and staff. 'He has a lovely way about him,' said one parent. 'Very paternalistic and knows the children.'

You can tell he did English: slightly dramatic, very witty, warm, possibly a bit of a luvvie, who we imagine enjoys his time 'on the stage' as head, but in the nicest way, with a self-deprecating sense of humour. Smartly turned out. Runs the school with great efficiency and warmth. 'He's completely aware of what is going on, but is happy to let his very efficient management team cope with the day to day minutiae,' was one parent's view. 'Pragmatic and takes difficult decisions at times, but deals with them with great empathy,' from another. Keeps in close contact with parents via email and social media. 'Very much on the ball,' was said more than once. All fourth form (they use the old fashioned descriptions of year groups here) pupils have tea with the head, and his dogs, who enjoy hoovering up crumbs.

Prep school head: Since 2008, Mike Schofield (50s). Studied history and sport at Bedford College; has been at Culford for 19 years, arriving as a housemaster from the state system. Still coaching local rugby teams and referees matches at Culford. Chatty and likable, knows all children well, again very paternalistic. 'Watching them perform on stage, it's like being a parent 22 times over.'

Academic matters: In 2017, 45 per cent A*-A/9-7 at GCSE 28 per cent A*/A at A level, 51 per cent A*-B. Good results for a school that does not claim to be highly academic. BTecs recently introduced in sixth form; pupils can study these and A levels if appropriate. Spanish, French and Latin available at GCSE and A level, and taught in prep as well. Latin for the top set only in prep. All senior school pupils do one language, not many do two and unusual for all three to be taken. Maths is most popular subject at A level. Children set from year 5, gifted and talented spotted early and nurtured. No parent could fault academic progress and all spoke of being kept well informed of progress and problems. Extra help available if needed, and problems quickly spotted. IT well embraced. Old fashioned IT rooms have disappeared, it's all about laptops here, note the trolleys in the corner of classrooms loaded with laptops. Pupils encouraged to try all subjects, including art and DT, which proves popular further up the school. Good to see boys do textiles as well. Mention must go to the drones that are now being used in the grounds.

'Pupils are made to feel important whatever their role in the play,' said one parent. 'There are no divas; everyone's contribution is treated equally'

Excellent facilities including shared new science block, fabulous new £2.2 million library and refurbished art and DT blocks; alumni have proved generous benefactors. Sixth form centre with kitchen, used by groups quietly working. The new library is more popular for quiet study. Prep school has its own excellent library, well used with plenty of workshops and visiting authors. All seniors bring their own laptops.

A school full of energy. Happy children, relaxed teachers, all keeping busy and enjoying life, but don't be fooled, they are working hard. Saturday morning lessons for all in senior school. Senior school finishes at 5.30pm after clubs and sports practices, or prep for non-participants. Extended day runs to 9pm at no extra cost. Supervised prep and supper provided. Popular with many hard working parents as no dreaded homework to be done at home.

Small classes mean there's nowhere to hide, and teachers know pupils well. Parents appreciate

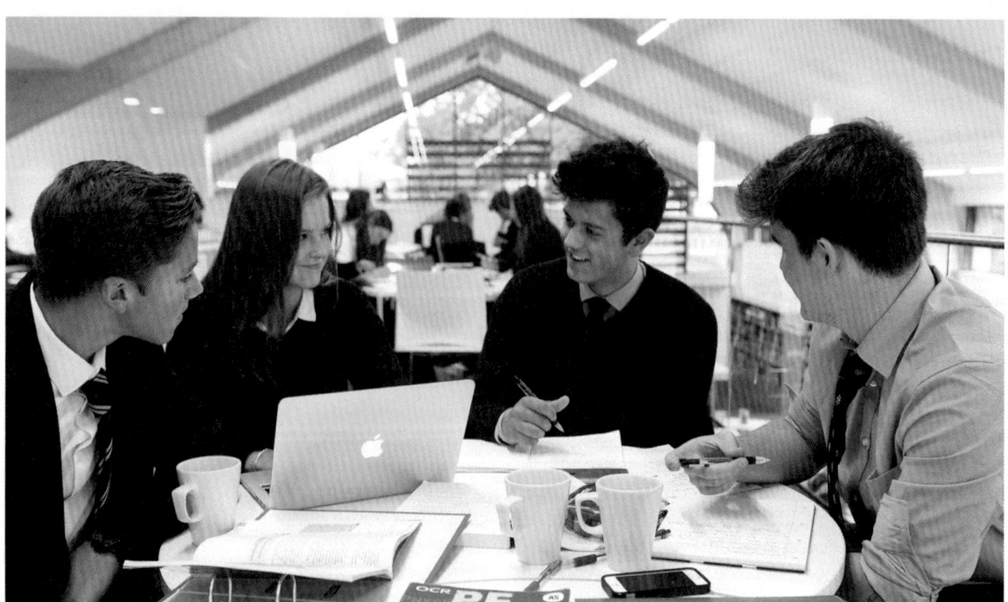

this and most said it was one of the main reasons for choosing the school. 'You can see the rapport on parents' evenings and it's good to hear the banter between teachers and your child; this reassures us that all is well.' We can vouch for this from our tour of the school. Average class size in prep is 17, 20 in senior and 10-12 in sixth form. UCAS preparation exemplary with one-to-one help for all. 'Amazing advice offered including what to look for on open days,' said one parent.

No pupils with a statement or EHCP but 55 on school action plus and school action. 'Learning support is excellent, staff are supportive and reassuring.' 'They know what is needed. My child was supported throughout the school to A levels and got excellent results.' Lots of one-to-one teaching if needed, or two-to-one where suitable. Plenty of feedback for parents. EAL pupils also well supported. Mainly group lessons, but individual if needed. Lots of long-serving staff.

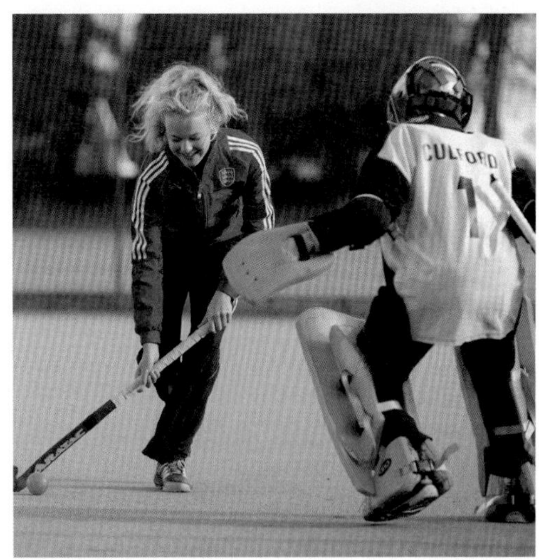

Games, options, the arts: Sport is king at this school, particularly tennis. Rated the best co-educational school in the country for tennis by the LTA, Culford attracts pupils from all over the world because of it. Elite athlete programmes on offer for many sports; these pupils have extra coaching and strength and conditioning classes, but never miss academic lessons. This lot are up with the lark and in the gym. Some 120 pupils play tennis all year round using the excellent facilities, including a four court championship standard indoor tennis centre. There are six grass, six hard and six Astro courts as well as numerous other pitches. Mention must go to golf as well, a new indoor studio with simulator and radar technology attracting golf scholars. More regular sports such as rugby, hockey and cricket (girls too) also extremely successful. Good to see there are teams for all, it's not just about the elite. Sports participation encouraged in the prep school; 'the unwilling are gently, but firmly encouraged,' says the head. This attitude prevails throughout the school. Large sports complex, lots of pitches and pavilions, excellent swimming pool, gym, studios – you name it, they've got it.

Music and drama also popular. Music centre in the beautiful old building, lots of rooms available for quiet practice. Many have individual singing and instrumental lessons. Loads of choirs, ensembles, orchestras and productions. 'Pupils are made to feel important whatever their role in the play,' said one parent. 'There are no divas; everyone's contribution is treated equally.' Loads of clubs and practices during lunch time and after school. Throughout the school are excellent works of art. All pupils welcomed us with open arms, happy to chat and proud to show work.

D of E and CCF well supported. 'Children are brought out of themselves and encouraged to try things,' said one parent. 'The children are encouraged to take ownership of the opportunities they are offered.' Plenty of school trips for all including a freshers' week for lower sixth with a trip to the Peak District for team building. Sixth form life seems to be very sociable, lots of dinners in the magnificent main house, the Highland Ball and numerous other occasions. 'We get through lots of dresses,' said our guide.

Boarding: One of the first genuinely co-ed boarding schools in the country; girls joined in 1972. Boys' boarding full, girls' growing rapidly. Flexi-boarding popular throughout. Pupils staying three nights a week always have the same bed. Offers 10 nights a term, part boarding of three nights a week or full boarding. Parents appreciate that there is always a bed available if necessary.

There are two houses for boys and two for girls. Co-ed house for prep school. All houses mix day and boarding pupils so strong friendships develop throughout. Extended day option available: pupils stay until 7pm, popular with many parents.

Newly refurbished prep boarding has eight in a dorm, four bunk beds, with years 7 and 8 mixed together. Very neat with pupils bringing their own duvets. 'We change our sheets weekly and sort our washing out,' we were told. Pupils' dorms checked daily by prefects. 'We stand by our beds and are dismissed only when our space is tidy.' Phones taken away every night. Lots of outings and trips for boarders: roller skating, cinema etc, and they have the run of the grounds as well, though younger pupils have to stay within certain areas. Supervised prep for all boarders.

Senior boarding houses not quite as tidy, a bit shabby, but homely. The tidiness instilled in younger years seems to slip a little, but teenagers will be teenagers. Years 9-13 in together with upper sixth having their own rooms. Most younger pupils share, and there is one dormitory of 16 for the year 9s which is very popular. Plenty of facilities for tea and toast making, and comfy common rooms. Sixth form flexi boarding very popular as Paddy and Scott's Café opens on Friday night for sixth formers. Pizza and snacks served here, very popular for socialising. Some sixth form boarders have their own cars. School fairly relaxed about toing and froing; they sign in and out using an app. Very much a family atmosphere with houseparents having dogs, pupils keen to walk them – it covers their D of E service module. Mention must go to the resident parrot as well. Boarders encouraged to have day pupils to stay. Plenty of trips, which day pupils can also join; Alton Towers particularly popular, London shopping and buses run regularly to Bury St Edmunds, making excursions to local town popular and encouraged.

Background and atmosphere: Located not far from Bury St Edmunds, the school is situated in beautiful grounds, just shy of 500 acres. Entering through impressive gates you drive through the estate past a very pretty church, used by the school and very popular for marriages of alumni, before rounding a corner to an 16th century magnificent mansion house, previously owned by the Cadogan family. The new buildings flow well and blend in, with plenty of space around them. The prep school is in the old stable block, built around a quad with the library in the middle. The nursery is housed in a separate building, cleverly located nearest the main gates so parents coming and going aren't noticed. Parents, staff and locals seen walking their dogs in the grounds, which are so large that pupils are easily absorbed, as are the large sports pitches and buildings. The 'Culford bubble' that parents and staff talk about is suddenly apparent. Easy to forget there is an outside world whilst cocooned in this cornucopia of beauty. School well aware of this, as are pupils, who appreciate how lucky they are.

Highland Ball and numerous other occasions. 'We get through lots of dresses,' said our guide

Founded on strong Methodist beliefs in 1881, the school is strong on moral values and there is much talk about the Culford Way. It is a relatively small school so a family atmosphere prevails; pupils and staff are friendly, jolly and welcoming. Everyone seems to know everyone. The school knows not just their pupils but the families as well. Pupils are smart with the senior girls in long, extremely long, skirts. 'They are brilliant,' said one of our guides; 'we can wear our pyjamas or tracksuit bottoms underneath when it's cold and no one knows!' Pupils encouraged to join in and try everything. 'Be the best person you can be each day,' is the prep head's mantra and it seems to work its way through both schools.

Pastoral care, well-being and discipline: Every parent we spoke to praised pastoral care. To be honest they raved about it. 'They pick up on problems – even at home – so quickly and are incredibly proactive,' said one parent. All spoke about the 'paternal' atmosphere and the sense of security the pupils, and parents, feel. House staff praised, and their dogs. Mental health problems quickly picked up on. School has focused on mental health for many years, 'long before it was flagged up,' says the head. Counsellors are well used, 'a good release valve.' Half of all staff are mental health first aiders, plans for every single member of staff to be trained.

Drugs have reared their ugly head in recent years and this is where the head comes into his own. 'Deals with problems empathetically, fairly but firmly,' was said by parents. Pupils and parents are kept well informed, nothing is swept under the carpet. Some miscreants leave, others given a second chance but have to agree to random drug tests. The head has had to have some fairly uncomfortable conversations with some worried parents. All parents spoke positively about discipline: 'They are tolerant to a certain extent but the children know where the line is drawn.'

Pupils and parents: A strong community of parents who are focused on a good all round education. These parents aren't just concentrating on exam results but on the development of well rounded individuals. Most parents are working hard to afford the fees and very grateful for flexibility school can offer with regards to boarding and late pick ups. Many second and third generation pupils, some even fifth. Most pupils live within an hour and a half from the school. Quite a large Forces contingent. Pupils happy and relaxed and do not show any signs of being under any undue pressure, but are obviously putting in the hard work. Mention must go to one of our charming guides, who had a disconcerting ability to walk backwards at full speed and hold a sensible conversation – we are convinced senior pupils practise this skill in the evening.

Entrance: Entry into nursery via taster sessions, pre-prep by day's assessment and taster session. Prep by entrance exam, entry to senior school automatic from prep, entrance exam if external student. Sixth form requires seven GCSEs including maths and English, grades A*-C/9-5. Flexibility is key. Unusual for a sibling to be turned away if they don't make the grade; 'we are a family school.' Largeish intake at year 7, mainly from the state, and larger again in year 9 from local prep schools, including the Cambridge contingent.

Exit: Very, very unusual to have a pupil not make the grade for transfer to senior school. And equally unusual for pupils not to make that. The odd one leaves to board elsewhere, usually following family tradition. About 10 leave in year 11, most to vocational courses or, again, to board elsewhere. Entry to sixth form denied if attitude doesn't fit, and school happy to verify this. One Oxbridge in 2017, six to universities in USA to carry on with sports. Most go to university, the odd one into Forces or family business. Arts and dance courses quite popular. Interestingly, apprenticeships not on the horizon. Gap years quite popular.

Money matters: Academic scholarships and exhibitions available offering 25 per cent and 10 per cent off fees for years 7, 9 and 12. Sports and music awards. Discounts for siblings and discounts for Forces families.

Remarks: This small school, housed in beautiful surroundings, really is a family orientated place; note the dogs and pets making it home from home. Happy children and parents. The school takes much of the strain away from busy parents. The Culford Bubble could be a disadvantage, but pupils are well aware life exists outside the grounds. Its strengths are small class sizes, excellent pastoral care and tremendous facilities. Once a Culfordian, always a Culfordian, it would appear.

Edge Grove Preparatory School

14

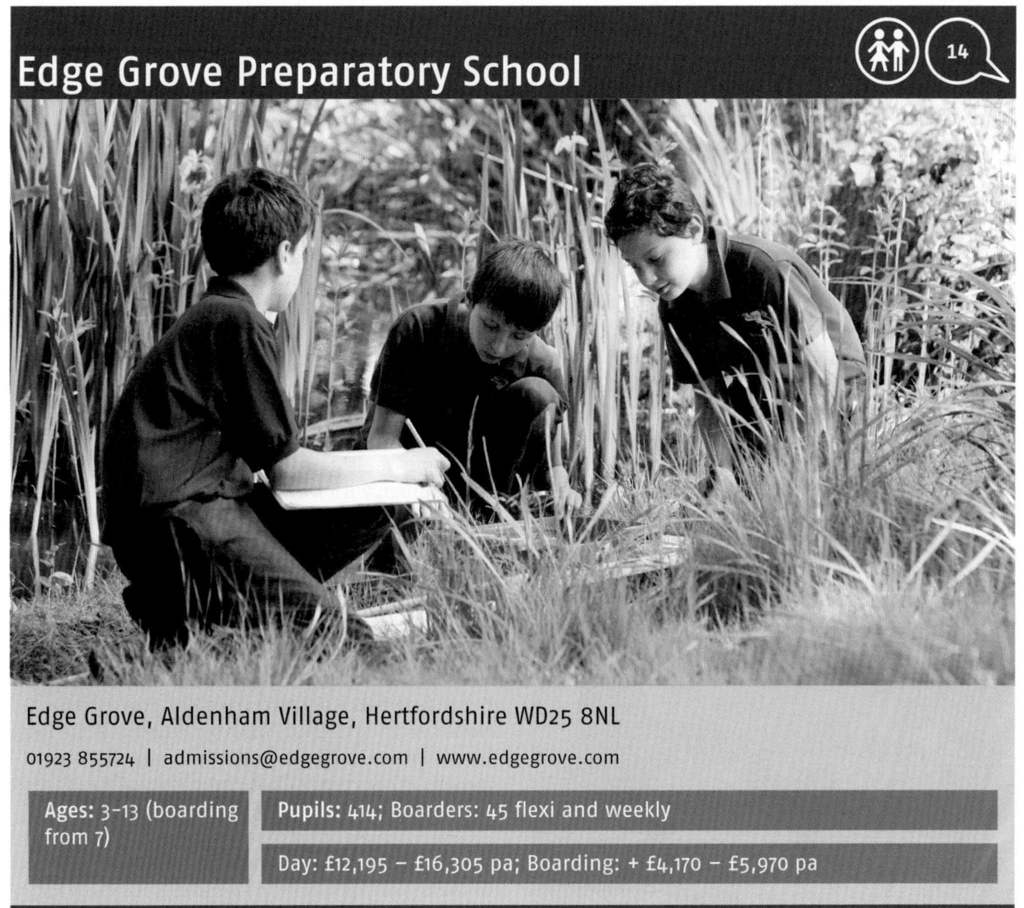

Edge Grove, Aldenham Village, Hertfordshire WD25 8NL

01923 855724 | admissions@edgegrove.com | www.edgegrove.com

Ages: 3–13 (boarding from 7)

Pupils: 414; Boarders: 45 flexi and weekly

Day: £12,195 – £16,305 pa; Boarding: + £4,170 – £5,970 pa

Headmaster: Since 2012, Ben Evans (40s). A Devon lad (mother still breeds Dartmoor ponies there) with a love of all things country. Head boy at Bramdean School before heading to Exeter University to read history and archaeology. Returned, armed with his degree and PGCE, to Bramdean where he 'learned to teach,' before taking up the post of head of history at Brighton College, later returning as deputy head to his alma mater.

Had a 'now or never' moment before hot footing it to Sri Lanka to teach at the junior school of the British School in Colombo, Sri Lanka, where he served a total of six years, the final four as head. Returned to the UK following the birth of his first child and found love at first sight with Edge Grove – 'exactly what I wanted,' he says. Laughingly says wealthy Sri Lankan parents provided good grounding for dealing with those of the ambitious north London variety, although parents say it is clear he is not trying to turn school into 'a typical north London hothouse.'

Lives in head's house at school with wife Alex – 'an absolute gem,' according to parents. Described as dynamic, likeable and no nonsense, she regularly rolls up her sleeves and gets stuck in in the boarding house, sorting things out 'with a deft hand,' says one mother.

During his first year in tenure, he scrapped Saturday lessons, made dramatic changes to the school day and really 'upped the ante' on the academic front. One parent said Evans had achieved more over the summer holidays (new adventure playground, gleaming home economics room and upgrades to textiles facilities) than they'd seen over the last three years. Just what Edge Grove needed after an unsettled patch with a revolving door of head teachers.

Entrance: Gently selective, with relaxed assessments and parental interview – 'we want parents to have chosen us for the right reasons,' says head. Little ones at 3+ and 4+ come for a short session where staff engage them in an activity and observe their skills in, for example, sharing and socialising. Currently oversubscribed for nursery and reception. Entrants at 7+ attend an assessment day and take verbal/non-verbal reasoning tests before spending a day in class to see how they fit in. 'We want the kind of children who will take advantage of all the things we have to offer,' says head.

No bursaries in the lower part of the school apart from those offered to military families. New scholarships introduced for existing pupils in years 7 and 8 to 'acknowledge their contribution to the school.'

Exit: Majority of girls leave at 11; others and most boys leave at 13. Girls to St Albans High School for Girls, Haberdashers' Aske's School for Girls, Abbot's Hill and Downe House, with St Albans Boys, Merchant Taylors' School and Harrow popular for boys; plus both to a range of co-ed schools including Rugby, Haileybury, Uppingham, Berkhamsted and Aldenham. A good handful of scholarships achieved annually, ranging from academic to sport and music. Conversations about next schools start with parents in years 5 and 6.

Remarks: When you arrive at this idyllic country prep it's hard to believe that it's just a stone's throw from north London and that the background hum is the M25. Set in grassy parkland with the requisite cows grazing next to the drive, Edge Grove – formerly the home of JP Morgan – is a world apart from many of its concrete-clad urban rivals.

Smiling boys and girls (school is now 50/50 and 'firmly co-educational,' according to head) in woolly red sweaters cheerfully and proactively greet you as you walk around, giving the impression of a happy, down to earth and confident cohort. Not surprising when you see the space they have to occupy – campus feels as if it could accommodate twice the number, with a huge open space for the nursery alone and separate science and art school buildings for older ones. Lovely manners abound, with classroom doors hardly opened before children leap to their feet.

Pupils and parents 'a really good mix,' according to head. About 20 per cent London based with the rest from around Radlett, St Albans, Elstree and Borehamwood and some from the Forces, based at Northwood. Ethnically diverse, reflecting the local area: 'wonderful,' say parents. Some discreet old money, others more flash and plenty of hard-working dual income first time buyers.

New school day structure popular with parents who say 'it just makes sense' to teach core subjects in the mornings when the children are most receptive. Activities take place either between 4 and 5pm or 5 and 6pm depending on year group and children can also stay for prep and supper, helping working parents or those further afield manage the pick-up. Saturday school has been replaced with

She regularly rolls up her sleeves and gets stuck in in the boarding house, sorting things out 'with a deft hand'

voluntary Saturday attendance to take part in fun activities like music and drama or the Edge Grove Award (like a mini D of E) and stay for lunch if they wish – 'the quality of what we offer is much better now,' he says. A fleet of new iPads were introduced for year 3 a few years ago, kicking the school firmly into the 'progressive' bracket as far as technology is concerned. Class sizes capped at 20 in the pre-prep and 18 in the prep school.

Head 'aiming for excellence in all subjects.' International Primary Curriculum taught in pre-prep, which also has a forest school curriculum. French taught from reception and classics from year 5 with setting starting in year 3 for English and maths, then for French and science from year 5. Recent new virtual language lab. Years 7 and 8 see pupils split into a scholarship set and two other common entrance sets. Parents talk about the 'academic rigour' being teased out of pupils and report a welcome increase in homework for younger ones. Mandarin, Spanish and Italian offered as after-school clubs for budding linguists.

Parents praise staff mix: 'some really old school, some young and dynamic,' although concede that 'some are better than others.' Communication between parents and teaching staff is reportedly 'excellent' in the main: parents are able to email class teachers direct and, with occasional exceptions, receive prompt, useful replies. Even throw-away comments in the car park are taken seriously and actioned, said one. Whole school communication 'getting better,' according to parents, with recent introduction of weekly email letting parents know of all forthcoming fixtures and trips to help pupils be better prepared. Head has introduced weekly staff training sessions to ensure consistent quality across the board. SEN and EAL limited to offering learning support to children with mild difficulties and no plans to increase provision.

Outstanding art taught in inspirational atelier style space with first class work in genres ranging from cubism to pupils' favourite, street art, on display. Host of shiny new sewing machines will no doubt add to pupils' textiles capabilities; home economics also on the curriculum. Classrooms alive with sound of music: head wants 'music to be happening all the time,' and is getting his wish with over 180 peripatetic lessons each week ('brilliantly timetabled,' say parents) and the director of music (ex Haileybury) is driving musical excellence in all its forms. Choral music is 'very strong,' says head and a lucky few get to try their hand in the school rock band – recently kitted out with four electric guitars, a drum kit and, most importantly, a soundproofed practice room. Plenty for budding thespians too – year 5 recently performed A Midsummer Night's Dream in the school's grounds, with a production of Bugsy Malone another success.

Sport taken seriously for both genders with a total of around 800 fixtures a year and specialist teaching from reception. Girls benefit from the guidance of an ex-England netball coach and the school has strong links with Radlett Cricket Club. U13 six-a-side football team current national IAPS champions, with other pupils reaching county standard for cricket, archery and squash and recent introduction of international tours for top teams. For less starry types, there are plenty of inter-house matches and tournaments which are fiercely contested, so everyone gets a go. Weekly swimming lessons and galas take place in the immaculate heated outdoor pool on the site of a former beautifully walled garden, mirrored on the other side by impressively sized, albeit slightly tired, tennis courts.

A lucky few get to try their hand in the school rock band – recently kitted out with four electric guitars, a drum kit and, most importantly, a soundproofed practice room

Around 45 flexi/weekly boarders, many forces' children, with a total of 50 beds to accommodate flexi-boarding. Recently appointed non-teaching head of boarding has made a 'huge difference,' to what was formerly a fairly chaotic boarding function according to parents, although many agreed that there is still some way to go in terms of organisation: very little wardrobe space (one wardrobe for seven girls) and no lockers lead to lost clothes, with one parent reporting having lost up to 20 pairs of socks and others on-going problems with lost sports kit. Occasional issues with bullying and bad behaviour are 'not dealt with badly,' for the most part but parents have high hopes that these issues will be eliminated altogether, to create a calmer and more nurturing boarding environment.

Bright, newly decorated dorms sleep up to eight pupils, with seniors (years 7 and 8) having their lounging and TV area incorporated into the dorm. There's also a games room in an annexe with snooker, table tennis and table football. Head, determined to avoid 'sleepover culture,' insists that boarders stay for a minimum of three nights a week from year 5, although they can stay for one in years 3 and 4, and all year 3 pupils are expected to board for at least one night during expedition week when years 4 to 8 head off site. Popular fun themed weekends twice yearly give all pupils a chance to taste boarding on a first come, first served basis.

Clubs galore – many of which are included in fees – from gardening and chess to taekwondo and war gaming. These are integrated well into the long school day and parents happily describe their children as 'very busy.' Two minibus services ferry years 3 to 8 to school if they choose, along routes covering Hemel Hempstead, St Albans, How Wood, Totteridge, Whetstone, Barnet, Brookmans Park and Shenley.

Felsted Preparatory School

15

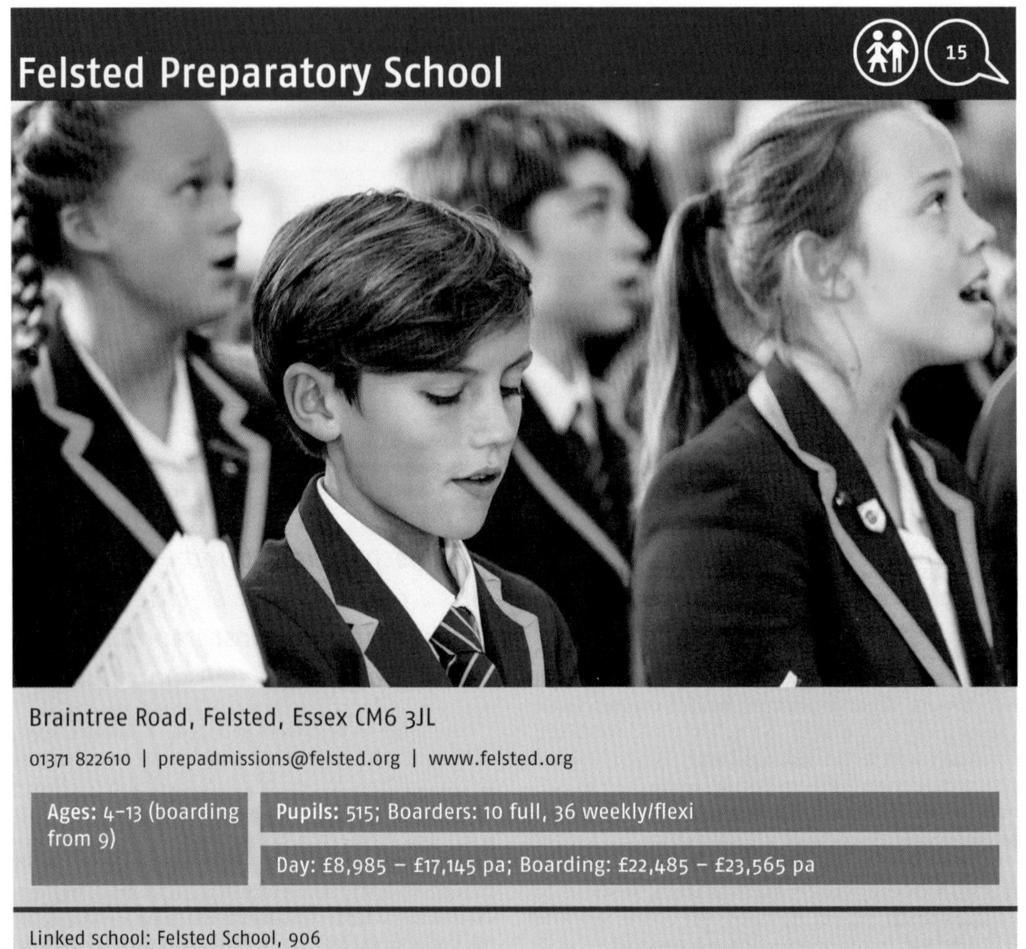

Braintree Road, Felsted, Essex CM6 3JL

01371 822610 | prepadmissions@felsted.org | www.felsted.org

Ages: 4–13 (boarding from 9)

Pupils: 515; Boarders: 10 full, 36 weekly/flexi

Day: £8,985 – £17,145 pa; Boarding: £22,485 – £23,565 pa

Linked school: Felsted School, 906

Head: Since September 2016, Mr Simon James BA PGCE (40s), whose degree is in history. He moved from Chigwell Junior School, where he was also head, before which he was head of Rossall School, Lancashire. Prior to that, he was director of studies at Kings School, Chester, a post he took up following various teaching posts at key stage 2.

He's relaxed, easy going and chatty – definitely more of a carrot than a stick man, and with an open door policy for children, parents and staff alike. But don't be fooled – despite his warm and cuddly exterior, this is a head that kids don't want to disappoint and who is not afraid of being proactive when it comes to improving school processes and strategies. 'He's out and about every morning at the school gates, which is a really nice touch,' one parent told us, and he teaches games and history 'to keep in touch with pupils.'

He lives a 10 minute drive away with his wife, Jill – who joined Felsted as a teacher four years prior to him – and their two daughters, who joined the school when their mum did. 'It made this a very easy move for me,' he smiles. A keen cricketer and ex-rugby player, he enjoys cooking and travelling with his family during school holidays.

Entrance: Various entry points including 4+ and 7+, with big intake at 11+ when prospective pupils submit a confidential report from their previous school and undergo interview and assessments in English, maths, non-verbal and verbal reasoning. 'Entrance isn't overly selective, but it is rigorous when it comes to the process involved,' one parent sums up. Entry lower down is less stringent, although interview and taster day still a must (and a school report, if they're moving from another school). Academic scholarships are available, covering up to 20 per cent of fees. There's also the Mary Skills award (a convenient surname, if ever we heard one) for talent in subjects including music, sport, art, design, technology and engineering, which covers up to £2,000 of fees. Some open bursaries are also on offer. Unlike many other preps, classes continue up to the end of year 8.

Pupils are able to board from age 9 (one per cent of boarders are from overseas).

Exit: More than 94 per cent proceed to the senior school, often to join older siblings. 'Caters for all types, so why look elsewhere?' The remainder head to other boarding schools (one to Harrow, one to Bishops Stortford College), 11 moving overseas and two moving for financial reasons (to state schools).

Remarks: The prep school is made up of a hodgepodge of buildings (some beautiful; some less so) directly across the road from its big sister, the senior school. With a few exceptions, these buildings are divided into four separate areas – each home to the school's four 'phases,' which move the pupils on towards greater self-reliance, focus and specialisation. Each phase has its own head, who – together with the director of learning and deputy head – make up the senior leadership team. Stewart House – home to reception, year 1 and 2 – is a contemporary, purpose built two storey building with lots of sunlight and stunning views, not to mention a huge, cuddly 'FelsTed' in the reception area. The classrooms are spacious and colourful, with plenty of imaginative artwork adorning the walls, and there's a library, multi-purpose hall and wide, bright play spaces instead of corridors. Years 3 and 4 are based in Frome Court – a series of prefab buildings, where pupils can use the dedicated contained playground or venture out into the bigger green space, shared with the older children. At this age, children start to be mainly taught by subject specialist teachers. Years 5 and 6 move up to Cloisters – based in (you guessed it) the old cloistered part of the school, and finally, there's Courtauld House for years 7 and 8, which includes a sociable common room. All share the new and shiny science labs, spacious ICT suite, Ross Hall (for assemblies, performances and some games) and art block as part of their impressive facilities.

The consensus was unanimously positive towards Saturday school among students and parents alike. 'You get to do activities like forest school and golf'

As with the senior school, parents here recoil at the thought of increased pressure and favour greater focus on individual educational plans, with the aim of ensuring maximum academic success – but not at the expense of other activities. Every pupil and parent we spoke to believes the balance is just right and we were impressed with the school's commitment to that overused term, 'holistic education.' Indeed, Felsted claims one of the biggest co-curricular programmes in the country, with LAMDA, golf, riding, cooking, gardening, Mandarin and judo just a few of the wealth of opportunities on offer for these lucky young things. There are also lots of trips – including overseas sports trips and a year 8 leadership weekend to Wales – and

the head was about to introduce a bushcraft trip for year 6 when we visited. Day trips to support the curriculum include Colchester Zoo (pre-preps) and parliament for year 8s. The five houses – known as leagues – bring some friendly competition to sports, music and drama. Plus, each league does its own charity work. 'It's a 24/7 school, so if you're not prepared to sign up to it, it's not the school for you,' warned one parent, but those who live it, love it.

The three classes per year group are kept to a maximum of 18 students up to year 3, which then rises to 20, and there's setting in languages, English, maths and science – usually with five tutor groups per year, with some exceptions (eg there are four groups for maths in years 6 and 7). There is plenty of personalised learning on offer for SEN, usually outside the classroom and for half hour lessons – as many as necessary per week. 'Welcome to my box,' laughed the head of SEN when we met her. But although her office is indeed compact, there are two other dedicated learning support rooms upstairs and children seem to like the environment – definitely no stigma attached. As for the very able, extension lessons are available for subjects where students have particular strengths, as part of the VAPs (Very Able Pupils) programme. For year 8s, this programme involves one-and-a-half-hour Saturday morning sessions available with a sixth form mentor. 'I've got a very intelligent child, who is also very strong-minded, and they've dealt with him brilliantly,' one parent told us. 'For example, they wanted him to learn Greek and he was adamant he didn't want to, so they agreed that if he translated all the Harry Potter spells from Latin into English, they'd let him off – and he did! They stood by their word.'

Languages are strong, with all pupils learning Spanish, to which they add either French or German from year 6. The brightest kids also take Latin from year 7. Homework is given twice a week from year 5 and three times a week from year 7 and woe betide anyone who hands it in late. 'They cut you no slack,' one student told us, despite the long school day. Indeed, while year 2s and under finish at 3.30pm, year 3s start to be introduced to lengthier days that, by year 8, last from 8.20am-5.55pm – that's longer than a lot of adults spend at work in a full-time job. 'At least, there's Saturday school,' a couple of students said – which is optional for years 5 and 6 (with around 60 per cent take up) and compulsory for years 7 and 8. Confused? 'Saturday school includes homework time,' they explain. In fact, the consensus was unanimously (and perhaps surprisingly) positive towards Saturday school among students and parents alike. 'You get to do activities like forest school and golf,' one student explained. Lots of development opportunities for teachers – one told us about 'a kind of speed dating event, where we had to share best practice in speed time, working our way round the room – it was really fun, and very useful.'

Drama is taught to all students weekly, with many choosing to take it as an extracurricular option on top. The result is a much talked about all school performance every year, plus extra ones from some individual years. Ditto with music – as in all students do it, and many do extra, including belonging to the orchestra, chapel choir or one of the many bands and ensembles ranging from the jazz band to steel drum group. Plus, around 60 per cent learn an instrument via peripatetic lessons. We particularly love the two art rooms – an Aladdin's cave of opportunity for budding young artists, who can try their hand at everything from textiles to pottery. 'The children particularly like getting involved in making props for the school plays,' the art teacher told us, and there is no shortage of proof – the huge elephant's head from the Lion King performance probably the most prominent.

Sport – of which the core for boys are rugby and hockey, while for girls, it's netball and hockey (and cricket for both in the summer) – seems to strike the right balance between healthy competition and inclusiveness, with regular fixtures for A-G teams in many sports. 'We like our A teams to do well, but we also like everyone to play because sport is such a central part of school life here,' says the head, and parents concur. 'My son is not naturally good at sport, but he enjoys it,' said one parent. That said, with players reaching county level in cricket and rugby – plus national finalists for hockey, netball and horse riding – there's plenty or silverware to keep the school cabinets glistening. Facilities are great, including five rugby pitches, three cricket squares and four tennis courts. There's also an outdoor swimming pool and sports hall. In addition, there are two all weather astroturf pitches,

We were introduced to a flamboyant woman who was painting not just plain walls, but some lively and modern murals

numerous netball and tennis courts (grass and hard) and indoor swimming pool (which needs updating) that they use over in the senior school.

Boarding is a major part of school life here, with Felsted Prep boasting its own – very uninstitutional – boarding house, which has a capacity for 64 students: one floor for boys, the other for girls. In reality, some 10 use it full time, while there are some 36 weekly or part time boarders, where parents commit to three specific days a week. One weekend in three is full boarding, one is optional and the third is an exeat, so the most a child would be continuously at school is likely to be three weeks, which we think is right for children at this age and a good preparation for senior boarding schools. Bedrooms have between two and eight beds, with children encouraged to personalise their space, and each floor has its own common room. Just as we were noting that the house could do with a lick of paint here and there, we were introduced to a flamboyant woman who was painting not just plain walls, but some lively and modern murals. Meanwhile, the 1970s-esque pine beds are being updated with more contemporary oak veneer ones – also a much needed move.

The boarding day begins at 7.45am for breakfast, while evenings include homework time, activities ranging from ICT to football (with different choices each night), and weekends include trips out ranging from cinema to the beach. The house is heavily staffed (with very low staff turnover) by a set of houseparents, a second set of deputy house parents (both have families, adding to the family feel), plus house tutors, resident matron and four gap year students who live on site in their own apartment. Even the so called 'domestic fairies' get stuck into the community feel, with lots of friendly notes from students to them, and vice versa, left on doors. Communication with parents is encouraged, with animated videos regularly sent home and unlimited phone calls allowed during sociable hours. 'We now have a boarding house administrator to help manage this communication,' the housemistress – a delightful, bubbly woman – told us. The children we spoke to enthused about boarding, while the parents rave about the pastoral support.

Pastoral care is a key strength back in the daytime part of school too, with each head of phase tasked with ensuring the children are happy, while a tutor system for the older children means those in years 6, 7 and 8 have their own personal tutor for three years, who acts as a single point of contact for parents and with whom the children have a weekly individual meeting. We think this is an excellent model to ensure no one slips through the pastoral net. 'These tutors know us well and make sure we feel comfortable talking to them,' one student told us. 'It's a talking community anyway,' piped in another. 'So if you didn't want to talk to your tutor for any reason, there's always an older pupil available via the peer support system. And I know my mum likes the fact that she often gets emails telling her if I've done well in something like spellings or maths. It's just very, very open.' There's a matron available too, as well as mindfulness classes. Bullying is rare, not just for these reasons, but also the fact that they do talks on what it is and how to recognise it, and students told us it is dealt with quickly and humanely when it does occur. The school is keen on giving the children responsibilities and has created many leadership roles, and it doesn't just pay lip service to the student voice, with the head meeting the pupil council weekly. There's a charity committee and global gang too.

While rewards are seen as being more effective than punishments to keep kids on the straight and narrow, misdemeanours are certainly not overlooked. Indeed, each child carries round two cards in their pocket, reminiscent of an old train ticket from the 1960s – green for good deeds and cream for bad ones. Teachers sign them when either happens (holding doors open might be a good one, while running in a corridor a bad one) and three signatures equals a house point or, conversely, a detention, either on a weekday – or for serious transgressions, a Saturday one with the headteacher.

'The children particularly like getting involved in making props for the school plays,' the art teacher told us, and there is no shortage of proof – the huge elephant's head

Many of the weekend activities, which the children tell us they adore and are keenly anticipated, are open to parents and the grounds are fully used on a daily basis. The children have built an outdoor pizza oven, there are outdoor classrooms and mini Duke of Edinburgh style award activities outdoors one afternoon a week. There are clear rules about where in the grounds children can explore but plenty of space for climbing trees and building dams. The head is keen to introduce even more challenge to the outdoor education programmes.

Food is good – we tasted it – although the dining space options aren't great for the younger ones. It's taken to pre-preps; years 3 to 6 eat on site in a small hall; and years 7 and 8 in senior school – to our mind, a great policy that helps older ones feel more independent and on their way to the senior school. In fact links with the senior school are increasing generally. 'In the past, it was seen as a separate school, but we're trying to make it a more seamless transition for the vast majority of students who go on to study there,' says the head – and that includes joint academic ventures, such as years 7 and 8 working with seniors on science projects and use of sports facilities.

Despite the school being located in rural Essex, it feels part of a much bigger world rather than existing as a primary school bubble – no doubt helped by things like their 'global centre,' complete with a skype wall, which enables pupils to communicate with a school they support in India. Families – who are a mixture of traditional farming families, the super wealthy, entrepreneurs, middle class professionals and no shortage of dual income families – can't get enough of it. 'Felsted is more of a way of life than a school,' one parent told us. 'And it's one the children know they are very lucky to have.'

Many schools claim to be child centred, focusing on each individual across a wide ability range, but not all achieve it. Felsted does, providing a busy, bustling and largely fun environment, where the ethos is all about doing the very best you can and finding your key strengths. This early growth mind set has many of the youngsters believing everything is possible – great preparation for the senior school, where an all round education is taken to a whole new level. 'This is a school that brings out the best in everyone,' sums up a parent. 'It's education to fit the individual child, not the other way round.'

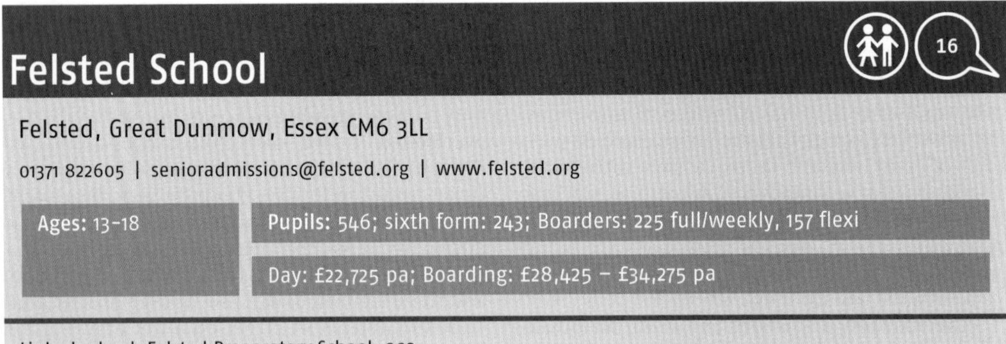

Felsted School

16

Felsted, Great Dunmow, Essex CM6 3LL

01371 822605 | senioradmissions@felsted.org | www.felsted.org

Ages: 13-18

Pupils: 546; sixth form: 243; Boarders: 225 full/weekly, 157 flexi

Day: £22,725 pa; Boarding: £28,425 – £34,275 pa

Linked school: Felsted Preparatory School, 902

Headmaster: Since 2015, Chris Townsend BA PGCE (40s), previously deputy head. Classics degree from Oxford, where he was an exhibitioner and won three cricket blues. First teaching post at alma mater Dean Close, then housemaster and head of boarding at Stowe, then to Felsted in 2010 as deputy head.

Students and parents alike revel in recounting the story of the moment his appointment as head was announced. 'The whole school – including staff and pupils – erupted into applause, which lasted for about 10 minutes!' we were told, with all parents, staff and pupils we spoke to enthusing about how 'excellent,' 'inspirational' and 'nurturing' he is. 'He has a huge amount of respect from everyone and knows every child,' one parent told us. 'He is absolutely committed to making education well-rounded so that every child's strengths are valued and nurtured,' said another. 'He leads by example and gets really stuck into school life,' a student told us, with evident pride.

Indeed, he teaches when he can (Greek and Latin), plays piano at school concerts, referees some of the rugby, as well as doing the corridor rounds and attending some school trips, including one to Uganda and Malawi in the summer holidays. But despite his larger-than-life reputation, he is not extrovert, loud, opinionated or loquacious. Conversely, we found him mild-mannered, quiet and unassuming – just the kind of chap you'd feel safe leaving shy, petrified little Johnny with on first day of boarding school. Not that he's afraid to discipline, as any student will confirm.

He couldn't live closer if he tried, with a door behind his office desk leading straight to home, where he resides with his wife Melanie (assistant head at another local school), their two children (both at Felsted) and a red setter.

Academic matters: Not overly selective, but each year a solid cohort achieves top grades across the board in both GCSEs and A levels: in 2017, 40 per

cent A*-A/9-7 at GCSE and 35 per cent A*/A, 66 per cent A*-B at A level. The broad ability range is big pull to many parents, including one who told us, 'My son got into a top grammar school, but I didn't want him in a highly pressurised, "work-work-work" environment – Felsted still gets good results, but it's more fun, offers a more holistic education and has a mix of people that better reflects real life.'

At GCSE, the strongest subjects are maths, English, sciences, RE and languages, with other popular options including geography and history. There's also a good creative uptake, with decent numbers of students and grades in DT, music and drama. At A level, students do particularly well in psychology, geography, RE and history – and, increasingly, maths and science. Other popular options include business studies and economics. 'This part of the world is known for its entrepreneurial buzz,' points out the head. More generally, the school has a reputation of bringing out the best in all and IB is taking off even among quite conservative local families – currently about a third of the sixth form opts for it: 33 average point score in 2017.

Year 9s all learn Spanish (the core language here), plus French, German or Latin, then in year 10 they can take up to three languages, with other options including Italian. Other languages also on offer as part of the IB, where they can be self-taught, with past students having done just that with Japanese, Russian and Mandarin. Parents praise the 'native speaking language teachers and high number of classroom assistants to make sure everyone stays on track.'

Setting (up to six sets per year) in maths, English, sciences and languages and class sizes are kept small, between 15-20 up to GCSE, and often considerably smaller in sixth form. Staff development encouraged, with both peers and pupils invited to provide feedback on selected lessons and suggest what constitutes good or outstanding teaching – all part of the collaborative ethos of the school. Projects with other schools also exist, with a view to sharing best practice. Teachers – all of whom are involved in pastoral care and who really get to know the children – are known for being a thoroughly committed bunch, with a positive and engaged staff common room.

We found him mild-mannered, quiet and unassuming – just the kind of chap you'd feel safe leaving shy, petrified little Johnny with on first day of boarding school

Homework isn't for the faint-hearted, although for the younger ones, homework sessions are built into the school day – a welcome relief, say parents, given that the school day lasts from 8.15am to 6pm and there's also Saturday school. IT is embedded into learning, with pupils encouraged to use Chromebooks, Google Classroom and even smartphones in some lessons (more of which, later).

SEN pupils, of whom there are many (albeit at the mild to moderate end – mainly dyslexia, dyspraxia, ADHD and autistic spectrum), have personalised support from the learning department, which has no stigma attached, not least because it's open to everyone, offering everything from intensive one-to-one tuition to drop-in sessions to help with prep. 'Why wouldn't you want extra support to help you do your best?' one student asked, rhetorically. 'My son has dyslexia and he wound up with As and A*s, thanks to the personalised support he got behind the scenes,' said one parent. EAL teachers also on hand, also in a specialist department.

Games, options, the arts: Traditionally sporty, with the school producing some outstanding cricketers and Olympic athletes, and there were three boys signed to professional rugby teams when we visited. In fact, hockey, rugby, netball and cricket (including for girls, now that it's replaced rounders) are all strong, with regular success at regional and national championships. Partnerships with professional clubs such as Saracens Rugby, Essex Cricket and Blue Hornets Hockey. But fear not if your child doesn't make the teams as the emphasis is very much on participation. 'Neither of my children are hugely sporty, but they still play in matches, which is great,' one parent said. Lots of other alternatives to keep you fit and occupied, including swimming, badminton, squash, show jumping, water polo and tennis, to name a few. Games fields and facilities stretch as far as the eye can see across the school's 80 acres and includes 12 pitches, nine cricket squares, two floodlit AstroTurf fields, 10 hardcourts, squash courts, gym, weight training – and the rather less impressive and tired-looking sports hall and indoor swimming pool, the latter of which was mentioned by almost every parent we spoke to as the 'main downside of the school.'

'My daughter has had the most wonderful experience when it comes to acting – she's got involved in absolutely everything and loved every minute'

Pupils are all expected to have a crack at music, in one form or another – and few complain, with lots of pride around the many choirs (including the elite chapel choir that sings at main services) and orchestras. The House Shout singing competition is a favourite event, and all students sing in chapel. Quite a few learn an instrument via a peripatetic teacher and there's an emphasis on percussion, including marimba players (a marimba was donated to the school by Dame Evelyn Glennie, who performed here). Regular opportunities for overseas tours – the choir was going to Italy at Eastertime during the academic year we visited.

Everyone does drama in year 9, then it's an option – but a popular one, with a few students going onto study it at university. Easily the best school play posters we've ever seen displayed on the walls – including Jesus Christ Superstar (which around 120 pupils took part in) and Joseph. Parents rave about the quality. 'My daughter has the most wonderful experience, when it comes to acting – she's got involved in absolutely everything and loved every minute,' one parent told us. Every two years, the school takes a production to America, including a past performance in a maximum security women's prison.

The art school, which is based in the old school laundry, is fabulously quirky and practical, with plenty of great facilities (although no dark room, we noticed) and an authentic feel. Popular at GCSE, IB and A level, with history of art and art options available. Extracurricular possibilities are plentiful, including weekly life drawing sessions. Evidence of some serious talent.

Foreign exchanges to a wealth of countries and residentials to practically everywhere you can think of. Biologists and geographers go to Bali; tennis players to Portugal; business studies students to New York; other sports tours to Australia etc etc. Back in the UK, geography field trip to rather less glamorous Swanage and plenty of cultural trips to the likes of Cambridge and London. Charity volunteers to Uganda, their partner school in Ethiopia and a former pupil's Magic Bus, which supports children in the slums of Mumbai – and there are links with Royal Docks Community School in the East End, which pupils regularly visit.

You won't find many schools with a longer list of extracurricular options – we felt exhausted just looking at the 50+ options including academic society, charity projects, amateur radio club, astronomy club, beekeeping, bridge, Greek club, life skills, Model United Nations, science film club. Huge take up of D of E – at the last count no fewer than 12 gold awards in the upper sixth – and 237 enrolled in CCF. Very much accords with Round Square school promoting IDEALS – internationalism, democracy, care for the environment, adventurous pursuits, leadership and service. Felsted has been a global member since 2010. And because students queue up for opportunities to break the 'Felsted bubble,' it all makes for very full days and busy weekends. No wonder it was pointed out to us time and again by pupils and parents that this school is not for the retiring, ill-organised or easily-wearied type.

Boarding: Some 80 per cent board, taking up one of these three options: full-time (mostly international and expat families, with a sprinkling in the UK), weekly (usually, when both parents work) or three-nights-a-week (mainly local families – some even in the village itself). 'We live in the village, but

'They're pretty strict on tidiness, but it's more a case of matron having a quiet word, rather than draconian room inspections'

I asked my mum and dad if I could board as you get the best of both worlds,' one student told us. 'There's always a waiting list – the boarders are really happy,' said a parent. 'They love the camaraderie and really enjoy the relationships with the houseparents, matron and the ladies who help with cleaning and ironing. There's a real sense of community, a great atmosphere and they form strong bonds,' said another.

Two day and eight boarding houses, five for boys and five for girls – plus co-ed boarding in the prep school from 9 years upwards. Separate upper sixth form boarding houses. Here, students get their own room and more freedoms – seen as good preparation for university. Each house has its own unique feel and ranges from being in the main building of the old school (traditional rooms – almost an Oxbridge feel) to the brand new, open-plan girls' boarding house. Ongoing investment means that a seven-figure sum was also about to be spent on upgrading one of the boys' houses when we visited. Every boarding house has an emphasis on homeliness and sociability, but also allows the children personal space – with dorms ranging from singles up to eight beds. 'They're pretty strict on tidiness, but it's more a case of matron having a quiet word, rather than draconian room inspections,' a student told us. 'Bedtimes feel fair – year 9s have lights out at 9.45pm, which goes up to 10.30pm in upper sixth,' said another, who added that mobile phones are handed in overnight.

While the boarding timetable is highly structured (in evenings, it's supper in main school, back to your house for prep, then quiet time, while weekends have a full activity programme, with chapel on Sundays), there's also 'lots of chances to catch your breath,' as the head puts it. Boarders particularly like the independence – for example, being able to walk to the local shop or getting a Chinese take-away from the village – which is well balanced by the feeling that this is a really supportive environment, with many of the houseparents having young families. There are no restrictions on parental visits and robust measures in place to help new and international students settle in. And although many local boarders disappear at the weekends, the stayers-in are rarely short of invitations to stay with local families, outings or on-site activities to fill their time. Likewise, there's no need for day pupils to feel left out, with one parent commenting, 'Both of my kids are day students and they were at school until 10pm three evenings last week. They often stay on for a house BBQ or pizza evening – it's all very inclusive.'

Background and atmosphere: Traditional, yet progressive, it feeds off its history but is not hidebound by it. Founded in 1564 by Richard, Lord Riche, Lord Chancellor of England, the school's original Guild Hall is still in use with other, later, attractive grade I and II listed buildings scattered throughout the village, interspersed with well-tended lawns and sports fields and cut through by the quiet Dunmow to Braintree road. Most recent additions include the music school, the Bathurst gardens for socialising and outdoor performances and the sixth form centre – a great space to hang out, play pool or enjoy regular social events where the odd glass of wine is permitted. Pupils particularly like the coffee shop – open to all in recreational times, although only sixth formers are allowed to work in there.

Some areas could do with an upgrade, notably the swimming pool and sports hall – and we'd hoped for more of a wow factor in the library. 'My husband went to Felsted and much of it doesn't feel look like it's changed from 30 years ago – but then again, it's not the facilities that make a great school,' said one parent. We can vouch for the fact that the food is good (new caterers had just been brought in, thanks to the student food committee, when we visited), and parents praised the fact that youngsters can now go up for unlimited helpings.

'My son is a strapping lad, so he needs it!' said one. As a C of E school, the chapel is at its heart and Felsted is one of only two remaining independent schools to have its own mission church in the East End of London, with links to the church and the young people in the surrounding area.

Overall impression of being a happy, happening place with parents content to be swept along for the ride. 'I'd be amazed if you found a Felstedian that wakes up and think, "I don't want to go to school today",' said one student.

Pastoral care, well-being and discipline: 'We have very well behaved children at all times,' says the head and although he's teasing, there's no doubt the balance of rewards and sanctions sets a high standard. This is a school with big expectations around behaviour and uniform, which seem to be unanimously welcomed by parents and local businesses – and even the children agree it's 'all pretty fair.' 'You're as likely to get rewarded for good behaviour as you are punished for misdemeanours,' one told us, explaining the school's card system, which involves each pupil carrying two small cards in their pocket – one for good deeds to be instantly recorded by teachers ('If we carry books for a teacher, for example') and one for transgressions ('If our uniform is really scruffy or we talk in class, for instance'). 'The principle is that any incident is dealt with at source,' explains the head, explaining that a full 'good' card gets you housepoints, while a full 'bad' one lands you in detention, of which there are various levels – Saturday ones being considered the gravest. Around a dozen temporary exclusions in the year we visited, mainly for serious bad language, bullying and alcohol abuse.

All this is balanced with some surprisingly lenient policies, including around mobile phones,

The stayers-in are rarely short of invitations to stay with local families, outings or on-site activities at weekends

which pupils are allowed to have throughout the day. 'Mobile phones are part of modern living. So there seems nothing to be gained by denying their existence, and much more to be gained by embracing them and it's for this reason that we sometimes ask students who have one to produce them during a lesson and use them to assist with learning,' one teacher told us. And because the school called on the student council to help write up the code of conduct around the use of mobile phones (students aren't allowed to walk around using them, for instance), the rules are respected and followed, say pupils – adding that this is a reflection of the seriousness with which student voice is taken at Felsted.

Pastoral care highly praised and attributed to a range of factors, including an atmosphere of openness and purpose; the house system that 'means everyone is close – and not just with people in their year,' said a student; peer counselling; and prefects being trained in child protection. Bullying minimal, doubtless for all the same reasons – and when it happens, it's dealt with swiftly on both sides. A life coach and a counsellor are on hand, and there's a new well-being centre 'at the heart of the school'.

Pupils and parents: Felsted produces self-starting, entrepreneurial and independent spirits – characteristics that are immediately evident among the ambitious, self-motivated and self-aware pupils, who have some of the healthiest can-do attitudes we've seen. The mix of students – who range from the highly-driven and academically-oriented to the more fun-loving and easy-going – is a breath of fresh air. And they are all pretty down to earth. Parents (many of whom went to the school themselves) love that this is no academic hothouse, yet their offspring still do very well, and they champion the provision of holistic education. 'If you're the kind of young person who just wants your head in a book the whole time, your parents would probably be wasting their money on Felsted because of the ridiculous number of opportunities on offer,' one student told us and parents concur.

'But if you think a lot is expected of the kids at Felsted, wait until you hear about the parents,' laughed one mother we spoke to. 'We're only into the second week of term and already we've had harvest festival and a charity event – and that's not including Saturdays spent watching sport.' But nobody says it with an ounce of irritation. 'I love it – we all do.'

Long list of notable OFs includes English test cricketer John Stephenson and General Sir Richard Dannatt, until recently chief of the general staff. Huge diversity of talent is reflected in the senior positions and success OFs have achieved in science and medicine, the military, politics and public service, academia, business, sports and the media.

While most live within a couple of hours of the school, it is increasingly attracting London-based families. Taking advantage of its proximity to Stansted Airport, international students make up some 18 per cent of pupils – getting towards the high end amongst schools in this guide. Lots of Germans, Spanish and Italians do IB and a similar number of students from Middle East and all round the world.

Entrance: A hundred pupils – split across three classes – come in at year 9: around 70 come up from the prep (having passed a transfer exam), with the remaining 30 from feeder schools including Holmwood House, Heathmount, Orwell Park and Edge Grove. Those taking CE are required to obtain 50 per cent in each paper. Others take a verbal reasoning test, interview and submit a confidential report from their current school. They may also take tests in maths, French and English for setting purposes. The same is true at 14+ entry. At 16+ (when the year group increases from 100 to 125), there is a similar entry procedure and pupils are required to obtain five GCSEs at grade B/6 or better including B grades in the subjects being pursued. Pupils who do not have English as their first language will be assessed by the head of EAL.

Exit: Around 80-90 per cent stay on to the sixth form. After A level, most to good universities such as Exeter, Brighton, Leeds, Newcastle, Birmingham and the top London universities. Three medics in 2017. Business-related subjects, humanities, law and the sciences popular.

Money matters: Academic, music, sport, art, design and technology or drama and all-rounder scholarships offering up to 20 per cent off the fees are available at 13+ and 16+. There are some assisted places up to 100 per cent on a means-tested basis or via open bursaries.

Remarks: At one time, the focus on catering for a wide ability range meant this school's reputation in the academic stakes wasn't as high as it could have been. Not so now, with a renewed focus on academic performance striking just the right balance with valuing individualism and quirkiness. No wonder there's such a sense of excitement as this school becomes increasingly recognised as a leading independent boarding and day school.

Framlingham College

17

College Road, Framlingham, Woodbridge, Suffolk IP13 9EY

01728 723789 | admissions@framcollege.co.uk | www.framcollege.co.uk

Ages: 2–18 (boarding from year 3)

Pupils: 710; sixth form: 185; Boarders: 215 full, 70 seniors + around 60 juniors flexi

Day: £8,409 – £19,176 pa; Boarding: Prep £36 – £39 per night, Senior £29,823 pa

Headmaster: Since 2009, Mr Paul Taylor BA. Read history and politics at Exeter University. Formerly lower master (deputy head) at King's School, Canterbury, and before that director of sport at Tonbridge School. Very friendly, charming without overdoing it and a good listener. Aims to 'produce a decent, rounded human being who looks you in the eye' and believes the school's good performance should be better known outside East Anglia. Wife, Amanda, is secretary of the Framlingham Society and they have four children – two at university and two at Framlingham.

Head of prep: Since 2016, Matthew King. History degree from Nottingham; began his teaching career in Surrey before moving to Dorset, where he met his wife Emily while both were teaching at Dumpton School in Wimborne. Deputy head and then head of Pennthorpe School in Sussex, where he spent eight happy years before being appointed head here. He is a keen sportsman and writer who has taught subjects ranging from geography to drama and from cricket to ancient history.

Academic matters: Setting begins early for English and maths in the prep, and higher up for other subjects. French in pre-prep and Latin from year 7. Help for mild difficulties, notably dyslexia, but the curriculum is not geared for those who seriously struggle. Extension programmes are developed for 'exceptional students' (head prefers this to 'gifted and talented').

Performs well at both GCSE and A level, though not highly selective – strong commitment to pupils of varying ability. In 2017, 49 per cent of A levels were A*-B, 23 per cent A*/A. At GCSE, 30 per cent A*-A/9-7 grades. Some sixth formers take EPQ, others BTecs. Computer science and graphic design recent additions.

SEN provision well established. Emphasis on supporting the pupils' needs – a register (updated termly) is kept to inform staff across the curriculum of any difficulties. Timetabled access to small group and individual tuition avoids pupil withdrawal from mainstream classes. All pupils must be capable of following the academic programmes at GCSE and A level. Provision for EAL also excellent – separate classes as well as individual tuition. Facilities well thought out, well designed and un-flashy. Exceptional library and design and technology building. Classes kept small, average size 12.

Games, options, the arts: Excellent provision for all sports. Artificial surfaces, new indoor pool and fitness centre (well used, especially by girls) – hosts many tournaments. Sport is important – all pupils take part competitively, whatever their level of ability. Music and drama popular too. New theatre/performance studio and many pupils take drama options at GCSE and A level. Well attended regular public performances – pupils recently took The Importance of Being Earnest to the Edinburgh Fringe. Concerts held in local churches – Framlingham and Orford, as well as Ely Cathedral. Big takeup for D of E, with numbers reaching gold awards. Curriculum also supported by extraordinary plethora of clubs and activities.

This is a school for exploring and enjoying; massive oak staircases, terraces on which to play games or take off into the ravishing grounds

Boarding: Prep school boarding is on the top two floors of the original building with spectacular views from every window, redecorated dormitories (mostly four to six beds) and common rooms – no twangy old sofas. Flexi-boarding very popular, and nearly every child from year 3 stays at least one night; 'The whole of year 7 and 8 seem to stay on Wednesday and Friday nights,' say pupils, partly no doubt, because there is Saturday morning school for these years.

Senior school boarding houses well planned and comfortable enough, though girls' quarters, unsurprisingly perhaps, are more home-like and with better decoration. Three houses for girls and four for boys. House competitions range from cross-country to crabbing. Pupils come and go with their own swipe card; most go home at weekends, unless from abroad.

Background and atmosphere: Founded in 1864 in memory of Prince Albert, Queen Victoria's husband (his statue takes pride of place at the front of the school). Senior school in imposing Victorian main

building in stunning setting, perched on a hillside with a gorgeous view across the valley to 12th century Framlingham Castle. A variety of buildings added over time, none of them particularly distinguished, but well planned to make good use of beautiful and extensive grounds. Stupendous view of the castle from many perspectives (head has bagged dress circle view from his first floor study).

Prep school in idyllic setting down the Suffolk lanes. The original manor house has been rebuilt and remodelled as a memorial to former pupils killed both world wars. Remembrance is taken seriously and VC citations are proudly displayed in the panelled hall. This is a school for exploring and enjoying; massive oak staircases, terraces on which to play games or take off into the ravishing grounds. The country house atmosphere of the main building is complemented by a modern, multi-purpose hall used for concerts, assemblies and plays and well-designed buildings for DT and art, science and technology. Newish classroom block is reached via a covered passageway; spanking new dance and drama studio; new multi-use Fowler pavilion overlooking hockey pitch and cricket square.

Nursery and pre-prep occupy their own purpose built accommodation and play areas, but are very much part of the same site. Notice boards with details of after-school clubs, sport and music cover the walls, including one headed Celebration, and pupils proudly point out their names and faces.

A tone of respectful informality throughout. Pupils well-mannered and noticeably calm, even at lesson changes and in the dining hall at lunchtime.

Pastoral care, well-being and discipline: Policy of incorporating day pupils into boarding houses is now well established and a great success. Many pupils do 'occasional' boarding. A parent told us: 'I can email the housemaster directly if my daughter wants to board at short notice – on the same day, on occasion.' Anti-bullying posters dotted around school and any incidents picked up on quickly. 'The housemaster got to the bottom of the matter on the same day,' said one parent, 'and the boys are still together in the same house.'

Keeping sixth formers in the house system creates opportunities for leadership. As a relief from house responsibilities, sixth formers have their own common room and social areas – plans afoot to create a technologically sophisticated sixth form centre. The head rightly lauds excellent pastoral track record but emphasises that 'the family is more important. Schools can over-claim for themselves'.

Pupils and parents: Pupils are mainly drawn from middle class East Anglian families. In some cases, several generations have attended the school. A strong body from abroad, notably Germany and the Far East. Head sees the school as poised to appeal as much to the Oundle and Uppingham market as to its Norfolk and Suffolk constituency. Excellent reputation locally and no problems recruiting.

Pupils well-mannered and friendly, very at-ease in their school, 'Not precocious, but not scared of adults either,' is how the head puts it.

Entrance: For entry to the nursery and pre-prep, pupils are invited to spend a day (or morning) for an informal assessment; same for year 3 upwards but their day includes an entrance test. Scholarships at 11+ for entrants to the senior school – academic, music and sport. At 13, pupils from the prep accepted 'on the nod' – assuming they can cope with the academic rigour of the college. CE and interview for everyone else, though tests in core subjects (English, maths and non-verbal reasoning) can be arranged for pupils from schools that don't do CE. The interview is key and head also takes prospective pupils' school reports seriously.

Stupendous view of the castle from many perspectives (head has bagged dress circle view)

Significant numbers enter after GCSE, with places offered conditionally on the basis of an interview, school report and a minimum achievement of seven A*-C/9-5 passes at GCSE/IGCSE or equivalent for those not following the British curriculum. Overseas candidates also sit tests in English and maths.

Exit: Everyone in the prep is prepared for common entrance. All but a handful transfer to the senior school (results help decide setting in year 9). Small number of leavers after GCSE. Almost all sixth formers go to university, with traditional universities well represented. Head is aware of need to identify and support Oxbridge potential early – one to Oxford and one to read medicine in 2017. Others go off to read anything from chemical engineering at Lancaster to equine management at the Royal Agricultural College to children's nursing at Kingston. The place of careers advice is stressed – head believes it should be seen as separate from the university application process. Parents rely on the school as an expert resource.

Money matters: A range of scholarships awarded for outstanding academic, musical, artistic and sporting excellence at 13+ and 16+. Further means-tested bursarial help is available as needed. Reductions for siblings and Forces families.

Remarks: A well run, unstressful school, with happy pupils and high levels of achievement in all areas.

Gresham's

18

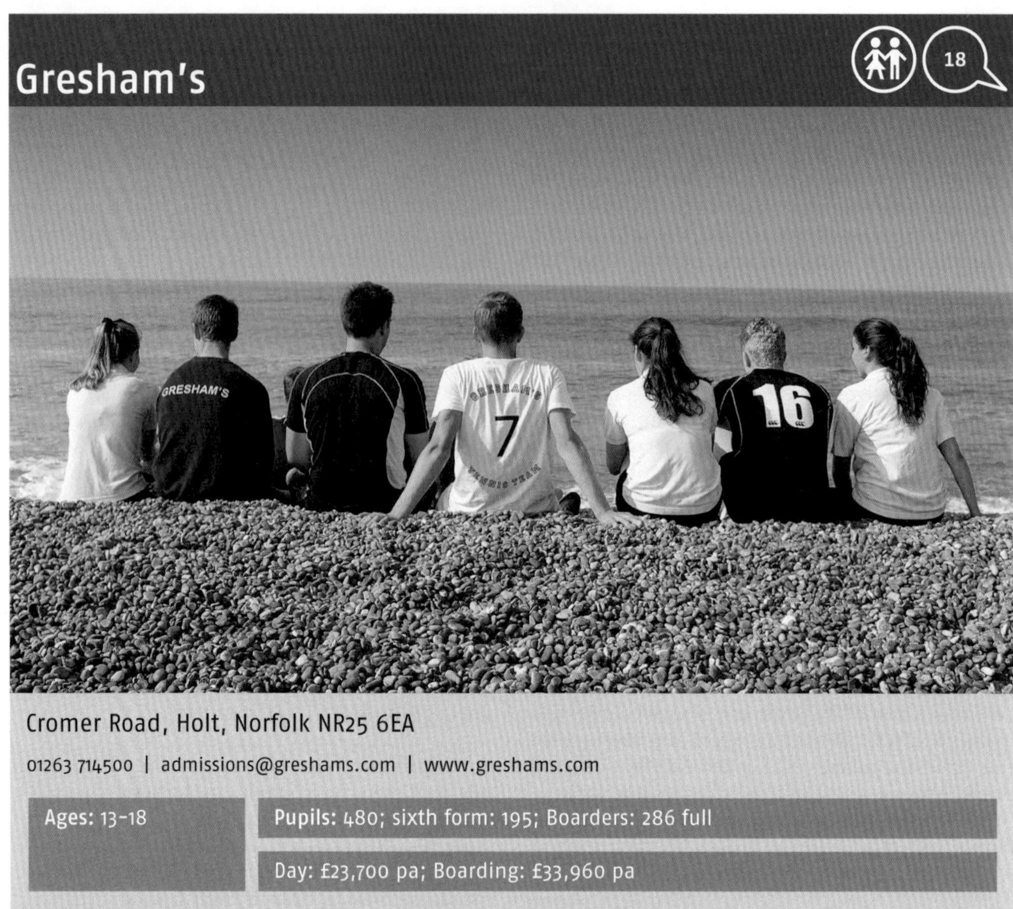

Cromer Road, Holt, Norfolk NR25 6EA

01263 714500 | admissions@greshams.com | www.greshams.com

Ages: 13-18

Pupils: 480; sixth form: 195; Boarders: 286 full

Day: £23,700 pa; Boarding: £33,960 pa

Linked school: Gresham's Prep School, 917

Headmaster: Since 2014, Douglas Robb MA (Edinburgh) politics, MEd (Homerton, Cambridge), previously head of Oswestry School. A post-university spell of teaching in Zimbabwe and at Fettes College helped decide his career. Following a post teaching politics and economics at Loughborough grammar, he taught and was a housemaster at Oundle for 10 very happy years which 'totally persuaded me of the benefits of boarding.' Quite a commanding physical presence (a former rugby player), extremely quick-witted and entertaining, a live wire. 'He is confident enough to be able to listen to us and sometimes change his mind,' we were told by a pupil, and it is clear that he has 'picked up the vibe' of the school. He thinks 'it is dangerous to try and change a school; find one that's good and help make it the best. A school has a life of its own; I am a caretaker for a short time.' Believes the house system is central to the success of pupils learning and integrating well into school life. It can also help during the teenage years with 'opportunities for conversation and friendships, both amongst peers, but also with staff.' Has high expectations of his staff and spells out the commitment at interview; 'I pin them down, no woolly promises to help will do. This job is a vocation.' He is scornful of phrases such as 'work-life balance', believing that, in term time, successful teachers must be prepared to involve themselves far beyond the classroom itself, including meetings at odd times; 'Ten o'clock in the evening is not unheard of.' Is fortunate to be inheriting sound finances and is planning new boarding and music facilities and a sixth form centre. Is keen to continue raising academic standards – 'I never heard of a head wanting to lower them' – and to emphasise the central importance of boarding to the ethos of the school. Will accept pupils 'so long as they are prepared to work hard,' and their parents are realistic and in support.

Is married to Lucinda and they have three children (all at Gresham's). He is enjoying north Norfolk life, 'countryside, dogs, getting to know people.' Maintains keen interest in rugby, also golf, skiing and travel and 'proper holidays'

Academic matters: Class sizes between 12 and 20, and setting for most parts of the curriculum, mean pupils get focussed attention. Parents think the size of the school allows for pupils to develop at their own pace, though several also mentioned, not as a criticism, 'there is definitely more push; things are less easy-going than in the past.' Pupils generally take at least 10 GCSEs; 43 per cent at A*-A/9-7 in 2017. For the sixth form, there is the choice of A levels or the IB with between a quarter and a third taking the IB. The requirement for one of the six subjects studied to be a language puts off a lot and, as an exam, it is perceived as 'stiffer' than A levels. The previous head's attempt to enforce the IB for all by 2016 met with strong parental resistance, and was abandoned as a policy in favour of the status quo: all may, none must. The present head is clear, 'IB is an excellent exam and we encourage it, but it is not, and never will be, for everyone.' Creditable results across the board at A level with 36 per cent A*/A, 59 per cent A*-B grades in 2017. Solid IB results: average score of 33 points.

Around a fifth receive extra help with SEN, mostly dyslexia, dyscalculia, sensory impairments and poor self-esteem. The need for help appears greatest in year 9 and 10 and lessens as pupils progress through the school, perhaps finding their feet. The department is well staffed with full and part-time teachers, one devoted to teaching ESL, and help is offered individually and in small groups. Care is taken to ensure that individual difficulties are made known to subject staff. New entrants are screened to flag any problems early on and close relations nurtured with feed junior schools. Charged as an extra, but there is a termly cap on fees at £500.

Games, options, the arts: Outdoorsy lot who make the most of the facilities and seem to agree with the 'healthy mind, healthy body' outlook. All the usual team sports: rugby, hockey (for boys and girls), netball and cricket, with lots of match play for everyone and good coaching for those taking things seriously. School also hosts training camps, some residential, in cricket, rugby and hockey, in the holidays. Swimming is compulsory in the lower forms and an extra activity higher up. Weights room, rowing machines, yoga and cross-country running all popular. 'I often go for an early run; it is one of the reasons I like boarding,' we were told by one girl, and it is obviously not a place for those who prefer stewing indoors. The few who seriously dislike team games are treated humanely and allowed to do shooting (this is Norfolk), sailing, fencing, cycling and swimming higher up the school. Pitches, Astroturf and courts for tennis and squash galore, and a rifle range (members of the club have been junior ladies champion four years running, and several pupils have been selected to represent Britain in the U19 rifle team). D of E popular at all levels, with around 30 reaching gold each year; CCF and the BASC course (British Association for Shooting and Conservation) are options.

Quite a commanding physical presence (a former rugby player), extremely quick-witted and entertaining, a live wire

The reputation of the school's drama department and facilities is renowned and the school has produced several professional actors, Olivia Colman (Broadchurch and Rev) most notable. With professional facilities (Auden theatre hosts touring companies as well as being used for several school productions each year – excellent sound and lighting systems, dressing rooms, proper auditorium, the lot), drama is a very popular extra activity: 'It was a reason to come here.' Parents loud in their praise: 'It is incredible what they can stage; lots of opportunities to develop a serious interest in stage management, lighting and sound as well as acting.' At least three major productions each year; it can be a real springboard for pupils who want to go on to study at drama school or university.

Music is equally valued – roughly half the school has timetabled instrumental tuition and there is a wide variety of choirs, ensembles, bands and orchestras. Despite a revamp for the Britten centenary in 2013, accommodation is under par and new facilities are a high priority on the head's

building programme, which includes the new music school and sixth form centre.

Well-designed building devoted to art, textiles, and DT – splendid displays of pupils' work, excellent facilities and all manner of projects undertaken. Opportunities to use oil paints from the start, life drawing classes regularly held and artists in residence inject their own talents and energy into this thriving department. Superb exhibition space, lots to feast the eyes on – a really dynamic place to develop a talent. Art and design have their own rather eye-catching building in the prep too, with spectacular displays of pupils' work (including designs on backs of chairs) and every inducement for creativity. 'We do textiles, mosaics, woodwork, mess generally'.

Boarding: Strong boarding feel, but day pupils are well integrated having their own bed and/or desk, in their house, and though flexi-boarding is not actively encouraged, 'We happily accommodate pupils overnight on occasions when they are here late for rehearsals, performances or other school events.' Pupils do swap around quite a bit; choosing to board in the sixth form is popular; others, sometimes for financial reasons become day. Houses are comfortable, well lit and decorated with thought given to making things home-like, for example decent-sized kitchens that are actually used for cooking and eating in, rather than miserable little kitchenettes with a toaster and electric kettle, standing room only. Houseparents and matrons are always about, pupils return to their houses at break and lunch; bedrooms mostly shared between two or four.

The academic/pastoral divide is blurred; house staff teach their own subject alongside their pastoral duties. Lots stay in at weekends and there are plenty of organised activities though not what the head calls 'enforced jollity.' Houses sit together at their own tables in the revamped dining hall. The food 'has improved, we get more salads' (this from a girl) but we thought it still a bit on the stodgy side – room for improvement. Some houses have fruit always available, but not all, a source of some grievance, we discovered. Straightforward uniform; jacket and trousers for boys ('suits' in the sixth form), calf-length tartan kilts and new, light blue tweed jackets (rather chic) gradually replacing the old blazers. Coats hardly worn and if needed (one thinks of bracing North Sea breezes), 'We wear what we like so long as it's not too outrageous.' How sensible. Home clothes once the timetabled day is over and at the weekends.

Background and atmosphere: Founded originally as a grammar school (1555), rejuvenated in 1890s by George Howson, a headmaster with 'advanced' views in education. He introduced the teaching of sciences, abandoned corporal punishment and encouraged pacifist thinking – practically unheard of then. Set in over 170 acres of woodlands and extensive playing fields, school buildings extend on both sides of the old Cromer road leading out of Holt (pupils cross via a bridge) and are a mixture of styles and quality ranging from magnificent Edwardian and art deco halls and libraries with grand staircases, stained glass etc, through to more run of the mill classrooms, the innovative art and design block and the famous Auden theatre. Pupils get plenty of fresh air doing the brisk walk between lessons in different parts of the site. There is a well looked after air about the place and a programme of refurbishment of various houses is under way together with further planned developments.

'I often go for an early run; it is one of the reasons I like boarding,' and it is obviously not a place for those who prefer stewing indoors. The few who seriously dislike team games are treated humanely

Pastoral care, well-being and discipline: Nothing but praise from parents; 'My three boys all settled quickly and never felt out of things as day pupils,' was a remark we heard over again. The school focuses particularly on those not coming up from the prep school in year 9, and there is a 'buddy' system in place. 'Our son found it hard to begin with, but the school continued to support him; they were brilliant and he is really happy there now.' The small size of the school means staff and pupils all know each other and relationships are forged, which can help if there are difficulties at any stage. Good interaction between the different year groups and friendly, still respectful staff/pupil relations.

Apart from usual minor misdemeanours, a well behaved lot.There is a clear anti-bullying policy (lots of awareness notices on walls), counsellors and a school chaplain as well as matrons and house staff all keeping an eye out. Well understood rules on illegal drugs (zero tolerance), and alcohol: over 18s may drink ('enjoy a pint ' is the phrase used) either in the school's own bar or the Feathers in Holt; no PDA (public displays of affection), but few overstep the mark. The need for teenagers, sixth formers particularly, to handle stress is taken seriously with regular sessions on relaxation and quick intervention if a pupil is struggling. Sixth formers also choose their own tutors: 'they have to teach one of the subjects we are studying, it helps with university choices but of course liking comes into it too.'

Pupils and parents: Friendly pupils, unflustered and polite, with just the right amount of door-holding and rather less hair flicking and self-conscious teenage behaviour than usual. Un-flashy, country school, 'It's a Barbour and boots place.' Day pupils are drawn from a large area of north Norfolk, many travelling for an hour each way; boarders from all over the country but predominantly East Anglia. Mostly farming, professional and business families with a sprinkling of county boarding families, plus lots from London – many choose the school for the contrast with the fiercely competitive schools in the Capital. Some move to Norfolk for this reason, both parents commuting, or one remaining in Norfolk during the week so children can be day pupils. About 20 per cent from overseas, mostly Europe.

Arts, sport, science and technology are all well represented amongst former pupils, who include Benjamin Britten, WH Auden, Sir Christopher Cockerell (inventor of the hovercraft), Sir James Dyson (vacuum cleaner), Tom and Ben Youngs (international rugby players), Lord Reith (first director-general of BBC), Prof Alan Hodgkin and Olivia Colman.

Entrance: Roughly 80 per cent of senior school have come up from the prep school, others from a mix of day and boarding preps, some from maintained sector. No common entrance; an assessment day is held for year 9 entrants in Lent term for following September. Tests in English and maths plus reports and references from current school. For sixth form, predicted grades (usually a minimum of A*/B in six subjects including those to be studied and minimum of C in English and maths) plus school report and interview.

Exit: A few to Oxbridge (five in 2017), sizeable numbers to London (Imperial, LSE, UCL) plus the other Russell Group universities. Wide range of subjects studied including a regular few to drama school and music colleges (Central St Martins, Guildhall). One to British Columbia and one to Groningen in 2017. Varying numbers (some 10 per cent) leave for pastures new after GCSE, usually in the maintained sector, plus the odd one for vocational work (gamekeeping a recent one). Head approves of pupils choosing vocational work and believes it reflects the diversity of the school.

Money matters: Thanks to a long association with the Worshipful Company of Fishmongers and its generous financial underpinning of the school's finances, a number of valuable scholarships and bursaries are on offer. Academic scholarships worth up to 50 per cent of fees offered for year 9 entry (can be topped up with a bursary, if financial need is demonstrated), drama, music, art and sport awards also offered, for up to 20 per cent. In the sixth form, scholarships are offered to those who do brilliantly at GCSE (if not already in receipt of an award) and help is forthcoming if families fall on hard times, at least to enable pupils to get through to the next public exam. Usual sibling discounts for three or more at one time.

Remarks: Well-established country boarding school with a deserved reputation for the encouragement of the arts, particularly music and drama. Its relatively small size and position make it a good choice for those looking for a broader educational experience within a school with a strong pastoral ethos. The twin paths of the IB and A levels will remain under the present head. Hard to think who would not thrive in this happy, well-run school.

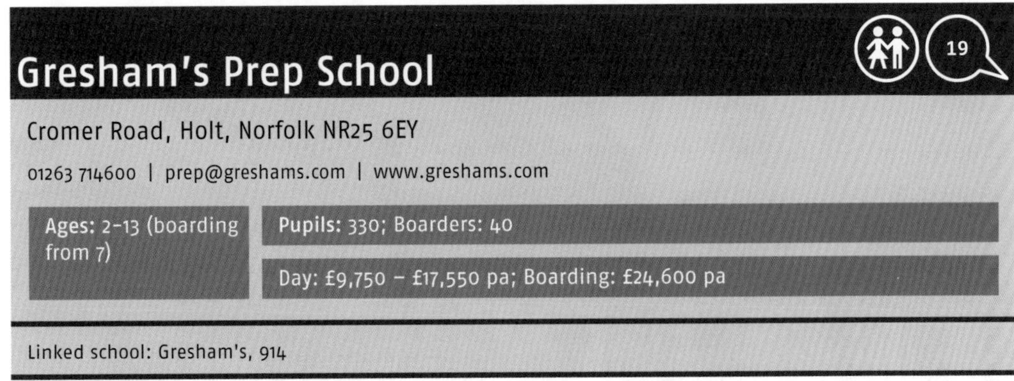

Gresham's Prep School

Cromer Road, Holt, Norfolk NR25 6EY

01263 714600 | prep@greshams.com | www.greshams.com

Ages: 2–13 (boarding from 7)

Pupils: 330; Boarders: 40

Day: £9,750 – £17,550 pa; Boarding: £24,600 pa

Linked school: Gresham's, 914

Headmaster: Since 2003, Mr James Quick (50s) BA in economic history, PGCE (Durham); began teaching at The Dragon School, then St Edward's, Oxford, where he was housemaster. Did teacher exchange at Geelong College, Australia before coming here. His wife, Kim, teaches English, history and Latin and their four daughters, all but one at university stage or beyond, were at Gresham's. Sparkling-eyed with a youthful appearance and manner, he is clearly at ease with both staff and pupils, but does not overdo the bonhomie in chance encounters. Has a modest manner and the attractive quality of being quick to praise colleagues. Says, 'Everyone can chip in ideas and rely on each other'. Continues to teach his subjects, history and classical studies, 'doing what everyone else does here'. Says there is no defined Gresham's 'product' as such, but believes hallmarks of pupils are 'the confidence to be themselves (we have room here for the odd squeaky wheel), kindness, a sense of humour, and being prepared to Have a Go.' Sees family in spare time and is a dedicated runner. He recently took part in the Round Norfolk Relay, volunteering for the Thetford – Diss leg at one o'clock in the morning. He is a happy head and in the right job.

Brilliant library, bursting with delectable titles and opportunities to enter competitions, and with an enthusiastic, full-time librarian

Head of nursery and pre-prep since September 2016 is Sarah Hollingsworth (30s), previously director of pastoral care at Oswestry School. She has had various early years and KS1 roles and is a trained ISI inspector.

Entrance: At all ages and stages from 3 (nursery and pre-prep), 7 and 11 in the prep school, although they will try to accommodate when possible at other times. Some year groups fill quickly, so first come first served. Accepts a fairly wide spectrum of ability, but admission is not a foregone conclusion. Informal assessment in the early forms, the same plus maths, English and verbal and non-verbal reasoning tests at 11. Pupils from the maintained sector often join for years 7 and 8 in preparation for the senior school.

Exit: Great majority, currently over 85 per cent, go through the school to year 8 and move up to the seniors. All take the 'exit' exam, those not likely to make the grade are warned in good time. Those wishing to go elsewhere at 13, and there are a few most years, are prepared individually for the necessary entrance exams. Ampleforth, Charterhouse, Framlingham, Norwich School, Oundle, Rugby, Stowe, The Leys and Uppingham are popular choices.

Remarks: On its own site, though only a brisk walk from the senior school, on the edge of Holt, North Norfolk's stylish market town. Certain facilities such as sport, swimming pool and the theatre are used at the senior school (which has recently added combined music school and sixth form centre) but in the main, it operates autonomously. Parents queue up to praise this relaxed and happy school where 'childhood still seems to last the right length of time'. One parent thought, 'My son came out of his shell here, he became a different boy'. A number of families have both Norfolk and London bases,

but choose Gresham's for its 'less pressured atmosphere' over the more hothoused approach found elsewhere.

No defined Gresham's 'product' as such, but believes hallmarks of pupils are 'the confidence to be themselves (we have room here for the odd squeaky wheel), kindness, a sense of humour, and being prepared to Have a Go'

Without the restriction of teaching for the common entrance (abandoned recently), there can be greater flexibility in the curriculum. Excellent languages: the younger years (2-5) learn a number of languages with the focus on fun and communication. French is taught from year 6 with Spanish and Latin options from year 7. Other languages (eg German, Mandarin) can usually be accommodated on request. Science taught in designated labs, sometimes using the more sophisticated facilities of the senior school. There is mixed ability teaching up until year 4, then setting in most subjects, though 'these are flexible and pupils move up and down'. Pupils have their ability stretched by differentiated targets, rather than being 'pushed'.

Educational support well-resourced, with five specially trained staff (two full-time) who are also class teachers. Caters for mild difficulties such as dyslexia, Asperger's, and other emotional problems, for example, low self-esteem. About a quarter of pupils receive help, either in one-to-one tuition, small groups, or support in the classroom. Brilliant library, bursting with delectable titles, displays, opportunities to enter competitions and with an enthusiastic, full-time librarian, who does everything to encourage reading as an enjoyable habit. Open all day long (boarders can use it in the evening for project work), the atmosphere is quiet: 'we don't insist on a deathly silence, but purposeful reading does need peace and quiet'.

The performing arts, particularly music and drama, have status, and are very well taught within the curriculum and as extra activities ('one of the reasons we chose the school'). Everyone sings in a choir in the lower forms, with auditions higher up for the senior and chapel choirs (runners up in the national Barnardo's Contest recently). Over two-thirds of pupils learn an instrument, some at the top grades, and there are many bands, ensemble groups and orchestras with frequent performances. Dance is on the curriculum in the lower forms and an extra activity later on. Drama is timetabled throughout the school; performances take place in the hall with larger productions in the Auden Theatre at the main school. Art and design have their own rather eye-catching building, with spectacular displays of pupils' work (including designs on backs of chairs) and every inducement for creativity. 'We do textiles, mosaics, woodwork, mess generally'. Loads of sport, all the usual team games, and though 'we understand not everyone is mad keen, but it's also important to have to keep going with something you wouldn't necessarily choose'. In addition, pupils can choose shooting or kayaking in years 7 and 8. A large number of fixtures, with parents often on the sidelines in support.

Mostly new buildings of one or two storeys, of varying design, set in the midst of extensive grounds, adventure play areas and piazzas; 'pupils have to play in sight of the gazebo'. Separate boys' and girls' houses, each with capacity for 40 or 50, in bedrooms of two to four. Exceptionally attractive and home-like decoration (strong Cath Kidston influence) and furnishings. Photographs of children enjoying themselves on every wall, bunting, posters; a mock-up of Giles Gilbert-Scott's classic telephone box houses the real telephone – no mobiles during the day or after bedtime. House parents and matrons always around, and pupils return to house at break and lunch.

Careful attention is paid to ensuring pupils' well-being and happiness. As well as the usual offers of counselling well displayed, there is a 'worry box' to post in 'anything they want to discuss, however small it may seem'. Staff keep a weather eye, particularly in changing room areas, which are always supervised. In the un-canteeny dining room, pupils are helped to make good food choices, picking from colour-coded categories, green (vegetables), red (protein) and yellow (carbs). Early supper ('children are all starving by 5:30pm') which day pupils often stay for if doing activities, and cereal/toast and hot drinks in the houses before bed.

Parents queue up to praise this relaxed and happy school where 'childhood still seems to last the right length of time'. 'My son came out of his shell here'

This is a happy, well-run prep that benefits from its connection to the senior school, but is definitely separate. Would suit most types but is not specially geared to preparation for common entrance or other highly competitive school entrance exams.

Haileybury

C of E | 20

Hertford, Hertfordshire SG13 7NU

01992 706353 | registrar@haileybury.com | www.haileybury.com

Ages: 11–18 (boarding from year 9)

Pupils: 784; sixth form: 315; Boarders: 506 full/weekly, 9 flexi

Day: £16,455 – £24,753 pa; Boarding: £20,796 – £32,784 pa

Master: Since September 2017, Martin Collier MA, previously head of St John's School Leatherhead. He read modern history at St John's College Oxford, followed by PGCE from London University. His first 10 years of teaching were in the maintained sector, at the 'fantastic' Thomas Tallis in south London and the 'tough' Weavers School in Wellingborough. He then moved into the independent sector and Oundle School, where he worked through roles of head of history, director of studies and second master. He also has many years' experience as an examiner with different boards, has been involved with the Qualifications and Curriculum Development Agency and has appeared as an examinations expert before the House of Commons select committee on education. In short, he has a broad experience and detailed knowledge of all things educational. Married with three older children.

Academic matters: A famous name in public school education, Haileybury has in recent years become equally well known for its enthusiastic participation in the IB. 'We began in 1998 because it promised a broader curriculum and a boost to boarding, but we're now totally idealist.' Today about 110 sixth formers follow the diploma programme, with about 40 arriving each year specifically to do so. A levels, however, are still very much on offer and the school does very well in both sets of exams, with 36 average IB points in 2017, and pleasing results at A level (40 per cent A*/A in 2017). Biology, chemistry and history notably strong. Though not the easiest thing to run a school with a dual set of qualifications, this is managed by highly-qualified staff (including a hefty sprinkling of doctorates), who generally teach across both systems. The ISI commended the 'often outstanding' teaching.

Lower down, IGCSEs in just about everything, with 63 per cent A*/As in 2017. Here, all do a compulsory core of maths, English language, science and RS ('because of its philosophical and ethical bent'). Languages include Italian, French, Spanish, Latin and classical Greek, with German also taught to the 15 or 20 native speakers taking the IB. Newish IGCSEs are computer science and positive psychology. Pupils are set in maths and languages from year 7, science and English from year 9. Reasonable numbers who require some type of learning support (typically 50-80), with two teachers to address their needs, one a specialist in language, the other in maths. A small number, too, have extra help with English as a second language. Overall high aspirations, with sane expectations. 'They work hard, but it's very unpressured,' said a parent. 'They expect you to try your very, very best.' Relationships with staff particularly good, both in and outside of the classroom.

Games, options, the arts: Co-curricular activities are very much part of Haileybury's raison d'etre and the school has an outstanding reputation for both sport and choral music. Sport compulsory for all throughout, with games afternoons twice a week and matches on Saturday. Plenty of teams too, often from A-D, so everyone gets a chance to show their mettle. Those who aren't fans of the playing field can do 'something less taxing,' with options including aerobics, badminton, trampolining, rowing, rackets, golf and sailing (currently boasts one girl who sails for Great Britain). Though boys triumph in hockey and football (where the school plays in the Boodles Cup) and girls in tennis, hockey, netball and lacrosse (competing at county and national level), rugby (boys only) and cricket (mostly boys) remain the 'communal sports.' 'Boys' rugby is the main thing,' said a girl, and the whole school turns out to cheer on rugby matches played on the front field. Facilities can only be described as superb, with a bright, modern pool, two Astroturf pitches and a professionally operated tennis club in the grounds. The rackets court is also considered one of the finest in the world and plays host to the world rackets championship. High Performance Programme (including training and lectures) aims to help talented sportspeople raise their game.

The school has a 30-year tradition of exceptional choral singing and won the BBC Songs of Praise School Choir of the Year some years back (it has reached the semifinal twice since then too). 'One of the things I enjoy most about the school,' said one parent, 'is the Christmas concert. It's just magnificent.' Chamber choir of about 30 ('very intense,' said one member) plus larger chapel choir of about 90. Wide range of other musical opportunities, from jazz bands to concerts and musical theatre. Twenty peripatetic music staff. 'You potentially can do any instrument,' said a teacher. 'We currently have pupils studying the steelpans, jazz piano and the organ.' New 'associated composer' will compose music for school events and lead class projects. The stand-alone music building, which already enjoys a charming beamed concert hall, has recently undergone a £1m refurbishment.

Art taught in its own large, light, purpose-built building, which not only caters for those doing GCSE or A level, but for leisure enthusiasts, seven days a week and in the evenings. Offers 2D and 3D, print, ceramics, photography and textiles, with exams tailored to individual interests. Dance lessons on offer for about 100 keen participants in jazz, ballet, street and tap, plus an annual dance show. 'Fantastic drama,' said a pupil, listing an energetic range from house drama to full-school musicals, which take place in the well-equipped studio theatre.

An abundance of trips. Sport (South Africa) and music (Slovenia, Prague and Venice), plus charity and subject specific (Uganda, Tanzania, Vietnam, and Sinai), as well as more modest outings to battlefields and cultural events.

Wednesday afternoons are devoted to community service, D of E and CCF for years 9 to 11, broadening out in the sixth form to take in activities like photography and web design. One extended weekend each term devoted exclusively to D of E and CCF (which flourish in equal numbers). Plenty of societies and lectures. Model United Nations particularly popular and the school recently played host to a world conference with 800 delegates. The head, who feels strongly that co-curricular activities build up life skills, has devised a specific year 9 programme which includes such fundamentals as outdoor pursuits skills and life saving.

Though Haileybury is ethnically and religiously diverse, everyone must attend services four or five times a week. 'It's here they learn the values that hold the school together'

Certainly you wouldn't enjoy the school if you weren't happy with a busy life. 'Everyone encourages everyone else and invites them to get involved. It's very full on,' said one pupil. 'You do have to learn to plan your time to fit in all your commitments, but you go to bed feeling fulfilled.'

Boarding: From year 9, about 70 per cent of pupils board, with a sizeable chunk of weekly boarders who leave late on Saturday and return on Sunday evening (except for five or six weekends annually, when all remain). Boarding ethos even for day pupils, who stay till 6.30pm and have their own beds at school. Seven boys' houses, five girls'. Four recently built, with light, bright rooms, the rest older but updated. All sit amongst pleasant greenery and house the boarders, overseen by a housemaster or mistress, plus a resident tutor. In the early years, eight to 10 pupils share a large, subdivided space; from year 11, single or shared rooms.

Girls do their own laundry, boys have theirs done for them. 'They think girls prefer that arrangement,' justified one pupil. Active inter-house social life and plenty of weekend activities for full-time boarders, with Saturday film nights and Sunday trips. Plus 'a lot of people have flats in London' or visit local pupils (with beneficent parents). Parents ('my son's housemaster is just wonderful – warm, jolly, intelligent, everything you could hope for in a male role model') and pupils ('my housemistress is the most reasonable woman') praise the boarding care.

Background and atmosphere: The school was designed in 1806 for the East India Company by William Wilkins (also responsible for the National Gallery and Downing College, Cambridge) as a training college for civil servants bound for India. In 1862, after the closure of the college, it was taken over by Haileybury, to be transformed into a public school for families in the professions and services, amalgamating, in 1942, with the Imperial Service College. The first girls were admitted in 1973. Today the school continues to occupy an impressive 550 acres of rural Hertfordshire, complete with magnificent neo-classical university-like buildings constructed round a traditional quadrangle. Later additions are sympathetic and well designed, with most subjects benefiting from purpose-built space. Beautiful, well-stocked and well-used library. 'If they don't have a book, they will get it for you.'

The school remains a Christian foundation with an Anglican chaplain who officiates in a domed chapel of cathedral-like proportions. Though Haileybury is ethnically and religiously diverse (with a fair number of Muslims, Jews and Hindus) everyone must attend services four or five times a week. 'It's here they learn the values that hold the school together.'

Charity work is taken seriously and the Haileybury Youth Trust, first set up in the East

Designed in 1806 for the East India Company as a training college for civil servants bound for India

End in 1890 by old boy Clement Attlee, has been working with impoverished Ugandans since 2006. It has been commended by the UN as a model of a small-scale charity, patenting a brick now used for building schools, kitchens and water towers.

Two further Haileybury branches now operate in Kazakhstan, the first British public schools to be opened in Central Asia. These help underwrite bursaries for UK-based students.

Pastoral care, well-being and discipline: The school essentially operates as two schools, a more-or-less self-contained lower school, running as a day prep from 11 to 13; and an upper school, from 13 to 18, which is very much a boarding school, with a full day of lessons and sport on Saturday.

Not a grand school in atmosphere. 'It's cosy and terribly, terribly happy,' said one parent. 'You could not think of a better place to have your teenager running around.' Food comes highly commended. 'It's one of the things people rave about,' said a sixth former. Three compulsory meals a day (plus an optional snack on games days), but with plenty of choice. The Costa Coffee, a latter-day tuck shop, is 'the' place to congregate. Manners are formal (new pupils jump to attention, teachers are addressed as Sir) but not stiff. All pupils wear uniform, tartan skirts and blazers in the junior school, plain navy suits in the sixth form.

Discipline runs the usual gamut from detention to permanent exclusion. Drugs dealt with firmly. First offenders are suspended for a week, and regularly drugs tested thereafter, second-time offenders are expelled – though the school 'can't remember excluding someone.' Strong prefect system, with 30 to 40 college prefects given additional responsibilities and privileges (more flexibility in uniform, better rooms, pub visits).

Pupils and parents: Largely from the surrounding counties – Hertfordshire, Essex, Buckinghamshire, Cambridgeshire. In general parents are 'City folk, business people, successful professionals' and as most live reasonably nearby, more involved than usual at boarding schools. Large numbers from Europe for the sixth form, particularly Germans and Italians; a trickle from Haileybury's sister schools in Kazakhstan. Pupils seem happy, confident, friendly and balanced.

Entrance: Fifty in year 7, a further 60 in year 9. Unusually, also a healthy intake (10 to 20) in year

10. Typically 50 new pupils enter the sixth form, including about 40 from overseas. At this juncture the school is heavily oversubscribed, with about three applicants for every place. Entrance tests at all levels in maths, English, verbal and non-verbal reasoning. Year 9 entry pre-tested by negotiation with the prep school 12 or 24 months in advance and CE used for setting. 'We are looking for somebody who wants to do their best, is B+ to A* academically and will throw themselves into the co-curricular.' Wide range of feeders includes Heath Mount, Edge Grove, Lochinver House and Keble.

Exit: About 10 to 20 leave after GCSEs, often for local day schools. Post A levels and IB, it's mainly to Russell Group universities (most popular choices include UCL, Warwick, Durham, Nottingham, Leeds, Bristol and King's College London), and increasingly, to Europe and the US. Five to Oxbridge in 2017 and three medics. Fourteen off abroad, including to New York University, McGill, Toronto, Switzerland, Spain, France and Italy (including one medic). Subject range from astrophysics to music. Good range of specialist advisers, for Oxbridge, medical school and North American universities. Three or four to art college.

Money matters: Music, sport, art, and all-rounder scholarships of up to 30 per cent of fees, plus a range of (generous) means-tested bursaries.

Remarks: A dynamic and energetic school, with a long established, successful IB diploma programme. Haileybury actually achieves what many boast about, a well-rounded education. Great fun for those who want to be involved in everything it has to offer.

Holmwood House School

21

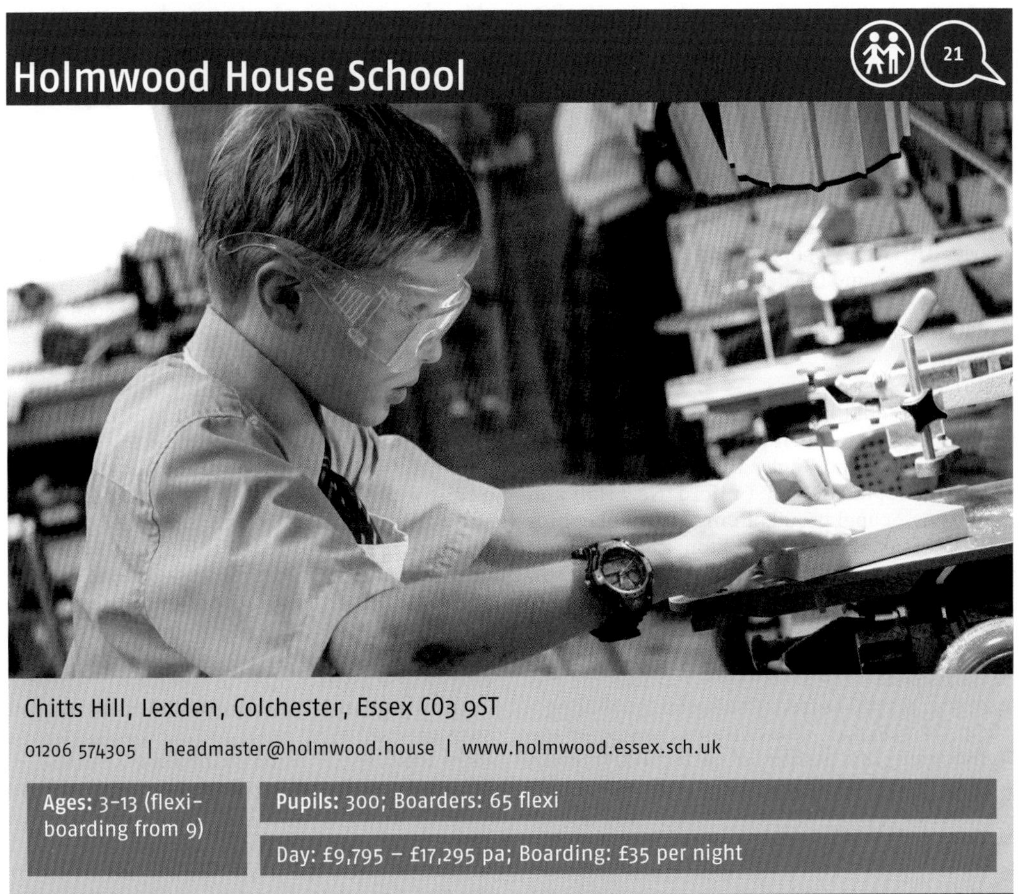

Chitts Hill, Lexden, Colchester, Essex CO3 9ST

01206 574305 | headmaster@holmwood.house | www.holmwood.essex.sch.uk

Ages: 3-13 (flexi-boarding from 9)	Pupils: 300; Boarders: 65 flexi
	Day: £9,795 – £17,295 pa; Boarding: £35 per night

Headmaster: Since 2009, Alexander Mitchell, 50s. Originally from Perthshire, though he worries the burr is fading, having spent more of his life down south than north of the border (not to Essex ears, it isn't). Educated at Napier in Edinburgh, with a degree in music from Colchester and PGCE from

Reading. Has taught in the state and public, single-sex and co-ed, day and boarding sectors, most recently for three years as head of the music school at Loughborough Endowed Schools and 10 years as director of music at Haberdashers' Aske's School for Girls. ISI inspector for 10 years. He's only the fifth Holmwood head in its 90-year history and the first ever not to have any past association with the school. 'Underneath his friendly, easy-going exterior there is a respected, efficient, deep-thinking workaholic,' notes a perceptive parent. Lives on-site ('handy for fire drills,' approved a pupil) with his wife Helen – head of PSHCE and registrar – and their two children, all in the school and ranging from year 4 to year 6. Conducting was his love, but he says he doesn't miss the music – 'I have plenty to be getting on with here as headmaster and our head of music and drama is outstanding; I'm very lucky to be doing what I feel I was meant to be doing, it's the best job in the world.' Still finds time to play bass guitar in the school's jazz band. 'Happiness is the key to progress,' he says. 'I can't promise a perfect school but I can promise a happy one.' Chimes with Holmwood's Latin motto, which translates as 'I was glad'.

Entrance: A third from the school's own nursery, which takes 53 children from 6 months and is set in an attractive rural building a few miles from the main school. The rest go off to good local primaries. Usual entry point to the main school is at age 4, straight into the dedicated reception, which takes two classes of 18 in each year. A handful more pupils arrive at throughout each year. Boys in the majority.

Exit: Year 8 children largely depart for Felsted, Framlingham, Ipswich or Oundle. One or two to Uppingham and Rugby and a similar number to Royal Hospital School, Culford, New Hall and Greshams. School proud of range of scholarships won. Occasional places at eg Eton, Harrow, King's Canterbury, Benenden, Ampleforth, Brighton College, Millfield, Stowe.

Remarks: The principles of the school have remained the same since it was founded on this very site, two miles from Colchester, in 1922 by a Mr and Mrs Duggan, whose aim was 'to develop the individuality and abilities of each child, to make him self-reliant and adaptable and to help him face reality.' A collection of semi-rural buildings punctuated by courtyards and outside spaces that cleverly maximise the opportunities for outdoor education (we've never seen so many woodland classrooms, play areas and nature trails in one prep school). Garden Block arranged around a tranquil garden in memory of a former pupil and treated by all with respect.

The Holmwood day is divided into lessons until tea at 4pm and then prep and activities until supper for boarders and more activities until lights-out. Flexi-boarding – minimum one night – is popular and most take advantage by year 8 ('I tell parents their children will let them know when they want to board,' says head). Houses are named after the elements and there are competitions and challenges all year round. Intriguing range of reward systems – golden leaves, superstars, as well as 'showups' and 'showdowns' for older pupils with the requisite number of showdowns leading to a detention ('I had one once,' confessed our guide. 'I'm not getting another one'). There's 'a week for everything' – English, Maths, Mental Health and Well-being, and when we visited a celebrated scientist was setting up ready to give a demonstration as part of Science Week.

Music and drama 'about to explode' under the direction of the new head of department, predicts Mr Mitchell. Matilda being rehearsed by years 6 and 7 throughout our visit

Reception children have their own little world, across a path from the main school. Cavernous for the two classes of 18 in the early years department – with airy classrooms and intriguing corners tailored to computer play and dress-up – it also has a lovely outside play area with a patch of age-appropriate, safe woodland to explore. The main pre-prep department houses years 1, 2 and 3 in spacious, modern, purpose-built accommodation. Moving into the prep, pupils are arranged by ability in English, maths, French and science and in years 7 and 8 into a scholarship and three further sets. A few new arrivals, but the head points out 'as the year group gets larger, the sets get smaller'. The scholarship set is made up not just of the brightest but those who have the 'emotional maturity to cope with the stretch and challenge'. Pupils from year 4 begin to move to specialist classrooms – 'you're exhausted for the first few days but you soon get used to it,' reassured our guides. Year 6s learn Latin. French in reception then a carousel of French, Spanish and Mandarin. A few drift off into the strong local state selective system at 11+ but the vast majority press on to 13.

Music and drama is 'about to explode' under the direction of the new head of department, predicts Mr Mitchell. Matilda being rehearsed with years 6 and 7 throughout our visit and, recently Pirates of the Curry Bean. Art room described (accurately) as 'humongous' by our guide, and full of unusual projects including animation installations by year 8s, who all received a still turned into a souvenir picture. DT is offered as an activity in a fully-equipped studio. Sport every day for those who want it. Rugby, hockey and cricket are major for boys, while girls play netball, hockey and rounders. Some 20 acres of the 34 are given over to sport, plus a vast newish sports hall and indoor swimming pool. On-site Lexden Rackets Club – financed by compulsory purchase of school land for the A12 decades ago – is heaving with fit young retirees on a dreary Wednesday morning, but also a superb resource for the school at other times. School has its own tennis and squash coaches.

Library with 12,000 books and an intriguing colour-coded filing system, presided over by the school librarian. Red sofas for the exclusive use of year 8 are as close as they come to a common room. Science labs in converted stables. Jubilee Hall with tiered seating for nearly 200, backed by professional-looking exhibition space – self-portraits when we visited. Dyslexia unit recently renamed learning support (although the sign-maker hasn't yet caught up). Excellent provision for SEN. 'We make progress here,' says the head. 'That might be a scholarship for one child, or an improvement in reading for another. We nurture strengths and support weaknesses and develop young people who are confident, and above all comfortable with whom they are.'

Boarding house open from Monday evenings to Saturday mornings – no full boarding. As well as using school sports, art, music and cooking facilities, boarders have a games room with pool, table football, table tennis etc in the main building cellar for evening recreation. Currently Saturday school for years 4-8, but this will be abolished in September 2018.

We've never seen so many woodland classrooms, play areas and nature trails in one prep school

Courtesy and respect are still ingrained at an early age and children here are at ease with anyone (the head swears by the 'train to Norwich test' – in a parallel universe as the proprietor of his own company, he would be sufficiently confident to put any Holmwood pupil on a two-hour train journey with his best client). 'Every child is well mannered and friendly,' agrees a parent. 'Even on the sporting field – win or lose, the children are always gracious.'

Surrounded by its own playing fields, Holmwood has the feel of a much larger school, but at its heart it's a small community of some 300 pupils which extends to embrace their families too.

Ipswich School

22

Henley Road, Ipswich, Suffolk IP1 3SG

01473 408300 | admissions@ipswich.suffolk.sch.uk | https://www.ipswich.school

Ages: 3-18 (boarding from 11)

Pupils: 1,059; sixth form: 241; Boarders: 45 full, 4 weekly/flexi

Day: £11,394 – £14,979 pa; Boarding: £23,463 – £29,010 pa

Headmaster: Since 2010, Mr Nicholas Weaver BA (30s). Read engineering at Jesus College, Cambridge. Previously deputy head (academic) at Portsmouth Grammar, and before that taught physics at the Leys School, Cambridge, the Royal Grammar School, Guilford, and Radley College. Tall, elegant, with an approachable, unruffled manner. He is keen to develop what he calls the 'growth mind-set' – a strategy for developing the potential of all pupils, with a particular eye on those identified as academically able. The Academic Excellence Programme is designed for this 'elite' group, although open to all comers. Changes to senior management structure have resulted in a more streamlined, collegiate approach; all posts are now advertised externally. He is married and has three children, all at Ipswich Prep.

Prep school head: Since 2009, Mrs Amanda Childs BA MA, Dip Ed (late 30s). Previously deputy head of Alleyn's Junior School, following a teaching career at various independent schools and an international school in Bangkok. Dedicated and determined to introduce the school to changed teaching practices, for example in teaching reading. Extremely au fait with all current educational fashions but steers her own course. Believes in clear boundaries and instilling in pupils respect for each other's differences. Married to Martin, a journalist, and they have two daughters, both in the prep school.

Academic matters: Prep school class sizes fluid, and range from 18 in reception to 24 in years 5/6. Form teaching in most subjects, with setting in maths and English from year 5, and specialist teaching for certain subjects in years 5 and 6. All pupils are screened on entry for specific learning difficulties and emotional/behavioural problems are quickly picked up on. The School Action Plus programme is designed to support struggling pupils with the aim of them being able to cope, eventually, in the senior school.

Pupils are encouraged, even pushed, to work hard. Whilst not an academic forcing house, there is no place for coasting in the senior school. The brightest of the bright will be fast tracked – lessons before school for some and there is a programme of enrichment, including lectures and seminars, geared specifically at these pupils – 'We are hoping the head doesn't over-do all the elitism and Oxbridge stuff,' commented a parent. Homework is now called PSC, which stands for Preparation, Stretch and Consolidation – 'No one remembers,' said several. Though selective, the school has quite a wide ability range, but despite the head saying, 'we recognise the hard-won B grade', there are not many of these in evidence. In 2017, 62 per cent A*-A/9-7 grades at GCSE. A level results saw 48 per cent A*/A grades. The head has made clear his priority to raise all teaching in the school to exceptional standard and school expects pupils to have the solid achievement of an A/7 grade at GCSE for subjects studied at A level. Sixth form is no place for slacking, with compulsory enrichment programme alongside A levels. No demand here for IB, as curriculum seems to be diverse enough.

Sixth formers allowed the latitude of wearing their own clothes. Conformity seems natural here though 'slight oddballs have been successfully integrated'

All year 7 entrants are tested for SEN, but as this is a selective school, the needs identified will often be to do with organisation, mild dyslexia, or for ESL, for which support is offered outside the timetabled day. Head has introduced drop in clinics at lunchtime so any pupil can seek help informally.

Games, options, the arts: A recent shift in emphasis in referring to the 'co-curricular' rather than the 'extracurricular', with a designated assistant head in overall charge (formerly head of sixth form). First division player in all the team sports – frequently area and national finalists, most recently in hockey. Sport is for all, and the school often fields teams from A-D. Other sports on offer, and played highly competitively, include karate, sailing and equestrianism. Also entered a winning pair in the national finals of Eton fives. School recently bought nearby sports centre, complete with sports hall, fitness gym and floodlit Astroturf hockey pitch.

Music is taken seriously, with a third of pupils taking individual instrumental lessons and a variety of orchestras, choirs and ensemble groups which perform throughout the year. The chapel choir, besides a regular slot singing evensong at St Paul's Cathedral, tours both at home and abroad. The Annual Ipswich School Festival of Music brings internationally-renowned musicians to perform at the school in masterclasses and workshops. Britten Faculty of Music is based in a state-of-the-art purpose-built music school, with a concert hall and recording studio still to come. School hopes this new facility to become one of the region's main musical hubs, attracting performers from Suffolk and beyond.

Drama GCSE is offered as an enrichment sixth form option (no theatre studies A level) and several productions are staged throughout the year. The sixth form recently performed Seussical-the-Musical, based on the works of Dr Seuss. Thursday afternoon activities include CCF and Duke of Edinburgh plus a long list of clubs and societies including photography, journalism and robotics. If the club isn't already there, it can be started.

Prep school walls covered with art/science work – some of it spectacular – and there is an interesting menu of music, drama and other activities, both within the school day, and at after-school clubs. All year 3 pupils learn a stringed instrument as part of the curriculum; new music school.

Boarding: The boarding house is a short walk away, occupying its own grounds – which include the school Astroturf – in a suburban road. Common room and boarders' kitchen; breakfast, dinner and weekend meals eaten in the boarding house. No Saturday school but EFL lessons available on Saturday mornings.

Background and atmosphere: The school has occupied its present site since 1852, but it has a medieval foundation (Cardinal Wolsey is an illustrious old boy) and the school's history is well-recorded and treasured. In addition to the original, rather gloomy Victorian structure, there are some fine and functional 20th century buildings which adjoin each other by a series of passages, steps and covered ways. Later additions include the sports facilities and sixth form building, which overlook the playing fields – a focus for relaxation as well as sport. There is a school chapel and a library of exceptional quality and design with windows by John Piper depicting the seasons. Everything is well cared for and maintained. Odd fusty corners in the older part of the school offset by displays of pupils' work, posters and subject information. Pupils by and large polite rather than courtly but clearly intent on their pursuits. Straightforward uniform policy, with sixth formers allowed the latitude

of wearing their own clothes. Conformity seems natural here though 'slight oddballs have been successfully integrated'; especially if they are clever.

The prep school has occupied its own purpose-built premises next to the nursery and pre-prep since 2006. An eye-catching building which, though striking and affording fine views of the town, has limited play areas and no grass whatsoever. Pupils are taken over to the main school playing field to let off steam in the lunch break, and have timetabled access to the sports facilities. At the end of the school day, the playground transforms into a car park for collecting parents.

Pastoral care, well-being and discipline: The prep school is quick to respond to problems as they arise with contact via email and the head available before school each morning. Pupils charming, though we felt that the ones we met (year 3) were inhibited by the presence of the registrar, acting as chaperone.

Usual house and year group tutorial system in senior school with a separate identity for years 7 and 8, each form keeping the same tutor. The school chaplain, a full-time member of the teaching staff, plays a key part in the pastoral set up. The matron has her room strategically placed near the hard play area, a reassuring presence at break and lunchtimes. There is a strong expectation that pupils are well-organised and can cope with the pressure, though all know where to turn if in difficulties. Despite the city location, little flouting of rules, and a system of merits and detentions seems to keep the odd backslider on track. Occasional serious offenders dealt with firmly.

Pupils and parents: Mix of farming, professional and business families from the rural reaches of East Anglia together with those from Ipswich itself or other towns, mostly in Essex. Quite a lot of parents are London commuters. Extensive network of bus routes bring many pupils to school, and of the 40 or so boarders, over half come from overseas, mostly Europe and the Far East. Boys continue to outnumber girls by about 2:1 in years 7 to 11; the influx of girls to the sixth form gives a better balance, though girls remain in a minority. Pupils appear to be well able to cope with the rigours of the school; perhaps not ideal for those lacking in confidence or who thrive on pushing the boundaries.

A library of exceptional quality and design with windows by John Piper depicting the seasons

In addition to Cardinal Wolsey, notable old boys include the author and illustrator Edward Ardizzone, physicist Sir Charles Frank and the writer Rider Haggard (King Solomon's Mines).

Entrance: Admission to the nursery is by registration. For reception and years 1-6 entrance assessment includes reasoning, English and maths. Children are also observed at play. Main points of entry are at reception, year 3 and year 5. Pupils come from a variety of schools and a wide catchment area, 'though half have a Colchester postcode'.

The majority join the senior school at 11 (year 7) with many coming up from the prep. All take the same entrance exam (results are used to organise setting in year 7). A report from the pupil's present school and a chat with the head are also required. At 13 (year 9), another 30 or so are also admitted via common entrance or school's own exam. Pupils do need to have above average ability to pass and to flourish. Entry to the sixth form requires six GCSEs with at least B/6s, preferably A/7s in chosen A level subjects.

For overseas admissions school will now consider UKiset applications (online testing system) rather than paper-based tests.

Exit: For most juniors, an easy transition to the senior school. A few leave for state schools (there are flourishing grammars in Essex). Any thought unlikely to cope in the seniors will have been given fair notice. Around 20-30 per cent leave after GCSEs. Majority of sixth formers to university with a leaning towards the Russell Group, particularly Exeter, Birmingham, Nottingham and London universities. Seven to Oxbridge in 2017, and four medics; the head is keen to push up numbers; one off to Hong Kong.

Money matters: Queen's (academic) Scholarships equivalent to 50 per cent offered at 11 and 13, based on pupil's performance in the entrance examination plus interview. Means-tested bursaries can cover the full fees if necessary. Scholarships are also available in music, art and sport at 11 and an all-rounder at 13. A full range are offered at sixth form, together with a number of means-tested bursaries.

Remarks: A well run, urban school, with many opportunities for bright, motivated pupils to excel.

Kimbolton School

23

Kimbolton, Huntingdon, Cambridgeshire PE28 0EA

01480 860505 | headmaster@kimbolton.cambs.sch.uk | www.kimbolton.cambs.sch.uk/

Ages: 4-18 (boarding from year 7)

Pupils: 980; Boarders: 47

Day: £9,855 – £15,300 pa; Boarding: £23,925 – £25,455 pa

Head: Since 2002, Jonathan Belbin (50s). History at Bristol followed by PGCE. Sporty so decided could combine sport and history by teaching. Spent a lot of time as sports coach. Joined independent sector by chance and never looked back. Moved around country expanding his roles before first headship

at Kimbolton. 'I liked that Kimbolton was co-ed and boarding and I could see lots of potential.' Very well established and popular with parents, 'a bit of a shining light,' said one parent. 'He's interested in the kids,' was another take. All spoke of his high profile around the school and at matches and productions. 'He's very professional, not gushing or effusive, slightly distant from parents, but in a good way. I don't want a friend, but a professional, which is just what he is,' said one perceptive parent. 'He has good people skills,' was said by another. Has handled tricky situations well according to parents, 'dignified and straightforward, measured in his responses and manages the school well, in good times and bad.'

Has overseen many building projects and refurbishments, bringing facilities up to date over the years, the most recent being the new science and maths block opened in 2015. Numbers have expanded by 150 under his tenure. Still teaching PHSE and history to certain years so knows all the children. Profile high around prep school as well. Smartly turned out, youthful looking, friendly and welcoming. We got the impression of a head very much on the ball and comfortable and confident in his role. His children have all been educated at Kimbolton.

Head of prep: Since 2015, Philip Foley (50s). Studied education, so could spend more time playing sports, before spending a year in industry, then drawn back into teaching, 'the best decision ever.' Kimbolton is his fourth headship. Establishing himself well and knows all the children. 'He is making positive changes, slowly without upsetting anyone.' Parents like what they have seen of him and say he is very accessible, and always outside at the end of the day. Softly spoken and mild mannered, teaches years 2 and 4 so getting to know children well. Daughter joined sixth form on his arrival.

Academic matters: In 2017, 56 per cent A*-A/9-7 at GCSE, 58 per cent A*-A at A level, 80 per cent A*-B. Results have steadily increased over the last few years. Spanish and French available at GCSE and A level, taught from reception. Not many take two languages at GCSE, nine or 10 a year. Half the year group take all three sciences. Pupils taught in mixed ability groups apart from maths, which is the most popular subject at A level. All parents, throughout both schools, spoke of excellent academic progress and close contact with teachers. Academic problems picked up on quickly and help offered in both schools. Lots of subject workshops and drop ins available and popular with pupils. Prep pupils taught by class teacher until year 5 when subject taught and pressure ramped up, subtly, with more homework, getting them ready for senior school life. Maths set from year 3 onwards.

Boarders housed in two houses at each end of Kimbolton's High Street (it's not very long) and never the twain shall meet

Excellent facilities throughout both schools, some – such as halls and sports – shared. Impressive new science block, please say hello to Colin the fish in one of the classrooms. Pupils working hard and more than happy to chat, pleased to show off their work. Very relaxed atmosphere between pupils and staff, but mutual respect apparent. Parents spoke of 'excellent teaching staff who know our children well and want them to succeed.' Most said, 'staff handled child well, knew them and brought the best out in them,' others spoke of their child 'flourishing.' One parent noted that 'the odd teacher appeared to be marking time and needed moving on,' but was sympathetic to the situation and said, 'these individuals are now a rarity here.' IT embraced, computing and programming taught to a high level and right up to date, so much so that our sixth form guides were slightly at a loss, we completely so. Excellent artwork on display in both schools. DT, textiles and cooking for all, particularly in prep. Sixth form offers 'life cooking skills' as an extracurricular course.

Class sizes small, average of 17 in prep, 21 in senior with an average of seven in sixth form, so nowhere to hide, which is appreciated by parents. Some 40 pupils receive extra support throughout both schools, but only two are statemented. A handful of pupils bilingual, 18 on the EAL register. One-to-one available for learning and language support if necessary. UCAS support exemplary; staff appear to be very much on the ball. Sixth form common room in basement equipped with comfy chairs. Very much their own space, with large study rooms also available, and well used.

Games, options, the arts: As expected with two heads who are ex-sports teachers, games plays an important part at Kimbolton. 'We aim to get everyone out at least once a year representing the school,' said the prep head. Lots of silverware in the cabinets and lots of choice, bar rugby, which is not played. Football plays a major part, along with hockey for boys and girls. Prep girls are campaigning for football and cricket teams and head is open to the idea. Swimming on site with own

The school bought The Castle from the Duke of Manchester in the 1950s for a reputed £11,500, and a further 200 guineas for the magnificent paintings when they were offered them at the last minute – they had a quick whip round

pool and lots of pitches within the grounds. Please note the lake where canoe practice takes place. Lots of teams for all levels. Plenty of sports clubs and after-school practices; 85 per cent of prep pupils stay after school. Most parents very complimentary about sport and facilities bar one who felt 'they don't have a great reputation for sport as it doesn't appear to be a priority. I'd like to see a director of sport.' All other parents spoke about the children being 'taught well and lots of choice.'

Music and drama popular and well represented. Lots of individual lessons, including over half of pupils in upper prep. Parents spoke of sensible way these lessons are timetabled, particularly in the senior school, so less academic do not miss essential teaching time. Dramatic productions spoken of highly in both schools. Lots of productions, choirs, orchestras, bands and after-school clubs. You name it, they have it.

CCF very popular with vast majority of pupils taking part from year 10 upwards. D of E also popular, up to gold. Lots of school trips, sporting and curricular.

Boarding: Boarding available from year 7. It's not a major part of the school, which is predominantly a day school with boarders making up about seven per cent of pupils. Boarders housed in two houses at each end of Kimbolton's High Street (it's not very long) and never the twain shall meet. Girls' house is full, boys' house has the odd space. Full and weekly boarding offered, flexi if space available. Some 45 per cent of boarders from overseas, others based just outside travelling distance, most within two hours. Quite a few children have parents in the Forces as the school is quite close to some RAF bases.

Parents impressed with boarding. 'The house is run really well and the weekly and flexi boarders are treated as full boarders, welcome to go on trips and excursions.' Parents spoke about children being kept well occupied, 'there is always a full term of events, booked in advance.' Parents of girls spoke about 'the mumsy chats' the staff have with their daughters. Curfews upheld and respected, older boarders given more independence. School happy for boarders to visit day pupils, with parental permission.

The two boarding houses are well equipped and modernised; tall boys will need to duck in certain rooms, with low ceilings and ancient buildings. Three in a room maximum, sixth form have own rooms. Communal common rooms for all age groups well used. We get the impression that because there are so few boarders they are a close knit little unit. Lots of encouragement to participate in sports and extracurricular life. Supervised prep for younger years, older ones do it in their rooms at set times. They cook their own breakfast at weekends.

Background and atmosphere: Located in the small pretty village of Kimbolton, The Castle, originally an ancient castle and now a magnificent Georgian mansion, dominates the village sitting at the end of the High Street. Very little teaching actually takes place in The Castle, but admin and head housed magnificently, with sixth form in the basement. The prep school, at the other end of the village, an old red brick purpose built Victorian school house, was once the senior school. Originally a boys' grammar, dating back over 400 years, the school bought The Castle from the Duke of Manchester in the 1950s for a reputed £11,500, and a further 200 guineas for the magnificent paintings when the governors were offered them at the last minute – they had a quick whip round to raise the money. Since then the school has thrived and succeeded, reflecting rather sadly on the opposite fortunes of the Manchester family. The Castle housed Catherine of Aragon when she was exiled from London. She died in what is now the head's office and historians still pay an annual visit to pay homage. This is not as macabre as it sounds, but do note the secret panelled door into the head's office.

The prep school was opened in the 1970s, and became co-ed at a similar time. Both schools are accessible via a brisk walk through parkland. There's lots of space, 120 acres, to absorb pupils, who make the most of their magnificent surroundings.

Very much a family orientated school, and being relatively small, this atmosphere prevails with the school seeming to know parents well too. Pupils know each other, and the staff, well. Parents really appreciate this and, for many, was the reason they chose the school. 'My child isn't lost in large numbers,' was alluded to many times. A jolly, relaxed atmosphere prevails with a warm welcome for everyone. The distinctive purple, black and white striped blazers dominate, possibly an acquired taste, not the easiest colour combination for everyone to look good in. Sixth formers wear black business suits. Purple dominates the school, it's their school colours and it's everywhere. Even the Christmas decorations are purple on the tree, matching the purple carpets et al. We're sure you get the picture. Food raised its ugly head with parents. It's raved about in the prep school, but standards slip when pupils move to The Castle.

Pastoral care, well-being and discipline: Every parent praised pastoral care. 'I don't know how they manage it,' said one parent who went on to praise the' kind, patient, supportive, caring teachers,' and believed this atmosphere is absorbed by the children, who behave in the same way. 'They pick up on problems quickly,' was said numerous times. Many parents spoke about the 'feel of the school' when they first visited, the friendliness of pupils and parents, and wanted that for their children. 'The children and parents are nice.' Friendship issues dealt with kindly and effectively. Counsellors available and well used.

A family orientated school. 'My child isn't lost in large numbers,' was alluded to many times. A jolly, relaxed atmosphere prevails with a warm welcome for everyone

Pastoral care and safeguarding so effective that the odd parent feels independence is being lost. But those with older children spoke about 'independence and more freedom in the sixth form.' Sixth formers a familiar sight in the High Street where they congregate at a popular coffee shop. Discipline at acceptable standards. 'They have high expectations which are usually met,' was said. Pupils in prep aware that if behaviour unsuitable they will not

be going up to The Castle. We are not aware of this happening in recent years so all appear to toe the line. Suspensions incredibly rare and low detention numbers. Pupils and parents happy that discipline is fair and appropriate. Lots of mentoring between pupils and effective school councils in both schools.

Pupils and parents: Most families rural dwellers from surrounding villages and small towns. Traditionally a farming and Forces school, this is now changing with many families moving from London whilst parents still work there. More families now coming from Cambridge's outskirts, so more medics and techy parents joining the fray. Most parents both working to pay fees and want a good value for money, all round education for their children, 'involved parents,' said the prep head.

Parents welcome flexibility school offers with boarding and late pick ups. Many children second, even third generation. Pupils happy and chatty and seem very relaxed, but ambitious and not fazed about leaving their rural idyll for urban sprawl; they are being well prepared.

Entrance: Pupils for reception assessed in small groups and teachers visit them at local nurseries to see that they are ready to learn. School happy to say no at this stage. Older children assessed and spend taster morning at school. No automatic transfer to senior school; all pupils take entrance exam. External candidates interviewed as well. Those from prep who won't make grade kindly weeded out in earlier years, but this is a rare occurrence.

Numbers double in senior school 1st year (year 7) with external pupils, 45 per cent, coming from up to 30 local primaries with a small intake in year 9. Senior school full, the odd place in prep. About 20 join the sixth form, virtually all from state schools, the odd one from independents. These pupils all interviewed by head and head of sixth form. Six GCSEs, grade B/6 or above needed including English and maths.

Exit: All pupils from prep went to The Castle in 2017. Occasionally one or two leave for other boarding independents, following family tradition. Nine or 10 leave after GCSEs, usually to vocational courses at local colleges, the odd one to board elsewhere in sixth form, again following family tradition. 'We don't cull,' said the head, 'they are good kids,' so those who want to go into sixth form usually do even if they don't make the grade, but must have the right attitude. Virtually all go to university, the odd one straight to employment, gap years minimal. Two Oxbridge places in 2017, as for most years. Apprenticeships not being embraced as yet, but school open to it.

Money matters: Scholarships available in senior school only, up to 20 per cent of fees, the vast majority academic, but the odd sports, leadership and arts available at 13+. Six means tested places at senior school per year group, most subsidised by at least 80 per cent of fees.

Remarks: This small school, housed in beautiful surroundings, appears to be a well kept secret, much to some parents' bemusement. 'Why is it not more well known?' said by many. We get the impression that there's no need; the school is virtually full, has an excellent reputation locally and is providing a good all round education for local families wanting to use the private sector. Pupils can spend their whole education at Kimbolton enjoying the benefits of a happy environment, small class sizes and excellent pastoral care. Those parents in the know appreciate that a Kimbolton education is money well spent. Shhhh.

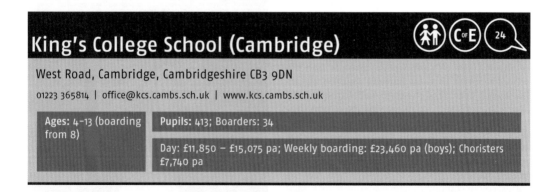

King's College School (Cambridge)

C of E 24

West Road, Cambridge, Cambridgeshire CB3 9DN

01223 365814 | office@kcs.cambs.sch.uk | www.kcs.cambs.sch.uk

Ages: 4-13 (boarding from 8)

Pupils: 413; Boarders: 34

Day: £11,850 – £15,075 pa; Weekly boarding: £23,460 pa (boys); Choristers £7,740 pa

Head: Since January 2018, Yvette Day, previously head of the Chorister School, Durham. She is also master over the choristers, in charge of the education and care of the boys who have sung in the college choir since the college's foundation by King Henry VI. Mrs Day was educated in South

Africa and in England, holds an MMus degree in historical musicology from the University of London and more recently completed a law conversion course with the College of Law. Her husband, Andrew, is also a headteacher.

Entrance: Some children registered at birth, or before. All 4 year olds spend over an hour with the pre-prep department, so 'we can get the feel of the child.' Be warned, they're looking for bright bunnies. Siblings, past pupils and fellows of King's given priority. Parents also have a chat with the head. Entry at 7 after assessment. Chorister scholarships for up to five boys in year 4. Open to any boy in the world if he passes the audition, and many try. All choristers (boys only) offered scholarships of up to two-thirds of fees or more, plus free piano lessons. Means-tested bursaries of up to 100 per cent at age 7, available for all. Children come from a wide commutable area, many from Suffolk and Hertfordshire, some boarders further afield. Many parents ex-Oxbridge, academics, medics, City people. Generally a good cross-section. All very ambitious and the driving force behind their offspring.

Exit: The occasional one at 11, but very unusual. No 'evictions'; they work hard, with the help of learning support, to keep them going, and then guide parents to make a 'sensible choice' for the next step. Only one has been 'moved on' in the last 18 years before age 11. Virtually all leave at 13. Over half to local independent schools in Cambridge, particularly The Perse and Leys. Eton, Uppingham, King's Ely and Oundle all popular too. Every chorister offered a music scholarship. About a third of all leavers get scholarships, many music, some academic.

They travel the world touring and, of course, there is that carol service every Christmas Eve and the service on Christmas Day. It's a big commitment with many sacrifices made, but very rewarding

Remarks: Founded in the 15th century to educate the choristers, now housed on one site off a leafy road a brisk walk from King's College. The choristers are an iconic sight walking through the streets in a croc in their Etons and top hats heading for chapel. Primarily a day school with 34 boarders, all boys, 24 of whom are choristers, the rest – some of whom flexi board – in the upper years. The choristers are an important part of the school, famous throughout the world, but are treated like any other pupils within lessons. But their life is different. Compulsory boarders from the age of 8 when they become full choristers, they attend six services a week at the chapel during the university term time, practice for an hour and half before school (in a purpose built acoustic room) and again in the evenings. Weekends during the university term means three more services. They travel the world touring and, of course, there is that carol service every

Christmas Eve and the service on Christmas Day. It's a big commitment with many sacrifices made by the families, but very rewarding, and the boys thrive on it. Every care is taken to make sure they don't suffer academically or personally. 'My son, a chorister, has struggled at times with his work, but the support from the staff is excellent.' They still get to play in the teams but practice is out; there just isn't time. If a boy's voice breaks before he leaves he is still included and part of the set up.

These children are bright and teaching is excellent, with some well-loved, gregarious characters amongst the staff. The special needs department, one of the first to be set up in the country, is very proactive. 'The school contacted me very quickly when my daughter started to struggle with her maths. She was offered extra help immediately, which was excellent.' Lots of support available if needed. All parents commented on how well the staff knew their children. 'We like the school for its "ballsy" attitude,' was said by one parent, with many commenting on the relaxed, but focused atmosphere. Lots of new computers available. Plenty of artwork about, modern science labs and a very well equipped DT room. A large, stuffed library attended by a librarian who appears to be a school stalwart. Knows every child, loved by all. Every parent was happy with their child's progress and had confidence in the school. Pace increases further up the school with a scholarship class in year 8. 'They are realising my child's potential,' came up more than once.

'The school contacted me very quickly when my daughter started to struggle with her maths. She was offered extra help immediately, which was excellent'

Lots of after-school clubs, chess highly recommended, but music dominates. A fabulous music department, and that's excluding the angelic-looking choristers. Virtually every child plays an instrument, many two or more. Lots and lots of chamber groups, choirs, orchestras and quartets. If you can think of it, they've got it. A new organ in situ, played by many, and lots of acoustic rooms for practice, including the church-like room for the choristers.

Music aside, sport is playing an increasingly big part in school life. Many more top-notch staff employed, with more teams available and better results. A new sports centre in the offing. 'Team selection can be a political minefield,' said one parent. 'I don't envy the staff but they handle it

Tuck boxes brought out once a week with matron providing more on Saturday evenings. Dog walks on Sunday morning. Very much a family atmosphere, with parents included, as they often pop in

well.' The playing fields are at the front of the school, giving the impression of lots of open space – a bit of an illusion: every spare inch of the site is utilised.

A friendly, happy school, pastorally excellent. Bullying usually nipped in the bud very quickly. One father mentioned that an incident had been allowed to escalate before being 'handled excellently.' A mother praised the handling of manipulative children by the form teacher. 'He was sensitive, calm and firm.' 'The school's policy of keeping parents at arm's length and bringing the children together is the right one,' said one wise mother. A school counsellor available for all and the children are happy to consult. Older pupils mentor younger ones with a buddy system.

The boarding house is also on site. Functional, but immaculate with modern facilities. Bright, airy dorms, duvet covers brought from home, sheets changed by the boys. Housemaster (sic – a woman) praised and loved by all. An open door policy for the parents and homesickness dealt with kindly. Misdemeanours dealt with quickly. 'Punishment comprises chores, just like I would at home.' Tuck boxes brought out once a week with matron providing more on Saturday evenings. Dog walks on Sunday morning. Very much a family atmosphere, with parents included, as they often pop in mid week and, if local, walk the choristers back from chapel.

Bright purple blazers and sweatshirts make the children stand out. 'My son hates his sweatshirt so gets through a blazer a year.' Girls' summer dresses not popular with parents or pupils. Do note the purple carpet throughout the modernised buildings. Sartorial whimsy, perhaps?

All parents seem happy that the school is on one site and many spoke of the 'family atmosphere.' Every parent we spoke to was delighted with the school and would strongly recommend it. We can see why; you can't help but feel the relaxed ambience. The children are bright and friendly, completely stress free and at ease with their teachers. But don't let that fool you. There is a rarefied atmosphere of intense learning – and you may get to hear some excellent singing as well.

King's Ely

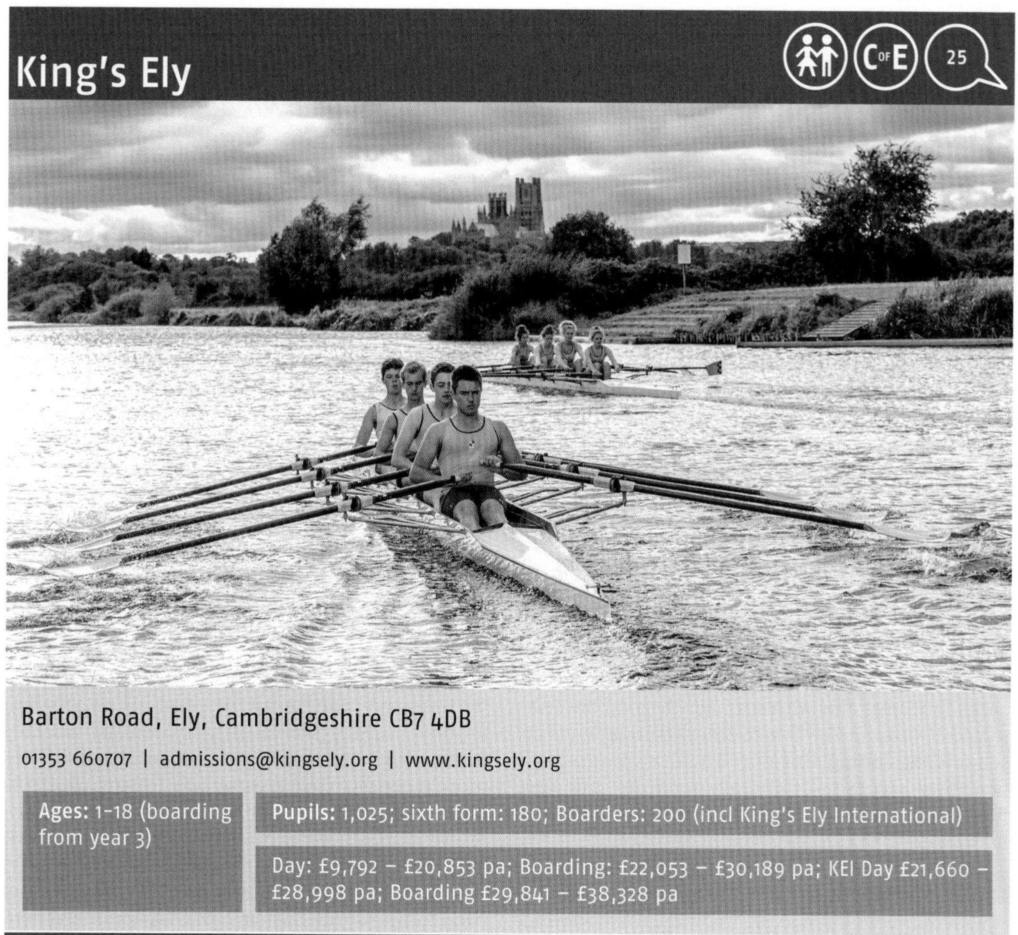

Barton Road, Ely, Cambridgeshire CB7 4DB

01353 660707 | admissions@kingsely.org | www.kingsely.org

Ages: 1-18 (boarding from year 3)

Pupils: 1,025; sixth form: 180; Boarders: 200 (incl King's Ely International)

Day: £9,792 – £20,853 pa; Boarding: £22,053 – £30,189 pa; KEI Day £21,660 – £28,998 pa; Boarding £29,841 – £38,328 pa

Principal: Mrs Sue Freestone GRSM Med LRAM ARCM (60s), who joined the school as head in 2004, and became principal in 2013. She is again in charge of the senior school, after the brief tenure of Alex McGrath as head. Trained at the Royal Academy of Music and Bristol University. Was formely head of Sibford School, and before that conductor and director of music at Colston Girls. Very energetic, approachable and unstuffy, with strongly held convictions and an expectation of high standards for herself, the staff and pupils.

Leaving in July 2019.

Head of the junior school: Since 2008, Richard Whymark BA (Ed) (40s). Previously head of Stonar Junior and before that head of boarding and deputy head of Salisbury Cathedral School. Has an engaging manner and a natural flair for communication – with pupils and parents alike. 'He is usually around at drop-off time', commented one parent.

Firmly believes a good head needs 'a strong voice and a reflective personality – no room for big egos'. Has an easy rapport with students and is clearly a respected presence – on hand to sort out spats. Art, travel and gardening are all interests but, clearly something of a romantic, his passion is for restoring Morris Minors. Has two children at King's and wife Joanna also teaches at the school.

Academic matters: Parents praise the emphasis on effort and progress in the junior school; certificates and prizes are awarded for these as much as for attainment. Both ends of ability spectrum well served, with support and extension classes available. 'Confidence is encouraged, but not cockiness', commented a mother. Tutor groups are reshuffled each year, to break up cliques and expand friendship groups. A buddy scheme operates throughout the junior school and problems are quickly dealt with. The top year groups use some of the senior school's facilities and are taught by specialist staff as a way of managing the transition from junior to senior. Setting in maths and English from year 3. Languages introduced early, with taster lessons in

Japanese, Mandarin and Arabic. French, and Latin from year 7.

Though increasingly selective at 11 and 13, the bar is not quite so high as for certain of the Cambridge schools close by. Considering the reasonably wide ability range, the school is achieving very respectable and frequently glowing results. Pupils are setted for most of the core subjects; close attention is paid to individual progress, and though not an overly pushy school, 'drifting along with little effort will be spotted', a mother remarked. Twenty-four subjects offered at GCSE (53 per cent A*/A and 7-9 in 2017) including single sciences, Latin and Greek. Religious and moral philosophy is compulsory. Twenty-seven subjects offered at A level with economics, mathematics and psychology all popular, and 36 per cent A*/A grades overall in 2017. Those with specific educational needs, such as dyslexia, are well accommodated. There is individual support available, together with a drop-in clinic, and a close eye is kept on subjects chosen at GCSE, with a flexible approach to certain subject choices allowed.

King's Ely Junior International offers 11-12 year olds intensive English language tuition alongside a wider range of subjects in preparation for 13+ senior school entry. King's Ely International prepares 14-16 year olds with sufficiently good English to take IGCSEs and be able to enter UK independent schools, including this one. The classrooms and boarding accommodation are separate, but the head is encouraging greater fraternisation with the main school: 'It can only benefit all pupils'.

Games, options, the arts: A strength of the school is what happens outside the mainstream academic timetable. Tremendous range of opportunities, from rowing at 6:30am to singing in cathedral services. Music predominates, with more than 50 per cent learning an instrument, and ensembles, choirs and orchestras galore. Junior school includes the 22 boy choristers, who alongside daily rehearsals, services and instrumental practice have a demanding schedule of recordings, concerts and broadcasts. The girls' cathedral choir recruits from the senior school. This is the first scheme of its kind in England, and is the inspiration of the present head, herself a professional musician. It will be interesting to see if the idea is taken up by other co-educational schools connected with cathedrals. The choir sings regular cathedral services, as well as touring and performing elsewhere. The musical training given to these girls will prepare them for advanced study and choral scholarships at university. A new initiative is sixth form male choral scholarships.

Rowing taken very seriously. The school has its own boathouse, pupils keen enough to be up with the lark

Sport remains central and important, though perhaps 'not the be all and end all as at some schools,' said a parent. Besides regular hockey, rugby and so forth, there is an emphasis on the more recondite sports, especially rowing, which is taken very seriously. The school has its own boathouse, pupils keen enough to be up with the lark and even some Olympic potential.

The Ely Scheme (outdoor pursuits programme) runs compulsorily in year 9 and 10, and many continue. It includes kayaking, rock climbing and navigation, and pupils are encouraged to join either the climbing or kayaking club. The culmination is a major expedition, which could be traversing the Cuillin Ridge or the Picos de Europa, or climbing in the Alps or the Himalayas. Teaches self-reliance, responsibility and leadership skills. Many join D of E too.

The teaching facilities for art and design are impressive – as is the teaching. Eye-catching displays of recent work are quite outstanding and several pupils, thus encouraged, go on to study at prestige institutions, notably in fashion and design.

Boarding: Boarding houses are clean and comfortable, rather than deluxe. Boy choristers live in the Choir House during term time, Christmas and Easter holidays, with the housemaster and his family. When not practising or performing they are encouraged to play outside and the housemaster takes them on excursions during stayovers. Girl choristers have their own boarding house, complete with grand piano in the common room. They have weekend chorister duties about once a month, and stayovers – periods of intensive rehearsals and services – at the beginning or end of terms and half terms. The Old Palace (former residence of the Bishops of Ely) is now a sixth form centre, with boarding space for 26 girls.

Background and atmosphere: Occupies a sublime position adjacent to the cathedral, partly within the close itself, but largely in a sprawl of buildings (some medieval, others purpose-built) nearby. Glimpses of the cathedral, the Ship of the Fens, tantalise from many windows, notably from the head's office, in the Old Palace; hard for conversation to compete with the Romanesque masterpiece behind. The cathedral's presence is both seen and felt, but the school also has a close relationship with the town through a variety of initiatives with other schools and local organisations. Frequent road-crossing is managed by pupils safely and with aplomb – it is just part of school life. Other buildings include The Monks' Barn, which houses the dining room (think National Trust restaurant – food, if anything, even better), jolly atmosphere, staff eating with pupils. The library has been reordered, also within the ancient fabric, but retains a monastic feel.

The junior school ccupies a site on the edge of the main school campus. Slightly bleak approach around the back of the senior school but the buildings themselves are well planned and designed. Attention is paid to the grouping of different classes, so years 3 and 4 (and so on up the school) are accommodated together, with their own suite of classrooms and play area. Youngest pupils cluster round a courtyard with a Tarzan trail for play time; years 7 and 8 slightly apart in their own building.

Glimpses of the cathedral, the Ship of the Fens, tantalise from many windows, notably from the head's office, in the Old Palace; hard for conversation to compete

Pupils and parents feel they are listened to, and heard. The school council, a forum to discuss new ideas, is taken notice of by the powers-that-be.

Pastoral care, well-being and discipline: The Christian foundation of the school has a strong influence on the community. Rules are few, though strictly enforced, particularly for those boarding, but there is an atmosphere of trust. The head is very aware of the pressures on pupils and feels 'peer perception' can be 'the hardest nut to crack'. Emphasis on enjoyment as well as achieving.

Pupils and parents: Largely professional, business and farming families, drawn from surrounding Eastern counties; Kings Lynn and Cambridge both send cohorts (quick, easy train services). School believes 'it is in no-one's interest for pupils to travel more than half an hour each way'. Overseas contingent (about 12 per cent) including those in the King's International Study Centre. Past pupils include Alan Yentob, the tenor James Bowman and Olympian Goldie Sayers.

Entrance: Assessment for entrance at 7 consists of diagnostic tests and informal interview. Entry to King's Ely Acremont for ages 1 to 7 (pre-prep, though this term is not used by the school) is by informal assessment and most progress up to the junior department. Screening for dyslexia and dyspraxia at entrance. Moderate difficulties can be accommodated but all pupils must be able to benefit from the full curriculum, with minimal extra support. Those applying as choristers (boys only) must also pass the necessary voice trials.

Own exam at 11 to senior school and at 13+ to senior school, through a common entrance style exam (or common entrance itself). About 75 per cent of senior school entrants have come up from the junior school and the remainder from a mixture of local-ish schools, Framlingham Prep, South Lee and the Cambridge prep schools. Numbers well up and competition for places is increasing. Entry for the sixth form – minimum of six grade A*-C passes at GCSE with at least Bs in chosen A level subjects.

Exit: Virtually all make the transition from junior to senior school at 13. The exam also decides setting for year 9. The occasional pupil not suited to the senior school is identified early and support given in finding another school in good time, but leaving is generally due to relocation. Up to 50 per cent of students leave after GCSEs, often for Hills Road or other sixth form colleges. Post A level, the majority leave for Russell Group universities to study a wide range of subjects, with a number going to colleges of art and design and performing arts courses; two to Oxbridge in 2017.

Money matters: Boy choristers in the junior school get a 50 per cent fee remission, with 33 per cent scholarships in the senior school for those who remain in the school choir, and for senior girl choristers. The sixth form choral and organ scholarships (open to boys and girls) offer a 50 per cent fee reduction. Up to 10 per cent off for clergy. Generous dynamic discount in addition to CEA for Forces families. Bursaries for those in financial need.

Remarks: The school has an atmosphere of purposeful learning, and provides plenty of opportunities for all types to shine. A strong, happy school where the Christian ethos is taken seriously.

The Leys School

26

Trumpington Road, Cambridge, Cambridgeshire CB2 7AD

01223 508904 | admissions@theleys.net | www.theleys.net

Ages: 11-18

Pupils: 562; sixth form: 198; Boarders: 250 full, 120 home

Day: £15,435 – £21,390 pa; Boarding: £23,295 – £31,965 pa

Headmaster: Since 2014, Martin Priestley. Oxford PPE graduate. Claims to be an accidental teacher. Originally wanted to be a diplomat and applied to join MI6: 'I fancied being James Bond.' Whilst waiting for vetting to join the fast stream civil service, taught, and caught the bug. 'The civil service was not for me, too much use of the in and out tray.' Previously taught at Uppingham and was head of Warminster before joining The Leys. Attracted to the school because of its size, 'it's a big small school.' Knows every child. 'I was worried when the last head left as he was so good,' said one parent, 'but Mr Priestley has been very impressive, I like his style, he is very open.' 'He communicates with parents every week via the schools comm; we are very much kept in the loop.' Another parent said, 'He has changed a lot, modernised the school and is making good use of social media.' 'He is at every function and moves around the pitches talking to everyone during matches.' A German speaker who doesn't have a long commute, through the door from the hallway of his impressive looking headmaster's residence. We were privileged to meet Twiglet, his blind dog, obviously a regular in his office.

Academic matters: In 2017, 71 per cent A*-A/9-7 in GCSE, 55 per cent at A level. Impressive results that seem to be achieved without a pressure cooker environment. Lots of clinics available for those needing extra support, most voluntarily seeking it. Parents kept well informed about academic progress. 'The children are taught to work hard and do their best; what more can you ask for?' French, German, Greek, Latin, Chinese and Spanish all offered at GCSE, many doing two languages. Pupils set in maths for all year groups and sciences from year 10. One parent would like to see more choice of subjects at A level. Most are covered but no politics or photography.

Excellent facilities, computers everywhere with iPads for each pupil. Very impressive art on display including pottery; lots of art rooms with fabulous smell of paint and oils. Sixth formers working on mezzanine floor. Fully equipped DT room including a whole computer suite. Beautiful large library, children encouraged to take books out, free reading periods up to year 9. Lessons we observed showed friendly staff and chatty children. A very relaxed atmosphere but don't be fooled, they were working hard. Noticeably less formal between teacher and student further up the school. Enjoyed listening to the discussions in A level theology; couldn't resist joining in – this lot were very harsh on drivers. Seemingly very young teacher who had the group eating out of his hand, but maybe we are getting old. School on Saturday, all day, for years 9-13, lessons as well as sport. They make good use of Cambridge; lots of chances to go to lectures and listen to eminent speakers.

Learning support lessons for some 50 pupils year 7-11, twice a week in small groups, sixth form weekly one-to-one lessons for 21. Around 16 other pupils monitored throughout the term to make sure their needs don't change. Good support offered and parents are pleased. 'My daughter was disengaged when it came to studying until the school spotted her dyslexia. They offered tremendous support, and still do. She is now completely focused.'

Some 15 per cent of pupils are from overseas, 35 different countries. Around 40 students have EAL requirements. These pupils have three English lessons a week and extra privately funded lessons available if required. Integration activities for all. Monitored throughout their time at the school to make sure language skills not holding them back academically. Many long serving staff, some living on site.

Games, options, the arts: This is a sporty school, renowned for it, with excellent facilities including all-weather pitches. Lots of teams for all year groups. Accepting of pupils who have outside sporting commitments and willing to offer extra support academically if needed. Interesting to see they have a girl in the cricket team; she's there on merit, excellent. Good to see that pupils play within their own age group whatever their abilities. 'It is good for them socially to be with their peers,' said one wise mother.

The school is very keen to emphasise that it is 'not just about sport.' And parents backed this up. 'Their plays are excellent, much better than some I've seen in Cambridge,' from one parent. Lots of drama clubs and productions throughout the year. An inspirational, enthusiastic drama teacher who pulls everyone along with her.

Music excellent, housed in its own school with a very proactive director. Eighteen music rooms including a recording studio and recital hall with excellent acoustics. Professional musicians perform at lunch times. Lots of music lessons, 200 a week. Many talented musicians including ex-choristers from the local prep schools. Loads of bands, choirs, orchestras and groups. Boarders often practise or jam in the evenings.

D of E compulsory in year 9 and 10. CCF from year 10; interesting that they don't have a RAF contingent, yet, but they do have a rifle range.

Many school trips to all over the world. Trekking in the Himalayas this summer, three weeks in Southern Africa for biology last year. Numerous sports tours and subject trips.

Boarding: Pupils are split between 11 houses, including three day houses, and assemble there for registration and notices. The day houses have the same facilities as the boarding ones but without beds. School offers two sorts of boarding, full or home. Home boarding pupils stay at school until after prep and go home about 9pm. They are allocated a space within the house and are in all aspects boarders, except they don't spend the night. A popular option with many parents and pupils. Some 70 per cent board, with 50 per cent of pupils being full boarders and 20 per cent home boarders. Very much a family atmosphere, pupils on first name terms with staff and obviously very tight with each other. Sixth formers share light out duties and often pop in to chat to younger age groups to make sure all is well.

Matron described as a 'superstar' by our guide. Parents agree. 'It really is home from home and they do all they can to make sure everyone is happy,' said one parent

Lots of house competitions for snooker etc. Year groups 9-13 housed together; sixth form have their own common room but often join younger age groups. One specific house for sixth form, mainly for new joiners. Lots of facilities including piano that is well used. Younger years share rooms, up to six in year 9, sixth form have their own rooms. Tea and toast-making facilities available, oven available for sixth form. Nice to see some of the dorms were messy. Clean, modern bathrooms, plenty of them. Matron described as a 'superstar' by our guide. Parents agree. 'It really is home from home and they do all they can to make sure everyone is happy,' said one parent. 'They are in a lovely environment and the housemistress really is a surrogate mum.' 'The younger girls have a "big sister" in the house that they choose and she will look out for them and help them settle in.' Prep supervised up to year 11; each pupil has their own desk in prep rooms. Phones and iPads taken away at night from younger years.

Lots of activities offered at weekends and evenings; they are kept busy. Sixth formers make the most of 'Cambridge boarding' and often head into town for dinner at the weekends, choosing to spend time in the city enjoying what it has to offer. Curfew of 10.30pm adhered to. Sixth formers also have a club with licensed bar. Pretty flexible approach to parties. If parents and host parents agree they are allowed to stay away overnight at weekends.

Background and atmosphere: Founded in 1875, The Leys is the only independent co-educational boarding and day school in Cambridge. Went co-ed in 1981. Situated on a 50 acre site a stone's throw from the centre of Cambridge. The buildings surround open playing fields so all feels very spacious. Lots of building undertaken over the years but fits in well with the original red-brick slightly gothic original ones that are beautiful inside and out. Founded by the Methodists, the school still has a strong sense of religious community with chapel services for all, whatever their denomination, happy to join in. Parent like the ethos. Note the original Wesley chapel, one of the earliest built, as a memorial to pupils killed in WW1,a perfect example of the arts and crafts movement. The school was evacuated to Scotland during WW2 with premises being requisitioned for a military hospital. Lots of talk of ghosts in the basement, but we didn't see any.

The big small school is an apt description. Large enough to be well supported and funded by generous benefactors, so offering excellent facilities and teaching, small enough to be intimate, with individuals recognised for who they are.

Pupils and staff lunch together, staff on a mezzanine floor, but many joining pupils. Delicious food we can vouch for. There was a quiet buzz within the dining hall: calm and orderly but relaxed.

Lessons we observed showed friendly staff and chatty children. A very relaxed atmosphere but don't be fooled, they were working hard

Pastoral care, well-being and discipline: 'We are hostile to bullying,' says the head. Problems usually picked up quickly within the house, often resolved by pupils themselves. The house system is very effective with tutors and houseparents, as well as matron, getting to know the pupils well. They spend a lot of time together and quickly pick up if there are problems. Plenty of counselling services on offer if needed. 'There is a very strong community at The Leys,' said one parent. 'I was surprised and delighted at how well the teachers look after the pupils.' Another parent said, 'Pastoral care is the school's biggest plus point. My child is so happy there and as they are happy they work hard.' 'My child has a voice and is listened to. Problems are dealt with sensitively and well.' It's not just academia here. 'They encourage the pupil to be the best they can be, and not just at studying.' Pupils are listened to. A new initiative is just being introduced by the pupils themselves offering a point of contact for those with race/gender/sexuality issues – very on trend.

Introduction to the school treated seriously. All year 9s invited to spend 24 hours at the school before they start in September, day pupils as well, a very effective method that our guide still spoke about. Lots of bonding sessions to create a community.

Discipline wasn't mentioned by any parent as it doesn't seem to be an issue. The head has had to exclude one pupil for drugs. 'We don't have a zero tolerance policy, but it's close to zero. I know teenagers dabble, but warnings are usually heeded. I'm a great believer in second chances, but not third.'

Pupils and parents: Parents are very much 'Cambridge,' academics, entrepreneurs and medics and many more doing the London commute, hence the popularity of home boarding. Popular with Fen farmers as well. Many pupils second and third generation to attend the school. Most live within an hour, boarders as well, apart from the overseas contingent.

Pupils mostly well-rounded and self aware, friendly, welcoming and chatty. They can see there is more to life that just qualifications. A 60:40 mix of boys and girls. No obvious divide between boarders and day pupils.

Entrance: Every child is interviewed prior to the test. Year 7 intake of around 30, mainly from state primaries. The main cohort, about 70, joins year 9, mainly from local Cambridge prep schools. St Faith's is part of the foundation and a feeder school. Competitive entrance exam. Their own English and maths plus standardised verbal and spatial reasoning tests. Oversubscribed so they can take their pick.

Sixth form entry five B/6s for current pupils. Same for new arrivals but As and A*s (7-9s) preferred. Between 25 and 30 join, mainly to board from day independents, the occasional state school pupil.

Exit: Some 25-30 leave after year 11, mainly to the excellent local state sixth form colleges. Very unusual to lose a pupil to another independent school. The occasional one doesn't meet GCSE hurdle, but again unusual. As expected most to university, RAU and Harper Adams represented by the farming contingent, others to eg LSE, Imperial, Newcastle, Reading, Exeter, Durham and Edinburgh. Two to Oxbridge in 2017. Around 20 per cent take gap years.

Previous pupils have included tennis player Jamie Murray, a couple of rugby union stars, journalist Martin Bell, the current King of Bahrain and a previous King of Tonga – an eclectic mix.

Money matters: The usual scholarships and bursaries. One full scholarship a year from the Wesley Foundation including all trips. The mindset behind this was so that no other pupil would know they were on a scholarship.

Remarks: A lovely place to study. You feel as though you are in the countryside but are minutes from the centre of the city of Cambridge so you get the best of both worlds. 'I don't begrudge a penny we have spent,' from one happy parent. Known locally as 'the friendly school,' we can see why, it is.

Lockers Park School

27

Lockers Park Lane, Hemel Hempstead, Hertfordshire HP1 1TL

01442 251712 | secretary@lockerspark.herts.sch.uk | www.lockerspark.herts.sch.uk

Ages: Boys 4-13, girls 4-7; (boarding from 7)

Pupils: 170; Boarders: 16 full, 40 flexi

Day: £10,350 – £16,920 pa; Boarding: £23,940 pa

Headmaster: Since 2013, Chris Wilson BSc PGCE Cantab (30s). Educated at Winchester House in Northamptonshire, where he boarded from the age of 6, and Oundle. Read rural economics at Newcastle before moving to Cambridge to take a conversion course to enable him to teach maths to A level, followed by his PGCE at Homerton College.

Returned to alma mater Winchester House for first teaching role, where he spent 11 years teaching maths and running first XI cricket and colts rugby, heading the boarding house for 10 of them. Moved to Lockers in 2012 as deputy head, drawn by its rigorous sporting culture, boarding heritage ('boarding is infused through the school,' he says) and pastoral approach, as well as its superb musical offering (although he cheerfully describes himself as 'woefully inadequate' in this respect). Headship came after a period which was, according to parents 'turbulent', with three heads of school in six years. He has reportedly 'steadied the ship brilliantly' and restored confidence to staff, with parents describing the change in mood after his appointment as 'palpable'.

Still teaches years 7 and 8 maths and revels in being able to 'physically see the path of the boys' development' in a prep school and having 'involvement in all spheres' of their lives. Parents describe him as a 'fantastic communicator' and say that he has returned a focus on academic achievement which had formerly been 'slightly lost'. A cricket fanatic, he likens the patience and thoughtfulness required for the game to his role as head. Intent that his charges will remember the fun side of school, believes in 'freedom within boundaries' and aims to 'fly in the face' of pushy parents to 'ensure Lockers boys have a childhood'.

Engaging and likeable with a relaxed persona, and ably supported by wife, Hayley, who fulfils a traditional head's spouse role as well as caring for their two young daughters.

Entrance: Newish pre-prep school housed in a purpose designed building welcomes girls as well as boys. From here, most girls likely to move to local girls' school, Abbot's Hill School, whilst boys move into the 'steadfastly single sex' year 3.

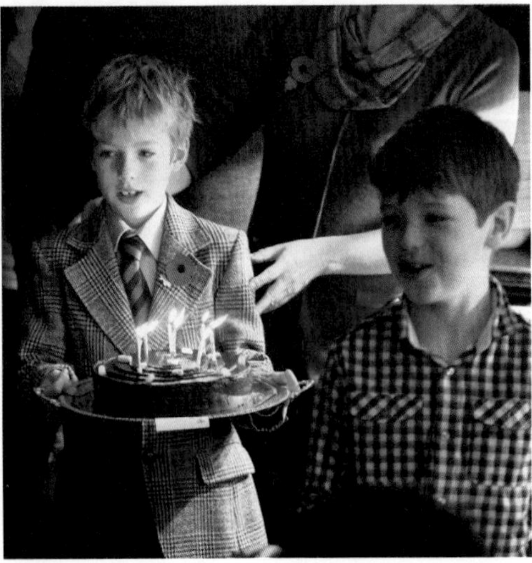

Ensembles and bands galore with an invitation to join the 'intensely serious' main choir considered a real accolade (dare we say cool?)

Not currently oversubscribed, although at highest ever numbers. Main intake into year 3 with a 'low key' assessment day including tests in verbal reasoning and maths. Scholarship day in February with applicants also observed in music, sport and a fun activity such as a treasure hunt. Head says they are 'not only looking for academic strength' but for children who can bring 'that certain something' to the school.

Pupils join mainly from state primaries, occasionally other preps (a large influx recently from Berkhamsted Prep), within a 20 to 30 minute radius of the school. Approximately half the cohort are day boys, with the rest doing 'some form' of boarding (two nights minimum). About 50 per cent of full time boarders are overseas pupils (typically Russian or Chinese) and some Forces.

Exit: The small number of pupils means they tend to leave in ones and twos to a broad variety of schools. Most recently to Aldenham, Harrow, Rugby, Eton, Bedford, St Albans and Winchester; in other years Berkhamsted, Stowe, Shiplake, Haileybury, Bradfield, Radley and Shrewsbury also popular destinations. The occasional one to state maintained grammars at 11+, although this is 'definitely not encouraged,' says head. Three or four scholarships achieved each year. Head deliberates carefully over choosing of senior schools 'on a very individual basis.'

Remarks: Adamantly traditional in its fabric but with a subtly modern feel (thanks to a rolling programme of improvements), Lockers was purpose-built in 1874, based on Mitchell House at Rugby School, and sits atop 25 glorious acres of woodland – a boys' own oasis in a drab Hemel suburb. The heart of the school is undoubtedly the stunning, light-flooded panelled dining hall, which typifies Lockers' success in juxtaposing the modern with the school's rich history, the names of alumni etched on its walls. Everything about the school is focused on bringing out the best in boys – from the 40 minute morning break where they can tear around fields and woodlands with just enough time for a bit of den-building before the bell calls them to lessons, to the pristine well-structured classrooms (if there was a GSG award for the cleanest prep, Lockers would be in with a good chance) and predominantly male staff. Staff know all the boys and are '100 per cent accessible,' say parents – 'clearly visible and just a phone call or an email away.'

The spacious, well-stocked library has a cosy feel, with armchairs and banks of computers, and the chapel can house the whole school at a squeeze. Art room large and airy with its own kiln, although feels suspiciously tidy – and whole school could benefit from more artwork on display, especially as standards are high enough to win a senior school art scholarship most years. DT recently rehomed into a modern block with two super rooms – one for design and one for work. A comfortable boarders' common room is supplemented by the 'boys' hall' and the old gym, home to table tennis and pool tables for boys to use in their free time. Engine enthusiasts will adore the 'train room' – a dedicated space for a huge model railway for boys to tinker with. Pianists practise on a baby grand situated in a very public space rather than tucked away in a practice room – 'great for getting them used to performing,' says head.

Tousled boys bomb happily around between classes with plenty of cheery greetings for staff and visitors. The uniform – or lack thereof – comprising a check shirt of the boys' choice and a pair of navy cords, sums up the collegiate learning environment where boys can be boys and the endgame is reached via a path punctuated with a lot of good, wholesome fun as well as academic rigour. 'Best' is when the jackets and ties come out – again the boys' own choice of jacket – reserved for school outings, concerts and away matches. School committed to small class sizes with between 10 and 15 in most forms – parents feel that school's bijoux size is its 'true strength'.

Long days – sometimes up to 11 hours for older boys – with all allowed to arrive at school from 7am and stay for breakfast and supper at no extra charge and with no prior arrangement, all of which helps to cement the seamless boarding vibe – parents say it's like 'one big family.' Boarding house is part of main school, with boys split over two floors according to age and presided over by a housemaster who is supported by a team of live-in matrons.

Bright, functional dorms housing four to six boarders slightly lack the personal touch, although boys can bring their own duvet covers. Clothes kept in the laundry room and matrons lay out boy's outfits each day. Exeats every third weekend, unusually from Friday lunch time until Monday evening, with Saturday morning school still going strong on non-exeat weekends, optional for pre-prep.

Setting from year 7 in preparation for CE with specialist teaching across all subjects from year 5. Modern languages exceptionally strong, with head describing French as school's 'stand out' subject and parents adding history and geography to the list. A brief audience with the head of modern languages certainly confirmed his passion for language and inspirational teaching techniques. Latin and ancient Greek also on the menu, although not considered by parents to be school's strongest suit. Maths and English 'on the up,' says head, due to recent staff changes.

Music 'firing on all cylinders', according to head, led by the 'most dynamic, committed' head of music who secures a music scholarship for at least one boy each year. Violin for all from year 3 and at least 96 per cent of boys continue with an instrument, some playing two or three. Choirs, ensembles and bands galore with an invitation to join the 'intensely serious' main choir considered a real accolade (dare we say cool?) and with parents saying it's 'totally normal for boys to be singing' at Lockers. Drama on curriculum from years 3 to 5 (replaced by Latin in year 6), with opportunities galore for budding thespians to perform in plays, poetry competitions, debating etc.

Intent that his charges will remember the fun side of school, believes in 'freedom within boundaries' and aims to 'ensure Lockers boys have a childhood'

Sport not the school's raison d'être but a good ethos in place – head laments the demise at some fixtures of the traditional post-match tea in other schools ('a bag of crisps and box of juice – just not the same') – and places huge emphasis on fair play and sportsmanship, fielding A-E teams whenever possible so everyone gets a trip on the bus whatever their ability. Sports department is making the most of its not inconsiderable facilities, including cricket nets, a renovated outdoor pool, tennis courts, and putting green. Sport every afternoon for all boys, with the timetable adjusted seasonally to allow for more light for outdoor fun. Occasional parental grumbles that less sporty boys are 'labelled' in the early years and don't get the same coaching opportunities as their more able peers. Tons of extracurricular from chess club to year-round skiing at the nearby snow dome. Lockers' own cub and scout packs thrive, and boys who take part generally stay the night afterwards.

Chapel every morning takes a 'general studies' approach and acts as a 'reflective, calming exercise' to start the day. Boarders' fun nights well attended by day boys and the anti-health and safety Dark Tower night, an unlit night time treasure hunt around the school, hugely popular. In summer, day boys stay over after evening barbecues and are 'swept along' with boarding activities throughout the year, some parents saying their boys never want to come home. Action-packed weekends for full-timers with activities split three ways between the cultural, educational and purely fun. All prep done in school – a popular move with boys and parents. School even has its own vernacular – with quirks so numerous that newcomers are issued with a handbook to decipher it all. Parents report that any incidents of bullying or upset are dealt with effectively in a 'supportive and understanding' way.

In all, a small but perfectly formed school which gives boys all the tools they need to continue on to top public schools. Lockers offers the best of both worlds – boarding for those who want it, with all the benefits plus their own beds at home for those who don't. In the words of one happy parent who moved two boys from another prep: 'boys are known and valued at Lockers, rather than unknown and undervalued'.

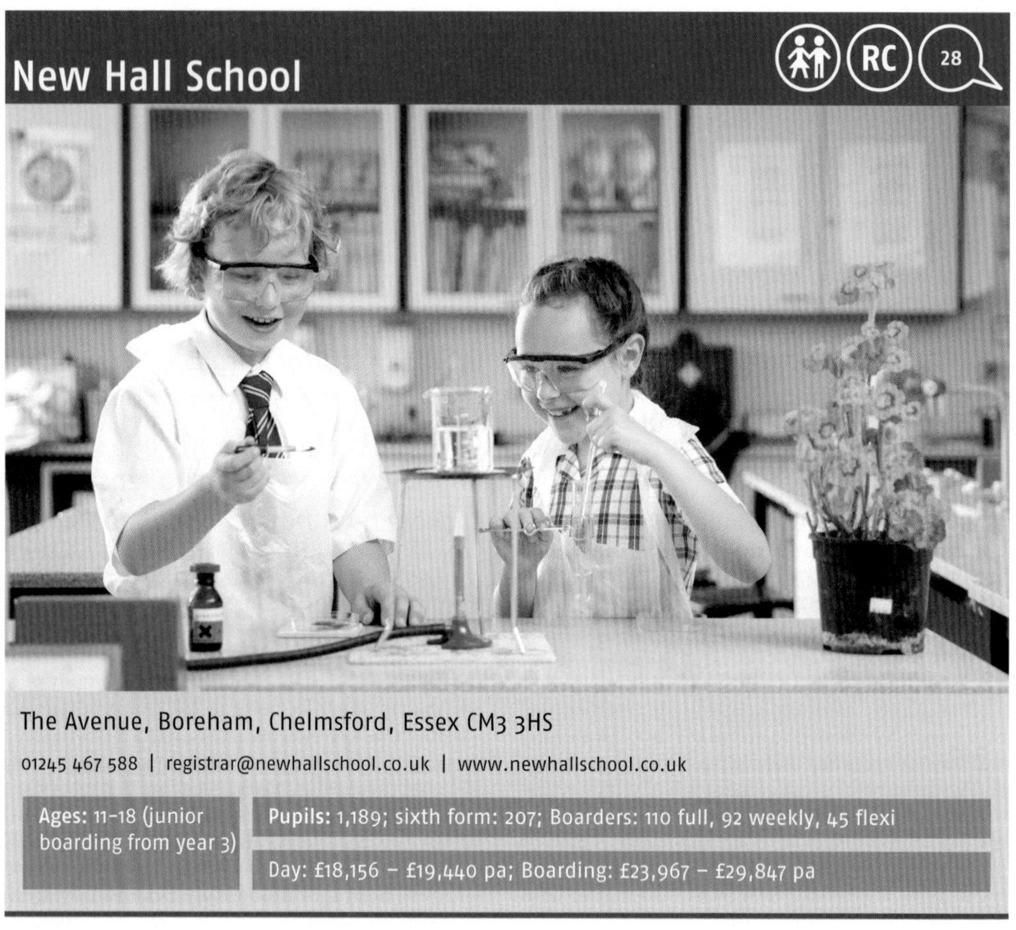

New Hall School

RC 28

The Avenue, Boreham, Chelmsford, Essex CM3 3HS

01245 467 588 | registrar@newhallschool.co.uk | www.newhallschool.co.uk

Ages: 11–18 (junior boarding from year 3)

Pupils: 1,189; sixth form: 207; Boarders: 110 full, 92 weekly, 45 flexi

Day: £18,156 – £19,440 pa; Boarding: £23,967 – £29,847 pa

Principal: Since 2001, Katherine Jeffrey MA PGCE MA (EdMg) NPQH. Previously an RE teacher at St Mary's School, Shaftesbury, head of RE at Woldingham School, deputy head at The Marist School, Ascot before coming to New Hall as its first ever lay principal and teacher of theology. Awarded the Institute of Directors' East of England Businesswoman of the Year Award, followed by a national Independent Schools Award for Outstanding Strategic Initiative. Since 2010 she has been a committee member of the Catholic Independent Schools' Conference. Mrs Jeffrey is married with four daughters – all educated at New Hall School.

Making the change from dyed-in-the-wool Catholic convent girls' boarding school of variable academic results to one of the UK's foremost successful pioneers of the 'diamond model' (co-educational prep school, single-sex teaching for ages 11 to 16, returning to co-education for the sixth form) took Mrs Jeffrey a speedy five years.

Presumably also nerves of steel, which we don't doubt pulse beneath her polished exterior. 'She oozes confidence and enthusiasm,' swooned one impressed parent, and many laud her 'efficiency'. Indeed, the school comfortably met all the targets it had set itself when adopting the 'diamond model', notably a student body of exactly half girls and half boys. When we visited, New Hall had recently trounced Harrow at rugby and Eton at tennis – to the transparent delight of Mrs Jeffrey. However, amid all this blatant success, at its heart – and its principal's – New Hall remains a Catholic foundation Christian community with core moral values to impart. 'My aim is to shape the adults of the future, form their characters as people of integrity and kindness,' says Mrs Jeffrey. 'We are a community – no-one is here in isolation.'

Academic matters: In 2017, 44 per cent of A level grades were A*/A and 76 per cent A*-B. Similarly impressive results at GCSE – 54 per cent A*-A/9-7. Interestingly, the genders at New Hall are on a par results-wise at GCSE, bucking the national trend for boys to fall behind by 10 per cent. More grist to the mill of the 'diamond model', allowing the teaching between 11 and 16 to be tailored to gender-specific learning styles, with co-ed lessons in the prep and sixth form.

French and Spanish are taught from year 7. Theology is compulsory up to year 11. In year 9, classics, Latin and critical thinking are introduced. GCSE students have timetabled religious studies, English, maths, science and a choice of modern language. Head of science has the final say in who takes separate sciences and head of languages gives the 'oui or non' or 'si or no', to students opting for two languages. Most students take 10 or 11 subjects, a few more or a few less according to ability. Each student in years 10 and 11 follows a tutorial programme including 'life skills' and careers education. Games afternoon once a week, with team sports and individual options. Staff reputedly bend over backwards to make sure students shoehorn in their favourite subjects – one parent reported the head of PE giving up his lunch for individual lessons with her son whose GCSE timetable was already full to bursting.

Gifted and talented is taken seriously with accelerated and differentiated learning in lessons and encouragement to take part in enrichment opportunities. The DELTA club promotes scholarly habits (including 'challenge', 'persistence and big picture thinking', 'intellectual courage' and 'metathinking'), and the OMEGA club is for the several each year with sights set on Oxbridge.

Games, options, the arts: 'Our co-curricular programme is not an add-on,' emphasises principal. Sport in particular is taken very seriously. Income has been ploughed into facilities – sleek, purpose-built gymnasium block stuffed with cardio machines and weights overlooks a sweep of sports pitches, 10 courts for netball or tennis (full-time tennis pro nurtures future stars), 400-metre cinder running track and chlorine-free pool in its own block with changing room facilities (also used by the Essex swim squad). A former equestrian arena is now an indoor sports hall with state-of-the-art flooring, while the many horse-related activities take place off-site. County and national athletes in many disciplines, including UK independent school golf and equestrian champions, not to mention star swimmers, cricketers, tennis, hockey and rugby players. A New Hallian athlete competed in the latest Commonwealth Games.

Staff bend over backwards to make sure students shoehorn in their favourite subjects – one parent reported the head of PE giving up his lunch for individual lessons

The first time we've come across a choir that's compulsory – year 7 boys and girls enjoy or endure a year before being given the option to remain. 'We have discovered some great voices that way – people who wouldn't have put themselves forward,' says head of music. Choice of choirs for those inclined, including Voces for the broken-voiced, plus instrumental ensembles of all kinds and the occasional rock and pop band. Organ lessons on the restored Norman & Beard organ in the school chapel. Many informal as well as the formal performances. Despite a good take-up at GCSE, a small handful study A level music and the odd one or two each year progress to conservatoires.

There are regular – and by all accounts, spectacular – drama productions all year round and involving all ages, and the Walkfares Centre is the venue for all performing arts. Annual dance show is a highlight and dance A level popular. Own dance company takes students from year 10 upwards and crosses over with the local community. ESB and LAMDA thrive. Around 30 a year take art A level – working away in a warren of atelier-style studios – and about a third continue beyond, though architecture tends to win out over fine art.

In keeping with the school's focus on community and charity, all pupils are heavily involved with the New Hall Voluntary Service, which for many becomes a way of life. One pupil recently received the Princess Diana award – for swimming the Channel to benefit Great Ormond Street Hospital – but all make a contribution of some kind.

Eight houses – unrelated to the boarding houses – contest in competitions of all hues.

Boarding: Cream sofas? Cushions? Can this be a boys' boarding house? For 7-13 year olds? Indeed it is at New Hall. Quite apart from Earle House's jaw-droppingly ornate cornicing and mouldings worthy of a royal palace, the place is spotless in the face of a most unforgiving neutrally toned décor – not a muddy rugby sock nor a mouldering trainer to be seen. Either the staff deserve a medal or this is a new breed of boy. The usual entertainment – large-screen TV, Xbox etc – but arranged in such civilised, convivial surroundings that one could happily invite one's grandmother for a spot of GTA. The dorms too are a revelation – again tidy beyond belief with all belongings stowed neatly into storage compartments hiding behind the ladder treads of ingenious high-sleeper beds, designed by the former New Hallian director of boarding and incorporating a study space underneath. Magdalen House, for girls in years 3-8, is more the usual fayre – though rooms for ones and twos rather than the multiples for boys (full boarders usually roomed with the flexi-boarders) – and a comfortable lived-in look with cheery décor chosen by the girls themselves. Four other houses – two for boys and two for girls as they progress through the year groups – accommodating the 33 per cent who board on a flexi, weekly or full-time basis. Up to 16 reserved places for junior (full and weekly) boarders from year 3 onwards.

Background and atmosphere: The original Palace of Beaulieu, ancestral home of the Boleyn family and thought to represent much of the attraction to King Henry VIII of his second wife (beheaded), perhaps with good reason. Henry expanded the existing building to create a most imposing and gargantuan edifice, with eight courtyards behind a 550-foot wide red-brick frontage and two enormous gatehouse towers. Channel 4's Time Team dug up evidence of the foundations of what appears to have been a nursery for Henry's first-born, Princess Mary. Having passed through a few hands (including those of Oliver Cromwell) after Henry's demise, in 1799 the palace became occupied by the Canonesses of the Holy Sepulchre, one of the most ancient orders in the Catholic church, established in Europe long before the English Religious Community was founded in 1642. Forced out of their home in the Low Countries by the French Revolutionary Wars, the Canonesses brought their school to the Palace of Beaulieu with the intention of offering a Catholic education to girls denied this in England in the Post-Reformation period. Thus, New Hall is the oldest Catholic girls' school in England.

Today's New Hall is (in terms of footprint at least) but a fraction of Henry's pile, but breathtaking nonetheless and approached via a mile-long avenue at the end of which one fully expects a National Trust ticket booth to appear. Perhaps one of the most impressive interiors is the chapel, with its original solid wood door and Henry VIII's coat of arms over the main entrance.

Behind the long façade of the main building, which houses an impressive entrance hall with waiting room, the chapel, classrooms and a boarding house, there is a dedicated arts block incorporating two large studio spaces (which host the school's popular Saturday dance and drama schools as well as lessons throughout the week). The Eaton Theatre seats 210 and is used for productions as well as lectures and year meetings. Large library with study area for all-comers and hanging with Apple Macs. Eight science labs. Spacious refectory reminiscent of the restaurant in an upmarket London department store with a choice of three hot options (the traditional fish and chips on the Friday we visited), plus a salad bar and other cold choices.

Sixth form is a tight-knit community of 250, presided over by staff other than those that continuing pupils will have met in their junior years. Sixth formers have their own wing of the arts block, with study space and chill-out zone including snack kitchen.

New Hall hit the education sector headlines when it became the first independent school in the country to enter a partnership with a struggling state primary school. The school now lends its expertise and guidance to Messing Primary School, 15 miles away – management input, plus New Hall

The place is spotless in the face of a most unforgiving neutrally toned décor – not a muddy rugby sock nor a mouldering trainer to be seen

pupil-run events, such as an international day and community carol service.

On Mrs Jeffrey's wishlist is a new science centre and a large auditorium with the capacity to seat the whole school together, but these she admits have fallen victim to the more pressing need to keep fees 'reasonable' for parents (minimal increases and none at all in one recent year; flexi-boarding rates have actually been reduced).

Pastoral care, well-being and discipline: 'Parents remark on the smiles here – on the faces of pupils and staff alike,' says Mrs Jeffrey and this does appear to be a rather serene community. Personal qualities, kindness in particular, are recognised and drawn out, and pupils we met were certainly happy in their own skin. This is a Catholic school and although those of all faiths and none are welcome, Christian values are at its core. Support and care for others, both in school and outside it, are fundamental to life here for even the smallest New Hall pupils. New Good Hope café donates proceeds to For Jimmy charity.

Parents too are comfortable in the fold. 'The school has always encouraged parents to give feedback and support the development of the site, by running parent forums and questionnaires,' said one satisfied parent.

Pupils and parents: One clearly in touch with her target market, Mrs Jeffrey appreciates the fact that her school is surrounded by a changing profile of local parents – from the traditional farmers and professionals to city commuters and the grammar school educated. 'Some have attended the historic Catholic schools such as Stonyhurst and Worth themselves and are now looking to us for their children,' she says. Being Catholic is not a prerequisite, but engagement with the religious life of the school very much is. 'If you come here you sign up to the whole package,' says Mrs Jeffrey. 'I would hope that our pupils would leave here well-informed on matters of faith, and that they would have absorbed our core moral and spiritual values.'

Buses zero in on the school from a myriad directions daily and boarders come from all over the south east, many from London thanks to the fast and frequent commuter train service – 35 minutes from Liverpool Street to Chelmsford, four miles away. The rumour is of a proposed new mainline station right at the end of the New Hall drive (no prizes for guessing Mrs Jeffrey's preferred name for it). Long a favourite with overseas pupils, about 45 per cent of boarders, who represent more than 30 countries.

Entrance: Year 7 has 120 places – usually three times oversubscribed. Around 40 pupils come up from New Hall's own year 6, although they too must go through the same entry procedure as external applicants – papers in English, maths and verbal reasoning plus a three-minute presentation to members of the senior school SLT. Lengthy admissions preamble – families have usually visited for at least one open day as well as a group tour including the opportunity to ask questions of the senior leadership team before beginning the formal application. Lower sixth has 150 places, with new entrants needing two A/7s and four B/6s at GCSE to be in with a whiff. 'Our A level classes are very fast-paced,' says principal, 'with pupils aiming for A* to B grades.'

Exit: Some 40 per cent leave after GCSEs. Six to Oxbridge in 2017, others mostly to their first choice of a range of universities to study subjects in all realms eg Southampton, Exeter, Edinburgh, Bristol and London unis.

Forced out of their home in the Low Countries by the French Revolutionary Wars, the Canonesses brought their school to the Palace of Beaulieu with the intention of offering a Catholic education to girls denied this

Former pupils are automatic members of the Old Fishes' Association (being rebranded as New Hallians) and this association numbers many notables, including international fashion designer Anya Hindmarch, CNN international correspondent Christiane Amanpour, artist and novelist Leonora Carrington, opera singer Stefanie Kemball-Read and Horrid Henry actor Theo Stevenson.

Money matters: Scholarships for Catholics, academic, music, all rounder, sport (general) and tennis, plus means-tested bursaries.

Remarks: There is the feeling that New Hall is much more than the sum of its parts, with personal qualities and integrity as central to the ethos as an application to study and success.

Old Buckenham Hall School

29

Brettenham Park, Ipswich, Suffolk IP7 7PH

01449 740252 | admissions@obh.co.uk | www.obh.co.uk

Ages: 3–13 (boarders from 7)

Pupils: 193; Boarders: 26 full, 18 weekly, 46 flexi

Day: £9,225 – £18,711 pa; Boarding: £16,041 – £24,378 pa

Headmaster: Since 2015, Tom O'Sullivan – a man who makes workaholics seem lazy. In two years, he has, through the power of his personality and brio, transformed his school. Educated at Pate's Grammar School in Cheltenham and Durham University where he read law; people always said that he would become a teacher but, for a while, he resisted, spending an extra year at Durham as JCR president before deciding that a career spent in a quest for silk was not for him. Work began in a variety of roles: as a graduate trainee for WH Smith, for a recruitment firm in Singapore, and in drug education for a pharmaceutical company. He then followed his destiny, taking a PGCE, specialising in science, at Homerton College, Cambridge. Here he discovered in the first 10 seconds of his first lesson that 'the buzz from teaching' was better than anything he had previously experienced in his working life.

Appointments at Beaudesert Park and a deputy-headship at Mowden Hall followed, before he assumed command of Old Buckenham Hall. A flamboyant individual – in many ways a sort of academic circus-master – he has clearly put an immediate stamp on OBH with his dynamism and determination. This has come as a major contrast to his predecessor, who did much for the school but, according to one of the year 8 pupils, tended 'to tuck himself away in his study'. This head is different and epitomises all that a modern leader needs to be. He describes OBH as 'absolutely brilliant' and that 'it's lovely when you wake up just wanting to go to work'. Thus far, he has made a series of what he claims are 'little tweaks'. This understates both the scope and significance of his reforms, especially in the recruitment of new staff (now well into double figures) and in his development of boarding.

OBH operates an 11-day model, a scheme that was instituted before the head took over, but has now been honed to include themed weekends such as The Masked Masquerade Ball, featuring chocolate fountains and mocktails, Grillin'n'Chillin and Secret Mission Sunday. Boarding numbers are up 40 per cent, around 40 children stay in for the weekends and the school is now financially buoyant. The word 'fun' dominates many a sentence as the head explains that if his boys and girls are here for 10 years then 'they have got to love it'. And they clearly rate him, senior pupils describing him as 'energetic and funny': he dresses up on themed nights as The Incredible Hulk or Michael Jackson, and runs discos from his jukebox – he admits to a liking for power ballads and American rockers REO Speedwagon......

Has now been honed to include themed weekends such as The Masked Masquerade Ball, featuring chocolate fountains and mocktails

And then there is his dog, a year-old Great Dane by the name of Scooby; a huge beast of a hound who brought to mind Conan Doyle, Baskervilles and Grimpen Mire. Scooby, though, is softer than cream and is predictably popular with everyone, especially the children, who seemingly at almost any time can pop into the head's study to pat their pet. The head lives in a flat in the main house, holds Tuesday night suppers for year 8 pupils, teaches science to years 7 and 8, likes refereeing rugby and directed the school play Joseph with a cast list of 190. Claiming not to 'do stress', he then reflects and concludes that it only strikes him 'on the odd day'. Far more than merely a whacky cousin or a spirited uncle, he is, we perceive, well able to crack the whip if required. He will be a terrifyingly hard act to follow.

Moving on in July 2018 to head Cheltenham College Prep.

Entrance: This is essentially non-selective. Taster days are available and children wishing to enter from year 3 onwards are assessed in English, reading and maths. Only if a child is exceptionally academically fragile will an offer of a place not be forthcoming. Bursarial assistance is available for military and clergy children whilst sibling discounts operate for parents with three children at the school.

Exit: Ultimately a major part of any parental verdict will depend on how pupils fare in final examinations. According to the head, 'expectations were not where they needed to be': OBH's senior schools were in a rather narrow geographical area, comprising schools such as Framlingham College, Oundle and Uppingham. Clearly these still feature, but 2017, 37 leavers had offers 16 different schools, amongst others Winchester, Radley and Benenden; 12 scholarships. Children have on occasion been offered Harrow and Eton places.

Remarks: Deeply embedded in the Suffolk countryside, a few miles from exotically-named villages such as Thorpe Morieux and Bradfield Combust, appears the splendid entrance to OBH. Lodge cottages frame the gates: an avenue of trees flanks the drive on which a pheasant sprints away to safety. The 80-acre estate opens up... Cambridge Blue flags edge the rugby pitches; red flags pin the greens of the golf course. The house, dating back to the mid-19th century, was the home of Sir Edward and Lady Warner until the former's death in 1955. Entering the building, we were struck not just by the gold lettered honours boards or the oak panelling, but by the fire that, even by mid-morning, had crackled its way through many a log. Sofas are voluminous; pupils bustle by on their way to lessons. A suit of armour stands in the corner.

OBH presents itself as a 24/7 school where, according to the sparkling registrar, 'The children rock around an old family house and are allowed to be children. They aren't treated as mini-adults.' The range of buildings and the way they have been adapted, in, for example, the old stable complex is impressive and we especially liked the South Lawn with its well-tended pond (large enough to accommodate a platoon of ducks) and a variety of trees that formed Sir Henry's small arboretum. The children are encouraged to climb them. Whereas many schools would have corralled off this area as some kind of health & safety danger zone, OBH boys and girls are encouraged (in a phrase grudgingly authorised by some inspectors) to make their own

'dynamic risk assessments' and gauge things for themselves. Predictably, a lifebelt at the edge of the pond does not look like it has been used for years.

All classrooms, whether in the nursery, pre-prep or in the more senior areas of the main school, are spacious and stylish; not really a verdict that we could pass on the library, which is on the small side. However, the science complex is a highlight as it incorporates three laboratories. Also worth a look are the DT centre (take note here of the textiled scarves and the model catamarans), the performing arts centre and the suite of music practice rooms. The Britten Hall – opened in 2003 and named after one of the more famous alumni of the school – houses not just a selection of classrooms but also a major facility which doubles up as a gym and as a theatre. Assemblies are also held here, which, given the fizziness of the staff, are sure to be more inspiring than the dog-eared and broken-spined selection of hymn books on show.

OBH stresses the significance of outdoor education and runs a modular programme based on acquiring skills, such as 'how to make silver birch tea and super-glue' and 'the knots that you should know'. Then there are the physical challenges which build through each year until year 8 pupils are ready to deal with their 100-length swim and the Gold Survival Expedition. This lasts four days, recent locations being the Welsh Peaks and Northumberland.

There's his dog, a Great Dane by the name of Scooby, who brought to mind Conan Doyle, Baskervilles and Grimpen Mire. Scooby, though, is softer than cream

Sport, music and drama are central to the school. Main sports are rugby, hockey, cricket and athletics for boys, and hockey, netball, athletics and cricket (increasingly popular) for girls. Swimming throughout the year. The spectrum of fixtures is impressive and every child represents OBH around six times each term. And there is so much more ... cross-country, golf, clay pigeon shooting. There is a cycle track in the woods. Musical opportunities are, if anything, still more striking. Four choirs, a jazz band, two samba bands and a string orchestra sing and play each week whilst dramatically recent productions include The Lion, The Witch and The Wardrobe and Mr Humbug sees The Light.

Learning support is co-ordinated by one of the two deputy heads – who switches more hats than a milliner as she is also director of studies and in charge of scholars – and takes place in the Learning Centre, situated in the heart of the school. LS caters for approximately 50 pupils out of a roll of around 200, including scholars who each follow an individually designed educational plan. Apart from the head of learning support, there are two full-time departmental staff who provide assistance in lessons, small groups and individually. A trio of external specialists are brought in if extra individual tuition is required.

There are exams three times a year and progress-tracking is clearly of a high quality. Class sizes are pegged at a maximum of 18; many are smaller.

There is a real enthusiasm for boarding, created not just by the head's ambition, but through the fact that, along with a squadron of matrons, six members of staff live on site. The girls' house is characterised by a pinky fluffiness, hairdryers and posters which advise the reader to Keep Calm and Love your Pony. Dormitories, such as Pankhurst and Sharman, are arranged by year group. The boys' accommodation is similarly configured, although curiously the names of some of the original residents have been retained. Thus, boys could be assigned to Elizabeth, Isobel or Maud. New junior boarding house and more plans afoot. This will no doubt give a boost to the standard of some of the furniture and fittings which, although perfectly adequate, do not quite have the wow factor. Amongst the boarders are around a dozen children from overseas.

Staff are full of praise for the way in which OBH is developing. One recalled driving up on her first day and sensing 'that this is a very special place'. Appreciative of being kept informed via daily staff briefings, they express confidence that the school is sufficiently flexible to attract working parents. The number of staff children in the school gives a further spur to their attachment and involvement.

Children and parents become almost misty-eyed when they assess OBH. The former think that 'it's all so easy to settle here'. Teachers are 'absolutely amazing' and one boy commented, between mouthfuls of lunchtime crumble, that 'I know everyone' – unlike his previous experience in a Singaporean school where he was one of 3,000. On the debit side, the grass on the football pitch is 'too long' and supper, at 5.50pm, is 'way too early'.

Parents are similarly full of praise, for the overall 'slickness of everything' and for the head who is 'extraordinary with the children'. They are kept superbly informed through a library of literature and the clarion call system which sends out electronic updates; 'the teachers cannot be faulted'. The Friends of OBH give a social appeal, organising bonfire nights, cake sales and lunches for new parents.

So, what could be better? The swimming pool could do with a roof. There could be a new sports hall; but our dominant impression is that OBH is very much on the rise. It makes much of its school colours – Oxbridge stripes of the sort that are found in Jack Wills shops. The head wears hooped socks in the same shades (matching Scooby's collar). Less is made of the school's motto Spero – Latin for I Hope. Doctor Johnson had it that 'Hope is perhaps the chief happiness that life affords.' Much of it can be found at OBH – original, brave and, above all, happy.

Orwell Park School

30

Nacton, Ipswich, Suffolk IP10 0ER

01473 659225 | headmaster@orwellpark.co.uk | www.orwellpark.co.uk

Ages: 2–13 (boarders from 7)

Pupils: 300; Boarders: 48 full

Day: £7,902 – £18,234 pa; Boarding: £21,096 – £25,122 pa

Headmaster: Since 2011 Adrian Brown MA (Cantab) PGCE. Early 50s. Previously spent 20 years at Ipswich school where he taught French and German before being appointed deputy head (pastoral). He thinks, 'It has been invaluable, as a prep head, to have taught in senior schools. I know what they are looking for and expecting. Being "in the know" is something parents can depend on for guidance in choosing senior schools and entering for scholarships.' Wants all pupils to 'discover their strengths and develop skills that will stand them in good stead throughout life'. Believes in allowing pupils to experience the sometimes-uncomfortable feeling of 'not getting things right first time': 'We are becoming risk averse as a society and sometimes we learn best by our mistakes.' Strong advocate of collaborative learning and developing resilience and good communication skills, which are 'essential for life no matter what career path they follow'.

Continues to teach his own subject (French), usually in year 6, and remains a dedicated sportsman; he was a Cambridge blue and played professional cricket at county level (Essex). His wife, Nicole, also a trained teacher, concentrates on organising major events such as the Leavers' Ball and dealing with design and decoration throughout the school. Strong approval from parents for the way the head and his wife greet all pupils as they arrive at school in the morning. 'It is so welcoming for the children and makes it so easy, as a parent, to have a quick word'. They have three grown up children who have all flown the nest.

Entrance: Main entry points are at 4+ and 7+ but places continue to become available throughout. Year group sizes increase year on year. Nursery and pre-prep places are non-selective (taster mornings in class and a home visit). At 7+ and 11+ tests in maths, English and reasoning plus a report from current school and an interview. Not overly selective but as school only offers learning support for mild difficulties pupils must be able to follow the curriculum.

Exit: At 13+ post CE. Excellent track record for winning scholarships (24 in 2017, including ones for singing, sport and art); usually over half the year 8 cohort win an award, some several, and to a range of senior schools throughout the country, including to the top drawer ones. No well-trodden path to favoured schools – fewer than five pupils go to the same school. In the last three years pupils have departed for over 19 schools including Ampleforth, Benendon, Eton, Gordonstoun, King's Canterbury, Oundle, Uppingham, Oakham, Rugby, Framlingham, Ipswich, Tonbridge, Harrow and Winchester.

Remarks: In a spectacular setting overlooking the River Orwell, it is difficult to picture more idyllic surroundings to grow and learn in; the splendid Blenheim Palace-style wrought iron gates open to reveal grounds of outstanding beauty with sweeping lawns, wisteria draped pergola, a ha-ha and the River Orwell glistening in the distance. A Georgian mansion, with significant additions (including an observatory) made by the Victorian philanthropist who then owned the estate, forms the core of the school. Many Downton Abbey features have been retained including the orangery (now used as an assembly hall), panelled walls, French windows and a roaring log fire in the entrance hall. Pupils revel in their surroundings and 'swimming in the pool and looking up at the trees', 'playing outside on summer evenings', and 'the view from the dormitories' were all mentioned as special; all seem aware of their good fortune. The recently built pre-prep department is a one storey building and stands in its own grounds close by.

Stepping through French windows from the head's study (size of a small ballroom) onto the terrace is an ageless experience, but the school is thoroughly 21st century. 'We want to prepare pupils for the uncertainties ahead and a job market that we do not yet know'. A recently appointed head of digital strategy oversees the introduction of interactive panels in every classroom, the adoption of Firefly (virtual learning environment) and individual iPads. Use of mobile phones, however, is strictly limited to off duty times. Each day begins with a tutor period or assembly and a service is held in St Martin's church, close at hand, every week. Serious emphasis on academic attainment with

Many Downton Abbey features have been retained including the orangery (now used as an assembly hall) and a roaring log fire

pupils' individual strengths encouraged and targeted support where needed. In the middle school (years 3-5), pupils mainly class taught with specialists for music, DT, art and languages. Seniors (years 6-8) taught by subject staff and in sets according to potential. Classics continue to have status with Latin taught from year 6 and Greek, for scholars, in year 8. A notice on the classroom door says 'Mistakes welcome here!' and pupils confirm this, 'You learn best if you can say if you don't understand'. How true. French continues as main MFL.

Learning support is for all with a drop-in centre open all day and into the evening with plenty of help available, including typing courses, interactive revision sessions and assistance with speech and language development from trained therapists. 'They spotted that my son needed some help without me having to ask and ask,' we were told; and 'there is such an atmosphere of acceptance and support and no stigma attached to receiving extra help'. Those who require more formal support can be withdrawn for one-to-one help and this is charged as an extra. Communication with parents considered vital, as it is with any outside agencies involved such as educational psychologists. Real focus on study skills with pupils encouraged to take responsibility for their learning and personal organisation, particularly in years 7 and 8 as preparation for senior school.

Potential scholars are identified and streamed in year 7 and go on to form the 'scholars' group' in year 8. School well aware of risks in labelling pupils too early as gifted and talented and the enrichment programme laid on to nurture scholars is open to all pupils, parents and the wider community. This programme includes a series of 'Orangery lectures' given on a range of subjects plus scholarship preparation for music, art, sport and drama. Pupils take part in off-site initiatives such as the Uppingham skills day and the Gordonstoun challenge. Debating workshops, musical soirées, plays and careers talks all nourish and support pupils' motivation and widen their horizons. For the same reason a link has been developed with Mayo college in India with exchange visits to take place annually.

Performance culture well established in verse, singing and public speaking, usually as inter-house competitions or with other local independent schools. Grounds perfect for letting off steam at break and play times, the ha-ha providing a natural boundary. Den building in the spinneys and copses together with a genuine assault course in the woods provide plenty of opportunity to run free and exercise as well as more formal games provision of rugby, cricket and hockey. Girls all play cricket these days, there is a nine-hole golf course, squash and tennis courts, outdoor swimming pool and an equestrian and ski racing team are all on offer. Art scholars have specially allotted areas for their work in the studio which they can continue with in spare time. Extracurricular activities include clay pigeon shooting and a stargazing club run from the school's own observatory.

The recent introduction of the OPS challenge, a sort of mini D of E with long hikes, camp-outs, bushcraft and outdoor pursuits holidays to Normandy in year 7 and the Ardèche post-CE provide opportunities for learning leadership skills – as well as enormous fun. Senior pupils are selected for the responsibilities of prefect, dorm captain, head boarder and house captains and the school has a head boy and a head girl, as well as two senior prefects.

Boarding increasingly popular, particularly in top two forms when it is seen as good preparation for senior school, but care is taken not to assume every child is on the path to boarding school. 'My son decided he did not want to board at senior school and we were supported fully in that decision.' Many begin with flexi boarding, later becoming full boarders, even when they live close at hand to the school. 'I like being with friends and we have so much fun'. Dorms, for six to 10, have recently been updated to a high standard.

The Purcell School

31

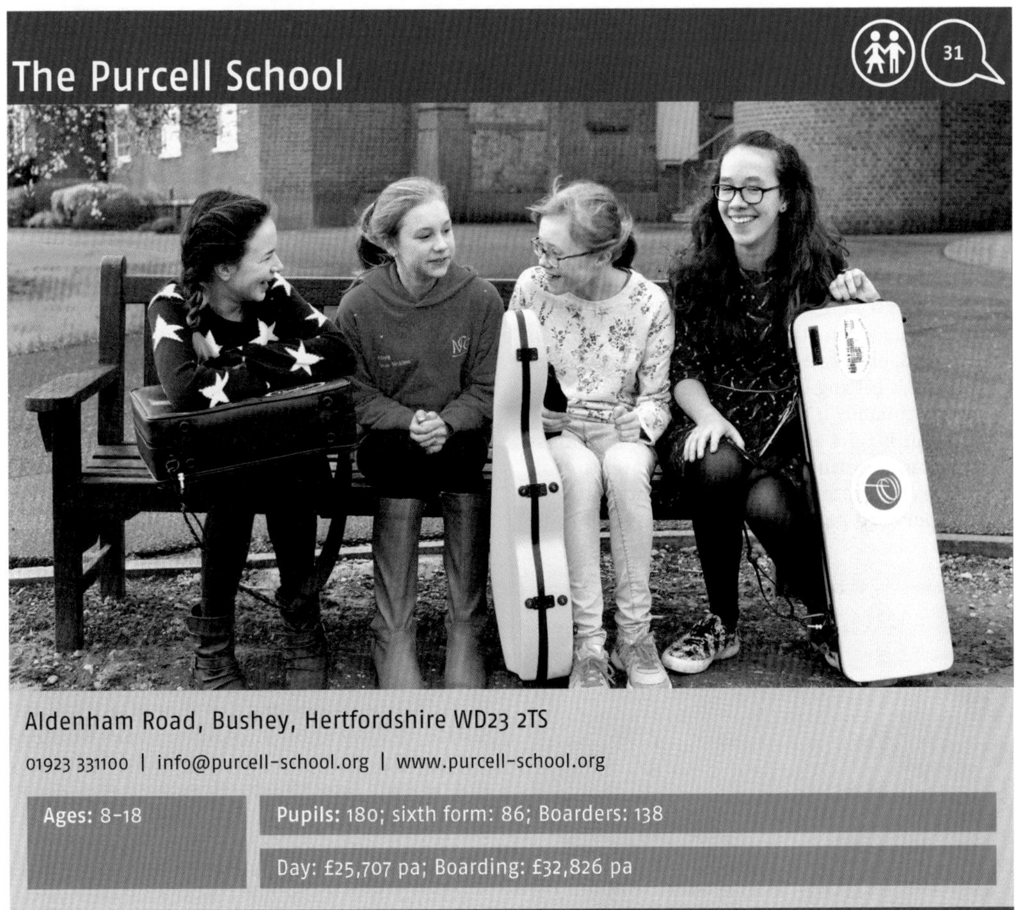

Aldenham Road, Bushey, Hertfordshire WD23 2TS

01923 331100 | info@purcell-school.org | www.purcell-school.org

Ages: 8–18

Pupils: 180; sixth form: 86; Boarders: 138

Day: £25,707 pa; Boarding: £32,826 pa

Interim head: Since January 2018, Dr Bernard Trafford. Read music at Oxford and was director of music at Wolverhampton Grammar before taking over as head there. He was also head of Newcastle Royal Grammar for nine years.

Academic matters: Not an obvious place for the academic scholar who also happens to be a musical prodigy, but then again this is not a place pretending to be a one stop shop all for the all-rounder: far from it. 'Music colleges don't require academic excellence...but we do want parents to trust that the academic side can be delivered.' Public examination results variable from year to year: 30 per cent of A level results graded A*/A in 2017 and 64 per cent A*/B. Subject range limited, and unsurprisingly by far the greatest number of takers are in the artier subjects (English literature, art and music tech consistently most popular), although the diminutive number opting for sciences tend to do quite well. School encourages pupils to take three A levels 'unless performance requirements get in the way'. What is surprising, though, is the spread of results for music A level which, as well as some starrier performances, has its fair share of Bs, Cs and even a smattering of Ds.

GCSEs respectable, with 46 per cent graded A*-A/9-7 in 2017, consistent with previous years. Pupils generally take no more than seven or eight subjects (compulsory music, maths, English language and science) – 'our pupils undertake a huge amount of practice; there simply isn't time'. There are so few pupils in years 5 and 6 that they are taught as a single group, and classes throughout are comparatively very small, but increase gradually towards the upper end of the school. Teaching staff vibrant and engaging in the main (occasional parental rumblings that some have been there too long) – with some new appointments really upping the ante. 'The academic side isn't stellar,' say parents (and it's true to say that it doesn't come close to measuring up to other nearby independents in that regard, either in terms of facilities or teaching), 'but it's getting better all the time'.

But ultimately it's all about the music. Pupils' days begin bright and early with pre-breakfast practice, and continue with instrumental tuition and rehearsals interspersed throughout the day, with supervised practice for the younger pupils.

'Everyone here is like us.' And if ever a real life school could mirror the Hogwarts wizards versus muggles effect, The Purcell is it

Blessed with music rooms containing two grand pianos apiece and genuinely inspirational music teachers, most of whom also have professorships or senior teaching posts at top music academies and colleges. Having observed one such maestro in action, we are hard pushed to think of a single more dynamic teacher of any subject we have seen (and the pupil was nothing short of breathtaking). Pupils have up to two hours of academic music lessons a day, around two hours weekly of individual instrumental tuition plus between three and (in the final years) up to five hours of timetabled practice per day. Theory not taught as a matter of course beyond grade 6 – a cause of consternation for some parents. School adamant, though, that it is on offer 'on demand' up to grade 8 for those who wish to continue (with exceptionally high results for those who do), and the recent accolade of the Incorporated Society of Musicians' Gold Award for the highest achievement at GCSE music (taken a year early at The Purcell) should give comfort that school has the academic side of music covered.

With one-to-one relationships so fundamental to teaching music, what happens if a pupil and teacher just don't click? 'School is amenable to change,' the parent of one such child told us, 'but parents need to be prepared to intervene.' Abundant performance opportunities from lunchtime recitals under the discerning eyes of peers and teachers to the full symphony orchestra at Cadogan Hall, and chamber ensembles series at London recital venues (Wigmore Hall, St Martin-in-the-fields).

Dedicated SENCo works with the 50+ pupils on the register, the majority requiring help with some degree of dyslexia, dyspraxia or dyscalculia but also some ASD (two statemented at time of writing) and ADHD. Assistance also provided to pupils with general organisational and planning skills, particularly around exam time. One-to-one support provided in lessons when required.

Games, options, the arts: Never have we been so reassured by the sight of a boot rack laden with well-worn football boots. Despite the all-pervading musical focus hanging in the air, and only one timetabled PE lesson per week, pupils still enjoy a range of sports including badminton, volleyball and football, mainly of the rather jolly, participative, uncompetitive sort, with the exception of one annual fixture against the Yehudi Menuhin School (the Purcell usually wins). Recent appointment of an enthusiastic young sports teacher has been met with rapturous appreciation. 'He asks the pupils what they want to do, then organises it for them'. Perfect. Sports facilities rather sparse – we were not voluntarily shown the ancient, draughty sports hall (cobwebs present), but see it we did and frankly it does the job, as does the very generous field at the school's rear. Yoga a regular and organised activity to benefit the young musicians' core strength and posture and help avoid injury, and those who wish to are able to use the gym and pool at nearby Bushey Leisure Centre.

Other options vary wildly as there's such a constant intake of new pupils with differing interests, but those with a specific passion are encouraged to start their own club, be it debating, chess or ping-pong. Choir is compulsory, art pursued to a high standard in the delightful stable block atelier adorned with cellos and bicycles hanging from the ceiling and some inspirational two and three-dimensional work – much of it music themed – on display. A dedicated art technician supports the teaching staff and keen photographers and potters can use the dark room and kiln. Drama 'very good' (and now on curriculum) according to parents, with pupils entering into the spirit with great enthusiasm and delivering some 'highly entertaining' performances.

Pupils' days begin bright and early with pre-breakfast practice, and continue with instrumental tuition and rehearsals interspersed throughout the day

Boarding: Majority of pupils involved in boarding life to some degree and they enjoy all the creature comforts of smart, cosy boarding houses. Littlies in years 6 to 8 are in homely co-ed Avison House, just a hop, skip and jump from the main school building. Run with a true family atmosphere, with its own garden, well kitted out common room (anyone for table tennis?) and spacious twin bedrooms ('we do have one single, but nobody ever wants it,' the housemistress told us). Accommodation has been designed to be totally flexible, thanks to a clever system of locking doors on the bedroom corridors to allow for fluctuations in the male:female ratio. Full programme of activities runs for these youngsters, including team building at the start of each year.

Sunley House, upstairs in the main school building, is where you'll find some of the girls from years 9 to13 (as well as Rupert, the house labrador), and offers modern rooms, lovely views – and pianos in the bedrooms of sixth form pianists. Peachy. The large, well-equipped common room doubles as venue for film nights, food nights and craft activities (dreamcatchers and crochet recent hits). Gardner & Graham offer the same high quality accommodation for years 9-13, arranged in single sex corridors. Parents praise house staff as 'wonderfully supportive' and 'so kind', with the only real grumbles relating to the food which, we must agree, was not up to scratch for a boarding school. Tuck box definitely required.

Weekly boarders head home Friday afternoon and the programme for those staying for the weekend is a mix of performance classes, practice and rehearsals with homely activities (baking, takeaways) in the house when time allows. So integral is boarding culture to the school that parents tell us their day pupils can 'feel a little bit out of it' at times.

Background and atmosphere: Not as old as one might expect, despite being the UK's first and oldest specialist music school. Founded in 1962 by Rosemary Rapaport and Irene Forster as The Central Tutorial School for Young Musicians and residing first at concert venue Conway Hall then Morley College in London before relocating to Hampstead. Renamed in 1973 and relocated to its current site – formerly the Royal Caledonian School – in 1998. The drab environs of Bushey and austere Edwardian façade of the school do no justice to the lightness (actual and metaphorical) and vibrancy that lie within. The pristine main school corridors are bathed in natural light and schools with three times the number of pupils would envy the space. First stop on our tour – via a welcoming modern reception area showcasing some 3D artwork – was the coffee shop, frequented by both staff and pupils, and decked out with brightly coloured sofas, tables and chairs. Spacious classrooms, kitted out with all the latest IT equipment, look out over a vast field that could almost fool you it was countryside. The icing on the cake, however, is the fabulous modern music centre at the school's rear with its multitudinous practice rooms, teaching spaces, studio theatre and concert hall. Even for a music school, though, we found the library somewhat lacking in...well, books. Pupils can take out any music score you could think of, but those looking for the latest David Walliams will need to consult Amazon.

So why choose a school like this over a mainstream school with a cracking music department? It's simple, according to the pupils, who are not just mainstream kids with a cracking aptitude for music: 'everyone here is like us.' And if ever a real life school could mirror the Hogwarts wizards versus muggles effect, The Purcell is it. Pupils have often felt 'different' in their former schools and joining The Purcell has enabled them to live, breathe (and probably dream) music in a school where everyone's agenda is the same. Even their senses of humour have a musical slant. Unexpectedly for a hotbed of such great talent, the temperature is pretty low and overall vibe laid back and friendly – pupils told us: 'everyone in the school is a friend... even the teachers'. Lack of uniform underscores relaxed, creative vibe and parents say 'it feels more like a college than a school.' Performance is all part of a day's work – our tour included a lunch time recital by a trio of year 13s, and nothing could quite have prepared us for the standard of music – we were buzzing for hours afterwards.

Pastoral care, well-being and discipline: Crucially, staff:pupil ratio is such that in the event of an issue they have ample time to spend resolving it. Pupils say that bullying is out of the question: 'Everyone respects each other and we're such a small community that a bully would be socially ostracised'. Homesickness in the boarding houses is dealt with 'with incredible patience and kindness', say parents. Despite vast talent pool, school assures us that 'pupils are no more neurotic than other kids', but that the necessary systems are firmly in place to support the pressures, which are different to those experienced by most young people: 'We ask them to work at adult level and need to be aware of the demands that are placed on them'. Pupils say school is very helpful with time management challenges and that they have 'lots of free time' to unwind from performance pressures. School 'extremely firm' around transgressions, according to parents, and alcohol or drug use results in expulsion.

Pupils and parents: Families from all walks of life and social backgrounds, some from the music world, many (around 40 per cent) from other creative industries and occasional bewildered parents who have no idea where their prodigy's talent came from. Tiger parents not an endangered species. A little less than 20 per cent of boarders come from overseas, with largest numbers from Korea and Singapore. Pupils bright and breezy, funny and articulate – totally at ease in this environment with their talent, commitment and work ethic. Former pupils include Oliver Knussen (composer and conductor), Nicholas Daniel (oboist and first winner of the BBC Young Musician competition), Catrin Finch (former harpist to the Prince of Wales), Lara Melda (winner of 2010 BBC Young Musician), Janice Graham (leader, ENO Orchestra), and Yiruma (Korean pianist and composer).

Entrance: Audition season runs weekly between September and March. Prospective pupils come

Families from all walks of life and social backgrounds, some from the music world, many (around 40 per cent) from other creative industries and occasional bewildered parents who have no idea where their prodigy's talent came from

for a preliminary, one-to-one audition and are invited back for a thorough going over by a panel if they are taken to the next stage. Key criteria is not what grade candidate has achieved but how committed they are to a career in music. About half those who audition are offered a place – staff talk about the 'wild glint in the eyes' of the selection panel when they see an outstanding talent. No academic threshold but school 'must be able to cater for them' and numbers for entry into any year group are a constantly moveable feast. The tiny numbers at the lower end of the school (10 pupils in year 6 at time of writing) quadruple by year 12, and there's a large intake post-GCSE.

Exit: Almost all to the great and good of music colleges, top universities to read music, and conservatoires. Strongest numbers to Royal Academy of Music, Royal College of Music and Guildhall School of Music and Drama, often with scholarships (nearly 60 per cent in 2017). King's College and Royal Holloway College, London frequent choices; usually one or two Oxbridge (none in 2017). The occasional pupil goes completely off piste and chooses to read anything from history to aeronautical engineering – no trends here, but we're talking one or two per year. Occasional premature departures back to mainstream education – often because families with more academic children struggle with the balance being so enormously in favour of music.

Money matters: With boarding fees now comfortably topping £30K it's up there with the top public schools, but very few pay full fees. The majority of places (currently over 140) are funded by the brilliant government music and dance assisted places scheme, school bursary or scholarship.

Remarks: In the words of one parent: 'proof that specialist music schools can work'. Not to be entered into lightly – particularly at the younger end of the age range – but here is a greenhouse of a school, providing exactly the right environment for its brilliant young students to flourish amongst like-minded individuals.

Queenswood

32

Shepherd's Way, Brookmans Park, Hatfield, Hertfordshire AL9 6NS

01707 602500 | admissions@queenswood.org | www.queenswood.org

Ages: 11–18

Pupils: 415; sixth form: 113; Boarders: 153 full, 68 flexi

Day: £20,925 – £24,825 pa; Boarding: £30,450 – £33,750 pa

Principal: Since September 2016, Joanna Cameron, previously deputy head of Ipswich High. Degree in environmental science from Surrey; she has taught science at St Mary's Wantage and was a member of the senior leadership team at St Gabriel's in Newbury. A keen sportswoman, with a passion for running, hockey and equestrianism, she is married to David and they have two sons.

Academic matters: A level/Pre-U results strong. In 2017, 77 per cent of grades were A*-B in the 23 subjects offered and 52 per cent A*/A. One third of students gained at least three A*/A grades. Broad intake, coupled with commendable performance, places school at pinnacle of Hertfordshire's value-added tables. Languages are hot here, with most girls taking two at GCSE and one to A level. Japanese really gaining momentum from year 8 up, thanks to enthusiastic teaching and a cultural visit to Japan (alternative for those staying at home is a week of Japanese visitors and activities). Latin from year 7 and the recommendation is that pupils either continue with it or switch to classical civilisation from year 8. Italian and Spanish also on the menu and girls encouraged to continue studies in their own native languages.

No one is refused a go at a GCSE – 'they're keen to push the academic students as much as possible, but are also prepared to coach and encourage those who are less academic and need a different approach,' noted a parent. In 2017, 67 per cent A*-A/9-7 grades. Teaching is mainly traditional with ICT increasingly used by all – every girl has a laptop. Sets for maths, French, English and science; class sizes not larger than 24, many smaller (DT scheduled against ICT in year 7 and textiles in year 8 to allow for smaller groups, for example). Pre-U English and history of art going great guns and EPQ alongside A levels (no IB here and no plans). RE growing in popularity with a dozen taking A level and one or two per year to study theology or philosophy at uni (often Cambridge). Government and politics a popular newcomer. Academic scholars have a staff mentor.

About 15 per cent have EAL needs. Support available for those with moderate dyslexia or other, mild SEN. Some 90 on register, many monitored and some receive one-to-one (max two lessons a week) from helpful and enthusiastic learning support co-ordinator. Most have SpLD type difficulties but a few with mild ADD, ADHD or ASD. School earnestly insists that parents matter. 'They're the ones who know the girls, what makes them tick, what causes them to crumble, so we're always keen to discuss issues, strategies and ways forward.'

Games, options, the arts: A school for budding international sports stars – 'We love watching sports and it's a joy to be part of a school that wins'. Lots of successes at regional and national finals. National hockey players include members of the England junior squad and one recent leaver is now a promising player on the international tennis circuit, another a world-class rower. School is a national LTA clay court centre and hosts the annual national schools' championships. School's tennis team were silver medallists at recent World Schools Tennis Championships and the Lawn Tennis Association recommends it for would-be tennis stars. With 27 courts in all – 12 clay, 13 all-weather and two indoors – 'you can play tennis at any level,' and at almost any time. One pupil is a national and international wheelchair tennis star. Budding stars in all disciplines are carefully mentored – help given with diet, fitness (fitness coach onsite who devises individual programmes), training, fixtures etc. Masses of inter-school competitions ensure sport for all. Facilities include large, modern indoor swimming pool, Astroturf hockey pitch, fully equipped fitness suite, aerobics room, professional dance studio and huge sports hall, with new sporting facilities under construction.

'You can play tennis at any level,' and at almost any time. One pupil is an international wheelchair tennis star. Budding stars in all disciplines are carefully mentored

More than half learn a musical instrument and many at least two. Ensembles for everything and very enthusiastic teaching – a lively percussion session was in full swing when we visited. School rock band. One pupil a BBC Young Chorister of the Year finalist recently. Meanwhile drama thrives, with half taking LAMDA lessons and awards for actors and public speakers. Lower and upper school productions every year, plus one for GCSE and A level students and scholar plays in between. Rehearsals for Sweeney Todd in the rehearsal space when we visited – great gusto on display. Dramatists visit Edinburgh Fringe. Celebrated its 120th anniversary in style with a music, drama and dance extravaganza at the Barbican Hall in London.

Thriving 3D art department with its own kiln. Around 10 a year continue to A level (upper sixth students have individual atelier workspaces) and a few move on to art school, while architecture is also popular. Artists are inspired on trips to Milan and Florence.

One of only 20 schools to run the elite Leiths cookery course in preference to food tech – taught right from the beginning (even including lessons on choosing the right wine to accompany). When we visited girls were whipping up macaroni cheese or rack of lamb with a herb crust, depending on ability. Timetabled lessons for years 7 and 8 and a club thereafter. Each student issued with her own set of Sabatier knives, uniform and Leiths 'bible' to keep. Leiths teacher was formerly a chef in the school's own kitchens.

Dance unsurprisingly popular and the school has its own dance team (puts on an annual spectacular and contributes to other school shows too). Model United Nations, Young Enterprise, debating society, plus charity works. Thriving D of E – 25 working on gold, 45 recently achieved bronze. School awarded silver level eco-school status.

Trips galore, especially with London on the doorstep (museums, galleries, Wimbledon etc). Year 9 girls have the opportunity to study for a term overseas, usually Australia or New Zealand. Language visits to Spain and Japan. Sports teams tour all over the world – all 'help the girls to develop independence, work as a team and cope when things don't go right'. Acknowledgement of the global community though exchange schools in Australia, New Zealand, South Africa, Canada, Japan. Girls work on education projects with schools in Malawi and Zambia. Closer to home, community work in local primary schools and with the elderly – developing 'generosity of spirit and the importance of giving, to counteract the materialism communicated by the media'.

Boarding: Cosy houses with contemporary interior design (and about to be refurbished) to please even the pickiest of teenage girls integrate day and boarding pupils – one for years 7 and 8, four for years 9, 10 and 11, plus sixth form houses. Day girls have the flexibility to board when they wish if a bed is free and this is encouraged. Some fixed 'in school' and 'home weekends,' otherwise boarders can spend full weekend at home with choice of Sunday evening or Monday morning return. A few traditionalists would prefer a return to full boarding, but most appreciate this is a move to meet 21st century family needs and preserve the boarding ethos.

When we visited girls were whipping up macaroni cheese or rack of lamb with a herb crust, depending on ability

Background and atmosphere: Founded in Clapham Park in 1894 and moved to purpose-built neo-Tudor building in 1925 (masses of later additions). Splendid grounds – glorious gardens open to the public at end of May and 120 acres of sports fields and woodland. Two miles from the M25, a 'commutable hour' from London. First-rate Audrey Butler Centre (aka the ABC) houses lecture theatre, language labs and masses of classrooms. Impressive new theatre and associated facilities a jewel in the crown. Science labs recently refurbed, as is Old Pool Hall, now the library. School is 'quietly fundraising' for a Queenswood Hall as an alternative to chapel.

Sixth formers have their own comfortable pad – the Bellman centre with individual study bases, social space and kitchen.

Girls are smart in grey and purple – 'unfussy and not ridiculously expensive,' approved a parent – with sixth formers in office-style apparel.

Pastoral care, well-being and discipline: There is a Queenswood way of doing things, which begins up high and 'permeates its way through the rest of the school,' commented a perspicacious parent. Certainly the school day reflects the level-headedness that typifies the school's approach to everything. The day starts with boarders' breakfast at 7.30am, then chapel (school is Methodist foundation but services are non-denom) twice a week at 8.15am and lessons from 8.45am until lunch, with a mid-morning break. Year 7s have a study hour incorporated in their day and all girls participate in their chosen activities – crafts, sport and other clubs – after formal lessons finish at 4.20pm. 'Balance is key,' says the school.

School's approach is to encourage girls to adapt and assimilate change – 'We applaud having a go. We tell them that failure is a part of learning and challenging themselves.' A secure support and pastoral network through housemistresses, tutors and friendly faces. The overwhelmed or anxious are free to confide in any member of staff with whom they feel comfortable. All keep an eye out in particular for girls who are stretching themselves thinly to take advantage of all Queenswood has to offer.

Houses are run by teaching housemistresses, with assistants and a team of academic tutors (around 10 tutees each). Pupil-teacher and parent-teacher relationships relaxed but respectful – 'we work in partnership with parents; we want them to take an active interest in the school and their daughter's education.' Now a large prefect team with specialist responsibilities. Girls who put themselves forward for head girl must present on stage to the whole school and everyone votes for the speech they found most compelling. Principal's choice from then on.

Range of visiting speakers use personal experiences to raise awareness of hard-hitting issues such as drugs, sex, HIV and alcoholism. Girls taking drugs 'lose their right to be a member of the school.' Rewards and sanctions system aims to reward girls for contributions to school life and help them overcome any problems they may have with that. Postcards of praise, gold badges and stars reward pupils; demerits and detentions aim to deter miscreants. Parents involved at early stages.

Food is 'delicious,' enthuses a self-confessed foodie year 8. Serving area a top hotel would crow about, even with its own showcase area where food is cooked to order. Option of outdoor eating in new picnic/BBQ area when weather permits.

Perhaps acknowledging the reason some girls opt to leave for sixth form, school now hosts joint projects with Bedford and Radley but school says Q girls never have a problem integrating in a mixed environment when they go to university – 'that's just a myth.'

Pupils and parents: 'The girls are self-confident and very resourceful,' says school, though adds that there's no particular type. 'They're real individuals, not moulded.' Nearly 50 per cent boarders. Twenty per cent from abroad – fair proportion from Hong Kong and mainland China, with some expats. All continents represented. EAL taken seriously. Scholars are well recognised around the school – 'there's no envy,' said our eloquent sixth former

guide. 'Everyone is inspired by them and shares in their success.'

Very much a 'sleeves rolled up' school for community-minded doers who are happy to get stuck in. Refreshing to find pre-teen girls as excited by camping out and playing hide and seek as they are by beauty and make-up sessions. Sixth formers articulate, poised, feisty but sensible.

Lots of first-time buyers, with both partners working. Masses from London. Drawn by Q's 'warmth and positive energy,' explained one. Strong parents' association much involved with social activities throughout the year and generous contributions to school development projects.

Old Queenswoodians' Association is arguably one of the largest, with more than 4,000 members and branches around the world, ready to befriend and advance Queenswood girls in all sorts of careers and all sorts of places. OQs include Sky Sports presenter Georgie Thompson, actress Helen McCrory, Professor Dame Alison Richard (former vice-chancellor of Cambridge University), journalist Carol Thatcher, tennis player Naomi Cavaday and GB athlete Jodie Williams.

Entrance: Early registration advised, but entry into most years if vacancies permit, either by CE or own entrance exam. Visits welcome by appointment, pupils act as tour guides. Broad ability intake but should be capable of gaining good grades at GCSE. Strong sixth form intake – candidates must get six GCSEs at B/6 or above, with A/7s in the subjects they want to study at A level. Pupils join from a number of schools, including Stormont, St Mary's (NW3), Lyonsdown, Beechwood Park, St Hilda's (Harpenden), Heath Mount, Maltman's Green, Duncombe, Edge Grove and Palmers Green High.

Exit: Up to 25 per cent leave at 16, usually lured by co-ed. Some come back. At 18 majority to wide range of universities eg London unis, Birmingham, Bristol, Loughborough, Warwick, York. One to Oxford in 2017 (history and Italian). Many gap years – school offers support with planning.

Money matters: Majority of scholarships are honorary, bringing glory and support rather than cash, though bursaries available in cases of need. Very much looking at what they can offer that will foster girls' talents rather than offering financial sweetener. Music (including organ scholarship), drama, art, tennis and sport scholarships. Occasional bursaries – means-tested. Discount for Forces families. From 2018, year 7 and 8 boarding fees reduced to widen accessibility.

Remarks: A modern girls' school to which others should aspire. A winning combination of traditional values with a broad, forward-looking education to equip bright young women with the integrity and self-belief to make a difference in the world of the future.

The Royal Hospital School
33
Holbrook, Ipswich, Suffolk IP9 2RX
01473 326200 | admissions@royalhospitalschool.org | www.royalhospitalschool.org
Ages: 11-18
Pupils: 750; sixth form: 220; Boarders: 334 full, 59 weekly, 27 flexi
Day: £15,081 – £16,416 pa; Boarding: £20,598 – £31,185 pa

Headmaster: Since January 2016, Simon Lockyer, previously second master at Portsmouth Grammar. Has also been housemaster and head of department at Wellington College. The son of a naval officer, Simon was educated at Blundell's School, Devon, on a military bursary after which he went on to gain a BSc in microbiology at Newcastle, a PGCE at Cambridge and a masters at Buckingham. His first teaching appointment was at Bishop's Stortford High School in Hertfordshire. He is married to Abigail, who grew up in Suffolk, and they have three young children.

Academic matters: Sits comfortably between the highly selective Ipswich schools and the maintained grammar schools over the county border. The introduction of day pupils and their increasing numbers mean that academic achievement is rising across the curriculum. In 2017, 33 per cent of GCSE grades were A*-A/7-9. Pupils have noticed the increased rigour of the timetable, bemoaning that 'he stopped games on two afternoons and we have to do science and languages instead'; not strictly the case, though games have been moved to an after-school slot one afternoon a week to make

way for lessons. A modern language is compulsory up to GCSE. All year 7s now have taster lessons in German, Spanish and Latin before selecting one, in addition to French.

Over 25 subjects offered at A level; maths and the sciences very popular. Sixth form purely academic; in addition to A levels, students follow the sixth form enrichment programme, which provides an opportunity to teach useful skills and gain extra qualifications; popular topics include ancient Greek, law, sports leadership training and a handy-sounding course, the seven habits of highly effective people. In 2017, 28 per cent A*/A grades, 57 per cent A*-B.

School has creditable results considering wide ability range, which includes some 80 overseas pupils for whom English is a second language (also responsible for stunning results in Chinese and Russian). Overseas centre can help them gain a good grasp of English. Over 100 have identified specific educational needs, but the majority of these are mild, and require only class-based support. More serious problems with literacy and numeracy, often a result of Forces families having a disrupted education, are given extra help from the start. Timetabled support can take the place of learning a second language. Mobile learning programme is seeing pupils issued with tablet computers.

Games, options, the arts: A big part of the school's attraction is the exceptional range of sports and activities. Games on three afternoons; all the seasonal team sports, and though not an elite sporting school, the variety is a big plus: rock climbing (largest indoor climbing wall in the area), squash, shooting and kickboxing a glimpse of the 70 plus activities. 'We never have nothing to do,' said one pupil, and it is definitely not for lazybones. Gigantic sports hall (or gymnasium), a separate enormous, indoor pool in another vast building and, if you've any energy left, 96 acres of playing fields. Plus the Graham Napier Cricket Academy for girls and boys.

Mouth-watering new music school opened by John Rutter, who is patron of the school's annual concert programme

But sailing remains key activity, with undreamed of opportunities for learning the craft and progressing in a sport that is often ruled out for many on grounds of cost. All year 7s receive a full week's instruction: 'We want to find ability among those who are not "dynastic" sailors,' says the RYA (Royal Yachting Association) instructor. Over 100 take to sailing seriously, on the water three or four times a week in one of a fleet including 60 dinghies – from beginners' boats to Olympic classes – plus four Cornish shrimpers and four powerboats, all replaced every three years. The beauty of the school is the location, overlooking the river Stour and near the Alton reservoir – no trek in a minibus, and 'nothing but the extremes of cold stop us sailing'. Many gain RYA qualifications, enter sailing competitions and have a recreation for life; Sailing Scholars get individual tuition from RYA advanced instructors. School teams compete successfully and there are sailing trips to the Med and further afield every year.

Mouth-watering new music school opened by John Rutter, who is patron of the school's annual concert programme, performed by home-grown and professional performers. Recitals hall with spectacular acoustics complete with two grand pianos, 10 others in practice rooms, all brand new and all Bechsteins and Faziolis (Rolls Royce in pianos). Composition suites bursting with equipment. Some 50 per cent learn an instrument; a plethora of orchestras, bands, choirs and ensembles to join. Pupils in the marching band that accompanies Divisions, the regular pupil parades, receive free music tuition.

Art, photography, graphics and product design all housed in separate building with large permanent display area with gallery for pupils' work. A separate print room (formerly manual training centre) harks back to earlier times, and there is serious encouragement for all craft and design skills, with many pupils working on projects outside class time.

Every spare moment filled with activities. Four sections of CCF: royal marines, navy, army, air force compulsory in years 9 and 10, but many continue: 'It encourages leadership and responsibility,' we heard from pupils as well as parents. D of E popular at all stages up to gold. Car maintenance, medieval society, Scottish dancing – choices for all tastes.

Boarding: Boarding houses are comfortable, with well-planned central areas for table tennis, pool and computers, huge kitchens for making snacks (all pupils have tuck lockers) and bedrooms, single or shared, are en suite. TV room stuffed with leather sofas said to be the least used space (though

The beauty of the school is the location, overlooking the river Stour and near the Alton reservoir – no trek in a minibus, and 'nothing but the extremes of cold stop us sailing'. Many have a recreation for life

it was the housemaster saying so). The infirmary is a 26 bedded medical centre with a full time nurse; there's a school doctor and dentist (NHS), and a counsellor who can be seen confidentially.

Background and atmosphere: Long, proud association with Royal Navy and seafarers gives a distinctive feel to this large co-educational boarding and day school, and many material benefits. The Royal Hospital School was founded in the early 18th century at Greenwich to educate boys for service in the navy. Moved to its present site in the 1930s, when school received a bequest from the estate at Holbrook together with a generous endowment. The old school building is now the National Maritime Museum. The current buildings and layout, on a grand scale, are inspired by the original work by Christopher Wren at Greenwich. The pillared entrance, a massive hall with columns, marble floors and oil paintings, is awe-inspiring and regarded by pupils with affection and pride. The grounds, with wide promenades and parade ground, have the well-kept air of a military establishment, but pupils revel in the space, the vista of the river Stour and the tangible connection to naval history.

Became co-educational in 1991. The phased withdrawal of naval funding, begun in 2005, came with a parting present of £18 million for building projects and a general sprucing up. Day pupils were introduced to broaden the intake and make up the financial shortfall, but school retains the naval connection. Pupils all use navy speak, such as Stations, Mess, and Civvies, and regular parades or Divisions are a regular part of school life. Saturday morning hymn singing in school chapel is a feature and not seen as an imposition. 'It's fun, who doesn't enjoy singing?' say pupils. 'They sometimes grumble, but generally enjoy the parades,' we were told by a parent. 'It is one of those bonding experiences looked back on with affection'.

Pastoral care, well-being and discipline: Friendly house system counteracts the (possibly) daunting size and scale of the school, and we heard nothing but praise. 'Excellent support in the house, matron was key in helping my child over a bout of homesickness'; 'Matron does a lot more than simply dole out medicine'; 'Staff seem extraordinarily available.' Cries of approval (pupils as well as parents) for disciplined atmosphere and several parents spoke of lives being transformed by all that's on offer. 'Motivation is more likely in school work if they are interested and busy out of the classroom.' Food neither praised or criticised; we saw hearty fare, perhaps not enough in the salad line. Day pupils are increasing in number and fit in to the house system, with many remaining well into the evening to take advantage of everything going on.

Older pupils allowed out at weekends, but taxi fare and trek to Ipswich dowse enthusiasm, especially as school operates The Nelson Arm (supervised bar) discos and other events. By the end, a few chafe at restrictions but most think the way things work is fair, and they all know what the position is on banned substances (expulsion) and relationships (courting allowed but strictly outside lesson time). For many there is never a dull moment – 'I can't imagine having more fun at university' – but quieter types fit in just as well.

Pupils and parents: At present the majority of pupils are boarders, of which 15 per cent are foreign nationals, mostly Chinese and German, with a sprinkling of other Europeans. Day pupils largely drawn from Suffolk/north Essex. About a third have a naval background (grandfathers count) and it is unsnobbish. Day pupil numbers likely to increase as naval boarding subsidy is withdrawn. Parents speak highly of school's social mix: 'He rubs shoulders with pupils from all backgrounds and this experience will be useful all his life'; 'There is no arrogance or sense of entitlement.' Great sense of ease and camaraderie between staff and pupils but courtesy insisted on. Pupils appear confident, open and friendly.

Entrance: The majority enter at 11 via entrance tests in maths, English and verbal reasoning. At 13 plus another 30-40, respectable common entrance performance needed, and there is another influx in the sixth form. A reference from the current school is essential and all prospective pupils have an interview with the head.

Exit: Around 30 per cent leave after GCSEs, mostly to sixth form colleges, the majority after A level for higher education. A wide choice of subjects and institutions chosen; not an Oxbridge factory – though four places in 2017 – but heavyweight universities eg Edinburgh, Durham, Bristol well represented. Significant numbers take a gap year, often for travel and following courses abroad.

Money matters: Complex range of awards and bursaries. School offers a limited number of academic, sporting, drama, music, art and sailing scholarships each year. The value of the award is at the discretion of the headmaster and can be topped up with a bursary. Bursaries of up to 100 per cent of fees, depending on parental means, and siblings get a 15 per cent discount. Forces families claiming the continuity of education allowance (CEA) are also eligible for discounted fees. Greenwich hospital bursaries for the children of seafarers also available, depending on family income.

Remarks: Long association with Royal Navy brings privilege and a sense of service. Would suit the socially outgoing, give-it-a-go types, especially sailors. Excellent full boarding provision.

Royal Masonic School for Girls

Rickmansworth Park, Chorleywood Road, Rickmansworth, Hertfordshire WD3 4HF

01923 773168 | enquiries@royalmasonic.herts.sch.uk | www.royalmasonic.herts.sch.uk

Ages: 11-19 (junior boarding from 7)

Pupils: 640; sixth form: 159; Boarders: 84 full/weekly

Day: £16,875 pa; Boarding: £27,495 – £29,835 pa

Head: Since January 2017, Kevin Carson, previously co-interim head at The Grammar School at Leeds. His teaching career began in a single-sex girls' school, following which he headed up the English and drama departments at Cheltenham College and subsequently Abingdon School, also taking on the role of resident tutor in boarding houses in both schools. He particularly championed equal opportunities for his female tutees within Cheltenham's co-educational environment.

Married to Sarah, they have two young daughters who Sarah is currently caring for at home, having previously worked as an equal opportunities officer for both Oxford University and the police. Outside of school, the family pursues a wide range of sporting and cultural interests.

Academic matters: Turning formerly dismissive heads and winning more and more parental votes with persistently improving results. In 2017, 49 per cent A*/A grades at A level and 53 per cent A*-A/9-7 at GCSE. Small class sizes (maximum 20) across the board and setting from year 7 in maths and French, with fewer than 10 in some lower sets. More setting (English, science) from year 9 but these are totally flexible, with one parent delighted that her child moved from the bottom to top of six sets for maths in the space of a year. Must be the 'outstanding teaching' that the school is so proud of. Teachers 'go the extra mile', say parents and pupils, and are happy to tutor any stragglers in their free time. Enrichment programmes and extra work for the gifted and lots of clinics to make sure nobody slips through the gaps.

Parents say it's a 'good all round school' where their children can have a go at 'absolutely anything'. They like the fact that the brightest children are made to feel so in this mixed ability environment rather than bumping along feeling average in a class packed with boffins, as they might in more selective schools. Geography and history most popular subjects at GCSE with sciences and maths coming to the fore at A level.

Both highly academic parents with children to match and those with less intellectual offspring feel that the school has the 'right balance' regarding achievement. Girls can choose to do between nine and 11 GCSEs depending on ability and those staying on in the sixth form to take two A levels in photography or art are treated with as much care as mathematicians and scientists taking four. To keep everyone happy, academic girls wishing to take arty subjects can take A2 exams in these in year 12, freeing them up to concentrate on their academic subjects thereafter. EPQ results are also impressive, with 25 per cent choosing to enter and all of these achieving grades A*-B. Strong languages on offer, with girls able to choose two plus Latin at GCSE; Mandarin on offer for the most gifted linguists from year 8.

Girls enthuse over chess and Chinese clubs as much as astronomy (in school's own planetarium)

Girls put on a carousel of arty subjects in years 8 and 9, dipping into subjects from ceramics and 3D design to home economics and DT. All taught by specialists in purpose designed (albeit a bit tired) facilities.

Good SEN, with individual lessons on offer to girls needing support. All pupils screened to detect literacy or numeracy difficulties on entry. Specialist EAL teaching for overseas pupils, charged as extra.

Games, options, the arts: Impressive sports facilities. Gymnastics, trampolining, dance et al take place in a jawdropping double sports hall that would give most public sports centres a run for

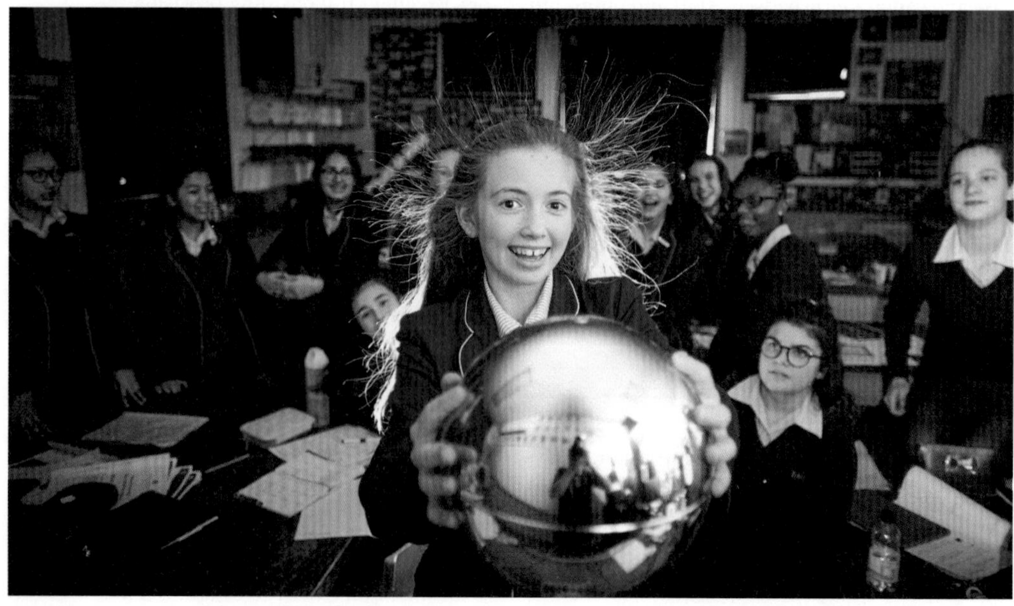

their money. Four squash courts and a multigym, available for the girls' use whenever they wish, also housed in the complex. Swimming pool is poor relation to the rest, functional at best. Acres of playing fields, great for cross-country and adventure training, and new all-weather pitch.

Lots of competitive sport with trophies galore of late – the school recently claimed the independent girls' schools golf championship title and the gymnastics team has just been placed nationally. Occasional grumbles from parents, however, that the school needs to work harder to engage more of the less obviously sporty girls in physical activities that are in tune with their lifestyles, claiming that some older girls get away with doing 'hardly any or no sport at all', although school disagrees: 'They have all sorts of options from year 10 including zumba, pilates and yoga.' Recent injection of young sports teachers has opened up more opportunities, including football and rugby.

School has strong artsy feel, offering a well-used photography studio and dark room, drama studio and 'loads and loads' of musical and theatrical productions throughout the year, according to girls. Music 'improving all the time', say parents, with 300 girls learning an instrument and plenty of opportunities to show their skills in concerts and shows.

Trips and tours of all sorts, for sports teams, choirs, curriculum and just for the fun of it. Vast array of extracurricular activities including very popular D of E and cadets means the school continues to buzz after lessons are over. Girls enthuse over chess and Chinese clubs as much as astronomy (in school's own planetarium) and taekwondo. Plenty of charitable works too, with prefects nominating a charity for the school to support each year. Others such as the Royal Hospital in Chelsea and schools in far flung places (Ghana, Japan) also benefit from visits and performances.

Boarding: Around 85 boarders live in three boarding houses. Boarding most popular in year 10 upwards with a mix of weekly, flexi and full time. Around 40 per cent from overseas – Europe, the Far East and, increasingly, Russia. Traditionally very popular with Forces families but this is in decline due to MOD cuts. Boarders are treated to an outing every Saturday (bowling, cinema, theatre, London attractions). Older girls allowed to London in groups for shopping and lunch and in years 12 and 13 to the cinema in the evenings. A renovation programme of boarding houses is under way. We visited the most newly refurbished which, like the rest of the school, was extremely spacious, clean and well-equipped with a pool table, DVDs and Wii in its large common room. Not as cosy and homely as many boarding houses we've seen but certainly not lacking in mod cons. Light, bright and modern

dining room, where boarders and day girls take all their meals, feels like a hub of chatter at lunch time, with girls seated at sociably round tables, enjoying freshly cooked meals which are, by all accounts, 'outstanding'.

Background and atmosphere: Founded in 1788 to educate the children of masons who had fallen on hard times, the current 150 acre site, built in the 1930s, is the school's fourth home. A vast campus (NB visiting parents – wear flat shoes, if not trainers, for your tour), more akin to a redbrick university than a suburban girls' school, with smart, identikit buildings surrounding two quadrangles ('teeming with girls chatting in the summer term'), and the longest teaching corridor in Britain. Became an independent school, open to all, in 1978 while continuing to fulfil its charitable obligation and still offering full bursaries to some 50 children in need of financial support at any time, although most staff don't know who they are.

Unlock your sons. RMS girls seem much younger and fresher than their more streetwise peers and are just the kind you would love your boys to bring home for dinner

New sixth form centre where all year 12 and 13 girls take the majority of their lessons. Fabulous common room, interior designed by pupils, complete with hot pink walls and matching sofas. All whistles and bells, with girls able to borrow laptops from the library, or bring their own, and log onto the centre's Wifi network. A senior team of 20 drawn from year 13, plus a head girl and eight deputies, elected by girls and teachers. Girls describe guidance at this stage of their education as 'excellent', with teachers giving up free time to help with personal statements and a dedicated Oxbridge co-ordinator on hand for brainboxes. Lovely rotunda library, one of the nicest we've seen: fingerprint withdrawal technology and plenty of space for quiet study.

Parents say the school is 'very into tradition' and this feeling permeates its very fabric. RMS is the only school in the country still to do 'drill': a spectacle of pinafored girls with pinned back hair performing something akin to synchronised swimming but without the water. Places in the squad are highly sought after, with dozens volunteering even for the reserves.

Pastoral care, well-being and discipline: School head is 'anti-clique' and works hard to minimise the inevitable girly issues. Sixth formers are trained as peer mentors by the school counsellor, with year 9 girls taking on 'big sister' roles to new year 7s when they join the school.

Serious disciplinary problems are few but parents say school has never been afraid to 'take a hard line' when necessary and has even been known to call in police to educate girls on the outcomes of certain scenarios if they rear their ugly heads – as in a recent inappropriate staff/pupil relationship. School claims alcohol is 'not an issue' and persistent bullying is dealt with by permanent exclusion. In a recent Ofsted boarding inspection, 92 per cent of girls interviewed said they had never seen or experienced bullying; 'an exceptional figure', says school, compared to most boarding environments. Year 13 girls are well prepared for the real world with a range of seminars offering advice on subjects from budgeting at uni and car maintenance, to getting the most out of gap years.

Chapel once a week, plus Sundays for boarders, taken by the school's full time chaplain. Boarders of other faiths do not have to attend Sunday communion, although many choose to. The whole school crams into this impressive space at Christmas for the traditional carol service.

Pupils and parents: Unlock your sons. RMS girls seem much younger and fresher than their more streetwise grammar peers and are just the kind you would love your boys to bring home for dinner. Confident and articulate without arrogance, they seem a genuinely grounded bunch. Good ethnic mix, reflecting the school's position on the London borders, with the vast majority taking full advantage of all the extras the school has to offer. 'Lots of bat mitzvahs to go to at weekends', said one parent.

Parents from all walks of life from the well-heeled to hard working, dual income, first time buyers. Some expats and international parents, largely of overseas boarders. Many from across the Chilterns and Hertfordshire, with an increasing North London crowd. The school provides an excellent coach service from all these areas, with the London brigade able to take advantage of the shuttle bus from the tube station. Parents of girls at smaller prep schools reported a bit of a culture shock when their daughters joined this vast establishment, but added that they felt totally at home 'after just a few weeks'.

Dining room, where boarders and day girls take their meals, feels like a hub of chatter at lunchtime, with girls seated at sociably round tables

Entrance: Increasingly selective, now parents are seeing RMS as a desirable option in an area of excellent independent and maintained schools. Majority join at 11+ but some places are also available for girls to join up to 14+. Candidates spend a full day during which they take the University of Durham online test to assess skills in English, maths and reasoning. The test is designed to accurately gauge girls' natural ability and – pushy parents be warned – cannot be tutored for. There's also a creative writing exercise, group activity and group interview. School is keen to find space for girls with 'something else to offer' and looks closely at report from current school as well as test results. Candidates for entry in later years sit tests in English, maths and non-verbal reasoning.

Around 170 girls compete for approximately 40 places with successful ones, about half from state primaries, guaranteed a place in all future stages. Good sibling policy too, a relief if younger ones aren't as starry as big sister. Approximately 50 per cent join from Cadogan House (these girls are guaranteed entry, making for a mixed bag academically). Around 25 new places are available in year 12, with girls being selected on GCSE results and extracurricular achievements.

In line with its charitable ethos, school has an ongoing social mission to offer a limited number of assisted boarding places to disadvantaged children from London boroughs of Hillingdon and Tower Hamlets, and Norfolk. Head says that integration of these girls, and that of the mainly international boarders, is 'fantastic'.

Exit: Majority of sixth formers to Russell Group universities, Birmingham, Nottingham, Leeds and Exeter all popular; one to Oxbridge in 2017, plus two medics, a vet and a dentist. Worth bearing in mind that as school's academic reputation continues to improve, Oxbridge places likely to increase as fresh talent filters through. A small exodus – around 20 per cent – at 16, recently to local grammar schools; perhaps girls wanting a somewhat more worldly environment, although head says all were for financial reasons.

Money matters: Capital expenditure is underpinned by an endowment set up by the masons and the school is a tenant of the site. Multitude of scholarships and exhibitions available at 11+ (academic, all-rounder, art, music and sport), and sixth form (adding performing arts to the list) offering a maximum 25 per cent discount on fees. Five per cent discount for siblings and 10 per cent for Forces families. Means-tested bursaries available.

Remarks: A school where girls can be girls and sing, act and run their way to well-roundedness in a safe and nurturing environment. Steadily improving academics over a number of years mean RMS has now secured its position as a serious contender in the competitive local market, and first class facilities help turn out real all-rounders.

A school that aims to draw the best out of everyone, whatever their abilities and turns out confident, rounded young ladies. Parents 'never mind writing the cheque to RMS', according to one. Eggheads and pushy parents might prefer some of the surrounding competition, though.

St Christopher School

35

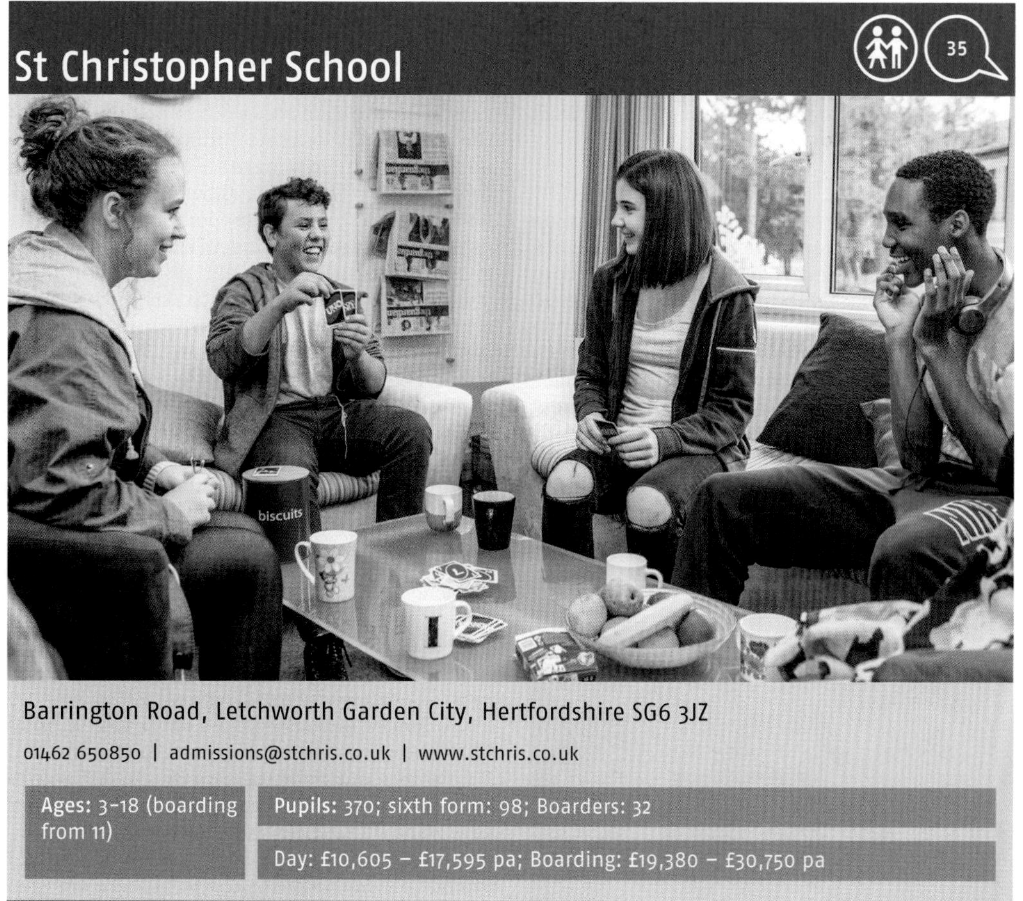

Barrington Road, Letchworth Garden City, Hertfordshire SG6 3JZ

01462 650850 | admissions@stchris.co.uk | www.stchris.co.uk

Ages: 3–18 (boarding from 11)

Pupils: 370; sixth form: 98; Boarders: 32

Day: £10,605 – £17,595 pa; Boarding: £19,380 – £30,750 pa

Head: Since 2007, Richard Palmer (50s), who first went to St Christopher as a gap student and then went on to get a first in education at Nottingham. He taught science, drama and design technology at several schools, eventually becoming head of DT and housemaster at St John's College School, Cambridge before finding his way back to St Christopher. He became head of the junior school in 2004 and has been head of the whole school since 2007.

Previously chair, now on the committee of the Society of Heads, he is also a school inspector with the Independent Schools Inspectorate, giving him an opportunity to see other schools in action. His office is full of mechanical toys and old cameras – a man who loves design and technology still managing to teach it to all in year 7.

Described by parents as well respected, level headed, genuine and a little shy. He does not overwhelm with charisma or charm but is clearly confident in his decision making and that clear decisiveness feeds down to the school. He allows for things to be liberal without being in the least slack. He wants the school to 'remain distinctive' with a breadth of education and for 'pupils to be able to work and live with difference'. He has some freedom to do this since pupils do not do Sats and they follow the national curriculum only loosely. He wants to create more dynamic middle school years and allow topic work and individual work to continue in those years before exams set in. He is keen to find ways to bring drama and philosophy earlier on in the school. So far from a complacent head, but one with vision and goals.

Academic matters: Not narrowly academically selective, yet clearly a school with an expectation that each child be hungry to learn and participate. Independent learning is encouraged throughout the school by teachers who are enthusiastic, energetic and creative.

Nursery has more space than usual with plenty of outside play areas – grassed, soft surfaced and a covered 'outside classroom' with lots of equipment clearly being well used for learning. Historically Montessori, so lots of practical learning, playing and making but now following the EYFS curriculum with clear evidence of more formal phonic learning and number work. Children seen in wellingtons in the garden as well as in wonderful fairy dressing up clothes. Children change into indoor shoes on re-entering school. Reception children well prepared for reading and writing when they are ready and lots of trips to the junior school in preparation for year 1 transfer.

In the junior school, topic based learning and much creative planning seems to allow students to develop and research ideas, which allows for more independent learning than usually seen in a junior school. Topic learning across all subjects very much in evidence – stretching the topic to music and maths not just in humanities. Small classes – 20 is the average – with a teacher and teaching assistant in each airy classroom. Desks grouped – a sign of collaborative learning with lots of space for carpets, beanbags, making and creating. Early introduction to democracy with class rules and ethos very much child instigated. The junior library is extremely well and widely resourced – a joy in this technology based era – with pupils and parents encouraged to take books out at any time even if the enthusiastic dedicated junior school librarian not available. Interesting to see extension maths in this non-selective school, allowing for more challenging work. Learning support staff (two) in the junior school take pupils out of class but pupils also given in class support.

Five one hour lessons each day in the senior school so no rushing between lessons with bags full of books, and as a result much less tension all round. Extra impressive therefore that they manage to give such a breadth of subjects (though no Latin or RS). Spanish and French expected for all students, where appropriate. Language exchange trips considered a rite of passage and something to look forward to in year 10. Geography trips also popular as is the history war graves trip to Northern France. The trips get more exotic as the students move up the school – Rajasthan one of the most original we have seen. Creative English learning involving role play, drama, filming, and journalism work. Setting in maths from year 7 then more subject setting in year 9. Separate sciences from year 9.

Sciences and maths get particularly good GCSE results as do English, arts and crafts and DT. Parents and students appreciate being able to choose whatever combination of 18 GCSE subjects they want with no timetable limitations or restrictions. Subjects include film studies, additional science, PE and Spanish. At A level there are even more subjects to choose from with the arts and sciences getting particularly impressive results. Career evenings and seminars to help students from year 11 onwards with choices for further education. Extension classes for Oxbridge candidates and extended project qualification for those with particular interests. In 2017, 33 per cent A*-A/9-7

Some students we spoke to were delighted to go to a gig in a north London pub and see one of their school bands on stage

grades at GCSE and 35 per cent A*/A at A level, with 58 per cent A*-B grades.

Dedicated learning support staff in both junior and senior parts of the school take students out of classes for extra (paid for) lessons as well as supporting in class. Touch typing taught before school if desirable from year 5 onwards and we saw several students with laptops as well as having amanuensis (teaching assistant writing for them – particularly useful in exams). The school takes some 25 per cent pupils with special needs, though these places fill early with cognitively bright dyslexic pupils and a few with autism spectrum disorders or ADD. Pre-screening for children with special needs, so apply by November in order to make sure the school has enough provision in place for individual needs.

Games, options, the arts: St Chris is often chosen is for its wider curriculum offerings. Art, music and drama not considered soft options but very valued subjects. A very lively music department with practice rooms for individual instrument learning as well as much music creation in music technology suite. Bands and groups abound – some students we spoke to were very delighted to go to a gig in north London pub and see one of their school bands on stage. Plenty of opportunities to perform at weekly Morning Talks. More jazz and rock and small ensembles than classic orchestras, although these too exist. Junior school choir and some singing.

A large theatre building ideal for drama classes and huge annual musical productions. All the school involved in these extravaganzas, and if you don't like to be in the limelight, lots of opportunities backstage, in production and stage management.

This school is well known for its visual art department which is marvellously well resourced – sewing machines, pottery studio, printing room, woodwork, metalwork, fine art in very mixed media. A whole room dedicated to displays of their work – and one rather wonderfully designed piece of woodwork even ended up in a shop window to display shoes.

The forest school site is generous and gloriously muddy and wooded and well used.

Despite the non-competitive ethos, successful sports teams despite that definitely punch above their weight for such a small school. Everyone is involved and the theory is that this brings up the weaker sportspeople – evidently it works. Matches against local teams and county games. Netball, rugby, football, tennis, volleyball etc. Swimming pool used from early years up – for swimming lessons and fun swim club as well as squad training. It is also an opportunity for older students to obtain a lifeguard certificate so they can work at school or outside in the holidays. Heaven to find a pool with a very civilised and warm temperature of 28 degrees. More sports in lunchtime clubs and after school – rambling, cross-country, cycling, jogging, dance, canoeing, trampolining, athletics and fitness training. Their spacious green fields much in use when we visited for an inter-school football competition with five games going on at a time.

An impressive climbing wall up the whole of one side of a classroom block. But there are also trees in the grounds that are specifically 'climbing trees' – any child welcome to climb in break time if they think they can get up and down. Such a joy to see kids climbing trees in these health and safety conscious days. Plenty of fruit trees and others growing in the extensive grounds. The apple trees are picked and juiced in October by the students who get a bottle to take home. Other growing areas including a wormery from which compost is made and sold locally or used here. Nothing wasted from vegetarian school lunches. A garden shed designed and built by students made from recycled plastic bottles and bamboo sticks provides a good greenhouse for seeds and plants before planting out. And the role of food is not only evident in the growing and composting, but of course in the cookery suite. The Vege Centre is a serious part of the school curriculum where students are taught to make meals not just bake scones. The enthusiasm for all these extracurricular activities was brought home, according to one mother whose son came home eager to show off his cooking skills one day and another time wanting to make a board game.

Students wear their own clothes, call teachers by their first names, are all doing projects and exploring ideas, and there are no bells between lessons

Once a week there is an enrichment programme allowing students to choose an activity to explore – film making, jewellery, yoga, tai chi, philosophy, dependent on the interests and skills of current staff, supplemented where necessary by external tutors. These are across the age groups so give an opportunity for different years to get to know each other and perhaps explains the familial atmosphere.

Boarding: Extremely flexible boarding available from year 7 upwards. Where there is space and availability, pupils can choose between 'day boarding' between 7.30am-7.30pm and includes breakfast, supper and supervised homework, flexi boarding just for the odd night, weekly boarding from Sunday evening to Friday afternoon or full boarding. Inevitably more full boarders as the students move up the school, especially for international students. Three boarding areas according to the age of the student, with some 20 year 13 pupils in a separate house on the school grounds, year 11 and 12 students in a very modern and light extension, and younger years in cosy traditional rooms in the heart of the school. Many of the rooms are single ones – privacy being part of the respectful ethos of the school.

Kind houseparents and gap students involved in weekend activities, and each teacher also responsible for one Saturday activity a year. Weekly evening activities available include movie night, cookery, games nights. Weekend activities almost always involve a trip away from school. Cooking facilities for snacks available to students, though older students have a good kitchen and cook for a weekly supper club. Meat meals are available for boarders after the vegetarian only daytime school canteen. Despite separate boarding areas, it felt very family-like, with older students and younger all hanging out together. We liked the rule that phones were taken away and charged overnight and only returned in the morning once beds were made (something to start in all homes perhaps?).

Background and atmosphere: Founded during the First World War, this school aims to treat children as individuals, to be non-judgemental and to encourage independence. The Quaker origins of one of the first heads are reflected in Morning Talk three times a week that always involves a period of silence. This opportunity for silence was also seen when we visited: in the middle of a lively lunch, one student rang a bell, the hall fell silent for a moment, and the pupil thanked the hall and the day continued. The right to ring the bell is clearly a privilege allowing for a moment of calm.

Ideal for a family with several children of mixed interests and abilities – how rare to find a school to suit both the artistic child and the mathematician, the reader and doer

Large grounds and airy classrooms with plenty of space also add to the atmosphere of calm. Set in a quiet road in Letchworth, and based around an arts and crafts building with wood panelled rooms, several newer buildings and extensions: a slightly ramshackle group of buildings, with plenty of opportunity to walk outside between classes. Immaculate grounds and planting and freshly painted and very clean rooms despite the fact that many of the buildings are old. The school exudes clean orderliness, which is surprising in view of the reputation it has for being liberal. Students wear their own clothes, call teachers by their first names, are all doing projects and exploring ideas, and there are no bells between lessons, little noise and a great sense of purpose. Teachers appear passionate and engaged, as do pupils. The friendly and efficient catering staff, ground staff and administrators all spoke of loving their jobs. One doesn't sense hierarchy here at any level. Parents said that they appreciate that the school concentrates on things other than uniform and it was one less thing to pay for and worry about. A parent said the school 'has fantastic facilities, is not selective and is all inclusive. What's not to like?'

Pastoral care, well-being and discipline: You wouldn't choose this school if you wanted a safe route or wanted to impose on your child, said one parent, but it really works if you trust your child to make their own choices and the school to nurture and empower them. Parents described it as 'non-pushy and non-selective but allows the child to pursue what they most want to do'. The pupils do choose – their subjects, the direction they want to take and how they work best. Classrooms were busy with students carrying out their own projects and working at their own pace. This is possible because the teachers work hard and there is so much mutual respect. First name terms with teachers – we saw pupils open doors for teachers and teachers waiting for pupils in the lunch queue. No pushing and shoving. Older pupils making allowances for younger pupils and sitting together at lunch. More like a family rather than exclusive year groups.

Dedicated head of pastoral care who liaises with heads of year, who in turn meet with advisors or tutors. The fact that students meet their advisors every day means that issues are fed back quickly up the school, and students and parents feel that they always have someone to speak to. Parents we talked to all knew exactly who they could speak to or email with questions or complaints or concerns.

Self-government (a way of introducing democracy and ensuring students are totally engaged in the school) is an important feature of St Chris according to students we met. Anyone can attend the school council, at which student representatives can vote. Any proposals that get passed by the school council go up to a meeting of the entire senior school where each student can vote. Resolutions passed by the school are enacted unless vetoed by the head (which almost never happens). Pupils we met loved the fact that even the youngest child in the senior school could make large things happen – like the building of the cookery Vege Centre.

Pupils and parents: Quite a large proportion commute from north London thanks to trains from Finsbury Park and school buses. Also some from Cambridge, and more who are either local or move to be near the school. A growing number of international students, especially higher up the school, who tend to be boarders. This is not a narrowly academically selective school and students and parents really reflect this – some making sacrifices to have their children at St Chris, some second generation St Chris families, some bursary students, some with quite significant special needs, some with multiple strengths and huge academic ability. Ideal for a family with several children of mixed interests and abilities – how rare to find a school to suit both the artistic child and the mathematician, the reader and the doer, and to value them all equally. Parents said they are 'encouraged to be involved' and 'can pop in at any time to ask questions'.

Entrance: The school has wonderfully popular open days (the head thinks the free lunch helps keep everyone cheerful for the day) and many parents visit several times to get a feel of the school. Applications are followed up with an interview – both of parents and, separately, the child – to make sure that expectations match. All applicants over year 4 are given cognitive ability assessment which is age related. They aim to accept 25 per cent with special needs if the school can match child's needs to school resources. Since all applicants are interviewed, the school looks for a match of school's ability to match the child's needs. Mild dyslexia well supported with extra individual lessons, high functioning verbal pupils with autism spectrum disorder seem to do well, and especially good for anxious children. The head says that 'some children need to be here', and they may well be given a place even if they don't meet the requirement that 'all prospective students need to show cognitive ability of at least 100 standardised score'. Oversubscribed senior school, and years 5 and 6 generally full too. Children with individual needs must apply by early November for the following year.

Exit: All early years move onto junior school, and almost all move from junior to senior school. Some movement at 16 (around 30 per cent) as London students get weary of the commute and move to sixth form colleges in the big smoke, and some are just ready for a change or move to technical colleges.

As for further education, interesting split between the large number who go on to do art and those who do engineering, science and maths. The art teacher was very proud to show that every single child who applied to art college got places at every college they applied to (including Parsons in New York, Bournemouth College, London University of the Arts). Some even applied for foundation art courses but were offered the art degree course directly since they were so well prepared by St Chris. A good range of universities – including many from the Russell Group – art schools and two to Oxbridge in 2017. A special extension group prepares sixth formers for entry into the most demanding courses.

Money matters: This school is built on solid foundations with good transparent governance provisions in place. Financially stable and well supported. The facilities show recent and regular investment and maintenance. Despite having to pay for extras like music lessons and individual learning support lessons, parents say that the school does its level best to keep costs to parents down as much as possible. There are some 100 per cent bursaries and small allowances (10 per cent fee remission) for art and academic scholarships for pupils at years 7, 9 and 12.

Remarks: Calm and orderly, busy without feeling hectic. Palpable sense of mutual respect between pupils and teachers, between pupils and other pupils and a sense of confident self-respect in the pupils themselves. Passionate, quietly self-confident and articulate students suggested that this was because everyone felt empowered thanks to their role in the school council and self governance. The ethos of respect included the school buildings – extremely well cared for with interesting wall displays, spotless toilets and no sign of writing on desks or chewing gum under desks. The pupils are given a voice at this school so there is no need for graffiti.

St Edmund's College

RC 36

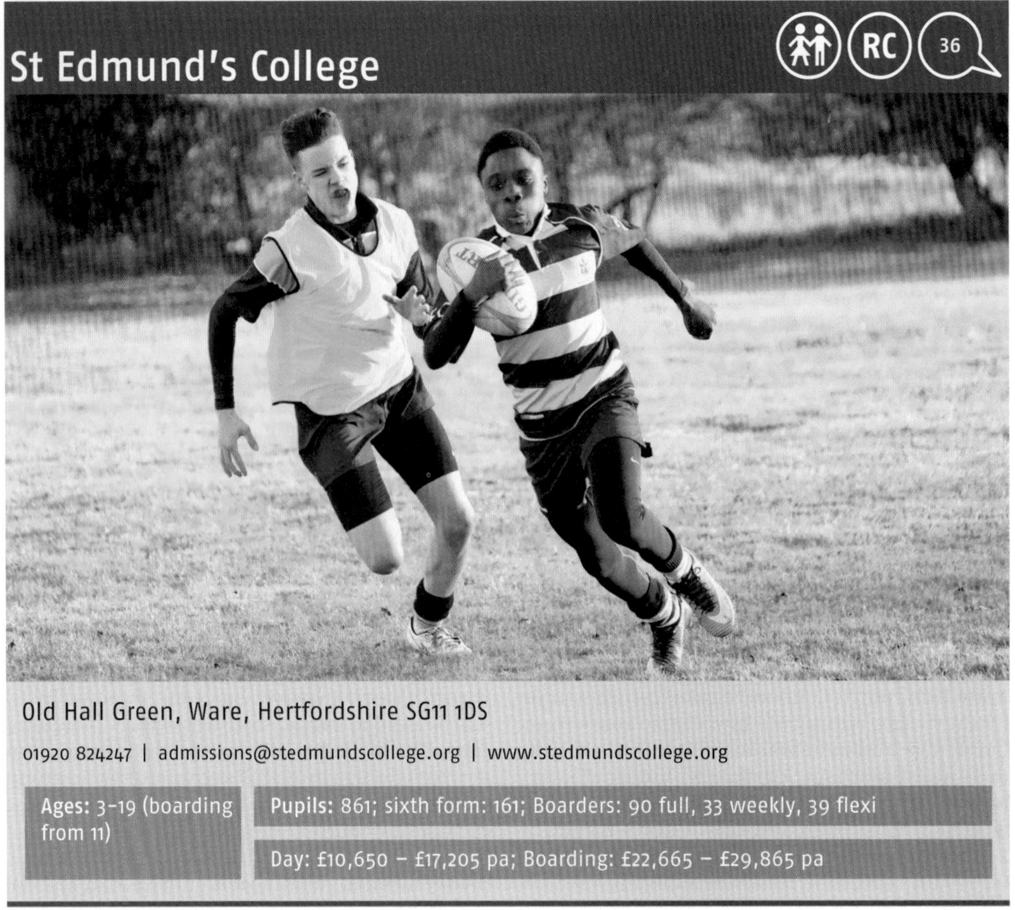

Old Hall Green, Ware, Hertfordshire SG11 1DS

01920 824247 | admissions@stedmundscollege.org | www.stedmundscollege.org

Ages: 3–19 (boarding from 11)

Pupils: 861; sixth form: 161; Boarders: 90 full, 33 weekly, 39 flexi

Day: £10,650 – £17,205 pa; Boarding: £22,665 – £29,865 pa

Headmaster: Since 2012, Paulo Durán BA MA (London). Educated at the London Oratory, King's College London and Heythrop College. Married to Alice, a teacher, with one daughter at St Edmund's. After spells at South Hampstead and Alleyn's, he took up a post as head of modern languages at Mill Hill School where he stayed for six years, before moving to St Edmund's as deputy head in 2009. After three years he was offered the headship, and, he says, would like to stop here. Parents hope so too. 'A very warm, very charismatic man and a very strong leader,' said one mother. 'Please don't leave!'

Prep school head: Since 2013, Mr Steven Cartwright BSc. Joined the school in 2009 as deputy head and became acting head before taking up the post of headmaster. Married with two daughters, one at St Edmund's. Interests include squash, climbing, running, 'my family, my school!' Popular with parents, who describe him as 'lovely'. 'He's such a nice man, very approachable,' said one. 'He's really good with the children,' said another. An enthusiast who wants the best for his students. 'I am passionate about this school. I do sincerely believe that we strive for the best, and we've got a very nice community.'

Academic matters: Broad curriculum in the prep, including French, with a learning support manager to provide help for those who need it; we liked the learning support room, which was welcoming and cheerful. At the other end of the scale, a child who was particularly gifted in French attended lessons over in the senior college, and all the children go there for science. 'The teachers always encourage the children not just to learn, but to understand and ask questions,' said one satisfied parent.

Generally a sound performance with top grades consistently accounting for around a third of results. 2017 figures, for instance were 43 per cent A*-A/9-7 at I/GCSE and 32 per cent A*-A at A level. 'Results are very good, and I want them to improve,' says head, but aims to achieve same 'without changing the children or the school. It's about moving up those league tables the hard way.' There are changes, however. Between 2014 and 2017, the school offered the IB alongside A levels (final average point score in 2017 33) – 'Catholic means universal, so we're already part of an international network.' However, clearly not enough take up for it to continue.

'The trip to Thailand was one of the most amazing things I've ever done,' said one girl, and other pupils were starry-eyed about their experiences in India and America

Broad curriculum comprises all the usual arts, humanities and sciences, with maths being a particular favourite. 'I like maths, purely for the fact that the teachers are so willing to help you,' said one boy, and his friends agreed. French, Spanish, German, Latin and Italian are on offer. All students learn French in year 7 and study an additional language throughout year 8 and 9. As you'd expect in a school of this ethos, religious education has a high profile, and RE is compulsory up to and including GCSE. The pupils aren't bothered by this, because 'the RE teachers are really good!' Bang-up-to-date ICT suites, and well-resourced classrooms and science labs. Food tech a popular option, and the children were proud of their achievements in the school bake-off. Lots of good quality work on the wall displays, and we were pleased with the standard of writing and spelling. The handsome library is surprisingly small for a school this size, but was lively and welcoming and regularly hosts visits from the likes of Kevin Crossley-Holland and Dave Cousins.

Our young tour guides were upbeat about lessons and about the amount of individual attention they got from teachers; the average class size is 21 (14 in sixth form). Parents described the teaching staff as 'really fantastic' and 'always there for the pupils', and praised the unwearying help given, in any subject, to students who needed it. 'If you're in the top set, you're pushed just as hard as you would be in a top academic school,' commented one sixth former. But a broad range of abilities is catered for here. The school currently has 105 children on its Learning Difficulties and Disabilities register, and pupils with SEN requirements are well-supported, both in class and at homework club, which happens four afternoons a week. EAL is also important here, because of the school's international intake. IGCSE second language English is offered to overseas students where appropriate.

The intake is only gently selective, which may account for the odd unexpected hiccup in student knowledge here and there. Talking to us about the school's history, a year 9 pupil told me, 'France wasn't Catholic back then, which is why the school moved here.' But the school's history is quite long and involved, and we were impressed by the pride with which the children talked about it. Everyone we spoke to was adamant that the school fostered a strong work ethic and helped all students to achieve their best.

Games, options, the arts: One happy parent, a musician herself, described the music as 'fantastic', and we certainly liked what we saw. The school's top choir, Schola Cantorum, regularly gigs at the likes of Canterbury and Westminster Cathedrals; chapel choir sings on Sundays during term time, and the chamber choir is much in demand for more secular school functions, such as weddings and dances. New music recording studio and vocal booth. Lots of ensembles including an orchestra and jazz band, ably supported by a 21-strong team of peripatetic music teachers who get the children up to scratch on voice, strings, brass, woodwind, percussion, piano, guitar, harpsichord and organ (there's a magnificent organ in the school chapel). The school is particularly keen to build on choral scholarships 'and to see where that takes us.' There's a musical production every year; Our House by Madness is a recent example, and Half A Sixpence at the nearby Broxbourne Civic Hall. 'They're a lot of work and a big commitment but they're absolutely wonderful!' enthused one student. Drama is also popular, with lots taking LAMDA exams, and student-directed productions such as – amazingly – One Man, Two Guvnors.

The last period of every school day (which finishes at 4.30pm) is given over to extracurricular activities, so all pupils participate in something. An extremely wide range of arts, crafts and other interests are offered, including CCF, D of E and Model United Nations. There are also some pretty special opportunities for travel. 'The trip to Thailand was one of the most amazing things I've ever done,' said one girl, and other pupils were starry-eyed about their experiences in India, America and Barcelona.

Wonderfully spacious campus means lots of playing fields plus tennis courts and Astro. Girls' sport is strong and includes hockey, netball and football. The boys' provision for traditional team games appears to be something of an issue. 'I'd like to see more organised compulsory training for the top teams,' said one boy, diplomatically. Parents (eager in their praise of all other areas of the school) were more forthright, criticising what they claimed was a 'lazy' lack of coaching for school teams who then had to 'go out and get slaughtered every week against better-trained sides.' Students confirmed that rugby/football practices were sometimes scheduled after the school buses had left, so that pupils, who travel in from an unusually wide geographical area, had no choice but to miss the sessions if they wanted to get home. The school counters by saying that the after-school clubs, targeted at mass participation, were scheduled at the request of parents, who had seemed happy to collect their children themselves. A sports academy focuses on the development of elite players in years 7 and 8. The less traditional sports – table tennis, golf, badminton, aerobics – are all flourishing, and there can't be many schools which can offer their students fishing (in the school pond) as an option.

Plenty of extracurricular activities at the prep too, with music and drama flourishing, and lots of

Less traditional sports flourishing and there can't be many schools that offer their students fishing (in the school pond) as an option

sports (football is particularly successful). 'This is a very sporty school!' said one little boy, enthusiastically. Children can use the senior school's sports facilities.

Boarding: Boarders (full, weekly and flexi) are very well looked-after, with lots of staff living on site, and the school counsellor is always on hand. 'Bullying here is mercifully rare, and we set the bar low,' said head, firmly. One boys' and one girls' boarding house (twin or single rooms), with a communal common room where they can socialise together after prep. The usual weekend theatre, cinema and shopping trips for boarders, who include pupils from 20 different countries; activities include themed cultural evenings.

Background and atmosphere: Founded in France in 1568 as a seminary for English Catholics when the Reformation's prohibition of Catholic education forced Cardinal William Allen to decamp to Douai in Flanders. A couple of hundred years later in 1793, the French Revolution had professors and scholars packing their bags once again and moving to the village of Old Hall Green just north of Ware, where a small (and very secret) Catholic school had formerly acted as a 'feeder' for the Douai seminary. On 16 November 1793 – the feast of St Edmund – the school was created. It weathered various changes of fortune during the 19th century, but celebrated its quarter centenary in 1968, admitted girls to the sixth form in 1974 and has been fully co-educational since 1986. The school lists 20 canonised saints and 133 martyrs amongst its alumni, and is proud of its history, which it commemorates throughout the building in drawings, paintings and artefacts. Now occupying the whole of the village of Old Hall Green, the site is spacious (440 acres), wooded, and stunningly beautiful.

If Catholic iconography makes you uneasy, this ain't the place for you. Pictures of popes, archbishops, cardinals and saints are everywhere, along with statues, shrines, relics, holy paintings, and even a graveyard, containing, said an earnest pupil, 'people who died for the school'. It was something to see students lining up, in their own free time at their own volition, to use the Scofield Chantry for a few moments of candle-lit private prayer. The prevailing mood throughout the school, even at its liveliest times, was one of calm benevolence and order. 'We pride ourselves on the way we talk to our students and the way they talk to each other,' said the head, and all the young people we spoke to were in agreement. 'Everybody is nice, everybody respects each other,' 'I love it here, all my friends are nice,' 'The atmosphere is lovely,' were typical comments. Prayers are said before every lesson, 'And some of the prayers are really nice!' cried a pupil, who then recited one for me with great affection, adding 'You don't have to join in, but everyone respects it.' The school's Pugin chapel is lofty and awe-inspiring, and is used for weddings, funerals and baptisms as well as for school services. It's flanked by the smaller shrine chapel, built to hold St Edmund's left fibula that was presented by Cardinal Wiseman in 1863.

The college is overseen not by a specific order but by the Archdiocese of Westminster, and the Roman Catholic ethos is completely central to the life of the school. Even the year groups are named after Catholic principles: Elements, Rudiments, Grammar, Syntax, Poetry, Rhetoric I and Rhetoric II. 'We're proudly and unashamedly Catholic,' as the head put it, but added, 'We're also proud of being inclusive.'

It was something to see students lining up, in their own free time at their own volition, to use the Scofield Chantry for a few moments of candle-lit private prayer

Located on the same beautiful campus as its big brother, the junior school benefits from an enviable degree of space and wooded tranquility. Whereas the main senior school building is grand and imposing, the prep is a smaller, cosier affair, housed in a former family home designed by Pugin and containing many of his hallmark features. The prep children have their own very appealing little chapel, which is in daily use, plus an outdoor amphitheatre.

Pastoral care, well-being and discipline: Everyone we spoke to was especially warm in their praise of this aspect of the school. 'It's really good, very strong,' 'The school is very nurturing,' 'A very, very welcoming place, my child settled in straight away,' were some of the comments, and the last ISI inspection report praised the pupils' spiritual and personal development as outstanding. The house system is the main source of pastoral care with each pupil having a tutor and head of house.

The prep school children we met were relaxed, happy, well-mannered and fond of their school. 'They're really kind here, and I've made a lot of friends,' 'I prefer this school to my old one, there's so much to do,' were typical comments. As one parent added, 'There's a very nice atmosphere within the school. We're really pleased, no complaints at all.'

A number of pupils and parents commented on the lunch queues, which, they alleged, were not always well-managed. Some children spoke of having to miss lunch if they needed to attend clubs, or even if the queue just was too long. 'She loves the meals, but doesn't always get to eat them!' said one mother, 'I can't understand why they haven't nailed that problem.' (School admits that the situation needs addressing, and says it is working on ways to improve things.) On the plus side, the boarding means that all pupils can stay for supper at the school when they need to – when there are concerts or parents' evenings, for instance – and generally students seemed cared for and contented, moving with calm purpose about the school; uniform was worn tidily and behaviour everywhere was good. The spacious, well-kept and eye-pleasing buildings themselves seemed to help create a relaxed and happy community of individuals, quirky and otherwise, with a refreshing range of life-aspirations: one student hopes to set up a museum dedicated to vacuum cleaner parts.

Pupils and parents: Day pupils make up the majority of students, and are bused in from all over Hertfordshire and beyond via a network of 17 different routes. Excellent scholarships and bursaries ensure wide social diversity. Significant community of international students, many of them from eastern Europe, Africa and Asia. About 40 per cent of pupils are from Catholic families. The rest are from other Christian denominations, and from 'all other faiths and from none'. ('We have a fantastic Diwali celebration every year,' the head told me.) Notable alumni include William Scholl the sandal designer, perfumiers James and Robert Floris, and Ralph Richardson.

Entrance: Entrance to nursery from the term following children's third birthday. Further admissions at 4 and at 7 by interview ('crucial,' says head) and informal assessment. Up to 20 children per class; the school prefers to keep them small. Around a third of the children are from Catholic families, the rest from all faiths and from none. Scholarships available at 7+ based on academic merit – applicants sit an exam in January. The school's popularity is rising, and they recently went to two form entry from year 3 in response to demand.

About 20 a year of the senior school entry come from the prep, for whom entry is automatic, provided they joined in year 4 or below. The rest, who come from a wide range of preps and primaries, sit entrance exams in maths, English and non-verbal reasoning. However, the report from the child's previous school is just as important, along with the St Edmund's interview. 'We interview everyone for at least 30 minutes, and for as long as it takes, really,' says head, who puts great emphasis on getting to know what the children are like. The school's popularity continues to rise and they are now oversubscribed, with around 220 applicants for the 80 available places. Small additional intake at 13+. Some join the school at 16+, for which they need five A*-B/9-6 grades at GCSE with at least B/6 in their chosen A level subjects.

Exit: Nearly all prep school pupils move up to the senior school. At 16+, around 40 per cent to state sixth form colleges, or, very occasionally, to other independents (one boy found he'd grown away from the Catholic ethos and wanted a change). The rest stay on for sixth form here. At 18+ mostly to university: Manchester current front runner, with Hertfordshire Uni another favourite, alongside several London universities. One to Cambridge and one medic in 2017.

Money matters: Academic scholarships at 11+ and 13+, awarded on performance in the entrance exam. Music, art, sport and all-rounder scholarships also available, often in combination with academic awards. Total awards can be extremely generous – we heard from one parent whose child's scholarship was worth 90 per cent of the annual fees. A few sixth form scholarships. Limited number of means-tested bursaries, covering up to full fees.

Remarks: A successful, flourishing, dependable school with real spiritual heart. Well worth considering.

St John's College School

C of E | 37

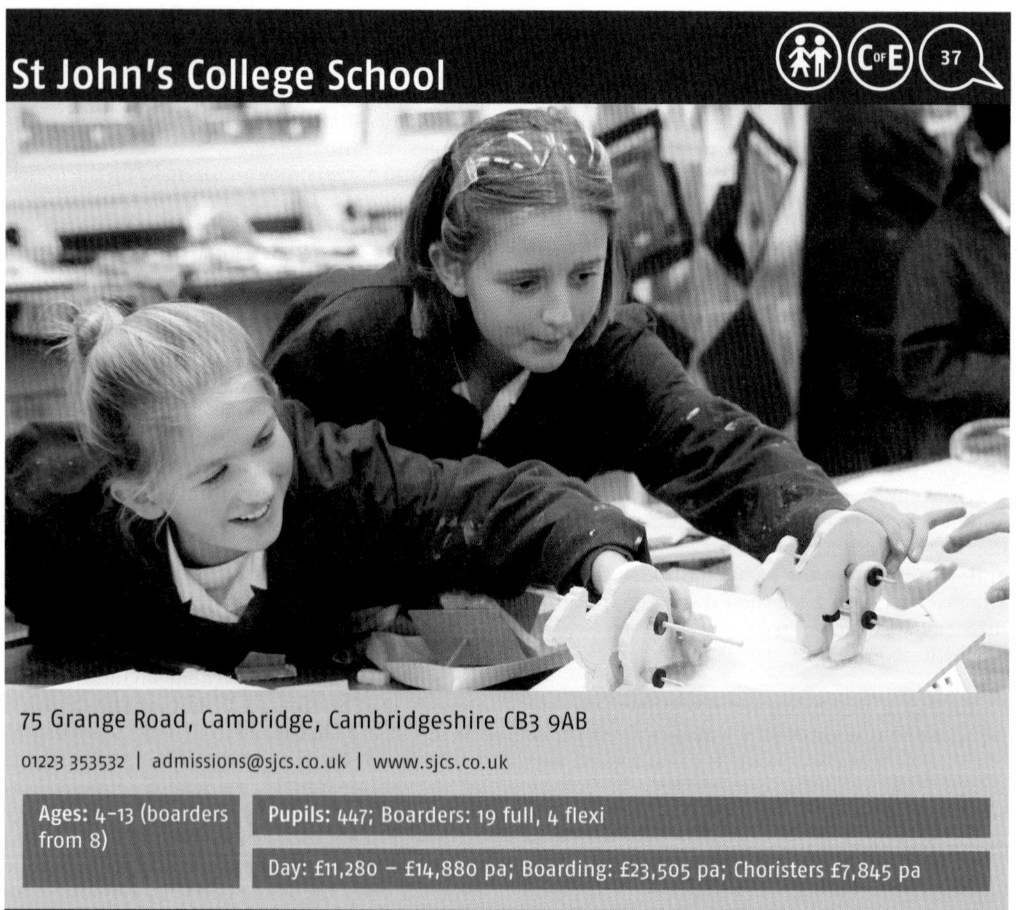

75 Grange Road, Cambridge, Cambridgeshire CB3 9AB

01223 353532 | admissions@sjcs.co.uk | www.sjcs.co.uk

Ages: 4-13 (boarders from 8)

Pupils: 447; Boarders: 19 full, 4 flexi

Day: £11,280 – £14,880 pa; Boarding: £23,505 pa; Choristers £7,845 pa

Headmaster: Since September 2016, Mr Neil Chippington MA (Cantab) FRCO (40s), previously head of St Paul's Cathedral School. Music scholar at Cranleigh, organ scholar at Cambridge, Fellow of the Royal College of Organists; music is certainly in his blood. Came to St Paul's from Winchester

College, where he was a housemaster for eight years, and having himself been a quirister (chorister) at Winchester Cathedral. He is a keen cyclist and runner who regularly takes part in half marathons and triathlons, usually for charity, and recently completed a 280 mile three day cycle to raise money for Leukaemia Research. In addition, he has a strong interest in travelling and has over the years led school trips to a wide range of countries including Jordan, Iran and Turkey. He is married to Leisle, who is also a teacher, and they have two sons.

Entrance: Oversubscribed but not overly so. For entry at 4 the children are 'assessed' – using sequencing and other methods which, even at such a young age, show their potential – as are the parents. 'We want parents to have a feel for the place and we see what they want for their child. If we agree, we can work together.' Don't be complacent; children here are bright. At 7, assessments in English and maths and child is observed during half a day at the school. 'It's all about the child fitting in and coping.' Chorister bursaries for up to five scholars, all boys, at 8, of at least two-thirds of the fees. Means-tested bursaries for those who would particularly benefit. At 11+, potential music scholars welcomed as boarders, with scholarships available. Siblings take priority and then boy:girl ratio to keep the numbers even. Children come from a wide commutable area around Cambridge, or further afield for boarders. The majority of parents are academics, medics from Addenbrooke's or employed on the Silicon Fen,with a Newmarket contingent as well. Many work in the City. All parents very ambitious for their offspring, but nicely so and welcoming to newcomers.

Exit: The odd leaver at 11 but very unusual, usually heading to the state sector. No 'evictions', but occasionally, after much discussion and agreement, the occasional one will be moved on to 'somewhere they will be happier at.' Virtually all leave at 13. Lots of help with future schooling. 'They guide us away from making the wrong choice.' Over half of the year get scholarships/awards, academic as well as music. At least 50 per cent go to local private Cambridge schools, the rest off to board: many to Perse Upper; St Mary's, The Leys, Uppingham, King's Ely, Eton, Oundle, Rugby and Stephen Perse Foundation all popular.

Remarks: The school is owned by St John's College and was originally set up in the 17th century to educate the choristers. Now housed on a leafy road in Cambridge opposite the college's playing fields, which they share, in three adjacent houses, recently redeveloped to include new outdoor woodland area on what was once the staff car park. On entering the main building the first thing you see are the choristers' gowns hanging in the hallway. They are very proud of the choristers, rightly so. They travel the world and are very talented. But once in the school they are just normal pupils. There are no 'stars' in this school so no cabinets full of trophies on display. They have them, but discreetly hidden in the dining room. The life of the chorister is slightly different to other pupils as they start practice at 7.30am, running through to the start of school at 9am, and again after school for a couple of hours. It's a massive commitment but handled well. The school ensures they don't suffer academically or personally.

'We are told very firmly to leave the education of our child to them and not to stress about exams. It works, the children are pushed, achieve highly but don't feel under pressure'

A very tactile school. 'If a child needs a hug it gets one.' Many parents spoke of their children 'being allowed to be children and not to grow up too quickly.' 'They are imaginative and modern about learning,' said one parent. 'We are told very firmly to leave the education of our child to them and not to stress about exams. It works, the children are pushed, achieve highly but don't feel under pressure.' No exams until the penultimate year. Children taught to have enquiring minds and embrace learning. Mindfulness is taught to all, even the little ones, and stands them in good stead for future years. Hugely supported by parents.

'All of the teachers are of a similar mindset and embrace the concept and love the children. They wouldn't be here if that wasn't the case.'

Lots of after-school clubs, but not until year 3. Enrichment programme each Thursday afternoon for 9-13 year olds explores cross-curricular work across arts and sciences, plus My Mind programme, which includes tai chi for year 4. As expected, loads of music, not just for the choristers. The majority of the children learn an instrument, many two or more. Bands, choirs, quartets galore. All the usual sports teams, well supported. Drama very popular. Very impressive artwork framed and displayed throughout the school. A large, airy, newly refurbished art room where the older children can pop in and set to. 'All children can draw by the time they leave St John's,' the very enthusiastic art teacher told us. Timetables are flexible. Extra tuition offered, some at no extra cost, very quickly if needed. Individual needs department proactive. They are on top of the children academically and extra time allocated towards subjects for those aiming for certain scholarships.

A small contingent – including all choristers – boards. 'It means we can manage their time well rather than it being wasted travelling.' Larger numbers boarding higher up the school, many weekly, some flexi. Clean, bright, mixed boarding house. Lots of comfy sofas, snooker and table football. A large kitchen with huge table. 'Our parents can come and see us and have a cup of tea with us after services,' said one chorister. Very much an open door policy for parents. Strict rules within the house. No child can enter another dorm. No mobile phones in the boarding house and, very contentiously for our chatty guides, no tuck. 'They decided the choristers were getting too much sugar so cut tuck to twice a week and have now cut it out completely,' was the outraged comment. 'So when we go home we beg our parents for sweets.' There used to be accompanied visits to town with the older ones going in threes, 'as long as one of us was wearing a watch,' but these have now been stopped. 'They said all we did was buy sweets, but we only had £2 so what can they expect?' from our opinionated guide, 'and how do they expect us to manage money if they won't let us out to spend it?' All said with very good humour and a big smile. We feel our guides have a bright future ahead of them. Homesickness handled well. One pupil allowed to bring her rabbit last term. Lots of contact with parents, though not before bed, in private phone booths. 'Please note the phone number for Childline is listed on our contact lists pinned to the door.' This guide will go far. Dormitories clean and tidy. Bunk beds, six to a room max. Boarders change their own bed linen. Duvet covers brought from home. Houseparents loved by all, children and parents. 'I couldn't ask for more from them and the receptionist is magnificent.'

Uniform stands out with bright red blazers. 'The uniform is too expensive,' said one rather disgruntled parent, 'particularly the blazers.' The girls wear a rather dowdy summer dress, far too dull for the bright, exuberant characters donning them. 'Pastorally excellent,' was said by every parent. 'There are issues, usually girls and their friendships, but the school handles them sensitively and effectively.' The year 8s mentor the incoming year 5s.

Nearly every parent we spoke to felt 'we are very lucky to have our children at St John's.' We can see why. Certain schools have 'that feel', and this one does. It's a joyous place that's buzzing. Lessons are alive, the children are working hard, utterly engaged. And they are happy, exuberant, confident little people, from the youngest up. Children being children, nurtured through some tough, turbulent times, meeting adolescence with equilibrium and well set for future schooling. Long may it continue.

St Mary's School, Cambridge

RC 38

Bateman Street, Cambridge, Cambridgeshire CB2 1LY

01223 353253 | admissions@stmaryscambridge.co.uk | www.stmaryscambridge.co.uk

Ages: 4-18 (boarding from 11)

Pupils: 622; sixth form: 94; Boarders: 84 full/flexi

Day: £9,438 – £15,324 pa; Boarding: £30,513 – £32,421 pa

Headmistress: Since 2007, Charlotte Avery (40s). English degree Oxford, PGCE Cambridge. Taught in various schools, deputy head at Highgate where she oversaw the transition to co-ed. St Mary's is her first headship. One of triplets, all with Oxbridge degrees. A formidable intellect who is determined

to get her point across. Dedicated to girls' education. Brisk and efficient but also kind and caring. Obviously stands no nonsense. Well liked and respected by parents. 'She can talk the hind leg off a donkey, but in the nicest way,' said one parent. 'She's brilliant, a whirlwind with great enthusiasm who carries everyone along with her.' Many parents spoke of her great vision and the 'huge changes she has made.' Others spoke of how she has promoted internally. 'A very nice person, tough and a great leader.' Very high profile and attends all school events. President elect of national Girls' Schools Association in 2017. Interesting to note that she is an Anglican but head of a Catholic school.

Head of junior school: Since 2016 is Matthew O'Reilly. Read German and politics at Newcastle. Travelled the world teaching adults English for large businesses and interpreting. Returned to the UK to do his PGCE and started teaching in senior schools. Disliked this, so turned to juniors instead. St Mary's was his first job and he has worked his way up to head. Very well liked by all parents and settling into the role well. 'He is a young man with a quiet, calm, manner and great enthusiasm. I was delighted he was appointed head.'

Academic matters: In 2017, 62 per cent A*-A/9-7 at GCSE, and 46 per cent A*-A at A level. Impressive results from girls instilled with great self-belief and a strong work ethic. 'The girls work really hard but have great fun too,' said one parent. Lots of support for all, whatever their abilities. Parents kept well informed about academic progress and spoke about 'prompt responses' from teachers. Science and maths very strong with lots of science clubs. Fabulous new science hub, incredibly well equipped. Year 10s were working hard at an experiment and good to see large sixth form groups doing sciences. Spanish, French, German, Latin, Greek and Mandarin all offered at GCSE. Many girls do two languages, though small groups for A level languages.

'She can talk the hind leg off a donkey, but in the nicest way,' said one parent. 'She's brilliant, a whirlwind with great enthusiasm who carries everyone along with her'

Inspirational quotes throughout the school from renowned women. Good to see a noticeboard about exam week and preparing for them. 'Don't panic' was one piece of advice. 'A very proactive school,' was one parent's comment. Another parent said, 'How I wish I'd had teachers like that.' Lots of computer suites and iPads filtering through to all pupils. Certain social media sights blocked – good. Food tech offered at A level. A younger age group was cooking when we were visiting – some delicious smells wafted our way.

The junior school is now a short walk away in Chaucer Road, in a lovely old house with lots of outside space. Girls taught here as per state system. One teacher for all subjects, but with specialist input throughout. Again lots of inspirational quotes, particularly from the founder, on the walls. 'They get a very good start here,' was said more than once. French for all and Mandarin taught to all but a few who have extra tuition when needed. All girls actively encouraged: 'You can do it,' is what a lot of parents said their daughters were being told.

Average class sizes of 20, smaller in the sixth form. Many teachers long serving. Learning support lessons for those that need it, about 100 SEN on the register, all with milder needs. 'My daughter needs extra support and time and the school couldn't have been more supportive helping her plan her work and revision as well as extra lessons.' Some 48 students have EAL classes, all in the senior school. Many more from overseas who no longer need this support.

Games, options, the arts: Quietly sporty and successful; cabinets full of silverware are testament to this. County cross-country runners, hockey players and netballers. Pitches situated a 10 minute minibus journey away. 'Sport for all and there are no sporting prima donnas,' said one parent. All talk about plenty of teams and 'masses of sports clubs.' Touch rugby on offer. Sixth formers have the chance to row. A jointly refurbished city rowing club's boathouse will mean that rowing will be available to all senior girls shortly. Gymnastics popular. Sports rotated throughout the year so always something for everyone.

Drama very popular with lots of productions, clubs and workshops. Parents very enthusiastic about performances. Drama GCSE one of the most successful subjects; most gained A*. LAMDA popular and encouraged for overseas students.

Art is big at St Mary's and it has a very strong reputation for it. Impressive art on display throughout the school. The art school is situated next door

A beautiful building that has recently been refurbished. Comfy-looking common room, kitchen (we spotted the toast and Nutella)

to the main building. Sixth form art scholars' photos displayed in the reception area. Each sixth form student has their own space; we admired the quality of the work, ambitious and eye-catching.

Music highly thought of here. Orchestras, choirs, bands, ensembles galore, in both junior and senior schools. Our visit coincided with mass rehearsals at the junior school. Every room was full of performers practising. Music as a career actively encouraged.

Numerous sports tours and subject trips. D of E for all, up to gold award.

Boarding: The boarding community is international. Some 20 countries represented, with those from south east Asia being the largest cohort. Currently 84 girls board, about half of whom are in the sixth form, and virtually all from overseas. The majority are full boarders, though flexi boarding is offered. All boarders now housed in Mary Ward House a short walk from the school on Brooklands Avenue. Up to five younger girls in a room, with double rooms for years 10-12 and year 13s in single rooms.

Girls are encouraged to personalise their space and taught to do their own laundry. One father couldn't understand why boarders were allowed so much freedom – 'why do they need to go into town to buy sweets?' – but we suspect the boarders disagree with him. They are kept occupied with church on Sundays, optional, and plenty of trips to Alton Towers and the like. Parents keep in close contact and are happy their daughters are 'safe and supervised.'

Disappointing to hear from sixth form day girls that the new boarders don't mix socially with them. Lots of effort made to include them in sixth form socials but not many takers and very few attend the Leavers' Ball. Doesn't appear to be the case lower down the school: parents spoke of daughters going to stay with friends who are day girls.

Background and atmosphere: Now the only girls' school left in Cambridge. Founded by Mary Ward, an innovator of education for girls, St Mary's opened in 1898. Based on a strong Catholic ethos that is reflected throughout the school. All religions, and none, are welcomed and embraced, with the spiritual welfare of the girls being of paramount importance. There is a resident chaplain, a small chapel where services are regularly held, parents welcome to attend as well, and whole school services regularly. A strongly Christian school that believes that 'every girl is of equal value and has something to offer.' This belief permeates throughout junior and senior schools.

Outwardly the school is not particularly attractive. Squeezed into the centre of Cambridge along a large part of Bateman Street, the 70s façade is quite low key. But once inside the school it's another matter. Modern additions have been incorporated well, including new science hub opened by Dame Mary Archer in 2016, and it's interesting to tour the school going from ancient to modern: it adds character and works well.

The original building, once a residential house, is beautiful. Now home to the admin and head's office. The magnificent staircase and large bay windows looking out onto large gardens reflect back to another era. The gardens are well used – the grass could have done with a cut when we were there – with plenty of benches, an outside gym and table tennis table.

Sixth form housed in a separate building that used to be the junior school, across the road. Smaller classrooms for teaching, a dance studio, gym and showers; please note the hairdryers and straighteners. A beautiful building that has recently been refurbished. Comfy-looking common room, kitchen (we spotted the toast and Nutella), and outside space for dining. Interesting to see a sign up in the kitchen to say only English should be spoken. Impressive library with sixth form girls quietly working. Silent study rooms and less quiet ones, but all working hard in them. Good use made of Cambridge and all it has to offer.

The junior school reflects the senior school, with large gardens and an attractive, airy building. Pretty sensory garden and vegetable plots for each year. Both schools are very much 'girls' schools.' The empowerment of women, strong women, is a theme throughout. The girls seem to absorb this. Unaffected and natural. Very little make up worn and no strutting divas to behold – thank goodness.

Pastoral care, well-being and discipline: All parents praised the pastoral care. Very few bullying claims. Happiness and joy with strong moral values is their mantra and the girls take this on board. But girls will be girls, and the school knows it. Spats and sniping dealt with calmly and efficiently, usually with very little parental intervention. Parents spoke of a happy school with 'no queen bees or cliques.' A junior school mother said, 'some parents get too involved, collaring teachers at every opportunity. They are too protective to the detriment of others.' But that's junior schools for you. Most parents trust the school and know their daughters are 'safe and happy.' School knows how to deal with girls and their problems. A counsellor and female lay chaplain available if needed, and staff appear to know the girls well.

Instilling self-esteem and confidence is very much an ethos of the school and many parents spoke about it along with the Mary Ward philosophy that they have great belief in. 'My daughter was very shy when she started but they have brought her out of herself and her confidence now is amazing.'

Pupils and parents: Parents are very much 'Cambridge,' academics/medics/professionals. Many are old girls. All spoke about the values of the school and how important that was to them. About a third are Catholic. All very pro single sex education, even the mother who said, 'I was very anti single sex education initially, but St Mary's suited my daughter best and she's thrived.' Girls from a 30 mile radius around Cambridge with about 25 per cent from overseas.

The empowerment of women, strong women, is a theme throughout. The girls seem to absorb this. Unaffected and natural, very little make-up worn

The girls were interesting. Charming and unaffected in both schools. It was quite revealing to see the sixth formers, slightly scruffy, but not in a bad way, and minimal make up. As one mother said, 'they don't care what they look like as there's no-one to impress.' Amen to that.

Entrance: Entrance tests for all, even the reception children, who have a chat with a member of staff, count, write and sort shapes, 'to see if they will fit in.' Don't be fooled: they are looking for bright sparks. Skype interviews for those overseas. Most girls are interviewed. The senior school is oversubscribed and the junior school full from year 5. Automatic entry from the junior to senior school, with only one girl in the last five years weeded out in year 5. Quite a large intake at year 9 when girls arrive from the local prep and state schools, and from abroad to board.

Exit: Around 40-50 per cent leave each year after GCSEs, mostly to the excellent state sixth form colleges in Cambridge. The odd one to a co-ed independent, but quite unusual. Sometimes a girl is advised not to return for sixth form, but it's very unusual, and as far as we could tell entry to sixth form was automatic for current pupils as long as they have a clutch of good GCSEs.

One to Cambridge in 2017; London a very popular destination, reflecting the international profile of the girls. Sciences, medicine, vets and engineering very popular. The head is embracing apprenticeships and encouraging girls to explore this option.

Money matters: Scholarships up to the value of 20 per cent of the fees awarded and bursaries of up to 50 per cent available. Two Ogden Trust mathematics and physics scholarships open to lower sixth candidates from the state sector, means-tested and can be worth up to 95 per cent of day school fees.

Remarks: A girls' school offering a tremendous education to young women. Being instilled with the belief of the empowerment of women from such a young age, these girls will go far. There'll be no glass ceilings for this lot.

Summerhill School

39

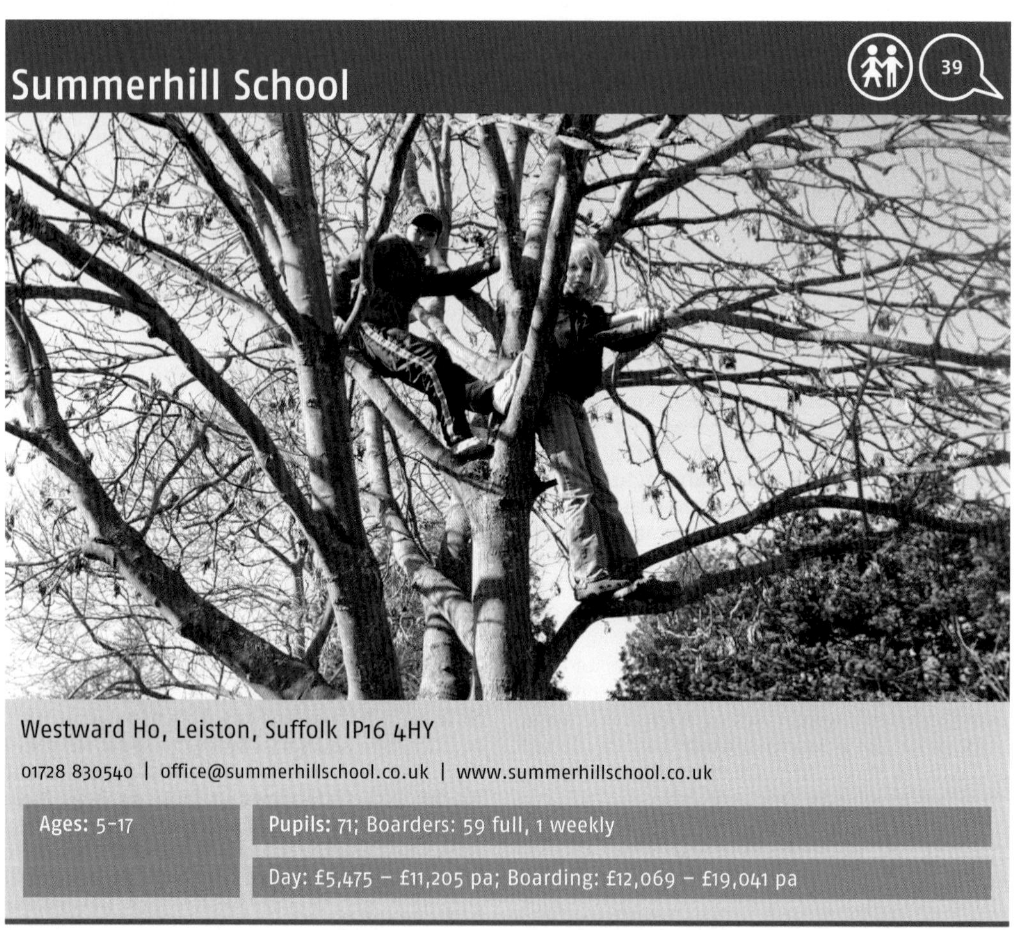

Westward Ho, Leiston, Suffolk IP16 4HY

01728 830540 | office@summerhillschool.co.uk | www.summerhillschool.co.uk

Ages: 5-17

Pupils: 71; Boarders: 59 full, 1 weekly

Day: £5,475 – £11,205 pa; Boarding: £12,069 – £19,041 pa

Principal: Since 1985, Zoe Readhead (a very youthful late 60s) – proprietor, keeper of the ethos and daughter of school's founder AS Neill. Literally born, bred and educated at Summerhill. Has been a staunch guardian of school's core values when lesser mortals would have wavered. Inspiring, uncompromising, down to earth rather than airy-fairy (is a qualified riding instructor), does not mince words. Married to Tony, a farmer, with four grown-up children all educated at Summerhill. In many ways a traditional family business: son Henry presides over the music studio; son William is deputy head and expected to take over running the school whenever Zoe retires.

Academic matters: Of secondary importance here. Summerhill is a 'free' school (NB in no way related to government-approved 'free' state schools) run on the principle that children have the same rights as adults and should be able to choose their own educational goals unfettered by the interference of anxious parents. Lessons are optional – some

Boredom is considered an important ingredient of education. Children become practical, hands on – can light a fire, cook, run a meeting

children will not attend a single lesson for a number of years, if ever. As the parents' handbook emphasises, 'remember, at Summerhill your kid could theoretically NEVER go to a lesson – they have that right. Staff members are not going to persuade, cajole or bully your child about lessons.' Play is considered as valid a part of a child's development as formal teaching: 'Many kids just need to play until they are ready to learn.'

That said, most pupils end up taking at least a few GCSEs, some take five or more. Results all over the shop from A* to G. 'My daughter might have got better exam marks at a different school,' a parent told us, 'but she got the grades she needed for the next step she was planning to take which is what mattered.' Prime emphasis is put on reading and writing, much of it delivered via one-to-one teaching. We observed a physics lesson which consisted of one seated pupil soberly facing a whiteboard where the teacher was instructing – curiously alternative and traditional all at once. A great environment for independent learners – the school brings this out in many of its pupils – but less ideal for those who thrive on a collegiate buzz and constructive competition from like-minded pupils. Nine full-time, live-in teachers, plus peripatetics, offer normal range of subjects plus environmental management, specialist music lessons, sound recording, drama, catering, psychology, French, German, Chinese and Japanese – staff try to accommodate kids' interests. Pupils are entered for Cambridge International O levels for some subjects rather than GCSEs.

One senses kid gloves in Ofsted's almost comically gushing most recent report (how times have changed from 1999 when it recommended the school be shut down): 'An outstanding feature is the way in which learning is closely tailored to match individual pupil's needs, including those with special educational needs and/or disabilities. A fundamental aspect of the school's curriculum is that learning takes place out of lessons as well as in them.'

'Special needs' not recognised here. Pupils labelled ADHD elsewhere are taken off the Ritalin and dispatched to play in the woods until they feel ready to learn. 'We take a rather old fashioned attitude to things like ADHD,' says Zoe. 'You've got to get on with it. Everyone is treated an individual here and there's so much one-to-one teaching.' However, school does apply for pupils to be given extra time in exams if they're eligible.

Games, options, the arts: Sports not high on the agenda and, despite its rather windswept tennis court, Summerhill is not likely to produce the next Andy Murray. Various games played, including Summerhill's own 'tork'. Swimming for the bold in unheated outdoor pool and for the meek at the Leiston Leisure Centre. Dance is an option and performance of all kinds is valued here. Music important with some excellent teaching and good facilities for music technology and studio recording. Similarly, drama is big among these arty kids and the school has a small theatre. Woodwork taken seriously, operating on same footing as English or maths – except it is probably more popular. Other activities include metalwork (new room joins the woodwork room and is apparently proving very popular), Japanese, Chinese, gardening, photography, calligraphy, film-making, crafts, riding, cooking in the café, camping in the grounds, making tree forts etc. But no-one is coaxed into any of this: at Summerhill boredom is considered an important ingredient of education. Children become practical, hands on – can light a fire, cook, run a meeting.

Boarding: Not a hippy wilderness – TVs and Xboxes in some of the dorms. Girls' rooms generally nicer than the boys' and fewer girls to a room. Pupils allowed out to Leiston town – a quiet backwater roughly 10 minutes' walk away. No Saturday activities or lessons – 'we just live' – but kids can ask for a lesson if desired.

'Special needs' not recognised here. Pupils labelled ADHD elsewhere are taken off the Ritalin and dispatched to play in the woods until they feel ready to learn

Background and atmosphere: Founded in 1921 by AS Neill near Dresden, Germany; settled in Leiston in 1927, where it became one of the most famous and controversial schools in the world. The school has been threatened with closure on several occasions, most recently in 1999 after a damning Ofsted report that called the pupils 'foulmouthed' and accused the school of failing the children educationally. Summerhill contested the notice of closure in court and four days into the hearing – in the face of enormous protest from current and former parents and pupils – the government's case collapsed.

Rough and tumble 11-acre setting includes large Victorian house, many single-storey additions, staff accommodation (one basic, hippy-style caravan left, treasured by its occupant – you've got to see it to believe it), wooded grounds. Spectacular beech tree for climbing, rope-swings and general play – a 'Summerhill thing', the pupils told us. Felt less full than on our last visit but school says its numbers wax and wane over the course of the year. Long holidays – five weeks at Christmas, five weeks in the spring and nine weeks each summer, but no half-terms or bank holidays – works well for overseas pupils. Annual festival-style camp for parents and former teachers over a summer term weekend.

Pastoral care, well-being and discipline: Far from being a place where you can do anything you like, Summerhill has more rules than any school we have ever visited. However, there are few fixed rules (other than the laws of the land). Everything is voted on at the Meeting, held twice a week. All children, from age 5 upward, have an equal vote, as do the teachers. No special authority invested in adults, indeed quite the contrary as they are vastly outnumbered. The Meeting is chaired by pupils and will sometimes make outlandish decisions eg to banish bed-times (sooner or later a glassy-eyed pupil will suggest they be reinstated). Misdemeanours are 'brought up' at the Meeting and an appropriate 'fine' is decided upon. Meeting proceedings surprisingly formal, with older pupils chairing on a rotating basis after first attending training sessions – lots of juicy educational stuff going on here. Pupils not afraid to voice complaints about their peers; bullying usually dealt with calmly and swiftly. As a former pupil told us, 'what Summerhill does give you is an ability to communicate with people, and it teaches you to just be nice.'

No special authority invested in adults, indeed quite the contrary as they are vastly outnumbered. The Meeting is chaired by pupils and will sometimes make outlandish decisions eg to banish bed-times

The school makes much of its claim that it allows kids to be kids. To us, however, at times it felt that it allows kids to be adults. Summerhill's freedom and democracy can extend into unsettling areas. The Meeting decides how to filter internet access and DVD restrictions. Sex is not officially sanctioned, but boys and girls allowed in each others' rooms and there is no effort made to discourage it. The school will assist pupils with contraception 'when it is thought necessary' and parents will not be informed unless the child requests it. Smoking allowed over age 14 but

Inspiring, uncompromising, down to earth rather than airy fairy (is a qualified riding instructor), does not mince words

pupils must announce that they are smokers at the Meeting and sit through an anti-smoking information DVD. Smoking rather more prevalent than last time we visited. Drug taking or drinking will get a pupil sent home for four to eight weeks, but a child would only be asked to leave if they consistently made clear they could not fit in eg for extremely disturbed behaviour or consistently failing to follow the community's rules. A young boy we saw walking through the school with an open evil-looking folding knife was chastised by an older pupil.

Everyone up by 8am on weekdays. At lesson times teachers await pupils for 10 minutes, then depart if no-show. Student investigation committee deals with any reported thefts. Food a bit basic, portions smallish, vegetarian option – can be a challenge for hearty or picky eaters, but toast and fruit always available. 'Poc' – weekly pocket money – handed out by age. The school recommends children not bring in extra money (though some do).

Pupils and parents: An international community. The school is well known abroad and around 65 per cent of children come from overseas: Japan, Korea, Holland, China, Germany, France, Poland, Russia.. the nationalities wax and wane over the years. Around half of pupils are receiving some sort of EFL help (if they choose to turn up). Recent drop in Japanese pupils (recession) made up for by upsurge in Chinese. Hodge-podge of languages can be heard as one meanders through the school.

Like home schoolers, parents at Summerhill tend to be ardent advocates of the school, born, no doubt, of having continually to justify their choice of this kind of education. 'A profound place,' said a parent. 'Love creeps up through the floorboards'. Parents here have taken the decision to 'let go' for the benefit of their children; keeping parents at arm's length so that the children can develop free of parental anxiety and interference is a key tenet. There are no school reports and parents will not be informed if their child transgresses. The school's literature says, 'what happens at school is usually considered to be the kid's own business, not necessarily to be shared by parents. Accepting this is part of learning to accept your new independent, free child.' Some children were previously home schooled or attended other alternative schools, though lots come straight from mainstream education. 'Many of us didn't get on in normal schools,' a pupil told us.

Entrance: 'Selection is based on whether we feel the child is suitable for Summerhill and vice-versa – the parents also need to understand and support the ethos of the school.' Takes children on up to age 11 – over 12s rarely enrolled. There are day places, but it is basically a boarding school with children going home twice a term for weekends (although they can ask at the Meeting and usually get away more frequently if they want to). Weekly boarding is an option for the youngest children or as a settling stage for pupils who will become full boarders later. Pupils may enter the school at the start of any term and, as they seldom start with a cohort, it is common for them to take several terms to fully integrate. Interested parents are encouraged to read about the school, and then to visit.

Exit: A few leave at 14 to attend a more traditional GCSE course elsewhere; most leave at 16/17; a small number stay on until 18. Majority go on to some kind of further education. Many proceed to sixth form colleges (and then university) although entering a normal school can be a jolt. Some end up working in skilled craft jobs. Children's writer John Burningham (The Snowman) attended the school, as did several successful actors, musicians, dancers, artists and scientists – others are off making tepees in the Welsh hills.

Money matters: Mega-cheap, but then they do not have the overheads of keeping up historical buildings, state-of-the-art sports centres, interactive whiteboards etc etc. Whole place runs on a shoestring with an air of frugality. Teachers' salaries lowish. Ten per cent fee discount, or more, for children of ex-Summerhillians. Some subjects – like Chinese, riding, dancing and music lessons – charged as extras. School squirreling away funds for the AS Neill Summerhill Trust, which will eventually be able to provide limited bursaries for existing pupils.

Remarks: You know tiger parenting? Well, this is the opposite. A living, breathing St Trinians of a school, and we mean that in the best possible way (indeed, its 1999 battle with Ofsted was made into a CBBC TV series). Other schools seek to incorporate watered-down elements of the Summerhill philosophy, but none provides such an uncompromising, full-on, 'free' education – accepting the good (enlightenment) and the bad (illiteracy) that may result. Thank goodness something like this still exists in 21st century Britain where exams and paper qualifications are almost a religion. Educational philosophies and government initiatives may come and go, but Summerhill glides serenely on.

Tring Park School for the Performing Arts

Tring Park, Tring, Hertfordshire HP23 5LX

01442 824255 | info@tringpark.com | www.tringpark.com

Ages: 8-19 (optional 3rd year in sixth form for dancers)

Pupils: 361 (267 girls, 94 boys); sixth form: 155; Boarders: 211 full

Day: £14,430 – £22,965 pa; Boarding: £24,540 – £34,710 pa

Principal: Since 2002, Mr Stefan Anderson MA BMus ARCM ARCT. Fifties, single, no children. A highly personable man whose Boris Karloff-like photo on the school's website in no way reflects his immense charm and humour. A classically trained musician, he grew up in Canada and attended Carleton University, Ottawa; then moved to the UK and studied at the Royal College of Music and Emmanuel College, Cambridge, where he was an organ scholar. He spent 12 years at Wellington as assistant director of music, then seven years as director of music at King's Canterbury, before taking up the principal's post at Tring in 2002. Very much involved in education nationally: an executive director of the Boarding Schools Association, and a trustee of the National Schools Symphony Orchestra. Universally liked and admired by parents and pupils. 'I think he's wonderful. He's absolutely spot on with the kids,' said one mother. 'They all respect him, but they can have a laugh with him,' said another. 'Kind and courteous and very professional,' pronounced a third. 'Makes time for you, easy to deal with, very helpful and very fair,' added a fourth. 'He's brilliant, a character,' said a father, 'There's a great fun side to him.' The feeling is clearly mutual. 'I love it here!' Mr Anderson affirmed. 'The students can be high-maintenance, but it's never dull.'

Academic matters: Tring's results are proof that for the right children, the chance to do what they love actually enhances their academic performance. Only half the school day is given over to academic lessons, and the students here are selected solely on their performing abilities (if they pass the audition, applicants sit academic tests for diagnostic purposes), yet results just keep getting better. In 2017, 42 per cent of GCSE passes were A*-A/9-7. You could be forgiven for wondering if these results were made up of non-academic subjects such as drama and dance, but no: they cover the full spread including sciences and languages. In 2017, A level results were 28 per cent A*/A and nearly 59 per cent A*/B, and 81 per cent got D or D* in BTec performing arts. Solid spread of academic subjects offered includes English lit, French, German, RS, history, geography, IT, and all the sciences. 'We push the academic side hard,' confirmed the head, who was brought in to improve Tring's profile in that area. Active and successful learning support department caters for wide variety of SEN, and roughly a quarter of students have either one-to-one or small group support. Parents report themselves very happy with the provision. One mother whose child has dyscalculia reported, 'She really struggles with maths, but she's had excellent support.' A boy with dyslexia told us, 'I've never had so much help as I've had here.' 'The support for dyslexia is brilliant,' said a father.

Those of us who remember the days when stage school was more often than not a byword for poor education can only marvel. But then Tring isn't a stage school in the old-fashioned sense, as the pupils were eager to point out, but a heady mix of high-level vocational and academic education, where the two strands rub together to produce very bright sparks. The former head boy has gone off to Manchester to read medicine, and one Tring alumna, a physicist, has recently started her doctorate. As the director of studies, herself a Cantabrigian, put it: 'It's very exciting working with students who are engaged and passionate with their lives. There's a joie de vivre here that spills into academic lessons.' That said, it's important to remember that this is a vocational school, one of only eight such in the UK funded by the DfE as centres of excellence for exceptionally talented young dancers and musicians. Tring's remit is to produce highly-trained performers who've received a rounded education; not lawyers and doctors who like hoofing.

Tring isn't a specialist music school – aspiring concert pianists would feel frustrated at having to break off and jeté every time they'd sat down to practice – but music is strong

Games, options, the arts: Believe it or not, Tring had actually played a football fixture shortly before we visited. They lost 11-0. 'But,' assured the head, 'we played with great passion.' Students do get together for an informal kickabout, or walk down the High Street to the local swimming pool, but there are no organised games on Tring's timetable, because there isn't time for them. Instead, half of every weekday is given over to vocational training, and,

say parents and students alike, it's amazing. 'Equal to the very best available in this country,' said one parent. 'Inspirational!' said another. 'Second to none, absolutely fabulous,' said a third. 'My son's physical fitness has improved dramatically,' said a fourth. And everyone else said something similar.

Children in the prep (years 4-6) receive training in acting, singing and dancing. Thereafter, students specialise in either dance or theatre arts. Dance training covers ballet, contemporary, tap and jazz; drama training does pretty much the same, but less intensively and also covers voice, improvisation, and other aspects of theatre technique. And of course there's musical theatre and singing too. Tring isn't a specialist music school – aspiring concert pianists would feel frustrated at having to break off and jeté every time they'd sat down to practice – but the music department is strong, with several excellent choirs and all students given the chance to learn instruments and play in ensembles.

Packed programme of shows, plays, musicals and other performances throughout the year, all of them done to an astonishingly high standard. Sometimes students have a chance to do external work – ballet dancers regularly join English National Ballet for productions of The Nutcracker, for instance – but not that often. The school doesn't encourage students to be absent, and children wanting a school that will act as their agent and find them regular professional work should look elsewhere.

Boarding: With limited space and funds, the boarding provision was only rated 'satisfactory' by Ofsted in 2011, and we have to say we thought it pretty basic; we saw seven girls to a room, for instance. On the other hand, the 9-12 year old girls in question didn't seem bothered. 'It's fun! Like we're one big family! And if we're having a row, the houseparents sort it out and then we're all best friends again!' Pupils are encouraged to do what they think will make their quarters nice: thus the girls' accommodation was a profusion of heart-shaped pink fluffiness, whilst the boys' was as fresh and tidy as you'd expect rooms shared by multiple boys to be. New boarding accommodation planned to start in 2018. Feedback about the food was very mixed, with a number of parents expressing anxiety about how much and how healthily their children were eating, and several stories of boarders needing to pop into town to fortify themselves at McDonald's (a behaviour not confined to Tring students, of course). We ourselves were given a pleasant and nutritionally-balanced meal in the canteen, so it's impossible to comment on this further. Third year sixth formers (the sixth form dance course is a three year course) sort out their own accommodation.

Background and atmosphere: Today's Tring grew out of the Cone Ripman School, founded in 1939 and itself the result of a merger between two previous dance schools. Originally located in London, the outbreak of war forced a move to Tring where the school shared premises with the Rothschild Bank at Tring Park Mansion House (strange bedfellows they must have been). In 1941, the school was able to move back to London but kept its Tring premises as a second school where boarders could be accommodated, and in 1947 both places were renamed the Arts Educational School, to reflect Grace Cone's and Olive Ripman's commitment to a proper academic education for their stage-struck charges. Gradually the two schools diverged, with London becoming more focused on post-18 training, while Tring continued to develop as a vocational boarding school. Eventually they became completely independent and in 2009 the Tring school changed its name to Tring Park School for the Performing Arts, in order to avoid confusion with its former partner. Originally for girls only, one boy was admitted in 1993, 'and that opened the floodgates'.

We arrived amidst cries of 'Five, six, seven, eight, and right! Two, three, four, and left!', while Guys and Dolls mingled jauntily with a more demure strain from the ballet class

Still housed in the gorgeously flamboyant mansion in which it took refuge over 70 years ago, Tring Park School literally sings with activity and joy.

Half the stunning wood-panelled entrance hall is glazed off as a dance studio, and we arrived amidst cries of 'Five, six, seven, eight, and right! Two, three, four, and left!', while Guys and Dolls mingled jauntily with a more demure strain from the ballet class next door. Everywhere we looked, we saw children enjoying themselves and eager to tell us so. 'Life here is amazing!' 'You get here and everyone has something to give!' 'Everyone's really welcoming!' 'It's so creative!' 'It just makes you want to dance more, being here. You get to see everyone's talent!' 'You have more time here for what you love, you're more connected!' twittered a group of frankly adorable young things. Parents agree. 'If you have a non-academic child, as we have, the enthusiasm and the passion motivates them to do better at everything. Our son loves it, he absolutely thrives on it,' said one mother. Another commented, 'The children are lovely, all so dedicated, and it really is like a family,' adding, 'When my husband and I are walking round the school, we wish we were there!' 'Every child comes out with poise and confidence from that place, they all know how to present themselves.'

The mansion's grade II listed status has hampered some necessary modernisation – it took years to get planning permission for Wifi to be installed – but the school boasts an impressive array of newly-built dance studios. It has also received funding for an even bigger and better theatre to supplement the existing 176-seat Markova Theatre, while the new art centre will move from the site of Baron Rothschild's zebra cage to a new home next to the theatre. The surrounding tree-studded gardens provide a tranquil and soothing backdrop to all the artistic fervour.

'We've always been taught not to compare ourselves to others, but to where we were last term,' said one sixth former. 'If their best friend gets the part, the others still give her a hug,' said one mother

Feathers do get ruffled occasionally. 'Inevitably at a school like this, there is competition, and I think there should be,' said one level-headed student. But everyone we spoke to insisted that the school also fostered care and affection amongst its students. 'We've always been taught not to compare ourselves to others, but to where we were last term,' said one sixth-former. 'If their best friend gets the part, the others still give her a hug,' said one mother. Another said, 'There is no real jealousy or one-upmanship over talent, and good performances are widely praised and discussed between pupils.'

Parents were less starry-eyed about school-parent communication, and everyone we spoke to agreed that it needed improving. 'Communications are not all they should be,' was a very typical criticism; 'they could be more regular and more informative.' Another said bluntly, 'We pay a hell of a lot of money for our child to go to Tring, and if I send an email I expect an answer.' The head acknowledged these criticisms with candour. 'I would absolutely agree. We need to upgrade our facilities so that we can have a parent portal. We email things weekly, but we don't have a newsletter as such. We have plans – our aim is to get a new iSAMs system (school information software). Staff are extremely busy here, but that doesn't excuse it, and I take it on board.' A new appointment, head of careers, was made recently to address concerns that families weren't getting enough information and help with students' UCAS applications.

We also heard disquiet from parents whose children hadn't been allowed to take the course of their choice at 14+ or 16+ after having already spent two or more years at the school. Specifics weren't forthcoming, but we gathered that this particularly applied to those with aspirations to a career in dance. 'This can be a more difficult adjustment than the school acknowledges, and it's you the parent who has to deal with your child's disappointment,' wrote one worried mother. But as other parents observed, a career in the performing arts is tough, and the head was adamant that the school always put the child's best interests first. 'I would dispute very strongly that we block anyone, but we try to get the child onto the course where we feel they'll succeed. If someone has unrealistic expectations, we speak to the child and to the parents. But 95 per cent of the time, parental, child and school expectations match up.' The great majority of parents we spoke to agreed. As one mother wrote, 'Tring provides a very supportive network for students who are struggling or who change their minds about whether vocational training is for them.' Another said simply, 'The support given by Tring's staff is exceptional. Our son is very happy there, and flourishing beyond our imagination.'

Pastoral care, well-being and discipline: To a person, parents praised Tring's pastoral care, with the boarding staff particularly singled out. 'The housemother was wonderful, and my son settled in really quickly,' 'A houseparent in a million' 'The houseparents are so switched on,' ''The houseparents comfort you if you're homesick!' 'They're amazing! They do so much for us!' were typical comments. The medical unit was also very highly rated: 'Informs you immediately if there are any problems,' 'The medical staff were exceptional,' 'Both pastoral and medical care have always been exemplary.'

Behaviour at Tring is exuberant but respectful. There are the usual sanctions for infringements, but the students want to be here and are generally keen not to mess up. Many parents commented on the children's excellent work ethic, and one boy added, 'My time management has become fantastic since starting here. You really do become reliable, hard working, responsible. You have to work hard.'

Pupils and parents: From a very broad range of backgrounds, and from all over the UK. Some from overseas (around 10 per cent of boarders), and EAL help is there for those who need it. Many of them new to boarding, or to independent schools, or to the world of performing arts, but all of them united by a common ardour. Inevitably, there are more girls than boys, with the current ratio being more than 2:1. Do the boys mind? 'No, because I'm friends with all the boys in my year,' said one young lad, 'and my confidence with girls has increased!'

Entrance: Children can join the school from age 8 to 16, but the commonest entry points are at ages 11-13, 14 and 16. Applications are increasing, particularly at 16+, and overall the school receives seven applications for every place. One-day audition process at which children show what they can do in dance, drama and singing. They aren't expected to excel in all three of these – although many do – but the school is looking for great talent and potential in the candidate's chosen specialism, 'and they have to show a real desire to learn,' says head. If they're successful in gaining a place but need funding to take it up, they're called to a second audition.

Exit: The majority of students continue on into the performing arts in one way or another. A few dance stars progress straight to major companies such as English National Ballet and Scottish Ballet; others might join the school's own dance company, Encore, for a rigorous third year of touring and performing, or take up places at dance schools such as The Place. Drama schools are also a popular destination: Laine Theatre Arts, Bristol Old Vic, etc. 'And we regularly turn out some good classical musicians,' adds head, although invariably these are singers – one recent alumna went on to train at The Royal Academy of Music and has already appeared with Garsington Opera and Opera North. Some go straight into professional work (Downton Abbey has mopped up several Tring alumni). And a number decide to go to university instead: one off to read physics at Durham in 2017, alongside one to New York University and another to the Julliard performing arts school in New York.

Still housed in the gorgeously flamboyant mansion in which it took refuge over 70 years ago, Tring Park School literally sings with activity and joy. Everywhere we looked, we saw children enjoying themselves and eager to tell us so

Much praise from parents and pupils alike for the way Tring supports and guides students' career aspirations. 'I'd love to get a job in a ballet company,' said one young male dancer, 'but my body doesn't work that way, I'm not flat-turned-out. But the teachers work with you to find other ways you can do things, and they're brilliant.' A parent whose son was now at college told us, 'He knows he can still call on Tring for help and advice, a relationship he really values.'

Money matters: Stonkingly high fees, as you'd expect with all this specialist tuition, but around one third of students are on some kind of support. Dancers who join the school at age 11, 12 or 13 can apply for funding from the government's means-tested Music and Dance Scheme. Dance students joining at 16+ may be eligible for DaDA scholarships (Dance and Drama Awards, another source of government funding). And Tring has its own scholarship fund for musical theatre and drama pupils, to which families can apply. Many Tring students come from families on modest or low incomes. Up to 100 per cent assistance available for those who need it.

Remarks: An extremely impressive vocational school that gives its students an excellent and well-balanced education. Children for whom the performing arts are central to their existence will feel they've come home the moment they walk through the door. As one mother whose daughter had been there eight years said, 'We cannot fault it. She's had a wonderful time, and the training has been amazing. Her work ethic is fantastic, she's very well-prepared for auditions, she's made friends for life, and she's grown into a wonderful young lady.'

Woodbridge School

Burkitt Road, Woodbridge, Suffolk IP12 4JH

01394 615041 | admissions@woodbridgeschool.org.uk | www.woodbridgeschool.org.uk

Ages: 11–18 (boarding from 13)

Pupils: 585; sixth form: 172; Boarders: 62 full

Day: £14,802 – £16,020 pa; Boarding: £29,985 pa

Headmaster: Since 2014, Neil Tetley, previously deputy head of Sevenoaks School. History degree and PGCE from Cambridge, then spent a year in Japan before taking up teaching. Ten years at King's College Wimbledon, becoming housemaster and then assistant head, with an interim year at the International School of Brussels. He has a great passion for Russian history, enjoys all things Italian and is an enthusiastic sportsman, particularly enjoying squash and cricket. He is married to Laura, a foreign languages teacher, and they have two young sons. Off in July 2018 to head Hastings School, Madrid.

Academic matters: Despite a keen eye for results, the school is not enamoured with league tables believing, as do many, that too much of a focus on the school's overall performance can lead to individual pupil's needs being ignored. Academically the right buttons are being pressed, with 40 per cent A*/A and 69 per cent A*-B at A level in 2017, 57 per cent A*-A/9-7 at GCSE. The arts, maths, sciences

'Pupils can have a crack at everything going – there is a niche for everyone'. Pupils themselves are friendly and polite

and languages perform particularly well. Though less eye-catching, the middle range ability pupils' results reflect their solid achievement and success. Pupils are banded from year 7 and setted in certain subjects eg maths. Classes around 20. Everyone takes French in year 7, adding Latin and Spanish or Mandarin in year 8; at least one modern language to GCSE, with Mandarin and Japanese optional extras and classics including Greek available in the sixth form. Around 60 pupils have mild learning difficulties; several full-time teachers offer support individually and in groups. The emphasis is on keeping pupils fully integrated into the mainstream classes. Strong EAL provision for overseas pupils. This is a school that works for all abilities.

Games, options, the arts: Impressive pitches and courts with the sports hall housed in the Eden Project-style Dome, which provides room for several classes at a time. Sport is for all and everyone has the opportunity to play competitively in the school teams, often trouncing the opposition. The Elite Sports programme is devised to encourage the most talented pupils, many of whom catch the selector's eye at county and international levels. Swimming is for the hardy in an outdoor pool. Friday afternoon is time tabled for the Seckford Scheme, an extraordinary range of non-academic activities in which the whole school (staff included) joins. All interests and tastes are encouraged: eg sailing, cookery, chess (school has its own Grand Master), and CCF is a top draw for many. D of E is also popular.

Music regarded as mainstream – no 'sporty' or 'aesthete' labels and half the school learns one or more instruments. It is 'cool to sing'. School has a close association with Aldeburgh and Snape with masterclasses, courses and recitals taking place regularly. Proliferation of choirs, ensembles, orchestras and bands. Drama also wildly popular with eight plays and shows performed annually in the impressive Seckford Theatre. Dance is increasingly popular. The school's international programme provides visits and exchanges throughout Europe, India, Australia, S Africa, China and Oman. Pupils spend periods of up to 10 weeks at linked schools.

Boarding: Boarders are virtually all from overseas – from a wide range of countries including Spain, Germany, Thailand, China and Hong Kong. They are fully integrated into the school, and as there are only 62 of them they have a close relationship with the boarding houseparents. They are free to visit the town after school and at weekends; some weekend excursions further afield organised to eg London or Cambridge, plus parties, paintballing etc. Help with language issues available.

Background and atmosphere: Founded in the 17th century, the school is part of the Seckford Foundation and has occupied its present site in the town since the 19th century. It has been fully co-educational for 40 years. School stands on extensive grounds on a hilly plot with the various buildings dotted around, giving a campus atmosphere. The immediate approach to the school passes the slightly unprepossessing boarding house. However, the school buildings are a mix of styles from the Victorian to the contemporary, including the recently-built Seckford Theatre and sixth form centre. Atmosphere in classes, library and areas for independent working is palpably studious. Time-wasting is frowned on and most pupils spin from lessons to sport to activities non stop. One mother commented, 'Pupils can have a crack at everything going – there is a niche for everyone'. Pupils themselves are friendly and polite; teachers, if anything, even more so. Unstuffy relations all round, and the staff give praiseworthy loyal service.

School has a close association with Aldeburgh and Snape with masterclasses, courses and recitals taking place regularly. Proliferation of choirs, ensembles, orchestras

Pastoral care, well-being and discipline: Enthusiastic endorsement by parents for vertical tutoring system, which operates from year 10 to 13. Younger pupils have the benefit of knowing older pupils well, and it provides leadership opportunities for sixth formers; 'most pupils know whom they would go to'. Few discipline problems.

Communication with parents is taken very seriously. As well as the usual parents' consultations, staff are available on a day-to-day basis via telephone or email. This care of the children is at the heart of such a happy school.

Pupils and parents: Pupils drawn largely from professional East Anglian families, many with a media background (Aldeburgh, BT close by). A fleet of buses brings pupils from as far afield as Norfolk, Felixstowe and Colchester. The school is very popular in the town and many parents have moved out from London to take advantage. Foreign students, many from the Far East, are encouraged to come for long or short periods, partly to ginger up what would otherwise be a very English school; about two-thirds of sixth form boarders are from the Far East, others from mainland Europe.

Entrance: Common entrance or test, together with a report from present school, and interview at 11 or 13. Two-thirds of intake at 11 transfer from The Abbey prep, the rest from local state and private schools. About three-quarters of those tested are accepted. Entry to the sixth form is based on an interview and GCSE predicted grades.

Exit: Few leave after GCSEs. Great majority leave sixth form for university; Edinburgh, Newcastle, Oxford Brookes and Reading currently popular, as are sciences, modern languages, English and business/finance courses.

Money matters: Academic scholarships worth up to 50 per cent of fees can be topped-up with means-tested bursaries. Music, sport, all round and art scholarships are also available. Some sibling reductions.

Remarks: A good all-round 'country school in the town'. Lively, and although selective, would suit quite a wide ability range. Exceptional extracurricular provision for what is, largely, a day school.

Midlands and Wales

Derbyshire
Herefordshire
Leicestershire
Lincolnshire
Northamptonshire
Nottinghamshire
Rutland
Shropshire
Staffordshire
Warwickshire
West Midlands
Worcestershire
WALES

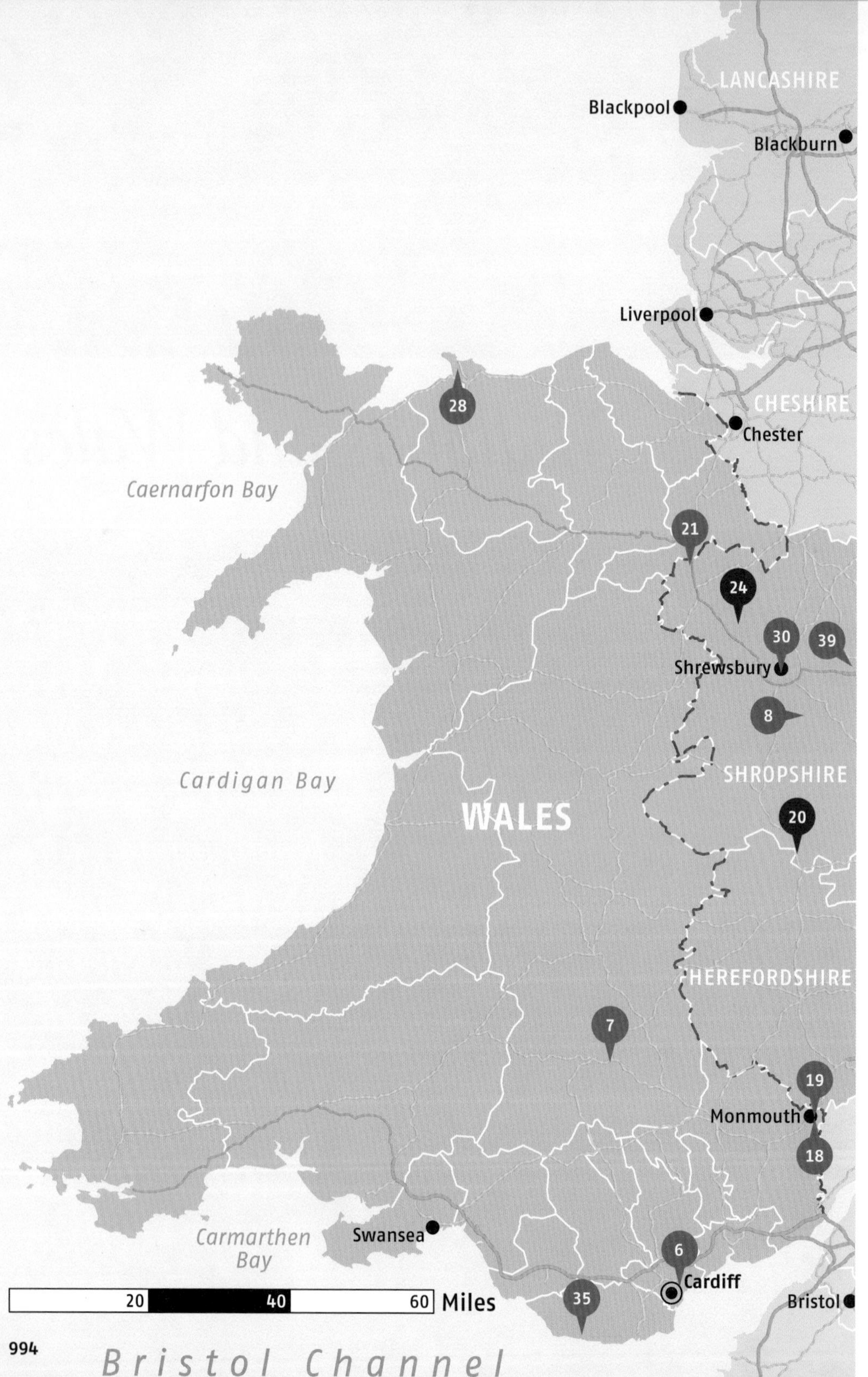
LANCASHIRE
Blackpool
Blackburn
Liverpool
CHESHIRE
Chester
28
Caernarfon Bay
21
24
30
39
Shrewsbury
8
SHROPSHIRE
Cardigan Bay
WALES
20
HEREFORDSHIRE
7
19
Monmouth
18
Carmarthen Bay
Swansea
6
Cardiff
Bristol
35
20
40
60
Miles
Bristol Channel

York
EAST RIDING OF YORKSHIRE
Leeds
Kingston Upon Hull
WEST YORKSHIRE
NORTH LINCOLNSHIRE
Huddersfield
Grimsby
Bolton
GREATER MANCHESTER
SOUTH YORKSHIRE
NORTH EAST LINCOLNSHIRE
Sheffield
13
27
Lincoln
29
DERBYSHIRE
LINCOLNSHIRE
NOTTINGHAMSHIRE
The Wash
Stoke-on-trent
Nottingham
Derby
25
2
38
14
12
STAFFORDSHIRE
22
31
33
RUTLAND
Stamford
Leicester
32
Peterborough
LEICESTERSHIRE
Wolverhampton
34
10
Birmingham
15
23
WEST MIDLANDS
Coventry
26
5
CAMBRIDGESHIRE
36
WORCESTERSHIRE
NORTHAMPTONSHIRE
4
1
Northampton
Cambridge
WARWICKSHIRE
Bedford
16
17
Worcester
Great Malvern
37
Brackley
11
9
3
Luton
Gloucester
HERTFORDSHIRE
Harlow
Oxford
GLOUCESTERSHIRE
OXFORDSHIRE
GREATER LONDON
Swindon
London
Reading
BERKSHIRE
Bath
WILTSHIRE
Basingstoke
SURREY

MIDLANDS AND WALES

Abberley Hall

Worcester WR6 6DD

01299 896275 | louise.brook@abberleyhall.co.uk | www.abberleyhall.co.uk

Ages: 2-13 (boarding from year 3)

Pupils: 235; **Boarders:** 84 (24 girls) full; 26 part

Day: £8,790 – £18,705 pa; **Boarding:** £12,705 – £23,490 pa

Headmaster: Since 2014, Will Lockett, previously classics teacher and housemaster at Bryanston. One of a small number of prep school heads who have moved from senior schools. In Will's case, the move was quite simply because he loves Abberley. An old boy of the school, he is reveling in the move to this age group. 'They are so refreshingly enthusiastic about everything', he says. He has a classics degree from Manchester, still teaches some and relishes it, no doubt contributing to the status the subject has with the children. A great believer in the value of routines, he says children respond to the structure of boarding and he has even introduced half an hour silent reading in bed before lights out. Everyone likes it. Will's style is brisk and vigorous. He knows exactly what is going on and children and staff are keen to keep it that way. 'He has respect without fear from the children,' a parent told us.

His wife, Beth, is fully involved, overseeing junior boarding and doing some teaching. A headmaster's wife to die for is the verdict of parents, who say she is very maternal and nurturing in her approach to the children. There are three Lockett children, the youngest at Abberley and the older two at Shewsbury. Will is spending his first few years at the school consolidating all the strengths and bringing new challenges in terms of independent learning and outdoor education.

Entrance: Non-selective. Children are assessed either before arrival or when they arrive to ensure there is clarity about educational needs and, with older children, to help determine which academic sets are appropriate.

Exit: The vast majority stay to the end of year 8. This is a school that is a serious player in the CE stakes. Over recent years secured a great many scholarships amidst the 45 year 8s and they are a range – academic, sport, art, drama, DT. The head says parents are very keen to seek advice on senior schools, which they recognise as objective and in the child's best interests, and school prides itself on pointing parents in the right direction. They feed a large number of senior schools nationally.

Co-educational include : Shrewsbury School, Cheltenham College, Gordonstoun, Malvern

College, Marlborough, Millfield, Oundle, RGS (Worcester), King's Worcester, Rugby, Stowe, Christ College Brecon and Uppingham.

Boys only include Eton, Harrow, Monmouth, Old Swinford Hospital, Radley, Sherborne and Winchester.

Girls only include Badminton, Cheltenham Ladies' College, Moreton Hall, Haberdasher's (Monmouth), Malvern St James, St Mary's Ascot and Tudor Hall.

Remarks: Ninety acres of park and woodland surround Abberley Hall, a 19th century edifice of some significance. The bluebells were out along the drive on our visit to add to the idyllic rural setting in which the children grow up. The buildings are on a slope and the gentle Worcestershire hills frame the school site. Inside, the first impressions are of a grand but comfortable past. While we talk to the headmaster, a glorious peacock pecks at the window as if he wants to join us. Many of the original features of the old house remain – large oil paintings on the impressive staircase, wonderful great wood framed doors, a family theatre now converted into a girls' dormitory with its original pastoral murals. The headmaster's study is the old library, apparently untouched since an era of leisurely scholarship.

But there is nothing leisurely about the scholarship at Abberley today. It is a high powered prep school that prepares children with great success for the top senior schools in the country. It offers a traditional academic curriculum. The older children have 30 hours of lessons a week. 'It would be nice to have a few less lessons,' one or two year 8s said to us plaintively. Languages are a huge strength – Greek is taught from year 6, there are three hours of French a week and two and a half of Latin. It pays off in terms of scholarship examinations, the head tells us.

Many of the weekend activities, which the children tell us they adore and are keenly anticipated, are open to parents

From year 3, the children have twice yearly exams. It is low key to start with but it means the children are getting used to tests. Science, maths, design and manufacture have a practical, cross-curricular emphasis that is impressive. When the children learn about pressure in science, they look at saturation diving in design and manufacture. It keeps the children fully engaged with the more theoretical aspects, the head of design and manufacture tells us.

The workshops are open at lunch time and after school for children to work on their own design projects – about a third of the school is engaged on one of these. Art is striking with a practising artist running workshops twice a week – 'It has been a huge help for the children preparing for scholarships', the head of art tells us. There are textiles, ceramics, print-making, painting onto canvas and use of different media. The head is keen to develop even further the profile and challenge of the creative arts.

The older children told us that the high academic standards were what made the school stand out. 'We can get help from teachers whenever we want,' they say, 'and we can sign up for extra academic coaching sessions'. The school is preparing the children for senior schools where they will need to take the initiative in planning and shaping their own learning and there is no doubt that the older ones get this. Parents are enthusiastic about the quality of the teaching. 'They go the extra mile,' was how one described staff. Once year 8s have completed all their exams, there is a challenging leavers' programme of events for them. The head says that feedback from senior schools is that Abberley children are notably good at grasping opportunities.

As the school is non selective, learning support is taken seriously. Class size is kept to 15 maximum, allowing for much individual support within the classroom. Then there is dyslexia screening in years 1 and 2 and careful scrutiny of ongoing assessments. Where a need is identified, the head of learning support will step in. The school may do its own further assessment or advise an educational psychologist's report to help tailor future learning. What happens next depends on the level of need and is very much individually determined. It may be two half hour support lessons a week, a teaching assistant helping within a class, curriculum adjustments, special exam access arrangements. Parents say that the children take needing extra help as a matter of course – there is absolutely no stigma attached.

The head says it is not what happens in lessons that distinguishes the outstanding boarding school, but what happens at weekends. Abberley Hall is committed to full boarding. There is no flexi-boarding but there is part boarding, where parents commit to specific days a week a term in advance. One weekend in three is full boarding, one is optional and the third is an exeat, so the most a child would be continuously at school is likely to be three weeks, which we think is right for children at this age and a good preparation for senior boarding schools. Many of the weekend activities, which the children tell us they adore and are keenly anticipated, are open to parents. Just before we visited there had been the annual fun run where everyone dressed up to complete various length runs around the grounds. The grounds are fully used. The children have built an outdoor pizza oven, there are outdoor classrooms and mini Duke of Edinburgh style award activities outdoors one afternoon a week. There are clear rules about where in the grounds children can explore but plenty of space for climbing trees and building dams. The head is keen to introduce even more challenge to the outdoor education programmes.

Extracurricular life is teeming – every teacher offers two activities a week. Music is highly valued and a big part of the school. Not only lessons but practices are timetabled for the children which, with 200 instrumental lessons going on, must take some doing. There is a lunchtime concert series and, as with other extracurricular activities, the emphasis is on everyone getting a chance to perform at some stage. Many take RSM exams and do very well and there are regular music scholarships awarded. A group goes each week to the CBSO Children's Choir in Birmingham, which opens up huge opportunities for music making. There are lots of instrumental ensembles and choirs. The senior chapel choir is invited to sing around the area, regularly performing at Worcester Cathedral. Parents describe the music as 'sensational' and are delighted by the high expectations from staff. There is a 'phenomenally ambitious' annual musical. 'The staff are not just wanting performance but perfection', one parent told us approvingly.

The school is considered to punch well above its weight in sport, which happens every day with matches on Wednesdays and Saturdays and sports tours. Facilities are brilliant. Rugby coaching is exceptional even by standards outside the prep school world. Girls' cricket is taken as seriously as boys' cricket. Lots of the children said sport is a great thing about the school, but even those who admitted to not being particularly keen appreciate the choice they have and the chance to be outside.

There is drama and beekeeping, run by the headmaster, fishing and film making, spy club and electronics; the list goes on. Children can bring their horses from home and ride round the grounds on their bikes. It is a day packed full of intellectual and outdoor activities – 'Gumboots and Greek' is the school's current strapline and it is a good reflection of what life is like. Parents like the lack of hierarchy in school activities. There is no sense that the rugby players are any more valued or respected than the grade 1 flautist. The school is also noted for its enthusiasm for discovering new talents – children are not labelled as 'a sportsperson' and that is that. All this does mean the days are long and, particularly for parents considering boarding, it is important to ensure their child is ready for this degree of activity.

There is drama and beekeeping, fishing and film making, spy club and electronics. Children can bring their horses from home and ride round the grounds on their bikes

Abberley has its own chalet in the French Alps and all year 5s and 7s have a couple of weeks out there each year to immerse themselves in a different culture and pick up a bit more French, which they are learning alongside Spanish, Latin and Greek. A Chinese school exchange is also planned.

The children we spoke to enthused about boarding. The accommodation is very non institutional, using the variety of spaces in the old buildings. Pastoral support is strong and the turnover of staff small. Head has introduced a new tutor system for the older children so years 6, 7 and 8 have their own personal tutor for three years, who acts as a single point of contact for parents and with whom the children have a weekly individual meeting. We think this is an excellent model to ensure no one slips through the pastoral net.

'We are not big on punishment', says the head and indeed the discipline issues with which staff are dealing are low key. The focus is on getting children to think about their own behaviour and how it impacts on others. Parents say that the school's attitude to problems has always been to leave it to school and not encourage parents to be very much involved. The new head seems to be changing this a bit, but everyone we spoke to seemed very confident in the school's ability to sort things out quickly and humanely and follow through on issues. The school is keen on giving the children responsibilities and has created new roles in the last couple of years to ensure the opportunities are there to learn about leadership. There is a visiting CofE chaplain and a traditional chapel service four times a week, with family services some Sundays.

Family backgrounds range from landowners and farming families to professionals and business people, and they are highly supportive of the school, generally living close enough to attend matches, concerts, Sunday chapel and the many other events. They had just helped organise a long distance walk to raise money to take out to a community in South Africa when the sports teams go on a tour. There are some children whose family connections with Abberley go back several generations. Parents and staff value the range of children – not just in terms of background but also in terms of their educational needs.

The children are strikingly open and unaffected, living witness to the head's belief that prep school children retain their innocence longer. They are unselfconscious, gutsy and ready to talk to adults appropriately. They are being prepared for a work hard, play hard culture. They love the outdoor freedom and they also know life is a serious and competitive business, which they are up for. The school is in its centenary year. It has much to be proud of in its past and everything to suggest the future is golden for the children lucky enough to come here.

Abbots Bromley School

CofE 2

High Street, Abbots Bromley, Nr Rugeley, Staffordshire WS15 3BW

01283 840232 | enquiries@abbotsbromleyschool.com | www.abbotsbromleyschool.com

Ages: 3-18 (boarding from 8)

Pupils: 245; sixth form: 75; **Boarders:** 107 (27 boys)

Day: £9,048 – £15,357 pa; **Boarding:** £17,040 – £28,305 pa

Principal: Since April 2017, Mrs Maggie Shackleton BA (40s), a historian. Described as a 'gold medal headteacher' by no less a sporting icon than Dame Katherine Grainger, Maggie has held senior leadership positions across the education sectors: comprehensive, grammar and independent, culminating in seven successful years as head of Sutton Coldfield Grammar School for Girls. Maggie's husband, Paul, is also a history teacher and they live on the school site with their two dogs. The dogs have become firm favourites with boarding students and are a familiar sight walking around the quintessentially English village of Abbots Bromley.

Prep school head: Since 2015, Mrs Wendy Gordon, previously deputy head.

Academic matters: This not a results or league table driven school. Abbots Bromley, referred to affectionately as AB, will not kick a pupil out if her GCSE performance suggests that her A level results will damage the school's ranking. When we asked some girls if that happened at AB they looked amazed and replied with tough logic, 'Of course not, you'd be offered more help and guidance.' There is plenty of advice and help given at AB but one of the advantages of being a small school is that it is possible to tailor girls' needs and aspirations to suit them. The recent inspection noted and applauded that. Instead of shoehorning pupils into subject blocks, the school, where possible, builds the curriculum around pupils' choices. At best this approach is seen as inspirational and encouraging and not an opportunity for copping out.

Exam results are commendable for a school which is non-selective; 47 per cent A*-A/9-7 at GCSE in 2017; 32 per cent A*/A at A level. Girls and teachers seem immensely happy with the opportunities they have to pursue the sciences. In a mixed school these are frequently seen as 'boys' subjects' but here they are pursued enthusiastically. Small classes are greatly appreciated, too. There is a mass of information about subject choices in the excellent booklets that come with the prospectus.

Maths and English are setted for ability but sets are not rigidly static: movement up and down is in response to progress and confidence. Good dyslexia help is available as well as EFL tuition for those 10 per cent who need it. Those we talked to from abroad spoke with genuine fondness of the school, the way in which they had been welcomed and their involvement with dance and other activities. One mother told us of her dyslexic daughter who had struggled agonisingly at her previous school, but once at AB had 'taken off. There's such a wonderful mixture of love and expertise at the school. She's blossomed.' Sixth formers help younger girls with maths and other subjects as a genuine extension of that 'family feeling' as well as points towards their Duke of Edinburgh Award.

Everything at the prep school is achieved within a framework of carefully drawn up curricula and an intelligent timetable. For instance, conversational French is taught from the kindergarten, as is swimming. The school trumpets healthily the fact that the ratio of teacher/pupil is much more generous than government recommendations – but then parents are paying for it. Early years education is seen by those with whom we spoke to be particularly good value for money.

Games, options, the arts: Two unique features of AB are the Alkins School of Ballet and the Equestrian Centre, adding depth and variety to a school experience which is genuinely broad and challenging. Ballet may be fun but, be under no illusion, it requires dedication, with a mixture of sensitive response, physical control and courage. Outstanding results for performing arts and dance BTecs. Vocational dance, by audition, involves about eight hours a week; the alternative is dancing for fun, for a sense of release, for 'enrichment'. Both involve commitment. Several students have gone on to perform professionally via the Royal Academy of Dance and other prestigious schools. The excellent director of ballet, a former examiner with the Royal Ballet, and his wife, a former international ballerina, know that the career of a dancer can be cut short and does not last as long as many professions. For that reason they encourage students to do three A levels along with preparing for their BTec and beyond. 'We want them to have the widest possible choice.' Marvellous equipment – lots of barres and mirrors – but more importantly, fabulous teaching in spacious studios.

The superbly equipped equestrian centre is reached via a beautiful tree lined avenue and clearly has everything a budding rider needs to move on to Olympic honours. Indoor, floodlit outdoor, bring your own horse or hire one of the school's – you name it. Girls may learn to ride from 6 years old and there have been a number of startling successes both at horse shows and with BHS examinations, the top one of which counts for over 100 UCAS points as well as a teaching qualification.

These two activities are more than hobbies: they really do contribute to the well-rounded character of the school. AB is not an academic hothouse nor a school for trendy air heads aspiring to have their pictures in Country Life: it is a school which offers education at its broadest and most stimulating. It challenges and nurtures the brain as well as plugging into a lively, creative life of spiritual freedom and energy, artistic expression involving movement in response to music, what the school calls 'enrichment'. The Renaissance was right to combine horsemanship with learning.

Art is exciting and popular with examples of girls' work all over the place, helping to make the passageways of the original 19th century building less formal and intimidating. Plenty of drama, with plays being written and performed by the pupils themselves in house competitions. One wing of the school is dedicated to music, with over 20 individual practice rooms where girls who are now grandmothers practised scales in the morning after cold showers. Now there are computers for composing on after warm baths, as well as a keyboard studio. Music and singing are very popular, with most girls learning at least one instrument and a much travelled chapel choir – Italy, New York, Paris, San Francisco, Lichfield – and a Cantoria Choir that sings regularly on Radio 4.

Matches against bigger schools (and most are) are played with much zest and skill, with county players in many fields. Another school commented to us, 'Abbots Bromley girls always play with tremendous determination'. 'That's part of the ethos of making the most of our abilities and opportunities,' a pupil told us without a whiff of self-consciousness.

Hockey, netball, football, cross-country, tennis, swimming, rounders and athletics are all on offer.

Girls very keen on boarding, 'but I can't get my mum to agree,' said one girl who is stepping up her nights of flexi-boarding. 'Perhaps then she won't notice I'm not at home'

One of the great delights of the Abbots Bromley Prep School adventure is what it calls 'enrichment' (what might more prosaically be referred to as hobbies). There is 'enrichment' before lunch four days of the week, and these periods of serve to alter the tempo of the day and tap into a different part of the psyche. Some activities are charged for, such as riding, dancing (Abbots Bromley, as a whole, is brilliant at both these activities), tennis coaching, speech, music and drama lessons. Members of staff follow their own interests and – the best moments for teachers – share what fires them up. Thus there is craft club, ICT skills, art club, choir, ukulele ensemble (all those little Georgette Formbys!). There are also masses of sporting activities including netball, football, swimming, trampolining and athletics. And you can revisit old haunts by journeying to the sports hall and swimming pool bang next to where the prep school once was.

Boarding: Boarding is increasing in popularity. Younger girls share with three or four others, sixth formers have individual bedsits of a rather higher standard than they are likely to find at university. Girls we spoke to were most enthusiastic about boarding, 'but I can't get my mum to agree,' said one frustrated girl who is stepping up her nights of flexi-boarding. 'Perhaps then she won't notice I'm not at home.' Two free taster nights are included in every term's fees, which means that the great majority of the girls experience boarding from year 3.

Boys' boarding house opened in 2015 to accommodate male sixth formers and students from new AB International College, which 'provides a variety of courses for overseas students'.

Background and atmosphere: The village of Abbots Bromley has a population of fewer than 2000 and was recently cited in the Sunday Times as an outstandingly good place to live. Most of the pupils and teachers at the eponymous school would agree. There are so many listed buildings in the High Street that the village is preserved at its best: handsome, understated and welcoming. The school itself has two sides: in fanciful terms the mind and the spirit. The academic and intellectual side is what you encounter when you enter from the street and thread your way past the large 1960s building, through narrow alleyways separating the 19th century buildings of the original foundation to the visitors' car park and thence to reception and the head. If you drive towards the equine block, however, you come to the sports fields, the huge Astroturf and the stunning view of Cannock Chase. Here, too, is the grass running track where the school recently had to buy new loudspeakers to make announcements heard above the sound of the girls cheering on their housemates and friends.

Originally two schools (St Mary's and St Anne's), AB was the first girls' school in the Woodard Foundation and is one of the oldest girls' public schools in the country. Woodard was unwilling initially to found a girls' school: he couldn't see the point of girls' boarding schools. Various friends, sensing Woodard's blinkered vision, persuaded him to accept the idea and ultimately he allowed Abbots Bromley into the Woodard Foundation. Six years later, on the other side of the street, St Mary's was founded as a less expensive sister school. The Woodard Schools are religious foundations, but Victorian Anglicanism was very class conscious and St Mary's was for the daughters of less wealthy parents. Later ages were more squeamish about such distinctions and in 1921 the two schools on either side of the road became as one. Later they were linked by name as Abbots Bromley School for Girls.

On the St Mary's side of the road there is a splendid injunction to motorists from a bygone age: 'Please do not stand your Motors on This Side of the Road'; on the other side of the entrance is a fiercer notice: 'Private property: no trespassing.' This is the home to the swimming pool, sports hall and medical centre (and previously the prep school, which has now moved across the road to join its big sister). The mixture of senior and junior parts of the school contributes to that sense of affectionate unity that pervades the whole place.

The 19th century builders were generous with the size of their windows. Whatever the original motives for such huge windows – wide open at night, no doubt – they are a delightful addition to the facilities and contribute much to the rooms, which are airy and spacious. The lovely and inviting library is in the process of being made even more attractive, science labs have been improved, IT is efficient and attractively laid out and the boarding facilities are homely and inviting.

The school chapel is, in keeping with Woodard's principles, the most obvious and memorable building. It has height, majesty and atmosphere and will be even more impressive when the lighting is improved. It is clearly central to the atmosphere of the school and though there is no longer daily chapel for all, one or two girls we spoke to told us that they sometimes went to sit there and think.

On Fridays the whole senior school attends eucharist and 'it's a wonderful place to sing in.'

The sixth form wing, with its delightful common room, cooking areas and comfortable bedsits, offers an induction into university. As part of the practical preparation for leaving home and school, sixth form girls do some cooking and are responsible for their own laundry.

The facilities of the prep school, back on the main school site, are excellent and the prep school children spoke excitedly – there was a lot of high octane energy around – about the satisfaction of navigating themselves around the building, the sense of being a part of the whole. One or two even volunteered the surprising view that the new set up is an improvement because if it's raining on Thursdays you can go to chapel without getting wet. Godliness and common sense: just what you would expect from a Woodard school.

Girls we spoke to, and how happy they were to talk, expressed huge happiness and delight in their school. 'If I have children,' said one sparky girl, 'I would definitely send them here.' Others nodded in agreement before she added, 'if I could afford it.'

Pastoral care, well-being and discipline: The old adage about family warmth and trust in each other is as true and apparent in AB as any school we have visited. It's partly the size. 'I know every girl in the school,' one happy inmate told us. 'That helps a lot.' Girls and staff greet each other with warmth and interest as they move about. We saw some inspirational teaching born of mutual respect and genuine interest. Classes were lively, active and worthwhile, and outside the classroom the willingness of staff to spend time with the girls and listen, advise or help is much appreciated.

There is much scope for interaction across the age range in the houses, whether it is in the dining room where houses eat together, playing and watching inter-house sport, performing together in plays and concerts, going on outings and trips. Clear anti-bullying policy and girls we spoke to said they felt happy and safe. As far as adults are concerned, girls can turn to their houseparent, form tutor, sixth form mentor, 'anyone whom they trust.' Some parents have moved to be nearer the school. That's always revealing.

Pupils and parents: There is a genuine elegance and style about the girls but they are not remotely pretentious or posh. Those we met were forthcoming without being arrogant and were innately courteous and good fun. Many spoke of the joy of being at AB because 'you don't have to pretend to be anything other than yourself'. They love the village and the village seems to love them; dads spoke approvingly of visits, 'do you know of any other school which is bang next door to a jolly good pub?' Mums spoke of the love and support given by the school and the fact that the girls are happily busy and involved. Those parents who were disenchanted by the previous regime are now coming back on board. The Commemoration Day, when the whole school walks down the centre of the High Street in costume and singing hymns, continues. 'We like the tradition: it's slightly mad but great fun.'

Entrance: Non-selective into the prep. Every child has talent. 'We accept boys and girls of all faiths and abilities.' Pupils may arrive at any stage, providing there is room. Obviously the start of term is the best time but the school is flexible about that. We met children who joined in the middle of a term and who spoke so happily about the way they had been welcomed in by everyone. Taster days are available.

Most of the girls at the prep school move on to the senior school, for which they are well prepared. Others come from abroad, locally and further afield. Entry is, by and large, non-selective: the school is looking for potential, for girls who will contribute and stretch their potential, for girls who will appreciate the variety of activities on offer.

Sixth form entrants – including boys – are assessed in English, maths and by interview.

Exit: Some 20 per cent leave after GCSEs. A mix of sixth form destinations from Oxbridge to art school to Royal Ballet to Case Western University, USA. Courses range from dentistry to animation to accounting and finance. There is no cloning these girls.

Money matters: The school offers scholarships into year 7, year 9, year 10 and year 12 (academic, dance, riding, music, art, sport and children living in the village). Riding and ballet are extras: expect some £800 a term for ballet and stabling around £90 a week. Bursaries may be available. Don't be afraid to ask the bursar.

Remarks: It is surely right to see AB as a special school, a school with delightful idiosyncrasies and unique possibilities; a school which really does nurture individuality, offering unrivalled opportunities to pursue dance, the performing arts, music and riding as well as good academic teaching. In 2014 the school celebrated its 140th anniversary and it is now leaping into the next decade with 'courage braced and faith rekindled.' These are exciting times for an exciting school.

Beachborough School
3
Westbury, Brackley, Northamptonshire NN13 5LB
01280 700071 | office@beachborough.com | www.beachborough.com
Ages: 2.5 -13 (boarding from 7)
Pupils: 382; Boarders: 5 weekly, 70 flexi
Day: £10,440 – £16,395 pa; Boarding: + £28 – £30 per night

Headmaster: Since April 2018, Christian Pritchard, previously head of Ranby House, the prep school of Worksop College. Degree from University College of Ripon and York St John and a masters in education from Oxford Brookes. A keen musician with a background in computer science. He has also worked

internationally as head of the British School in Amsterdam and head of the junior school at Taipei European School. He is married to Zoe and they have two daughters.

Entrance: Main entry (non-selective) in September, but can and will take from any time, with the school having grown by 100 pupils since the start of the recession. An informal 'taster' day, with teacher-led assessments, gives the school some idea of a child's strengths and weaknesses; applicants for year 3 upwards assessed in English and maths. Some financial assistance is available for parents in difficulty via means-tested bursary provision.

Exit: Around half of year 8s leave with scholarships and all reach the pass rate for their chosen schools, the most popular of which are nearby Stowe and Bloxham, with others including Oxford High, Abingdon, Akeley Wood, Tudor Hall, Magdalen College School, Oundle, Millfield, Mount Kelly and Headington. A few leave at 11 for schools like Royal Latin, nearby grammar.

Remarks: Set in an impressive rambling country mansion, once owned by MP Sir Samuel Scott, the school has a good range of modern blocks surrounding it, the newest of which is a huge sports hall that many senior schools would be proud of. Others include a very good sized school theatre, science block that usually has Bunsen burners in full swing, and a smart Boardroom Building, where children from nursery up to year 4 are based. There's also staff digs, where many of the 40-strong teaching staff live, including head, two deputies and the head of boarding. All the classrooms are light, airy and inviting. The school hasn't always been based here, however, having originally been founded in Folkestone in 1910, after which it moved to Ewell, Purley and then Stockbridge, finally settling three miles from Brackley in 1942.

The fact that the children use the same school entrance as visitors says it all – this school is all about inclusivity. So whilst the reception areas still have the typical 'smart hotel' look of many rural private schools, there's a refreshing emphasis on displaying children's artwork and there are practical touches like the fridge (albeit hidden behind tasteful built-in cupboards) by the front door so pupils can collect anything they've made in cookery lessons on their way home.

Total of 30 acres of lush countryside for pupils to enjoy – and they really do. We happened to visit on a sunny April day and at break-time, children were running and jumping all over the front lawn, but on rainy days they simply don boiler suits and wellies. School has its own farm and sells its own sausages, and there are plenty of dedicated gardens dotted around, including the nursery sound garden and early years vegetable garden. Forest school means you'll often see pupils taking classes outside, and when we visited there was even a replica of a trench in one field. This formed part of the school's 'enrichment week', where the timetable is regularly collapsed so that teachers can focus all subjects on a single topic, in this case World War I.

'Enrichment week' and a few other examples aside, lessons up to year 6 are based on the national curriculum. In addition to core subjects of English, maths and science, all children learn history, geography, French (from age of 5), Latin, religious studies, art, DT, music, computing, drama, PE and games. Years 7 and 8 geared towards CE and scholarship exams. Subject specialists teach children from year 5 upwards. Three sets for English, French, maths and science from year 3 upwards. Average class sizes of 14 to 18 with two or three classes in a year group.

In the past, Beachborough wasn't regarded as very academic. But whilst a previous head referred to it as a 'gentle' school, it now prefers the description of 'happy, ambitious and challenging' – a combination that pupils and parents agree pretty much sum up the changes brought in, ie encouraging a greater academic focus which stretches pupils, although never aggressively. So whilst year 1's computing lesson might focus on coding and older children can expect lectures from the likes of Professor Matt Jarvis from Oxford University on black holes, you'll also find display walls throughout the school celebrating the efforts of the less academically inclined.

Good provision for those requiring extra help (dyslexia, dyspraxia), via the learning support department. No charge is made for this – nor, incidentally, for tea and prep time after school; before- and after-school care; or most residential school trips, which include a year 2 trip to Amersham, whilst older year groups go to PGL, HMS Belfast, Spain, Paris and the Lake District. There's also a focus on gifted and talented via the school's able child programme. Self-assessment and peer-assessment are priorities and there's a big push for children (especially the gifted and talented) to be encouraged to allow themselves to take intellectual risks with a view to learning from them, rather than getting stuck in the notion that they must achieve the best marks first time.

Pudding known as 'bird seed' (Rice Krispies coated in custard) easily the best loved course. Children eat calmly at long wooden tables, with teachers sitting at each end

Sport is central, with some pupils at regional or national level in sports such as trampolining and cricket. But this isn't a school where only top athletes are celebrated. Every child is involved in team games and team photos displayed around the school are not just of the A and B teams, but also the Cs, Ds and Es. Moreover, whatever their level of sports prowess, children get to compete against other schools, enjoying match teas and hearing their names read out in assembly. The school regularly puts out four or five sports teams to play against other schools. Girls play football and cricket too, which one parent says reflects 'how Beachborough isn't a boys' prep school with girls, but a proper, genuine co-ed school,' where incidentally there is pretty much a 50/50 gender split in every year. Swimming club every week at Stowe School's pool, four miles away, and the newest sport in the school is triathlon, in which 30 children take part every Saturday.

Music is big here, with around two-thirds playing an instrument ranging from piano to bassoon, and all year groups have weekly class music in a charming music department at the top of the school. Year 1s and 2s get to try out the violin, recorder and percussion keyboard for 20 weeks before deciding if they want individual lessons. Two choirs, chamber choir and junior choir, for all year 3 and 4 children. Music tours include places like Bruges.

Weekly drama and art classes for all year groups too. Year 8s perform a Shakespeare play every year, while years 7/8, 5/6 and 3/4 also perform annually, with recent examples including Treasure Island and Pirates of the Caribbean Curry Bean. Years 2 and under do a Christmas play. Art – which is overseen by not just a head of art but professional artist – is imaginatively displayed throughout the school, and other activities include Young Enterprise, golf, Mad Science, tennis, archery, craft clubs and dance.

USPs include no Saturday school and a flexible approach to boarding. This includes up to four nights a week, and nearly half the children aged 7+ stay over at least once a week. This is no sleepover, though, with organised activities for boarders, a clear boarding school culture and all the strict rules you might expect, such as bedtime for oldest pupils at 9.15pm and silent reading before lights out. Dorms, which are located on top floor of main school building and which have girls' rooms on one side and boys' on the other, are well kept, welcoming and cheerful, with stunning wall art (Narnia for girls; war planes for boys). Long-serving school matron is based here. As one pupil said, 'Some of us have never boarded and you don't feel left out because of it.'

Food is popular, with one pudding known as 'bird seed' (Rice Krispies coated in custard) easily the best loved course. Children eat calmly at long wooden tables, with teachers sitting at each end, and grace is said before and after each meal.

The code of conduct is clear, including 'being friendly is easy and it can make the world of difference' and 'always do your best, whatever the challenge.' By and large, the children seem to live by them, with pupils (and indeed parents) saying the school feels like one big family. Bad behaviour taken seriously, with a naughty bench for the younger children (although it's not called that), but the focus is on prevention and there's a new well-being programme. School says that whilst it's natural for children to fall out from time to time, they don't allow this to descend to bullying, which they put down to an anti-bullying policy, great pastoral care, a focus on rewards for friendly behaviour and the fact that little problems don't grow due to positive interventions. Parents and pupils agree. Active school council, which had just voted in increased choice in school meals when we visited.

The pupil body is almost exclusively white and, besides the 10-15 per cent Americans, almost all English. But this is unsurprising, given that the majority of children are local, with some coming from Towcester, Bicester, Banbury and Milton Keynes. Parents mainly from farming industries, motor racing employees (Silverstone is round the corner) and hedge-fund managers. Lots of family events, with the Beachborough Association putting on things like murder mystery evenings, coffee stops, quiz nights and an annual camp-out on the front lawn, for which tents were starting to appear when we visited.

This is a happy, nurturing school, set in beautiful surroundings that are truly utilised. We found the children to be confident, polite and animated and completely lacking in arrogance. 'I've done things I'd never have thought of – like archery,' said one pupil. 'I love the fact that we're always celebrating people. I've learned that everyone is good at something,' said another.

Parents talk about the 'special atmosphere' and 'emphasis on inclusivity', as well as the 'individual attention that each child gets.' 'This place is a hidden jewel,' says one parent. 'The children are encouraged in whatever direction they want to go and the staff have a way of getting the best out of them.'

Bilton Grange School

Rugby Road, Dunchurch, Rugby, Warwickshire CV22 6QU

01788 810217 | admissions@biltongrange.co.uk | www.biltongrange.co.uk

Ages: 4–13 (boarding from 7)

Pupils: 302; **Boarders:** 34 full, 15 weekly, 68 flexi

Day: £9,780 – £18,870 pa; **Boarding:** £23,850 – £25,710 pa

Headmaster: Since 2013, Alex Osiatynski. This is a head who has the right school and a school that has the right head. He has managed to distil the essence of the school into an inspiring package. He has an impeccable background to understand the heritage of Bilton Grange and a vision for how to maximise this heritage in order to create a 21st century education for children. His own education was at Dulwich College and Oxford; he came to Bilton Grange from being director of music at Loughborough Endowed Schools, and has worked at Gresham's and the British School in the Netherlands. He is married to Freya and has two sons. Freya is a theatre design professional and her creative eye is visible in the imaginative decor around boarding areas and elsewhere. 'She is busy teaching professional theatre lighting skills to the children for the next school production rather than being the traditional tea pouring headmaster's wife,' Alex tells us.

He is Polish by ancestry, and his family's close involvement in the Polish struggle for liberal democracy makes him acutely aware of the need to educate children in political global awareness – something in which he is clearly succeeding, judging by a group of older children who told us earnestly how important it was that every single person voted and had thought about it.

He has overhauled communications with parents and this has been much appreciated. 'Boarding staff and academic staff get back to you so quickly and they often tell you things before you have had time to ask,' a parent told us. He is a head who is seen as having time for people, has high standards and is open and collaborative in style. He is generally considered to have driven a lot of change, some of it a bit rapid for a few parents, we gather, but Alex is now committed to those small steps that can take everyone along.

Entrance: Two or three form entry. Slightly more boys than girls (particularly amongst boarders) but it's not obvious looking round. Non-selective, though the school says they are looking for children who can access what is, in an age appropriate way, an academic curriculum. Applicants are interviewed by the head. If places become available, children can enter at any stage. A number come in from London at 11+ for the final two years, to get the boarding experience or just to get away from the London hothouse.

The school is very keen to offer means-tested bursaries and is working hard to forge partnerships to increase these. There is, as a result, a slightly wider social mix that you find in many country prep schools.

Exit: Parents felt very well advised by the school about appropriate choices at 13+. A few leave to go to grammar schools at 11 but mostly it's senior boarding – around half to Rugby but also Eton, Uppingham, Repton, Oundle, Bloxham and Stowe with a number of scholarships each year. As you might expect, the focus is on 13+ and the head is not keen on 11+. 'It puts a lot of pressure on children much too young', he says. 'They lose out on years of childhood'.

One group was busy designing Bilton Grange's own Cluedo while another was reviewing designs for a trebuchet. Others were writing policy papers for a mock election

Remarks: Set in 90 acres of its own countryside and woods, the Pugin designed buildings stand as a symbol of stability, tradition and British cultural heritage. The children can't but be reassured and uplifted by the glorious wooden panelling and carvings of chapel, library and staircases, the huge windows, the period wallpaper sourced from the Houses of Parliament. Within this, modernity in the form of ongoing building development sits comfortably. Not all the 20th century builds are as stunning as the Victorian heart but buildings are being adapted and renovated – science labs are bright and fresh and lots of the classrooms have had a complete and attractive overhaul.

Academically Bilton Grange does very well both by its high flyers and by those who are not going to get the big public school scholarships. Most subjects are taught in ability sets by year 7 and although this clearly causes some angst, by and large parents and children are on board. The

children in particular spoke about the benefits of being with a group that learnt at your sort of speed. A number of parents who have moved children out of the London pressure cooker told us that while Bilton Grange is less in your face, academically pushy than its London counterparts, it does get children to the best schools and even more importantly, it creates highly motivated and self-driven children who succeed well beyond 13+.

The school takes in children whom they expect to access an academic curriculum, and within that can work positively with those who might be considered to have a mild learning difficulty. Small class sizes (around 12 to 16) allow for a lot of individual support within lessons and the increasing setting as they get older allows for further tailoring to meet specific needs. Where difficulties are identified, a team of specialist staff works with parents and develops an individual learning plan which may involve a range of strategies – one-to-one sessions, in class support, Saturday literacy enrichment, for example.

The school identifies high flyers who might be heading for senior school scholarships during year 7 and is about to look at year 6 as well. The children are offered various opportunities and teachers watch how they respond to the stretch and challenge. The children say the teachers are always ready to help when they need it and don't want them to have to do masses of work in the evenings. These children don't feel under tremendous pressure but get the scholarships without it.

We visited as academic scholarship exams had finished, and one group was busy designing Bilton Grange's own Cluedo whilst another was making a trebuchet scaled up from some carefully worked out computer calculated designs. Others were writing policy papers for a forthcoming election in school to mirror the June general election manifestos. 'Our children are moving beyond party politics to think about policies', the head told us – a very enlightened and much needed approach, we all agreed.

While the curriculum is fairly traditional, the focus is on encouraging what the head calls 'flexible' learners. The school now teaches the three sciences together rather than separately as in a secondary school. 'That's not what life is really like,' says the head. 'We want children to see the connections.' This leads to an emphasis on the applied aspect of science – the children had a talk from a Jaguar Land Rover designer recently and have been creating their own rocket-propelled cars. DT is a real strength. Even young children work on scary machines and love it. The school encourages them to make cross-curricular links all the time. The options and curriculum enrichment programme, which runs after school and on Saturdays, is extensive and includes academic extension subjects such as Japanese as well as lots of creative opportunities

in technology and science. Teachers' continuing professional development is taken seriously – there are weekly staff meetings where teaching and learning ideas can be shared and everyone benefits from hearing about the excellent practice.

After a talk from a Jaguar Land Rover designer recently, pupils have been creating their own rocket-propelled cars

The school is also traditional in terms of its values and behavioural expectations. There is an emphasis on courtesy, respecting one another and the community but this in no way inhibits the children's enthusiasm, which is celebrated round every corner of the school. Parents, too, are expected to uphold the school values and the head has very little time for those who don't. While traditional, the school is certainly not static, however. 'We are constantly future gazing', the head told us. 'We have stopped the pattern of doing great strategy plans every four years or so and changing dramatically at that point: we are thinking about the future and introducing small developments on an ongoing basis. Modern institutions can't wait for the old pattern of management reviews: they need to be much more nimble.'

The school runs a lecture series for years 7 and 8, their parents and the wider community three or four times a year that aims to bring into the school leaders from a wide field to help the children become aware of the vast number of life opportunities that are now available.

There are other forms of outreach going on – though the head has found some of the DfE generated initiatives pretty school-unfriendly. One success is the Scout group, started and still run by the head. It is now the biggest in the district and gets together very regularly with other packs for scouting activities.

School welcomes parents in and considers their needs thoughtfully. This is regarded as a huge strength. There is a lounge area in a charming stone-slabbed Victorian conservatory for parents who are waiting to pick up a second child, or just want to chat or browse the senior school brochures, with a little play area for tinies. Talks that are regarded as important for parents to hear are videoed and sent to parents who can't make it. 'The school really understands working parents', one family told us. 'We need all-encompassing care so we know if BA lets us down on a flight back from a meeting, a phone call to school will ensure the children can stay and are cared for. It's brilliant.'

Most don't start boarding until year 4. The school is very careful to try to ensure that boarders are emotionally ready for it – and indeed that their parents are. Some flexi-boarding is possible but by year 8 most are full boarders. There is deliberately gradual transition. Saturday mornings are optional for year 4s, with an exciting new programme called the BiG Saturday that should tempt many back before afternoon sports matches. By year 6, there are some lessons on Saturdays for everyone as well as the vibrant enrichment options. In years 7 and

Day children are welcome to join boarders for prep; boarders are encouraged to invite their day friends in for the odd sleepover

8, everyone is in for academic morning lessons and games in the afternoon. If you are not actually in a match, you are in a training session.

We enjoyed the food, which caters for various special diets as well as provided keenly anticipated treats such as roasts and steaks. Matron is on the door to ensure plates contain a variety of colours. Boarding accommodation is refurbished on a rolling programme and the rooms, most of which house about six, are fresh and unregimented. The boys have a playroom with Scalextrics, table football, a model railway and snooker. The girls have a charming sitting room with plenty of books. Day children are very welcome to join boarders for prep and boarders are encouraged to invite their day friends in for the odd sleepover at weekends.

Pastoral care is high on the school's priorities. Staff are caring and clearly love children. They are also well trained and knowledgeable about theories around children's mental health. The PSHE programme aims to tackle the issues that start to cause anxiety as the children head towards the teen age years. No-one was worried about bullying; yes, normal friendship ups and downs, but nothing the school isn't highly experienced at resolving. Although it is a school where masses seems to be going on all the time, staff are conscious that children also need to relish quiet times and these, too, are built into the day.

Sports facilities are good and sport is relished as only healthy, active children can relish it. School encourages non-team sports (golf, clay pigeon shooting, zumba, trampolining) though the head also wants everyone to experience the community values playing in a team can bring. The children love the fact that they can do sport more or less every day and they like the fact girls play cricket. One family, whose children are clearly sporting stars, felt a bit more of the 'winning at all costs' drive wouldn't come amiss, but that was not a general view, most going along with the sport for all approach. In fact the school does do well against other schools and the top players participate at county and, indeed, national level. The grounds lend themselves to a vigorous relationship with the outside world. Some of this is formalised – a science garden, a gardening club – but probably more important is the tearing about outside that goes on around lessons. There is an Astroturf within a Pugin walled garden but what strikes us most is that there is simply masses of space with which the children engage in every way they can.

Drama thrives and much use is made of the theatre. 'Being able to participate in plays has really given my son the confidence he lacked before coming to Bilton Grange,' one father told us. The head is a musician by training and keen to develop music facilities. The director of music's regular hymn practices are apparently highly entertaining and eagerly anticipated. Lots of the children play instruments (about 80 per cent have individual music lessons each week) and there is a wide range – the harp as well as the mainstream orchestral instruments. There are many performance opportunities for the various ensembles and choirs, both in the school and outside – the choir has sung in Coventry Cathedral, the Royal Festival Hall and St John Smith Square recently.

Bilton Grange is unpretentious despite its splendid buildings. 'Not posh enough for some,' the head told us, with some pride. It has been co-educational for many years and there is none of the alpha male feel of some prep schools. It has a genuine child-centred core – children are not there just to fulfil parental expectations and not allowed to be mini-teenagers plugged full time into the cyber world – they are there to experience and enjoy childhood.

There are many highlights to make both local families and those from the south east sit up and take note. Not least the recent improvements to the perennial school problem of car park space – which allows the school to make the most of its magnificent façade and is one of the most efficient systems we have seen.

Bromsgrove School

5

Worcester Road, Bromsgrove, Worcestershire B61 7DU

01527 579679 | admissions@bromsgrove-school.co.uk | www.bromsgrove-school.co.uk

Ages: 13–18

Pupils: 944; sixth form: 446; **Boarders:** 425

Day: £16,020 pa; **Boarding:** £23,775 – £35,850 pa

Headmaster: Following a glittering career in New Zealand that embraced the state and independent sector, Peter Clague joined Bromsgrove as head in 2014. Attracted by its sense of heritage and purpose, Peter says it was Bromsgrove's challenge to the traditional public school image that clinched the deal for him. He is a huge supporter of IB and believes that its genuinely international spirit suffuses the whole school, bringing with it a progressive liberalism and excitement about modern educational developments. He has introduced more flexibility in the timetable, with longer lunch breaks for pupils to pursue co-curricular interests, and aligned the prep and senior school more closely, but perhaps the biggest changes are in the importance he is giving to the arts. There is more music and drama than ever before and a huge investment into the building of a new theatre at the prep school and concert hall at the senior school.

'He is not as scary as he looks', said one girl to us, which is more a comment on his height and presence than anything else because he is universally seen as charming and warm. The school is proud of its international leader and feel he mirrors the increasingly global outlook of the school. They like also the way in which he respects the traditions of the school but helps them all to look critically at what works and change what could be better. He is described as a visionary and also praised for being in touch with reality. 'He's not all idealism – he has his finger on the business pulse and is very data focused', one senior member of staff told us. He is a skilled wood turner and works beside staff and students building stage sets. He is an 'awesome' public speaker, pupils told us: 'we never know where his metaphors are taking us'.

His litmus test for everything is 'Is it good for the pupils?'

Academic matters: This is a school that really does embrace and value the vocational and the academic. A Level, IB and BTec are all on offer in the sixth form and each has its strong supporters. The IB group loves the small, but growing, tightly knit IB community and tells us that they get all the very best teachers – but the other groups said the same, so we assume there are just a splendid lot of wonderful teachers. A Level students assured us they get the breadth through all taking the EPQ (Extended Project Qualification). Geography is 'amazing', politics is 'brilliant' and both attract large A level groups. Science and maths flourish. There are currently nine sets taking single maths and three further maths groups. Results are strong. At GCSE, 60 per cent A*-A/9-7 grades in 2017. At the end of the sixth form, virtually all BTec results are double distinctions, the average IB diploma score was 39 in 2017 and at A level 80 per cent of grades were A*-B and three-fifths A*/A.

The only criticism on curriculum breadth came from parents who wanted the school to be offering much more on the home economics and cookery side of things, but apparently the school is taking this on, and other than that there is an impressive range of opportunities.

Impressive arena with seating for 400 where the national indoor hockey finals take place. The pool and gym are open at weekends

Saturday mornings are not compulsory but a large proportion of pupils are likely to be there, not least because that is when some of the additional academic classes take place – whether in the form of catch-up and support 'surgeries' or Oxbridge preparation. There are plenty of other academic interest groups running too for anyone not falling into those categories. For those who miss a Saturday, there are departmental tweets that keep you interested.

Learning support is highly rated, though one parent gave a word of caution that moderate learning difficulties were beyond the scope of the school. There is a very attractive and well-used learning resources centre on three levels and we were delighted to hear it is open till 10.00 in the evening and at weekends. This is the sort of opportunity that makes boarding so attractive to the serious student as well as those who want one long sleepover.

Games, options, the arts: Everyone was at pains to tell us that this is not just a rugby school. Well it certainly brings home the rugby silverware, winning the last two national finals, but then the girls' netball team are national champions too. There is genuinely a big variety of sport on offer with D teams that inspire just as much enthusiasm as the A teams. The school was ranked fourth in the country this year in School Sports Magazine. The elite senior rugby players do have to make the sort of serious commitment you would expect at national level, so it is not really an option to be in the U18 squad and play the lead in the school play. Sports facilities are excellent as you would expect, with a particularly impressive new indoor arena with pull-out seating for 400 where the national indoor hockey finals take place. The pool and gym are open at weekends for boarders.

There is an exciting variety of clubs and societies and the school has invested heavily in staff on the co-curricular side to make a strong offering for all. Everyone was rightly proud of a girl who had entered an international competition to build an electric car and had ended up racing it at Rockingham. Drama, even before the new theatre is completed, is big and lots of departments – including art and DT – contribute to productions. Music is getting stronger all the time with smaller lunchtime concerts as well as the big school showpieces. There is Model United Nations and the school sends pupils to the European Youth Parliament. Pupils and parents were keen to tell us that the school looks for what every individual is good at and helps them find their niche and passion.

All year 10s do CCF. Some continue and others take up Duke of Edinburgh awards separately. There are service projects running so everyone makes a community contribution at some stage.

Boarding: At first the size may be a little intimidating but it is that which ensures the wide opportunities and it is ameliorated by the house system. Each house has its own internal family structure with older pupils acting as mothers and fathers and the younger ones as children. At the end of year 11, students can move to a sixth form house, but some can't bear to leave their first boarding house, home from home, at that stage. Apart from those in the sixth form house, everyone eats in a central dining room. There are separate day houses and one with day pupils and boarders. A full cycle of impressive refurbishment is just about completed.

House tutors have about eight in a group and, with a 50 minute weekly session timetabled, get to know their tutees well. Sixth formers say that if you act like an adult, tutors treat you like an adult. Houses are good at communicating with parents and pupils – there are house newsletters and blogs as well as balls that help create a strong house identity. House competitions are seen as big bonding experiences and we were urged to get onto the school website to enjoy the full splendour of house music competitions.

Contact with ex-pupils is maintained so that current pupils can get advice on careers and university choices and the chance to practise interview technique

The medical centre is highly praised. The nurses visit each boarding house every night to check all is fine and the focus on well-being, which includes bringing in outside speakers, is welcomed. Boarders say it is a 'full on' school. If you want to spend your weekends and evenings on a couch, the Bromsgrove experience would be wasted on you.

Background and atmosphere: Teaching staff come from a range of educational backgrounds – Oxbridge as well as the old polys – and this gives a sense that the school is grounded in the realities of life outside. There is a drive to ensure an authentic connection with the local community, who use the sports facilities and will be enjoying the new performing arts additions. Senior pupils have links

with local state schools through CCF, D of E and university preparation. There's a sense of energy and hard work. The days are long for boarders and day pupils but they are full of purposeful activities.

It is a large campus, 100 acres, in the middle of Bromsgrove, a medium sized Midlands town. Buildings vary in age and the overall impression is of a site loved, cherished and very well maintained. Teaching blocks are attractive with wide corridors and big classrooms, all well lit. There is a delightful little school museum in the old chapel which is just one of a number of reminders of the school's heritage. There are 11 houses, all but one single sex, some in modern buildings, some in charming older ones; the only co-ed house, in a converted hotel a few minutes from the main campus that was once the home of A E Housman, is a real stunner. The 'new' chapel is very prominent on the school site and there are assemblies three times a week for everyone.

There is a popular café, open all day, for older pupils – but we were assured by sixth earnest formers 'it is never a substitute for a proper lunch'.

We were impressed by the careers department where there has been a serious investment in staffing. Year 11 and sixth form pupils have a number of one-to-one interviews and these are supplemented by a Bromsgrove Futures programme of weekly visiting speakers. The contact with ex-pupils is also strong, so current pupils can get advice on careers and university choices and the chance to practise interview technique. There is a diverse intake and the careers department is well aware it is catering for wide range of needs – another example of how, despite its size, the school is interested in individuals.

Pupils clearly feel the school is good at listening. The head boy and girl lead regular school forums with no member of staff present and they told us the very positive results from these meetings. Pupil voice is increasingly bedded into all aspects and creates an atmosphere that pupils really are at the centre of this school.

Pastoral care, well-being and discipline: The pupils do need a degree of self-discipline to flourish, parents told us. They need to manage themselves to some extent especially as they get older – which is seen as excellent preparation for life beyond Bromsgrove for those who succeed, but some parents knew pupils who had struggled with it. Discipline is seen as being robust and fair and pupils need to be prepared to accept it without arguing the toss. Uniform regulations are enforced strictly. Punishments for serious breaches of school rules ('but it's very rare,' pupils assured us) are consistent and take sensible account of the culprit's previous history, but there is very little debate round drugs or sex – you are out. The underpinning rule is that you must not stop others from learning.

The pupils we met were delightful and genuine. They were articulate and thoughtful and all quite different from each other, which was refreshing

Pupils and parents spoke very warmly and appreciatively about members of staff both on the academic and pastoral side. The overriding sense is that well-being and the whole person really do matter to staff.

Pupils and parents: The school sits somewhere between highly competitive Birmingham and posh boarding school clientele. Families typically have both parents working and are fairly diverse, but probably not a lot of old money and a quite a number of military families. It attracts English families who want an international community – there are boarders from all over the world – and a choice of routes post-16. Bucking national trends, there has been an increase in British boarders and prep boarding in recent years. The pupils we met were delightful and genuine. They were articulate and thoughtful and all quite different from each other, which was refreshing. The situation of the school is an asset – it is in a good central England location, easy to reach from all corners of the country.

Head is very conscious of need to widen access and play a part in promoting social mobility. He is building a bursary fund

Entrance: At 13+ tests in English, maths, verbal and non-verbal reasoning and essay writing. The largest cohort from the school's own prep. No automatic entry, but parents seem to feel that plenty of warning and advice is given if a child is unlikely to be accepted to move through. At sixth form level, entry depends on GCSE results and an interview for UK candidates.

Exit: There is a seriously impressive range of courses, universities and countries in terms of pupil destination that reflects the wide sixth form clientele. In recent years, pupils have gone on to do catering, boat building, digital games study as well as maths at Cambridge, PPE at Oxford and mainstream academic subjects at strong UK and global universities, including lots of future doctors and engineers. Four to Oxbridge in 2017 and three medics; UCL the most popular destination; scholarships to NYU in Abu Dhabi, the University of British Columbia (International Leader of Tomorrow award) and the University of Mount Olive (international scholarship).

Money matters: You are paying for the excellent facilities and opportunities as a boarder or a day pupil. Learning support is included in the fees as is ESL tuition. The head is very conscious of the need to widen access and play a part in promoting social mobility. He is actively building a bursary fund and currently there are 98 children on significant fee reduction. He tells us that past pupils are very receptive to raising funds for bursary support. Scholarships are on offer for academic, sporting, artistic and musical talents.

Remarks: Bromsgrove manages to combine the feel of a local family day school with an international boarding school, attracting pupils both for its sporting reputation and also its academic offer and results. It is a carefully crafted hybrid that works. There is a culture of hard work and hard play and an earnestness about the pupils that is beguiling, far from the arrogant outcome some parents fear in independent schools. The arts side of the school is definitely in ascendency, both in terms of the huge financial investment and in the mindset of the community. We want to be invited back for the first performances in the new theatre and concert hall – we expect them to be world class.

Cardiff Sixth Form College

6

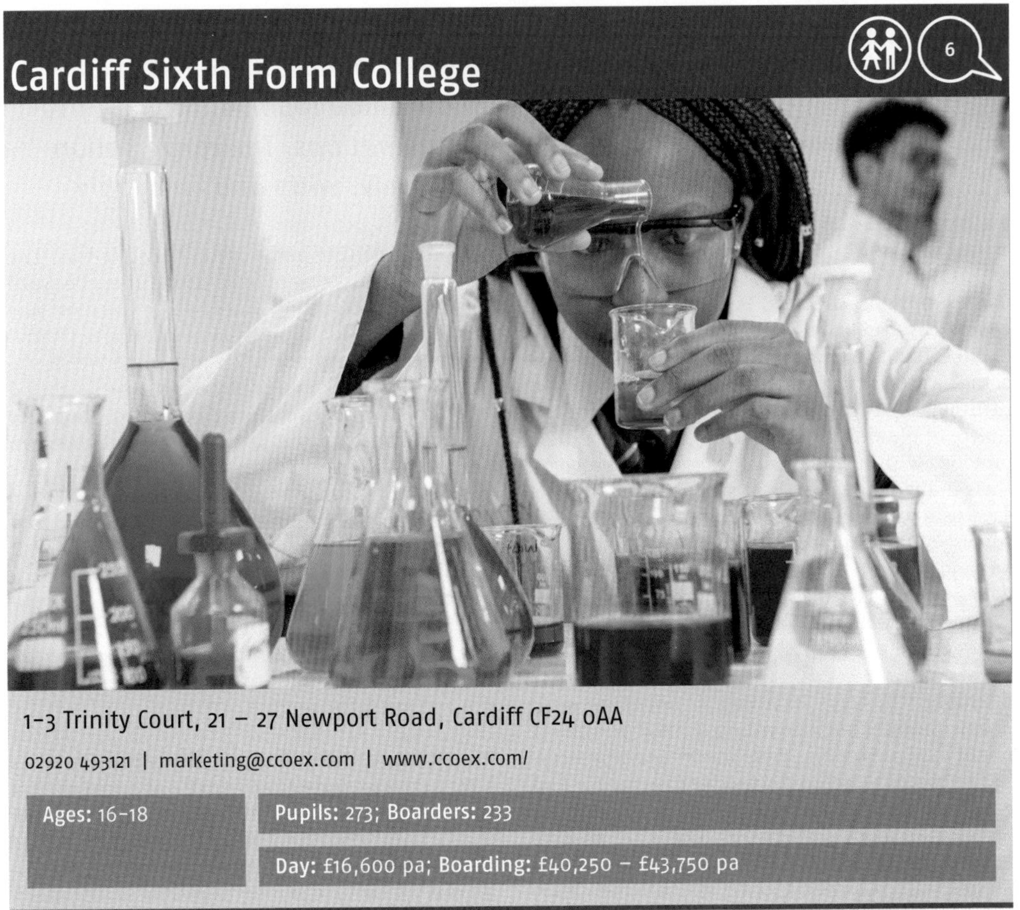

1-3 Trinity Court, 21 – 27 Newport Road, Cardiff CF24 0AA

02920 493121 | marketing@ccoex.com | www.ccoex.com/

Ages: 16-18

Pupils: 273; Boarders: 233

Day: £16,600 pa; Boarding: £40,250 – £43,750 pa

Principal: Since October 2016 Gareth Collier, previously head of business development here. Georgraphy degree from Dundee and PGCE from Leeds in geography and PE (outdoor activities). Has taught at schools in Tanzania and Kenya as well as being a houseparent at Gordonstoun, director of sport at Moreton Hall and international registrar at Taunton School.

Academic matters: The recent BBC programme entitled Britain's Brainiest School did not encourage everyone. Although we were sent a CD of the programme we did not watch it before we visited, but people who had watched it insisted on telling us what they thought. Some were impressed by the professionalism of the approach, the overall success of the pupils and the astonishing A level results 'that would help pupils get into any university.' For those who like statistics, 92 per cent of A levels were A*/A and 99 per cent A*-B in 2017. That's one side of it. 'But they must get an awful grinding,' others said. By the time we arrived we had been dragooned into expecting a hothouse atmosphere of gritted teeth, furrowed brow and clenched fists.

In fact from the moment we set off on our tour, during break, we met with something else. We came across pupils and staff lolling around in passageways, talking and laughing with all the ease of natural friendship. The leading actors in The Lion King were effortlessly discussing the play with the producer, who happened to be head of maths. We were generously drawn into the animated and entertaining conversation and invited to watch the extracts being performed during the Evening of Culture later in the week. We met a student who was reading Milton for English A level and who discussed it with zest and perception; other students were involved in critical thinking, politics, business studies, economics et al. Of course maths, further maths, chemistry, physics, biology – the usual suspects – were there. Best of all we were almost literally locked into a small room with about five mathematicians. The conversation was lively, witty and enjoyable. These were highly experienced and committed maths teachers who were blissfully happy because they no longer taught in schools where they had distracting responsibilities. Instead they were teaching/sharing the subject they loved, and to such bright and enthusiastic pupils. Later, during our visit to the Cultural Evening, we saw those Einsteins appear in a song and dance routine. The chorus went something like 'the more Maths you do, the better looking you become'. These teachers were a wonderful demonstration of scholarship and fun.

Games, options, the arts: Pupils looking to play competitive rugby or football, cricket or golf will find it difficult, though it is possible. 'Physical well-being,' as the school calls it, is more practical and utilitarian: health and leisure facilities are the centre of physical activities and 'students will be provided with custom-made fitness plans based on their individual needs......' It's all there in the prospectus: a balance to the more cerebral side of their time studying. All carefully and sensibly worked out and supported by a professional medical team who come on a regular basis. There are numerous sports clubs including football, netball, swimming and tennis. But not in the school's grounds.

Boarding: The term 'boarding' is not quite what people familiar with boarding schools in the UK might expect. Boarding here means literally sleeping in rooms which offer modern furniture and excellent facilities for working in – as good if not better than many universities. There are specific houseparents dealing exclusively with boys or girls in their houses, as well as other staff around checking the students in and out and qualified counsellors who lend an expert ear to anyone who needs some TLC. The delightful person who showed us round seemed to know everyone's names. The atmosphere is calm, friendly and inviting and the building, which is over a coffee shop, is just over the road from the teaching block. Clean, comfortable and safe.

There is a tremendous amount of preparation for university entrance including much interview practice

Background and atmosphere: This is a multicultural atmosphere with students from 40 different nationalities. One of the students told us, 'Internationals, while mixing with other nationalities, of course, keep their nationality. There's no compulsion but we appreciate the freedom to express ourselves. We are different and we rejoice in that. One of the obvious expressions lies in the different costume worn with pride and dignity on special occasions.' We witnessed this during the Cultural Evening and very exciting it was. The atmosphere was one of open friendliness between pupils and staff, a friendliness which was most generously extended to this ancient interloper. Overall it seemed a happy place. We met some Welsh students, all of whom were obviously clever – they'd been given very generous scholarships – but they are very much in the minority. One of them, in particular, is a very promising rugby player, who replied in response to our questions, 'I love the opportunity of meeting so many people from around the world.' He's global as they all are. It was very good to see so many alumni coming back for the evening and being cheered in.

We were almost literally locked into a small room with about five mathematians. The conversation was lively, witty and enjoyable

Recently bought by Dukes Education; an investigation by the Charity Commission into suspected financial irregularities relates to former trustees, not current management.

Pastoral care, well-being and discipline: Students have tutors to support and advise and told us that staff overall were very friendly and understanding. Certainly the atmosphere is cheerful as well as purposeful. There is a tremendous amount of preparation for entry into universities including much interview practice and many tutor-led societies exploring eg critical thinking, extended learning, various competitions such as senior maths, debating, Model United Nations, study skills – on and on it goes. No wonder the entrance level into universities is so high. As for discipline there are groups, called houses and given classical names. Apparently they are looked after by individual masters but there was no mention of that during our visit. Perhaps it's all done so well that it's taken for granted. Certainly the students were courteous and well behaved in a natural, friendly manner.

Pupils and parents: Parents mostly come from far away, but we met one delightful, happy parent who had made the journey from the far East especially to discuss the possibility of another of her children joining the school. 'They all keep us in touch,' she said, and, 'Skype is wonderful, though when my daughter first left home I was very sad.' At the Culture Evening we met many, many parents who were thrilled to be there and part of the whole occasion, enjoying the food and the dancing. We heard nothing but praise and appreciation, including from those (few) parents who live in Wales.

Entrance: Everyone takes entrance tests and are interviewed (by Skype if necessary). International students may be accepted purely on these results, as long as they have a high level of English fluency (IELTS 6.5), or if they already have at least six A*s at I/GCSE including their proposed A level subjects. Day students must obtain at least six A* grades at GCSE (those applying for scholarships must get at least nine A*s, or numerical equivalents), plus passing the entrance test and interview.

Exit: In 2017, 19 to Oxbridge, with 63 off to the London colleges, plus many to top universities round the country to study courses including medicine, law, engineering, economics and PPE. Large numbers of medics generally include some going to universities in Hong Kong, United States and Ireland.

Money matters: There are generous scholarships for locals – up 100 per cent for those with all A*s/9s at GCSE – and those we met seemed very happy. Scholarships of up to 50 per cent for overseas applicants.

Remarks: People who spoke to us before we visited expressed suspicion. 'It must be very tough, very restrictive, utterly humourless. Think force-feeding: the embodiment of Brave New World; robotic machines.' Such were the comments we heard from people who had not visited. This ageing GSG scribbler came away impressed by what was being achieved. There is, of course, a difference between education and the achievement of excellent grades. One might be seen as infusion for life; the other might be seen as stamp collecting. But what we saw was youth working hard to achieve results worthy of their talents and for which they deserved credit. The teaching is excellent and, most important, morale seems high with delightful relationships between staff and pupils.

That wonderful evening of music and dance, energy and liveliness with bags of skill, humour and well-tuned banter revealed the synthesis of this society. National dress, a variety of hats and music. What a colourful evening of creativity, happiness, joy and delight. One member of staff sitting next to us leaned over and whispered, 'and this is the collection of young who are described by critics as ground down, overworked and harassed. Remember!' We will remember, and with much pleasure.

Christ College, Brecon

7

Brecon, Powys LD3 8AF

01874 615440 | enquiries@christcollegebrecon.com | www.christcollegebrecon.com

Ages: 7-18 (boarding from year 5)

Pupils: 400; sixth form: 145; **Boarders:** 178 full, 21 flexi

Day: £8,889 – £17,988 pa; **Boarding:** £16,788 – £27,792 pa

The head: Since September 2017, Gareth Pearson (40s), previously senior deputy head at Lord Wandsworth College in Hampshire. Has also been a housemaster at Wellington College and maths teacher at Millfield, as well as a captain in the Royal Marines for eight years. Mechanical engineering degree from Loughborough, teaching qualifications from Plymouth and Bath and a masters in character education from Birmingham. He is married to Rhian and they have two children.

Academic matters: One of the really tedious pictorial clichés published by so many schools in August is of groups of pupils leaping up into the air clutching their A level results – or so it is to be assumed. It's a silly picture because it's so obviously lacking in any spontaneity and you feel the leavers have been treated like performing fleas. 'One, two three, now jump into the air as high as you can,' encourages the photographer absurdly. The pictures are enforced as useful advertising for the school. Humbug!

Christ College, Brecon does not go in for that sort of silliness though, naturally, they are happy to share their delight. After all, they have a lot to celebrate. They have always had their bright pupils moving on to Oxbridge and top medical schools but overall results have improved, and in recent A level results CCB came in the top 100 schools in the Daily Telegraph league tables. In 2017, 44 per cent A*/A grades at A level. The most obvious way of showing academic prowess is through endless grid systems. Statistics. Statistical junkies can get a fix here, of course, but the celebration and relief that accompanies success here is more human than most. This school is less about numbers, it's about human beings and their deserved achievements. A recent publication contains a wonderful account of two boys, great friends, and the academic rivalry which they shared for most of their time in the school. The writing is superb, like a short story. In fact there is genuine suspense as we read on, wondering who has indeed performed better overall. It's typical of this wonderful school that they should invest statistics with such human interest.

Having said all that the overall statistics are impressive and not to be ignored. They should be celebrated, but above all they should be put into perspective against the background of superb teaching, mutual respect and, yes, friendship between staff and pupils. Classes are small and that helps, though not as much as is frequently claimed. After all, small classes with lousy teaching will produce lousy results. We witnessed some absolutely tremendous teaching. The facilities and classrooms are generously laid out and the pupils respond fearlessly. They spoke to us unashamedly of the exciting quality of the teachers, the energy and fun they injected and the extra time teachers were prepared to offer for catch up and clarification. We saw sparky language teaching, lively music and drama, history, sciences, maths, biology: all demanding subjects – no raffia dolly-making here – and all warmly appreciated by pupils. It pays dividends. Medicine, science and engineering courses are the most popular. GCSE results are excellent, demonstrating the popularity and success of technical and creative subjects. In 2017, 46 per cent A*-A/9-7 grades. The overall academic standards of the school have improved without the aggressive insistence on the importance of grades adopted by so many schools. Here the grades are merely the boxes: it's the contents that matter and the way those contents are treated.

Brecon is the HQ of the army in Wales. The CCF is enormously popular, and when you've met the man who runs it you're half way towards understanding why

And what about those people with SEN? There aren't many at CCB who have SEN and those who do have been described as 'moderate mostly'. But it's almost worth cultivating some SEN in order to be closeted with the highly qualified, approachable teacher who presides in her classroom ever ready to help anyone who drops in. A previous GSG scribbler referred to those visits as pit stops and that's how the SEN guru likes it to be. She perceives her visitors as engaged in learning to overcome weaknesses, developing a sense of belonging and togetherness, of readiness and enhanced expectations. Let them stop by when they want to. She is full of wisdom and compassion. Every Thursday afternoon is tea party time: often, we were told, pretty lively. The parents we spoke to about her 'couldn't find the words to do her justice.' One final joy: most schools charge for help with SEN. At CCB pupils and parents pay with heartfelt gratitude and affection.

Games, options, the arts: Rugby is regarded by many as the number one sport at CCB. However, there is a strong move gathering impetus in the medical world and parts of the media to ban tackling throughout inter-school rugby. Oblivious to that, some ailing schools have turned themselves into something like rugby academies with much emphasis on wooing the biggest and the fastest players. Previous head, who enjoys watching rugby, spotted the potential dangers of such one-sided games and decided that the fixture list should change to ensure safety and competitiveness. It was a sane and sensible decision but initially brought her considerable flack from those who felt that boys should learn to deal with hard knocks and a broken bone or two. However, she stood her ground formidably before eventually winning her point. Rugby is still extremely popular with continued investment in the sport and its coaching with a former rugby professional appointed as director of rugby in recent years.

But rugby is by no means the only game. There is some football played, a lot of hockey – the school has a number of international hockey players, past and present, boys and girls. The boys as well as girls have been recent Welsh champions at U18s, U14s and U12s and there are outstanding netball teams. Lots of cricket, including a 20:20 Festival involving players from the UK and abroad. There's masses to do and much to be admired. Most pupils enjoy getting involved with a variety of sports and activities. Just as well. One pupil told us that he had been selected for five different sports 'and I'm not much good at any of them. But it was terrific fun and we didn't lose them all.'

Brecon is the HQ of the army in Wales, as a trip to the nearby cathedral with its regimental chapel confirms. The CCF is enormously popular, and when you've met the man who runs it you're half way towards understanding why. When we met him he was busy polishing up a trophy to return. Internet news suggests it's back in CCB, along with two silver medals won by what sounds a formidably tough, determined and clear-headed cadet. CCF is compulsory in yrs 9 and 10; girls as well and female staff.

Drama is driven by a dynamic head of department who enthuses not just the pupils but all members of the school community to tread the boards and join in. With an annual community project to rope such amateur thespians in, as well as an ambitious school production for the different age groups, it really does produce some of the highest quality productions. Their Les Mis was 'jaw-dropping', according to one West End fan we met who had seen the Christ College version.

Music is terrific. We were shown round by the director of music and met some delightful and talented pupils practising for a concert at the end of the week in the recently enlarged music building. It wasn't difficult to persuade us to return two days

later for a concert at the Royal Welsh College of Music and Drama, part of the school's celebrations of the 475th anniversary of its foundation by royal charter. It was a thrilling concert full of energy and skill, sensitivity and passion, from the youngest to the most senior. Choral singing that might have been written for Polly Garter, for as the Reverend Eli Jenkins murmured, and many of the audience might have done that evening, 'thank the Lord we're a musical nation'. Orchestras of all or most ages playing together; a delightful pupil making an excellent debut on the drums; from the youngest – who were wonderful – to the oldest instrumentalists who played with such skill, the evening was moving and exciting. Eli Jenkins was right.

We met a lot of parents at the school concert and no, they were not selected for their unique loyalty. They had come to support their children and the staff and what they all said in reply to our questions about academics was that it was 'cool to work'. One parent volunteered the notion that the pupils worked hard 'out of inspired interest and loyalty.' That seemed to sum up everything. Another phrase that remains is about the school, overall: 'Whatever they do, they do well.' The results of a recent survey would suggest that fewer than five per cent of parents would disagree with that.

Boarding: Boarding is convenient, of course, that's part of it all, but it ignores the fact that for many boys and girls, boarding is fun. The rooms are designed and built to be attractive. One or two of the students, who had older siblings at university, recognised that the rooms in which they lived were much nicer than they would get at most universities. They're nicer than many homes: snooker table, luxurious, comfortable sofas, large screen televisions, efficient showers and always friends to talk to. But they have responsibilities, and many to whom we spoke talked of the satisfaction they feel in being given positions of authority and so opportunities to pay back the treatment they had received. How ominous that would have sounded 100 years ago. Nowadays it's part of the rhythmic pattern of the school; the feeling of continuity and progress: history in the making. All staff are involved in boarding.

The six day and boarding houses include Alway House, where year 5 and 6 pupils from St Nicholas House junior school can weekly board with the year 7 and 8s.

Background and atmosphere: Founded in 1541 by Henry VIII on the site of the sacked and wracked Black Friars' church, victim of the Dissolution. Students are touchingly proud of this ancientness, as of the crowned 'h' tag, which is the school's logo, and of the fact that the chapel where they meet every morning has been worshipped in continuously since around 1250.

Wonderful new junior school: the St Nicholas House for boys and girls aged 7-11 (opened in 2014) and Alway House (boys and girls aged 11-13) which is, unbelievably, over 50 years old. A joyous building and full of intelligently conceived fittings and decorations, an area for sleeping, playing inside and out, ICT for researching particular topics and always kind, creative helpers from all walks of the school and not just walks, because on Fridays they go for a country run. Delightful, challenging

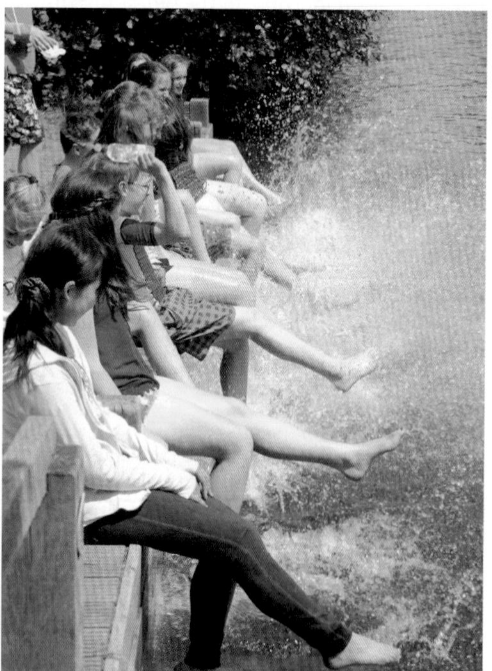

A delicious lunch in the wonderful ancient refectory in the company of delightful sixth formers was a real pleasure

climbing frames guiding young adventurers to the distance, where always and for ever the hills beckon and invite. How lucky those very young are and how appreciative everyone seems, from the youngest to the lower sixth volunteers.

Numerically this is a small school, though it has grown in numbers recently. It is amongst the happiest we have ever visited. From the genuinely warm welcome with which we were greeted at reception – something commented on by many parents – and thence throughout the whole tour (with a thoughtful and entertaining mixture of guides) we were treated with courtesy and spontaneous good will. Lunch with delicious food in the wonderful ancient refectory in the company of delightful sixth formers was a real pleasure. Our hosts were confident and entertaining without a hint of arrogance or self-consciousness; informative in their effortless appreciation of the school and generous minded about each other and the staff.

Pastoral care, well-being and discipline: The happiness is palpable and high spirited and that says much about the discipline. Pupils and staff walk around greeting, smiling and chatting and, when they see visitors approaching, focus the eyes and smile inclusively. At some schools visitors are greeted with pasted smiles and glazed eyes: well-trained but fundamentally indifferent. Staff and pupils clearly get on well with each other. Discipline is based on common sense and mutual consideration, and that is presumably what is meant by well-being. We were told stories of incidents in which anxieties and problems were spotted and addressed by teachers, class assistants, senior pupils and ground staff. Everyone is everyone's responsibility. In reply to our question about the school's tangible happiness, one sixth form girl told us: 'It's like a jigsaw: everyone seems to fit in.'

The head of school and deputy (one boy and one girl – this year the head of school is a girl) are selected by the head following nominations from staff and pupils, and there are 15 prefects. Duties? 'Not arduous,' said one. 'People are pretty reasonable.' 'Cowed?' Certainly not. 'Comfortably co-ed' – no difference of opportunities.

Pupils and parents: Most pupils come from a radius of, say, 50 miles or so, the sons and daughters of army officers, farmers, businesspeople. The usual suspects but, in our experience, considerably more loyal to the school than blasé parents in the home counties. 'Fewer demanding expectations,' we were told by parents with experience of both areas. Most boarding schools these days have a number of students from abroad and CCB is no exception. But here you do not get the impression, as with some schools, that they have been imported in lorry loads simply to boost grades in the sixth form. In the nicest possible way, those 17 per cent or so of pupils from China, Hong Kong, Japan, Nepal – there's a strong contingent of Gurkhas in Brecon – and Germans in the sixth form are almost invisible at first visit. The school seems much better at fully integrating pupils from abroad so that many get stuck in to rugby, cricket and choir singing. Those pupils from aboard whom we met were genuinely happy and involved.

Entrance: Into year 3 for St Nicholas House via an entry morning with 'a range of academic and creative activities', plus small group meetings with the college head and the head of St Nicholas House. Into years 7 and 9 by English and maths assessments and IQ test, plus interview and school reports. Sixth form entry by GCSE predictions, IQ test, school report and interview.

Exit: About 10 (on average) leave after GCSEs. Not because they're unhappy, we were assured by prefects and senior pupils, but often for sporting reasons or simply for a change – occasionally geographical. We did not detect any specific grumblings or rumblings of discontent. Of those who stay, most go on to university and to a wide range of subjects. The very helpful literature potential parents and pupils receive in reply to expressing an interest will clarify that. That literature is, incidentally, amongst the best of its kind we have ever seen and read: informative without being chest thumping, elegantly expressed and genuinely interesting. You could read it in bed without falling asleep and that's not true of all prospectuses. These ones would sit easily at the Hay Literary Festival.

Sixth form leavers to eg Cardiff, Exeter, Bath, Swansea, Liverpool and Reading to study subjects such as architecture, biomedical sciences, computer science and mechanical engineering.

Money matters: There are scholarships and bursaries available for the able and needy. Don't be afraid to ask. Incidentally there are no inescapable extras – in fact The Good Schools Guide recently voted CCB in the Top Ten Value for Money Boarding Schools in the UK. We do not have shares in the school.

Remarks: When you step back from GCSEs and A level grades; from rugby results and hockey triumphs; from CCF marches and medals; when you pause to marvel at the hills around, enfolding the school and beckoning; when you listen to the wonderful singing in the chapel founded nearly 800 years ago and restored by Gilbert Scott about 600 years later; when you consider that at the time the English Bible was being hammered out by that group of scholars and fanatics presided over by James 1, the Scottish King, Christ College Brecon had already been in existence for nearly 100 years, it is not difficult to feel that much has been absorbed from history and the world around. Perhaps it is not too fanciful to think that the extraordinary atmosphere of friendship, mutual loyalty and academic endeavour has emanated from the variety and insistence of the past. Like many schools of ancient foundation CCB hasn't always been in a good place, but it certainly is now. What's more there is history in the making. Ask about the expansion into the Far East. Great things are being delivered, even more is promised and this is a school that warrants admiration, loyalty and, above all, trust. Go and see for yourselves.

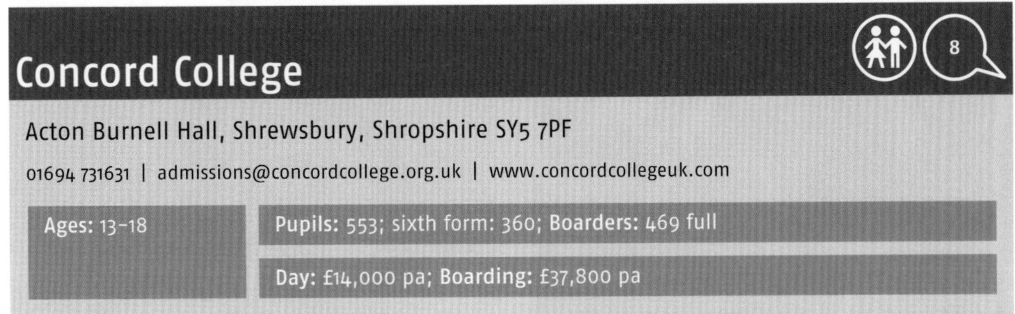

Concord College
8
Acton Burnell Hall, Shrewsbury, Shropshire SY5 7PF
01694 731631 | admissions@concordcollege.org.uk | www.concordcollegeuk.com
Ages: 13-18
Pupils: 553; sixth form: 360; Boarders: 469 full
Day: £14,000 pa; Boarding: £37,800 pa

Principal: Since 2005, Neil Hawkins MA (50s), a Cambridge historian whose previous posts include director of studies at The Leys and head of history at Sevenoaks. He has built on splendid work of his visionary predecessors – built and how! As we visited, a new science block with 22 laboratories including a research laboratory was going up, and boarding houses were being extended and kitted out with ensuite rooms. But it is the underlying ethos of the school, its commitment to internationalism, to excellence, to a global, harmonious meritocracy that has kept Neil and his wife at the school, though he admits the gorgeous views of the Shropshire countryside from his spacious study have helped.

Parents, staff and students clearly respect him hugely. They say he listens and empowers, that he is liberal and takes everyone with him in the drive for excellence. He comes across as approachable and incredibly enthusiastic, with a vision not just for the school but for the world. He feels the responsibility of educating the next generation of global leaders and wants to share his commitment to rigour and gentleness. He models the warm, unpretentious, positive and driven behaviours that he wants in the students. 'I have in my mind whenever I speak to groups of students, what values will these young people be passing on to their grandchildren. I want those values to be the core Concord ones of decency, trust, responsibility and service'.

Engaging, warm and welcoming, with a bubbling sense of humour and an air of inner calm, Mr Hawkins clearly delights in being at Concord – 'As a historian, it is wonderful. Look out there. Over to the right the castle and to the left the Parliamentary Barn'. As principal, he talks with infectious enthusiasm about the students, the staff and the whole set up, cheerfully and convincingly dealing with common misconceptions of the college.

Neil's wife Vanessa runs marketing, and does some teaching and pastoral leadership. They met at Cambridge where their son now studies after five years at Concord.

'He really cares about us,' said a student. 'He knows our names, comes into lunch every day and asks us how we're getting on and he listens to our answers. That is why so many student-led initiatives are implemented.' 'He certainly has his finger on the pulse,' said one parent. The right man for the job, and during his reign the college has gone from strength to strength. No school will stand still under Neil's leadership.

Academic matters: Whichever way organisations choose to produce exam league tables, Concord is coming in the top few elite selective schools in the country. This, of course, is the big draw for international students and it is this that keeps the school growing. A level results at A* and A hover around 80 per cent (85 per cent in 2017). At GCSE, 82 per cent A*-A/9-7 in 2017. Huge numbers take maths, further maths, economics and the sciences – very few humanities or languages – hence the need for more lab space.

Students and teachers agreed that the atmosphere is competitive – noticeboards feature top students from last year's exam cohort – but it's also highly supportive

Class sizes are small and the whole emphasis is on individual attention. We visited as A levels were kicking off and teachers had provided students with a list of all their non-contact time each week so students knew when each teacher was available for individual support. The results reflect the high

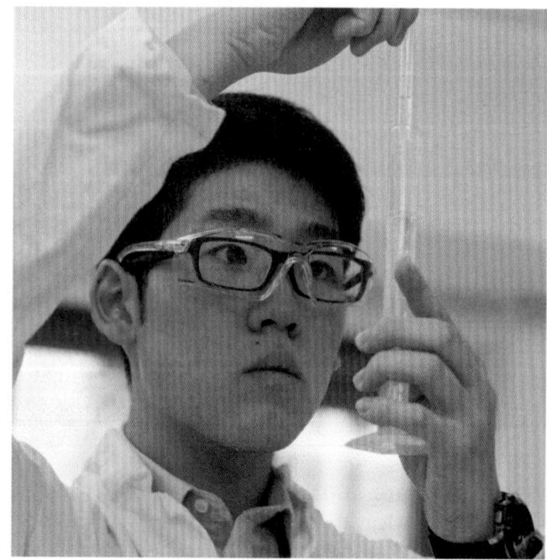

quality of teaching staff, the high regard in which they are held both by the students but also by the management, and the fact that students come from backgrounds that are very goal orientated (85 per cent are from overseas) and believe that education is important. Expectations are stratospheric. After the Saturday tests that run for year 10 upwards every week, teachers are bombarded with students wanting to know how to move their 98 per cent to 100 per cent. But teachers say that is only part of it – students are curious, love discussions, ask questions and feed off each other's intellectual passions. Many are aware they are exposed to a very different education to that offered in the top schools in their own country and they relish the relative liberalism.

Teaching is fast paced and teachers find they get through twice the material in a Concord A level lesson that they would expect to in other schools. The English lesson we observed had the students making their own notes, contributing to quick fired questions and shooting them back equally fast. Staff say students are united by a desire to succeed. They demand a lot of their teachers but are incredibly appreciative. The sixth formers were planning the Teachers' Day as they came to the end of their exam classes – an occasion to be able to express their gratitude in a number of creative and heartfelt ways. Both students and teachers went out of their way to explain that yes, the atmosphere is competitive – there are noticeboards with the top students from last year's external results featured – but also highly supportive. The students want everyone to achieve and helping each other is seen as part of the principles of a Concord education.

This may be the case for some but parents did raise questions about what it must feel like to be a student there when they don't get into Oxbridge or get top grades. Student after student to whom we spoke was high octane. They had ideas pouring out of them. They wanted a school with a brilliant reputation and results so they could go on and be significant players on the global scene. They knew that is not just about their sharp intellect but also about wider awareness, and they were just as keen to grab that too with both hands.

A level choices are what might be considered the safe, traditional subjects and one student commented that there was a limit to the combination of subjects that were possible. There are no 'ologies' taught, and drama and PE are available at GCSE but not A level – both largely practical courses. Music is offered as a BTec rather than GCSE and as an EPQ in the sixth form, again with a practical emphasis. These are for high quality recreation rather than purely academic study.

Most students are able to learn very quickly and the small class sizes allow for regular one-to-one support within the normal lessons to work on individual short term difficulties. At sixth form level, the admissions process selects those who will cope with the fast pace of A level teaching, though there is English language tuition available at all levels and students told us that they find this efficient and helpful. A few students require extra support which takes the form of extra lessons targeting language and/or literacy skills, with progress being closely monitored, mostly without extra cost.

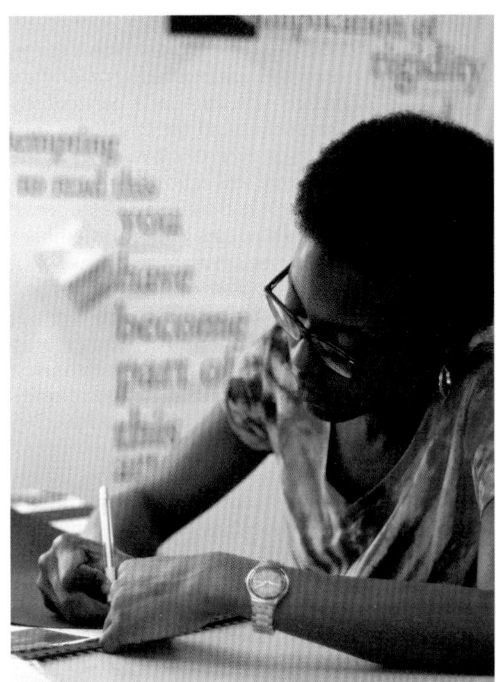

Games, options, the arts: 'Sport', one teacher told us, 'is not God here. It is a recreation for everyone and something you are expected to manage as part of your daily life.' That said, there are PE periods timetabled for everyone except the final year students during the week. There are a lot of matches against other local schools with stirring write ups of the games. There are the usual sports and probably more of the minority sports than you find at other schools – badminton, table tennis, basketball, volleyball. The facilities are marvellous, as you would expect, and going to be further extended with the recent purchase of a large field adjacent to the main school site. There is a popular fitness suite and swimming pool. There are links with local and regional sports clubs to support the elite sportspeople and the college boasts the occasional national champion. On the other hand, one father told us his son disliked sport and coming to Concord had been a huge relief to him.

There are wonderful performance opportunities for the musically gifted and a lot relish these, unsurprisingly given the number taking individual music lessons. But again the emphasis, particularly in the house competitions and international society cultural events, is on everyone having a go. The day we visited, everyone was talking about a concert the night before that had consisted of students' own compositions and students leading ensembles. Like a number of other performances, it was also a fundraising event for a local social enterprise charity. It had been professionally recorded by a music producer – the school has its own recording studio – and CDs were being sold in aid of the charity. There is an emphasis on celebrating musical traditions throughout the world, classical and folk. Top musicians enter local and national competitions and many sit music examinations. The school takes the students to concerts around Shropshire and hosts professional concerts itself in the 300 seat theatre and concert hall.

Student are high octane, they had ideas pouring out of them. They wanted a school with a brilliant reputation so they could go on and be significant players on the global scene

Performing arts generally consciously draws on the international dimension, offering ample opportunities for creative expression within a culture that is familiar but also exposing students to ones that are less so. The house arts competition is hugely popular and includes songs, poetry, dance and ensembles.

The art department is housed in the old village primary school and offers a brilliant space for high quality work. We saw bold projects in a great variety of media that showed the students pushing the boundaries of their creativity as well as indicating their ability for detailed research.

There is a myriad of other societies including the important international ones. 'It is good preparation for university where international societies are a valuable anchor for some of our students', the deputy head told us. Everyone commented on how open the college was to any new ideas for societies. There is none of the 'You can't do that because that is when rugby practice always happens' at Concord. Many of the societies are student-led and intellectually based – behavioural psychology, CED (Create, Engage, Discover – the Concord answer to Ted talks).

There is a real awareness of social issues in a college where first-hand experience of developing world problems is common. A committee that coordinates charity outreach and there is a lot going on which requires a level of business acumen.

There are outdoor education opportunities and a number of visits as well as workshops run by professionals of various kinds. All year 9s do a Duke of Edinburgh bronze award.

Boarding: Boarding has been slightly reorganised to reflect the needs of a larger college. All the lower school boys are now in one house and the lower school girls in another. Some students are housed outside the main school campus around the village. Not all parents are completely comfortable with this, so getting the younger ones on site is a good move. House monitors undertake leadership training and their antennae are always out for any concerns, the head of lower school told us. The single sex culture of the boarding houses is deeply ingrained so there is no having to constantly police this. In fact the guidance is so taken for granted that on a recent ski trip there was the same discipline observed with no challenges. The quality of the accommodation is high with an increasing number of single en-suite rooms and security is unobtrusive but rigorous. The food was praised – there is lots of variety and, not surprisingly, an international or fusion flavour.

Students spoke warmly of the relationship between staff and students. After academic lessons finish, boarders' time is carefully structured when they are younger and becomes less so, as the habits become ingrained. Weekends are pretty packed with the school facilities being well used and plenty of day trips organised. Sixth formers can go into Birmingham on Saturdays if they wish. There is always a lot to do. One group of boarders commented that it was a very trusting community and speculated on how prepared they would be for the more edgy outside world. Everyone commented on what a close and warm community the lower school is and how welcoming the college is to newcomers.

Background and atmosphere: Not only is the site breathtaking, with its views and sympathetically designed modern buildings blending with the 18th century and medieval parts, but it is a site that looks loved. There seems to be an army of support maintenance staff who take as much pride in the site as the principal. The school responds quickly to new ideas. It is not bogged down in sacred past traditions and will let students run with whatever the passion of the day might be. Recent student-led initiatives include beekeeping and an outdoor movie event as well as a buggy competition, where it was good to see the girls playing as leading a role as the boys. The initiative behind the new research lab was also something encouraged by the students themselves.

The school was founded after the Second World War as an attempt to start the healing process through language teaching and personal warmth. The word Concord means harmony and this principle value is still absolutely at the heart of the college today. It is an intellectual powerhouse but a calm and gentle one. Community and service are held in as much esteem as individual success.

Parents felt there was a slight difference between the atmosphere in the lower and upper parts of the school – which is to be expected. The lower school does have the genuine family feel. At sixth form level, the big influx of new students – some two-thirds of the school are sixth formers – results in some dissipation of this. One or two felt that the new students just saw Concord as a means to an end – top universities – and life was more hard edged. 'But that's what their lives are going to be like', commented one parent philosophically.

Pastoral care, well-being and discipline: The worst thing that the principal can say to anyone is, 'I am really disappointed in you'. The students want to please. They hold teachers in high regard and behavioural problems, even the low level class disruption that you often find in years 9 and 10, simply do not occur at Concord. 'The students self regulate,' staff told us. If occasionally a new student is not focussing in class, it is his classmates who get him in line. Students wear their own clothes and show that uniform has nothing to do with inner discipline and motivation. But everyone knows there are boundaries, and if someone brought drugs into the college, they would soon be heading out.

There is an impressive, all-embracing pastoral structure that includes outside counsellors, a psychotherapist, student counsellors and lots of staff training, as well as tutors, house staff and those in the leadership team with pastoral responsibilties. The school runs a self-esteem profile test on entry and the emphasis is on early identification of any problem, followed up with targeted support. It has a reputation for training young people to acquire the organisational skills needed for success and personal fulfilment. As it has grown, there is efficient use of electronic communications. Staff, students and parents assured us that there were a lot of safety nets in place in cases of concern. PSHE lessons with outside speakers reinforce key pastoral issues.

Pupils and parents: Parents are largely from the international business community. They choose Concord because they know results matter but so do the softer skills and a breadth of outlook. They are not families who want or need the social cache of a traditional English public school. These international parents are not interested in their children absorbing an English privileged culture – that is just a tiny part of their world, worth experiencing, yes, but so is all the other cultural exposure that Concord offers. Local Shropshire parents of day students are particularly keen on the cultural, racial and religious mix. Parents and students respond to the unpretentious atmosphere and the lack of historic baggage. There is an informal feel about the college, in part reinforced by the lack of uniform, that appeals but doesn't dilute the palpable rigour.

The students clearly love the place and can't speak highly enough of what it is giving them in terms of tools to build success. They pack their days with serious work and purposeful activity. About 80 of the 550 or so are from the UK and others come from a great variety of countries – the majority from Asia. The ones to whom we spoke were articulate and confident but unassuming – most just very natural and charming but among them, you could also spy the next mandarins – carefully considering our questions and weighing up their responses.

They are very aware of the opportunities they have been given to achieve academically in an environment that can offer more than at home. Many respond to the glorious countryside and some are just pleased to be away from the noise and distractions of city life.

Entrance: Entry in year 9, year 10 and year 12. Highly selective, particularly at sixth form level, and getting more so. There are three strands to admissions – tests (overseas students take the UKiset pre-test), school reports and interviews. Senior staff travel the world conducting interviews but if all else fails there is always Skype. Students joining year 12 need competent English; those coming in at 13+ have more time to get it up to standard. Many come from international schools where they are already learning in English.

Exit: The influence of the family background can be seen in the patterns of higher education choices. Parents have done well themselves in business and they value degrees in economics and finance as well as medicine, law, maths and the sciences. Having said that, more go on to study architecture than you would find elsewhere and the art department (though tiny) has considerable success with the London art schools. One boy was heading off for a bespoke tailoring course at Central St Martins when we visited. In 2017, 22 got into Oxbridge and there were 26 off to study medicine, with UCL and Imperial the most popular destinations. Preparation for university is taken very seriously and not left to chance or to a belief that bright, hard working children are sure to get where they want. The sixth formers get the chance to visit a number of universities and attend workshops and lectures. There is structured work for the various different entrance exams now required for different universities and different courses. Right from the start of the sixth form, there is a focus is on university entrance. The college makes excellent use of its international alumnae network to support current students in providing advice and opportunities for their next stage.

Money matters: Fees are high but you get the impression no expense is spared when it comes to the goal of academic excellence. Facilities are superb and always improving. The school is working on developing its own bursaries and scholarships so it is not solely dependent on the wealthy elite, and some students attend on scholarships from their own government. Fees include being able to stay at half terms and for, sixth formers, during the Easter holidays. There is bursary support available for day students.

Remarks: Concord is never going to suit a child who really doesn't want to work and is made uneasy by a fierce pace of academic progress. It may not be right for a child who is solely interested in the arts and struggles with maths and sciences – not because they wouldn't find high quality and wide ranging arts teaching but because they might not find enough like-minded peers. There is an English support department, but a student with weak English would undoubtedly struggle because of the pace of lessons.

It is as near perfect a place as you could want for the student who is scientifically academic. Parents whose child had suffered in a school where they were the only bookish one told us Concord had saved them from utter frustration. If you have ever looked round university campuses or watched groups of late teens and despaired at the culture of drinking, the lack of serious work or even serious thinking, the mindless use of social media, then visit Concord. This is where the next generation of global high flyers is being nurtured. If you want your offspring to have a chance in this stratosphere, want them to engage with issues outside the shores of the UK or just want them to make lifelong international friendships, then do look at Concord. It is in a league of its own and one that is increasingly in high world demand.

The Downs Malvern

9

Brockhill Road, Colwall, Malvern, Worcestershire WR13 6EY

01684 544100 | registrar@thedowns.malcol.org | www.thedownsmalvern.org.uk

Ages: 2–13 (boarders from year 3)

Pupils: 260 (two-thirds boys); **Boarders:** 51 full, 10 flexi

Day: £6,933 – £16,599 pa; **Boarding:** £12,567 – £22,050 pa

Linked school: Malvern College, 1047

Head: Since 2009, Alastair (known to everyone as Sam) Cook. Previously head of Pembroke House in Gilgil, Kenya, he is a graduate from Westminster College, Oxford. There is something of the gentleman's club about his study. The comfortable chairs, old school photos and stirring mountain landscapes speak of a man and school at ease with the world. Alastair Cook certainly is that and much

more. He has energetically meshed three schools (The Downs merged with Malvern College Prep in 2008) together into a now seamless unit, worked on relationships with Malvern College to mutual benefit and made himself much respected and loved by parents and the children whom he places firmly at the centre of everything. He teaches, does sport with the pre-preps and runs a swimming club. 'He is always around when the children arrive, there with his dog, at matches, just all the time', said one parent. He knows all the children, even those who have just arrived. 'You would never worry about approaching him over anything', said a mother.

Entrance: Entrance is non-selective – can support all but those with serious learning difficulties. Informal observations and interviews on taster days, combined with discussions with parents, lead to offers. Depending on the age of the child, may also request information from the current school.

Exit: More or less all take the common entrance and most go onto Malvern College – there is a strong flow through in curriculum terms. A smattering goes to other local schools or further flung public schools. If there is a problem academically, parents are told at an early stage and alternative plans discussed.

Remarks: The Downs has the feel of a much loved school with bucket loads of unspoilt charm that you find in the very best rural preps. It spreads over the Malvern Hills and the only downside we could see were the narrow roads and precipitous bends on the way there. There is a flexibility and breadth about everything. Pick up times are to suit parents not the school, boarding can be when families need it – it is all about individuals growing up in a community that cares, and for which families too care and show respect. The curriculum has all the academic rigour combined with creativity that you would hope for – strong science in suitably equipped labs ('We get to use proper chemicals,' one 10 year old was bursting to tell us), French is all the way through with Spanish or German in years 7 and 8, Latin from year 6, art has its own kiln and there is masses of music.

Perhaps what best sums up the school's charm is the little steam train that runs through the grounds

All of this spills out of the classroom into the rich extracurricular programme that runs at lunchtimes, after school and on Saturday mornings (not compulsory but much loved by parents). There is sport galore (including girls' soccer), gardening, chess, Chinese, pottery, cookery, world history, computer coding, current affairs, science in the news, touch typing, debating, Scrabble, endless drama and music and so it goes on. Perhaps what best sums up the timeless charm is the little steam train that runs through the school grounds. The oldest miniature light railway in the world, this is a serious educational tool. The children learn to drive and maintain it. The wholesome environment too is fully utilised – the children are outside as much as possible, soaking in subliminally, we would like to think, the awe-inspiring rolling landscape, but also using it for serious geographical and scientific measurements and as inspiration for their artwork, which is of a seriously high standard.

There are plenty of links with the world outside the school. Its own first rate facilities are supplemented by some use of Malvern College – its theatre, chapel, swimming pool, for instance. The choir sings locally and the school hosts national music and art events for other schools. About three quarters of the boarders are from overseas (11 different countries when we visited) and parents commented on how well the school integrates the day pupils and the boarders. The school offers excellent preparation to overseas boarders wanting to brush up their English and understand British values ready for senior school. There are fun and cosily low key events organised at weekends for boarders – a visit to the circus, theme parks, ice skating, Christmas shopping. The flexi-boarding is popular with parents who want to give their children a taste of boarding before the full immersion as they move on to Malvern College. The boarding accommodation is in The Warren – rightly named as it rambles round the centre of the original school buildings, not smart but very homely.

Parents say the teachers are very quick to pick up on any individual needs and that they take huge pride in the children's small achievements. 'Go to Friday assemblies', parents urged us. 'Everyone is invited and we really get a sense of how much the school praises the children, how the discipline works in practice, the clear moral message the school is getting across, and we can see the opportunities all the children get for developing confidence through public speaking.'

The head told us, 'care comes first and then education'. Parents and children praised the flexibility and common sense – no rigid rules that stunt children. Fairness is the basis of the approach to discipline. Teachers want to find out what the situation actually is by spending time talking to children involved in any difficulties – and then it is a quiet word and a real attempt to equip the children with the skills to move forward.

'So what do you give school out of 10?', we asked one boy. 'Ten+++', he said with a big grin.

Elmhurst Ballet School

249 Bristol Road, Edgbaston, Birmingham B5 7UH

0121 472 6655 | enquiries@elmhurstdance.co.uk | www.elmhurstdance.co.uk

Ages: 11-19

Pupils: 170 (108 girls, 62 boys); sixth form: 52; **Boarders:** 143 full

Day: £18,564 – £19,239 pa; **Boarding:** £23,793 – £25,650 pa

Principal: Since 2010, Jessica Wheeler BA NPQH (30s). There can't be many people in the world, never mind the UK, who combine professional dance experience with top notch educational management expertise. But Elmhurst has found it. Laban trained, she then became resident with the Laban dance company. Moved into teaching as freelance and guest teacher. Tough London comprehensive that employed her to teach dance spotted the charisma, energy and determination and she was fast-tracked to assistant headship before moving with a team of super fixers to work magic in one of the worst schools in London.

Aspirations since arriving at Elmhurst are to make it the dance school of choice in the UK and beyond. Her vision is a holistic one – to ensure talented dancers are also healthy and wise – and this is being realised through detailed, methodical planning, management and monitoring. She is stunning in every sense, and warm with it.

Brilliantly supported by artistic director Robert Parker, the driving force behind the increasingly world-class dance side of the school. He had a meteoric career through the Royal Ballet School, into the company and to Birmingham Royal Ballet as principal dancer. He knows the industry inside out and inspires huge respect in the young dancers. Coming from a Billy Elliot background, he is driven and self disciplined but also hugely charming, brimming with enthusiasm and cares passionately about the experience Elmhurst gives its young dancers. And he has collected a commercial pilot's licence along the way.

Academic matters: Given that admission is entirely done on dance potential, results are good and the

Most dance schools give up on academic side at 16, but there is a philosophical commitment here to the value of an academic training

principal and new deputy are determined to continue the upward trajectory for GCSE and A level results. Eighty-seven per cent of pupils got 9-4 for both maths and English GCSE in 2017 (35 per cent A*-A/9-7 grades). At A level, 24 per cent of grades at A*/A in 2017, 52 per cent at A*/B. Academic staff are up against students who say all they want to do is dance, but while they might be guided by their hearts, they are surrounded by adults who know you can't dance for ever, however talented you are.

Principal and her team have brought in changes to ensure any dip in academic performance is picked up and acted upon swiftly. She is building a curriculum that will play to the strengths of young dancers who are increasingly getting their GCSE grades. Baseline testing for children coming in to allow individual target setting and tracking of progress year on year. Most importantly, there is now transparency for students and parents about where things are heading.

School is rightly proud of its serious A level programme – dance, music, art, English and maths are on offer – and hopes to introduce geography and biology. Most dance schools give up on academic side at 16 but there is a philosophical commitment here to the value of an academic training, heavily underpinned by the practical consideration that a student who is seriously injured at 17 or has simply grown a bit too tall must have alternatives to a dance career.

Classes are around 20 – smaller once options are chosen. A real strength, parents tell us. Some streaming for EAL students and English exams are very careful chosen to meet the individual's best needs. Teachers all comment that the discipline and focus of the dance studio infuses academic lessons. The issue is sometimes getting the students to speak at all (they are so used to the silence of dance class). Teachers are very conscious that many of the students are kinaesthetic learners and match their teaching styles to maximise this.

Games, options, the arts: This a rigorous training for the most gifted and resilient. The artistic and dance side of the curriculum takes up about a third of the students' time up to 16. Then, as they head towards their three-year National Diploma in Professional Dance, it takes up two-thirds. Training is in classical ballet but there is also a strong emphasis on jazz, contemporary and other supporting dance styles. There is an assessing out process in year 9 and year 11, when students who have not developed as dancers as expected are asked to leave. Process is done as compassionately as possible and warning given in good time for families to find an alternative. About eight per cent of the cohort assessed out across these two key stages; however a percentage leave at the end of year 11 of their own accord to go to dance schools offering a different sixth form curriculum.

Recent major review of the programme drew on the views of the professional dance companies,

ensuring students are prepared for the demands of the dance industry today. Increasing number and diversity of visiting artists, directors and choreographers, running workshops, masterclasses and lecturing to enrich the students' experience.

Partnership with Birmingham Royal Ballet (reason why Elmhurst moved to Edgbaston 10 years ago) is the icing on the cake for the artistic side of the school. It means getting top quality dance teachers is much easier than anywhere else outside London and students get the chance to perform regularly with the company. Even the youngest can audition for children's parts in productions like The Nutcracker. Also allows for easy professional exchanges.

Dancers simply don't do risky contact sports but Elmhurst is keen for them to try everything else and takes its responsibility for overall fitness very seriously. Attractive fitness suite has been created and staff and students are encouraged to use it, and there's a new multi-use games area. They also share sports facilities and coaches with a nearby mainstream school.

With no sports fields, there are no obvious spaces for younger children to run around but school's pretty, landscaped grounds give a sense of openness to the site.

The school is ahead of the game – linking with university researchers to ensure pre-emptive strategies are in place to keep the students dancing at their peak

Friday afternoons have been developed as an off-timetable fun time for learning new skills and offering enrichment and students love it. Sport, art and craft, academic clubs, drama, student-led choreography projects and yoga. Keen to showcase the students' talents outside dance, the school takes part in a host of national competitions – poetry and short story writing, for example, have seen recent successes.

Heart of the school is the excellent 250-seater theatre where the many performances take place, culminating in the outstanding end of year productions.

Boarding: Accommodation for the vast majority who board (just under nine per cent from overseas) is excellent, with many single and double rooms. When we visited the girls had set up their own beauty studio for pamper time with the help of a beauty-trained member of the house staff.

Sixth form accommodation has now moved into a purpose-built space nearer the main campus. This better links the sixth form experience and the rest of the school. Prior to this, one parent felt that when the children were younger they were in a very protected, small environment and then at 16 were suddenly launched into independent living. Students and parents commented on the recent increase in weekend activities, making the most of Birmingham, once Saturday classes have finished.

Background and atmosphere: The moment you walk into Elmhurst, you arrive in a huge dance studio, where there is invariably a class going on. From that point, you are in the ballet world. Students move around the corridors as though they are still on stage. They are graceful, hold themselves beautifully and even when they are chatting outside a maths classroom manage to group themselves as though in a corps de ballet. Most of the time they are either in dancewear or tracksuits in which they naturally look elegant and purposeful.

Staff comment on the maturity with which students relate to adults. Students we spoke to were articulate, able to express themselves confidently and had plenty to say. No bells and the atmosphere is calm and quiet. Something about the absolute dedication to a highly disciplined vocation infuses the whole place. Drive is there in academic as well as artistic classes. 'I have never been in classes with fewer discipline problems,' one teacher told us. 'The children succeed more than they would in other schools because all the time they are asking "how can I improve?" They do that in their ballet and they have that attitude to their GCSEs too.'

School's recently developed 'live, dance, learn' slogan captures the holistic approach to dance education. This is also underlined by 'the Elmhurst way', four statements posted all over the school to remind students and staff what it is all about – choose the right attitude, be there, make someone's day and have fun. We like the sentiments – they give an adventurous and humane dimension to the gruelling discipline of the ballet world.

Pastoral care, well-being and discipline: There has been a huge amount of heartbreak over the years about 'assessing out,' the process at the end of years 9 and 11 when students are told if they are good enough at dance to carry on. Elmhurst has done much soul searching as to how they can make this stressful time as bearable as possible for everyone concerned. They have introduced pre-assessment, which allows teachers to give early indication to both students and parents if things are not looking good. In some cases it can be turned around and every opportunity is given, but sometimes, no matter how much they work, it just can't. At least everyone knows sooner rather than later

Dancers simply don't do risky contact sports but Elmhurst takes its responsibility for overall fitness very seriously

and the school support swings into action, looking for other alternatives (of which there actually are a lot). Pupils may not end up as Giselle at the Bolshoi but they could still have a career in the dance industry.

Overall, Elmhurst has moved way beyond the usual pastoral care. Students' health and well-being is at the core of everything and systems are in place that recognise the unique nature of vocational ballet training. Dedicated medical centre, with qualified nursing staff, on-site GP appointments, physiotherapy services, dance psychology, dance nutritionist, sports massage and chiropractor. New health and well-being centre aims at a holistic approach, fostering 'a closer working relationship between healthcare, artistic and boarding staff'.

The school is ahead of the game – linking with university researchers to ensure pre-emptive strategies are in place to keep the students dancing at their peak. More in the pipeline – working with international researchers to develop motivational programmes based on the psychology of success. Probably because of the emphasis on well-being, there are virtually no cases of anorexia. Principal told us that during her time at the school there have only been two diagnoses (both of which had positive outcomes) and that this is proportionately far fewer than at her last school (a large comprehensive).

The school holds student inset days, much like those for staff. Outside agencies come in to run workshops and talks on subjects like e-safety, cancer, injury prevention and choreography. Staff make every effort to ensure that parents have the same information to complete the circle and ensure maximum input for the students.

'The children are simply in love with what they are doing,' one houseparent told us in an attempt to explain the enthusiasm and buzz about the boarding experience.

Pupils and parents: Most are encouraged to apply by their ballet teachers and all are there because they want to dance. There is a real warmth in relations between staff and students and between the students themselves. One boy told us: 'I have finally got friends who have the same interests as me.' Everyone we spoke to stressed the very special people here and the friendships made. 'I have become a different person,' said one girl. 'I am independent and confident now that I am doing what I love.' Parents commented on the way the school by its very nature encouraged independence. 'Our son is noticeably more mature and independent that his contemporaries at other independent boarding schools,' observed one father.

Not surprisingly, parents are quite intense. They are acutely aware of both the dangers and the strengths of opting for a specialist vocational education at 11. A number choose the school because they can see that it tries very hard to keep the academic doors open.

Parents are more obviously desperate for their children to succeed than those in other schools (although given the limited employment opportunities with the world top ballet companies, they know that not many can). This gives an edge to how they relate to the school, and one or two thought some parents were reluctant sometimes to approach the school with criticisms. The last thing they want is for their child to be asked to leave. Those with children about to start auditioning for their first jobs were unsure if the school was doing enough to support them, although they recognised it did as much or more than other dance schools. A parent whose child had just had a minor injury wanted to see even more physiotherapy and counselling support. But even the most anxious parents agreed that their child couldn't be happier.

Former pupils (known as Old Elms) include actresses Helen Baxendale, Hayley Mills, Juliet Mills, Jenny Agutter and Joanna David, singer Sarah Brightman and ballet dancers Dame Merle Park, Diana Fox and Isabel McMeekan.

Entrance: Entrance is entirely on artistic merit. Auditions are held at various times in the year in the UK and overseas, although the overseas auditions are increasingly conducted via DVD submissions and then by Elmhurst staff travelling to host auditions overseas. Children will have had ballet lessons before they come and the school has links with some of the best local ballet teachers around the country. The school also runs its own associate classes for the under 11s in Birmingham, Sunderland, Manchester and Plymouth as outreach. Also visits some very challenged primary schools to talent spot. Students are reauditioned at the end of the third year (year 9) and fifth year (year 11) and places are either confirmed or not.

Exit: Around 60-75 per cent leave after GCSEs, though 90 per cent of these leavers go on to further dance training. More than 80 per cent of sixth form graduates enter dance related employment within six months of graduating – increasingly to join internationally prestigious companies. A graduate placement scheme has been introduce to allow students who don't gain immediate employment to stay at the school to sustain audition-ready fitness. The odd student for whom the idea of a ballet career has palled by the time they are 19 head to university. When we visited one had just got an offer from York to read English.

Money matters: Given that the fees include all the specialist ballet tuition, they are reasonable. Many UK families are able to take advantage of two government funded, means-tested, bursary/scholarship schemes: music and dance scheme (MDS) for those aged 11 to 16 and dance and drama awards (DaDa) for the sixth form. Awards are highly competitive but all credit to the government for ensuring highly talented children can get the specialist training they need, regardless of parental income.

Remarks: The only purpose-built ballet school in the country, this is the ballet school to watch. Elmhurst isn't afraid to look beyond the intense and sometimes claustrophobic ballet world. It challenges the conventional thinking that young dancers must be silent sponges soaking up the technical knowledge of their teachers. With the school's rising academic profile and development of pupil voice, the dancers coming out of Elmhurst are critical learners ready to take ownership of their own careers.

Elmhurst is not the Royal Ballet School and in that sense it has to fight really hard to prove itself. There are no laurels to rest on here. It reinvented itself when it moved to Birmingham and it has the drive and energy of a young institution hungry for success. The Royal Ballet School is still the first choice for the majority of families but Elmhurst is biting at its heels, offering something new and very special.

The Elms School

C of E 11

Colwall, Malvern, Worcestershire WR13 6EF

01684 540344 | office@elmsschool.co.uk | www.elmsschool.co.uk

Ages: 3-13 (boarders from 8)

Pupils: 162; Boarders: 109

Day: £8,910 – £19,860 pa; Boarding: £23,655 pa

Head: Since January 2018, Chris Hattam, previously a senior housemaster at Sedbergh School, where he also taught philosophy and RE and coached rugby, cricket and hockey. Degrees from Edinburgh and Manchester; worked as a probation officer with young offenders before turning to teaching. He is married to Jess, with three children (and three spaniels).

Certainly enjoys life, throwing himself into anything he does, believing that he can't ask others in his community to do what he isn't willing to. He sees that value in giving every child the opportunity to explore their potential and be excited by what lies ahead of them. The outdoor elements of the school and giving children the chance are both close to his heart, whilst ensuring that the academic potential of each and every one is unlocked. Deep understanding of the all-encompassing remit of a boarding school for all pupils whether they board or not and how to prepare boys and girls for the next stage.

Jess, a paediatric nurse, is fully involved in all aspects of school life. Enjoys hosting the 'Tuesday lunches' with Chris for the pupils, ensuring that all the children get to enjoy lunch and social time in the headmaster's family home.

Entrance: Entrance into Montessori early years at 3, regular intake at 7 and 8. Most children from Herefordshire, Gloucestershire, Worcestershire, Monmouthshire and Powys. A few Forces families and a handful from overseas. Entry is by assessment rather than selection, and children who are intending to board can stay the night to test the waters. No scholarships but means-tested bursaries of up to 100 per cent for those 'who could benefit from what we offer'. 'We can and do get our children into leading public schools but we also support children who struggle'.

Exit: On exit the children go to a variety of schools eg Malvern College, Cheltenham College, Cheltenham Ladies', Radley, Marlborough, Eton, Rugby, Winchester, Wellington, Harrow, Millfield, Oundle, Shrewsbury, nearly half with scholarships.

Remarks: The oldest prep school in England, founded by Humphry Walwyn in 1614. Facing away from what passes for the main road in the village of Colwall, near Malvern, it opens out onto a site of 150 acres full of lovely green spaces and beautiful gardens. The school itself has rather the feeling of a collection of period houses that have grown together, sometimes in a slightly idiosyncratic manner. However, the school is much more than its academic buildings. For a start it has enviable sports facilities – including Astroturf, games field, swimming pool, a large sports hall, stables for about 15-20 ponies (boarders can also bring their own) and a new outdoor riding arena. Sport obviously important – riding and shooting particularly so; the school has its own pistol and rifle shooting clubs. Then there is the school farm – rural studies compulsory up to and including year 7– which boasts a prize Hereford bull as well as Gloucester Old Spots, walked by the children round the grounds, a large flock of hens and a rather lovely vegetable garden. Each year group has a plot in which it is expected to grow its own vegetables. The children clearly love their involvement in the farm and take pleasure and pride in it. And they all speak very highly of the food – beef, pork and eggs come from the farm when available.

Boarding and teaching accommodation require some modernisation. The boarding facilities are a little overcrowded, although homely and tidy. Every child in the prep school (not pre-prep) has a designated bed; there are rest periods after lunch every day. This means that day children can board when they want.

Enviable sports facilities – Astroturf, swimming pool, a large sports hall, stables for about 15-20 ponies (boarders can also bring their own) and outdoor riding arena

The children are genuinely charming – friendly, respectful but responsive, confident and very happy indeed; well motivated and thoroughly self disciplined – we saw groups working on their art, music and sports during break, all purposeful, focused and notably unsupervised, teachers within range if needed but leaving them to their own devices if not. There is an impressive auditorium/theatre with some good music practice spaces, a beautiful new grand piano, and good sized music classroom attached at the back. A good art room too – full of innovative, varied and careful work. Parents say their children are very happy.They appreciate the variety of activities offered and the freedom of each child to 'be a little bit eccentric' if they want to.

Relatively high fees fund a staff:pupil ratio of about 1:7. Academically sound with many long-serving staff who say relationships with children are excellent, respectful but friendly and that parents are extremely supportive. Two ICT rooms, a new teaching block including state of the art science labs, a pleasant library, not much prep as Saturday school is compulsory, and most reinforcement/prep style work is done within the classroom. Traditional curriculum includes a strong classics department. Follows a policy of moving children through classes as the need appears – the school calls this the ladder system – which can mean that the brighter sparks might spend the last two years in the top class. However, it is clear that the school is sensitive to parental concerns and in reality the majority of pupils are taught within a cohort of their own age. Groups are very small and no class is larger than 15; the smallest we saw was seven. The teaching model seems to work well and certainly destinations on exit don't point to any major hiccups.

On the whole a very traditional feel – there is something of the flavour of the Famous Five about the place – which may raise the hackles of some potential parents. Boys wear cord shorts and tweed blazers, girls wear kilts and jumpers, the children go out for a walk before breakfast and have outdoor activities every afternoon. There are no mobile phones, no cash, no sweets and no straying out of the school grounds. Chapel four times a week with visits from the local vicar and Catholic pupils taken to mass once a week. There are proper napkins at mealtimes, and grace is said. Some staff keep dogs in their classrooms and there is a 'pet palace' for the children's own rabbits and other small animals. Some parents may think it too sheltered by far, others will breathe a sigh of relief when they find it.

Weekend activities range from The Elms Tetrathlon to bugboarding to Nerf Gun War. Children might also go off geocaching in the Malvern Hills, paintballing or ice skating, or on a shopping trip to Cheltenham.

A school which wears its differences from the mainstream with pride. With its farm, fields and outdoor ethos this is a glorious place to get muddy while you learn – and somehow it manages to preserve childhood while fostering independence.

Foremarke Hall (Repton Preparatory School)

12

Milton, Derby DE65 6EJ

01283 707100 | registrar@foremarke.org.uk | www.foremarke.org.uk

Ages: 3–13 (boarding from 7)

Pupils: 443 (two-thirds boys); **Boarders:** 40 full

Day: £8,982 – £19,299 pa; **Boarding:** £21,144 – £24,993 pa

Linked school: Repton School, 1083

Headmaster: Since 2011, Richard Merriman, who easily matches his surname as he fizzes along into his late 50s and dresses in tasteful tweed, entirely in keeping with the kind of country school that Foremarke is. Educated in Loughborough, both at the grammar school and the university, he took a multi-faceted teaching degree in PE, sports science and geography. Like many a prep school headmaster, he trained as a secondary school specialist and spent the first phases of his career in senior schools in Kent and Dorset, before moving, at the end of the 80s, to a position as director of sport at Kimbolton. Throughout this time, he still developed other interests: securing, for instance, an MA from Leicester University in English local history – special subjects being churchyards and gravestones – whilst his flair for singing saw him as the front man of a band, Johnny Cool and The Iceboxes, who warmed things up in Kentish pubs and clubs with their early rock covers. Now his shoes have changed from blue suedes to brogues.

He then progressed to two headships, initially at Wolborough Hill in Devon, before moving to Birchfield School in Shropshire. Now in his fifth year at Foremarke, he is clearly in his element, endowing his school with an assurance and an ambition that can only be sparked by his kind of varied experience.

His study is a room of some glory and very much reflects the man. Elizabethan and Georgian portraits of Foremarke's former families embellish the high walls – some other heads might have been myopic enough to have taken them down in favour of some 'marketing shots'. Copies of Wisden are lined up on one of the alcove bookshelves, revealing his life-long love of the sport and his times as a minor county cricketer. He still plays for the MCC.

Popular with his staff, for the work he does and the example he sets; they describe him as a 'kindly person who inspires confidence' and 'clearly wants the best.' When he arrived, so colleagues advised us, the school was rather departmentally driven – no doubt meritorious but fragmented in its operation. Now it is very much a single entity. Pre-prep staff, for example, from their base in a splendid new building, are included in everything. Training days are inclusive. Failure is acknowledged. All share in success.

A century ago, RM would have been the sort of character whom men would have wanted alongside them in the trenches; for the inter-dependence of Foremarke's children, staff and parents is obvious. As we left his study, we noticed, somewhat tucked away, a silver-framed photograph of the head in filmic James Bond dinner dress; unshaken, pistol raised to the sky.

Retiring in December 2018.

Entrance: This is essentially non-selective, although those who wish to enter from year 3 onwards will be given introductory papers to assess their abilities in English, maths and reasoning. The expectation and the reality is that children will progress to year 8, ultimately following either scholarship or common entrance systems of study. The learning enhancement department numbers four and works both in and out of the classroom, providing individualised and small-group guidance for those in need of assistance, especially in literacy and numeracy. There are up to 20 overseas students (all who have been assessed) and this international spread is encouragingly wide, students coming from Japan and Russia, Hong Kong, Spain and China. There is an EAL department to assist in their transition.

Girls from year 3 said 'best things about the school' were flapjacks on Wednesdays and 'golden time' – 'where we can do drawing'

All admission matters are in the hands of the school's registrar, Ruth Merriman, a character full of Irish warmth and wit. The role of headmaster's spouse, especially in a boarding and day school, is a trappy one and, in certain institutions, Fawlteyesque squabbles for supremacy can ensue. This could not be further from the truth here, where headmaster and registrar are a conspicuously strong duo. Their daughter joined Foremarke in year 4 and is now at Repton, so empathy with parents is a given.

A range of scholarships and awards are available – for academic prowess at 7+ and for prowess and promise in music, sport and drama at 11+.

Exit: Being Repton's preparatory school, it is hardly a surprise that around 90 per cent of year 8 students advance to the senior school. Other popular schools, from a wide selection include Eton College, Harrow School, Uppingham School, Rugby School

and Oundle School. Alumni include Georgie Twigg – a GB hockey gold medallist at Rio, the actor Tom Chambers, and England U21 footballer, Will Hughes.

Remarks: Shakespeare had it that 'all that glisters is not gold'. Foremarke's website is amongst the best we have seen; dazzling with high-quality photographs and text, a selection of enticing videos (one of which reminded us of an opening sequence to the Great British Bake-Off) and more menus than one would find in a chain of restaurants. Like many, it claims to be 'the leading prep school in the Midlands' (a phrase increasingly reminiscent of the 'best beer' Heineken advert) but does it live up to its promise?

Certainly, it makes a stunning start as, at the end of a long, well-tended, rhododendron-fringed drive, the Georgian hall comes into view, resembling part of a wing at Blenheim Palace. As we drew up, a gardener (hard to credit in early November) was cutting one of the perfect grass rectangles. Everything is immaculate. Sweeping steps herald the entrance to the front hall where sofas and log fires deepen the style. Home-made biscuits are served with coffee.

Throughout the school the facilities are impressive. Many join the pre-prep where play areas, consisting of a wooden adventure trail and a green area with tunnels and mounds that looks like something out of Tellytubby land, introduce the new building. The great majority of Foremarke's infrastructure is presented with similar polish.

The quad development, along with the adjacent Thomas Davies building, features rooms of a scope and flair that would in no way be out of place in a senior school, and, indeed, would be superior to many. Tremulous pupils, however, might not be too encouraged by the sign on the door of the history room which instructs entrants to 'abandon hope'.

The library will inspire, as will the theatre and the sports hall. The triple highlights, though, are the Charles Jennings music school (named after Handel's librettist) and the exceptional art studio and DT centre. We especially liked the pencil portraits in the former, while the latter is the pit-stop for four electric racing cars. These compete on circuits such as Goodwood and Rockingham, the school holding the course record at Aintree, on the track – adjacent to the Grand National fences – that used to host the British Grand Prix.

It is a truism that the most important factors in a school's success are the students and the staff, but the buildings and the beauty of the grounds at Foremarke all help to set the tone. Taste for the best of both the ancient and the modern is all-embracing.

This was also evident in our tour of the boarding houses. Full, weekly and flexible boarding options are available and around 40 students are in on weekends, cared for by the dozen members of staff who live on site. The girls' house, Nightingale, has a cottage-style feel to it and could have been decorated and furnished by a joint design team from Laura Ashley and Cath Kidston. There are two boys' boarding houses, Francis and Burdett. Francis' rooms take their names from their original function: hence there is the Gun Room and the Wine Cellar, the Still Room and the Butler's Pantry. As in Nightingale, the rooms are spacious and elegant.

> *Triple highlights are the Charles Jennings music school (named after Handel's librettist) and the exceptional art studio and DT centre*

Consequently, the only carbuncle is the dining room, where space is cramped (we are told there will be a brand new facility in summer 2018). So, staggered sittings have to operate; all of which impacts on ideal timetable patterns. The food, however, is fantastic; as evidenced by our spectacular Thai curry. (Foremarke won the Tatler Award for the Best School Food in 2014, whilst The Week magazine awarded a similar accolade in 2016).

At lunch, we talked with some girls from year 3 whose 'best things about the school' were flapjacks on Wednesdays and 'golden time' – 'where we can do drawing'. On the same table was a year 8 boy, hopeful of a place next year at Eton, who was of the outlandish opinion that Foremarke was 'the most rounded school in England'. We challenged him to detail his knowledge of all schools from Durham to Cornwall. He smiled, and without a touch of Trump-like arrogance, coolly explained that he could not imagine a better school, 'for all that it has done for me'.

And it is clearly not just because it prepares the way for students to enter some of the best senior schools. The extracurricular holy trinity of sport, music and drama sparkles. Girls play hockey, netball and rounders, boys football, hockey and cricket. A multiplicity of teams exists for sportists at every level and the school celebrates the Foremarke Football League which runs alongside the pattern of school fixtures. This year Barcelona (still without Messi) were the winners. There is sailing on the lake, athletics, fencing (a year 6 girl has recently won The IAPS national épée title), swimming, triathlon and even an equestrian team.

Music fills many pages in the Foremarke yearbook – The Preptonian – detailing the calendar of concerts, both in and out of school, and the excellence of orchestras, ensembles and choirs. The chamber choir sings at Remembrance Sunday at the National Arboretum in front of 5,000 people. This year's senior dramatic production was Twelfth

Night. There are class plays too, and visits from the Young Film Academy and the Young Shakespeare Theatre Company.

Given this whirligig of opportunity, parents gush about the Foremarke brand of education. One Russian mother, for example, who had met the head in Moscow, had scoured England for a school that would be flexible enough to allow her daughter to develop her high class ice-skating. According to her, 'everything is superb'. Another reported that her family's transfer from Yorkshire had gone well because of 'the excellent academic experience and also the experience of life that Foremarke gives'. A third said that... 'Staff cannot be faulted. They take them way beyond the curriculum.' When asked about the lead up to year 8 examinations, the view was that 'they are very good at managing the pressure and making the hard decisions regarding common entrance and scholarship selection.' Parents kept well-informed by the school's weekly newsletter (the Foremarke Flyer), text-alerts working smoothly if triggered by late cancellations. We were left with the words .... 'Children have such fun. They're tired and they love it.'

And so, does Foremarke, founded in 1945, live up to its marketing promises after its first 70+ years? If it is affordable – fees might be too much of a stretch for many – our visit confirmed that the shimmering straplines are justified. It is, perhaps, an indication of the school's standing that, in the county of Derby's recently produced edition of Monopoly, Foremarke has been awarded a green square: rather appropriately, given its heritage, Regent Street. As all Monopolists know, the third green property is Bond Street; where jewelled gold glitters. There is plenty more to be discovered at Foremarke.

Lincoln Minster School

13

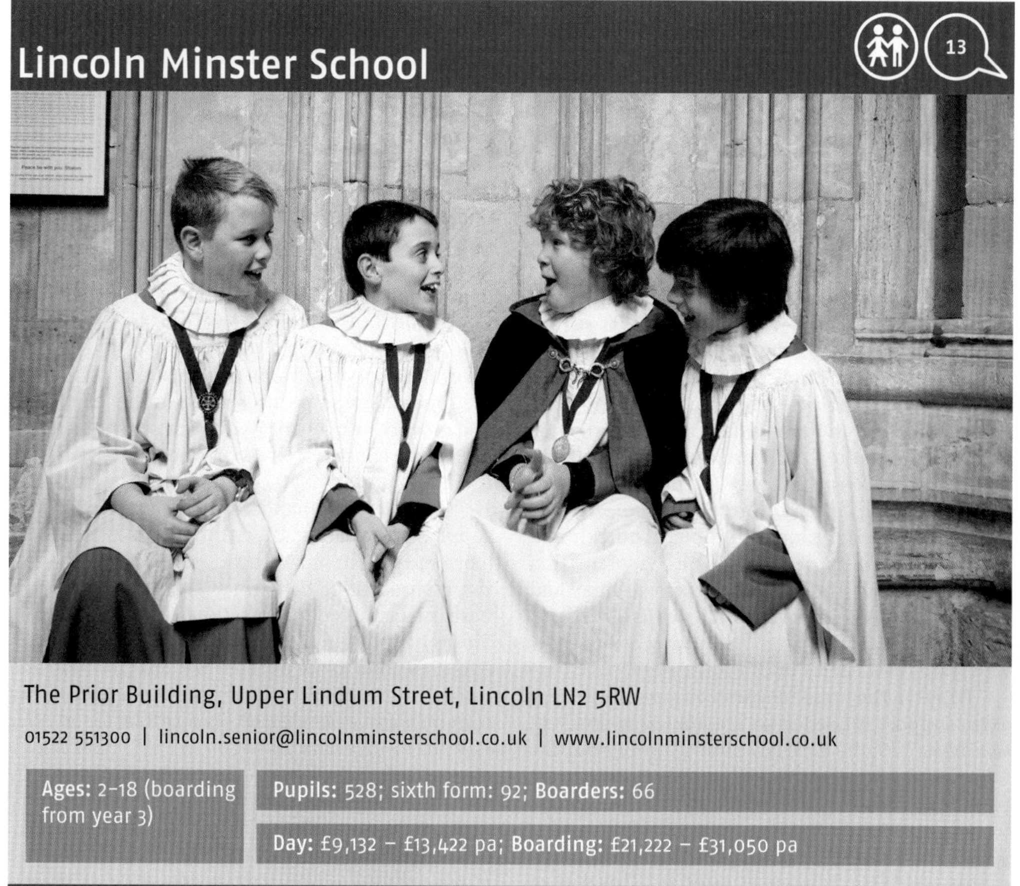

The Prior Building, Upper Lindum Street, Lincoln LN2 5RW

01522 551300 | lincoln.senior@lincolnminsterschool.co.uk | www.lincolnminsterschool.co.uk

Ages: 2–18 (boarding from year 3)

Pupils: 528; sixth form: 92; **Boarders:** 66

Day: £9,132 – £13,422 pa; **Boarding:** £21,222 – £31,050 pa

Principal: Since 2015 Mark Wallace (40s). A mathematician from Northern Ireland. Studied at Queen's in Belfast. From a banking family and took the same path, working in offshore banking in Jersey before becoming disenchanted. Spent time working for Camp America and decided wanted to teach. Very sporty and an ex-international hockey player. Previously taught at Caterham and Kingston

Grammar; this is his first headship. Wanted to be at a non-selective school 'so I can make a difference.' Very aware of need to increase profile of school and numbers. Approachable, friendly and competent and well aware of his remit. Popular with parents, 'a delightful young man,' 'approachable,' said by all. 'He's ruffled a few feathers, but in a good way,' was another comment. All parents commented that he knew all of the children by name, and was very high profile within the school and starting to be within the city. 'He's keen to increase the school's profile and is putting himself out there to do so.' One parent called him a 'top bloke with a lovely way about him.' Works closely with heads of junior and pre-prep schools.

Prep and pre-prep school: Headed by Fiona Thomas since 2012 (50s). A warm, welcoming lady with a great deal of Welsh charm. Originally from Cardiff, this is her third headship, the previous one being in Spain. She heads both the junior and pre-prep schools. A lady who inspires confidence and has managed the post-merger transition of both schools successfully.

Academic matters: In 2017, 32 per cent A*-A/9-7 grades at GCSE; 58 per cent A*-B at A level with 25 per cent A*/A. Solid results for a non-selective school. High flyers encouraged, less able nurtured. French, German and Spanish on offer at GCSE. One language for all, a few do two but, disappointingly, not many. iPads being rolled out for all. Plenty of computers available with up to date IT suites. Lessons we observed showed engaged pupils and articulate teachers. Pupils set in year 8 in most subjects. Excellent facilities, most of them modern. Parents kept up to date with academic progress and all commented that problems were picked up on quickly. Most spoke about the small classes being a huge selling point of the school. 'We are made aware of any academic problems quickly and support on offer immediately.' The school instils a good work ethic: 'They come home from school and get on with their homework with no fuss,' was said more than once. All parents commented on how well staff knew their child.

Pupils in the junior department usually getting extra support if needed so are able to keep up in senior years. Some 82 SEND pupils throughout the school. Individual learning plans after assessment; parents spoke highly of support offered. 'My daughter was struggling to keep up at one point, they spotted it, put her into support and she quickly caught up. We much appreciated it.' This sort of comment came from many parents. Support available in lessons for those that need it and staff aware of how to teach these pupils. Parents very much involved. EAL requirements for 28 pupils, mainly sixth form. A minimum of two hours help a week offered, more if required, particularly in year 11. One year pre-A level course, including GCSEs in key subjects, offered to international students.

Boarding is pretty relaxed for the older children with school friends allowed to stay overnight. The Mount, for boarders up to year 8, includes most boarding choristers

Children get a good start here with lots of academic support and diligent, enthusiastic teachers pick up on any learning needs. The non-selection ethos means there's a broad spectrum of abilities, coped with well. Brand new IT suite and well stocked library. Languages taught from an early age by specialist teachers. Spanish in pre-prep, French from year 3, with a chance to sample the more exotic linked in with other subjects: Arabic, Mandarin and even a smattering of Welsh. Children taught as a class with separate subject teachers. Interesting to hear that pupils practice for 11+ papers, but Lincolnshire is a grammar school county.

Games, options, the arts: Sport rapidly improving, helped no doubt by enthusiastic support from the head. His arrival seems to have rejuvenated the department. All abilities encouraged to take part. Rugby and football for all, girls too. Rock climbing, judo, polo and squash all on offer. Squash team very successful. Lots of silver in cabinets: U15 girls tennis are regional champions, successful hockey teams and cross-country strong with one star ranked first U15 in the country. New sports hall a few years ago including a basketball court and indoor cricket.

Music very popular here; it is a choristers' school, supplying the cathedral with 25 of its 40 choristers (boys and girls in separate choirs, which sing at separate evensongs). Until recently all choristers at school here; now children from any school can audition. This is happily embraced by the head and some parents. 'It's good to see as there was a bit of them and us from some chorister parents,' said one. It's a big commitment. Practice starts before 8am for an hour every day with evensong beginning at 6.15pm. A long day, helped slightly by not having late finishes only every other evening. Choristers mostly join the choir in year 3; boys usually out by year 9, girls a little later. Choristers lead the way musically but many more pupils involved as well. Lots and lots of bands, orchestras and other choirs, very keenly supported. Lots of practice rooms including a drum room: drumming very popular, apparently.

Drama also popular. Lots of productions in junior and senior schools, some student-led, others include whole school. Modern theatre with sound and lighting box and new drama studio. Recording studio too. Art students support productions by creating backdrops and props. Excellent art facilities with fabulous views over the city; sixth form artists have their own work space.

Loads of after-school and lunch time clubs including strong debating club. Sports and music as well as homework club to enable later pick up for parents. D of E to gold and school trips far and wide.

Boarding: Boarding offered from year 3 but not many at this stage. Just over half of boarders are sixth formers, with 70 per cent of these from overseas (Brits are all weekly boarders, most living with an hour of the school), in three separate houses. Boarding facilities good. Pretty relaxed for the older children with school friends allowed to stay overnight. The Mount, for younger boarders up to year 8, includes most boarding choristers. Senior girls in Hillside, adjacent to the main school, with panoramic views. Senior boys in Eastgate a large period house with massive gardens, also a stone's throw from the main school building. Easily accessible to the city. Close links with local hockey and rowing club, with boarders encouraged to join in. Gym nearby and weekend trips for overseas students. Use made of Forces links with trips to nearby bases and museums. Lots of social areas with tea and toast making facilities, modern bathrooms. Pupils eat at the main building. Supervised daily prep for all ages. Younger boarders do lots of baking and competitions. Maximum of three to a room, which are large and airy – and tidy. Older pupils, mainly sixth form, have their own rooms. Boys planning a garden, designing and planting it themselves. Chapel not compulsory on Sundays. Despite numerous nationalities and languages, a cohesive atmosphere prevails and freedoms do not appear to be abused.

Background and atmosphere: Formed in 1996 by the amalgamation of the Cathedral School for Boys, St Joseph's School for Girls and Stonefield House School. St Mary's Prep School merged with them in 2011 to become the junior school. Lincoln Minster is now the only private school in the city, housed on three separate central sites, a stone's throw from the cathedral. The main building, the senior school, is a combination of old and new. Aesthetically pleasing modern building, opened in 2002, which has blended well with the old, offering large church-like windows and sweeping, modern curves. Its curving corridors are particularly attractive. Sixth form housed in separate wing. Good facilities with comfy common room and eating area. The junior school is a short walk away. On this site since 2014, an attractive old building with modern extensions, bright and airy, with a well-used outdoor classroom, sitting rather incongruously within a modern housing estate. It was once a city farm and school has large, leafy grounds and is well hidden from suburban sprawl. Each site has plenty of room around it with outside seating areas and large playgrounds. Pre-prep, up to year 2, on a separate site within a walled garden with the cathedral looming over the wall. Lots of space and play areas within a very secure setting, delightful surroundings.

Close links with the cathedral, not just the choristers, and ties are getting stronger, with work experience offers.

The pupils are easily spotted in their distinctive green, white and blue striped blazers, the junior girls wearing kilts – thankfully with a navy blazer; stripes and tartan would be a step too far. Sixth formers wear smart business suits and look the part. A friendly bunch.

Pastoral care, well-being and discipline: 'They know what they can get away with,' said one parent, 'and if they cross boundaries there is retribution.' All parents supported the school's stance on discipline. 'My child was given detention for something pretty innocuous. But they knew the rules, got caught, so fair enough.' Children excluded if necessary or given time out and taught in isolation – doesn't happen very often, but parents made aware of situation. 'What happens in school is dealt with by the school, which is as it should be,' said a parent. All parents commented on quick responses to emails and good communication from the school, including the head.

Pastoral care excellent, according to all parents, and the school prides itself on being nurturing. All the pupils are known to every member of staff and

their development closely monitored. 'Problems dealt with confidentially and appropriately,' was said more than once. Niggles eased before they have chance to escalate. Support offered and coping strategies put in place for those struggling. Two counsellors and a school nurse available. 'We have a close rapport with our teachers,' said one of our rather earnest but delightful guides.

Pupils and parents: A strong community of parents. Professionals, medics, London workers, academics from the university and a strong contingent from farming and the RAF. All very supportive of the school. All we spoke to happy with their child's progress and would recommend the school. 'If my child is happy then I'm happy.'

Pupils chatty and friendly and willing to engage in conversation. Independent and well rounded and obviously very comfy and happy at their school. We got the impression of a very tightly knit community with firm friendships.

Entrance: All applicants and parents are interviewed; English and maths exams for 11+ and 13+ entry. Reports requested from previous school and prospective pupils offered a taster day prior to joining. Automatic entry to the senior school from junior. Many year 7 entrants from state primaries. Overseas boarders join for sixth form, after entrance exams. Sixth form entry subject to GCSE results: 'grades need to reflect their subject choices.'

Exit: About 15 per cent leave at the end of year 6, many to state grammar schools. School aware of this and does practice 11+ papers. Another 20+ per cent leave after year 11, mostly to study vocational subjects. School happy to advise and guide at this stage.

Around a third of sixth form leavers to Russell Group unis. Very occasional Oxbridge place. Higher level apprenticeships actively embraced by the school along with school leaver programmes. Some 10 per cent to Forces, Harper Adams and Royal Agriculture College. Gap years minimal.

Money matters: Fifty per cent scholarships for choristers whilst they are in the choir; other awards possible afterwards and some have music scholarships. Academic, sports and art awards also available, plus means-tested bursaries; discounts for siblings.

Remarks: We feel the school has rather sat on its laurels in recent years, having no private competition, but that is all changing with the newish head. He is well aware of local competition from the grammars and an excellent academy in the city, and is working hard to raise the profile and standards. He's making inroads. The school prides itself on its pastoral care, has excellent facilities, gets solid results and, its real strength, has small class sizes.

Loughborough Grammar School

14

Burton Walks, Loughborough, Leicestershire LE11 2DU

01509 233233 | admissions@lesgrammar.org | www.lesgrammar.org

Ages: 10–18

Pupils: 972; sixth form: 300; **Boarders:** 61 full, 1 flexi

Day: £12,126 pa; **Boarding:** £24,357 – £27,411 pa

Headmaster: Since 2016, Duncan Byrne (40s). Languages degree from Cambridge (choral scholar) followed by MEd from Buckingham. From a teaching family, 'so it was always in the back of my mind.' Didn't fancy being behind a desk all day, 'working with young people is unfailingly interesting and varied: there's always something unexpected, often humorous, that happens most days.' Very keen on single sex education for boys, 'they take more risks intellectually.' Encourages boys to contribute to local community, 'it makes them feel part of something and helps with wellbeing.' He's settling in well and making his mark. Parents like him, and we can see why, he's charming, affable and chatty. 'He's very easy to talk to,' was said more than once. Parents appreciate communications from him and follow his blog and social media posts. All say they like him and he feels very welcomed by community. Two boys, one at the school, another still in London, a chorister at Westminster Abbey. A musical family; head was attracted to Loughborough because of its music

credentials. Lives on site in headmaster's house. Teaches languages to year 7s. Attends all home matches and has a high profile around the school.

Academic matters: In 2017, 65 per cent A*-A/9-7 at GCSE; 57 per cent A*/A at A level, 82 per cent A*-B. Excellent results but remember the school is fairly selective, though 'not as selective as you might expect,' says the head. French, German, Spanish, Latin and Greek all taught to A level. Head very keen for languages to flourish; 33 per cent of boys do two languages, 35 per cent study classics including Latin to GCSE. Maths is king, with around two-thirds studying it for A level. Sciences also very popular. Results have improved in the last few years with tracking of pupils becoming more effective. This means intervention is more prompt. 'Some boys are naturally lazy if they are not pushed,' says the head. Parents back this up, commenting on 'outstanding teachers who push the boys.' Parents kept well informed of progress. Lots of clinics for different subjects. Boys take advantage of these. 'They get lots of homework,' said one parent, who talked about the headmaster's blog explaining that the boys needed to do more at home. School well aware of boys and their foibles. All homework online so no excuses. iPads for all from year 8. The jury is out, with the head and parents unsure about the effectiveness of these as an educational tool. Half of the boys' work is handwritten so still lots of emphasis on 'old fashioned' skills.

The school is cleverly laid out with defined areas for each subject. Impressive library with spiral staircase in oldest part of the building. Chapel now used as a classroom, but small services still held here. Boys working hard and taking part in discussions in classes we viewed. Each science subject has its own block with impressive labs. Setting in maths. Lots of artwork on display. Mention must go to DT: a massive department, with state of the art equipment, run by a very enthusiastic teacher. Please note the electric racing car, built by the boys. Some 25 boys study DT at A level. The boys are taken driving round a local race track in the cars they have restored and built, age of 14. Sports car being restored, and driven on sports day, funded by parents via the PA. Many more boys who are not studying DT join in with restoration work. The school has the UK Young Engineer of the Year winners for 2017 and many go on to engineering careers, including in motorsport. Some sixth form subjects are taught with the girls from Loughborough High: psychology, music, languages and politics.

Lots of clubs but a nod must go to bridge and chess, and the slightly more unusual beekeeping

Some 40 boys on the SEN register, one boy with an EHCP. Five per cent of these are seen every week by learning support at no extra charge, as yet. Around 120 boys are on the monitoring list. Diagnostic testing for all boys in year 7, 9 and 12. Class sizes average 16 in the main school, 10 in sixth form.

EAL support is very good. There is an EAL co-ordinator who works four days a week helping the boarders, in particular, who are offered at least two hours a week support. Day boys can also use this service. Many boys, in line with the ethnic diversity in the area, speak a second language at home.

Games, options, the arts: Sport is compulsory right into the sixth form; 'it's good for them,' says the head, and boys are expected to participate and contribute. Rugby very popular and successful. Hockey, cricket and football also well supported, as are cross-country and athletics. Plenty of teams for all. Sport rotated and varied, so even the least sporty boy can find a niche. Excellent facilities a short minibus ride away at Quorn, their 70 acre site where most sports are played. On site are a swimming pool, large gym and cricket pitch. Parents happy that sports stars not favoured; 'they all muck in together,' said one parent. Another said their son 'didn't miss out by not being sporty.' One parent did complain about 'the amount of sports gear we have to buy. Do they really need at least two sets of shorts and so many different tops?'

Fabulous music school that is shared with the other schools in the Loughborough Endowed Schools foundation. Please note the grand piano in one recital room; this is a Steinway School. Many boys have individual music lessons. As [typo] expected, music excellent and parents rave about the concerts and reviews, 'they have an amazing choir.' There are over 40 weekly ensembles that the boys can take part in. Plenty of orchestras, bands, choirs, most combined with the girls' schools in the foundation. Lots of instruments lying around the school during our tour. Drama and school plays talked about a lot by parents. 'They are well co-ordinated with lots of rehearsal time.'

Far too many clubs to mention but a nod must go to bridge and chess, and the slightly more

The school has the UK Young Engineer of the Year winners for 2017; and many go on to engineering careers, including in motorsport

unusual beekeeping. The head was very pleased to be presented with a jar of honey shortly after his arrival. CCF very well supported, joining forces with the girls. D of E popular and lots of school trips including trekking in Vietnam and plenty of sports tours. As one parent said, 'there is so much available, it's up to the boys to take advantge of these opportunities. They are pushed to try things, which is excellent.'

Boarding: Nearly half of the boarders are in the sixth form. Virtually all of them international, the vast majority from Hong Kong and China. LGS has been an international boarding school for 25 years. There are two boarding houses: one, the old headmaster's house, within the main quad, the other in a refurbished Victorian property next to the main offices. Most boarders start in year 9, the odd one in year 8, but that is quite unusual. Lots of cultural trips for the boys including trips to London, Oxford University and a pantomime at Christmas, as well as many more local trips to nearby matches. The boys are kept busy, encouraged to join the CCF and take part in the musical activities.

Very experienced housemasters know the boys well. 'The common room is the heart of the house,' said one; during the refurbishment he made sure that there was room to sit all 31 boys together. There is a house meeting every day at 6.30pm, even if it's only for five minutes. The newly refurbished dormitories house up to four boys; sixth formers usually in pairs. Each boy has his own desk where homework is done. Very cleverly supervised, but allowing independence, doors are propped open between 6.30-8pm. Computers and phones allowed but Wifi use closely monitored, any misdeeds picked up immediately.

Sport compulsory three evenings a week, usually basketball, which is very popular. Boys allowed into town, which is a five minute walk away, but have to be in at least pairs and out of school uniform. With all this activity it's easy to keep the computer nerd off his laptop. English language classes held in the house. Unlimited supply of hot water greatly appreciated by the boys. Note the chickens in the garden; boys enthusiastically collect eggs for breakfast.

Background and atmosphere: Established within the town since 1495, the school has been at its present site since 1852. A state grammar school until 1974. Sited just on the edge of Loughborough, a town not noted for its aesthetics, the school itself is something of an architectural revelation. Part of the Loughborough Endowed Schools foundation which comprises four selective independent schools, Loughborough Grammar, Loughborough High School, Fairfield Prep and, since 2015, Our Lady's Convent School. Loughborough Grammar shares a campus with the High School and Fairfield.

Located on a massive site, next to the other schools, this handsome Victorian red-brick school is built around a quad. Modern extensions, which have blended in exceptionally well, are difficult to tell from the old. As you enter under an arch, which is a memorial to fallen pupils, the school stretches out in front of you. Neatly mown grass, which only the upper sixth – and your guide – are allowed to walk on. Over the years the school has bought most of the Victorian and Edwardian houses on the opposite road so boys can roam safely in a traffic free environment. It is slightly confusing trying to find the main office; luckily a friendly sixth former took pity on us and guided us in the right direction (across the road). Very confusing, we imagine, for visitors. Upper sixth boys have their own car park, boys in the year below are not allowed to use it – the privileges of being in your final year.

Boarders enjoy lots of cultural trips to London, Oxford University and a pantomime at Christmas. Boys are encouraged to join the CCF and take part in musical activities

A large school, both in number of boys and area covered; there is plenty of space for everyone. Lots of outside space for boys to let off steam. A school of all creeds and colours, the boys all seem to rub along well together and the atmosphere is cohesive and cordial.

Pastoral care, well-being and discipline: The head was honest enough to say that in a school of this size bullying does exist but is dealt with rapidly. Backed up by a parent who talked of problems on the school bus 'that were dealt with effectively and fairly.' All parents were happy with discipline, many of them saying, 'the boys are not allowed to step out of line, standards are to be met.' Good. Heads of year play an important part in the boys' welfare and discipline. Parents spoke highly of them and said 'staff know my son.' Boys understand sanctions that are handed out and reasons for them.

School very attuned to mental health issues and is proactive and preventative. 'We want the boys to know and like who they are and learn to be good at being themselves.' Very keen to ensure boys have a balanced lifestyle, hence plenty of sport and music as well as studying. Certain parents need to have this balance explained, school happy to do this. Parents happy with pastoral offerings. 'The reverend and his team are always available if necessary.'

Pupils and parents: Boys travel from about a 25 mile radius covering Leicestershire, Nottinghamshire and Derbyshire. Busses from all areas. The school has a broad social and ethnic mix with a number of pupils speaking a secondary language at home. Families vary from old county families, where a pupil could be the fourth generation to study here, to university staff, academics, professionals, engineers, as per the area, and many medics. All parents want a broad independent education; interestingly not many showed a strong preference for boys only. Parents have high expectations and most are working hard to be able to afford the fees. Boys mix well and strong friendships are formed. Good to see that the geeky quiet boy is as accepted as the rugby stars.

Entrance: Entry into year 6 is small, 17, and not publicised. Mainly to accommodate families with older siblings. Most boys, 131, join in year 7, with a third coming from the affiliated prep school Fairfield, the rest from state primaries. Entrance exam; they are looking for bright sparks. A small number join in year 9. Another 25 or so join the sixth form, 10 overseas boarders, the rest from the state system, mainly to study maths and sciences. Five B/6s at GCSE as an absolute minimum are needed for the sixth form, higher for certain subjects including maths, sciences and languages. Most new entrants have a fistful of A*/8-9s. School happy to turn a boy away if attitude and work ethic isn't right.

Exit: About 20 leave at the end of year 11 to mixed colleges in the town. Virtually all go to university, 80 per cent to Sutton Trust Top 30 group. Six to Oxbridge in 2017, many more medics (eight in 2017) and engineers, 'it's in the genes,' says the head. Gap years and apprenticeships not mentioned.

Money matters: Scholarships – music and academic – and bursaries on offer of up to 105 per cent of fees.

Remarks: A large, traditional, urban boys' school offering a good, well rounded education. It's not just about grades, albeit these are an important part; these boys are turned out as grounded young men with a broad outlook on life. Fees are excellent value for money, deliberately kept low. The parents appreciate this.

Maidwell Hall

Maidwell, Northampton NN6 9JG

01604 686234 | headmaster@maidwellhall.co.uk | www.maidwellhall.co.uk

Ages: 7–13

Pupils: 118; **Boarders:** 92 full

Day: £16,995 pa; **Boarding:** £19,596 – £26,100 pa

Headmaster: Since 2001, Robert Lankester MA PGCE (50s). Educated at Charterhouse and Selwyn College, Cambridge, where he read history. Military family – and he has a touch of it in his demeanour although never served; decided to leap into teaching after seven years in the City ('the best decision I ever made'). PGCE at Durham then 13 years at Uppingham, 10 as a housemaster. Exudes an air of calm confidence that pervades entire school and, as is often the case with outstanding leaders, his charges (averaging around 127 in number) have acquired in spades his self-assured qualities as if by osmosis. Was responsible in 2010 for the introduction of girls ('an interesting journey') who are now fully established at around 40 per cent of the cohort.

Adored and revered by parents who say he is 'a figurehead, and incredibly all-seeing'. A teacher at heart, still teaches CE history six periods per week and mingles with pupils at mealtimes. Lives on site with multi-talented wife, Carey ('a very special person,' say parents), a Montessori trained teacher also heavily involved in Maidwell life as tutor, swimming coach, teacher of drama and PSHCE and reader of bedtime stories to the younger boarders. Two grown up children: a daughter training to be a teacher and a son, the 'very popular' head of history at Maidwell ('an amazing teacher and perfect role model,' parents told us). With such idyllic rural surroundings, there's probably no need to escape to the country, but when the Lankesters do, it's to their home in Carmarthenshire, where they enjoy walking. Other leisure pursuits include skiing and – recently – golf.

Entrance: 'Pretty comprehensive' is how head describes intake. Fifteen to 20 join school into year 4, with handfuls joining each year thereafter, resulting in numbers almost doubled at top of school. Small numbers of pupils join aged 7 and are taught with year 4, repeating the year. Very gently selective ('I can count on one hand the number of children we have turned away over the past 10 years,' says head), prospective pupils assessed in maths, spelling, reading and NVR, plus short interview.

Majority join from pre-preps or other prep schools, very few from state primaries, and live within a 90-minute radius of school (East Anglia, Suffolk, Cambs, Derbyshire, Herts and Bucks). Very few London families, Forces 'significant'. Less than 10 per cent international; small numbers from Spain, Japan, China and Thailand. Old Maidwellians include Earl Spencer, novelist Boris Starling and Masterchef judge William Sitwell.

Exit: Almost all girls as well as boys stay until 13+, progressing to (mainly co-ed) public schools. Greatest numbers to Uppingham, followed by Stowe then Oundle. Boys in ones and twos most years to Eton and Harrow, a few more to Radley, with girls only very occasionally opting for the single sex route, eg Queen Margaret's, York or Roedean. Extremely rare exits at either 11+ or to day schools 'tend to be for financial reasons'. Some scholarships, although head says, 'We don't push them. They can be a weight around your neck and ruin your last year of prep school. We'd rather good grades at CE than shaky scholarship results.'

Remarks: How many prep schools of such modest pupil numbers can boast such riches in terms of breathtakingly spacious grounds? Maidwell's extensive gardens, five rugby pitches, trout-stocked lake, six hole golf course and 'wilderness' – where its pupils can climb trees ('only to three times our own height,' we were earnestly assured) and build dens to their heart's content – are framed by spectacular Northamptonshire countryside and farmland as far as the eye can see, the school instantly seducing visitors with its quaint Swallows and Amazons feel ('as soon as we drove in, we knew it was the one', said one parent). Founded in Derbyshire in 1913, school moved to this picturesque spot in 1933, making use of the 17th century turreted hall itself as main school building and boarding accommodation, plus recent additions. To compare the fabric of Maidwell to many other boarding preps would be as to compare Sandringham to Beckingham Palace. Here you will find no trace of architect designed theatres or gleaming new boarding houses (they did think about one for the girls, but parents vetoed it, preferring to keep their daughters in the characterful main school attic dorms) but a low-key wealth of facilities that's right in line with the lifestyle of the well-heeled parent cohort. There's a croquet lawn, used for family tournaments in summer (we were honoured to have last year's champion as our guide); a carpentry shed where pupils can create, well, anything in their spare time; rowing boats for year 8 leavers to bob around on the lake in summer months; a shooting shed and clay pigeon shooting activity on Sundays. The idyllic frieze could only have been improved on the day of our visit by the presence of the head's golden lab, who was otherwise engaged at the time, and we're willing to bet that the Range Rovers picking up pupils at leave-out are of the proper, mud-spattered country variety.

The overall vibe of the school is wholesome, jolly and humane. No abrasive bells to signal the end of lessons or break: 'This is their term time home,' says head, 'and we try to make it feel as homely as possible.' Also: 'We have less a uniform and more a code of dress, allowing pupils to express their individuality'. The result of this is an absolutely charming array of corduroy trousers or culottes, a striped or checked shirt and tie of choice (boys and girl prefects only), topped off with a jacket tailored in pupils' own choice of tweed. Screen time is almost non-existent, save the occasional sports match projected onto a giant pull-down screen or the news for prefects. Phone calls home are made from one of a few good old-fashioned landlines situated in nooks and crannies around the school and the tradition of a compulsory weekly letter home to parents continues to thrive. Free time, or 'muckabout' as it's known, is spent running around the vast grounds, taking part in one of the plethora of activities and sports on offer or – we were delighted to see – reading. An actual book. 'Reading rest' takes place after lunch each day, with pupils kicking back on their beds with their choice of ripping yarn and help on hand from learning support for anyone who needs it. Parents love that their children 'are not just getting an education, but a childhood too'. The 21st century has not bypassed Maidwell, though, and technology is very much alive and kicking in the classroom, with all pupils now taking a standard issue iPad to every lesson. These used to great effect with teachers accessing the latest educational apps or facilitating online research for projects or artwork.

So, we asked, what kind of 8-year-old goes full boarding these days? Head very clear that Maidwell pupils are not 'sent away' from home as was often the case yesteryear. Boarding here is 'always a positive choice' and 'to be honest, the children clamour for it', he says. All have a 24 hour boarding trial in the summer prior to starting and, as far as we can make out, it's consistently a hit. About half of parents are 'old school', with the rest 'a lovely smattering of everybody else, but definitely not flash', we were reliably informed. Those we spoke

to – most having had the debate at some point about the benefits of weekly versus termly boarding – were keen advocates of the full boarding model, grateful that their children are not subject to the weekly upheaval of lengthy travels, the emotional switch between school and home life or constantly exhausted without a chance to fully recharge between Saturday tea time and Sunday evening. They also appreciate the fact that they're all in the same boat and there are no lonely 'remainers' wafting around a near empty school at weekends. 'Parents choose us because we're small,' says head. All were keen to extol the virtues of the high quality family time, either when the children come home for their four day leave-outs twice every term or at one of the multitude of fun family days laid on by the school, where 'everyone mixes in'.

Small class sizes of up to 15 but more often around 12. All lessons taught by subject specialists, many of whom are trained secondary teachers, which 'enables us to be teaching at almost GCSE level by the time pupils leave', says head. Two streams in each year, with pupils set separately for maths. Trad curriculum (languages are French and Latin, with Greek for potential scholars taught outside of usual timetable). Parents of very academic children full of praise for teaching, with staff spending their break times to offer extra tuition to scholarship candidates around exam time. Exam technique covered in detail at frequent revision seminars in the run up to senior school exams and all CE pupils create revision plan with deputy head, with up to eight hours' extra independent study expected at key times: 'we make sure they are always in the right place at the right time', he says. High praise, too, from parents of the less academically stellar who, if necessary, are 'taken off quietly by the incredible learning support department', often resulting in pupils becoming 'unrecognisable' in their outcomes. Mild dyslexia, dyscalculia or dyspraxia all in a day's work 'but pupils do have to be mainstream', says head. Mild ASD (mainly undiagnosed) also fine but 'I dislike labels and won't allow them', says head. 'The structure of a boarding school plays to the favour of children who may have been told they have ADD or ADHD – we work with it as we would anything else'. Specialist EAL teacher supports international students, who are often withdrawn from French or Latin. We loved the vertical tutor system – there are no forms and pupils have the same tutor from the start of their school career to the end and meet weekly in groups of six to eight – 'it engenders a lack of hierarchy among the pupils', says head. Behaviour and manners a major strength of school: 'we are very strict, although pupils don't really realise it and parents comment on improvements after just a few weeks', says head. Mothers concur: 'if you want a well-mannered child, send them to Maidwell'.

On top of all the academic subjects (history was the pupils' firm favourite when we asked), very strong art, led by the 'young, fizzy' head of department, and drama equally impressive. One 'massive' production every year (recently The Wizard of Oz, Oliver, Romeo and Juliet), described by parents as 'brilliant – so slick and fresh.' About two-thirds take peripatetic music lessons in the somewhat makeshift music rooms adjacent to the boys' boarding floor. 'Not ideal, but it all just happens,' says head, although watch this space for news of an all-singing-all-dancing performance space and library over the next few years. Perhaps Maidwell will get a touch of architectural gloss after all. Sport six days a week with 'everyone in the teams' and plenty of match day success. It's rugby, hockey and cricket for boys, and girls – whose sport is 'good now', thanks to new head of girls' games – play netball, hockey and rounders, albeit sometimes in mixed age groups to make up numbers. Great to see girls' football on offer as an activity – how about cricket next? Girls would also like to see some more 'serious' gymnastics and dance. Older pupils jet away on fabulous sports tours (eg hockey to Barcelona, rugby to Dublin and cricket to Antigua). Weekly swimming in school's indoor pool, also used for free swims during activity time. Activities aplenty, with two compulsory during the generous 45 minute morning break and three in the evening each week, from various sports to street dance and climbing (trees and walls) or origami and Airfix. Squash and pool ladders also popular.

Boarding quite literally at the heart of the school with boys' dorms up a sweeping staircase off the main entrance halls and girls (who have to access their dorms via a different route in the evenings) on the charming attic floor above. Pupils allowed to board weekly during their first year

No bells signal the end of lessons: 'This is their term time home,' says head, 'and we try to make it feel as homely as possible'

– and can even choose to be a day pupil throughout their Maidwell career if they so wish – but very few do. Dorms for both sexes sleep six to seven pupils, with boys' clothing kept centrally and dished out as required by matron. Dorm captains – top year pupils placed to keep an eye on their younger peers – in every room 'to make sure everyone's happy – and tidy.' Super, homely feel to all dorms, with spectacular views across the grounds and surrounding countryside (beds in turrets most coveted) and the girls' rooms in particular, with their sloping ceilings, lending themselves to festooning with cheerful bunting. When we visited, pupils were buzzing in anticipation of the competition for most festive dorm decorations (whilst on the subject of Christmas, we are told that the carols round the tree, with the tradition of head boy/girl placing the star on top and youngest boarder a glass dove on a lower branch, followed by an 'amazing' Christmas lunch, are 'magical'). No boarding parents per se but head and his wife, a director of boarding, two matrons and three gappies live on site.

Whole school assembles each morning in the entrance hall cum library with prayers read by a pupil and a thought for the day from a staff member ('some more interesting than others', pupils told us) and there's a service in the church – conveniently situated next door to school, negating need for own chapel – every Sunday, with plenty of parents in attendance. Meals all taken in quite the loveliest prep school dining room we've ever seen. Cleverly combines the ancient walls of the original hall with a modern glass ceiling that floods the room with sunlight, and homely farmhouse-style tables and chairs beneath the beams. Family style meals ('the food's amazing,' said pupils – and we can vouch for Friday fish and chips) served out by either a member of staff or, for the older ones, a pupil. Lunch is fairly formal, with grace at the beginning and end announced by head's hand bell, and the tradition of a box of boiled sweets passed round to finish. Breakfast and supper are less so and pupils can sit amongst their friends or siblings in different year groups. Weekends in school are action packed, with lessons on Saturday morning generally followed by a sports fixture and relaxed evenings in with pizza and movies. After church on Sundays, there are trips (eg ice skating, trampolining or Woburn) or friendly sports matches. As one parent told us, 'there really isn't time for homesickness'. House system in place with head boy/girl, house captains and fiercely fought competitions for absolutely everything, from general knowledge or croquet to debating and baking.

Maidwell parents 'couldn't be more delighted' with their choice. Traditional in the most positive sense, parents describe as 'extraordinary' the extent to which staff know their children and love the fact that school allows its pupils to elongate their childhood, free from the pressures of social media and the internet, whilst packing a hefty academic punch and shimmying them smoothly into their next schools.

Malvern College

16

College Road, Malvern, Worcestershire WR14 3DF

01684 581500 | enquiries@malcol.org | www.malverncollege.org.uk

Ages: 13–18

Pupils: 646; sixth form: 309; Boarders: 484

Day: £24,534 pa; Boarding: £36,927 – £38,217 pa

Linked school: The Downs Malvern, 1026

Headmaster: Since 2008, Antony Clark MA HDE (50s). Widely regarded as a safe anchor for the school, he has been at Malvern long enough to make his own significant mark. He brought all his experience of being head at two schools in South Africa, and Gresham's for six years, to Malvern. He has focused on growing the school (it is now up to capacity, he tells us) and on developing the academic culture within the school, and is overseeing the three international school offshoots in China and Egypt. His wife is a lecturer in law and enjoys being involved in the school as much as she can.

Antony is seen by the pupils and parents as a measured and balanced head, a bit distant, but the pupils feel he does know them and they respect the aura of authority that exudes from him. He sets clear boundaries and parents as well as pupils know just where they stand with him.

Academic matters: The school offers an interesting academic dynamic. On the one hand, there are super bright European students who are there for the IB and do very well indeed. Then there are the home grown pupils who are much more mixed ability. The common entrance pass mark is a relatively modest 50, and about 20 per cent of those coming in at year 9 receive some level of learning support. A levels at 39 per cent A*/A in 2017, and 56 per cent A*A/9-7 at GCSE, but school is coy about giving average IB points. The school says that it wants to be open to as wide an ability range as it can, partly because it is interested in a broad range of talents and partly because the it wants all the family to come, not just the bright one of the clan.

Parents rave about the level of academic support. There are carefully tailored individual programmes, and whatever their level, pupils say their teachers really know their strengths and weaknesses. Pupils are highly encouraged to focus hard on their academic work. Some parents feel there is rather too much pressure and the school is expecting pupils to spin an awful lot of plates, but others recognise that this is what gets the results that would not have been forthcoming in a school with less resources to put into teaching and learning. Parents are full of praise for the availability of teachers and the tight level of communication between staff that ensures each pupil is getting the academic support and challenge they need.

The head has upped the academic profile in the school by very visibly encouraging intellectual societies to flourish, with a range of top quality outside speakers as well as opportunities for sixth formers to present papers reflecting their own intellectual interests. Here is the stretch and challenge that the bright sixth formers need. The head has also been keen to develop ideas about teaching and learning among his staff, has established a staff group to move ideas forward and initiated peer to peer observations to help share the very best practice.

In terms of subjects, the range is much what you would expect in a well-resourced school catering for a mixed ability range where the sixth form is split more or less exactly in half between IB and A level. Parents talk about how strong history, economics, English, maths, classics and modern languages are. Sixth formers also enthuse about politics and business studies. Science had a real boost with the opening of a modern science centre named after a past pupil, the current prime minister of Malaysia, Najib Razak. Teachers and parents told us that there is a lot of effort put into constructing sixth form timetables that will really play to the strengths of the pupils, resulting in some strong results and a thoroughly valuable sixth form experience for those of fairly modest academic ability as well as the high flyers.

Academic facilities are strikingly good across the board. The internet access has recently been speeded up, much to everyone's satisfaction. Not every department has the spanking new facilities of the sciences, but music, which is housed in one

of the older buildings, shows that energy, enthusiasm and high achievement are certainly not dependent on buildings alone. The library has all the aura of an ancient seat of learning with the buzz of a 21st century learning resource centre. Pupils commented on the helpful library opening hours.

Games, options, the arts: Sport is outstanding – and there is a lot of it. The sports facilities are excellent, with a splendid new sports centre that incorporates a generous function room for lectures and dinners, all of which are available for community use on occasion, and a new water based professional surface hockey pitch. We were pleased to hear of the girls' football teams' successes. There are special programmes for the elite sports players with high quality coaches and professional contacts, but everyone is expected to participate in games at some level. We spoke to parents who had specifically chosen the college for its sporting excellence and were delighted with how it had delivered, but also to one or two with unsporty children who resented the amount of time they had to spend on games, especially if they had really strong other passions – such as music – that required a big time commitment. We would recommend a parent whose 13 year old is clearly not sporty to think hard about whether the other, considerable, attractions, outweigh all that compulsory games.

It was wonderful to see pupils encouraged to work on a large scale, with great big canvases giving the senior art areas the feel of an art school

The other attractions certainly are there. The art is phenomenal and spreads way beyond the art building itself. The whole school is enhanced with a great deal of the pupils' artwork in a brilliant variety of media. It was wonderful to see pupils encouraged to work on a large scale, with great big canvases giving the senior art areas the feel of an art school. Pupils told us that they are invited to use the art building outside of lesson time and it is clear that there is much enthusiasm for doing this. DT is another strength, and both boys and girls spoke passionately about projects they were undertaking there. Drama is housed in a well-adapted old gymnasium, and again there is masses going on, both within the houses and at school level. Thespians benefit from the very close proximity of Malvern Theatre, which has a number of pre-West End runs, and there are house trips to see

various productions. Music is very strong too, particularly choral and chapel singing, but there is a huge range of ensembles and orchestras. Every year 9 learns a musical instrument. Those looking for choral scholarships at Oxbridge are well prepared, and the school has had success here. The music offers welcome links with the local community – the brass band played at the switching on of the Malvern town Christmas lights, and the choir were doing three carol services in the town during the week we visited.

Most of the school is involved in CCF at some stage and D of E is also offered. The school makes the most of the wonderful Malvern Hills, with various hill runs being an important part of the annual school calendar. Both IB and D of E candidates involved community service, and the school has links with a local school for blind children.

'It offers all a great school should – and more', one parent told us.

Boarding: Eighty per cent of the school are full boarders. There is no flexi-boarding (though day pupils can stay the occasional night for official school events) but there are two compulsory weekends out of school each half term. Day pupils are incorporated into the boarding houses and have the same study space as the boarders. Pupils eat in the houses and house staff make the most of this opportunity to understand exactly what is going on in the daily life of their charges. Non-house staff and other visitors eat with the pupils at lunchtimes too, and the atmosphere is warm, stimulating and highly conducive to developing the best social manners. Pupils and parents say they know the house staff are there for them and will give unstintingly of their time to offer support.

The school suits high energy all rounders and there is a tremendous amount on offer round the clock. One or two parents felt the demands on the pupils were almost too great, with very little down time, but the pupils we met absolutely thrived on the high octane atmosphere and recognised the diversity of gifts that make up a flourishing and healthy community.

Malvern is a delightful and slightly quirky town to wander around – pupils can go out to do a bit of shopping or have a coffee

Background and atmosphere: The school is very cosmopolitan in feel and outlook – about 35 per cent are from overseas, and there are about 40 different nationalities represented at the moment. This global feel is grounded in the quintessentially British landscape of the Malvern Hills. The site is stunning, set on the side of the Malverns with spectacular views. There are 11 houses (six boys' and five girls') around the 250 acre site – many in huge 19th century villas that could well have been the houses of the successful financiers of the Empire who made their home in this health resort for the Victorian rich. Malvern is a delightful and slightly quirky town to wander around – staff and parents can feel as relaxed as they could anywhere in permitting pupils to go out to do a bit of shopping or have a coffee.

The Victorian foundation of the school, 1865, with that glorious mid 19th century architecture that exudes confidence in Church and Country, is an essential part of the school's feel today. Everyone goes to the chapel four times a week for a broadly Church of England service, where hymns are still sung and prayers said although the emphasis is on wise words that will speak to those of all persuasions. There are non-Christians in the school – dietary and other religious observations are happily accommodated – but this is a Church of England foundation and you do feel that is a living reality. The head tells us that past pupils really value the regular worship as they move out into the wider world.

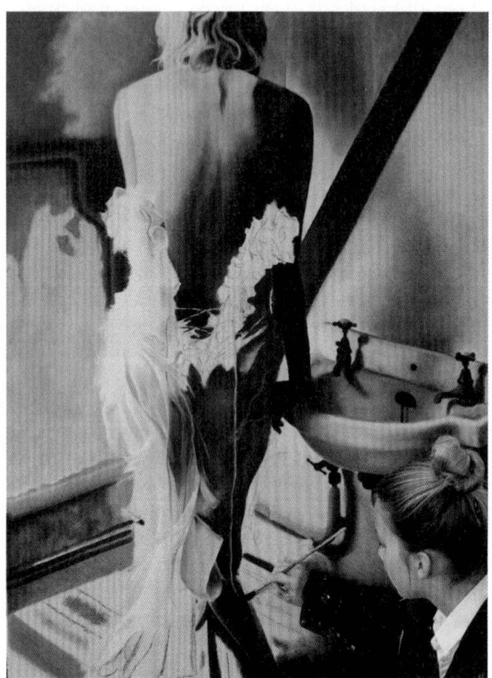

Pastoral care, well-being and discipline: Everyone to whom we spoke valued the pastoral care highly, even parents who had other grumbles. The emphasis is on the individual needs – there is no one-size-fits-all here. One parent told us how accommodating everyone was when her daughter suffered a bad sports injury, and pupils spoke about the staff with genuine warmth. Staff, too, showed a strong sense of loyalty to pupils who had come up through the school, wanting to ensure they had the smoothest possibly transition to the next stage and making it clear each pupil was valued for themselves not just for their A* exam results. The atmosphere felt well-disciplined without being too formal. The rules are clear and everyone recognises a no-nonsense approach to any transgressions, but it is rewards rather than punishments that reinforce the school's strong moral values.

Pupils and parents: Among the alumni of the college are at least two Commonwealth prime ministers, two Nobel prize winners, an Olympic gold medallist and many other notables from the worlds of science, law, the military, business, politics, sports and literature – including CS Lewis. The school produces an eclectic range that bears out its claims to suit the all rounders.

There are a lot of wealthy families forming the backbone of the school. Bursary help is available and we heard of families who were pooling generational resources to send children to the college, but one or two parents speculated that this might not be a comfortable school for a child whose parents were really having to push the boat out financially to pay the fees. The international clientele rubs shoulders with the children of successful Hereford farming families, of London commuters, and of the technological elite who can choose to live in such a delightful part of the country.

The school has been co-educational for about 20 years and there are now more-or-less half boys and girls. Some said that the families put children under some pressure to look good as well as do well, and we certainly saw none of the much publicised childhood obesity here. Housemistresses are aware of teenage girls' desire to look slim and beautiful and on the alert for any obsession, but the girls we met relished the outdoorsy, sporty opportunities of the school and didn't appear to be under pressure to present as cover girls. Both boys and girls appeared pleasingly extrovert and outward-looking. Perhaps not a school for the very quiet and reflective who need a lot of time to themselves.

Entrance: Most families start looking two or three years before entry and some houses fill up faster than others. There are open days, but most families have personalised tours. In some cases there is pre-testing, but the main admission is through common entrance at 13+, or for those coming from non-common entrance schools, the school's own tests in maths, English and science. About 50 join the sixth form each year and they normally do tests in the subjects they want to study at A level or IB, including an English and maths paper as appropriate. The interviews are important too, as are school reports.

Exit: Almost all the sixth form go on to higher education. Those staying in the UK are attracted to campus and collegiate universities like Durham and Exeter or the big Russell Group names eg Imperial, UCL and Bristol; six to Oxbridge in 2017 and three medics. About a quarter go on to US, Canada and mainland Europe top institutions, and may put in UK applications as well to see what comes up. In 2017, 23 off abroad, 22 of them to the US, including two to Harvard and four to other Ivy League unis.

Money matters: This sort of education, staffing level, facilities, opportunities and general ambiance does not come cheap. There are means-tested bursaries and scholarships for a wide range of talents. Pupils can accumulate these but learning support and EAL tuition come as extras.

Remarks: This is a school for the international set, and those who come from the local area, or even 'over the hill' – as the other side of the Malverns is described – undoubtedly benefit by having their horizons expanded beyond the comfortable values of the English shires. There are huge opportunities for pupils to learn from different cultures here and the college does well to work on its links with the local community, so it is not just the mon-eyed international culture that pupils assimilate, delightfully appealing though that is. There is a wholesomeness about Malvern for those who lift their eyes to the hills that can balance the daily busyness. The offshoots in China and Egypt will add to the global dimension and set everyone looking to the far horizons – not just at the opportunities but also, we hope, at the challenges. This is a school deeply bedded in the British public school tradition but with its sights now set across the globe to prepare the pupils for world citizenship.

Malvern St James Girls' School

17

15 Avenue Road, Great Malvern, Worcestershire WR14 3BA

01684 584624 | admissions@malvernstjames.co.uk | www.malvernstjames.co.uk

Ages: 4–18 (boarding from 7)

Pupils: 400; sixth form: 90; **Boarders:** 152 full, 20 weekly, 25 flexi

Day: £8,445 – £19,005 pa; **Boarding:** £19,065 – £35,475 pa

Headmistress: A historian (Leeds), Olivera Raraty arrived in 2016 with impeccable girls' school credentials. Senior deputy at Notting Hill and Ealing High, assistant director of studies and head of history and politics at Wycombe Abbey, history specialist at Francis Holland NW1. With Junoesque presence and a warmth that has captivated the whole community, Olivera has brought the academic clout of her former roles with her, and while she loves the breadth of the ability range at MSJ, she is determined to build on the academic drive started by her predecessor to showcase the intellectual force blossoming in the school.

The girls say there has been a bit of general tightening up since Olivera's arrival but no worrying dramatic changes. 'She is there at everything', they note. She has got the staff on board because they can see she puts in the hours, loves the school already, has masses of exciting ideas for focussing the academic life of the school and the confidence to move things forward. 'She is just great to work with', we heard over and over again from her colleagues.

Parents are pleased to have a mother of two daughters with whom to share the ups and downs of adolescence. Both Olivera's daughters are now safely through the teenage years.

Marina Stentiford (history degree from Worcester) set up and has run the prep school since 2008. She is regarded as 'lovely' by parents and totally committed to the development of the whole child. Staff see her as collegiate and keen to support career development in her staff. She is enthusiastic and revels in the advantages for her girls of the all-through school.

Academic matters: The school prides itself on its tailored approach to the individual in all areas of academic and personal development, and has been awarded 'excellent' in both categories by the ISI. Academic strength is growing throughout the school. GCSE results have been improving steadily with 63 per cent at A*-A/9-7 in 2017, and 39 per cent of the year group achieving eight or more A*-A/9-7 grades – impressive for a school that is by no means highly selective. 2017 A levels show this – 28 per cent of all entries achieving an A*, 53 per cent A*-A; nearly 90 per cent of sixth formers are studying one or more STEM subjects (60 per cent are doing maths A level) and the school has targeted this as an academic area to promote. As a result, an unusually high number go on to study some form of engineering. The team got into the finals of the UK Maths Challenge in 2016, putting it in the top two per cent of whizzy UK maths schools. There is computer science on offer at GCSE and A level as well as DT product design. In fact the sixth form offer is unusually broad and undoubtedly one of the strengths of the school. There are bespoke kitchens for the Leiths Food and Wine course, which you can combine with Greek and Mandarin if you so wish.

Nearly 90 per cent of sixth formers are taking one or more A level STEM subject and an unusually high number go on to study some form of engineering

The school is working on building an active learning approach where girls take responsibility for their own attitude to school work. In the classes we watched, there was a sense of real engagement in learning and teachers were enthusiastically promoting creativity and challenge. The prep department stresses independent learning, so the girls who move up already have a strong basis which is then developed through a new year 7 curriculum that includes a Philosophy for Learning course.

Teachers and senior girls report that the new head has breathed fresh life into the academic life of the school. The offer for the most able is being refined with a coherent progression from one stage to the next. There are academic enrichment

opportunities for everyone who wants them and some who may need a bit of initial prodding. The extension programmes include exciting outside lecturers, the prestigious Somerville suppers and various debates. There are new mentoring and coaching programmes being set up for the high flyers as well as masterclasses.

Staff report it is an exciting place to teach and they feel free to try out innovations. The impressive senior team is keen to take the school's enthusiasm and expertise outside its grand walls and is busy plugging gaps in the local area by providing all sorts of opportunities for local primary schools – modern languages days, maths challenges, technology workshops – that get out the message that academic rigour can be fun and creative. The new head is developing closer links to teacher training providers, particularly around the STEM subjects, so the teachers can share their expertise more widely in the profession.

Careers education is far reaching, including an increasing input from alumnae. With various old girls in the Debretts/Sunday Times 500 Most Influential Britons list, the girls are getting contact with well established women who are at the top of their careers and wanting to give back to their alma mater. 'My friends at co-ed schools always have to sit through talks from lots of old boys,' one of the sixth formers told us. 'Our alumnae are all important women'.

There is a stunning library, well stocked and with long opening hours. The librarians are enthusiastic and fully involved with curriculum innovation across the school. They are passionate about developing students' critical literacy – vital for independent learning, and understanding and interpreting information sources.

Learning support operates at various levels. There is a drop in session for juniors during prep. All staff have training on learning difficulties and there are two full-time SENCos in addition to literacy and numeracy specialists. Support is provided within a graduated framework after a problem is identified. This may include short term focused group work as well as one-to-one lessons (extra charge) – all designed round the needs of the individual.

The prep department is at the heart of the school, not just physically but also in its ability to access high quality facilities and specialist staffing. Not that the movement is all one way. The department offers excellent practice for all the school in its creative curriculum design with cross-curricular enrichment at its core. A recent Toy Story theme allowed the girls to get to grips with mechanics while the woodland school lets them get messy and use serious tools to make tree dens. We spoke to a number of parents who had moved girls from state primaries for the range of opportunities the prep department offers.

At the other end, the sixth form is going from strength to strength. More girls are joining at 16+ and fewer girls leave than in the past because the message is out there that the sixth form is intellectually exciting and tailor-made for you. Tutors and tutees are matched as far as possible by interests and support is coherent – enough to ensure they learn how to maximise their potential without floundering when they leave. The size (about 60 in each year) means the school can be fleet footed when change and innovation are needed. EPQs are increasingly popular and topics reflect the diversity of interests – How to Organise a Tough Schools Day, Training a Racehorse, The Drawbacks of Volunteering Abroad.' 2017 saw an almost clean sweep of A*-A for EPQ entries.

Games, options, the arts: Given the size of the school its sporting success is amazing, and the head is determined to take it still further in line with some parents' views that there could be even more wins. There are a number of elite national athletes – at hockey, lacrosse, rounders, golf, cricket, fencing, athletics, eventing – and the school receives lots of accolades for its willingness to support individuals when they are off competing. The excitement around sport is reflected in the girls' very small wish list where bigger sports facilities came pretty near the top. We thought they were very generous already. The school attracts girls who are very talented in specific ways and parents tell us that one of the strengths is the emphasis on ensuring that individual requirements can be met.

Interest groups abound. Quest, a liberal religious literacy group, got a special mention. Model United Nations is popular and MSJ works with state secondary schools to help them get involved. Year 9s ran a mock election for the whole school and the staff are keen to develop the girls' confidence in public speaking. There is a STEM club where much of the enthusiasm for all forms of engineering is born. MSJ is really doing its bit to redress the gender imbalances. 'Coding is boring until you see the application', one enthusiastic teacher told us, 'Hence the STEM club'.

Drama is flourishing and much loved. Some girls and parents say music is the strongest department in the school. It certainly offers lots of performance opportunities for its high quality choir and various music ensembles. Visual arts are vibrant. There is lots of evidence of large art works as well as some painterly high quality pieces. Textiles is notably strong.

The prep department has its own plethora of activities. Everyone is involved in the marvellous annual production – this year it was Alice in Wonderland. The year 5s and 6s designed the costumes and the set.

Boarding: There is one junior boarding house for years 3-8, two for years 9-11 and two sixth form houses, one of which is in the main school building (much coveted by those who want to stay in bed a bit later and those who want to burn the midnight oil in the library). Other houses are in nearby lovely Malvern properties with large country gardens, high ceilings with light and fresh air flowing through. The houses nicely reflect the age of the girls – the junior one has teddies everywhere.

The school works all the time on improving communications with parents and parents report great strides. Staff email replies to parental concerns very promptly.

There is a strong and experienced pastoral team. Pastoral care plans are put in place quickly and unobtrusively when necessary to provide additional support to girls.

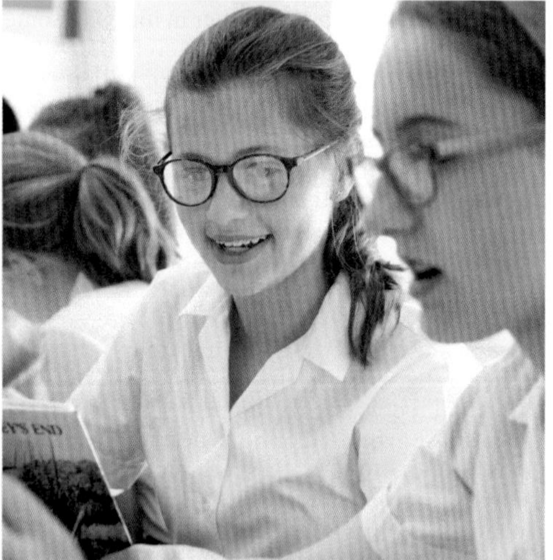

Weekend activities are highly rated and are compulsory up to year 9. There is a full programme of events and there is never a dull moment at weekends. Girls are very positive about relationships between day girls and boarders.

Boarding houses are in nearby Malvern properties with large country gardens, high ceilings and plenty of light and fresh air flowing through

Food in the newly designed dining hall is fresh and diverse, catering for a cosmopolitan set. There was a healthy eating week when we visited that certainly sold the concept to us. Boarders take their meals in this main dining hall.

Background and atmosphere: Opposite the railway station, with good links to Birmingham and London, the main school buildings were once the imposing and gracious Imperial Hotel. The spirit of grandeur and spaciousness still hovers above the busyness of the daily school life. Malvern St James is the result of the 2006 merger of Malvern Girls' College (founded in 1893) and St James's School (founded in 1896). The fallout from the merger is now a thing of the past.

Having the prep department in the centre of the school gives a light and fun atmosphere. This is certainly not a school that feels dominated by teenage angst. The younger girls dart around a glorious copper beech, reminding everyone in the summer term when we visited that there is a life outside GCSEs and away from computer screens. 'They look up to the seniors who they see around all day – it gives them something to aspire to,' the prep head told us. While it is clearly a whole school and everyone loves that, each phase has its own distinctive features. 'We dress up a lot in the junior department and parents are in and out all the time.' Senior girls get involved with the juniors in lots of ways: prefects from the senior school are attached to the pre-prep, there are house links, junior girls sit on the school anti-bullying and food committees – so in the dining hall, used by all ages, there is much waving and smiling between the different age groups.

We were pleased that the school has lots of much loved traditions. There is the exchanging of prefects' gowns ceremony, the annual staff pantomime and ships' events (the competitive houses – as distinct from the boarding houses – are called 'ships' here and run from the junior department right through the school.) The juniors have their own keenly anticipated traditions – a secret Santa for everyone. But it is not a school weighed down by tradition. It is a place with the imagination to go with the creative ideas that the girls come up with, celebrating the quirky as well as the more mainstream.

'It's warm but not fluffy,' says the head and we think that just about sums it up.

Pastoral care, well-being and discipline: The school prides itself on its tailored, personal, family feel. There is a lot of careful, professional attention given to defining and meeting individual needs and the decision to offer an unusually broad range of options, particularly at sixth form level, supports this principle. Girls tells us that they stay at the school because its size means everyone looks out for everyone else.

The growth mindset philosophy is being well bedded in for both girls and staff and builds on the can-do mentality the school has historically cultivated. A new year 10 course looks at negative and positive coping strategies and the school intends to encourage parents to get to grips with current mental health theories, recognising that in such matters school and home need to be giving the same message.

Mental health issues are discussed very openly. There is a 'brilliant' health and well-being centre, the girls tell us, and staff are complimentary about how well the centre communicates with the rest of the school. Girls have access to an external counsellor.

Behaviour is exemplary, as you find in so many girls' schools. Staff and girls scratch their heads to think of naughty actions, but if they find something, there is a range of the usual sanctions – detentions, withdrawal of privileges. But staff say an awful lot of listening and talking works as prevention.

The management team has been looking at extending leadership opportunities for everyone. This is just as true at year 6 as at year 13. The girls appreciate this and relish the chance to try new roles in a fairly small and safe environment.

The head is seen by parents as being absolutely on top of e-safety and anti-bullying strategies.

Pupils and parents: These are girls who are comfortable in their own skins. They are accepted for who they are and give others the same respect and kindness. It is not nerdy to like science, we were told, and if you are not good at sport you can still have fun on the games field.

There is that unique feature you can find in non-city girls' schools – a gentleness combined with a sassy competitiveness. These are girls who are well connected through social media, so know what is trending globally, but who also love a hike in the rolling Malvern Hills.

It's a school where many of mothers and fathers work. The junior school reports the rise of older parents with just one child.

While families are in the main pretty well-heeled, bursaries and scholarships dilute this a little. There are old farming families, those working in the new Worcestershire high-tech areas, businesspeople and professionals from the local vicinity and overseas.

Entrance: There is an element of selection but it is not ferocious. Up to year 3, the girls are invited in for a day to see how they get on. After that there is some assessment through tests. The juniors sit the same 11+ tests as external candidates but if teachers think they won't cope with the step up, there are early discussions about where would be more suitable. Nearly all of the juniors do move up, forming about half of the new year 7. Eleven plus and 13+ entrants are often moving from co-ed preps. Sixth form entrants take papers in their three A level subjects, plus an EAL paper if English isn't their first language.

Exit: Some 60 per cent to top 10 UK universities. Five to Oxbridge in 2017; others to study eg bioengineering at Sheffield, veterinary science at Liverpool, criminology at Cardiff and music at Trinity Laban. Decreasing numbers (around 30 per cent) leave at 16+ for co-ed schools.

Money matters: About average scholarships for top girls' boarding schools, of up to 10 per cent of fees, plus means-tested bursaries up to a total of 40 per cent. There are academic scholarships available at year 7 and year 9 as well as art, music and sports ones, drama, technology and riding are added at year 9 and for the sixth form. The prestigious Founders' Awards Scholarships are for top-notch scholars and all-round ambassadors. There are additional assessments and interviews for these. Wrap around care is available at no extra cost.

Remarks: MSJ is not smart and shiny but has more the air of elegant intellectual eccentricity – there is something of a Bloomsbury feel about it, but a Bloomsbury fit for the 21st century. Operating in a competitive area, MSJ is continuing to carve out a niche for itself as being at the forefront of thinking on girls' education. The fact the new head has come from the GDST stable is helping this still further. The school feels driven and full of girls who are going to change the world, but keeps a sense of a small, close knit community. Undoubtedly brilliant for the all-rounder, but increasingly meeting the aspirations of the high flying academics.

Monmouth School for Boys

Almshouse Street, Monmouth NP25 3XP

01600 713143 | admissions@monmouthschool.org | https://www.habsmonmouth.org

Ages: 11–18 (junior boarding from 9)

Pupils: 516; sixth form: 163; **Boarders:** 157 full

Day: £15,354 pa; **Boarding:** £19,500 – £30,828 pa

Linked school: Monmouth School For Girls, 1059

Headmaster: Since 2015, Dr Andrew Daniel, who has a breadth of educational experience from the liberal, global atmosphere of his own student days at UWC Atlantic College, the University of East Anglia and Washington, Seattle, to the established British independent schools where he has forged his career – including head of maths at Taunton and senior deputy at Wellington School, Somerset. His PhD was on mathematical modelling of plate tectonics in Patagonia, though we refrained from questioning him on this. Andrew comes across as wise and experienced, a man you would seek out for educational advice.

He has looked at the Monmouth site with a fresh pair of eyes and is focussed on new buildings and refurbishments. His attention has been on the science facilities where a big investment is in the process of being rolled out, the 60s boarding house, and creating new classroom spaces as well as improving the dining hall. He is keen to exploit further the strengths of collaboration between the five schools that make up the Monmouth Haberdashers' family – it is in their combining strengths that he sees the huge potential for growth.

He has the unbeatable mixture of people skills ('He really gets on well with grown ups as well as us,' we were told, with some awe, by the boys), a sharp, analytic approach to the business side of running a school and an academic's passion for educational research. He is very clear on the school's priorities. It is academic work first for everyone, then sport and enjoying all the wonderful range of extracurricular activities.

Married to Alison, an oceanographer; they have a son, at boy's prep and a daughter at the girls' school. Andrew's interests include mountaineering, cycling, walking, coaching squash and playing the French horn.

Academic matters: Selective but not frantically so, which makes the results even more impressive. At A level, 54 per cent at A*-A in 2017 and 75 per cent

A*-B. At GCSE, nearly 62 per cent A*-A/9-7 grades in 2017. Value added scores are impressive. Maths is very successful and popular, as are the sciences. Economics, history and classics all get much appreciation from the boys. Computer science is a big growth area.

In the sixth form, there is much collaboration with the girls' school up the hill – and indeed it will become a joint sixth form from September 2018. Minority subjects may be taught at one or another school and combinations that might not work at one school can often work across both. Everyone we spoke to saw this as a real strength. The school also collaborates with Monmouth state schools on the Monmouth Science Initiative, which brings young people together regularly to work with specialists in the science world, who come and speak at the schools, plus twice yearly visits to Cardiff University.

The school believes that single sex academic classes up to GCSE mean the boys flourish in the creative arts and languages as well as maths and sciences, unperturbed by narrow gender stereotypes. Parents say the teaching staff 'get boys', know how their brains work and can get them inspired academically. There is much praise from both boys and parents for the high quality of the teaching.

There is a learning support department to work with boys with mild learning needs either for a few sessions to help with such difficulties as time management and organisation or by offering a longer term programme for ongoing difficulties such as dyslexia. Both approaches are considered effective by the relatively few boys who need them.

Games, options, the arts: There is a phenomenal sports programme. Although the jewels in the crown continue to be rugby and rowing, other sports are getting a look in and gaining considerable success. Some, such as swimming, are now putting out mixed teams. Although the first teams do very well regionally and nationally, everyone agrees the coaches show the same respect and commitment to the thirds, who in fact also do very well – the 3rd 11 football team being the most successful in the school last season. There is an impressive fixture list with up to four teams per year group out most weeks. The sports centre is open day and night for senior and junior school boys and incorporates a private members' sports club for the public and parents. It is home to a canoeing club, pilates studio, huge all purpose sports hall and gym. An impressive sports pavilion with a terrace cum large social space overlooks the playing fields that fall away to the Wye river, with the Welsh hills rolling away as a backdrop to this inspiring scene. The quality of the pitches is professional, the wicket county standard, with the grounds staff to support this.

But that is only a part of what is on offer outside lessons. There is lots of quality music and drama. Drama, often jointly with the girls' school, includes musical theatre as well as the big drama classics. Large scale as well as smaller music performances take place throughout the year. There is a wide range of ensembles including choirs, who sing at various church and cathedral venues as well as in school. DT is a vibrant department, very well equipped. We visited as the finishing touches were being given to the very high quality GCSE and A level projects. The department runs a number of challenging enrichment activities – eg tear down club where they strip apart ordinary household items such as a washing machine to see how they work, creating a green powered car, a rocket competition.

Sports programme is phenomenal. Professional standard playing fields fall away to the Wye river with the Welsh hills as backdrop to the inspiring scene

And the list goes on. There is a CCF, literary and debating societies, reading groups, science clubs. Many sixth form clubs are combined with the girls. Lots of the residential and overseas trips are also for both boys and girls.

Boarding: Monmouth is a delightful small town and it is very safe, so the boys walk out of the school gates into the life of the town, avoiding the isolation bubble that can sometimes be a boarding experience. The school is very committed to its boarding and the boarding houses feel very much part of the whole school. About 60 per cent of boarders are British and there are pupils from a range of countries. Houseparents, who are also teachers – something parents value – are totally devoted to the school and boys. There is a boarding house for juniors in years 5-8, three for years 9-12, and then year 13s all come together in a house designed as a stepping stone to fully independent university life. Here the boys learn how to cook on a budget and how to operate a washing machine. They also all have their own en-suites – a luxury they might not experience at university. The houses are all different physically, ranging from Georgian town houses to a 60s block which is about to have an extensive, swishy face lift. Older houses have a quirky feel adapted creatively to the needs of today – no boring regimentation here. 'Relaxed and purposeful' is how staff describe the atmosphere in the houses. Staffs regularly tour overseas to meet international parents. There are activities with the girl boarders some evenings and at weekends.

We appreciated the large poster in the sixth form house centred round the statement 'I haven't any homework to do tonight', with a lot of very valuable suggestions.

Background and atmosphere: The school was founded in 1614 by William Jones, a member of the Haberdashers' Company, as a local school. It expanded its boarding throughout the 19th century. The 400th anniversary was commemorated by, among other things, the creation of a new building with classrooms, offices and meeting spaces, all ecologically high quality. There had been a major rebuild in the 1880s in magnificent Jacobean style, so the campus embraces a mix of architectures from the almshouses where offices are now located, to the highly modern builds, to the sensitively refurbished chapel that now acts as a library.

This is a school that inspires a lot of loyalty, both from parents, old boys and the wider Monmouth community. The head noticed on his arrival a marked lack of 'town and gown' division and the crowd at the big rugby matches is swelled by locals. The school theatre, The Blake, is a brilliant resource for the town as well as the schools, showing NT Live streams and hosting a number of touring companies as well as local arts groups. The school runs computer programming classes for the local community. There is a much-loved tradition where the school parades through the town to church for the annual commemoration service, and all the key local dignitaries are invited to events such as the carol service.

The school feels friendly and purposeful. There is a wholesome sense of balance about the whole place.

Boarders in their last year of sixth form live in a house designed to prepare them for university life. Boys learn how to cook on a budget and how to operate a washing machine

Pastoral care, well-being and discipline: Mental health issues do not dominate the pastoral agenda here as they seem to be increasingly doing elsewhere. Some staff say this is down to very strong and flexible support systems so everyone has someone to go to if anything starts to fall apart. The head says it is also the consequence of sport for all, quoting research which shows how good physical exercise is for warding off serious mental health problems. The boys themselves are serious about the emotional problems that can occur, happy to talk openly about them and agree staff are hugely supportive.

Staff say discipline problems are largely pre-empted. Behaviour expectations are made very clear and it unusual for boys to overstep the line. If they do – an example was given of playing football in the bedroom – a very clear reminder is given of the reasons behind the prohibition, followed up, if there is any recurrence, with a sanction such as extra tidying up duties. But usually, one of the house staff tells us, there is just a lot of trust and respect on both sides.

Parents comment on how responsive staff are to queries or concerns. getting back swiftly by email or phone.

Pupils and parents: Families come mainly from the south west, the Bristol/Cheltenham area and South Wales, with some families leaving the south east for a more healthy lifestyle option without having to compromise on education. A lot of parents buy into the Habs' Monmouth suite of schools and the schools are increasingly making it easy for parents to have the whole family in the group. This family-friendly approach is seen in the school bus policy, with routes adjusted each September accordingly to where the children in all the schools live. We thoroughly approve, though some parents comment on how expensive the service is and, like so many other schools, it is not possible to take into account everyone's after-school commitments.

Parents are a cross-section both professionally and financially. Teachers and parents comment on the easy social mix. The boys seem very comfortable in their own skins, welcoming to newcomers, completely unpretentious and conscious of how fortunate they are to be at such a wonderful school in such a wonderful location.

Entrance: Most of the boys at the prep move up to the senior school and they are joined by about as many again from outside. At 11+, assessment has a three pronged approach – exams in English, maths and verbal reasoning, an interview and a report from the present school. At 13+, by common entrance or the school's own exams in maths, English and French with interviews. Sixth form entry depends on GCSE results, an interview and report from existing school.

Non-nationals must speak reasonable English, although the school does offer EAL support.

Exit: Some 20 per cent leave post-GCSE. After A levels, the school is proud of the range of universities and courses to which the boys move on. Three to Oxbridge in 2017 and four medics. One off to Hong Kong to study mechanical engineering. The majority choose science based-subjects, but there is a fair smattering of languages, humanities and the arts.

Money matters: For escapees from the south east, the comparatively low level of fees brings tears of joy to the eyes. This school offers excellent value for money. There is bursary support and scholarships at each level: academic, music and sport.

Remarks: An excellent school for the all rounder who wants to work and play hard. It is a place of high aspiration in the most idyllic setting, far away from the city scramble but not isolated socially or intellectually. It would probably not be ideal for those who detest sport or who want to be hot-housed for a scholarship to Harvard.

The family of schools work closely together and undoubtedly gain strength not just from having the Haberdashers behind them but also from the collegiate approach at leadership level. Perhaps the fact that leadership is not the usual lonely business is one reason for the tension-free atmosphere of palpable enjoyment that cascades down from the senior levels.

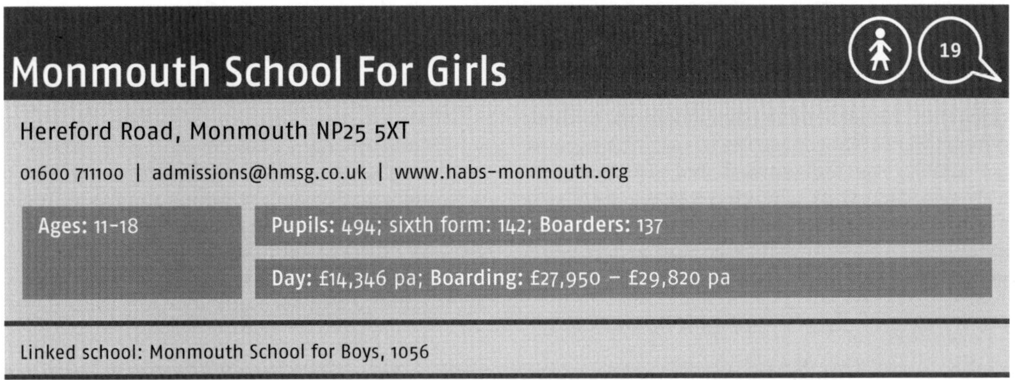

Monmouth School For Girls

19

Hereford Road, Monmouth NP25 5XT

01600 711100 | admissions@hmsg.co.uk | www.habs-monmouth.org

Ages: 11–18

Pupils: 494; sixth form: 142; Boarders: 137

Day: £14,346 pa; Boarding: £27,950 – £29,820 pa

Linked school: Monmouth School for Boys, 1056

Headmistress: Since 2014, Mrs Caroline Pascoe (40s), previously head of Truro High School for Girls. Microbiology degree from Bristol, member of GB rowing squad at 1992 Barcelona Olympics, still adores sport. An officer in the RAF Volunteer Reserve. Worked in Himalayas and continues to lead high altitude trekking expeditions. Married to a very supportive husband, with a son at Monmouth School, and very involved as a family, in town and county life. Much admired and respected by the girls. She knows everyone's names and it is widely held that she 'walks the talk'. As far as encouraging girls to take risks is concerned, in addition to joining them on outdoor pursuits adventures, she learnt a One Direction tune on the recorder and played it in assembly. We were impressed, and so were her pupils. She has developed a Confidence for Life programme which is all about moving outside your comfort zone. She has also encouraged a higher profile for the creative arts on a regular basis – assemblies have been transformed and are much anticipated, being regularly used to showcase dance and music.

Her appointment of an assistant head to lead co-curricular activities is part of her drive to give breadth, as is her development of the expeditions programme. She is creating a generation of proactive girls with high levels of resilience – no worrying about a glass ceiling here. Breadth isn't just about trips to India; Caroline also wants to keep raising academic horizons – 'Girls don't read enough after year 10, ' she tells us. 'We want to see a continuing love of learning here'. She is also committed to building the boarding, which has grown since her arrival.

A can-do, action head, Caroline leads from the front and her constant presence round school, from eating with the girls to supporting everything they are involved in, creates a buzz around the place. The energy and pace you feel everywhere

here is coming from the top. Parents find her very approachable and feel she has ambition for the school to drive it forward to greater things.

She is off in July 2018 to head the International School Bangalore.

Academic matters: The results at GCSE and A level are very good and the school says it achieves this without putting the girls under too much pressure. In 2017, 72 per cent A*-A/9-7 grades at GCSE and 54 per cent A*/A, 75 per cent A*-B at A level. Art, modern languages, maths and science are popular choices. At sixth form level, Monmouth School for boys and the girls' school come together – and indeed it will be a joint sixth form from September 2018 – allowing 30 subjects to be on offer across both schools, which ensures virtually everyone gets the combination of subjects they want. It means some girls will be taught in some subjects at the boys' school and boys at the girls'. This works well. The girls say they like the different perspective the boys bring to subjects and comment on an often-repeated observation that it is noticeably that the girls think before they speak, unlike the boys.

Parents say that the school doesn't heap unreasonable amounts of pressure on the girls, but that doesn't mean that HMSG has any lower expectations that the big London day schools, with which parents were often comparing it. Learning support is available on an individual/shared basis from suitably qualified staff. The girls say teachers will always make time for them if they need a bit of extra help on a less formal basis. Most departments run surgeries for individual help, too.

Links with outside organisations enhance the academic work. Renishaw plc sponsored a STEM competition recently that led to further work supported by the school staff, which led in turn to two girls exhibiting their invention at the NEC, pitching it on Dragons' Den and selling to national retailers.

Games, options, the arts: The school has a deserved reputation for being very sporty, and clearly even the girls who aren't games mad are very proud of the reputation. Those girls told us that respect and resources are given to the arts as well and there is a policy of introducing girls to different sports to help them all find some physical activity that appeals. Girls regularly represent the region and Wales in a variety of sports. One parent told us that her daughters had asked the PE staff if they could start a gym club. Within a few months they had it – well resourced and competing nationally.

Atmosphere is one of calm and sunny good manners, relationships between girls and staff are excellent

Drama and dance are popular, with excellent facilities shared with the local community. Music is strong with 50 per cent taking some additional music lessons. The annual inter-house Eisteddfod gives an extra frisson to these activities. The glass atrium is hung with house flags on such occasions. Art is popular and high quality – lots is displayed

around the school. Parents praise the standard of the drama productions.

At senior level, most of the extracurricular performing arts are done with the boys' school along with CCF, shared visiting speakers and a number of societies. It would be nice to have even more, the girls tell us. D of E and other local community service opportunities as well as fundraising for overseas projects. Girls are committed to these ventures both for their own personal development but also, we felt, out of a genuine desire to serve others.

Boarding: The boarding houses are on the school site and are purpose built. They are strikingly attractive and friendly in feel. From year 11 up, girls have rooms of their own. Below that they share in twos or threes. There is a lot organised for the boarders outside lesson time, some trips including the boys' school. Much sport goes on at weekends and in the evenings. There is shopping, cinema trips, salsa evenings, BBQs and generally a purposeful but relaxed atmosphere, which is very appealing and might account for the very low incidence of illness, despite the attractions of the medical facilities – there are soft toys on every bed. It might also account for the equally low level of law breaking. The girls really struggled to think of naughty things that anyone did. The worst seems to be not doing your kitchen duty or being late to breakfast (punishment – go in early the next day).

Boarding is flexible but that hasn't meant the school opts out of providing after-school and weekend activities. This is an active school with high energy pursuits on offer throughout the days and weekends. The meal menu is wide and quality good with meals served in an attractive extended dining room.

Background and atmosphere: Founded in 1892, to offer girls the opportunities that Monmouth School had provided since 1614, the Girls' School was funded by the original bequest of a local man, William Jones, a member of the Haberdashers' Company who made his fortune in Russian. The livery company is responsible for the school and provides financial support and stability, which reassures staff and has allowed for continual development of facilities. Although the boys' school is not far away, the girls' school has its own extracurricular facilities such as an Astroturf and swimming pool. The original Victorian buildings have been enhanced by imaginative, modern expansions such as a glass atrium and sixth form centre.

The school works hard at being a part of the Monmouth community and from those we spoke to, it is liked and respected. We arrived in the middle of the Monmouth Literary Festival – Carol Ann Duffy had been speaking the night before – which is organised entirely by the sixth forms of the three Monmouth secondary schools, the two Habs schools and Monmouth comprehensive. A remarkable achievement involving contacting agents, organising programmes, ticket sales and so on. There is another serious collaboration through the Monmouth Science Initiative, where state and independent schools work together with Cardiff University to bridge the gap between A level science and university science.

The girls really struggled to think of naughty things that anyone did. The worst offences seemed to be not doing your kitchen duty or being late to breakfast

There is a lovely sixth form centre with study areas and a cool common room café – 'The boys love it', the girls tell us. 'We have to remind them that they are here for lessons not to drink hot chocolate all day'. Sixth formers still wear a uniform, suits, and tell us that they like it as they don't want to feel separate from the rest of the school. The dropout rate between year 11 and the sixth form is quite small – girls can't wait to wear suits and go to the café, we are told.

Pastoral care, well-being and discipline: The atmosphere is one of calm and sunny good manners. The relationships between the girls and staff are universally praised and we saw lots of warm and relaxed exchanges. 'They are interested in you and what you want to make of your life', sixth formers say. We heard about the much-anticipated annual satirical review put on by staff as part of the sixth form Christmas entertainments, a good indication of strong relationships. There are anti-bullying ambassadors and a buddy scheme working between year 7 and year 13. The girls tell us they would like even more integration between year groups. Prefects apply for their role and are eager for an opportunity to give back to the school. 'It is the school empowering us to experience responsibility', we were told by a successful applicant. The head has opened up the subject of social media and bullying and the girls are aware of the effects this can have and are being helped to combat it. The school is less focused on punishment and more concerned that the girls understand the dangers and causes.

A coloured card system operates for minor disciplinary infringements throughout the school – three yellow cards for something like late homeworks leads to a detention. 'It is really to help us get caught up,' the girls say. There are orange cards for uniform matters – zero tolerance for nail varnish: it gets that naughty. Parents say problems are nipped in the bud early and the staff are open and honest in their communications on pastoral issues. Pastoral care is outstanding, we were told.

Pupils and parents: Pupils come from a wide local area. There are buses coming from Cardiff, the north Bristol area, the Monmouthshire border, Hereford, Newport and the Ledbury area. The calendars for both day and boarding pupils are coordinated across the five Haberdashers' Monmouth schools, which is clearly a huge advantage for parents.

The bursary scheme ensures a good social mix. There are émigrés from the home counties, old Monmouth families, families with very little in the way of income and lots with both parents

Fresh, clear air from the Welsh hills permeates the whole ethos. It is lovely place to live – for staff as well as boarders

working hard to afford the fees. Staff commented to us that you find none of the sense of entitlement that some schools engender – pupils seem grateful to be at the school.

The head takes parents' surveys very seriously and we were impressed by how positive she was about parental criticisms. She wants the school to be on a constant improvement journey and uses parental feedback to keep raising the game. School council is valued by her as well as by the girls. This is an example of a school that pays more than lip service to parent and pupil voices. Parents complimented the school on its proactive approach to keeping them aware of current problem issues such as e-safety. 'They are taking care of my education as a parent,' one mother told us. Parents' view of the HMSG 'product' is one of engaging, confident, interesting girls who are keen to try new things, unaffected and enthusiastic. We would agree.

Former pupils include Lisa Rogers, Sandra Huggett and Jackie Ballard MP.

Entrance: About a third from their own prep school, Inglefield House, a third from other independent schools and a third from state schools. Entry is by entrance exam, interview and junior school report. At 13+ by own exam or common entrance. Some join at sixth form following an interview and good GCSE results.

Exit: There is less of the problem than some girls' schools face with large numbers of year 11 leaving for mixed schools. A few will go for financial reasons or because A levels really aren't for them, but most (some 75 per cent) stay on for the final two years. Sixth formers and parents say the school prepares girls very well for university and beyond. There are lots of links with old girls – staff meet up semi-formally with those who are London-based very regularly. There are plenty of opportunities to visit universities and the girls are starting to think about the possibility of apprenticeships. At the moment virtually everyone goes to university – one to Oxbridge in 2017, the majority to Russell Group universities and others to do niche high quality courses such as stage management and technical theatre, agri-food marketing, anthropology and media. A number study science, including medicine (three in 2017) and engineering. A few go overseas – one to an art foundation course at

Rhode Island School of Design and one on a rowing scholarship to the Academic Center of Exploratory Studies at Connecticut in 2017.

Money matters: One in five receive financial assistance through a means-tested scheme that reassesses every year from endowment income.

Remarks: Habs has been in Monmouth for 400 years and reinvented itself over that time. The current structure is a selling point, so parents tell us. They like the all through concept with co-ed for the little ones in Agincourt and at sixth form level. Parents frequently used the word 'honest' when describing the school. You feel the fresh, clear air from the Welsh hills permeates the whole ethos. The location is very inspiring. From the sports fields you look out along the Wye Valley and from anywhere in the school you have views down to the rest of Monmouth and beyond. It is a lovely place to live – for the boarders, but also for staff and for families moving into the area.

We wondered if it was all a rather awful shock when girls had to move outside the Monmouth bubble, but we were assured that the school was anything but parochial. There are lots of visits to far-flung parts of the globe and the head's background in overseas work has re-emphasised the idea of a global village. Having said that, there is no doubt that Monmouth feels a very long way from Cardiff or Bristol, where a number of day girls live – no doubt part of its appeal for many families. It has the ambitious feel of a big city school without any of the traffic jams and tower blocks.

One parent summed up the feel of the school well: 'HMGS may lack a little of the pomp, ceremony and glitz of some public schools, but what you get is genuine care and a commitment to help your child reach her potential, whatever that may be.'

Moor Park School

RC 20

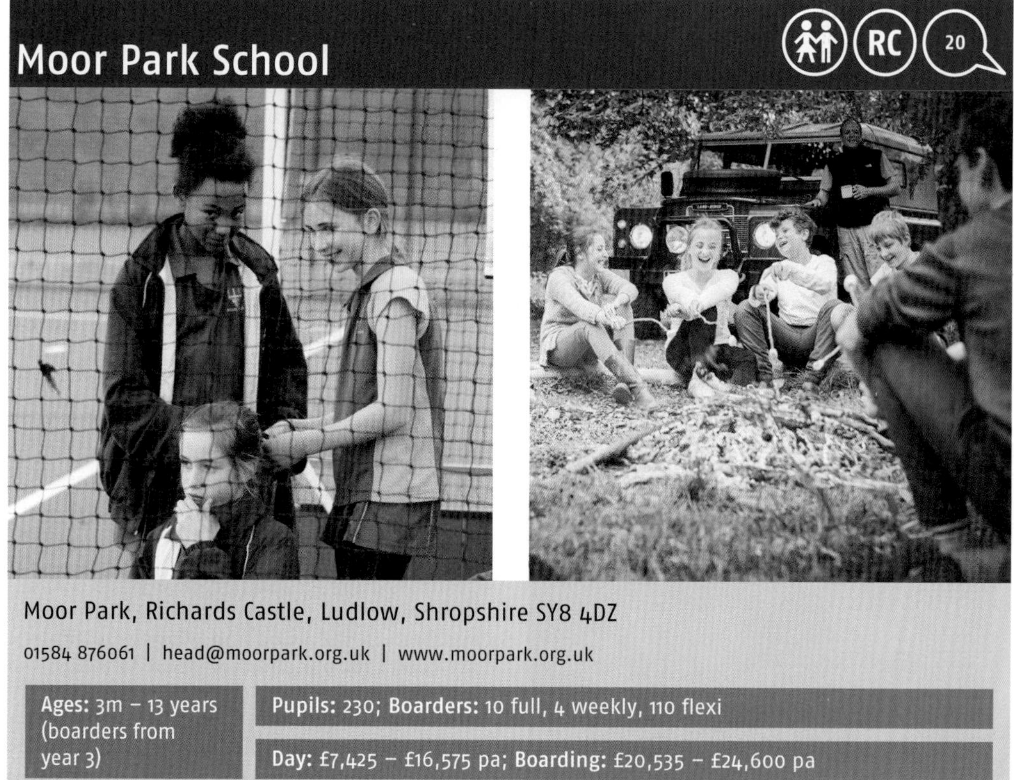

Moor Park, Richards Castle, Ludlow, Shropshire SY8 4DZ

01584 876061 | head@moorpark.org.uk | www.moorpark.org.uk

Ages: 3m – 13 years (boarders from year 3)

Pupils: 230; **Boarders:** 10 full, 4 weekly, 110 flexi

Day: £7,425 – £16,575 pa; **Boarding:** £20,535 – £24,600 pa

Headmaster: Since 2015, Charlie Minogue. It is never easy taking over from a popular longstanding head, but the word among parents is that Charlie is different and brilliant. He has won their hearts by singing Can't Stop Me Now with the parents' band at a school ball, wearing his kilt. Before Moor Park, Charlie worked at Aldwickbury School (deputy head), Harpenden and St Paul's Cathedral School, having started his career in a secondary state school, an experience that has shaped his educational values. 'That first school taught me to never give up on a child and always be aware of what else is going on in their life. No-one is only a school pupil.' He is not a practising Catholic but very drawn to the moral framework that the Catholic foundation provides and subtly underpins everything about Moor Park.

There is a gravitas about Charlie that is balanced by boyish good looks and a twinkle in his eye. He knows all the children by name and what they are up to. The children are clearly keen to win his approval and attention. While we visited, one boy came up to him to arrange to be his partner in a golf match on the school's nine hole golf course that evening and it was clearly the highlight of the boy's week.

The dormitories are at the top of the old house – quirky rooms with slanting ceilings and irregular lines

Charlie, his wife and two children are loving the open air life that the Shropshire 85 acre estate allows after the restrictions of the south east. Both children are at the school and Charlie says that when they went back to Harpenden to meet up with friends, his son commented, 'It was nice seeing them, Dad, but we can be outside so much more now and never seem to use our mobiles much'. Smartphones are not a feature for the family at Moor Park – there is far too much climbing trees for that. Charlie's wife is totally involved in the school, entertaining visitors, teaching the double bass, running the marketing. 'She's fantastic,' one parent told us. She exudes charm and common sense and is a very reassuring presence for parents of boarders. The couple have exciting plans for the school, including a performing arts development. Parents like the fact Charlie has an open door policy for them. 'Don't moan in the car park', he says, 'Come and tell me'.

Entrance: The school is non-selective. Assessments take place either prior to or at joining to establish educational needs. Some children come from the nursery all the way through the school, but more join throughout the years. Some parents send them for the last few years as a preparation for senior full boarding.

Exit: The UK's best known senior schools figure as destinations including Eton, Winchester, Rugby, Cheltenham, Harrow, Moreton Hall, Christ College Brecon, Malvern College, Hereford Cathedral School and Downe House. School prides itself on the advice it gives parents regarding the most appropriate senior schools for their children.

Remarks: In physical terms, this is the site to die for. Parents talk of the delight of seeing distant deer appear through the early morning mist as they drop their children off. The original house is Queen Anne, much developed in the late 19th century and includes arts and crafts features such as Morris stained glass. The entrance hall is inviting, with a big fireplace and imposing staircase that boasts remarkable tooled leather wallpaper and leads up to the boarding area for older children. Just off the entrance hall is the chapel, the old ballroom with a wonderful ceiling. The 85 acres includes a deer park, lake, terrace, lots of woodland and lawns.

But this is no sterile stately home. The delight of the grounds and buildings is that all are used both formally and informally for the children to have a full outdoor life and rich childhood. The dormitories in the old house are in the quirky top rooms with slanting ceilings and irregular lines. The old coach house has made a spacious pottery and art space. Outside, full use is made of the stream as part of an assault course – mud runs are the fun activity of the moment. There is an outdoor classroom in the woodland where the children have poetry lessons and there is an Astroturf. The night before we visited, there had been a bonfire in the woods where the children had baked their own bread. 'Awesome', said the year 8s. Around the main house are lots of small outdoor areas and as you turn a corner, you find a swing with a group of girls playing, then round the next a small grass area with half a dozen boys playing cricket, then you see individual raised beds for vegetable growing for the incipient gardeners. You couldn't get further from the typical urban fenced-in school playground. There is a big sports hall, a swimming pool, excellent outdoor sports facilities as well as a large multi-purpose space with banked seating for performances and whole school assemblies.

The school is non-selective and caters for the full ability range. There are two children on formal SEN statements and also a lot of academic scholarships to highly regarded senior schools. When children join, there is an assessment of their academic needs and if necessary a plan is put in place with the SENCo ('She's a brilliant asset,' says the head). The school works successfully with children who have dyslexia or dyspraxia or are on the autism spectrum. One parent told us how quickly the teachers picked up on her son's dyslexia, despite it having been undiagnosed for years at another school. There are two forms most years with up to 16 children in each form, so class sizes are small enough for a lot of one to one support as a matter of routine, which the children are quick to point out and appreciate.

The children do well in terms of acdemic outcomes and the head is delighted that, having created a new academic committee, teachers are starting to talk to each other more about teaching initiatives. A new post common entrance programme brings real enrichment to the educational experience of the year 8s, preparing them for the challenges ahead. The maths department runs a shares competition, and there is a developing emphasis on emerging technologies, thinking and creative skills.

Art is undoubtedly one of the outstanding strengths of the school – the standard of work is way above what you would expect for children of that age. The DT workshop is home to an enormous crocodile made by the children that hangs from the ceiling and the emphasis is on teaching crafts using the professional-looking array of tools and equipment. The children have made a compostable loo for the woods and a hovercraft as well as tables and chairs that can actually be used. Everyone up to year 2 has woodland time each week.

The children say there is always lots to do and that the best thing about the school is the freedom. Sport is huge and very successful – the girls' U12 hockey team had just been in the national finals when we visited. Children take part in equestrian eventing and triathlons feature. Many are involved in out-of-class musical activities. We were impressed by a flautists' group that arrived in the school chapel for their lunchtime rehearsal and just got on with it before any teacher appeared. Those involved in speech and drama regularly take part in local festivals and competitions and again do very well. There are school plays and concerts. Weekend activities are wildly anticipated. These are often themed – a Bake-Off weekend, a Camo weekend with the highlight being Capture the Flag at night. They also climb trees.

The emphasis is on flexi-boarding. There are full boarders, some of whom are foreign nationals coming over for perhaps a year or even a term, mainly from Europe. A lot of children dip in and out of boarding on a weekly basis and that works well both for the children and families. Everyone is welcomed for special boarding weekends. It all feels very relaxed. There is a separate purpose-built boarding house for younger children, The Tree House, a wooden building that has impeccable eco-credentials. This allows for 10 girls and 10 boys to board at any one time and children typically stay for two or three nights a week. Parents see this as an excellent introduction to boarding.

Pastoral care is regarded as outstanding. The children say that staff sort out any problems very quickly and the head tells us that he was very struck, coming new into the school, how very positive the weekly staff pastoral meetings are, with is a sense that everyone is supportive of the holistic approach to pastoral care. The children and staff comment on how the children all look after each other, particularly in the boarding context, where the older and younger children play together all the time. Parents describe how if there is a relationship upset between the children, the staff are very good at dealing with it sensitively, getting everyone to sit round and have a general discussion about being kind and thoughtful.

The old coach house has made a spacious pottery and art studio. Outside, full use is made of the stream – mud runs are the fun activity of the moment

There are daily assemblies in the middle of the morning to give the children a sense of calm and something outside their busy daily lives. Mass is held each week and although now most children and staff are not Catholic, that tradition is very visible and very much a part of the school's fabric. The children said that one of their most memorable events in the school calendar was the Benedictus at the end of the Michaelmas term. 'They trust us to hold the candles and the sheet of paper with the mass on', we were told by awed children. The school is concerned to ensure that those who board have some time just to be quiet by themselves, and the small bedrooms help this. Having said that, children who were very introspective or fixated on their play technology might not settle here. The head said that staff have to like the outdoor life, and we would say the same for children. If your child really doesn't enjoy getting muddy, Moor Park would be a bit wasted on them.

About half the children are fairly local – school minibuses bring children in from the rural areas. Traditionally it has been a school for established farming/land-owning families and those wanting a preparation for the big Catholic boarding schools. Nowadays there are increasing numbers of escapees from the home countries. Families tend to share a belief in a holistic education and want their children to enjoy every minute of their childhood. 'Moor Park is unflashy', one parent said. 'Everyone's car is dirty'.

Moor Park is the most magical bubble. Children have a childhood experience that will never be forgotten and will shape them whatever life brings. The school develops skills that prepare them for life outside. They leave with the ability to interact positively with others of all ages, with a striking degree of self-reliance, and a sense of knowing themselves and knowing the delights of our natural world – things which can never be taken away. Parents can't bear to think their children will ever have to leave. 'It is a blessed place,' one said to us.

Moreton Hall School

21

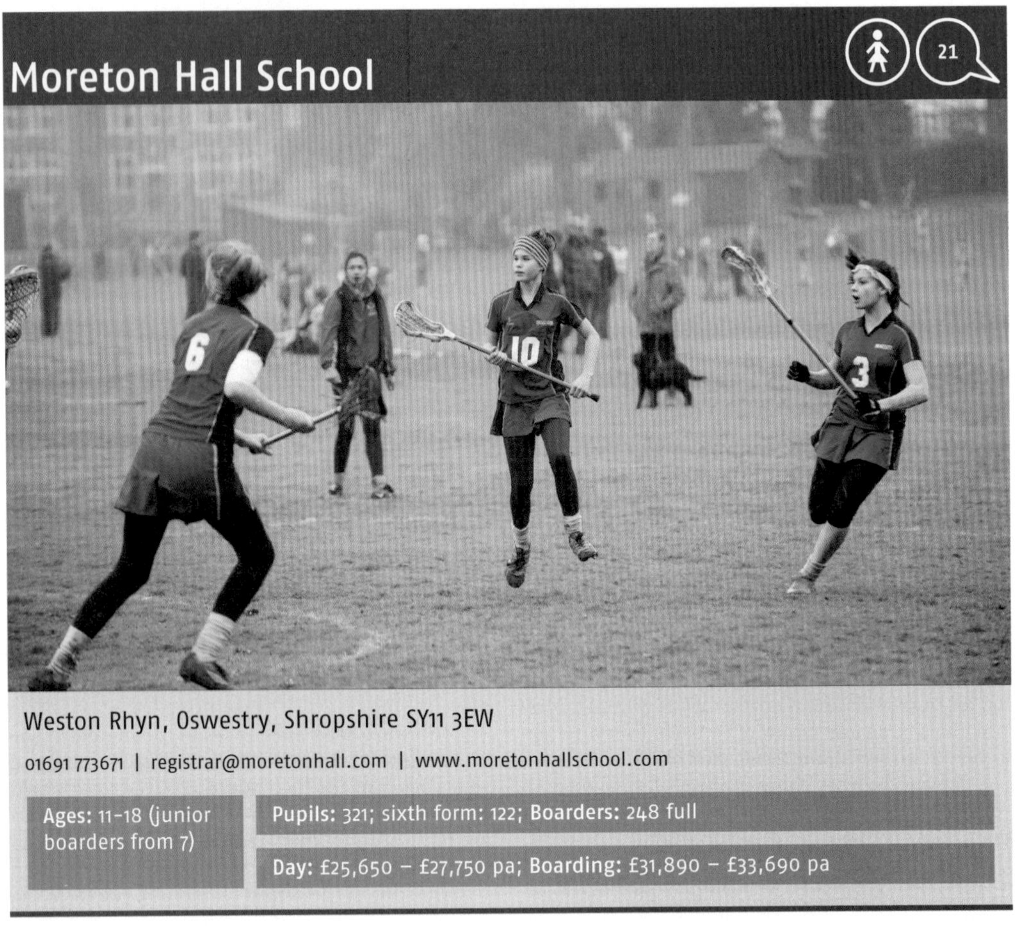

Weston Rhyn, Oswestry, Shropshire SY11 3EW

01691 773671 | registrar@moretonhall.com | www.moretonhallschool.com

Ages: 11-18 (junior boarders from 7)

Pupils: 321; sixth form: 122; **Boarders:** 248 full

Day: £25,650 – £27,750 pa; **Boarding:** £31,890 – £33,690 pa

Principal: Since 1992, Jonathan Forster BA PGCE (50s) who still 'just loves every day at Moreton Hall'. His daughters have been through the school and he and his wife, who's heavily involved in school life, can testify as parents to what a wonderful place it is bring up children. Jonathan – who has a degree from Leeds and was previously housemaster and English teacher at Strathallan – rescued the school from imminent closure, and he has continued to drive it at a pace that speaks of a life-long mission and endless creative energy. He is always ahead of the game, ensuring the school leads not follows market demands. He has kept true to the liberal educational vision of its founders and provided that liberalism with a modern twist, to give Moreton Hall girls the edge when they enter the adult world of work. Jonathan says he has been empowered by the environment, and it must be mutual, because his entrepreneurial spirit, his thinking outside the box, shows in the girls and in the whole ethos of the place. He has done remarkable things and when he eventually does leave, it will take someone very special to take his place.

Academic matters: Academic results are strong, with an improvement at A level to 53 per cent A*/A grades; GCSE 50 per cent A*-A/9-7, and the value-added scores at both GCSE and A level are usually huge. Its increasing success draws in star teachers and bright girls, so it's mostly on an upward trajectory. With lots of living accommodation on site, the job becomes a lifestyle choice for teachers as well as families. There is no deadening insistence on the latest Department for Education pedagogy here. The principal is far more interested in bringing in people who have done things – the English department boasts a writer, the art department has practising artists and the girls told us that their chemistry teacher had been testing perfumes before joining Moreton Hall. There is a strong science drive in the school (innovative science centre includes medical science facility – the first for any UK school) and well over half are taking at least one science A level. Close links to Keele University and the orthopaedic hospital at nearby Gobowen.

Though edging up all the time, the ability is quite wide on entry, which makes the results particularly encouraging. It's down to excellent teachers as well as small class sizes. The girls describe their teachers as 'passionate and enthusiastic' and are very aware that they are there literally all the time. 'They give you as much extra as you need,' said one sixth former who told us that when she was working late on a piece of work, she had emailed her teacher with a query at 11pm and had a reply that night.

There is no extra charge for learning support, whether it is Oxbridge preparation or getting through GCSE maths. Teachers are there for the girls whatever their needs – no sense of children having to fit into rigid school systems here. One parent commented on the flexibility the school offered in terms of curriculum – girls can study more or less any combination of subjects they want at GCSE and A level.

Games, options, the arts: It's in this side of school life where its radical and constantly progressing nature really shines. In sport it embraces that most traditional of girls' sports, lacrosse, where the Moreton Hall teams win everything this side of London and a fair bit nationally as well, but there are masses of other successes and opportunities with the fabulous sports facilities on site – a nine hole golf course and grounds that mean cross-country really is cross country. Cricket popular summer sport – now has indoor nets. Elite sports scholarship programme gives access to top quality coaching.

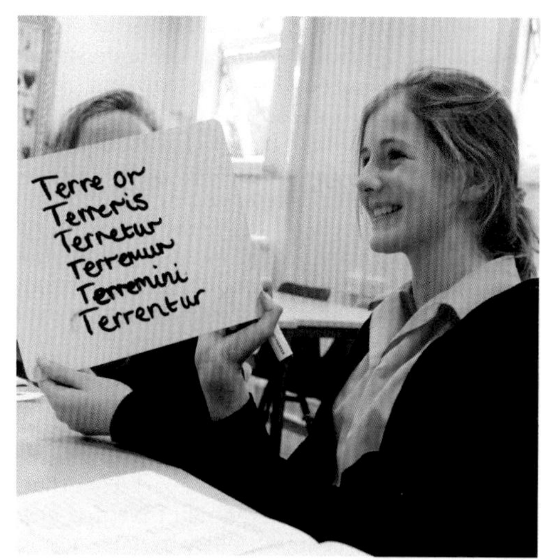

Lots of music goes on, classical and popular, with girls performing regularly to both large and small audiences. Drama is hugely popular and professional. 'Musical theatre can consume everything', said one non-thespian parent, worrying about exam results, but the girls are queuing up to take part.

Astrophysicist Dame Jocelyn Bell Burnett had just been when we visited, and strong links with Keele University produce a steady flow of high-powered speakers

All this is nothing like enough for Moreton Hall. The school is strong on connections and is extraordinarily well linked with a network of influential men and women whom Jonathan brings into the school for inspirational talks. Outside London this is not easy, and you would never guess this school was in the depth of gorgeous Shropshire. Dame Jocelyn Bell Burnett, world famous astrophysicist, had just been when we visited, and strong links with Keele University produce a steady flow of high-powered visitors. These not only enhance academic lessons but often come to speak at one of the many societies to which parents also drop in. There is wine-tasting, a feminist society, a medical science group, share dealing and so it goes on, reflecting the scope of opportunities for young women in the 21st century world.

All the girls get involved in the English Speaking Board to enhance confidence, presentation skills and the ability to think on their feet. One parent said, 'Everyone gets a 2.1 from Bristol or wherever these days, but Jonathan Forster really understands that the girls will need a lot more than that – he is giving them the life skills to succeed.'

Moreton Enterprises is part of this – a unique business venture consisting of a shopping mall run entirely by the girls. There is a branch of Ryman's stationery, Barclays Bank and home grown shops. The girls have business mentors, but basically the lower sixth operates as a small business turning over £50,000 a year. It is seriously impressive. Moreton Connect aims to create a network of OM and parent contacts for careers advice and work experience opportunities.

Boarding: About 90 per cent are boarders, and there is Saturday morning school, but apart from that, it is pretty flexible. One parent felt that girls new to boarding could be unsettled by friends coming and going, but we didn't find any girls who worried about this. The school wants girls to love boarding there and they do, partly because of the very special staff and partly because there is so much going on. 'It's like a long sleep-over but with loads to do as well,' said an enamoured 13 year old who had started as a day girl and then converted to boarding after a few taster nights.

We asked the sixth formers whether they felt a long way from all the city lights and boys, but were assured they saw quite as much as they wanted to of Shrewsbury School boys and often stayed Saturday night with friends in Manchester or Birmingham if they could fit it in between rehearsals, choir, talks. 'But it is just so lovely to come back,' they said with heartfelt sincerity.

The girls have business mentors, but basically the lower sixth operates as a small company, turning over £50,000 a year. It is seriously impressive

Senior boarding accommodation is single or double (very popular in holidays with overseas adults as well as children), adding to the home from home feel. Junior girls and boys, often boarding one or two nights a week, have their own cheerful dormitories.

Background and atmosphere: As you would expect from girls who run a business at the age of 16, they are confident and at ease with themselves. They work and play hard, but there is something in the rural Shropshire surroundings (the school is set in 100 acres of parkland) that takes any unattractive

'Girls have time and space here, you don't get a frenetic atmosphere building up where no one has room for anyone except themselves'

edge off the ambition and drive. We felt that every girl in England should have at least a term in this environment.

The school was started by women educationalists 100 years ago, and Jonathan holds firm to their liberal view of education. He has used the school's centenary year to ensure the girls know about the strong female role models in the school's past. 'It was never meant to be like other schools,' he tells us. 'The Lloyd Williams family wanted a school where girls could enjoy the country and experience a rounded education that would set them up for life and all the different people they would meet'.

The very English country landscape and original school building, a moated Tudor house with the current façade dating from William and Mary, are balanced by new state-of-the-art purpose built areas. There is a stunning new science block, planned in a collaboration with Keele University and local state schools. The facilities are used by the university to run science taster session for local students with a particular emphasis on medical careers. The library is both welcoming and very modern. One girl talked about working in the library before her GCSEs and being able to take her kettle, mug and biscuits in there for a real go at her revision – good for the librarian.

Pastoral care, well-being and discipline: The principal wants the girls to love Moreton Hall as they would love their home, and to care for the school and each other in the same way. From what we saw, they do. There was a genuine warmth between the older and younger girls and a sincere appreciation for their surroundings and the attention they receive from teachers and boarding staff. Given the entrepreneurial energy about the place, the girls are amazingly relaxed. One member of staff said, 'They have time and space here so you don't get a frenetic atmosphere building up where no one has room for anyone except themselves'. These are not privileged princesses who think the world owes them. They are self-disciplined young women who have learnt in school that you can make a difference and live happily together. The centenary pageant included everyone who is a part of the school – not just teachers and girls. It's an inclusive place. Discipline was not a word we heard mentioned, and for a school that can happily host tribute bands in the outdoor amphitheatre on the last night of the summer term without a qualm – who needs lots of rules and punishment?

Pupils and parents: Some 80 per cent of the boarders are from the UK, a deliberate policy, and about 90 per cent of those girls are from within one to two hours travel. The school caters for business, diplomatic and professional families where often both parents are working and see the boarding option as a lifestyle choice, with the girls having endless activities and friends on tap. Communication, both formal and informal, works very effectively. Overseas parents tell us the school makes brilliant use of modern technology and emails are responded to very quickly by both the head and staff. Parents are supportive both in terms of social events and also by acting as mentors for the business enterprises. They can drop in to more or less any event going on, and the division between home and school seems very fluid compared with many schools. One parent said, 'There are very traditional families who find it all rather liberal, but the principal soon shows them it works'. The principal and staff are well known for their assiduous attendance at school events and their detailed knowledge of the girls and their families.

Alumni include Zanny Minton Beddoes, editor of The Economist, Thea Musgrave, composer and musician, and Dame Linda Dobbs, high court judge.

There is a separate study centre for overseas students and multi-activity holidays for children and their parents.

Entrance: Many of 11+ entrants from co-ed junior school, Moreton First. Then further entry points at 13 and 16 into the sixth form. Number from overseas capped at 10 per cent. Test, interview and school report to determine entry. Oversubscribed at various points, particularly in sixth form. Once girls are there, the school sticks with them and very few leave – including hardly any year 11 leavers (some 10 per cent).

Exit: Up to a quarter leave after GCSEs. Almost all sixth form leavers to university. Leeds very popular (including for physics and biology), then Bath, Exeter, Liverpool and Oxford Brookes. In 2017, four to Oxbridge, plus a medic and a vet. Not surprisingly, given their experience in school, a remarkable number of Old Moretonians are running successful businesses.

Money matters: The school has worked hard to increase means-tested bursaries, particularly to allow local girls from state schools to join the sixth form. Everyone pays something, but the aim is to give girls who would otherwise not have the opportunity a chance to experience the high-powered, aspirational world of Moreton Hall.

Remarks: It is outside the radar of parents who don't look beyond the home counties but more fool them – they are the ones missing out here. When asked why he had chosen Moreton Hall for his daughters, one parent looked vaguely bemused and said, 'Well, why wouldn't you?' We agree. This is a school with a difference, rigour in everything but going about it in a way that shows girls they can lead the world in a new way. And they will.

Oakham School

22

Chapel Close, Market Place, Oakham, Rutland LE15 6DT

01572 758758 | admissions@oakham.rutland.sch.uk | www.oakham.rutland.sch.uk

Ages: 10-18

Pupils: 1,035; sixth form: 396; Boarders: 559 full/flexi

Day: £16,905 – £20,025 pa; Boarding: £20,145 – £32,520 pa

Headmaster: Since 2009, Mr Nigel Lashbrook (50s). Educated in one of the last grammar cohorts at King's Heath Boys' Technical School in Birmingham. Only pupil in his year to get into Oxford (Hertford College – chemistry plus lots of rugby), first in his family to go to university. Part of his final year at Oxford involved running some undergraduate classes; 'Have you thought about teaching?' he was asked (in a good way) so DPhil plans were changed to teacher training. 'I just loved it', he says.

His first post was Manchester Grammar School where he taught chemistry and coached cricket and rugby. After eight years he went from this academic day school to an academic boarding school, Tonbridge. At Tonbridge he was head of science and chemistry, a housemaster ('I finished being a housemaster just before the advent of email', he says with a smile), plus a term as acting head – good preparation for his next move, the headship of King's Bruton in Somerset.

Seven years into his Oakham headship and Mr Lashbrook seems to be a man in his element. Parents describe him as 'very friendly', 'affable' and 'approachable' and so he is, although that relaxed bonhomie belies the super-efficiency with which his school is run. We thought Oakham had a particularly collegiate air – Mr L is obviously extremely good at picking the right staff and delegating to their strengths. He's also forward thinking and alert to shifts in what Oakham parents want from their boarding school. At the time of our visit a new boarding package was being launched to replace the three nights a week 'day boarding'. There is now a five-night option (costing 95 per cent of the full boarding fee). Apparently it's something that families who live further away have been asking for.

He identifies parental attitudes as the biggest change he has seen during his career. While he feels that parents wanting to be more involved is a cause for celebration, 'the pressure of unrealistic expectations can be a great cause of anxiety for children. We work hard to get parents to see the bigger picture.' At Oakham, as elsewhere, the emphasis is on enabling children to become independent learners, to see 'fail' as 'first attempt in learning'. 'We want to unravel the cotton wool,' says the head.

Mr Lashbrook still manages to do 'a tiny bit of teaching' and as part of his commitment to lifelong learning plans to take diving lessons; 'the pupils like to see staff doing new things.' To this end Oakham supports staff who wish to undertake study for masters or PhDs (in education related subjects, of course).

He lives on site during term time but has a family house nearby from where he 'commutes' in the summer and Easter holidays (when Oakham's commercial directors 'sweat the assets', running high profile sports academies and other events). His wife is an economics and geography teacher – 'they make a great team', said a parent – and two of their three now adult children were educated at Oakham. Down time is for golf, cricket and the theatre. Is there anything he wishes he'd been able to do? 'Play the saxophone'. Retiring in July 2019.

Academic matters: In 2017, 42 per cent of A level/Pre-U grades were A*/A, 69 per cent A*-B, with 58 per cent A*/A at GCSE (IGCSEs in core subjects). Double award science only (IGCSE), French, Spanish and German are the language options. Around a third of sixth formers take the IB and results are impressive: 2017 average of 36, 22 per cent of takers gained 40 points or more and one pupil achieved the maximum 45 points. Geography seems to be the most popular choice of A level, followed by maths, biology and economics. Two subjects – business and sports science – available as BTecs as well as A levels. We were a little surprised not to see more A*s at A level, especially given the very respectable number of leavers off to medical school and Oxbridge – proof of above and beyond teaching at all levels. 'Look at the bigger picture,' says a voice in our ear (it's the headmaster ...). We always do, and so do parents who choose Oakham for their children: 'We like the way they celebrate hard work as well as good grades,' said one.

We heard a great deal from Mr Lashbrook and his staff about the Oakham approach to teaching and learning. Words such as 'holistic' and 'enrichment' aren't just eduspeak here; lessons we observed were hands-on, pupils were working at their own pace and one felt that teachers saw them as individuals rather than a class. In the DT department (school has Design Mark) we came across a group getting to grips with ancient history in the form of early video games, telephones, cassette recorders and a BBC Micro. 'So what is a mix tape?' we heard one ask. Sigh.

The learning support department was settling in to new top floor premises when we visited – lots of technology but quiet, calm spaces too. Staff had chosen some wonderful pictures, all by 'our' pupils, we were told proudly. 'Mild' SEN – mainly dyslexia but also dyscalculia and dyspraxia – catered for via small group teaching, individual lessons or in-class support. Lots of study, organisation and revision support, all described by parents as 'brilliant'. What's even more brilliant is that there is no charge for this service.

Words such as 'holistic' and 'enrichment' aren't just eduspeak here; lessons are hands-on, pupils work at their own pace and teachers engage with them as individuals

Senior academic mentor (formerly the formidable sounding 'master of scholars') is responsible for intellectual stretching of those with academic awards and Oxbridge candidates. We couldn't help feeling that this role (especially under its previous title) seemed a little un-Oakhamian. Not at all, we were told; the scholars' society is 'elitist but not exclusive', members aren't necessarily academic scholars: some have been talent-spotted by housemasters. After all, there are established pathways to extend and develop sporting, musical and artistic talents. Chosen pupils attend a seminar programme designed to play to particular specialisms and nurture 'genuine intellectual curiosity'. Whole school enrichment week in the autumn term is also designed to challenge and surprise all pupils. Most recent theme was the enticing sounding, 'rules and rebellion'.

The Smallbone library (named after a former head), is impressive, the foyer doubles as an exhibition space and was full of pupils' art work; it's also used for parent meetings. Upstairs though it is absolutely silent. Certainly no talking, no whispering and no headphones. 'Up here pupils can hear themselves think', the librarian told us (very, very quietly).

Games, options, the arts: A word to the wise: don't trot out the cliché 'sport for all' if you're visiting Oakham – unless you want to run five times round a rugby pitch and do 100 press ups as punishment. Director of sport actually shuddered at such a last century idea. The distinction is a bit lost on us because that seems to be what happens, even if the emphasis these days is on health and fitness as much as competition. Huge choice of over 30 sports, from sailing on nearby Rutland Water (Oakham's sailing coach devised and hosted the inaugural Water Quidditch World Cup) to polo (water and four-legged variety), and all take part, whether by competing or supporting. Outstanding facilities including 40 acres of grass pitches, two floodlit all-weather pitches, multi-purpose sports hall, squash and fives courts. The cricket square hosts county matches as well as school fixtures.

Over 100 pupils played in national finals in lots of different sports and the school will create 'pathways to foster individual talents, whatever they are.' Oakham's recent sporting honours are evenly spread between boys' and girls' teams with the girls' 1st X1 football team carrying off the Independent Schools Football Association trophy and the U15 rugby team reaching the NatWest Vase final. The 1st XI boys' hockey team came runners up in the U18 Hockey Schools Cup Final.

Drama and music are big news with countless opportunities to perform at all levels. The aim is to maximise participation as well as foster individual talents – at whole school plays, hymn practice or small in-house showcases to build the confidence of first timers. Over 300 pupils sing in school choirs and the chamber choir recently reached the finals of Songs of Praise School Choir of the Year. We were lucky enough to join an audience of townspeople and pupils at one of the weekly lunchtime concerts in All Saints Church. Young and old sat rapt in the pews, listening to virtuoso trumpet and oboe soloists give spellbinding performances. When asked, 'Why Oakham?' a prospective parent sitting nearby simply said, 'It's the music.'

Impressive numbers of A*/As for art and DT at GCSE; specialist teachers in all disciplines including sculpture and textiles, visiting artists run workshops. The courtyard of four art studios was formerly the town prison and the new exhibition space was a workhouse – Oakham can truthfully say that its art takes no prisoners.. Wonderful sculpture studio where pupils can create in clay and mixed media on a large scale and even learn stone carving. Not huge numbers taking these subjects at Pre-U/A level but the results are excellent. Pupils regularly go on to top art schools and to study architecture.

New Exploring Learning camp for younger Oakhamians is a swashbuckling, Treasure Island-themed, problem-solving adventure in the countryside.

Boarding: Over half the pupils board and what with lessons on Saturday morning plus matches and other activities in the afternoon, day pupils probably feel as though they do as well. Parents of younger day pupils acknowledge this but say that the children like the chance to finish homework before they leave and enjoy time out in the common rooms. Quite a few local day pupils turn up for the Sunday goings on too. Food is praised by all – parents and children alike. All food is prepared in house and everyone eats together in the Barraclough. There doesn't seem to be any falling away of deliciousness as the day goes on – we heard no complaints about dreary boarders' suppers here.

Emphasis is on enabling children to become independent learners, to see 'fail' as 'first attempt in learning'. 'We want to unravel the cotton wool,' says the head

The homemade bread and soups, carvery nights and Sunday brunch came in for special praise.

One 'leave-out weekend' each half term. 'Transitional' boarding (two to five nights a week) is offered to lower school pupils (10-13 year olds) but the day boarding option of up to three nights a week for upper school pupils has been retired. 'It didn't meet the needs of families who live more than an hour's drive away,' we were told. Instead parents can opt for an up to five night a week package that comes in at 95 per cent of the full boarding fee.

Boys' and girls' middle school (age 13-17) boarding houses are on either side of a large playing field known as 'Donkey' (Doncaster Close). All upper sixth (known at Oakham as 'seventh form') pupils are based in two houses in Chapel Close, next to the market place. There are four lower school houses (two boarding) away from the main campus where younger children can enjoy their own space. Rooms that we saw were fairly standard issue – cabin beds with desks underneath, two or three to a room in the lower years, individual study bedrooms on the ground floor for the lower sixth. All the doors we looked behind in the boys' house featured, as ever, empty noticeboards, massive shoes and Lynx. Common areas are large and well maintained with the usual exhausted soft furnishings, big wooden bowls of apples ('we keep trying,' smiled the housemaster, indulgently resigned to choosing fruit on the basis of what makes the minimum mess if used as a missile), pool and table tennis tables. Year group integration fostered by lots of competitions and activities.

Youngest boarders do prep in the house library supervised by a member of staff or prefect until they're ready to work independently. Sensible rules about screens of all kinds, Wifi turned off at 10pm; youngest must hand in everything before bed. The term's programme of matches, activities, exam dates, UCAS deadlines and the like is up in an A3 frame near the entrance and makes exhausting reading. 'We like to do a lot,' said the housemaster, adding, 'This isn't babysitting, we put our heart and soul into boarding at Oakham.'

Background and atmosphere: Drive into the charming eponymous town (there's a butcher, baker and by the looks of things no shortage of artisan candle makers), past the Whipper-In hotel (Oakham is home to the Cottesmore, one of England's oldest hunts) and in the corner of the cobbled market place you will see Oakham School announced in fine wrought iron. Oakham and its near neighbour Uppingham were both set up as free grammar schools by Archdeacon Robert Johnston in 1584 to teach Latin, Greek and Hebrew to the sons of their respective towns. The two schools' fortunes and size waxed and waned over the next 300 years – as late as the end of the 19th century the original one room school house was still Oakham's only teaching premises.

The main site is a horseshoe of teaching and boarding accommodation and if there is a lack of fine or grand architecture then it is more than amply compensated for by the bright green fingers of a first-rate grounds team. If there were Good Schools Guide awards for best-kept school grounds then Oakham would certainly be on the podium. School is very proud of the courtyard garden with its grass-free lawn designed by near-neighbour Bunny Guinness. It's overlooked by the biology labs and no doubt the 30 varieties of native plants that make up the lawn provide a useful study in biodiversity.

Oakham itself is a charming town, home to a butcher, a bakery and, by the looks of things, there's no shortage of artisan candle makers either

Fair bit of Monopoly-style buying up of town sites – latest is a former pub which is about to be reborn as a performing arts centre; the town's old police station is set to become school's pastoral hub (we don't know who will occupy the cells). Town and gown weave seamlessly in and out – one of the first lessons new pupils receive is about road safety, although we imagine that motorists are held up by pupils crossing, more often than the reverse. Our sixth form guides observed the school's road safety rules to the letter, despite absence of any traffic, we're pleased to report.

Sensible uniform of black crested blazers, white shirts, ties (boys only) and below the knee black and white kilts for the girls. All seems to be worn as intended: smartly and un-customised. Seventh formers sport the dreaded business dress – although apparently it's not dreaded at Oakham. 'We really look forward to wearing it,' our sixth form guide told us.

Pastoral care, well-being and discipline: Pastoral care was singled out for its high quality and 'generous scope' in most recent inspection report and we couldn't find anyone who disagreed. The parents we spoke to commented how observant teachers were – quick to spot and then get to the bottom of changes in mood or attitude. Like most things at Oakham the pastoral system is commendably well-organised and implemented with genuine interest and concern, not a whiff of weary lip-service to a box ticking set of 'guidelines'. The head of pastoral care told us how important it was that she and her fellow tutors teach: 'it keeps things real', she observed. Tutor groups are small and pupils keep the same tutor throughout their time in each section of the school. Boarding house matrons are all trained in youth mental health care and are 'eyes and ears' and girls often pass on concerns they may have about boys (who can find it harder to talk). Add to this a 'house family' and buddy system and every child should know plenty of adults or fellow pupils to whom they can turn if necessary. All pupils do a body and mind course that stresses the interdependence of mental and physical wellbeing. Respect, for oneself and others, plus very clear boundaries, govern relationships between pupils.

Pupils and parents: 'You get all walks of life here,' a parent told us. According to Mr Lashbrook the Oakham demographic is solid middle class, 'definitely not socially elite'. Pupils we met officially were clean cut and refreshingly uncynical (they always are) but those we saw from a distance didn't appear to have revolutionary tendencies either. Oakham probably isn't the place for determined bohemians or incipient Bolsheviks, but we've no doubt that the school would welcome them with a smile and find them plenty to do. Around 15 per cent from abroad – mostly Europe. Former pupils include Stuart Broad, Tom Fell, Josh Cobb (cricket); Alex Goode, Tom Croft, Matt Smith, Lewis Moody (Rugby); Crista Cullen (Olympic bronze, hockey, 2012); Matthew Macfadyen, Greg Hicks, Richard Hope, Lydia Rose Bewley (actors); Miles Jupp (actor/presenter); Thomas Hescott, Katie Mitchell OBE (directors); Phoebe Gormley, Sarah Curran (fashion/business).

Entrance: At age 10 and 11 from over 30 different preps and primary schools – exams in maths English and verbal reasoning. At 13+ CE mark of 55 or over or, for entrants who don't take CE, school's own papers in English, maths, French and science; pre-test available in year 7. For lower school pupils (age 10-12) progress to middle school is automatic. Around 50 new pupils enter the sixth form each year; they need a minimum of seven Bs at GCSE including the subjects they wish to study, plus satisfactory personal and academic references from previous school. All candidates are interviewed.

Exit: Some 15 per cent leaves after GCSEs. Around 70 per cent to Russell Group universities, good numbers to medical schools, others abroad. School employs a Yale Fellow who oversees preparation of candidates for US universities. Six to Oxbridge and four medics in 2017; one to Switzerland, two to the Netherlands, one each to France and Spain, three to North America. And five to drama schools. Oakham has been awarded the Career Mark for its excellence in careers guidance and several parents commented on how good the higher education, apprenticeship and careers support was.

Money matters: Comparatively good value, especially the boarding. Even more so if you consider that SEN support is free of charge and parents of day pupils are not charged for evening meals if their children have to stay late at school for activities. Wide variety of scholarships at 11+, 13+ and sixth form. Means-tested bursaries also offered, applications considered on individual basis. Ten per cent discount for Forces families.

Remarks: 'The Oakham of today started when we went fully co-ed in 1971,' the head told us and it's true that though the school is proud of its origins, four centuries of history are not its defining feature. This is a clear-eyed, energetic, forward-thinking school, aptly summed up by its motto, 'Et quasi cursors vitai lampada tradunt' ('And, like runners, they pass on the torch of life').

Oundle School

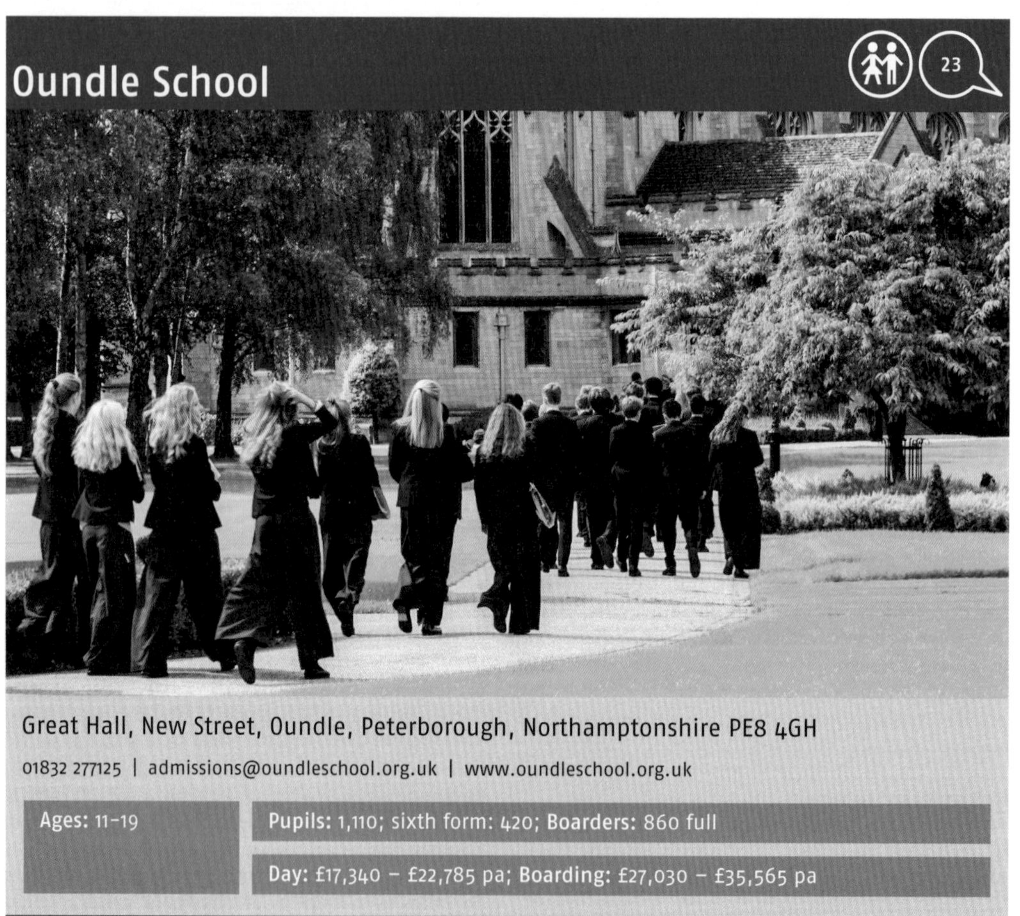

Great Hall, New Street, Oundle, Peterborough, Northamptonshire PE8 4GH

01832 277125 | admissions@oundleschool.org.uk | www.oundleschool.org.uk

Ages: 11-19

Pupils: 1,110; sixth form: 420; **Boarders:** 860 full

Day: £17,340 – £22,785 pa; **Boarding:** £27,030 – £35,565 pa

Head: Since 2015, Sarah Kerr-Dineen MA (50s), previously warden of Forest School in London, is the first female head of Oundle. Seeing her name inscribed on the board outside the school's entrance hall, coming after 450 years' worth of (doubtless splendid) male heads, certainly gives one pause for thought. Mrs Kerr-Dineen was brought up in rural Sussex and educated entirely in the state sector. Both her parents were teachers and she describes herself as a bookish child, 'I read whatever was put in front of me.' After studying English at Cambridge, she went on to Oxford to begin research into the literary reception of the Elgin marbles for a DPhil. Marriage and children pressed pause on her studies (and we got the impression it definitely still is 'pause') and instead she took up a post at the Open University where she taught literature and was a tutor counsellor – despite having told her teacher parents she was never going to go into the family business. This was followed by part-time teaching at Kelly College, where she worked alongside her husband, a music teacher, and then it was back to Oxford where she spent two years at Oxford High and 13 years just down the road at St Edward's, teaching English, heading up a new girls' boarding house and finally becoming director of studies.

'I am basically a teacher,' says Mrs Kerr-Dineen; 'I will always teach.' And she does, as part of Oundle's recently introduced Trivium course for third formers (year 9s). 'We do the grammar, rhetoric, logic of cryptic crosswords, it's great fun.' So that's year 9 sorted out, but how does she get to know the rest of the 1,100 plus pupils? By going to as many events as possible, looking at photographs and 'working very hard to try and remember names'. The practice is paying off – several parents mentioned how impressed they'd been at her recall. Entertains the lower sixth to supper in her sublime 17th century house, Cobthorne, and eats with pupils in their boarding houses.

Mrs Kerr-Dineen, and other members of staff we spoke to, are keen to dispel the myth that Oundle is exclusively full of confident, high-achieving 'alpha' children and that it has a somewhat hard-line attitude to boarding. While we saw little evidence to support the former, there probably was some truth in the latter; cue moves to 'breathe more flexibility' into the system. From 2018 another exeat has been added to the long first half of the Lent term for all pupils: 'It's a dark corner of the year and a change of scene is necessary,' says the head. 'But,' she continues, 'apart from exeats, when we are in session, we are all here.' And if a child is tired, ill or just needs a break? There are no hard and fast rules, it's always about the individual and a 'conversation with the housemaster or mistress.'

Mrs Kerr-Dineen possesses both the breadth of experience and the cultural and intellectual heft that such a demanding and high-profile role requires, but without the excess of ego that could accompany it. Parents concur, while conceding that her appointment initially set off a 'bit of chuntering' among the 'more traditional types.' 'Her parent talks are excellent, she has a clear vision and has made good appointments.'

One of the head's first actions was to set up an anonymous telephone questionnaire for parents and she has, apparently, applied herself 'forensically' to the responses. 'She absolutely understands the importance of the individual in such a large school. There were one or two blurry lines when it came to pastoral care and she addressed these straight away.' One parent thought that in the past it might have been possible for a pupil to pass through Oundle 'unnoticed,' but that this 'definitely wouldn't happen now'.

One change noted by several parents is perhaps atmospheric, rather than material: 'We don't seem to hear so much about suspensions and expulsions now – not that there were loads before. There just seems to be a different mood when it comes to discipline.' 'School is listening more – to pupils and parents.' And, last but not least, 'It's terrific to have a female head, not to mention women in the school's other significant positions. They're great role models.'

Academic matters: A big school means a broadish intake at year 7 and 9, hence there's room for Cs and Ds, even the odd E, among the many As at GCSE and A level. Nor has school adopted the habit of kicking out GCSE underperformers. In 2017, 82 per cent A*/A at I/GCSE and a pronounced dip to 53 per cent A*/A at A level/Pre-U. Most favoured A level subjects are maths, chemistry, history, biology, physics, English lit and geography – a healthy mix. And, hurrah, modern foreign languages are up there too, with great results and as many opting for French A level as economics, psychology and religious studies. Spanish and Latin aren't far behind. Music and drama are popular options at I/GCSE, but only a handful choose to continue with them to A level – although both are keenly pursued as extracurricular activities.

It takes something very special to render us almost lost for words – but Oundle's Patrick Engineering Centre (design, engineering and technology), did just that

Oundle has a proud engineering heritage and, from what we saw, is determined to ensure the subject has an equally bright future. We are accustomed to the arms race of facilities in independent schools so it takes something very special to render us almost lost for words – but Oundle's Patrick Engineering Centre (design, engineering and technology), part of a newly completed STEM campus, did just that. We felt we'd walked out of a school and into a high-spec, high-tech light engineering company. Not only, we were told, does it have the largest footprint of any design and technology department in any school in the country, the equipment is so specialised there are probably businesses, and definitely universities (Imperial College London and Swansea University are partners), green-eyed with envy. Whatever next? We would not be surprised to hear that plans were underway for Oundle's own version of the large hadron collider.

Our notes became more and more phonetic as the head of design, engineering and technology proudly showed us one piece of kit after another (if you're interested a full list is on the school's website). 'We're the only school in the country that can 3D print in any material – elastomers, rigid plastics, clear resins, carbon fibre and titanium – pupils can even design their own materials.' He showed us a small model of himself, 'I was scanned and then printed in 3D!' Model racing vehicles made by Oundle's year 9 won first, second and third place, best engineered car and fastest vehicle at the regional finals of F1 in schools.

'It's not all about pressing buttons,' we were told. Pupils in the lower years start by learning 'artisan techniques' such as welding and use of traditional lathes – there's even a forge. The fact that the whole set up feels nothing like a school is deliberate, it's an environment in which pupils are 'challenged to develop their own creative problem-solving skills'. Around a quarter take DT for GCSE and half of those progress to study it at A level.

Science facilities are equally impressive and well equipped, if somewhat more recognisably 'school' than the Patrick Engineering Centre. We dropped in on a lower sixth class occupied with an extension work practical – making their own analgesics, 'They're putting into context what they've learnt on paper,' the teacher told us. EPQ students can set up and run their own experiments in dedicated project rooms.

Pupils in the lower years start by learning 'artisan techniques' such as welding and use of traditional lathes – there's even a forge

STEM may be the school's showcase area, but those subjects which require little more than book and pen are taught to an equally high standard. The modern languages department is housed in the Adamson Centre, one of the older buildings. Seven languages including Russian, Arabic and Chinese, are offered as two or three-year courses up to GCSE level and all bar Arabic can be taken at A level. 'We're bucking the trend of language decline at A level,' the head of department told us, 'it's all down to inspirational teaching – what happens in the classroom is what makes pupils choose a language.' Extension opportunities for sixth formers include the school's Quadrivium (Quad) course. Like the third year Trivium course, Quad features rhetoric and public debate and challenges pupils to read widely and think laterally.

The pace is fast but support is there for those who need it – whether via Academic Voluntaries, weekly drop-in sessions for pupils who want one-to-one help with any aspect of their work, or from the educational support department. The department has six specialist staff who support pupils with (mild to moderate) SEND and EAL requirements. All pupils are screened for learning difficulties on arrival. Parents tell us that pupils are stretched and challenged, rather than pushed, 'they really want them to do well'. Nevertheless, Oundle probably isn't going to be first choice for a child who really struggles with organisation or needs significant support.

Games, options, the arts: Forget the STEM campus – that was last year, now it's all about the Sports Masterplan. We hurried as fast as our note-taking allowed behind former England rugby player and now Oundle's visionary director of sport, Danny Grewcock. The existing facilities looked pretty good to us, but little do the swimming pool, athletics track and car park know that they are about to be flattened to make way for a new pool, sports centre and 'hospitality suite' overlooking the cricket pitch. This will also provide a much-needed whole school venue – none of the existing buildings is large enough.

Mr Grewcock wants to build on Oundle's undoubted sporting strengths in rugby, cricket, hockey, swimming and netball, develop rowing, and focus on other activities such as dance and cycling that may appeal to the ball shy. School has four floodlit Astros, masses of pitches, two boathouses and an indoor and outdoor shooting range. Developments seem to be a little tardy on the girls' sporting options front, with girls' cricket only introduced in 2017 and football and rugby still offered only as recreational activities. That's set to change under Mr Grewcock, whose focus is not only on competitive sport, but also on encouraging pupils to develop a life-long interest in physical well-being and challenging traditional gender stereotyping in sport.

Standing in beautifully tended gardens is the Yarrow Gallery, built in memory of Eric Yarrow, a former pupil who was killed at Ypres in 1915. It was originally a science and art museum but is now the school's exhibition space for both pupils' work and that of visiting artists. When we visited the gallery was exhibiting A level exam work of astonishing maturity and skill: intricate paper cuts, pen and ink drawings, light box work, collages and a surprising amount of sculpture – beautifully detailed portrait busts and some very lifelike iguanas basking on rocks. A level art and Pre-U art history are offered; emphasis is on fine art (drawing, painting, sculpture). No separate textiles or photography A levels but these can be pursued as part of the art A level.

A level artwork of astonishing maturity and skill: intricate paper cuts, pen and ink drawings, and sculpture – portrait busts and some very lifelike iguanas

Oundle has a great tradition of choral singing and everyone gets to participate, whether in one of the school's four choirs or at weekly congregational practice. Apparently, the thing is to ensure that Oundle's rendition of Jerusalem is louder than Uppingham's at matches. There are multiple orchestras, ensembles and chamber groups and any number of performance opportunities, from popular weekly lunchtime concerts in the town to playing at CCF ceremonies. School has not one, but four, organs and what started out as a small festival dedicated to that instrument has grown into the annual Oundle International Festival – a celebration of music, film and theatre organised by the Oundle Music Trust and enjoyed by the whole town. Compared to other areas the music department did look a tiny bit tired, but fear not, it is, we were told, next on the list for enhancement.

School plays are programmed alongside performances from national touring companies at the Stahl Theatre, converted from a former chapel in the town. The theatre has its own director, technical team and support staff who work with pupils to give them experience in all aspects of putting on plays in a professional setting. House plays are entirely run by pupils; houseparents are not involved at all – 'That's very Oundle,' said a parent.

Nearly half the pupils participate in CCF (army, Royal Navy and RAF). It's compulsory for all pupils in the fourth form (year 10) and many continue with it afterwards. For those who don't want to do drill on a Wednesday afternoon there's the community action programme, so successful and popular that the organisers have had to look considerably beyond Oundle – as far as Kettering, Corby and Peterborough – for worthy causes. Pupils work in special needs schools, supervise riding and rowing and help with primary school sports coaching and homework clubs. They can take part in environmental enterprises, work in local museums or even get involved in renovation projects at the Nene Valley Railway. We had a welcome sit down in the community action office – staff are genuinely proud of the difference pupils can make in the local community and the way in which they develop through their voluntary work.

On Tuesday and Thursday afternoons it's Vols time, with pupils choosing between reading, music commitments, academic surgeries and activities and societies. There are nearly 50 options including debating, climbing, design engineering and technology, or taking a turn running OSCAR, the school's radio station that broadcasts from its own studio in the music department. One pupil decided to make use of the facilities in the Patrick Centre to restore his family's 1940s bread van, a real labour of love.

Boarding: Oundle stands firm against the prevailing trend to dilute school boarding to a homeopathic version of its original self. There are no flexi, part-time or weekly options, it's either boarding or day. The resulting consensus makes for a very stable, cohesive community and all the boarders we spoke to – not just our 'official' guides – were genuinely positive and insightful about the choice they and their families had made. There are eight boys' houses and five girls' houses plus Laxton, a house for the 200 or so very local day pupils and Berrystead, a 'transitional' co-ed boarding house, for the 40 boarders in years 7 and 8. From 2018 day pupils in years 7 and 8 will enter a mixed junior day house adjacent to Berrystead. This move is designed to allow greater specialist provision for the youngest pupils, graduating their transition to the senior school and maximising opportunities for friendships between day and boarding pupils.

Like practically everything we saw at Oundle the houses, which are spread across the town, are spacious, well-resourced and very efficiently run.

The head said that Oundle works because the house system subdivides it effectively into mini schools, and we saw this in action as we enjoyed a delicious lunch in Sanderson, one of the girls' houses. All meals are taken in house, giving staff frequent opportunities to check how pupils' days are going, pick up on any changes in mood or follow up quickly on anything that may have happened earlier. Each house has its own chef whose competencies are by no means exempt from the fierce inter-house competitive spirit. 'We lost our French chef – he went to another house. He was so good at puddings,' one of our lunch companions sighed. We felt it was our solemn duty to test the new chef's pudding skills and enjoyed every last morsel of scrumptious banoffee pie – not part of the standard French repertoire. 'Pupils are expected to eat what's on the menu', but they meet with the house chef every fortnight to help plan meals. Food in the boys' houses is, apparently, 'very different.'

Saturday is a full school day with lessons in the morning and sport in the afternoon until 5.30pm; Sunday is 'more relaxed', breakfast is optional (and can be eaten in pyjamas), although chapel isn't. Chapel services (Sunday plus two in the week) are on a rota because it's not large enough to hold the whole school. We asked boarders what happens for the rest of the Sunday: 'catching up with work' was one option, but going into a coffee shop in town for a 'full cooked breakfast, wearing chapel clothes' sounded like a better bet. Parents and grandparents can also visit for the day and will often scoop up friends whose parents live abroad and take them out for lunch too. International families like the fact there are no exeats and appreciate that a night away from school could be arranged if they happen to be in the country – on a case by case basis.

On Sundays 'catching up with work' was one option, but going to a coffee shop for 'full cooked breakfast, wearing chapel clothes' sounded like a better bet

Rooms we saw were spacious and comfortable; accommodation varies between individual houses but usually it's small dorms of two or three in lower years and single rooms or bedsits for sixth formers. In Sanderson the head of house has her own bed sitting room, complete with stag's head on the wall. Of course each house is different, but that difference comes from its occupants as much as a predetermined identity. It's traditional for pupils to join the same house as a parent who attended, but apart from that the advice is to try and ignore 'reputations', consult the website and then visit a few before deciding.

Background and atmosphere: Oundle's earliest origins have been traced to the 15th century when it was a school serving the town's 29 guild houses. Officially it dates from 1556 when wealthy Oundle merchant, Lord Mayor of London and Master of the Worshipful Company of Grocers', Sir William Laxton, left some of his London properties to the Grocers' Company to endow his former school. Oundle's fortunes waxed and waned and waned again – beset both by poor choice of headmasters and wider troubles such as the civil war and the Great Fire of London (the latter destroyed many of the Grocers' properties, including those bequeathed by Laxton). The 19th century wasn't much better, with more sub-par headmasters and an outbreak of typhoid threatening the school's future until in 1892 the Grocers appointed complete outsider, Frederick Sanderson, as head. Sanderson was not only a scholarship boy from a poor family, for his time he was also an educational radical, believing that science, engineering and modern languages were as important as the classics. Despite initial resistance, his ideas about offering boys a wider education proved popular, not just at Oundle but throughout the public school system, and numbers increased. During the first world war Oundle deployed its scientific and engineering facilities as workshops, producing horseshoes and metal parts for shells and torpedoes

– the tradition of 'workshop weeks' actually continued until the 1990s. Oundle went co-educational in 1990 and is now the third largest boarding school in the country.

The market town of Oundle and its eponymous school (or is that the other way round?) combine to make a large campus that is both public and private. The school's centre is a cluster of mainly late Victorian buildings (cloisters, great hall, chapel) and boarding houses, playing fields and teaching departments fan out from there. Townspeople enjoy the school's gardens, make use of its sports and leisure facilities and attend events and exhibitions; pupils and staff must dominate every aspect of the town in term time and are no doubt much missed by local businesses during the holidays. Pupils are on show as they move between houses and lessons – uniform (girls distinguished by their beloved long culottes) is worn by all, but some kind of unofficial consensus means bags are carried by none, so new pupils must learn quickly to negotiate some busy roads while balancing a pile of folders and books. A five-minute period of grace has now been introduced to allow for travel time between lessons.

Pastoral care, well-being and discipline: All of the above came in for unsolicited praise from parents. 'The houses are really well run, they're just the right size and the unit works brilliantly.' Tutors are pupils' and parents' main point of contact and the system was described to us as 'robust, in a good way'. That confidence notwithstanding, several told us that things can be tough at first for the youngest boarders, more so if they haven't come from a boarding prep, 'The size of the school is a bit daunting at first, but they soon find their group and community.' Day pupils are really well integrated and every effort is made to 'eliminate the difference.' Laxton, the day house, even has its own PTA (not usually found in boarding schools) and parents organise socials, second hand uniform sales and raise funds for travel bursaries.

Head was keen to talk about the importance of well-being and mental health, praising the structures that were already in place when she joined: 'It's something we all talk about a lot, everyone who works at the school has a role to play. In addition to house parents, tutors and prefects who are all alert to potential problems, we also have a dedicated suite of rooms where pupils can make an appointment or call in and talk safely and confidentially to a trained, independent listener.'

While many agree that the additional exeat was long overdue, we found little demand for additional exeats from older pupils, and definitely none from the parents we spoke to: 'It's much better than in one weekend and out the next, that can be unsettling,' and 'It's the best thing in the world, especially in the lower sixth. No parties – you're free to focus on work – my daughter loves it.' (We didn't get the daughter in question's take on this.)

We heard plenty of comments to the effect that Oundle is 'not a hand holding school' and the same applies to pupil relationships: hand holding or other PDA is a very serious disciplinary matter. A mother observed: 'It's not fast – boys and girls have pretty healthy relationships as friends, those girls don't take any nonsense'. School sets high standards and expects pupils to learn quickly, take responsibility and 'self regulate'. 'It's the implied contract of the place,' said another parent.

Pupils and parents: Consensus is that school is 'pretty good at picking the right pupils – and parents'. Pupils come from all over the country, about 20 per cent from abroad (full boarding makes it popular with expats). 'It's definitely not London-centric,' said one parent; another thought that while some families were wealthy, it wasn't a 'glossy' place; 'Lots of pupils have bursaries, but no one knows (or cares) who they are', they added. That was our impression too, we didn't see any pupils taking liberties with uniform, hair or make up. Even the sixth form girls we met hadn't fallen out of love with their culottes. 'We heard the new head might get rid of them' confided one, 'but it was just a rumour.' Phew. No mutterings about fundraising for high profile building projects either, 'They think very carefully about how they spend money – it's needs driven.' Governing body publishes a very readable annual review with key facts, figures (including income and expenditure) and 'objectives'. Top marks for transparency.

Oundle stands firm against the prevailing trend to dilute school boarding to a homeopathic version of its original self. There are no flexi, part-time or weekly options, it's either boarding or day

Old Oundelians (OOs) include writers Al Alvarez (poet), David Edgar (playwright) and Roderick Gordon (children's novelist), Bruce Dickinson (singer with Iron Maiden – do Google why he was expelled), Arthur Marshall, Sir Alan Budd, Sir Peter Scott and Professor Richard Dawkins, plus any number of engineers, industrialists, soldiers and public servants.

Entrance: Most join from prep schools: Witham Hall, Beeston Hall, Orwell Park, Old Buckenham Hall and Belhaven are the principal feeders. Modest but growing number from preps in the south east eg The Dragon, Summer Fields and Ludgrove. Parents are advised to plan ahead – entrance at 11+ and 13+ is very competitive. Trusty registrar makes it his business to ensure only those who will succeed are entered. Not many sixth form places going spare so bar is high. Minimum for entry is three As and three Bs at GCSE (or numerical equivalents), but successful external applicants will typically have all A*s and As.

Exit: Very few leave post-GCSE. University destinations are the usual Russell Group suspects – Newcastle, Bristol, Exeter, Durham. Mixed views on Oxbridge preparation, 'fantastic' say some, one or two thought it could be 'a bit' more proactive; 16 places in 2017. Increasing numbers to US universities. History, modern languages and engineering are the most popular degree choices.

Money matters: Boarding and day fees in line with similar schools. Wide and widening range of bursaries – around 30 per cent of pupils receive some fee remission, with the average bursary award just over 70 per cent of fees. Scholarships bring honour, but make little dent in the termly bill.

Remarks: 'Flying high', 'On top of its game', 'There's a real buzz.' Oundle has always been one of the UK's top-performing co-ed boarding schools, but parents sense a new energy about the place. We too were bowled over by this dynamic, innovative, forward-thinking school. Oundle challenges itself, as well as its pupils, to be prepared intellectually, personally and spiritually, for whatever the future holds.

Packwood Haugh School

24

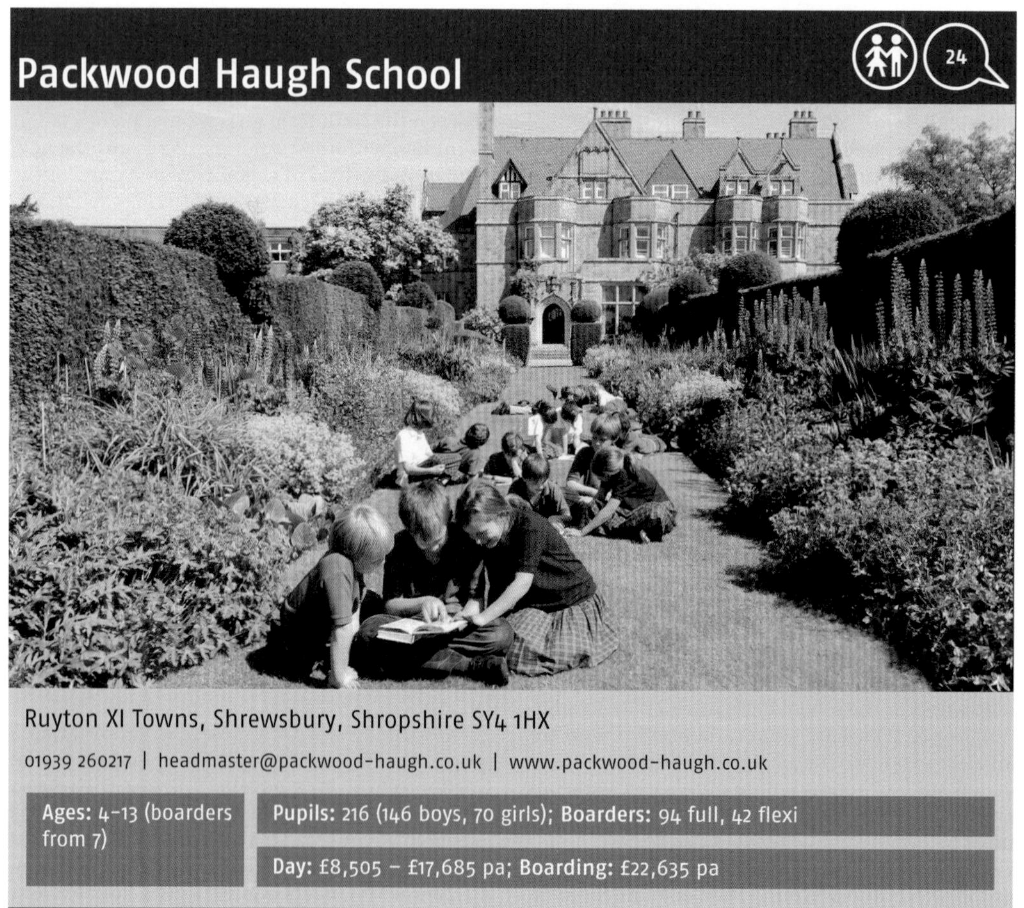

Ruyton XI Towns, Shrewsbury, Shropshire SY4 1HX

01939 260217 | headmaster@packwood-haugh.co.uk | www.packwood-haugh.co.uk

Ages: 4-13 (boarders from 7)

Pupils: 216 (146 boys, 70 girls); **Boarders:** 94 full, 42 flexi

Day: £8,505 – £17,685 pa; **Boarding:** £22,635 pa

Headmaster: Since 2012, Clive Smith-Langridge. Limbered up for the role by spending 16 years in marketing before switching to boarding schools (was previously deputy head at Walhampton). Brings essential savvy plus the experience of having captained a Chile cricket XI vs Brazil. In an evolving boarding market, Packwood is lucky to have his sort of business nous and strategic expertise: finances are sound, numbers healthy, pupils and teachers audited and fine-tuned. Appointed in tandem with his wife, Sally, who glories in the possibly puzzling title of headmaster's wife, a post you'll find in many prep schools. Hers is a salaried role with responsibilities on the pastoral side. Parents very much like this proxy-parent, family-feel arrangement. Clive and Sally have two daughters.

Entrance: Co-ed (some two-thirds boys), non-selective. Informal assessment for prep – Eng and maths. No assessment for pre-prep, Packwood Acorns. Range of scholarships. Bursaries for Forces families and local children, one of whom is off to Eton. Children come from all adjoining counties and north Wales. Some, sons and daughters of devoted former pupils, journey from afar. Less than 10 per cent from overseas – Spain, Japan, China.

Exit: Packwood has long furnished the top public schools. Lots to Shrewsbury, others to usual suspects, including Rugby, Malvern College, Eton, Harrow, Wycombe Abbey, Moreton Hall, Stowe, St Edward's. They know it's important to get it right, so a smattering to Sedbergh, Ellesmere, Wrekin College. Eminent one-time pupils include Mark Rylands, Bishop of Shrewsbury; Tom Salt, head chef at Manicomio; Tom James MBE, double gold medal winning Olympic rower; and Rhys Bevan, Toby Fairbrother in the Archers. There were 25 scholarships in 2017, including six to Shrewsbury.

Remarks: A time honoured top tier prep school which celebrates its headmasters by inscribing their names in gold on the panelled ceiling of the entrance hall. Co-ed since 1968; we await the first headmistress. Former pupils celebrate glorious character-building idiosyncrasies, all now superannuated (Molesworth, where art thou?). Packwood is fully C21-compatible with heritage values: country prep school, 'proper boarding', traditional values, old-fashioned manners, fresh air, friendship, give it a go, play out of your skin. The food's great – official. So nothing here evokes St Custard's. But there is a skool dog, the head's border terrier Belle, never more cheerful than when egging on the troops from the touchline on match days.

There's none of your oligarch-magnet hotel quality accommodation and associated blingy 'facilities' here. We're not talking spartan, we're talking quite comfy enough – in the case of the girls' dorms, very nice indeed (the difference perhaps being boys here tend to call each other by surnames, girls by first names). What else do you want? Purpose built theatre? Tick. Sports hall? Tick. Swimming pool? Tick. All weather surface? Tick. Er, golf course? Yep. Lamasery? Oh yes, got one of those (it's a quiet room set aside for contemplation.) Spinney? Yes, that's where we go to make dens and Packwood Acorns have their outdoor school. Everywhere you go you don't see children staring moodily into the middle distance of their smartphone screens. None, we asked? None, said the head (a non-negotiable no). Don't need them. They can skype home from their dorm in the evening. All good.

Traditional values, old-fashioned manners, fresh air, friendship, give it a go, play out of your skin. The food's great – official. So nothing here evokes St Custard's. But there is a skool dog, the head's border terrier Belle, never more cheerful than when egging on the troops from the touchline on match days

Packwood is a classic country house prep school set in a mere 66 acres of lark-filled Shropshire. It is not set haughtily apart, though; you happen on it off a side road, you don't motor up an avenue to get to it. It adjoins the splendidly named Ruyton-XI-Towns (always XI) with which the Smith-Langridges have forged friendly relations on several fronts. There are collaborative links with local schools; many who work in the school live in the village and Packwood boys and girls sing in the church choir. There are activity days to which all and sundry are invited. Some prep schools orbit real life. Not Packwood.

Honours boards, honours boards everywhere. There's no mistaking what's expected of you. Oppressively so? Not so far as our inquisitorial investigations revealed. Aspirational, more like. In any case, pupils know perfectly well who their brainy peers are and where they stand in relation to them. More to the point, how does it feel to be in the wake of them? For one dyslexic pupil, no problem, the learning support is great, some of the brightest have it too and anyway your friends don't measure you by how many marks you get. Hats off to the teachers, though, for an open access school all these scholarships represent an extraordinary achievement. Hurrah for the SENCo, too. Parents praise the way their children are 'pushed and stretched'. Mr Smith-Langridge has upped the game in terms of monitoring individual progress and thereby also the effectiveness of the teaching. He likes his data and he wants more of it. But he doesn't want to run a hothouse or a sweat shop. For him it's all about making the best of all the opportunities of the long, boarding day – and not just academic opportunities, either. He and his colleagues delight in the richness of achievement of all their charges according to their lights, not just their 'honours board worthiness'. Art is good, drama on the up, music ubiquitous and top notch.

Weekends are busy with numbers boosted by those returning late on Saturdays from sports fixtures in faraway schools. Boys are in the big house, hugger-mugger, as they like it. Girls have their own residence. Beds are cosy and teddy comes too

If boarding isn't done well, 'twere well it were not done at all'. Packwood has intelligently reinvented it and, just as important, made it a specialism, because no one wants to board at a school where most children go home at night. Boarding is phased in, there's a range of flexi-options and the majority graduate to full-time in preparation for their senior school. Weekends are busy with numbers boosted by those returning late on Saturdays from sports fixtures in faraway schools. Boys are in the big house, hugger-mugger, as they like it. Girls have their own residence. A number of teachers live in school, there are houseparents and there are lovely matrons. There's masses of care and oversight from warm, watchful adults who know these children and mind about them. There are bright posters bearing improving/banal quotes on the walls (we'd have preferred quotes by the children). Beds are cosy and teddy comes too. But take a look at the boys' washbasins, tidy as can be, and you'll see there's rigour here. This is no sleepover city, it is home from work; talking after lights out is a big no-no. A happy school is a deceptively rigorous place and all the happier for it. All parents praise Packwood's code of conduct and the way the children buy into it. Said one parent: 'They know when they've done wrong and genuinely feel contrition'. Another indicator of emotional health: Packwood children are no respecters of age and happily chat to those below and those above. There are boarding captains, older children to whom the younger ones can turn for counsel. And here's the point; we were accompanied by a viscerally antipathetic visitor to whose mind boarding is a bad, weird thing to do to a child. She visibly melted, the more she saw and heard, and ended up easily envisaging her grandson here, happy as a sandboy. One recent parent wistfully said she wished she'd known about Packwood for her other two girls.

Yes, the children really are terrifically nice and lit up, their manners are excellent, they're very at ease among adults, they're great company. It's easy enough to see how an outdoorsy, sporty child will thrive here, and the school aims to enable every single child to represent the school at something. There's a big games playing tradition at Packwood, another heritage touch, and not just in main sports. To survey the offering all round is to find yourself muttering clichés about punching above their weight. Like all knackered clichés, it exactly pinpoints the truth.

So what of the ones who are indoorsy, solitary, geeky? They're the ones you worry about, so we pried. Unlikely as it may seem, more than you'd think take to fencing; indeed, Packwood is nationally famed for its swordsmanship. And for its horsemanship. Some take to cross-country running (very strong here). We learned of one child who managed deftly to schedule guitar lessons in games time. All the parents we spoke to assured us that eccentricity in all its guises is simply not an issue. And then Mr Smith-Langridge recalled the boy who loved knitting.. and no one gave him a second glance. It helps to be gregarious, though, obviously, it's in the nature of the place. And at least a bit fresh-airy. Outside, after all, is where it happens every afternoon.

Packwood has a devoted fanbase of parents. Former pupils keep in close touch and their feats serve as an inspiration to the present generation. The school has shrewdly and effectively remodelled itself to align with the needs of today's working parents and carried with it the best of the old values. Our view: you get the best of both.

Repton School

25

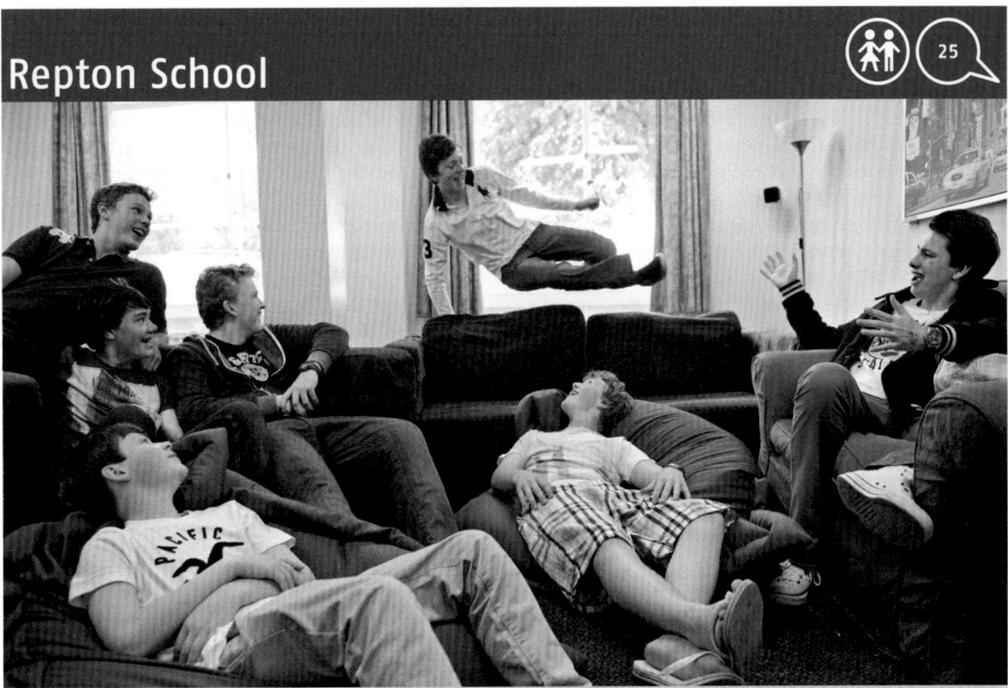

Repton, Derby DE65 6FH

01283 559222 | registrar@repton.org.uk | www.repton.org.uk

Ages: 13–18

Pupils: 646; sixth form: 287; **Boarders:** 441 full

Day: £25,746 pa; **Boarding:** £34,707 pa

Linked school: Foremarke Hall (Repton Preparatory School), 1034

Head: Since April 2016, Alastair Land MA (Cantab), (40s). Educated at Manchester Grammar School and Trinity College, Cambridge (first class hons in natural sciences). He comes from a lineage of skilled horticulturalists who nurtured his early interest in science and his family has 'deep ancestral roots' close to Repton, in Derbyshire and Cheshire. A man with a vocation to serve, he seriously considered a career in the armed forces (and hasn't closed the door on one in the church), but above all he 'always knew he wanted to teach.' His first job gave him the opportunity to combine the two and he spent nine years at Eton as biology teacher and commanding officer of CCF. Thence to Winchester College where he was master in college and senior housemaster, and Harrow School where he spent four years as deputy head. In the rarefied world of 'proper' full boarding schools that is a well-nigh impeccable pedigree, so the polite, but firm 'no' when we asked Mr Land if he had any plans to introduce weekly or even, ahem, flexi options at Repton was hardly a surprise. He describes boarding as a 'profound and enriching experience' and believes that young people benefit greatly from being part of a community and engaging with different adults, 'from houseparents to coaches.'

Mr Land may come across as rather a serious, cerebral kind of chap, but he's a man of action too – don't forget that he nearly went into the army. Parents like his style: 'Very impressive', 'listens and responds straight away', 'quick to get things done'. Pupils also approve, 'he drops round to houses for lunch and makes a real effort with everyone' and 'he's very involved, very visible'. Our sixth form guide seemed particularly impressed (that's probably why he was our guide): 'He takes a section of CCF and he goes to the gym.'

Mr Land welcomes the fact that parents now want more opportunities to be involved in their children's boarding school life; he also wants to create more channels for 'pupil advocacy and voice'. To that end he has established a parents' forum and what could be regarded as pupil focus groups: The Captains' Club for 'those who lead in sport' and the Academy for 'those who lead in academics' (forgive our levity but those names sound a bit like 1970s 'nite' spots). He hopes the last two will provide insight into what's on pupils' minds, 'what's important to them.' Requests for girls to be allowed to wear trousers were given a swift green light and DT and music practice rooms now have longer opening hours. Whether he would be as sympathetic to some of the other pupil wishes we heard, namely on-site Starbucks and McDonald's, remains to be seen. Our money's on a very dusty answer.

Mr Land credits his English teacher at Manchester Grammar for introducing him to reading for pleasure. In his case it was a Graham Greene novel, The Power and the Glory, that did the trick. With this in mind he has compiled – with the help of colleagues – The Head's Reading List, an inspiring and eclectic selection of fiction and non-fiction by writers from Chinua Achebe to Bertrand Russell.

With a big school to run, not to mention a young family, Mr Land would seem to have his work cut out. Even more so since his wife (who is French) lives in London, where she teaches maths at a girls' independent school. The couple have two young sons and the eldest attends Repton's prep, Foremarke Hall.

Academic matters: Repton sits securely among the top co-ed boarding schools for academic achievement, but we detect a little sharpening up, refining perhaps, on the teaching and learning front since Mr Land's arrival. English, government and politics, geography, art and maths appear to be the most popular A level choices and results in 2017 were 47 per cent A*/A. Unusually there are more takers for music, French and even German A levels than for drama. We salute the recent solitary drama A level pupil, but wonder how they managed – lots of monologues perhaps? GCSE/IGCSE results showed a dip in 2017: nearly 58 per cent A*-A/9-7, but no notable subject problem areas. Very small tail of D, E and even a few F grades, but vast majority of pupils are getting top grades across the board.

Whole school gets involved in the biannual fashion show, with everything from outfits, models, marketing and social media to music and graphics done entirely by pupils

First stop on our itinerary was the Science Priory, a glass-fronted temple to – you guessed it – science. Laboratories, seminar rooms and lecture theatres with 3D projectors, all very high spec and high tech, more university than school and probably better appointed than some universities. We're not easily won over by technical wizardry but it's hard not to be impressed when an animated diagram of a human kidney appears inches from one's eye line. Each science has its own floor and there's even a bijou observatory on the roof – perfect for those dark Derbyshire skies. The building is full of natural light and the double height wall against the open staircases affords exhibition space for art students who like to paint a large canvas – we loved the huge dodo, wistfully regarding the busy, busy non-extinct species rushing up and down to lessons. In the top floor library we discovered the Repton village retirement group who come for tea and delights old and new such as bingo and IT support, provided by sixth formers as part of their community service.

Pupils are streamed on arrival and this is reviewed the same year after school exams, but there's sufficient flexibility for them to 'find their own level.' Lessons are 40 minutes long with an eminently sensible five-minute change over between to accommodate cross campus dashes. Learning support is either one-to-one or small groups; all pupils are tested on entry and there's effective liaison with teaching staff to monitor progress and implement strategies.

Pupils were falling over themselves to praise the dedication of teaching staff, especially the out of hours help available for GCSE and A level subjects during exam times. Parents agree, singling out 'brilliant' support for those applying to Oxbridge and US universities.

Games, options, the arts: 'Rugby's not big at Repton' we were told. You can play rugby here 'for enjoyment' but the oval ball finds itself in the unaccustomed category of a minority sport. On the plus side, an average player is likely to get first team matches. Repton is a hockey school (ditto football, cricket, tennis...). All pupils play hockey and can do so all year round on two floodlit water-based Astros, a sand-based Astro and indoor pitches. Facilities are so good that the GB men's squad trained here. Repton girls have won the national under 18 hockey finals a record 10 times in the last 12 years and boys were U16 and U18 national champions in 2015 and 2016. Repton's first football match was in 1878 and several boys have, more recently, gone on to play professionally for clubs such as Watford, Derby County and Sheffield Albion. School's 12 pitches are regarded with envy by visiting teams. Girls play in the Midlands league. Cricket too has a venerable history, Repton has produced 152 first class players and three England captains. On the day of our visit a prep schools cricket match was being hosted and diminutive figures were padding up ready to walk out onto the famous square (overlooked by a thatched pavilion) at the heart of the school. No complaints about teams lower down the alphabet being sidelined and no shortage of alternative options such as sailing, golf and riding.

CCF (army or RAF) has a distinguished history at Repton and is compulsory for all pupils in their first year. Attendance at week-long training camps during the Easter or summer holidays is also 'expected', as is parental support for these out of term activities. Those who choose not to carry on with CCF do either D of E or a school-run 'skills and service' activity. Mr Land has, apparently, 're-energised' Repton's CCF and regards it (and also D of E) as hugely important; 'both can teach powerful life lessons', he says. Interesting if worthy-sounding selection of co-curricular or subject based societies. Debating society is enjoying something of a roll, winning Nottingham University's schools' debating competition and reaching the national finals of the English Speaking Union's Mace competition in 2017.

Pupils' art is exhibited in the village gallery (former shop) and displayed all over the school. A level art is a popular choice and almost all candidates get A* or A; results for photography and textiles, though few, are similarly top notch. All teachers in the art department are practising artists and they and the two artists in residence have studios within the school. Textiles may not get many takers at A level but the standard of the

work we saw during our visit and the enthusiastic and knowledgeable staff were inspiring. All pupils do at least a term of textiles and there are drop-in classes on Tuesdays and Thursdays for those who want to do an 'off timetable' GCSE in the subject. Whole school gets involved in the biannual fashion show, it's run by the sixth form and everything from outfits, models, marketing and social media to music and graphics is done entirely by pupils. The event is held in the 400 Hall where the stage can be extended to form a catwalk, it plays to 500 people over two nights and raises over £2,000 for charity.

Double height wall against the open staircases affords exhibition space for art students who like to paint a large canvas – we loved the huge dodo

The DT department offers an educative mix of traditional and modern: pupils can programme their designs for 3D printing or forge metal in the furnace. Head of DT proudly showed us lovingly maintained industrial standard lathes and milling machines supplied by local Midlands manufacturers.

'Opportunities for music are incredible' and the teaching is 'phenomenal,' we heard. Music is for all and house singing competitions are as keenly supported as diploma level soloists. Impressive programme of visiting musicians who give concerts and masterclasses – Julian Lloyd Webber recently judged the school's music competition – and plenty of opportunities for pupils to perform, whether at informal lunchtime concerts or main school events. Music school has pianos aplenty, including a harpsichord and a Steinway Grand Model D; 'It's wonderful to have the chance to play something so beautiful,' a pupil told us. School chapel is home to a 'magnificent' Harrison & Harrison organ. As elsewhere, very few take music A level, but school maintains good record of Oxbridge organ and choral scholarship awards.

On Sundays after chapel pupils can sign up for SLOPs (Sunday leisure options) – anything from shopping in Leicester to clay pigeon shooting or white-water rafting

1930s Hollywood swashbuckler Basil Rathbone first trod the boards at Repton and one imagines he'd be mighty impressed by the professional standard facilities enjoyed by today's actors. Drama is enthusiastically pursued at house, year group and whole school level and performance spaces include a black box studio and the 315 seater Auditorium Theatre. But alas, alack, the subject is only slightly more popular than German as a GCSE option and with barely a handful of takers at A level, the repertoire must be pretty limited.

Boarding: Ten boarding houses, six boys', four girls', are spread throughout campus and village. Girls' houses are newer and purpose built, rooms are smallish, as are windows. Boys do a bit better in terms of original features and historic atmosphere – rooms are larger, ceilings higher. B Block (Repton-speak for year 9 pupils) share three or four to a room; sixth formers get individual study bedrooms. In addition to houseparents, their families and pets, all houses have live-in matrons and a resident tutor. We found no inclination on school's part to persuade prospective parents that the houses are the same, but the reasons for a particular house's reputation are often more to do with practicality than glamour. For instance, the 'musical' house is the one closest to the music department, attracting musicians because it offers the least distance to travel to reach practice rooms. Parents recommend visiting at least four houses before selecting one and talking to any pupils you come across, not just the ones showing you round. Sound advice. Individual house profiles on the website are a useful starting point and some, but not all, have their own Twitter feed. Several parents told us they really enjoyed keeping up to the minute with house happenings via 140 characters.

All meals are taken in house – more and more unusual these days – which means that pupils are frequently back and forth, giving staff ample opportunities to observe how an individual's day is going. Teachers take their meals in different houses, as do visitors, and pupils become accustomed to entertaining whoever lands at their table. We ate a delicious lunch in School House (boys) and enjoyed hearing their observations on Repton life, some of which were lost to posterity amid the clatter and chatter of many boys refuelling for an afternoon of cricket and athletics.

Ten separate in-house catering operations, plus the same number of laundries, may be a bursar's nightmare, but pastorally and in terms of cohesion it's hard to beat. 'House is everything' was a phrase we heard again and again – not just from pupils but from parents too. A pupil told us: 'Boarding means you make really close friends, it also makes you behave more maturely – if there's a problem you have to sort it out. You can't be petty.' Competition between houses (in anything from singing to sudoku) is fierce but positive; it seems to create a kind of extra energy that propels all pupils along in its wake.

So, what about evenings and weekends? When lessons finish boarders can change into home clothes for supper and then it's prep and/or music practice (7-9pm). On Saturdays there are lessons in the morning, matches or other sporting activities in the afternoon and regular themed 'socials' in the evening. Socialising takes place in Grubber, pupils can have a Grubber account and buy snacks and drinks with a thumbprint. Sixth formers get together in the JCR. On Sundays after chapel pupils can either have a relaxed day, catch up with work or sign up for SLOPs (Sunday leisure options) – anything from shopping in Leicester to clay pigeon shooting or white-water rafting. Rehearsals for plays and concerts are also scheduled at the weekend. 'They keep them busy', a parent observed. Indeed they do. Each boarder has two privilege weekends per term, Saturday and Sunday nights that can be taken out of school by prior arrangement. Pupils may also go out of school on a Sunday after chapel to have lunch with parents, returning by 9pm.

Background and atmosphere: Repton was founded on the site of a 12th century Augustinian priory by bequest of Sir John Port in 1557. In return for their education pupils were obliged to pray for the Port family's souls – many parents today might consider this a much less painful form of recompense than school fees. The next 300 years saw acrimonious legal disputes, fluctuating pupil numbers and a general decline that was not reversed until the middle of the 19th century. Fragments of the original priory buildings remain, notably parts of the

'House is everything' was a phrase we heard again and again – not just from pupils but from parents too. 'Boarding means you make really close friends, it also makes you behave more maturely'

arch that marks the entrance to the school (moved to its current site in 1906) and a tower that was incorporated into the building that now houses the head's study and offices. The school started taking girls in the 1970s and was fully co-ed by 1991. Time and social change have not diluted school's Christian foundation: 'Repton is a Christian School and for all our values, not least Respect, our guide is the Scripture.' We hope values of respect and tolerance are similarly explicit in Dubai and Abu Dhabi where Repton has international avatars.

School and village merge harmoniously – the Spar shop must see a dramatic fall in its profits during the holidays, likewise the butcher who makes 'the best' sausage rolls. The 'Repton bubble' doesn't stop at the arch, there's an air of prosperity here, plenty of places for parents to take their children out for lunch at the weekend, and property prices are inflated by demand from both staff and parents who want to live close at hand. The Derbyshire address somehow makes Repton seem more remote than it is; as the school's website is keen to point out, London (Euston) is 75 minutes away (plus a taxi to the station).

Pastoral care, well-being and discipline: 'The teachers really know the children', or words to that effect, was what several parents told us. They describe pastoral care as 'completely joined up' so that, for example, if a pupil has a music exam or a national sporting trial, all members of staff know and will act accordingly. Because staff eat in different houses and at different tables every day they gain insight into all aspects of the pupils' academic, social and personal lives. 'You observe body language and can pick up on any tensions,' a teacher told us. The year groups are mixed at lunch which also fosters good relationships. A sixth form pupil who had joined from a state school ('for the maths and the hockey') told us, 'I worried about whether I'd fit in, but everyone accepted me straight away.' Universal praise for the way in which day pupils are integrated into houses, but be warned, the Repton 'day' doesn't finish until after prep at 9pm. It's also a long week, what with Saturday lessons and matches and even compulsory Sunday chapel for those who live near enough. Day parents tell us that traffic around Repton is pretty snarly in the mornings and recommend getting pupils in for breakfast at 8am to avoid the queues. No wonder it's common practice for parents of day pupils to buy or rent houses in or very near Repton village itself.

Pupils and parents: Still very much a 'local' boarding school, majority of families from Midlands, Cheshire, Yorkshire, Lincolnshire, Lancashire; smallish contingent of international boarders. In addition to 152 first-class cricketers, many eminent military and clerical chaps and MPs both red and blue, former pupils include Roald Dahl and Jeremy Clarkson (neither of whom recall their time with affection), poet James Fenton, comedian Graeme Garden, novelist and screenwriter Christopher Isherwood, artist Anthony Gross and recent field hockey Olympic medallists Georgie Twigg and Ellie Watton.

Entrance: Around half join from Repton's nearby prep, Foremarke Hall; others from preps such as S Anselm's, Malsis, Orwell Park. Common Entrance pass of around 50 required. Some 30 or so pupils enter the sixth form, minimum five GCSEs at B or above or numerical equivalents (As for chosen A level subjects).

Exit: Very few leave post-GCSE. Nearly all go on to Russell Group universities, four to Oxbridge in 2017, plus three medics. Growing numbers to top US universities (one to Harvard in 2017)– many with athletic scholarships for eg tennis, football and hockey.

A sixth former who joined from a state school ('for the maths and the hockey') told us, 'I worried about whether I'd fit in, but everyone accepted me straight away'

Money matters: Range of scholarships and exhibitions – some titular only, some worth up to 20 per cent off fees. Fees broadly in line with similar schools. Considering six-day week and 9pm finish, day fees look like good value, but you may have to factor in the cost of a house in the village.

Remarks: This is a grounded, friendly school with high academic standards and secure moral values. It will hardly come as news to parents north of Watford, but whatever your child's strong suit – scholar, musician, artist, athlete or enthusiastic all-rounder – Repton could be just the right fit.

Rugby School

26

Lawrence Sheriff Street, Rugby, Warwickshire CV22 5EH

01788 556216 | enquiries@rugbyschool.co.uk | www.rugbyschool.co.uk

Ages: 11–18; 13–18 from 2018 (boarding from 13)

Pupils: 808; sixth form: 367; **Boarders:** 656

Day: £21,804 pa; **Boarding:** £34,752 pa

Headmaster: Since 2014, Peter Green MA PGCE (early 50s), previously head of Ardingly. Educated at St Joseph's College, Dumfries, then University of Edinburgh, where he read geography. Although he comes from a family of lawyers and judges he always wanted to be a teacher. Studied for Cert Ed in religious studies and PGCE at St Andrew's Foundation for Catholic Teacher Education (now part of the University of Glasgow). First job was at an inner-city comprehensive in the Gorbals. He taught at St Olave's Grammar in Orpington and then Strathallan before moving to Uppingham, where he was head of geography, a housemaster and introduced all-rounder scholarships. Spent five years as lay second master of Ampleforth, followed by seven years as head of Ardingly College, where numbers rose by a quarter under his watch.

A vastly experienced and engaging head (wearing fetching bright pink socks when we visited), he talks fast, sensibly and enthusiastically and is full of good tales and ideas. He says 'the whole person is the whole point of education at Rugby', and while this isn't a unique declaration for a head he believes Rugby is 'uniquely placed to make the claim.' Doesn't teach these days – 'I'd sack myself,' he jokes – but spends as much time as he can talking to pupils and staff and observing lessons. On the day we met he arrived hotfoot from discussing Lake District geomorphology with the youngest pupils in the school.

He's enjoying his job at Rugby – 'we have fantastic children here and it's a wonderful environment to work in,' he says. He finds the school's history a huge inspiration but emphasises that while Rugby is 'traditional,' it isn't 'traditionalist.' Delights in the fact that he's sitting in Dr Thomas Arnold's study – with a portrait of the great man, Arnold's own (surprisingly small) desk, a hidden key rack above the fireplace and the spiral staircase in the corner that pupils used if they wanted to talk to him privately.

The head says that Rugby is 'phenomenally strong' but is always looking for ways to improve – whether it's blended learning, flipped classrooms, character development, teaching tolerance and respect or engaging pupils in STEAM (science, technology, engineering, arts and maths) subjects.

He's particularly proud of the fact that there isn't a Rugby type. 'The duckbilled platypus and the behemoth can be equally at home at Rugby School,' he says. Like his predecessor (Westminster head Patrick Derham), he wants Rugby to remain as inclusive as possible. The Arnold Foundation offers 100 per cent funded boarding places to pupils whose parents are unable to afford the fees and since 2003 well over 100 youngsters have benefited from the scheme.

Wife Brenda is an English and learning support teacher at Rugby. They have two children, a son who has finished university and a daughter still there. In his spare time he enjoys reading, opera and the opportunity 'to pray and be silent.'

Academic matters: Rugby has a tradition of innovation – it was, for instance, the first school in the country to teach science as part of the school curriculum in the 1850s – and this continues apace. The school offers the IGCSE in most subjects and A levels in 29 subjects (plus the Pre-U in physics, chemistry, biology and art and design). Around 50 students a year take the Extended Project Qualification (EPQ), which was developed at Rugby via a pilot qualification called Perspectives in Science and involves an extended piece of research on a topic they choose themselves.

In 2017, 60 per cent A*/A grades at A level/Pre-U. At GCSE, 79 per cent A*-A/9-7. 'The head is definitely on an academic mission,' a parent told us. French, German and Spanish offered at GCSE and A level, with exchange trips to Montpellier, Vienna, Madrid. Wonderful new language block, with 11 classrooms, two language labs and computers and software in every language. Sixth formers can study an ab initio language, such as Russian or Japanese. Pupils also write, edit and code their own online magazine, Page Polyglotte.

The head is particularly proud of the fact that there isn't a Rugby type. 'The duckbilled platypus and behemoth can be equally at home at Rugby school,' he says

Most do three separate sciences at GCSE. The sciences are housed in an imaginatively refurbished Victorian building, with lecture theatre, seminar rooms and labs. Learning development department offers some support for those with mild difficulties or EAL, either one-to-one or in small groups. Enrichment programme for all pupils, with additional weekly sessions for academic scholars (140 currently). All pupils have their own laptops, supplied by school and charged to parents.

Teachers are skilled and experienced. Many pursue their own academic research and the school is producing its own document on approaches to teaching and learning at Rugby. School runs parallel sets (including two top sets) in English, maths and the sciences.

Games, options, the arts: Rugby has overseen a huge investment in sports facilities in recent years. It has the only listed gym in the world and, of course, the famous School Close, where William Webb Ellis first ran with the ball in 1823 and invented the game of rugby football. Members of the 1st XV are very proud to play on it, along with leading players and teams who visit from all over the world. More than 200 TV crews pitched up to film at Rugby ahead of the 2015 World Cup and the school featured in the opening ceremony (Prince Harry and Jonny Wilkinson had cameo roles in a video shot at the school). Immaculately maintained playing fields, with 13 rugby pitches and five cricket squares. Locals use school's three Astroturfs, tennis courts and 25-metre indoor pool.

Sports centre, with squash courts, polo pitches and fitness centre. Boys play rugby, hockey, soccer, cricket, tennis and athletics while girls' main sports are hockey, netball, tennis, rounders and athletics. Other sports include badminton, fives, rackets, basketball, fencing, gymnastics, tai chi, pilates, dance, aerobics, riding, polo, clay pigeon shooting, sailing and triathlon. One girl is the current under-19 British champion in wakeboarding. Huge number of sports tours – recent expeditions include hockey and netball to Australia and Singapore, rugby to Japan and Canada and cricket to Sri Lanka and Dubai.

Music department has more than 40 practice rooms, a recording studio and small concert hall.

Music is magical, with masses of orchestras, choirs, ensembles and rock bands. Total of 600 music lessons a week. An impressive variety of drama productions at school's fully equipped theatre. Pupils stage a major school play and musical every year, plus a house drama season and annual arts festival. Art, design and photography flourishing and a third of sixth formers study related subjects at art school or university. Lewis Gallery, a light, airy space cleverly converted from old squash courts, runs programme of exhibitions by pupils and outside artists.

Boarding: Sixteen houses in total – eight for boys, seven for girls, plus Marshall House, a co-ed house for year 7 and 8 boys and girls (all day pupils), which will close in 2018 and is no longer accepting applications. Each boarding house has up to 60 pupils and the furthest is no more is than a 10-minute walk from the heart of the school. We visited soon after the school's annual pushcart race, hotly contested by all. The victorious house had a jaunty skull and crossbones flag fluttering from a top window.

Pupils eat breakfast, lunch and supper in their own houses – 'it encourages a real sense of community,' a parent told us. Food gets the thumbs up and there's plenty of it, including snacks in morning and afternoon breaks and in the evening. In a recent move, all but the sixth formers hand in their phones, tablets and laptops before bed each night. The new rule has brought a few grumbles from pupils, 'but nothing but parental support,' said a housemaster.

Houses are very wholesome. The boys' houses used to be less ritzy but are in the process of being upgraded. A house we visited boasted a cinema room, neat as a pin laundry, tuck shop (the 'stodge' in Rugby-speak) and individual studies for all. Each year group has their own common room and dorms vary from singles for sixth-formers to dorms of four to six for younger pupils. 'Your house is your home,' one boy declared.

Housemasters and housemistresses all live in (many with their own families) and see pupils as they come and go during the day. Youngest have to be back in houses by 9.30pm (lights out half an hour later), while sixth-formers return by 10.15pm (they don't have to be in their rooms till 11pm, though). Tutors are house-based and see their tutees formally at least twice a week, as well as when they're on duty.

Background and atmosphere: Founded as a grammar school in 1567 by Lawrence Sheriff, purveyor of spices to Elizabeth I. Moved to its present site in the centre of Rugby 200 years later. Home of the famous Dr Arnold and immortalised in Tom Brown's Schooldays. With its red-brick, Victorian schoolhouses the site feels rather like north Oxford.

A house we visited boasted a cinema room, neat as a pin laundry, tuck shop (the 'stodge' in Rugby-speak) and individual studies for all

Pupils like being based in a town, close to shops and cafés. One told us: 'You get a sense of the real world. We aren't in a bubble.'

Glorious Victorian library, the Temple Reading Room, provides a quiet, inspiring place to work. Pupils attend chapel three mornings a week and on Sundays. Chapel – Thomas Arnold is buried beneath chancel steps – is majestic and awe-inspiring, with walls adorned with tablets in memory of famous Rugbeian writers like Lewis Carroll and Rupert Brooke. School chaplain describes the chapel as 'the base' of the school and pupils say it's a place where the whole school sings its heart out.

School went fully co-ed in 1993 and boy/girl ratio is now 55/45. All wear smart uniform for lessons. Girls sport distinctive ankle-length grey skirts, now redesigned so they can run in them. Girls say they really like their skirts – they suit everyone and you can wear woolly tights and leggings underneath to keep warm in winter, they told us. The only gripe from boys is that their tweed jackets get 'a bit smelly' in the rain. Prefects – or levée as they are known – wear different ties and gold buttons on dark blazers. Four buttons for heads of school (boy and girl), three for heads of house and two for school prefects – a simple and subtle way to work out exactly who's who.

The sixth form has impressive new Collingwood Centre, housed in a former Catholic secondary school on the edge of the site. Careers, economics, philosophy, business studies, art history, PE and politics departments are based there (politics classroom is set up as a mock House of Commons, even down to the green leather seats) and centre is used for studying, socialising and school events. There's also the Saturday evening Crescent Club, where sixth formers are allowed a maximum of two drinks (wine or beer) with food.

Pastoral care, well-being and discipline: School has put an enormous amount of time and effort into its pastoral care. It is also one of 10 schools across the UK chosen to work with the PSHE Association on the development of a new character curriculum, which aims to develop skills and attributes like motivation and resilience.

Each pupil is given a copy of the school's Guidelines for Life, which covers everything from its anti-bullying policy to relationships and where and when boys and girls can be in their free time.

Policies on smoking, alcohol and drugs all clearly laid out. Expulsions are few and far between – two in the last five years. Public displays of affection (PDAs) between pupils banned – 'couples must behave in a way which would be appropriate if a member of staff were in the room,' says the school.

A host of opportunities for pupils to make sure their views are heard. 'Councils are huge here,' declared the head boy. He's right – there's a social council, music council, academic council, sports council and changes council. School is good at picking up on problems before they escalate. 'There are lots of people looking out for them,' a teacher told us. Cleaners spot things and chefs notice if a pupil hasn't eaten much at lunch.

Pupils and parents: Pupils come from all over, many from London, Oxford or locations within two hours' driving distance. Around 10 per cent international students. Parents are very supportive of the school. Many are sons and daughters of Rugby alumni and one described pupils as 'unpretentious, natural, spontaneous, courteous, tolerant and unstuffy.' Illustrious former pupils include Rupert Brooke (a girls' house is named after him), Lewis Carroll, Robert Hardy, Tom King, Salman Rushdie, AN Wilson and Anthony Horowitz. Not forgetting, of course, Harry Flashman and Tom Brown.

Entrance: No more 11+ admissions. Local children can sit exams in year 6 for deferred entry in year 9. Others sit aptitude pre-test and interview in year 7. CE pass mark is 55 per cent but average is higher. Boys and girls come from more than 300 feeder schools across the country, including The Dragon, Bilton Grange, Packwood Haugh and S Anselm's.

Around 40 new pupils (mostly girls, but some boys) join in the sixth form. UK candidates need at least three A/7s and three B/6s at GCSE. They sit sixth form entrance exams and have a house interview. Potential scholars are invited back at a later date for scholarship interviews. Keen competition for sixth form places.

Exit: Virtually all to university – around 94 per cent head to Russell Group universities most years. Bath, Bristol, Durham, Edinburgh, Leeds, Manchester, Newcastle and UCL are popular choices. Usually around 10 Oxbridge places a year (five in 2017, plus four medics), with three others off to US/Canada. Gap years 'less fashionable' than previously and interest in US universities is growing.

Money matters: Complex range of bursaries and awards. School offers academic, music, drama, art, DT, computing and sport scholarships – it led the way in 2003 by limiting scholarships to 10 per cent of the school fees, although this can be augmented to 100 per cent if family need can be shown through a means test. Bursaries of up to 100 per cent of the fees, depending on parental means.

Remarks: This famous public school takes huge pride in its history and traditions – and quite right too – but it is genuinely innovative and forward thinking, especially when it comes to academic matters. Boarding houses have a real sense of community, pupils are welcoming and unpretentious and facilities are second to none.

S. Anselm's School

27

S. Anselm's Preparatory School, Bakewell, Derbyshire DE45 1DP

01629 812734 | headmaster@anselms.co.uk | www.sanselms.co.uk

Ages: 3–16 (boarding in years 3–8)

Pupils: 262; **Boarders:** 40 full, 30 occasional

Day: £10,500 – £19,800 pa; **Boarding:** £24,900 pa

Headmaster: Since 2012, Peter Phillips. Head of Cundall Manor in Yorkshire for 13 years; built up school from around 80 to some 400 pupils. Started as a surveyor before seeing the light and becoming an English teacher. Head of English at Yardley Court and Dulwich College then director of studies at Cargilfield in Edinburgh.

A tall man, by any standards, he does not belong to the pinstriped, lapel-tugging, bullfrog school of heads. He is a thinker, a man of intelligence and vision, of great kindness, strong-minded and determined, and not easily swayed. Above all, he is dedicated to the welfare of the pupils. He does not like being pushed about by autocracy, but will listen for hours to children's worries and concerns.

Some parents have complained that he is something of a recluse, that he doesn't come out to see them. The pupils we met – and they were marvellously forthcoming and natural – said how much they like him because he takes such a keen interest in them, makes a fuss of them when they are sent by their teachers to show him a good piece of work, and so obviously cares about them.

Though he denies being a Luddite, he knows nothing of computers and announced early on in his time at S Anselm's that he did not do emails but was always willing to talk. All emails go through his wife, Sarah, who has a delightfully zany sense of humour and helps look after the girls in the evening. He teaches 18 lessons a week and referees some matches. Pupils enjoy his lessons and he enjoys the contact.

He has encouraged some of the older staff to leave, causing some disquiet among a few parents and indignation from those staff. The overall feeling amongst the parents we talked to was a sadness that even teachers have to move on, but an acceptance of the inevitability. This has not been a St Bartholomew's Day Massacre of the not-so-innocent over-50s: he has displayed considerable wisdom in retaining some of the finest teachers on merit, reputation and – importantly – a willingness to accept his enlarged expectations. One experienced teacher said that due to the new demands of helping at weekends she now knew the pupils better.

Perhaps most exciting has been the arrival of a cohort of young, lively, talented and dedicated staff. Many of them followed Mr Phillips, along with children and families, from Cundal Manor. Their arrival caused much excitement among the parents and children, and they are a most delightful and engaging group. Parents queued up to tell us of the new buzz in the school, the energy and drive, the sense of purpose and fun, the fresh air. Even we could feel it.

Boarding is becoming ever more popular. Weekends are action packed and hugely enjoyed. 'He doesn't want to come home,' one parent told us

Mr Phillips has given up the rather grand and slightly intimidating study of his predecessors, and now inhabits a smaller but delightful room overlooking the beautiful gardens. As the visitor glances around he sees a rugby ball in the (unlit) fireplace, a set of bagpipes on a table, a model steam train made by one of the science masters (an inspirational teacher whose lesson we had observed earlier), and a pile of papers. No badges or hints of office, no pomposity or sense of importance. The same is true of the website. Search as you may, you will not find one of those proprietorial messages from a head looking like a stockbroker or as if they were fresh from a stylish garden party, urging you with false modesty and marketing acumen to come and visit. With a dash of daring, S Anselm's has done away with all mentions of the head and doesn't have a prospectus. 'The school belongs to, and exists for, the children.' You'll only find the

head's name on the copy of the recent inspection report, and pretty good it was. He doesn't do swank nor is he interested in suits and tailors. He greeted us in bright, pinky-red trousers and sweater.

Head of S Anselm's College: James Mortimer BA (Oxon) PGCE MA.

Academic matters: Mr Phillips has restructured the timetable in the junior prep. English and maths is the staple diet in the morning, 'when the children are at their most alert', with other subjects in the afternoon. We listened to an exciting and challenging science lesson. When asked to describe their teacher, pupils said, 'distinctive, epic, fun, super, funny and heroic.' They were still yelling out adjectives as we left the room. We saw groups of young Romans planning a three course dinner which included stuffed doormice. They were off to Chester soon to explore all things Roman there. 'Don't mess with this man,' said our guides as we entered the classroom of a gentle-looking man. 'He teaches karate.' A woman was teaching the value of a sensible diet in a brilliant lesson incorporating geography, chemistry, history, common sense and health.

Another of the head's ideas is for the whole school to share a topic and approach it from all angles. When we visited it was lighthouses, so there were pictures of lighthouses everywhere, calculations of light travelling, weather maps etc. Teachers described the excitement of approaching a topic right across the school from the youngest to the oldest, the way that seems to unite the pupils in a common aim, enabling them to share and exchange knowledge. A visit to a Northumberland lighthouse involved camping: the buzz, the fun and the almost unnoticed accumulation of knowledge.

Saturday mornings are voluntary up to year 6, but the take-up is enthusiastic. There is the excitement of starting to learn Spanish, and Latin and Greek are, in the words of one distinguished exponent, 'full on'. First set of GCSE results in 2018.

Games, options, the arts: Terrific facilities include a well-designed music block where we watched children rehearsing for an arts evening. About 90 per cent of them learn an instrument. Art teacher wearing spectacularly bright trousers; 'I love getting messy in art,' said one enthusiastic painter with rainbow coloured hands and face. Excellent artwork everywhere, not just in the large-windowed studio. The wonderful sports hall is, perhaps, even slightly improved following the recent fire during the winter holidays. No doubt the excellent food contributes to the success of S Anselm's sport, which is taken seriously and played with zest and skill. County players abound in all areas, and there is huge excitement, though not at the expense of academic work. Or so they say. New Astroturf. The library is being extended and improved, a proud 10 year old librarian told us. Now there are plans for a real farm with real animals and the real hard work that goes with it, and a domestic science building.

Boarding: Boarding facilities are excellent and improving all the time. In fact, under the 'amazing and seriously mad' master in charge of boarding, according to parents and children, it is becoming ever more popular. Weekends are action packed and hugely enjoyed. 'He doesn't want to come home,' one parent told us, and talking of home, not long ago a group went up to Sheffield to help with the Archer Project. On that occasion it took the form of sleeping on cardboard on the streets in the rain with some young homeless people and some hardy members of staff. A thought-provoking experience. 'Boarding is just the greatest fun!' children said to us over and over again.

Background and atmosphere: The school has been through a turbulent period over the last few years. Numbers dropped, morale amongst many parents and staff dipped, and they told us that a few years ago they were very worried. With the arrival of fresh blood and new energies, numbers and morale are looking up, with a doubling of intake into reception and increased numbers in the main school, and now a secondary school too.

Pastoral care, well-being and discipline: Feelings of excitement, pleasure and happiness seem to permeate right through the school – including the gardeners and maintenance staff and the charming and friendly cooks. (We had the most delicious lunch of roast pork and all the trimmings.) All of them are, of course, vitally important contributors to the overall happiness and smooth running of the school.

Senior school heads like the lively, inquisitive appraoch of Anselmians, their willingness to get stuck in, their courtesy and friendliness

Pupils and parents: One parent told us with huge appreciation of how her son, joining as a boarder a little later than the main group when the family moved up from London, had been welcomed with kindness and consideration by boys and housemaster, and had settled in very quickly. When we wandered out during break and saw the running, the chasing, the laughter, the sense of timeless delight, it felt as if we had taken a detour with Thomas Traherne: 'Boys and girls tumbling in the street, and playing, were moving jewels. I knew not that they were born or should die; but all things abided eternally as they were in their proper places.'

Entrance: Mostly into the nursery and pre-prep, which is superbly run with first class teaching, according to happy parents. The overall head of the pre-prep is 'wonderful' and children in the prep look back with fondness and an early whiff of nostalgia. But anyone may apply at any stage if there is room.

Entry to the senior school in year 9 via common entrance.

Exit: The school has an excellent reputation for scholarships, achieved through excellent free-range teaching rather than force-feeding. Parents talk of the way teachers assess their pupils realistically and sensitively. A few parents, of course, have unrealistic demands and expectations, but the head is good at nudging them towards greater reality, even though that doesn't always endear him. Public school heads said they appreciate the lively, inquisitive approach of Anselmians, their willingness to get stuck in and their articulate courtesy and friendliness. Varying numbers to Eton, Harrow, Shrewsbury, Oundle, Fettes, Uppingham, Winchester, Downe House, Repton and Malvern. But school has expanded to secondary level, with its first year 11 in 2017/18, so many stay on.

Remarks: S Anselm's celebrated its 125th anniversary with an elegantly produced book, with a forward signed by The Duchess of Devonshire. In it the writer comments on the founder's choice of motto: 'Esse Quam Videri......to be and not to seem to be'. It's a wonderful motto extolling the virtues of honesty and, to use that overworked word, transparency. Several people have suggested to us that Mr Phillips fits the message behind that motto. He may not be universally popular – people who need to make changes rarely are – but he is now presiding over a deeply happy school with parents falling over themselves to tell us how pleased they are with the current set up. Such bubbling enthusiasm is rare.

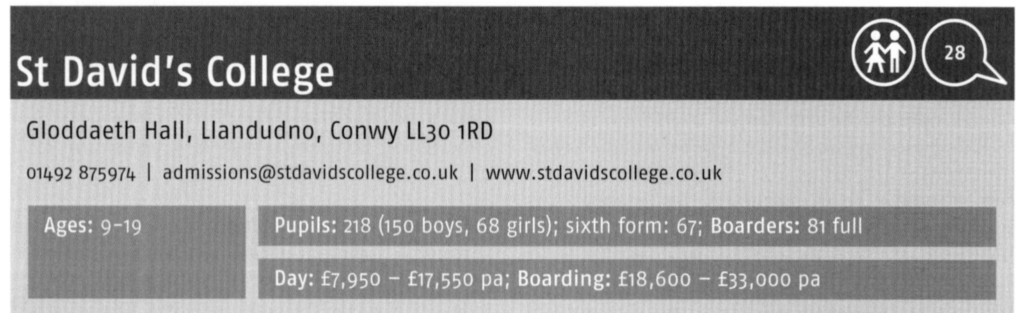

St David's College

Gloddaeth Hall, Llandudno, Conwy LL30 1RD

01492 875974 | admissions@stdavidscollege.co.uk | www.stdavidscollege.co.uk

Ages: 9–19

Pupils: 218 (150 boys, 68 girls); sixth form: 67; **Boarders:** 81 full

Day: £7,950 – £17,550 pa; **Boarding:** £18,600 – £33,000 pa

Headmaster: Since 2017, Andrew Russell, previously acting head. Degree in accounting and economics from Southampton and PGCE in maths from Bangor. He has taught at St David's for his entire career of over 25 years (maths, business studies and IT) and risen through the ranks as head of year, head of department, housemaster, assistant head and deputy head.

Academic matters: What a joy it was not to have examination results and league tables thrust under our noses. There is a belief in some quarters that education is dead and has been replaced by a slavish seeking after grade levels and that dreaded, often misused, word 'targets'. At St David's there are individual goals for each pupil but they are personal rather than political. Education at its best is very much alive and shining here. The reticence they have in not trumpeting their grade results is for no reason other than the firmly held conviction that grades are not the most important aspect of life at this school.

Average class sizes are 10 and every teacher is a qualified dyslexia teacher. An infinitely better system than that where a pupil is given one session of help a week and then goes back to a class where the teacher is making no allowances at all. That happens in a number of schools. This school was one of the first to adopt a multi-sensory teaching policy and we witnessed some marvellously lively, creative and stimulating teaching from a staff who seem universally dedicated and fun. None more so than those we met in the Cadogen Centre, a specialised building where each pupil enjoys one-on-one teaching with a programme individually planned for them after careful discussion with their class teachers.

'Community' is a word which sits easily on the lips of pupils eager to talk about their school. They really do feel as if the school belongs to them and they to the school

The facilities for IT are excellent and we had a wonderful time with some very bright sixth form pupils who were about to go off for an exhibition. Not only was the work they were doing as part of NVQs in CAD outstandingly good, but so were the fluent and perceptive comments which accompanied the work. 'Dyslexics often think out of the box,' a teacher told us. Recently a young man from St David's, who while there had attended one-on-one lessons, graduated in architecture at Manchester University. Another is reading nuclear physics. There are so many success stories.

Games, options, the arts: To gaze down from the beautiful terrace in front of the house is to marvel at the immaculate state of the games pitches, the superb Astroturf and the lure of mountains beyond. Virtually every game you can think of is on offer, and other schools talk of the verve and energy with which St David's teams perform. In addition there is a shooting range, an indoor climbing hall and vast amounts of equipment for outdoor activities, one of the distinctive features of the school. The excellent prospectus and online introduction to the school reveal the depth and breadth of the activities on offer. There is an activity, an expedition, a challenging outing once a week, but lest anyone think this is an attractive offer replacing academic pursuits, think again. The school academic day continues until 5pm Monday to Friday and there are additional lessons, activities and games sessions timetabled on Saturday mornings. When questioned about Saturday morning lessons, 'Fair enough,' said the boy we asked. Sixth formers can take a BTec in sports (traditional or outdoor ed).

A particularly popular activity is 4x4 off road driving in a spectacularly battered and mud caked old Land Rover. The school really is a paradise of activity, challenge, determination, broadening horizons and going beyond the syllabus.

Very lively art in an old building where budding artists can express themselves without worrying about spilling paint. Those are often the best buildings for producing the exciting art work. There was plenty here and in the photographic section adjoining. Such creativity and such joy, delight and encouragement.

Boarding: The boarding houses (three for boys and one for girls) are bright, airy and friendly; the house teams dedicated and involved. Boarding seems to work well, which is probably one reason why pupils come from so far afield from throughout the UK. Huge variety of indoor and especially outdoor activities available at weekends.

Background and atmosphere: In 1965 a deputy head from Cheshire, John Mayor, upset by the way boys and girls with learning difficulties were smothered, if not dismissed, because they were seen as lazy or stupid, decided to found a school where their needs were addressed. It was founded on three main principals: a determination to respect, understand and help the pupils; adventurous outdoor activities where the young could experience freedom and excitement; and all this within a gentle Christian ethos. Over 50 years later the school largely continues to follow those guidelines. And it shows. We met happy pupils who spoke confidently and unselfconsciously about how miserable they had been on arrival, with a bleak and cheerless outlook on life and no self-esteem at all. For some, St David's was last chance saloon, and some of them were far from home. They spoke of the warmth of the welcome they received from the whole community.

'Community' is a word which sits easily on the lips of pupils eager to talk about their school. And that's not a cliché either: they really do feel as if the school belongs to them and they to the school. There's a very real closeness. They talk of the increasing delight they derived from their lessons;

the love and interest shown by the teachers; the friendliness of their contemporaries. 'It's just everything,' said a young boy, struggling to articulate the indefinable. 'Surely there must be some things you don't like?' we pressed. 'Of course,' came the reply, 'but there's far less to worry about than there was at my previous school. It could be very depressing there and a bit scary on occasions.' What they all agreed on was the 'overall atmosphere'. They looked surprised when we suggested that that came from them. These young have not been stuffed with cheesy old clichés raked off that useful pile plundered by professional prospectus writers or that irritating band of media trained heads. These are real people making real discoveries about themselves.

Pastoral care, well-being and discipline: Within the academic, as well as the sporting and sporty side of life at the school, there are practical and generous ways in which pupils help each other. This is manifest by the way in which older pupils help younger pupils with academic subjects as well as more personal, private anxieties. The people we spoke with were unanimous in the feeling that there was always someone there to help. A word they were fond of evoking is 'banter.' Affectionate teasing. One of the most moving moments of our tour was when our guides pointed out the Prayer Garden, 'or whatever you like to call it. You can approach it in any way you like, but it's essentially a place for reflection. You can take it or leave it.' It's a lovely touch, and the statue in front, created by Nick Elphick, an old boy of the school, is a thought-provoking addition. This is not a threatening environment. Discipline is sensible, thoughtful, considerate. It seemed as natural as breathing.

There is an activity, an expedition, a challenging outing once a week, but lest anyone think this is an attractive offer replacing academic pursuits, think again

Pupils and parents: From a wide range of primary and prep schools. Day pupils from across the whole of North Wales. Boarders from all over the UK, a small number from overseas. Inclusive entry helped by quite a number of pupils being funded by their local education authorities. Apart from those with special educational needs, many parents choose the school because of its broad all-round education and its small class sizes. Recent extension to boarding provision due to increase in pupil numbers.

Immaculate games pitches and the lure of mountains beyond. Virtually every game you can think of is on offer, and other schools talk of the verve and energy with which St David's teams perform

Entrance: The majority enter aged at about 10 after an interview and a report from their school (although some join age 9 into year 5). A large number come from local primary schools, but others come from far afield. We heard how sensitively the business of arrivals is handled. Always a sign of a happy school. A few leave and a number come into the sixth form, attracted by the reputation of the teaching and the breadth of subjects on offer. The sixth form handbook says that the most important qualities for entry into the school are commitment and enthusiasm. That handbook is, incidentally, one of the best of its kind we have ever seen.

Exit: Around 15-25 per cent leave at 16. The school goes to tremendous lengths to help the boys and girls choose the courses that match interests and abilities. The vast majority do go on to further or higher education eg product design at Bangor, fashion buying at Manchester Met, maths and economics at Trinity College Dublin. Technical subjects seem the most popular, but not exclusively so.

Money matters: The school works hard to keep the costs down. The wonderful expeditions are very carefully budgeted. No swanky hotels. Parents we spoke to said that they felt the school was very thoughtful about money matters and we got the impression that those who ran into severe financial difficulties would be carefully listened to.

Remarks: This is a very special school, almost a magical place. Pupils develop in an unsentimental atmosphere of love and generosity. The staff are almost as amazing as the pupils and, yes, there is plenty of banter along with the seriousness. Over the years a strong bond has matured with Kampala. Pupils and gap year students are deeply and genuinely involved. 'The projects we are involved in come from the dreams of our own pupils,' says that handbook. The same could be said about the school as a whole.

St Hugh's School (Woodhall Spa)

Cromwell Avenue, Woodhall Spa, Lincolnshire LN10 6TQ

01526 352169 | office@st-hughs.lincs.sch.uk | www.st-hughs.lincs.sch.uk

Ages: 2-13 (boarding from year 3)

Pupils: 168; **Boarders:** 10 full, 40 weekly/flexi

Day: £8,748 – £14,706 pa; **Boarding:** £20,013 pa

Headmaster: Since 2013, Chris Ward BEd, late 30s; first headship, previously deputy head of Worksop College Prep. He spent several years as director of music at St John's-on-the-Hill School in Monmouthshire, though now does some science teaching. Approachable, visible and welcoming to pupils and parents. A keen and competitive rugby player, spends Wednesday and Saturday afternoons refereeing matches or supporting from the pavilion, mingling with parents over a cup of tea.

Believes that St Hugh's is unique in Lincolnshire, as a stand alone co-educational prep school, providing all round care and catering for everyone. Is proud that 'when St Hugh's pupils leave they are able to stand on their own'. Parents feel that he has given the school 'a new lease of life' which they hope will continue.

Recognising the shift in the demands of modern parents for flexible boarding, he is transforming boarding under newly appointed houseparents and UK gappies to a more cosy, warm and family experience. Keen to build and strengthen the nursery provision to provide sustained growth in pupil numbers over the years and enhance the structure and shape of the school day.

Married to Angharad, who has traditional prep head's spouse's role, with three children, all pupils at the school.

Entrance: Majority of the children rise through the ranks of the school's nursery and pre-prep with some recruitment in year 3 and 4. Prospective pupils spend a day at the school for assessment. Six minibuses bring children from wider areas.

Exit: Seventy five per cent go on to independent senior schools in Lincolnshire and the A1 corridor, Uppingham, Oundle, Oakham, Repton, Stamford. Further afield Sedbergh and Barnard Castle. The remaining 25 per cent get places at local grammar schools, usually at 11 (some go at 13).

Remarks: Located in the attractive, former Victorian spa resort of Woodhall Spa, in the midst of what was RAF heartland, St Hugh's is situated in a leafy avenue of traditional, Edwardian villas. Founded by the Forbes family in 1925 as a boys'

boarding school, loyalty to the school has been strong and successive generations of often farming families continue to be educated here. A charitable trust since 1962 and co-educational since 1981.

Whilst first impressions are of a modest establishment, once through the door the extent of the buildings and facilities become immediately apparent and the newly acquired playing field now allows the grounds to be described as extensive for a school of this size. New astroturf; this addition to the functional yet well maintained sport hall and swimming pool provides sporting facility gold, particularly for the hockey players. An adventure playground and nature pond – increasing use of the natural environment, staff undertaking forest school training, part of a green school kitemark. Boarding facilities in the upper echelons of the main school house, well away from classrooms.

Small number of full time boarders are well looked after at weekends and kept busy. Everyone (children, teachers and parents) agrees that the food is 'fantastic'

Nursery and pre-prep classrooms flow through a building across the playground from the older children. Bright, well resourced and full of colourful displays. Corridors adorned with interesting displays and children's work provide a sense of pride and commitment from staff. Good specialist facilities for science, music, art and DT with whiteboards in each classroom, a dedicated ICT suite and wireless connectivity throughout the school.

St Hugh's pupils have been successful in achieving scholarships, particularly in sports, music and arts, and it is the head's plan to strengthen further the number of academic and all-rounder awards. In the early years foundation stage, the new department head has developed numeracy work, and investigational skills in mathematics is a focus of teaching and learning. Specialist French starts in nursery, increasing across subjects so that by year 5 all teaching is by specialists, with German and Latin being introduced and setting for mathematics and science. Classes are grouped according to ability from year 5 with an average of 14 in a class. Whilst teaching broadly follows the national curriculum, there is a weekly session for senior pupils to enhance independent learning. Ten per cent SEN, mainly dyslexia and dyspraxia though several children with statements/EHC plans. Personalised learning plans, good coordinated strategies between SENCo and teachers, with one-on-one support where required.

Everyone is given the opportunity to contribute to the school, either on the games field, musically or in drama, but it's sport that rules the roost. Focus on traditional team sports and swimming, and everyone encouraged to play in a team. Good fixture list mainly against local independents but outlying location involves lengthy travelling times. It really is 'sport for all' – no one is left out. Hosts an annual netball tournament using boarding accommodation for teams from far afield.

Music flourishes with three quarters of pupils from year 3 playing an instrument up to grade 8. Plenty of performance opportunity with termly concerts and musicals, and public recitals for the two choirs; two orchestras with seniors scaling symphonic heights; string and wind ensembles. Joint production with drama each year – recently the Wizard of Oz and Bugsy Malone – though plays, sketches and nativities, as well as assembly presentations, give lots of scope for budding luvvies. Elocution competitions too.

Expressive arts thrive in well equipped, dedicated rooms with specialist art, pottery and design technology workshops and weekly scholarship classes. Textiles and cookery are included throughout the curriculum.

St Hugh's pupils get out and about on numerous curriculum enriching visits and outings. Years 5 and 7 have residential French trips and year 8 has a week's outdoor pursuits experience. Biennial hockey and rugby tours to Dublin and South Africa.

Positive reinforcement is key to rewards and sanctions, with gold points accumulating for the benefit of the pupil and their house. Not just academic achievement: effort, good behaviour and citizenship are all equally recognised. We were wowed by the Wow board where individual exceptional achievements are displayed. When needed, clearly defined sanctions escalating through report cards to detentions. Parents feel very well informed about their children's progress through teacher emails and regular reports.

Pupils and staff are polite, friendly and welcoming; evidence of real rapport between teachers and pupils, anecdotal comments tinged with humour and respect; no doubt that every child is known well here. Citizenship prized – and awards presented at weekly assemblies. St Hugh's Award for actions above and beyond – recently presented to one of the house captains who went home for a night to bake a cake to cheer up a young house member who had sustained a complicated broken femur on the rugby pitch. Strong house structure (named for three previous heads) with sporting, general knowledge and arts competitions and fundraising activities. Peer mentors in years 7 and 8; worry boxes discretely placed for confidential concerns.

Attuned to changing needs (and a declining number of Forces' children), the metamorphosis of boarding has seen a rise in the number of children deciding for themselves to board weekly or occasionally. A programme of investment has provided houseparent accommodation and upgraded bathrooms, and will create common rooms available to all and improve storage space, much needed as the bedrooms accommodating up to nine children are not large – though not always full. Friday nights are the most popular – great fun, and for the price of a babysitter, no early morning rising for parents to make Saturday school. There is a small number of full time boarders, who are well looked after at weekends and kept busy. Everyone (children, teachers and parents) agrees that the food is 'fantastic', with plenty of choice. The place is absolutely spotless throughout the boarding and school sides.

Parents tell us that they 'love the wonderful family atmosphere' and that the children 'mix throughout the year groups and are very supportive and encouraging of each other'. One parent told us, 'I have seen older year groups, unprompted, clapping and encouraging the little ones as they walk through the dining hall to go to perform in a play, which gave them such a boost'.

St Hugh's turns out well rounded children who are polite and self confident. Happy children – and parents.

Shrewsbury School

30

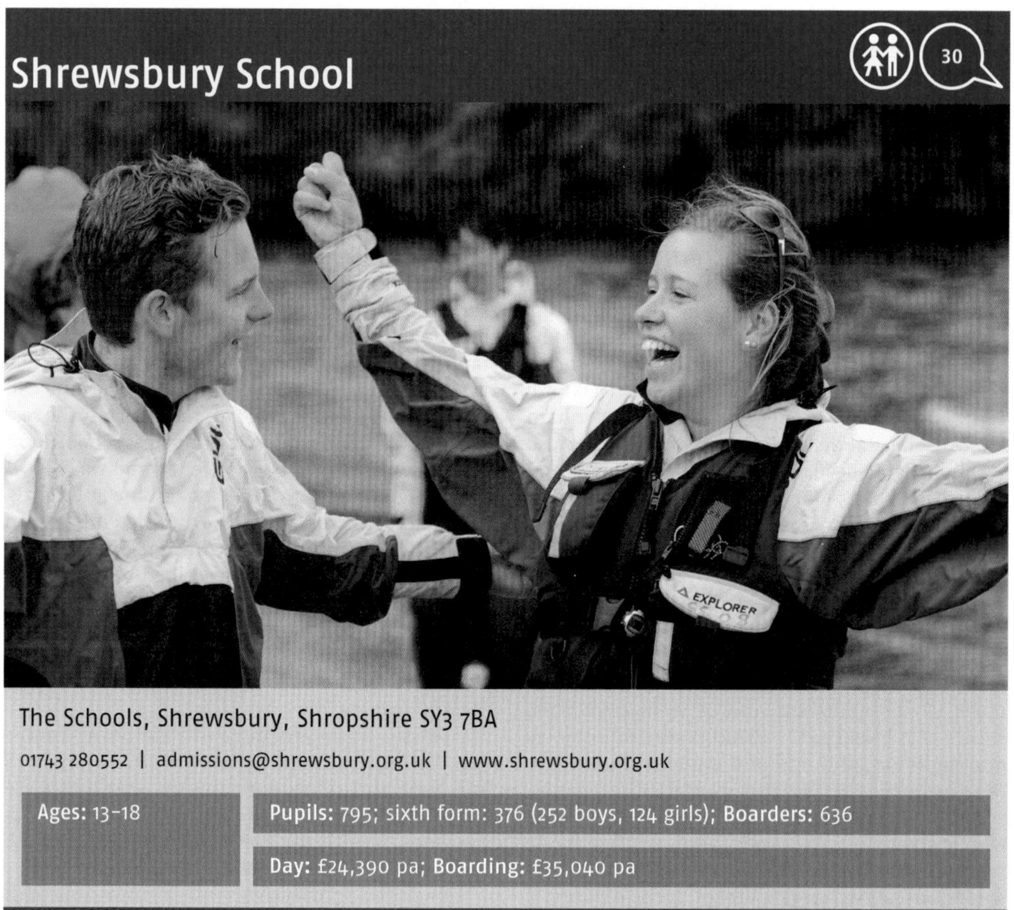

The Schools, Shrewsbury, Shropshire SY3 7BA

01743 280552 | admissions@shrewsbury.org.uk | www.shrewsbury.org.uk

Ages: 13–18

Pupils: 795; sixth form: 376 (252 boys, 124 girls); **Boarders:** 636

Day: £24,390 pa; **Boarding:** £35,040 pa

Headmaster: Since 2010, Mark Turner MA PGCE (50s). Educated at Rossall School where he was head boy, followed by Mansfield College, Oxford where he was an army scholar and read geography. Served with the Royal Artillery for four years before completing a PGCE at Cambridge. Housemaster at Oundle and then headmaster at Kelly College (now Mount Kelly) in his early 30s, followed by Abingdon for eight years. Married to Elizabeth, also an Oxford graduate, who teaches religious studies; they have two sons. Spends spare time in Devon where he can indulge his twin passions of bass fishing and lobster potting.

A 'crisp and keen administrator' who wants to 'retain the best of the past with the cutting edge technology of the future' and to up the academic ante. Having a close look at teaching styles and practice and work ethic, but does not want the school to become overly selective – believing in rigour rather than elitism. Cuts a slightly remote figure; parents and boys still feel that they hardly know him. Abingdon parents felt that Mr Turner's military demeanour and focused approach was just what that school needed – and we agree – but while many Shrewsbury parents feel that discipline did need tightening up, some are concerned that he is bearing down on eccentricities and traditions, and is too pernickety and keen on process. Capable and ambitious.

Stunning cricket pitches described by Sir Neville Cardus as 'the most beautiful playing fields in the world'. Top class indoor cricket centre also used by local and regional clubs

Moving on in July 2018 to head St Michaels University School in Canada. His successor will be Leo Winkley, currently head of St Peter's School, York. Read theology at Lady Margaret Hall, Oxford. Taught at Ardingly College and The Cheltenham Ladies' College as head of religious studies; has also been managing head at Bedales. A keen runner and follower of sport. Married to medical oncologist Jules; they have three young children.

Academic matters: In 2017, nearly 79 per cent A*/B at A level/Pre-U and 50 per cent A*/A – a comforting indication that this is a school that does not chuck out kids at 16. Particularly good showing at maths and further maths. Sixty-five per cent A*/A in IGCSE (most subjects) and GCSE in 2017. Wide choice at A level/Pre-U – usual academic subjects plus ceramics, photography, computing, design, theatre studies, PE and most combinations can be accommodated. 'Clinics' offer support for anyone who is struggling. Vibrant academic life outside main curriculum – voluntary complementary study programme in sixth form, some examined and some not eg global perspectives Pre-U, BTec in public services, extended project, sports leadership programme, Russian, Arabic, law and book-keeping for beginners as well as debating societies and Model United Nations. Range of academic societies with presentations by pupils and visitors. School hosted the International Young Physicists tournament and received a gold medal in the British Biology Olympiad.

About 130 pupils with SEN – mainly mild dyslexia. One full- and five part-time members of staff provide support. EAL offered but pupils must be able to follow the curriculum. Plenty of careers and university advice includes help finding work experience and talks on what employers are looking for. The school offers tuition for SATs (American university entrance exams) and is a registered SAT centre. Lectures from universities, agricultural and art colleges and the world of work plus lower sixth talks on interview technique and an interview coaching course (charged for).

Low turnover of staff – loyal band, some were at Shrewsbury themselves. Increasing number of NQTs but most changes come from retirements. Hugely supportive staff who 'bring out the best in everyone and take children as far as they want to go academically'. One parent told us, 'The school has brought out things in my son that none of us knew he had'.

Games, options, the arts: Sport taken seriously here both at house and school level but still with an emphasis on 'fun, friendship and fitness', as the school puts it. Wide range of sports; big on rowing, girls are now also afloat in numbers – lots of national competitions, significant presence at Henley and many Shrewsbury boys have represented their country on the water. Newish Yale boathouse with training room and indoor rowing tank. Newish head of rowing is from Abingdon – so interesting times ahead on the river. The elite can take it as a major sport for all three terms, the rest compete at house level. A leading fives school (Eton variety) with 14 courts – a recent pupil was one of the first girls to be awarded a half blue at Oxford.

Venerable cross-country running club known as The Hunt is prominent on national circuit. Stunning cricket pitches described by Sir Neville Cardus as 'the most beautiful playing fields in the world'. Top class indoor cricket centre also used by local and regional clubs, funded by the Foundation. Recent winners of the national boys' cricket 20:20 championships.

Masses of non-team sports including canoeing, kayaking, climbing, mountain biking, and sub-aqua club. Outdoor pursuits and hill walking weekends to Tally, the school's own cottage in Snowdonia, with the aim of having 'serious fun'. Thriving CCF and Duke of Edinburgh up to gold.

Rich and impressive musical tradition with numerous ensembles and choirs (places in the chapel choir particularly sought after), annual house singing competition. Pupils often take productions to the Edinburgh Fringe and perform concerts in London and Birmingham. All new pupils offered a free lesson on an instrument of their choice and there are several Steinways and an organ to practice on. Two major drama productions a year a well as house plays.

Buzzing art department with mezzanine art gallery where upper sixth students can hold solo art exhibitions – particularly strong ceramics. A number go on to art school each year.

Dozens of societies, both academic and not so academic, from millinery and wine tasting to bee-keeping and the green power electric car racing team. Witty and irreverent school magazine follows in the satirical tradition of the Old Salopian founders of Private Eye.

Community service popular, but not compulsory; involves work in old people's homes, schools, charity shops etc – oh, and a trip to Malawi. School has close links with Shrewsbury House community centre in Liverpool, known as The Shewsy; sixth formers can spend a week there and see another side of life and children come back for a return match to Shrewsbury.

Boarding: Now seven boys' boarding houses, of about 60 beds – refurbed eighth is now a girls' house, making four in all, mixed day and boarding; there are also two day boys' houses. Housemaster or mistress, matron and team of four or five tutors in each house. Boys' houses scruffy and comfortable – girls' houses newly built or refurbished with en suite bathrooms – some harrumphing from the boys about this but their houses next on the list for refurbishment. Boys start off in dorms and then graduate to study bedrooms as they move up the school.

Background and atmosphere: Founded in 1552 by Edward VI, the school throve, faltered and then revived in 1882 when it moved across the river into the old workhouse-cum-lunatic-asylum. It was named as one of the 'great' public schools by the Clarendon Commission in 1886 along with Eton, Harrow et al. Set in 100 acres high above the river Severn with distant views to the Malvern hills. Sir Arthur Blomfield's chapel was one of the first buildings to be built and is very much the centre of the community, with its vibrant red and blue interior, striking modern ceramics and pew runners representing the River Severn. Not everyone can fit in the chapel so houses take it in turns to have a Sunday lie-in.

Pupils take productions to the Edinburgh Fringe and perform concerts in London and Birmingham

Elegant Edwardian houses cluster round the cricket pitch connected by immaculate lawns and fine avenues of trees. Programme of refurbishment under way and new buildings (more to come) blend into the landscape overseen by imposing statues of

famous old boys Charles Darwin and the warrior poet Sir Philip Sydney.

The ancient Chained Library, open on Sunday mornings, contains some remarkable books including John Gower's Confessio Amantis, printed by Caxton in 1483, and Newton's Principia, which the school bought on publication in 1687, as well as books, manuscripts and letters of Charles Darwin.

The first girls joined sixth form in 2008 and school started taking in girls at 13+ and 14+ in 2014, aiming for 65:35 ratio with scope for numbers to increase to 780. Parents divided on this change between the huffers and puffers and those who felt it was a bit of a pity but probably inevitable. The blow softened by the evident high quality of the current sixth form girls, and the long lead time that means that all who joined for a boys' school with girls in the sixth got just that. In our view Shrewsbury boys will adapt well to co-ed – a civilised and courteous lot.

Pastoral care, well-being and discipline: Strong sense of community and a family atmosphere with many staff living on site. 'Staff totally committed and often find it difficult to leave' but still a healthy number of young teachers. Comfortable relationships between staff and pupils who are still expected to call teachers 'Sir'.

The house system 'preserves the innocence of school days but makes sure children are ready for the next stage,' said one happy mother. Children not allowed out on Saturday night without good reason (granny's birthday dinner likely to be as exciting as it gets) and they mostly keep to their side of the river anyway. It is too far away to 'bunk off to the King's Road on a Saturday night', said another. Strong house loyalty with lots of inter-house competitions in music, drama and sport. Enormous dining room where everyone can eat together – pupils sit in house groups with tutors. Food much improved in recent years – lots of choice, praised by children.

A school with a genuine sense of individuality, 'where you can really be yourself and where everyone's personality has a place,' according to one sixth form girl

Sixth form common room, known as Quod (no one knows why) with separate social and study areas and a shop, is run by a committee of sixth formers who organise talks, lectures, film nights and socials. Sixth formers choose their own tutor and anyone who wants to be a prefect, known as a praeposter, has to write a letter of application to the headmaster.

The chapel is central to school life but Catholics can attend services at the cathedral across the river and other faiths are accommodated. Whole school policy on bullying is underpinned by extreme vigilance from housemasters (a comfortable and friendly crew): none of the parents we talked to mentioned bullying as a concern, and we heard no grisly stories from the boys either. If there is clear evidence of drug taking a pupil will be asked to leave, if it is unclear they have to comply with a testing regime. When asked about drinking, children said there was 'no point as you would only get caught', and there is no doubt in their minds as to how Mr T would react.

Pupils and parents: An eclectic mix of landed gentry, City money, local farmers and intellectuals, all happy to keep their children away from the rat race of the south east. From all over the country including London but most live within a couple of hours of the school. About 10 per cent from overseas. Fleet of coaches ferries children home for exeats – as one father said, 'the school has something special and it is worth the long journey'. Lots of children of Old Salopians, sometimes fourth or fifth generation.

A school with a genuine sense of individuality, 'where you can really be yourself and where everyone's personality has a place,' according to one sixth form girl. Described by a parent as 'interesting, interested and able to get on with people from all backgrounds'. Lovely quirky Salopian sense of humour can be seen in the Blue Chair Charity set up some years ago to raise money for leukaemia research. Old Salopians take two blue chairs with them on their gap year and photograph them in unusual places – they have been spotted outside the Blue Mosque in Istanbul, and at the Taj Mahal; one fell down a ravine and had to be rescued and another was being held hostage on the Somali border and an £8,000 ransom had been demanded. The 8,000 members of the old Salopian Club have a great bond and sense of community. Most famous old Salopian of all is Charles Darwin, who was at the school from 1818-1825. Others include Sir Martin Rees, cosmologist and astrophysicist, Richard Ingrams, Willie Rushton and Christopher Booker, who cut their satirical teeth on the school magazine The Public Nose and went on to found Private Eye, and Paul Foot, who was a major contributor; also Michaels Palin and Heseltine.

Entrance: Fairly broad church and also looking for potential. Most come from about 12 preps within about two hours of the school. Entry mainly via CE (55 per cent required) or academic scholarship (held in the May before entry). School's own tests in English and maths for those at non-CE schools. A few join in the fourth form (year 10) if things have not worked out elsewhere but must be able to 'hit the ground running'. Some 25 boys and 50 girls join for sixth form – a number of boys come from local state schools.

At sixth form entry they are looking for candidates who will make a contribution to school life – sport, music academic, drama. Assessment weekend in Nov prior to entry – candidates can choose three or four subjects in which to be assessed, plus a reference from current school, interview and personal statement.

Exit: About 30 per cent take a gap year – Shrewsbury International School in Bangkok useful source of employment for gappies; travel scholarships available for interesting and challenging gap years. About 98 per cent to university, six in 2017 to Oxbridge; otherwise mainly Russell Group – Bristol, Newcastle, Leeds, Edinburgh. Anyone who does not achieve at least five Bs/6s at GCSE will be asked to leave – parents get plenty of warning if this is likely to happen.

Money matters: Scholarships and bursaries a tradition since the school was founded. Not a rich school but very supportive Old Salopians and parents put their hands in their pockets for the annual Foundation appeal, a telephone campaign staffed by sixth formers and recent leavers. Range of Foundation awards and scholarships worth up to 50 per cent can be topped up with a bursary – testing, interviews and consultation with prep schools (and some primary schools) for talented children who can't afford fees. Academic, sports, all-rounder, drama, music, DT and arts awards offered. Sixth form Margaret Cassidy Sports Scholarship worth up to full fees for talented footballer, cricketer or oarsman, and Alex Wilson day boy scholarship also worth up to full fees, for academic and sporting excellence (we assume girls not eligible for these).

Remarks: A school where individuals and individual talent are truly celebrated and where there is a 'breadth of opportunity without pressure cooker atmosphere'. Produces people with a wonderful and quirky sense of humour who are not afraid to be different.

Stamford High School

31

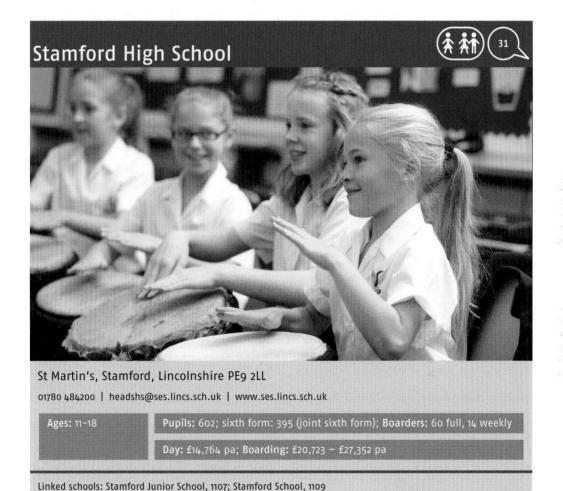

St Martin's, Stamford, Lincolnshire PE9 2LL

01780 484200 | headshs@ses.lincs.sch.uk | www.ses.lincs.sch.uk

Ages: 11–18

Pupils: 602; sixth form: 395 (joint sixth form); **Boarders:** 60 full, 14 weekly

Day: £14,764 pa; **Boarding:** £20,723 – £27,352 pa

Linked schools: Stamford Junior School, 1107; Stamford School, 1109

Head: Since 2015, Mrs Vicky Buckman, 50s. The daughter and sister of heads, she grew up in the schoolhouse of a large urban grammar school in Cheshire which she later attended. Never planned to follow in their footsteps, but in her final year at Leeds University (BSc agricultural and animal sciences) she decided teaching was for her. Her first post was at Christ's Hospital in West Sussex where, at the age of 25, she became the youngest ever housemistress. 'It was a way of life and was great fun,' she says. 'I get how girls work. I got used to championing them.' In 2006 she moved to become deputy head of City of London Freeman's School. Has always worked in the independent sector.

Comes across as friendly, approachable and positive. One of her first jobs was to move her office 'from the back of beyond' to the ground floor so she could see what was going on. Teaches biology to year 8. 'I think it's important everyone sees the head teaching and writing reports,' she says. 'And it keeps my hand in.'

When Mrs Buckman started she asked pupils to give her time to get to grips with the role and explained that, initially, they might not see that much of her. The girls say she's now out and about – eating with them in the dining hall, attending concerts and supporting sports teams on the touchline. Clearly wants to be visible.

Every Wednesday from 8 to 8.30am she has Open Door when girls can go to her office and talk to her about anything on their mind. They seem to like this.

A trained ISI inspector, she is also a keen musician, gardener and swimmer and a qualified open water scuba diver. She believes in responsible risk-taking, something that particularly resonates with girls, she says.

One younger pupil pointed out, 'It's nice having boys close by but good you don't have to see them all the time.' And a sixth former added, 'It's been the perfect mix for me'

Married to Stephen, a vicar; they have a son and daughter, both in their 20s, and a family cat called Borodin 'who is large, fluffy and ginger,' she says.

Mrs Buckman feels she has been very lucky getting the headship and we get the impression she is there for the long haul.The ISI inspected the school in the third week of the 2017 autumn term. At the time of writing she had seen a copy of the draft report. 'It was good and fair,' is all she will say at this stage.

Academic matters: The head believes if girls work hard, listen to advice and take advantage of all the opportunities anything is possible. 'I want them to be the best they can,' she says. It is certainly no academic pressure cooker. There is pressure and competition but girls we spoke to said this comes from each other rather than teachers. As one year 11 pupil said, 'The school pushes us to work hard but teachers also encourage us to take a step back before launching ourselves completely into revision. A lot of the pressure comes from ourselves because we want to do well. Our teachers are so passionate about their subjects and that rubs off on us so that we become passionate too.'

One pupil went as far as saying, 'They inspire me. I thought I wanted to become a lawyer but I'm now thinking of becoming a teacher.'

There's mutual respect here and you get the impression that although expectations are high the school has a friendly, caring environment where girls can ask for help and support if they need it. Class sizes around 20 with no more than 14 pupils for A level subjects. Teaching staff ratio of women to men is 50:50. The head's senior leadership team comprises mostly women.

Stamford High School forms part of Stamford Endowed Schools (SES,) which also includes Stamford Nursery and Junior Schools and Stamford School (boys). SES uses the diamond model which involves girls and boys being taught together in the junior school, separately in their senior schools then together again in the sixth form.

The girls seem to like this approach. As one younger pupil pointed out, 'It's nice having boys close by but good you don't have to see them all the time.' And a sixth former added, 'It's been the perfect mix for me. Having just girls around in senior school allowed me to grow up freely. In the sixth form it's felt like starting a new school and I've enjoyed mixing with the boys.'

The head believes more and more schools will follow Stamford's example: 'We became a diamond school in 2000 but we will always be true to the founding principle that we are a single sex school with a mixed sixth form. Girls thrive in lessons here in a way that they don't in a co-ed school. They ask questions, they are supportive of each other. Classes are more productive and teachers are teaching in one style to meet the needs of girls. Inevitably, in a co-ed school you tend to teach to the boys rather than the girls. The model works well because it offers the best of both worlds.'

Automatic entry from the junior school. Everyone else sits an entrance exam (non-verbal reasoning, maths and English). This means the ability range is quite broad. Most take 10 GCSEs including three sciences and a language; in 2017, 59 per cent of grades were A*-A/9-7. Rich choice of languages on offer: French or Spanish in year 7 then can add German or Russian in year 8. The brightest currently take French a year early (70 per cent get A*) then complete a short course in Spanish, although this is under review.

The five GCSEs at grade B/6 boundary for progressing to the sixth form doesn't seem to be set in stone, according to some parents. We checked with the head who says each case is treated individually and there is flexibility. 'Ultimately we want our girls to achieve something for their efforts over two years,' she says. 'For some, a coursework approach may be better.'

Some 26 subjects offered at A level plus BTecs in sports science and business. Most study three A levels. Most popular and strongest performing subjects, with girls as well as boys, are biology, chemistry and maths. The joint sixth formers achieved 62 per cent A*-B in 2017 (a slight drop from 2016, which the head attributes to the curriculum changes); 33 per cent A*/A grades.

The school currently has no statemented pupils but has a watching brief on 195 girls who are on a learning needs list. These are pupils who have a below average score on a test that measures skills such as verbal reasoning, working speed and memory, mostly pupils with dyslexia. All teachers are aware of those pupils on the list and make adjustments in the classroom to meet learning needs. Extra lessons also available for those with English as an alternative language. No charge for special support although a nominal fee is added if a pupil gets extra help over lunchtime.

Many go on to Russell Group universities, but the head accepts that university isn't for everyone and says an increasing number are applying for apprenticeships, which she supports.

Games, options, the arts: Plenty of sport on offer including hockey, netball, cross-country, gymnastics, tennis, athletics, badminton and sailing (at nearby Rutland Water) with success at county, regional and national level. The U14 hockey team is currently county champions.

We counted some 18 hockey teams and 24 netball teams so there seems lots of opportunity to have a go whatever your level, particularly lower down the school. For hockey, some age groups field three or four teams and at U12 there are five.

Girls in the top teams are expected to commit to several training sessions a week and a match at the weekend, not unusual in the independent sector. As one parent pointed out, 'If you are sporty, a lot is expected of you.'

Boarders have the use of a fully fitted kitchen where they can make toast, bake cakes and even do their own laundry if they want to

Fantastic facilities available – a £6.1m SES sports centre complete with all mod cons including fitness suite and 25m indoor pool. These are a 20-minute walk away at the boys' school – not ideal, but part and parcel of being a town centre school. Swimming also available at the junior school's pool. Stamford High School does have its own on site sports hall, which has recently been updated to house a fitness suite.

Some 176 music lessons every week with plenty of concerts (string and band), choirs and ensembles. Dance productions too. A state-of-the-art performing arts centre at Stamford School is the venue for large scale productions, such as Grease and Les Misérables. A production of the musical Hairspray at planning stage. The High School has its own hall

but it is too small to stage large productions. The head is determined to increase its capacity. More than 280 pupils take speech and drama and many are prepared for the LAMDA (London Academy) exams.

Regular visits to art galleries and exhibitions and recent overseas trips to Italy and Paris. No Saturday morning school but more than 80 voluntary activities offered such as bridge, golf and driving lessons for 16 year olds. Thriving CCF – this year's new recruits in the army section numbered 12 boys and 31 girls. Around 40 gold D of E awards each year. Girls encouraged to volunteer and get involved in the local community through charity work.

Boarding: This is a day school with about 10 per cent boarders. Around a quarter of these are from overseas and the school is actively recruiting with recent trips to mainland China, Russia, Ukraine, Thailand, the US and Nigeria. The rest are mostly local girls with parents in the Forces; Lincolnshire is home to several airbases.

Three boarding houses. We looked at Welland (11 to 16 years) – just around the corner from the school's main site and a 10-minute walk into town. It has a homely feel with two big TV rooms complete with large sofas and beanbags. Four or five students to a dorm with sixth formers sharing two to a room. Pupils also get the use of a fully fitted kitchen where they can make toast, bake cakes and even do their own laundry if they want to. There is a lovely large garden at the back. This is also home to two rabbits, which the girls help to look after.

Girls seem to enjoy a fair amount of freedom here. They are allowed to walk into town from year 7 at different times provided they are with another pupil. The houseparent is keen to encourage independence: girls can attend sleepovers or parties at the weekend with day girls provided parents give permission. The girls we spoke to loved boarding. One said if she didn't board she wouldn't do her prep – compulsory every night in the school library.

Boarders can opt for a three, four, five or seven night package. Around 22 girls stay on a Friday evening with 16 or fewer on site on a Saturday. A new service, aimed at busy London families, offers accompanied travel to and from King's Cross on Friday evenings and Monday mornings.

Background and atmosphere: Beautiful mellow limestone buildings, quirky narrow passages and stunning riverside views. What's not to like about Stamford? The SES schools sit at the heart of this picture postcard town with its 600 listed buildings (the TV adaptation of Middlemarch was filmed here). Stamford High School was founded in 1877 as part of the legacy left the schools in the Browne's Hospital Trust. It still occupies its original site on the south side of the River Welland.

The school entrance is not very obvious. We were so busy gazing up at the town's beautiful architecture that we missed it. But then we spotted a group of pupils who were obviously from SHS. The uniform is distinctive – navy blazer, long pleated below-the-knee navy skirt, white open shirt and black shoes (no heels). It sounds old fashioned but we liked it and, more importantly, the girls we saw love it. If they do have a gripe it's to do with tying their hair back, a rule the new head introduced. Parents support the head on this one, we believe.

Beautiful mellow limestone buildings, quirky narrow passages and stunning riverside views (the TV adaptation of Middlemarch was filmed here)

Once inside the atmosphere is calm and orderly. Girls move about the corridors with a sense of purpose. No rushing around or shouting. On the walls hang pictures and short profiles of inspiring alumnae including Sarah Outen, the first woman to row solo across the Indian Ocean, and international Emmy award-winning actress Lucy Cohu.

Girls are friendly and come across as confident, cheerful and relaxed around their teachers. The ones we spoke to were certainly not snooty. A couple of spirited sixth formers were keen to take us on a tour, pointing out the newly-refurbished dining hall and home economics centre recently opened by former Bake Off judge Mary Berry.

They then showed us the new ideal classrooms, an initiative being rolled out as part of the head's drive to use the latest ideas and approaches in class. Interconnecting desks are covered in interactive whiteboards enabling pupils to write on their desks, save information and use digital technology to share it with the rest of the class.

Pastoral care, well-being and discipline: All girls have a form tutor who is a main point of contact for both pupils and parents. One pupil said, 'Everyone is so friendly and the teachers are so nice. If you have a problem you can go to anyone.' And a parent added, 'Pastoral care is very good. I contacted the school about an eating issue and the school was fantastic.'

Strict rules around the use of mobile phones. Years 7 to 9 must keep them in their lockers during the school day. Boarders have to hand in all devices 15 minutes before they go to bed. Some girls have tried to get round this by having several devices but the houseparent is one step ahead of them. Main sanction is being gated.

Pupils and parents: Mostly local families from a large catchment area and from all walks of life, thanks to range of bursaries available, with lots of military families who like a modern boarding option. For day girls an extensive network of bus routes from as far afield as Newark in the north to Peterborough in the south.

Some parents looked at the grammar school option but chose SES because they like the diamond model – particularly those with sons and daughters. One parent with a daughter in year 11 and a son at Stamford School said she loved the feel of the place when she looked round. 'It has a warmth about it. My daughter was very unhappy at her junior school. It was as though I had lost her, then when she started at Stamford High School I got her back. When my son and daughter come home after the first day of term they are so excited they can't stop talking. The schools are like one big happy family.'

One parent who had two daughters at the school said it suited both girls despite them having different strengths. 'My oldest is into science while my younger daughter is more into the arts and drama. But there are opportunities for both. The school is good all round.'

Another acknowledged her daughters had been very happy and had formed incredibly strong friendships. All said that given their time again they would still choose Stamford High School.

Entrance: Automatic entry from the junior school at 11. Entrance exam for outsiders and those after a scholarship.

Sixth form entrants (internal and external) schould have at least five GCSEs at grade B/6.

Exit: Around 20-40 per cent leave after GCSEs. Nearly all sixth formers into higher education (many to Russell Group universities) with a few to apprenticeships. Two to Cambridge in 2017 and three medics; one off to Amsterdam to study linguistics.

Money matters: Bursaries means-tested and up to full fees, scholarships worth between £500-£1,000 pa. Academic, music and sports scholarships available at 11+ and art, drama and all-rounder scholarships added at 13+. Similar number in the sixth form.

Remarks: Traditional atmosphere but with modern teaching methods turning out spirited, well-rounded, confident girls keen to get out there and test themselves. Former pupil Flight Lt Kirsty Moore, the first woman pilot in the Red Arrows, says, 'I arrived a shy, 11-year old and seven years later I felt ready to step out into the world and make it my own.' We think plenty more will feel inspired to do the same.

Stamford Junior School

32

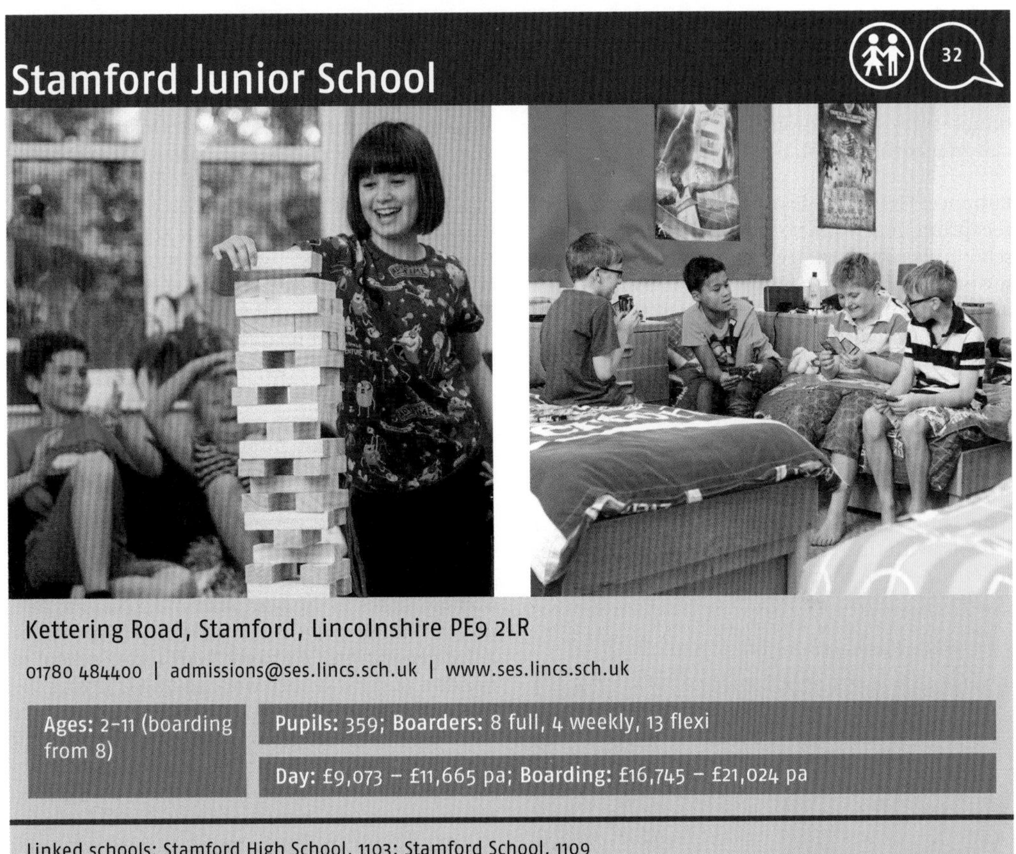

Kettering Road, Stamford, Lincolnshire PE9 2LR

01780 484400 | admissions@ses.lincs.sch.uk | www.ses.lincs.sch.uk

Ages: 2-11 (boarding from 8)

Pupils: 359; Boarders: 8 full, 4 weekly, 13 flexi

Day: £9,073 – £11,665 pa; Boarding: £16,745 – £21,024 pa

Linked schools: Stamford High School, 1103; Stamford School, 1109

Head: Since 2012 Emma Smith (early 40s). Convent educated in Berkshire, early years BEd from Kingston University. From a Forces background, husband and sister still serving. Previously worked in the state sector in and around London. Bit of a baptism of fire at previous school. Hired as deputy head and within weeks made acting head due to a suspension. 'I had a very young staff [she was hardly Methuselah herself] with no leadership team. It was an intense experience that I enjoyed, but knew after two years I needed a change. My husband has family in Stamford, so I was delighted to get the job and go back to just teaching for a while.' Starting to get itchy feet when previous incumbent retired and was appointed head. Nice to see a rather glam head – black fingernails et al.

She's ambitious, with big plans that are coming to fruition. Reception classes have been moved into a newly converted stable block. A recent bespoke year 6 block. The school is getting larger, but with smaller class sizes, under her leadership. 'I think emotional intelligence is vital. If you are honest with children they respond well. And never underestimate them. They need to appreciate that they won't get on with everyone in life but need to treat people, particularly their contemporaries, with courtesy and respect. I want the children to bounce through the door in the morning, have an amazing day and then bounce back out again, full of what they've done. My aim is for them to learn to love learning and have a good work ethic.'

Parents are very supportive. 'She has great vision for the school and is making very positive changes,' said a year 5 parent. 'She ruffled a few feathers at first, but listens to people and has learnt to communicate with parents very effectively. Her handling of a very sad, horrible accident involving one of the pupils has been exemplary. Parents have been kept informed throughout, so avoiding any unnecessary speculation,' said a parent with two children at the school.

Entrance: First come first served into nursery and reception. A few places available higher up the school, via tests from age 7. Quite a large and growing junior school with most children coming from a 20 mile radius. Families attracted by the fact that you can almost certainly stay in the Endowed system until 18.

Exit: Some leave for other schools after nursery, but the majority go into reception. Automatic entry from year 6 into the senior schools means that from year 5 there's a sharp increase in numbers. A big chunk (some 47 per cent) go up to the senior schools, with the rest going to state sector or other independents. A couple each year are warned early

Boarding house is a lovely, honey coloured stone building. Large garden with climbing frames, chickens and rabbits

that they might not cope with the senior schools. Handled sensitively.

Remarks: Part of Stamford Endowed Schools with its diamond structure. Co-ed in junior and sixth form, single sex 11-16. The junior school is situated just outside the historic town of Stamford. Feels very rural, on a very quiet, leafy, green site in a delightful setting with a very pretty playing field set in a dell. The recently converted stable block housing reception class adds to this, along with the recent nursery building. New-ish year 6 building awash with iPads etc. Lots of outside space, climbing frames and toys obviously well used. The classrooms spill into the outside space down here through large French windows, which were flung wide during our visit. Lots of newly-planted seedlings in the garden. All year 5s do nursery duty at lunch time and go down to help the toddlers. The main building is surrounded by pitches, grass and astroturf. New learning garden and adventure area by the river. Fresh air seems to be king at this school. Windows are flung wide and the garden is inside with vases of flowers everywhere – all bright and cheerful.

Many parents relocating to Stamford from London, often returning to their roots, choose the school. The town was recently voted by The Sunday Times as the best place in England to live, and we can see why. A lot of pupils are second or third generation. 'We came from a state school in London and I was very worried about fitting in,' said one parent. 'We couldn't have been made more welcome, by the school, or other parents. I think it's a fabulous school. My children have gone from strength to strength and will try anything now, whereas they were very cautious before.'

All children learn musical instruments. Recorder for the early years, strings from year 2 (poor parents) and piano in year 5 and 6. Lots of clubs, ranging from chess to gardening, sewing, sports and orchestra, and there's even a left handed club. New clubs for year 6 include DR, science awards and gardening club, plus Saturday cookery and craft sessions. Artwork all over the place, and it's good. One of the teachers has her work displayed and on sale, great for the pupils to see.

Sport is thriving and open to all. School gymnasts are 'Under 11 Mixed Floor and Vault National Champions'. Rugby, hockey, netball, tennis and swimming teams are doing well. 'The sport is tremendous, but I am disappointed that as a latecomer to the school my son has found it hard to break into some of the A teams, as there are "invitation only" squads for the best players,' said a parent. 'It is hard to improve and catch up if these squads are getting extra coaching. That said, both of my children are very happy and it's my only gripe'.

A lot of learning is through play in the early years. 'We came from overseas where a lot of emphasis was on academic success. I worried at first that the children didn't seem to be pushed hard enough. But I soon accepted that the softly, softly approach works well. My children have been transformed and are so much more relaxed and happy.' 'What I really like about the school is that it feels like a local school and very much part of the community,' another parent told us.

Spanish and French taught from year 3, Italian also available. They have a thumb scanner for the library; we enjoyed that. Every child reads for 15 minutes in class daily. Science week when we visited. Lots of excitement about making false blood for homework – from pupils and parents. ILIC – independent learning and intellectual curiosity – is a big ethos throughout all three schools, and they start them young, instilling a good, enthusiastic work ethic.

Special needs not overlooked. Some 63 have SEN status. SENCo teachers praised by parents. 'My child joined in year 3 and is on the autistic spectrum. The bedding in period took a while, but the school was very accommodating and listened to professional advice. My child has gone from strength to strength and is thriving'. Another mother said, 'My son is dyslexic and gets lot of support. Extra lessons, spelling groups and assistance are given if needed, but he is not made to feel different.'

Boarding starts in year 3. Most boarders are flexi or weekly, with handful of Forces children full time. Boarding house is a lovely, honey coloured stone building situated in the dell. Large garden with climbing frames, chickens and rabbits. We were welcomed by two slipper clad boarders who showed us every inch, chatting all the while. Definitely home from home; they even have jobs to do, with a rota. Nice and bright and airy. No phones upstairs, taken away at night, and no social networking. 'The children need to interact and be sociable, not glued to a phone,' the likeable housemistress told us. Homework supervised and lots of weekend trips: a forthcoming visit to the Natural History Museum involving a sleepover eagerly anticipated. Scruffy the dog is very much part of the boarding family.

There's a very strong parents' association that offers huge support to the school, providing funding for various trips and talks. They're listened to as well. The head is reducing class sizes because of parental pressure – mutual respect is the impression we got.

Parents didn't need to tell us that this is a happy school; we could see it for ourselves. Our delightful guides were proud, chatty and cheerful. Food is good, we were told, particularly the lasagne. Everywhere we went we were greeted with a cheery smile. A joyful place, offering a happy, positive start to education. A very good grounding to take to the increasingly impressive senior schools. Hard to see why you'd go elsewhere locally.

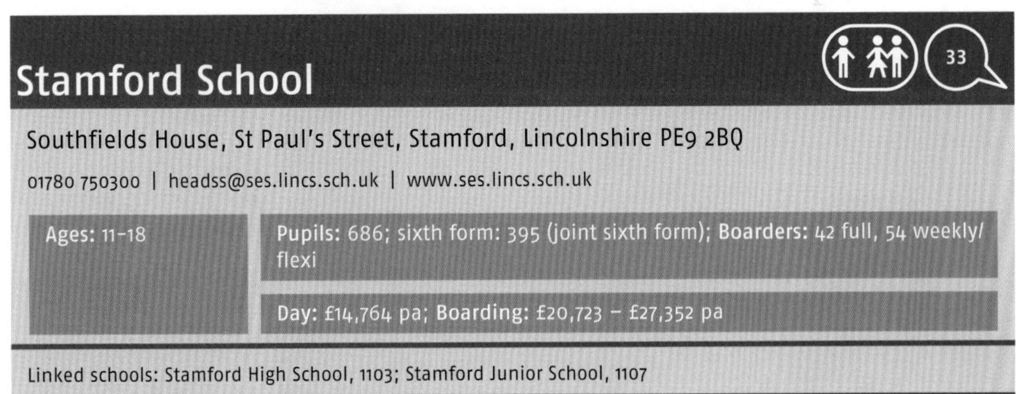

Stamford School

33

Southfields House, St Paul's Street, Stamford, Lincolnshire PE9 2BQ

01780 750300 | headss@ses.lincs.sch.uk | www.ses.lincs.sch.uk

Ages: 11–18

Pupils: 686; sixth form: 395 (joint sixth form); **Boarders:** 42 full, 54 weekly/flexi

Day: £14,764 pa; **Boarding:** £20,723 – £27,352 pa

Linked schools: Stamford High School, 1103; Stamford Junior School, 1107

Head: Since 2016, Nick Gallop, previously assistant head and head of sixth form at Portsmouth Grammar. Politics degree from Durham; he has also been head of department at Loughborough Grammar, and at Wellington College, where he was later a boarding housemaster. He has coached first XV rugby; married with two young children.

Principal of all three schools since September 2016 is Will Phelan (40s), previously head of school. Read medieval and modern history at Royal Holloway, followed by PGCE at Reading and MBA in education management. Formerly deputy head at Warwick, head of sixth form and director of rugby at Abingdon School, and head of year at Royal Grammar School, High Wycombe. Considered a career as a professional rugby player until injury forced a different direction.

Originally planned to study economics and 'make money' but didn't quite make the grade, so headed to Australia to consider his future. 'Not getting my first choice turned out to be the making of me,' he says. A year as a boarding master in Australia, where he also coached rugby and cricket, made the decision for him. 'I loved being at the school coaching and being with the boys, so decided that I wanted to teach. I've spent 20 years with boys and I know what makes them tick. The boys from Stamford are some of the nicest boys I've met. The school is spread out over a large site, which is perfect, as I don't think boys should be on top of each other, they need room. A Stamford boy is a tryer – he's stretched, but not stressed.'

He is charismatic, very well liked and respected by boys and parents alike (we're sure the mothers love him). Married with three children. A huge man, he towers over the tallest of boys (well, he was going to be a rugby player).

Academic matters: Consistent, solid results. In 2017, 43 per cent A*-A9-7 at GCSE, and 30 per cent A*/A at A level (nearly 59 per cent A*/B) – results for joint sixth form (Stamford High School and Stamford School). Most boys take 10 GCSEs in a wide range of subjects. French, German, Spanish, Russian and Latin are language options. DT is strong (the workshops and work produced are impressive; two self-propelled vehicles built by the boys caught our eye). Twenty-eight subjects offered in the sixth form that is joined with the High School, most popular being maths and the sciences, with economics and business studies rising fast. Philosophy and ethics rated highly throughout the three schools.

We were shown every nook and cranny by the younger boys, who told us about boarders' outings to the cinema, Alton Towers, and local Leicester Tigers' matches

The lessons we observed showed involved, enthusiastic boys. The year 8 Latin scholars were wriggling in their seats, they were so keen – well disciplined, though. Lots of arm raising in the year 11 philosophy and ethics debate and diligent studying in year 9 maths. All boys leapt to their feet when we entered the classrooms. The year 13 lessons had a very different atmosphere. Much less formal but strongly focused pupils. Determined and interested, these boys had their eye on the end game. You could feel expectations of the staff and boys were high.

Learning support is available for boys who need it. Around 80 boys with SEN and 40 or so get learning support. One boy has a statement of special educational needs. Extra support also offered to invited boys on Saturday mornings.

Games, options, the arts: Sport features highly – even the non-sporty boy is encouraged to have a go. A strength of the school is the number of teams in different sports, so even the boy who is 'rubbish' (our words, not theirs) gets to play. But don't be fooled. Stamford's 1st XV was unbeaten last year and are formidable opponents. Eye-catching rugby kit, but one unimpressed mother wanted to know 'why do they make the sixth form play in white shorts? I just can't get them clean'.

Some of these boys are playing at county level, others selected by local premiership sides, and the captain was invited to represent England in the U18 squad, while a previous captain is now playing professionally. The cricket team is largely unbeaten (ex-England international Dean Headley coaches), the squash squad has been unbeaten for three years, and the basketball team (including another national player) too. They're pretty good at hockey and swimming as well. Their first year with a triathlon team resulted in a GB squad selection (and the school had to teach the boy in question to swim).

A parent told us that if a boy was yellow carded in any sport at the weekend he was up in front of the headmaster on Monday morning to explain himself. Excellent. Parents are happy and trust the school. The odd grouse about sporting stars possibly being cut more slack (sour grapes maybe?) but every parent we spoke to was happy and 'hugely impressed.'

The new £6.1 million sports centre dominates the skyline, looking out over the rugby pitches, and offers gym facilities as well as a 25m pool (pity they don't brush the walkways more often) and is well used by all the school.

Music and art are equally strong. SES is the largest independent centre for LAMDA exams in the country and six boys recently opted for music or music tech at university. A visit to the music department revealed a stash of new Macs for composing and music tech as well as the usual instruments.

The combined productions with fellow endowed school, Stamford High School (girls), are very popular (can't imagine why): recent production of Les Misérables involving all three schools was a sell out. Thriving choirs, bands and orchestras, ranging from big band and jazz to full orchestra. House singing and music competitions are hotly contested. New drama and music block.

Artwork is displayed throughout the school. Portraits seemed to be popular, albeit mainly from the upper school, in the more prominent spots. Arty boys are encouraged to spend time in the studio.

CCF section is one of the largest in the country (combined with the girls' school from year 10 up), with opportunities to go flying if you're in the RAF section. The shooting team is good (they have their own range), winning the Bermuda Cup at Bisley

Boarding: Although Stamford is predominantly a day school,15 per cent of the pupils board. Most are weekly or three night boarders who live within 100 miles of the school. There are also boys from China, Poland, Holland and Russia. The boarders are divided into two houses – years 7-10 (Byard House) and years 11-13 (Browne). More boys board in the latter years and most have single rooms. Facilities recently updated – new furniture, lots of snooker and table tennis tables, all clean, bright and tidy, with posters on the walls (nothing inappropriate though). The older boarders must be the fittest around as the gym is a regular haunt in the evenings after prep. Co-ed junior boarding house in the grounds of the junior school, with climbing frame, rabbits and chickens in the garden.

We were shown every nook and cranny by the younger boys, who enthusiastically told us about boarders' outings to the cinema, Alton Towers, paintballing, go karting and local Leicester Tigers' matches, as well as table tennis tournaments. All age groups said how like home it is – boys change their own sheets and can bring their own duvet covers – and how much they like the boarding staff. There are televisions, but they don't get used a lot. More time is spent on Xbox and table tennis, after two hours of supervised prep every night. Boarders eat together in the main dining hall and seem happy and relaxed with each other.

Background and atmosphere: Founded in 1532, Stamford School still operates from its original site in the middle of the town (recently voted the best place to live by The Sunday Times). The school chapel, surrounded by its immaculate lawns, is at the heart of the school. Stamford School is part of the Stamford Endowed Schools (includes Stamford Junior School and Stamford High School). Each school is run separately – with its own head but a common principal. Teaching at the Stamford Endowed Schools is via the diamond structure – mixed junior and sixth forms, single sex 11-16 – which seems very successful and strongly supported by the parents. 'Lots of info on drugs, drink, driving and sex, which the boys seem to find easier to take in a single sex environment,' one parent told us. A year 8 parent commented: 'My son is just hitting adolescence and they know exactly how to handle him. The single sex education is a godsend.'

Sixth form teaching is split between the two schools, so there's a 10 minute walk across town if there is a site change in the timetable. This gives the school a collegiate feel and allows the sixth form boys a certain degree of independence. There's a lot of trust involved but it doesn't seem to be abused. Because of this constant walking – great in the summer, not so good in the winter – the boys are highly visible in the town. The local shops can no doubt set their clocks by hordes of hungry boys dashing in for sustenance for the 'long walk' through the beautiful town. (The school food used to be awful, now greatly improved, we're told). No driving is allowed between sites. Woe betide any boy who is caught doing so. We understand keys have been confiscated on occasion. There is also the 'six-inch rule' to be considered. Six inches must be kept between a boy and a girl at all times...

Boys are very involved with the wider community and help out with many of the local charities. The Evergreen Trust in Stamford and Help for Heroes get lots of support. Year 7 boys took part in the Sleep for Shelter Night, spending a night in a cardboard box in the school grounds.

School site is spread over a large area, giving the boys plenty of room. Part of the site features beautiful, honey-coloured stone Georgian and older buildings with beautiful gardens. Perhaps one of the most iconic features of the school (probably to their disappointment) is the incredibly ugly footbridge that connects two parts split by a very busy road. We were told that plans are afoot to improve it.

Boys we met were courteous, friendly and grounded. In school's own words, a 'Stamford boy is well rounded and up for anything'

Pastoral care, well-being and discipline: Discipline is hot and any problems nipped in the bud quickly. School doesn't deny bullying exists, hooray, but it's dealt with promptly, quite often by the boys themselves. Mentoring system means older boys mentor the younger ones (years 7-11) and there is a one-to-one mentoring system between year 10 and year 12 boys. Lots of banter, but lines aren't crossed. The atmosphere is friendly and happy – these boys seem to like each other. Quite how the introvert sitting in the corner fares we're not so sure, but we were assured by a parent that 'the school knows their boys.'

'Support is there if you need it; you just have to ask,' a pupil told us. A younger boy's mother said: 'Parent mail is a fairly new system. We can access the school portal and see what and when homework is due. We are very quickly told if deadlines are missed, so my son knows he is being watched very closely by us all and knuckles down and gets on with it. A great improvement.'

Parents say that 'communication is very strong both ways.' One told us: 'We have needed pastoral help and the school has been very supportive and dealt with matters calmly, effectively and efficiently.'

Pupils and parents: Boys mainly from a 30-mile radius, slightly further afield in the sixth form. Mostly from professional families who value the all-round education of their sons rather than a well-known name. Boys we met were confident, courteous, friendly and grounded. In school's own words, a 'Stamford boy is well rounded and up for anything.' Boys are encouraged to get involved and say that if you get stuck in (and everyone does) 'you fit in.'

Every parent we spoke to gave glowing references: 'Excellent, I would recommend it every time; they turn out grounded, confident boys,' said one. 'My son loved being there so much he says he will send his own son, if he has one,' said another. A third told us: 'They take in boys and send out confident young men, and they guide them through really well.' A few parents felt Stamford was undersold, but they're working on that, and a couple felt communication between the two schools in the sixth form could be improved.

Old boys include General Sir Mike Jackson, former Chief of the General Staff, Nick Anstee, former Lord Mayor of the City of London, Colin Dexter (Inspector Morse), Iwan Thomas (Olympic athlete), golfer Mark James, conductor Sir Malcolm Sargent and Simon Hodgkinson (England rugby international).

Entrance: Entry is mainly at year 7, based on an entrance exam covering maths, English and verbal reasoning. The main feeder is Stamford Junior School, just under 50 per cent, with an automatic transfer; the remainder come from local primaries and preps. Forces families are well represented, as are farming families.

There's a smaller intake in year 9, based on performance or CE, and in the sixth form five GCSEs at grade B/6 or higher (internal and external) are required.

Exit: A handful (some 20 per cent) leaves after GCSEs – a couple to other sixth forms, usually boarding, a few to the local college for vocational courses. Most boys head to a Russell Group or other top universities. One to Oxbridge in 2017, and six medics (including one to Immanuel Kant Baltic Federal University, Russia). Popular are Durham, Newcastle, Loughborough, Leeds and Sheffield; one off to Sciences Po in Reims to reading international relations. Engineering, business and sciences slightly favoured but too many choices to judge. One or two into the Forces, the odd boy straight into employment, eg an engineering apprenticeship with Audi, another spending his gap year as a Deloitte scholar.

Money matters: Means-tested bursaries (up to full fees) and academic, sports and music scholarships, all funded by the school. A Stamford School boy could have a parent who is CEO of a multi-national company or be a postman in the town, a huge strength of the school. Many boys are second or even third generation pupils.

Remarks: Stamford is surrounded by some very big hitters – Uppingham, Oundle and Oakham spring to mind – so can be overlooked, as it doesn't seem to have the same kudos. But Stamford more than holds its own, academically and sportswise. It's a hidden gem but we doubt it's going to be hidden for much longer. It shouldn't be. Prosecco rather than champagne, but better value for money and preferred by many.

Uppingham School

High Street West, Uppingham, Rutland LE15 9QE

01572 822216 | admissions@uppingham.co.uk | www.uppingham.co.uk

Ages: 13–18

Pupils: 785; sixth form: 345; Boarders: 773 full

Day: £25,305 pa; Boarding: £36,150 pa

Headmaster: Since 2016, Dr Richard Maloney MA (theology at St Andrew's) PGCE (Cantab), early 40s, previously head of Bede's Senior School. An alumnus of Latymer Upper School, Dr Maloney began his career in West Yorkshire. In 1997, he became head of RS and, later, head of sixth, at Chigwell School, during which period he completed an MA at King's College, London. In 2006, he was appointed deputy headmaster of Sutton Valence. During his tenure there he became a PhD but left after three years to take up the Bede's headship – whilst still in his 30s. We described him at Bede's as 'A man of palpable energy – physical and intellectual – complemented by equal measures of compassion, dedication, ambition and vision'. He has transformed that school and become hot educational property.

He is married to Tracey, who runs an educational consultancy, and they have two children.

Academic matters: Although the emphasis is on holistic education, academic matters do not suffer. It was obvious from talking to pupils that teachers relish challenging the most able to get as far as they can. All abilities are making excellent progress and exam results are strong, but parents hastened to inform us that Uppingham is no academic hothouse, and compared the approach to education very favourable to what they see as the stressful academic day schools of Cambridge and London. In 2017, 48 per cent of A levels were at A or A* and nearly 80 per cent were at A* to B. At GCSE, 71 per cent A*-A/9-7 grades in 2017; this stays fairly steadily in the high 60s, low 70s year on year.

The school considers all subjects to be strong, pointing to outstanding results and large numbers taking both science and arts subjects at A level. Pupils enthuse about the history, religious studies and politics, but also approve of the various innovations that the stunning new science block has inspired, including the outdoor science classroom. The new labs are designed with one half for practical work and the other half for the theory – a great improvement to the traditional labs where students make notes between the gas taps and Bunsen burners. With 29 A level subjects on offer, there is a superb range. The post-16 curriculum is under close review but current view is that a combination of A levels, Pre-U, and the Extended Project will offer lots of stimulus for all in the sixth form. Average class size is 16, and nine in the sixth form. There is support for those with mild learning difficulties and those who need help with English language (at extra cost).

Games, options, the arts: You would expect a school that prides itself on its holistic education to provide a rich extracurricular offer and Uppingham doesn't disappoint. Facilities, which are also used by the local community, are outstanding – the biggest stage, the pupils informed us, of any school they had heard of, and drama is supported by fantastic teachers and professional technicians. Endless sports on offer and, pupils assure us, it is for everyone, not just the elite. One year 13 boy spoke with considerable enthusiasm about his engagement with a lowly rugby team. As well as 'major' sports there is a plethora of others – just as well, given that it is compulsory to do something.

Some houses are in the centre, minutes away from teaching areas, others are further out and have the advantage of more space – one boasting its own swimming pool

Music is outstanding – one parent said that all independent schools say their music is good, but at Uppingham it is really good. Everyone mentions whole school congregational singing in chapel. There are House Shouts in which everyone seems to get involved, and then highly selective choirs and orchestras for the specialists. These groups tour in the UK and overseas as well as having endless performance opportunities in school. Masterclasses given by eminent musicians are regular features. Recording studios, a radio station and music technology encourage those who aspire to find renown in more celebrity spheres, honing their acts along the way in the school Battle of the Bands.

Everyone does CCF, though there is an opt-out for older pupils, who can get involved in community service. Some help in local primary schools, including teaching a Latin programme; others visit

elderly people, ride with disabled people or take part in various overseas aid projects.

The art is vibrant and diverse – taking place in the Leonardo Centre, named after the Renaissance Man, the ultimate model for the Uppingham student.

Boarding: All but a tiny handful board. Everyone says it is a school for children who really want the full boarding experience – no flexi approach countenanced here to ease the way for those valuing their own 'me time'. There are separate girls' and boys' boarding houses spread over the small market town. Most are vertical – pupils from every age group – but there is also a sixth form girls' house, as more girls join the school at sixth form level. Some houses are in the centre, having the advantage of being minutes away from teaching areas, others are further out and have the advantage of more space – one boasting its own swimming pool. Prospective families are normally taken to see just a few of the houses, though you can see all 15 if you really want.

Music is outstanding – one parent said that all independent schools say their music is good, but at Uppingham it is really good

Boys' houses have around 50 pupils and girls' about 60. Each has a housemaster or mistress living there with their own family. There are resident tutors and a team of non-resident tutors attached to each house. Meals are taken in the house and house staff share the tables with the pupils. There is a rota of other staff circulating around the houses, so the students are very used to visitors.

Background and atmosphere: Uppingham is a boarding school with no half measures. Only a handful of pupils go home for the night – it is a school for those who want people around all the time and masses to do. 'Much too much, really,' said one boy who knew his AS results could have been a bit better if there weren't just such a brilliant amount going on all the time. However, one mother who spoke to us said that the houseparents have a close grip on this sort of problem and can usually sort things out early on.

When we dined at one house, the boys were completely charming – enthusiastic about everything at school and genuinely interested in their visitors. These are young people whose emotional intelligence is being unobtrusively developed on a daily basis. Separate girls' and boys' houses add to the individual flavour of each house. They can come to breakfast in their pyjamas and experience single sex norms as well as the hurly burly of co-ed in the classroom. Parents who had visited a number of houses before the children joined Uppingham said that every houseparent they met had credibility, and had proved to be inspirational.

With all the high quality activity on offer both in regulated and not regulated time, you would have to work very hard at being bored round here. Sixth formers have their own social centre, which is open once a term to other years, but most pupils are dashing from sports fields to drama studios to art rooms to music rehearsals, getting the most out of every minute.

Pastoral care, well-being and discipline: A lot of thought goes into settling in new pupils. They have a mentor in the year above and a sixth form mentor in their house. House staff make sure there is plenty going on at the weekends, so new pupils are quickly immersed in the busy life of the school. We got the sense that the staff all loved communal life, and their enthusiasm is infectious. Pupils all talked about their close friendships – 'My friends are always there for me and probably always will be,' said one year 13, starting to contemplate life beyond Uppingham.

There are school counsellors and a school psychotherapist, and all the pupils we spoke to felt there were plenty of staff to whom they could take any concerns. As part of the curriculum, there is health and social education that supports the usual

areas of teenage angst, with self-help techniques as well as information and advice. Sixth formers are trained to support the younger pupils.

There are very firm rules and sanctions about bullying, drugs, smoking and alcohol use. Spirits are taken more seriously than wine. Everyone knows the score, and where a pupil has fallen foul of the sanctions, parents have accepted the firm and clear way the school has dealt with the matter.

Pupils and parents: The large map in the registrar's office with its pins indicating where in the UK families come from shows, not surprisingly, a preponderance from the wealthy parts of the country – largely home counties, but there are plenty from the Midlands and the north too. Parents are mostly from the professional and business classes. A steady 12 to 15 per cent of boarders are from overseas. Parents like the real mix of nationalities. They also like the school's approach to the family. 'The school gives you the sense that it is the whole family joining the school; they really want us to get involved too.'

Pupils are aware of how fortunate they are. They are not taking all this for granted, and the ones we spoke to were determined to make the most of all their opportunities

The pupils are fully aware of the preconceptions that others have of them. 'But we are not arrogant,' they assure us. 'The school actively teaches us humility. We are confident, but when you are living with lots of different people and learning how to get on together, it tends to make you confident.' Parents say they are delighted with how Uppingham pupils turn out – they are engaging, personable, gregarious and go out into the world with enthusiasm and interest in other people.

Alumni include John Schlesinger, Stephen Fry, Rick Stein, Jenny Willott, Rowan Atkinson, John Suchet and Tim Melville-Ross.

Entrance: As you would expect, the admissions process is a very well-oiled machine. Many families start the process three years before the actually date of entry. It is all very welcoming and informative. Most join at 13+, but there is also a significant entry at 16+, particularly from girls who have been in a single sex environment. Most of these girls (typically 25-30 a year) are housed in the sixth form girls' house, The Lodge.

There is a pre-testing round at 11 (year 7) with papers in maths and English, an interview and references from current school. Places are then conditional on further tests in year 8, when pupils can sit common entrance (55 per cent average pass mark) or the school's own exam, consisting of maths and English with a further interview.

At sixth form level, there is a six GCSE at B/6 grade minimum requirement for everyone, but virtually all existing pupils get those. For those coming in from outside, there are also sixth form scholarship and non-scholarship exams, plus two interviews – a house one and an academic one.

Exit: Very few leave after GCSEs. In 2017, 10 to Oxbridge. Bristol, Newcastle, Oxford Brookes, Edinburgh, Durham and Exeter also popular. There is a good range of subjects, business, history, sciences, politics and international relations coming out top. The careers advice and particularly support with UCAS applications are highly regarded, with subject staff and house staff all contributing.

Money matters: A serious number of scholarships are awarded at both 13+ and 16+: music, art, DT, sport and all-rounder as well as academic. There is also a new sixth form science scholarship. Typically, in a year group of about 150, there will be 35 scholarships awarded.

There is also some means-tested bursary support available – the registrar says the approach is flexible to respond to the very individual needs of a family.

Remarks: Even though it is big and spreads throughout the small market town of Uppingham, everyone tells us the school has a homely feel. We know just what they mean – though it is probably Homes & Gardens homely rather than the average urban semi. It is a rather wonderful bubble, and feels a world away from the relatively close Midlands cities. Uppingham is charming English small market town, with its own theatres (owned and run by the school) and its own cafés and shops that the pupils wander round relatively freely. Parents and pupils love it.

We had some sense that by the time the pupils leave the school, they are hungry for the wider world, but that is a good thing. A sixth former who wanted to party hard might start to find it restricting, but the community feel is energising enough for most. The pupils are aware of how fortunate they are. They are not taking all this for granted, and the ones we spoke to were determined to make the most of all their wonderful opportunities. They were enthusiastic, curious and positive – as one would hope for from a liberal, holistic education. Will they change the world, lead the revolution? Probably not. Will they spread sweetness and light wherever they go? We think probably yes. Will they be responsible citizens of the world? Another yes.

UWC Atlantic College

35

St Donat's Castle, St Donat's, Llantwit Major, Vale of Glamorgan CF61 1WF

01446 799000 | studentenrolment@atlanticcollege.org | www.atlanticcollege.org

Ages: 15–19

Pupils: 378; Boarders: all full

£33,000 pa

Principal: Since April 2017, Peter Howe, previously head of college at UWC Maastricht in the Netherlands. Degree in accounting, finance and economics from Queen's University in Ontario and PhD in art and architectural history from University of Toronto. Had a brief stint in sales and marketing at Procter and Gamble before switching to teaching, and spent 13 years at Canadian universities. His UWC career began in 2005, as the IB coordinator and head of economics at the Italy-based UWC Adriatic. Later, he became the school's deputy head and director of studies and ultimately, its rettore (head of school), before moving to Maastricht in 2012.

Academic matters: Education starts with the IB but, like the battery-powered toy bunnies in those long ago TV ads, keeps on going long after other schools have ground to a halt, courtesy of the Diploma Programme, the compulsory, wrap-around co-curricular programme introduced in 2012.

Diploma extras take up a good 30 per cent of pupils' time, 'and probably more,' requiring the academic component of the IB (no picnic at the best of times) to be breezed through in just five mornings plus an afternoon in the classroom each week. Pupils choose one of four 'experiential' faculties, each big on the redemptive powers of active, selfless participation (very Kurt Hahn), that add to the IB's magnificent seven and tick off its creativity, action and service component en route.

There's outdoor (focus on those in peril on the seas – past pupil and teacher developed now best-selling RIB boat, then, combining brilliance and philanthropy in equal measure, selflessly donated patent to the RNLI); social justice (first hand encounters of a robust kind, including work with refugees and prisoners' families); global (everything from organising peace events to sharing a dorm with traditional enemies); and environmental, where commitment to sustainability is no light matter (students, who recycle everything, deeply miffed by college's failure to consult over green disposal of fittings following boarding house refurb).

It's education the immersive way, students picking a theme that interests them and following its thread through their studies – real world, practical applications dovetailing with academic side. Someone with an interest in Middle East might study Arabic, prepare an extended essay in world studies, help set up a project week in Jordan and, through this, 'understand the UWC mission in the way they choose to develop their strengths,' says head of curriculum.

At its best (which is much of the time) diploma activities feed back into lessons, making for a buzzy classroom atmosphere where passionate debate is a way of life. There's nothing like hearing about refugees' experiences then discussing them back at base to add bite to economics or geography lessons. 'Makes it much more interesting and stimulating. I think it affects their exam grades, too.' Worked wonders on inspectors too, who assumed students leading lessons (spreading the word to peers in other diploma facilities is part of the syllabus) were teachers and had graded them outstanding before misunderstanding pointed out.

Structure won't be for everyone, particularly those with league-leaping performance as sole aspiration. College holds trenchant views on results, which are 'meaningless after a few years. It's the outcome that is important. We measure the success in the effect our students have on the world'. Average IB score of 35 in 2016, but school says it's 'not publishing 2017 IB results'.

Hot spots include spectacular languages (nine mother tongue or foreign options and a further 21, including Khmer, Mongolian and Welsh, as self-taught subjects). Maths and science are also very strong, say students – big clue to expectations the vast university physics textbook toted with pride by first year student.

Generous with their time (lots of one-to-one sessions in final run up to IB exams), teachers praised for effective problem-spotting system that kicks in early

With run of the mill IB students elsewhere already reckoned to be worked more intensively than A level counterparts, it's useful to arrive with work ethic fully formed and be good with stress, say students, who rapidly acquire super-efficient learning techniques.

Pre-diploma programme sees some 20 15-16 year olds who aren't yet ready for full-on IB experience doing one year IGCSE course (26 per cent A*/As in 2016) alongside co-curricular activities. This programme will not be offered after 2017.

In the main, it's attitude of mind that determines student suitability. 'Not for the weak-hearted,' thought one. Just as true for teachers, many with similar international background. Total conversion to college philosophy the norm and few move back to conventional posts afterwards. Once recruited, becomes a forever post, others paling into comparison. 'You're spoiled for life', thought one, while college newsletter praised students' freedom to 'chase academic hares into the undergrowth of learning [...] keeping an eye on the syllabus and sometimes even a blind eye'.

Generous with their time (lots of impromptu one-to-one sessions were under way in final run up to IB exams), teachers praised for effective problem-spotting system that kicks in early, tutors the first point of call, subject specialists alerted and involved as necessary.

Other areas (notably EAL, learning needs, gifted and talented), formerly a bit piecemeal but are having policies written and in some cases coordinators, including SENCo, appointed. Essential, given some pupils' patchy educational history and/or imperfect grasp of English (no minimum language requirement for EU students). Lack of screening during committee-based recruitment system also means learning needs (mostly mild Asperger's, SpLD and ADHD) will only be picked up on arrival, though good to see real commitment to disabled access. Wheelchair access determinedly provided wherever possible, whole classes relocated if necessary when it isn't.

Overall, exceptionally demanding curriculum covers emotional, intellectual and practical terrain that many adults would find hard going. Though something you'd hesitate to impose elsewhere, impressively mature bunch here take it in their stride. Only student doubt was perception that college is putting greater focus on IB scores. College is adamant this isn't the case.

Games, options, the arts: Whichever diploma faculty they choose, students are unlikely to spend much time sitting on their hands, all areas being long on activity. Derring-do comes with the territory no matter what the gradient, acquisition of skills in graceful failure as important as trappings of success (fallibility reckoned by Kurt Hahn to be essential part of the learning process). As a result, there isn't much pupils here would say no to, from consorting with top scientists and politicians at climate change summit in Fiji to qualifying as a music therapist.

Outdoor faculty is the most obviously action-packed of the bunch. Students join either aquatic water activities team (kayaking and surfing on offer but highlight lifeboat training at college's own RNLI station) or sign up to Terra Firma, which features mountain walking, navigation, emergency first aid and climbing (Brecon Beacons, a few miles inland, the venue for unlimited yomping).

Setting – in 800-year-old castle by the sea – is out of this world and much appreciated by production companies (has featured in Dr Who)

While physical activity is compulsory, organised sport isn't. Stems from character building the Kurt Hahn way, which almost heretically relegates organised games to an 'important but not predominant' position in the hierarchy. The newly built 'Moondance' gym and sports hall is a 'purpose-built and fully equipped facility with a student social centre to complement a student wellbeing agenda.'

What happens and whether it happens at all is largely down to pupils. Though specialist coaches visit (pupils seemed slightly hazy about the details), there's no head of sport and activities vary from year to year depending on each cohort's enthusiasms. As a result, vast games field is intermittently used. Only sound on a fine spring afternoon was the bleating of newborn lambs from on-site farm. Anyone expecting pitches groaning with glory-seeking team endeavours may well be in for a bit of a shock.

Similarly, though IB studies are efficiently catered for with public showcases including drama reviews and weekly music recitals, there's not much in the way of large scale musical or dramatic endeavours.

Boarding: Seven boarding houses. Their distinctive characters, reflected in not always flattering secret student nicknames (we know what they are, too, but had to promise not to tell), are home to just under 50 pupils each. Pastoral care efficiently provided by brace of well-liked houseparents. Facilities are 'simple', says college, and they're not wrong. Perfectly acceptable though, with extensive communal drying rooms and welly racks (essential given climate) and enough single showers to ensure sufficient privacy for those who find communal versions problematic. Pre-diploma pupils have their own house.

There's the odd idiosyncrasy when it comes to equipment – irons are allowed in dorms, kettles are not (one boarding house has recently been rebuilt following a fire). But this is outweighed by impressive, all-round sensitivity, subtle pooling of kitchen equipment in mixed common rooms avoiding distinctions between haves and have-nots, daily deliveries of communal food essentials.

Background and atmosphere: For mood and idealism, think educational version of Star Trek, the crew's goal less about finding 'strange new worlds' than improving the one they're in, one dilithium crystal at a time. While hippies might give peace a chance by putting flowers in gun barrels, Hahn's solution to unify Cold War ridden world of the 1960s and ward off what he saw as the physical and moral decline of the young was to found a school (two, if you count Gordonstoun, many more if you allow Round Square schools).

Here, the aim was to create a harmonious blend of nations and cultures, pairing opposites of every sort, oppressors and oppressed, poor and rich, who by living and studying together would develop shared outlook and common purpose (though took until 1967 before they got round to adding girls).

College remains a one-off in the UK and was the first of what is now 12-strong United World Colleges international movement. Its niche status and relatively low profile (even amongst heads, let alone the average parent) is, however, in inverse proportion to behind the scenes clout. Former students are embedded in some of the most powerful organisations and political administrations in the world, from the Chinese and US governments to top banks, providing under the radar alternative to conventional old boys' (and girls') network and one with huge clout.

Setting – in 800-year-old castle by the sea – is out of this world and much appreciated by production companies (has featured in Dr Who). In addition to as many corkscrewing staircases as you can shake a medieval flail at, castle interior features terrific library, galleried and home to municipal quantities of books including Harry Potter (a college favourite) in assorted translations.

Lessons in many cases a perfect match for surroundings. History lessons compete with hard to improve vistas through arrow slits to wooded hill

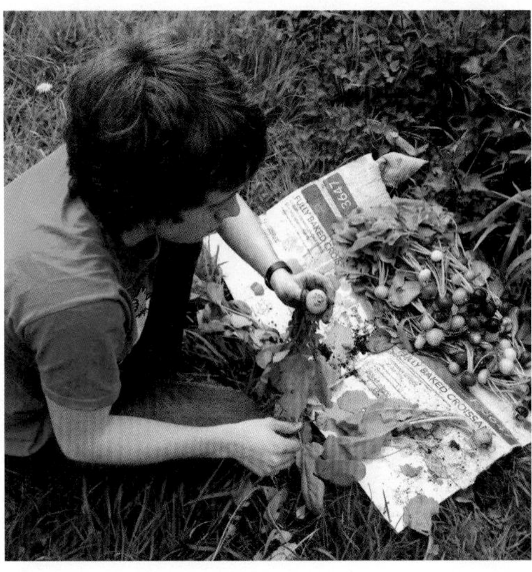

beyond, art and music located in nicely converted stable block. Other subjects are taught in three 1970s teaching blocks (science and maths, perhaps appropriately, in crumbliest and flakiest), all apparently constructed, together with admin centre, by embittered town planner having a bad day and featuring urban-style mini-underpass. Recent developments as described (in somewhat corporate language) by the school include The Agatha Christie Library, a 'modern resource and IT centre, fit for purpose for the 21st century', the Great Hall, a 'fully-resourced meeting and conference facility in the heart of St Donat's Castle to support our education programme' and The Seafront, 'refurbished accommodation and teaching areas to provide a centre for outdoor activity courses, and for schools and community groups.'

With just one communal TV to its name, a climate that's far from tropical and the nearest cinema nine miles away by land (or 13 if teamed with a bracing swim across the Bristol Channel), this is a place that needs decent social events more than most. Until recently, though, it wasn't getting them, felt pupil. Far better now, with weekly disco (noise levels bravely borne by principal, who lives opposite), boarding houses charged with weekend event organisation, and much more to do.

The sense of being a body apart is reinforced by two-term structure that follows the beat of the IB drum – with the result that pupils only have four days off between January and May and are then off on holiday until early August when second year pupils arrive back for a week's bonding before new intake turns up.

Policy of picking room-mates for differences, the more apparently irreconcilable the better. 'We would always put Israelis and Palestinians together'

Physical apartness makes it something of unknown quantity within the local community. 'Out of my league,' thought one local. 'Feels exclusive – if you can afford for your kids to go there, you're doing well'. No wonder the college is contemplating a hearts, minds and meters job to get locals, starting with taxi drivers, who are probably the college's most frequent visitors, on side.

Pastoral care, well-being and discipline: New arrivals are paired with 'excellent' buddies, big on tea and sympathy (favour returned when it comes to exam time). Their first task is probably to settle nerves after meeting and greeting ceremony, where they're drummed in with chorus of pots and pans pillaged from common rooms by second years ('it leaves terrible dents', said one pupil, who as kitchen monitor was charged with subsequent search and rescue mission).

With full boarding the only option (though parents can come and stay nearby at beginning and ends of term), inner core of steel probably helps, given policy of picking room-mates for differences, the more apparently irreconcilable the better. 'We would always put Israelis and Palestinians together'; college is spearheading drive to recruit Syrians from both sides of current conflict.

Pupils aren't just in favour of approach but drawn to college because of it. Beliefs that elsewhere would be on collision course (there's a strong LGBT movement, for example) spark enduring friendships and sometimes more, with potential for heartache when relationships breach cultural barriers.

Whether deliberately or by chance, student bonds are well and truly cemented by decision to involve them in the nuts and bolts of college operations. Open book policy on everything from finances to rebuilding ensures that student voice isn't merely heard but is a force to be reckoned with, from spontaneous orations in assembly on whatever issues take their fancy, college-related or otherwise (polemic following death of Mrs Thatcher made for edgy listening) to indignation over any perceived high-handedness. 'If they give us a voice, that's what they have to expect', said one.

Impressive maturity means that nobody sweats the small stuff. Courtesy on both sides is a given, teachers generally liked (only one got thumbs down) and while big issues go to the wire, there are minimal rules elsewhere, nous and good sense taken as read. 'We don't need a rule about using phones in lessons when it would clearly be rude', a pupil told us.

Pupils and parents: Easy to gush over pupils' self-assurance and intelligence which carries all before it (just one non-show in recent memory, pupil so overcome with nerves that unable to board the plane). A sassy bunch, it's no surprise that many have persuaded their parents that this is the place to be and in one case at least secured the sponsorship to pay the fees.

Though fees are 'low compared to other top boarding schools', says college, they are still high enough to skew social mix towards luxury ingredients rather than salt of the earth. Or in UWC words, 'similar people simply born in different places'. A pupil said that this 'isn't the place for the materialistic or those who believe the world can get better with money alone'. Parent philanthropy is a way of life, one family funding not only their own child but three others, too. Similar acts of generosity both widespread and long term.

Five-strong development department works with alumni who include King of the Netherlands, chairman of Shell and vice-president of European Bank to get that giving feeling early. And give they do. Vocal and passionate espousal of college and ideals often continues for life, endorsements from everyone from Nelson Mandela to Queen Noor of Jordan setting the tone. It's resulting in growing numbers from the poorest and most war-torn regions of earth.

Some local recruitment, extending to deprived Liverpool, Birmingham and Valleys schools, requires a bit of careful eggshell treading to avoid Orphan Annie connotations, college raising grateful poor to a life of privilege. So far so good.

Entrance: 'The world is our catchment area', says college (90 nationalities currently). Makes a refreshing change from same old distance from home criteria, but downside is labyrinthine admissions process requiring minotaur-seeking levels of persistence (though no string). Think Oxbridge inter-college pupil swapsies at admissions time, add international dimension requiring agreement between parents, students and UWC staff who may all be on different continents, and it's not surprising that entrance process is officially badged as 'extremely complicated'. On the surface it's highly competitive, too, with nearly 100 nations jostling for places, just 20 available for UK nationals and a further 17 places in other UWC colleges.

Would-be pupils submit applications either to one of 140 UWC national committees, often staffed by alumni, or direct to colleges – specific requirements as individual as they are. Though they can express college preferences, they're assumed to be signing up to UWC aims rather than a location, and so could end up being offered a place somewhere completely different. Loving care is advised to ensure that focus on community work and support for UWC ideals shine through. Also useful to ensure academic endorsement (no GCSE minimum grades specified, every application considered on merit) is from teacher '... who supports the idea of you going to a UWC'. (Our tip: use the word 'mission' at least once.)

Shortlisted UK candidates have an overnight stay at the castle, followed by informal 20-minute interview with committee members, alumni and, unusually, former rather than current teachers. Final decision communicated around three weeks later (though can take longer). Whole process is an excellent Kurt Hahn-style challenge and, if you meet the age criteria (students normally start aged 16 or 17, though there's some flexibility), there's the chance to do it all over again the following year.

Exit: It's off to better things not just for pupils, but with 70 per cent ultimately ending up in humanitarian-linked careers, for the world as a whole. While US admissions tutors zoom in early, like dealers at a jumble sale before the doors open to the general punters, other top unis aren't far behind.

Pupils are impressively mature. Courtesy on both sides is a given, teachers generally liked and while big issues go to the wire, there are minimal rules elsewhere. Nous and good sense taken as read. 'We don't need a rule about using phones in lessons when it would clearly be rude'

US is the most popular university destination overall with close to 40 per cent of places (college doesn't train students to take SATs, but is a test centre), followed by UK (28 per cent – vast majority to Russell Group members, including three to Oxbridge and two to study medicine in 2017) then Canada and Europe, with a few to Asia. Recent destinations include Harvard, Cambridge, Brown, MIT, Yale, Princeton, UCL, Sherbrooke and Cornell.

Around 18 per cent take a gap year or go off to complete national service. Courses many and various. A pupil we spoke to hoped to major in physics with laudable aim of investigating travel across vacuums in outer space.

Money matters: Admissions process supported by large fundraising and development department working overtime to bring in the dosh. Latest initiative themed to college's 50th anniversary (think of a number, any number, with a 50 in it and hand it over) is generating over £2 million a year, almost all used to fund scholarships. Other countries chip in, too (Norwegian government funds 10 of its own students, for example). In all, over 55 per cent of students have some sort of financial support.

Remarks: Once a glorious experiment, still out on a limb (and, we suspect, in no hurry to shed iconoclastic status), Atlantic College provides an education as remarkable as the feisty, impassioned students it attracts. The ticking of admin boxes may annoy, but it's a necessary evil that parents will welcome. Its location may be isolated but its perspective, genuinely global, is anything but. Just don't expect a picnic by the sea.

Warwick School

36

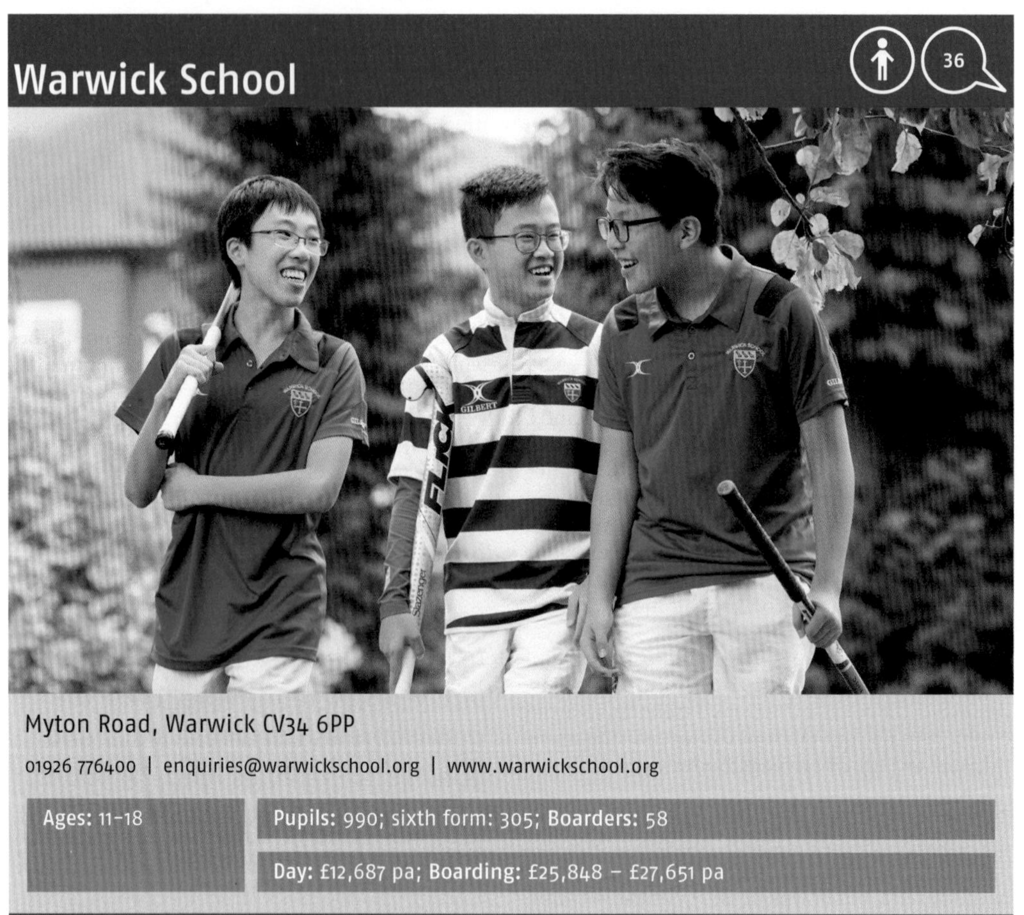

Myton Road, Warwick CV34 6PP

01926 776400 | enquiries@warwickschool.org | www.warwickschool.org

Ages: 11–18

Pupils: 990; sixth form: 305; **Boarders:** 58

Day: £12,687 pa; **Boarding:** £25,848 – £27,651 pa

Head master: Since 2013, Mr Augustus (Gus) Lock, MA Oxon (late 30s). Educated at Haberdashers' Aske's School, Elstree, he read ancient and modern history at Oxford. First teaching post was at The Manchester Grammar School, thence to Merchant Taylors' School in Northwood, where he became head of middle school and met and married Alison (a French and Italian teacher). Mr Lock then moved to Warwick School, where he served as deputy head before taking on the headship. Gus and Alison have three young children, two of whom attend Warwick Prep School.

Leaving in July 2018 to head his alma mater, Haberdashers' Aske's Boys. His successor will be Dr Deneal Smith, currently under master (senior deputy head) at Westminster School. A Cambridge graduate with a first class degree in mathematics and astrophysics, and a PhD in observational astronomy, he began his teaching career at Winchester College before becoming head of sixth form and then director of studies at Magdalen College School, Oxford.

Academic matters: It is clear that academic work is a top priority and taken seriously by most of the boys. The pace is vigorous and demanding – for pupils and staff alike – and the overall results are impressive. When we asked if there was any truth in the rumour that Warwick was an exam factory, one boy replied, 'Well, if it is, I haven't noticed it. There is lots of work but you expect that. You just get on with it.' One ex-teacher at Warwick confirmed that the pace was demanding. That word 'pace' crops up a lot – Warwick is a very busy school with lots to offer. It may be a day school but, in the words of another boy, 'it never seems to close. With all the extracurricular activities on offer, a 12 hour day starting at 7.30am is not that unusual.' League table junkies can pore over the statistics, salivating at the various permutations, but here's a quick fix: of the 27 subjects on offer for A level, maths, economics, physics, chemistry, biology and politics account for some 250 entries; English, history, French and Spanish, 50. Just an observation but it does reveal the breadth of subjects on offer and the strengths of scientific subjects in the sixth form. How well they do overall is confirmed by the consistently high percentage of A*-B at A level (95 per cent in 2017, and 57 per cent A*/A). GCSE results from 28 subjects are impressive too: in 2017, 78 per cent of papers were graded A*/A. This is clearly not a school where boys spend time during their first few years 'settling down and making friends' before starting to work seriously.

The facilities for teaching and learning are impressive. Foremost is the new science building of which the school is justifiably proud. Like most of the new buildings at Warwick, it is superbly designed, both aesthetically and functionally. From the moment you enter the large bright foyer, decorated with a fascinating creation stretching up through two floors like a curling spine, you are in a genuinely stimulating building. In this instance it is all about experiment, discovery and excitement. Each of the three floors is allocated to a science, with spacious laboratories designed in consultation with the teachers themselves. All the latest gizmos and terrific teaching to go with them. One huge laboratory is used for extended projects where budding Nobel laureates are joined by the no less budding girls from King's High and students from other local schools. Certainly no sign of science declining in popularity here – many boys go on to university to read science-based subjects. How some of them must pine for the excellence of the facilities at Warwick. But it's not just the scientists who are well served; we hear many reports of excellent teaching in other subjects too. The delightfully designed lecture theatre hosts talks embracing all disciplines from within and beyond the curriculum.

Musicians perform all over Europe (financial support given if necessary); recently four bands were awarded platinum, two golds and a silver at the National Concert Band Finals

If the heartbeat of real education is a library, Warwick is very healthy. The library is housed in The Masefield Centre, named after an old boy, charmingly described to us by a current pupil as 'some kind of a poet, I believe.' A superb set-up with over 20,000 books, it is an invaluable centre for reference resources and information files as well as CDs, DVDs and now e-books. The school even has e-readers to lend out. The wonderfully enthusiastic librarian told us that the issue of books had recently risen by 30 per cent, and inviting pamphlets, one with an encouraging foreword from the headmaster, explain and exhort. Those pupils we spoke to genuinely appreciated the facility.

Everyone entering the school is screened for dyslexia and those with learning difficulties receive help from the 'very good' learning support team. Curriculum support is also available to those who encounter academic difficulties.

Games, options, the arts: Naturally sport plays an important part. However, this is not a hearty school where prizes and recognition are given only to games players. Colours are awarded for music and drama, for instance, and one boy we spoke to, a confessed non-sportsman, said he didn't feel an outcast in any way. 'There are plenty of opportunities for taking exercise. In fact I'm almost spoilt for choice.' Nevertheless, the ethos that permeates the school – 'if you're going to do something, do it to the best of your ability' – is much in evidence on the games field. In the winter term, for example, over 20 rugby teams could be turning out on a Saturday afternoon. The 1st XV has a very strong fixture list and is renowned for its prowess, but the great thing is that everyone who wants to has a good chance of playing in a team. However, 'it's not all about rugby,' as somebody once said. In addition there is hockey, cricket, swimming, tennis, cross-country, athletics, rowing, canoeing, clay pigeon shooting: you name it. No wonder the boy who didn't like rugby didn't feel left out. Facilities are excellent with a top rate swimming pool (they have been national schools water polo champions more than once), squash courts, tennis courts, a superb sports hall, including an indoor hockey pitch, and games fields that seem to stretch on for ever. A recent cricket tour to Sri Lanka, golf to Spain and rugby to Ireland are just some of the opportunities to play abroad; boys who cannot afford to go are supported financially.

Music is excellent (ask for a copy of their DVD) and generally regarded as cool. Harmony maintained by a charismatic director with a wonderful team of teachers, most of whom are concert players themselves. In a recent and highly successful initiative, new boys were lent an instrument of their choice and given free tuition for a year; the enthusiastic take-up means the music department now has 720 lessons a week to organise. Five orchestras, three wind bands, three jazz bands, rock groups, quartets and much more. Huge programme of concerts and the chapel choir sings every Sunday morning during term; local parents, old boys, friends of the school and boarders attend. The musicians perform all over Europe (as with sports tours, financial support given if necessary) and recently four bands were awarded platinum, two golds and a silver at the National Concert Band Finals – the Little Big Band got a platinum award for the third consecutive year and as a result was presented with a consistent achievement certificate.

Proximity to Stratford may account for the school's high achievements in drama. The superb Bridge House Theatre is kitted out to professional standards with proper lighting and sound equipment, adjustable stage and seating arrangements for 300 people and musicians; it is used by community theatre groups as well as for school productions. A number of boys have taken small parts at the RSC; recently a year 9 pupil played Gershom, first born son of Moses, in Exodus, and a few go on to take theatre studies at A level. One ecstatic mother told us of the huge encouragement given to her young son when he was given a demanding role. 'It boosted his confidence right across the board,' she said. Warwick productions have won awards at the National Student Drama Festival, the only school to have done so. There are large scale drama productions every term as well as pupil led plays, many shared with girls from King's High.

School's aims may be serious and pursued with determination but there is an underlying sense of well-being and community which extends to the town

Art and DT very good. All pupils have a double period of art and design a week for their first three years and can then go on to GCSE and beyond.

Astonishing range of clubs and societies to try – debating, scuba diving, robotics (UK champions several years running). Boys can also sign up for D of E, Young Enterprise and CCF. Wonderful opportunities enthusiastically seized. Exam factory, forsooth.

Boarding: Upstairs from chapel in the old building is a little corner of Asia where the 50+ Chinese boys in the sixth form live with the housemaster, a resident tutor and a matron. Boarding is available from year 9. Warwick has been taking Chinese students for many years now and those we chatted to seemed very happy and proud to be there. Activities sensitively arranged to reflect both boys' cultural background and traditional British life – there's Autumn Moon Festival and bonfire night; Christmas and Chinese New Year. Trips, many suggested by boarders' council, include photographers' visit to London and football-themed visit to Manchester, taking in United game.

Background and atmosphere: The gates to the main entrance hint at the tradition of the school. In addition to the Tudor Rose and the school's coat of arms depicting, significantly, the Warwickshire bear without chains, you can read the dates 914, 1545 and 1958. These refer to the traditional dates for the founding of the school by Edward the Confessor, its reinstatement by Henry VIII and the visit of the Queen Mother when the school was once more in the ascendant after a period in the doldrums. From a succession of sites in the town the school moved out to its present position beside the Avon in 1879. The neo-Tudor building with lovely oriel windows is typical of 19th century public school architecture, though to some, apparently, the colour of the brick is reminiscent of a hospital. A fascinating archive room with old photographs of school groups and haunting pictures of teams from 1914, testifies to the pride the school takes in its past. After all, isn't this one of the oldest boys' schools in the country, nay, the world?

The current site is a mixture of old and new buildings, increasingly dominated by the new, close but not jostling. Always an interesting insight into a school is to ask for directions and note the response; those boys we asked were uniformly helpful and charming, courtesy and good manners are the norm here. One new boy told us not to worry; 'Just ask,' he said, 'you can't go far wrong.' He spoke with feeling of the help he had received on arrival. All schools trumpet 'the excellent relationships between pupils and staff'; unobtrusively and naturally, this school demonstrates it. We witnessed a number of conversations between staff and boys and were struck by the obvious mutual respect and friendliness between them.

The school's aims may be serious and pursued with determination but there is an underlying sense of well-being and community which extends to the town; the civilised behaviour of the boys was acknowledged by the residents to whom we spoke. Sixth formers are allowed, with permission, to have lunch in town; so are senior girls from King's High. 'What we almost take for granted,' said one elderly resident, 'is that there is no arrogance about them. No swaggering and showing off. Not like those public school kids.' An interesting observation. Much is done for charity, an excellent way of combining community spirit and awareness of those less fortunate. Along with girls from King's High, teams have twice swum the Channel. According to the records the boys' team was the 50th ever two-way swim; the 13th ever successful swim by any UK team and the first by a boys' school team.

Proximity to Stratford may account for the school's high achievements in drama

Impressive chapel with college seating where services take place most days of the week, and new 1,000 seater Warwick Hall for assemblies etc. Plans afoot to move King's High out to a new building on the Warwick School campus, with shared sixth form centre.

Pastoral care, well-being and discipline: Typical of the caring efficiency of the school is the trouble it takes to welcome new boys and blend them in.

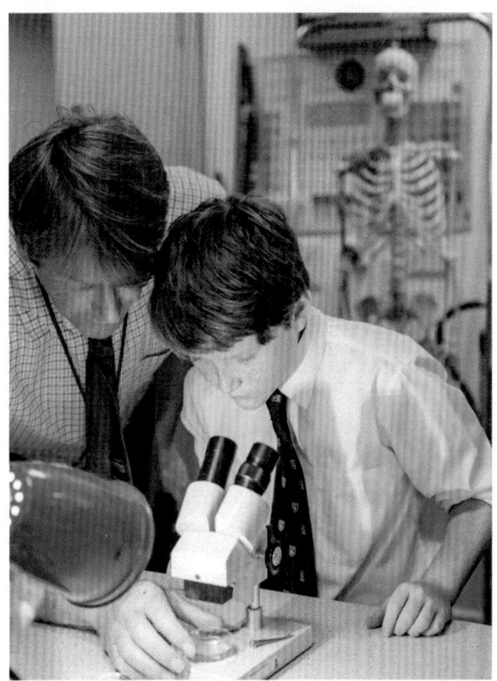

There are unobtrusive but clearly delineated policies to ensure 'there is always someone to pick us up' and the welcome package, is helpful, informative and encouraging. The effortlessly friendly atmosphere that pervades is, perhaps, because boys know where they stand (a phrase oft repeated when we asked). Prefects, selected by peers and staff, regard it as one of their prime functions to ensure boys are happily integrated and that consideration for others is maintained. Rules and guidelines are clear and thorough, even down to expectations of behaviour in the classroom; uniforms are smartly worn. One parent, talking about a boy who had been excluded – a rare event by all accounts – spoke of the trouble the school had gone to ensure the boy was well established in his next school. 'They really do care about the individual, but however friendly, they are strict about implementing the rules.' 'We know what is required of us. Mostly it's common sense,' a senior boy told us. 'Firm but fair.' No-one – boys or staff – claimed that bullying could never happen here, but parents we spoke to said it was quickly and sensitively dealt with. 'Staff are very approachable and understandable,' more than one boy told us.

Pupils and parents: Warwick has a large catchment area, a result not only of its excellent transport links but also the determination of parents and boys to make the effort. By bus, by train, by car, they come; from as far afield as Oxfordshire and Northamptonshire. Just under half the year's intake comes from the junior school and others from local primary schools and nearby prep schools. This is not a toff school; parents come from a broad cross-section of society, mostly professional middle classes, and thanks to the availability of bursaries many who might otherwise not be able to afford it do send their boys. The head and governors plan to raise funds and offer more.

Eclectic is the word that springs to mind when considering notable old boys. Currently there are two MPs, Iain Pears the novelist; Marc Elliott of East Enders; Christian Horner, Red Bull motor racing; Michael Billington, theatre critic; an Italian rugby international, an Australian rugby international, an England Sevens player and, from the ranks of the departed, the poet John Masefield. More evidence of breadth.

Entrance: The school is selective and competition is strong. It's not just the strongest academics who are awarded places; lively, quirky boys who can keep pace and bring with them special talents will be given consideration. Entry points are 11 and 13. Details of the examinations are on the website and follow the usual pattern. For entry to sixth form at least five B/6 grades with A grades needed in some subjects to be studied at A level.

Exit: Most – about 85 per cent – of boys stay on to do their A levels (others join) and nearly all go on to university. As well as purely academic subjects eg maths, classics, English, history, PPE, recent leavers have gone on to read marine vertebrate zoology, management with entrepreneurship, forensic science and architecture. Six to Oxbridge in 2017, plus five medics and three vets. Popular destinations include Birmingham, Durham, Leeds, Nottingham, UCL and Loughborough.

Money matters: The school is fortunate in benefiting from a number of ancient charities, some specifically aimed at boys living in the town of Warwick. Scholarships are offered in music and academics but not for sport. About a quarter of boys in the school are assisted financially.

Remarks: This is a winning school and achieves success right across the board. 'I don't know how we do it,' a boy told us in genuine amazement; 'there must be some reason for it.' There are plenty of reasons why this is such an excellent school although, like all good schools, it won't suit everyone. But for those seeking a day school that offers more excellent facilities and opportunities than many boarding schools; for those who are possessed of energy, stamina and self-discipline; above all, for those who can match the pace and plunge in, this might very well be the school. Not a school for drifting in, a school for striking out through the waves. Even across the Channel.

Winchester House School
37
44 High Street, Brackley, Northamptonshire NN13 7AZ
01280 702483 | registrar@winchester-house.org | www.winchester-house.org
Ages: 3–13 (boarders from year 3)
Pupils: 283; Boarders: 24 weekly, 62 flexi
Day: £10,800 – £19,035 pa; Boarding: £24,090 pa

Head: Since 2014, Emma Goldsmith (40s). Born and educated in Durham before reading English at Manchester. Landed first teaching job at Oakham where she threw herself into coaching netball, D of E: 'The last thing in the world I wanted to be was a teacher,' she says, 'but from that point on, I was committed to boarding schools.' Later recruited to help set up sixth form girls' boarding at Rugby and whilst there visited Bloxham School for a sports fixture. She loved it and was recruited to introduce girls and to manage the transition to co-ed, including setting up the first girls' boarding house, rising to deputy head.

Both of her children attended Winchester House, and she was asked to join the board of governors, so approached the headship 'from a unique position.' 'Bowled over by the quality of teaching and level of dedication and commitment of staff.' Focuses on every child leaving with a 'tool kit' for success in their future school. Parents approve, and describe her as the kind of person they would want running their business, as their best friend or their sister: 'She's fantastic,' they say. 'She is everywhere and has time for everyone...which has stopped all the tittle tattle because you can ask her anything.'

Warm and attractive, 'a brilliant communicator,' in the words of one happy parent, with a gentle humour (happily swapped places with a pupil for Comic Relief day) – and the chicest office we've ever seen. Still teaches year 7 English and 'occasionally' umpires netball matches, reads stories in pre-prep and on the odd occasion serves lunch. Children attend Bloxham, where husband is a teacher.

Entrance: Non-selective into pre-prep with automatic entry to prep. All assessed prior to entry into year 3 and above to identify learning needs.

Pupils mainly local (within 10 miles) with those joining after pre-prep mainly either from families moving out of London or from local state primaries and pre-preps. Strong old school, rather than aspirational, bias. Lots of former pupils in parent cohort. Some year groups oversubscribed.

Exit: The school prides itself on sending its pupils to a broad range of destinations. Marlborough, Oundle, Radley, Rugby, St Edward's and Stowe to name but a few current favourites. Popular day choices are Magdalen College School, Warwick and Headington. The 2017 leavers gained 17 scholarships to some of the top schools in the country in all the disciplines – academic, sport, drama, computing and art – but particularly sport.

Strong focus on 'right school, right child'. Conversations regarding moving on start in year 5, with 100 per cent heading off to their first choice school.

Remarks: Set in a former hunting lodge approached directly from the charming village high street through grand wrought iron gates, opening into a Tardis-like 18 acre campus, school sits astride a small country road which separates the pre-prep from the main prep school. Delightful pre-prep setting where classes are taught in large, bright classrooms with every possible millimetre of space adorned with creative offerings and the ceilings festooned with bunting and mobiles. Seamless transition for the youngest from on-site nursery, housed in a light and spacious recent extension. Years 3 and 4 housed in own building, with much evidence of the 'creative curriculum' followed on display.

Traditional – makes no bones about its boarding culture and preparation for public school

Good facilities across the board – many secondary schools would envy the enormous sports hall and new full-sized Astroturf. A lovely outdoor pool (although parents would like it used more) and cricket nets sit among the manicured lawns of the walled garden with the main playing fields across the road. Each year group has its own play area – some with super modern equipment and all with new, rainbow striped 'buddy benches.' The real magic of Winchester House, however, is in its enchanting and unique features: a secret garden tucked through a tiny archway, where year 8s are allowed to 'hang out' and lower years tend allotments and sit around camp fires; a beautifully paneled dining room where lunch is served family-style by teaching staff; tongue in cheek rules on the walls of the girls' boarding house (our favourites: no whining, laugh a lot and break the rules...sometimes) and vibrant works of art created collectively by visiting artists and pupils.

Fully co-educational (girls first introduced in the 80s), with a charming cohort of pupils who mix easily together and come across as children enjoying being just that – no ties, lots of untucked shirts and not a hiked up skirt or gelled quiff in sight. Our lunchtime hosts were bright-eyed, chatty and full of the joys of boarding – quite something for 11 year old boys. A traditional vibe prevails and school makes no bones about its boarding culture and preparation for public school, but it's by no means stuck in the dark ages. Technology is up to date (the ICT room recently upgraded) and the curriculum strikes an excellent balance of remaining traditional whilst moving with the times. The innovative 'creative curriculum' followed in the lower part of the school is well established and revered by staff and pupils alike – head speaks passionately about its execution: staff burying artefacts to be found by children with metal detectors (Romans) and children arriving at school to find snowy footsteps leading to their classrooms which were draped in fur throws (Frozen Worlds).

Science a huge strength with all three sciences taught separately by specialist teaching staff through 'as much practical work as we can manage,' according to the physics teacher. Outstanding computing, too – our year 8 guide lost us totally in a conversation about coding, but her enthusiasm and knowledge was clear to see. Pupils we spoke to unanimously voted history their favourite subject, thanks to the inspirational young teacher. French from reception by native speakers ('they only talk to children in French,' says head), Spanish from year 5, Latin from year 6 and Greek from year 7. Setting

Art department focuses on 'much more than just drawing,' with visiting artists offering masterclasses

from year 3 in maths and English, when pupils start to move between teachers, leading to entirely specialist teaching from year 5.

All screened on arrival for SEN to identify areas for either support or extension. Dedicated SENCo 'aims for as little withdrawal from the classroom as possible,' with small groups to 'boost' performance where needed, although those with greatest need withdrawn from Latin to receive extra support. Can accommodate mild to moderate dyslexia and dyscalculia and mild ASD.

A school alive with the sound of music – 'we're very much a singing school,' says head and parents concur, describing the termly concerts in glowing terms. With around three-quarters of all pupils playing an instrument, it's music for all with choirs (both auditioned and otherwise), bands and ensembles aplenty for musicians of all levels. Performance is 'one of the key aspects of the school,' says head, but 'you don't have to be brilliant to perform – we're building pupils' confidence all the time.' Specialist taught drama on curriculum to year 8 and around 60 per cent take LAMDA activity, although parents would like to see more productions. Strong art department (recently upgraded) focuses on 'much more than just drawing,' says head, with visiting artists offering masterclasses on disciplines from woodcarving to animation.

Head says sports department is 'successful and ambitious,' but also clear to point out that they are keen their charges 'learn to fail.' Inclusive approach with everyone getting the opportunity to represent the school – sometimes with up to 10 teams each for boys and girls representing the school each week. Recent introduction of graduate gap year coaches keeps things lively for the children.

Pupils able to board from year 3, and some do, in one of two single sex boarding houses – boys upstairs in the main school building, girls in a purpose built block. Unsurprisingly, the girls' house with its cosy dorms, sleeping up to 10, has a homelier feel than the boys', although both are spacious and comfortable, with plenty of spaces for down time. Head says boarding 'really takes off' in years 7 and 8, with an 'all or nothing' approach for the oldest pupils who are required to board all week rather than occasionally as is allowed lower down the school, although there's no boarding on Saturday nights and Saturday school has now been abolished altogether for years 4 and below. Prep kept quite light and boarders have their own schedule of after-school activities, with all catering for both sexes. Boarders describe food as 'amazing' – and having sampled the kitchen's roast beef followed by banoffee pie, we can't disagree.

Awareness of pupils' pastoral needs dramatically stepped up under the present head. School's unique Learn to Lead programme encourages pupils to take risks and approach failure with a sense of humour to build emotional resilience, through expeditions and on-site activities. Recent appointment of retired staff member as 'well-being mentor' ensures pupils – who are well informed on the 'circle of support' within the school – have someone to turn to if things go wrong. Head's visibility and approachability also seen as having 'made school a friendlier place', particularly in keeping 'alpha' parents in check. Pupils in year 3 and above are each assigned a tutor who keeps a beady eye on their pastoral and academic well-being, stepping in to help them handle heavy workloads around exam time or making sure they keep up their sporting commitments when academics threaten to take over.

New, open approach to extracurricular (welcomed by parents, who say it was previously a bit 'cloak and dagger'), focuses on three pillars – creative, enriching and physical – to give balance and breadth. Importantly, activities on offer are now communicated clearly to parents. Many, such as squash, chess, gymnastics and debating are included in fees, with those such as skiing (at Milton Keynes) and golf charged as extra. For working parents, children are able to arrive at school from 8.10am with pre-prep children cared for until 4.45pm and from year 3 onwards until 6.30pm, when they can be collected having done activities, prep and eaten supper. Daily minibus services bring children to school from locations including Chipping Norton, Bloxham and South Newington.

Under the present head, Winchester House is one to watch. In the words of one year 8 parent: 'I wish my children were starting from the beginning now. In a few years' time, Winchester House will be one of the top preps in the country.'

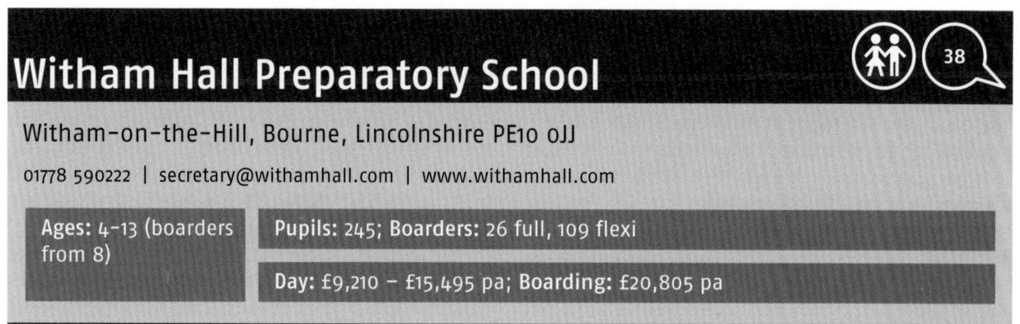

Witham Hall Preparatory School
38
Witham-on-the-Hill, Bourne, Lincolnshire PE10 0JJ
01778 590222 | secretary@withamhall.com | www.withamhall.com
Ages: 4-13 (boarders from 8)
Pupils: 245; Boarders: 26 full, 109 flexi
Day: £9,210 – £15,495 pa; Boarding: £20,805 pa

Headmaster: Since 2009, Charles Welch (40s). Studied PE and geography at Exeter. From a farming background and always expected to return to the farm. Sport took over and decided that teaching was for him. Started in a small school in Yorkshire, developed sport there and told to move on (in the nicest way) as had done all he could before taking over as director of sport at Oakham, his alma mater. His appointment coincided with that of new head Tony Little; 'we thought the same way and he became a bit of a mentor.' Took the boys' rugby to Twickenham, and won, and girls' hockey soared. 'I love targets and had achieved what I wanted at Oakham.' He met his wife at the school and they looked for a prep school that wanted a husband and wife team, and came to Witham in 2009. 'We wanted a very good school to make great.'

Tall and imposing, he's a highly visible figure around the school. Well liked by parents and pupils alike. 'He wants the best for the children.' Another parent said, 'Mr and Mrs Welch are lovely and do the best they can. Keeping everyone happy must be tricky at times – I wouldn't want his job – but he does it excellently and efficiently.' Parents perceive them as a team, Mrs Welch highly thought of head of boarding who deals with pastoral care, often counselling parents as well. 'They are a very good team. She is like the mummy of the school and he is brilliant, good fun but strict and the children respect him. He's very visible, we all know him and he knows all of us and our children.' Lots of refurbishment and development since his arrival, culminating with a new sports complex opening shortly. Awarded Best Head of a Prep School 2016 by Tatler magazine. Two young children both at the school, the elder one flexi-boarding even though they live on site.

Entrance: The school is oversubscribed all the way through but don't hesitate to approach them. To guarantee a place in reception it's wise to register before child is 2. First come first served in this respect. Non-selective in the pre-prep but don't be complacent. Every child is interviewed – as are the parents. A taster day is offered before a place is guaranteed and parents looked at closely too. Reception children come from local nurseries; more join throughout the pre-prep – most from local primary schools. Many children registered to come in year 4, and many more turned away as no places. Children tested for entry from year 3. Again, every child interviewed along with parents. Children come from a wide area, many traveling up to an hour, further afield once boarding starts in year 4. Traditionally a country school for 'old money,' local landed families and gentry; we duly noted the pair of wellies in the corner of the head's office. Less so these days with a larger London contingent now joining the fray, albeit many of these with connections to the area. Many second generation pupils, the odd third. The blend seems to work with all parents talking about how 'sociable and friendly' the school is.

Exit: Very unusual to lose a pupil at 11. These will usually go to the local grammar school or follow siblings. Very, very unusual to have an 'eviction' – one in eight years; they work hard to keep them going. Some 99 per cent stay until 13. Oundle is where their largest contingent move on to, Repton, Oakham and Uppingham all popular too. The odd one each year to Eton and further afield. Virtually all children go on to board. About 60 per cent each year get scholarships, all rounder, academic, creative, performing arts and sports.

Remarks: The school is less than 60 years old, housed in the old family home of the founder, having started in 1959 with six children. A fantastic setting, fabulous limestone mansion set in beautiful grounds. It couldn't be more quintessentially English. Over the years new buildings have been built and old ones adapted so that the original house is now home to the boarders, oak-panelled dining room and admin staff. Teaching is in two separate buildings within the grounds.

The school day is long: all pupils from year 4 stay until 5.15pm with supervised prep sessions (the pre-prep day ends at 3.30pm, but clubs and activities carry on till 5pm). Supper is then served with most pupils staying for one of the many after-school club or sports practices and picked up at 7pm. Parents like this, as 'we don't have to sit and do the dreaded homework after school.' Many parents commute to London and this is why flexi-boarding is so popular. Saturday morning school for all from year 4, followed by matches. 'If you choose Witham you have to commit to the school and buy into the lifestyle,' said one parent. 'School has to come first, but it's worth it,' was another comment.

Traditionally a country school for 'old money,' local landed families and gentry; we duly noted the pair of wellies in the corner of the head's office. Less so these days

Academically, parents are happy with progress, 'particularly now they have sorted out the maths department.' Pupils graded for ability further up

the school and all parents spoke about how easy it is to get in touch with a teacher. Regular reports on progress. All children tested for dyslexia in year 2. Twelve pupils with SEN, some offered one-to-one support, others one-to-two. All parents said their teacher knew their child well. Many commented on the discipline. 'They don't stand any nonsense.' We can vouch for this. One miscreant was writing lines during a lunch time detention before being spoken to, firmly but kindly, by his form teacher. Good to see. Sound advice offered about future schooling by the Welchs, appreciated by the parents.

This is a sporty school with lots of it. But not just rugby, hockey and netball. Yoga for reception and fly fishing on the school lake as well as a nine hole golf course. One parent spoke about 'sporting stars being favoured and not enough teams for the less able.' Strongly denied by Mr Welch, and our guides. But with him and his wife both being ex-sports teachers it is a large part of the school, and successful. As is art. Very impressive work on display in the converted stables that are now the art rooms. Special room given over to the scholarship students. We can see why so many win art scholarships. Music and drama also a strong part of the school with enthusiastic teaching. Most of the children learn an instrument.

'The staff eat with the children at lunch time and attention is given to good table manners and behaviour, which I think is excellent,' said one mother

Pastoral care excellent according to all parents, with Mrs Welch being given glowing praise. 'She sorts out any niggles and problems, quickly and efficiently.' Very much a caring place, with staff well aware of any mental health problems that can develop. Counseling offered if needed. One mother talked about the emphasis given to good manners. 'The staff eat with the children at lunch time and attention is given to good table manners and behaviour, which I think is excellent.' Many staff and their families live on site, or within the village, adding to the family atmosphere.

Boarding must be a logistical nightmare, but it works. Some 120 of the 160 pupils in the prep department board over the course of the year. Around 35 are weekly boarders but the vast majority are flexi-boarders, varying from one night a week to five. Even children living in the village board, usually at the pupil's behest. Many board on the same night as a friend or because they have a club. This means some bed-hopping and lots of sheet changing, but all handled well to fit in with parents. Boarders staying two or more nights stay in the same bed. Friendly boarding staff and house matrons. Boarding housed in the main house in large, airy, freshly decorated dorms, housing up to 10 pupils. Pupils encouraged to decorate dorms with competition for the best one. Wednesday nights are the quietest because of match fixtures. Remaining pupils have 'family nights' with the houseparents, joining the young family for pizza. Mobile phones are not allowed in the boarding house and definitely no social media. Girls' and boys' sections have comfy lounges where pupils have hot chocolate, cake and 'downtime.' Trips feature bowling and such like, and pupils have the run of the grounds during the summer. Croquet on one lawn, but headmaster's lawn sacrosanct.

Very much a community feel, and most parents chose the school because of this. 'We fell in love with the place as soon as we walked through the door.' 'It's a delightful place; my children are so happy here.' The children are cheerful and chatty. Working hard, but seemingly not under great pressure. Witham offers a tremendous start to their education, they are taught to focus and strive. 'Do the best you can.' But it's not just books and learning: they are encouraged to try new things, spend lots of time outside and are taught the importance of courteous, thoughtful behaviour. Perfectly set up for the future, with parents queuing up to get this start for their child.

Wrekin College

39

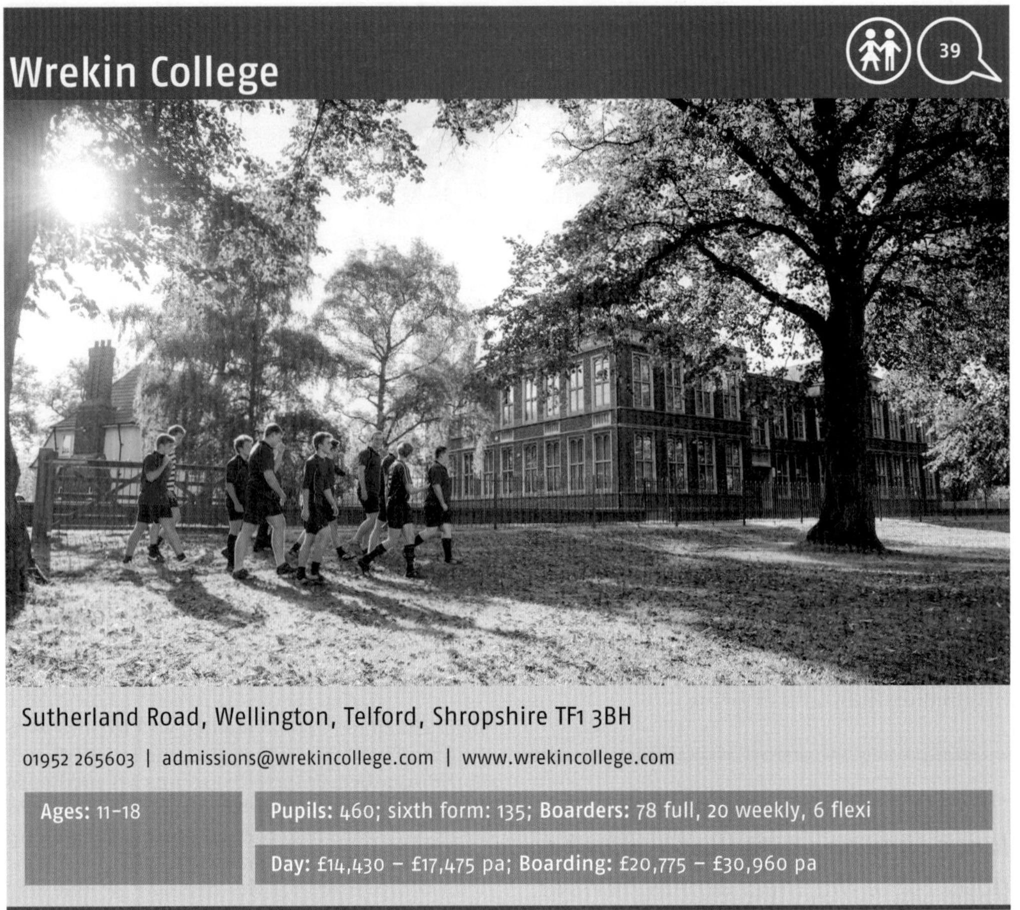

Sutherland Road, Wellington, Telford, Shropshire TF1 3BH

01952 265603 | admissions@wrekincollege.com | www.wrekincollege.com

Ages: 11–18

Pupils: 460; sixth form: 135; **Boarders:** 78 full, 20 weekly, 6 flexi

Day: £14,430 – £17,475 pa; **Boarding:** £20,775 – £30,960 pa

Head: Since September 2016, Tim Firth, BA English Literature, Sheffield University, PGCE Oxford University. Previously deputy head and then acting head at Hurstpierpoint College, West Sussex; came to the school after Wrekin's unfortunate run of heads (three in quick succession). Nothing Lady Bracknell-ish about losing all these heads, just a quirk of fate. And possibly one that has benefited Wrekin since it resulted in the arrival of Mr Firth, who is, according to parents, a 'great fit', a 'dynamo who is very energising' and brings 'solid leadership'. Parents like him; children like him. They say he is approachable and chatty and after the first few weeks of him arriving, 'everyone relaxed'. Being the warm, funny, open sort of chap that he is, we imagine that he will be very adept at taking people with him on what he plans will be an 'enlightened evolution' of the school. We hope everyone's ready: his development plan, outlining numerous aims including targets for value added to pupil grades and a reformed appraisal system for teaching staff, suggests the evolution will be pacey.

In the past parents may have selected Wrekin for its happy vibe and reputation for pastoral care, rather than its academics. Mr Firth has set about addressing this. A big change has been to introduce Challenge Grade Review cards; parents tell us that they finally know where their child stands academically. Clear targets are given to each pupil based on his or her ability, regarding where pupils could be if they successfully carried out measurable tasks. They are given clearly defined 'stretch' work to enable them to meet these challenge grades (head describes the process as a coaching manual) and teachers are able to see which pupils might need a bit of extra support (one on one, for example). Having recruited new heads of lower and middle school to work alongside the tutor system, he says there is now a whole team around each child academically. Greater coordination. Greater tracking. The head says they want to harness the excellent pastoral care that allows frank but supportive conversations about academic achievements

So far so (very) good; the 2017 GCSE results were the best on record. A level results were solid and we predict this uplift will settle into a trend. Number of students has also increased – an extra 50 have been lured in by the Firth factor over the last 12 months.

While raising the school's academic profile is a clear goal, head is also acutely aware that young people are entering a competitive job market and their employability needs to be equally strong. To that end a new Business School opened in 2016, which focuses not just on CV and interview preparation, but also offers a wide programme of career talks on practical topics like 'what an office is like' and industry-focused subjects, such as engineering. Pupils are introduced to apprenticeship schemes and discover what could work best for them as individuals post school. The centre's curriculum is designed to include pupils of all ages. While Mr Firth has far too much humility (and realism) to claim these aims are unique, the dedicated nature of the centre perhaps is. He describes it as a 'standalone temple to employability' – not a phrase you hear very often. It's certainly shaping up into a significant USP and is especially popular with those parents who are in business and want their children to be better prepared for the world of work.

Mr Firth recognises that the straight A student, who may have been a bit spoon fed along the way, does not always make the most agile, creative, resourceful presence in the workplace. The centre is dedicated to resolving that conundrum. His ambition is for Wrekin students to be more stalagmite, less snowflake. He refers in passing to the high number of golds in the Duke of Edinburgh awards (17 in 2017) clocked up by Wrekin students, testament to their sturdy, resourceful characters.

Above all, Mr Firth is keen for Wrekin to continue to be an inclusive environment, one which reflects a broad spectrum of children. Or as one impressed parent put it, quoting the head's words in his first communication with them, 'no one under the radar, no one on the bench'. That phrase went down like manna with parents. He says he relishes the diverse intake because it reflects the real world and this mix 'breeds thoughtful teachers'.

Mr Firth is a keen sportsman, particularly interested in cricket (he was a cricket blue), loves reading, particularly poetry, and Bob Dylan (he has 60 albums). He and his wife, Jane, have three children: two at university, the third, a daughter, is at Wrekin.

Academic matters: Wrekin offers a broad curriculum to suit its diverse intake, including BTecs and A levels in subjects like accounting and psychology. Languages are fairly healthy: 52 per cent of students take one or more language at GCSE; 12 per cent continue to A level. School is very supportive of apprenticeships and does not automatically assume that university is the right path for everyone. Classes are small: typically no more than 20 for the younger pupils and 8-15 at A Level.

The 2017 GCSE results were Wrekin's best ever with 44 per cent A*-A/9-7. A level results were steady; 26 per cent A*/A and 48 per cent A*-B. Most of the A* at A level were in maths and further maths with a sprinkling across languages.

Business School focuses not just on CV and interview preparation, but also offers a wide programme of career talks on industry-focused subjects, such as engineering

Tutoring system means each pupil has personalised academic support. Pupils' academic progress is closely monitored with twice weekly meetings. The mix of pupils means teaching, as Mr Firth explains, is all inclusive but differentiated, depending on stage and ability (this might manifest itself in slightly different homework).

The Franklin Society is in place to challenge the most academically gifted pupils. It is aimed at developing logic, science and the arts (game theory, science projects, study of the classics, architecture). After a rebranding, there are now timetabled weekly lessons. Pupils are chosen from second form upwards based on their performance in non-verbal reasoning and/or exams (pooling all the academic data). About 10 out of 60 students in a year get the nod.

There are also the usual subject-related extension activities, mind-expanding lectures and

academic challenges in national and inter-house competitions. Parents say head has added polish to the teaching and upped ambition in pupils. (Although one parent wondered if staff might be a bit stretched, master of a lot of roles.)

Good learning support team for mild to moderate difficulties. A learning profile is drawn up for all pupils, identifying strengths/areas for development, as well as strategies to help teachers. All have agreed termly targets. Progress is measured against these targets and reassessed each term. Support also available on a temporary or permanent basis for pupils experiencing difficulty with a particular area of the curriculum. No extra cost.

Games, options, the arts: House system provides a healthy platform for competitiveness, team playing and support. Parents say it results in every child wanting to participate in a range of activities and have a go; it 'puts fire in their bellies', as one parent said.

All the usual sport is on offer (vast grounds, lots of playing fields), netball, rugby, football, rounders, cricket, cross-country, tennis, athletics. Also fives and fencing. Large sports halls, gym and tip top swimming pool. Very good to see the girls have a strong six-a-side football team. Netball teams seem to excel, frequently ending up county champions.

Very vibrant art department with an annual exhibition and trips to back it up, like a recent Photoshop workshop with a local artist. Around 200 pupils have music lessons every week and there

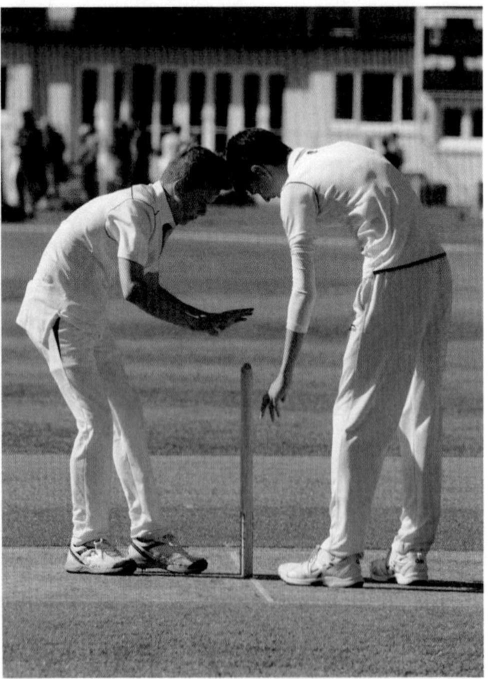

Cheerful studiousness might best capture the atmosphere, students going about their business with a smile. It all feels very friendly

is the usual array of orchestras, bands of all types (rock and jazz) and choirs. A regular programme of school soirées ('soirees at six') recitals and concerts means heaps of opportunities to perform for all, including house singing competitions and house concerts. Also, Wrekin Musician of the Year competition, concerts off site at eg Shrewsbury Abbey and overseas tours. Recent very ambitious production planning of Carmina Burana involved 200 singers. Music is a clear strength of the school. At least one whole school play per year and lots of house productions, from Macbeth, to Shadowlands. House drama competitions allow senior students to manage younger ones.

Around 130 pupils each year are involved in CCF. Duke of Edinburgh popular – remember that healthy stash of gold awards.

Lots of trips, including annual house camping; cultural visits to Hampton Court, Tate Modern, design and business trip to Jaguar Land Rover.

Boarding: One girls' boarding house and two boys'. Rooms are fine, not huge – pretty standard boarding fare. Younger years share four or five to a dorm, older students have their own study bedrooms, some with ensuites. Communal facilities are okay, some have had a refurb so are a tad smarter. All houses have common rooms with decent sofas, cushions, relaxed vibe, kitchens (fridge, toaster, microwave) and games rooms (pool tables). Boys can visit the girls' common rooms for a short time after prep; one girl called their common room a 'social hub'.

All well supervised, houseparents on hand along with matron and prefects, who have a duty roster. Phones are allowed but wireless turned off at 10.30pm. Day pupils don't go into the boarding areas but common rooms for day students, within the houses, are open to boarders so there is a fair bit of downtime mingling. On site medical centre staffed throughout the day and a nurse is always on call overnight.

Lots of trips into nearby Shrewsbury, Ironbridge, Chester, Birmingham and London. Also, there are a great many clubs on a Saturday morning from squash to jewellery making, horse riding, archery, rowing, maths.

Background and atmosphere: Founded in 1880 by Sir John Bayley on a large and lush site above

Wellington, a market town in Shropshire, Wrekin is a combination of old and new buildings (no eyesores), on a large campus with plenty of green space. It became co-ed in the 70s and in 2006 merged with The Old Hall School, which moved on to the same site.

Cheerful studiousness might best capture the atmosphere, students going about their business with a smile. Classrooms have an old style charm, some with the smell of refurbs, like the chemistry labs. In the corridors displays don't jump out at you, but it all feels very friendly and 'community-led' with all the information and updates pupils need.

Inevitably, lots of hoofing required to cover distance between boarding houses and buildings – our legs could tell we had walked a fair distance by the end of our visit.

Pastoral care, well-being and discipline: By all accounts, a massive strength of the school. As one parent said, every day their son 'had gone to school with a smile on his face and come home with a smile on his face'. Others spoke of a happy and secure environment where children are social, look people in the eye and are making the best of who they are.

While every school says there is a caring environment, the students we saw and spoke to – who really did smile and make eye contact without knowing who we were – looked cheery. We also noted the impeccable manners – door opening, standing aside. They didn't seem formulaic, just natural consideration, true courtesy.

Lots on for boarders including day trips and Saturday morning clubs for interests such as squash, jewellery making, horse riding, archery, rowing and maths

A very inclusive environment; most parents seemed to think the house system was instrumental here – the spectrum of inter-house competitions (a house play, a house singing competition etc) all offering a sense of identity. The children relish being part of a group, not wanting to let the group down. First and second form (years 7-8) are all in Lancaster House, which parents said was an excellent stepping stone and a good way of introducing them to the whole school. From the third year, they join one of three boys' or two girls' houses. Parents say pupils all look after each other and being part of the house is viewed as an honour.

Experienced counsellor on site and all the usual assemblies on pastoral matters. Pupils can train as mentors, identified by a distinct badge to encourage others to approach them. Every new pupil is issued with a school handbook and it is genuinely useful, packed full of all the information necessary (mobile phone use, security, map, routines, who does what on the staff).

Wrekin is a Christian foundation and worship – four times per week – is very much part of the makeup. Services are also an opportunity for pupils to perfect their public speaking – prefects often give 'thought for the day' talks on topics such as 'determination to achieve goals'

Our House is a week's compulsory boarding for sixth formers who have to cook and clean for themselves – good preparation for university

Pupils and parents: Pupils are friendly, social, polite and without a whiff of arrogance or entitlement. As the head says, Wrekin's broad mix ensures its leavers are rounded and prepared for the world beyond school.

Parent demographic is similarly broad; many have business backgrounds (this is a part of the country where manufacturing still thrives); others are professions or from the farming and county set. Head welcomes parents' support – and their high expectations. Those we spoke to said home-school communication is good and they appreciate the open door policy. Head has also started discussion forums where parents can contribute ideas and give feedback about the school.

Entrance: Around half come from the on-site prep, Old Hall. Rest from local primaries and preps including Packwood Haugh and Prestfelde. All candidates sit 11+ exam, papers in maths, English and non-verbal reasoning, but bar is not set too high for entry. Entry at 13 + by Wrekin entrance exam.

Exit: Nearly all sixth form leavers head for university and the spread is typically broad for both subjects and locations. Parents praised the UCAS support. Most choose northern, Midlands or Welsh universities: Leicester Bangor, Cardiff, Keele, Leeds, Manchester, Hull, Sheffield, York. Economics, engineering, business management and sports courses (sport science, sport and health education) seem popular. Not many takers for arts degrees, just a few for English lit and languages.

No places in 2017 for Oxbridge or medicine, but two for law. This may change as aspirations are raised under Mr Firth's leadership. Several of the parents we spoke to had children who were holding offers to universities in the south and the number of Oxbridge candidates has increased significantly. Some pupils move on to apprenticeships which might include sponsorship through university.

Money matters: Boarding and day fees are somewhat lower than similar schools further south. In a nod to today's economic climate interest free monthly payment plans are offered, as well as a reduction loyalty scheme for those who attend its associated Old Hall prep.

Remarks: A wonderfully nurturing and inclusive school which is on the up academically but also offers something rare: the chance for pupils, in this tough old world, to hone their employability factor.

Northern England, Scotland and Northern Ireland

Cheshire
Cumbria
Durham
East Riding of Yorkshire
Greater Manchester
Lancashire
Merseyside
North Yorkshire
Northumberland
South Yorkshire
Tyne and Wear
West Yorkshire
SCOTLAND
NORTHERN IRELAND

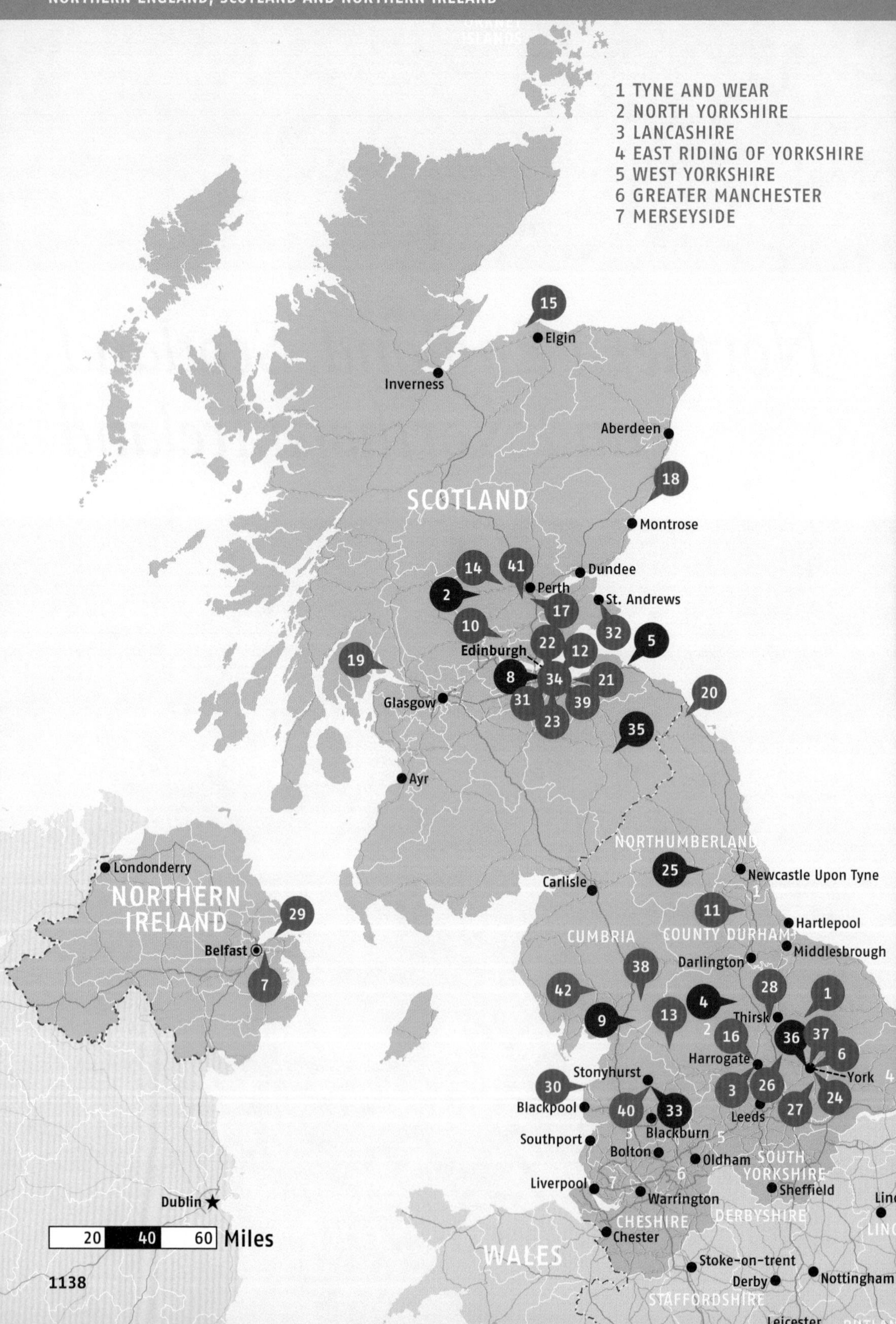
1 TYNE AND WEAR
2 NORTH YORKSHIRE
3 LANCASHIRE
4 EAST RIDING OF YORKSHIRE
5 WEST YORKSHIRE
6 GREATER MANCHESTER
7 MERSEYSIDE
SCOTLAND
Elgin
Inverness
Aberdeen
Montrose
Dundee
Perth
St. Andrews
Edinburgh
Glasgow
Ayr
NORTHERN IRELAND
Londonderry
Belfast
Dublin
NORTHUMBERLAND
Newcastle Upon Tyne
Carlisle
CUMBRIA
COUNTY DURHAM
Hartlepool
Middlesbrough
Darlington
Thirsk
Harrogate
York
Stonyhurst
Blackpool
Blackburn
Leeds
Southport
Bolton
Oldham
SOUTH YORKSHIRE
Sheffield
Liverpool
Warrington
CHESHIRE
DERBYSHIRE
Chester
WALES
Stoke-on-trent
Derby
Nottingham
STAFFORDSHIRE
Leicester
20 40 60 Miles

NORTHERN ENGLAND, SCOTLAND AND NORTHERN IRELAND

Ampleforth College

RC 1

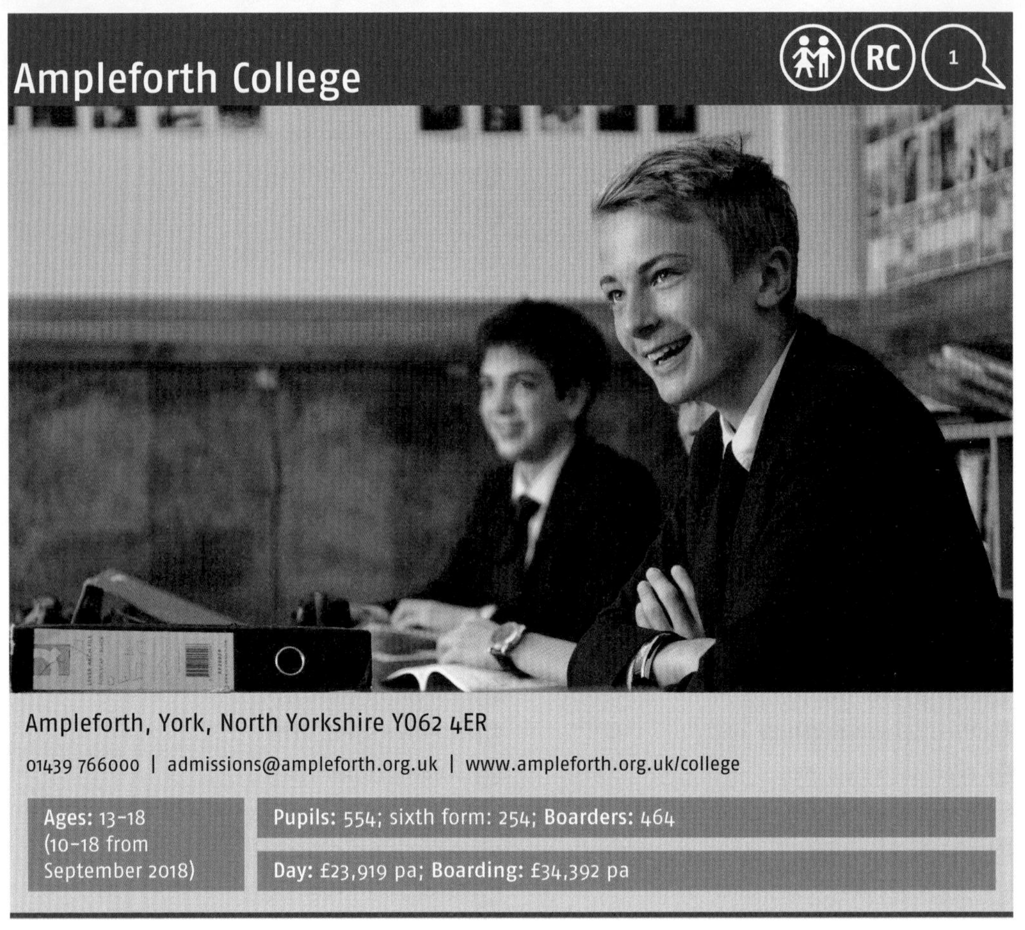

Ampleforth, York, North Yorkshire YO62 4ER

01439 766000 | admissions@ampleforth.org.uk | www.ampleforth.org.uk/college

Ages: 13–18 (10–18 from September 2018)

Pupils: 554; sixth form: 254; Boarders: 464

Day: £23,919 pa; Boarding: £34,392 pa

Headmaster: Since December 2016, Fr Wulstan Peterburs OSB BA PhD, who was previously interim head from June 2016. Fr Wulstan first taught in the school in 1994 as a lay teacher of Christian theology and history, entering the monastery in 1998. He was subsequently head of Christian theology and housemaster before being appointed as procurator of Ampleforth Abbey and College in 2010.

Academic matters: Top of the Catholic league but proud of non-elitist intake – from A stream scholars to IQs around 100, who get extra help with English and maths. Ninety per cent of the slowest workers get three A levels, which bears out the college's mission statement – an extract from the Rule of St Benedict: 'the strong should have something to strive for and the weak nothing to run from'. Determined to stress academic rigour and unashamedly and successfully pushing up A and B grades at A level (2017: 39 per cent A*/A, 67 per cent A*-B), 'though these are not laurels on which we are proposing to rest'; still aiming higher and the value-added score increases all the time, especially at A level. GCSE: 60 per cent A*-A/9-7.

'They never discard,' says a parent. 'The pupils gain self-respect, the staff have an ability to unlock potential.' School prudently adds that sometimes pupils cannot or will not cope: 'We try to reach an agreement with parents about them leaving'. Overall aim is for everyone to fulfil, and preferably exceed, their academic ability. The most able are challenged by membership of an unashamedly intellectual discussion club.

Core curriculum plus Christian theology throughout, Latin and Greek too, and now computing GCSE. Half GCSE year takes separate sciences, half (of all abilities) double award. English department now doing IGCSE. Humanities traditionally have more takers and the edge at A level, but maths and science continue to strengthen, and computing now available. English very strong (most get A or B); history and Christian theology regularly successful and enormously popular.

Dyslexics taught 'for the most part' in mainstream; additional specialist one-to-one teaching available. EAL provision for pupils whose first language isn't English.

Games, options, the arts: Traditionally powerful games school. Strong first XV, respected throughout the North. Hockey exceptionally strong for boys and girls, netball, lacrosse, athletics (own track), squash, golf (own nine-hole course), fly-fishing, renowned independently-owned beagle pack, shooting (brace of pheasants recently spotted hanging on coathanger outside boarding cubicle). Phenomenal 20 rugby sides – 'We want wide participation in school teams', 10 cricket sides, eight tennis teams, and so on. Sports hall, Astroturf, 25-metre pool. Very successful voluntary CCF and it has been known for the girls' platoon to teach the boys a tough lesson by winning the CCF challenge. Flourishing D of E.

Music outstanding – Schola Cantorum choir tours regularly, singing in Catholic and Anglican cathedrals, also impressive girls' Schola Puellarum. Talented chamber music group and the biggest school pipe band south of the border, with own Ampleforth kilts. Enthusiastic singing by whole school in the abbey church, though sometimes, by their own admission, 'more Twickenham than heavenly hosts'.

No longer offers A level, but hugely impressive work on display – a direct result they say of 'an interaction between inspirational teaching and the environment'. New all-singing-and-dancing performing arts theatre (literally – includes sprung floor, wall mirrors and ballet barres) and also smaller studio theatre, popular with pupils, who would like to do even more. Annual pilgrimage for seniors to Lourdes. Own charity, run by students, raised funds to build school in Nepal and to sponsor East European students in school's sixth form. Also several other eye-openingly worthwhile international projects.

The St Laurence Cookery School was opened in 2016 by Old Amplefordian and MasterChef the Professional's star Joey O'Hare. The 12 week Leith's Cookery Toolbox course takes place twice a year and helps students to grasp a range of key cookery skills including time planning, food safety, hygiene, healthy eating and knife skills.

A new staff appointment has strengthened careers advice, including preparation for university and after. It's a work in progress but a deliberate and concerted change – 'it's a meritocratic world and our students need to be prepared'. Long list of extracurricular activities, including some rarer options such as croquet; also the opportunity to strip down and build a Land Rover. And they usually win the regional school shooting range challenge, 'though not quite sure where that fits with the Benedictine philosophy.' Activities are compulsory between 5-7pm and though a small number wriggle and squirm, most are happy to take part because apparently 'being busy makes you happy'. This is definitely a busy school – boarding philosophy through and through and even day pupils do everything (except sleep) here.

Boarding: Houses vary considerably in character, with deliberate spread of ability – seven for boys and three for girls. Charming and articulate boys and girls rub very comfortably alongside each other, the girls raising the bar in a number of areas and the boys raising their game in response. Rolling programme of improvement in boarding houses; 'I have a power shower!' exclaimed one girl proudly. Home from home, clearly, and it matters, especially to the girls. Some girls' houses have nominated 'guardian angels' as peer mentors; varying approach across individual houses, boys tend and befriend as necessary, usually without being asked. A real plus with the boys is that 'this is a place where you don't have to choose between singing in the choir and playing rugby' – it's acceptable, even cool possibly, to do both. Lunch with houseparents each day, central dining room and cafeteria system in use for other meals. Apparently (according to pupils) 'the food is good – for school food', a guarded mix of fierce loyalty and sensitive disclaimer.

Fly-fishing, renowned independently-owned beagle pack, shooting (brace of pheasants recently spotted hanging on coathanger outside boarding cubicle)

Background and atmosphere: Founded 1802. Girls originally in sixth form only but co-education introduced elsewhere in 2010 and now growing throughout school. Magnificent setting in 3,000 acres of stunning countryside, very calming to the soul with the Abbey as its central focus, physically and spiritually. Though fairly remote, 'in fact easy to reach – with some determination – from all parts of the country and world'. Beautiful Victorian gothic main wing plus Giles Gilbert Scott's huge abbey church and school buildings (1930s), with late 1980s and more recent additions.

School keeps in touch with outside world through excellent lecture programme and faraway projects, eg Chile and E Europe. No exeats except for two in winter term, otherwise half-terms. Handy list of local hotels, restaurants and B&Bs sent to parents in very comprehensive booklet, Your Questions Answered. Not unknown for parents to rent a local cottage during their child's time at Ampleforth. Warmth of hospitality legendary, 'Part of the Rule of St Benedict is to welcome guests as Christ welcomed his'.

Pastoral care, well-being and discipline: A key change in recent times is that of the deployment of monastic personnel: there are fewer monks and they no longer perform the role of housemasters. This role has been taken over by families who serve as houseparents – 'very civilising,' was the comment. Monks now act as chaplains to the school houses, 10 chaplains for 10 houses and parents and pupils commend them for being both priests and friends.

Consciences worked on rather than harsh restrictions imposed, all with the aim of turning students into responsible adults. It appears relaxed on the surface; essentially you are 'allowed it until you misuse it'. Fair enough. At the same time, 'this means clear structure and boundaries.'

Tough on bullying – those directly implicated and also bystanders – no one ever implicated in bullying can reach the position of monitor at the top of the school; 'a moment of madness can cost you dear.'

No uniform as such, but dress code in place.

However, recent press articles on the treatment of historic alleged sex offenders (and now a Charity Commission investigation) plus the premature departure of a recently appointed head suggest all may not be well in this part of North Yorks. If/when you visit, it might be worth asking questions because, at the very least, whilst pupils may well remain unaffected, these will almost certainly have proved a distraction internally.

In 3,000 acres of stunning countryside, very calming to the soul with the abbey as its central focus, physically and spiritually

Pupils and parents: Numbers close to full and consistently so. Pupils from all over the UK and beyond, 30 per cent Yorkshire families, 40 per cent elsewhere UK (often with OA connections), remaining 30 per cent from overseas. Five per cent of overseas pupils are expats, rest mainly European mix of French, German, Swiss, Spanish. The recession has gently pushed up overseas numbers and reduced the number from the rest of the UK. 'We're a long way from London and you have to pass a lot of good schools to get here.' That said, many do, the main attractions being the Catholic Benedictine tradition and – bucking the trend here – full boarding provision; 'the school doesn't empty at weekends'. Scions of top and middle Catholic families (80 per cent); the rest mainly Anglican, but special welcome for orthodox.

There's a sense of comfortable ease between parents and school – 'if you want to be involved and constantly in touch, that's possible, If you want to take a more relaxed approach, then that is fine too'. Former pupils include Rupert Everett, Hugo Young, Lord Tugendhat, Lord Nolan, Sir Anthony Bamford (JCB), Michael Ancram, Sir Anthony Gormley, Lawrence Dallaglio, Joe Simpson, Lord Fellowes, James Norton.

Entrance: Own prep St Martin's Ampleforth closing in September 2018 with years 6 up moving here. Common entrance (50 per cent), or school test, and interview. Exceptions 'for faith or family', but no one admitted if he or she won't be able to cope with curriculum. Sixth form entry: at least five GCSEs at B/6 or above. Non-Catholics expected to take full part in school's religious life.

Exit: Up to 20 per cent leave after GCSEs. In 2017, four to Oxbridge and four medics; around half to Russell Group universities; Edinburgh and Bristol also popular. Overseas destinations include Boston, Trinity College Dublin, Vienna and three off to Segovia, Spain.

Money matters: Generous financial help. Academic, music and all-rounder scholarships. Nearly 13 per cent receive means-tested bursary help. In last two years some pupils have attained scholar status after entry.

Remarks: It has been said that people who leave Ampleforth take with them a 'compass for life', a spiritual direction finder, which allows them to hold on to their moral bearings. Three fundamental college aims underpin the thinking and approach here: for parents to call up and say their son/daughter is 'having a whale of a time', to succeed academically and finally, while 'not all super pious', to 'treasure a place in their hearts for the spiritual side of life'. The pupils we met confidently achieved all three.

Parents like and appreciate the 'strong moral feel' of the school 'encompassing faith and learning, as well as 'the welcoming atmosphere'. They describe it as 'surely one of the most beautiful places to go to school', hoping (and praying) that it can 'live up to the challenge and expectations in coming years', that particular challenge being one of 'raising the bar academically with first rate and inspiring teachers'. School is listening and has taken note but NB our comments on recent press reports.

Ardvreck School

2

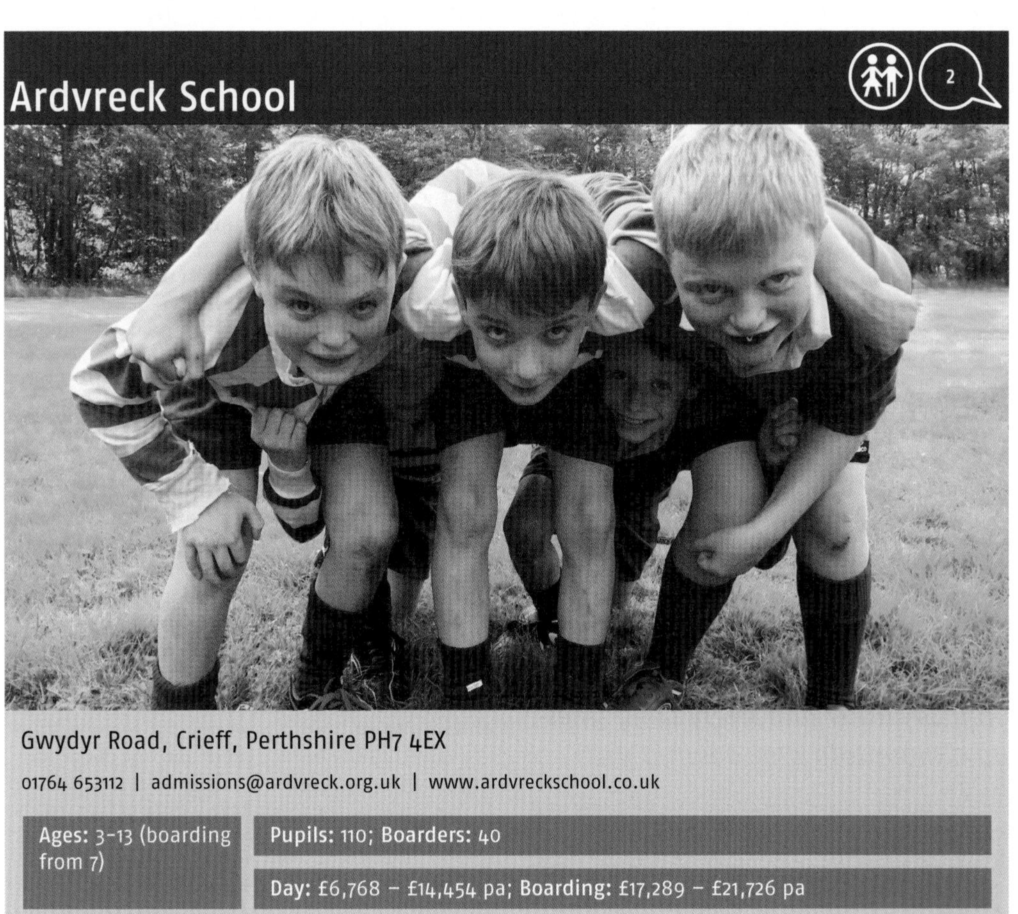

Gwydyr Road, Crieff, Perthshire PH7 4EX

01764 653112 | admissions@ardvreck.org.uk | www.ardvreckschool.co.uk

Ages: 3-13 (boarding from 7)

Pupils: 110; Boarders: 40

Day: £6,768 – £14,454 pa; Boarding: £17,289 – £21,726 pa

Headmaster: Since 2015, Dan Davey MRAC DipHE (environmental sciences) BEd (Oxon). This is his third headship. He is married to Nichola, a modern languages teacher and housemother for junior house. They have three sons, two of which are at the school. He loves outdoor pursuits – hunting, shooting and fishing – and has a keen interest in music, including playing the bagpipes (badly, he claims).

Entrance: Children come from all over Scotland, although the majority are from Perthshire and surrounding area. A smallish number join the pre-prep or Little Ardvreck. This is being developed into a full-blooded Montessori nursery running on forest school principles, ie children under 6 should have most of their lessons outside, encouraging an appreciation of the environment. Most children, however arrive between the ages of 8 to 10.

Exit: The majority to public schools in Scotland and England. St Mary's Ascot, Radley, Oundle, Uppingham, Fettes, Strathallen and, of course, a sizeable proportion to nearby Glenalmond College, which historically has a close relationship to the school. In 2017, 14 scholarships, including all rounder, art, music (one for piping), sports and academic.

Remarks: A lovely, warm, friendly and nurturing school. One parent said they were sold on the place after coming up the drive and seeing some boys bursting out of the bushes with rosy red cheeks, play-fighting with sticks. We hate to use that hackneyed comparison Famous Five, but gingerbread, crackling fires and pop for tea really springs to mind. It's a beautiful setting, perched on a rather steep incline, just west of Crieff. Its central core is a rather austere Victorian lump of a house with a straggly collection of satellite buildings (like many schools), but nestling around it is 42 acres of woodland and breathtaking scenery. A truly idyllic environment if you like the idea of fresh air and outdoor pursuits for your children.

But not everything in the Ardvreck garden is completely rosy. With the change of headship, of course, comes a 'new broom' and some different ideas, not all of them universally liked. Ideas like doing away with prep and integrating it into lessons, so that the children can enjoy clubs and activities in the evenings. Not all the parents we spoke to, were thrilled by this. 'This is not what I sent my children to prep school for.' 'I had real concerns that once they got to senior school they wouldn't know how to organise and plan their own study.'

Three times a year the school closes on a Saturday and every child goes up a mountain and down a glen

But many others could see the benefits and were delighted with the way it allowed their children to de-stress in the evenings. 'When our eldest left we couldn't have had a more rounded, happy child.'

There were also concerns about changes in staffing at the school. 'Evolution not revolution would have been better.' Although another parent said, 'We needed new blood and now that the changes have happened hopefully everything will settle down.'

So our impression? Well, we saw Mr Davey as being full of both confidence and ebullience and with a real passion for the job. And certainly the children seem to love his enthusiasm and drive. 'All the children adore Mr Davey. He engages with them all, he knows them all and his pastoral side is second to none: whether dealing with homesickness, bereavement, you name it, he's excellent. He's perhaps better with children than parents.'

'We want children to embrace the wonderful surroundings. We value talking to each other and one of our important tenets is that Ardvreck allows children to be children'

So a few grumbles and misgivings from parents at the top end of the school, but many more appear to have great faith in Mr Davey's plans for the school long term. There was mention of the 'excellent' deputy Alison Kinge, and what was also clear was the very strong belief among parents further down the school. 'Great family spirit.' 'It's easy to pick holes, but it works.' 'It's still got a huge amount to offer.' Above all, most parents said their children were very happy at Ardvreck.

Dan Davey says they've appointed a number of new members of staff to their fold over the last couple of years. These new members include a director of studies to focus on academics and improve 'our already good levels of academic achievement'. A scholarship and a common entrance set now from the fifth form. They've invested in a new science lab and new computers in all their classrooms. They have a set of iPads for form 1 and the whole school has ready access to an IT room for lessons. 'This is an area we want to develop, along with the new director of studies.' Head says he believes it's a careful balance between embracing technology in teaching and controlling access to the internet. 'We do allow it in the boarding houses, but we want children to embrace the wonderful surroundings. We value talking to each other and one of our most important tenets is that Ardvreck allows children to be children. They will have plenty of time in the future to come to terms with the full world of internet and the media.' We couldn't agree more.

With Ardverck positioned in the middle of an area of outstanding beauty, outdoor education is clearly important, and to this effect they have recently appointed a new specialist who can teach kayaking, skiing and archery and is a trained mountain leader. Put it this way, we wouldn't challenge him to a race for a bus. This charming and enthusiastic member of staff has already swept up a Pied Piper type following and has embraced the school's outdoor ethos, ie every child will camp, or Barvick as it's known (we have no explanation, we're afraid), and three times a year the school closes on a Saturday and every child goes up a mountain and down a glen.

'We do everything from bushcraft skills to knife craft, fire lighting and cooking over an open fire.' (Famous Five again.) Dan Davey says this is so that they can avoid force-feeding facts, but rather introduce ideas and encourage the children to think for themselves. 'We want them to have the courage of their own convictions and have the ability to think for themselves and to convey their views confidently.' Sounds good, and both the parents and the children are more than on board for this part of the Ardvreck experience.

If ever a boarding school can be a home from home, then Ardvreck probably fits the bill. It's not glamorous and it's not very modern, but it has a cosy charm which we could imagine younger children feeling very at home with. They have just appointed a new head of boarding, so changes may be afoot, but the current model – which has junior boarding in the main building, graduating to chalet type accommodation for the top two years with common rooms to match – seems to work.

They describe themselves as a full boarding school with only two exeats a term. What this means, in effect, is that 30 per cent are full boarders, but 60 per cent 'step up' to part-time boarding. Step Up is a package where they can board three or four nights a week to prepare them for full boarding at senior school. They say they're trying to avoid the term flexi-boarding although we're not quite sure what the difference is.

Once in the senior years the children are encouraged to take more responsibility for themselves: they have separate activities from the juniors and are given the chance to take on chores such as doing their own washing. There is plenty of opportunity to mix between the sexes, with the girls sometimes visiting the boys' common rooms, but as with most girls and boys of this age they like their own space and Ardvreck provides that.

Another full-time appointee is educational psychologist Daryl Van Blerk. Head says, 'I think at some point all children need support in their learning and I believe Daryl's teaching is outstanding in this respect. He has already brought improvements, introducing new learning techniques to enhance academic learning.' The school has also become a provider for BACS 3, a form of psychological screening, which they believe will help them tailor their teaching methods further. All learning support is free.

Ardvreck maintains a very high sporting profile for rather a small school, fielding an impressive array of teams in a wide variety of sports. They have their own swimming pool (covered by what looks like a strawberry tunnel) and have just hired a new swimming coach. One parent told me that they 'wipe the decks' in terms of swimming competitions. Every year the school hosts the ARD challenge, which is a 14 mile yomp with five

command tasks: air rifle shooting, simulated medical disaster, rifle shooting, moving 'explosives', walking through a minefield and a memory test. We're exhausted just writing about it, but it does sound both challenging and fun. It finishes on the banks of Loch Tay with a BBQ, spit roast and the school's wood fire pizza open ready to rustle up some tasty 'scran'. Lots of hearty exercise and food.

Last but not least a very good pipe band. This intrepid group played Highland Cathedral on top of Ben Nevis. You just can't keep an Ardvreckian down, or indoors for that matter

Art and music seem to be rather strong too. They've just appointed a new art teacher and the school is proud of its record in art scholarships. Musically they seem very active: woodwind group, choir, ceilidh band, brass group and last but not least a very good pipe band (essential for a good Scottish prep school). This intrepid group played Highland Cathedral on top of Ben Nevis. You just can't keep an Ardvreckian down, or indoors for that matter.

Ashville College

3

Green Lane, Harrogate HG2 9JP

01423 566358 | ashville@ashville.co.uk | www.ashville.co.uk

Ages: 11–18

Pupils: 570; sixth form: 168; Boarders: 110

Day: £13,785 – £14,220 pa; Boarding: £21,735 – £28,920 pa

Headmaster: Since September 2017, Richard Marshall, previously head of Bury Grammar Boys. Biochemistry degree from Birmingham and masters in science communication from Imperial. He joined Bury in 2006 as head of chemistry, and was promoted to head of science, deputy head academic, second master and then headmaster in 2013. He has also been head of sixth form at Queen Elizabeth Grammar School Blackburn. A basketball fanatic, he played for England as a schoolboy and for the British University England team and captained the university first team. He still enjoys playing, watching and coaching it. He is married to Kimberley, also a teacher, and has three young children who have joined Ashville.

Academic matters: Good value-added, especially at GCSE – 32 per cent A*/A in 2017. Science, mathematics, economics and PE all very popular at A level (32 per cent A*/A grades in 2017, 61 per cent A*/B). Not a shining star in the league tables but most pupils exceed predicted potential and very able pupils do particularly well. Good choice of subjects at GCSE; A level offering includes history of art and government and politics.

Average class size 16, max 22, dropping to 10, max 16, in the sixth form. Years 7–9 follow broad curriculum including at least two modern foreign languages (Italian now offered); set for mathematics and languages. For GCSE years, pupils split into ability bands A and B; A are taught Latin and B do extra lessons in English, geography and ICT. Majority take three separate sciences, a few dual award, all at least one modern foreign language.

All year 7 pupils (and year 3 in the junior school) are screened for dyslexia, with further testing and screening as necessary. No pupil has a statement of special educational need/EHC plan, but over 130 pupils receive some additional help for 'mild dyslexic tendencies' – individual support if deemed necessary. Those with dyslexia thrive thanks to the kindly environment and carefully planned programmes of study; indeed in recent years few haven't got the benchmark five A*-Cs at GCSE, and most gain at least a B (or numerical equivalent) in English.

A basketball fanatic, he played for England as a schoolboy and for the British Universities England team and captained the university firsts

Over 60 international students require English as an additional language, mostly taught alongside mainstream English. Target is Cambridge FCE by year 11 and all sixth form sit Cambridge IELTS in year 13. Also offers a US international studies programme for students aiming to return to education in the US or apply to an American university.

Games, options, the arts: Facilities – two gyms, 30m swimming pool, fabulous climbing wall, squash courts, fitness room and ample pitches, including a new all weather surface pitch – show importance of sport. Further proof by way of sports centre's £3 million refurbishment, updating changing rooms, gym and adding fitness studios and dedicated BTec sport classroom. Teams and fixtures galore in traditional team sports. All usual suspects on offer plus American influenced disc golf – something for everyone. Director of activities recently appointed to provide even more challenging outdoor opportunities.

Well-resourced and well-used music centre – a third take individual instrumental or singing lessons. An array of choirs and bands, from chamber to soul and jazz to strings. Talented musicians play in the National Children's and National Youth Orchestras, but plenty of playing and performing opportunities for those just starting out too: Verdi Requiem in Leeds Town Hall, Messiah from Scratch for charity.

Dedicated art studios and drama facilities always busy. Unusually for a boarding school, a 4pm finish and no Saturday school, but plenty of choice of after-school activities and clubs and supervised prep until 5.30pm; D of E from year 10. Trip for older students to Malawi ties in with charity fundraising to support the Open Arms Orphanage, which has close links with the school.

Boarding: School viewed as a day school with boarding – under 20 per cent board, and half of these are sixth form; firmly in the school's sights to improve these statistics. Three senior boarding houses, two boys' and one girls', are comfortably furnished with usual facilities: kitchens, common rooms, games areas and computers.

Approximately one-third of boarders are from South East Asia – this has reduced in recent years. More emphasis on weekly/flexi boarding and more recruitment from the Forces. Girls and boys encouraged to socialise, with trips regularly organised at weekends and half-termly theme evenings. Plenty of activities on offer after school but all optional. Cultural differences mean not much integration with day pupils after school hours.

Background and atmosphere: Founded in 1877 by the Methodist Church as a senior boys' boarding school, co-ed since 1984. Pleasant, well-maintained site is in a leafy residential area, with a swathe of pitches and playing fields fringed by the trinity of schools (college, junior and pre-prep), sports centre and boarding houses. Evacuated to Windermere during the war as the premises were requisitioned for the war effort and used by Air Ministry.

Plenty of well-kept facilities – atmospheric Memorial Hall is home to lectures, meetings and some concerts, with larger gatherings filling the school hall. Recent, much-needed, extensive refurbishment programme to most classrooms, with the library now excellent. Investment in ICT infrastructure and hardware and more planned. New head of sixth form and review of academic offering, pupil monitoring and facilities in sixth form centre.

Pastoral care, well-being and discipline: Methodist ethos underpins the pastoral care and the school is committed to the development of the full potential of each individual. Parents praise excellent standard of care and say it's what they like most about the school. Hot on manners and respect, 'instilling values and standards which are often overlooked in the 21st century'. Strong culture of inter-house competition between four houses, from poetry to public speaking; the prized Rigg Cup for sport. Unusually, continuity of house membership from pre-prep up – adds to house loyalty and vertical bonding. School believes in picking up problems quickly to 'fix it small' and then 'partnership between school and parents'. This is recognised by parents, who said that the school 'tried very hard to get it right'.

Pleasant, well-maintained site is in a leafy residential area, with a swathe of pitches and playing fields fringed by the trinity of schools, sports centre and boarding houses

All year 7s are taken to the Lake District for a bonding weekend early in the autumn term; this receives rave reviews not only from the new pupils but also from sixth formers, who work as liaison prefects and, if assigned to year 7, go too.

Fines if caught smoking, with possibility of exclusion for repeated offences. Drugs: out for supplying or intending to – no issues in recent times.

A genuine sense of community that keeps ex-pupils in contact long after they have left the school gates.

Pupils and parents: Mainly from local professional and business families, extending from Ripon to north Leeds and surrounding villages. Quite a few first time buyers; Americans from nearby Menwith Hill military base add an interesting dimension. For about 10 per cent of pupils English is not a first language and overall approximately 14 per cent come from a variety of minority ethnic backgrounds, mainly Chinese, Nigerian and European. Thriving Friends of Ashville runs regular, well-supported activities.

Old boys: Ian Dodds (designer of the Moon Buggy), Commander Ian Grieve (head of anti-terrorism Scotland Yard), Jim Carter (Downton Abbey actor), Simon Theakston (director of Theakston's Brewery and chairman of the Yorkshire Agricultural Show) and Peter McCormick (lawyer to the Football Association).

Entrance: For year 7, a day in January with English, mathematics and non-verbal reasoning papers followed by practical activities, plus a report from previous head. Usually a three form entry of 60 pupils, though recent demand has increased this to four forms.

Majority of pupils come from own junior school and nearby preps: Belmont Grosvenor and Brackenfield in Harrogate, Richmond House, Moorlands and Frobelian in Leeds, plus local state primary schools. Six bus routes in operation starting in Leeds, Thorner, Addingham, Ripon and Bramham.

School believes in picking up problems quickly to 'fix it small' and then 'partnership between school and parents'

Sixth form entry is via interview and satisfactory reference; five grade Cs with minimum grade Bs (or numerical equivalents) in subjects to be studied. Exams, interview and reference are norm for entry at other times.

Exit: Around a fifth leave at the end of year 11, most to state sector, further three per cent at end of year 12 – mostly starting afresh, some to foundation courses. Majority of sixth formers go on to higher education, sometimes a couple to Oxbridge, rest to a wide range of universities including a third or so to Russell Group, Northumbria currently most popular, then Liverpool and Leeds. One vet in 2017.

Money matters: Academic, music, sports, art and drama scholarships. Scholarships are awarded on entry into year 7, year 10 and sixth form and are reviewed at key stages. Means-tested bursaries of up to 100 per cent of fees are available either in conjunction with scholarships or on a stand-alone basis. Additional discounts are awarded to the children of Methodist ministers and parents in the Forces.

Remarks: A successful all-round day school with a boarding ethos. Plenty of happy pupils in a caring and supportive environment. Academics and teaching being strengthened. Offers a trinity of schools providing seamless transition through each stage of education, obviously popular with many parents and pupils.

Aysgarth School

Newton-le-Willows, Bedale, North Yorkshire DL8 1TF

01677 450240 | enquiries@aysgarthschool.co.uk | www.aysgarthschool.com

Ages: Boys 3-13, girls 3-7 (boarding from 8)

Pupils: 203; **Boarders:** 75 full, 52 weekly and flexi

Day: £19,035 pa; **Boarding:** £24,780 pa

Headmaster: Since 2015, Rob Morse, previously head of Perrot Hill, with his wife Lottie and their children, Daisy and Harry, and black labrador, Nel. Moved from Somerset, though no newcomer to the north as former deputy head at S Anselm's in Derbyshire.

Entrance: Non-selective, but for prep an interview and assessment (no exam) to look for boys with a 'willingness to get stuck in', 'We try not to turn anyone away'. A few scholarships of between 10-25 per cent and some bursary help, which can be up to 100 per cent. Siblings and Forces discounts available.

Exit: Excellent record to public schools: Marlborough, Harrow, Eton, Ampleforth, Uppingham, Radley, Sedbergh, Shrewsbury, Stowe, Fettes and Winchester. Good sprinkling of academic, music and sports scholarships.

Heads and senior staff of senior schools spend one weekend a year at Aysgarth meeting boys and parents after chapel and at social events.

Remarks: Quiet, rural setting with glorious views in 50 acres of parkland, feels remote but only a short distance from the A1. Approached through a sleepy village, purposely anonymous except for landmark of the splendid school tower on the horizon. A grand, purpose built, 19th century school building, including a gem of a chapel, complemented by modern facilities. As you journey from the entrance your eye is caught by the profusion of discarded balls in the grounds, underlying a parent's description of 'a place where boys can be boys', though girls are welcomed into pre-prep.

Pre-prep established in 1993 in Oak House, a gentle amble from the prep school. Well adapted with well-equipped, secure, outdoor play area running along the front of the attractive building. The curriculum is traditional and broadly based on the national curriculum, though French is introduced in reception.

The weekly early years' newsletter helps parents understand the real learning outcomes from the play-based activity in EYFS, nursery and reception. This becomes more formal in year 1 with specialist teaching beginning to be introduced for French, PE and music. In year 2 concepts are developed through creative topic work. Transition is high on the agenda in year 3, with boys preparing for the prep school and girls for their next step at another school. House captain and other responsibilities allow the children to develop confidence. Golden time in assemblies celebrates rewards for academic achievement and good deeds, focusing on a difference aspect each week.

Families are a mix of old school and new, many first time into boarding, including some who say they had previously neither considered boarding nor single sex

The rural setting provides the natural habitat for the forest school in 'Mr McGregor's garden' and the woodland areas. All the usual opportunities for music, drama and sport, with fixtures from year 3 and swimming for all. Good range of extracurricular clubs on offer, sport and choir with cookery, forest school and multi-activity acorn club – ballet at an additional charge. Pre- and after-school care is on offer from 8.00am – 6.00pm and there is school transport from Ripon and Asenby, all at extra cost.

In the prep school, small class sizes (max 16) with traditional and demanding curriculum; setting and streaming from year 5. Extraordinary continuity over the years in gaining places at top public schools. Challenge is to keep abreast of 'subtle shifts' in senior schools and 'keep improving in every sense' as the bar gets higher to top schools. SEN provision improving all the time as the school becomes an even more 'broader and kinder place'.

Top notch sports facilities, especially cricket field, swimming pool and newly built sports hall. The Aysgarth game of COW – cricket off the wall – is a love of Aysgarthians old and new, the real challenge being to hit the ball from the playground into the head's garden. Sport is high profile and they play to win, while still managing a well done and a slap on the back for the chap who comes last. Rugby, football, shooting, fishing, sailing, riding, golf and climbing all on offer. Won Rosslyn Park National Sevens Rugby tournament relatively recently.

Art is strong and design technology is popular in well-equipped rooms where the boys can get their hands on serious equipment and tools. Four classrooms which provide light, stimulating spaces for the first year of the prep school. Music is outstanding with over 70 per cent of the pupils singing or playing an instrument. Boys – both the very musical and the less so – can be seen enthusiastically practising their musical instruments in dorms and classrooms at reserved times. They can play anything here, including bagpipes if they so wish, and the choir is 'as cool as being in the first XV' and a joy to hear. Drama lessons and lots of performance opportunities in newly built 200 seat theatre. Good to see boys enjoying reading sessions in the library after lunch.

Boys – both the very musical and the less so – can be seen practising their musical instruments in dorms and classrooms. They can play anything here, including bagpipes if they so wish

Many of the boys look as though they are about to take Eton in their stride – happy, confident and courteous, without being arrogant, they are both charming and endearing but clearly relish this boy friendly atmosphere where you can 'be your own man'.

Staff know the boys well and, although the phrase is often over used, there is really a 'family feel' about this place, thanks chiefly to great enthusiasm and care from the top. Very much focused on full boarding – in fact, north of Oxford, it's the only all boys' boarding prep in England and parents come from both north and south of the border and say, 'It's worth the journey'. Day boys are welcomed, though certainly in the minority, and they follow the boarding routine.

Extraordinary continuity over the years in gaining places at top public schools. Challenge is to keep abreast of 'subtle shifts' in senior schools and 'keep improving'

Boarding accommodation on the top three floors of the school, includes ranks of sinks, where boys have to be reminded to wash occasionally. Cheerful dorms, a mix of beds and bunks, yet mainly unadorned walls, where caring staff keep a close eye, tidying up after them and providing a homely feel. Delightful to see much-loved soft toys adorning many a bed – in the senior dorms as well.

Common rooms on ground floor showing signs of good wear and tear. Extensive after hours activities for boarders include both pillow and water fights (though not at the same time) and it's fine to get down and dirty and build dens in the grounds as well as engaging in debating. Full boarding with diverse range of weekend activities and breaks at exeats only.

Food is ample, prepared in-house using fresh ingredients and 'not bad for school food' (though the boys did say they would like a little more salmon and duck on the menu, please), served in a pleasant if slightly old fashioned style dining room, long tables and benches, where good old fashioned courtesy and table manners count.

Clientele mainly solid (upper) middle class from the north and midlands, with a few Forces families from Catterick. Strong full boarding ethos attracts families from further away, Scotland and Northern Ireland, with 10 per cent international boarders from Europe, Middle East and Russia. Families are a mix of old school and new, many first time into boarding, including some who, interestingly, say they had previously neither considered boarding nor single sex. Initially a little reluctant to let go, these parents place huge value on all that Aysgarth has to offer, both in and out of the classroom, the end result being that their sons are well prepared for the next school, commenting that 'Aysgarth boys are both in demand and popular'.

Governors very active and close to headmaster. There's a lively Old Aysgarthian association. Old boys include Sir Matthew Pinsent and Robert Swan OBE, whose achievements espouse the Aysgarth ethos.

Belhaven Hill School

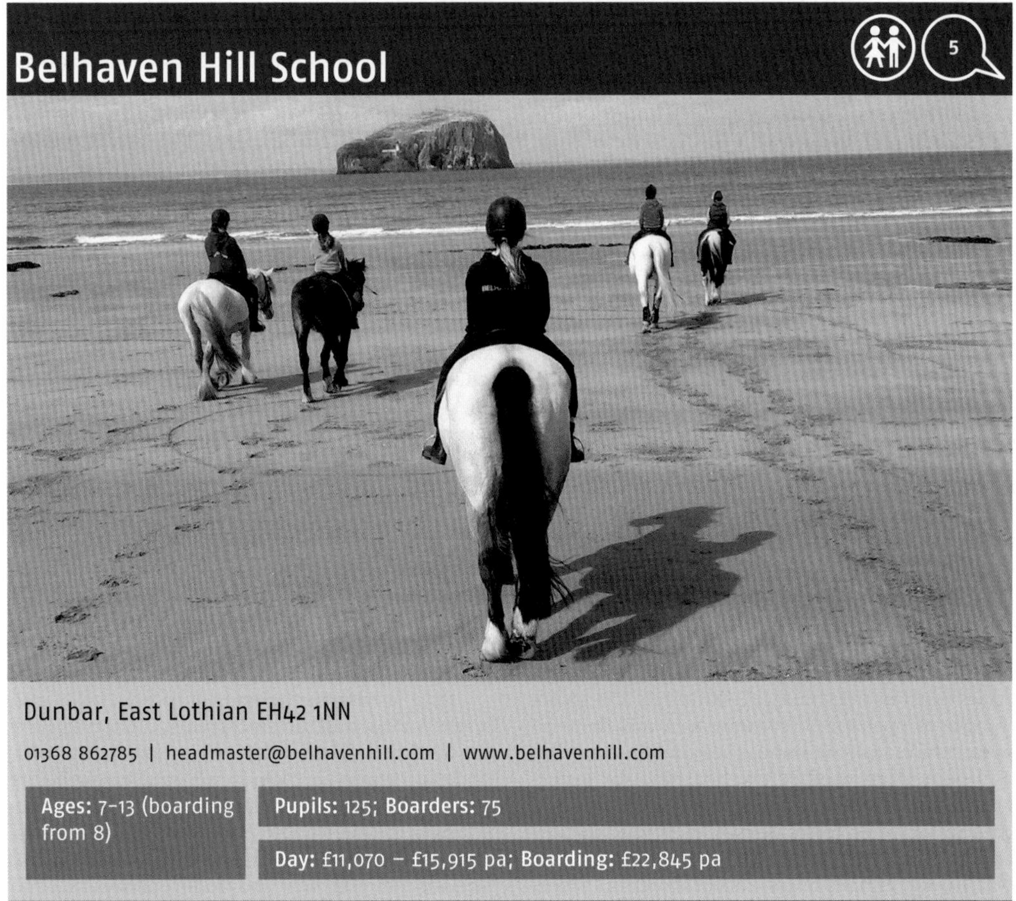

Dunbar, East Lothian EH42 1NN

01368 862785 | headmaster@belhavenhill.com | www.belhavenhill.com

Ages: 7-13 (boarding from 8)

Pupils: 125; Boarders: 75

Day: £11,070 – £15,915 pa; Boarding: £22,845 pa

Head: Since September 2016, Henry Knight, previously head of Woodcote House. BA in classical civilisation (Royal Holloway), PGCE, MEd (in his 40s). Before he took up teaching he ran corporate hospitality for Berry Bros. He started out at Woodcote as an English teacher and housemaster and ended up as headmaster for seven years before his move to Belhaven. He still teaches English to the middle school and also keeps his hand in on the sports side by coaching the 2nd XI cricket team. A down to earth, straight talking man, popular with parents and children alike. Parents report that he's 'very normal', 'approachable', 'well liked', and the children loved that he spent time in the first term with a large, red L plate stuck to his back. Married to Susannah who heads up pastoral care (we hear 'she's great, brilliant with kids and parents'); they have three children, two currently at the school.

Entrance: No formal test but register as soon as possible. Children spend a taster day (and sometimes a night) the year before they come. Here they attend lessons and take part in sport and activities as well as taking a short (20 minute) informal test.

Exit: Oundle, Rugby, Glenalmond, Fettes, Queen Margaret's, Ampleforth, Eton, Harrow, Wycombe Ab-bey, St Mary's Calne, Radley plus the other big English and Scottish schools. At present the split is about 60 per cent heading south of the border while 40 per cent stay in Scotland.

Remarks: Originally a boys' boarding prep school, it went co-ed in 1995 and thereafter welcomed day pupils. The heart of the school is a mid 18th century country house with various add-ons out the back. The location, at the edge of the town of Dunbar, close to an 18 hole golf course and the beach, is peachy. Pretty house with delightful grounds. This editor would happily relocate there.

Eight classrooms all tightly grouped around a pond at the rear of the main house. Light, bright rooms and very easy to nip between classrooms. Class sizes 'generally 12-ish'. Two computer rooms. Setting from age 9 – in maths, English, science and languages. Latin and Greek both on offer. No separate scholarship stream: potential scholars have extended learning and additional tuition; 12 scholarships or awards in 2017.

Learning support in a revamped building (The Hub). Team of four LS teachers. One-to-one teaching, small groups – whatever is needed. Children can pop into The Hub during quiet reading time (every day after lunch) for a catch-up on any subject. If a child has particular difficulties school 'wouldn't say no' to parents employing additional support but would try to find other solutions first to prevent the child 'standing out or feeling different'.

Drama and dance very popular. Plays for all, nativity for the younger ones. Public speaking encouraged through the annual competition: every pupil has to speak on a topic of their choice for four minutes. Inspirational art that is clearly celebrated and displayed around the school. Woodwork/DT room where tasks involve creativity and problem-solving with a healthy dollop of fun. It's not all about curriculum learning – 'we don't just want to be a sausage factory'. On the day of our visit, fabulous ramshackle boat creations all lined up ready for an America's Cup moment on the school swimming pool.

Sport for all. Two cricket pitches, tennis courts (grass court in the summer), Astroturfs and swimming pool, open for the summer term and first half of autumn term. Swimming lessons once a week and pool often used by the boarders for muck-abouts at the weekend. Annual school swimming gala in summer term. Boys play rugby, hockey and cricket while the girls' main sports are netball, hockey and rounders. Lots of sporting success but also an ethos that sport is for all and everyone gets a shot at representing the school. Tennis, golf, skiing, athletics and football also on offer. Functional sports hall, which doubles as theatre for school plays. Lots of extracurricula activities from taekwondo to croquet, fly-tying and horse riding. Piping very strong; lots of music lessons and choir.

The children loved that he spent time in the first term with a large, red L plate stuck to his back

All of the 7 year olds and most of 8 year olds are day pupils. The majority of older pupils board. School operates a bi-weekly boarding programme, finishing every other weekend on a Friday at 1pm or occasionally 3.45pm. Buses operate on these weekends – to Perth, Stonehaven and Thornhill (Dumfries) – to help parents who live further afield. Pupils return either on the Sunday night or first thing on Monday morning.

Day pupils from form 4 upwards are expected to attend school every other Saturday from 8.30am to 4.30pm for lessons and games matches. For the boarders, Sunday kicks off with a chapel service taken by the headmaster or visiting preachers. Headmaster has introduced new fun-packed activities on Sundays for boarders – bubble football being a particular favourite. Head has done much to improve communications with parents through his new blog, Facebook and Instagram, although some parents of boarders miss the now discontinued fortnightly newsletter – this was an 'important piece of communication'. Manners are important and any bullying is kept firmly under control – 'educating the children and talking about it is key'.

Walled garden is well kept but not manicured and children can plant up garden plots of their own. The plots are blank canvases – from vegetables to pond digging

Boys' dorms in the main building. Light and bright rooms, dull tartan curtains. Older boys have new snazzy desk/bed combos – very smart and popular. Small communal room for juice and biscuit before bed. Girls accommodated in a fab new building separate from the main house. Super cosy, homely dorms, very prettily decorated. Big pinboards, floral curtains. Circular common room (Rosy room), plasma telly and piles of beanbags. On the dorm front, the girls have definitely lucked out. Head tells us that plans are afoot to redesign the boys' boarding house to create more beds and give the boys a proper common room space. Boarders aren't allowed phones but can phone home from their dorms. iPod shuffles allowed for music. We hear that the 'matrons are lovely' and the 'pastoral care fantastic'.

Children tell us that food is good ('great match teas') and there's plenty of it, although a couple of junior gourmets reported that the breakfast sausages were 'way more tasty than the ones at supper time'.

Walled garden is well kept but not manicured and children can plant up garden plots of their own. The plots are blank canvases – from vegetables to pond digging to tractor tyres, some major earthworks, anything goes. These mini gardens aren't show pieces for visitors but are for the children to have the freedom to guddle about and have fun in. Fierce competition for the annual garden trophy.

Time to mention the animals.... Let's kick off with ducks. These are in a tidy enclosure near the girls' boarding house. Children are encouraged to feed them and collect the eggs, which are used for baking. Then there are the dogs. Lots of them. Some teachers bring their dogs into their classrooms, where they can be petted between lessons and sit quietly once the lesson begins. There are 11 'school dogs' at the moment. Rather than causing merry chaos, both the dogs and the children seem to be happy and calm in each other's company. Next on the list, but not yet in residence, are the pigs. We look forward to meeting them on our next visit.

Still perceived as Scotland's school for toffs and grandees, although head tells us that now 30 per cent of parents are first time buyers. Some children of former pupils, some from south of the border – often with Scottish connections. However, the base has widened out somewhat with many more families from East Lothian and the borders. Lots of social parents and good friendships. Numbers are still high but slightly down from last year. No plans to change to weekly/flexi boarding. Head says, 'we see ourselves as the pre-eminent full boarding school in Scotland'. We saw so many well mannered, happy children on our visit, and time and time again we hear that parents are 'delighted with the school'. This is a traditional prep school in a beautiful setting with an all-round approach to education that is hard to fault.

Bootham School

Q 6

51 Bootham, York, North Yorkshire YO30 7BU

01904 623261 | admissions@boothamschool.com | www.boothamschool.com

Ages: 3–19 (boarding from 11)

Pupils: 576; sixth form: 162; **Boarders:** 111

Day: £6,930 – £17,865 pa; **Boarding:** £18,330 – £31,170 pa

Head: Since September 2016, Chris Jeffery BA PGCE (50s). Educated at Bristol Grammar School, history at York University, PGCE at Exeter University. Taught history and head of house at Bristol Grammar (eight years); head of middle school and deputy head at The Perse, Cambridge (eight years), head of The Grange School, Cheshire (11 years). Currently teaches personal, health and social education here, has taught history, English and RE.

Very committed to pupil well-being (founding chair of Headmasters' and Mistresses' Conference well-being working group) – genuinely cares as much about pupils' happiness at school and in their future lives as their academic prowess and greatly values the school's primary focus on relationships and Quaker ideals (wearing a white as well as a red poppy when we visited – plus a very jolly multi-coloured tie). Good sense of humour, modest and approachable: pupils address him – and all staff – by his first name and have, he says happily, no inhibitions about visiting him to express criticisms of school matters. 'Inspirational and very child-focused,' said a parent. 'Quickly knows every child, and their parents, by their first name.'

Married to Carol, a nurse; two adult sons and a daughter at Bootham sixth form. Enjoys song writing and performing, all sports (supports a number of 'spectacularly underachieving teams', as he puts it), 'Spotify addict', walking, travel and attending church.

Junior School: Since 2013, Helen Todd BA MEd (late 30s). Attended All Hallows RC High, Macclesfield, then English at Warwick University. Taught English at Durston House, head of English Aysgarth School, deputy head Edge Grove. Appointed vice chair of Independent Association of Prep Schools for 2018. Does various teaching at Bootham. Married to David, IT manager at Cundall Manor School; boy of 10 at Aysgarth, daughter of 12 at Bootham. Enjoys amateur dramatics, walking, travel.

Genuinely cares as much about pupils' happiness as their academic prowess and greatly values the school's primary focus on relationships and Quaker ideals

Dynamic – lots of energy and 'ambitious for the school'. Has broadened curriculum to cover cultural studies and focus more on skills, as the most appropriate form of preparation for the children's future in the twenty first century. Revels in the learning opportunities afforded by freedom from the constraints of SATs. Straightforward, businesslike, flexible, approachable, supportive and 'very present', say parents.

Academic matters: Steady results at A level: 2017 43 per cent A/A*; 72 per cent A*/B. Standard choice of subjects including classics, Latin, extended project qualification; strong modern langs (French, German and Spanish), maths, physics, chemistry, psychology, art. Good gender balance for maths and science uptake. Average sets of 11.

GCSE achievement strong across the board – including Latin language/Latin literature – with no gender difference on five A*-Cs with English and maths measure; 2017: 57 per cent A*-A/9-7. Options include classical civilisation, sport and PE. After school astronomy in historic observatory, with use of original William Cooke telescope – in 1850s was one of the first schools to have its own observatory; open to state school students too. DT product design the only technology offered. Sets of 15-20.

Year 7 curriculum includes thinking skills, classics, health and the environment. Latin, German and Spanish (in addition to French) added in year 8. Maths and French sets from year 8; classes of around 18. Creative approaches, eg building a model medieval castle competition.

Inclusive gifted and talented policy: the able & interested network – talks from outside experts; students undertake ambitious and imaginative projects, such as building an eco car to race in the Greenpower Challenge, creating an astronomy GCSE textbook, displaying dreams of refugee children from different parts of the world on a large dream catcher. Much involvement in the York independent-state schools enrichment partnership. Success in national competitions – modern foreign language debating, chemistry, maths.

Well qualified SENCo; mainly covers a wide range of mild to moderate learning difficulties but would consider more challenging pupils to see if school could meet their needs. Reading test given to all pupils at the start of each year to identify literacy support needs; initial dyslexia screening within department on referral (free), charge for full exam access arrangements assessment. Years 7-11 small support groups. EAL individual and small group support; older students prepared for IELTS (no extra charge).

Junior school: enlightened curriculum: core skills plus cross curricular topics, using creative and flexible approaches to learning with practical tasks, eg building a flood proof house, cooking with war-time rations. A different European language studied each year from years 2-4, including cultural studies; Latin and Mandarin for years 5 and 6. Thinking skills taught through philosophy-4children. ICT skills developed through topic work and dedicated lessons. Plenty of opportunities for the very bright and talented, such as challenge and enrich workshops, also open to state schools. Big focus on outdoor learning and trips – specialist outdoor education and forest school trained teacher for outdoor skills, from whittling to fire lighting. Classes of 15-20 higher up, can be as small as 10 or 12 lower down.

Children monitored for additional needs such as dyslexia as they progress (high praise from a parent about support for this; another spoke of a child's emotional needs being 'subtly and gently addressed') – very capable SENCo, who works closely with senior school SENCo, says she can tell by years 3 or 4 if a child needs a more appropriate school and will help family to find it and child to settle in. Younger children have in class support, mainly small groups outside the classroom for the older ones; families helped to pre-teach topics. EAL support available – many children from overseas.

Unusually, has a very engaging resident therapy dog; we were less taken by the (caged) snake in the foyer.

Games, options, the arts: Abundant sports facilities, including climbing wall. Wide choice of standard (success at regional level) and additional sports. Recent high achievers: an international fencer, Olympic swimmer and cyclist, national orienteering competitors, plus academy footballers. Tours to, eg, California and Spain.

Thoughtfully equipped playgrounds – we particularly liked the covered picnic tables with built in games boards and the outdoor oven. Yurt for quiet time in breaks

Very attractive arts centre with colourful, large, collaborative cranes mobile and studio-sized concert hall doubling as a lecture theatre. Free weekly lunchtime programme of arts performances and lectures in Georgian recital room open to public. Quantities of very high level and varied music – over 20 different ensembles, more than 60 per cent learn an instrument (some win scholarships to top music colleges), has hosted York guitar festival. Recent drama productions include Shakespeare, The Wind in the Willows, Peter Pan. No cultural opportunities wasted – poems posted on loo doors by head of English!

Excellent art in a variety of media on display throughout the school, including several more collaborative pieces. Has artist in residence and all art teachers practise and exhibit. Outstanding DT department produces an unusual number of Arkwright scholars and successful engineers, male and female – much work to promote careers in engineering. Exceptionally well equipped: 3-D printer (used to make a Dalek!), laser, three cadcam machines; finished artefacts look professional. Links with the real world, eg designing antarctic research station task set by an engineering consultancy. Good percentage of girls do DT at GCSE and AL.

One-hour timetabled leisure activities session every week day – huge choice (up to 80), including bell ringing, juggling, candle making, hip hop, mini drone flying, world shaper action group. Natural history society goes back to 1834. Community service is very big, as you would expect from a Quaker school, via D of E and the Bootham Challenge: awards at four levels for the development of soft skills through extra curricular activities. Sustainability also taken very seriously – aiming to achieve 50 per cent fall in energy use over five years: very high standards in new buildings; environmental action group successfully conducted switch-off-fortnight to cut use of gas and electricity; eco schools' Green Flag award. Thoroughgoing careers programme: a wide range of visiting speakers, including former pupils; year 10s do work experience.

Many local trips, exploiting York's cultural and gastronomic advantages, and visits to South Africa, the Americas, Europe, Asia; sixth formers make an annual pilgrimage to sites of Quaker importance in the Lake District; exchange visits with a Quaker school in Washington.

Junior school: varied PE and extracurricular sports activities. Recorder learned in year 2, violin opportunity in year 3; choir, orchestra, flute and recorder groups. Drama thrives: much active contact with York Theatre Royal – workshops, performing, play reviewing; years 5 and 6 use the senior school hall for annual musical, such as Pirates of the Curry Bean, Romeo and Juliet and A History of the World (Abridged). Lots of interesting art in different media on display. Very well equipped ICT and food tech rooms – we were pleased to see a boy, in a fetching apron, critically sampling his hot savoury dish. Strong links with senior school DT department give opportunities for woodwork, mechanics and computer aided design. Good choice of extracurricular clubs; residentials for all, from, unusually, a much enjoyed night in a tent at school for Reception to year 6's five nights at an outward bound centre.

Boarding: Rowntree, the girls' house, consists of three elegant Georgian houses (one belonged to Josiah Rowntree), including shared flats for sixth formers as preparation for university; comfortable common room furnished with leather sofas and

armchairs, kitchen, cheerful shared bedrooms. Similar modernised Georgian houses for the boys' house, Fox: the single room we saw looked very cramped, but the shared ones are more spacious; kitchen with four ovens; two basement common rooms with games consoles, drum kit, pool table and mega TV screen, plus challenging outdoor climbing frame. Additional sixth form boys' house. Full, weekly and flexi-boarding. House staff supported by recently graduated university students. Good programme of weeekend activities and treats following Saturday morning school, eg late Sunday morning brunch. Happy boarders, apart from the odd grumble about things taking a while to get repaired.

Background and atmosphere: Situated in the centre of York in a nine acre estate. Gracious Georgian frontages and interiors with skilfully harmonised modern additions. The main building, the original house, has a warm, homely atmosphere – attractive dining room with wooden furniture and red and cream curtains; the original library has been supplemented with a modern mezzanine floor and is lavishly supplied with reference and fiction books.

Founded 1823 by the Society of Friends (Quakers) for boys, fully co-ed by 1983. Only a minority of Quakers now, but Quaker values and ethos are central and make it distinctive. Relationships, based on mutual respect, come first; co-operation, peaceful approaches to conflict, individuality and equality are all fostered – staff and students are currently working on a new chapter of expectations that applies to both groups; school council pupils interview teaching candidates. The goal is to produce young people who are 'happy in their own skins, confident without being arrogant' (head), who assume they will find purpose and contentment in life through contributing to the community and wider world – many go on to work in the voluntary sector – rather than just pursuing materialism and competition: people who recognise and develop 'that of God' in themselves and others. Facilities widely shared with state schools and the community.

The morning Meeting – a short period of silent reflection – is valued by the pupils: 'When I was in year 7 I thought it was boring, but now I appreciate it' (year 9 boy); 'It gives you time to think about what you want, or not think at all'; 'It's a good time to relax, not be busy'.

Fab choice of high quality food made in house: hot and cold, carnivore and veggie – we can understand why many parents are keen to take up the open invitation to have lunch as a family on Saturdays (no charge), after the optional Meeting, and term it the 'best restaurant in York'.

More relaxed (and cheaper) uniform than most – years 7-9: polo shirt, hoodie, black trousers/tartan skirt; years 10-11: smart casual, but no jeans; sixth: free choice so long as appropriate for school.

Junior school acquired 2002; purpose built, intimate size, with corridor walls in a warm yellow. Extensive grounds with playing fields (shared with senior school), courts and thoughtfully equipped playgrounds – we particularly liked the covered picnic tables with built in games boards and the outdoor oven. Yurt for quiet time in breaks, peace garden, plus amphitheatre for small-scale performances. Attractive spacious classrooms with colourful displays; delightful early years/before and after school area (wrap around care 7.30am-6pm).

Quaker values displayed on the walls and developed, for example, through encouragement to be active citizens – discussion of politics, school council, charity fundraising, eco projects, singing carols in old people's homes. We liked the 'disposition boxes', containing tokens for displays of independence, resilience, being collaborative, creative, reflective and adventurous – not competitive, other than aiming to improve on the previous term or year, though plenty of matches and house competitions on offer as well. Strong sense of community, being mutually supportive, nurtured; individual achievements seen as the result of group effort. Children take the initiative, eg bid for funds raised by the (very active) PTA, then choose and order equipment; interview teaching candidates; year 6s plan and lead their residential.

Parental praise for chef, who cares about the children as individuals and provides a great diversity of high quality food. They also appreciate the staff's eating with the children, encouraging them to eat correctly, and the amount of time the year 5-6s spend at the senior school, which helps them to adjust easily when they move up. 'The school is very good at developing confidence and self worth and sees the children in a holistic way – they want to know about any outside school difficulties as well and are very helpful with them.'

Pastoral care, well-being and discipline: Well-being a particular focus. Usual tutor groups, heads of year structure. Pupils talked appreciatively of readily accessible health centre services, 'You can go there whenever you want, even if you're in a lesson'. Access to a counsellor. Programme of external speakers on mental well-being much appreciated – a parent of three boys of different ages reported: 'The material has been new and interesting; they understand things from a young person's perspective'. Sixth formers provide a peer listening scheme.

Space given to discussing politics (in lessons and morning Meetings) and its practice – eg the recent mock election (Labour won – just) and EU referendum (Remain won 70:30)

Punishment seen as an opportunity for the offender to learn more about the reasons for their behaviour and its effects on others. Education in downsides of mobile use – restricted for younger boarders at night; older students only allowed them in relaxation time.

Pupils and parents: Day pupils mainly from York and the surrounding area, up to a 25 mile radius, from the junior school, prep schools, state primaries. Boarders from the UK plus over 20 other countries including Europe, the Far East, China, Nigeria, Russia, USA. Parents from a range of backgrounds – business, professionals, public service, academics; ethnically mixed. 'Our parents want their children to become good people, have purposeful, meaningful lives,' says head; they value the Quaker ethos and educational values. Parents we spoke to in general delighted with the school – just the odd comment about occasional failures of communication.

The pupils we met were impressively thoughtful and mature, articulate, open, relaxed. They spoke warmly about their teachers, 'They care about you and your development as a person..They want to know how you are and feel'. Space given to discussion of politics (in lessons and morning Meetings) and the practice of it – eg the recent mock election (Labour won – just) and EU referendum (Remain won 70:30). They also appreciate the priority given to relationships, the non authoritarian and relatively relaxed atmosphere, with freedom to speak your mind in lessons, friendliness and sense of community.

A deeply impressive number of very distinguished old boys dating back to the 19th century. Scholars such as physicist Silvanus Thompson, who worked alongside Michael Faraday on electro-magnetism (plus 16 more fellows of the Royal Society); mathematician Lewis Fry Richardson ('father of fractals'); historian AJP Taylor; child psychiatrist Michael Rutter. Politicians, such as the Anti Corn Law leader John Bright and Olympic athlete and Nobel peace prize winner Philip Noel-Baker. A tradition of social reform exemplified by members of the Rowntree family and actor and disabled champion Brian Rix. More recently: Olivia Garfield, CEO of Severn Trent Water (one of 2013 Fortune Magazine's top 10 highflyers under 40), Elizabeth Waterman (in list of top 50 women in engineering), Emily Sutton, artist and illustrator, Benjamin Leftwich, singer-songwriter

Entrance: Junior school: non selective. Taster day – a normal day in school, with future classmates, to allow child and teacher to get to know each other and ensure school is a good fit, plus meeting with head and report from current school. Year 5/6 entry has English and maths test included.

11+: initial 30 minute interview with the headmaster before enrolment about what the child enjoys most/least at school and leisure activities; reference from head of current school (child needs to be at least at national average level for reading, writing and maths). Optional taster Saturday morning in autumn term before entry. Assessment day in January: science and art activities, challenges, brief maths and English comprehension tests.

12+,13+ and 14+: all do maths and English papers; years 9 and 10 also do French/German/Spanish paper; short interview with head or deputy head.

Sixth form entry: minimum of seven GCSEs at C/4 or above (or six GCSEs, of which three must be at B/6 or higher), including maths and English, and requirements of chosen A level subjects (20-25 join).

Exit: Almost all junior school pupils progress to the senior school. Small number leave post 16 for more vocational courses at local sixth form colleges. Several to top universities (occasional one or two to Oxbridge), to study a broad range of subjects, including art and music. Sheffield and Newcastle popular.

Money matters: Means tested bursaries awarded according to need and academic performance in 11 and 13 plus exam. Music scholarships of up to 50 per cent of fees based on tests and audition plus performance in entrance assessment. Bursaries for children from Quaker families from age 3. Means-tested scholarship/bursary for candidates from state-maintained schools who gain a minimum of eight A*-A/9-7 grades at GCSE.

Remarks: Strikingly friendly and calm atmosphere, with priority genuinely given to the development of emotional intelligence, as the way to future happiness, and respect for individual differences, rather than on academic and other kinds of achievement. Not that results don't matter – parents say they bring out the best in children in all ways and that talents are cultivated to the highest level.

Campbell College

7

Belmont Road, Belfast, County Antrim BT4 2ND

028 9076 3076 | hmoffice@campbellcollege.co.uk | www.campbellcollege.co.uk

Ages: 4-18 (boarding from 11)

Pupils: 920; sixth form: 240; Boarders: 150

Day: £2,630 – £8,120 pa; Boarding: £13,685 – £19,175 pa

Headmaster: Since 2012 Robert M Robinson MBE BSc MEd PQH (NI). Married to Sharon; they live in a house in the grounds and have two grown up children. He grew up in Belfast and went to Methody (Methodist College) and read chemistry at Queen's, where he also took a masters in education. He had planned to go into the church and says he 'fell into teaching'. His first job was at Glastry High School where he 'learnt to bring out the best in each pupil and how good teaching could transform lives'. He taught chemistry at Regent House before moving to Rainey Endowed School, where he spent 10 years as headmaster – he transformed the school and was awarded an MBE for services to education – he collaborated with other schools in the town and shared best practice which broke down barriers – 'it was a very exciting time,' he says.

Softly spoken but passionate about the school, he says, 'you can feel the 120 years of history in every corner of the place'; 'I would not have moved for any other position'. He says that joining a boarding school was a leap of faith as he expected it to be grim dorms and iron bedsteads; he was pleasantly surprised and would now like to grow the boarding. 'The ethos here is simple and complex,' he says, 'to encourage every boy to be the best he can, be as this will breed confidence and success.' 'Boys will jump as high as the bar is set'. 'Our aim is the development of character and leaderships skills, and we want boys to believe they can truly make a difference to society'. He believes that single sex education suits boys as 'they tend to showboat for the girls, and here they don't have to worry about perceptions and can feel comfortable about getting involved with the choir or the arts.' He is approachable and easy to talk to, and is a regular on the touchline at matches and at school pick-up time. He sends signed birthday cards to every boy in the school, 'a lovely touch,' says a mother, 'and makes the school feel like a huge family'. Ever modest, he says, 'I fear I am one dimensional, as my great pleasures are reading, playing the guitar, walking and running and the church'.

Three of the five families living on site are called Robinson, in fact it is almost a requirement for working here, and causes some wonderful confusion with emails.

Academic matters: Only 70 per cent of pupils joining at 11+ are academically selected which puts these results into context. In 2017, 24 per cent of grades at A level were A*/A (50 per cent A*/B) and 26 per cent of grades at GCSE were A*-A/9-7. Offers 26 subjects at GCSE and 27 at A level, and curriculum tweaked each year according to demand. Good range of hard, academic subjects including politics offered at A level as well as media studies, leisure studies, PE and BTecs in hospitality and sport. The most popular and successful A levels are maths, history, physics, chemistry and business studies.

As well as the usual subjects, computing and ICT, business studies, hospitality & catering, motor vehicle studies, leisure & tourism and Chinese offered at GCSE. Most take individual sciences but dual award offered and a handful take the single award. All taught in quite old fashioned labs– a new science block is on the headmaster's wish list.

Numerous academic competitions and trips: physicists visit CERN and technology students often take part in Sentinus Young Innovators finals at Ulster University. Business studies students visit the BMW factory in Munich and there is a history trip to the battlefields and war graves of northern France.

Some subjects shared with Strathearn Girls' School – girls come over for drama and boys go to Strathearn for media studies. German is shared between the two schools with good results, thanks to an inspirational teacher. All boys study home economics for the first two years, with particular emphasis on healthy eating.

The headmaster says that 'every boy has the right to be pushed academically' and there is subject streaming from year 8 (English year 7). GCSE class sizes about 18, dropping to 14 in sixth form and as low as three for some subjects like further maths.

Very low turnover among the staff, which gives stability and a sense of belonging. Says the head, 'Once you teach at Campbell it gets into your bones'. Still a good age range and balance of male and female staff, with almost half being female. 'Teachers know their stuff and go the extra mile for us,' said a pupil.

Warm, light-filled library with a full time librarian as well as pupil librarians, well equipped with computers and printers, a popular space for studying. Busy careers department with three staff. 'Boys need to see the context of what work can do and need to meet people in the work place,' says the headmaster. Old Campbellians are keen to give back to the school and come to give talks about the world of work via the Leaders in Society programme, eg what it is actually like to be a young barrister. They also help with personal statements, interview technique and how boys should present themselves. Boys expected to do three days of work experience in year 13 (English year 12) – old boys very helpful and school has a good network of contacts.

Busy careers department with three staff. 'Boys need to see the context of what work can do and need to meet people in the work place,' says the headmaster

Fairly large SEN department with a SENCo and a team of assistants who can liaise with external agencies if necessary. Most are identified by screening and careful observation by staff or self-referral. Pupils taught in mainstream classes with extra help as required in one-to-one sessions or small groups. Those needing any extra help are given an IEP, the SEN department works closely with teaching and pastoral staff and parents are kept up to date. Those with literacy difficulties can choose not to take both English GCSEs. About 28 statemented children in the school, with conditions ranging from autism and hearing difficulties to wheelchair users – managed discreetly so boys can join in as much as possible and take part in some sports.

EAL team of three – about 70 pupils need some form of assistance; department offers pastoral as well as language support and international students see the head of EAL as their first point of contact. Pupils can take a GCSE in their own language and the department will prepare pupils for the IELTS exams.

Games, options, the arts: 'Sporting prowess is part of the fabric of the school,' says the prospectus. Rugby and hockey the main sports but school also fields three football teams. Badminton, basketball and table tennis popular with the international students. Rugby is king here and the top rugby players are heroes. The school has won the Ulster Schools Cup 23, times and boys have represented Ulster and Ireland. Matches played all over Northern Ireland as well as south of the border and on the mainland, and there is a rugby tour to South Africa, Canada or Australia every three years. 'You don't have to be brilliant, though and boys have a lot of fun at the lower levels and it is even ok not to play at all,' said one less sporty boy. Athletics and cricket the main summer sports, with two cricket teams per year group.

Eleven rugby pitches, including the hallowed first XV Fox's Field overlooked by Stormont. Two synthetic pitches for hockey, a 25 metre pool, a fitness suite, two sports halls and a running track; boys can play golf at the local Shandon golf club. The school has its own rifle range and has a good record of success at Bisley – although some of the younger boys complain that they don't get a chance to shoot. The school will support boys who want to take part in outside activities, for example, one keen showjumper put together a school team to take part in local competitions.

New head of music reinvigorating the department – about 120 learn an instrument and performance is part of the new remit. There is a large choir, chamber choir, orchestra, jazz band and string quartet.

Active drama department, with 120 seat theatre and drama studio – girls from Strathearn come over to join in and the two schools collaborate on large scale musicals.

Well-equipped technology department which offers CAD and a laser cutter, and impressive art and ceramics displayed around the school; we were particularly struck by a red chalk drawing of a boy's grandfather. Not that many take art and design at GCSE, but those who do get very good results with vast majority of grades A*/As.

Wide range of after-school activities every day. Campbell College has one of the largest combined CCFs in the UK with over 300 members – all voluntary and includes a pipe band. The army is by far the most popular but many attracted to the RAF as a way of getting a pilot's licence. Members of the CCF can take a BTec in public service.

About 85 boys involved with D of E with 12-15 each year getting gold. One sixth former has contested and won Youth Parliament elections and represents East Belfast in the MYP. About 40 do Young Enterprise each year with recent projects including selfie sticks and software for keeping track of your phone.

CS Lewis attended the school for a short time, and it is rumoured that the gas lamp in the drive inspired the one in the Narnia books

Boarding: 'The ethos of boarding runs through the whole school' and many staff and their families live on site all year round. Numbers have grown recently and there are now 150 boarders from all over the world: Northern Ireland, including some expats, rest of UK and Europe, especially Spanish, and what the headmaster calls the far away pupils – about 40 from Hong Kong and China and usually a handful from the Cayman Islands and the UAE, who come for the rugby.

They live in School House. The original dorms were for 50 boys each but now junior boys (11-13 year olds) share small rooms of up to five and all senior boys from year 11 (English year 10) have their own study bedrooms. Upper sixth have a separate house with ensuite bathrooms, which also accommodates up to 16 girl boarders from Strathearn School (separated by locked, alarmed doors). The conversion of the original Victorian building has posed a few challenges but all the rooms we saw were light and airy and extremely tidy. Dedicated head of boarding (another Mr Robinson) and a team of staff look after the boys and the girls have their very own Miss Honey to take care of them.

Some local boys go home for the weekend but usually 90-100 in on Saturday nights. Sports and activities for all on Saturday mornings and most of day boys come in. Sundays are quieter but weekend activities are consistently being reviewed. Boys can take a taxi into Belfast and go to the cinema or karting or a rugby match – boys organise and staff facilitate. Plenty organised during the week and boys have access to the fitness suite every evening and to the swimming pool on Thursdays and can play squash or take part in house football, badminton and basketball competitions. 'Sport is a good way to socialise and get to know people,' said an international boarder. House cookery is popular and boys are allowed to go to Tesco on Monday nights and cook their own supper. Library for junior prep as well as a games room, sitting areas and a television and Xbox rooms – 'although we hardly ever watch television,' said one boarder.

Background and atmosphere: Founded in 1894 with a bequest from Henry Campbell, a philanthropist who had made his fortune in the linen trade and wanted to give something back to society, the school is set on a 100 acre wooded site in East Belfast. The main building is a monument to imperialism with an imposing, red-brick façade complete with clock tower, and radiates high Victorian ideals. Inside it is all wooden panelling and displays of silverware with an open fire in the entrance lobby. The galleried central hall with a stained glass rose window is at the heart of the school and is used for plays, concerts, assemblies and chapel services. The school is very conscious of its history and traditions – pictures of the fallen from both world wars line the walls, but it is not a backward looking place and respect and tolerance are part of its fabric. C S Lewis attended the school for a short time, and it is rumoured that the gas lamp in the drive is the inspiration for the one in the Narnia books.

Boys are smartly turned out and wear black badged blazers and black trousers with a white shirt and house tie. Whole school charity strategy driven by the boys – all vote for the school's charity of the year and raise about £6,000 a year. They run large and small events – pumpkin carving at the local hospice, a touch rugby family festival, Christmas market, a jingle bell run which brings in the local community.

A kindergarten and junior school for boys aged 3-11 in the grounds opened in 2006, replacing the Cabin Hill School. It is quite separate from the senior school, but shares some of the facilities, including the swimming pool and sports pitches, and boys come up to the main dining hall for lunch. A very well designed multi-purpose space with an opening roof and classrooms leading off. Has its own ICT suite, library, Astro and sports hall. Lots of outdoor learning, including a mud kitchen, and boys can build dens in the woods.

Produces confident, friendly boys who are able to stand up and do a presentation by the age of 7. They are made aware of the world of work from an early age, and doctors and dentists visit the school to talk about their work, to help make learning real. Boy-friendly approach to reading and writing with male authors coming in to give talks, and artwork is linked to topics. Boys from the senior school act as mentors and positive role models, and are trained to help with reading sessions – this works both ways as also looks good on a UCAS form.

Wrap-around care is available from 8am until 6pm to help working parents and those with sons in the senior school.

Pastoral care, well-being and discipline: Six houses for day boys and one for boarders, with healthy competition between them in the form of debating, assemblies and sports day. Each has a housemaster and all boys have a personal tutor attached to the house, who is also the first point of contact for parents. Boys can take risks and learn that it is ok to get things wrong. The ones we spoke to were very happy with single sex education: 'It means we can focus on our studies and get good grades and play lots of sport'. 'It is a lovely environment to learn in,' said a parent, 'where boys can be boys but are treated as young adults, and are encouraged to do everything to their full potential'.

Everyone eats lunch in the enormous dining hall, though despite the good and plentiful food – even the bread is baked on site – some prefer to bring in a packed lunch.

The school has a robust set of policies to deal with any misdemeanours – immediate suspension if a boy seriously breaches the school's code of conduct, which can lead to permanent exclusion, but issues dealt with on a case by case basis. Bullying is not tolerated and the house system means tutors know boys well and can nip it in the bud.

Boys can take a taxi into Belfast and go to the cinema or karting or a rugby match

A counsellor comes in one day a week, and several members of staff are also trained as counsellors – parents and staff can refer pupils or boys can self-refer. Quick to pick up problems and get in touch with parents if they are concerned. A close eye kept on time management to make sure boys don't take on too much, especially in sixth form.

Pupils and parents: Some parents very affluent and others struggle to send their children here, but all want to give their sons the very best education and are supportive of the school. About 40 per cent of boarders are foreign nationals, mainly from Europe and the Far East – the headmaster goes on marketing trips to Hong Kong. Some of the Europeans only come for a year and can take a pared down GCSE course.

There is no PTA but a parents' forum helps them feel involved in their sons' lives. Three progress cards and one report per year plus ongoing communication makes parents feel part of the community, and a parent Campbellian gives parents a voice and acts as a way of raising concerns. Old boys are extremely loyal to their school and the Old Campbellian Society has over 5,000 members spanning four generations. They support scholarships and international exchange visits and there are a number of get-togethers throughout the year including dances and dinners and the Boxing Day rugby fixture.

Distinguished list of old boys with a good representation from the army including a VC and an air chief marshall, rugby players, numerous MPs, film makers, judges, media people and journalists as well as Tim Martin, founder and chairman of Wetherspoons and actor David Caves of Silent Witness fame.

Produces well rounded boys 'of management quality' who are ready for life after school.

Entrance: Entry to the junior school at 3+ or 4+. Most boys join the senior school at 11+ or 16+, but will take applicants at any time if space available. Eleven plus entrance is via the Northern Ireland CEA and GL assessment (similar to the English 11+ and with similar problems with over-tutoring). Language test for non-native English speakers – their English must be good enough for them to be able to access lessons. A minimum of six GCSEs at grade C/5 or above including English and maths plus a specified number of points required to join the sixth form – both from within the school and external candidates. Sometimes it is suggested that a boy might take a different path.

Exit: Nearly all junior school boys move up to the senior school. About half of senior leavers go to Russell Group universities. Queen's University, Belfast is the most popular followed by the University of Ulster, but about two-thirds venture further afield to a wide range of universities, mostly to the mainland, including one to Cambridge in 2017, but also to Europe and the USA. Boys study a wide range of subjects including biomedical sciences, business and media studies, art & design and computer science – STEM subjects are increasingly popular.

Money matters: The school is a Voluntary B grammar school, which means that fees for senior day tuition for EU passport holders are under £3,000 pa (over £8,000 pa for non-EU). All tuition, teachers' salaries etc are paid for by the state but the school has to pay for the upkeep of the buildings. The senior boarding fee for EU citizens including tuition is £13,685 pa, nearly £20,000 for non EU citizens. Academic scholarships for up to 50 per cent of fees and the school offers bursaries of up to 100 per cent of fees based on academic performance for boys on free school meals.

Remarks: A highly successful all boys' school with a strong sense of history, where academic achievement and excellence on the rugby pitch are highly rated – but still a tolerant and inclusive community with strong pastoral care. A school which deserves to be better known by the wider community.

Cargilfield School

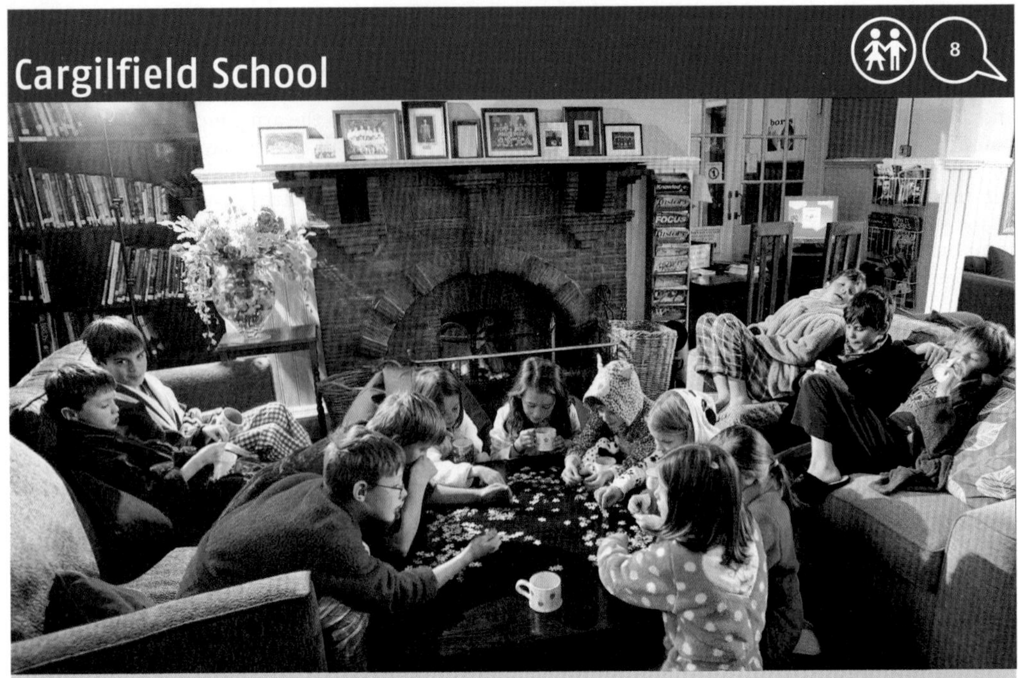

45 Gamekeeper's Road, Edinburgh EH4 6HU

0131 3362207 | registrar@cargilfield.com | www.cargilfield.com

Ages: 3–13 (boarding from 8)

Pupils: 309; **Boarders:** 25 weekly, 31 flexi

Day: £9,984 – £15,384 pa; **Boarding:** £18,879 pa

Headmaster: Since 2014, Rob Taylor, previously registrar at Harrow School. He has also been head of Ashdown Prep School in Sussex. He is married to Sarah, and they have three children. Took over from acting head following the abrupt departure in October 2013 of previous head and his wife.

Entrance: Nursery and pre-prep popular; upper school numbers have grown enormously; places pretty well guaranteed through pre-prep but tests if learning difficulties suspected. Wannabes assessed: occasional places may occur throughout the school – logistics.

Exit: Fettes, Glenalmond, Oundle, Eton, Uppingham, Rugby, Winchester, Wycombe Abbey, Harrow, Queen Margaret's, York, Merchiston, Ampleforth, Gordonstoun, St Mary's Ascot, Radley, Sedbergh, Strathallan, Loretto amongst currently popular schools.

Remarks: Cargilfield had a bad case of wobbles with rapid head turn-over. We arrived to find the school covered in scaffolding and wondered about a new, new-build, but no, just roof repairs. (The £1.2 million games changing rooms are up and running.) This former parent of the pre-prep (still brill) regrets the reduction of play area (previously 23 acres now 15: posho pads equal new builds); the sports hall (a 21st century prerequisite) impinges on the games pitch, alongside a couple of cedar-clad (rather grand inside) huts, which blend well, but look like early huts for battery hens (or photographs of Bletchley Park), and provide a new teaching centre plus a 10-room (soundproof) music school with a mini-concert rehearsal room, used for drama too. A stonking 80 per cent take extra music. Strong choir, which tours 'down south', and terrific strings ensemble: 'our top area and they have won major awards at the Edinburgh Music Festival'; pop group. Pipe band is second to none, taster sessions for all in pre-prep, they were practising on the games pitch as we left, certain amount of interesting baton chucking.

Impressive two-storey classroom block for English, ICT and history, with colonnades, cloisters and walkways. Certain amount of internal restructuring, with dorms becoming classrooms (and vice versa).

Pipe band is second to none; taster sessions for all in pre-prep; they were practising on the games pitch as we left

Pupils setted and streamed, maths from age 8. Most year groups divided into three: scholarship stream (currently boasting some 14 pupils) for the last three or four years plus two mixed-ability classes. French from nursery, Latin from 9 or 10; ancient Greek at 11, classical civilisation, Spanish for the last two years. (German and Mandarin clubs.) Fantastic learning support (known as learning development), all assessed on entry; head of learning support plus two and a half staff. One of the best departments in Scotland, combining individual and co-teaching: max 5.5 hours per week. Currently has a parent-underwritten (ie they pay school fees and for a dedicated teacher) unit for two pupils who have very special needs, (previous) head hesitated for a moment, but agreed this was still in place, 'an unusual arrangement'. But isn't this what the independent sector is about? School can no longer accommodate many of the weaker brethren, unless they are, in fact, brethren. Jolly Phonics and any 'other combination that works' on the reading front.

Founded in 1873, the school moved to its purpose-built site in 1890. Girls' boarding house is full, difficult to find space for flexis. Jolly sitting-rooms on ground floor (along with showers etc) and some of the prettiest dorms we have seen in a long time. Odd space in boys' dorms: trad old school dorms, huge, with sofas and games tucked into corners – given the choice, chaps preferred more mates to smaller bedrooms. Chaps in bunks, girls have drawers below beds, total replacement of furniture and fittings factored in every three years. Two-weekly boarding for all (max 74 boarders at any one time). Day pupils regularly join boarders for a huge variety of weekend activities (though all must stay for three nights and can't just pick and choose). Mega weekend activities, no Saturday school ('children more relaxed and less tired on Mondays'). Nine year olds camping in the Highlands, 12/13 year olds at Hadrian's Wall.

Kayaking, shooting, international coaching in fishing, fencing, judo, hockey, skiing both at Hillend and the real thing. Two small Astroturfs. Eighty clubs on offer – chess champions with boards set up all over the place (and visiting chess master). Trips all over, both at weekends and longer ones abroad to Rome and France. Much use made of resources in grand Scots cities. New website.

Discounts for MoD children (handy for Scottish Command). Hundred per cent bursaries on offer: means-tested – five or six pupils on this kind of bursary (but not necessarily every year), graduated sibling discount. Mixed bunch of parents, grander than previously, FWAGS now thinner on the ground, one or two proper foreigners, tiny ethnic mix. Boarders from Yorkshire, the Borders, West Coast, Aberdeenshire, Angus and Perthshire. Bus on Sundays from Angus, and daily from Saxe Coburg Place in Edinburgh and Fife but, as children often stay until after 8pm, parents must collect them themselves.

Pre-prep and nursery based in stunning £3.5m building with cherished (quite small) Astroturf and enclosed play area, share big school facilities. School not keen on folk using the nursery as a springboard for a couple of years and then heading off elsewhere (like this editor!).

Casterton, Sedbergh Preparatory School

9

Kirkby Lonsdale, via Carnforth, Lancashire LA6 2SG

01524 279200 | ajm@sedberghprep.org | www.sedberghprep.org

Ages: 6m–13 (boarding from 9)

Pupils: 200; **Boarders:** 63

Day: £8,010 – £15,600 pa; **Boarding:** £18,735 – £23,055 pa

Linked school: Sedbergh School, 1262

Headmaster: Since September 2017, Will Newman, previously deputy head of Taunton Prep. He has also been housemaster and head of boarding at Edgeborough Prep in Surrey. Education degree from Exeter; won a commonwealth scholarship to study at the University of Victoria, Canada, where he got an MA in PE. Interested in sport and music: currently concentrates on the guitar. Married to Liz, a science and maths teacher, and they have two children who have joined the school.

Entrance: Assessment by head's interview and previous school report for younger children; English, maths and cognitive ability tests for year 4 upwards.

Exit: Around 80 per cent to Sedbergh senior school.

Remarks: Eggs, 'laid with love' (says the sign) from the free range chickens here, plus the goats and the rabbits bring out the 'softer side of a prep school'. The children, while not quite 'free range' (tiger mothers and helicopter parents need not worry), have an abundance of outdoor space and room to breathe. They mostly ignore the glorious views and the weather that changes almost hourly; they are too busy enjoying their childhood.

Housed in a range of buildings, with plenty to spare; specialist science labs, inspirational art studios, music and superb sports facilities, these prep and pre-prep children are enjoying all the benefits of this former senior school. With reference to the relatively recent merger, parents say, 'it was the best thing that could have happened' – Casterton parents with older girls may disagree somewhat, but undoubtedly the feel-good factor is back and they are bucking the trend in this northern demographic with excellent post-merger recruitment figures and a good solid number of boarders. This is no mean feat in a school tucked away with no passing traffic; you have to seek it out, but advice from parents is 'if you are at all unsure, go and take a look – and take your children with you, that'll do it'. Most of us have at some point seen teary parents and weeping children at school gates at some point – well, here the children were weeping because they'd been for a taster morning and didn't want to leave.

It's so quiet here that one boarder told us he falls asleep each night to the sound of the birds singing

Variously described as a 'broad church' and 'a good all-round education', the facilities are matchless for a prep school, having originally been designed for pupils up to A level. Note the six full size science labs, massive sports hall with cricket nets and a bowling machine, swimming pool, Astroturf, music practice rooms and much more besides, and they make full use of every bit of it. Nothing precious about it; parents say the children 'live in it' rather than 'just exist', and whilst they are quick to add that 'it's the people who really make the place', they also tell us they feel as though they have 'hit the jackpot here'.

You can bring your bike, you can also bring your horse – though not essential if you have a love of riding, as the school has 10 ponies that they happily loan. Work hard and play hard could be the school's motto, though presumably only if translated into Latin; the energy is astounding, before, during and after school. Rugby, hockey, cricket, netball and much more besides mean that there is no

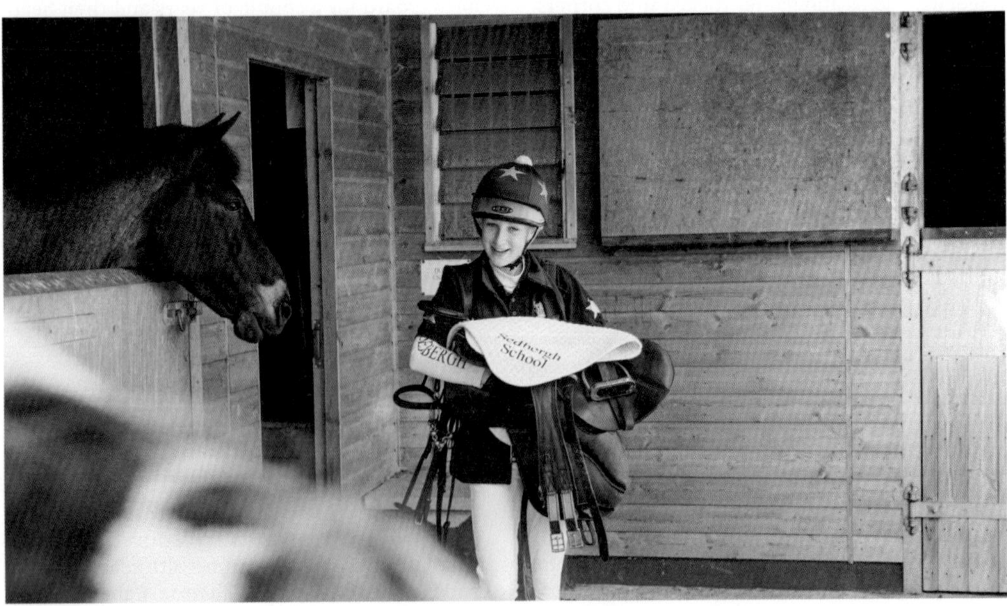

lack of fresh air and exercise. For obvious reasons, the location means that boarding makes sense, and it also allows you to join in with activities ranging from a parachute regiment leadership day to abseiling, bouldering, go-karting, clay pigeon shooting, bushcraft and (for the gentler soul) cheese-tasting; essentially, you just 'don't stay in'.

The pupils are a refreshing and captivating blend of childlike naivety and honesty alongside a wisdom that belies their years. Shoe-polishing night for boarders, fastening your top shirt button and a ban on chewing gum are happily tolerated by pupils, but, for them, the deal-breaker would be bullying, 'a real no-no', as is anything which essentially 'makes the atmosphere less friendly'. All meals are prepared in-house from, as far as possible, local produce; adults sit with the children in mixed age groups and apparently the curry is legendary.

Boarding accommodation, in rooms with views to die for, is spacious and homely; there are kitchens for extra toast-making and generally hanging out, plus a sitting room with TV and games for the boys; similar though slightly smaller and prettier accommodation for the girls with the obligatory One Direction posters. It's so quiet here that one boarder told us he falls asleep each night to the sound of the birds singing outside, and then they wake him up again in the morning.

Parents are a mix of medics from Lancaster, local business owners and landed gentry; tweed is somewhat de rigueur – practical and stylish, as befits the place. It's only a 15 minute drive to the senior school from here so parents and staff can and do manage both. Parents say it 'doesn't matter what car you drive, or even if you land your helicopter on the back field, you're made very welcome here'. House staff use Twitter to keep parents of boarders up-to-date, regular photos home of joyful, smiling children.

Clearly the merger and change of status required careful handling, but thanks to good management and huge parental advocacy, they've not only survived but thrived. A portrait of old girl Charlotte Brontë still hangs in the sitting room, and although it's still slightly old school here (and all the better for that – good manners and etiquette still count), she'd hardly recognise the warm and happy place it is today.

Dollar Academy

10

Dollar, Clackmannanshire FK14 7DU

01259 742511 | rector@dollaracademy.org.uk | www.dollaracademy.org.uk/

Ages: 5-18 (boarding from 9)

Pupils: 1,217; sixth form: 151; **Boarders:** 82

Day: £9,414 – £12,591 pa; **Boarding:** £25,956 – £29,133 pa

Rector: Since 2010, Mr David Knapman BA (maths) MPhil (40s), previously deputy head of Hampton School in London, where he still has a foot on the property ladder. At Hampton he established a no-nonsense reputation but was also notable for his work with charities and the local community. Educated at Morrisons, 'doon the road', followed by Sheffield and Exeter. Married to Brigitte with two sons (younger one attended the school). His mother lives in Dunblane and 'is my fiercest critic; she keeps her ear to the ground'. Plays tennis regularly and enjoys 'playing the piano badly'. Wife also a teacher, came from a country background and is 'pleased to be in Scotland', they like walking the hills and are planning to tackle Ben Lomond this summer (Munro bashing very popular around here).

They live in a stunning Georgian street which houses a collection of school buildings – much in demand by film crews no doubt – we yomped to the burn to see Mylne Bridge (built and named for the local minister and first rector, who opened the school in 1818, to give him a short cut to the kirk) and were told that if it 'weren't for that pine tree, we could see Castle Campbell' (we googled it – it is pretty impressive).

Has a dry sense of humour; hugely enthusiastic and 'very popular – going down well' and 'doing just fine,' say our spies. Sits in on classes, walks round every day and never misses a match, concert or play. Boarding numbers going up and examination results at a record high last year.

He was mentored by Dr Ken Greig, rector of Hutchesons Grammar in Glasgow (we hadn't realised that heads had mentors too) who seems to have grown a beard in solidarity. A mixture of young and old teachers, housing not cheap in the Dollar area but it is the perfect place for families.

Assistant rector and head of prep and junior school: Since 2010, after four years in big school, Mrs Alison Morrison, BSc (Cantab) PGDE (40s). Economics graduate, following spells in the City, advertising and television changed course (professional graduate diploma of education) at the University of Edinburgh, and has one of the most stunning collection of reviews on Rate my Teacher we have ever seen.

Academic matters: There is no formal setting in the prep and junior school with pupils receiving differentiated teaching and learning within each class. Efficient support for learning in place, with rector getting progress reports. One-to-one, small groups and supported learning in class. Variety of reading methods used, but Jolly – or unjolly come to that – Phonics in the main.

Not quite all singing and dancing new computer system (rector says 'could do better'), touch-typing for all, strong on techy subjects. We found a lovely gang of 8 year olds happily making intricate ribbon pictures (for calendars?) in the fabric/home economics room. Some of the chaps were enormously imaginative. Our attempts were rubbish.

Aged 10 (J1), pupils move to junior school, where they are looked after by Sally Horne, assistant head of the junior school, certain amount of specialist teaching in specialist rooms: hist, geog, science plus art, PE and music, by senior school staff. French, German and Spanish (the former two more popular – contrary to the apparent national trend) from J1. Three parallel classes J1, moving to four parallel classes in J2. Junior school is seen as a transition between prep and senior school.

Strong academic tradition, particularly science with a compressed science option on offer for 14-16 year olds and large numbers for medical school; English and mod langs good (housed in new Westwater Building, which won a couple of design awards); German and French more popular than Spanish; Mandarin available; Latin, Greek and classical studies (heroes for zeros) all on offer and four dedicated classics teachers. All three langs from junior school plus some Japanese, Russian, Italian, philosophy, car mechanics and other jolly options. Broad streaming for English (with EFL if needed), tight setting for maths and mixed ability in most subjects, plus. Large business department offering economics, business management, finance and accountancy.

Rumours abound whether the monies came from slavery or piracy but they were certainly augmented by bribes from ship owners

Rector and/or senior staff have a 20 minute meeting with every pupil (and their parents, who usually keep stumm during the interview) to discuss their personal subject choice. Pupils choose the subjects they want to study and classes are worked round them, rather than the trad system of block choice. There is a distinct emphasis on the academic rather than the vocational.

School follows a mixed bag of courses: National 5 (plus National 4 in maths), Intermediate I and II; Highers, Advanced Highers and the Scottish baccalaureate – which doesn't seem to have many followers outside Dollar. In 2017, a record 67 per cent of Highers and 54 per cent of Advanced Highers were A grade; 55 pupils got five A grades at Higher.

Classes of 6-24. Efficient support for learning in place; one-to-one, small groups and support learning in class all on offer. School has a positive approach to those with ADHD: pupils can drop into the dyslexia centre at any time. Serious homework, carefully spelt out in a smart little green book full of info for parents which interestingly persists in referring to the school as the Academy. 'Whatever else, we expect that all pupils in the Academy should have enough work to occupy their evenings and any child who indicates otherwise misunderstands.' Not quite all singing and dancing new computer system (school report says 'could do better'), touch-typing for all, strong on techy subjects – most to Advanced Higher level.

Games, options, the arts: No sport is compulsory. That said, boasts a first XV rugby team unbeaten for the first seven years of this century. Shooting 'phenomenal'; always a strong showing at Bisley. Hockey hot stuff. Regular tours to Europe and further afield: Canada, Japan, Italy, Argentina et al. Numerous individual county reps in major and minor sports – golf, skiing and badminton, as well as more esoteric activities such as shotput, curling, table tennis, equestrian vaulting (gymnastics on horseback) and triathlon (NB Clackmannanshire ain't that big), plus national and international team members eg Scottish rugby U18 squad. Mass of games fields, 63 acres of school grounds, much-used hall and swimming pool. Amazing circular Maguire Building – sports, arts, drama – million pound bequest from FP Brian Maguire; formidable school art on display and used for external exhibitions too – even the Scottish Examinations Authority asked for a painting for their new premises. Second bequest from the Price family resulted in a new 5.3 metre inflatable for the navy section. All weather surface was opened by Linda Clement, Scottish Ladies' hockey captain. Presumably by bullying off.

Strong volunteer CCF – good following, not just because of the trips to Canada. Three pipe bands, who all sport the Campbell tartan; the B band was third in the national CCF championships this year. Two orchestras, jazz bands, oodles of choirs; the annual Christmas concert in the Usher Hall was a sell-out with almost 2,000 in the auditorium. Drama timetabled with masses of productions – the rector believes that 'pupils gain confidence through performance'; lots of smaller concerts – 'six performers, 30 in the audience'; that sort of thing. Hot on debating, all sorts of trophies as well as representation in the winning Scotland team at recent world champs in South Africa – a tour de force. Ballroom dancing on Fridays; participants learn Latin American and rock 'n' roll, Japanese dancing the latest wheeze but no medals for this nor for Scottish country dancing. Prize winners sport their bronze, silver, gold or Scottish Awards proudly on their blazers thereafter.

His mother lives in Dunblane and 'is my fiercest critic; she keeps her ear to the ground'. Plays tennis regularly and enjoys 'playing the piano badly'. Wife also a teacher

Munro bashing, D of E, exchange and trips, work experience at home and abroad, go-kart racing at Knockhill, skiing, motor mechanics, surfing, falconry. Clubs for everything, usually post school, late buses nightly. Fabric technology timetabled. Over 70 options in total; terrific facilities; powerful charities committee (15 mile sponsored walk raised over £50,000, staff, parents and doggies all included).

Boarding: Boarders from age 9 (though not a lot of them); all boys share one dedicated house: two individual (Victorian villas) houses for girls, recently revamped – and dead posh they are too. The boarding houses are small, two with up to 24 girls in each, one for boys that takes up to 49; all three have had recent million pound facelifts, stunning.

Usual range of after-school and weekend activities – cooking to sub aqua.

Background and atmosphere: Captain John McNabb, a former herd boy who rose to become a ship's captain and, latterly, a ship husband – literally looking after ships in port – died in 1802, leaving half his fortune, £55,000, to found a school to educate children of 'the parish wheir I was born'. Rumours abound whether the monies came from slavery or piracy but they were certainly augmented by bribes from ship owners eager to be first past the post. After much shilly shallying, the Rev Andrew Mylne, a trustee, commissioned Playfair to build a 'hospital' which finally opened in 1818. The first co-ed in Scotland. McNabb's corpse was rediscovered in the 1930s and proudly brought back to Scotland, and cremated. Gruesome or what. His ashes are entombed in the wall above the main Bronze Doors; this has to be the only school in the land where pupils pass under the founder every day. By 1830, the grounds at Dollar had become an Oeconomical and Botanical garden, boasting some of the rarest trees in the country – certainly the most northerly tulip tree, as well as a Corsican pine, and specimen sequoias. Pupils originally had their own plot of garden, though we are not sure whether this was for ornamental purposes or whether they were expected to augment the school kitchen. The interior of Playfair's original building was gutted by fire in 1961, which allowed a certain amount of internal rearrangement. Zinging concert hall (the Gibson Building), improved science block. Current wish-list includes a new technology, engineering science and earth science building – to be built out of 'funds'. The grounds are open to the public daily. And the library is no longer lollipop pink.

Has a long tradition of looking after the children of tea planters, missionaries and engineers

Formerly a direct grant school, Dollar became independent in 1974 – a day school, with a boarding element, around 50 per cent of boarders international. Easily accessible from most of Scotland and just a short hop from the Forth Road Bridge and Edinburgh Airport. Wet weather a feature of the place and masses of matches are rained (or snowed) off (school says very rarely due to new all-weather Astroturf courts and pitches). NB The school uniform includes beanies (first time ever for us on a clothes list) and macs with fleecy linings. Rector says he doesn't mind what they wear on their heads, as long as they are warm.

Pastoral care, well-being and discipline: Automatic out for drugs. Lousy work equals detentions post-school or early morning – dead unpopular with parents, plus out if 'The pupil is not deriving benefit from being at the school or indicates by his/her conduct that he/she does not accept the rules of the Academy.' Pupils not particularly streetwise – but modern studies popular and strong politics and international relations society.

Victorian values, with clear rules; many of the petty restrictions have been done away with.

Pupils and parents: The vast majority comes from within a 30 mile radius – impressive number of buses, plus Forces children and a contingent from the Scottish diaspora worldwide. Dollar itself has the reputation of having the highest percentage of graduates of any town in the country. School has a long tradition of looking after the children of tea-planters, missionaries and engineers – still. Perhaps a tad parochial and 'mercifully' free of Sloanes. Exceptionally strong and active FP network, including Sir Frank Swettenham, the first Governor of Malaysia, Sir James Dewar, the inventor of the vacuum flask, and the sculptor, George Paulin. The governing body is mostly FPs, which ensures that the place has freedom to develop but an awareness of its history shapes the thinking – no bad thing.

Entrance: Pupils come to junior school at 5 or 10: the latter by fairly selective entrance exam. To seniors usually at 11 or 12, by examination, which is quite selective. Generally oversubscribed for entry at fifth and sixth forms; each case individually considered; good GCSE or National/Intermediate grades required plus good refs and an ability to put something into the school. Open day in September, but parents and prospective pupils are welcome to visit at any point of the year, which gives the opportunity to see the school in action.

Exit: Virtually all go on to senior school, though the occasional one may peel off for trad schools ('very very rare for someone to leave,' says the rector). A handful to Oxbridge each year (two in 2017). Otherwise most students head for the Scottish universities: Edinburgh, St Andrews, Glasgow, Aberdeen, with under a quarter going south or abroad. Eight medics in 2017. Low gap year take up: either a reflection of the recession or the 'get on with it' mentality. The chairman of governors and his wife have set up a trust with more than £1 million to encourage the youngsters to take up challenges involving travel. If that doesn't persuade entrepreneurs overseas.

Money matters: Collection of means tested-academic bursaries at 11 and 12, plus ESU, Forces and boarding bursaries (usually means-tested, with tuition not covered). Fees very reasonable; governors tough on non-payers.

Remarks: Very sound – this large, solid, co-ed school provides education in the best Scottish 'get on with it' tradition, facing the 21st century with the expectations and values of an earlier age, mercifully free of most of the excesses of the 60s. 'Robust teaching and meritocracy' are important here. Up there with the best of the merchant schools.

Durham School

11

Quarry Heads Lane, Durham DH1 4SZ

0191 7319270 | admissions@durhamschool.co.uk | www.durhamschool.co.uk

Ages: 11–18

Pupils: 388; sixth form: 159; **Boarders:** 62 full, 31 weekly, 3 flexi

Day: £13,791 – £15,993 pa; **Boarding:** £22,041 – £31,767 pa

Headmaster: Since 2014, Kieran McLaughlin (early 40s), previously deputy head (academic) at Rugby. Studied natural sciences at Cambridge, specialising in physics and theoretical physics. Has been head of science and technology at Sevenoaks and head of physics at City of London Girls. Attended selective boys' school St Edward's College in Liverpool, having won an assisted place. In the past was the bass player in an obscure Liverpudlian rock band, as well as pursuing the ancient martial art of jiu-jitsu to black belt level. Married with three young children.

Feels that after some change the school needs time to consolidate. He brings experience of a variety of schools (Durham is his sixth): single sex, co-ed, city day, day and boarding, traditional boarding. Although only 15 per cent of pupils are regular boarders (25 per cent when occasional/flexi boarders are included), he says, 'The school feels like a boarding school', and we would agree.

His focus has been on delivering the school's message in the city and beyond. He believes that 'the school is much better than is generally perceived at delivering its core purpose'. Emphasis is on holistic educational experience, evidenced by the value added at A level being in the top 10 per cent of independent schools. Reminders, too, about academic success, and work is in progress to drive standards higher without being 'an academic hothouse'. Durham is a city where education really does matter and word of mouth really does count. One parent we spoke told us that they had researched in depth seven schools before selecting Durham School.

Has a collegiate management style; teaches physics to year 12. Has an easy manner, and when walking around the school it is obvious he is a visible head to his pupils. Very strong vote of confidence from parents, with one summing up the tenor of the parents we spoke to: 'He is an asset to the school and clearly has a firm grasp on the challenges within education and the strategic development needed to stay ahead and maintain standards of excellence'.

Currently not too distracted by the Durham International Schools initiative – a franchising joint venture with Indian company Infinity, looking to clone Durham ethos in the UAE.

Academic matters: A level 36 per cent A*/A, 68 per cent A*-B in 2017. Probably why school is working to develop academic aspects of the sixth form ('more rigour', a study centre, supervised study time, more intellectual societies). Wide choice of subjects includes economics, politics, psychology, philosophy and ethics, government and politics, classical civilisation, photography, theatre and business studies. EPQ now available together with an enrichment programme which includes a lecture series and five societies, supervised by staff but run by students: Academic, Politic, Heretics, Tristam (scientists) and Medsoc (would-be medics). Very good support with university applications and Oxbridge/elite university preparation.

GCSE results 40 per cent A*-A/9-7 in 2017. Mathematics, two English, separate sciences or dual award and a modern language compulsory. Option choice includes Latin, classical civilisation, ethics and drama, music, PE, DT graphic products and Greek, off timetable. German or Spanish added to French in year 9 (can also do Latin) and language awareness days, with themed meals. Most recent inspection praised pupil-staff relationships, teaching and use of monitoring, but commented on some marking inconsistency, which school is addressing.

Plenty of opportunity to showcase their dramatic talents – big musicals like Les Misérables in Durham's Gala Theatre or plays like The Great Gatsby in the school's own space

Classrooms tend to be traditional, with just one computer plus projector (only a few interactive whiteboards), some darkish, but also some new ones and some modern ICT facilities with a stock of iPads. 'Bring your own device' has been introduced. Wifi connectivity has improved and there's a VLE.

Strong learning support department – well qualified, flexible, sensitive; can cope with most needs apart from severe behavioural problems. The spread out nature of the campus could be a problem for anyone with major physical disabilities. Screens all new entrants for dyslexia and ESL, if from overseas (extra charge for ESL – full-time specialist – and learning support sessions); trains other staff. Thorough-going gifted and talented policy – systematic identification and monitoring, early maths GCSE, fourth A level and extra, challenging activities.

Games, options, the arts: Astroturf, functional swimming pool, sports hall, playing fields, very good rowing facilities and access to top flight coaching. Individuals and teams successful at regional, county and national levels with rugby first XV reaching the Natwest Trophy semi finals and the hockey teams getting to the National Schools regional finals recently.

One of the oldest rowing clubs in the country (dates from 1847) – the whole 1970 crew represented GB and has current international stars. Water polo taking off in a big way, ski team reached finals of English Schools' Championships, a GB fencer; also cross-country, golf, squash, boxing, rifle shooting, wind surfing and climbing. All pupils participate in 4.5 hours of sport and physical activity per week, still partly compulsory in the sixth form. Girls have more chance of being in teams through being in a minority.

Very accomplished choral singing – TV appearances, radio broadcasts, including Radio 4's Sunday

Worship and a number of CDs. All Steinway school so plenty of pianists. Orchestras, jazz band, rock group; performance opportunities abound with concerts at The Sage, Gateshead and Durham Cathedral plus foreign tours.

Plenty of opportunity to showcase their dramatic talents in a variety of genres and settings – big musicals like Les Misérables in Durham's Gala Theatre or plays like The Great Gatsby in the school's own performance space, The Luce. Also more informal performances take place in the school's modern studio theatre.

Inter-house competition is rife with the show-stopping annual music competition (staged alternate years in the Sage and the Chapel) top of the bill. Sporting and drama events are staged throughout the year with much-coveted trophies for the winners.

Wide choice of activities from creative writing to computer programming, peer support to the languages film club. D of E and CCF (all three sections). School participates in BBC School Report (writing news bulletins and reports) and the lively and entertaining school newspaper, The Durham Eye, printed in house, has reached the finals of a national schools media competition. Careers education now expanding using network of Old Dunelmians.

Just enjoy the view; mellow sandstone buildings flank grassy lawns leading to the hill that ascends to the chapel

Lots of fundraising for charity and foreign trips – staff and pupils seem to have bags of energy and enterprise; Chinese exchange visit to Chengdu; World Challenge to Borneo, Africa, Ecuador, Vietnam or India, cricket tour to Antigua, hockey tour to Portugal, rowing camps in Belgium and Norway, winter walking in Scotland, ski trip to the Alps – plenty of opportunities to do good and see the world.

Boarding: With boarding all is possible – full, weekly and part time. Four of the five houses include day and boarding pupils – three for boys and one for girls. The majority of boarders are from overseas (plus Forces children) – most from Hong Kong, mainland China and Europe – and room allocations mix nationalities. Each house, located along a street outside the main campus, has studies (shared or single), common rooms, kitchen and leisure facilities, and have had some refurbishment. The boarding provision was graded good in the last inspection – a relaxed atmosphere, flexible

eating arrangements on Sundays, plenty of activities. Good range of food (we can recommend the home-made veg soup), but boarders we met wanted a more substantial meal later in the evening, after their sports training.

Background and atmosphere: One of oldest schools in the country – goes back to Cardinal Langley's refounding of Durham Cathedral in 1414; at the end of the last century became more or less independent of the dean and chapter. Originally situated on Palace Green, next to the cathedral; moved to present site on other side of River Wear, 1844, only five minutes' walk from city centre.

The entrance to the school provides an attractive glimpse of the site – though there is no time to enjoy it if arriving at break times. Hordes of pupils stream across the car park on the way to their houses, seemingly oblivious to any car navigating its way to the tightly packed parking bays.

Once stationary, just enjoy the view; mellow sandstone buildings flank grassy lawns leading to the hill that ascends to the chapel. The 98 steps all commemorate old boys who died in the two world wars. On Remembrance Day the whole school lines the stairs at twilight, holding candles, while a wreath is laid on the memorial plaque, which must be very moving. Stunning view of viaduct, cathedral and school from the top. The 1926 traditional chapel has pews etched with the names of all leavers.

Further up is the Astroturf and beyond, up again, are rugby pitches. You need to be pretty fit just to get to them, let alone train and play. The sports hall and sixth form centre can be found in this vicinity after passing the quirky classics building.

There is a real feel of a traditional rural boarding school, with lovely views of sports fields and gardens containing many mature trees. Although the majority of the pupils don't board (day ends at 6pm), each has a house where they have common rooms and their own space to retreat to before and after school and during breaks in the day. Registration is held here each morning with the houseparent and there are strong bonds between fellow house members.

Girls were introduced into the sixth form in 1985 and Durham became fully co-educational in 1998. Girls feel that there has been a move in recent years to fully integrate them in what is now a true co-educational setting. They are outnumbered 2:1 by the boys, but feel 'very comfortable with the balance,' having single sex houses.

There is a strong sense of community and leadership opportunities with house captains and monitors (prefects) who are now selected through written application and interview.

One of the oldest rowing clubs in the country (dates from 1847) – the whole 1970 crew represented GB and has current international stars. Water polo taking off in a big way

Chapel plays a central role in school life with three assemblies a week. There are also strong links to the cathedral with services and concerts held there. Various school councils and pupils told us that they feel their voices are heard. A parent told us that 'The school finds where the individual can develop and works with it'. Not only discovering academic, sporting or musical latent talent but 'developing confident individuals with great self belief'. Parents like the house system, providing 'ever greater maturity and acceptance of responsibility' to pupils – and the competition too, 'They all get very involved'.

Pastoral care, well-being and discipline: Pastoral care centred on form tutor and house staff, plus chaplain – rated outstanding by inspection, which glowed about relationships in general and moral and social development. Bullying not seen as a problem – pupils we met felt should it occur, it would be dealt with quickly and effectively (school would exclude if necessary), anti-cyber-bullying policy devised by staff and pupils. There is a clear escalation of staff to speak to about any problems, academic or pastoral. Pupils we met told us that they knew who they were and would be happy to talk to a number.

Senior prefects and school and house monitors support younger pupils – 'It's a very caring environment: the house system works very well'. A sixth former who joined in year 12 from a state school spoke of how quickly he had been integrated into friendship groups 'who conducted themselves so differently' from his previous school.

New children have an acquaintance day in the summer term before entry, an induction day just before term starts and a 'buddy' in their house when they arrive. Prep school pupils will also have used the senior school facilities regularly and visited for a day in year 5.

Pupils and parents: At 11, most from the prep school, the rest from state primaries; at 13 and 16 from a range of state and independent schools. Many of day and weekly boarding pupils from within or close to Durham, others from as far as Sunderland, Newcastle, North Yorkshire and the Borders. A range of ethnic and financial backgrounds but mostly professional or self-employed.

Plenty of contact with generally satisfied parents – weekly e-letter, website, academic diaries, meetings, a parents' forum. Forthcoming, well-mannered, confident pupils. Proud of their school and appreciative of what they have gained; one boy told us, 'I often wonder what person I would be now if I hadn't been at Durham'. Certainly, new sixth formers joining from local secondaries are bowled over by the collegiality, welcome and attitude to learning.

Entrance: At 11+: short tests in English, maths, VR and non-VR; 13+: all have to take tests in English and mathematics plus short interview. Above average ability but a wide range. Sixth form entrants need five GCSEs at B/6 or above with a minimum C/5 in mathematics and English; also by interview and school report.

If overseas applicants can't sit the entrance exam, they can get in with a school reference, but need a good level of English – for sixth form need level 5.5 IELTS. Some stay in sixth for three years – special programme for first year. Has top rated tier 4 boarding sponsors' licence.

Exit: A small number leaves at the end of year 11 for vocational courses or jobs and a few at the end of year 12, after some more maturing. Northern redbrick and 'new' universities favourite, north and south of the border: Newcastle, and Northumbria top choices, Edinburgh, St Andrews, Sheffield, York, Liverpool and Durham popular. A few to Oxbridge and US universities sneaking in. Wide range of subjects: civil and chemical engineering popular choices as well, as business, biomedical sciences and psychology, plus a few medics (two in 2017) and lawyers. One off to Japan (environment and information studies), one to Ghent (commercial engineering) one to the Savannah College of Art and Design, USA and one to Israel (mechanical engineering) in 2017.

Money matters: Various academic, music, drama, art and sports awards, at 11+ and 13+, Burkitt and Peter Lee Scholarships at 16+. Sibling, Forces and clergy discounts. About 150 pupils have means-tested assistance and 105 non-means-tested admissions scholarships of a maximum of £1,000.

Remarks: A sense of community and history binds the pupils together, underpinned by the strong house system for day and boarding pupils alike. In recent years academic results have been record breaking. The school produces well-rounded, confident young people, who have opportunities to develop a wide range of talents to a high level in a supportive, peaceful and very attractive environment.

Fettes College

12

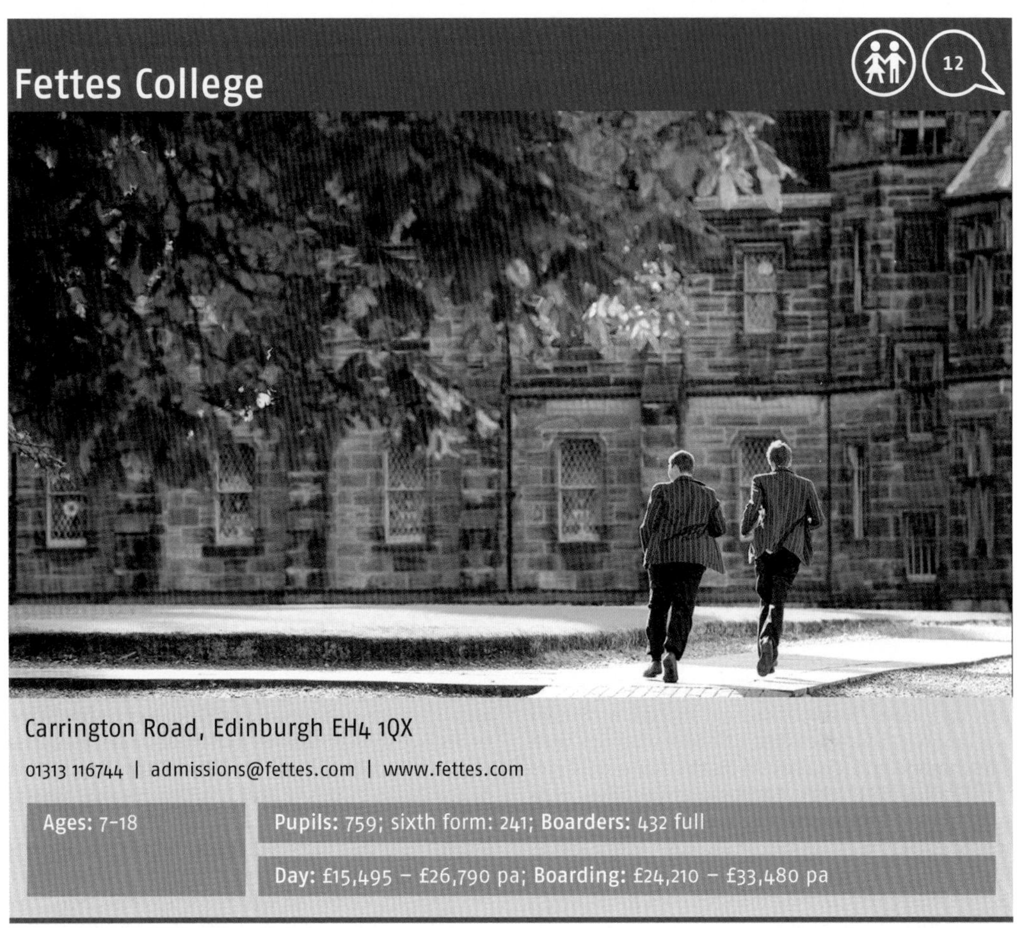

Carrington Road, Edinburgh EH4 1QX

01313 116744 | admissions@fettes.com | www.fettes.com

Ages: 7–18

Pupils: 759; sixth form: 241; **Boarders:** 432 full

Day: £15,495 – £26,790 pa; **Boarding:** £24,210 – £33,480 pa

Headmaster: Since August 2017, Geoffrey Stanford, previously deputy head at Sevenoaks. Classics degree from Oxford, captain in the Grenadier Guards and worked in the City before joining Millfield to teach economics, business studies and Latin. Has also been boarding housemaster and head of department at Pangbourne. He has rowed for Eton, Sandhurst and the British Army at Henley, completed the Marathon des Sables and Devizes to Westminster canoe race, and taken part in a succession of expeditions to the Himalayas, including leading an international team to the summit of Mount Everest. He also enjoys playing the French horn. He is married to Susanna and they have two young sons.

Head of prep school: Since 2003, Mr A A Edwards BA London (mid-40s). Formerly a housemaster at Gresham's School, Norfolk. Married to Jill; three sons and one young daughter. A history graduate and a talented sportsman.

Academic matters: Prep school has tiny classes, excellent remedial, super facilities and plumb in the centre of Edinburgh. Latin early, computers everywhere.

Almost all senior school heads of departments have changed during the past few years – 'new young staff', 'very good', 'strong', 'Edinburgh is a strong draw'; and, having played the Scottish versus the English system along with all the other big players, added the IB in 2006. Pupils can choose whether they want to specialise, therefore do A levels, or take the broader IB syllabus: excellent IB results – average score 37 in 2017; will not provide separate results for A levels as 'it gives competitor schools an unfair advantage'. At GCSE, 75 per cent A*/A grades.

Three sciences on offer throughout, plus trad French, German and Spanish, as well as Mandarin (available for beginners as well as for native speakers). No particular bias – physics, chemistry, history and geography outstanding at GCSE level, maths and English almost equally strong; results in all disciplines equally impressive at A level. Art results outstanding throughout the school. Tranche of outstanding French GCSEs taken early. Strong tradition of classics; government and politics and history of art available at A level. Broad range of subjects, but not the biggest take up at A level in langs, classics or further maths.

Foreign pupils with minimal English are no longer accepted willy-nilly, unless they happen to be particularly bright or have siblings in the school. EFL is on hand, but pupils who don't have 'a pretty good working knowledge of English' are encouraged to do an English lang course before they arrive (Edinburgh School of English is popular).

Good staff:pupil ratio. 'Computers zooming ahead' – wireless networked throughout, with all senior school students having their own laptop.

Games, options, the arts: Wide range of opportunity for games. 'Rugby is strong, though no longer a religion' (73 blues to date). Needle matches with Glenalmond and Merchiston on the rugby field and Strathallan in hockey. Lacrosse impressive, girls play hockey and netball as well; sixth form not forced to play team games at all – 20+ other sports including swimming and aerobics also available. Big sports centre and swimming pool providing a wide range of other sports, old pool now an exam hall/ceilidh and disco area.

Music 'a huge strength' with loads of bands, orchestras, three choirs and a string quartet etc etc, two popular concerts in spring and autumn plus carol service all in aid of charity. Keen drama with imaginative productions; pupils often perform at the Edinburgh Festival (and win awards). Frankenstein the most recent production with over 100 pupils involved. New art centre in pipeline (still) and 'very inspirational head of art' (another one, if you follow) recently appointed. Pipe band popular. CCF, community service, D of E etc. Masses of trips, everywhere, for everything.

Boarding: Two prep school and eight senior school houses, all single sex, for day and boarding pupils, with tutors attached. Newish posho boarding house – Craigleith, dead modern – to accommodate the expanded sixth form, which is due to increase by 25 per cent. The sixth form centre houses 125 upper sixth pupils in two identical wings (surely this should be 126 or 124?) each with their own individual room and provides a transition between the disciplines of school and uni with pupils being able to cook their own meals if they want to.

Background and atmosphere: William Fettes (later Sir William), the son of an Edinburgh grocer, made his fortune during the Napoleonic Wars when 'he became Scotland's leading contractor for provisions for the army'; his only son died in 1815, and William in 1836. Whilst he had originally intended to found a hospital, he later 'decided to create a school for orphans and the needy'; and – after prudent investment – the trustees decided that with £166,000 in the kitty, there were enough funds to acquire land, and both build and endow a school: Fettes opened in 1870 with 200 boys.

He has rowed for Eton, Sandhurst and the British Army at Henley, completed the Marathon des Sables and taken part in a succession of expeditions to the Himalayas

Vast Grimms' fairy tale of a building, turreted and with acres of wood panelling and shiny black floors (are they granite or stone flag underneath the tarry surface?) purpose-built in 1870 by Bryce. Part of the main building still has the original steam-driven heating which starts up twice a day with alarming groans and wheezes – ripe for the engineering museum, methinks.

Various Victorian edifices scattered about the school's wonderful 90 acre grounds plonk in the middle of Edinburgh. 'School uses Edinburgh much more now.' Spectacular development after school sold 'redundant' acres to build Fettes Village, a collection of neat little boxes which splits the games field and provided the cash for much-needed expansion. The collection of new and converted buildings that house the prep department are much bigger than they look from the outside, an example of space well used, and about to be extended. Fettes North is new block housing 25 classrooms plus music school, art school, history of art building and sixth form studio and workshop.

The school has gradually metamorphosed from famous trad boys' school to genuinely co-ed. The flavour has changed from home-grown Scots to more exotic (school says '75 per cent UK, 15 per cent British expats, 10 per cent foreign nationals with over 40 countries represented in this').

Pastoral care, well-being and discipline: Despite colourful stories in the Edinburgh press in past years – drugs, booze, etc, grossly overstated, says the school – there is a clear framework of discipline that is well understood by all. This is a school with a zero tolerance policy on drugs. Edinburgh is the drugs capital of the north and running a school in the middle of it is no joke. Under-age drinking is an acknowledged problem. Three tier system on the discipline side: housemaster/deputy head/head = rustication/formal warning and suspension or expulsion. Ditto smoking. Very clear house-visiting rules – no overt demonstrations of affection; bonking equals out. And yes, they do lose the occasional pupil for all these misdemeanours, ditto bullying. Strong anti-bullying ethos. Prefects very responsible – imaginative anti-bullying code involves culprits writing down what they must or must not do and signing it. Expulsion is always an option.

Pupils and parents: School topped up with many non-Brits in the old days, now the mix is veering more towards the British norm but still collections of internationals – Russians, Chinese, Japanese, Americans, Ukrainians, but fewer Bulgarians than previously. Increasing numbers of locals and Scots from all over. 'Pupils from 40 different countries, East European connection sadly dropping off.' Very strong old Fettesian stream, plus loads of first-time buyers, intellectuals etc etc. Good vibrant mix. Old Fettesians include John de Chastelaine, Ian McLeod, James Bond, Tilda Swinton, Lord Woolf and Tony Blair – remembered fondly for 'his acting ability'.

Entrance: To prep by assessment test and interview.

CE or school's own exam to senior school for those not coming from UK preps. Approx 40 students a year join the sixth form after GCSE elsewhere, currently much sought after as pupils pile in from other, mainly Scottish, schools.

Exit: Virtually all juniors to senior school – internally set exam for entry. Hardly any leave post-GCSE. Most to university – Aberdeen, Durham, Edinburgh, Exeter, Glasgow, King's College London, Manchester, Newcastle, St Andrews, Warwick etc to study eg engineering, English, maths or law. Three to Oxbridge in 2017, plus three medics.

Money matters: Well-endowed with scholarships including academic, music, sports, all-rounder, piping, art, up to 10 per cent of fees. Also means-tested bursaries: 'The level of these awards depend upon parents' financial means and can cover up to the full value of the fees'.

Special (Todd) bursaries for Old Fettesians, 12.5 per cent discount for Forces (not so many of these around). Having initially failed the charity test for spending insufficient fee income on subsidising children from low income families, it later passed.

Remarks: Undoubtedly the strongest school in Edinburgh – possibly riding too high? To quote one governor, 'It is better to have a challenge, otherwise we become complacent'. School adds, 'No danger of becoming complacent; the most dangerous thing in a school is to stand still.' Exciting cosmopolitan mix in an exciting city.

Giggleswick School

13

Giggleswick, Settle, North Yorkshire BD24 0DE

01729 893000 | enquiries@giggleswick.org.uk | www.giggleswick.org.uk

Ages: 11-18

Pupils: 360; sixth form: 136; Boarders: 226

Day: £15,135 – £20,385 pa; Boarding: £20,700 – £32,760 pa

Headmaster: Since 2014, Mark Turnbull MA, previously deputy head of Eastbourne College. Studied geography at Liverpool University and did an MA in London; taught geography at Sevenoaks, where he was also head of department, housemaster and head of boarding. An active hockey, cricket and rugby coach, he has led charity and international projects. Married with three children.

Academic matters: In 2017, 41 per cent A*/A grades at GCSE and 67 per cent A*-B at A level. Improved academic standards 'spectacular with the same intake', due to personalised learning, with setting in French, maths, science and humanities, focused learning support and 'aspire' programme for gifted and talented. Combined with individual monthly assessment of effort and attainment measured against targets, with tutor sessions to motivate further improvement. All available online to pupil and parents, together with full reports three times a year. Success breeds success and has allowed the school to turn down the odd pupil.

Broad curriculum with separate sciences and a taste of three modern foreign languages and Latin in year 7, reducing to two language subjects by year 9. Choice of 19 GCSE subjects – usually nine or 10 taken. Committed staff, a blend of age and experience who 'provide inspiration to the pupils and are very positive and caring'. 'A pretty impressive bunch' a general view from parents, articulated by one. Small class sizes, less than 20, and significantly smaller groups, down to four pupils, study a selection of the 22 A level courses offered. Sixth form enrichment through the EPQ plus Open University YASS modules – offered alongside A levels for those who require stretch and challenge. Most interests and abilities catered for though those wanting to pursue purely vocational courses are directed elsewhere at 16. No massaging of results here – if you study for a subject you sit the exam. 'Failure not necessarily a bad thing,' says school. 'Sometimes it can provide a much needed wake-up call.'

Special educational needs support tailored to individual need and provided through support in the classroom on the whole. Full time special educational needs co-ordinator and successful buddy system where older children with experience of a learning difficulty mentor younger ones. EFL provided (two to four lessons a week), one-to-one, in study periods, but anyone arriving from abroad must have a basic level of English.

Art and design a real strength with resident artist changing annually, impressively ambitious design work allowing some pupils to skip university foundation courses

Lots of computers, including some in each boarding house; every pupil has email and a computer link in their study bedroom.

Games, options, the arts: Rugby, cricket, cross-country and hockey loom large in the (very full) fixture list. International coaching over the past few years has led to such success that the school has had to drop traditional fixtures in search of more competition. With impressive investment in indoor and outdoor sports facilities almost any and every sporting interest is covered. Seven hard and three grass courts, together with the opportunity to train in Portugal, ensure continued popularity of tennis.

Keen drama started by Russell Harty – several OGs and some pupils active in the profession, but luvvies and their tantrums not tolerated. The Richard Whiteley Theatre, named after the late TV presenter, who was an old boy and governor, provides a suitable and flexible venue for such recent

diverse productions as We Will Rock You and Alice in Wonderland.

Art and design taken seriously – a real strength with good facilities across the disciplines, resident artist changing annually, impressively ambitious design work allowing some pupils to skip university foundation courses.

A third of pupils learn an instrument (some play professionally), heavenly chapel choir and lots of bands regularly tour home and abroad. Plenty of opportunity to perform in front of a home crowd with a programme including recitals, concerts and annual rock concert, not to mention the fiercely contested 'themed' inter-house Singing and Speaking competition.

CCF compulsory in year 10, those that carry on can gain silver and gold D of E awards and earn an additional four A/A* GCSEs through the CVQO Public Services BTec scheme, in addition to military qualifications. Making the most of its glorious Dales location, outdoor pursuits activities abound; conservation projects and all the usual opportunities too.

Boarding: Seven houses – four boys', two girls', one junior (years 7 and 8 together with junior school boarders). Different character to each of the boys' houses (not surprising with 500 years of history), not so for the girls. All pupils allocated a bed, room mates usually a mix of day and boarding. Small dorms for years 7 and 8, study bedrooms for years 9 and up, shared until year 11 (boys) or sixth form (girls). Senior house staff tutor years 7-10, with pupils choosing their tutors from year 11. Exeats – four a term. Few full junior boarders, though some flexi-boarding in the eight-bedded dorms in the junior boarding house. Full activity programme and a new year 5 boarder spoke glowingly of kindness, good dinners and fun.

The boarding houses we visited were comfortably furnished and in good order though the boys' evidenced more wear and tear. Rooms were reassuringly 'lived in', personalised with posters, photos, soft toys and general clutter. 'Keep calm and carry on' seems to be the universal mantra. Sixth formers play an important role in the smooth running of the house and are rewarded with single rooms. Year 9 prep is done in separate study areas and monitored by sixth formers. Common rooms, displaying fine examples of residents' art, are filled with squashy sofas, board games, puzzles, a Wii, DVDs and music. Strict rules on TV watersheds but Saturday night is film night.

Background and atmosphere: Set in the western margins of the magnificent Yorkshire Dales beneath an imposing limestone escarpment, 60 minutes' drive north of Manchester and Leeds (so the brochure says). Founded in 1512, moved to present site in 1869. Attractive buildings overlook

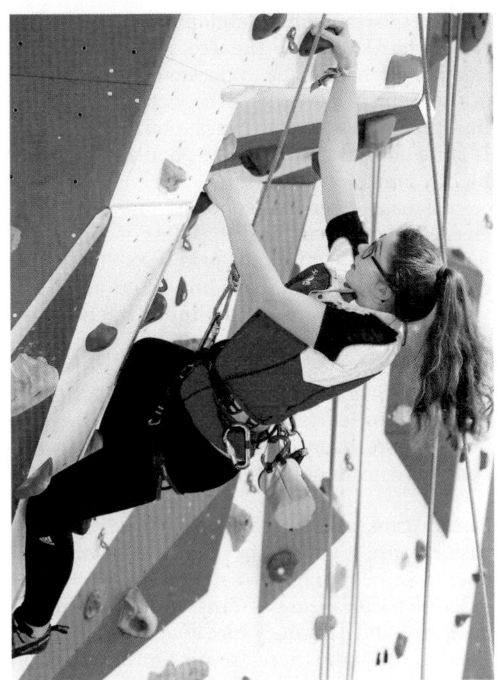

Giggleswick village beneath the fabulously restored chapel, complete with landmark copper dome, a fitting reward for the walk up the steep hill.

Immaculate and comfortably sized school campus (big enough to be roomy, small enough to retain a real sense of community) with a calming oasis of lawn in its midst. Happy, relaxed but purposeful atmosphere, knots of pupils engaged in conversation amongst themselves or with staff. Polite and smiling welcome from everyone; a real sense of community.

Sixth form centre with bar on the edge of the main campus – current cohort trying to find ways to make it more 'happening'. Alcohol allowed at weekends

Promotes a real 'can do' philosophy, encouragement and support for pupils to have a go at anything and everything. Evening prep, activities, clubs, house events, rehearsals and sports practices mean it's a 12 hour school day, with little respite on Saturdays. All the pupils we spoke to seemed to thrive on it, though Sunday evening chapel was popular for the lie in it provided. Not surprisingly, day pupils opt to use their bed in their boarding house on occasions – for a fee.

Recent sympathetic development has included the Richard Whitely theatre, sports halls, all weather pitch, upgrade to classroom facilities and at the heart of the school, the wonderful Sharpe library, where there's always a buzz of activity. IT suite and internet café are popular venues for nightly prep.

All meals eaten in the modern dining hall (cafeteria system, separate sittings, lots of choice and pupil endorsement that the food is good). Boarders can supplement with toast, hot drinks and other snacks they prepare in the house kitchenettes (girls' facilities more extensive than boys' – surprise, surprise).

Sixth form centre with bar on the edge of the main campus– current cohort trying to find ways to make it more 'happening'. Alcohol allowed at weekends but consumption strictly monitored.

Pastoral care, well-being and discipline: Parents see pastoral care supported by medical centre, school doctor and chaplain as a major strength. They describe pastoral care as 'fantastic', 'the staff are dedicated and genuinely care about the children'. Correspondingly, there are no significant pupil behaviour problems, though lack of accessibility to temptation in this rural location may help. Chapel is an integral and important part of the school but faith more important than denomination and appreciated by a number of parents who believe 'it adds a special personal spiritual experience'.

Thorough drugs checks (this is no-nonsense Yorkshire) – sniffer dogs brought in termly; compulsory drugs testing used on known and suspected offenders and anyone dealing faces immediate expulsion. Smokers required to attend cessation clinics.

Comfortably sized school campus (big enough to be roomy, small enough to retain a real sense of community) with a calming oasis of lawn in its midst. Happy, relaxed but purposeful atmosphere

More traffic from boys to girls' houses, visits welcomed but permission must be sought to move away from public areas. Behaviour between sexes 'should not cause embarrassment to anyone'. Staff vigilant for anorexia and similar – system in place to check on pupils suspected of skipping meals, including height/weight monitoring and meal attendance cards.

School engenders a non-bullying culture and staff vigilant for anything that may make a child feel isolated. Sixth formers charged to look out for anyone feeling wobbly. House masters maintain good communication links with parents.

Pupils and parents: Some 55 per cent fully board, the rest are local children from a large catchment area; school transport system. Numbers stable though reduction in boarding. Recession has seen families release property equity by moving to the area – children remain as day pupils; parent commutes to work. Healthy 60:40 ratio boys to girls. School fully co-ed since 1983. Seventeen per cent overseas, 16 per cent expats and Forces – popular with all these. Parents in business and the professions. OGs: James Agate; Richard Whiteley; William Gaunt; Sarah Fox. OG society well established on the internet.

Entrance: At age 11 Giggleswick entrance exam, at age 13 normally CE together with interview and previous school's report. Entrance into sixth form is by a minimum of five GCSEs at grade B; around 35 new sixth form entrants per year. Giggleswick Junior School, the main feeder for Giggleswick at age 11, shares campus.

Exit: Around 15 per cent leave after GCSEs. Sixth formers to a range of mostly northern universities; one to Oxford in 2017. Others to Sheffield, Southampton, Hull, Durham, Leeds, Liverpool and York.

Money matters: Scholarships and exhibitions for academic, all round achievement, sport and music are awarded at 11+, 13+ and sixth form, with art at 13+ and sixth form and sixth form only design, drama. There are 15-20 awards annually, ranging in value from 10-50 per cent of fees a year, the majority for 20-25 per cent. Means-tested bursaries can increase fee reduction to 75 per cent for scholars who could not otherwise take up an offered place. School has benefited from large gifts from OG Norman Sharpe and more recently Graham Watson (late governor).

Remarks: An 'all round' education with support and encouragement across a spectrum of academic and extracurricular activity, for any willing to take on the challenge. It is a warm and welcoming school with no sign of snobbishness (as you would expect in Yorkshire); secure in its strong moral foundations. As one of our guides said, 'you just have to be prepared to give everything a try, and if you fall out of line there's always someone to help pick you up.'

Glenalmond College

Glenalmond, Perth PH1 3RY

01738 842000 | registrar@glenalmondcollege.co.uk | www.glenalmondcollege.co.uk

Ages: 12–18

Pupils: 392; sixth form: 175; Boarders: 309

Day: £16,470 – £21,954 pa; Boarding: £24,858 – £33,180 pa

Warden: Since 2015, Elaine Logan. 'I'd follow that woman to the ends of the earth': well, how often have you heard a member of staff say that about a headteacher? No – us too. So we think it's fair to say that Elaine Logan has already really left her mark on Glenalmond College. Not to say that there wasn't a surprised shiver running through some parents and teachers when they announced the appointment. Ms Logan is not only the first female warden (about time!), but she has taken on a school that is famously traditional and which had been slumbering and dribbling on its laurels for too long.

So, the facts: Elaine Logan is married with three adult children. MA University of Edinburgh,PGCE Moray House, PGC counselling Heriot-Watt University, PGC pupil support University of Aberdeen. Her career began in state schools in Fife, before teaching posts at nearby Dollar Academy and Loretto outside Edinburgh. Rising to assistant head at Loretto over a period of 14 years, she was well-liked and respected, but was raised to near iconic status by stepping into the breach when the headteacher role was unexpectedly and hurriedly vacated. Far from papering over the cracks, she steered a floundering school towards calmer waters with great aplomb and sensitivity. Top marks.

Academic matters: One of the biggest changes since Elaine Logan has arrived at Glenalmond has been 'improving academic rigour and ambition'. This has been achieved by introducing the Learning Project – a big name for a radical restructuring of the way the children and the teachers are monitored and taught. Ms Logan says that when she took over there was an opportunity to look at the school in a stark and pared back way and re-evaluate what 'we're good at and what we can do better'. Head of learning, Dr Matt Gibson, says, 'We did lesson observations, we trailed kids for the day, we did surveys and we did questionnaires.The warden fully embraced this.'

The idea is that 'no-one is alone and that everyone is supported'. Teachers now routinely observe each other's lessons to spread good practice and help eliminate the bad and are coached and supported if improvements are needed. Meanwhile, the pupils' academic and social movements are now closely tracked, with regular meetings between house teachers, academic teachers and senior staff to evaluate progress and pastoral needs. Prep is now being monitored for all but upper sixth (one parent told us their child was thrilled by this development as they were actually getting work done). In addition, there are tutorials to help pupils develop core skills for learning including essay planning, revision strategies, mind-mapping, time management, literacy and numeracy foundation skills.

'I'd follow that woman to the ends of the earth': how often have you heard a member of staff say that about a headteacher? It is fair to say that she has already made her mark

Housemaster Guy Draper Colford says they are all discussing pupils and their welfare far more than they used to. Sharing best practice is common and all the house staff have meet every week to discuss pupils and their progress. Senior management aren't being left on the shelf either. They're being trained to manage their departments in a more effective and supportive way.

So a huge upskilling all round, but is it working? Apparently! Education Scotland is recommending they spread this good practice asap. Meanwhile, parents we spoke to felt that both the children and the teaching standards are beginning to reap the benefits. '[My son] actually looks forward to his supervised study...incredible. He says Mrs Logan should be the next prime minister.' 'For the first time in ages, there's a real buzz about the place. And they love Elaine Logan. She's disciplined, fair and gets their vote every time.' 'They really like her. They respect her. She's a real dynamo and gets things done.'

Glenalmond will never be an academic hothouse, but Elaine Logan wants us to judge them on how much the pupils improve on their journey through the school. 2017 saw one of the best GCSE performances ever with 54 per cent A*-A/9-7 grades. At A level, 39 per cent A*/A and 68 per cent A*-B, with many surpassing expectations. As Ms Logan says, 'There were far fewer parents and pupils outside my door looking worried after the results compared to previously.'

Subjects on offer cover the usual spectrum from politics to history of art (26 subjects on offer at A level) and are now being supplemented by Mandarin and computer science at GCSE and computer science at A level. Now offers 13 subjects at Higher level.

A significant proportion of the school is involved with the learning support department at some level. This ranges from extra time in exams all the way through to a reader and a scribe. There is a policy of free screening for all pupils who enter the school in second, third or fourth form. Thereafter there are charges for eg additional assessments and individual support sessions.

There's a prep club at break and lunchtimes so more support on offer then.

The staff ratio is particularly good at 1:7 and class sizes rarely exceed 16. The bottom sets may have as few as six or seven pupils. They recruited heavily for new staff recently (there was a lot of stagnation to deal with in our view) and the results are new faces with enthusiasm and drive. Another school head has commented that there seems to be a real buzz about the school and they are attracting some real talent to their ranks.

Games, options, the arts: One of the major changes is a complete restructuring of the sports department so that it functions co-educationally ie boys' and girls' games are given equal billing (rather than the rugger buggers hogging the limelight). This change has been implemented by a new director of sport, Andy Rowley, who was a headmaster down south, but wanted to get back to the coal face of teaching, apparently. He comes with a new head of rugby, Graham Smith, who as a former Fife development coach brings new links to the rugby pathway system and possible international progression. Touch rugby has also been introduced for girls. In fact the school now has heads for hockey, lacrosse and rugby and hopefully soon tennis, golf and cricket. Andy Rowley says one of the best things about Glenalmond is the great support the parents give to sport.

Parity has also been brought for the firsts lacrosse team, who now share the former firsts rugby pitch, Neish's, as it's known. This has been revamped and a new stand has been built (this time facing the right way ie towards the beautiful hills). The sporting facilities also include a first class swimming pool and now an Olympic standard water-based hockey pitch, which has already hosted some international players.

They're not the most amazing sporting facilities that you will come across but, as elsewhere in the school, the ambition seems to be big. There are also plans to make more of what is a truly fabulous outdoor location. There is a school golf course and the possibility of fishing on the river Almond, which flows through the school. Duke of Edinburgh Awards are enthusiastically pursued, as are clay pigeon shooting, tennis, white water rafting, skiing. The activity programme is booted up further at the weekend, and at Cairnies, the newly created junior boys' house (second and third form), there are compulsory activities so that they are kept busy.

Neighbouring boys' house Patchell's is the Testosterone Towers of the school, housing a lot of the rugby boys in long dorms in something akin to horseboxes

Expressive arts has always been somewhat understated at Glenalmond, but there are plans to improve this starting with the introduction of dance at GCSE. With the old warden's house now being repatriated as an admin hub, there is also a permanent display area for any artistic endeavour, while neatly putting it in front of any prospective parents.

Boarding: Girls are being given a bigger slice of the pie and are being 'promoted' to the Quad. This is the Oxbridge-style area at the heart of the school, traditionally the site of three boys' houses. Now one of them, Goodacres, has been made over to girls. Neighbouring boys' house Patchell's is the Testosterone Towers of the school, housing a lot of the rugby boys in long dorms in something akin to horse boxes. They seem to love it, though. Another house, Cairnies, formerly for fifth form girls, has been turned into a junior house for second and third form boys – increasing in numbers apparently due to more pupils arriving from destinations other than traditional prep schools.

Elaine Logan says that one of the USPs of the place is that all of the staff live on site, so the pupils get to see them in their civvies and leading a normal life. Relationships tend to be stronger because this 'really is a full boarding school', but be warned if your child doesn't fit in, there is very little escape.

Background and atmosphere: 'How many schools have a front and back avenue, Mum?' Well, probably more than we realise, but it does emphasise the sheer grandeur of the place both in architectural and scenic terms. Going down the drive on a warm summer's day (they do happen, apparently) or a crisp winter one with snow on the hills can be an uplifting experience. The school was founded by the former prime minister William Gladstone to keep young men free 'from the sins of the city', and to a certain extent that still happens. Sadly, after years of dodgy mobile phone reception, the pupils can call out with ease, but there is still a feeling of beautiful isolation which helps keep the worst offenders out of trouble, and if your child is sociable and likes the outdoors, they will probably form friendships to last a lifetime. Be prepared to blink when you see the school uniform. The boys are traditional in grey flannels and blazers, with tweed jackets for upper sixth. But the girls, well the girls have navy floor-length skirts. 'Victorian parlour maids' was one description, but according to the school the girls are adamant they won't have it any other way. Reports say they enjoy wearing their pyjamas and wellies underneath in bad weather, so who could blame them? And Mrs Logan believes it helps with evening out those body image crises that so many other schools have to deal with.

Pastoral care, well-being and discipline: The school has now appointed a deputy head of pastoral care who oversees the eight housemasters/mistresses and there is far more exchanging of information so that nobody slips through the net. House staff and teachers meet weekly to discuss pupils, especially any there are concerns about.

Discipline appears to have improved since the arrival of the current warden. Drugs have never really been an issue at the school, but alcohol could be. This, parents say, has definitely been tightened up, although the occasional lapse still occurs.

Pupils and parents: A high 70 per cent are UK boarders. The school has traditionally been the 'county' choice, or 'tweed central', as some have dubbed it, so many from surrounding Perthshire, Angus, Fife and Aberdeenshire, and the other 30 per cent are international with Germany leading the table. You are less likely to get hard-working lawyer or property developer parents and more likely to see well-heeled farmers and castle dwellers.

Entrance: Common entrance is on the wane, apparently with less coming in from the prep route, so the school tests independently for maths and

English. There is no waiting list so entry is fairly straightforward at the moment if you wave a cheque book, but with the new buzz around the place this may well change.

Exit: Around half to Russell Group universities including Oxbridge (one place in 2017), with a trickle to American universities.

Money matters: They stress they don't buy in talent, so no 100 per cent scholarships for the rugby gorillas, but they do support four pupils every year on a bursary basis of 90 to 100 per cent. This isn't based purely on academic potential, but if there is a child who would clearly benefit from the boarding experience then they will try to help. The total remission pot is £2 million a year of which the lion's share goes to bursaries. Scholarships get the usual 10 per cent reduction. Most applicants will try for both.

Remarks: Get in fast, Glenalmond is on the up and up. Inspirational is one of those over-used words but it really does seem to apply to the warden Elaine Logan. If they can continue to combine academic rigour and making use of their spectacular setting then Glenalmond is set for a cracking future over the next few years.

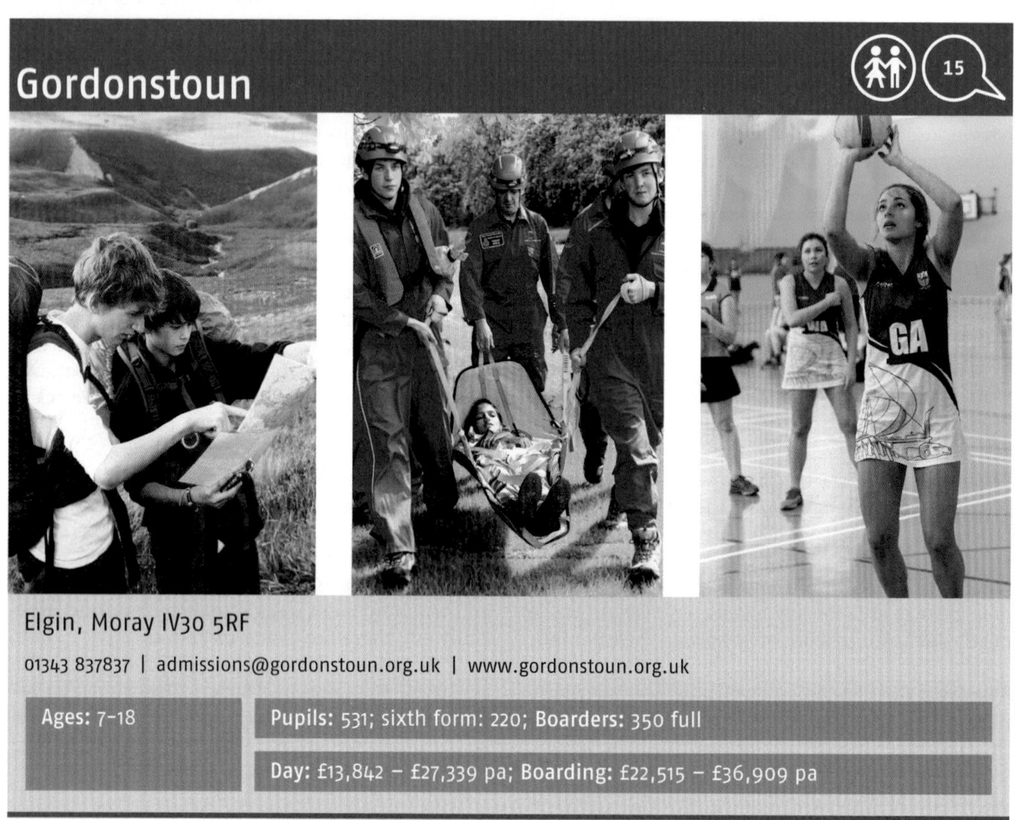

Gordonstoun

Elgin, Moray IV30 5RF

01343 837837 | admissions@gordonstoun.org.uk | www.gordonstoun.org.uk

Ages: 7–18

Pupils: 531; sixth form: 220; **Boarders:** 350 full

Day: £13,842 – £27,339 pa; **Boarding:** £22,515 – £36,909 pa

Principal: Since September 2017, Lisa Kerr, previously a strategy and PR consultant to a range of businesses. Music degree from York; has worked as a radio producer and director and ran a group of local radio stations before going on to represent the sector, latterly as director of strategy at RadioCentre, the industry body for UK commercial radio. Set up her own PR agency. She has been a governor at Gordonstoun 2006, and is its first female principal, as well as, unusually, coming from a business rather than education background.

Titus Edge, previously deputy head, is headmaster. A history teacher, he also has senior leadership experience at Dulwich College. He has three children at the school and comes from a family where three generations have attended Gordonstoun.

Head of junior school: Since 2003, Robert McVean, BSc (40s), who has taught science at the junior school from 2000. Educated at Hurstpierpoint College, he read environmental biology at Swansea, thence five years in the state sector, followed by

Edinburgh Academy. Married to Laura (bubbly and fun; she helps with SEN), two children in the school ('all been huge fun, wouldn't have changed a thing').

Academic matters: 'Students are here for the whole broad experience'; 'The balance is important'. Huge range of ability, from those 'at the lower end of the academic scale', to all A* candidates. 'School getting more academic.' In 2017, a third A*-A/9-7 grades at GCSE, nearly 45 per cent A*/A level. 'What is worth noticing this year is that the highest number of students achieving above their predictions, whether that is at A* level or below. This is far more important than detailed examination results and highlights the distinctiveness of our broad curriculum and ethos'. Native speakers can do A levels in their own langs. One year GCSE course for year 11 international students moving to the English system. Classes setted for maths and English from 13. Networked computers throughout, wireless connection in all boarding houses. Bespoke international citizenship course new kid on the block: not PSHE or RS but 'examining real problems against a global background'. Good remedial support – all pupils screened on arrival. Will scribe for exams. EAL available at all levels.

Games, options, the arts: Community service is important at Gordonstoun. All do service training aged 16 and choose which discipline to follow: the fire brigade (the most popular), mountain rescue, coastguards, canoe life guards, ski patrol, first aid, technical, marine training and rescue, conservation, pool life guards. Number of exchanges with other Round Square schools – Canada, Germany, Australia. Local projects and joint international expeditions to India, Sinai, Thailand, Kenya, Honduras to work on conservation/ecological schemes. The latter are expensive – students are encouraged to fundraise to meet own costs. Outdoor pursuits expeditions, sleeping in snow holes, add a whole new dimension.

School has its own 80 foot sail-training yacht, Ocean Spirit of Moray, timetabled sailing weeks (when the weather can be 'pretty wild', according to the skippers, ditto the crew). Tall Ships' race a regular feature; school has a new 28 foot training cutter and a rash of new Lasers (which could make for interesting sailing).

Mainstream games on course but long distances to other schools for matches cause problems. Reid says 'school plays locals and rugby league'. New sports hall opened by Olympians Heather Stanning and Zara Tindall. Those over 16 can be in charge of swimming pool and do lifeguard training. Outstanding Ogston theatre, new extension, performing arts studio with sprung dance floor. Newest drama studios look stunning. We were shown the previous green room, now a storage area of monumental proportions, in detail; how anyone finds anything in the place goodness only knows. Par hazard, our guide was the daughter of a long time friend; our other guide was a most charming clever-clogs about to hit global mathematical hotspots (from Norfolk, full blown scholarship). A level pupils lead dance workshops in local primaries. Each year group has 'headmaster's reels' of a Saturday, with a caller.

Grounds and setting lovely – half a mile from the Moray Firth with cliffs and beaches nearby, and not as cold as one might think (Gulf Stream). Cunning music rooms

Trips all over – Europe, Australasia, points west. Magnificent art, lots of disciplines, graphic design impressive. Particularly strong DT with pupils learning not only to make lights but also cost them effectively.

Boarding: Houses spread all over, some quite a hike from the main school (you would never guess they were originally army huts). Recent HMI/Care Commission inspection awarded 'excellent' for two out of the five categories and 'very good' in the remaining three. Minimal exeats – distances are huge (even more so for 30 per cent overseas boarders), but pupils often do not want to go home, regular socials (by block on Saturdays), films and formal dinners. This is a school that has to make its own entertainment. Flexi and weekly boarding recently introduced for junior school pupils (some 20 or so takers). Weekend jam-packed with activities. Shopping bus to Elgin on Friday, but only the upper sixth can visit on Saturdays and can 'have meals out in the evening'.

Certain amount of re-jigging houses: a £10.5 million (apparently no problem getting dosh) refurbishment of the Round Square boarding house and making the old building above accessible to all 'by creating a curriculum centre for international and spiritual citizenship'. Girls' houses bung full, but some boys' houses (sixth form particularly) could be busier, but junior boarding a run-away success. Boys' Duffus House now on main campus in refurbished premises. Prospectus lists nearby hotels, B&Bs (with prices) and ways of getting to school (a good four hours from Edinburgh but less than that flying from London). Non-stop social life which swings right through the holidays – caveat for Southerners.

Background and atmosphere: Founded in 1934 by the German educationalist, Kurt Hahn, Jewish refugee, founder of Salem School in Baden-Württemberg and believer in educating and developing all aspects of children, not just the academic. Grounds and setting lovely – half a mile from the Moray Firth with cliffs and beaches nearby, and not as cold as one might think (Gulf Stream). Gordonstoun House is a former residence of Gordon-Cumming of card-cheating fame. Beautiful circular stable block (hence Round Square) houses the library and boys' house. Cunning music rooms round exotic chapel (shaped like an open book – magnificent, but repairs to the pews are sadly botched).

School has its own 80 foot sail-training yacht, Ocean Spirit of Moray, and timetabled sailing weeks (when the weather can be 'pretty wild')

Rather jolly and purpose-built junior school in the grounds of senior school with self-contained classrooms and dorms all in the same building, the dorms, strategically placed on the second floor, with glorious views.

Pastoral care, well-being and discipline: Occasional problems with drugs, smoking and alcohol (not to mention the P word) – 'not totally whiter than white'. No automatic expulsions; pupils get alcohol or smoking points, and school negotiates with the parents. 'The Code of Conduct is not on our website but is posted to every parent before their child joins the school and is re-sent if there are any changes', in other words, the goal posts have changed. Drugs: straight to the head, usually straight out. Will take pupils who have had to leave other schools: contract in place. School tough on perpetual offenders, particularly bullies – 'Children have eventually had to leave the school as a result'. Commendably clear rules. Girls and boys can visit each others' houses but only allowed in the opposite sex's 'mixed common room' (sounds a blast) and nowhere else. Each pupil has an academic tutor, boarders have houseparents and assistant houseparents in every house. God worshipped in a Christian fashion, more than lip-service to other faiths. Local minister can prepare for confirmation.

Pupils and parents: A third English, a third Scottish and a third from the rest of the world – wide diversity of students, some deeply rich, some less so, with the less so benefiting from serious scholarships. Numbers of first time buyers. Parents dropping off their young have been known to stay 'for a few days'. FPs include royals; William Boyd; Eddie Shah; the composer of The Flower of Scotland – Roy Williamson; Martin Shea; Alan Shiach; Lara Croft; Sophie Morgan, who commentated for Channel 4 for the Paralympics; 2012 Olympian gold medal winner, rower Heather Stanning. Numbers currently down.

Entrance: Juniors enter by assessment and interview plus report from previous school. Dedicated scholarships for juniors, who will lose them if they don't keep up to snuff. Many senior pupils have come up through the junior school (usually automatically, at 13), with others from Ardvreck, Cargilfield, Belhaven and prep schools south of the border. Assessment for those joining at year 10 (about 10 each year) and influx to sixth form. Pupils are assessed both academically and for personality. Odd places sometimes available for pupils, 'at any level of the school for short periods – although not normally less than one term'. Keen to keep up its intake from outside Scotland – may pay travel/hotel bills for prospective parents. Gordonstoun challenge – usually in June – invites UK prep schools to send teams of four or five, all expenses paid for a three day jamboree at Gordonstoun. The idea, of course, being that the little darlings will be so impressed, that whatever school they had previously considered will be cast aside.

Exit: Nearly all juniors move up to the senior school and hardly any post-16 leavers. To universities all over eg Edinburgh, Bath, St Andrews, Newcastle, Leeds, Nottingham. Courses range from aerospace engineering to philosophy and linguistics, and from classics to creative computing. Seven to the US in 2017, including one with a scholarship to the American Academy of Dramatic Arts in New York;

others to countries including Canada, Holland, Spain and Switzerland.

Money matters: Set fee; parents can 'opt above', and some do, 'notably so'. Scholarships and bursaries awarded after means-testing. Hardship fund. Success of flourishing international summer school helps with dosh. Fundraising doesn't seem that difficult. Stunning new bursaries for children of fisherfolk. Second hand clothes shop. Picked up the tab when Aberlour House was closed (it was losing money); the buildings were sold and funds realised more or less paid for the stunning new build, Aberlour, in the grounds.

Remarks: Children and parents appear happy. Fashionable, co-ed outdoor pursuit-ish boarding school with vast range of pupil backgrounds, not overtly academic, though school vows it is getting more so. Increasingly popular junior school in the grounds has been an enormous addition. Budget airline flights to nearest airports popular with southern-based families as well as those further afield. Regular direct links from Inverness to Amsterdam: Aberdeen to Frankfurt, and thence to points global. It is still a long drive from Edinburgh and Glasgow.

Harrogate Ladies' College

16

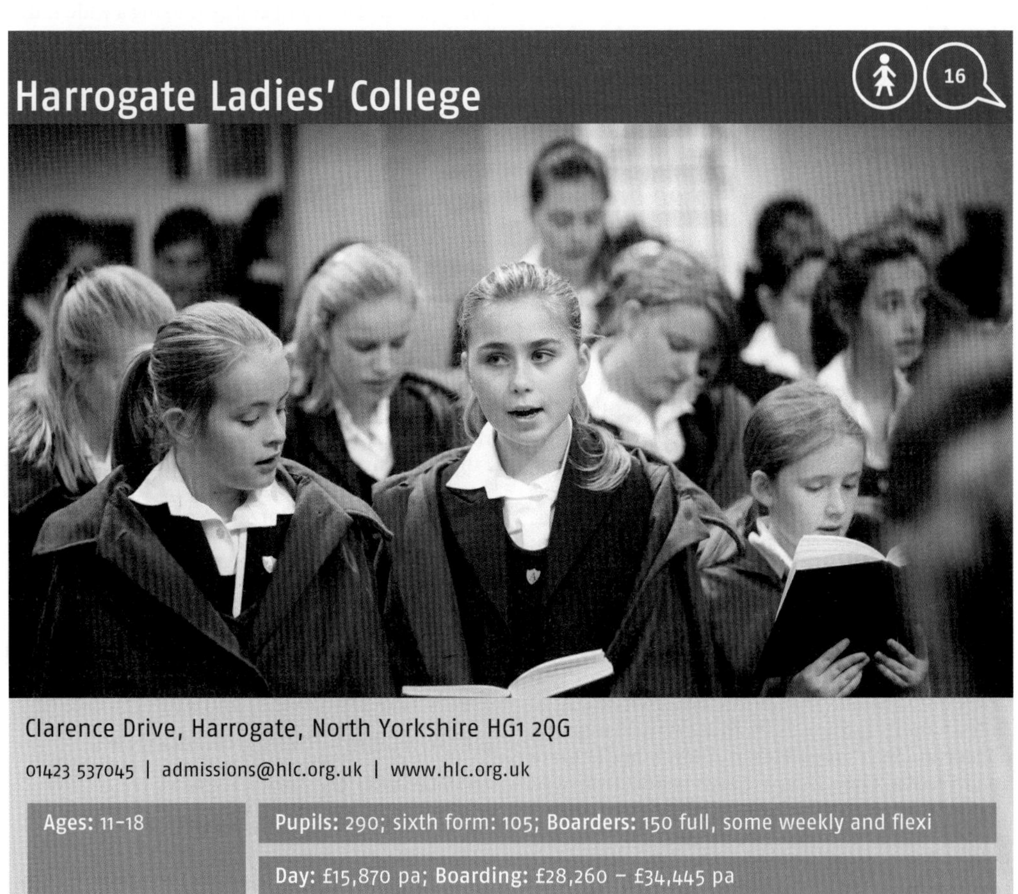

Clarence Drive, Harrogate, North Yorkshire HG1 2QG

01423 537045 | admissions@hlc.org.uk | www.hlc.org.uk

Ages: 11–18

Pupils: 290; sixth form: 105; **Boarders:** 150 full, some weekly and flexi

Day: £15,870 pa; **Boarding:** £28,260 – £34,445 pa

Principal: Since 2013, Mrs Sylvia Brett BA MA (40s). Read theology at Durham, followed by masters in philosophy and religion at University of London. Worked in alumni relations and as moral tutor at Durham for four years before joining the Royal Masonic School as RS teacher and sixth form housemistress. Then lay chaplain and head of RS at Caldicott followed by head of lower school, RS teacher and year 7 housemistress at Downe House, before being appointed as sole deputy at Roedean.

Head believes in ensuring girls are 'jolly good at lots of different things' when they leave HLC. Breadth of curriculum and extracurricular opportunities vital and girls 'are encouraged to be brave' in extending their comfort zone and trying new activities.

Open, engaging and caring, has a 'passion for deep learning' and getting to know the young people in her care. Declared by sixth formers as 'more personable' than predecessors, impressed with her interest in them and knowledge of special events in their lives. Parents see the head as 'a traditional headmistress who genuinely cares about the school and its pupils' and as 'a strong, reassuring presence, confident and approachable'. More traditional than her predecessor, say girls, who have noted a downturn in emphasis on 'girl power', and parents who, without complaint, felt the drive is 'less towards cutting edge and 21st century'.

Head believes in ensuring girls are 'jolly good at lots of different things' when they leave HLC. Breadth of opportunities vital and girls 'are encouraged to be brave'

Married to Justin, a classics teacher, and has one daughter who is a pupil at the school. When time permits her interests include music (singing and piano), art, swimming, family and friends.

Academic matters: In 2017, 36 per cent A*/A grades at A level and 69 per cent A*-B. 2014 results of 71 per cent A*-B placed HLC as top performing school at A level in Harrogate, but they were just pipped to the post for that position in 2016. Interestingly, in recent years almost half of sixth form pupils, predominantly international boarders, have been new to the school.

Good range of subjects on offer though numbers can restrict options. Historically, strength in mathematics and sciences, a particular bias in the sixth form, but modern languages are fine – normally only the odd D at GCSE, otherwise all A*-C. Only a handful (groups as small as two per language) opt for modern languages at A level, but achieve good results. Over the past four years, a third of girls have pursued a business-related degree course. Launched 2010 in purpose built business suite, the Business School has increased business-related subjects to include accounting, business studies, economics and psychology, which remain popular choices. Wider purpose continues to promote enterprise and entrepreneurship throughout the school. Extended Project Qualification introduced for older pupils; just over 10 per cent uptake so far.

Consistent 61 per cent A*/A at GCSE in 2017, up from 45 per cent in 2013; value added 1+ grade per subject. Strong performance in all three sciences, English literature, modern foreign languages, humanities and drama. Broad curriculum and, common with most schools dual award or single sciences recommended after first year of course, one modern foreign language compulsory and a standard range of options. Statistics offered in addition for top set mathematics.

Teaching is generally very good – friendly, good-humoured staff, and girls feel both known and supported on the whole. Generally a willingness to learn and good manners makes teaching a worthwhile experience here. As one parent said, 'Teachers go the extra mile for pupils regularly'. Plenty of new blood though: across the school 95 per cent of staff have less than 10 years of service, with movement in and out of the independent and state sectors.

Practical subjects good too – impressive art throughout the school and girls using a wide range of complex design and technology equipment. Well-equipped food technology room used up to GCSE. Enrichment programme for first year GCSE and sixth form to widen horizons in preparation for higher education. Plenty of IT facilities but an iPad free zone – 'no gimmicks' says the head; 'IT must enhance learning'.

Class size maximum 24, some as low as 12. Parents' evenings and full reports twice yearly, always discussed with head or tutor prior to being sent home. Displays everywhere still a feature – a striking balance of pupil work and thought-provoking material, alongside posters from house captains rallying the troops.

Overseas students encouraged to sit exams in their native language; additional English language tuition available (and certainly encouraged). EAL students used to sit IELTS rather than GCSE English, but pilot study of integration with mainstream English classes in years 10 and 11 has proved highly successful and continues to be the way forward.

Declared by sixth formers as 'more personable' than predecessors, impressed by her interest in them and knowledge of special events in their lives

Across the whole school over 10 per cent SEN catered for in and out of the classroom by dedicated learning support. Generally, in class teacher support free with scale of charges for a more individual programmes. Needs span support in cognitive and learning, communication and interaction, emotional and mental health, and sensory and physical.

Games, options, the arts: Sport, the life-blood of the school, is keenly pursued by all with lacrosse

Musicians regularly run away with prizes at the Harrogate Festival, chapel choir were semi-finalists in a BBC competition, the challenging baroque opera Dido and Aeneas has been staged and there's a wealth of choral performances

('lackie') embedded in the school's culture. Current holders of U13s northern schools' lacrosse title, with good representation at county and regional level. Good range of competitive team sports with recent successes in tennis, district champions in U13 and U15, Harrogate area U14 netball and North Yorkshire Schools Games winners for rounders. Good, much-used, sports facilities include plenty of tennis and badminton courts, multi-gym, 25-metre pool and an enormous indoor general-purpose sports hall which doubles up as a venue for social events, speech day etc.

Dedicated music house accommodates ensembles galore, from samba to string with four choirs. Music is a real strength and majority of girls learn an instrument or two. Musicians regularly run away with prizes at the Harrogate Festival, chapel choir were semi-finalists in a BBC competition, the challenging baroque opera Dido and Aeneas performed, and a wealth of choral performances in cathedral services, at the Royal Hall and on tour, most recently Barcelona.

A level theatre studies on offer, with plays and productions acted out in the suitably-equipped drama studio. The Merchant of Venice staged in Leeds as part of the Shakespeare Schools Festival and annual competitive inter-house drama filled with theatrical thrills and spills. Curriculum supported by regular trips to concerts, theatre and cinema. Many girls take LAMDA lessons (honours and distinctions the norm).

Art, photography and textiles all on offer at A level. Good facilities and the results of talented artists on show around the school. Careers education taken seriously – two weeks' work experience for all followed by presentation and lunch.

An extensive extracurricular menu with over 20 creatively named clubs ranging from Apprentice to Babel Fish and Legobots, with interesting business breakfast club. Golf, sailing and ski trips as well as keen D of E and masses of charity and community work. Burgeoning participation and success in Leeds Young Enterprise. Enterprise days held in the summer term.

Boarding: Four well-presented boarding houses each have attractive study bedrooms, a common room centred on the TV, kitchen and games room, with room for 30 in two houses and 45 in the third. Upper sixth only in Tower with room for 40. Distinction made between 'home' and school by no pupil access to houses during the school day.

Up to four can share a room in lower school, but currently able to spread out a little more. Most sixth formers have their own room with internet access for all in studies and bedrooms. Two taster nights per term offered to day pupils without charge. A growing number of flexi and weekly boarders, but full boarding offers weekends full of trips and activities, off and on site, with over 90 boarders remaining in school most weekends.

Friendly, comfortable feel, no inter-house rivalry: girls mix well with the sense of a supportive sisterhood and good relations with staff. Encouraged to mix across the ages with a buddy system operating for new pupils. A reward system in place for kind deeds, tidiness and helping out. Celebration of international festivals brings an appreciation of different cultures.

Upper sixth housed in Tower – a half way house between school and university where pupils prepare and eat breakfast and a couple of evening meals in house and have greater freedom than lower down the school (team-building exercises at start of upper sixth aid the bonding process). At 16+ girls are allowed out one night a week.

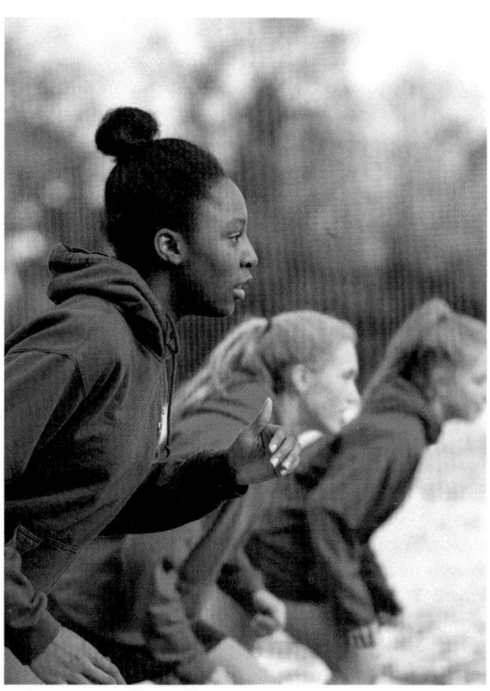

Background and atmosphere: School founded in 1893 on a nearby site and is one of the Allied Schools. Within walking distance of the busy town centre, in the heart of Harrogate's leafy prime real estate, originally part of the Duchy of Lancaster. The pleasant Victorian mock-Tudor buildings with sympathetic additions blend gently with the locality. C of E (own chapel, resounding hymns et al) in small doses for all without exception. New assembly hall officially opened in 2013 to mark school's 120 year anniversary. Separate sixth form centre in main school complete with common rooms, study centre, kitchens, AV room etc with use of business school café. Unique sixth form studies valued by girls as their space and used for personal study until 9.00pm each evening.

Over 20 creatively named clubs ranging from Apprentice to Babel Fish and Legobots, with interesting business breakfast club. Golf, sailing and ski trips as well as keen D of E

'Being the best you can be', the school motto, is at the heart of the ethos here. Resilience, curiosity and confidence are the aims, engendered by an individual knowledge of each girl by their teachers. The school is proud of being in the top one per cent for value added at GCSE, adding 1+ grade per pupil per subject (the top 5 per cent of schools add on average 0.6+ of a grade).

School council meets regularly, though girls would like it to be less of a talking shop and to exert more power. Uniform throughout the school, predominantly navy with tartan skirts, a nod to the traditional colour scheme, perpetuated by the retention of the green cloak for chapel. Dress code for sixth form – business wear – recently more rigorously enforced.

Food is now provided by external catering company, which has seen a marked improvement in the choice and quality of meals available; recently refurbished dining room. Staff and girls dine together in main dining room, self-service with occasional formal dining. All meals here for boarders during the week, only snacks available in houses for L6 boarders and below. Dinner served in the boarding houses for all boarders at the weekend.

Pastoral care, well-being and discipline: Girls we spoke to are happy here. Manners strictly monitored. Clear guidelines for good behaviour that pupils understand and few challenging misdemeanours. Head has introduced a more positive points system, which is seen by girls as less draconian. Occasional links with other schools, but not into creating artificial exposure to boys. Drugs and similar problems uncommon and treated with firmness – head retains discretion, expulsions rare. Health centre, specialist counsellor, tutors and staff all on hand to help if things go wrong.

Pupils and parents: A widening catchment for day, flexi and weekly boarders, from Ilkley to York and beyond. Looking to attract pupils from Borders and Scotland; currently the majority of boarders are from overseas, particularly in the sixth form. There are around 24 nationalities in school though 40 per cent of boarders are from south east Asia. Within the boarding houses there are shared cultural celebrations and activities, but day girls told us that close bonds with their Pacific Rim peers are the exception rather than the rule.

Parents predominantly from the usual professions, many Harrogate notables, also self-employed and some farming families, popular with the Forces. Turns out informed, assured, polite and articulate girls, cooperative rather than competitive. Strong OG network, including Coki Van der Velde, 2015 Barclays Woman of the Year; Julie Mulligan, police and crime commissioner for North Yorkshire; Juliet Bremner, TV news reporter; Laura Winwood, former president of the Oxford Union. Building a network for more recent leavers to stay in touch.

Entrance: Main entry points are 11, 13 and 16 but school flexible. For Y7 entry, taster day in autumn term, school entrance test (mathematics, English, non-verbal reasoning) and interview taken on January assessment day, together with reports from previous school. Highfield Prep is the linked feeder school though recently only a small number have transferred to the college. Both school and parents gave the reasons as competition from excellent local state provision with families cherry-picking stages of independent education.

Minimum five GCSEs at grade C or above required for entry to sixth form, international pupils tested in English and appropriate subjects. Scholarship assessment programme.

Exit: Retention of day pupils at 16 has seen a recent improvement but historically some 15 per cent leave at 16 for local state or independents. An influx of international pupils – currently more than 60 per cent of sixth formers are boarders – results in a sixth form of some 100+ pupils.

Sixth formers leave for a widespread selection of universities, including London colleges, Exeter and Bath, though northern locations preferred, eg Durham, Edinburgh, York and Manchester. Two to Oxbridge in 2017 and 75 per cent to Russell Group. Wide range of courses: economics and business feature strongly but includes international relations and politics, 3D design and architecture, medicine, PPE, engineering, mathematics and law.

Money matters: A range of scholarships of up to 15 per cent of day fees. Fee reductions of 15 per cent for UK armed forces and 10 percent for offspring of former pupils. Means-tested bursaries up to 110 per cent of day fees to include transport, uniform etc.

Remarks: An 'in-town' girls' day/boarding school that shouts 'girl-centred' education, firmly holding onto its roots whilst reaching out to widen opportunity for its pupils to allow them to blossom in their post-school brave new world. Academic results particularly good at GCSE and a dazzling array of out of classroom opportunities means happy girls and supportive parents. Looking at ways to communicate its distinct offering at home and away to combat the pressures from increasingly competitive North Yorkshire schools.

Kilgraston School

RC 17

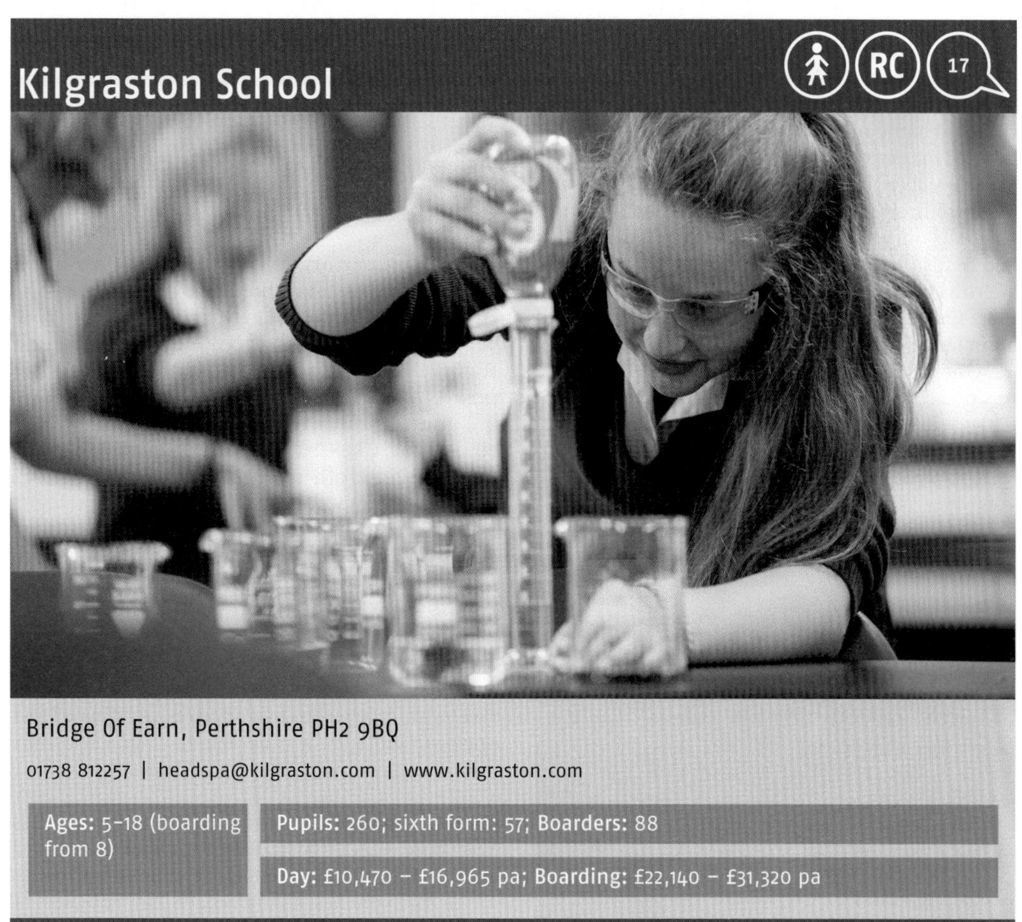

Bridge Of Earn, Perthshire PH2 9BQ

01738 812257 | headspa@kilgraston.com | www.kilgraston.com

Ages: 5-18 (boarding from 8)

Pupils: 260; sixth form: 57; Boarders: 88

Day: £10,470 – £16,965 pa; Boarding: £22,140 – £31,320 pa

Principal: Since 2015, Mrs Dorothy MacGinty, previously head of St Francis' College in Hertfordshire, where she has also been head of biology, head of games, boarding housemistress and deputy head. She is married to Frank and they have three children, the youngest in lower sixth here. Hobbies include playing golf, swimming, theatre, art galleries and spending time with the family.

Head of the junior school: Since September 2017, Anne Fidelo DipEd (from Moray House College, Edinburgh University). Has taught at the Royal High Primary School, Edinburgh Academy and Cargilfield Prep; in between, has headed a kindergarten and been head of junior school at the Banda School, both in Nairobi.

Academic matters: Unusually for a Scottish boarding school, Kilgraston works within the Scottish education system. That means that apart from offering one A level (in art), all other qualifications are Highers and Advanced Highers. Mrs MacGinty says this is a careful choice on the part of the school as they believe the two year long A level system suits boys better than girls. Also the Scottish system offers a much broader spectrum and doesn't narrow down the girls' choices too early on. 'The girls make their UCAS applications at the end of lower sixth and if they change their mind, they can pick up different subjects in upper sixth. So it's such more flexible.'

Although the girls don't sit any public exams during their first two years of senior school, S1 and S2, the school has introduced the Kilgraston Diploma. This involves a mixture of academic achievement, community service, learning a new skill and some outdoor pursuits activities, and it is based on the five goals of the Sacred Heart (faith in God, respect for intellectual values, social awareness, community building and personal growth). Mrs MacGinty says, 'We think it gives them focus and helps to introduce them to the school ethos. We're a Catholic school, and we are actively providing a Catholic education to girls of any faith and of no faith.'

One parent we spoke to said the academic side was one thing that the school did extremely well. 'They seem to know how to handle girls. It's very relaxed, but they have a good instinct for when to start applying a little bit of pressure.'

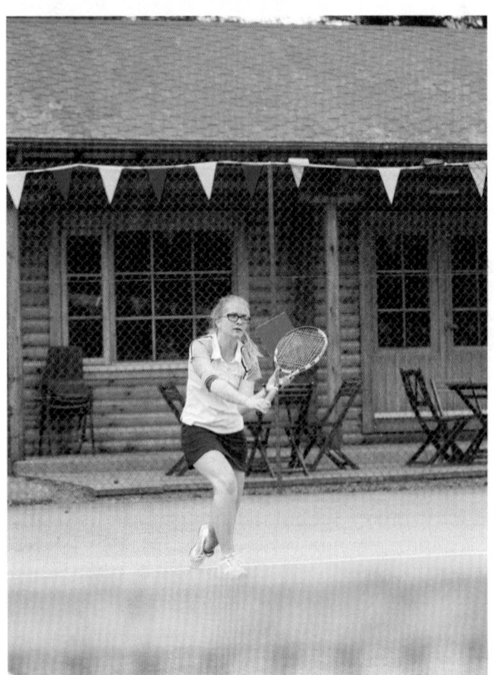

Mrs MacGinty says they are currently undergoing a curriculum review, considering other additional subjects such as psychology, for example, but she stresses that they want to keep the breadth of subjects currently available. The school clearly has a strong science department as they regularly send 40 per cent of upper sixth to university to study STEM subjects. Head says time and again statistics show that girls in a single sex school are more likely to choose STEM subjects than if they are in a co-ed environment. Languages are well catered for too, with Latin taught all the way through and regular exchange opportunities through the Sacred Heart network.

'We're a Catholic school, and we are actively providing a Catholic education to girls of any faith'

In fact, performance in all academic areas seems equally strong and this is borne out by the Higher and Advanced Higher results. In 2017, 42 per cent A grades at Advanced Highers. As for their Higher results, 55 per cent A grades; nearly 58 per cent As at National 5s.

Learning support is free and is covered by a specialist unit (CReSTed WS) with dedicated teachers for dyslexia and other learning difficulties. The head of learning support is an educational psychologist (which we assume saves going outside for testing). Twenty-five per cent of the girls at the school have some kind of learning support. This includes regular one-to-one teaching and small groups, although normal class sizes rarely exceed 12. The school layout, with many stairs, is not ideal for children with mobility issues, but head says, 'We have two girls with cerebral palsy and we have adjusted the environment and the timetable eg language lessons are brought down to the ground floor.'

Games, options, the arts: Mrs MacGinty says, 'Sport is huge here. Very important to the school as a whole,' and the facilities on offer are certainly impressive. Three Astro pitches, an impressive 25m pool, lots of grass pitches, equestrian facilities. 'We're the only school in Scotland with its own equestrian centre. We run the Scottish championships for dressage, show jumping and cross-country.' Currently seven ponies at livery at the school plus 16 school ponies which anyone may ride, and around 40 per cent of pupils do so.

From fifth form (15 years old) they start choosing what they want to do in PE: eg zumba, fencing, yoga, climbing wall, karate, archery, Scottish country dancing, skiing. Hockey, netball, rounders, tennis and swimming are the main inter-school competitive sports (although one parent told us it was far too much 'hockey, hockey, hockey'). Director of sport is Pauline Stott, an Olympian who captained the British hockey team at the Sydney Olympics. (She has an MBE for contribution to Scottish sport, hockey in particular.) Head says, 'We invest a lot in sport.'

We loved our tour of the arts and music areas at the top of the main building. Our enthusiastic tour guides (one had just secured a scholarship to Edinburgh School of Art) were brimming with information. Lots of impressive artwork and a busy practice schedule was clearly underway in the music department which nestles, quite literally, under the eaves of this impressive building. Plenty of scope here to play with jazz club, fiddle group, brass and wind ensembles, sing in chamber choir... the list is endless.

And for relaxation and fun there are plenty of clubs eg chess, Chinese culture, ethos club and, rather charmingly, the Jane Austen Film Club (bet Colin Firth and his wet shirt feature.).

Mrs MacGinty says they've been working on getting the whole school to be as outward looking as possible. 'We've established a link with a school in India – pupils are going out there for the first time in October. We chose it because it's a Hindu school. We've been working on understanding geographical differences in immunisation projects. We want them to open the girls up to different issues that affect different societies.'

Boarding: Very small boarding numbers, with currently only 16 junior boarders. There are three boarding houses: juniors in Butterstone, most in large rooms with dividers so each has her own space; 13-16 year olds in Mater each with a single room each with washing facilities; 16-18s in Barat or Swinton. Wifi access is moderated. School stops at 4.10pm on a Friday, but there are masses of activities to keep them all busy – from theatre trips to dog sledding. Charming and well-used chapel, which is obviously important in a Sacred Heart School.

Background and atmosphere: Founded in 1930, Kilgraston is one of a 200 strong network of schools and colleges within the Society of the Sacred Heart. Vast, grand, Palladian style mansion with stunning stairway and upper entrance hall. That said, the atmosphere is far from stuffy. 'We have one daughter, aged 15, who still hangs upside down from trees at Kilgraston. Our other daughter wants the full Kardashian birthday party. It really seems to cater for all.' We certainly found the girls charming, relaxed and quite confident. No self-conscious hair flicking or tinkling laughs here. They seemed very relaxed about how they looked and talked. Quite happy to be hearty. The grounds are lovely and secluded with plenty of space to roam around.

'A number of schools have gone co-ed,' says Mrs MacGinty, 'but I think the value of girls' schools is underestimated. It's about promoting confidence and inner resilience. Our girls will take risks in leadership because they don't have the boys here. They have space to develop all those skills that they might be more reticent to try out at a co-ed school.'

The junior school is situated in a brilliantly converted stable block with a glazed central atrium. It's increasingly being run on forest school principals, which encourage the girls to get outside as much as possible. Numbers have been dropping recently, however, the nursery has closed, and there has been some parental concern over composite classes. Mrs MacGinty assures us that this is only a temporary issue, however, and future numbers are on the rise.

'We introduced composite classes for P4 and P5 last year, as well as a composite P1, 2 and 3 class, and the rumour mill suggested we were going to have composite classes further up, but that's not true. Top class P7 is going to be two separate classes because the numbers have grown.' So not bursting at the seams. It will be interesting how the junior school fares under its new head.

Pastoral care, well-being and discipline: Would you be surprised if we told you Kilgraston has its own BFG? In fact it has a whole load of them. Nothing to do with giants, you understand, but instead a fantastic buddy system to help younger girls. (Big Friendly Girl, in case you were wondering.) We actually saw it in action as one of our tour guides was nearly felled by a little person hugging her BFG.

Our enthusiastic tour guides (one had just secured a scholarship to Edinburgh School of Art) were brimming with information. Lots of impressive artwork

The school stresses that the girls get plenty of interaction with the opposite sex. Many of the girls have brothers at Merchiston and there are regular joint social events – debating as well as parties. (Lucky Merchie boys as they are the social foils for Edinburgh girls' school St George's as well.)

The girls are divided into houses and there are house meetings or year group meetings every Friday morning. Tutor meetings every Tuesday and regular PHSE sessions. Social studies in the sixth form also covers age relevant well-being topics. One big school concern is the amount of stress girls are under through social media. 'We drum home the message that appearance is not important. We want to motivate them, celebrate their achievements. We don't want them to feel under pressure.'

Pupils and parents: Boarders from around 14 different countries worldwide, but the majority of the girls are from Scotland (many from Perthshire). A good number of first time buyers. Although the school is RC, there are plenty of non-Catholics.

Entrance: No entrance exam. Mrs MacGinty meets every girl and her parents to make sure that they're offering the right style of education. Then a report and reference from the previous school.

Exit: The school is proud of its record in getting their girls into Scottish universities eg Edinburgh, St Andrews, Glasgow, Robert Gordon, Caledonian, Abertay, Dundee, with others to eg the Sorbonne (physics), Brunel (aviation engineering with pilot studies) and Derby (special education needs and disability).

Money matters: Up to 10 academic, art and music scholarships. Also riding, tennis and sporting scholarships. Almost one quarter receive assistance of some sort. School is 'good at finding trust funding' for those who have fallen on hard times.

Remarks: Kilgraston occupies a unique place in Scottish education as the only all girls' boarding school north of the border and the only public school to adhere to the Scottish education system. And it seems to suit them. They get good results and provide a non-pressurised, relaxed, sporty, happy and non-overtly religious atmosphere for their girls.

Lathallan School

18

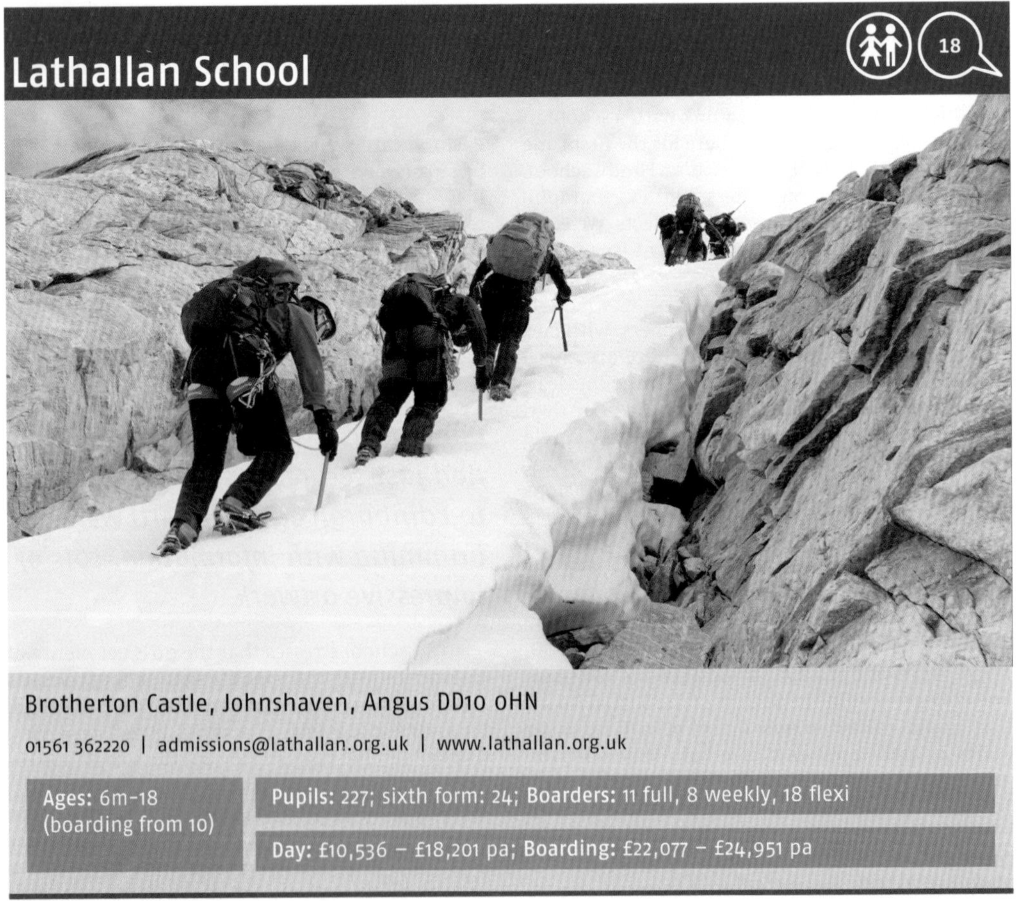

Brotherton Castle, Johnshaven, Angus DD10 0HN

01561 362220 | admissions@lathallan.org.uk | www.lathallan.org.uk

Ages: 6m–18 (boarding from 10)

Pupils: 227; sixth form: 24; **Boarders:** 11 full, 8 weekly, 18 flexi

Day: £10,536 – £18,201 pa; **Boarding:** £22,077 – £24,951 pa

Headmaster: Since 2009, Mr Richard Toley BA MPhil PGCE (40s) who joined Lathallan in 2006 as director of co-curriculum from nearby High School of Dundee. Educated at The Merchant Taylor's School, Liverpool, followed by St David's Lampeter MPhil at St Andrews and PGCE at Strathclyde. He and his wife live on site, with their young now in school.

Six years down the road (Toley was catapulted into headship after an 18 month apprenticeship) he is comfortably confident in his role. (We usually pop in for a quick check on our way down from Aberdeen, though alas this time we were both caught in traffic and had to do some crisis management, so missed our meet.) School moved from being 'just' a prep school with a hugely popular and often oversubscribed nursery in 2006, to building up a senior base year by year.

A historian, charming and relaxed, Toley teaches classics (as in classical studies) and history 12 periods a week in the senior school, and runs school with senior school head, Mr Duncan Lyall BSc PGCE (40s), an Edinburgh lad, and Mr James Ferrier BA (Cantab) PGCE (50s), head of junior school since 2011, having first come to school in 2001 from Moor Park in Shropshire. Lyall, who read mechanical engineering at Edinburgh, is married with a brace of young, and came to Lathallan from Peebles High, having previously taught in both the borders and Aberdeen.

Ferrier lives on campus with his wife, was educated at Hardyes School, Dorset, read humanities of Christ Church, followed by PGCE at the University of Kent, and runs his part of the Lathallan empire with gentle humour.

Impressive collection of uber-powerful governors plus parent governors, 'tremendous backing'.

Academic matters: Scottish curriculum: 17+ subject options at all levels. As ever, we ask for individual results per subject, with number of candidates in each subject and results (as in 12 did English Higher, two got A, four B, five C – that sort of thing). Whilst school 'does hold such results, it does not divulge them'. So now you know. School is non-selective and for some a C or a D may be a real achievement (some 80 per cent of Highers were A-C in 2017). The staff whom we have met over the years have been bubbly and enthusiastic.

Variety pack of langs on offer – Mandarin – whenever (number of native speakers in school) plus French (from P1) and Spanish (S1) (native speakers). Not a lot of take-up in the former, though occasional outstanding results at all levels. Pupils study both French and Spanish throughout S2 before opting for one or t'other for Nat 5s.

Latin from aged 11 (classical studies at Higher and Advanced Higher), crash course in Italian (ab initio) – offered at Higher level, but no take-up – plus the usual suspects: maths, English, three sciences, history, geography (pleasing and popular), business and classical studies, art, PE and drama, and managing environmental resources (MER). This is penny number stuff, occasional glitch.

Civilianship the latest addition – ie how to open doors, ladies first, that sort of thing; school is talking to exam boards as to how they could make this an examinable subject. Think finishing schools, think nanny, think how clever.

All assessed for dyslexia et al on arrival. Two dedicated learning support staff, one-to-one, clusters, or co-teaching, throughout school. Costs the same as a piano lesson. Back-up for the bored and the brightest. Class sizes around 13 (max 16), pupils streamed for maths and English both taught in refurb'ed classrooms in the castle, interactive whiteboards all over.

Ten acres of playing fields overlooking the North Sea and own beach (bracing). Lots of jolly rugby trips and netball tours

IT impressive – Dell computers plus Apple Macs in senior school. iPads for all seems to be the current flavour of the month (last time we did a round up it was the 'virtual learning experience'). Only for those in the dyslexia stream at Lathallan. We were told that Toley 'was not convinced' by rolling 'em out across the board.

Science still in a hotch-potch of temporary buildings beside the nursery complex: but zinging new science centre more than a couple of metres off the ground (as ever, near the nursery complex). We have a natty brochure with pics, showing three dedicated science labs plus one for environmental study and junior science lab. Plus accessible loos, shower – got to have 'em now and pupil inspired 'treehouse' (to enhance outdoor learning experiences). Natty brochure has fundraising options, so we hope there is enough dosh to complete the

project. Impressive sounding new head of science Ian Smith comes from Cults Academy where he was head principal teacher of chemistry.

Staff whom we have met are young, enthusiastic and fun. Twenty-six on the books and six part-timers. Peris pulled in for the more esoteric subjects (or instruments). No apparent problem in attracting staff, particularly in the current financial climate, when property prices have in some quarters reached basement level. The Aberdeen catchment area was pricey.

Games, options, the arts: Music everywhere – bagpipe boxes all over the porch and hall, both girls and boys in pipe bands much in demand for charities and have entertained Princess Anne of late, played in the Angus show, the Glamis gathering, the Scottish parliament etc. Pipes and drums played at the battlefields in Belgium during the Great War memorial year and compete in the Royal Pipe Band competitions with success. Scottish country dancing no longer has parental input; marvellous photographs in the porch of a junior Scottish country dancing lesson – note the kilt loops and the ecstasy on the faces of the young. Strong drama: new head of music previously with Aberdeen Youth Theatre; no orchestra per se (yet) but wind and ceilidh bands.

Music everywhere – bagpipe boxes all over the porch and hall, both girls and boys in pipe bands much in demand for charities and have entertained Princess Anne of late

Toley has introduced a new formal school-wide traditional PE programme, which 'through age-appropriate indoor exercises aims to improve co-ordination and mental agility both in and outside the academic classroom' (sounds a tad Steiner-ish). School thinks this sounds harsh. 'We have a real focus on sports/PE and outdoor education but this sounds almost military'. 'We realise the importance of exercise.' 'We want our pupils to be well-rounded by participating in PE/sports and outdoor ed.'

Thrashing all comers in under-16 rugby 7s, new games pavilion (board member head of SRU); 7s rugby team toot to Dubai on the cards, but 'mainly it is regional' with all points south of Gordonstoun. All 7+ year olds play sport daily, tennis courts double up for netball (Astroturf), 10 acres of playing field overlooking the North Sea and own beach (bracing), plus refurbished gym. Lots of jolly rugby trips and netball tours. Sea at the bottom of the garden, but no sea sports – too rough. Impressive games area adjacent to junior/baby school. Astro: tennis: you name it; plus dedicated gym (though hall in main school building equally adaptable).

Head of outdoor education is Monro-potty, 'probably climbed them all three times,' says Toley. D of E timetabled and huge numbers – school claims 'highest percentage of participation in the D of E scheme in all of the country (Scotland)'.

First two years of senior school spend six days in the mountains, mountain rescue, navigation (shades of Round Square). Skiing, both at home and abroad for all. Huge emphasis on outdoor education, self-resilience, and leadership training. New 50 foot long zip wire in the wood (100 foot drop). Scary. Six pupils and guides did an unsupported, exploratory exped to Eastern Greenland last August. (Scary again). Recent trip to Iceland has even more scary photos.

ISCO (careers guidance) enrollment (as ever) and ongoing advice as to 'what happens next'.

Boarding: Influx of foreign boarders since full boarding reopened: 30 boarders housed in separate wings of the castle (previous staff quarters), co-ed boarding tidily arranged, mainly oil-y children, from Thailand, China, Spain, Nigeria, Russia. Scottish Guardian Overseas Association oversees them (and individual guardians have to pick up the flack if their charges are sent 'home', ie gated). Some locals, bed and breakfasting available. ESOL on hand to help with language glitches. Interesting to see whether boarding numbers hold up during current oil turn-down.

Background and atmosphere: Founded in the imposing Victorian Brotherton Castle (1867) in the early 1930s. Originally trad boys' boarding prep school, set in 62 acres of woodland which catered for 'the folk over the hill'; now a thriving nursery (handful of real babes being pushed out in three prams when we visited; good North Sea air) through to Advanced Highers co-ed offering full, weekly or flexi-boarding (from age 10).

Regular exchange programmes with 'smallish' schools in Canada, Switzerland and Australia; the latter were enjoying their six weeks in Angus during a previous visit. More than 25 clubs; 'we rotate them,' says Toley.

William Bruce house-lets (which pre-date the castle) guard corners of the long abandoned formal garden which makes a splendid play area. Library and resource centre in main building with classrooms and nursery in bright converted stable block with massive additions (and home to new science build but see above). Some lessons in temporary classrooms. Irritating steps both too shallow and too wide link the two sites. Nursery/junior wing surrounded by play/games areas, stunning nursery playground. Collection of toddler sized loos and mini basins: one wonders how they cope at home.

Newly refurb'ed common room for senior school pupils. School uniform provided in house, with jolly fleecy waterproof jackets which staff wear too. Staff all have to take the minibus test.

Pastoral care, well-being and discipline: School small enough for every child to be known (cherished is a word that comes to mind if it didn't sound so soppy), strong anti-bullying policy. Occasional gatings for wickedness, no child yet asked to leave. School is 'bespoke, focused'.

Pupils and parents: Increasing number of first time buyers. FPs supportive, strong parental input, parents will drive many miles out of their way to drop off their tinies in the nursery. Return buses for older children from Stonehaven, Edzell and Aberdeen with coaches from Brechin, Forfar and Montrose.

Aberdeen business community plus local farmers, commuters, usually from within 90 minute radius (which takes you to Dundee). Rob Wainwright an old boy (and does the odd spot of coaching), ditto Ian Lang (Lord Lang of Monkton).

Niche school: perfect for the occasional non-performing refugee from bigger trad schools: Fettes, Merchiston, Robert Gordons. Children thrive in the smaller environment. 'We care'. (Those parents to whom we spoke fell into the latter category. Their relief was palpable.)

Entrance: Lathallan nursery: from six weeks, 80 tinies registered but no more than 49 at any one time. Entrance to junior school seamless from nursery test-ette for problems and 'nearly all go' (95 per cent). Juniors are checked 'carefully' and if problems obvious, they get a 'proper test'.

Entry to senior school at any time to any year group if places available, many come via junior school. Otherwise form 5 (P7: 11, 12 year olds). Taster day. Informal tests in English, maths and verbal reasoning, but not a selective school. Numbers up from prep school, 10/12 a year. Currently full first three years of senior school (and nursery and pre-junior school ie ages 5 and 6).

Exit: Tiny trickle leave for trad independents age 13, occasional departure age 8, otherwise the odd relocation. Sixth formers head in the main to the Scottish unis: St Andrews, Edinburgh, Aberdeen, Heriot Watt, Stirling and Glasgow.

Money matters: Money matters 'under control', up to 100 per cent bursaries (and extra help if necessary): huge raft: academic, sports, rugby 7s, netball, music and pipes and drums. Sibling discount. Secondhand clothes shop. Will keep child if parents fall on hard times with the usual caveat of being up front about the problem.

Lathallan nursery in partnership with Aberdeen County council (discounts). Hours roughly 7.30am to 6pm but check fee structure, deeply expensive if child not collected by designated time (emergency cover and charged by the quarter hour). This is a 50 week nursery with two weeks off for Christmas.

Remarks: This is the tail that wagged the dog. We have visited Lathallan over the past 20 odd years: six headmasters. This was a school which had – quite frankly – been toiling. Sometimes it had a nursery which took babes from 2 months, sometimes from 3 years. In any case it was a boys' boarding prep school with an increasingly dismal roll call (even after they took girls and day pupils) and a glorious view. Two (or was it three?) heads ago, the brave decision (we thought nuts) was made to expand, on a year by year basis, to become a fully fledged school, with Highers and Advanced Highers and all. We were wrong. Very wrong (and we won't rehearse further the various decisions down the line). Remarkable success story which keeps on growing.

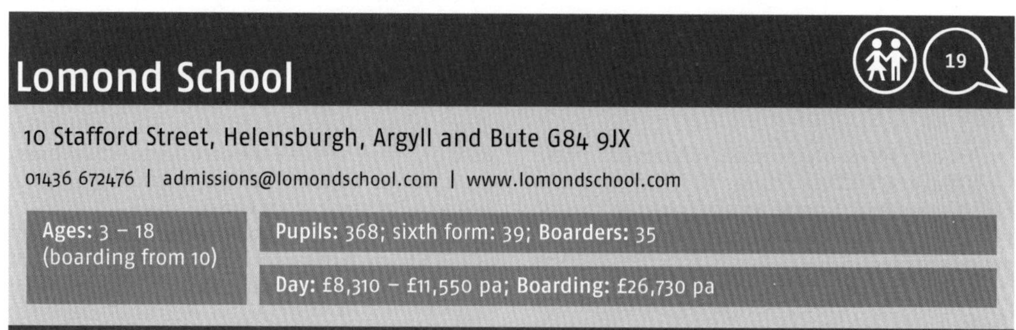

Lomond School

19

10 Stafford Street, Helensburgh, Argyll and Bute G84 9JX

01436 672476 | admissions@lomondschool.com | www.lomondschool.com

Ages: 3 – 18 (boarding from 10)

Pupils: 368; sixth form: 39; Boarders: 35

Day: £8,310 – £11,550 pa; Boarding: £26,730 pa

Head: Since 2014, Johanna Urquhart, previously depute head (academic) at George Watson's College. She has a degree in maths and statistics and a masters in education, specialising in leadership and management. She has also been depute head at Breadalbane Academy.

Academic matters: Setted in English, French and maths at the age of 12, French taught from age 5, German from 11. Huge range of subjects on offer, including such esoteric ones as graphic communication, modern studies and business management, as well as French, German and Spanish. Three sciences. Latin GCSE taught by video conference link and distance learning. In 2017, 78 per cent A-B at Highers.

Maximum class size 20. Sixth form were working supervised (which is unheard of at that age) in the library when we visited. Homework very important – children keep a diary and expect to do at least two and a half hours each night in their National grade year. Has strong links with private schools in China, Germany and US. Computers everywhere, networked, and all have access to the internet; keyboarding skills for all, electronic interactive whiteboard presentations for all by all. Tutors for all. Good learning support (and provision for those with dyslexia, ADD or ADHD). English as a second language on hand.

Games, options, the arts: Huge playing field just along the (tree-lined) road. Full-sized floodlit Astroturf hockey pitch. Rugby and hockey the two main winter games, with tennis, cricket and athletics in the summer and oodles of add-ons. Swimming in the local pool, option of squash, riding and badminton. Inter-house matches popular. Mass of lunch time clubs, D of E popular and, of course, sailing, The Scottish Islands Peaks Race, Lomond Challenge (a beastly tough triathlon) – not a school for sissies. Newish games hall, adjacent to the Astroturf, includes badminton courts, climbing wall, dance studio, fitness suite and indoor cricket lanes. Further development to include another smaller Astroturf.

John Logie Baird's school report, displayed in the dining room, expresses the hope that he will eventually 'go on and do something with his life'

Traditional Scottish music important – clarsach players, fiddlers, pipers and singers are in regular demand. Strong music, based in the old stables – one wall entirely covered with guitars, not just for decoration, judging by the enthusiasm the guitar teacher generated. Recording facilities in place. Big bands and chamber orchestras, over 20 instruments on curriculum with some 150 individual lessons. Sparkling art department, with old school desks press-ganged into use. Huge variety of disciplines – photography with spit-new kit, magical screen printing, jewellery making, as well as the more prosaic (which it wasn't) sculpture, painting and etching. Tremendous enthusiasm here – enchanting flower costume, complete with design, basque and wings, made for last summer's play, on show. Strong drama.

Boarding: Burnbrae now the most modern boarding house in Scotland – boys and girls (boarders from age 10) share the same building but are separated by a state-of-the-art security system using biometric readers.

Background and atmosphere: Based on the northern edge of the posh, sleepy, seaside town of Helensburgh, originally housed in a series of Victorian villas. Present school is an amalgam of Larchfield, founded in 1845, and the girls' school, St Bride's, founded in 1895. The schools combined in 1977; later a stunning rebuild. The resulting school is a curious combination of old and new, with three floors replacing the original two and subject rooms being grouped in series. Most impressive – massive amount of glass, super new dining hall, good gym and terrific entrance hall with glorious views out over the Clyde. All pupils wear uniform (kilts for females) – neat and tidy with ties and a thoroughly purposeful air.

Pastoral care, well-being and discipline: Strong anti-bullying procedure in place – the 'no blame' circle appears to be the most effective. Confidential suggestion boxes all over the school are really part of the anti-bullying programme. Good PSD programme. CCTV cameras throughout. Children not 'given a lot of rope', eg any substance abuse leads to suspension, 'pending a discussion of their school future'. Dealing equals straight out. Smoking is apparently 'not happening just now', but smoking in uniform is 'not on'.

Pupils and parents: An upmarket lot – solid middle class, from the surrounding area (they organise the buses), some from as far away as Glasgow. Number of Forces families (Faslane naval base next door) and some from further 'round the bay' send their children here (the local state school thought to be too state). A few mainland Chinese usually come for most of their secondary schooling, plus connection with Germany, whence the occasional pupil comes for a year or a term – not much take-up of Scots going to Germany in exchange.

Bonar Law was educated at Larchfield, as well as John Logie Baird – his school report, displayed in the dining room, apart from showing that he was 14th out of 14 in maths, expresses the hope that he will eventually 'go on and do something with his life'!

Entrance: Either up via nursery or from local state primaries.

Exit: Usual dribble away after National grades and could fill up the resulting places several times over, trickle leaves after Highers; some, eg those going south to university, tend to stay and do their Advanced Highers. Most will end up at university – destinations include St Andrews, Edinburgh, Glasgow, Aberdeen, Stirling, Strathclyde, Swansea.

Money matters: Not a rich school. Will support pupils in financial difficulties; an increasing number of means-tested bursaries (up to 100 per cent) available at the age of 10 and 11 and post-National grades.

Remarks: A jolly, busy school, perfect for those who want to keep their children at home without the hassle of going daily to Glasgow.

Longridge Towers School

20

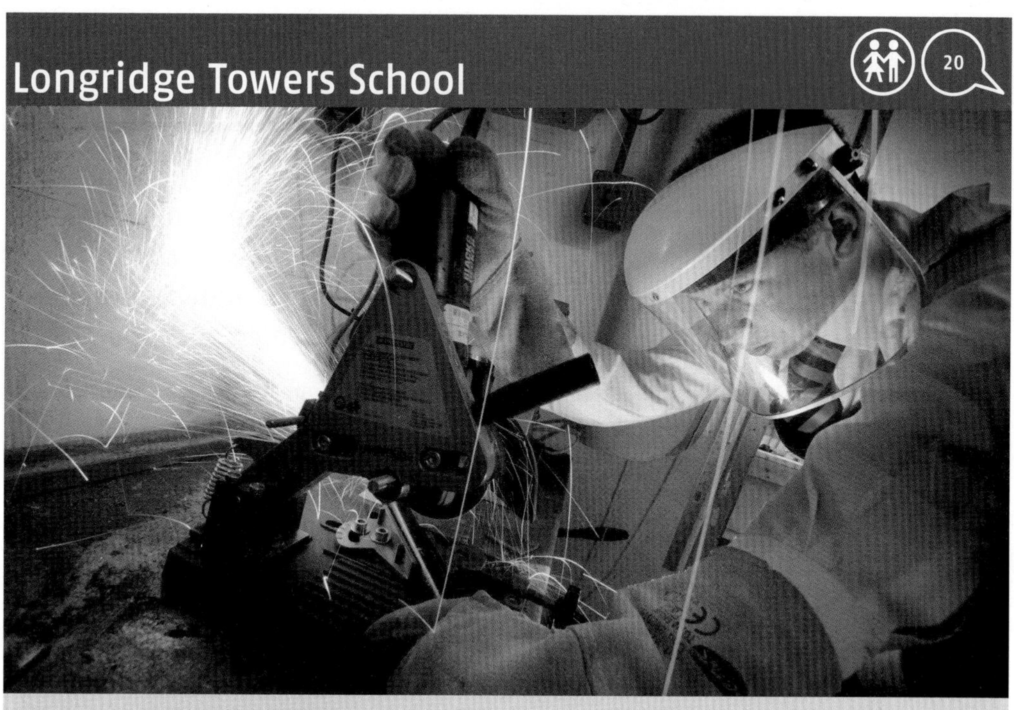

Berwick-upon-Tweed, Northumberland TD15 2XQ

01289 307584 | enquiries@lts.org.uk | www.lts.org.uk

Ages: 3-18 (boarding from 8)

Pupils: 207; sixth form: 42; Boarders: 22

Day: £8,481 – £13,233 pa; Boarding: £19,461 – £26,943 pa

Headmaster: Since September 2016, Jonathan Lee, previously housemaster and maths teacher at Uppingham. Maths degree from St Andrews and is a qualified accountant.

Academic matters: All-through school from 3-18, with French started at 7 and German at 11. Spanish, Italian and Latin as extracurricular but can be taken at GCSE, as can Chinese. Wide range of GCSE subjects with flexible time timetabling based on the needs of each particular year group so that 95 per cent get to take what they want. English, Eng lit and maths for all plus six other options (can include three – or two – separate sciences or science and additional science.) Usual subjects plus ICT, CDT (done in a well-equipped but basic hut in the grounds), sports studies, drama and music. Consistently sound record with a good sprinkling of A and A* in biology and maths and a few in Eng lit and elsewhere. Almost everyone takes drama and IT, both with solid results and no significant weaknesses, though art a bit up and down. In 2017, 51 per cent of GCSEs were A*-A/9-7.

At A level, 23 per cent A*/A in 2017 and 54 per cent A*-B. Choice includes the usual subjects plus economics with business studies, sports science and further maths; general studies AS for all now replaced by critical thinking after rather iffy results; while psychology can be taken at AS over two years. Dusting of A*/As across most subjects and a consistently solid 'pass' rate but also quite a smattering of C/D. Inevitably small groups – will put on a mainstream subject for one pupil in sixth form. Anyone with 5+ Cs/5s can take As though B/6 preferred in subject concerned.

SEN support offered mostly by individual withdrawal with personal education plans used to keep teachers aware of needs. English help for pupils from China etc and efforts to provide extra stimulus for the very bright.

Juniors start from early years foundation stage (tiny classes of five to 10 only) on Oxford Reading Tree, supplemented by lots of Jolly Phonics and Ginn letters and sounds.

Classrooms pretty modern with a few interactive whiteboards and computer projectors, lots of IT including laptop trolleys for use in amazingly antiquated though very adequately equipped labs. The smartest lab is in the junior school building for 7-11s. Called Stobo after a benefactor, the junior school is still clean and new looking with state of art (though cheerfully decorated) classrooms, cloakrooms and hall etc. Early years to junior 3 have humbler but thoroughly refurbished quarters absolutely brimming with colour, imaginative stimulus material and even recorded birdsong. A pleasant fenced outdoor area for tinies and some smashing all weather play equipment, in enthusiastic use.

Games, options, the arts: Sport flourishes with highly successful seven-a-side rugby reaching finals in county tournaments – they struggle to produce a top-level full teams from a small co-ed school but are outstanding in sevens. Recent leavers at Scottish, English and Great British U20 championship level, soccer just starting, lots of hockey for girls with several county players, a school champion skier and masses of opportunity for basketball, volleyball, badminton, cricket, tennis, curling (Scottish school finalists) etc. Spacious sports hall (takes a marquee inside for prize days and dances), defunct swimming pool left by previous convent school so minibuses take them to Eyemouth pool but grounds lend themselves to hosting local cross-country etc. At last has Astroturf.

Hammer-beams sporting snarling monsters with grotesquely bared teeth, an imperial staircase and an elaborate portico added to shelter the Prince of Wales' carriage

Lots of choir, orchestra, jazz groups etc with star pupil in Northern Youth Orchestra but little take up of academic music beyond GCSE. Informal lunchtime concerts much enjoyed by all. Special centre for peripatetic music in a pretty gothic house in the grounds which the previous head rejected as a home. Drama in the round in strange theatre converted from former convent chapel, with jazzy lighting, provided by the enterprising parents' 'school development association'. Recent production is Billy Liar. Art seems a bit marginalised in a building seven minutes walk from main school but is looking to a new art teacher to hot it up next year. Ambition is to reincorporate this in a new sciences and practical subjects building. The school is now full and seemingly growing, so hopes to revamp abandoned plans for new labs into a more inclusive facility.

Boundless activities! Almost all day pupils including juniors stay till 4.40pm for an hour of activity which can include supervised study, tutorials, extra coursework or teaching. Falconry is clearly the latest craze – the juniors couldn't stop talking about it – but also the tip of an impressive iceberg: archery, athletics, lacrosse and other sports, debating, wildlife gardening (with a good muddy pond), yoga, a new Radio Longridge, science and engineering clubs, cheerleading, war games and lashings of other things. School comments that having rearranged activity times to suit staff and pupils better, the staff can do what they really like. Bags of trips: German exchange, sport to Canada, South Africa, Iceland etc. Charitable

Unusually friendships across year groups are not uncommon, especially valuable in such a small and variable boarding situation

links with Borneo and others. D of E for seniors and Adventure Service challenge for juniors.

Boarding: Boarding on two floors (girls above, boys below) has spacious mostly two-bedded rooms, some with en suite showers. Their height makes them a little stark though inmates are allowed locked doors and a free-ish hand with posters and personal paraphernalia. Pleasant and well-planned recreation room, with spotless kitchenette and generous supplies of luscious fruit.

Background and atmosphere: The extraordinary Victorian Tudor extravaganza built of sandstone ashlar in 1880s for Sir Hubert Jerningham, a liberal MP, on the estate inherited by his wife Annie, Liddell was designed to impress (it does!) by the Buckleys who redid Arundel Castle. It features battlemented stone chimneys, magnificent great hall, now for concerts, with hammer-beams sporting snarling monsters with grotesquely bared teeth, an imperial staircase and an elaborate portico added to shelter the Prince of Wales' carriage (though history is silent over whether he actually arrived to use it) all making Longridge the grandest house in the area. Set in 80 acres of parkland, it became a hotel, then in 1949 an Ursuline Convent school. In 1983 it was restructured as the co-educational Longridge Towers School.

In a fantastic rural setting with imaginative use of the castellated grand areas, the school also has the problem of making stone staircases, high ceilings and a warren corridors of work for 21st century education. The original library had a cunning makeover with a gallery providing working space and banishing the previous nightmare scenario of children on ladders to glass (non-safety) fronted bookcases. There's lots of help on hand and an ambitious programmes of visiting authors etc. 'Service wings' house boarders, dining rooms and kitchens – some tasty dishes (pupils actually like it on the whole) made on site with a few home-grown veg. All obviously well used and well cared for but lots of echoey passages and stairwells, improved by pupil artwork (not always the right way up, though it's hard to tell). Most noticeably some stunning Aboriginal hangings done for a drama performance liven one of the central stairways. Everything clean and mainly litter free, well used and not unnaturally tidy.

Pastoral care, well-being and discipline: Independent Schools Inspectorate really praised pastoral care. Qualified nurse in boarding and system of tutors and year heads (form teachers for juniors) and three school houses which run vertically through juniors to senior school. Pupils respect and value system and genuine interest of staff, so problems are picked up quickly and children tend to monitor and report issues like bullying before they become serious. New junior school council is prized by pupils. Plentiful contact between all ages with seniors helping with reading and games. Unusually friendships across year groups are not uncommon, especially valuable in such a small and variable boarding situation. Strong sense of community enhanced by boarding and also by the school's involvement with its neighbourhood. Activities provided supplement rather than compete with local amenities such as junior golf. Pupils are ready to take responsibility as elected prefects etc within and without school. One sixth former even combined his school duties with being chief coastguard for Lindisfarne.

Pupils and parents: Masses of bus routes bring pupils coming from a scattered area which includes not only Berwick-upon-Tweed, the surrounding border country in both England and Scotland, but also the Holy Island (Lindisfarne) population, whose children need to board on days when the tide cuts off their journey to or from school. Hence boarding has a special wing for them where siblings can be together and the provision has a more temporary feel than the full termly boarding, though they share its amenities and supervision. So boarding at Longridge is more 'flexi' than most and the population fluctuates. Boarding seems to be on the increase with about 22 current maximum and applications going up. A few boarders from abroad, mainly China, otherwise a largely British intake.

Falconry is clearly the latest craze – the juniors couldn't stop talking about it – but also the tip of an impressive iceberg

Uniform is in a state of flux though everyone looks quite smart. New blue blazers, white shirts, grey trousers and knee straight skirts with prominent kick pleats in blue, white and grey tartan look neat and innocuous, while tinies wear blue and white cotton summer dresses.

Parents run a dynamic programme of events and raise significant amounts for equipment etc. Governors take an active interest in the school and the local worthies, whose families give the names to houses etc, support it with visits and interest.

Entrance: By assessment at all levels but school will take anyone capable of benefiting from what's on offer. Since Longridge pupils come from Scotland and England with different systems involving changes of school at 7, 11, 12, 14 and even different age cut off points, September for England but February for Scotland, need careful induction and class sizes are unpredictable. Now started a class for 3 year olds in response to local demand.

Exit: Some leave from juniors at either 11 and 12 (English and Scottish systems) mainly to independent, Ampleforth, Merchiston Castle etc, though not usually to local state schools. There is more than a trickle (15-45 per cent) after GCSE to local and Newcastle sixth forms and a few to independent boarding. Those who stay to upper sixth go mostly to uni, a few to blue chip and a surprising quota of sports degrees. Some to academic courses too. Popular destinations include Newcastle, King's College London, Leeds Beckett (vocational courses), York, Edinburgh, Northumbria, Central Lancashire.

Money matters: Not a rich school but awards available for academic (up to 50 per cent), sporting (up to 10 per cent) or musical (free tuition) excellence are offered to those qualifying by exam, achieving county sports honours or by audition. Pupils from Holy Island are sponsored by the local authority, which would otherwise be unable to provide adequate hostel accommodation.

Remarks: Small, with all the advantages of good supervision, care, close-knit community and friendliness a small school can give. Copes very well with the disadvantages of scale, so pupils do not lose out on activities, subjects etc. Berwick-upon-Tweed is jolly lucky to have this alternative at hand.

Loretto School

21

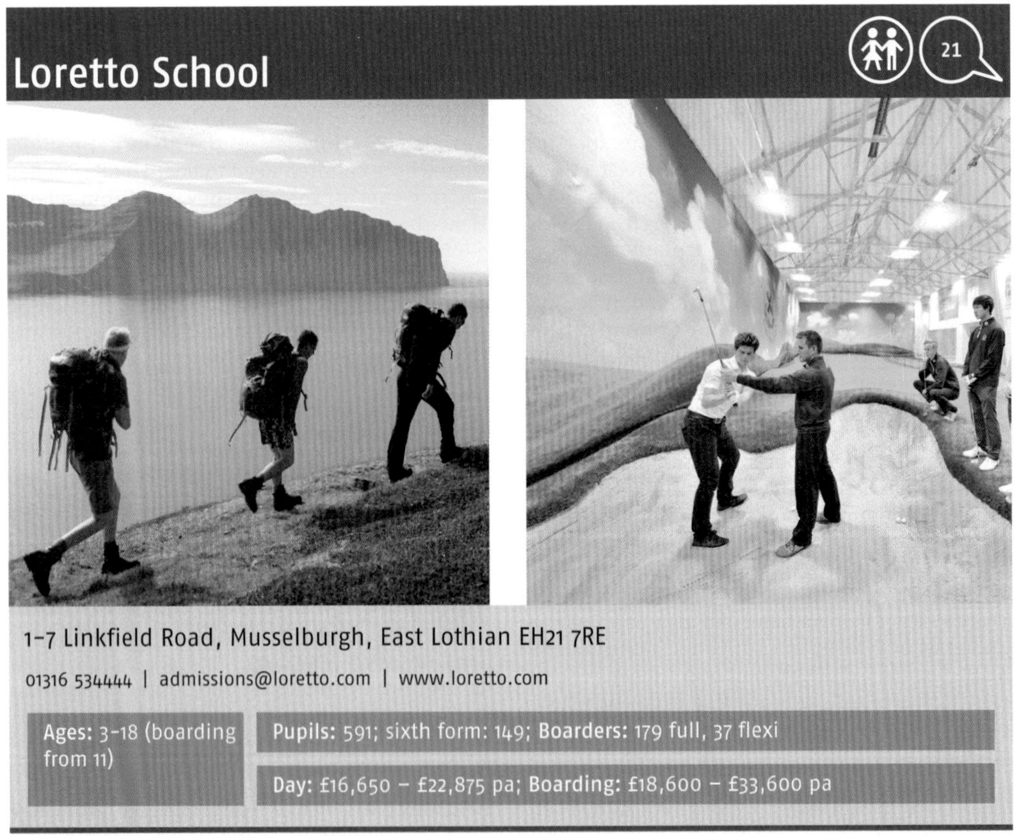

1-7 Linkfield Road, Musselburgh, East Lothian EH21 7RE

01316 534444 | admissions@loretto.com | www.loretto.com

Ages: 3-18 (boarding from 11)

Pupils: 591; sixth form: 149; Boarders: 179 full, 37 flexi

Day: £16,650 – £22,875 pa; Boarding: £18,600 – £33,600 pa

Headmaster: Since 2014, Dr Graham Hawley (BSc, PhD, PGCE). Previously headmaster of Kelly College, a co-educational HMC boarding/day school where he stayed for six years. Educated at Mill Hill School in London, he holds a first class honours degree from Durham University (natural sciences) and a doctorate. A keen sportsman, he represented Middlesex U18s at cricket. Before his teaching career his scientific research expeditions took him all over the world. He's a thinker but without an ego – clever, articulate and happy in his own skin. We are told (by parents not by Dr Hawley) that he greets all the pupils as they arrive each morning. Parents report that 'he is very approachable and astute'. Married to Rachel (rave reviews from parents, 'she's terrific – bright, friendly and observant') with two teenage young.

Pupils tell us that on his appointment as headmaster he worked at the coalface to establish exactly how the school ticked, alongside the teachers, cleaners, groundskeepers and the catering teams at all hours of the day (and night). As well as providing him with a good working knowledge of the school it also earned him a great deal of respect from his pupils.

Junior school: Since the departure of Philip Meadows, Dr Hawley is currently acting head of the junior school. The new head from August 2018 will be Andrew Dickenson, currently head of junior school at Kelvinside Academy. MA (50s); studied modern history at University of St Andrews. Started off teaching career in London in early 1990s, then The Edinburgh Academy Junior School (deputy head). Passionate about promoting digital learning across the school as well as outdoor learning. Married with two grown-up daughters.

Academic matters: Senior school follows the English education system of GCSEs and A levels. No plans to introduce IB, headmaster is 'comfortable with A levels' and doesn't see the need for 'constant tinkering' with the system. In 2017, 39 per cent A*/A grades at A level and 45 per cent A*-A/9-7 at GCSE. Results have stepped up recently despite still being a 'broadly unselective school'.

Music, drama and PE can be taken at A level and GCSE. Psychology A level a recent introduction. Boy/girl ratio fairly even across all subjects possibly helped by new female head of science. Economics, business and accounting are now available as separate A levels and are popular choices. History and politics department also thriving with excellent record of public examination success. Main modern languages are French and Spanish.

Learning support available throughout junior and senior schools – one learning support teacher plus two assistants. In sixth form support is timetabled on a needs basis.

Interactive whiteboards and networked computers throughout. More digital content in lessons is being introduced. Various societies for brain boxes and those keen to learn more – Reimann Society for those mathematically gifted. Mavor Society – lectures given by the sixth formers on any topic that interests them – an opportunity to extend an academic passion. Excellent visiting lecturers each week (recent lecturers include Olympians Heather Stanning and Steve Cram); pupils spoke about the lectures with real enthusiasm.

Open classroom policy at lunchtime for staff to help pupils if required. Senior pupils tell us that there's always someone available to help them with their studies and that the teachers are very approachable. Interview practice for sixth formers and individual support with UCAS personal statements.

The art room in the junior school is a thing of wonder and clearly run with dollops of passion, skill and imagination. Fantastic creations of every shape and form

Junior school teachers get excellent feedback from the children and parents. 'Nothing is too much effort and if there's a problem or a child needing help they will always sort it out'. One young pupil told us that she liked her maths lessons as it was the first time any teacher 'had made maths fun' for her.

International English Language Testing System (IELTS) available for international pupils who need it.

Games, options, the arts: The junior school uses many of the senior school facilities such as the main theatre, the chapel and the eyeball searing, blue Astroturf ('the smurf turf').

Sport is a big deal, with pupils in regional and national teams from rugby to judo. In general sport is laid out on traditional lines – boys play rugby in the autumn term, hockey in spring and cricket in summer. Girls play hockey in the autumn term and lacrosse in the spring. Lots of teams so everyone is included not just the sporting legends.

This inclusion is a double edged sword with some parents thinking it's a huge positive that all children have the experience of playing in a team. However, one junior school parent commented that 'they don't always put their best teams forward and this is a shame as the teams could be more successful than they are'.

Rugby is strong as is girls' lacrosse – a specialist coach from the USA and girls representing Scotland at U17 and U19. Cricket – for both sexes – is well catered, with excellent training facilities and links to Cricket Scotland.

Many of the children in the junior school that we spoke mentioned 'sport' as their 'favourite' part of school life and the parents say that 'the children are very proud of their sporting teams and their success'.

And so, to golf. The Golf Academy, established in 2002, is Loretto's USP and is top in Europe, attracting young golfers from around the world. To the east of the school lie the golf courses which provide the fairway for the Academy – Craigielaw and Archerfield. The school has on campus facilities with a Huxley 9 hold artificial putting green, driving bays and bunker and chipping areas. In 2015 they opened the Golf Academy Indoor Centre on the site of the school's former swimming pool complex. Includes a studio with video analysis and Trackman and enables year round, whatever-the-weather, teaching.

Golf is offered to all 600 pupils at Loretto and is part of PE curriculum for the junior school. In their final two years at the school, the 'senior squad' can choose to play golf as their sole sport over all three of the terms. Success rate is high with eight national titles and seven of these in the last four years. Summer residential golf camps ensure that the school is earning its keep over the holidays while at the same time showcasing its facilities to potential new pupils. Golf scholarships are available and carry a fee reduction of up to 10 per cent of the fees.

Parents tell us that on his appointment as headmaster he worked at the coalface to establish exactly how the school ticked, at all hours of the day (and night)

Singing and music remain popular with a terrific choice in the junior and senior schools. Chapel choirs, training choirs, jazz bands, rock bands, chamber ensembles... new groups spring up depending on who wants to play or sing. The junior school choir have been runners up in the BBC Songs of Praise School Choir of the Year competition. The choirs tour regularly in the UK and abroad (Limousin in June – can we all go?) and have made a number of CD recordings. Parents in the junior school commented that music, both instrumental and choral, 'is tremendous and is taken seriously' and that it's seen as 'cool', 'all the children want to be in the choir, no coaxing is required'.

However we hear of slight wobbles in the Music Department of the senior school. According to parents the department staff are in 'a state of flux' at the moment with one parent telling us that 'the situation needs sorting out' and that 'music isn't as strong as it used to be or as strong as in the junior school, which is disappointing as it was fantastic'.

Other excitements – the conversion of the old exam hall into a dance studio. Highland, hip hop, ballet and a range of other styles for all ages and growing in popularity (still more with the girls than the boys – Footloose the Musical is coming soon). Highland dancers often accompany the tiptop pipe band to major events. Pipe band has per-formed with Sir Paul McCartney (twice) and entertained the Pope on his visit to Edinburgh.

Drama is all inclusive with opportunities for individual excellence. Drama workshops include puppetry and stage fighting (small boy heaven). Substantial productions in both junior and senior schools. At the time of our visit the junior school was warming up for the end of term production of Treasure Island. Grease paint, bloomers and

Major changes, new catering company brought in with excellent results. Great choice on offer when we were there – we'd happily go back for seconds

enthusiastic cutlass wielding in evidence – happy children.

Art department (senior school) has multiple studios and a dark room – pupils can also work with clay, stone and wood. A level students (at present all girls but we are told – more boys next year) have their own studio allowing them to work in an atmosphere similar to art college. There was a degree of artwork on display around the school but not in particularly prominent places which seemed a shame as there was an abundance of talent evident in the department.

The art room in the junior school is a thing of wonder and clearly run with dollops of passion, skill and imagination. Fantastic creations of every shape and form and much of it displayed around the school. Impressive and outstanding.

Loretto Radio launched in 2009. Children can choose 'radio' as a weekly activity, learning about technical operation, presentation and production skills. Radio presenter from Forth 1 (FM radio station for Edinburgh & East of Scotland) trains small groups of pupils.

One society worth a mention – Borealis Society. For sixth formers, an opportunity to go on major trekking/academic expeditions to northern areas. 2017, destination Iceland for five weeks under canvas to climb five of the highest mountains in the country and study birds and Artic flora. Serious stuff and a major undertaking.

CCF compulsory in fourth form, voluntary later (good take up). Focus on adventure. Army and navy only.

Boarding: The junior school now only caters for day pupils, all boarding has been phased out, with both boarding and day options available in the senior school. Senior boarding can be in any shape or form – full, weekly or flexi (very popular). There's no 'hot-bedding', so even the flexiest of boarders has their own bed.

Sixth form boarders can leave the school grounds at weekends and can make full use of the city in terms of cinema, shopping, concerts etc. Many of the full time boarders stay with local school friends at weekends but apparently 'staying in' is popular too with lots of activities organised within the school, social events and the opportunity to venture into town. This is a 'proper' boarding school (70 per cent of senior school board) but one that takes advantage of its proximity to a major city.

There are six boarding houses, all different in character and with their own distinctive layouts. The pupils are in boarding houses from years 2-5 (senior school up until lower sixth form) and the sixth formers are in separate houses. Study bedrooms in sixth form houses and lots of communal areas and mixed common rooms for boys/girls to visit.

Background and atmosphere: The school, founded in 1827 is Scotland's oldest boarding school. Fully co-ed in 1995. Located in Musselburgh, a small coastal town on the outskirts of Edinburgh. Proximity to the bright lights of Edinburgh works in its favour – pupils can take full advantage of the art galleries, drama and music as well as the opportunities for sport and leisure.

Campus is quite spread out and somewhat disjointed (lots of walking) with the junior school (known as The Nippers), nursery and some playing fields north of the River Esk (footbridge crossing). Junior school feels separate from the senior school and that is due to the geographical layout rather than any difference in the ethos of the two schools. Nippers have to be escorted by staff to use senior school facilities as they have to cross public areas. The impression that is given is that this doesn't happen on a daily basis and that the Nippers use the senior school areas for matches and special occasions. Not ideal but it seems to work and there's little that can be done to change this.

Summer residential golf camps ensure that the school is earning its keep over the holidays while at the same time showcasing its facilities

Senior school is bisected by a main road (with a tunnel to enable safe crossing). Buildings predominantly painted in the traditional East Lothian yellow ochre, while the attractive stone built Pinkie House (boys' boarding house plus headmaster's house) overlooks a pretty walled garden (good party venue according to our young guides, used as wedding venue in the holidays).

Excellent Communication and Resource Centre situated at the heart of the campus incorporates the library and sixth form centre. Popular with students during the day when there's no time to return to their houses to work – encourages independence and a university ambience for the older students.

Elegant and unusual chapel (Tardis like – appears small/intimate but seats a lot of bottoms), good sized theatre (240 seats), shooting range and squash courts.

Red blazers for all pupils and the tradition of no ties still remains. Kilts on Sundays. Flat shoes – strictly no heels.

Dr Hawley has overhauled the catering operation. Major changes, new catering company brought in with excellent results. Great choice on offer when we were there – we'd happily go back for seconds.

We heard time and time again from pupils and parents about the friendliness of the school. That there was 'no pupil hierarchy' and that 'the pupils mix well between the year groups'. The overwhelming feedback that we got from parents is that their children are 'incredibly happy and confident' at the school and many parents felt that this was as important as academic results.

Pastoral care, well-being and discipline: Ladder for punishments but each misdemeanour treated on a case by case basis. Gatings and letters to parents for smoking. Pupils automatically expelled if supplying drugs but for 'experimenting' with drugs – suspension and then onto a drugs testing programme. Suspension for alcohol and then a final warning before you're out. Bullying and cyber bullying is taken seriously with an escalating series of sanctions depending on the circumstances.

Buildings predominantly painted in the traditional East Lothian yellow ochre, while the attractive stone built Pinkie House (boys' boarding house plus headmaster's house) overlooks a pretty walled garden (good party venue, according to our guides)

House parents and live-in house tutors provide pastoral care for boarders. In the sixth form the allocation of a tutor provides another support layer and help with academic targets. Pastoral care reinforced by weekly PSHE lessons, including seminars and tutorials. Parents report that the pastoral care is exceptional.

Pupils and parents: Twenty per cent international pupils (some expats) from 21 countries, highest proportion from Germany. Large numbers of OLs' sons, daughters and grandchildren, but also a good many first time buyers. Not particularly a Scottish grandee or Sloane Ranger school, although there'll be a smattering. We hear that 'parents are very friendly' and 'quite a diverse mix' and that 'it's easy to make a network of friends'. Old Lorettonians (OLs) include Lord Lamont, Andrew Marr and Alistair Darling.

The Golf Academy now attracts pupils from further afield than ever before. Parents are supportive of this, even the non-golfers, saying 'it has resulted in broadening the mix of pupils which can only be a good thing'.

Good bus service to just about everywhere: East Lothian, central Edinburgh and even down to the Borders.

Entrance: Entry at all stages throughout the junior school. Informal interviewing for all. Years 5-10 verbal reasoning, maths and English tests, school report. Sixth form have the same plus two exams from Loretto's curriculum. Minimum of six GCSEs, grade C/4+, to include maths and English.

Senior school has its own entrance exam for children coming from Scottish or northern prep schools. Scholarships and means tested bursaries are available.

Exit: Nearly all the Nippers move up to the senior school at the age of 12 and most stay right through to the end of sixth form.

Sixth form leavers to a broad selection of universities – Edinburgh and Aberdeen are popular. A few to study in the US and elsewhere abroad. Three Oxbridge offers in 2017, plus one medic.

Money matters: Scholarships (10 per cent of fees) awarded for general academic, music, art, golf, sport, drama and piping. No scholarships are awarded until year 9 (age 13).

Some means tested bursaries are available for pupils who will contribute well to the school but whose parents cannot afford the full fees (up to 105 per cent of fees, the extra 5 per cent is to cover transport, uniform etc). Bursaries are automatically reviewed on an annual basis. Fifteen per cent bursary for children from Forces families. Sibling discounts also available.

Remarks: A famous Scottish public school that's warm, friendly and has a rounded approach to education. The parents we spoke to all said that it is a place that is small enough to include everyone but big enough to let children go the distance and achieve their potential. It is a school where the individual matters.

Not an academic hothouse, although strong academic results are important (one parent commented that Loretto is 'as academic as you want it to be'). Ethos is to educate the whole person 'in mind, body and spirit'. Headmaster tells us that it is a school 'to prepare pupils for the rest of their lives'.

Loretto sells itself on being a 'small school with a big heart and big ambitions' and fulfils the brief – and more.

The Mary Erskine School

22

Ravelston, Edinburgh EH4 3NT

0131 347 5700 | admissions@esms.org.uk | www.esms.org.uk

Ages: 12–18

Pupils: 757; sixth form: 114; Boarders: 20

Day: £11,298 pa; Boarding: £22,101 – £22,668 pa

Linked school: Stewart's Melville College, 1266

Principal: Since 2000, David Gray BA PGCE (60s). Educated at Fettes College, read English at Bristol where he also did his PGCE. He spent six years in Greece teaching in a language school, taught English and modern Greek at Dulwich and was head of English at Leeds Grammar. Before his arrival here he was head of Pocklington School in East Yorkshire for eight years. Born in Scotland, he was brought up in Inverness and left Scotland at the age of 19 to return to Edinburgh at 45, bringing a wealth of experience with him.

An intense man, not showy or shiny. Clearly passionate about education and the responsibility that he holds. Being principal of ESMS (Erskine Stewart's Melville Schools) is 'his life, a vocation... to prepare the next generation... the future is theirs'. Beneath the intensity is a sense of humour, quiet charm, determination and kindness. Years of teaching have not jaded his enthusiasm – 'what we do here matters'.

He is a hands-on head and this garners respect from the pupils. Keen triathlete: pupils report that he's to be found ploughing down the school pool at 7am every morning without fail ('I can't do my job properly unless I'm fit'). He cycles to work (he now lives off site), teaches English and coaches a first year cricket team. Married with three grown up children.

Keen triathlete: pupils report that he's to be found ploughing down the school pool at 7 every morning

Mr Gray runs the twin senior schools (Stewart's Melville College and The Mary Erskine School) with two heads and the head of the co-ed junior school. He spends part of the week in each school (separate campuses) with offices in both.

Head of Mary Erskine is Linda Moule. She will take over as principal from David Gray in August 2018. She is also vice principal of ESMS. After graduating in theology from Manchester University, she has held positions in the teaching profession in Bristol, Stockport, Manchester and was deputy head of Holy Trinity College, Bromley, before becoming vice principal of New Hall School, Chelmsford in 2004. She was appointed head of Mary Erskine School in 2009, and became vice principal of the ESMS in 2016. Mrs Moule is married with two sons, both of whom have attended Stewart's Melville College.

Her successor will be Kirsty Nicholson, who has taught geography at both Stewart's Melville College and The Mary Erskine School, was a very successful head of house at Mary Erskine and, through her role on the management team in charge of S1 and of admissions for the whole school, has very much been its public face in recent years.

Academic matters: ESMS follows the 'diamond' model of education. The boys and girls are educated together at the junior school, separately in the senior school from 12-17 and back to a co-ed set up in their final year. The principal and his heads of school are all strong advocates of this system: 'we can tailor the teaching for boys and girls'.... 'boys and girls learn differently'. The pupils 'look forward to sixth form and don't lose contact with each other as they go through'. Class sizes of around 20-22 for first two years – S1 and S2 – reducing in size to 20 or less for S3-S5 and then between 12-15 for the final year (sixth form). Parents of boys and girls see it as a 'better learning environment' and pupils say that 'the separation doesn't affect the friendships between the boys and girls'. Many of the sixth formers say 'we have the same group of friends, boys and girls, as we did in the junior school; we don't lose touch'.

Pupils tell us that if there is anything academic that they need help with there are drop-in centres every lunchtime where a teacher is available – in all subjects

Pupils study for eight National 5 exams in S3 and S4. English, mathematics, a science and a modern language are compulsory at this stage. In their penultimate year (S5), they study for five Higher exams while in their final year, they study for Advanced Highers in twinned classes with Stewart's Melville College.

Many pupils do three Advanced Highers (some do more) with considerable success. For these exams pupils have to undertake a dissertation and, in some cases, a scientific investigation which teaches them the skills of independent study that will be necessary at university. Recent results are strong for both exams with 87 per cent of Highers and 82 per cent of Advanced Highers awarded A/B in 2017. French, German, Latin and Spanish all on offer to Advanced Higher. The principal tells us 'there is a strong work ethic here'. This was echoed by parents – 'it's a school that produces conscientious children'.

Strong links with the Merchant Company, whose members offer all final year pupils mock interview practice.

Firefly Learning, an online virtual learning platform, has recently been implemented throughout the school. This allows teachers and students to publish and access information from anywhere with an internet connection. Parents, staff and girls appreciate the effective system to keep track of homework, study tasks, school events and individuals' progress in learning. Pupils do not bring in their own laptops but can sign out and use a school laptop (kept in school library) whenever they need to. However, pupils are still encouraged and expected to use books for their academic research as well as online resources ('both are important skills'). Strong learning support both in and out of the classroom. We hear reports of 'great classroom assistants'.

Great achievements in hockey. For those not so enamoured with team sports, there are plentiful options, including cycling, golf, climbing and cross-country

Pupils tell us that if there is anything academic that they need help with there are drop-in centres every lunchtime where a teacher is available to help them – in all subjects. Big, bright custom-built common room for sixth formers and study areas available.

Games, options, the arts: As you would expect for the largest (joint) independent school in Europe, sport is massive. Great achievements in hockey with the 1st XI team winning the Scottish Schools' Cup. There are successes across the more minor sports as well with national accolades in athletics, badminton, dance, curling and swimming. Dance is popular and available at Higher level. Basketball has also become very popular. For those not so enamoured with team sports, there are plentiful options, including cycling, golf, climbing and cross-country. The school offers 30 extracurricular sports clubs.

Outstanding drama – principal says 'sport and the performing arts are equally strong here'. We hear from parents that drama is 'quite extraordinary'. It is part of the curriculum for younger pupils and can be taken up to Higher and Advanced Higher. The Tom Fleming Centre for Performing Arts, at the Stewart's Melville site, can seat audiences of up to 580. It's a renovated Victorian assembly hall – an impressive venue with comprehensive production, sound and lighting facilities. Drama is for all, with plays and performances throughout the year for all age groups with regular performances at the Edinburgh Festival. Masses of orchestras and choirs at all age groups (22 bands, orchestras, ensembles and choirs running). Annual house music and house rock competitions, both keenly fought with performances described by one parent as 'bloody amazing'. Choir performs annually at the Royal Edinburgh Military Tattoo. More than 200 girls have instrumental music lessons and there are 45 visiting music teachers. Pipe band thriving.

A staggering variety of clubs and societies on offer to all. It's all here – from video editing to curling and everything in between. These take place at lunch time and post school. Many of the clubs are sporting – squash, football, netball – but there's certainly something for everyone in the lineup.

Voluntary CCF very popular with over 300 pupils involved. Strong RAF section – over 100. Even split between boys and girls.

ESMS are the biggest provider over D of E in Scotland with over 70 pupils awarded D of E Gold in 2016.

Splendid art – and up to date displays around the school, wondrous paintings from this year's art exams already up and framed on the walls. Schools often display fabulous art that we then discover has been hanging there for years. Here the boys and girls can see their creations being valued while they are still at school, when it matters most.

Design and manufacture is available as a Higher and Advanced Higher. Exceptional displays of the girls' product design projects line the corridors.

Boarding: Only a tiny percentage of pupils board; this is still predominantly a day school. Erskine House can accommodate up to 29 boarders. The house isn't purpose built and it feels more like a large family house. The bedroom sizes vary and accommodate between one and three girls. Sixth formers may have their own room depending on numbers. The house is well furnished and very well equipped.

At weekends the boarders have planned activities such as surfing, cinema trips etc but they may also go into the city centre if they wish. The Sunday morning service in the local church remains compulsory to all boarders. They are free to use the school sports centres (pool and fitness suite) in the evening and over weekends.

Up to date displays around the school, wondrous paintings from this year's art exams already on the walls. Schools often display fabulous art that we then discover has been hanging there for years

Flexi-boarding is also on offer – but only if there's space available.

Boarders come from Scotland, south of the border and also abroad, often with family connections to the school (offspring of FPs), expats. Predominantly UK citizens rather than foreign nationals.

Background and atmosphere: Mary Erskine was founded in 1694, as the Merchant Maiden Hospital, and moved to its present site in Ravelston in 1966, changing its name to The Mary Erskine School and amalgamating with the boys' school (Stewart's Melville College) in 1972. The majority of the buildings are from the 1960s (designed by William

Kininmonth in 1964). White and cube-like (could be mistaken for a hospital), but light and spacious inside. These buildings surround the pretty, but somewhat overwhelmed, Ravelston House, built in 1800 by Alexander Keith in the late Adam manner.

The attractive grounds here are much more expansive than those at Stewart's Melville (and there's more car parking space too). This means that the girls play nearly all of their sport on site and don't need to be bussed out to other playing fields.

Senior pupils share the site with the nursery pupils and the lower half of the ESMS junior school. Final year pupils who are back in the co-ed set-up with Stewart's Melville are bussed to classes between the two school campuses (they're situated about a mile apart). Mind boggling timetabling but, according to both pupils and staff alike, it runs like clockwork.

Coaches from Dunfermline, Bathgate, Eskbank and Haddington as well as around Edinburgh.

Pastoral care, well-being and discipline: The school runs a tutorial system for the first year with groups of 20 girls led by their form tutor, after which the school is divided into six houses. Each has a head of house and an assistant head who together look after the girls as they move through school. These houses are common to both Stewart's Melville and Mary Erskine, so the various inter-house competitions have mixed teams. Weekly inter-house challenges range from maths quizzes to basketball matches. Sixth formers are under the divided into small tutor groups with a personal tutor, under the umbrella of the director of sixth form.

We hear from parents that 'any bullying shenanigans or friendship issues are handled very well and quickly', that there is 'fantastic pastoral care' and pupils are made to feel 'valued and that they belong'

Excellent anti-bullying policy. Principal says that 'cyber bullying in school aged children now more of a threat than normal bullying' and that they have a full programme to educate the pupils and make them aware of the pitfalls. We hear from parents that 'any bullying shenanigans or friendship issues are handled very well and quickly', that there is 'fantastic pastoral care' and pupils are made to feel 'safe, valued and that they belong'. Sophisticated PSE programme throughout the school.

'Zero tolerance' and expulsion if pupils found in possession of, or dealing in, drugs of any kind. Booze and smoking normally end in suspension – principal says 'unacceptable but not an issue in school'.

Pupils and parents: A real mixture of parents. Many first time buyers and children of FPs (former pupils). Parents report 'a broad cross section of families', mostly from central Edinburgh and suburbs. Not really a toff school, although there will be a smattering. Taking over a third of Edinburgh's independent secondary pupils, it is less elitist than some of its neighbours. Children living far out can spend the night when doing evening activities (as long as there's room). Alumni include Tom Fleming, actor and broadcaster.

Entrance: At age 11, 12, 13, fifth year and sixth form. Automatic entrance from junior school. A broadly non-selective school. Children are assessed (English, maths, verbal reasoning) before entrance. Numbers are up. The waiting lists remain 'first come, first served' and there are no plans to cherry-pick the more able pupils. The principal was adamant about this.

Exit: Minimal leakage pre-Highers with most going on to university. Some 65 per cent to Scottish Universities – Aberdeen, Glasgow, Edinburgh, Dundee, St Andrews and Strathclyde popular. Around 35 per cent to English/Irish/European/American universities. In 2017, four to Oxbridge and seven medics. SATS (for American colleges) not a problem. School has recently started promoting Dutch universities (Amsterdam, Groningen, Maastricht, Leiden) as an option – good transport links, less expensive than some UK universities.

Money matters: Bursaries – up to 100 per cent – and scholarships throughout. Those doing well in the entrance exam are invited to sit a scholarship exam. Music scholarships (together with free music tuition) are also available.

Remarks: This is a big school with big ambitions. With terrific success stories on every front, not just academically, it is a formidable operation. Not every child will thrive as a small fish in such a big pond, and such a large operation may leave the non-conformist with less room to manoeuvre. However, its sheer size has tremendous benefits – parents report 'the school pulls in great staff' and provides pupils with 'incredible opportunities'. Well mannered, ambitious children leave the school with self-confidence and 'a strong work ethic'. Parents across the board say they 'can't fault it'. An outstanding school with impressive results.

Merchiston Castle School

23

294 Colinton Road, Edinburgh EH13 0PU

01313 122201 | admissions@merchiston.co.uk | www.merchiston.co.uk

Ages: 7-18

Pupils: 450; sixth form: 140; Boarders: 300 full, up to 46 step up

Day: £14,595 – £23,505 pa; Boarding: £20,280 – £31,650 pa

Headmaster: Since 1998, Andrew Hunter BA PGCE, educated at Aldenham School, Elstree and Manchester University, where he read combined studies (English, theology and biblical studies). An expat, he was brought up on a Kenyan coffee farm and started his schooling at Kenton College, Nairobi.

Began his teaching career at Worksop as housemaster of Pelham House (eight years) and then on to Bradfield, again as a housemaster, for another eight years. Keen sportsman – squash, tennis and ex-county hockey player.

Married to Barbara – parents report she's 'immensely likeable', 'great, hands on', 'into the arts' and 'totally up to speed with what's going on'. She is also an expat, from Uganda. Three grown up children.

Passionate about the arts and theatre and what the city of Edinburgh has to offer. His devotion to the school is evident. A man of charm, easy conversation and high energy. Parents report that he is 'intelligent, well read' and 'a well-liked, kind man' who 'cares about the boys and really understands them'. Leaving in July 2018. His successor will be Jonathan Anderson, currently senior deputy head at Worksop College. Geography degree from Queen's Belfast; has also been housemaster at Christ's Hospital.

Head of the junior school (Pringle): Since 2012, Niamh Waldron, first came to the school in 2005. Junior school parents sing her praises and say that she's 'really wonderful, warm and motherly', 'fun with a great sense of humour and completely dedicated to the children'.

Academic matters: Junior school pupils start at J4 (primary 4, age 7/8) and stay in the junior school until they finish year 8 (S1, age 12). The tinies (age 7-9) are taught in the Pringle Centre classrooms and move up to take lessons in the main school aged 10. Set from aged 11 and follow three individual sciences from age 12. At 13 they move seamlessly up to the senior school without taking an entrance exam. Languages taught from the start, specialist teachers for maths, science and the arts. Pupils in the junior school also have access to a bank of iPads in the Pringle Centre.

School continues to follow the mainly English system. A few do sit a combination of A levels and Scottish Highers. In 2017, 47 per cent A*/A grades at A level, 61 per cent A*-A/9-7 at GCSE. Tiny numbers doing Advanced Highers (two in Mandarin, one in music in 2017) and a small number Highers (90 per cent A -B grades in 2017). All boys must do two separate sciences at GCSE and many go on to study science at A level. Maths still the most popular subject at A level. Sciences and English are also strong. No plans to change to IB; head says, 'we looked at IB twice but it wouldn't suit us and wouldn't work for the majority of our boys'.

The science labs are well kitted out with full multimedia facilities and video microscopes – they are also equipped to do a certain amount of genetics work. Much to the delight of most of the boys there is also a menagerie of animals including a boa constrictor, a chameleon and a tarantula. Recent developments include Mount Olympus, a suite of classrooms for geography, classics and economics which also includes the popular Masterchef kitchen. This was launched in 2011 with the aim of preparing leavers for life after school. Each boy in their final year has six sessions to learn basic cookery skills. For the ambitious there is the annual, hotly fought and popular Masterchef competition where the boys can showcase their skills.

Interactive whiteboards and projectors in many classrooms and an increasing use of computers as teaching tools. Own iPads are required from S1 (age 12) onwards with laptops or iPads required for the final three years. Good IT suite and more computers can be found in the spiral staircased, double decker Spawforth Library.

Pupils' support needs are assessed before admission and progress is monitored on an ongoing basis. Pupils are taught either individually or in small groups in timetabled classes in the learning support department. Support is there for actual diagnosable problems but also for getting some boys up to speed. Good feedback about this department – 'it's all dealt with' and 'good communication with the parent's'.

We hear that at weekends boys don't necessarily rush home when their rugby matches are finished – many choose to stay on the touchline to support their first team

Parents report that the teaching staff in general are 'top drawer' and 'go out of their way to help the boys'.

Games, options, the arts: Merchiston has long been associated with a tradition of sporting excellence, in particular on the rugby pitch. Sport is played along traditional lines with rugby in the autumn and spring terms and cricket and athletics in the summer. The school is currently represented at national and international level in many sports, including athletics, cricket, rugby and target shooting.

Make no mistake, rugby is still big here – 66 Merchistonians have played at full international level. Parents say, 'hockey and football are becoming more popular but rugby is still the main sport'. However with six senior and 12 junior teams, there are opportunities at all levels and everyone is given a chance to represent the school. Boys are enormously proud of their rugby heritage. We hear that at weekends boys don't necessarily rush home when their rugby matches are finished – many choose to stay on the touchline to support their first team. Team tours, including overseas.

Sports facilities are good with a rifle range, golf nets, putting green, fives, tennis (three all-weather floodlit courts) and squash courts, an indoor swimming pool and sports hall. The boys are encouraged to be involved in sport outside the 'core sports' during the school week.

Senior boys often help coach the younger children – works well, clearly popular with the younger ones and the coaches.

The school established a tennis academy in 2007 with 13 players and it has now grown to around twice that size. These players pursue a bespoke academic timetable and an individual tennis programme. Students join the academy by invitation, after passing an assessment.

The golf academy (in association with Kings Acre Golf Club), likewise, provides an environment where young golfers can maximise their potential. The academy takes part in junior and senior tournaments throughout Scotland and the UK with plenty of success stories, and there's help with applying for golf scholarships in the US.

School is embarking on the biggest sporting development for a generation which will include a new sports centre, 25m pool and a 3G synthetic pitch for football and rugby.

Strong DT department, subject available at A level. Super art, painting displayed in the department and around the school. Music for all. Two-thirds of the boys play a musical instrument. Chapel choir, choral society (over 120 pupils), jazz band, ceilidh band. Fantastic junior and senior pipe bands. Plus many other formal and informal music groups. Many of the weekday school assemblies include music performances. Parents report that the boys 'sing and dance with great enthusiasm' and 'they don't think it's uncool to be in the choir'.

Flourishing CCF with rifle range built into school wall. Sister school – St George's School for Girls – has recently joined as a cadet company and the schools train together at Merchiston during the summer term.

Drama in partnership with St George's. At least two main productions each year, with a biennial musical, for all year groups. Merchiston Juniors also have their own musical in alternate years.

Boarding: Traditionally a boarding school; 65 per cent of the boys are boarders and this rises to 80 per cent in sixth form. Junior school offers what they call 'step-up' boarding (flexi), reviewed termly – subject to beds being available. Pringle House (juniors) can sleep a maximum of 46 boys. Lovely cosy house, enclosed in its own secret garden. Homely dorms, spacious kitchen and comfy dayroom, supervised by the head of juniors, resident tutors, a housemother and a team of prefects chosen from upper sixth formers.

Modern and well furnished, all rooms are on-suite and more akin to a new-build hotel than a traditional boarding house – lucky boys

In the senior school the boys are divided 'horizontally' rather than 'vertically', so all in each year group are in the same house. Four houses: those for the first three years have a combination of shared and single rooms; when the boys reach lower sixth they move into the impressive Laidlaw House. Boarders are split between Laidlaw North and South, with Evans House accommodating the day pupils. Laidlaw is pretty super dooper. Modern and well furnished, all rooms are on-suite and more akin to a new-build hotel than a traditional boarding house – lucky boys. No wonder boarding numbers increase in sixth form. Six kitchens, in-house laundry, gym and stunning views of Edinburgh.

The only boys-only boarding school left in Scotland. Traditional, warm and personal school – small enough for everyone to know everyone

No step-up boarding in the senior school. A day boy may sleepover for up to three nights per week but beyond this he has to pay the full boarding fee, if beds are available.

Sixth form prefects are billeted to a house for the year to act as mentors. Parents report that the boys 'look up to the prefects mentoring them' and they are their 'role models'. The boys have a different housemaster each year and have to learn to build a new relationship with a senior person, which is 'an important lesson and skill to have,' say parents.

For boarders and day boys alike, Saturday is a normal school day. Lessons in the morning and sports fixtures after lunch. Entertainment in the evening – pizza/DVD evening, cinema or theatre trip or an evening with a sister school – disco or ceilidh. Sundays have either a whole school service (boarders and day boys) or a morning or evening service for boarders only. Often there are Sunday trips for the boarders – into Edinburgh city centre, bowling, swimming, go-karting, hill-walking. Boys may go out and visit friends or family by arrangement with their housemaster.

This is a 'proper' boarding school, not one composed of flexi-boarders who empty out every weekend. Lots of weekend activities. Each house has telephones for pupils to use and set rules about mobiles. Computer available in Pringle for Skyping.

Background and atmosphere: School was founded in 1828 by Charles Chalmers. Moved to Merchiston Castle, an early 15th century tower, in 1833. In 1930 moved three miles down the road to the current greenfield site at Colinton, four miles from the centre of Edinburgh. Present day buildings date from this time, though the original Colinton House now houses the science department.

Buildings set within 100 acres of park-like playing fields. Beautiful mature trees and exceptional views – lovely setting. Compact campus, buildings all quite close together – easy for boys to get from

A to B quickly. Nothing flashy but everything well kept and in good heart.

Juniors in Pringle House are cosily tucked away in the south west corner of the school grounds but still have easy access to and use of entire campus.

Sick bay with visiting sports physiotherapist and own ultrasound machine. Dining hall with servery and buffet service. Boys quick to praise the food: 'it's good and there's always enough'.

First floor Memorial Hall doubles as chapel and dance hall. An impressive space with balconies all round and a stage at the front, it can seat the whole school – lots of tartan. Big on Scottish reeling. Girls are regularly bussed in from sister schools – St George's (Edinburgh) and Kilgraston (Perthshire) – for reel parties and socials. Girls can visit at weekends and join the boys in the sixth form club.

Uniform of blue blazers, white shirt, tie. Dark, grown-up suits for sixth formers (popular with the boys – badge of honour). Kilts and green jackets for outings/special occasions.

Impressive website – information on just about everything. Full disclosure on academic results – by year and subject. A great window into the school.

Pastoral care, well-being and discipline: The feedback that we got from both boys and parents about the matrons and the nurses was second to none – 'top notch', 'fantastic', 'they're lovely', 'totally on it'. The boarders reported that they keep in touch with their previous house matrons as they move up the school.

The horizontal house system works well for controlling potential bullying. Good PSHE programme. Each house has a well-being prefect with whom other pupils are encouraged to confide.

Smoking dealt with on a case by case basis. Punishments: detention or clean up task. Smoking within school buildings results in suspension. The school tries to educate pupils about the risks in consuming alcohol, which is dealt with on a case by case basis.

Drugs: instant expulsion for supplying. Expulsion also for drug use except in 'exceptional cases', where a 'supportive regime' may be offered. However this option is 'unlikely to be applied when drugs are used on school premises'.

Pupils and parents: Parents strongly middle class. Many have family connections to the school – former pupils. Plenty of first time buyers as well. Lots from Edinburgh but also boarders from further afield, Perthshire, Borders, Stirlingshire – many from Scottish prep schools. A few from south of the border. Around five per cent expats, 22 per cent from overseas – from 22 countries, particularly Hong Kong and Germany. The boys we met were all open, friendly, confident, well-mannered and proud of their school. Manners matter here.

Entrance: Entry into junior school by assessment using computer based InCAS software – measuring reading, general maths and mental arithmetic. Online screening assessment also required, plus interview. Automatic entry to the senior school from the junior school (around 40 pupils per year).

Senior school entry at 13+ from preparatory schools via common entrance, or by mathematics, English and science exams, plus interview.

Sixth form entrance depends on GCSE or National 5 performance, or entrance exams, plus interview.

On Sundays boarders see friends and family, explore Edinburgh or else go bowling, swimming, hill-walking etc

School supports boys with a range of needs – dys-stream, Asperger's, ADHD. Broadly non-selective school, but boys 'must be able to access the curriculum'.

Exit: About a quarter to Scottish universities – particularly Edinburgh and Glasgow – and 70 per cent to English universities. Four to Oxbridge in 2017, plus four medics; Newcastle and Exeter popular choices. A few to Europe and America.

Accounting and finance, economics, business management, engineering, social and political science top subject choices.

Money matters: Academic scholarships at 13+, 14+ and sixth form – school's own examinations. All-rounder scholarships, music, sport, art & design. No money off fees – awarded for the honour alone. Parents may apply for means-tested assistance (up to 100 per cent of the fees). Reductions in fees for siblings attending 'sister' schools (St George's School for Girls, Edinburgh; Kilgraston School, Perth and Queen Margaret's School, York).

Remarks: The only boys-only boarding school left in Scotland. Traditional, warm and personal school – small enough for everyone to know everyone. Charismatic powerhouse of a head. Blessed with lovely grounds, with the bonus of having Edinburgh on the doorstop and well placed to attract good staff. Rugby is still very much a religion here but don't underestimate the rest. They're no slouches off the pitch either.

The Mount School

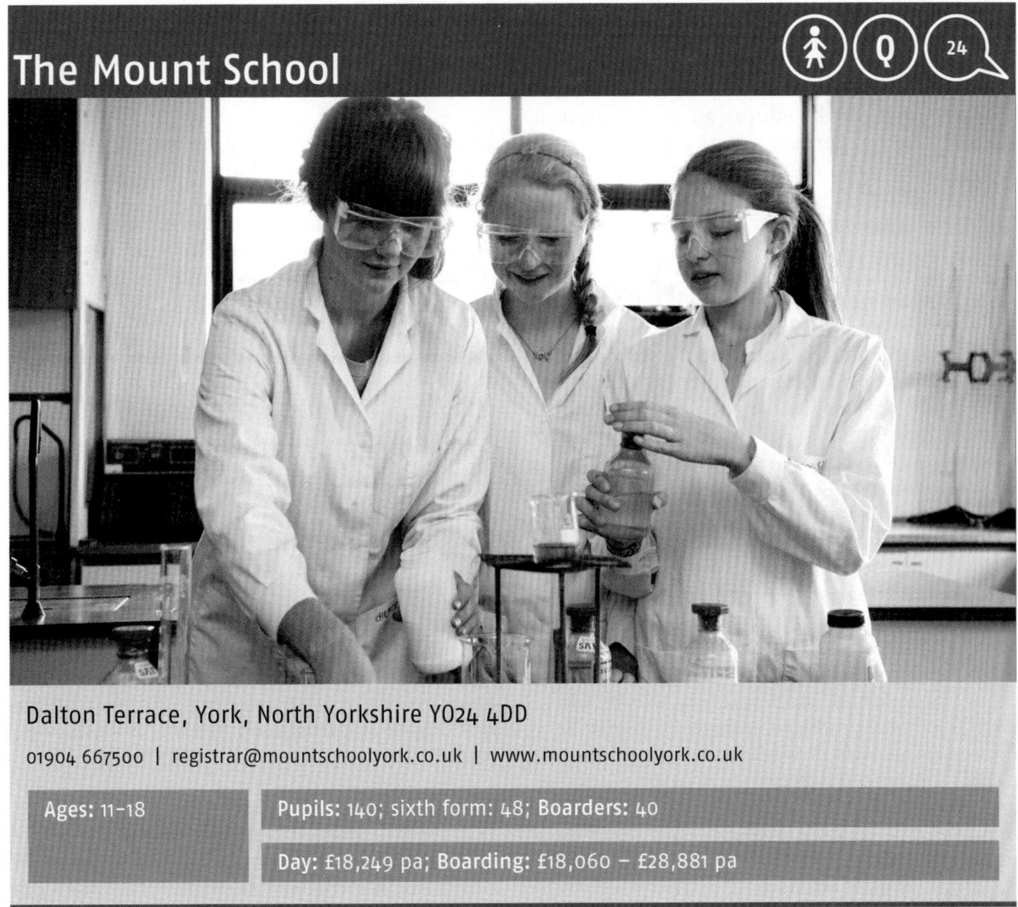

Dalton Terrace, York, North Yorkshire YO24 4DD

01904 667500 | registrar@mountschoolyork.co.uk | www.mountschoolyork.co.uk

Ages: 11-18

Pupils: 140; sixth form: 48; Boarders: 40

Day: £18,249 pa; Boarding: £18,060 – £28,881 pa

Principal: Since January 2016, Adrienne Richmond, previously deputy head at Durham High School for Girls. She has also been director of studies at Newcastle Central High. She studied maths at Newcastle and trained as a maths teacher at Manchester. She is an ISI inspector and a D of E award leader, enjoying hill walking and camping.

Academic matters: A level results 55 per cent A*/A in 2017, A*/B 74 per cent. Traditional A levels with biggest uptake in maths and sciences (perhaps due to recent recruitment of more international students to sixth form) though class size remains small 'with nowhere to hide,' said one sixth former, smiling ruefully. PE, theatre studies, psychology and business studies on offer too. Ever-expanding enrichment programme with weekly lectures, community and global focus. Strong uptake of EPQ – now extended down to GCSE years.

At GCSE, 33 per cent A*-A/9-7 in 2017. Good choice of options, 10 subjects standard, MFL either French or German (Spanish GCSE on offer in sixth form). Maths setted in year 7 onwards, English in year 9 onwards. Good IT provision – Wifi and iPads throughout, interactive whiteboards in most classrooms and two modern computer suites plus dedicated department clusters; qualifications including vocational OCR Nationals taken in middle school and sixth form.

Pupils and parents alike comment on the quality and commitment of teachers; girls enjoy lessons. 'They are kind, supportive, encouraging, nurturing as well as being fantastic teachers': one pupil voice spoke for many. A parent told us, 'When she has had a wobble, the teachers have been there supporting her; her form teacher understood and knew my daughter straight away'.

York used for local cross-curricular and thinking skills work via Investigating York in year 7; archaeology is part of history in younger years; links with university. Elements of the Peacejam programme, devised by Nobel Peace Laureates, introduced to the sixth form, form part of a weekly enrichment carousel of activities within the curriculum for whole school.

Selective, though does well with all abilities including EAL – support available. Specialist learning support teaching provided in and out of classroom dependent on need.

Very good careers education, skills-based in year 10, work experience post-GCSE in year 11. Focus in sixth form is university preparation, particularly for medicine and Oxbridge, some jointly with co-educational Quaker school Bootham.

Games, options, the arts: Beautifully kept grounds with grass and hard tennis/netball courts, sports fields for hockey and athletics, an indoor pool and sports hall including a fitness suite. Successful at traditional competitive team sports and offers non-competitive options such as rock climbing, dance and outdoor pursuits. Has players at county and country level in several disciplines.

Very strong and varied musical life, from classical to rock; all abilities participate in Christmas concert; regular concerts with other Quaker schools. Almost half of pupils learn instruments at school. Regular speech and drama successes, regional winners of Poetry by Heart, best delegate at Model United Nations conference and regional team finalists in Rotary Youth Speaks. Annual school production, most recently The Witches; sixth form play produced entirely by pupils. Very impressive artwork throughout the school encompassing ceramics, photography, sculpture, textiles and graphics. Design and technology studied up to A level – no cooking, except for fun; sixth form university preparation.

Huge range of after-school activities, eg jewellery making, photography, ultimate Frisbee – a non-combat, self-refereed game originating in the US; all take part. D of E popular – strong tradition of community involvement. Emphasis on understanding the wider world and global issues is important – Peacejam, Ibba school in Southern Sudan, electronic links to Quaker schools in Palestine and Lebanon.

Boarding: Sixth form boarding is across the road from the main school building with younger boarding in the upper echelons of the main school building. Accommodation is comfortable and homely, recently refurbished. Three to four to a bedroom still the norm – no single rooms in sixth form.

It's like entering the Secret Garden, though beautifully maintained, stretching beyond the eye to green fields. The girls make the most of the outdoor space

Whilst 75 per cent of boarders are in school at weekends, the high number of sixth form boarders with right to opt out of activities means smallish numbers and a wide age range. Regular organised off-site activities and freedom for unescorted paired trips to the city centre from year 9.

Background and atmosphere: Origins go back to 18th century; present building, close to the centre of York, has a very fine 1857 façade with modern additions. Approached through iron gate from the car park, it's like entering the Secret Garden, though beautifully maintained, stretching beyond the eye to green fields – an unseen total of 16 acres. The girls make the most of the outdoor space, some practising their tennis strokes, others deep in conversation, and even 12 year olds are not too cool to race to the garden swing at break times.

Classrooms are a mix of old and new, very traditional library, which the girls enjoy, and a spacious and light dining room, serving excellent fare, decorated with posters to inspire the girls to reduce food wastage. Attractive and well-designed new sixth form study centre has revitalised the top end of the school, giving private study areas as well as allowing extra activities such as cookery and social gatherings.

Though only a small percentage of staff and girls are Quakers, the ethos is at the heart of the school, manifest in respect for everyone in the community, a high degree of tolerance of differences, caring for others and democratic practices. 'It provides girls with a moral compass,' says the principal. 'They are valued for who they are'. 'Very little herd mentality,' say parents; pupils are demonstrably happy to be themselves. The head girl is

Though only a small percentage of staff and girls are Quakers, the ethos is at the heart of the school, manifest in respect for everyone in the community, a high degree of tolerance of differences, caring for others and democratic practices

appointed by the school, as the 'girls have a strong sense of fairness and justice'; the school council, conducted on Quaker business meeting lines, discusses internal affairs and, unlike most, really does have a voice. Morning Meetings include a period of silent reflection. Widespread involvement rather than bald achievement is regarded highly, and girls view additional activities, such as lectures from visiting speakers, as 'opportunities not to be missed'.

Pastoral care, well-being and discipline: Pastoral care onsidered very important – an absolute strength of the school. Girls feel they have an identity, are known and receive a lot of individual attention. Size helps, and activities transcending year groups with good integration of international boarders promote cohesiveness from sixth form down, resulting in the friendly and happy environment. There is a lot of social interaction between year groups, observed in mixed ages, day pupils and boarders all round the same table at lunchtime. Peer mentoring from sixth form for younger pupils.

Non-confrontational approach to discipline, huge amount of trust around the place, which girls appreciate with a typical common sense approach. 'If you mess up, you mess it up for everyone'. Time is given to listen to pupils and they are encouraged to speak and have a voice – in a respectful manner.

Exclusion only for persistent offences or major breach of rules, though the current leadership has not had to deal with incidents involving drugs or alcohol. Even more extraordinary, there is no litter and no evidence of chewing gum. School puts this down to 'pupils having a strong culture of ownership of their school'.

Plenty of contact with parents – school website, weekly newsletter. Termly forum where parent representatives meet the senior leadership team to discuss topics of mutual interest.

Latest ISI report criticised some aspects of staff recruitment checks, though praised the teaching.

Pupils and parents: Not just those with Quaker connection (it's the only all-girls Quaker senior school in England) – large number of local parents, often without an independent school background; not a county set school but local family loyalty over several generations. Wide range of religions or none. Over 60 per cent of senior school board – half are in the sixth form; the majority are full boarders from Pacific Rim, South America, USA and a variety of other countries, though 'not too many from any one language group'. Some European, mainly German Dresden Scholarship pupils plus several MOD funded. Girls wear white shirt, tartan skirt and blue jumper; no uniform for sixth form – 'relaxed' dress code. Famous old girls include Dame Judi Dench, Margaret Drabble, Antonia Byatt, Mary Ure, Kate Bellingham, Laura Sayers.

Entrance: Assessments for years 7-10 entry in English, maths and verbal reasoning plus interview with principal, who looks for 'spark – interesting girls with wide interests'. School report also important. Average and above average abilities catered for. Six GCSEs A*-C/9-4 and interview for sixth form.

Exit: Around a quarter leave post-GCSE, most for local sixth form college. Otherwise to a variety of universities, predominantly Russell Group – Exeter, Nottingham and Bath currently popular. Two to Oxbridge and one medic in 2017, one off to Cornell University in the US.

Huge amount of trust around the place, which girls appreciate with a typical common sense approach. 'If you mess up, you mess it up for everyone'

Money matters: Year 7 academic and music scholarships; year 9 academic, art and design, sport, music and drama; lower sixth (College) academic, art, sport, drama and music – all give five per cent remission of fees, to which a means-tested bursary of up to 100 per cent can be added. Music and drama scholars get free lessons. Separate bursary fund for Quaker children.

Remarks: True to its Quaker ethos, evident in the school's caring and cohesive community of multi-faith and international students. Girls are highly motivated self-starters, with teachers who prepare them well for life outside the school gates. Articulate, mature, collaborative rather than competitive, but nevertheless driven by a determination to do as well as they can.

Mowden Hall School

Newton, Stocksfield, Northumberland NE43 7TP

01661 842147 | info@mowdenhall.co.uk | www.mowdenhall.co.uk

Ages: 3-13 years (boarding from 8)

Pupils: 181; **Boarders:** 85 full/weekly, 59 flexi

Day: £8,970 – £16,500 pa; **Boarding:** £22,890 pa

Headmaster: Since 2014, Mr Neal Bailey BA PGCE (30s), previously directeur of Sauveterre, the French school which hosts the year 7 Mowden children for a term each year. He has also taught at Cothill, where he was once a pupil. Educated at Eton and Newcastle University (international business management), he worked in the City before turning to education, having realised he 'was not destined to sit behind a desk looking at numbers'. He'd dipped his toe in educational waters as a gap year student in New Zealand and France, but the real game-changer came when his first son was born, and it would seem he is now living the dream since crossing the Rubicon into prep school life.

Teaches French and maths and is a talented sportsman, particularly keen on football, cross-country and tennis, plus skiing, surfing, camping and bushcraft. Parents love his 'neon-wearing enthusiasm for all things outdoors'. He loves a challenge and took it upon himself to learn to play the drums as per his mantra oft heard by the pupils that 'everyone should have a go at something new'. 'Every child,' he says, 'has a golden thread and it's our job to find it'. He and his wife, Nici, also a qualified teacher, are a strong, warm and hugely welcoming team, and with dog and family they are clearly at home here. Their two young sons attend the school and they all pile in the car for the long drive to a bolthole in Devon for family holidays.

Entrance: Prospective parents visit most days. Be careful with open days – we spoke to one family who visited on one with no intention of enrolling their children but 'were so overwhelmed with the fun and happy atmosphere and the setting that we made a decision on the spot'. Wide ability range – non-selective, but then again 'not just anyone': maintaining the school's ethos and dynamic is important, so if it really wouldn't work for a new a child alongside existing pupils then the head is prepared to say so. Informal assessment, usually during a taster day spent in school, plus interview with head. Vast majority of pre-prep transfer to prep. Pupils local or from prep schools all over the north of England and southern Scotland – Northumberland, Yorkshire, Cumbria, Dumfries and Galloway, Scottish Borders. Small number of overseas boarders (mainly Spanish), and although

He'd dipped his toe in educational waters as a gap year student in New Zealand and France, but the real game changer came when his first son was born

some teachers are TEFL trained, applicants must have a 'reasonable command of English' to be offered a place.

Exit: Sedbergh up in popularity; Oundle, Shrewsbury and Ampleforth remain popular, as do Stowe and Uppingham. Fettes, Rugby, Eton, Newcastle High, Radley, Queen Margaret's and RGS Newcastle all feature, plus a good few others. Over the last three years, 23 scholarships achieved amongst 74 leavers. Few, if any, leave at 11.

Remarks: Mowden Hall School was founded in Darlington by Mr Frank Marchbank in 1935. The school was evacuated to Fallbarrow, Windermere, at the start of the war, before acquiring its present impressive site at Newton Hall, near Newcastle-upon-Tyne, in 1945. Originally a traditional, boys-only, boarding prep, Mowden Hall welcomed girls in 1982, and opened a pre-prep department in 1993. Much work was done in the school's early years at Newton to convert the former home of the Joicey family, built in 1835 by the distinguished northern architect John Dobson, into a fully-functioning prep school. Now part of the Cothill Trust, a group of seven mainly prep schools spread around the UK.

Splendid setting, on a 50 acre site with fine views. You can get a mobile signal here, but it's irrelevant, at least as far as the children are concerned. No mobiles, iPods or electronic devices allowed other than Kindles for bedtime reading. Boarding pupils communicate with home via the old fashioned means of weekly letters, email/Facetime/Skype (access after supper) or use of the two payphones. No complaints from pupils and parents are both delighted and relieved.

The dormitories, dining room, common rooms, library and headmaster's house are all in the main building, with an adjoining classroom block and IT rooms. The original stable yard was converted in 1992 to house additional classrooms, science labs and a gloriously colourful art room. The pre-prep building was designed specifically and built adjacent to the school in 1993. The nursery, in a brand new wing, was officially opened in 2014 and shares a number of hard and soft play areas with the pre-prep, allowing learning inside and out. Other additions include a swimming pool, used year-round by everyone, plus sports hall and theatre.

All facilities and resources are shared by children throughout the school, right from nursery. A couple of temporary classrooms add valuable teaching space for the older children but, if the head has his way, their days are numbered and (hopefully) soon to be replaced by something both more permanent and more attractive. No lack of rigour – essential if they are to maintain or even improve on current CE success; expectations are high and the children respond accordingly. Plenty of teaching from subject specialists. Smartboards are gradually being replaced by Clevertouch interactive boards, linked to the use of iPads as teaching tools.

Prep children are set for English and mathematics for years 4 and 5, streamed from year 6. The top class studies Greek and a number sit scholarships (good track record). Maximum class size 17: 'any bigger than that would contradict our ethos,' says the head. French for all from nursery; Latin from year 5. Good and imaginative teaching at all levels. Pre-prep classrooms especially attractive, prep could do better on classroom displays. 'Our teachers make learning exciting', said one pupil to a chorus of nodding heads. SENCo with specialist dyslexia qualification provides support throughout the school; one-to-one support is available (charged) if required.

Focus on CE kicks off in year 7 after the unique experience of 'entente cordiale', a term spent at Château de Sauveterre near Toulouse, immersed in French and the French way of life. Away from home and their mother-tongue, this is where the children find their inner coping mechanisms, and most describe it as a major highlight of their time at Mowden. Many understand little during their first 10 days at Sauveterre but then quickly develop a

real sense of empowerment as they become fluent in the language – 'confidence is a valuable commodity,' say the staff. The children enter a number of competitions – writing, art and the like – both locally and nationally. They are allocated to one of four houses, named after illustrious northerners, with plenty of healthy, inter-house rivalry.

The unique experience of 'entente cordiale', a term spent at Château de Sauveterre near Toulouse

It's not all work. In addition to the wide sporting programme, the nurturing is clear. Staff:pupil relationships are good with high levels of trust and support, seen as a real boon by parents. Music is strong, with choirs, bands, orchestras and plenty of individual music on offer. Art and drama are popular, the school is a centre for LAMDA and public speaking is big: even if it's announcing the hymn numbers for assembly, everyone finds their voice. That, and the ability to look people in the eye when speaking, is another valuable tool with a generation usually more used to looking down at screens. These are well-mannered children with more of a sense of responsibility than entitlement. Links with the Kenyan school and also a local school for children with disabilities keeps it real.

There's a croquet lawn that (unusually) really is used by the children, alongside impressive sports fields, tennis courts and cricket nets. Hidden from sight just off the main driveway are terrific new all-weather pitches, a major recent investment and transformational in that they allow year-round matches, even this far north. There's an hour of games every day. Trad team sports are popular – rugby, football, hockey and netball with rounders, tennis and cricket during the summer and swimming and gymnastics year round. Away from the school site the children also enjoy a range of other activities including fishing, paddle-boarding and horse-riding.

Bags of enthusiasm from sports staff and gap students, a number of whom live on site. This 50 acre site also encompasses a large woodland which provides a muddy but exciting landscape for den-building competitions and a BMX trail. Manicured lawns host an annual garden fête, barbecue and leavers' matches, and a beautifully-kept rose garden provides all the floristry for speech day and is also a cherished location for the delivery of common entrance exam results (weather permitting). New sports kit has proved enormously popular with all – gone are the heavy rugby shirts and old-fashioned kit, recently replaced by quick-drying, body-wicking fabrics and hoodies, appreciated by both pupils and parents. Interestingly, old kit, along with old uniforms and desks, has been shipped out to a partner school in Kenya, for whom the children raise money on a regular basis.

Smiling, bright-eyed year 6 pupils shared their joy of a recent camping trip to 'some random place in the countryside' where the wind was howling, the rain was relentless and they had an 'amazing time', sustained by the school's (allegedly) famous camping stew and doughnuts. Lunches are cooked in-house and very popular; old-fashioned dining room with trestle tables, conversation is encouraged and children clear the tables afterwards. For these busy and active children food is clearly important and they describe the food on offer in school as 'incredible', favourites being fish and chip Fridays, including an offer of smoked salmon and mackerel for more refined tastes, and mint lamb kebabs and fajitas for midweek suppers. There is, of course, also a salad bar.

Boarding numbers are strong, 85 per cent and growing. Some only live a short walk away but such is the pull (from the children, not the school) to stay overnight that parents are drawn into the boarding bubble. About half are full boarders, the rest flexi. Separate accommodation for girls and boys in dorms with four or six beds. Rooms are spacious and colourful and children personalise their own space. Super live-in housemistress with bags of experience is running the show with the support of the head, his wife and matrons. Weekends are busy and fairly structured, plenty of staff on hand and no time to be bored. Boarding is especially popular on a Wednesday night as there's no prep and it is also tuck night. Speaking of prep, it's one hour of supervised homework most nights (usually two subjects) for the older children, Latin prep is apparently 'challenging' – schola obdurate, clearly.

It's a rural school so no surprise to see corduroy trousers, kilts, checked shirts and tweeds as part of the school uniform, mostly green and navy – it's attractive and they like it. A rare heatwave allows shirt sleeve order and ties are removed after supper. You'll notice the wellies in the school porch as you arrive. They are out in all but the very worst of the winter weather. Scooters, go-carts, bikes and rip sticks are hugely popular. Sensibly, the pre-preps wear waterproof boilersuits, enabling them to make the most of the school's wonderful outdoor environment without ruining expensive school uniform. There's even a woodland classroom where the children drag logs across the soggy ground to build dens, bake bread on camp fires and experience the enjoyment of whittling. There's a wide range of extracurricular activities– all the usual suspects plus badminton, computer coding, ballet, nature detectives, golf, Airfix model-making, tapestry, Japanese, jewellery-making, magic tricks, cookery and, if it's your thing, cross-country running with the headmaster.

The next step is a big one and the school has close links with a wide range of day schools (independent and state) and boarding schools across the UK. Choices helped by regular reporting through prep years; effort and attainment grades every three weeks; ranking every quarter; full written report each term. Pupils de-stress after CE with a diverse and challenging three week leavers' programme. During our visit they had been tasked with rehearsing and producing a play in the school theatre – in three days from beginning to end.

The parent profile is diverse, reflecting the local demographic. There's a daily complimentary bus picking up from Jesmond and Gosforth for busy parents wishing to avoid the sluggish early morning commute from Newcastle. No school transport on offer at the end of the school day but there's plenty of sensible lift-sharing going on. It's a staggered finish with a wide range of after-school activities for day pupils as well as boarders; day pupils tend to do everything – except sleep – at school, though even that's a popular option on Friday nights.

Good traditional prep school with lots going on, exuding energy from the top down. Concentrates on developing confident, well-rounded individuals whilst still aiming for those highly competitive top scholarships. A number of parents say the school has 'surpassed their expectations, engaging and developing all the children and bringing out the best in them – an excellent equilibrium of sport and scholastics'. Were it in a different neck of the woods, geographically speaking, it would be bursting at the seams, but its boarding prowess may eventually encourage a few from overflowing southern schools to venture north – and why not? You'd struggle to find better.

Queen Ethelburga's College

Thorpe Underwood Hall, Ouseburn, York, North Yorkshire YO26 9SS

01423 333330 | admissions@qe.org | www.qe.org

Ages: 14–20 (junior boarding from 6)

Pupils: 519; sixth form: 331; **Boarders:** 478

Day: £15,375 – £16,455 pa; **Boarding:** £29,916 – £37,380 pa; International Boarding £36,588 – £46,104 pa

Principal: Since 2006, Mr Steven Jandrell BA (50s), married to Margaret, with a young son at Chapter House. Warm, friendly, genuine and approachable, he understands education and enjoys discussing it. Well-respected and liked by staff and pupils, he's part of the furniture, having been here for many years as head of music and deputy head. Long-standing parents describe him as 'the best head so far'; 'He's a good listener who doesn't bat you away with standard answers'.

Academic matters: Splits into two streams at age 14, the College and the Faculty.

The College is the straightforwardly academic stream, with all students aimed at the EBacc at 16 and A levels (a choice of 23, but no classics) at 18. In 2017, 80 per cent A*-A/9-7 grades at I/GCSE (overseas students' English accounts for a large percentage of the C or lower grades). College students rarely get less than a B at A level: 85 A*/A in 2017. Subject choices are dominated by maths, languages (largely Russian and Chinese) and economics – indicative of the strong overseas contingent. UK university destinations are strongly weighted towards business- and science-related subjects at good universities; psychology, maths and law also popular. Around couple a year to Oxbridge, and indeed two in 2017. Five timetable slots in the sixth form, four for A levels and one for 'enrichment' – Faculty has the same pattern.

The Faculty has a much broader remit, with an emphasis on BTecs. There are quite a lot of pupils here who struggle even with English and maths at GCSE (69 per cent got at least a grade 4 in both in 2017) – 30 per cent of grades were A*-A/9-7 (lower without the Chinese and Russian home languages). A smattering of A levels – mostly maths and home languages, giving the 76 per cent A*/A headlined on the school website – and a strong emphasis on business studies BTec where the results are even better: around half D*D*D*. Vocational rather than academic university destinations, mostly business-related or sport at middle-ranking universities with strong reputations, but an increasing showing in recent years from creative subjects and division 1 universities.

The division, though, is not as simple as that. Some College pupils do a BTec among their A levels; one 2015 Faculty student who went to read engineering at Imperial had four A*s at A level. There's a difference in style – eg self-motivated vs needs mentoring – which affects how pupils are allocated.

Some parents of Faculty pupils clearly feel that they were not sufficiently involved when the choice between Faculty and College was made. QE agree that they tend to insist on their views of which suits each pupil – leading in some cases to unsurprising emotional friction given parental views (which we often encounter) that BTecs are a second-class option with second class outcomes. That's not, though, how the dozen or so Faculty alumni we have communicated with have seen it. They have felt much more in tune with the style and approach built into BTec: more project-based, more continuous assessment, more real. They praise their teaching and the support from their teachers. They formed strong friendships across Faculty and College, and are still in touch with many of them. They chose university courses that worked well for them (careers guidance much praised), and look back with much fondness to their time at QE.

Huge solid oak tables fill the room with comfortable seating on the balcony above, alongside exciting sculptures courtesy of Amy Martin's late uncle

Low to mid-range universities are happy to accept BTecs; you'd have to be a truly extraordinary candidate to get to Oxbridge on one (it has been done), other Russell Group vary – business courses at Durham accept openly, equivalent courses at Exeter do too, but not obvious on their website, so do check carefully.

In both Faculty and College pupils as a whole do much better than you would expect from their earlier results.

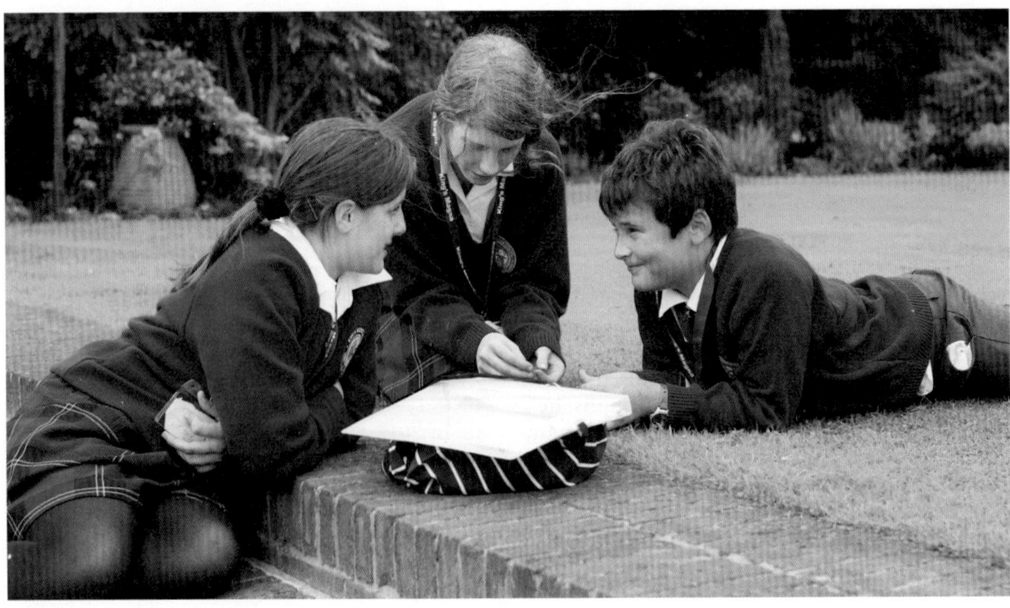

Small classes, unashamedly setted, with regular testing for all – pupils say 'it's good for us'. Reports from parents lower down the school are good. Many parental comments on rapid teacher turnover, and the difficulties and disorganisation that this sometimes engendered. The school puts this down to rapid expansion and says 'now that a decision has been taken to remain at around our present number, this problem should no longer be the case; there were only five new appointments for this year out of 180 teaching staff'.

Dyslexia help available. All children tested on arrival in the prep school during the first half term, ed psych's report if necessary, usually individual lessons for free twice a week, if more needed then extra charge. Five specialist teachers of specific learning difficulties. EFL free throughout the school.

Games, options, the arts: Music (for all) very strong, with frequent opportunities for performance. The old refectory (now the Phoenix Centre) contains no fewer than four practice drama and dance studios and a dedicated theatre – most impressive. Art good but not emphasised.

Thirty-four acres of floodlit pitches for hockey, soccer, rugby, high jump, netball, basketball, volleyball etc and six Astroturfs. CCF popular, clubs for IT, archery, fencing, golf. A new swimming pool too. The giant sports centre (sports village, as the school calls it) is an eye-watering, Olympic-level provision; you can look at the main school website and not see a sign of it, but go to www.qesportsvillage.org and prepare to be blown off your feet. This provides a home for the eight 'performance sport' courses (notably rugby and netball) – as one of their five timetable slots, students push their sporting aspirations, with professional coaching, and individual strength and conditioning programmes prepared by staff from Leeds Beckett. A long string of individual and team successes, as you would expect from provision at this level.

D of E with plenty of gold participants. Lots of extracurricular activities – the list is (almost) endless, most free, but a charge is made where there is a strong element of personal tuition (riding, archery, fencing, tennis, golf and kick-boxing).

Boarding: From age 7 (at Chapter House). International students from 66 countries (most notably south east Asia and the various parts of the former USSR) make up about two-thirds of the boarding community; most of the other third are Forces children. Modern boarding accommodation consists of smart and well-equipped bedrooms, all now with private bathrooms, all with flat screen TVs (in fact two TVs in some twin rooms – just in case these lucky pupils wish to watch different programmes..) on timers so they do not get in the way of prep or sleep. DVD players, telephones with voicemail, fridges, electric kettles, microwaves, air conditioning, trouser presses and room safes – pretty much everything except a mini-bar, in fact. Great attention to detail and, it would appear, no expense spared – newer boarding houses have fantastic limed oak doors, skirting boards et al. A classy medical centre that resembles a private hospital and oodles of huge common rooms – all with leather sofas, toasters and TVs. Houses for the younger ones surrounded by squidgy playgrounds filled with serious kit. Boys' and girls' accommodation is separate. Day pupil centre for day children plus B&B available if needed. The campus has a strong mobile signal.

Houseparents occasionally express concern that individual facilities are so good that pupils, particularly senior (Chinese) boys, are loath to leave their bed/study rooms and join in communal activities. No Saturday school, but full range of activities on offer during weekends – trips to Whitby, the latest cinema preview. After their first term sixth formers can nip into York or Leeds on a Saturday night, but must meet the pickup by 10pm at the local station (or be in by 10.30pm if they miss the train).

Background and atmosphere: Twenty-five minutes from York and Harrogate and a 10 minute drive from the A1. Run by a collegiate board, chaired by Amy Martin, who lives on site and whose family have been involved with the school since 1991 when she was a student at QE. Has been the driving

force behind the school's development over the last few years. Thorpe Underwood dates back to the Domesday Book, where it is described as Chirchie, Usebrana and Useburn, before becoming part of the monastery of Fountains Abbey in 1292. The hall was rebuilt in 1902 in best Edwardian Tudor style and the extensions have been sympathetically carried out with leaded paned windows to match the original. The place is a complex mix of old and new – in style and attitude – and full of surprises.

Impressive newer facilities include a vast dining room (The Undercroft) that doubles as an assembly hall – though the acoustics are pretty grim and mealtimes can be a deafening experience, say some staff. Huge solid oak tables fill the room with comfortable seating on the balcony above, alongside exciting sculptures courtesy of Amy Martin's late uncle. Fruit available at all times with good salad bar, home-cooked food with a veggie option. Self-service queuing system moves around barriers like a busy post office. A lift has been installed for wheelchair users. A popular activity centre has been established on the perimeter of the campus.

The original Hall – previously the home of the Martin family – houses a traditional library, the Phoenix Centre and some notable taxidermy.

Has benefited from millions of pounds' worth of Martin investment. Good, if not lavishly stocked, library, banks of computers, Wifi everywhere. Almost 50/50 boy/girl mix, boarding numbers up, and reasonable fees have brought a considerable flow of day pupils.

All faiths and none are welcome. In fact anyone who can afford it is welcome really – with little academic selection and a determination to meet all needs.

Faculty and College mix well outside the formal school day: activities and boarding are entirely mixed. The Faculty is larger and has more UK students than the College.

Relationship between the genders is good, as are relationships too between nationalities: most Brits make good foreign friends. Has a reputation for turning out well-mannered young people. Much-remarked upon omnipresent CCTV is not now monitored in real time, but still proves useful for 'security, serious disciplinary matters and for lost items of value'.

Pastoral care, well-being and discipline: Parents tell us that the pastoral care here is really good – 'Can't plug it enough'. Tutorial system – tutors change yearly, no more than 20 tutees to each. Has recently introduced THRIVE@QE, an initiative to 'proactively support all pupils' emotional health, well-being and resilience through activities, resources, clubs, workshops, clinics and more.' Charming and encouraging leavers' letter.

Smart and well-equipped bedrooms, all now with private bathrooms, all with flat screen TVs (in fact two TVs in some twins)

Discipline is described as 'sensible' – exclusion for violence and selling drugs, possibly also for taking drugs, 'depending on what it is'. Reserves the right to search boarders' rooms and to test for drugs and alcohol – and does.

There was much comment in the press following a critical report from the Independent Schools Inspectorate on the efficacy of QE's child safeguarding systems. ISI has now given the school, which has made substantial improvements, a clean bill of health.

Further press attention expected when the former Provost stands trial in 2018 on allegations of historic sexual offences.

Pupils and parents: Lots of first time buyers, pupils come to board from all over: Scotland, Wales as well as East Anglia and locally on daily basis. Nine buses collect day pupils from all over Yorkshire (not cheap), buses collect from local station. Many overseas students, as above.

Quite a lot of the parents we talked to felt that QE could be better at communicating with them, and at creating a community among parents.

Entrance: Many via Chapter House, but generally aged 14; A*-As/9-7 at GCSE for potential A level candidates in the College, broader intake (Bs/6s accepted) to Faculty. External candidates come from other independents, local state schools or out of the area. Pupils below year 10 accepted at any time during the school year 'if places available'. Promotes itself heavily locally, nationally and internationally – regular pop-outs from Good Housekeeping and the like. Informative DVD which plays in English, Chinese Simplified and Traditional, German, Japanese and Russian. The heaviest prospectus bundle that we have ever encountered, though fear not, it is fairly repetitive. Entry to all schools is based on CAT 4 test, interview and positive school reports plus Oxford Online English Test or IELTS if appropriate.

Exit: Quite a substantial exit after GCSE – 30 per cent or so, with overseas students typically changing school and UK ones headed for sixth form college. After A levels, most College students off to study law, maths, politics, psychology or medicine recently, a large proportion at Russell Group unis (two to Oxbridge in 2017 and two medics). Business much the most popular course for Faculty students, who virtually all do vocationally-flavoured courses at mid-ranking (recently some division 1) unis: accounting/economics/information management, a wide range of creative subjects (eg fashion design with marketing and music with enterprise) and some science and sport. Several off to Switzerland to study hospitality, and two to pre-medic courses in Paris and Chicago. No hoofing out mid-course.

Money matters: The school is well underpinned financially but quite expensive (especially so for overseas pupils) and 'you pay for absolutely everything,' say parents. Countered a little by masses of scholarships, plenty of awards (32 per cent discount for Forces and FCO). Add to that list sports and music scholarships and many, many more. 'You can also pay by Barclaycard or Amex.' Very streetwise management and 'all awards granted will be repayable in full, if the school fees bill is not paid seven days prior to the commencement of each term, and, or, if a pupil does not complete their education with us for any reason, regardless of commencement age, until the completion of the end of year 13...' etc etc. Read the small print very carefully. We have great reservations about these terms.

Remarks: Has come a long way, not just in its facilities but also in its academic provision. Making a success of looking after both the academic and the less academic. If it carries on like this it will end up with a grand reputation.

Queen Margaret's

27

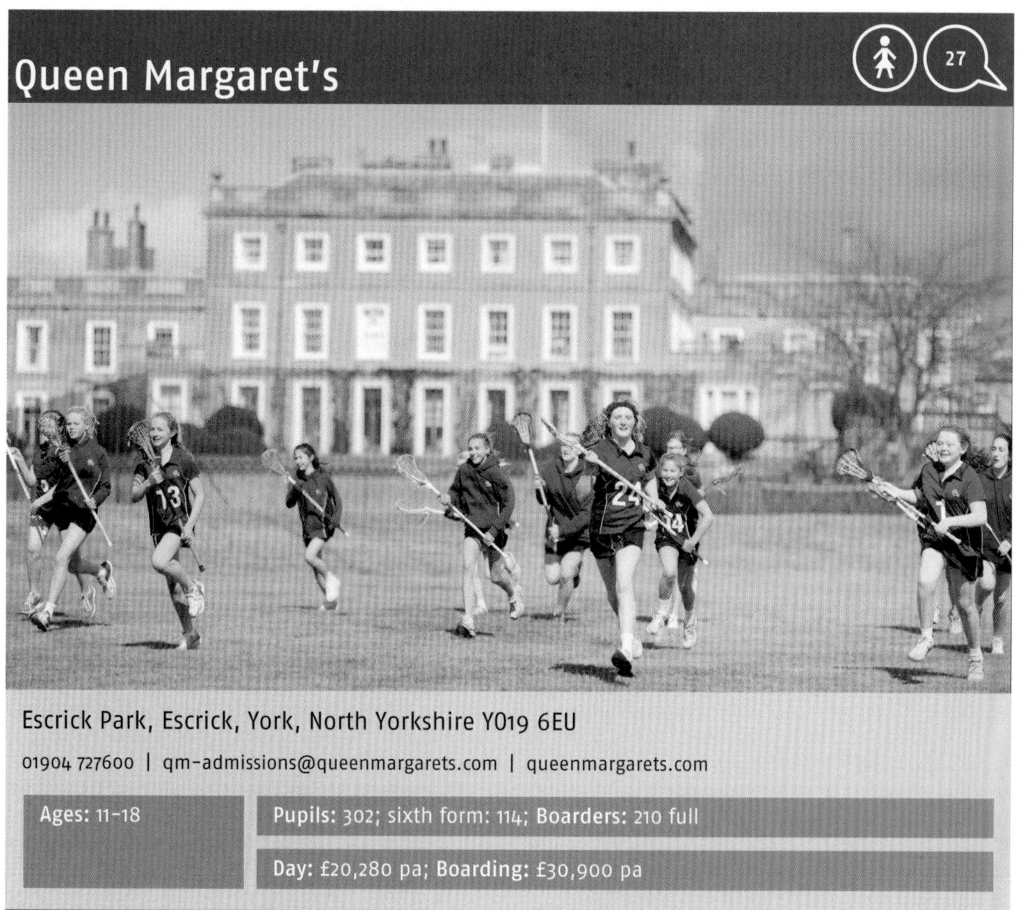

Escrick Park, Escrick, York, North Yorkshire YO19 6EU

01904 727600 | qm-admissions@queenmargarets.com | queenmargarets.com

Ages: 11-18

Pupils: 302; sixth form: 114; **Boarders:** 210 full

Day: £20,280 pa; **Boarding:** £30,900 pa

Head: Since 2015, Mrs Jessica Miles MA PGCE (late 40s). Educated at girls' boarding school Farnborough Hill in Hampshire and a scholarship student at Oriel College, Oxford graduating with a degree in modern languages. Worked for short time in arts administration, then did PGCE at King's College, London. First teaching post at Dulwich College, where over 11 years she became head of Spanish, deputy head of upper school, head of sixth form and director of rowing. After a move to Dorset in 2007 and a year teaching Spanish and French at Sherborne School, she moved to Leweston School as deputy head. She is the first female head of Queen Margaret's since 1982.

At Oxford was a member of the university drama society touring in Japan and Russia; she also rowed for her college. Fluent Spanish speaker, who once wanted to be a flamenco dancer. Married to Paul, a former teacher who now works in cricket development for Help the Heroes; two young sons at local schools.

Warm, charming and refreshingly genuine, has fantastic press from all that meet her. Tries to keep a day a week clear in her diary to observe first hand classroom and outdoor activities and matches, keeping her finger on the pulse of the school. Obviously pays off as girls find her very approachable and parents, using girl-speak, say 'she's cool'.

Lauded by parents, who say 'she is spearheading the move to banish the need for "perfectionism" in our daughters and replacing it with courageous bravery. Bravo indeed'

Believes the school's special quality is the strength of its community, having 'a real family feel', and certainly this was top of the list of likes for many of the girls we spoke to on our visit. Head is passionate about the school 'having a heart and soul with kindness, honesty and openness as its core values'. Parents speak of her glowingly, saying that 'she has met any difficult challenge head on with intelligence and compassion'.

Her focus is preparing each girl for life beyond university, 'providing skills and helping to shape values for use in their lives and to make a difference in society'. Wants to 'unlock their self-confidence key' and believes in building resilience, teaching girls to be brave, take risks, cope with failure and be able to move forward. Recognised and lauded by parents, who say, 'she is spearheading the move to banish the need for "perfectionism" in our daughters and replacing it with courageous bravery. Bravo indeed'. Has introduced a sixth form diploma as a tool to complement the academic curriculum and as a culmination of earlier co-curricular opportunities to assist each girl to reach her potential.

Emotional maturity and well-being feature high on her list and has introduced mindfulness in the PSHE curriculum. Wants to further strengthen the link between boarding and academic staff, is mindful of the increasing mental health problems faced by young people, and aims to ensure that girls realise that there is 'no shame in feeling down and are very aware of the enormous support there is for them'.

Current priorities are looking to strengthen Oxbridge preparation, careers advice and business links and to enhance the 'outstanding teaching' by improving the library facilities for independent study. Constant improvement to boarding facilities is taken as read. Staff development is top of the list to ensure school recruits and retains top teachers.

Academic matters: Excellent academic results almost taken as read by parents and success matters despite entry not being particularly selective. Overall A level performance consistently good, though 2017 grades 42 per cent A*/A and 70 per cent A*/B the lowest of the last five years' results. Mathematics, biology, economics, English, chemistry, languages and the arts popular and no weaknesses; psychology a new addition.

Improving and pleasing GCSE results: 73 per cent A*/A grades in 2017. Mathematics, sciences, humanities and art all tend to have an excellent proportion of top grades.

Wide range of subjects available at examination level with 31 subject choices at A level. Along with usual three subjects, the girls complete an enrichment activity under the umbrella of the QM diploma, and are encouraged to complete one activity in each of its five strands, which cover excellence inside and outside the classroom, independent thought, learning and research, emotional maturity, and community and school activity and participation

No option blocks and 23 subjects at GCSE – timetables are built around each girl's subject choices though the usual STEM subjects are compulsory for all and most take one MFL. French, Latin and a choice of either Spanish or Mandarin are on the timetable for the first two years. German is introduced as an option in the third year when girls choose three subjects from French, Spanish, German, Mandarin, Latin and classics; all are on offer at GCSE and A level. Around 50 girls have individualised programmes for EAL taught by suitably qualified specialist teacher; small group and individual sessions according to need, leading to international recognised qualifications.

Class sizes around 10-12, maximum 16, and we saw evidence of interactive teaching and engaged pupils across a number of subjects, notably a history lesson considering WW1 propaganda posters.

IT embedded in the curriculum but not given high profile, though plenty of computers and Wifi site wide. Surprisingly no overt computing or programming clubs, though the head of physics is a Raspberry Pi educator and led the QMSKYPI project, which culminated in a high altitude balloon launch for Margaret the knitted teddy bear.

The jewels in the boarding crown are the upper sixth cottages: 'something to look forward to,' the girls say

Around 90 girls receive some sort of SEN support, mainly mild difficulties and dyslexia (all pupils have a screening test as an entry requirement). A team of two teachers works closely with academic colleagues to provide classroom and prep support where needed, some one-on-one where girls have slightly reduced timetables.

Games, options, the arts: Sport for all here – lots of healthy outdoor and indoor life with games keenly contested at house level and a full inter-school fixtures list. Stunning facilities – floodlit all-weather pitch, two swimming pools (one indoor, one outdoor), sports hall, tennis/netball courts, dance studio, new sixth form cardio suite etc – hard to find something that's not on offer. Riding popular (private riding school on campus); some girls bring ponies, school keeps a number.

Traditional team sports, winter lacrosse, hockey and netball and summer tennis, athletics and cricket. Links with local sporting clubs and training offer opportunities for talented sportswomen, scholars receive weekly sports conditioning session with a personal trainer. School supports and encourages girls whose sporting prowess involves competition at regional, national or international level. Sports tours – most recently to Sri Lanka.

Music on rotation for the first three years then timetabled. About a third of girls have individual instrument lessons with plenty of ensembles to showcase their talents, from wind to rock band, orchestra to songwriters' collective. Catiamo year 7 and 8 choir compulsory, training for the senior chamber choir, together with close harmony pop up group covering popular repertoire. Weekly informal concerts, summer and Christmas concerts, annual musical production. Usual outreach performances, including singing in local cathedrals but no tours.

Fabulous drama facilities for aspiring luvvies. Two productions a year, one in collaboration with the music department – most recently an open air Midsummer Night's Dream (a brave decision in Yorkshire) and a musical version of the edgy and gritty Bad Girls.

Not overwhelmingly 'arty' school but plenty of choice across the genres, textiles and photography as well – though no electronics, product design or resistant materials. A handful of girls go on to the top performing art and fashion colleges each year.

Home economics for all through to small uptake at A level with Leith's food and wine certificate part of sixth form enrichment. Inter-house Masterchef competition hotly contested and first year tea party a high spot on the calendar.

The extensive range of extracurricular activities offers something for everyone and extends to clay pigeon shooting, driving remote control cars and climbing walls. QM diploma for sixth formers pulls together five strands of achievement and challenges them to achieve at least one element from each strand in two years; Leiths Food and Wine now available. A breadth of activities ranges from science and mathematics Olympiads to dance and music qualifications, Duke of Edinburgh gold to Queen Margaret's Princes Trust, Model United Nations to Amnesty International and takes great note of full participation in school life.

Boarding: Horizontal boarding structure: girls live with their year group all the way through. Really liked by both girls and parents. 'Enables great camaraderie and the foundations of life long friendships,' observed one pleased parent. As the girls move up through the school, their experience changes and grows with them, allowing for greater independence and personal study space. For 11 year olds Red House is a welcoming home from home with a Cath Kidston inspired kitchen for tea, toast and conversations around the Aga. For the next three years girls will be in houses at the top of school buildings whilst year Vs (15-16 year olds) move out into the grounds to purpose built boarding house, Winnie's (named after old girl, journalist and writer Winifred Holtby). Dorms generally have between four and six beds, though there are some twins, but don't feel cramped: clever use of mezzanine in high ceilinged rooms to create more space.

Good sized bunks with drawers and hanging space. Individual study space only provided in Winnie's; school used for prep for younger girls.

Lower sixth are in the heart of the school in Cloisters and enjoy the privilege of sitting and walking on the quad lawn. 'Modern loft-style living' twin rooms with individual study areas enable girls to be well organised for busy lives. It is expected they will be actively involved in many aspects of school life.

The jewels in the boarding crown are the upper sixth cottages: 'something to look forward to,' the girls say. Reminiscent of the Emmerdale set, stepping back in time, the line of cottages leads to impressive wrought iron gates with the village of Escrick beyond. Head girl has the first pick of houses; all have large kitchens, 'great for entertaining', and communal sitting rooms; cottage life has the feel of a college campus. Individual study rooms, breakfast and snack preparation, responsibility for all their laundry, non-uniform dress code all contribute to the girls' transition to post-school independent living.

Confident, articulate girls show great loyalty to their school and say, 'we know we're in a bubble but we know what we're in for'. Lifelong friendships are forged

No flexi-boarding but day girls, a quarter of pupils, all have allocated beds and can stay for a nightly charge. House activity nights for all on Fridays, a programme of weekend trips and visits and shared café and social spaces encourage girls of different ages to mix. Community weekends four times a term require girls to stay in school but at other times about 70 per cent remain. From year 4 girls are allowed off campus to the village garage – rather a shock for those who like to shop – though York on a Saturday afternoon allowed the following year. Greater freedoms for sixth form which they are careful not to abuse – cars allowed, York at free times on Wednesdays and Saturdays, supervised Cellars bar open on campus on Saturday nights – alcohol allowed with parental permission.

Termly room changes based on getting at least one of your choice of friends. If unhappy then a girl can be moved but house staff do encourage tolerance and social responsibility. Plenty of opportunity for Skyping or phoning home and parents uniformly mentioned the accessibility of staff when needed. Parents commented that their daughters feel hugely supported by house staff who 'adapt their life around ours'.

Background and atmosphere: Founded in 1901 as a Woodard school in Scarborough; moved to Escrick Hall, a John Carr built Georgian country house in 1949. Independent from Woodard since 1986, the flag flies proudly from the rooftop as you spin up the sweeping drive past 70 well kept acres of North Yorkshire's finest. A large yet compact and cohesive campus with a number of Victorian additions, clever conversions, complementary new-build with award-winning centenary theatre, chapel and indoor swimming pool. A throw back to earlier times – a cluster of timber cabin classrooms – add a quirky touch.

An Anglican foundation, the whole school meets four times a week in the stunning modern chapel for communal worship or communion. Catholics go to nearby Thicket Priory for mass and confirmation by visiting priest; half-termly vigil masses in school; girls prepared for annual Anglican confirmations by school chaplain.

Superb Mouseman reference library doubles as function room, wood panelling everywhere, open fire with huge windows looking out on to lawns – yet rather soulless. Small separate fiction library but both facilities need upgrading – on head's wish list.

Circular dining hall (once an indoor lunging school) serves all meals to award winning standard, with school rarities such as a cappuccino machine and balsamic vinegar; younger girls envious of the privilege of pain au chocolat delivered to sixth form houses for breakfast – all very civilised. Breaktime snacks provided, excellent cakes and fruit, girls on school council keep a watchful eye over food provision and choice.

Girls are expected and encouraged to think big here, challenged to break out of their comfort zone and aim high. First class academically for some time, the focus is now very much on the whole individual, providing each girl with the confidence, strengths, maturity and values for an unknown future. 'A greenhouse not a hothouse,' says the head. Confident, articulate, reflective girls show great loyalty to their school and say, 'we know we're in a bubble but we know what we're in for'. Hard working and committed to their peers, lifelong friendships are forged here, a hallmark of the school. The many house activities, communal social areas, buddying, mentoring and guardian angel schemes, not to mention the size of the school, make this a very supportive and close knit community.

Whilst 20 per cent of boarders are from overseas, this is not an international school. Girls find that where there are wide cultural differences this can preclude close friendships: 'we're friendly but not all best friends,' say sixth formers. Parents comment on the overseas pupils 'whose priorities are different and they are not so interested in sport or drama' – they would not like to see this number grow. Cultural festivals are celebrated communally in house.

Good exposure for girls to global and topical issues through debating, extracurricula organisations and mock elections such as Brexit hustings and vote. Parents aware that this is a privileged life and take responsibility for widening their daughters' experiences, though would like to see the girls do more in the community.

Girls encouraged to take responsibility for completion of prep and, if need be, learn by getting it wrong. As they progress through the years they choose where and when they do it – all part of building independence. Girls are kept pretty busy but told us 'teachers are understanding if we require a bit of extra time on occasions'. Lots of support for new and younger girls who are monitored to check they aren't overdoing it and taking on too much in the early days.

Uniform is an attractive tartan and charcoal – no skirt lengths above the knee were observed – a first for us. Own clothes worn after tea – don't provide anything that you wouldn't want boil-washed. Relaxed smart casual dress code rather than uniform for sixth form.

Pastoral care, well-being and discipline: Parents cannot speak highly enough of the pastoral care: as one put it, 'compassion and kindness run through the veins of this school'. Staff say, 'we want to get it right for the girls, so they feel very secure and know that there's always someone there for them'. Together with house staff each girl has a personal tutor who meets boarding staff daily with any concerns to SLT weekly. Some parents commented that in their experience the quality of tutor varied; maybe that's why strengthening this link is on the head's to do list. Currently there are around eight girls per staff member (including the head), and the system runs on a three year cycle. Sixth formers have a personal mentor who acts as a guide in their subject of choice to provide extra reading advice and support university applications.

Girls and parents feel the rules are very clear. Zero tolerance for smoking, unsupervised alcohol and drugs. There's a sanctions grid which escalates according to misdemeanour or repeat offenders, but girls and staff were quick to point out that behaviour is not a problem here with no full exclusions in the last two years.

Six houses promote lively competition through house points tally and a plethora of events: popular fun song with dance routine, choral soft song, sports day, Masterchef, drama, art – the list is endless. An army of sixth form posts of responsibility: head girl with three deputies, prefects covering the gamut of school life and six house captains.

Evolving from meditation groups, mindfulness is a recent introduction to PSHE lessons for first and fourth years and lower sixth (and at lunchtime for a group of staff). The head has introduced a 10 session course on mindfulness-based stress reduction and cognitive therapy delivered by a trained practitioner. In its early stages there is already an impact, with girls asking to meditate to calm themselves before examinations and one group cascading their learning to house mates by conducting a 'beditation' before lights out.

Pupils and parents: Welcoming, self confident girls, open and friendly, proud of their school, clearly enjoying the many benefits of living and learning in such a lovely environment. A real sense of collegiality across the campus, lots of smiling faces – a combination of the strong links forged through in-year boarding and full-on inter-house activity across the age range. Girls aim high in every arena – whatever their talent; higher education is a foregone conclusion.

There is already an impact,with girls asking to meditate to calm themselves before examinations

Parents mainly upper and middle class: landowners, farmers, professionals. Boarders – some 20 per cent from overseas – span 10s of nations and four continents; head using Spanish and South American networks to widen further. Many from Scotland, Cumbria, East Anglia and of course Yorkshire. Essentially the main catchment is the east coast train line – head keen to open the eyes of London prep schools to God's own county, unexplored territory for many.

OMs include Winifred Holtby (author), Ann Jellicoe (playwright), Sarah Connolly (opera singer), Dame Justice Eleanor King (High Court judge).

Entrance: Own assessments at 11, 12 and 13; mathematics, English, dyslexia screening and observation of group working in two classroom activities. Additional intake into sixth form: two A/7s and three B/6s at GCSE/IGCSE, at least a C/5 in mathematics and English and a minimum of a B/6 in the subjects proposed for study at A level. Interviews for all admissions. Taster days for new boarders prior to admission with buddies for first years and guardian angels for third years, most popular boarding entry point.

Exit: Virtually all sixth formers to higher education nationwide – a strong showing of Russell Group universities, with Durham and Edinburgh both popular. Courses cover a wide spectrum and include engineering, business and finance, languages, law and 'ologies'. Heartening to see numbers going on to prestigious art colleges eg Central St Martins.

Post-16, each year a few girls (some 20 per cent) becoming restless and move to co-ed, local sixth form colleges or boarding schools like Uppingham and Oundle, usually 'for a valid reason not a worrying reason,' says the head. A number goes and looks elsewhere before deciding to stay put.

Money matters: Scholarships at 11,13 and sixth form; academic, art, choral, dance, drama, music and sport scholarships. Means-tested bursaries. Sibling remission of five per cent, maximum 15 per cent for three or more sisters in school.

Remarks: A supporting and enabling atmosphere where girls thrive and their talents developed, whether they are academic, sporting or arts based. All rave about the pastoral care and the breadth of opportunity on offer. Girls prepared go to on to post-school life with their eyes open. As a number of parents told us, it seems 'they've got the balance right'.

Queen Mary's School

28

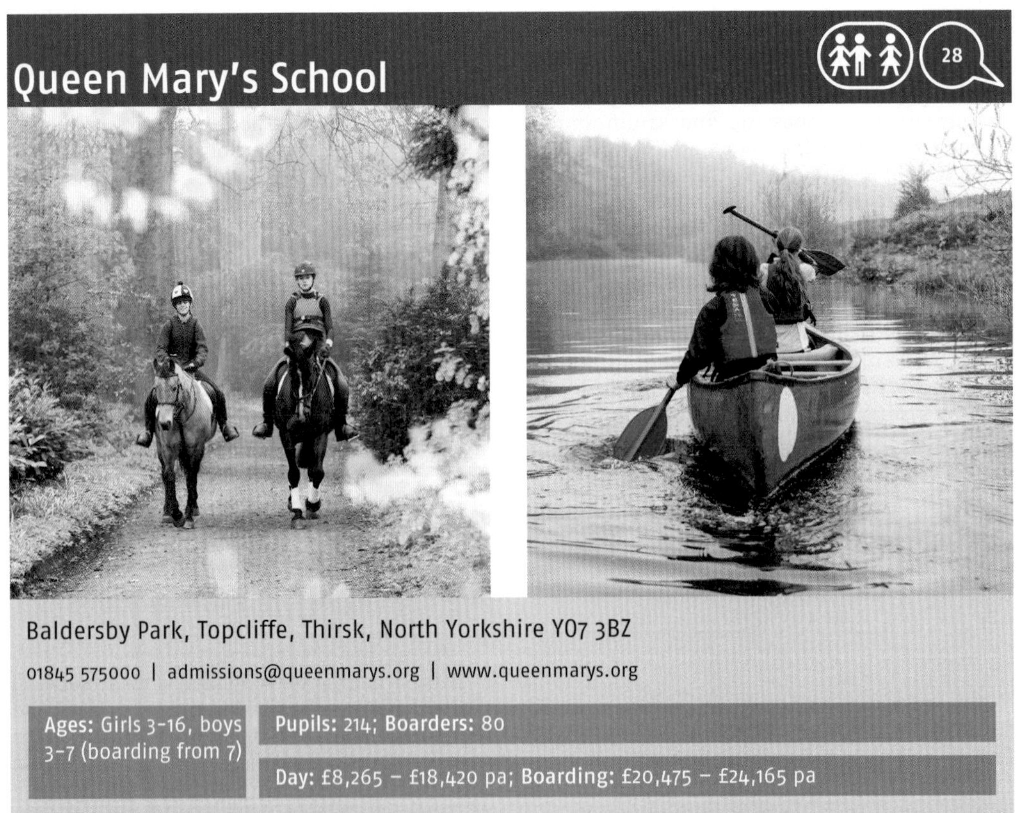

Baldersby Park, Topcliffe, Thirsk, North Yorkshire YO7 3BZ

01845 575000 | admissions@queenmarys.org | www.queenmarys.org

Ages: Girls 3-16, boys 3-7 (boarding from 7)

Pupils: 214; Boarders: 80

Day: £8,265 – £18,420 pa; Boarding: £20,475 – £24,165 pa

Head: Since 2015, Carole Cameron, previously acting head at Queen Margaret's School in York. Geography degree and MA in education management; she has also been head of Highfield, the Harrogate Ladies' College prep school. She worked in schools in Nottinghamshire, London and Leeds before spending 10 exciting years in international schools in the Caribbean while her family lived in Grenada and the Cayman Islands. She has two grown up daughters.

Academic matters: Play-based learning and participation in junior department productions builds confidence in nursery, with care available until 4.25pm each day and flexibility in the number of sessions. From reception, core learning is in numeracy and literacy – and tinies have computers too. Emphasis is learning through fun, creativity and exploration. Each reception child can take the lead and organise a school trip for their class to enjoy – helps too if parents are farmers. Very small numbers allow interaction with older children at meals, playtimes and in celebrating special events.

Unique to years 1 and 2 are Thrilling Thursdays, when the day is spent out of school in a new experience, or in school with a special visitor. Specialist teaching extended to French and IT, where curriculum has been revamped, as has dance; cross-curricular projects using art and IT.

Girls in prep, years 3 to 6, are accommodated in the main school building and are taught in small, mixed-ability classes for all subjects. Fun, cross-curricular learning such as when an English lesson in invitation writing blossomed into a full-blown tea party for parents. A request to let them make cake – and they did.

Pleasing GCSE results in 2017 with 52 per cent A*-A/9-7 grades. A very mixed ability school, non-selective intake – all take English, maths, dual sciences, religious studies; nearly all take French as well. Two sets of French in year 7; top set add German and bottom Spanish in year 8. Lots of role-play, telephone conversations and presentation work in lessons. 'Amusing yet educational,' seems to be the general opinion of the pupils. No exchanges but Spanish and French pupils regularly spend one term here. Classics and Latin on timetable and available as GCSE options, bringing GCSE subject choice to 17 – pretty good for a school this size. German and music results consistently good and the humanities well represented.

Introduction of bespoke challenge curriculum, on timetable and led by outdoor adventure instructor, to develop 'collaborative working, leadership, problem solving and resilience alongside presentational skills, ability to research and evaluate'.

Very small tutor groups and tiny classes, setted and streamed. Lunch with form tutor; termly target setting with 'grades, a trigger for conversation'. Saturday morning school followed by drama rehearsals, choir practice and matches. Staff/pupil relationship exemplary – seems that school never closes and girls can be found wandering around in the Easter holidays having been 'doing extra workshops' with dedicated staff, who never seem to take holidays either. Parents also say staff very good at motivating their daughters without them feeling under pressure.

Good and sensitive SEN, most commonly dyslexia help; either two sessions of one-on-one or shared in a small group. Library used extensively, reading encouraged through wide selection of fiction.

Recent improvements in IT network, high level security where every device in school logged, necessary when lots of own devices; iPads provided in library and dedicated IT suite. Specialist teaching from year 1 with focus on upskilling rather than software package training; programming, network design and logic with project work cross-curricular – though not available as GCSE option.

Outdoor adventure is where the school comes into its own – adjacent River Swale popular for canoeing and the occasional swim (hardy girls up north)

Prepared for life post-16 through life skills curriculum alongside GCSE – first aid, cooking, managing finances etc. Good careers library, Cambridge profiling, interview training and work experience organised.

Games, options, the arts: Traditional sports, daily, full fixture list with lacrosse, athletics and tennis teams all doing well. Own tennis courts, all-weather pitches and small indoor swimming pool. Outdoor adventure is where the school comes into its own – from adjacent River Swale, popular for canoeing and the occasional swim (hardy girls up north), wild running assault course (aptly named Wolf), and even a 160 feet bungee jump as a special treat. No wonder the girls say, 'You learn to face your fears'. Secret missions, overnight camps and canoe expeditions for juniors – led by outdoor teacher – lay the foundation for what's in store in senior school.

Music is very important and the place hums with junior and senior choirs and delicious concerts open to the general public as well as for inmates – impressive for a school of this size. Chapel choristers wear much-coveted green sweatshirts and give regular performances both home and away. Lots of opportunity for instrumentalists – classical focus though annual battle of the bands competition.

Bright, colourful art in the attics including creative textiles, ceramics; sewing machines in the DT room. Drama good and well supported, musicals popular, though lacking good performance facilities. Cooking timetabled and enjoyed by all.

Superb equestrian facilities; children can and do bring their own ponies and ride daily, girls enjoy mucking in – and out – in the stables at weekends, after lessons and occasionally before breakfast. Outdoor manège of Olympian size, as well as rides across the local landowner's fields, school in constant negotiation with neighbours to increase riders' scope, cross-country course on site. Tadcaster polo club is nearby and looks like becoming the next horsey activity.

Wide range of after-school clubs including the unusual pheasant plucking club, with fruits of their labours enjoyed at a dinner with invited guests. Superb selection of residentials, expeditions for all, plus D of E.

House activity – usual sport and performing arts plus boundary run and Wolf assault course. Fundraising for local and international charities – adopted school in Madagascar, support for child in Sherpa school in Kathmandu.

Boarding: Girls have a sense of ownership of their mansion – no showpiece, consequently shows signs of being well-used, a little shabby in places. Boarding in top echelons; girls 'like sleeping in stately home'. Rash of good-sized dorms, three to five to a room; top bunks for flexi-boarders used only up to year 8. Bathrooms receiving a timely refurbishment; furniture tired in places, some with limited storage, though additional lockers on ground floor. Common rooms small and underwhelming, though totally underutilised, according to head of boarding. 'The girls have such a busy life there's no time for TV,' she said. Dorms on the balcony over the Great Hall are a rite of passage for those in their last year. Girls encouraged to flexi-board from year 4. Often younger sisters of senior girls, their family home usually within 60 mile radius of the school. Some Forces' families, though declining, no international boarders. Very small number of junior boarders stay in school at the weekend; those that do enjoy outdoor activities, local attractions and have 'fun on a shoestring' with their older counterparts.

Unique to years 1 and 2 are Thrilling Thursdays, spent out of school in a new experience, or in school with a special visitor

Very few have never boarded and who can blame them, with pillow fights, mattress surfing down the great hall staircase and abseiling over the banisters as boarder activities. Discos, film nights and socials with Aysgarth boys (strong sibling links) for the younger pupils.

Background and atmosphere: Founded in 1925, moved from Duncombe Park to its present rural setting Baldersby Park in 1983. Said to be the first Palladian mansion built in Britain by Colen Campbell, 1721, and Jacobethanised following a fire in 1902. Impressive approach, long curving driveway bordered by pastures – like stepping into a Gainsborough landscape.

Well-proportioned, former drawing room now a head's study to die for. Glorious main hall used for daily service, with the girls sitting on the carpet, head sitting in front of the stairs, the choir ranged behind in serried ranks. When it is not being used for formal occasions, and even sometimes when it is (aerial performance at Christmas concert by pyjama clad outdoor education teacher to accompanied singing Walking in the Air), girls can be seen walking the trapeze from balcony to balcony high above the main hall, wisely harnessed; not a rite of passage but, as with most things here, girls encouraged to 'have a go'.

Beyond, leading off narrow corridors, a warren of classrooms, a number displaying 'dogs in residence' signs on their door. Home from home applies to staff canine pets as well as pupils. Girls like it and say they find a pooch pat mid lesson beneficial. Classrooms in the main building and converted outhouses; science department boasts a greenhouse and freshwater pond for hands-on experience.

Tucked round the corner from the Palladian mansion is the pastoral setting for the single storey timber classrooms that cosily house early years to year 2. They open out into a secure and spacious play area, and the boys and girls also have use of the main school facilities. Pre-prep is currently a girls' only zone; children receive a lot of individual attention and the department has been awarded the local authority's gold award for quality assurance.

School uniform evolves over the years with girls graduating from beige to green jerseys and royal hunting Stewart tartan kilts. Some rationalisation taken place; senior summer dresses culled.

School food is good quality, wholesome home cooking and girls' earlier wish for 'a visit from Jamie Oliver' to liven things up has almost been granted with appointment of a chef manager who trained in one of his restaurants.

Charming chapel, a peaceful haven for all; school has its own chaplain; school is keen that religion should be 'part of the school routine' but not rammed down the throat. Staff and girls are happy with the relaxed atmosphere – like an extended family (all ages mix) with a mass of sisterly teasing. Younger girls like to play and build dens in the woods, 'benign supervision' allowing a sense of freedom with a nod to health and safety. The early assumption of seniority (at 16 rather than 18) gives girls confidence and maturity – a great balance with the younger girls happily staying young and the older girls demonstrating early maturity and the ability to take on responsibilities.

Wide range of after-school clubs including the unusual pheasant plucking club, with fruits of their labours enjoyed at a dinner with invited guests

They love 'the opportunity to try lots of different things' and the 'enduring friendships' they feel they are making, but some feel rural isolation and would welcome more social interface with other schools – work in progress.

Pastoral care, well-being and discipline: Like home. No petty rules and others which are bendable, but an underlying sense of organisation. Definitely carrot not stick, detentions rare; house points with head's awards for a tally of five; woman of the week award – much wider than academic achievement. Badges pepper senior pupils' uniforms – awarded for contribution and achievement across a wide range. Prefects elected by head, staff and year 10 ballot.

Parents' requests granted when reasonable. Not a sophisticated place, no obvious sin, just an occasional ticking off for a girl wearing make-up, but it's few and far between.

Most board – flexi-boarding popular from year 4, building to weekly and termly boarding by year 10. Boarding staff and NZ gappies organise 'fun on a shoestring' weekend activities for around 15 to 25 girls; seniors don't have to join in. Boarding notice boards display weekly winners of 'good egg' and 'make a smile' awards.

Pupils and parents: Local as opposed to county school – combination of first time buyers, local farmers, landowners and professionals – 'not as Tatler and Vogue as some of its competitors'. Relaxed 7.30am drop off time for working parents. Quite a lot of army families though number reducing – Catterick is just up the road – some of whom pop their daughters into the school 'while they are based in Yorkshire' and are so pleased with the place that they leave their daughters there, younger sisters often joining them, when they are posted elsewhere.

Offers six routes on school minibuses – encompassing Aysgarth, Masham, Helmsley, Ripon and Wetherby.

Parents and pupils can use school facilities in the holidays. No real overseas presence, one or two expats, a couple of Spanish and French for a term, but boarding holding up and no wish to change its nature.

Entrance: At any time, middle of term if needed. At all ages. Entry test at senior level – year 7 applicants have an assessment day in January – but, places permitting, only those with special needs beyond the school's capability are liable to be turned away. Senior school feeders local prep schools and primaries.

Exit: At all ages. Some take common entrance at 11, and a small number at 13. Girls have previously mainly gone to Queen Margaret's Eskrick, with one or two to Tudor Hall, Heathfield or co-eds Uppingham, Millfield, Rugby. Senior girls go on to do A levels at Ampleforth, St Aidan's, Ripon Grammar, Sedbergh, St Peter's, Uppingham etc etc. Good collection of scholarships – music predominates, plus academic and sports.

Money matters: Not a rich school and not endowed, though has benefited recently from generous donations. Scholarships for academics, music, art and sport, plus discount for clergy daughters, sisters and Forces.

Remarks: Girls' – predominantly weekly – boarding school without a sixth form or international pupils. Queen Mary's is a very jolly place, a home from home, with muddy wellies on the doorstep, smiling cheery girls and teachers; a predominance of four-wheeled drives in the car park and very dog-friendly.

It provides a good solid education focusing on creating girls with confidence, a 'have a go' mentality and freedom to grow into their own skin. Fierce competition locally, shows in numbers lower down the school. It's possibly too small for those at the sharp end – but many would thrive here and the girls say they 'wouldn't change a thing'.

Rockport School

29

15 Rockport Road, Craigavad, Holywood, County Down BT18 0DD

028 9042 8372 | info@rockportschool.com | www.rockportschool.com

Ages: 3–18 (boarding from 12)

Pupils: 220; sixth form: 20; Boarders: 47

Day: £6,435 – £14,895 pa; Boarding: £14,460 – £25,800 pa

Headmaster: Since 2012, George Vance LLB BEd PQHNI (50s). He joined the school in 2007 as deputy head. His teacher training was at Stanmillis University College, part of Queen's University Belfast, and he read law at the University of Ulster. His first teaching post was at Regent House School, where he would spend 25 years, 22 of them as head of DT. His two great ambitions when he became headmaster were for Rockport to join the Round Square group of schools and to open a sixth form, both now achieved. As a student teacher he read an article by Kurt Hahn which made a lasting impression, and one of the reasons he joined Rockport was because he felt it was a 'Round Square school in waiting'.

'He lives and breathes the school, is approachable and welcoming and is just right for the school,' said a father. 'Kids warm to him as a person but also respect him as the headmaster, and no parent or child would hesitate to knock on his door'. He wears a gown for official events, can be spotted bicycling round the grounds, and The Belfast Telegraph likened him to Mr Chips, but he will put his shoulder to anything – 'he can be super smart,' said a pupil, 'but will also round up the chickens when they escape'.

A qualified mountain leader, he is passionate about the Morne Mountains and takes every child over the age of 8 hillwalking. He loves the outdoors and has been involved with the D of E for over 30 years. He keeps his hand in by teaching DT as cover. He lives on site with his wife, Susan, a special needs teacher at a local school, and they have three grown up children.

Academic matters: Not really selective and will accept all children who can access the curriculum. The environment is much more nurturing and supportive than at local grammars, and the breadth of ability means they can welcome whole families. It is not unusual for children to leave for the grammars and then come back. 'The children are not pushed but gently supported', said one mother, but another felt that perhaps they could be stretched a bit more. In 2017, 27 per cent A*/A at GCSE – impressive in terms of value added with most pupils outperforming their predicted outcomes by at least two grades. The small year groups mean that the statistics are less meaningful than in a larger school. The sixth form opened in 2015 with the first cohort of six pupils taking their A levels in 2017 (36 per cent A*-B grades) and nine due to sit them in 2018. 18 subjects offered at GCSE and science can be taken as three separate subjects or as a double or triple award. Apart from the usual subjects, the school offers media and business studies and learning for life and work. Can accommodate a range of abilities within one class and the average size is 12, but there are sometimes as few as five in a GCSE class and three in an A level class. The choice of A levels at the moment is very much pupil driven and includes the popular moving image arts, sports studies, ICT, art and geography.

The headmaster had to have difficult conversations with some members of staff a few years ago and now has a dynamic team of teachers who are happy to go on courses and update their skills.

A qualified mountain leader, he is passionate about the Morne Mountains and takes every child over the age of 8 hillwalking. He loves the outdoors

CAT tests all pupils annually and sets individual targets, and most improve on predicted grades – the school likes to call it the Rockport effect. Teaches separate sciences from year 8 in newly refurbished labs and uses the grounds and the beach as outdoor classrooms (as well as a bespoke forest classroom). Home economics (which can include child development) from year 8 is popular with boys and girls at GCSE. Well-equipped ICT suite – there are over 90 computers throughout the school.

SEN is housed in the cottage in the grounds with two full time dyslexia specialists and part time specialists in maths and dyspraxia, who all work closely with the teaching and boarding staff. Seven statemented children in the school, two with classroom assistants. Very supportive and inclusive and the school has a record of success with school refusers from elsewhere.

EAL support teacher comes in once a week – usually one-to-one teaching but depends on the need. Will even take a child with no English.

Lower sixth required to do a week's work experience – parents are very supportive and often offer work shadowing.

Games, options, the arts: Pupils have to take part in some sort of sport until they are 14, with rugby, hockey, football and netball being the main team sports. The school is probably too small to win any of the big rugby tournaments, but boys play with great enthusiasm and two are in the Ulster development squad. 'The Astro is our new baby,' said a pupil, 'and we can now host tennis and hockey matches.' The school also hosts a netball tournament and barbecue for 600 children, and the junior team recently won the Northern Ireland tournament – everyone is put forward for trials and 'they push us beyond our boundaries,' said a pupil.

Children are encouraged to try new things like kayaking from Rockport's own beach and sailing from Ballyholme Yacht Club. The latter is offered from the age of 3, culminating in the annual Rockport Regatta – the school has produced four international sailors, half the Irish team and a Commonwealth Games team member who is now in the pre-Olympic squad for Tokyo. They have also set up the Rockport Golf Academy and everyone plays golf once a week from the age of 3. There are five affordable courses within a few minutes' drive and school keen to spot talent and bring it on through development and elite squads – the junior girls' team are Ulster and Irish champions and a boy has recently won the Junior Irish Open. 1970s sports hall also used for exams, tests and speech day, with swimming at the local Aurora leisure centre. Rockport runs its own Wimbledon tournament – all involved, no one is left out and finals are held on the front lawn followed by a barbecue. Everything is a family affair and usually involves drinks and food for parents.

About 20 per cent learn an instrument, some up to grade 8, or take singing lessons. 'Singing is massive,' said a pupil, and there are two choirs run as clubs as well as a string quartet and a woodwind group – the school is not big enough for an

orchestra. Pupils sing at Holywood music festival and everyone takes part in the summer concert, which is preceded by canapes and fizz on the lawn.

Art particularly strong, with A level art being the most popular subject – the visual arts programme is mentored by an artist and the children exhibit their work at the Belfast museum; 'we love it when the artists come in', said a pupil. We were particularly struck by the beautiful stained glass windows in the art department.

Rockport runs its own Wimbledon tournament – all involved, no one is left out and finals are held on the front lawn followed by a barbecue. Everything is a family affair and usually involves drinks and food

Energetic drama department with something going on most terms. Senior and junior drama societies and GCSE plays – very inclusive and we 'pick children who would not necessarily volunteer'. Also have the opportunity to get involved with stage management and lighting is linked in with ICT.

Range of after-school clubs, many outdoors based, such as the fly fishing, angling clubs, orienteering and hillwalking clubs, most gain silver D of E and 12-15 take part in the Young Enterprise scheme – projects have included commissioning, branding, marketing and selling granite candlesticks, paperweights and pampered pet pouches. Outings include a visit to a potato crisp factory and a print workshop, theatre trips and a physics trip to Queen's University, Belfast.

Boarding: Offers full, weekly and flexi boarding and can accommodate the occasional casual boarder, but doesn't have much space. Some 47 boarders from the age of 12, with about 20 in at weekends. No Saturday school but outings like swimming and ice skating are arranged and 'we try to make it as much like home as possible,' says the matron. Lots of investment in boarding areas and a cosy family feel – boys in single or double rooms, younger girls in small dorms and older girls have their own rooms. Comfortable sitting room with tartan sofas and a television and boarders can make toast and bring in food. Reward night on Thursdays – maybe go-karting, movie night or trampolining. Boarders have structured evenings with a supervised second prep with staff on hand to help; sixth formers are given more independence. International boarders often come for just a term and have a week of outings in the summer when everyone else is doing exams.

Background and atmosphere: The school was founded in 1906 by Geoffrey Bing with the aim of 'preparing boys for the Public Schools and the Royal Naval College, Dartmouth.' It was built as a private house in the 19th century and is set in 25 acres on the shores of Belfast Lough on Northern Ireland's gold coast. It is the only fully independent school in Northern Ireland, has no church involvement and there are no clergy on the board of governors – unique in Northern Ireland. The school is not secular but has a light touch Christian ethos and has a long relationship with the parish church where the Remembrance Day and carol services are held, but mostly plays down religion and welcomes families from all faiths and none.

The new sixth formers are delighted with their social and study area in a chalet in the grounds overlooking the lough. As the school is so small everyone has to mix between years and join in. Academic achievement is only part of the picture and there is a strong sense of community, but it's not highly competitive – there are cups for everything but winning is not the be all and end all.

Attractive school uniform; the main school pupils wear a green kilt or grey trousers and green jumpers with blazers for best. There has been much consultation about the uniform for the new sixth form and they have settled for grey trousers or a Black Watch skirt and navy blue jumpers.

The school became a global member of the Round Square in 2016 and the education at Rockport is underpinned by Kurt Hann's six IDEALS of internationalism, democracy, environment, adventure, leadership and service, which fit well with its ethos. There are often exchanges with

Environment is more nurturing and supportive than at local grammars; breadth of ability means they can welcome whole families

other Round Square schools, two pupils recently attended the global conference in Singapore and four sixth formers represented the school at the Cape Town conference. There are elections for everything and a strong culture of service. The junior choir sings in old people's homes at Christmas and sixth formers volunteer in charity shops and at the Camphill Community for those with severe learning difficulties, and all get involved in the annual sponsored walk. Pupils are taught to think about what they can do for others and offer a helping hand. 'Never give up, rise to the challenge, do what you enjoy and treat everyone equally wherever they come from.' 'They don't tell kids what they can't do but what they can,' said a parent.

Pastoral care, well-being and discipline: Children can talk to anyone and everyone if they are struggling, school contacts parents immediately if there is a problem and a full staff briefing every morning keeps everyone in the loop. 'Everyone knows each other and there are no invisible children at Rockport', said a parent. Children also have access to an external counsellor.

The usual social media issues, but zero tolerance of bullying: 'it is nipped in the bud and we all look out for each other', said a pupil. The school has a team of student anti-bullying ambassadors who attend a training session to become peer mentors, with particular focus on social media. There has not been a drugs issue in living memory.

The school hosts the Amazing Brains programme to help students cope with the stress of revision and exams. Two houses, Green House and White House, which compete against each other in the founders' day cross country-race, swimming gala and declamations.

All meals made from scratch and the food is 'the best – even better than my mum's', said a pupil (not necessarily what a mother wants to hear).

Pupils and parents: Almost half are from local postcodes but a good train line means some from as far as 40 miles away – the local station is only a short walk. Combination of old money, professionals and self-made entrepreneurs with about a third receiving some financial assistance with the fees. Most children are from Northern Ireland but a growing international community in Belfast means that it is often the school of choice for expats. There is a large American contingent and the school now hosts a Thanksgiving dinner. Parents very engaged and generous with their time and money and the Parents' Association is involved with the planning of the numerous social gatherings and fundraising events such as the camping weekends and the quiz night, and are very welcoming to new parents. A parent described the children as 'well rounded and confident, will stand up for themselves and speak out and are willing to swim against the shoal'. They have a strong sense of right and wrong and are very understanding of those who are not doing well.

Former pupils include rugby star, Paddy Wallace; the rock band, Snow Patrol; former Lord Mayor of London, Sir Peter Gadsden; and the leader of the House of Lords, Natalie Evans. The school promotes free thinking, says the headmaster, and has produced a number of MPs and life peers representing the full range of political opinion.

Parents kept informed via regular progress reports and regular meetings and the headmaster's witty and informative Friday newsletter.

Entrance: Not hugely selective. Most children from the prep school move on to the senior school and there is a big intake from local state schools at 11.

Pupils are taught to offer a helping hand. 'Never give up, rise to the challenge, do what you enjoy and treat everyone equally wherever they come from'

Exit: School will prepare children for the transfer test to the grammars at 11+ as well as common entrance to independent schools on the mainland. Some leave after GCSEs for larger schools with a wider choice of A levels – Gordonstoun and Glenalmond are popular choices – but increasing numbers choosing to stay for the sixth form. The first cohort of sixth form leavers headed for Queen's University, Belfast and Scottish universities.

Money matters: One third have some financial assistance including 5-10 per cent on full bursaries. Academic, music and golf scholarships worth up to 20 per cent of fees, which can be topped up to 100 per cent with a with a bursary.

Remarks: A charming, gentle small school on the shores of Belfast Lough which feels like one big family, where 'there is top down happiness from the headmaster and staff to the children and everyone seems to be smiling'.

Rossall School

30

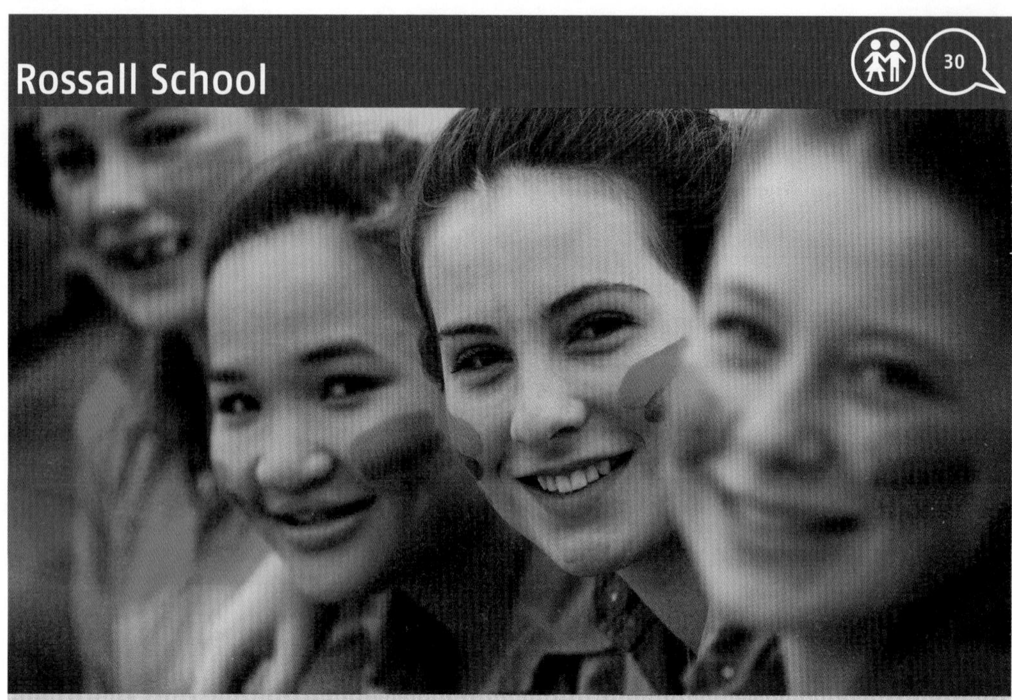

Broadway, Fleetwood, Lancashire FY7 8JW

01253 774201 | admissions@rossall.org.uk | www.rossall.org.uk

Ages: 11–18

Pupils: 444; sixth form: 182; **Boarders:** 220 full, 14 weekly

Day: £10,470 – £12,750 pa; **Boarding:** £16,920 – £36,450 pa

Head: Since 2013, Ms Elaine Purves BA PGCE (mid-40s). Brought up and state educated in Scotland and then in Nottinghamshire, studied English and German at Hull University. On graduation she worked briefly for agricultural manufacturer John Deere in Germany before going to Durham to do her PGCE. She nearly returned to East Germany to teach English at Leipzig University, but after the Berlin Wall came down everything became uncertain and she ended up taking her first teaching post in the UK – at Oakham School in Rutland – and she has worked in the independent sector ever since. From Oakham she went to The Royal High School, progressing through the ranks from head of languages eventually to deputy head. After 13 years in Bath, in 2006 she became head of Ipswich High School for Girls, where she stayed for seven years before moving her whole family from Suffolk to Lancashire to take the job at Rossall.

One aspect of Rossall that attracted her was its international intake (50 per cent of pupils come from abroad, and that figure rises to 60-65 per cent by the sixth form). She says: 'Another reason why I wanted to come and work in a school like this was for my children. I wanted them to have that global perspective'. She and her husband have a son and a daughter who are both pupils at Rossall. She says 'they've really thrown themselves into it' here. Her husband was born in Preston, so the family did already have some ties to the north west. The excellent local golf facilities seem to have been a draw for him. And now they live in the head's house on site. She says it's a 'nice thing' to live on site and, although she acknowledges that she pretty much is on call 24 hours a day, she doesn't seem to mind in the slightest.

The first female head at Rossall, Ms Purves still likes to get into the classroom teaching languages and, although she comes across as approachable and softly spoken, we had no doubts that she could command both a class and a workforce. Parents say she's 'fantastic', 'hands-on' and 'approachable'. Several parents said how impressed they were with the way she listens both to parents and to pupils, and they also note approvingly that she turns up to every rugby match.

Leaving in July 2018.

Academic matters: Rossall provides an all-round education – aiming to meet the needs of every pupil within its broad intake. Usually class sizes of 18-20 in years 7-11 (an absolute maximum of 22) and a maximum of 18 in the sixth form. The head identifies maths, the sciences, English, technology and art as departments that are doing particularly well. Food studies, Mandarin and drama recently added to curriculum. Parents we met were very happy with their children's attainment. One mother told us how impressed she'd been that the school offered to take her bilingual children, raised until recently in France, out of mainstream French lessons to teach them separately so that they could continue to study French as a first language. But there's a comprehensive and inclusive ethos here. Parents felt that the school was about much more than academia and that it doesn't focus resources and attention on high flyers at the expense of those in the middle or who are struggling. 'They don't single out the star pupils,' said one parent. 'They give praise subtly and they don't make a big song and dance of it.' 'Mine are never made to feel inferior,' said another mum. 'They do their best and they get praise for that.' There's no streaming but there is setting in some subjects. Parents said that sets were constantly under review and so 'you're not stuck in your set'.

Parents told us that even the highest performing sports players would never be discouraged from getting involved in the school play or any other creative endeavour

Results reflect the broad intake. In 2017, 34 per cent of GCSEs entered were awarded A*-A/9-7 and at A level that figure was 17 per cent, with 44 per cent A*-B. Roughly a third of sixth formers choose to do the International Baccalaureate rather than A levels and in 2017 they achieved an average of 27 IB points per pupil. The school languishes in the bottom quartile of the independent schools league tables but, unlike the high-flyers in the league tables, Rossall is not a selective school. It's also one of the most international schools in the UK, meaning that a large proportion of the children sitting those GCSE, A level and IB exams (about 60 per cent of them) don't have English as a first language.

International students can enter the main school if their English is already close to fluent. Those whose level of English would hold them back from achieving their potential academically are placed in the International Study Centre. This isn't as separate as it sounds; it's really a stream within the main school where pupils receive intensive English language support. Some pupils only stay in the ISC for a term or two, others stay for a year or more and some complete an intensive one-year IGCSE course there to prepare them for entering the sixth form in the main school.

The school supports pupils with a range of special educational needs. A full-time SEN support teacher has recently joined the school. There may be an additional charge to parents of children with SEN if a very high level of support is required.

Games, options, the arts: This is a very sporty school. Ian Botham sent his son, Liam, here and many alumni have gone on to play rugby, hockey or cricket professionally. More than a dozen pupils – male and female – currently play hockey for Lancashire. And there are countless sports options beyond the more obvious team games: pupils can also play basketball, squash or badminton, or lift weights, climb, dance or shoot, and there's now a golf academy. As you'd expect, there is an extensive range of top quality pitches, playing fields, squash courts and the like on campus; almost all sports offered have on-site facilities apart from horse-riding, ice-skating and golf. The 25-metre indoor swimming pool looked particularly inviting – although we didn't jump in – and we weren't surprised to see a large bank of seats on the poolside for crowds of supportive pupils to cheer on their peers. Sport is a unifying force at Rossall: one day the children might be competing fiercely in one of the many inter-house tournaments and the next day they'd be whooping with pride when another pupil scores a winning goal or try against a rival school. Rossall sport is steeped in tradition; Ross-Hockey is a unique game – a hockey-rugby hybrid played only on the beach next to the school; and the school regularly competes in rugby fives tournaments at prestigious public schools as well as hosting its own national Rossall Fives tournament each October.

One pupil we spoke to hinted, diplomatically, that the school could maybe invest a little more in girls' sport – particularly hockey. A couple of mums agreed. One said that the school hadn't traditionally pushed girls' hockey as much as the boys' game, but that she felt things are now improving and that the school has been responsive to criticism. But another mum said there was still some under-investment in the girls' game. She said that her daughter recently went to training, only four girls turned up and there was no coach. 'It's demoralising,' she said, 'because the ones that do want to play are a bit ignored... and I can see my daughter's face – you know: "Why am I here marking four players on my own?"'

Beyond sport the extracurricular opportunities are seemingly endless – with a particularly wide range of opportunities for arty and musical children and for outdoorsy types. Some more unusual examples include stage set design, costume making, film making, cryptography, psychology, jazz band, knitting, Warhammer and astrophysics (the school boasts a space science centre – complete with a planetarium, Victorian observatory and a telescope – and a resident astronomer). And this is just the tip of the iceberg. Many students are working towards their Duke of Edinburgh Award and pupils from year 9 and above can join the CCF.

Rossall has a diverse tradition in the arts. Choral music is strong here – closely bound in with the life of the historic chapel – but students play different types of music in various performances and concerts throughout the year; and they can learn instruments at school with visiting tutors – for an extra fee. There is also a literary society, which meets regularly to discuss poetry, books and culture. The school puts on two plays a year in one of two well-equipped performance spaces. The drama department also has links with a local theatre school and casting agency, which has enabled some pupils to appear in national radio and television productions. Keen artists are allowed to use the well-stocked workshops and studios every day after school. Each year in the Lent term Rossall devotes a week solely to art, music and drama and parents told us that even the highest performing sports players would never be discouraged from getting involved in the school play or any other creative endeavour.

Boarding: Pupils can board just five days a week or at weekends too. If day pupils want to flexi-board – which they often do – then they always stay in spare beds within their own house. Flexi-boarding allows day pupils to stay at the school for a night or longer – for pretty much any reason. Parents love it because it gives them a night off (or a weekend in Paris...) but, more importantly, the kids can't get enough of it. They typically flexi-board on a Friday night if they have to be at school early the next morning for a match or on a Saturday night if they want to tag along on the boarding house's Sunday outing.

The houseparents we met were warm and affectionate – they seemed to love the job and that was reflected in the way the children spoke about them: 'yeah, they're very supportive'

Although there are no classes on a Saturday, it tends to be a busy day with sports practices and fixtures. Every Sunday boarders can, at no extra cost, go on an outing – examples include bowling or crazy golf activities or trips to Alton Towers or the Manchester Christmas markets. Just over 42 per cent of boarders are international and these will be met at and delivered back to Manchester Airport by a representative of the school at the start and end of term. They don't have an option to stay in school during the holidays, though. If they can't fly home then they'll need to have a UK guardian to look after them.

The boarding houses, including the junior house for 7-13 year olds, are very homely – softer and more cosy than a typical university hall of residence. The boarding houses are a home from home where any pupil can come to relax and socialise during lunchtimes – and consequently there's lots of scope for different age-groups and both local and international pupils to mix. There are some single rooms available and a few are en-suite, but the majority of boarders share with one or two other pupils and share a bathroom on the corridor. Each pupil has a desk in their room and the freedom to put up pictures and customise their living space. Each house has a pair of live-in houseparents – who are either teachers or support staff. The houseparents we met were warm and affectionate – they seemed to love the job and that was reflected in the way the children spoke about them: 'yeah, they're very supportive,' said one sixth former and another added 'they look out for you and you can talk to them about anything'.

Background and atmosphere: An aerial photo in the school's prospectus shows the campus green, soft red and light blue. It is expansive and grassy; the buildings red-brick, grand and turreted; and beyond them stretches a thin strip of pale yellow beach before the misty sea. Even on a grey, murky day the space is picturesque and peaceful. 'Yes, it's a bubble,' one mum said to us, 'but it's a lovely bubble to be in.' This is one of the happiest schools that this reviewer has visited: pupils raved – with no hint of cynicism – about their friends and teachers, the school's traditions and jolly japes in the boarding houses.

The fact that it's a boarding school – and a very international one – is integral to Rossall life. The house system connects boarders with day pupils: all day pupils are assigned to a boarding house and from year 9 onwards they meet there, in cosy common rooms, each morning for registration. Even if they're not staying for a sleepover, this is a school where older pupils in particular just don't want to go home. They can stay late for prep (with teachers on hand to help) and have their tea at school. There's even a licensed bar and café on site, open to sixth formers three nights a week. One dad told us how pleased he was that when his nearly 17-year-old son stays out late, he doesn't need to wonder where he is or what he's up to because he knows he's safe and happy with his friends at school.

Tradition is very big here. Every year during Christmas dinner in the imposing, oak-panelled dining hall, the pupils sing The 12 Days of Christmas – each house taking a different verse. No-one tells them to do it, the pupils explain, 'it just sort of happens, spontaneously'. It gets quite competitive – each house singing more boisterously than the last. One pupil told me this tradition summed up what's special about Rossall. Might some prospective parents baulk at the hearty traditions, the special public-schooly Rossall sports, the sense that this could be the setting for an undiscovered Enid Blyton saga? Certainly we found no hint of social snobbery – we simply saw young people having a deliciously happy time at school. If grand old traditions make you cringe then Rossall may not be the perfect fit for you as a parent – when it comes to the pupils, though, the school is so warm and good-humoured, and there is such opportunity and encouragement to become the person you want to be, that we felt even if your teenager is something of a non-conformist he or she would still stand a good chance of finding a niche here.

Pastoral care, well-being and discipline: Several parents identified the quality of pastoral care as the single thing they most appreciated about Rossall. They raved about how well their children are known by staff. One dad was full of praise for

a teacher who stayed in regular contact with him, by text, to keep him updated on a particularly protracted UCAS application process. 'Teachers always remember what's going on with your child,' said another parent. 'It's just great that there's always that concern... and so I don't worry about my children here at all because I know the staff are really looking out for them.'

Religion is significant in school life: there's a full-time Church of England school chaplain and the whole school attends chapel every Friday. But, particularly with the diverse, international intake, the school takes care to ensure that worship is inclusive and that other faiths get a look in too.

Even if they're not staying for a sleepover, this is a school where older pupils in particular just don't want to go home. They can stay late for prep

Discipline is firm here. Serious breaches of the rules would be dealt with case-by-case but expulsion is a possibility. If you're caught smoking three times, you're out. (Although pupils told us that some of the German boarders are stalwart smokers so, presumably, they're good at not getting caught.) Pupils couldn't think of any instances of bullying in their experience and they spoke with real conviction about how caring an environment this is. They said that pupils wouldn't tolerate bullying – that they would tell a teacher and offer support to the victim. Parents knew of no bullying either. Like most schools, Rossall has a stringent anti-bullying policy. We were impressed that parents told us that they knew of several pupils at the school who had come out as gay – with minimal fuss or drama and complete acceptance from their peers. Parents felt the school was very accepting of difference – perhaps also because of the diversity that the international students bring to the community.

Pupils and parents: The parents are a mixed bunch. A good few are alumni of Rossall but many others were state educated. Some get help with fees from grandparents or from the school's own means-tested bursary scheme. The kids are also diverse. Across the school, 50 per cent are international – coming from a very wide spread of countries and cultures. Further up the school, more than 60 per cent are international. But there are far more British children than those of any other single nationality. The pupils seem inclusive and grounded. And they were positive and polite.

Parents felt the school was very accepting of difference – perhaps also because of the diversity that the international students bring

Alumni include Booker-Prize-winning novelist JG Farrell; Father Thomas RD Byles, the Catholic priest who refused to leave the Titanic so that he could help other passengers; eminent figures in the world of sport, music and industry; and a few bastions of the Establishment: a governor of a couple of colonies; a private secretary to Queen Victoria; and the magnificently-named Sir Walton Clopton Wingfield, who patented the game of lawn tennis.

Entrance: There are entrance tests in English, maths and non-verbal reasoning but it is rare to say no to a prospective pupil: this would normally only be done if the school couldn't meet his/her needs.

For international students, the admissions procedure is largely a question of assessing their English. The school has a Skype conversation with every student before a place is offered. They must have at least some English: if they can't hold a Skype conversation they can't come here. If their English is already good enough that it won't hold them back academically then they can go straight into the main school. If not, then they may need to first of all come to the International Study Centre (see above in Academic for more information.)

All pupils need to achieve five GCSEs at grade A*-C/9-5 to enter the sixth form. If they don't they can either repeat the year or leave.

'Yes, it's a bubble,' one mum said to us, 'but it's a lovely bubble to be in.' This is one of the happiest schools that this reviewer has visited: pupils raved – with no hint of cynicism – about their friends and teachers, the school's traditions and jolly japes

Exit: Everyone sits the senior school entrance exam but, for children already here in the juniors, it's just used as a baseline assessment and to assess for scholarship, rather than to determine who transfers.Some 35 per cent leave after GCSEs. Most sixth form pupils go on to university, some 15 per cent to Russell Group. Two medics in 2017; desinations included Manchester, Reading, Leeds Beckett, Queen Mary, University of the Arts. Plus International School of Management, Hamburg, Kosice, Slovakia, North Eastern Boston, USA and Vienna. Two joined the Forces and one is in Team GB for triathlon.

Money matters: The school has been in very good financial health for a number of years – the influx of international students has really turned its fortunes around. About six per cent of pupils in the senior school receive significant means-tested bursaries (a 50 per cent reduction of fees or more). There are also some scholarships available for high performers in sport, music, drama or academia.

Remarks: This is a very happy school. Its population is so diverse, there's no one type of child who would fit in better than another. But we did feel the school would particularly appeal to busy parents who perhaps don't have a lot of support locally or who find domestic life to be somewhat relentless – because the school offers a round-the-clock home-from-home programme of activities which could ease the pressure on families at times of stress. It's no academic pressure-cooker and less able pupils will be praised for their efforts just as much as the high flyers but there are excellent teachers, facilities and opportunities that should give the brightest pupils every chance to excel. Overall, Rossall is a warm, inclusive and remarkably happy place to be. Staff and pupils seem to genuinely love it here – and there's not much higher praise you can offer than that.

St George's School (Edinburgh)

31

Garscube Terrace, Murrayfield, Edinburgh EH12 6BG

01313 118000 | admissions@stge.org.uk | www.stge.org.uk

Ages: 2-18 (boarding from 11)

Pupils: 800; sixth form: 177; **Boarders:** 46 full/flexi

Day: £8,265 – £13,410 pa; **Boarding:** £25,290 – £28,035 pa

Head: Since January 2017, Alex Hems, previously deputy head of Wycombe Abbey. English degree from Oxford; has also been head of sixth form at North London Collegiate, head of senior school at St Paul's Girls and deputy head at Francis Holland. She is married to William and they have two daughters.

Academic matters: School no longer narrowly academic; girls follow English or Scottish system as best fits the bill. League tables are meaningless in this school, given that two systems are followed. Current exam boards' status on either side of the border is nothing short of chaotic; St G's timetabling both systems must be a nightmare. 'Absolutely no thought of moving to the IB'. Some impressive results in both disciplines, though rather more glitches than we have seen previously, and quite a number of soft subjects with tiny numbers: early education and childcare, media studies, travel and tourism, all at Higher level. We have no difficulty with penny numbers doing langs, but to have one each taking graphic communication, information systems and computing, and two doing modern studies cannot make economic sense. Results include those from the Royal Environmental Health Institute of Scotland: number of pupils have achieved introductory (two hour course) or elementary certificates in food hygiene (six hour course).

Possibly more followers of the Scottish system, physics and geography strong (oil?). As ever the English system popular for art and design, religious moral and philosophical studies, hefty showing in Highers. 'Lots of flexibility' in course selection (this editor reckons too much; but no doubt horses for courses). School employs VLE – Virtual Learning Environment; students can access/collect coursework, or refer to staff notes online. Claims to be the 'top school in Scotland for A levels and Advanced Highers'. As do many others, though perhaps not both at the same time. In 2017, 57 per cent A grades at Higher level and 52 per cent at Advanced Higher; 33 per cent A*/A at A level (art & design and Russian). At GCSE, 47 per cent A*-A/9-7 grades. No particular bias: English, maths, langs; French, German, Spanish, Latin and classical Greek. Latin for all in L4 (top end of the junior school), thereafter girls must choose from a 'revolving carousel' of double period tasters in Spanish, German, Mandarin. The latter popular with both pupils and parents in the school's Chinese centre. Thirty-six native speakers in school, many pupils host sessions in their native languages: Russian, Chinese, Gaelic; and can study for individual A levels (or whatever) in those langs. School will arrange specialist tutors. Four or five parallel classes in the upper school, max class size 21 and down.

Latin from age 10. Certain amount of tinkering about with what age is taught where, sounded immensely complicated, but the gist of the argument is that by moving girls around and splitting the junior school into two, the tedium of being in a single sex school for up to 15 years might not appear so drear. P5-P6 (11/12 year olds) are taught in the main campus, before they move to lower school proper for a couple of years before they move back to main school. Got it?

Much to-ing and fro-ing with local unis, pupils and staff combine on various projects, 'and take part in an impressive outreach programme which encompasses both the academic and the appreciation of the wider world'. 'Joint seminars in a plethora of subjects with an eclectic collection of schools, the state sector as well as other independents (in all disciplines: sport and music as well as academia)', according to the school. Good general studies, curriculum choice support and careers advice (careers breakfasts), 500 options in careers dept.

Comprehensive learning support, pick up early, can deal with most of the dys-strata and ADHD; laptops encouraged. SENCo on site, four specialist teachers plus rash of assistants. Small ESOL department to help non-nationals (charge). Drop-in centre for instant problem solving, 'weekly support sessions in every subject, plus subject clinics at lunch time, in break, before school or by email in the evening' (so presumably pupils have access to staff emails). This is what we like to hear. Buddy system: older girls help tinies with reading and much else besides. All girls in junior schools (combined) are assessed for learning hiccups; as with senior school, pupils are withdrawn from class: one-to-one, small clusters, or helped by assistants in class.

Drop-in centre for instant problem solving, 'weekly support sessions in every subject, plus clinics'

School split into three distinct departments – junior, which encompasses the nursery, lower and upper (senior in GSG speak). Head has offices in both lower and upper. School not totally wheelchair friendly but will make allowances and change classrooms if necessary (lift in junior school new build), chairlift in the main building; no problem with boarding houses. Hearing loops.

Games, options, the arts: Fabulous centenary sports hall with viewing area over hall and squash courts; much-used lacrosse pitches, floodlit all-weather pitch. Trad games played with a vengeance: lacrosse tours, hockey tours, swimming, judo, cycling. Local sports clubs use facilities: Grange Junior Hockey Club et al. Robertson Music Centre houses untold numbers of choirs, ensembles, three orchestras, over 600 musicians (can be hired for functions, popular with Alex McCall Smith's Really Terrible Orchestra, as well as National Youth Choir of Scotland, Edinburgh Youth Orchestra and Waddell School of Music). Impressive collection of music results. Vibrant art department, pottery, textiles, sculpture et al. Drama and theatre good, timetabled, not much pursued at higher level. All juniors use senior school facilities, gym, music, drama, games pitches.

Oodles of D of E, dozens of bronze but tails off somewhat as girls grow older. CCF, Outreach outdoor education from age 10. Sixth formers join forces with Merchiston for dances, sport, art, music, drama etc. Zillions of after-school clubs that offer everything from keyboarding to extra IT. Hot on exchanges: girls as young as 12 whizz off to spend a month or so in Canada, Hong Kong, Australasia, Chile, wherever.

Boarding: Boarders, from 11, 50 per cent overseas, live in a couple of converted Edwardian villas behind the tennis courts in an uninspiring road full of equally dreary (if upwardly mobile) villas. Hardly swinging Edinburgh. Purpose-built bungalow for sixth formers, singles or twins, all very jolly, lots of extra activities, but perhaps not very stimulating. Serious revamp recently; re-wired, new heating. Mixture of real foreigners and long distance Scots who can have friends to stay (charge). Flexi and weekly boarding options.

Background and atmosphere: St George's High School for Girls, a member of the Girls' School Association, founded in 1886 as a training school for women teachers, transmogrified into St G's in 1888. The purpose-built, colonial neo-Georgian 1914 complex by A F Balfour-Paul is pure Jean Brodie, and sits uneasily with inspiring new additions. Lower school in converted former boarding house (plus ugly add-on); magical extension for junior school, complete with dance studio (that hall again) and dedicated nursery area has a cantilevered first floor over a bungee surface popular with senior pupils as well as a strategic undercover play area for tinies. Stunning dining hall (exit bridge known as Bridget), entertainment area below has released valuable space for extra libraries and study. Parents can (and do) use the dining centre as a coffee shop.

New uniform compulsory for all within the year, certain leeway in upper sixth. Kilts for all from lower sixth down, in St G's ancient red millennium tartan, with optional trimmed fitted jackets, 'kilts not more than six cm above the knee' (most appeared much longer). Otherwise pretty standard, check dresses, blue gym tunics, navy tights, red or blue wellies. No problems with headscarves (number of Muslims in the school), presumably like the hair bands they will need to be in school colours. Sibling-led house system.

Long-running romance with the Edinburgh Academy fractured by EA's decision to go co-ed, though they still share the same bus routes. St Gs tells us that links with Merchiston Castle are very much alive; the Edinburgh rumour mill, not to mention the local education rumour mill, assured this editor that St Gs had made an approach to Merchiston to link up on a more formal footing some time ago. Everest dissed this as a canard, but numbers are less buoyant than previously, particularly lower down the school (despite St Margaret's untimely demise).

Student council includes both juniors and seniors, terrific charity input/output; latest wheeze was to approach posh Edinburgh restaurants for their chef's fav recipes, publish them in a book and charge the restaurants to advertise. Help with City Mission. YPI with the (oily Sir Ian) Wood Foundation gives girls practice in marshalling arguments and persuading fund to dosh out for good causes. God followed broadly via Christian principles, regular assemblies, PSE cross year on Fridays, business on Mondays, year groups Thursdays and Fridays. Local minister for high days and holidays. Loads of staff jollies: keep fit, choir, and dedicated welfare programme.

If it is a challenge they need then they must go south, for there is nowhere in Scotland that can hold a candle to St George's, in academe or global awareness

Pastoral care, well-being and discipline: Miscreants are given heavy hints that they should 'move elsewhere' (and sometimes they do). 'No need to break out; this is a liberal environment.' 'No sniff of drugs.' Good PSE, positive behaviour policy which incorporates 'the best of human rights legislation'.

Pupils and parents: The Edinbourgeousie: middle class Scots, professionals, incomers, wannabes and first time buyers. Boarders from the Highlands and Islands, the Borders and the Scottish diaspora abroad (alma mater stuff). Handful of real foreigners. Skype useful. Global links and exchanges. Trad. Lots of parent/pupil forums on every subject under the sun; Friends of St George's for social events. Quick poll round parents (in address book) produced no surprises: non-stimulated girls were bored at the top end, parents were fed up at having to buy a new uniform for such a short time (not in secondhand shop yet), sixth formers seemed to be working (and playing) hard. Particularly the latter. School shouldn't be so petty about make up. Not really a sophisticated bunch, and probably not yummy mummys' school of choice.

Entrance: Entry via nursery or interview aged 4/5. 'Unashamedly academic in outlook' was how we previously described this school, indeed there was a time when wannabe parents coached their 5 year olds pre school interview. School maintains, 'not so strict an entrance test; important that we can meet a child's needs'. At 11, will welcome a girl who is able to keep up with the pace of academic life but who seems set for Bs and Cs rather than A*s. Assessment, school report and interview. Entry to sixth form is more or less automatic for home-grown pupils; external pupils by interview and school report. Demands for sixth form places heavy. 'Skype handy for interviewing girls from abroad'.

Exit: Nearly all juniors move up to the senior school. Some leave after GCSEs/National 5s to go co-ed; otherwise gap, uni, and higher education of all sorts – Scots law popular, as are the sciences, medicine (four medics in 2017, and seven lawyers) and business management. Around 60 per cent opt for Scottish universities, eg Aberdeen, St Andrew's, Edinburgh and Glasgow. Bristol, Durham, York and London unis also popular; odd bods to US, Ireland, France, Hong Kong, Thailand.

Money matters: Means-tested bursary scheme now replaces assisted places; 'mustn't let the really bright down'. Full bursaries available, plus help with school uniform. Will keep child if parents fall on hard times, as long as bursar is kept in the loop. Sibling discounts. Joint discount with Merchiston Castle School. After being told to provide more help for pupils from low income families, school passed the charity test in 2013 and has maintained its charitable status.

Remarks: The top girls' school in Scotland (pace chaps in nursery); more liberal than previously. Tatler calls it the 'St Paul's of the north', but with only four girls' schools in Scotland (two of which are overgrown dame schools and one of which takes boarders and ponies) there's not much competition.

At regular intervals this editor is asked for advice by parents who have had their little darlings at St George's since they were in nappies and are looking for a change of scene in sixth form (teenagers being what they are and Edinburgh being what it is). We have to say that, in all honesty, if it is a challenge they need then they must go south, for there is nowhere in Scotland that can hold a candle to St George's, be it in the realm of academe or of global awareness.

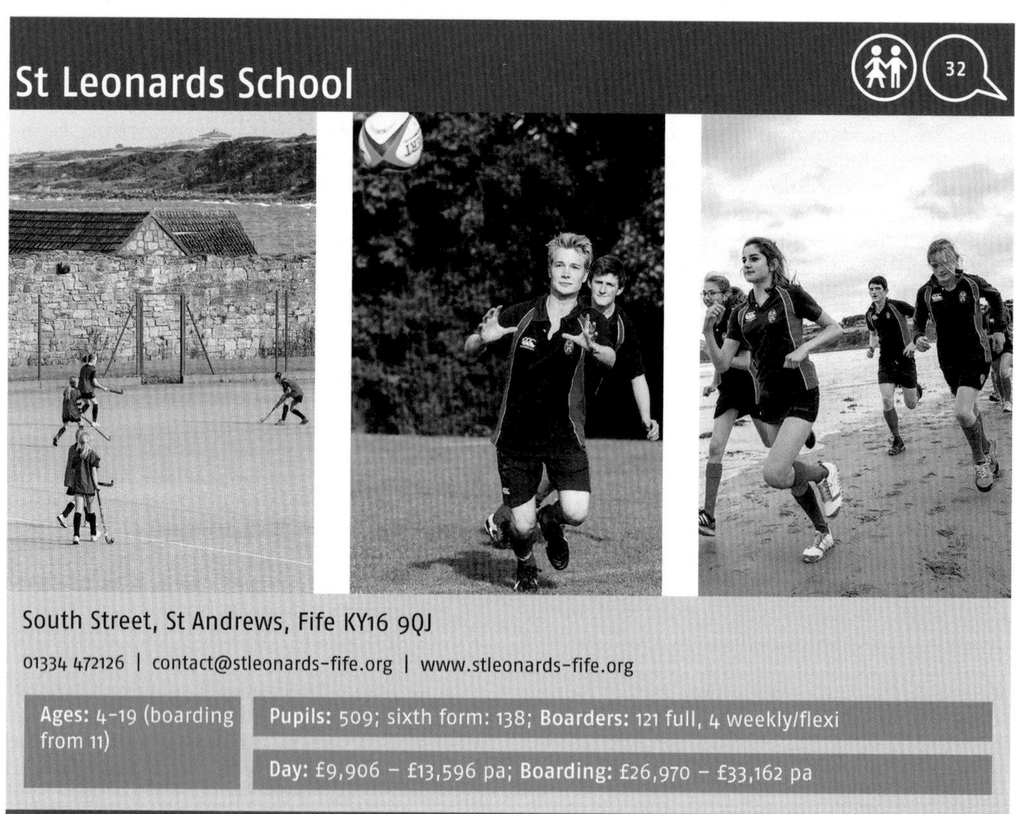

St Leonards School

32

South Street, St Andrews, Fife KY16 9QJ

01334 472126 | contact@stleonards-fife.org | www.stleonards-fife.org

Ages: 4–19 (boarding from 11)

Pupils: 509; sixth form: 138; **Boarders:** 121 full, 4 weekly/flexi

Day: £9,906 – £13,596 pa; **Boarding:** £26,970 – £33,162 pa

Headmaster: Since 2008, Dr Michael (Mike) Carslaw BSc MBA PhD (early 50s), educated at Merchiston, read zoology at Newcastle, spent three years doing VSO in Ghana ('discovered I loved teaching') followed by PGCE at Exeter ('where I met my wife'); comes to St Leonards via City of London Freemen's and Ardingly (responsible for more heads than you can shake a stick at). A Scot and a weedgie (as is this editor: work it out) he is a shoo-in and won The Tatler public school head of the year a couple of years back (he would have won ours too, but we don't do that sort of thing). St Leonards now has a head with vision, common sense and ambition, this is real CEO stuff; school is back on track, after suffering a variety of slings and arrows from a previous collection of headless chickens.

Academic matters: School prides itself on 'high quality education right from the preparatory school through to the senior school.' Scotland's only all-IB sixth form – focuses 100 per cent on the IB (average 33 points in 2017). 'We haven't taken any half measures with the qualification by offering alternative post-16 options, we have dedicated ourselves to it and we believe that's to the great benefit of our students.' New IB subjects include business management, computer science, psychology and sports science. Sixth formers help out in junior school as part of the charitable leg of the IB (CAS) with up to 50 hours' assistance 'reading, 'riting, 'rithmetic sort of thing.

Most pupils take GCSES/IGCSES in the normal way (39 per cent A*/A grades in 2017), before seamlessly switching disciplines; however, is introducing the IB Middle Years Programme for years 7-9. A one year pre-IB course ticks all the boxes for those joining school age 15 (often refugees from state systems) as well as international students who sit fewer IGCSE/GCSEs, and, if needed, get up to speed in English (about a fifth of non-native English speakers need some EAL help, and must pass a written proficiency test – ESOL). St Andrews Uni fields a raft of international speakers, St Leonards boasts help in 'a wide range of native langs in all year groups'...'be aware that some of this tuition may be subject to an additional charge', 'dependent on number of students and lang'.

When we visited (the week before summer half term) those taking the diploma were done and dusted: exams over, pupils were now home (think pay for six terms, school for five and a half: though, to be honest, 'yearly fees are divided, for the convenience of parents into three equal instalments'.. 'students can, and do, remain in school after their IB exams if that is easier for them, until prize-giving and leavers' ball'). Pupils know their results by first week in July.

Head says, 'The IB is probably the least tinkered about with qualification in the world – its basic philosophy of keeping a breadth of subjects going into the sixth form but also studying three to a level comparable to Advanced Higher or A level has remained.' 'Native lang' for IB may be English, Russian, German, French, Mandarin (currently on offer) or whatever, while Latin qualifies as a foreign language, as well as French, Spanish, German, Italian (ab initio). UCAS gives points for individual subjects studied under the IB system which means that non-linguists/mathematicians, previously

disadvantaged in the overall IB grading, now get full credit for their strong subjects.

Most study two or three langs, with all doing French from year 1 and Spanish and/or German/ Latin from 10/11. Max class size 20, smaller for practical or specialist subjects.

Senior pupils have access to the university library and regularly attend lectures. (Lots of profs' children so no dearth of academic governors or visiting speakers)

School appoints a St Leonards Associate Researcher or two, often a PhD student at St Andrews, to liaise with pupils and point them at the joys of research – or, as we said previously, 'helping them to develop an appreciation and knowledge of research'. Quite. Senior pupils have access to the university library and regularly attend lectures. (Lots of profs' children and consequently no dearth of academic governors or visiting speakers.)

Dyslexia/dyspraxia support – 'no statemented pupils accepted' – mostly provided for 'a small proportion of pupils' in mainstream teaching, but a good programme both withdrawal, group sessions and one-to-one if necessary (stunning, said one thrilled parent – 'saved our lives') at extra cost. School tests if they reckon extra help needed; specialist staff of four straddle both senior and junior schools.

Games, options, the arts: Proper matches for chaps as well as chapesses. Think Edinburgh schools,

Robert Gordon's... Full range of sporting options – rugby, lacrosse, hockey against Glenalmond, Strath and Dundee High: the hallowed main school site (birth of lacrosse in the UK) now boasts rugby matches et al (roll over Dame Louisa). Girls' sports still strong, with usual mass of international lax players. Practice matches held on beach if games pitches frozen.

Loads of individual sports and international coaches – needle chaps' tennis match in progress during our canter: judo, trampoline, skiing, badminton, swimming – university uses pool for water polo; snowboarding and surfing; rock-climbing as well as expeditions to the Alps. Annual skiing trips both at home and abroad; sailing now thoroughly embraced, ditto windsurfing and all 'local water sports activities' – and about time too. Local (and not so local) race-horse trainers use beach for exercise, as does the Scots Guards polo team, now based at Leuchars and St Andrews uni polo team. It being St Andrews, golf reigns supreme with about a third of the school playing; all lucky boarders can and do become youth members of the St Andrews Links Trust (as residents in St Andrews) so they can play the Old Course.

Nearby well-equipped BHS riding centre (moderately expensive, but not over the top) with a hot horse shower (wow!) offers a variety of options, from bringing your own nag to renting one of theirs. 'Weekly lessons available for keen able riders'.

Great new all-weather pitch, despite prolonged problems with Historic Scotland about floodlights, 'which would damage the fabric of the city wall': v expensive telescopic solution finally arrived at. Currently fundraising for new sports hall development.

Full range of sporting options–rugby, lacrosse, hockey: the hallowed main school site (birth of lacrosse in the UK) now boasts rugby matches et al (roll over Dame Louisa)

Outstanding art department, attracting pupils outside normal lessons as well as curricular – huge range of alternative media, dark rooms, textiles etc. Current craze is for zig-zag (as in card zig-zagging) art work. Fun, but difficult to live with, perhaps.

Head of art was hanging fiendish model birds from the ceiling during our visit – complete with two elderly black labs – preparatory to the next biannual art show – open to the public. Artists in residence. Regularly in the ribbons for local photography prize – the Kodak Cup – 10 times since 2002.

Music strong in fabulous Bob Steedman (husband of four heads ago, who, alas, died recently) designed centre. St Leonards Junior School pupils sang in front of the cameras at the televised St Andrews Royal Wedding Breakfast celebrations. Rash of bands/orchestras, 'choir for every day of the week', ambitious singing programmes. Pipe band; we were treated to a brilliant rendition by an 11 year old, who warned us that his favourite piece was 14 minutes long. We heard about four (though it seemed to take him longer to find his pipes).

Drama on the up; school performs twice a year in the revamped nearby Byre theatre in St Andrews (popular with both school and public) students must study history of theatre as well as pounding boards. Drama types take shows to Ed Festival and go on mega drama-fest to Broadway every other year. Trips (one per subject per year) planned on a two-year cycle. D of E of course. Youth Enterprise with goodies often sold in aid of local school-adopted fav charity TICCL.

Boarding: Weekly and termly boarding from year 7: emphasis is on day. Fairly harem scarum boarding houses, passages littered with rather grand bookcases and rows of servant's bells – relics of a former age. Day pupils in the sixth form included in house system with 'day rooms' in boarding houses. Couple of small dorms, mostly single rooms, usual teenage tip sort of thing, but they were in the midst of revising. Stunning shower (and this was in a house about to be done up!). £3 million refurb of all three boarding houses started recently – first revamped one opened recently (design brief: 'country house style'): 'Aspects of the interior patterns have been created using a sketch by a current student (and art scholar) – a Bishopshall Toile has been created of signature St Leonards scenes, and appears on all the curtains as well as cushions in the boarding house'.

No Saturday lessons. We were concerned at possible lack of organised activities for boarders at weekend, but were assured, several times, 'that they were too busy with their various IB projects'. Various jaunts to Edinburgh and Dundee were mooted but we are still a tad concerned. Head adds 'Boarders generally are taken up with sport on Saturdays, there is a boarders' outing every Sunday, the last few have been Elie (sic) (Ely?) Watersports, beach kite buggies on west sands, go karting, bubble football etc etc.'

Off duty gear as you might expect. School praised for high standard of pastoral care for boarders by the Care Inspectors.

Background and atmosphere: Founded by dons and wives of St Andrews's profs for their daughters in

1877 in what was once a medieval priory, backing on to the sea wall, the sprawling hotch-potch collection of impressive-looking granite has neither form nor symmetry: think Topsy. Dame Louisa Lumsden was first head (Dame Frances Dove, who succeeded her many years later, founded Wycombe Abbey in 1896).

Carslaw an IB enthusiast, 'better to have scientists who can write essays'; the IB is popular with international pupils, of whom there are over 30 different nationalities

Once Scotland's girls' academic (boarding) school of choice, St Leonards has weathered the storm caused by so-called brother schools opening their doors to the fairer sex to counteract (their) falling numbers (NB: fairer sex originally chosen on looks, rather than academic ability – how's that for daft?). School more or less went into free fall. Day girls were welcomed. Chaps were encouraged into the sixth form (for free – all two of them). A sixth form stand-alone college was trialled. Junior school (aka St Kats, St Katharine's) dissed boarders. Certain amount of family silver was sold.

The breakthrough came when junior school absorbed local co-ed prep, New Park, in 2005: chunk of New Park Educational Trust kicks in (took a wee while: rest of this moderately rich trust is devoted to 'providing equipment, project costs and bursaries', 'primarily in North East Fife – occasional individual bursary': so now you have chapter and verse). Boys and girls work their way up the school in true co-ed fashion: roughly 50/50.

In 2006, St Leonards adopted the two year IB as standard for all in sixth form; now adopting its middle years programme. Brave stuff: going IB all the way is expensive; staff need to be trained, with mandatory follow-up courses both in and out of house. Fees need to be paid, by staff and pupil alike.

Carslaw an IB enthusiast, 'better to have scientists who can write essays'; the IB is popular with international pupils, of whom, as we write, there are over 30 different nationalities; and is 'still delighted to be part of such a vibrant school community with so much going on.' Obvious good rapport with both staff and pupil: fun; our canter round the school was a delight.

Having moulded the three parts of the school into a cohesive unit, with sixth formers having more-or-less university privileges – tickets to the uni-library, can use uni gym and go 'by arrangement to lectures of interest', relaxed trips to approved cafés – that sort of thing; Carslaw now has a double-edged mission. The university town of St Andrews is a great draw, as is (whisper it soft) the golf; but school could still do with more punters. Both Carslaw and his marketing manager make global trips to far flung places pour encourager international students to both enjoy the St Leonards and the St Andrews experience. They also employ agents. Dividends are paying off. Numbers are up: particularly on the boarding side, where the elegant Edwardian houses no longer quite resemble the Marie Celeste.

An ongoing rolling programme of upgrading (where £2.5 million is a sum regularly bandied about). The external fabric is in need of serious help (sea breezes are hell on paintwork): some windows and sills are flaking, though much has been done within the neglected exteriors. A full time painter has been employed – think Forth Road Bridge and multiply him by 10 and they would still be toiling.

Curious combo of gracious living: elegant house drawing rooms reminiscent of Country Life plus lawned courts nestling among old stone building in dreaming spires style, combined with faintly scruffy corridors, classrooms, common rooms. (Bursar/cabinet maker needs to be shot: steel screws: Georgian half moon inlaid card table – pschaw.)

St Leonards inhabits a notoriously windswept corner of Fife, on the sea, bracing air, bone-chilling easterly gales, tracksuits popular for games. Nay, essential.

Golf, riding and the beach all great draws, as well as trips up town and forays to the surrounding countryside. Castle and cathedral a couple of minutes away. Mega library and selection of 'Maryana' in Queen Mary's House (oddly flanked by a boys' loo). Library much in use by those in sixth form, but available to all. Mary Queen of Scots and King

Charles II reputed to have stayed at Queen Mary's Library when it was a private house, but not, of course, at the same time.

Founded by dons and wives of St Andrews's profs for their daughters in 1877 in what was once a medieval priory, backing on to the sea wall, a sprawling hotch-potch collection of impressive granite

Splendid menu posted online: lunch we had was sumptuous and imaginative. All food scourced 'locally' (ie within 100 miles). International students can and do cook their own dishes. Veggie option, naturally, and fresh fruit available whenever. Central dining room recently given an internal overhaul: outside still pretty rank.

Comprehensive buses for day pupils: Dundee, Kirkcaldy, (Auchter)muchty, Perth, the East Neuk, and presumably special pick up at Leuchars following deployment of Scots Guards. Juniors can be dropped off early (8am) and collected late (5.30pm). (This represents a reduced school day but incorporates time for activities, which has 'settled down well and parents appreciate it'). Otherwise return journey leaves 5.40pm.

Sixth formers wear suits (or a fair approximation thereof) during the working day. Boys rather tidier than some we have seen at that age; girls less so: sixth formers adopt a theme (or two) in black – quite short shorts and thick tights apparently ok (skool says quite short skirts...). Machine washable blazers and blue tartan kilts for girls, grey breeks for chaps are senior/junior school uniform with blue woolly pullies. Ah but we hanker for the cloaks of yesteryear. Second hand shop run by the 'bullish' PA which also organises family fun tennis etc.

School is proud of its Scottish heritage and tradition – Burns Day celebrated though Scottish Country Dancing is apparently only taught in the junior school.

Pastoral care, well-being and discipline: School rules feature punctuality, security and civilised behaviour; the student handbook has a rash of rules, most of which are sheer common sense: L-drivers may not drive other pupils and the like. But members of the sixth form have a mass of privileges – can visit some (some definitely out of bounds) local pubs if aged 18 and over, smoke off-campus – je m'en doute in these days of stalag Scotland ('but not if I feel they are bringing the school into disrepute and are identifiable as St Leonards pupils,' says head) and are generally expected to behave like grown-ups. No smoking on campus, no under-age drinking and absolute zero tolerance of drugs. Parents like the drugs policy – random drugs testing and testing on suspicion, out for pushing, forfeit right to remain in school for using – depends on individual and other factors and for how long, and pupils may be allowed back under fairly arduous conditions. Suspension for continued failure to observe the booze rules. Police are called for theft. No chaplain but team of local ministers who regularly preach. Plenty of fundraising for good causes.

Pupils and parents: No boarding in junior school, hence strong Scots contingent in senior school; small number of UK boarders but most from abroad, particularly at sixth form level, when incomers swell the ranks to follow the IB course – a boon. Those pupils whom we met (either IB or newbies) were a more sophisticated bunch – particularly the former – than we would normally expect in a school which is so geographically challenged...with sea on three sides.

Eclectic mix of international and first time buyers: Fifers see school as a viable option. Think butcher, baker, candlestick maker, farmer, landed estate owner and very senior CEOs. Think oligarchs, think wannabe Donald Trumps. No longer does this ed hear from mates that 'we put Amelia/Georgina/ Freddie into St Leonards, but really it didn't take'. Parents, both past, and present are now positive about the place.

Many do a gap year, armed with addresses of welcoming Seniors throughout the world

St Leonards has a strong old girls' network and many at the school are offspring or grand offspring of Seniors; Seniors must now be referred to as FPs. Some concern previously from Seniors about school's new direction though others welcomed its new impetus. Famous Seniors include Betty Harvey Anderson, Dame Kathleen Ollerenshaw (previous president of St Leonards), past head Mary James, Gillian Glover of the Scotsman (who didn't last the course), Stella Tennant (ditto), Baroness Byford and Anji Hunter.

Entrance: At any time. Mid-term ok. Accepts CE, but usually own (written) entrance assessment (English and maths) or scholarship exam. Seamless transition from juniors to seniors. Six GCSEs or equivalent for sixth with A/7s and B/6s in subjects to be studied at higher level in the IB. 'We usually pick up 15/20 at sixth from entry' for IB. School prefers to meet with international applicants but, if pushed, will Skype.

Exit: 'Minimum' drop out at transition from juniors to seniors and some (20 per cent or so) depart post-GCSE (only accept good English speakers to sixth form). Around 90 per cent to universities – mostly Scottish and northern English destinations eg Durham, Newcastle, Warwick; one medic in 2017, and 10 off overseas, including two to Maastricht to study law. Many do a gap year, armed with addresses of welcoming Seniors throughout the world (a boon for worried parents).

Money matters: A means-tested, assisted places scheme in operation from year 5; open to application from existing parents in financial difficulties: sibling discount. Raft of scholarships: though only of nominal monetary value, and usually only lasting a couple of years – ranging from academic through music, drama and sport – golf scholarships very popular (as you might imagine).

Remarks: The IB is a winner. Dr Carslaw has the world in his hands: St Leonards runs seamlessly from age 5 to 18. the IB niche gives it an academic edge with an international flavour. All he needs is more punters, though currently boarding is full, with waiting lists in some years.

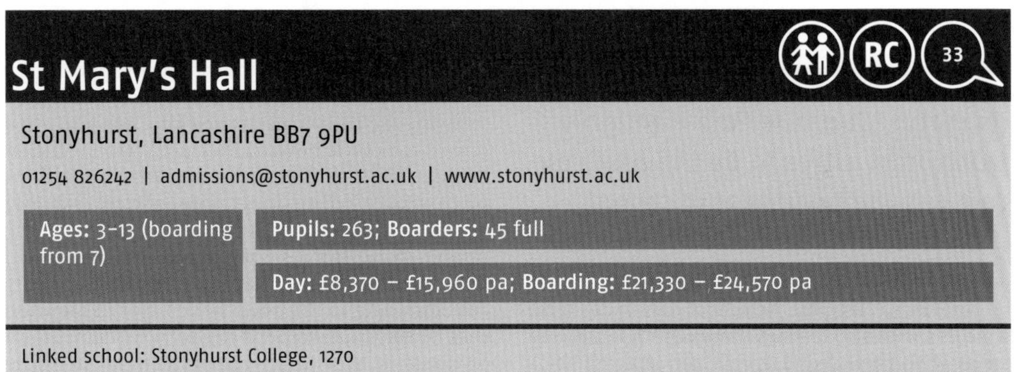

St Mary's Hall

RC 33

Stonyhurst, Lancashire BB7 9PU

01254 826242 | admissions@stonyhurst.ac.uk | www.stonyhurst.ac.uk

Ages: 3–13 (boarding from 7)

Pupils: 263; Boarders: 45 full

Day: £8,370 – £15,960 pa; Boarding: £21,330 – £24,570 pa

Linked school: Stonyhurst College, 1270

Headmaster: Since 2014, Ian Murphy (Durham BA, PGCE), previously Head at All Hallows, Somerset. Charismatic and open; his vision of education is about formation: helping to 'form' young people to be their best selves and excel. This view and his vocabulary are, in part, born of the spiritual values underpinning the school. Its motto, Quant Je Puis – roughly translated, strive to be the best you can – is the heartbeat of school daily life because unlike many a concocted mission statement, this is no hollow refrain: it rests upon an impressive 400 year heritage.

The heritage, however, is only part of the story, as Ian Murphy is a force for energising change in the here and now. Viewing academic excellence as a 'given' for SMH, he has focused on reinvigorating the arts and sport, allowing for greater inclusivity and honed excellence for the talented. He has also been busy instigating enhancements to the fabric of the school, moving the music department from stuffy attics to a swanky new ground floor wing with cutting edge technology. A new tennis dome was opened in 2017 by Tim Henman. And an idyllic garden created for younger children to grow vegetables, understand life cycles and handle animals. Very Mr McGregor and utterly charming.

On top of this, he has revitalised the curriculum, integrating the Stonyhurst crown jewels (its jaw-dropping private collection of 70,000 artefacts, including the First Folio of Shakespeare) into lessons as teaching tools to nurture intellectual spark. Parents say he has brought great energy, leads by example and has had a 'massive impact' academically.

Acutely aware that the school needs to be tuned into the modern world, head's innovatory zeal is a continuum; currently he is assessing the benefits of Saturday morning school (nicely aligning with parent feedback, saying the children get very tired). Innovation, he suggests, complements the school's spiritual values and refers to the Jesuits centuries ago being pragmatically alert to the need to evolve. The school's literature reinforces its Jesuit heritage a fair bit, making it clear worship is part of the school's make-up. So if you desire your child to have a Catholic upbringing this is marvellous, and those parents we spoke to certainly emphasised the immense personal importance of this to them. But what about other faiths?

The head is sensitised to Catholic schools sometimes struggling with their message in this area. So let's be clear right now in this review: make no mistake, this school is accessible to all, supportive of all and utterly inclusive. If you are not Catholic, as we are not then, yes, accepting worship as part of pupil life and unfamiliar lingo – references to Our Lady, to saints – is part of the experience. But do not, whatever you do, let lingo get in the way of embracing this school's wonderful ethos. The spiritual values the school holds are about forming wise, eloquent, generous young people. An uplifting aspiration which cuts across humanity, no matter which jack in a box of faith you spring from.

In fact, it is very telling that one of the elements which drew Ian Murphy to the school was the fact that its pupils used their own pocket money for charitable donations (as opposed to them being added to the parental bill). It's about forming people who think beyond themselves and become their best selves. Back to that motto again.

Its motto, Quant Je Puis – roughly translated, strive to be the best you can – is the heartbeat of school daily life

Inevitably, leading the school dominates term time (his wife also teaches there), but holidays are spent with their teenage children sharing their mutual love for sport and music. Personal reflection comes walking the dogs in the breathtaking Ribble Valley.

Entrance: Admission is via a meeting with the head and staff; pupils are invited for a day. Those transferring from another school provide school reports and reference. Students who speak little English are welcomed. Those entering in year 7 sit an 11+ exam.

Exit: Virtually the full cohort transfers to Stonyhurst for year 9. (A few overseas boarders may return home.) There is an exam at the end of year 8 but this is not related to the right to transfer (just preparation for the senior school world). Ian Murphy says it is not pressured, includes structured revision guidance; the results are important to the 'hand over' process.

Remarks: Although day pupils greatly dominate, this is a boarding school in outlook: most day pupils stay for prep until 7pm. All mix in Playrooms – year groups – though they are also members of Lines, which are akin to houses in that they encompass all age ranges and meet for sporting and special interest Interline competitions.

Ages 3-7 years attend Hodder House, a delightful building, packed with colour. The focus is on social development, literacy, numeracy, art, PE, swimming and French. There is outdoors teaching, exploring woodland and insects. Children have access to iPads. The whole school comes together for assemblies, easing the transition to the main building.

Within SMH, pupils' academic progress is rigorously measured by assessments, diagnostic tools to ensure all are on track and to identify those excelling and those who need extra help. A detailed picture of each child is built up, including pastoral well-being. Parents spoke of the school working on little weaknesses with the children, who didn't feel pressured, didn't notice 'tests'. Average class size is 15-18.

The national curriculum, enriched by the International Primary Curriculum, integrates cross-curricular themes, providing an opportunity to utilise the extraordinary Stonyhurst collection: studying the Tudors means touching Anne Boleyn's prayer book or Thomas More's hat. Wow. Evolution lessons, viewing dinosaur poo (oh yes). Artefacts in this astounding collection enliven learning as pupils are asked what it tells them about the human story. And it's not just the artefacts either; Lord of the Rings must have extra sparkle knowing Tolkien wrote in the guest rooms. Not to mention that Oliver Cromwell, the cheeky wee scamp, slept on a school table before the battle of Preston. The grounds are used for activities from fossil hunting to looking at natural landforms.

Every class has an interactive whiteboard. Older pupils have timetabled access to a desktop PC (a well-equipped IT suite). Internet safety is impressed from the start; portable laptops (there are 50) are used across the school to help pupils develop discerning research skills.

Currently 20 per cent of pupils receive learning support. School develops individual plans, ranging from one-to-one to group interventions to in-class support. Staff receive specialist training in areas like dyslexia. One parent whose child had been in a 'not very academic' box at his previous school said he blossomed academically after transferring to SMH. Another slightly dyslexic pupil had benefited enormously from teachers picking up she needed a worksheet next to her, rather than looking at a whiteboard; she is now 'flying academically'. High performers receive extension work.

Years 7 and 8, whilst still living and learning in SMH, are taught mainstream academic subjects by Stonyhurst teachers, some in college classrooms.

A newish director of music has expanded opportunities considerably: orchestras, choirs, big bands, the ukulele Odd Bod band. Some 75 per cent of pupils have music tuition and there are lots of concerts. While we visited, the Interline music

One teacher said informality in the dining room meant staff could pick up eating problems; it might seem relaxed but vigilance prevails

competition had unleashed pupil enthusiasm to the tune of 270 auditions.

There is a cracking theatre, an auditorium with sloping seating and state of the art lighting/ sound. Each year group performs a show: Grease, The Jungle Book, Bugsy Malone. Some older pupils prefer the technical side, acquiring new digital skills. Public speaking is encouraged; pupils had a Question Time style Brexit debate in 2016 (a trip to the Supreme Court in London the day before saw them meeting Dominic Grieve MP QC). Parents waxed lyrical about the confidence-imbuing aspects of all this. One talked about her previously shy daughter flourishing to become head girl.

The sports facilities are tremendous; new tennis dome, huge sports hall, netball courts, athletics field, cricket pitch, rugby fields, use of Stonyhurst's Astroturf pitch, heated pool and nine hole golf course. Other activities include fencing and horse riding. Parents enthused about increased sporting fixtures since Ian Murphy's arrival; one parent was astonished that her previously unsporty daughter was keen to join a netball summer school.

Frequent educational trips but the annual trip to the Somme stands out. Each pupil is given a photo of a SMH pupil who died in the Somme and asked to research their life. Parents say they 'adopt that person' and are immensely moved on finding their grave. Visits from charities, like the Society for the Blind, also widens the perspective beyond me me me. They are educated about poorer countries, farming in harsh environments – one pupil insisted her birthday money be donated to a charity.

Some super clubs, like Big Thinkers (philosophy, neurology) and astronomy club. Parents said children were encouraged in whatever area they showed interest.

Head feels all pupils benefit from the familial pastoral set-up in place for boarders. While in their playroom, a pupil can wander over to a teacher and mention a worry. One teacher said informality in the dining room meant staff could pick up eating problems; it might seem relaxed but vigilance prevails. Weekly staff pastoral meetings mean any worries are logged and monitored. Each child's pastoral log stays with them their entire time at SMH and Stonyhurst

Mobile phones are not allowed during the day. Boarders have phones for 45 minutes a night. Certain day pupils are permitted them to travel on school transport but they are signed in and out. Day pupils join boarders in mass each week in the theatre (the magnificent chapel can't host the whole school).

The 45 boarders are there seven days per week, sleeping in galleries of up to six. The boys' gallery seemed a little functional (though with breathtaking views of lush green hills), the girls' cosier with cushions and photos. One parent wished for more storage space. Lovely gender-specific sitting rooms; a joint playroom and kitchen. Staffing levels are 1:7. One of the houseparent couple, a former pupil, exudes enthusiasm and writes an effusive weekly newsletter (about pupils watching Man United play, a trip to Blackpool Tower, snooker games, watching a movie).

Parents spoke of excellent communication. One parent of a boarder praised staff who nursed her son after he broke his hand in a sports match and her daughter when she hit puberty: 'This level of support for teenage girls is vital'. Parents said the tiniest query is sorted the same day.

This ancient school, is set in magnificent grounds amidst beautiful scenery. The vibe within the school is a little two-tonal: corridors which have been Ian Murphy-ed are light, bright, covered in large photos of pupils in action which, he says, 'tell the story of the school'. They do, and it feels uplifting. Other corridors, lined with traditional annual school photos, seem an echo of the past; as one parent politely put it, 'shabby chic'.

Studying the Tudors means touching Anne Boleyn's prayer book or Thomas More's hat. Wow. Evolution lessons, viewing dinosaur poo (oh yes). Artefacts enliven learning

The playrooms for each year group however – the social and pastoral planks of the school – are full of inspiring pictures, quotes, games tables. They are terrific and age-appropriate, each room having its own distinct identity.

Parents are a blend of entrepreneurs, professionals and old money. No competitive inquiries, 'why isn't Jimmy reading Tolstoy now he's 8?' but empathy with the school's ethos and respect for its heritage. Certainly the parents we spoke to placed great emphasis on their children acquiring a broader view of the world, an awareness of the plight of others less fortunate. (Life beyond 'selfies'.)

In one of the playrooms, there is a fabulous poster of St Ignatius saying: 'Go forth and set the world on fire'. These children are being emboldened, their intellect and sensibilities refined, to do just that.

St Mary's Music School

Coates Hall, 25 Grosvenor Crescent, Edinburgh, Edinburgh EH12 5EL

0131 538 7766 | info@st-marys-music-school.co.uk | www.st-marys-music-school.co.uk

Ages: 9-19

Pupils: 80; sixth form: 12; Boarders: 34

Individually assessed

Head: Since 2013, Dr Kenneth Taylor BSc PhD PGCE PG Dip (50s); scholarship to Dulwich College, read chemistry at Edinburgh university and spent three years as a research chemist (we do like heads to have done something in the real world) and came to St Mary's from Biggar High where he was depute head, having skipped around the maintained sector in the borders.

A sportsman and musician (hill-running a passion – latest feat The Pentland Skyline Race: 16 miles, 6,200 foot climb), he played the piano and violin when younger and still sings (a bit) and plays the viola. Lives in Edinburgh with three young and regularly cycles to school (across Edinburgh). Delightful and outgoing, he enjoys encouraging the young in all manner of disciplines and has a deprecating sense of humour.

We previously dropped the school from the Guide because of a couple of cases of (historic) sexual abuse and Taylor mentions this to the whole school about once a term, systems now in place, but he advises any pupil who feels uneasy about any member of staff (or indeed anything) to talk to head of guidance, any (other perhaps) teacher or tell their parents. At The Good Schools Guide, we do not dwell on past problems unless they are still causing angst: St Mary's has moved on, and the somewhat shambolic 'luvvie' environment replaced by a rather more efficient regime. Taylor is unhappy about our mentioning this now historic abuse, but as there are screeds on the internet, we would look foolish if we ignored it.

Academic matters: Complicated. In the junior school, pupils from P5/7 often form a composite class: follow standard subjects with IT tabled throughout. Splendid triple class room with interactive telly: iPads being introduced. Delicious old-fashioned desks – alas without the Bakelite inkwells. Tiny classes (as you might expect with annual intake of only 10 per year); German and French from early: essential for singing. Latin mandatory S1/2 – and available at both Advanced Higher and SQA.

From P5-S6 school moves seamlessly through to Nat 5s to Highers and Advanced Highers. Highers are successfully crammed (well, smaller classes) into three and a half hours a week rather than the usual five to eight. Results impressive across the board. School really too small to supply individual subject results. Maths (strong), English, Higher music at S3/4 and Higher English S5. Now Cambridge Pre-U for music – harmony, counterpoint, composition.

Spent three years as a research chemist (we do like heads to have done something in the real world). A sportsman and musician (hill-running a passion)

Arrangements in place for pupils who need extra support; those with personal statements have one-to-one sessions, otherwise withdrawn from class and IEPs. Dyslexia and dysgraphia the main culprits.

The junior school is composed of choristers and instrumentalists, more of the former (both boys and girls – the latter introduced in 1976, though young instrumentalists since 1972). Choristers, both boys and girls, leave school at 14 (broken voices, sexual discrimination, that sort of thing – can't chuck out 14 year old boys unless girlies go at same age). Some may re-audition and return as instrumentalists.

Games, options, the arts: Small art room more or less adjacent to head's office stuffed with tables and art work on shelves. Both flat and 3D stuff on display.

Catch-all rather sad-looking all-weather surface area (school rather grandly calls it a sports court) serves its purpose. No gym (so mandatory one hour PE per week must be achieved by other means); boarders are members of Drumsheugh baths, a

Pupils regularly do their own thing, performing both a Schubert string quartet and 'a specially commissioned piece' plus jazz

stout half mile distant, and the local running club. Didn't see too many fatties on our wander round, so something seems to be working.

All pupils, both junior and senior, spend roughly 50 per cent of their time doing some form of music, be it practice or individual lessons: we came across a variety pack. 'Coaching sessions with an accompanist (gets them used to it),' says Taylor and we found one young piano-accompanied flautist sharing her lesson not only with a splendid Steinway but also with a somewhat overpowering organ.

Hideously complicated timetable, but sung evensong most evenings at 5.30pm in the cathedral and regular rehearsals either in Song School or cathedral itself (latter has 'soft' acoustics: 'ideal for singing but not practical for orchestral practice').

Music, of course is what the school is all about, with an emphasis on chamber music: regular concerts at venues all over Edinburgh. School itself has nowhere big enough for both orchestra and audience – former chapel too long and thin (Taylor says 'small'), dining room (beastly 60s excrescence) too low and cramped.

Any and every instrument played with peris pulled in for the more esoteric. 'No problems in getting staff', school handy for Haymarket (and Glasgow): tries to arrange a full day's teaching for visiting (musical) peris; odd orchestral player, 12 full-time staff.

Director of music takes instrumentalists to the odd concert (28 last year), and usually manages to get reduced rate – 'one or two quid sort of thing' – to boost ranks of punters – though full whack for some events (we originally wrote popular – as in the Latin – but Taylor preferred 'some'). Regular masterclasses: annual Nigel Murray masterclass – school sources suitable spaces for numbers: 130 violinist and their teachers last time; 60 cellists, that sort of thing; always oversubscribed. Occasional foray into performing at the Edinburgh International Festival (gives concerts three Sundays on the trot at St Mary's Cathedral). Pupils regularly do their own thing, performing both a Schubert string quartet and 'a specially commissioned piece' plus jazz in Dumfries and Galloway. Friday evening concerts and strong input on the charity front: this ed has been entertained by St Mary's young at a variety of fundraisers (and private homes).

Highly acclaimed and popular Saturday morning classes for up to a 150 youngsters aged 4-13; serious stuff and not just an airy fairy introduction to music. 'These classes are an enjoyable introduction to music,' says the head. Quite: those whom we know who take part say they are enormous fun: which is perhaps a better accolade than an 'enjoyable introduction'.

Boarding: Two floors of accommodation for boarders in Coates Hall; mainly twins with a few triple rooms, all en suite. Free time mostly spent practising.

Background and atmosphere: Tucked away in an enchanting corner off Grosvenor Crescent some 300 metres from the Cathedral. St Mary's was founded in 1880 as song (choir) school for The (Episcopal) Cathedral Church of St Mary the Virgin (funded by spinster heiress sisters Barbara and Mary Walker and built to a design by George Gilbert Scott in 1879). Based in Old Coates Hall and the Song School, the latter still used for daily practice (magical Phoebe Traquair murals) within the cathedral precinct until 1995, St Mary's (name changed 1971) bought Coates Hall, which had closed in 1994. Neophyte Anglican priests had rather fallen off the radar; the 18th century Old Coates Hall (part of the original bequest) is now the Edinburgh Theological Institute, providing accommodation, teaching and meeting rooms for both ordained and Anglican seminarians, albeit on a smaller scale.

Coates Hall, built in 'baronial style' by David Bryce in 1850, and bought by the Edinburgh Theological College in 1891, when Sydney Mitchell (better known for banks and psychiatric hospitals) added the splendid gothic chapel to the right of the main door – is too small for concerts. However, it boasts a fine-looking but non-functioning organ and an amazing turquoise decorated grand piano, which looks as though it is covered in potato cuts: paint job is apparently worth more than the piano itself. Bryce also designed the gatehouse. Extensive-ish grounds (for the middle of Edinburgh) filled with trees, badly parked cars (as ever in danger of small children with balls), and a couple of ugly modern teaching blocks. Plus the inevitable catch-all 'sports surface'.

Considering the expense of maintaining a highly complicated Victorian roof, the building is in remarkably good if complex heart, though we weep at the carving of rooms into offices. Head's study is in a former garage.

The main building is rabbit warreny in the extreme, with staircases going off in random directions – five steps here sort of thing – leading to a hotch-potch of bedrooms (seminarians had great views), now almost all en suite, twins and singles (school is let in hols to boost funds – which is why one of the practice rooms boasts a basin). Wiggly Ikea mirrors grouped in pairs throughout, and myriads of photographs – often with tinies overwhelmed by the size of their instrument.

Pastoral care, well-being and discipline: All choristers are day pupils. No reported disciplinary hiccups; pupils are more likely to be found discussing some obscure German 15th century composer than indulging in verbal point scoring. During our visit (break time) four really quite small people came out to the playground, one fell and was immediately surrounded (not sure about tears) by her own peer group and some elder children who were close by, who picked her up and escorted her back inside. Now that is what we like to see in a school.

School uniform for all, and worn with pride.

Pupils and parents: Pupils come from all over. No obvious social grouping, many pupils from musical families. Terrific parental support. Youngsters from abroad need local guardians.

Entrance: Audition in either discipline, at any stage, half way through term if space available: though most join at the start of the academic year. 'Looking for musical ability and potential'. School 'mushrooms' towards the top.

Exit: All choristers age 14 (though may come back as instrumentalists); rest usually after Advanced Highers to some form of tertiary education. Possibly

It boasts a fine-looking but non-functioning organ and an amazing turquoise decorated grand piano, which looks as though it is covered in potato cuts

95 per cent may go to a conservatoire or into music college, but this is by no means written in stone and one of the most promising recent musicians is currently studying engineering. Regular careers talks from FPs who emphasise how difficult it is to make a proper living out of playing in an orchestra and how few openings there are for soloists.

Money matters: Oodles of bursaries. Taylor told us to check online for fee info: two hours later we were still in the dark. Would appear to be in line with current fees elsewhere. Cathedral covers 50 per cent of all choristers (who get a couple of quid or so for weekly performances and rather more for weddings and funerals), Scottish government contributes a chunk (aided places) and music school doles out bursaries – rigorously – with financial background of applicants tooth-combed. Fair to say that no musical prodigy from any background would be left wanting.

Remarks: Exciting times. Watch this space.

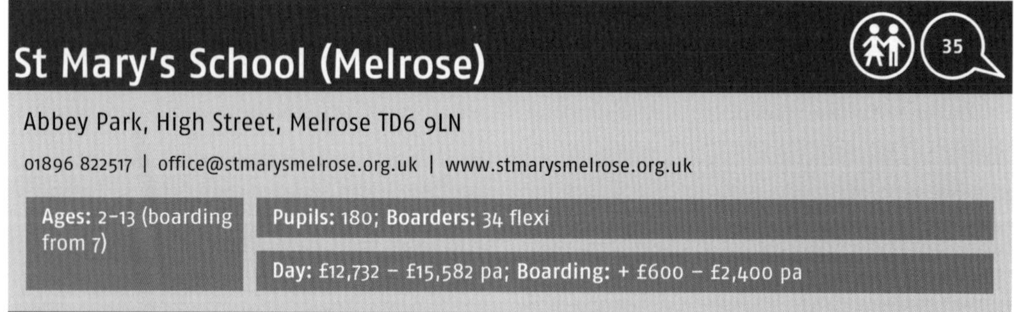

St Mary's School (Melrose)
35
Abbey Park, High Street, Melrose TD6 9LN
01896 822517 | office@stmarysmelrose.org.uk | www.stmarysmelrose.org.uk
Ages: 2-13 (boarding from 7)
Pupils: 180; Boarders: 34 flexi
Day: £12,732 – £15,582 pa; Boarding: + £600 – £2,400 pa

Headmaster: Since 2010, William (Liam) Harvey BEd (40s). The son of a local doc, and an FP, he went on to George Watson's followed by a BEd in PE at Liverpool John Moores University. Taught PE to A level in the state secondary sector before moving to Belhaven as housemaster and head of history and PE.

We met Harvey's Canadian wife, Marnia, efficiently organising the mysteries of the gap student's computer. Their daughters are in the school.

Entrance: All things to all men. The only independent school in the borders; children come from within a 50 mile radius, can come mid-term at any time if space available, otherwise automatically up from kindergarten. The odd state child has been known simply to come for an '18-month blast' before going back into the maintained sector, but this is rarer and rarer and none this year. Some come at 11 to do CE.

Exit: 'Most but not all' stay on until they go to their senior school at 11, 12, or 13 (the occasional toff pops off to Belhaven, Aysgarth, but none so far under the new regime), preferred secondary schools used to be Glenalmond, Fettes, Merchiston, Loretto, St George's in Edinburgh or Longridge Towers in Berwick, Queen Margaret's York and whilst these did indeed feature in our random poll, increasingly numbers are more likely to be turning south, Sedburgh gaining in popularity, Ampleforth and even Harrow. Winchester, Eton next?

Remarks: Wow. Didn't recognise the place. Totally transformed since our last visit and some of the most exciting (and cleverly sited to act as a windbreak) skool buildings we have ever seen. The Hamilton building opened in 2010 was funded by a gift from 'an anonymous benefactor'. Guestimate cost? A million near as dammit. Named after John Hamilton who founded the school in 1895 (good, if somewhat belated, way to celebrate a centenary).

Two non-parallel buildings with terrific reception area, full of photographs – though a tad Nuffield in aspect (think neutral carpets and comfy seating). Only thing missing is the coffee machine, although we were topped up with copious amounts – the head had his own insulated mug. Reception area littered with prospectuses of senior schools – not, as previously, concentrating on the Scottish mafia, but Shrewsbury, Uppingham, Cheltenham and Harrow. Quite a change, though those whom we asked mainly seemed to be heading North. Wide corridors – one outside the art dept was recently turned into a drawing 'road' where parents and pupils depicted the best aspects of their childhood (and jolly good some of them were too – we particularly liked the footballer). Photographs everywhere in main building, the art building – with yet more light, airy, and huge classrooms has walls filled with pupil offerings and classrooms for younger pupils.

Robert the chef comes complete with starched chef's hat and sparkling white uniform. Cor. He also makes scrumptious millionaire's shortbread

We previously described St Mary's as a 'Jolly useful little school, incredibly flexible, with flexi, weekly and day pupils; one or two toffs, but mostly farmers and local professionals who stay to the bitter end, plus 'masses of' first time buyers.' But gosh. Still tiny classes, max 18 but usually much less, only one stream, scholars will be 'hived off' and set at 10 if necessary and 'provided with evening tutorials with subject teachers'. Latin from 8, languages from 5, taster term of French, then specialists in French for common entrance. Fantastic and envy-making French trips when the entire form decamp to a monastery for a week. Science taught separately for the last four years, and pupils move round the staff (from age 9 – a transition class).

'Strong' dyslexia department, all singing and dancing and recently reorganised, oversees regular testing, and support for the very bright. Withdrawn help and support staff (masses of 'em, chaps as well as chapesses) go into class too – 'pretty flexible' (might be the school motto). Keen on handwriting. Interactive whiteboards abound, all classrooms are computered to the hilt, state of the art. Loads of staff changes since head's arrival (but see below), certain number of redundancies, and terrific young buzzy staff abound (think policemen). School now boasts 'a strong academic team'.

Drama strong and timetabled, the school has links with local borders youth theatre. Good music, rehearsals and lessons in functional school hall, whilst pre-prep has own gym, with Noah and his ark drawn by the young. The somewhat surprising cloistered classroom corridor (the 'veranda classrooms') have been relegated to music, a theatre store room, boarders' activity room, music and a thrift shop.

Day children can stay from 7.30am (and breakfast in school) right through to 7.30pm, by which time they will have done their prep and had supper, kindergarten can stay till 4pm. Tinies wear delightful green and white check tabliers and girls evolve from gym slips to proper kilts; we checked, most were eight pleats thick. Dining room with weekly menu, over-high benches for littlies to sit at table. Brown bread only and lots of sugar-free puds, mainly organic as far as possible. Robert the chef comes complete with starched chef's hat and sparkling white uniform. Cor. He also makes scrumptious millionaire's shortbread for the head's guests – not sugar-free at all, and has lost a mega amount of weight since we last saw him... now deeply into marathons. One is always told to beware the skinny chef, but he is still triumphant, and gives the boarders special cooking lessons (it was Burns night/lunch during our visit, and the haggis was piped in with aplomb). Pheasant (plucking lessons and all) on the menu next.

The Harveys live in the main school house, with dorms above, separate corridors for boys and for girls – room for up to 30 flexi boarders. The girls live in somewhat cramped conditions in a conversion of what used to be the main drawing room – fantastic ceiling, but divided into three – with what must be one of the grandest ceiling-ed bathrooms ever. Jolly dorms upstairs, all brightly painted with splendid stripy duvet covers. Very homey; bunks, the odd poster, random teddy bears – and currently being upgraded. B&B charged per night.

Squads and teams triumph all over the place. Swimming off-site in Gala(shiels) and main games pitches just across some National Trust land. Smashing little school.

St Olave's School

Queen Anne's Road, York, North Yorkshire YO30 7WA

01904 527416 | enquiries@stolavesyork.org.uk | www.stolavesyork.org.uk

Ages: 8–13 (boarding from 11)

Pupils: 351; **Boarders:** 13 full, 9 weekly/flexi

Day: £11,985 – £14,520 pa; **Boarding:** £22,485 – £24,810 pa

Linked school: St Peter's School, York, 1258

Master: Since 2005, Mr Andy Falconer MBA BA (40s). An ISI inspector, recent chair of IAPS as well as a Walter Hines Page Scholar. Previously deputy head at Chafyn Grove School and before that was head of geography at Craigclowan School. Married to Lesley, a nurse, with three young daughters. Enjoys skiing, grew up near a Scottish ski resort and is a qualified instructor, former travel writer and currently into marathon running, otherwise free time is family time. Kind, charming, with a soft Scottish lilt and a delightful manner. Chats very comfortably with pupils, knows who they are and equally they know him – pupils tuck their shirts in when they see him coming. He misses nothing, touring school with a watchful eye, even turning off lights in empty rooms – 'a Scotsman in Yorkshire,' he grins. Hugely knowledgeable about and committed to the education of children, up to speed on all the latest developments, cherrypicking the best and applying them with skill and understanding to enhance the learning experience. Parents and children trust him implicitly, never doubting that he has the children's best interests at heart. A rock solid practitioner.

Entrance: Automatic from Clifton Pre-Prep (takes ages 3-8), otherwise selective but not massively so, looking for cognitive ability scores of 100+. All

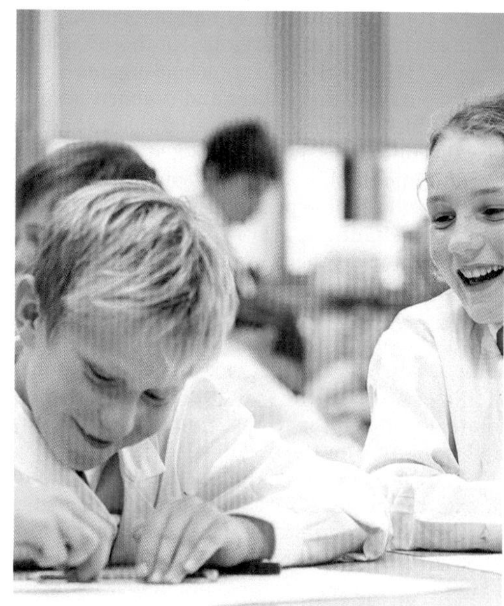

entrants are tested in maths, English, reading, spelling, and reasoning. Entrance examinations end of January.

Exit: Almost all to St Peter's School, York. A few to Queen Margaret's, Bootham, Queen Ethelburga's and local state schools.

Remarks: Sited in the former Queen Anne's grammar school buildings – a number of mums are old girls. The buildings have been adapted, extended and improved to create a more welcoming space for children and their parents. It's a very grounded school, not stuffy in any sense. Footbridge to senior school makes it easy to get from one campus to the other, 'distinct and separate, yet linked' (is the official line, and it seems to work).

Good facilities, shares Astroturf and indoor pool with senior school, but has own sports hall with indoor nets; music block; science lab; language rooms; DT; cookery, not as a discrete subject but linked eg to maths, DT, languages (recipes in French); art and ceramic studios; dining hall, Shepherd Hall for assemblies and regular productions, medical room and veg garden.

Parents delight in the school's 'responsiveness', answering questions, dealing with any concerns and, importantly, 'never underestimating children'. Stretch and challenge include sparky discussions on current events in assembly that then continue over supper at home and the ability of staff to 'see qualities in children that others might overlook'. PTA members are busy with social and fundraising events twice a term varying from murder mystery nights to wine-tasting and a denim and diamante evening.

Invariably over-subscribed at 11+, year on year; some leakage of girls at year 6 to girls' schools, but only a handful and they are 'easily replaced,' we are told. Roughly equal numbers of boys/girls.

Doing something right as the library bucks the trend by being packed with boys at breaktime (clever librarian – great choice of 'boy' books)

Almost 40 per cent of boarders are from overseas, third armed forces, the rest from across the UK or even local – one boarder (currently six boys and seven girls are full boarders) lives close enough to kick a rugby ball into his own garden. Saturday morning school for everyone 'allows a broader curriculum and more time spent with your mates', says school; 'great fun but requires stamina,' say parents. Parents of day pupils (that's most of them) pass the time having coffee or shopping, almost 50 take to school rowing boats on the river, it's all part of the service. Day pupils travel from as far afield as Scarborough, Harrogate, Selby and Wetherby – short cut to the railway station makes it possible. The train is a good idea because parking is tricky – has to be a quick drop off in the mornings though the playground is opened up so that you can 'park and pick up' after school.

No common entrance or national curriculum testing here yet plenty of rigour. For those heading for public schools beyond York school organises own testing/entrance procedures and supports accordingly. Healthy outlook on education, 'you've got to play the long game,' says the head; 'it's more about learning and thinking and less about testing', quoting that old Chinese proverb about 'not fattening a pig by weighing it'. Doing something right as the library bucks the trend by being packed with boys at breaktime (clever librarian – great choice of 'boy' books) and academic standards, across the board, are high. Average class size 18 with maximum usually 20. Chapel twice a week, traditional C of E service. No issue with bright dyslexics, have strategies to help, specialist tutors, extra lessons and extra time for those who need them.

Staff are encouraged to 'share the learning journey' – the head is learning to play the drums (and gives the children regular updates on his progress in assembly); others offer four week courses to their colleagues (teaching and non-teaching) in a range of subjects, skills and challenges. Years 6 to 8 have all their lessons with subject specialists, younger children gradually work towards this. There is setting throughout for maths and for French and Latin in the top two years. Carousel for French/Spanish/German/Latin in years 4 and 5, pupils choose post year 7.

Music is high profile, a school concert sees two-thirds of pupils taking part. Years 4 and 5 have three class lessons of music each week; add to that the usual choirs, brass groups, sax and clarinet groups, recorder, woodwind and cello groups – plus the school rock band Stereo Flair. Some phenomenal art on display; 'talent is recognised and nurtured,' say parents.

Sport is impressive here, plenty of teams and older pupils competing at national level. Bigger schools such as RGS Newcastle and QEGS Wakefield provide serious challenge; smaller preps may struggle to compete with the first team here. Sporting successes include four times winners of the National Rugby Sevens Tournament; winners of national JET Cup cricket; national finals for hockey, soccer and cricket. Outdoor pursuits, yacht sailing with Ocean Youth Trust and rowing (school has rowing machines as well as river access and own rowing club) plus an Easter ski trip and sports tours (years 5 and 8) keep pupils busy and active all year round.

Lots of extracurricular choice including enterprising young apprentice-type challenges and history model-making club, which essentially means making weapons from wood. Pupils also enjoy charity days and fundraising, pink day for breast cancer, organised by pupils, and green day in support of NSPCC, among recent events. Wide range of after-school clubs and activities, including prep clubs for day children of working parents.

Pupils eat and register in their mixed age houses, helping everyone to 'know the school vertically and horizontally'. Strong house identity (that children describe as 'Harry Potter-esque'), linked to pastoral care. A teacher/mentor follows through with groups of children year on year, a type of wraparound care valued hugely by parent body. Homemade lunches prepared by chef, the legendary Dave.

Smart (ish) navy uniform, different from and more appealing than the brown of the senior school; sports kit is linked across the schools.

St Peter's School, York

C of E | 37

Clifton, York, North Yorkshire YO30 6AB

01904 527300 | g.daniells@stpetersyork.org.uk | www.stpetersyork.org.uk

Ages: 13–18

Pupils: 573; sixth form: 255; **Boarders:** 130

Day: £17,550 pa; **Boarding:** £29,160 – £30,600 pa

Linked school: St Olave's School, 1256

Head Master: Since 2010, Leo Winkley MA MEd (40s), previously managing head at Bedales. Read theology at Lady Margaret Hall, Oxford. Taught at Ardingly College and The Cheltenham Ladies' College as head of religious studies. Still teaches religious studies and contributes to the global perspectives programme for sixth form: he enjoys teaching – 'it keeps you honest'. A keen runner and

follower of sport. Married to medical oncologist Jules; they have three young children. Committed to the breadth and all-round nature of independent education as lessons for life – says 'school should be serious fun', currently encouraging all parties to 'think big'. Pupils tell us he has 'smartened things up a bit and increased pupil involvement', parents say he is a 'fine chap' and has 'got the bit between his teeth'. You get a very warm welcome from this clear-sighted, ambitious strategist; he was born into the world of independent education, son of a headmaster, so knows the perils, pitfalls and joys.

Leaving in July 2018 to head Shrewsbury School.

Academic matters: Consistent achiever, sets the bar high in a robust local market. Strong work ethos with plenty of stretch and challenge, normal to try hard but fine-tuning from the top is pushing to 'broaden the pupil experience' ie accumulation of exam certificates is great but balance is also important.

Takes the academic rigour for granted; bright pupils will always do well, but hard workers also do well here, hence the very positive value-added. Believes good results are down to having really good teachers as well as selective but not highly selective intake; no weak subject areas; staff know what is expected and are multi-talented and self-driven. 'Learn Something New' is a St Peter's initiative that persuades staff to share interests and learn from each other with a range of activities across the school(s) encouraging staff to try out and learn new skills – 'learning teachers teach better' is the head's strapline.

Class size averages 18 in the middle school (maximum 24) and 12 in the sixth form. The occasional D or E grade creeps in at GCSE, but 71 per cent of passes A*-A/9-7 in 2017. IGCSEs being taken in maths, science and languages. At A level, 42 per cent of grades were A*/A and a commendable 77 per cent of all entries graded A*-B in 2017.

The school has responded swiftly by bringing in a second careers advisor and opening up careers events and visits plus 'exploration week' for the lower sixth

Some support for the handful with mild dyslexia – must be bright and able to cope. Part-time dyslexia specialist. Approximately 10 per cent have an ed psych report; five per cent qualify for extra time in exams. Third modern language replaced by extra English and study skills for some. Gifted and talented programme in place but doesn't target top 10 per cent. 'All the children here are bright; it would be wrong to concentrate on a handful.' Olympiads and similar challenges stretch those with real talent. Global Perspectives an additional course for sixth form with Horizons introduced for middle school. Does not allow students to take any GCSE early and moving towards more challenging IGCSEs.

Careers advice and support flagged up by parents as something to be worked on and improved, especially important for boarders whose parents are not around to have those all-important conversations. They are getting pupils into good and great universities, but what next? Both pupils and parents feel they would like more guidance and direction as life beyond university becomes tougher and more competitive. The school has responded swiftly by bringing in a second careers advisor and opening up careers events, visits, conferences plus 'exploration week' for the lower sixth – 'life after St Peter's' is a drum they will keep on banging.

Games, options, the arts: A surprising amount of outdoor space; you'd never guess it is so close to the city. Nearest to the school is the hallowed ground of the first XV rugby pitch, but there are plenty of others beyond. Sport is compulsory for all. Facilities include two sports centres, one with super climbing wall, multi-surface pitch, fitness centre, indoor swimming pool, extensive well-kept playing fields, boathouse and tennis and squash courts. Rugby popular and strong, rowing crews regularly pick up national honours and awards, boast 20 international rowers in the last eight years. Hockey, rowing and netball are the most popular girls' sports but tennis, athletics, squash, swimming and usual suspects on offer for all. Generally put best coaches with best teams but playing opportunities for all via B teams and house competitions. Competitiveness and fair play are a prominent feature of the school and success is universally applauded at weekly assembly. D of E and CCF flourishing. Plenty of trips including expeditions to Morocco, sports tours to New Zealand and South Africa, language holidays and music tours to the USA, Prague, Italy as well as singing in York Minster.

Very good art facilities, including super gallery. Art department appears in the Guinness Book of Records for a remarkable 100 per cent A*/A grade pass rate achieved four years running, though recent years have seen lower grades creep in – 'we were pleased, it took the pressure off, allowed the pupils to experiment, be more creative rather than formulaic,' said one art master. Many learn a musical instrument or two, 300 individual lessons each week with professional specialist music staff, 160 strong choir and plenty of opportunities to perform; director of music described as 'inspirational'. Each boarding house has a practice room with piano. Over 100 pupils involved with Community Action projects and all participate in charity fundraising.

Boarding: Around a quarter of pupils board, of whom 30 per cent are from overseas. Most are full boarders but a few stay on a flexi/weekly basis. Six day and four boarding houses, the latter well equipped with a selection of common rooms, games rooms and a kitchen for snacks (all eat in school dining hall). Pupils and staff strike a good balance between amity and mutual respect. Houses are headed by husband and wife teams and supported by resident and non-resident assistants. Good pastoral care, 'just wonderful,' say parents. They describe house parents as 'something out of the ordinary', creating boarding houses that are 'home from home' with all the care and support that may be needed and equally 'a kick up the jacksy as required'. Staff vigilant – invariably have one or two they're watching for eating problems etc.

Background and atmosphere: The school was founded in 627 AD by Paulinus, first Archbishop of York, and is one of the world's oldest schools, 'only two older', we are told. In 1844 it was established on its present, impressive, green, grade 2 listed site in Clifton, with 47 acres, river access and all within walking distance of York Minster, the city centre and station.

Beyond the imposing main building, others are a mix of ancient and modern. Some classrooms and corridors are a bit tatty round the edges; we get the sense that it's not a priority – it's a workhorse, not a show pony. Good range of facilities, with all angles covered, though pupils tell us they are pestering the head for a new sports hall; 'it could be so much better'. It's one of the head boy's pet projects, though not on the agenda (yet) – might have to settle for a new boathouse instead. Pupils rave about the new swimming pool, opened by Olympic diver Tom Daley. Other recent additions include four bright biology labs, a sixth form microbiology lab, chemistry lab and design and technology room with Cad Cam technology; new maths and languages building under construction. Three computer rooms are complemented by clusters of computers throughout the school and houses – virtual learning environment with Wifi throughout the campus.

Pastoral care, well-being and discipline: Advice, help and support may be sought from tutors, house staff, resident health centre staff or the school chaplain. Pupils tell us that the unforgivables are drugs and bullying; if caught smoking it's three strikes and you're out.

Pupils are allowed to visit town twice a week (more in older years) and for younger ones a timetable of supervised events is on offer. All eat in the modern dining hall. Menus offer a wide choice with mixture of typical school meal fare, continental options, salad bar, sandwiches, fruit and healthy eating options. Pupils say food is 'great', with 'boy-sized portions'; Sunday brunch is legendary.

If it were a car, we'd probably describe it as a Volvo, albeit a top of the range high performance 4WD version with sporty extras such as a ski rack and tow bar

Pupil voice has grown and developed through a pupil symposium. Head's question time is chaired by the head boy or girl – 'direct government-type stuff' – raising all kinds of ideas and questions from the downright silly to the well-considered and serious.

Middle school uniform uninspiring, disliked, yet (bizarrely) defended, by pupils – when push comes to shove there's nothing more conservative or radically opposed to change than your average 15 year old: brown blazer, grey trousers for boys, and brown checked skirt for girls. Apparently the current line is 'brown is good'. Sixth form (boys and girls) wear dark business suits.

Strong Christian ethos; pupils meet thrice weekly for collective act of worship in school chapel – the chaplain has 'livened things up a bit,' pupils tell us with a grin; assemblies at other times.

Pupils and parents: Day pupils mainly from North Yorkshire, Harrogate, Leeds conurbation, York, and surrounding villages. Majority of boarders live within an hour's drive but others from wide area in the UK. Parents in business and the professions, a popular choice for Forces families, minority from overseas – 'it's a world view we need to develop,' says the head. Mix of Hong Kong, China, Russia, one or two others – about 25 per cent overall.

'Parents,' say school, 'are interested – but not helicopters', ambitious and driven; quite a few first time buyers here but also dynasties with names all over the honours boards.

Old Peterites include Guy Fawkes, Alcuin (eighth century scholar), Greg Wise, John Barry, Laurence Eusden (poet laureate), Harry Gration (journalist, TV presenter), C Northcote Parkinson (inventor of Parkinson's Law) and Clare Wise (previous director of the British Film Commission).

Entrance: Automatic entry from Clifton Pre-prep to St Olave's (St Peter's junior school) and then from St Olave's to St Peter's. Seventy per cent follow this route, rest by CE and school's own entrance test at any age including 13 or 16 (minimum six GCSE grade B/6 passes). Assessment and filtering does take place in prep and pre-prep to weed out those who won't cope with the demands of St Peter's, but it is rare. Generally entry to St Olave's requires a child to have a reading age at least a year ahead of chronological age (sympathetic to siblings). Will take pupils who pass exam at any time provided a place is available. Other main feeder schools: Terrington Hall, Cundall Manor and Aysgarth, some state schools also.

Exit: Around 10 per cent leave at the end of year 11. Of those leaving after A levels, 95 per cent go directly to university, vast majority selecting Russell Group. Four to Oxbridge in 2017 (though UCL and Imperial often favoured by high fliers); others to Hong Kong, Utrecht and Melbourne. Edinburgh, Newcastle, Birmingham and Sheffield also popular; some 15 per cent applying next year; a few to employment. Eighteen off to study medicine in 2017.

Money matters: Not a rich school but has increased bursary funding considerably over the past few years. Means-tested bursaries available at 11, 13 and at sixth form regardless of previous school. Qualification criteria for bursaries on a sliding scale from 10 to 100 per cent based on need, and typically if household income is less than £45,000. Honorary (ie no dosh) subject scholarships are awarded; music awards, including fee remission, available for tuition and instruments.

Remarks: Very much the big brother of the 3-18 triumvirate of St Peter's schools, encompassing Clifton Pre-Prep and St Olave's junior school ('continuity, but difference' is the mantra here) and you get the impression that this is where it all becomes rather serious. If it were a car, we'd probably describe it as a Volvo, albeit a top of the range high performance 4WD version with sporty extras such as a ski rack and maybe a tow bar. It can accommodate the whole family and you can't doubt the quality, reliability and solidity of the product it delivers, pretty much unfailingly, in all areas.

Sedbergh School

38

Malim Lodge, Sedbergh, Cumbria LA10 5HG

01539 620535 | enquiries@sedberghschool.org | www.sedberghschool.org

Ages: 13–18

Pupils: 540; sixth form: 236; **Boarders:** 523

Day: £24,030 pa; **Boarding:** £32,625 pa

Linked school: Casterton, Sedbergh Preparatory School, 1163

Head master: Since 2010, Andrew Fleck (geology at Nottingham; MA at Sussex), a period which he describes as the happiest years of his career.

The uniqueness of Sedbergh, he suggests, lies in its location (cocooned within the rolling hills of the Cumbrian countryside) and the fact it is a close and supportive full boarding community (in other words, a vast distance away from youth-distracting razzamatazz and the potentially toxic influences of flashy urban street corners). So while extracurricular activities are of great importance within any school, they are of colossal importance here. The rural setting effectively means pupils must draw on inner resources and 'go find' interesting things to do in rain or shine (not difficult, frankly, out of the mind-boggling array of sport, performance activities and societies on offer). So as a parent you won't get your child fiddling about with Snapchat in the local Costa. There is no local Costa. What you get instead is something altogether more interesting and nurturing of individualism – which is very Andrew Fleck.

At school in Marlborough, he discovered his entrepreneurial side when a housemaster gave him the space to do his own thing (building kayaks in the laundry block and getting a little business going). He says being given that opportunity, that sense of empowerment and freedom, transformed his life, and ever since he has felt a responsibility to pass on such opportunities to pupils, whether they want to be a scientist in Cambridge or become a top equestrian.

Keen to open the vistas of the world for pupils, he is currently working with global companies and universities to put together a plan for a Centre for Advanced Technology and Science (which will also support other schools in Cumbria). A visionary, he can see the professions are changing with the encroachment of automation and that employers' needs will be very different in a decade when technical skills are likely to be highly prized. If the plan comes to fruition, it will teach crucial skills like laser cutting, 3D design, complex composites. In short, a unique blend of commercial academia.

He is, however, equally tuned into traditional academic challenge for pupils; the 9 star programme for top scholars (around 10 per cent of each year group) is aimed at helping pupils discover new ways of thinking. Head says it also acts as a seed of inspiration for the rest of the year group. He is aware that the fundamental shift in the higher academic end is about moving children from concrete to abstract thought. It therefore tackles a number of innovatory areas, like game theory – a sub-field of economics and maths, all about strategic decision making. Pupils may later be invited onto the Oxbridge development programme.

His, frankly fascinating, comment pieces in the school magazine grapple with the challenges of the modern working world. In one column he talks about creating an environment where pupils are willing to take intellectual risks (acutely aware that it is only through challenge that children can claim they have achieved their very best). In another column, he addresses the fact that children are having to contemplate the shifting sands of reality in a world where the term post-truth prevails.

He is, though, also thoroughly grounded in the here and now of the school; as one parent said, he is always on the touchline, cheering away. Personable and easy to approach.

The rural setting effectively means pupils must draw on inner resources and 'go find' interesting things to do in rain or shine (not difficult, frankly)

No surprise that the school has recently garnered an award from the Boarding Schools Association for its deployment of social media. As the Twitter revolution started, Andrew Fleck immediately saw its benefits and created a role within the school to manage social media. Parents adore it (one parent said she 'lived on it'): it plugs them into the mainframe of their child's life in a more immediate way. It's a small but telling example that the head, ever-alert to innovation, is most definitely not a man to let educational grass grow under his Sedberghian feet.

Academic matters: Andrew Fleck cites geology as a strength (the geology classroom, crammed with a huge collection of rocks, with desks sloping upwards like a university lecture room, is

The school responds to its broad intake by setting pupils from year 9 by ability. A tutor monitors progress, liaising with subject teachers. Added value is measured for every level of ability (though those stats weren't available to us). There is a broad curriculum; year 9 takes up French, and German or Spanish is on offer (though very few take languages at A level). More offbeat options are available at GCSE, like jewellery design. There are alternative options in sixth form beyond A level – a BTec in agriculture in conjunction with Newton Rigg College in Penrith.

A 2017 inspection report states 'assured and inspiring teachers with high expectations and expertise in their subject successfully encourage most pupils....to achieve their potential and fulfil their ambitions'. Where pupils would benefit from extra lessons, they are arranged. Everything is on tap, this being a full boarding community.

ICT is deployed to support learning, such as organising notes or recording class discussions. There is also what are described as 'pioneering academic opportunities', like the 100 hour revision challenge for years 11, 12 and 13 over the Easter holidays (as in, 21 days hol, five hours a day etc).

Some 120 pupils have learning difficulties; most of the extra support is around dyslexia or dyspraxia and is often one-to-one. Learning support works across both ends of the spectrum, though, including the 9 star programme. One parent, whose son was on the programme, felt he was flying academically. Another parent felt the academic side of things was generally 'on the rise' due to Andrew Fleck's lead.

Results are good overall (bearing in mind the very broad spread of intake) and on the up for the last few years. Particular strengths are English, English literature, maths, biology, chemistry, physics and geography. In 2017, 42 per cent of GCSEs were A*-A/7-9.

At A level in 2017, 38 per cent A*/A and 63 per cent A*-B grades, plus 22 out of the 85 taking BTec in agriculture got A*.

Games, options, the arts: Sedbergh has a national reputation for sports prowess but while the school is staggeringly good within this arena, this is only part of the story. (The old perception that this is a school for rugby players is past its sell by date.) Sedbergh today offers something wonderful for everyone. Frankly, it was a joy hearing the rugby-playing sixth former, who had set his sights on Cambridge, wax lyrical about the music department and refer with awe and respect to a recent school production of A Christmas Carol as 'very professional – dead arty and stuff'.

So, back to sport: each house fields teams for the inter-house competitions and the school itself continues to have a reputation for excellence. Pupils clearly love the Saturday sports matches where the whole school turns out to support. There is a vast array of activities on offer: lacrosse, athletics, horse riding (Sedbergh has an equestrian team), but also orienteering, fishing, kayaking, mountain biking, fell running, badminton, sailing, shooting, squash, tennis. The facilities match all this but are about to get a whole lot better as a new sports centre is being built for summer 2018. Expert sports coaching is also available, often with video analysis. The relationship between sport and good mental and physical health has long been established and here the regularity of sport seems to be a fundamental part of Sedberghian life. Staff are very aware of its benefits and note the increase in requests for early morning coaching around exam times. Parents also enthused about the freedom Sedbergh offers; that while care and safety were paramount, children get to experience activities like river bathing, mud sliding and wild camping (usually off menu in a lot of red tape schools). The expression 'it toughens them up' was used a lot by parents. (Here, a note of caution; the school's 'joining in' ethos might mean those more apprehensive by nature, or naturally introverted, may not be so well suited.)

Pupils effervesced about the school's 125 year old Wilson run (a 10 mile cross-country fell race, described by the Guardian newspaper as 'hell in the fens')

The pupils we spoke to effervesced about the school's 125 year old Wilson run (a 10 mile cross country fell race for 16+ pupils, described by the Guardian newspaper as 'hell in the fens'), about the camaraderie it engendered, the 'supporting each other through' it, the rapturous applause at the finishing line. It's all very reminiscent of the Brownlee brothers' spirit, because this is a run which requires grit and a can-do attitude which pretty much sums up what Sedbergh is all about. Its caring ethos and multiplicity of extracurricular activities nurture resilience and teamwork (qualities which most of the working world is crying out for right now).

Performing is dominant too, with high numbers taking LAMDA. School plays attract great interest; a recent production of Les Misérables had a cast of 78. While acting is good for confidence, head rightly values 'theatre' for its mind-expanding qualities and spoke of his relish in listening to pupils debate the concept of redemption in Les Mis. Likewise in Cabaret, the moral dilemmas, the lack of courage, were chewed over.

Pupils spoke to us casually about regular debating competitions, about having to prepare a topic quickly and thinking on their feet. They didn't seem fazed.

Musical opportunities run the spectrum: choral, orchestra, swing band (a big jazz and swing night had the pupils entertaining 150 guests). Everyone participates at some level; there is a house singing competition, for example. Professional musicians give concerts but there are also scholars' concerts and small informal musical soirées. The choristers get to sing in vast spaces like Durham Cathedral and recently went on tour around Italy. One pupil made it into the national youth choir. It's all on tap, again; you can pitch up at the music school before or after lessons and have a practice.

Unless they have the head's permission, all join the school contingent of the CCF. Teamwork and leadership are the primary motivators for this and exposure to new experiences – scuba diving, gliding, piloting. That said, the pupils we spoke to had done voluntary work instead of the CCF – helping in local schools – and seemed to have got a great deal of satisfaction out of it.

In addition, pupils are prepared for the finer things in life: events to practice etiquette, confidence-builders for social settings (balls). This is all reinforced by the fact that staff and pupils have three civilised meals a day together in each house.

Loads of trips, some to incredibly exotic climes, like an ecology trip to Madagascar.

Some fantastic clubs for those with big academic appetites (there is also an inter-house academic challenge): Polyglots (languages), the Invisible society (science), classics soc, Rogers society (economics).

Boarding: As this is a full boarding school, it has the pastoral care to go with it. The 2017 inspection report puts it thus: 'Boarding provides pupils with a safe, happy, fulfilling platform from which they can pursue their academic and other interests'.

There are nine houses (six boys, three girls), each with its own style and character to foster a sense of belonging: its own library, common rooms, computer suite, dining room. Each with a houseparent, resident matrons and associated house tutors.

One of the housemistresses we met had extraordinary powers of recall about every detail of the pupils in her care. She was a tour de force of warmth and intellect; she knew who would be sitting next to whom at lunch, what vegetables they liked and where each of them were. She exuded quiet competence, iron grasp of detail and seemed to possess mountains of energy. The newest girls' boarding house opened in 2015; a delightful building, all whitewashed stone walls, individual rooms with bow windows and fireplaces lending much charm (each room for year 10s upwards has a desk – year 9s do prep together, supervised by prefects). The house communal rooms have lovely furniture (piano, chandeliers), a super dining area, veranda, bright cushions and clean kitchen areas. A big TV is tuned into the news to top up their current affairs knowledge.

The lower years share, usually around five to a room. Older children are two or three to a room, sixth formers are on their own. The configuration in each room changes every term. While pupils put in requests to share with someone, the houseparent uses their good judgement to make the final decision (with the best will in the world, problems bubble up and, as one pupil muttered, term times can feel intense).

Any worries – eg homesickness – are fed back to parents from the houseparents. One parent spoke of visiting her sons' boarding house for the first time, seeing a row of black wellies outside the door and being struck by how homely it all was. Discipline, she felt, was good as the boys respected the housemaster.

Pupils are allowed to use their phones outside lesson and prep times but not at night.

Background and atmosphere: Founded 1525 by Roger Lupton, a provost of Eton, it nestles amidst the fells in the beautiful old town of Sedbergh. It has a huge campus with gorgeous old stone buildings. Lots of fresh air involved in walking from building to building. The school corridors, lined with traditional photos, have an old world charm about them. Nothing too edgy – the biology lab had geraniums on all the windowsills. Great exhibition space for art, nice DT workshops, decent labs and IT equipment. The library is out on its own in a beautiful old building. Views of hills to make the heart sing.

She exuded quiet competence, iron grasp of detail and seemed to possess mountains of energy

Girls joined in 2001 and now make up around 40 per cent of students. Sedbergh merged with Casterton School in 2013. The Sedbergh juniors moved to the merged junior school on the Casterton site (known as Casterton, Sedbergh Preparatory School), whilst the Casterton seniors moved to the merged senior school, named Sedbergh School, on this site.

Pastoral care, well-being and discipline: Andrew Fleck says they regularly seek pupils' views in discussion groups, run anonymous surveys and take safeguarding extremely seriously. The safeguarding board will always follow up on any concern voiced by a pupil, no matter how slight. Any hint of bullying is tackled immediately.

Older pupils can wander into town. The pupils have many socials on campus, though: Caribbean evenings, fancy dress parties, sketch shows. Minor disciplinary issues (being late for lessons) mean you will get endorsements, and too many of those means you may not attend socials.

One parent, whose son had been sent home due to a teenage misdemeanour, praised the calm way with which it had been dealt and said how easy it had been to reintegrate on his return due to Andrew Fleck's easy manner.

The school is open to all faiths and runs Sunday worship. The chaplain is an extra layer in the pastoral system.

There is a health centre with a doctor, nurses and physio.

Pupils and parents: In addition to Sedbergh's prep school, Casterton, pupils come from prep schools usually within a three hour radius: Scotland, Newcastle, York, Lancashire and Derbyshire. The net has started to be cast out wider, pulling in some pupils from the home counties who want this type of experience for their children. Around 60 per cent boys, and 20 per cent from overseas (there is specific information for Chinese students on the admissions page of the website).

Pupils spoke to us casually about regular debating competitions, about having to prepare a topic quickly and thinking on their feet. They didn't seem fazed

Parents are described as enthusiastic, keen to work with the school to solve any problems. There are parent invites to garden parties and dinners and everyone congregates in the local hostelry, The Dalesman, after sports matches for tea.

Parents praised the excellent communication (although one expressed disappointment that a week-long trip to Cambridge had been called off without explanation and not rearranged). Generally, though, it was felt updates were frequent and staff very accessible.

Entrance: The school is modestly selective. Most admissions via common entrance but the bar is not set too high. So the intake tends to be a broad mix. Pupils joining at a later stage in the school take maths and English exams.

Exit: Around half to Russell group universities with the odd trickle to Oxbridge, some applying post-A levels. It's fair to say there is latitude here for improvement, which may well come via initiatives like the 9 star programme.

There is a real blend and variety of destinations and subjects. More traditional subjects like art history, law, chemistry, classics and maths sit alongside the professional vocational ones; engineering, dentistry, and medicine. There are also a sprawl of more modern courses; sport science, international business management, fashion design, broadcast journalism.

Money matters: A number of scholarships available across academic, music, art, DT, drama, sport or even for being an all-rounder (with regard to the latter, we rather suspect Andrew Fleck would approve of polymaths). There are also means-tested bursaries.

Remarks: The caring enfold of this beautiful school gives young adults an opportunity to find their passions, draw on inner resources and reach their academic and personal potential. If you want your child to have an outdoorsy experience and be imbued with the robust spirit of a self-starter, this is the place. Couch potatoes or teenagers with a partiality for clubbing probably shouldn't apply.

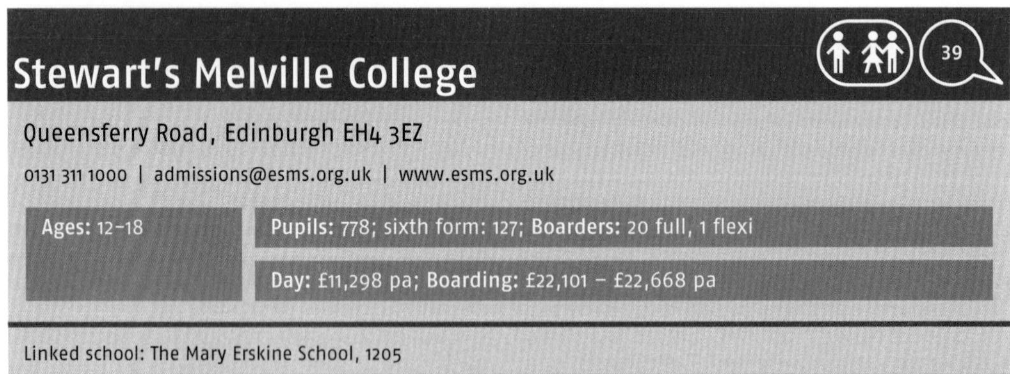

Stewart's Melville College

Queensferry Road, Edinburgh EH4 3EZ

0131 311 1000 | admissions@esms.org.uk | www.esms.org.uk

Ages: 12–18

Pupils: 778; sixth form: 127; Boarders: 20 full, 1 flexi

Day: £11,298 pa; Boarding: £22,101 – £22,668 pa

Linked school: The Mary Erskine School, 1205

Principal: Since 2000, David Gray BA PGCE (60s). Educated at Fettes College, read English at Bristol where he also did his PGCE. He spent six years in Greece teaching in a language school, taught English and modern Greek at Dulwich and was head of English at Leeds Grammar. Before his arrival here he was head of Pocklington School in East Yorkshire for eight years. Born in Scotland, he was brought up in Inverness and left Scotland at the age of 19 to return to Edinburgh at 45, bringing a wealth of experience with him.

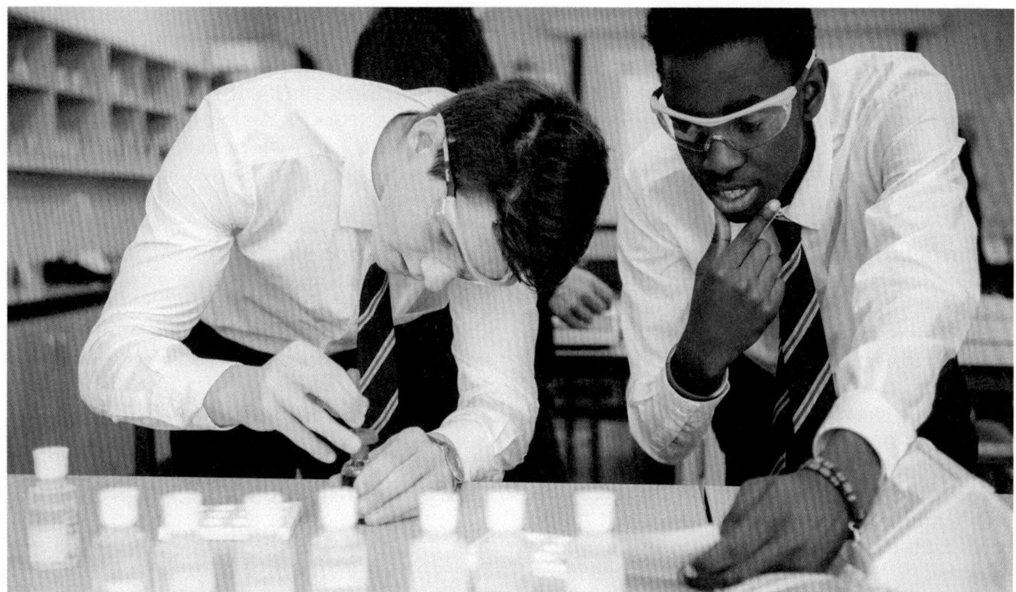

An intense man, not showy or shiny. Clearly passionate about education and the responsibility that he holds. Being principal of ESMS (Erskine Stewart's Melville Schools) is 'his life, a vocation... to prepare the next generation... the future is theirs'. Beneath the intensity is a sense of humour, quiet charm, determination and kindness. Years of teaching have not jaded his enthusiasm – 'what we do here matters'.

He is a hands-on head and this garners respect from the pupils. Keen triathlete: pupils report that he's to be found ploughing down the school pool at 7am every morning without fail ('I can't do my job properly unless I'm fit'). He cycles to work (he now lives off site), teaches English and coaches a first year cricket team. Married with three grown up children.

Mr Gray runs the twin senior schools (Stewart's Melville College and The Mary Erskine School) with two heads and the head of the co-ed junior school. He spends part of the week in each school (separate campuses) with offices in both. Standing down in August 2018. His successor will be Linda Moule, currently head of The Mary Erskine School.

Head of Stewart's Melville: Since 1999 is Neal Clark, a grammar school boy, studied English and came to ESMS via Kirkham Grammar School, Lancashire and then King Edward's School, Bath.

Academic matters: ESMS follows the 'diamond' model of education. The boys and girls are educated together at the junior school, separately in the senior school from 12-17 and back to a co-ed set up in their final year. The principal and his heads of school are all strong advocates of this system: 'we can tailor the teaching for boys and girls'.... 'boys and girls learn differently'. The pupils 'look forward to sixth form and don't lose contact with each other as they go through'. Class sizes of around 20-22 for first two years – S1 and S2 – reducing in size to 20 or less for S3-S5 and then between 12-15 for the final year (sixth form). Parents of boys and girls see it as a 'better learning environment' and pupils say that 'the separation doesn't affect the friendships between the boys and girls'. Many of the sixth formers say 'we have the same group of friends, boys and girls, as we did in the junior school; we don't lose touch'.

Outstanding drama – principal says 'sport and the performing arts are equally strong here'

Pupils study for eight National 5 exams in S3 and S4. English, mathematics, a science and a modern language are compulsory at this stage. In their penultimate year (S5), they study for five Higher exams while in their final year, they study for Advanced Highers in twinned classes with Mary Erskine.

Many pupils do three Advanced Highers (some do more) with considerable success. For these exams pupils have to undertake a dissertation and, in some cases, a scientific investigation which teaches them the skills of independent study that will be necessary at university. Recent results are strong for both exams with 87 per cent of Highers and 82 per cent of Advanced Highers awarded A/B in 2017. French, German, Latin and Spanish all on offer to Advanced Higher. The principal tells us 'there is a strong work ethic here'. This was echoed by parents – 'it's a school that produces conscientious children'.

Strong links with the Merchant Company, whose members offer all final year pupils mock interview practice.

Firefly Learning, an online virtual learning platform, has recently been implemented throughout the school. This allows teachers and students to publish and access information from anywhere with an internet connection. Parents, staff and girls appreciate the effective system to keep track of homework, study tasks, school events and individuals' progress in learning. Pupils do not bring in their own laptops but can sign out and use a school laptop (kept in school library) whenever they need to. However, pupils are still encouraged and expected to use books for their academic research as well as online resources ('both are important skills'). Strong learning support both in and out of the classroom. We hear reports of 'great classroom assistants'.

Pupils tell us that if there is anything academic that they need help with there are drop-in centres every lunchtime where a teacher is available to help them – in all subjects. Big, bright custom-built common room for sixth formers and study areas available.

Games, options, the arts: As you would expect for the largest (joint) independent school in Europe, sport is massive. In 2016/2017 there were 680 sporting fixtures. Hockey, football and rugby are all strong (winners of U18 and U15 Scottish Schools' Hockey Cup, of Scottish Schools' Rugby Cup, of the Scottish Independent Schools' FA Cup), but there

are successes across the more minor sports as well with national accolades in swimming, kayaking, orienteering, golf, judo and climbing to name but a few. The main sports of rugby or hockey and cricket or athletics are compulsory for the younger pupils, but the choice widens further up the school. So, for those not so enamoured with team sports, there are plentiful options, including cycling, swimming and cross-country. The school puts out a very high number of teams so many pupils – around three-quarters – will get a chance to play matches against other schools.

The David Rhind main building is large and Victorian gothic in design. Think fairytale pile, now surrounded by some necessary modern additions

The pitches at Stewart's Melville are used mainly for the curriculum PE lessons and for afternoon sport boys are bussed to further school pitches at Inverleith. Swimming is popular and the school has a 25m swimming pool on site.

Outstanding drama – principal says 'sport and the performing arts are equally strong here'. We hear from parents that drama is 'quite extraordinary'. It is part of the curriculum for younger pupils and can be taken up to Higher and Advanced Higher. The Tom Fleming Centre for Performing Arts, at the Stewart's Melville site, can seat audiences of up to 580. It's a renovated Victorian assembly hall – an impressive venue with comprehensive production, sound and lighting facilities. Drama is for all, with plays and performances throughout the year for all age groups with regular performances at the Edinburgh Festival. Masses of orchestras and choirs at all age groups (22 bands, orchestras, ensembles and choirs running). Annual house music and house rock competitions, both keenly fought with performances described by one parent as 'bloody amazing'. Choir performs annually at the Royal Edinburgh Military Tattoo. OMore than 200 boys have instrumental music lessons and there are 45 visiting music teachers. Pipe band thriving.

A staggering variety of clubs and societies on offer to all. It's all here – from video editing to curling and everything in between. These take place at lunch time and post school. Many of the clubs are sporting – squash, football, netball – but there's certainly something for everyone in the lineup. Good home economics. Voluntary CCF, very popular with over 300 pupils involved. Strong RAF – over 100. Even split between boys and girls.

ESMS are the biggest provider over D of E in Scotland with over 70 pupils awarded D of E Gold in 2016.

Splendid art – and up to date displays around the school, wondrous paintings from this year's art exams already up and framed on the walls. Schools often display fabulous art that we then discover has been hanging there for years. Here the boys and girls can see their creations being valued while they are still at school – when it matters most.

Boarding: Only a tiny percentage of pupils board; this is still predominantly a day school. Dean Park House can accommodate up to 30 boarders. Handily located on site; boys only have a few minutes' walk into their classes each morning. The house isn't purpose built and it feels more like a large family house, well furnished and very well equipped. The bedroom sizes vary and accommodate between two and five boys. Sixth formers may have their own room, depending on numbers.

At weekends the boarders have planned activities offered to them such as surfing, cinema trips etc but they may also go into the city centre if they wish. The Sunday morning service in the local church remains compulsory to all boarders. They are free to use the school sports centres (pool and fitness suite) in the evening and over weekends.

Flexi-boarding is also on offer – but only if there's space available.

Boarders come from Scotland, south of the border and also abroad. Often with family connections to the school (offspring of FPs – former pupils), expats. Predominantly UK citizens rather than foreign nationals.

Background and atmosphere: Stewart's Melville campus is based around the magnificent Daniel Stewart's Hospital. Designed by David Rhind, it was opened in 1855 by the Merchant Company of Edinburgh. When Daniel Stewart (whose wealth came from India) died in 1814, he left a sum of money and instructions that, once it had reached £40,000, it should be used to create a hospital for needy boys within the city. The hospital was transformed into Daniel Stewart's College in 1870. In 1972 the school merged with Melville College. The David Rhind main building is large and Victorian gothic in design. Think fairytale pile, now surrounded by some necessary modern additions. Games pitches to the front, mostly used for PE and by the junior school and car parks front and rear, chock full at the time of our visit.

Senior pupils share the site with upper junior school of ESMS. Sixth formers, who are back in the co-ed set-up with Mary Erskine, are bussed to classes between the two campuses, about a mile apart. Mind boggling timetabling but, according to both pupils and staff, it runs like clockwork.

Coaches from Dunfermline, Bathgate, Eskbank and Haddington as well as around Edinburgh.

Pastoral care, well-being and discipline: The school runs a tutorial system for the first year with groups of 20 boys led by their form tutor, after which the school is divided into six houses. Each has a head of house and an assistant head who together look after the girls as they move through school. These houses are common to both Stewart's Melville and Mary Erskine, so the various inter-house competitions have mixed teams. Weekly inter-house challenges range from maths quizzes to basketball matches. Sixth formers are under the divided into small tutor groups with a personal tutor, under the umbrella of the director of sixth form.

Excellent anti-bullying policy. Principal says that 'cyber bullying in school aged children is now more of a threat than normal bullying' and that they have a full programme to educate the pupils and make them aware of the pitfalls. We hear from parents that 'any bullying shenanigans or friendship issues are handled very well and quickly' and there is 'fantastic pastoral care'. Sophisticated PSE programme throughout the school.

'Zero tolerance' and expulsion if pupils found in possession of, or dealing in, drugs of any kind. Booze and smoking normally end in suspension – principal says 'unacceptable but not an issue in school'.

Pupils and parents: A real mixture of parents. Many first time buyers and children of FPs (former pupils). Parents report 'a broad cross section of families', mostly from central Edinburgh and suburbs. Not really a toff school, although there will be a smattering. Taking over a third of Edinburgh's independent secondary pupils, it is less elitist than some of its neighbours. Children living far out can spend the night when doing evening activities (as long as there's room). Alumni include Tom Fleming, actor and broadcaster.

Entrance: At age 11, 12, 13, fifth year and sixth form. Automatic entrance from junior school. A broadly non-selective school. Children are assessed (English, maths, verbal reasoning) before entrance. Numbers are up. The waiting lists remain 'first come, first served' and there are no plans to cherry-pick the more able pupils. The principal was adamant about this.

Exit: Minimal leakage pre-Highers with most going on to university. Some 65 per cent to Scottish universities, the rest to English/Irish/European/American universities. In 2017, one to Oxbridge and two medics (Stewart's Melville College). SATS (for American colleges) not a problem. School has recently started promoting Dutch universities

(Amsterdam, Groningen, Maastricht, Leiden) as a good option – good transport links to UK, less expensive than some UK universities.

Money matters: Bursaries – up to 100 per cent – and scholarships throughout. Those doing well in the entrance exam are invited to sit a scholarship exam. Music scholarships (together with free music tuition) are also available.

Remarks: This is a big school with big ambitions. With terrific success stories on every front, not just academically, it is a formidable operation. Not every child will thrive as a small fish in such a big pond and such a large operation may leave the non-conformist with less room to manoeuvre. However, its sheer size has tremendous benefits – parents report 'the school pulls in great staff' and provides pupils with 'incredible opportunities'. Well mannered, ambitious children leave the school self-confident and 'with a strong work ethic'. Parents across the board say they 'can't fault it'. An outstanding school with impressive results.

Stonyhurst College

RC 40

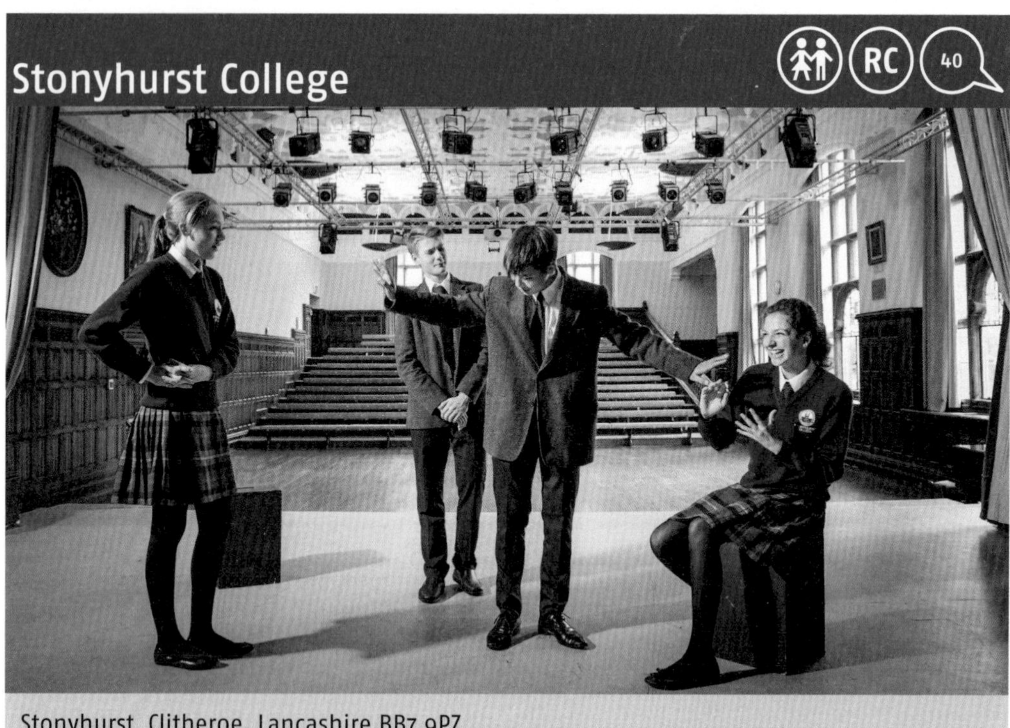

Stonyhurst, Clitheroe, Lancashire BB7 9PZ

01254 827073 | admissions@stonyhurst.ac.uk | www.stonyhurst.ac.uk

Ages: 13–18

Pupils: 458; sixth form: 209; **Boarders:** 310

Day: £19,560 pa; **Boarding:** £35,610 pa

Linked school: St Mary's Hall, 1249

Headmaster: Since 2016, John Browne, BA (Bristol, music), LLB, MBA (40s), previously head of St Aloysius' College, Glasgow. Says it was a blend of accident and design that led him to teaching: as organ scholar at Westminster Cathedral, he 'fell' into the choir school by accident, later diverting to law and then an MBA because 'teachers need to think strategically too'. Taught by Jesuits at St Ignatius College, it was the Jesuit chaplain of Westminster Cathedral Choir School who first asked John, 'when are you going to be a teacher?' This was not to be for another two years as he completed his LLB, but as the City beckoned so did music, and instead he took up his first post as assistant director of music at The Latymer School, returning to the Westminster Cathedral Choir School as the youngest headmaster (then aged 32). From there to Ampleforth as deputy head, then to Glasgow and now Stonyhurst.

Strategic thinking very much in evidence both internally – he has made changes to Stonyhurst's leadership infrastructure – and globally: Stonyhurst is opening a school in Malaysia in 2020. He has appointed five new assistant heads to be responsible for pulling pastoral and academic together in each year group (and who follow pupils through the school), so each pupil is viewed holistically. One parent (a big fan) told us that when he started, head asked a retired Independent Schools' Inspector to review Stonyhurst afresh and held open consultations with staff and parents. An MBA style approach, perhaps, and one senses that continuous improvements will be a defining characteristic of his leadership. Stays on the pulse of the school by meeting five students per week for lunch, which he describes as his 'five-a-day'. They 'help him see what needs to be different.'

He is a big believer in punctuating school life with unforgettable moments (for him, it was going to the Royal Albert Hall to perform every year). He feels the opportunities Stonyhurst offers, trips to the Vatican for example, are crucial. They light the spark. 'If you find a child's passion, the rest falls into place.' This fits neatly with the overall ethos of the school, its motto, 'Quant je puis' (What is the most I can achieve with what I have?) is a dominant backbeat. 'What can I do to change the world?' is what the head wants his students to ask themselves. The spiritual thinking which underpins this philosophy is clear, but he is keen to stress that while worship is part of the school's makeup (60 per cent of pupils are from Catholic families), as a Jesuit school it is very much outward looking.

There was no better testament to his effectiveness than the two boys who were selected at random to show us part of the school. (The selection was so random, in fact, that with the desperate air of an adolescent Just William, one of the boys was furtively and desperately trying to smarten himself up, tucking in his slightly bedraggled shirt as we went along.) 'The head sorts everything out', one said, with a knowing nod to the evening academic clinics, designed to help students with work problems. 'Oh, they've always been there', the other pointed out. 'Yes, but they actually work now, they're good, they're longer', his friend asserted. The pair exuded colossal pride in the school, able to reel off its heritage with enthusiasm you just can't fake.

The head's recreation is walking his dogs in the Ribble valley and spending time with his wife (Marie, a company director) and son. We left him on the day of our visit pondering which object he should take from the vast Stonyhurst collection of treasures to illustrate a talk he was due to give that evening. He 'loves objects which tell a story'. He refers to the writers who have passed through (Conan Doyle was a boy here, Tolkien a resident whilst his son was an English master, the poet Gerard Manley Hopkins taught here). Apparently Tolkien's middle earth was meant to be close to the River Hodder. He wants to bring everything all together, connect the past and present.

Academic matters: Broad curriculum allows students to follow their interests. Psychology A level recently introduced. Languages are strong; around 75 per cent take two languages at GCSE, 14 per cent at A level. The IB is predominantly taken by international students, but popularity is steadily increasing (27 candidates in 2017, compared with 15 in 2015).

History lessons must be much enlivened by articles such as Sir Thomas More's hats and the gunpowder plot vestments. Art lessons can draw on original works

At GCSE in 2017, 51 per cent A*-A/9-7 grades; 42 per cent A*/A, 71 per cent A*-B at A level. Lots of A*s and As in maths and economics. IB average was 34 and two candidates achieved 40 points (out of 45). Mixed ability intake (school accepts all siblings) makes results all the more impressive. Small class sizes, 20 max.

The head is enthusiastic about how IB educates the whole person. The IB's CAS components

– where students design their own projects around the creativity, activity and 'service to others' modules – are now applied to the whole school. School is also rolling out the IB careers programme.

Academically, each child is tracked and results analysed for patterns. If they are a bit below their target, why? The whole person is looked at, all knowledge, both academic and pastoral, pooled to provide answers (back to those new assistant head roles). For those needing extra help, there's learning support in the form of bespoke programmes, including use of mentors and educational psychologists. Parents say some of the teachers are truly inspirational.

If pupils feel they need to brush up on an aspect of the curriculum, the evening subject drop in clinics do the trick. Or as the head puts it, if the target grades are down, then a clinic 'becomes a priority'. Back to the motto again – all that I can: the benchmark is set high for all students and they are encouraged to aspire.

Conan Doyle was a boy here, Tolkien a resident whilst his son was an English master, Gerard Manley Hopkins taught here

A unique aspect of teaching at the school is its integration with the Stonyhurst collections (started in 1609). Artefacts from these extraordinary collections are deployed to bring the curriculum to life. We actually got to touch Shakespeare's First Folio and saw Mary Queen of Scots' Book of Hours. History lessons must be much enlivened by articles such as Sir Thomas More's hats and the gunpowder plot vestments. Art lessons can draw on original works by Turner and Rubens. These and other remarkable items are currently being curated into a small museum ('The story of the collections and English Catholicism'). The school's heritage is very much part of the learning experience in the here and now; even the observatory in the grounds is put to full use and ties up with head's desire to bring together past and present.

Games, options, the arts: Impressive array of sports facilities: tennis dome, squash courts, golf course, shooting range, swimming pool, heaps of sports pitches. Clay pigeon shooting, which used to take place off site, is now done on site. Dazzling successes in boys' and girls' sport (rugby team won the Lancashire Cup and the girls had just returned from netball tour to Dubai). CCF compulsory in year 10 and most continue thereafter. Duke of Edinburgh strong.

Art is nurtured here; there is an artist in residence and head would like to extend similar hospitality to a poet. Music runs the gamut with big choirs, big bands, orchestras, ensembles. There are headmaster's concerts as well as weekly performances. Dance is on offer in all its genres – street, tap, modern, zumba – with some nicely ambitious productions to showcase those skills (Moulin Rouge and Wicked). The Stonyhurst dancers recently got to spend time with the Birmingham Royal ballet (doubtless one of those unforgettable experiences so valued by the head).

There is a good drama space with professional sound and lighting and a chain of performances from the ubiquitous Les Mis, to Fiddler on the Roof and Hedda Gabler. A wonderful Much Ado, condensed into 45 minutes, was performed in a modern style with a Christmas morning setting. Students pitch in from backstage too, with lighting and costumes.

Clubs include politics, philosophy, robotics, astronomy, economics. Impressive range of speakers, recently Professor Robert Winston, historian Lord Hennessy, plus academics and politicians (we imagine Jacob Rees Mogg was thought-provoking at the very least).

Steady stream of big canvass events, like a fashion show with African couture, a literary festival (biannual) and all the usual balls. Trips include South Africa, China and closer to home: museums (Louvre!), Houses of Parliament and top universities. Interline (house) competitions in everything from tennis, maths, croquet to poetry reading.

Boarding: Most of the boarders are full time so lots of cinema trips and outings to York and Manchester. Boarding houses are called playrooms (a recent review concluded that Stonyhurst should retain horizontal boarding, saying it builds strong friendships across whole year group). Each pupil has a tutor (and an online pastoral log) who meets them in small groups every week. The new assistant heads will preside over this process to ensure everything is joined up.

Boarders start off sharing five to a room; single rooms for older pupils. Rooms are fairly trad, many have magnificent views over the grounds. 'Every morning it looks different', one pupil said. Some corridors and rooms have had a basic refurb: carpets, fresh paint and the faint aroma of Travelodge. More will follow suit. Boys' and girls' rooms differ only in that the girls have made theirs cosier. Showers and loos not palatial but in good order.

Girls' boarding area has rooms clustered around a central glass office with staff on duty – very reassuring, we thought. Sitting room looked comfortable and there was a well-equipped, homely kitchen with washing machines. Day pupils also have a desk in the boarding areas.

Background and atmosphere: Founded in 1593 in France, the school moved to its present site in the beautiful Ribble valley in 1794. The building and its grounds, with their formal waterways, have a stately grandeur that certainly inspired former pupil, Sir Arthur Conan Doyle – the description of Baskerville Hall, the family seat in The Hound of the Baskervilles, is based on Stonyhurst.

The ancient historical libraries are something else. The fact that students have seminars in these rooms must set the tone for high achievement

The library in main use has a very grown up feeling, but the other ancient historical libraries are something else. The fact that students have seminars in these rooms must set the tone for high achievement. Wonderful college chapel, St Peter's, lends a Brideshead grandeur.

Multi-million pound restoration developments are the norm here. Like any great estate, its treasures need to be maintained and extensive projects are ongoing to give its ailing beauties, such as the canals and the baroque gardens, some TLC.

There can be no radical modernisation in a listed building and it is all the better for it. True, the school's 'slightly worn in places' interior vibe prevails – indeed, approach it with the wrong mind set and certain corridors might seem a little gloomy. Nevertheless, classrooms are cheery, there are decent science labs, dance and drama studios, and don't forget all those incredible sports facilities.

Plenty of wall displays, not dominant or dazzling but interesting; we commented on some pictures of famous scientists to a couple of pupils. Shame so few women scientists, we think, looking at all the men displayed. 'What's the name of the woman who was part of the team who discovered DNA? She should be up there,' we say, racking our addled brains for her name. 'Oh, you mean Rosalind Franklin', came the reply, barely missing a beat. (Yep, we think to ourselves, impressed, that's the one.)

Pastoral care, well-being and discipline: The playrooms at break times certainly seem friendly places, a mad throng of chat. Parents enthused about the seamless blend of day and boarding and liked recent initiative to invite day pupils to spend three nights in the school for free.

On site health centre. Lots of school talks and workshops for students on walking tall, building resilience and looking at the nuances of behaviour; how you can subtly exclude someone and the impact that can have. The latter being particularly relevant to the complexity of girls' friendships. Head of pastoral/boarding said the girls will flag up concerns about others and it's a very supportive environment. The real aim is to give students the skills to deal with issues themselves. Mild concerns were expressed in this area by one or two parents who suggested perhaps students needed 'a bit extra' pastorally; others thought the same for the academic side of things (some pupils need extra cosseting, some need pushing). Mr Browne's five new assistant heads should go some way to bridging this perceived gap.

Phones are allowed during the day, but must not be taken out in lessons or they will be confiscated. In the evenings, phones permitted but Wifi is switched off.

The spiritual runs through the school, mass is celebrated each week and each playroom goes on an annual retreat. Yet although many parents say the school lives the Jesuit ethos, some felt its Catholic values should be celebrated more and 'shouted about'. We imagine it's a delicate balance for the school between inclusivity and celebration.

Pupils and parents: Pupils mainly come from the north of England and London (families looking for something less pushy). Good mix of international boarders; recent increase in European pupils who come for the IB.

Overseas parents are emailed frequently, relaying what their children are going to be studying and details of their performance. Parents in the UK described the comms as superb, saying you heard back from a teacher within a couple of hours of emailing.

School has the second biggest alumni association after Eton (handy for work placements)

The chain of connection goes on well beyond leaving Stonyhurst; many parents are themselves former pupils. School has the second biggest alumni association after Eton (always handy for work placements). The head sees all ex-pupils as ambassadors for the school.

The pupils we spoke to seemed a down to earth and diverse bunch. The head refers to the first hockey team, 'the cool kids', lobbying him to help with the refugee crisis. He was keen to impress the importance of the real commitment on them (helping is not a whim). The end result was the head of the Jesuit refugee service came to give a talk and the village is now looking to host a Syrian refugee family.

Entrance: One third of students come from school's prep, Saint Mary Hall. Entrance exam plus reports and reference for candidates at 11+, 13+ and 16+. Overseas students are assessed for English level to check that they will be able to tackle the subjects with ease.

Exit: Leavers go on to study a broad spread of subjects at universities all over the UK. York, Manchester, Bristol, Exeter and Newcastle currently popular. Four to Oxbridge in 2017; two medics (one at Oxford) and a vet. International students to universities in Europe and US. Popular subjects seem to be management/ business studies.

Money matters: Boarding fees in line with similar schools. Scholarships (music, sport, academic and all-rounder). Scholarships and means-tested bursaries up to value of £3 million annually for students who would benefit from all that Stonyhurst has to offer but whose family would find the finances a struggle.

Remarks: An outward looking and inclusive Catholic boarding school where students are encouraged to become their best selves, give back to the world and aspire to great heights academically.

Strathallan School

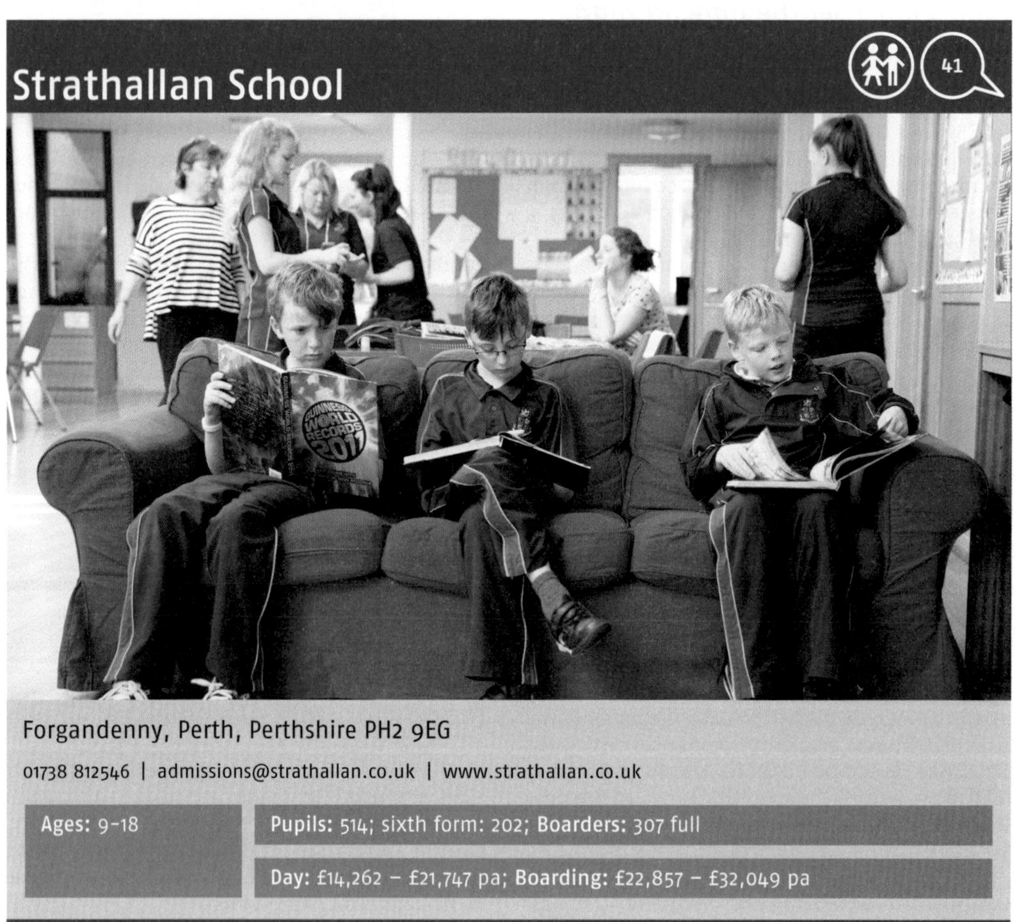

Forgandenny, Perth, Perthshire PH2 9EG

01738 812546 | admissions@strathallan.co.uk | www.strathallan.co.uk

Ages: 9-18

Pupils: 514; sixth form: 202; **Boarders:** 307 full

Day: £14,262 – £21,747 pa; **Boarding:** £22,857 – £32,049 pa

Headmaster: Since September 2017, Mark Lauder, previously head of Ashville College (40s). Did an MA in English literature and history at Aberdeen, spending his junior honours year at the University of Oregon, Eugene, USA. After graduating he embarked on research at St Edmund Hall, Oxford, where as well as winning a graduate scholarship, he achieved two half blues in rowing. Has also been deputy head and head of boarding at Felsted School, Essex, head of history and then housemaster at St Edward's School, Oxford, and before that head of history and master in charge of rowing at Shiplake College, Henley-on-Thames, coaching rugby and rowing throughout.

Married to peripatetic piano teacher, Caroline, with two teenage sons. In his spare time, he continues to restore his 17th century Yorkshire home, goes hill walking with his family and wild camping on Scottish islands.

Housemistress of Riley (Junior House), is Mrs Emma Lalani.

Academic matters: Not tremendously academic (school says 'strong academic record' – umm: 2017 A level results showed 43 per cent A*/As; Highers 31 per cent As; GCSEs 43 per cent A*-A/9-7s). Splendid mega million quid (expandable) computer suite, where 'the young are given screwdrivers to dismantle the things and sixth formers then expected to fix 'em', to quote the charming hands on head of computing. 'Problem solving skills' more important than rote. Three network engineers on site. Intranet access all over. Mandatory keyboarding in first form, then 'can catch up online'.

Strath not following blindly (as have so many others) into the Virtual Learning Experience where pupils are expected to work exclusively online (with teachers correcting and parents informed – online). We were enchanted to find a history teacher carefully hand marking (slightly scruffy) handwritten exam papers. Trips to battlefields, and re-enactments the norm.

Strong on langs – particularly Chinese (Chinese counsellor on staff), Spanish and German – native speakers perhaps? – French a poor relation. On our delightful trip round the school in blazing sunshine (groups of ad hoc revision classes squatted on the grass: tieless teachers and pupils – this was shirtsleeve order stuff) we met the head of foreign langs, who was introduced as 'teaching Russian'. Confusion reigned: Russian is not an offered option, though native Russian speakers may get tuition to get them up to speed for A levels ('can do public exams'). Ditto any native speaker. Classical civilisation. Latin still in the frame.

Class size around 20: usual thing, smaller for practical stuff and as pupil specialisation kicks in. GCSE for all, 'no Scottish qualifications below age 16,' says school. Nine or 10 GCSEs the norm; all do each science, although around a third take the dual award.

Twenty assorted A levels on offer: school plays the system, both Scottish and English. Seventy-five per cent follow the A level route; others opt for Highers over two years. School tries to please parents but the choice between A levels and Highers is always contentious. Highers are particularly popular for wannabe medics as school is one of the few to offer human biology. In 2017, 65 per cent A-B grades.

Mixed age common room: discrimination 'even to raise the subject of age.' Staff live on campus with their families, a boon for younger staff who might otherwise be reluctant to commit to somewhere with no nearby university for PhDs or MBAs (think Open University). Finding a new head of physics proved a (finally solvable) nightmare. Head of academics, a fairly recent appointment, comes from Dean Close: good to get fresh and experienced blood in the place.

Stupendous music. Enormous diversification. Pipe major plays with Red Hot Chilli Pipers (as do many of his pupils). Seventy-strong boys' choirs

School has always had a welcome reputation for supporting weaker brethren (siblings in particular) and has a small but effective learning support system which had a smashing HMI report with talk of 'systematic identification', 'sensitive support', 'informative advice' (yawn yawn). All pupils screened on entry with ed psychs brought in where necessary. One-to-one, small groups, plus after-school clinics in various disciplines which act as drop-in centres. Two full-time trained staff, plus ancillaries, cover entire age range. Extra time for exams. Regular assessment orders for all. 'Rarely costs extra.' School can cope with mild Asperger's/autism and the dys-stream: if SEN is on your radar, check out its comprehensive 'can-do' list below: physical infirmity not a problem, most classrooms on ground floor and lifts whizz you up to top floor of all new builds complete with disabled bathrooms in head of house. Massive EFL input for those who do not have English as their mother tongue: 'normally no extra charge for this.'

Tutors per year group, meet weekly, max 10 per tutor. Strong features of support for learning include: systematic identification of pupils with specific learning difficulties and sensitive support for individual pupils; well-planned arrangements for pupils requiring special assistance with examinations; informative advice to teachers on the learning needs of pupils requiring support; an appropriate range of programmes for pupils for whom English was an additional language; effective use of the expertise of external specialists such as educational psychologists; and after-school 'clinics' run by a number of subject departments. The priority is to provide long term support for individuals and groups of pupils and to respond positively to the needs of pupils referred from individual departments. Teachers have been provided with briefings on issues such as dyslexia and the focus in the last year has been on helping departments adapt approaches and materials to pupils' different needs. The department consists of two full-time members of staff with the help of three other teachers.

Games, options, the arts: Plaudits fail. We are gob-smacked. School has county, national, international, Commonwealth and Olympic presence across the board and at all ages: from rugby, footie, tennis, hockey, netball; fantastic swimming (speedos, goggles and shaven chests); silver at recent Commonwealth Games. Team and individual. Shooting: clay and small bore (plus popular CCF – boys and girls, voluntary) fencing, own golf course, sailing.

Reel parties by year group and Scottish country dancing an essential. Raft of hobbies: beekeeping current craze (apiarist on staff, and senior girls love it)

School mag and termly news catch up bung full of smiling prize winners/competitors (mebbe this ed is blind/stupid, but couldn't find an essay, poem, trip description anywhere). School says 10 pages of art and DT work in centre of skool mag: this ed was hoping for an essay or a poem.

Think Millfield of the North. Rugby squad thrashes all comers, beat Glenalmond 79-4. Coll now refuses to play them, abandoned rugby and gave out that Strath were importing South Africans and Kiwis to boost their front line. Fact: only one South African (son of a Strathallian) has played for the XV, his little bro comes shortly. South African exchange students come in the hockey term. Tennis academy triumphed in all three of the UK senior finals recently. Serious and successful skiing. County/national/international coaches in most disciplines. The list of sporting achievements is endless and impressive. And look at new head's interests.

To celebrate its centenary, school gave itself a fitness/weight-training centre (open at night), dance and drama practice area and possibly the most enormous covered sports area this ed has ever seen to complement the 70s sports hall (complete with climbing wall) and utterly delicious 20s gym. Think snow. Think footie, think tennis, think space age.

State-of-the art school over three floors with marvellous light and inspired work (we said that last time but it is still top of the pops) – current conundrum is how to retrieve two ginormous feet which were finalists in the Saatchi Schools competition. Enthusiastic head of art opens art rooms whenever: 'can always work on my own projects'; always open three nights a week. Unusual screen printing/photography combination involving rough-hewn branches and strange frame: eye-catching and imaginative (but one rather wonders.). Darkroom, pottery, kiln, very much in use, fabric design and inspired corsets on display (for outside rather than inside wear, you understand) some slightly uninspired work in progress.

Art/history combined field trips to Venice, Prague and the like.

Good music. Stop here. Stupendous music. Enormous diversification. Pipe major plays with Red Hot Chilli Pipers (as do many of his pupils). Seventy-strong boys' choirs for house music competition blow the roof off, choristers at St Ninians in Perth get paid a less than living wage – choral scholarships on offer, church music popular 'and fun,' said our guide. Headmaster's Music (freebie) in Perth Concert Hall (which holds 1,000 and is always full) has musicians (often the same musician) swapping seamlessly from complicated classical concertos to self-composed electronic dance music and rock. Several of the young have professional contracts under their belts. This is exciting stuff.

Loads of drama: small theatre, previously the dining hall, insides scooped out (which doubles as exam hall); new dance and drama studio.

Mass of charity work: mega Kenyan input. Help in charity shop. D of E. (Granny bashing apparently a thing of the past: pupils used to give them computer lessons... times change).

Break time when we visited, fresh fruit, milk, buns and fairy cakes with sports coaches huddled on sunny wooden benches working out next matches, plus Parker – said to be the most ferocious guard dog.

Boarding: Houses new and newish, boys and girls have own study bedrooms for their last four years, lots of kitchens and common room areas on each floor. New girls' house completed with an increase in girls. Heads of girls' houses have disabled type loos (lifts): an interesting juxtaposition.

Random books (which is what we like to see) in common rooms, plus mandatory CDs. And tuck shop – seemed to be over-full of cereal packs.

Much general to-ing and fro-ing, but co-ed works well here; girls' houses out of bounds to boys on Sunday mornings so that girls 'can laze around in their dressing gowns if they want.' PR whizzo disputed this: silly PR guru: our guide confirmed it as 'brilliant' (school says 'still not the case').

Chapel every other Sunday, new chaplain in the wings (ex RAF, natch). School facilities much used by groups during holiday period. New girls' house the furthest away, but otherwise houses fairly cloistered.

Background and atmosphere: School founded in 1913 by Harry Riley, based in 19th century red sandstone country house with masses of sympathetic additions, set in 153 beautifully manicured acres. Couple of double-deck libraries, one with the carpet reflecting the plaster work in the ceiling; adjacent media rooms – cosy and useful. Fairly utilitarian chapel (children quite rude about it) and refurbished dining room, million quid – ceiling dropped, new floor – though not sure it is that good for dancing. Main classrooms 150 yards away beyond the old stable building which has been transformed into junior house, Riley, boasting an atrium plus library and music practice rooms etc. Just across the valley from senior school (a splendid and accessible wooded dell) where youngest boarders and day children have dedicated sports and play area. Drop in centre for both day and boarders, tellies, prep tables (older pupils come and give the occasional hand) and computers for Skyping and the like. Games room.

All eat in dining room, with younger pupils getting a head start – think that means they eat first – rather than pigging all the grapes.

Classroom blocks clustered and cloistered on t'other side of the valley now refurbed, latest improvements include three state-of-the-art chemistry labs, 'nother new lab this summer. Not an overwhelming school, beautifully landscaped, though some of the signs – to car park et al – are out of kilter. School council operates under aegis of head girl and boy. House council meetings plus international council.

Reel parties by year group and Scottish country dancing an essential. Raft of hobbies: beekeeping current craze (apiarist on staff, and senior girls love it: suspect they may get some honey). Trippettes to Perth and Edinburgh at weekend, riding nearby (sleek collection of bays in neighbouring field). Girls have a dressmaking enthusiast on tap and one of 'em made her own ball gown last year – to the amazement of her peers. (Leavers' Ball a wow).

Pastoral care, well-being and discipline: Seven houses in senior school, four for boys and three for girls. Houseparents live on site with two staff on duty in each house every night. B&B in senior school only. Academic tutor attached to each pupil and tutorial team in every house. Tutors often using the time available for informal chats.

Staff 'aware that things happen' and talk of rustication and drugs testing 'in case of suspicion'. Automatically suspend for drugs and contact police. Tiny glitch recently, all aware of legal highs 'always a concern'. Random tests on suspicion.

School works hard on bullying awareness, lots of briefing – expectations, ownership, relationships, 'be reasonable'. 'Like running a huge great family,' with a 'good cross age group.' Boy/girl relationship 'works well'. Punishment system for misdemeanours of 'fatigues' – jobs around the buildings and grounds – 'no shortage of them'.

Assemblies on Fridays. Loads of medals and congratulations all round. Oodles of trips, both fun and cultural – skiing much enjoyed. Prague, Vienna, battlefields of France and concentration camps in Germany ('eerie,' said our guide).

Food said to be 'excellent'; 'fresh bread and milk every day'. Fruit everywhere.

Pupils and parents: A quarter of the pupils from overseas, mostly expats, plus 80-odd foreign pupils from Spain, Russia, Africa, China, Eastern Europe, Hong Kong, Germany, currently 23 different nationalities. No exeats, guardians needed for half terms

(our guide seemed to think that there 'was always a house available for those who prefer to stay in school'; 'not so', said the school). Popular with Scots (regional accents of all kinds), well-placed, an hour from both Edinburgh and Glasgow, plus a small contingent from south of the border. (School claims it is 'two hours from London Heathrow': three from Heathrow or Gatwick more like.)

Day pupils allocated to one of the houses; daily buses to and from Perth, Kinross, Auchterarder, Stirling, Crieff and Dundee. About a third or more come daily, with younger day children converting to boarders on going to senior school age 13.

FPs Dominic Diamond (computer games whizzo), Colin Montgomerie (golfer), Sir Jack Shaw, (Bank of Scotland), John Gray (former chairman of the Hong Kong and Shanghai Bank). Not a toffs' school, despite brief showing in the fashion stakes when David Pighills took the school co-ed. 'Very good relationship with parents,' says the school. Grandparents, whom we met couple of days ago were over the moon: granddaughter just left, 'loved it to bits' (and thought head a star): grandson ('deeply difficult') 'doing well at uni'. Couldn't praise the place high enough.

We only saw pupils in shirt sleeves or sports kit. Girls wear elegant (washable) tartan skirts which make the most of the strangest of shapes, long kilts on Wednesdays – seems a funny way to predict a cold spell.

Entrance: Entrance to the Junior House is at age 9, 10, 11 or 12 by school report and assessments, or scholarship held on entrance day in early Spring. Senior entrance is at 13+, via open scholarship examination (Late February/early March), common entrance (June) or/and school report. Sixth form entry is either via the sixth form scholarship examination (November) or on the basis of a satisfactory school report and/or GCSE/National 5 results. All pupils screened for learning difficulties on entry and IEPs plus ed psychs rolled on if necessary. Excellent route map for parents unfamiliar with public school entry procedures.

Exit: More than 95 per cent to range of universities – two-thirds Scottish, nearly all the rest English. Forces popular. Odd gap year.

Money matters: School financially strong. Mega centenary appeal 'helped the most recent developments'.

Junior scholarships, open scholarships and sixth form scholarship plus academic, all-rounder, sport, music, cathedral and art scholarships. Parents can apply for means-tested help with fees – 'moving towards bursaries' for all.

Many parents in oil industry: school had downturn last time oil went belly up but appears to be weathering this current hiccup: industry covers school fees when parents based abroad, but not when either in Europe or the UK.

Remarks: The school is in fantastic heart and at ease in the local community. Not for the would be Brideshead contingent. Can't fault it.

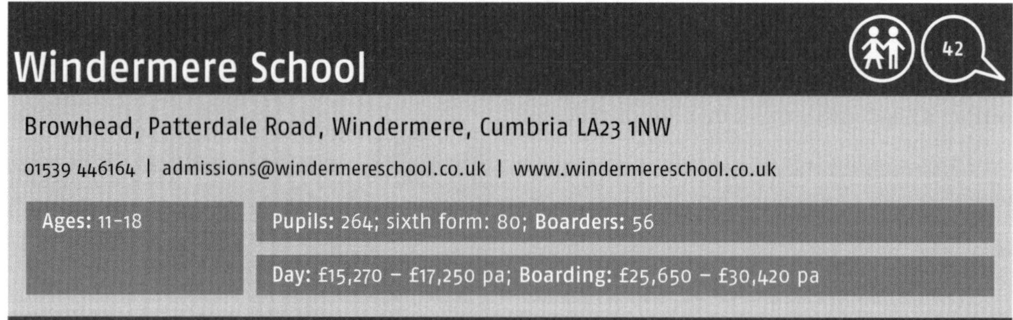

Windermere School
42
Browhead, Patterdale Road, Windermere, Cumbria LA23 1NW
01539 446164 | admissions@windermereschool.co.uk | www.windermereschool.co.uk
Ages: 11–18
Pupils: 264; sixth form: 80; Boarders: 56
Day: £15,270 – £17,250 pa; Boarding: £25,650 – £30,420 pa

Headmaster: Since 2009, Ian Lavender MA (Oxon) NPQH. Has a strong background in independent secondary school education, boarding and the Round Square ethos, having been a housemaster at Gordonstoun School for 11 years and before that a chemistry teacher at Cranleigh School and Eton College. He also has broad experience that extends well beyond teaching, including an early career in management consulting and service with the Territorial Army. His wife is a GP and they have three children. A quietly spoken, measured and thoughtful man, parents say 'he cares deeply about the students...and is an impressive headmaster'. Now in his sixth year at the school, he is beginning to 'see things more clearly'; there is no lack of ambition: his vision is that Windermere becomes 'the best small school in the country'.

Academic matters: Windermere pupils might not be dancing right at the top of the league tables

but they appear hard-working and happy. Due in part to the broad intake, the results at GCSE, whilst undoubtedly solid (45 per cent A*-A/9-7 in 2017), can't compete with bigger, more selective schools so it focuses on its considerable international appeal. Crucially, however, it is the highest performing independent school in Cumbria post 16, not least because there is no A level on offer here; it's the rigour of IB or a small choice of BTecs, and that's it. Exams and the choice of exams are a natural sieving process and the school's choice of the IB route means the game is raised considerably in sixth form; average IB point score 35 in 2017, with six students getting 40+ points. Now accredited to teach the IB careers' programme alongside the diploma. With small classes (around 12), teaching is up close and personal, there's nowhere to hide, and pupil-teacher relationships appear warm and relaxed. Personal academic tutors guide and, if necessary, hand-hold, helping students in their choice of subjects and mentoring them along the way. Parents tell us 'there are many inspirational teachers here', with a number of them prepared to offer extra tutorials on request at lunchtime or after school.

French, German, Italian and Spanish are all taught in this language-rich environment, with Latin and Greek being offered off-timetable as extras, classes running every Thursday evening. Outside of class, eager young linguists who keep their ears open can experience over 20 languages being spoken around school. Students are given the opportunity to participate in worldwide exchanges by spending up to a term in another Round Square school. There are also annual language trips to France and Spain and Germany.

Full-time head of learning support, dyslexia specialist and two part-time assistants; it's a strong department. Parents are charged for the support according to whether it's in-class or on an individual basis.

Games, options, the arts: Built on a slope; the site brings its own challenges and there aren't acres of pitches here; the biggest area of flat ground is the lake, so that's where most activities take place. Better suited to small team sports, and there are probably more expeditions than fixtures, but they do have an Astroturf and a sports hall for year-round play.

Eager young linguists who keep their ears open can experience over 20 languages being spoken

Whilst they can't compete with the big boys at team sports, they take it seriously and offer the full range of usual school sports and others besides, including equestrianism, sailing and kayaking. Hodge Howe, the school's own watersports centre and the only school centre in the country to hold RYA champion club status, has two boathouses, a private beach and a pavilion with a classroom (also available for wedding receptions..) and a fleet of sailing boats and kayaks. Other outdoor activities include camping trips, fell walking, ghyll scrambling, orienteering, caving and climbing, so if you are the adventurous type and not joined at the hip to your hair straighteners or worried by a patchy mobile phone signal, there's plenty here for you. All students in years 7, 8 and 9 complete the Windermere Adventure Award. They also spend one morning a fortnight outside school doing anything from mountain biking to conservation and environmental work.

Art takes place in the old stables; super natural light and plenty of Apple Macs for those with a penchant for design and design technology, and kilns for keen potters; it's an appropriately messy yet inspirational space. Drama is popular; it's a small school so very inclusive, and everyone who wants to take part can do, whether centre stage or behind the scenes.

Lots of individual tuition in music and the Holst Room, a space designed for its acoustics, is a valuable teaching and performance space. It's not the strongest subject, here according to parents, so a particularly musical child may not be able to shine, but there is undoubtedly a 'have a go' attitude to the subject, as with everything else.

The school supports community projects in South Africa; each year students help out with resources and provide physical help to a project with Tiger Kloof School – in fact just mentioning the name of the school brings a warm smile and glow of pride to the faces of the older students, who view it as an extension of their school life at Windermere.

A highly rated international summer school is proving increasingly popular and has effectively added a fourth term to the school year.

Boarding: Despite the national park location, it's only 90 minutes to either Manchester or Liverpool airports (outside London considered a safer option by some nervous parents), three hours to London by train and the school has a fleet of shuttle buses catering for students' many and varied travel needs.

Word of mouth is the biggest factor in attracting parents, both locally and overseas. There are a few expat Forces parents who love the leadership challenges here, and whilst more than half of the students are from within the UK, the rest represent around 24 different countries far and wide, including China, Germany, Hong Kong, Lithuania, Poland, Romania, Ukraine, Spain and Russia.

School's own watersports centre has two boathouses, a private beach and a pavilion with a classroom (also available for wedding receptions...)

Customary dorms in single sex houses on site for boarders aged 8-16 (only a handful of junior boarders); there are a few single rooms but not many choose them, most preferring to share. Plenty of messy individualisation of space with One Direction posters, soft toys and family photos. Each house has a staff house 'family', comfortable shared common rooms with views across the lake for socialising, karaoake and TV watching, and well-equipped kitchens for snacking. In the girls' house at least, baking seems popular with Mary Berry cake recipes much in evidence. Food cooked in-house, good quality and plentiful, just as well with all that fresh air.

Well-behaved sixth formers earn the right to have more space and freedom in self-contained flats in a co-educational house on site, still supervised, of course, but a step along the road to preparation for life beyond school. A sixth form bar allows (with parental permission) two drinks with dinner on a Saturday night; younger pupils love the occasional takeaway, shared with friends in the boarding house. If that sounds a little tame, there's not much else you can get up to here (a definite plus for many parents), but cinema visits and occasional weekend trips to the Trafford Centre in Manchester or Alton Towers keep restless adolescents happy. They are also very busy after school, so much so that a parent of a day boy told us they relocated to be on the school's doorstep simply because their son was 'reluctant to go home after school – way too much going on'.

Background and atmosphere: On this site since 1924 and co-ed since 1999, there is a good mix of boys and girls here. Extensive additional building took place in the '70s and '80s, but the national park setting places real limitations on new building – essentially it's all about how the place looks from the lake. Some attractive newer and recently refurbed buildings are scattered around the grounds of the Victorian mansion of the original Browhead estate, some boarding facilities, others classrooms and labs. Highlights are the Jenkins Centre for music, performing arts, languages and a superb dining room and Crampton Hall – a spacious auditorium for theatrical and musical productions.

Round Square is a worldwide association of schools that is all about the whole person – the Kurt Hahn view that says students can only understand life by experiencing it in exciting and challenging ways. Opportunities for travel and exchanges to other Round Square schools bring extra opportunities, and they welcome international students who wish to experience British culture whilst bringing with them their own perspective and world view. There is a real sense that, although surrounded by mountains here, their hearts and heads go way beyond the valley and into the wider world beyond. The core of the IB diploma programme encompasses many of the Round Square principles, making the curriculum ideal here. Daily reflection is an important start to the day and something valued hugely by the students themselves. 'It lifts you up,' they tell us; 'you're in school, lessons haven't started yet but you're saying hello to everyone'; 'it's a nice place to be' and it is often, apparently, like a mini TED talk to start your day, food for thought and a valued and laudable touchstone. Outside speakers are welcomed as regular visitors and students also attend conferences and exchanges worldwide.

Pastoral care, well-being and discipline: Many parents are attracted by the fact that the school isn't especially selective – telling us they didn't want their offspring to be a 'public school product' but rather they 'wanted their individuality to be valued'. They appreciate the weekly online newsletter and feel that they 'could walk into the school at any time if they had any concerns at all'. Also of great value to parents is the way in which 'teachers respond very promptly to even the smallest queries...pastoral care is excellent,' they say. Overseas parents enjoy a 'close relationship' with the staff and love the fact that their offspring often enjoy tea or dinner with the head and his wife.

Staff do, of course, keep a careful watching brief, but essentially Windermere pupils are encouraged to be self-disciplined. Problems are rare, as older and younger students jog along happily in the knowledge that they want for nothing (except perhaps a Starbucks) in this sprawling, healthy and supportive environment. Strong views from the sixth formers themselves on smoking – 'why would you?' It seems there's a degree of self-policing going on.

Students appear comfortable and relaxed but with an uncommon sense of responsibility too; they recently 'simply couldn't stand back and do nothing' following the recent earthquakes in Nepal, and within hours were actively fundraising within the local community in support of the victims. Charity fundraising such as this, alongside work in a soup kitchen and orphanage, affords them a 'very different reality,' say parents – 'one which puts their very privileged life into sharp focus'.

Pupils and parents: Any passing traffic is likely to be either hikers or tourists, so recruitment is a challenge, though undoubtedly helped in the overseas market by the Beatrix Potter and Peter Rabbit connection. It's a lifestyle choice living here in the Lake District, and some parents have huge commutes to city offices, whilst others are simply escaping the city altogether. Fewer landed gentry than in days of old, more hardworking hotel and restaurant owners or young semi-retired professionals who have made their money in the City and moved here for a breath of fresh air.

There is a real sense that, although surrounded by mountains here, their hearts and heads go way beyond the valley and into the wider world beyond

High on the list of attractions for many is the extensive programme of adventurous outdoor activities – something the pupils coming through from the school's own prep department have already enjoyed in abundance. It seems to result not only in hardy pupils but also in a 'can do' attitude, parents buying in to the opportunities for growth and independence in a safe environment. The words 'warmth' and 'friendliness' are oft repeated by parents when talking about the staff; they are aware that this is more typical of a small school and for them, it's a valid and valuable trade off for bigger and better facilities.

Entrance: Nearly all juniors move up to the senior school, making up the majority of the 11+ entry. The school likes to look for 'potential' rather than performance and 'well-rounded students with a genuine interest in education in the broadest sense of the word,' say staff. Candidates for entry (below 16+) sit papers in English, mathematics and non-verbal reasoning. Year 12 places conditional on a minimum of five GCSEs at grade C or above.

Exit: Some 20 per cent leave after GCSEs. Most sixth form leavers continue in higher education at home or overseas, some via gap years. In 2017, high scorers to UCL and popular Scottish universities, plus one to New York University Shanghai and one to University of Milan. A handful have gone on to key musical success. Notable former pupils include dressage Olympian Emma Hindle and internationally respected soprano Claire Booth.

Money matters: Non means-tested scholarships are available in performing arts, visual arts, general academic subjects and sport. There are some means-tested bursaries available.

Remarks: The photograph on the cover of the school's prospectus looks like an oil painting – and yes, that really is the view from the school. A glorious backdrop in which to learn and grow, and the school makes full use of it. It's not the ideal destination for the child without a cagoule or for whom manicured lawns and extensive sporting facilities are key, but you do have all the amenities of the Lake District at your disposal, so give even those indoor types a month or so and they'll be away from their Playstations and kayaking with the best of them.

On a sunny day you can see for miles. On other days you can't see your hand in front of your face. The weather can change in an instant, but no one allows that fact to get in the way of an existence where hard work, good friends, rosy cheeks and fresh air in your lungs are all part of the package. The introduction of the International Baccalaureate has upped the game academically at the top end and also encouraged a more diverse intake, with pupils introduced to a wider range of subjects with exceptional extracurricular enhancements.

State boarding schools

SCOTLAND
Edinburgh
Glasgow
NORTHERN IRELAND
Belfast
Dublin
Newcastle Upon Tyne
Keswick
Ripon
Leeds
Bradford
Kingston Upon Hull
Liverpool
Sheffield
ENGLAND
Stoke-on-trent
Nottingham
Leicester
Norwich
Birmingham
Coventry
Cambridge
Colchester
WALES
Oxford
London
Cardiff
Warminster
Southampton
Brighton
Exeter
1
2
3
4
5
6
7
8
9
10
11
12
13
14
15
16
17
18
19
20
21
20 40 60 Miles

STATE

Brymore Academy

Cannington, Bridgwater, Somerset TA5 2NB

01278 652369 | office@brymore.somerset.sch.uk | www.brymoreacademy.co.uk

Ages: 11–17

Pupils: 300; Boarders: 150

Day: free; Boarding: £10,170 pa

Head: Since 2011, Mr Mark Thomas (acting head since September 2010). Originally from Cornwall, Mr Thomas came to Brymore from Courtfields School, Wellington where he had been deputy and acting head. Previously deputy head at Brittons Academy in Rainham, his early teaching career was mainly in London. Down to earth, no-nonsense and determined, he is married with one young son – 'too young to think about Brymore yet!' – and his wife teaches locally. He spends several nights each week in his school house in the grounds. Sport is both his subject and his hobby though he says, cheerfully, that he hasn't had time for anything except Brymore since his appointment. Determined to 'keep the unique identity and nature of Brymore but create a truly secure atmosphere while raising academic expectations and achievement'. The pride of boys and teachers in their achievements, their interest in academic as well as practical work, as well as the national 'Raise Online' statistics, give strong witness to how much he has achieved in four years. Parents were a little apprehensive about changes, particularly the number of new staff and higher academic expectations, but now feel 'it has all come together'.

Academic matters: Since Mr Thomas' appointment there have been huge changes, with nearly three-quarters of current teaching staff appointed since 2011. Five of these are Brymore alumni, so tradition has certainly not gone out with the bathwater.

The farm and gardens are the heart of learning at Brymore. Practical hands-on farm work: tractor driving (from 13), milking, winter and summer feeding of cattle, pigs and poultry, calving and lambing, cultivation of vegetables and maintenance of the grounds. Getting up at 6am, come rain, come shine, come snow and ice, for seven days a week, making and maintaining heavy equipment, means learning to keep yourself fit and disciplined enough to do it all. If, in the past, the academic curriculum has taken second place, this balance is being altered in a major curriculum overhaul.

From year 10 up boys are now in sets (so a boy may be in a fast set for one subject and a more supportive group for another according to individual need) and years 7 to 9 are three streamed groups. A six day timetable gives 30 one hour lessons (doubles for practical subjects). Much more flexible options now with horticulture and agriculture compulsory for first three years but for not for exam years (10 and 11). This makes room for choice and art, modern foreign languages, history and geography, though there is still huge and successful take up in practical land-based subjects. Sadly for Brymore, these subject results won't register in the new league tables, though Mr Thomas is fighting the cause! Modern foreign languages haven't worked though to results yet, but there is a big take up of French in the lower school. Engineering can be taken to 'Industry standard' and DT is a core subject. Academic expectations are high. One boy aiming at an engineering career told us he hoped to go on to grammar school to study maths, higher maths and economics A Level, while another, readily admitting to struggling with English, relished his reading and was an exceptionally articulate living proof of success. In 2017, 53 per cent got 5+ A*-C/9-4 GCSE grades including maths and English; 10 per cent A*-A/9-7 grades.

Classes average 16, though there are much smaller groups for boys needing more help and every boy has an individual learning plan. Mentors regularly discuss progress, both academic and personal, and help boys to set and achieve appropriate targets. Very comprehensive learning support is managed by a SENCo with a team of 10 full time, qualified learning support assistants. Most are subject specialists working in their subject area, and the others plug gaps. Resourceful staff are dedicated to improving achievement, and initiatives such as reading nights – just being read to – for younger boys, house points for reading journals, triple input marking, which encourages boys to correct and learn from their own and others' work, are clearly having an impact. Statistics for improvement in maths are not quite as impressive as in English, where the school is in the top three per cent in national stats for improvement, but are OK, and the maths department is still developing new strategies.

Games, options, the arts: Brymore is a sporty school with good rugby, doing respectably at district level – no mean achievement with year groups of under 30 in competition with year groups bigger than the whole Brymore population. Hockey, mountain biking, with an exciting new track and bikes sponsored by Sport England, daily training on the MUGA (multi usage games area), a small Astroturf area, and above all, the Chad Hill daily run: three and a half miles of cross-country which is all but compulsory ('expected' is official terminology).

Sport and activities are partly in curriculum, partly after school, but central to everything is the agricultural and horticultural practice and theory.

Taught elements are in the teaching day but in addition every boy has to take his turn in the routine of the farm, boarding for a seven day week in order to be up 6am and be permanently on hand for emergencies. DT and engineering centres round farming. One boy explained that a few days fencing showed him the need for an efficient trailer for fencing materials. Brymore's metal and wood workshops, including smithy and foundry, enable really professional work, from handy little metal hammers made by beginners to roadworthy trailers and specialist tractor accessories – things with real practical value on the farm.

Horticultural minded boys can have personal plots in the walled garden and use of the potting and tool sheds to grow their own crops

There is a farm manager and a head groundsman, but all the work on the farm and maintaining the grounds and gardens is done by boys. There is nothing to make you understand better why people shouldn't trample across a perfect lawn than mowing it yourself! Horticultural minded boys can have personal plots in the walled garden and use of the potting and tool sheds to grow their own crops – Brymore's kitchens happily buy salad, potatoes and veg from them. Art and music are newly available as options. Languages and other options may be taught outside the main school day.

Boarding: Since a major refurbish, boarding is comfortable and clean, the slightly institutional layout softened by posters of giant tractors, 'great big combine harvesters', animals and sport and no institutional smell. Bins outside the doors of the two newish boarding houses take muddy farm clothes and sports gear. Dorms sleep four, except in the main house, where it's up to six. Very tidy – a few unwashed coffee mugs in the boys' kitchen sink confirmed that it is actually lived in. Each house has its own houseparents and relief team for continuity.

Background and atmosphere: Brymore was founded as a School of Rural Technology in 1952 for sons of Somerset farmers on an impressive 60-acre farm on the edge of Cannington, between the Quantocks and Bristol Channel. Half a mile of tree-lined drive ends in a cluster of farm buildings which surround the original 13th century house, much added to over the centuries, and once owned by the Cromwell's financier John Pym. Exceptionally loyal ex-pupils meet and encourage the current generation at the annual, misleadingly named, Pym's Night. Boys really seem to value the traditional standards of Brymore and are proud of taking part in the local church festivals – harvest especially – and of their reputation among local farmers: Brymore boys are useful on the farm. Shoes are miraculously clean despite farmyard mud, smart black uniform sports the Brymore spur and motto Diligentia et Labore on the pocket. It is also emblazoned on the walls in each boarding house, as the boys' chosen decoration. Parents and staff praise Brymore as 'feeling more like an independent school'. 'The noise of 180 boys singing out at full volume nearly knocks you out,' a proud parent commented after her first carol service.

Pastoral care, well-being and discipline: Brymore had a reputation as a pretty tough place in the past, but its toughness now focuses on the personal resilience and responsibility of the boys rather than rough and tumble rivalries. 'Resilience, Responsibility and Resourcefulness' is used as a strap-line by staff and pupils alike and there is no doubt constant reference to it has rubbed off on the boys' approach to academic and farm work. Day and boarding pupils mix in the three houses (not to be confused with the boarding houses), with house masters and tutors, who meet them weekly. Vertical tutor groups means the oldest mentor the year 7s and get to know all age groups. Year 11 boys take the usual prefect duties (hotly contested) and supervise younger ones for milking and feeding duties. Currently, they are very keen on creating an anti-bullying atmosphere, and are super-watchful over the newly-admitted first years. Down to earth matron on duty all day and liked by boys. Food said to be 'better than it was' but still a cause of some contention.

The Chad Hill daily run: three-and a-half miles of cross-country is all but compulsory ('expected' is official terminology)

Pupils and parents: The farming community both local and much further flung (boarders from Hong Kong, France, Norway and midlands) definitely dominates, but boys and parents are beginning to demand a wider outlook and academic curriculum. Past pupils visit frequently and are still part of school life. One, teaching blacksmithing at Brymore alongside his own small business, makes an excellent role model. Others include MEP Neil Parish, Mark Irish, England U21 rugby player, Alex Wright, British race walking champion, and Robert Watts, Brymore's head of boarding. Both alumni and parents fundraise enthusiastically.

Entrance: About 50 pupils, 28 boarders and 22 day boys, admitted to year 7. Currently there is a similar intake to year 9, though this will inevitably diminish once the early years are full. Now oversubscribed. Day places on the usual Somerset criteria, a combination of first come first served and distance from the school. Boarding places also now oversubscribed, open to any boy qualifying for UK schooling and 'suitability for boarding'. Brymore is good with boys who haven't thrived in mainstream, but increased demand has meant that the academic profile of the school is now higher that previously.

Exit: A few boarders stay on to year 12 but attend all courses at Bridgewater College. A large contingent to agricultural colleges, Kingston Maurward, Duchy College Cornwall, Bridgwater College (Cannington Centre) and all over the country. 'Brymore boys often get fast tracked at college,' said one farmer dad. A significant interest in engineering, and some boys go on to do A levels with a view to uni places. Lack of modern foreign language teaching has been a bit of a barrier with local sixth form college, so it's as well it's now on offer. Good number join the armed forces or work within local government, the medical profession or vet sciences; others to apprenticeships and a significant number end up running their own businesses.

Money matters: Fees only for boarding, not tuition, so miles cheaper than the independent sector, despite recent fee rises. Some pupils obtain educational grants from home LAs. All day boys, known as 'out boarders', have to board and pay for the weeks they are on farm duties, though some have found educational grants for this..

Remarks: There are still too few schools like Brymore and, though more are being established, it will be hard to rival its atmosphere and achievement. Articulate, friendly boys are not afraid of the pressures and daily grind of farm work. If this is what hands on experience and responsibility gives to children, schools could do with more of it. No hayseeds at Brymore – more business aware agriculturalists who understand the need to supply food and respect the land that grows it. Parents appreciate that every member of staff is there to give the very best possible education to their children.

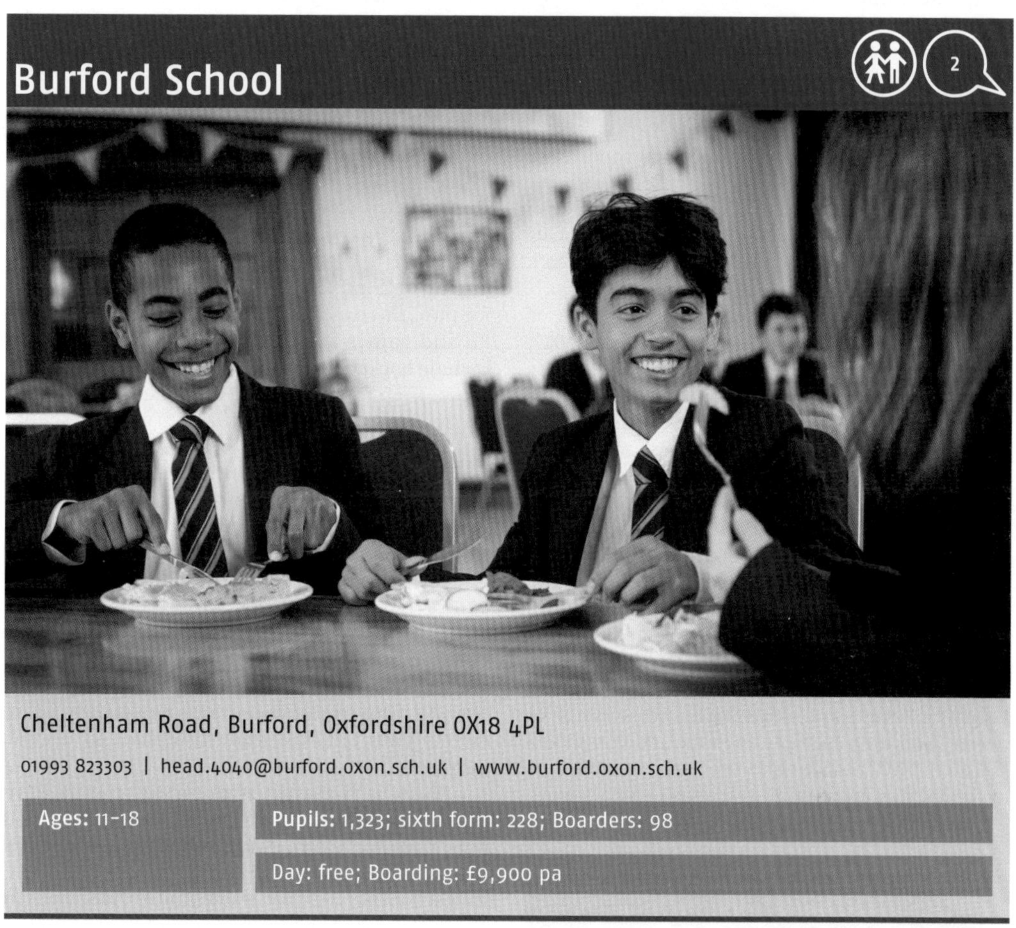

Burford School

Cheltenham Road, Burford, Oxfordshire OX18 4PL

01993 823303 | head.4040@burford.oxon.sch.uk | www.burford.oxon.sch.uk

Ages: 11–18

Pupils: 1,323; sixth form: 228; Boarders: 98

Day: free; Boarding: £9,900 pa

Headteacher: Since 2008, Kathy Haig BA MEd (40s). Educated at Burford School herself (her family lived at nearby Shipton-under-Wychwood), followed by Leeds University, where she studied food science and nutrition. Taught at schools in Hull, Keighley and Preston before moving to Ellesmere Port Catholic High School in Cheshire. Spent 12 years there, rising to be deputy head. Made a point of focusing on teaching and learning from the minute she arrived at Burford. When it comes to making decisions she always asks 'does it improve the teaching and learning?' If it doesn't, the school doesn't do it. Her approach has paid dividends. GCSE and A level results have risen year on year over the last seven years and the school received a letter of congratulations from the schools minister on being in the top 90 secondary schools in England for sustained improvement.

Outgoing, full of ideas and a good listener, she says that 'the culture of inclusivity and mutual respect' is key to the school's ethos. Parents told us that she is 'very down-to-earth,' 'easy to approach' and knows every pupil by name (no mean feat in a school this size). Her open-door policy means that if her door is open pupils can stop by and chat. When a group of boys mentioned that they'd like to play chess at lunchtimes she immediately put the idea into action. Now there's a chess league four times a week and Burford competes against other schools.

Head still teaches five hours a fortnight (child development GCSE to year 11 pupils). 'I love teaching and I think that it does the staff good to see that the head still has to do reports,' she says. Married to management consultant and has two teenage children, both at Burford.

Academic matters: A large, rural comprehensive that takes boarders (it's one of only 30 or so state boarding schools in the country). Offers wide range of subjects to wide ability intake but expects everyone to work hard and fulfil their potential – in line with head's belief that if you have high expectations then 'children will live up to what you expect of them.' Curriculum is mainly academic, with a small number of vocational qualifications. Most pupils take nine or 10 GCSEs and homework plays integral part, with parents asked to sign children's student record books once a week up to GCSE.

Exam results are very good – 80 per cent of pupils got 4-9 in both English and maths in 2017, with 26 per cent at A*-A/9-7 grades. At A level, 31 per cent at A*/A and 64 per cent A*-B. Thirty A level and BTec subjects on offer at A level – all the usual, plus economics, psychology, media studies and photography. EPQ and AS critical thinking also available.

Lessons are largely taught in form groups, apart from maths and French, which are set according to ability. Class sizes of 26 up to GCSE (20 for practical subjects) and average of 12 to 14 in the sixth form. Languages compulsory at key stage 3. All students do French in years 7 to 9 and can add a second language in years 8 and 9.

Learning support is housed in own block – The Learning Zone – and deals with a wide range of needs, including speech, language and communication difficulties, autistic spectrum conditions, dyslexia, dyspraxia and dyscalculia and social, emotional and mental health needs. Help given to children who arrive with lower than average literacy and numeracy as well as those with EAL requirements and the gifted and talented. There's also an inclusion room called The Bridge for students who temporarily need to study away from the main classroom. A mother whose daughter had to undergo spinal surgery was full of praise for it. 'Lessons were brought to her there,' she said. 'Potentially she could have had four months being home-schooled but thanks to The Bridge she only missed two or three weeks of school.'

In keeping with its rural setting, school has an outdoor classroom called The Acre. As well as being a base for GCSE course in environmental land based studies it has chickens, ducks, rabbits, two miniature donkeys and a vegetable patch.

Games, options, the arts: With acres of green space for pupils to run around in, Burford is very sporty. PE and games are compulsory – sports offered include hockey, football, rugby, netball, tennis, athletics, keep fit and dance. As well as games fields (including a cricket square and pavilion), school has a gym and sports hall, netball and tennis courts. Loads of matches with local state and independent schools (rugby, hockey and netball teams particularly successful). Burford also hosts schools from Argentina and Australia every year for rugby, hockey, netball and cricket. School has its own equestrian team and runs an inter-house riding competition in the grounds every summer – everything from best turned-out pony to show-jumping and dressage. If there's a sport pupils want to do, 'we will try and put in on,' says the deputy head, citing girls' cricket and volleyball as recent examples.

Music is fantastic. Around 300 pupils have instrumental lessons – 'you name it, we play it,' said one of our sixth form guides. Wide range of orchestras, string ensemble, wind band, jazz band and rock school plus a music residential for 100 pupils in North Wales in the summer. School hopes to build its own concert hall and recently became music hub for the area, offering workshops by visiting specialists, the chance to play in professional concerts and master classes at St Anne's College, Oxford. School stages musical every two years – they'd just done Sunshine on Leith when we visited – and a drama production in the intervening years. 'We try and involve everyone,' said the assistant head.

Well equipped art block, with different areas for art, design, photography, textiles, plus computers, scanners, colour printers and digital cameras that professional studios would give their eye-teeth for. Loads of voluntary extracurricular activities – during lunch breaks and after school on Monday, Tuesday and Thursday (late buses put on so everyone can attend).

We loved the feel of the place from the start. There's no keeping up with the Joneses. There are people from all walks of life'

D of E and Young Enterprise on offer and lots of trips to foreign climes. The school is rightfully proud of its 20-year tie with a school in Uganda. The first group visited Uganda in 1995 and since then an annual exchange has taken place. Burford pupils visit partner students in Uganda one year, then host them in Burford the next. Along the way Burford has raised money for everything from a library and computer room for its partner school to two cows.

Boarding: The head says she could fill boarding places twice over and we're not in the least surprised. Parents pay for children's accommodation but their education is free. 'State boarding schools show that you can have it all, but at a fraction of the price of independent schools,' the mother of a sixth form boarder told us. 'We loved the feel of the place from the start. There's no keeping up with the Joneses. It's very diverse and there are people from all walks of life.'

The 90 boarders (half of them boys, half girls) live in Lenthall House, a listed building in Burford itself and a 10 minute walk from the main school (uphill on the way there, downhill on the way back). As we said last time, it's a bit of a Tardis – a maze of interconnecting buildings with bright, newly refurbished rooms and excellent facilities. The school has created a flat within the boarding house for five sixth form girls – to help them prepare for the university years. Boarders come from all over, from down the road in Oxfordshire to Hong Kong and China. Most are full boarders (a couple of weekly boarders when we visited) and staff put on loads of evening and weekend activities. Everything from go karting and ice skating to theatre trips and craft sessions. Supervised prep every night and in-house structured revision during GCSE and A level study leave.

Pupils eat breakfast (full English on Saturdays and croissants on Sundays) and tea at the boarding house – food cooked by own catering staff – and lunch at the main school. Boarders can invite day pupils to tea and there's a formal dinner at Christmas, plus monthly lunches for local OAPs. Six live-in staff, including head of boarding and his wife. Boarding head moved to Burford from the independent sector and says: 'There is more drive and purpose among the boarders here. They are keener to do well and to take advantage of all the opportunities we offer.'

Application form on school website for boarding places. School asks for reference from children's current school and prospective pupils are invited to attend a taster day during term time. Students from overseas (30 per cent of total number of boarders) welcome as long as they have a relative or host family living in the UK.

Background and atmosphere: Founded as a grammar school for boys by charter in 1571 and still celebrates Charter Day in October each year. Main school is situated on the busy A40 on edge of beautiful Cotswold town of Burford (just over an hour away from London in reasonable traffic). Moved to its present 36-acre site in 1960, with boarders moving into the original grammar school at the bottom of the high street.

School still maintains many old grammar school traditions, including house system, prefects and smart uniform (blazer and house tie) for all but the sixth form (who wear their own clothes but are expected to dress appropriately – no ripped jeans or Ugg boots). This year's first XV rugby team have opted to wear smart suits when they travel to matches – a custom they reckon will continue.

Sixth formers have their own block, with common room, study area and more freedom. Year 13s are allowed off-site at lunchtime and if they don't have lessons. Some drive to school. 'We get treated like grown-ups,' an appreciative youngster told us. The only grumble we heard was that they'd like more parking places. Students keen to be head girl or head boy write their own manifestos, take part in hustings and are voted for by staff and fellow sixth formers.

Like the pupils themselves, the atmosphere here is busy and purposeful. Ofsted's 2014 report judged students' behaviour to be outstanding and when we visited we were impressed by pupils' politeness, charm and enthusiasm for the school.

Pastoral care, well-being and discipline: Well-defined rules set out in excellent student record book – smart hardback given to each pupil at the start of the year, with ruler and whiteboard they can hold up for plenary sessions in class. Contains everything from equipment needed for school to spelling lists and what to do if the school bus is late.

School's core tenet is that 'everyone will act with care and consideration to others at all times,' and it clearly works. School governor told us that Burford is 'very caring' and 'takes great pride in how we look after our youngsters.' There's a strong Team Burford ethos, with students keeping in touch for years after they leave.

Excellent induction programme for new pupils. Year 7s are mentored by trained year 13s and also get a three-day residential trip early in first term to help them settle in. Year groups are divided into seven or eight forms, each with own tutor, who's also responsible for registration and PHSE. All pupils belong to one of four houses named after school founders and benefactors – Falkland, Heylin, Warwick and Wysdom. Houses are fiercely competitive, with lots of competitions, from rugby and netball to art and even forensics. School council with four reps from each year group. Pupils have assembly twice a week – once for the whole school and once for their year group.

Pupils say the food has improved a lot and offers a daily choice of hot meals, pasta, salad bar, vegetarian options and baguettes. Cashless canteen – biometric system reads students' thumbprints.

Pupils and parents: A real mix. Pupils come from a wide variety of backgrounds, from disadvantaged to quite posh. Some have lived in the area for years, others have parents who commute to Oxford or London every day. Relatively few from the town of Burford itself – steep house prices mean properties tend to be owned by older residents and second-homers. School gives financial support 'very discreetly' to pupils whose families can't afford to pay for school trips.

Old pupils include Gilbert Jessop (cricketer), Simon West (film director) and Alice Freeman (rower).

Entrance: Children living in the catchment area and attending one of Burford's nine partner schools are virtually guaranteed a place. Thirty-five to 40 per cent of pupils come from outside the catchment area, from as far afield as Hook Norton, Faringdon and Bourton-on-the-Water, with priority given to those with siblings already at the school. Additional pupils arrive in year 9, including up to 30 a year from local private schools. 'We've had to put in an extra year 9 form,' says the head.

Up to 20 new pupils a year join the 220-strong sixth form (minimum of two B/6s and four C/5s at GCSE required by all, plus some subject-specific requirements).

Exit: Around 40-50 per cent leave after GCSE – for vocational courses at local FE colleges (including Cirencester, Abingdon and Witney and City of Oxford), apprenticeships and employment.

Three-quarters head to university after A levels – to study everything from biomedical science to fine art. One medic in 2017; others to eg Edinburgh, Durham, Cardiff and Exeter. School has a full-time careers adviser – professionally qualified and very experienced – who organises higher education and apprenticeships evenings, mock interviews, a careers convention and work experience (for year 10s and year 12s) and sees students one-to-one. School is creating strong links with local businesses too.

Remarks: A happy and successful comprehensive school with an impressive 'can-do' attitude. Pupils are keen to succeed and rise to the challenge admirably.

Colchester Royal Grammar School

3

6 Lexden Road, Colchester, Essex CO3 3ND

01206 509100 | info@crgs.co.uk | www.crgs.co.uk

Ages: 11–18

Pupils: 931; sixth form: 372 (including 115 girls); Boarders: 30 (sixth form, currently boys only)

Day: free; Boarding: £13,200 pa

Headmaster: Since 2015, Mr John Russell BSc MA ARCS, previously deputy head of Cranbrook School. Physics degree from Imperial College; first job in a Loughton comprehensive school before becoming head of physics at Ilford County High.

Gracious, unintimidating and refreshingly honest and transparent, he is a hands-on head, who teaches physics to at least one year group every year, and has plans to do more. Students regularly pop into his office unannounced, usually to tell of their successes. 'If I grant them a leave of absence – which I sometimes do for competitions as far away as Poland – the criteria is that they have to tell me how it went afterwards.' We noticed he pays the same level of respect to students as they give to him in conversations – it's all very mutual, with no draconian rules around standing up when he walks into a classroom etc. 'He's not like a headmaster – he's one of the team and the students love him for it,' a parent told us. He has a weekly drop-in session for parents and staff say he is highly supportive and consultative.

He lives five minutes' walk away with his wife, Michelle, a chemistry teacher, and their three children, two of whom are at the school. Describes himself as an enthusiastic sportsman if not a very accomplished one, with a particular enjoyment of football and racket sports. Also has a passion for music.

Academic matters: Extremely high academic standards, with the school's A level results nearly 70 per cent A*/A and 91 per cent A*-B in 2017 – having made them number one in the government league tables for most of the last 10 years. 'One student recently got nine A*s and 2 As, and that was at A level,' says the head. For GCSE, 72 per cent A*-A/9-7 grades, including maths and English.

So what's the secret of their success? One word – teaching. Students rave about the teachers here

No setting in years 7 or 8, French and maths setted from year 9 – 'but this is only a question of pace,' says school. 'Set 4 pupils will still be expected to achieve A* at GCSE.' French and Latin in year 7, plus additional choice of German or Greek in year 8. One of the very few state schools to offer Greek to A level – for a state school, an above average number go on to study classics at university. No areas of weakness to speak of at either GCSE or A level, with particularly outstanding results in humanities, maths, sciences, DT and economics. 'We have lots of further maths students,' says head. If the school doesn't teach a subject that a student desperately wants to do, they'll try to provide one lecture a week if the student agrees to self-teach the rest. 'We've done this with government and politics, Mandarin and a number of other subjects in the past,' says head.

So what's the secret of their success? One word – teaching. Students rave about the teachers here, notably their commitment to keeping every single pupil intellectually stretched and on track to meet their targets, providing extra support and revision clubs as necessary, and being available out-of-hours via email. 'There's lots of talk about where you should be at and how to achieve it.' Then there's the sheer quality of teaching. 'They keep it imaginative, fresh and innovative at all times.' 'They're not afraid to throw the textbooks aside.' 'You are never bored in a lesson.' 'Their enthusiasm is contagious.' Etc. Not a single inattentive expression spotted during our visit – these youngsters are hungry to learn and the teaching is a feast, in every sense. 'It's made very clear that it's ok to fail – that's how you learn – and my son has thrived because of it,' said one parent. 'It's not just intellectually rigorous and stimulating, it's relevant too – showing boys how what they're learning fits into today's world,' said another. 'It's more than about getting these youngsters to pass exams – it's about where this learning is going to take them in life.' Homework levels are, according to students, 'reasonable – and if you haven't been able to do it, there's a culture of support, rather than an immediate sanction.' Maximum of 30 in a class lower down; 25 at GCSE; and 20 in sixth form.

Some SEND pupils with physical disabilities, including visual impairments, and a fair number of Asperger's, plus a few dyslexic. Support is mainly classroom-based, and parents could not praise it more highly. 'With our son, they have taken a difficult autistic boy and grown him into a wonderful young man – coping with his complexities and outbursts in their stride, and celebrating every minor success. The staff should be getting an OBE, in my opinion,' one parent told us. Any EAL pupil will have had a high enough standard of English to pass the selection tests.

Games, options, the arts: Cricket and rugby strong. Regular fixtures against state and independent schools, with some representation at national level. Increasing strength in athletics. Netball, and now rugby, for sixth form girls. 'That's the one thing I'd change – I really think there could be more on offer for girls,' one told us. Other sports available as extracurricular activities, including sailing and weight-training. Also plenty of non-sporting activities. 'Sport here is inclusive – it's not all about the top players,' parents assured us. Extensive playing fields five minutes' walk away – 'less than ideal, but that's the way it is,' says head. Within the school, there's tarmacked playground, which is regularly used for sport, plus a heated outdoor pool.

Exciting music department, which takes up a whole (on site) three-story house, with loads of opportunities for any pupil with any musical ambitions. 'Our son is musical, but I didn't know what to expect with this school because it's better known for the academia, but the opportunities for learning and performing have massively impressed us,' said one parent. No shortage of instruments (many donated by old boys) and break-out rooms. Live music in every assembly; choirs and school orchestra; ensembles and bands, many student led; and 200 learn an instrument with a peripatetic teacher. 'I came here with no musical experience whatsoever and I'm now much more confident and enjoying the piano,' one boy told us.

Trips include cycling and visiting Cambridge, but mostly boarders seem content to hang around school. Sport and music facilities are open evenings and weekends

Drama only offered as extracurricular, but popular, with a much-talked-about annual performance, with examples including Fame and West Side Story. Rehearsals for a French play when we visited, as part of French lessons, highlighting their commitment to cross-curricular teaching. Spacious and light art block boasts a kiln, dark room, printing press etc and although there is some seriously talented artwork on the walls, the more average work is equally celebrated. 'If I'm honest, art is not my son's strongest subject, but he still wanted to do it for GCSE and he's been encouraged at every turn – the school understands that the benefits of art aren't just for those who are brilliant at it,' said one parent. Around 12 do art GCSE art, and similar figures for A level. DT rooms also spacious, and clearly well-used and loved.

Big on extracurricular, with lots of clubs and societies held during breaks, lunchtimes and after school, many of which are student-led eg sixth-formers run the law and medical societies. Very strong public speaking society, which regularly competes. 'You should see them – watching one of the boys talk is like watching Tony Blair,' says the head. Lots of sport and music themes among the clubs, plus the likes of BBC Young Reporters' Club, right through to more obscure ones such as Rubik's cube club, Swedish club and even a colouring club. 'Our philosophy is that we value our students excelling in anything – and that includes things like sport and Rubik's cube club,' says head. Students enter so many competitions that even the head loses track, although he's now got himself a 'little black book' to record them in. Day trips to London for cultural days out and year 7s were at Colchester Zoo the day we visited. Plus residentials eg classics trip to Italy; languages trips to Germany; sports tours to Italy.

'We do bonding trips too, including taking all year 7s to the cinema at the end of the first term, and we recently took year 12s on a bowling night,' says the head. Plenty of charity work, including an award-winning mental health charity, Time to Talk, which was set up by students themselves.

Boarding: Two boarding houses – one directly opposite the library in the main old building; the other a self-contained building behind the sixth form block – both with a mixture of single and double bedrooms (generally, you share in year 12 and get your own room in year 13). There are cooking facilities and a communal area in each house, and four resident staff members for the 30 boarders. These boarders – currently all sixth form boys, but school is developing girls' boarding provision – are mainly those who would have too far to travel to school each day and pupils from abroad; particularly popular in Hong Kong, where a member of staff visits each year to interview potential sixth formers, with these students now making up around half of all boarders. Head is a big supporter of boarding – 'it contributes to the school environment and the international element. I'd like to expand numbers,' he says.

After school finishes at 3.40pm, there's free time, followed by dinner at 6pm and study time from 7-9pm. Lights out at 10.30pm on weekdays and 11pm on weekends. Plenty of freedom to go into town, albeit with a strict signing in and out system. 'Some go into London too, as well as to stay with local friends, although we need permission from their parents for that,' the housemaster told us. Organised trips out include cycling and visiting Cambridge. But, for the most part, they seem content to hang around school, where they are permitted to use school sports and music facilities during evenings and weekends. The gym – which had unfortunately flooded when we visited – is also popular. 'Staying here also gives us a chance for a weekend lie-in,' one boarder smiled.

'It's all pretty relaxed,' more than one boarder told us – and with bedrooms not quite as tidy as in many schools we visit, we weren't surprised when we were told by the housemaster that 'we do guidelines, rather than rules. These are young men, and we treat them as such – but with the pastoral structure very firmly in the background,' he explains. Lots of transition work, especially for the Hong Kong contingent, where boys get to meet each other before they arrive and are given plenty of information to help them prepare. The result of all this is a very happy bunch of boarders, who are in no way seen as separate from the rest of the students. In fact, our only criticism was that some of the rooms could do with a bit of TLC, but then again this is state boarding.

Background and atmosphere: Directly descended from a Colchester town school that existed in

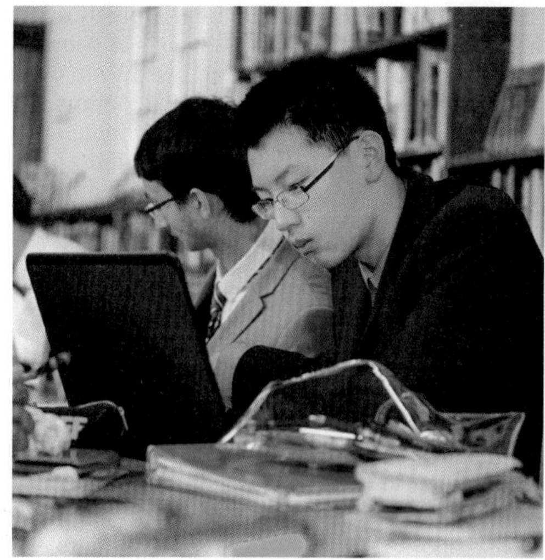

1206 and was granted royal charters by Henry VIII in 1539 and Elizabeth I in 1584. Set in an affluent residential area of Colchester, the main buildings date back to the late 19th century. These are home to some classic grammar school classrooms, with big windows overlooking the shiny floored corridors, plus a very traditional, well-stocked library, complete with oil paintings of old headmasters on the wall, and additional silent room at the side.

Newer additions – which include blocks for science and engineering, computing and art and renovated music and drama facilities – fit well with the attractive old school buildings. The new George Young Building serves as a concert hall, performance studio and lecture theatre, while the even newer Jenkinson Building boasts state-of-the-art science labs (with air-con – a godsend on the hot day we visited), and ICT suites. Wonderful to see sixth-form engineering students hard at work on imaginative projects (top secret, we were warned when we busily scribbled down the details – but all proper real world stuff that could potentially change lives). 'Students looking to study engineering can cut their teeth on it here, while others can explore if it is really right for them,' a teacher explained.

The sixth-form centre is home to a lively common room, with a large, all-school, cashless refectory to the side, serving a wide variety of food that nobody had any complaints about. Lovely, well-tended gardens of a standard unusual in a state school, featuring quiet and private sitting areas for students – in full use when we visited. The only thing the head said he'd like to add to facilities is 'more room for sixth form private study, but I think we're lucky with everything else.'

Despite the emphasis on academic brilliance, the atmosphere here is supportive, caring and – according to some students, 'almost family-like.'

'Everyone assumes it's a hothouse, but it's really not. And we have such a diverse range of people – some are natural brainboxes; others have to work really hard to get on.' The common denominator, they say, is that everyone is a self-starter and highly motivated. 'If you're inclined to slack off, it's probably not school for you.' We encountered lots of laughter and fun banter, including with teachers. At sixth-form, there's a particularly cohesive unit of students, 'which makes for a much tighter knit group than you'd get at sixth-form college. It's lovely.' 'There's something very special about the ethos here that quite a few of us parents get quite emotional about,' one parent said.

Everyone welcomes the addition of girls at sixth form. 'They settle in very quickly and tend to be very sociable, bringing the boys out of their shell,' explains the head, who points out that this year's school captain is a girl. Uniform includes a vivid purple blazer, and for sixth formers, it's smart dress. Loud, old-fashioned bell system that's a bit of a bone-shaker until you get used to it, but it certainly gets kids moving swiftly from one class to the next.

Pastoral care, well-being and discipline: Excellent standard of conduct and not many discipline problems, yet nobody describes this as a 'strict' school. 'There's nothing onerous about the discipline here. In fact, there's plenty of space to make mistakes and learn from them,' said one parent. 'They have this gentle, reward-based, quite soft culture that brings out the best in everyone,' said another. Punishments, when they do happen, include loss of privileges and lunchtime and after-school detentions. No permanent expulsions in the head's time at the school, although around three temporary ones. Zero tolerance of drugs – possession leads to expulsion – with no cases in recent years.

Lots of staff leadership roles, which helps create a strong pastoral system. Beneath the deputy head is the head of lower school, head of sixth form and heads of year. Big focus on promoting mental health and healthy lifestyles. Buddy schemes; part-time school counsellor; plenty of emphasis on transition to make sure year 7s and new year 12s settle in well. Minimal bullying. 'My first school assembly of the academic year is on how we celebrate difference in this school,' says head – and pupils concur that there's an atmosphere of supporting and looking after each other. 'I can't imagine anyone bullying here,' said one student, incredulous at the thought. Inevitably, there's stress, particularly around exam time – but there's support. 'My son had a wobble due to the pressures of work and the school dealt with it very compassionately, gathering together the relevant teachers to support him and keep us informed.' Students enjoy their leadership roles too, although they said other prefects got to do little more 'than

'There's nothing onerous about the discipline here. In fact, there's plenty of space to make mistakes and learn from them,' said a parent

wear a different tie – there definitely needs some changes there.'

Pupils and parents: Years 7-11 mainly from Colchester and surrounding area, but students travel up to an hour each way each day, including from Ipswich and even east London. Students come from a complete mix of families, both ethnically (including international, especially in the sixth form boarders contingent) and in terms of wealth and class. All feel extremely grateful – rarely have we come across such an appreciative bunch. Very active parents' association (called CRGSA), which raises funds for the school – there had just been an Autumn Fair before our visit – and they're always present at parents' evenings and social events too.

Old boys include Telegraph columnist Giles Smith, economics commentator Tim Congdon, costume designer and double Oscar winner Jim Acheson, founder of Freeserve, John Pluthero and former BBC education correspondent Mike Baker. 'Our alumni are very supportive,' says the head. 'If we have a big project on the go, they always try to help and they are very keen to support anyone who is in a financially vulnerable position – those who would otherwise miss out on an opportunity. They are also supportive when it comes to careers, helping sixth formers move on, offering internships, interview advice and networking.'

Entrance: Highly competitive September 11+ exam, made up of English (including verbal reasoning) and maths papers. Places are awarded in rank order to the top 120 boys who have named Colchester Royal Grammar School as a preference (the school is expanding, so while there used to be 850 students, they're increasing that figure to 1,000). The exam is set by the consortium of selective schools in Essex, which has 12 members, and is held in September at the school. Candidates do not have to live in Essex. Around 450 apply. Head discourages tutoring your way in, but is sensible enough to know he can't eradicate the practice and is therefore trying to offer more support to able local primary school students who can't afford it. No preference for those on pupil premium.

Minimum of four A/7 and two B/6 grade GCSEs for entry into sixth form for internal and external candidates. 'But because places are awarded in rank order, in reality they'll need a lot of A*s,' says the head. Around 450 external entrants apply for the 100 or so places (half of them girls), who also require a school report and must satisfy the school's academic requirements. Candidates for sixth form boarding places must meet the academic requirements first. Overseas boarders must be British or EU passport holders.

Exit: Some 90 per cent stay onto sixth form – 'the five or so boys who leave usually do so because we aren't offering the courses they want,' says head. Sixth formers virtually all to university, mostly to Russell Group including Imperial, LSE, Durham, Bath, Bristol and increasingly, St Andrews. In 2017, 26 to Oxbridge and 24 medics/vets/dentists. Four to Hong Kong unis (medicine, engineering, dentistry, accounting & finance) and one to study engineering at MIT. Popular courses include sciences, economics, history, English and languages.

Remarks: 'This is the best education that money can't buy,' was a favourite expression of the head's predecessor – and we think that's still the case. One of the country's top selective boys' state schools, which rivals many independents, but without the hard edges that schools of this calibre can have. 'It's exceeded our expectations,' was the most common phrase we heard from parents. Any academically able and hard-working boy (and sixth form girl) should thrive here.

Cranbrook School

4

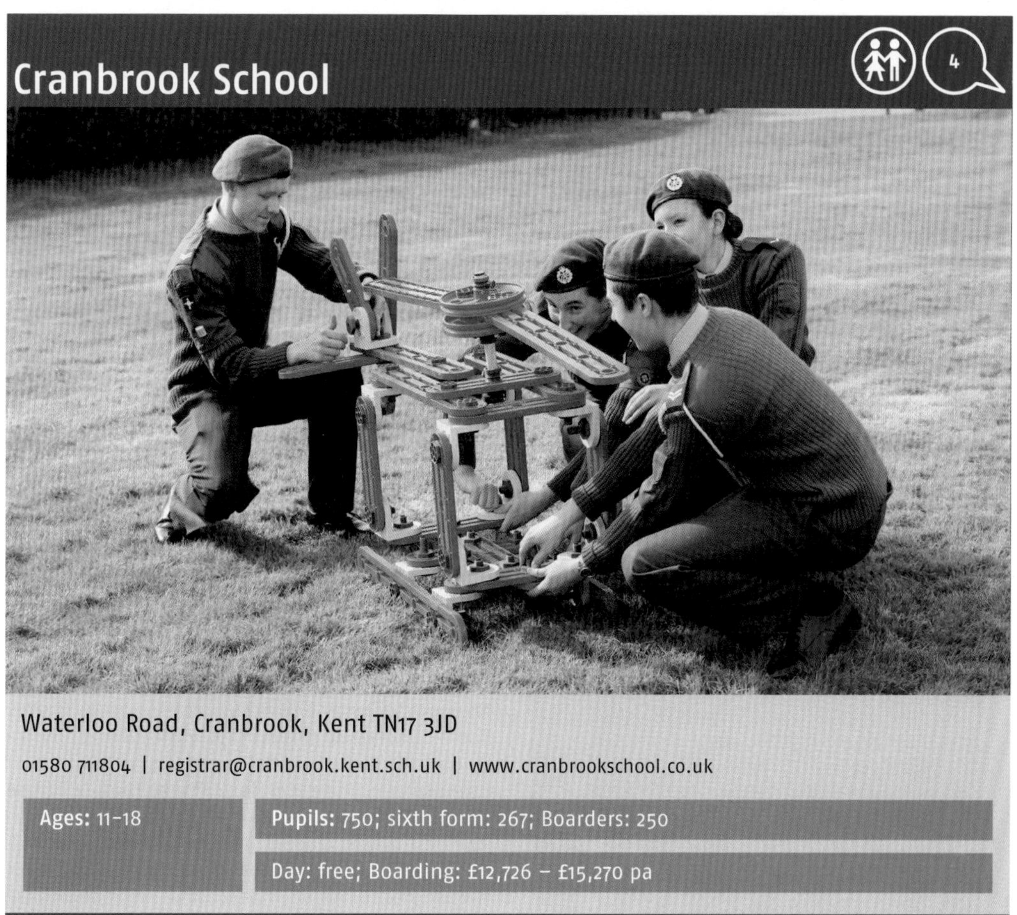

Waterloo Road, Cranbrook, Kent TN17 3JD

01580 711804 | registrar@cranbrook.kent.sch.uk | www.cranbrookschool.co.uk

Ages: 11–18

Pupils: 750; sixth form: 267; Boarders: 250

Day: free; Boarding: £12,726 – £15,270 pa

Headmaster: Since 2012, Dr John Weeds MA MPhil EdD (50s). Read classics at Pembroke College, Cambridge and his academic studies have long been part of his life. He jokes that he didn't want to be outdone by his talented micro-biologist wife, but the letters after his name attest to a driven and committed educationalist.

His most recent thesis was on the subject of the gifted and talented, which will come in useful here. But having consciously chosen to work in the state sector, he is very concerned with equality of opportunity too. He has an eye on re-balancing Cranbrook's increasingly independent school intake; he has ensured there are some less financially demanding school trips and wants to see the girls at Cranbrook given more of a voice too.

His first year was described to us by the tactful as 'a difficult period of adjustment' and by the more forthright as a 'baptism of fire.' The head heartily agrees with the latter, clearly enjoying the calm for now – although the thought of having to tackle performance related pay next makes his hair stand on end.

He found the school somewhat laid back, and hasn't been afraid to grapple with it – 'some traditions I'm prepared to take on,' he told us. One of the contentious changes was suits for sixth formers five days a week. 'It's created a different feel – more businesslike and focused,' he says. Understanding that parents 'really do want best grades,' he aims to deliver consistency of performance and to retain the focus on the academic. 'I don't want to lose sight of the diverse extracurricular offer, but we need more balance,' he says.

The parents we spoke to are right behind him. One told us: 'He is not a slick performer but the benefit is that I believe he listens and engages with both students and parents.' Another said: 'I feel his quest to raise results is to be praised and supported.'

He has three university-age sons.

Academic matters: A level results generally on upward curve; 71 per cent A*-B, 37 per cent A*/A grades in 2017. There have been tweaks all round, including a new approach to mock exams. Pupils know what is expected of them and are fired up to achieve it.

Some subjects notably outperform others by a mile, namely the large cohort of talented mathematicians. The school has been a specialist science school for years and has a new observatory equipped with telescopes. A third of pupils take science A levels, with chemistry particularly popular with the girls, and almost all taking single sciences at GCSE. Strong humanities, but English seems to be a weak spot. Head says the new assessment framework is challenging. Numbers taking languages fall off at A level, to only 10 per cent. Most seem pretty focused on traditional curriculum subjects but a sixth form enrichment programme offers additional choices such as astronomy, sports leadership and psychology.

Boarders can invite day pupils over after school and it's easy to see how self-sufficient youngsters can be here, without the need of the rural parental taxi service

At GCSE in 2017, 56 per cent A*-A/9-7 grades. Pupils study 11 or more (mainly academic) subjects at GCSE, excelling at maths, physics, Latin, IT, French and art. Maths and RE are out of the way a year early. A third of maths whizzes currently take home an IGCSE too, with year 9 and 10 students winning a clutch of gold medals in national maths challenges. Languages on offer are French and Spanish, with Chinese for native speakers.

More than a third of teachers have been at the school for longer than 10 years. The head assured us that only two staff left last year but parents are less concerned about turnover. They approve of the new focus on performance and are keen on removing the few 'dead wood.' One told us: 'There are a handful of teachers who struggle to control the class and some who could explain their teaching and homework better.' Other teachers singled out as inspirational. The pupils we spoke to said teachers will stay behind to explain things if they don't understand something, while RS and physics teachers were praised for their revision guides and pre-university preparation. The brilliance of the maths results is due quite simply, says the head, to 'the best maths teacher in Kent.'

Parents seem split between those who think the amount of homework is about right and those who think there should be more, particularly in the holidays. A pupil said: 'Teachers will always give you more if you ask for it' – clearly a loophole for the less inclined, but there don't seem to be many of those here. The online parent portal keeps parents up-to-date with progress and there are half-termly assessment records for effort and attainment.

Two full-time student support assistants offer additional support for specific difficulties (outside the classroom). SENCo is a dyslexia specialist and admin assistant is also listed as having mentoring skills. Between 10 or 20 pupils each year with special educational needs (whether or not recorded by the local authority as such).

Head told us with feeling: 'We're very committed to supporting those with particular needs. We will do just about everything we can.' If pupils need a laptop they don't necessarily need to bring one – the school will find one. Pupils won't slip under the radar here, he said, and added: 'We will pick up those who can become hard on themselves and down, and won't forget other children who can achieve great things.' A handful with EAL needs – EAL tuition is offered free of charge for anyone who needs it.

Games, options, the arts: School has a strong sports tradition. Fifty acres of sports fields and everyone participates. High-calibre cricket and rugby teams, with a growing fixtures list. One pupil told us he'd left a prestigious local grammar specifically to join the Cranbrook rugby first XV (he'd played against the team and admired it). Hockey and netball strong too. Some pretty glamorous sporting tours – South Africa for cricket, Fiji and New Zealand for rugby. A team of under-15 girls recently became British fencing champions. Facilities include an outdoor heated pool, squash courts, Astroturf, plus sports hall with dance studio (currently offering Bollywood classes), climbing wall and gym (popular in the evenings with sporty boys).

Not much consensus about music here. Head claims it's the 'story of the year' but some parents not so ecstatic. One told us: 'One concern is that the extracurricular music programme is not as strong as it could be. There are great facilities and talent but this is not always harnessed effectively.' It's certainly a well-resourced and vibrant part of school life, with several choirs, an orchestra, jazz and rock bands, folk, string, sax and brass groups, charity concerts and community carol services. Total of 150 students take individual instrument lessons, with many learning more than one and working on higher grades. Lots of pupils trying an instrument for the first time. Live music at every assembly and whilst pupils still seemed a little wrapped up in their early morning fugs we saw teachers toe-tapping along to a jazz band which could easily take a turn at Ronnie Scott's. However, no longer offers music GCSE or A level due to funding cuts.

The more artistic may be in the minority – only a handful taking art A level. Having tackled exam performance as her first priority, art teacher is encouraging boys into the classroom (now one third of pupils). Art room is open all hours and cool graffiti art pop-ups grab the attention of everyone

as they move around the school. Large, well-used facilities for DT and food technology.

The Queen's Hall is the home of the drama department and is a fully equipped and recently refurbished theatre – largely run by the pupils, but also used by outside touring companies. Annual house plays as well as junior, senior and whole school productions.

What Cranbrook does well is encourage pupils to be self-reliant and take responsibility, whether that is through CCF or D of E, fundraising for the charities they care passionately about – no standard Sports Relief here – or being given the freedom to set up any clubs they're interested in (40 at the last count, including curling club which promptly won a county-wide competition).

Annual trip to Tanzania to work on health and education projects is a stand-out opportunity. Pupils compete for a place and work hard to raise the money themselves. 'It was the best thing I have done in my life,' said the head girl. There's also an exchange partnership with a school in Kerala for two weeks at the end of the autumn term. All richly eye-opening, and no doubt contributed to the school's International Schools Award from the British Council.

Enrichment programme for years 9 and 10 means pupils go off timetable for two weeks. 'We take them out of their comfort zone,' said the head. 'They have to research and do presentations on what they've learned. This year they met everyone from a policeman to a prisoner. It gets youngsters who are bright to think.'

Boarding: Boarding houses are a bit of a lottery architecturally – some old, some modern. The year 10 dorms we visited in one house were more like tiny ships' cabins, with multi-tasking bunk-beds/desks, but as pupils get older they often get more space. There's a rolling programme of new carpets, curtains and bathrooms and we were impressed by the accommodation – squishy sofas, polished wood, no institutional paint colours (tasteful greys). Washing gets turned around in 24 hours – setting the bar quite high for when pupils return home – and there wasn't the slightest whiff of a less than fresh sock. Boarding pupils can invite day pupils over after school and it's easy to see how self-sufficient youngsters can be here, without the need of the rural parental taxi service.

Background and atmosphere: Founded in 1518 and given a Royal Charter by Elizabeth I in 1574. School's buildings straddle the main road into the pretty Kent town of Cranbrook and are a jumble of every architectural style, from 1970s accommodation blocks to a fine Georgian mansion. Local church of St Dunstan's is in the middle of the campus – very much part of the community.

The fact that Cranbrook is a selective state school with a large boarding contingent gives the place a unique feel. The alumni society is awash with hugging groups from reunited houses. Total of 12 houses – seven for boys and five for girls. Day pupils are grouped geographically to start with to help out of school socialising.

Art room is open all hours and cool graffiti art pop-ups grab the attention of everyone as they move around the school. Good facilities for DT and food tech

A parent told us that the school offers 'a balance of high academic achievement and extracurricular activities that is the equal to many public schools.' Another described Cranbrook as 'a very intriguing mix of competitive and laid-back.' They added that 'it places responsibility on the students rather than spoon-feeding them, which means that students need to step up.' Pupils want to go places here – it's not uncool to be clever.

Pastoral care, well-being and discipline: Pastoral care is highly praised. On arrival each child is allocated a tutor who will monitor their academic and activities programme, social progress and work with their head of house. As one parent pointed out, the houses and tutor groups are something of a haven. Pupils return to their houses regularly throughout the day – which helps to prevent the build-up of any bullying.

Mentoring is a word that crops up a lot (peer to peer, sixth form to younger pupils, staff to pupils). There is a smart new medical centre (like a mini hospital, with beds for sick boarding pupils), and counsellors offer appointments four times a week. Head has tightened up on discipline and believes the behaviour of pupils is now excellent (a view backed up by parents). Good liaison with parents, plus contracts for good behaviour.

Pupils and parents: Head says that youngsters who are 'particularly interested in learning' and have 'a real spirit of enterprise and adventure' will thrive here. Parents reckon school is ideal for self-motivated, well-rounded pupils who have capabilities beyond the academic, and are organised, not overly sensitive or under confident – or 'the engaged, interested and aspirational'. The place 'may not be suited to students expecting to be hand held,' although quieter children have found their niche too. Independence is held in exceptionally high esteem.

Parents tend to be less the super-rich and more middle class professionals with increasingly high expectations. Definitely a varied bunch, suggesting there's a good chance of finding like minds. Some parents are reputedly stirred up and vocal about the recent changes, whilst every other parent we spoke to was quick to say they liked to be 'hands off.' Head cites strong relationships with parents and a tradition for supportive involvement, particularly with careers teaching.

Notable alumni include Es Devlin, superstar stage and costume designer of the 2012 Olympic closing ceremony, Tim Smit, founder of the Eden Project, astronaut Dr Piers Sellers, comedian Harry Hill, designer Ptolemy Mann, journalist Sir Charles Wheeler and sports commentators Peter West, Brian Moore and Barry Davis, plus many high up in the Forces.

Entrance: Selective, catering for the top 20-25 per cent of the academic ability range. Has historically started at 13, but had first 11+ intake, of day pupils only, in 2017. This will gradually increase, from 30 places in 2017 to 90 places from 2021 (all day pupils), whilst the 13+ places decrease (from 162 to 72, including 52 boarders).

There is an 8.5 km preferred catchment, pushing up house prices even further nearby (inaccurate addresses taken very seriously). Applicants previously often came from the Cranbrook state secondary, The High Weald Academy. Now the competition has shifted up a gear – a strong intake from prep schools such as Marlborough House, Dulwich Prep and St Ronan's. Boarders mostly come from just outside the catchment area – most within 40 miles, including London and the home counties. About one third are based overseas – they must hold an UK or EU passport.

The 11+ admissions are via the Kent test – multiple choice English, maths and reasoning papers, plus a writing exercise, held in September of year 6 with the results given before the local authority application deadline. Sign up in June of year 5. The 13+ entrance exam (day pupils in January, boarders in November) is a three-hour, multiple-choice verbal reasoning test, plus the school's own papers in maths and English. As for some other Kent selectives, now a more rigorous English entrance exam, including 20 minutes of free writing, looking for flair beyond the basics. The maths test is based on the national curriculum, but designed to root out those performing at the higher and lower ends.

Only room for a few new entrants into the sixth form – 16 or so day students and a few new boarders. They require 11 points at GCSE (or equivalent) with A*=4, A=3 and B=1 point, but given lack of spaces, likely to be far more demanding in reality. Anyone who does not achieve the 11 points at GCSE is asked to leave.

Exit: Around 25 per cent a year exit at year 11. Parents and pupils feel the school prepares well for university, and helps with gap years too. Around 95 per cent of sixth formers head to university. Ten to Oxbridge in 2017, three medics/vets; a large contingent to Russell Group. Popular destinations include Bristol, Nottingham, Leeds, UCL, Warwick, Exeter and Birmingham. Many traditionally academic subjects, but also Asian studies, criminology, anthropology, product design and psychology.

Money matters: New academic scholarships for year 9 entry – 'identifying those who are not just just strong at their subject, but passionate as well'. Small financial reward but inclusion in high achievers' scheme.

Remarks: Recent changes have definitely left everyone a little shaken and stirred, but if the school's recent results are anything to go by Cranbrook is raising its game nicely. As an alternative to the high pressure Kent grammars, with the facilities and atmosphere of many private schools and the fun of boarding too, it's an excitingly different proposition for the adventurous young teen.

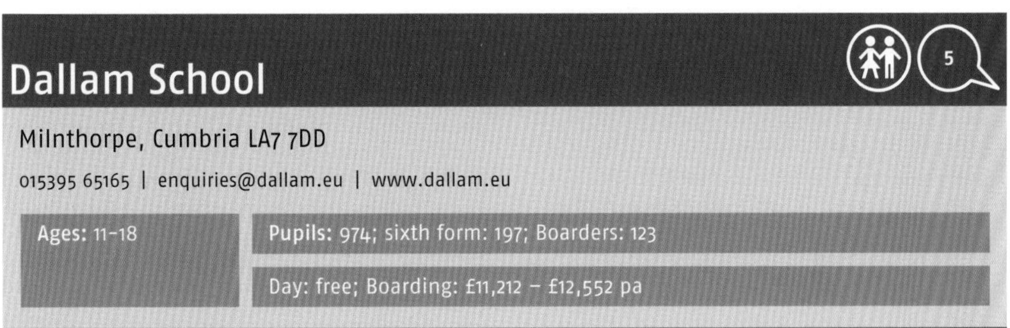

Dallam School

Milnthorpe, Cumbria LA7 7DD

015395 65165 | enquiries@dallam.eu | www.dallam.eu

Ages: 11–18

Pupils: 974; sixth form: 197; Boarders: 123

Day: free; Boarding: £11,212 – £12,552 pa

Headteacher: Since 2013, Mr William Bancroft, 50s, previously head of Settle College. Has a BA in history, though no longer teaches, plus PGCE, postgrad diploma and NPQH; currently chair of the South Lakes Federation of Schools. Warm and welcoming, nothing brash about the man; he's quietly spoken yet at the same time commands both attention and respect, giving the clear impression that he knows what he's doing here. And there is no doubt that he does: he has plenty of headship experience, this is his third to date and both pupil numbers and results are up. He commutes from Lancaster and enjoys walking and skiing when time permits, but acknowledges (without complaint) that school is somewhat all-consuming. Plenty of staff changes since his arrival, which inevitably upsets the apple cart a little, but all appears to be running smoothly now – in fact the place runs like clockwork: prior to our visit they certainly won our prize for speedy and effective communication, which is usually a good sign.

Leaving at the end of May 2018.

Academic matters: 'Learning for All, Learning for Life' is both the school's motto and its mantra. Excellent track record of outstanding achievement in exams with the full range of GCSEs, BTecs, A levels and International Baccalaureate (IB) on offer. Despite the broad intake, it sits very comfortably alongside selective schools in the area, beating national averages: 74 per cent achieved 4-9 in both English and maths GCSE in 2017, with 15 per cent A*-A/9-7 grades; 27 per cent A*/A, 51 per cent A*-B at A level. All very creditable, alongside an IB average of 33 points, with one student getting 42 points out of 45 and 60 per cent getting bilingual diplomas

– clearly something here for everyone. As the only IB world state school in Cumbria, it flies the flag for high achievement; of particular note were strong performances in Spanish, English, history and biology where many students achieved maximum marks. Most stay on into sixth form post-16, around 30-40 per cent following the IB route. Also offers the IBCP or IB career-related programme, which includes at least two diploma programme courses plus career-related studies.

The school is proud of its inclusive ethos, so those with special educational needs are well catered for, and proud of its approach to independent learning, teamwork and activity – didactic teaching methods aren't welcome here. There is a bilingual option for year 7 starters, though competitive so not guaranteed. Good primary liaison helps a smooth transition, important with more than 40 feeder schools. Teaching areas are well-equipped and unusually tidy, as are corridors and shared spaces. There are seven science labs and impressive teaching suites for design technology and food technology.

Spanish and French taught throughout, Italian and German on offer for the sixth form. Super-keen linguists can access other languages through the school's community education wing. Class sizes are around 30, apart from sixth form, where they are smaller. In addition to a range of sport and music options, lunchtime and after-school clubs offer curriculum support in science, art, maths ('Help with Homework'), business studies and a curiously-named 'Geek club' – seems good to us that this is somewhere where it's acceptable to be a geek.. because whatever it is, we'd like to be part of it.

Attracts a strong pool of teaching staff, the adventure learning programme proving a great added attraction. Add to that the fact that you can train to teach here under the South Cumbria SCITT umbrella, the school widens and deepens the pool in which it can fish for good teachers, embracing energy, enthusiasm and talent from those new to the profession.

Games, options, the arts: Two great sports halls at the Milnthorpe site, fitness suite and Astroturf plus multiple pitches nearby, so the school is well-equipped for year-round sport. Add to that a further sports hall at Heversham (home to the boarders) alongside all-weather tennis courts. They are serious about their sport but don't claim to beat all-comers, perhaps because they don't major in any one sport, preferring to offer a wider range than most; that said, we met a lovely netball player currently playing at national level, so no lack of inspiration or aspiration. The BTec outdoor programme sees students paddling rivers, surfing waves, capsizing canoes and mountain walking, clearly fearless in all weathers. A good range of sport is also on offer as twilight sessions for local primary pupils plus Easter and summer holiday sports camps, offering 'classic adventures'; sounds a bit Swallows and Amazons, but we are in the right part of the country for that and they are open to all and hugely popular.

Dallam was the first in the UK to gain Adventure Learning School status. Taking advantage of proximity to both the Lake District and Yorkshire Dales national parks, students and staff participate in canoeing, hiking, camping and other assorted adventurous pursuits. Year 7 students have a residential experience at Borrowdale and year 8 at Ennerdale, and the principles of outdoor challenge are embedded across the whole curriculum. Typically this will involve different subject departments working together with students on extended

studies, often of an investigatory nature, proving learning need not be entirely classroom-based.

Excellent music teaching here with the usual range of instruments available for individual tuition plus various choirs and two bands, including a swing band, and a strong ensemble. Christmas celebrations include a visit to the village church for nine lessons and carols with the music department featuring large. Drama is strong and popular and students tell us that these are the areas where the younger ones have the opportunity to work alongside the sixth form – something they clearly value. High quality drama productions are enjoyed by parents and pupils alike – much talk about the recent production of Oliver!

High quality artwork on display in many areas – pride is clearly evident here. A drama studio, separate dance studio, theatre and large sports hall add to the mix on offer; there's even an outdoor performance area with covered stage that would probably be used much more than it is were it not in Cumbria.

Boarding: For boarders there is even more on offer here. Lots of extra sport plus weekend shopping trips for those needing a retail fix, overnight camping in tepees, paintballing, waterfall and mountain hiking, cinema outings, ice-skating, visits to the theatre and opera, attending pro football and rugby matches, raft-building as well as seasonal activities such as carol singing and bonfire night.

Boarders enjoy shopping trips, overnight camping in tepees, paintballing, waterfall and mountain hiking, ice-skating and visits to cinema, theatre and opera

Boarders' home-from-home is the former Heversham Grammar School in the tiny upmarket village of Heversham. It's not far from school but far enough and different enough to feel like home, at least during term time. If you are up in time, you take the minibus shuttle into school each day and back late afternoon or evening. If you're a late riser you'll have to walk and make your excuses when you get there. Parts of the building are Hogwarts-ish: the charmingly named 'big school' is a communal space within the former school hall, with high ceilings, impressive fireplaces and honours boards of former pupils on display.

A plethora of outbuildings and green play space house a music studio, all-weather floodlit tennis courts, sports hall and a wet store housing climbing ropes, wetsuits and kayaks. There is also

a fives court much loved by old boys and an allotment and chicken house. Staff are lovely – buckets of warmth and care and very much on their game. Well-behaved sixth formers have individual ensuite rooms, all in very good nick; younger boarders are in rooms of two, three or four – less space, but it's their space and that's important. Updating and improving of facilities is ongoing – this isn't the smartest accommodation but it is more than adequate. Unusually, girls outnumber boys in the boarding stakes, but only slightly, and for peace of mind there is fobbed and timed security into all the main buildings and also between boys' and girls' dorms.

Twenty-one different nationalities make up the boarding set – 'a multi-cultural dimension from which everybody benefits,' says the head. There is some clustering, mostly down to word-of-mouth approval and recommendations from existing and former parents – currently the largest groups of boarders are from Italy (the school is apparently big in Tuscany), Majorca and the Emirates. A small on-site build is part of a plan to expand boarding a little by 2018, with a view to admitting more home-grown boarders as part of a plan to future-proof the facility. The boarders are important on many levels. They add real diversity to the community: 'Some of the most interesting people I've met here are from other countries,' said one pupil; they also, crucially, make the sixth form and IB provision viable in a rural area which really couldn't sustain either of these options without them. Home-cooking, all on-site with menus adapted according to national and international preferences (though the request for sushi hasn't yet been met) and staff keep busy with relentless laundry, all very motherly rather than matronly – there's real warmth and pride in looking after their charges here.

Background and atmosphere: A long and interesting history has created a school with traditional values within a modern setting. The original school was founded in 1613 by Edward Wilson (whose descendants still live locally and continue to work with the school). It all began a mile or so away with the former Heversham Grammar School, now home to the boarders and Dallam community education. The main Dallam School teaching hub is on the site of the former Milnthorpe secondary, all of which has benefited hugely from £12m investment in recent years, creating an attractive, multi-purpose teaching site. Predominantly low level buildings with green paint, the site is very well-maintained with a good car park, plenty of recreational space and residential housing at the perimeter fence. The mountains of the Lake District can be seen in all directions, and whilst on the edge of the large and pleasant village of Milnthorpe, you are a very long way from a Starbucks. The students don't seem to mind this in the least – they describe feeling 'safe' here, a fact which, according to them, allows them more independence, and indeed it does exude a calm yet purposeful atmosphere. The academic challenge is self-evident, but there are also plenty of opportunities for community involvement, public speaking and charity events for those happy to take up the additional challenges on offer – in fact if you don't, 'you'd be missing out,' say parents.

Pastoral care, well-being and discipline: They tuck their shirts in when they see us approaching and girls are nudged into compliance if their skirts are too short – so they know who's in charge. 'We're pretty well-behaved here, it's because we're rural kids,' said one sixth former, summing up the general view. Of course with a mixed intake of teenagers they, like every school in existence, have a few angry young men and scowling girls, but they're definitely in the minority and are carefully monitored and gently prodded into line. Peer pressure being what it is, conformity is the watchword here and parents praise the highly effective Dallam Learner Profile, an achievable and measured reward system of 'soft skills' in years 7,8 and 9 that leads very conveniently into D of E later. Parents tell us that communication is good, 'most staff return calls swiftly, parents are taken seriously, our concerns addressed and we are kept informed of outcomes. Online Parentmail and reliable and useful reporting systems are a bonus'.

Staff are visible in and around the school site, keeping a watching brief, and relationships between staff and pupils manage to appear both friendly and businesslike at the same time. Plenty of responsibility given to pupils, which they like; everyone seems clear on their role in keeping the place ticking smoothly.

Pupils and parents: The parents are mixed and far-flung many with interesting career profiles; liberal-minded university types from Lancaster, plenty of local teachers and headteachers, professionals, farmers and businessfolk from Kendal, Morecambe, Grange and beyond, who are attracted by a school that feels rural yet doesn't suffer the restraints of small rural secondaries elsewhere in the area. It may be sited in a large village, but strong numbers means there are no problems in generating sports teams, maintaining a healthy sixth form and being able to offer good facilities, making it the envy of others.

Well-behaved sixth formers have individual ensuite rooms, all in very good nick; younger boarders are in comfortable dormitories of two, three or four

Pupils are a likeable bunch, at ease with themselves and their surroundings but with no lack of aspiration and ambition. Prefects set an example in all areas; sixth form prefects have walkie-talkies giving them direct access to staff if they feel the need to bring in the heavies whilst on duty and amusingly, even in this digital age when all carry a mobile phone, their walkie-talkies are the envy of younger prefects. They describe their teachers as 'friendly and supportive,' which is always good to hear. They also tell us that the food is good, 'better than it used to be,' apparently, and the bacon buns, if you arrive for breakfast, are 'legendary'. Uniform is smart with a trad blazer badge and lapel badges indicating awards and honours; shirts and ties for all; most are very well turned out and the head will let them know if they don't meet the required standards. For sixth form it's a dress code which appears a little vague in interpretation – no jeans, T shirts or hoodies is clear enough, but there's possibly too much wriggle room in the term 'business wear', certainly for the girls.

Entrance: Over 40 feeder schools, some large, some tiny rural schools, from near and far. No appeals as yet, all wanting a place have one, but that may change in the near future with growing demand. For year 7 day pupil entry, apply via the local authority (unselective). Sixth form applicants need to have at least five A*-Cs/9-4s at GCSE (or foreign equivalent), including English and maths, to study on the IB or A level programme. IBCP students need to have a minimum of four Cs/4s and two Ds/3s at GCSE. Boarding applicants must have right of residence in the UK and be 'suitable for boarding'.

Exit: Some 50-60 per cent stay post 16, a small number move on to sixth forms elsewhere (mainly because of subject choices), others to apprenticeships. No NEETS here; all have a career plan. At 18 the majority go into higher education, one or two to Oxbridge each year (to to Oxbridge in 2017, and two vets), a good number to Russell Group and with overseas students pushing aspirations, some to university overseas (seven in 2017, all in Europe) – the Netherlands is currently popular (and free). Notable former pupils include: Times cartoonist Peter Brooke, opera singer Emma Stannard and BBC journalist and presenter Rob Broomby.

Money matters: Fees for boarding but not for tuition.

Remarks: 'It's ambitious for all its pupils and is small enough to know each one,' a parent told us. Certainly the academic challenge is wider than most and rigorous, too, but there's plenty of room for all-comers, at least for now. Though as a state school with boarding and the IB option to boot, interest in the school is, unsurprisingly, growing from far and wide.

Gordon's School

6

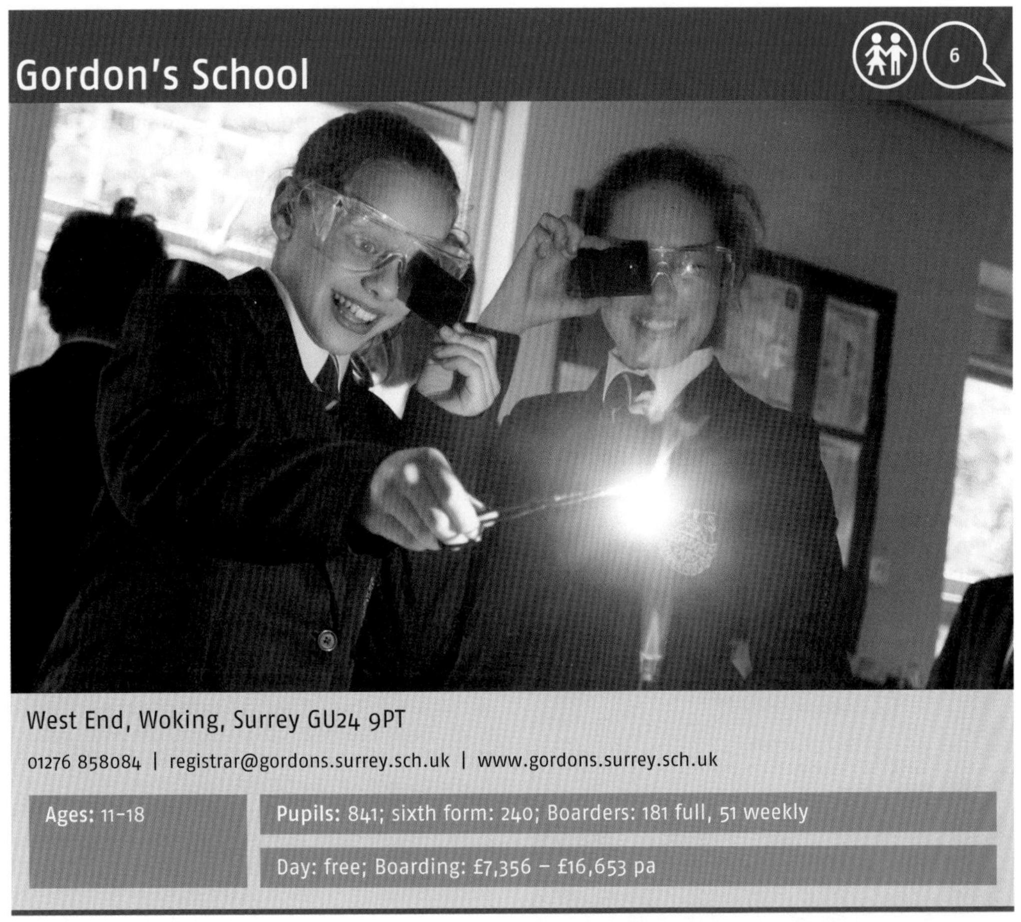

West End, Woking, Surrey GU24 9PT

01276 858084 | registrar@gordons.surrey.sch.uk | www.gordons.surrey.sch.uk

Ages: 11–18

Pupils: 841; sixth form: 240; Boarders: 181 full, 51 weekly

Day: free; Boarding: £7,356 – £16,653 pa

Head teacher: Since 2010, Mr Andrew Moss BA MEd NPQH (40s). Started teaching in 1992 and has worked in a variety of boarding and day schools, including most recently a headship in a Cognita independent school. Before that he was a deputy head in Hampshire, and deputy, director of studies and housemaster at Wymondham College (also a state boarding school). 'He's a breath of fresh air,' said one in the know, 'bringing the school forward, without losing the best parts.'

He's less of a father figure than his predecessor, who transformed Gordon's from plodding to premier league, but is equally enthusiastic about this rather unusual school. 'I'm in the best of both worlds,' he says. 'We have the sort of heritage and behaviour you'll typically see in an independent, but with more grounded, authentic people around, people from all walks of life.'

Every parent we spoke to described him as 'professional', then variously as 'dynamic', 'pleasant' and 'ambitious', although some admitted they did not know him very well yet. 'He speaks well at meetings, seems a good manager and has a very business-like manner,' said one, 'but he hasn't put himself out to get to know people'. Yet all agree he has a good handle on the school and is well-respected by pupils, from whom he'll take no nonsense. 'If he told my children to jump, they would simply ask "How high, Sir?"' said one. Interviewed by pupils in the school magazine, they said of him, 'His signature stern, tough chapel talks have become synonymous with his presence itself'.

He's undoubtedly got strong ideas, but does use staff and parents as a sounding board and talks about 'empowering people' and 'decentralisation'. 'You can't build capacity all by yourself,' he says. 'You need good people to get involved and play a role in ideas and delivery'. Wasted no time in making his presence felt – investing in several projects including building new and revamping existing facilities, improving reporting systems and assessment methods and sorting out better communications with parents.

Keeps a finger on the pulse by taking PSHE lessons on economics and finance once a week. Has two children of his own (both at the school) and is a keen skier in his spare time.

Academic matters: Among the very best state offerings in the country, with an academically rigorous curriculum. It is an all-ability school, for which pupils are not selected via entrance exams, yet its results are top notch. In 2017, 94 per cent of pupils got 4-9 in both English and maths, with 43 per cent A*-A/9-7 grades. At A level in 2017, 37 per cent A*/A and 72 per cent A*-B grades.

All three Forces are represented in Gordon's combined cadet force – quite a feat to manage a naval unit in landlocked Surrey

Its secret? Head puts it down to school's balance of traditional and modern methods – everything from reading out loud and spelling tests, through to use of peer assessment and mini whiteboards. Parents like its size (small), the emphasis on setting (rather than mixed-ability teaching) and its boarding school ethos.

Although two-thirds of its pupils live at home, the school is structured as a boarding school, with these 'day boarders' (as they are known) organised the same way as the wholly residential boarders in an extended school day. So everyone is in a house, with houseparents, and following the same programme, including supervised homework, until 7.30pm.

Everyone is set for English, maths and science (out of four) and also for languages in years 7 and 8 – a language is compulsory at GCSE; either German, French or Spanish. Lowish requirements for additional support; some seven per cent have one-to-one EAL help and four per cent have statements/EHC plans, led by full-time SENCo and delivered in small groups and individually. 'Although it's a regimented place, the school does adapt well to individuals', said one mother. 'They are very good at saying, this person has issues, let's sort him out – and I've seen some children really blossom here'.

They plough through the work, books filled at a pace, and there are plenty of practice papers and timed tests to make sure everyone is well prepared for GCSE. 'The new linear exams will suit us,' says AM. 'In fact we will gain as our work ethic is all about keeping it together to the end'. School has never been keen on the 'retakes' culture which fuelled much of the GCSE discontent.

Parents praise a strong and disciplined teaching team with high expectations that pupils will be self-disciplined to work hard and be courteous at all times. Good systems in place ensure that nobody slips through the net. 'Monitoring is really good', said one parent. 'If someone isn't working at the expected level they will be pulled into a clinic to get them up to scratch'. One of AM's tasks has been to improve the process still further, with more informative, more frequent reporting, particularly for key stage 4/5. On top of an effort grade, pupils now receive target and working grades and every half term they receive significant feedback on what they need to do next. Lessons are fairly formal, there's an atmosphere of calm, but pupils are fully involved. Word on the street is that supply teachers find covering lessons at Gordon's a pleasure – they do not get ripped to shreds as in some state schools.

Homework is 'reasonable' – homework diaries are an important part of keeping on top of everything, really well used, signed every week by parents and school. 'They have to have it with them at all times and it's great for day to day communications, gets them organised and responsible,' said a parent. 'It's almost like the children are on report at all times,' said another. 'But it's for good comments too – they can get a stamp (like a gold star) and sometimes we'll get a note from a head of department or a housemaster if they've done something wonderful'. Evidently the regime can be stressful for some. 'My son cried for half an hour when he lost his homework once,' one mother said.

Around 180 at sixth form take 'facilitating' A levels (serious subjects that will win students places at Russell Group and other leading universities). No vocational qualifications on offer. 'We retain those for whom the sixth form is suitable,' says AM. Parents like it that sixth formers are not allowed off-site during teaching hours, so are more likely to work during their free periods – school calls them 'study periods, there are no frees'.

Ofsted rated school as 'outstanding'; its glowing report is littered with superlatives like 'exceptional' and 'beyond excellent'.

Games, options, the arts: It's all going on, both during the school day and as extracurricular options. After what would be the end of the school day at most state schools, the extended day here begins with 'period 6' – anything from sport to cooking, calligraphy to mountain biking or ultimate frisbee. It's compulsory, and costs over £7,000 a year, although if pupils have a bona fide after hours activity not available at the school there will be a dispensation.

Masses of sport on offer, with good facilities on site – more than 40 acres of playing fields, and all the usual football, rugby and hockey pitches, to the less usual (for a state school) shooting range, Astroturf and indoor heated swimming pool. Gordon's teams are happy to take on the toughest opponents and often play independent schools. Next on AM's wish list is a new sports hall – you don't doubt he will get one. 'Sport is a great release for everyone here,' said one mother. 'There's so much for them to do so that it's not all about pure academia. It's more of a lifestyle, there's a total mix of ages on the parade square after school and always someone around to kick a ball with'. 'I love that my son's outside instead of on his Xbox,' said another. 'The amount of physical activity is great.'

Great tradition of hard-fought inter-house competition gets everyone involved, regardless of ability; not just in sport but also in art, music and drama, with specialist facilities for all – an outdoor theatre is the latest addition. There are two annual art exhibitions and two full scale productions every year. Music very big, as well as an orchestra, choir and concert band, there's a pipe and drum band which, together with marching practice, is a major focus of the school.

Boarding: There are five day houses and four residential houses – all well used by both day and full boarders, who mix well. Boys and girls are allowed freely in each other's houses, but no boy is allowed upstairs in the girls' boarding houses and vice versa. Boys' houses with pool and table tennis tables, girls' centred more around comfy sofas and bean bags. Full boarding houses include common rooms, study areas and dormitories with study/bed units – all homely and understandably more relaxed and not as tidy and regimented as other parts of the school. Ofsted's inspection of boarding facilities pronounced them 'outstanding' in every respect. One boarder said that he doesn't 'go home' in the holidays, saying that he and his parents considered the school to be his main home.

Background and atmosphere: Ceremony and discipline is in the DNA of Gordon's, which was founded in 1885, at the behest of Queen Victoria, as a national memorial to General Gordon who was killed at Khartoum. The reigning monarch has been the school's patron ever since.

Every pupil learns to march and takes part in every one of the eight parades and chapel services held each year, accompanied by the previously mentioned pipes and drums marching band. There is marching practice every Friday, and once a year pupils go to London and literally stop the traffic when they march down Whitehall to the Cenotaph, ending up at the bronze statue of General Gordon on the Embankment. Although right up the street of the keen musicians in the band, it can be rather a chore for the others. 'I wouldn't say the marching is universally popular, but they get used to it – it's just what they do, everybody does it, it's part of Gordon's,' said a parent. 'And in fact after they have left school I think that trip along Whitehall will be a really special memory for them.'

Head puts school's success down to balance of traditional and modern methods – everything from reading out loud and spelling tests, to peer assessment and mini whiteboards

Day to day things are rather less regimented, but all very orderly – AM likes to describe the atmosphere as 'purposeful calm'. The school is built around a large quadrangle, quite bare and military in feel, with the odd bench here and there, where the students hang out during break and lunch if they are not in their houses. Alongside the original Victorian buildings are some less pretty 1960s additions, and (much better) 21st century facilities, including the new music and drama centre, science block and sixth form centre. Classrooms are large, light and spacious, in both the older and newer buildings, and well resourced. Stunning chapel, built in 1894, which houses numerous school treasures, including a book which lists the names of all the Gordon's boys killed in the two world wars. Pupils are never for a moment in any doubt about their school's heritage.

Pastoral care, well-being and discipline: A very disciplined place; 'Without good order there can be no learning in the classroom,' says school. Generally not much allowance for anyone stepping out of line, but for those obedient souls happy to stay within the set boundaries there are plenty of rewards and responsibilities on offer. Pupils quickly pick up on what's expected of them at Gordon's – they get it and are generally hardworking and appreciative of what's on offer. 'It's brilliant fun' and 'not one horrible teacher', our tour guides told us. They don't even seem to mind their 'boarders' duties' – vacuuming and emptying the bins.

School terribly keen on simple good manners, insists that pupils are courteous and considerate of others. Similarly picky about uniform. If a girl's skirt is deemed too short (and we didn't see any) she will be given a week's grace to get a new one. Everyone attends the chapel twice a week. Very close companionship among pupils who say they trust each other. New peer mentoring system working well. Need we mention zero tolerance of bullying, alcohol, drugs and associated misdemeanours? Strong culture of 'telling' to house parents and tutors is encouraged from the off. One longstanding parent convinced it's the combined support from house parents, tutors and teachers that underpins the academic success here.

Pupils and parents: Although it's a state school, most parents have money, certainly parents of boarders who have to cover the boarding fees. Parents of day boarders must be able to afford the £7000+ day boarding fees and will be in a certain socio-economic demographic to live in the catchment; of necessity they must live practically next door and some will move house to get this education for their children. 'We may have spent time and effort moving so close, but we saved on tutoring for entrance to a selective school and are continuing to save a fortune in comparison to the level of fees we'd pay for an independent school now,' said one. Aside from these locals, parents are a huge mix of professional, diplomatic and Forces. Weekly boarders typically live within an hour's drive, full boarders come from all over the UK, with about 15 per cent from overseas.

Pupils seem friendly, happy and very proud of their school; all regular young people, not quiet and cowed by the rules and regulations, but confident and ambitious types who seem to thrive in the order of everything.

Parent/school communications have improved – still a way to go, but would have been more of a criticism a few years ago. Text messaging system, emails, more frequent newsletters and bulletins are all AM innovations and remodelling of website is next on his 'to do' list.

Entrance: Tough. There are typically 400 applications for the 108 year 7 places on offer (76 day boarders – around 300 applicants – and 32 full/weekly boarders) and around half of these are generally swallowed up by siblings. Non-selective, so no entrance exams. Full or weekly boarder places prioritised by 'need to board'. This usually means children from Forces families from the UK and overseas – the school foresees increasing numbers of such children following recent changes to legislation.

For admission as a 'day boarder' think purely of location. Catchment varies but typically you'll need to live no further than 600m from the school. Mother of a baby was enquiring when we visited and local estate agents are well used to dealing with desperate parents who've left it rather later, but want to move next door. A small number of places allocated each year to children with statements of special educational needs.

Some additional places are available for the sixth form, where the entry requirement for both existing and new pupils is five GCSEs A*-C/9-5 (including English and maths) with B/6s for subjects to be taken at A level.

Exit: Around 40-50 per cent leave after GCSEs, some to more vocational courses at nearby Brooklands College. Most sixth formers on to university; around half to Russell Group. Three to Cambridge in 2017 and two medics.

Money matters: The education is free, but parents pay for the boarding, and even parents of day pupils ('day boarders') must pay for the compulsory post 3.30pm element of the day, house system, Saturday school, lunches and teas. Some bursaries available.

Remarks: A very different state offering – more like a private school without the price tag and elitism. Committed to traditional values, high standards, good discipline – doesn't share its 'semper fidelis' motto with the US marine corps for nothing. Those happy with the 'heads down and work' ethos are rewarded with an all-round, top notch education, pastoral care par excellence and enviable opportunities for sport. Suits focused, self-directed types, rather than a rebel who would be exhausted by the discipline. It's a school for achievers – a child with no oomph or aspirations would be lost among these go-getters.

Haberdashers' Adams

7

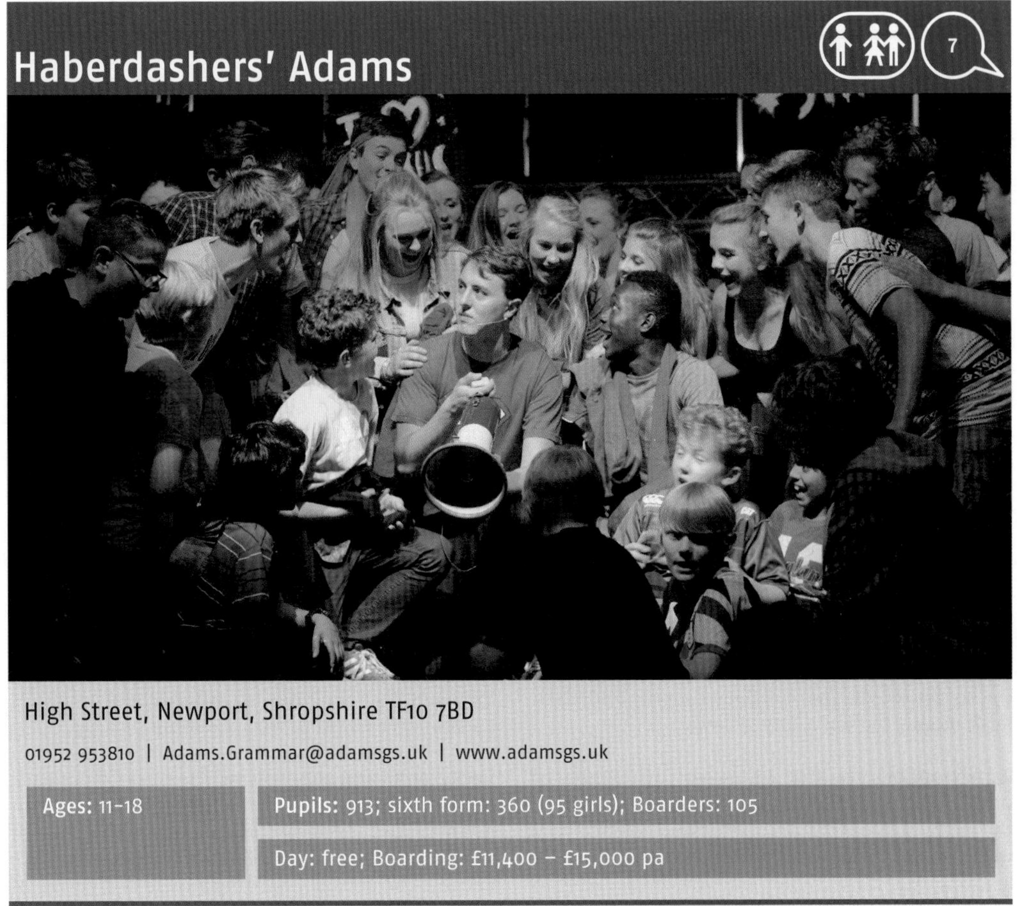

High Street, Newport, Shropshire TF10 7BD

01952 953810 | Adams.Grammar@adamsgs.uk | www.adamsgs.uk

Ages: 11-18

Pupils: 913; sixth form: 360 (95 girls); Boarders: 105

Day: free; Boarding: £11,400 – £15,000 pa

Headmaster: Since 2015, Gary Hickey, previously deputy head. Degree in music and drama from Manchester Met and a PGCE from Birmingham City, and has been awarded a Teacher Fellowship by Cambridge University. Gary is a man of many talents: he scooped a special commendation for 'extraordinary work in drama' in the 2000 National Teaching Awards, and lectures globally on raising the achievement of boys. He is also an award-winning theatre director and a professional musician.

He joined Habs' Adams in 2009, understands it through and through and knows just what potential he has been handed.

Academic matters: Strong results, as you would expect in a selective school boosted by girls coming into the sixth form. A levels were 60 per cent A*-B grades in 2017 and 34 per cent A*/A. GCSEs were 59 per cent A*-A/9-7 grades. Value added is great too. There is a real ethos of hard work from the word go. Staff know students well enough to stop the sort of coasting you can often find with boys after the first year or so. Form teachers are known to email parents after just one late homework and parents find that reassuring. Chemistry and physics results are particularly good – but so is English. Class sizes up to 30 at the lower end of the school but much smaller groups in the sixth form.

Day boarding is an optional extra for boys in years 7–9. It includes tea, after-school activities and then supervised prep, with a 7.30pm pick up

Curriculum is a traditional grammar school one – except there is no classics other than Latin, which is offered along with Mandarin and Polish as an after-school or lunchtime class. Though music and art are encouraged, the numbers taking them at A level are small. One or two slightly unusual A levels such as geology, government and politics and PE. DT popular; has just embraced a Life Bike Design project where the boys are enthusiastically rising to the challenge of building their own bikes.

Very few statemented children and a small number with milder learning difficulties, all of which are broadly dealt with in the classroom, though a part time SENCo has recently started. Students testify to plenty of support from staff if things get tough. There is peer support and sixth form mentoring for younger boys.

Games, options, the arts: A long-serving member of staff told us that the school used to be known as the rugby school that did maths and science very well. Things move on. The science is still excellent and rugby is thriving, but you are as likely to find the students throwing themselves into music and drama as much as into games. Sport itself has expanded, and although we heard one request for girls' rugby, the sporting offer is considered wide enough to suit most tastes. The swimming pool has been covered and even football has controversially been introduced, and students say they love their sport, whatever the weather. House sports competitions include cross-country in the beautiful grounds of the junior boarding house, to get even the less athletically inclined involved, and the emphasis is on inclusion, not solely on the gifted few. But those with the expertise are encouraged to play at regional and national level as well as for the school. Biannual rugby, hockey and netball tours abroad for senior teams.

Performing arts, which also blossomed under the previous head, looks set to continue to grow under the current one, with his degree in music and drama. The tremendously popular house drama and music events draw the whole school into the arts. There are opportunities for the very best actors, actresses and singers in the big school productions – The Crucible, Les Mis, Romeo and Juliet and Grease in recent years. A refurbished art space, although not enormous, stimulates some pretty sensational artwork that is seen around the school.

CCF is very strong and many ex-students join Sandhurst, the Royal Air Force College or Royal Naval College. There are plenty of Easter and summer camps on offer, and boys can join the CCF marching band. There is a good range of clubs and societies. A poet in residence brings in the culture that is not as readily available in the heart of Shropshire as it would be in a big city.

Boarding: New senior boarding house, Beaumaris Hall, close the main school entrance with every room en suite and 'super kitchen'. Junior boarding is idyllically housed about a mile away in a gorgeous Georgian mansion. 'Grade 2 listed buildings cost'; school has clearly spent money on the interior here. There are 100 acres of land attached to the house, used by the whole school for various sporting activities. Boys are bussed to and from the main school. The number of boarders about at weekends varies but there are always full boarders there. Activities centre round games, with some visits and other offerings depending on numbers and popularity. Day boarding – an optional extra for years 7-9 – includes tea, after-school activities and supervised prep, with a 7.30pm pick up.

Background and atmosphere: The school dates back to 1656 – it was founded by haberdasher William Adams – and is one of the Haberdashers' group of schools, adding Haberdashers' to its name in 2017. Behind the senior boarding house is a series of more modern and imaginatively refurbished specialist teaching areas; the new music block is in a converted coach house. The new areas such as the sixth form centre are impressive but there is further to go on refurbishment.

Everyone talks about the house system. The school has managed to generate house energy and vitality without losing a basic allegiance to the school. 'It's not nasty competitiveness', said one boy, 'it's nice tribalism', and we heard about one excellent dancer teaching those in rival houses how to move. The various house competitions encourage everyone to try new areas and the strong narrative is that everyone has a contribution to make. 'It is a great day whoever wins,' one boy told us. 'You have the freedom to choose whether to take part, but everyone wants to because you would be letting the house down if you don't.' There are school and house traditions that apparently take a bit of getting used to but are much loved.

It is unusual to find a predominantly boys' school tackle headlong and consistently the prejudices that can plague all male institutions, so Habs' Adams' very active and visible commitment to celebrating diversity is hugely refreshing. What used to be casually swept aside as male 'banter' is now no longer acceptable and is rigorously scrutinised for racist, sexist or homophobic overtones by the boys themselves. One of the heads of house who pioneered the work told us that initially there was a raised eyebrow or two amongst colleagues, but soon everyone was behind the work. Relevant news articles are routinely circulated, there is a dedicated school noticeboard and dedicated tutor time. The governors have had a presentation and such matters are the standard fare in school assemblies. Girls coming into the sixth form still report a certain amount of 'laddishness' at first, but 'we roll our eyes, get on with our work and they soon get over it.' Students spoke easily about such matters as respect, community and equality, and see a major strength of the school as encouraging everyone to be themselves.

Staff say it's a lovely place and all want their children to come. 'Every year someone's child doesn't get through the exam and it is a real sadness for everyone'. Parents say it is warm and friendly and has the intimate feel of a small school. Pupils spontaneously want to share not only personal news but also what they have been reading or hearing. There is an informality about the relationships and a sense of mutual respect. The occasional child who doesn't flourish is probably the one who doesn't talk to staff or take opportunities.

Pastoral care, well-being and discipline: The school rightly prides itself on its pastoral care and we got a strong sense that not only were all the staff alert to individual needs but the students looked out for each other. There is close communication between the boarding house staff and those running the whole school house system, where pastoral responsibility securely sits. Misdemeanours are dealt with very promptly using a traditional range of sanctions. We were pleased to note frontline staff reported full support from parents. 'We know they will back the school to the hilt when it comes to having to punish someone'. None of the 'my child right or wrong' attitude increasingly common in fee-paying schools. Counsellors attend regularly and the school is very well staffed in non-lesson time.

There is a zero tolerance approach to drugs, parents told us. Other offences are firmly stamped on and the boys know from the start that the school will take any deviation from their high standards very seriously. However, the nurturing goes hand in hand with this and the comment from all the parents we spoke to was that discipline and pastoral care were spot on.

Pupils and parents: The boys are unselfconscious and articulate. They look smart, and the accolade of having won a place at Habs' Adams acts as a real boost to the less confident. The majority of day boys come from a 20 mile radius of the school, which includes Wolverhampton and Telford, so there is more racial and social diversity than you would expect from a school that draws on the Shrewsbury set and is in deep Shropshire countryside. The school does some work with local primaries to try to widen access, but the overall impression is that most students come from middle class professional backgrounds.

Boarders come from across the country and the world (some eight per cent from overseas). If parents are looking for budget boarding with excellent exam results, this is hard to beat. Habs' Adams is one of only a very few academically selective state UK boarding schools.

The school has taken girls into the sixth form since 1993. They are still in the minority, about 95 in a sixth form of 300, which means, according to one girl, that they form a very close community. The type of girl who does well (and, probably, who

applies in the first place) is likely to be feisty and willing to speak her mind – 'just like the women who work here,' said one male teacher somewhat ruefully.

The only kind of child who might not thrive here, one parent speculated, is the one who has been heavily coached for the entrance exam. 'The boys put themselves under pressure: they are all very ambitious and only one can be top,' another parent said.

Old boys include Blue Peter presenter Radzi Chinyanganya, disc jockey Simon Bates, Labour leader Jeremy Corbyn and England rugby player Graham Kitchener.

Entrance: About four or five applicants for every place. The exam is one used by other selective state Midlands schools and is administered centrally, away from the school. It aims to be something which it's hard to coach for and includes reading comprehension, maths and non-verbal reasoning. For sixth form entry there is an expectation of at least five Bs/6s at GCSE, but most have much higher results.

For boarding places, after looked after children, places go to those performing highly in the entrance tests, with Forces children and then boarding need the next in priority order.

Exit: At the end of year 11 a few go to sixth forms that have a wider range of subjects. Vast majority of sixth formers to university – eight to Oxbridge and 11 medics, plus two vets and a dentist in 2017; Birmingham and Cardiff currently the most popular destinations.

Money matters: Tuition is free. The only charge is for boarding, with an optional day boarder fee for an extended day. Lots of flexibility.

Remarks: Amazing value for money as far as boarding is concerned – exam results, academic rigour combined with the community boarding ethos. But this being a state school you are exposed to the vagaries of the political climate and funding constraints of a particular government.

As good as it gets for boys in a single sex school in its determination to prepare them for a world where white patriarchy is no longer the default model. It is a particular type of girl who blossoms in a predominantly male environment – those who do, no doubt have brilliant advantage when they move on.

There is a charm about Habs' Adams that is part to do with its rural catchment, part with an unaffected enthusiasm and part a thoughtfulness – not a combination that is easy to find.

Hockerill Anglo-European College

8

Dunmow Road, Bishop's Stortford, Hertfordshire CM23 5HX

01279 658451 | admin@hockerill.com | www.hockerill.com

Ages: 11–19

Pupils: 837; sixth form: 251; Boarders: 294

Day: free; Boarding: £12,021 – £16,263 pa

Principal: Since 2013, Mr Richard Markham MA. An Oxford historian and former international hockey player who represented Wales, he began his teaching career at Marlborough College in 1994, where a variety of roles (including teacher of history and history of art, deputy housemaster, master in charge of hockey and IB coordinator) culminated in director of studies for his last four years. Insists the differences between Marlborough and Hockerill are 'not as pronounced as most people think', with key similarities including boarding and academic rigour. Whilst he inherited a school that was by no means complacent about its continued success, staff and students agree that he has pushed for a rounder education than his predecessor, believing that 'exam results are important, but a good education is about so much more.'

Relaxed but self-assured, he manages that winning headteacher combo of putting people immediately at ease, whilst still retaining a clear air of leadership. Staff clearly feel valued, able to explore innovative teaching techniques, and are never micromanaged, but woe betide any who go to him with a problem rather than a solution. Regularly dines with groups of students to seek their feedback, pointing out that with 92 per cent of day students eating lunch on site, the refectory is 'a good place to keep your finger on the pulse.' Meanwhile, year 12 students in his history class are taught at the conference table in his magnificent, spacious office.

Married with two children, he lives on site; interests include reading history, as well as playing and watching most sports, notably cycling, golf and hockey, the latter of which he coaches at Hockerill. Favours the term principal over head.

Academic matters: One of the most successful comprehensives in the country. In 2017, 58 per cent A*/A grades at GCSE. Also top non-selective state school post-16, with an average IB point core of 35 in 2017 (and two got the full 45 points) – excellent by any standard.

Part of the DNA of the school is to bookend GCSEs with the IB, with an IB middle years programme that means all pupils continue with a language, arts and technology. Class sizes average around 24, dropping to 18 at sixth form. Setting in English and maths from year 7 and science from year 9. Students expect to (and largely do) work hard and study hard, with Saturday morning school compulsory and plenty of prep (two hours a night by year 10). But this isn't just a school for the academically gifted; it has a wide mix of ability. 'You're not pressurised to get good grades, but you are expected to do your best,' said one student. Another, who has now left to study A levels at an independent school, said, 'Unlike my current school, which is all about teaching you how to get top marks, learning exam techniques, and basically being an alpha student, Hockerill's ethos is that education should be much broader, and I love that I left with so much more than a bunch of qualifications.'

Head claims the biggest change for him was 'coming to a school with a curriculum model I had not seen anywhere else.' Indeed, even in the gilded private sector, you'll be hard pushed to find a school where years 8, 9 and 10 are taught geography and history in either French or German – a programme with 80 per cent participation and which really sets the pace for this truly international school, where languages are genuinely embedded in the curriculum. Seven languages as separate subjects also currently on offer, including Japanese and Mandarin, with less than a handful of students doing fewer than two languages.

Day boarding pupils can be dropped off at 7.15am and picked up at 9pm, great for those living a distance away or working long hours

Truth be told, nothing here is taught in siloes, with students expected to link humanities with languages, languages with art etc. Lots of self-appraisals of work are encouraged throughout the school, especially at sixth form, and teachers are particularly praised for making subjects exciting and offering careers support in their topic area. 'There's a real passion among teachers about preparing us for both university and life beyond university,' said one student.

The college had 15 children with a statement of SEN when we visited, including one wheelchair user, extreme dyslexia and Asperger's, all of whom are dealt with by the SEN co-ordinator, both in and outside the classroom. 'The transition in year 7 was faultless, with the school knowing all about our daughter and her needs before she'd even started,' said one parent, who added, 'The reviews are excellent, the head of SEN is accessible and there's a great emphasis on any extra help being made to be enjoyable.' Meanwhile, the EAL co-ordinator helps the international students who need assistance with language and settling into a different way of teaching. 'We keep abreast of teaching styles in the countries these students come from,' explains head.

Games, options, the arts: The IB requires a mood of involvement and pupils here lap this up, with over 70 popular clubs which run on weekdays from 4-5pm, including fencing, public speaking, knitting and dance. 'Younger students really get stuck in, trying new things out before they find where their interests lie,' said one student. Sport is strong, with girls playing mainly hockey, netball, rounders and athletics, whilst boys are largely drawn to rugby, cricket and football. Fixtures against both state and private schools in all these sports, with the school pulling above its weight, and there's some exceptional individual talent too, with national champions in golf and karate, among others. Facilities are good, with two outdoor courts, a full-size Astroturf pitch, two rugby pitches, two training pitches and a rather tired indoor hall (although there are plans in motion for a new sports hall).

Music, drama and art part of the curriculum until year 10, with music including music technology, and 388 individual musical instrument lessons a week, including the organ (the director of music is an organ scholar). Regular performances from the popular orchestras and choirs, with a good balance of classical and modern, of which one parent said: 'You always go away with goosebumps because they're just so good.' There's a rotating pattern for drama performances – one year, there's a whole school production; the next, there's a dance show; and the next there's an art-based competition. Art and DT boast good facilities and interlinked rooms.

Given the global theme of the school, it will come as no surprise that there are some impressive international trips, including to India and Uganda, as well as language exchanges in years 8, 9, 10 and 12, whilst in school pastimes include Amnesty International and Model United Nations.

Boarding: Nearly all boarders are full time, with just a few weekly. Also on offer is a day boarding pupil option, which enables pupils to be dropped off at 7.15am and picked up post-prep at 9pm, a great asset for those living a distance away or working long hours. 'You do everything the boarders do, except actually sleep here,' explained one student.

Year 7s start off in Winchester (girls) and Canterbury (boys). At 13, boys move onto Durham, and at 15, girls move onto Rochester. Rochester takes girls aged 15-16, whilst Roding is for girls aged 15-18 and then there's the pupils' favourite boarding house, Thames, for boys aged 15-18. All the boarding houses (where the teachers also have flats) are world class – bright, well-maintained and welcoming, with all pupils having a study bedroom, sharing until year 12, then winning their own private space in their final year. Regular room inspections ensure pupils keep their belongings tidy, with downstairs reception rooms in Thames boasting polished floors, leather Chesterfields, beautiful fireplaces and large windows, whilst the other more modern boarding houses including comfortable and homely reception rooms.

All boarders are cared for in relaxed manner by housemaster (male or female), some with own family. All meals are in the refectory. Supervised prep sessions for all boarders, as well as plenty of opportunities for clubs and organised activities, events and trips. In fact, boarders enjoy the vibrant lifestyle so much that many choose to hang around even on exeat weekends. School prides itself on constantly evolving its boarding offering according to student feedback, and there are several forums (eg entertainment committee and food committee). Pastoral care praised. 'My eldest was horrendously homesick for a very long time, and the school was brilliant,' said one parent. 'They make sure there's a real sense of community among the boarders,' said another.

Background and atmosphere: Compact and leafy site close to Bishop's Stortford town centre with

For students who are willing to knuckle down this is an exciting and dynamic place to learn, knocking the socks off many fee-paying schools

an attractive mix of arts and crafts, 1930s and contemporary buildings, including a new boarding house. Boarding schools are a relatively rarity in the state system, but this is very much first and foremost a boarding school, with two large senior boarding houses pre-GCSE and another for those entering the sixth form. (Teachers have flats within the boarding houses.) The school's calendar is similar to a conventional independent boarding school, with longer holidays to allow boarders to return home for two weeks at October half term, three weeks at Christmas and nine weeks in the summer. Pupils make good use of the extra time – 'It allowed me to go to China,' said one. Boarding houses are bright and well maintained and all pupils have a study bedroom, sharing till year 12, then winning their own private space in their final year. Classrooms are quiet, teachers politely addressed. Very strong community feel, with everyone getting involved. 'Not just a place to be – a place where you grow up,' said one remarkably mature young man. Strong sense of mutual respect between teachers and pupils: 'Teachers give a lot. We want the knowledge and the teachers help us to learn'.

Pastoral care, well-being and discipline: A traditional but non-denominational school, where teachers are called Sir or Ma'am and everyone has sensible haircuts and wears uniform (blue in the lower school, black and white in the sixth form). Not excessive on school rules, though, with more of an emphasis on expectations of politeness, kindness and punctuality. 'If you set the right tone, you avoid major issues,' says the head, with low level prep-related detentions about as harsh as it has to get on the discipline front. Attendance problems and defiance non-existent, which students attribute to being well aware there are 10 applications for every place. 'There's an ethos that we are fortunate, and with that comes responsibility,' explained one. Incidents of bullying extremely rare, with incidents of unkindness dealt with quickly. Pastoral care is praised.

Pupils and parents: The latest school photo shows mainly white faces, but by no means exclusively, and even those are by no means all English. Indeed, 40 per cent of boarders (who are required to hold an EU passport) come from overseas, with significant numbers from mainland Europe eg Spain, Germany, Italy and France. Twenty-four nationalities altogether. Weekly boarders generally from 1.5 hours travelling radius, whilst day students tend to be local families. Pupils are articulate, mature, friendly and confident, appearing genuinely to enjoy interaction with adults. 'I walk into school, knowing I'll be stopped and asked how I am and that they really mean it,' says head. Certainly no signs of teenage diffidence, where students avoid eye contact. Parents are grateful. Hockerill Parents and Friends Association, which includes both current and former parents, is an active fundraising and social community responsible for changes such as refurbishment of the library and chapel, and which runs staff bids in the summer term which have resulted in eg 3D printers and a camera for sixth form.

Entrance: Eight hundred plus applications from over 60 primary schools for 120 places in year 7. Hertfordshire residents are allowed four choices at year 7, and you can use two of these to apply for both a day and boarding place. Places are allocated on the basis of siblings, language and music aptitude tests, children of staff and distance. For boarders, priority is given to Forces and diplomatic personnel plus boarding need. Those looking to board are interviewed – away from their parents – to assess how well they would adapt to life away from home. Boarders pay for board and lodgings, but all academic provision is covered by the government. About half of the 130 year 12 places are reserved for boarders.

Exit: Around 40 per cent leave post-GCSE, some because they prefer A levels, some because they don't meet the entrance criteria and some because they fancy moving to a sixth form college or other local school. Post IB, over 90 per cent get first choice of university, with around three-quarters to Russell Group universities (Nottingham, Exeter and Leeds are particularly popular) including four to Oxbridge in 2017. Quite a few to a range of overseas universities. 'We get lots of help to apply for universities, both here and overseas,' said one student. Very wide range of subjects – languages, humanities and medics (four medics and dentists in 2017), disproving the myth that IB makes it harder to get into medical school. Pupils would like to see more alumni involvement, and the school and sixth form are working on it.

Money matters: Boarding fees far cheaper than a conventional independent boarding school, with a day boarding option at £6,000+.

Remarks: 'There is no such thing as a typical Hockerill student,' the head girl wrote in a speech she was about to deliver when we visited, and you really do feel variety is the spice of life at this extremely well-run school, where students are encouraged to gain a genuinely holistic education, but with enough opportunity to follow real passions. For students who are willing to knuckle down (and this doesn't necessarily mean they have to be highly academic), this is an exciting and dynamic place to learn and grow up, knocking the socks off many fee-paying schools.

Lancaster Royal Grammar School

9

East Road, Lancaster LA1 3EF

01524 580600 | theaton@lrgs.org.uk | www.lrgs.org.uk

Ages: 11–18

Pupils: 1,042; sixth form: 296; Boarders: 64 full, 103 weekly

Day: free; Boarding: £10,650– £11,700 pa

Headmaster: Since 2012, Dr Christopher Pyle MA (Cantab) PhD (Cantab) NPQH (mid 40s). Previously a deputy head at Perse School, Cambridge and before that head of geography there, particular interest glaciers, hydrology and climate change. Briefly a manager at Anglian Water before taking up teaching. Married to Sally, a mathematics teacher at a local school, with three young sons, two of them pupils at the school. Headed north back to roots in the Lakes and lured to LRGS as 'the nearest thing to an independent school'. Parents and pupils comment positively on the visibility of the head.

He has been churchwarden and PCC member of a large Anglican church. A keen runner, he has also completed the Devizes to Westminster canoe race for charity, and is a fan of the Lakeland fells.

Academic matters: Superb tradition – regularly in top 100 schools nationally at A level; consistently near top of regional table at GCSE; strong value-added results. Perhaps explains why Ofsted data dashboard not a focus for head. Aiming high taken for granted, as is 'getting stuck in' to support it. In 2017, 43 per cent of A level grades A*/A; 66 per cent of GCSE grades A*-A/9-7. Very much the traditional grammar school ethos, challenging boys to fulfil their potential in a competitive environment. Mathematics outstanding, stronger classics than a lot of independents.

Wide choice of subjects at A level and Cambridge Pre-U including classics and philosophy – a third do four A levels, a quarter add on EPQ. An expectation to lead and be involved with the wide range of extracurricular; sport top of the league; CCF and D of E, volunteering – home and away with InspirUS (LRGS outreach gifted and talented programme) and the Erasmus programme.

GCSE: exceptional mathematics results and strong science as might be expected. HPQ (stepping stone to EPQ) recently introduced. Narrow ability range, setting in mathematics, English and French up to GCSE; class size averages 28. Ten GCSEs the norm; all do technology up to GCSE – school historically had technology, languages, mathematics and computing specialisms. French, German (with annual exchange) and Spanish timetabled, twilight sessions of Mandarin Chinese on offer. Sciences taught separately up to GCSE and all three are popular sixth form options – seen as a 'sciencey' school, says head. Special needs (eg dyslexia, Asperger's) looked after in-house. The especially gifted are stretched by further enhancement schemes and wide-ranging extracurricular provision.

Librarian works closely with English department to encourage reading – using an accelerated reading programme in years 7 and 8, collecting points per book with results published in a league table. IT infrastructure investment so Wifi throughout school but hardware lacking; some netbooks, but BYO not discouraged.

Games, options, the arts: Team games rather than individual sports dominate though increasing opportunity for minority interests that will last a lifetime. Strong rugby and cricket, taken seriously – they beat most independents. Frequent tours – Hong Kong, Australia, Japan and the 'Windies'. An impressive list of other sports, plenty of outdoor pursuits in nearby Lake District and rowing on the Lune leading to some successful pairs at Henley. Much encouragement to join in – no place for couch potatoes.

Music popular; 10 per cent take individual lessons in school practice rooms in the boarding houses. No need for Gareth Malone – choirs popular and everything instrumental from blues to philharmonic on tap. Annual musical drama production in city theatre (often with Lancaster sister school). Very good art and design results.

An extensive and eclectic range of extracurricular, humorously titled to suit all tastes or none (Texas Hold'em Society?) from Bad Boyz Bakin through Doctor Who Catch Up to PhilThy. These are on top of all the expected sport and fitness, debating, D of E, CCF, expressive and performing arts.

Boarding: Boarding gives the school an edge and identity and attractive facilities have understandably brought a resurgence of interest from 'first generation' boarders, often from the Lakeland valleys. Some 10-12 per cent of boarders in years 7-9, increasing to 20 per cent in year 10; few international boarders. Weekly boarders are the majority but about 60, mainly older boys, are full boarders. Fees for weekly or full boarding are the same so boys have flexibility to stay weekends, often influenced by sports fixtures.

An impressive list of other sports, plenty of outdoor pursuits in nearby Lake District and rowing on the Lune leading to some successful pairs at Henley

Junior boys have a splendid boarding house with views to die for and a back garden of immaculate cricket pitches with the stunning backdrop of the Ashton Memorial. Dorms are bunk-bedded, cheery, comfortable and well-furnished, with sitting rooms and homely kitchens for tea and toast after school. Seniors have a choice of two houses, School House and Ashton House, each with different character and design. School House is an attractive and well-designed conference centre-style building adjoining a Victorian villa, with some comfortable ensuite single studies alongside relaxed sitting rooms and a modern kitchen, allowing the boys both privacy and companionship as and when required. Ashton House is more traditional, with bigger rooms of up to four beds, but similar recreational spaces and kitchen facilities. The houses exude family atmosphere (with gardens, tree planting and chickens) and the boys speak warmly of collegiality and that this really is 'home from home'.

All the house staff have an academic role and there are now communal study areas in each of the houses for homework, as well as a desk in each of the dorms. Boys are given some freedom (Lancaster is a small city) and there are organised activities most Sundays, whilst Saturdays are taken up with prep and sports fixtures for many.

Catering is considered 'acceptable', no complaints so must be a positive. Dining room has had a recent cosmetic makeover with the addition of rainbow coloured chairs. New Grab and Go café in award nominated new City View building voted a great success by all.

Background and atmosphere: An ancient foundation, in existence by 1235 and endowed in 1472. Moved to its current location in 1852 when Queen Victoria donated £100, hence its 'Royal' tag – and the school still receives the same amount (sadly not index-linked) annually from the Duchy.

An extensive though fragmented site skirting either side of hilly East Road around a busy crossroad – pedestrian and vehicular. Building styles change from gothic to modern from the lower to upper site, and timetabling can mean crossing two roads between lessons, but boys take it in their stride and 20mph speed limits are enforced. Mixture of Victorian houses and purpose-built blocks in traditional style, leading to newer additions (science and business/design centres, new boarding houses). Parking is tricky but most walk or use public transport.

Though there is some resemblance to its independent competitors, lack of funding is evident in some parts of the school. It doesn't necessarily matter, as the school's focus is rightly on excellent teaching and positive learning outcomes, but it does mean the place can look a touch untidy at the edges. Extensive areas of the Old School House have been decommissioned but, at last, it seems priority school funding is coming to the rescue, and the head certainly has grand designs for the building.

Real sense of history and tradition about the place: 'Best of the old and the new' is the head's mantra. Boys bustle purposefully between classrooms that range from tired-looking utilitarian to smartly refurbished. Older parents will be reminded of the grammar school of their youth – 'no-nonsense, no-frills,' said one successful and grateful old boy. An ambitious and exciting 50-year master plan is attracting support from old boys and several years in, there is evidence of some success in the green shoots of improvements.

Pastoral care, well-being and discipline: Boys respond to the no-nonsense direct approach of staff in a school that thoroughly understands them. The school looks to recruit 'schoolmasters' (of either sex) rather than 'teachers'. Thorough care systems for both boarding and day work well – pastoral staff heavily committed to pupils' welfare and relations between boys and teachers admired by parents and inspectors. High personal standards expected. Not much evidence of real wickedness; school suspends for possession and would expel for dealing – and the boys know it.

Junior boys have a splendid boarding house. Dorms are cheery and comfortably furnished

Thriving mentor scheme where senior boys spend time with junior boys with similar interests and prefects have weekly tutor time with year 7 helping with pastoral and organisational issues. All the pupils (and parents) we spoke to commented on the sense of community and excellent staff/pupil relationships.

Pupils and parents: Lancaster is a city with a small town feel – boys come from every walk of life and are a very genuine mix. Head says the school is not about one size fits all. 'We take quirky characters who are valued in school and can say that there will be clubs for you'. Still 'the school on the hill' to some, yet no wish for this to become a middle class enclave – rather it is open to any boy, from any street, who can cope with living and working alongside a future Oxbridge don. Local day boys given preference; about 40 places go to those further afield. Boarders come from all over but must be a UK subject or have an EEA passport and a UK guardian (some 18 per cent overseas boarders from 10 countries).

Boys and parents very proud of school and its regional standing. As one boy put it, 'LRGS is an awesome place to be'. Parents comment that their sons are thriving academically and relishing life as a boarder. Old boys include Prof T Hugh Pennington, microbiologist; Kevin Roberts CNZM, CEO Worldwide Saatchi and Saatchi (retains the link with six summer internships for U6 boys each year); Jason Queally, Olympic cycling champion; Brigadier Alex Birtwistle, foot and mouth star; Tom Sutcliffe, journalist; and Sir Richard Owen, dinosaur man.

Entrance: By oversubscribed competitive exam at 11 (English/maths/reasoning). Three strands of entry: local day, regional day, boarding. Boarders considered separately but all 'must be of an aptitude and ability suited to an academic curriculum'. All must complete a personal statement and attend an interview for sixth form places: 'Tell us why we should give you a place here' – great practice for university UCAS or even the real world. Minimum of six grade Bs/6s at GCSE needed, with at least 5s in English and maths, and grade 7 in maths to study it for A level, for both internal and external candidates. Regularly increasing intake at 16 and growing interest from independents for sixth form places – grab a boarding place whilst you still can.

Exit: A few – around 20 per cent – leave after GCSE; vast majority to good universities, mainly in the Midlands and North, eg Durham, Edinburgh, Manchester, Newcastle, Warwick and York, though some dipping a toe into southern universities such as Bristol and Bath. In 2017, 11 to Oxbridge and two medics.

Remarks: Vibrant, selective grammar school with big reputation in the region; chiefly a day school but also offers excellent boarding provision. Has managed to retain marked degree of independence as an academy, offering a curriculum above and beyond the norm, including classics.

Unashamedly academic but takes all-round education seriously and delivers – recognised by pupils and parents alike. LRGS is a fabulous school which offers a wealth of opportunities to all boys. Besides academic progress, skills and interests are nurtured and developed which adds to the confidence of pupils.

Old Swinford Hospital

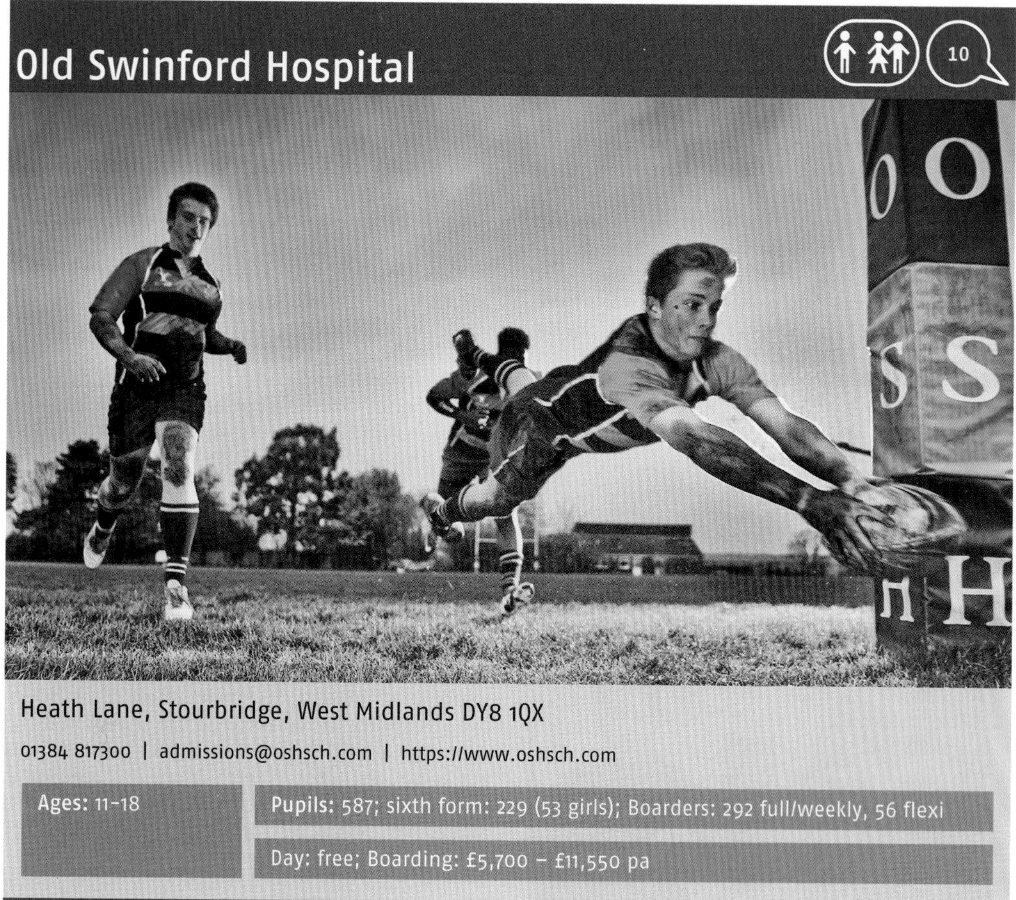

Heath Lane, Stourbridge, West Midlands DY8 1QX

01384 817300 | admissions@oshsch.com | https://www.oshsch.com

Ages: 11–18

Pupils: 587; sixth form: 229 (53 girls); Boarders: 292 full/weekly, 56 flexi

Day: free; Boarding: £5,700 – £11,550 pa

Headmaster: Since 2014, Paul Kilbride, who came from Bethany School, Kent where he was deputy head. He had previously had experience in the state and independent sector, both day and boarding, selective and non-selective, single sex and mixed. His own education was at a British Army school in Germany from where he went on to Magdalen College, Oxford to read modern history.

He exudes energy, charm and engagement. Totally committed to boarding, he loves the traditions of the ancient foundation at OSH. Parents and staff say he has taken on the challenge of pushing up academic standards with mounting success. He is regarded as excellent at leading the work on preparing young people for university, ensuring they have high aspirations and are very well supported. His engagement with all aspects of school life is legendary and he is seen as having brought a fresh vision of 21st century boarding into the school. The pupils, one parent told us, 'simply love him'.

Paul is married to Emma, another Magdalen alumna, and they have three young sons.

Academic matters: The school is partially selective at year 7, with prospective boarders taking an aptitude assessment. GCSE results are strong – 43 per cent A*-A/9-7 grades in 2017, showing an upward trend on previous years; generally around 90 per cent of grades are C/4 or above.

At sixth form, 23 per cent A*/A grades and 43 per cent A*-B grades. These are a bit more variable year on year, but overall there is an improving picture. Although there are entrance requirements for sixth form, they are less demanding than many independent schools and sixth form colleges. The school takes in quite a number of pupils at sixth form level who may have been taught in a less effective way than the 'home grown' groups, and this, too, explains the variability of results here. Partly because of the range of academic ability in the sixth form, the school has recently introduced BTecs in sport and science, and vocational qualifications in business and ICT. The sciences, maths and psychology attract large numbers at A level and get impressive results. The school encourages the uptake of EPQ, which it sees as teaching pupils how to manage and test information for themselves.

Boarding allows time for all the extracurricular activities on offer. Families love the idea that everything is on site

The school does standardised assessments in years 7, 9 and 12 for baseline tracking. Learning support is provided through careful differentiation in class, some setting as the children move up through the school and a strong SEN department. Value added for those needing learning support is particularly high.

Pupils do well, not by being forced or drilled but by increasingly cutting edge pedagogy. At the key stages, the teachers provide lots of extra help. Year 13 are encouraged to contact teachers when the teacher has free periods to clarify any last minute exam preparation. The head has introduced rigorous use of data, encouraged more timely interventions and tightened up punctuality to lessons by introducing sessional bells. He is generally considered to be excellent at holding staff to account, ensuring the whole school community is doing its job at the highest standard possible.

Games, options, the arts: Traditionally this has been a big rugby school, well able to hold its own with the large independent schools and won the NatWest Bowl in 2017. There is a variety of curricular sports. Rugby still is huge and a draw for a number of families, but now there is far more emphasis on broadening the offer both within sport and beyond. For those who try rugby and decide it is not for them, there are recreational sports groups, a multi-sports and a fitness programme. The sixth form girls play netball, join in cross-country, have fitness sessions and can opt for social walking.

Music is 'phenomenal', we were told by parents and pupils. A number of orchestras, bands, ensembles and choirs perform in the school and in outside venues, including on music tours. There are strong links exist between the school and the Birmingham Conservatoire. Drama productions are keenly anticipated and a dance competition is popular with boys and girls. There is CCF, D of E and opportunities for voluntary work in the local community for older pupils.

The head has been encouraging more activities. Participation in co-curricular activities is high and carefully monitored by pastoral staff to ensure everyone is as involved as possible in the broader life of the school. There have been considerable attempts recently to ensure a realistic co-curricular timetable so all the opportunities for, say, year 8s, don't fall on the same day of the week. The school is responding to requests from pupils to introduce a coding and a STEM club, with others in the pipeline. For senior pupils, there are opportunities to coach junior teams and run clubs. Pupil requests are also increasingly shaping the Sunday activity programme, which includes go-karting, raft building and paintballing as well as museum visits. Some activities are charged as extras, though pupil premium money is used to ensure no one need be left out. The aim of the co-curricular programme is increasingly to prepare the pupils for a rich and rewarding life beyond school.

A further manifestation of this aim is the eagerly anticipated enrichment week at the end of the summer term. The offer is huge here, reaching out to all interests, needs and pockets.

Boarding: There is an amazingly flexible boarding offer here. The school is highly committed to boarding but doesn't insist everyone is a full boarder from day one. House staff are aware of what a jump it is, particularly for younger boys and especially for those who come from a small prep school. Parents told us of boys who started off staying one night a week, then when they felt ready, increased it to two and three and then all week. We thoroughly commend this approach.

Boys who want to board need to subscribe to the values of the school, the head tells us – respect for self, respect for others. One aim of boarding is that boys learn to live with those from all walks of life. There is also the increasingly popular option of flexi-boarding where boys stay overnight a few nights each term.

Boarding allows time for all the extracurricular activities on offer. Families love the idea that everything is on site – no traipsing for hours to take different members of a family to different activities every evening and weekend.

The present head did away with Saturday lessons. Instead there is a full programme of activities and space for relaxation. The sports hall and music school are open in the evenings and at weekends. There are trips out every Sunday. The head has also set up a year 13 boarding house, which is very popular and seen as a bridge between the tight structures of the rest of the school and the independence of university living.

There are seven houses altogether – one for year 7s only, five for years 8-12 and one year 13 house. We like this approach. Parents are very drawn to the idea of a separate house for the youngest boys, and the year 13 house allows for an independence that is not possible with a mixed aged range. The houses we saw were very well appointed, airy, light and looked loved.

Boarding life for those coming into the school is very structured. Bed times are adhered to, there are no devices allowed at night. Housemasters feel they are able to give the boys a secure structure and routine that is not always there at home but helps the boys grow into stable adults.

Parents and boys say that house staff pick up very quickly on any small unkindnesses that can occur in day to day living and deal with them before things have time to develop. Houses encourage the pupil voice in various ways and concerns can be raised anonymously. Each housemaster is well supported by a team of house tutors and matrons who are the human face of this corporate parenting.

Induction is taken seriously. There are no academic lessons in the first week for year 7s: instead, a programme of activities aimed at bonding the group together. For the first half term, homework is a consolidation of year 6 work, aiming at getting everyone used to working in silence for an hour. There is an equally thoughtful induction for new sixth formers and they regarded it as an important factor in their speedy assimilation into the life of the school.

Background and atmosphere: The school was founded over 350 years ago by the local ironmaster and MP Thomas Foley to provide residential places for 60 boys so they could eventually be apprenticed to a trade. It is a mixture of highly atmospheric historic buildings dating back to its foundation and very attractive modern additions. In some places the older exteriors have been preserved while the interiors have been completely renovated. The campus, considering that it is in the middle of a Midlands town, is unexpectedly spacious and green. The music school and sports hall are just adjacent to the main campus. Sports fields are situated both on and off site.

The school is relatively small by secondary school standards and everyone said this

contributed to a strong sense of community. It has a very stable staff but that includes a healthy age range. We sensed excellent relationships between staff and pupils and this is certainly a core goal for the head in the drive for ever improving academic and pastoral standards.

This is a school that exudes clarity of purpose. The pupils and staff know what they are there for, expectations are absolutely clear and there is a dynamic structured feel about all aspects of school life. The school does take children whose family backgrounds mean they are crying out for this approach, but everyone to whom we spoke responded positively to it.

Pupil requests have shaped the Sunday activity programme, which includes go-karting, raft building and paintballing, as well as museum visits

Girls can join as day pupils in the sixth form and their number is capped at about 25 per cent of the year. Girls who come are clearly highly motivated and speak very positively about their experience. They often choose OSH as they want the structure of a school rather than a college. There is no doubt they are joining a boys' school, and some say that for the first few weeks the boys are quite territorial and socially awkward with them, but it soon settles down. The girls throw themselves into house competitions; there is girls' netball and plenty of drama, music and debating opportunities for them.

Pastoral care, well-being and discipline: The wide range of backgrounds and needs of the pupils make it essential that the pastoral care here is effective, and it is. Some boys are on carefully monitored welfare plans but all benefit from the considerable experience of the pastoral teams.

The school tackles mental health issues on different levels. Some areas are covered through personal education sessions. Mindfulness is encouraged with the younger ones. There is peer mentoring. It promotes an online facility run by a cyber charity that offers confidential advice. There is a school counsellor.

Pastoral care extends beyond the school. The head will intervene if he hears of unregulated pop-up or house parties. He is keen to work with parents, who are highly supportive of the school's efforts.

The underlying ethos is that families matter and the school is very conscious that it is educating the next generation of parents. Parents see the school as standing for traditional family values, and while they love all the modern technology it embraces, the ethos of decency and respect for others is central to its continuing popularity.

There is a traditional approach to discipline. Expectations are high, pupils are absolutely clear about the rules governing good behaviour and the consequences of someone falling short. There are a range of sanctions including Saturday detentions and exclusions. Considerable thought is given to integrating boys back after a temporary suspension. The school has a zero tolerance policy on illegal drugs.

Pupils and parents: There is a genuine range of backgrounds. A number of families have dipped into the independent sector at junior school age or with other siblings while there are also children who are sponsored to board through a charity because of home circumstances. In most families, both parents work. This led to one slight concern, common to many boarding schools: when term finishes at lunchtime or early afternoon, parents have to take a day off work to collect. Although some children come from further afield, the majority live within an hour or two of the school. It is been a popular choice for Forces families. We spoke to parents who had specifically chosen OSH over independent schools because of the social diversity of the pupils.

Parents regard communication between home and school as strong and appreciate the fact the school is always trying to improve it. A new communication in real time about sports fixtures has been much welcomed. One parent spoke appreciatively about how closely the school had involved her in decisions about the best ability set for her son to join.

Current parents are encouraged to attend open days and induction days to share their experiences with those just starting out.

Entrance: It may take you a bit of time to work your way through the terminology here. There various different options for year 7 entry. There are termly, or full, boarders. There are weekly boarders who can choose to go home on Fridays after prep. There are flexi-boarders who do everything a termly or weekly boarder does except routinely stay overnight – the only requirement is to stay over three or four nights a term. They can arrive for breakfast and leave after prep. Then there are day pupils who arrive in time for registration and finish after lessons. Application deadlines are different for various groups, so do check carefully.

There is no entry testing for day pupils. Flexi-boarding pupils must take a sport, music or academic aptitude assessment. Boarders are assessed for suitability for boarding via an interview and school reference. Most join at year 7. A few join in year 9, but only as weekly or termly boarders.

Sixth form offers are based on a minimum of seven GCSEs at A*-C/9-4, including maths and English (or an agreed equivalent for overseas candidates.) They recommend a B/6 grade or higher in subjects to be studied at A level, with some subjects expecting A*/A-9-7s. Sixth form entrants come from state and independent schools.

To be eligible for admission to OSH, all applicants must have full UK or EU/EEA, Swiss, Norwegian or Icelandic nationality or have other approved UK residential status.

Exit: A relatively small number leave at the end of year 11 to go to sixth form colleges where there is a wider range of non-A level courses and an atmosphere that is more college and less school. Sixth form destinations in 2017 included medicine at Bristol, nursing at Birmingham, biotechnology at Imperial, law and Spanish at Leeds and chemistry at St Andrews.

The former polys are popular with those who are looking for courses with a high practical element. Quite a few get prestigious apprenticeships.

Money matters: If you are considering boarding, OSH represents amazing value for money and is well worth a visit. Tuition is free is free and parents just pay for the boarding side. The school has a link with a major charity that funds some families in need so they can board even though their family could not afford the fees.

Remarks: Parents increasingly compare traditional independent Midlands boarding schools unfavourably with what OSH has to offer at a fraction of the cost. They like its diversity of family backgrounds, which you don't find often independent boarding sector. But although the boarding life of the school can certainly hold its own with the independent sector, this is a state school and like all others it is currently having to re-examine its budget. One or two less popular A level subjects will not feature on the curriculum next year and according to the head, everyone is 'rolling their sleeves up' to protect the front line teaching. Another response is to grow the school from the bottom end, so year 7 is larger than in previous years.

Day and flexi-boarding places at 11+ are highly sought after – it is regarded as the best state day school in the area. It is worth noting, though, that not all co-curricular activities are available to day pupils, which is why families are keen to opt for the flexi-boarding option.

This has a very British feel compared with some other boarding schools. The historic buildings contribute to this, as does a real sense of continuity. The chair of governors, for example, has an association with the school which goes back to the early 1990s: his son was a pupil here and now his grandchildren are at the school. The founding Foley family still have an interest in the school, with a family member having always sat on the governing body.

OSH probably best suits those who are looking for a stimulating, rounded education that is not too academically or socially exclusive.

Peter Symonds College

Owens Road, Winchester, Hampshire SO22 6RX

01962 852764 | psc@psc.ac.uk | www.psc.ac.uk

Ages: 16–18

Pupils: 3975; Boarders: 74 full

Day: free; Boarding: £13,200 – £14,160 pa

Principal: Since 2013, Stephen Carville BA (French and German, Southampton), MA MBA, at Peter Symonds since 2002, first as assistant, then vice principal. Previously an Ofsted inspector, and manager and teacher in sixth form and FE colleges.

Parents who know him, like him: 'He's great. Very caring, very nice.' 'Bright and capable.' Another said 'I've never actually met him...', which is not so surprising in this huge college, where the role of head is perhaps closer to that of vice chancellor of a university.

Academic matters: Often chosen for academic prowess, results here are excellent: in 2017, 62 per cent A*-B, 34 per cent A*-A; 'head and shoulders' above other options, said a student. This largely non-selective college achieves impressive value added: up one grade across three A levels. 'Staff in schools often tend to focus on the GCSE hurdle', explains the head: here the focus is entirely on sixth formers, and they evidently benefit from this. 'Education is most important here', said a student, describing, wearily, how in some schools everything is important; 'here: education', she said simply.

A good variety of A levels on offer, including the less usual environmental science, commercial art and graphic communications. Offers a few BTecs, including health & social care, music technology and sport. Only maths and science are selective (A/7 at GCSE), with students in maths and biology consistently achieving top grades.

Students here are treated as young adults. Boarders' time is not structured, although they are expected to study during quiet time from 6.30-8.30pm

Students said they would like more information on non-secondary school subjects and methods of teaching before they start – 'can go in and love or hate'; but they do have a taster day, when they try each of their subjects and get a course overview; they can also take four subjects with the flexibility of dropping one after the first year.

Students report some subject gender divide, more girls taking sociology, English, classics and law; more boys taking economics and computer science; but sciences and maths are well balanced.

The EPQ is available...'ah, love it', said the group of students we spoke to, 'if you have a burning passion...' ; although students said around half of the EPQ class drops out because of the need to work over the summer. But nice to escape the restrictions of A level, said one student; the 'write this argument'; and '[I got a] reduced offer from university because of it...'.

Classes are mixed ability, with 16-20 students. An experiment putting maths strugglers into small sets with the best teachers showed they did no better; the conclusion: that working with peers who are motivated and succeeding does more for struggling students. Additionally there are three sorts of workshops in every course: support workshops, for the struggling (attendance might be obligatory); extension workshops, to push the able; and structured workshops, for exam revision.

There's not the coercion you get at school, say students, who like this: 'Because you choose the subject, failing is only your own fault. So pull yourself up – and people do'. It's a different vibe to school, one explained: 'it's cool to do well'.

In this supportive student body 'uppers help lowers,' said a student, or teachers will help out. Study support is very good, said a parent: 'Grand at helping you study independently...if you seek it out'. It's not a place for those who need hand holding, parents agree: '...if you're concerned with being cool and a bit embarrassed about seeking help...you might need shoving a bit more'.

The SEN unit supports 900 students with mild-severe physical or sensory impairments, or mental health needs. 'This college places great value on SEN and the tools we need to do the job', said head of SEN gratefully. '[We are] very very supported by senior management'.

Range of support includes one-to-one sessions, in class support and other assistance: the physio room with plinth means that students in wheelchairs can come and take a rest; a frame allows another student to work in a standing position. A student with narcolepsy comes in to sleep during her free periods, and they have supported one with muscular dystrophy who could only move his head and one hand slightly. 'We work hard to find creative way to meet student needs...if we need additional support we go out and find it'.

The unit will help any students who want to develop independent study skills – 'not just a special place for special people', said head of SEN earnestly, but the onus is on the student to seek help. One parent told us her mildly dyslexic son gets extra time in exams, but that's it. '[He] muddles along with essays – doing ok, but they could hand hold him a bit more'. The help is there if he asks for it, thinks the parent, but her son is 'slightly embarrassed and lazy...'.

Careful preparation for competitive university entrance, with interview practice for anyone who needs it, and a dedicated Oxbridge tutor. The independence and responsibility of college prepares pupils well for university, and parents report a smooth transition between the two.

Students can make an appointment to explore their career options, but a certain amount is laid on for those who aren't likely to do this, such as careers week and the careers fair.

Games, options, the arts: Students must take part in one activity, and there are plenty to choose from, including rock challenge, national dance competition, colouring club and young Liberals. The college supports many activities which are set up by students: Symonds Speaks, the debating club,recently beat Winchester College, which the head understandably finds pleasing.

A number of students do community service as part of the D of E, but the head would like there to be more of it, and ponders how to give students an understanding of the value of volunteering which is independent of the utilitarian desire to pad out a CV. A programme to encourage volunteering will be launched soon.

Peter Symonds is home to Hampshire Specialist Music Course: just 12 places on this highly selective course, but it is the cream of music provision: students get one and half hours of individual tuition a week, as well as opportunities to form chamber groups and orchestras.

Anything Goes was the latest musical, performed in the Theatre Royal in Winchester with a full orchestra from Peter Symonds. Productions are of good quality, said a parent, but there's not that much drama (compared to independent schools).

Peter Symonds is the national leading sixth form for games, and if you excel at sport, the chances are you will quickly be in a team, but just the one team: keen sportspeople must choose their favourite sport. There are usually four teams for each sport, and those less talented can be part of the recreational team ('limp offering if just for fun,' said a parent). It can be a shock for those who were a big shot on the school rugby team to arrive at Peter Symonds, compete against 500 others, and not make even the fourth team. One parent told us her kids opted to take up lacrosse: a new sport to most, so an assurance of a place on the team.

Sun pours through the slanting glass roof of the art block, which has doors that open out onto grass; a nice space to work in, though no designated spaces for individual students, so work can't be left out. Students in the vibrant textile department consistently achieve high grades; a recent project with the neuroscience department at Southampton university involved developing dresses inspired by mental health problems; schizophrenia was a dress with long arms tied behind and a metal cage on the head. In 3D sculpture, dismembered Barbies and Ken were hanging from the ceiling in willow balls, alongside blown up blue latex gloves; curiously lovely, resembling some rare aquatic flower.

Boarding: '[It's a] boarding facility, not a boarding school', said head of boarding firmly. 'Not like the packed schedule for boarders at Winchester College, and students should not have these expectations', said a parent, although boarders are taken out for a team building day at the beginning of the year, and have various themed dinners. They can use the gym and sports hall three times a week after school hours.

Students here are treated as young adults; time is not structured, although they are expected to study during quiet time from 6.30-8.30pm. Safeguarding is taken seriously: students are always monitored in house, and day parents get students up – or attempt to – if they've got an 8.30am lesson. Each boarder has a care plan, which records everything that happens to them. But you 'don't have to go out; don't have to go to dinner', said a student who'd experienced independent school boarding, with evident relief. Students don't have to sign out to leave the campus, and just need to be back by the generous curfew times: 10.20pm during the week, 11.00pm on Friday and Saturday for lowers, 11.30pm for uppers. ('Many of the students have part time jobs', explained the head of boarding.)

Peter Symonds is the sixth form for the Falklands Islands (and very different to home they find it), although they account only for a small number of the 75 boarders, who come from the Forces, and across the country.

'[There are] close communities in both boarding houses, particularly the smaller house', said a student, and they try and match students up to their preference after visiting. Both houses have separate floors for boys and girls, locked down at night. School House is smaller and older; Falkland Lodge distinguished by its ensuite twin rooms and a feeling of Premier Inn. Each house has its own study room, common room and kitchen, where students help themselves to breakfast. There are rotas for kitchen duty (only the odd prompt necessary, say houseparents), and students do their own laundry.

Background and atmosphere: The college sits in an expanse of daisied green, a mixture of the old grammar buildings and modern additions, the swish and the less so. There's no space on campus which can accommodate all 4,000 students at once: the largest space on campus, the Varley theatre, seats 320, so everything is done in batches of students.

Peter Symonds is the sixth form for the Falklands Islanders (and very different to home they find it), although they account for only a small number of the boarders

One pupil compared its vastness with the size of a small town, but said that the numbers mean that you can act as an individual: you don't have to fit; 'cat girl', mentioned a student; 'oh, cat girl,' chorused the others: ears, eyeliner, tail 'n'll; but there are communities of people within the vastness, which come down to subject passions: '[with] such diversity of subjects... you can find someone whose views and interests are like yours. No one goes through without making a friend'.

The atmosphere here is relaxed, though purposeful and confident. '[It's a] stepping stone from school to university', says the head; 'freer and more open than school'. One parent told us her daughter opted to leave private education for Peter Symonds – 'she wanted to throw off the shackles of school'. Her daughter likes the informality, and 'being in control of her own destiny' (although her other children opted to stay in the school environment with rules).

As at university, there's a student union, which 'is prominent and has a strong voice', said the elected members, who meet with SMT – and would like to more frequently.

The college is packed with technology, with no suggestion of any shortages: 'austerity is not an issue here,' said a student: there are 211 PCs and 170 laptops in the library alone, and a huge range of magazines, journals and newspapers. They will get hold of any book a student needs, either buying it in, or by inter-library loan.

The biggest problem here has been finding space to study. The library fills quickly and early, particularly in the exam season. There are lists of free classrooms, which can be pinged to students' phones on Snapchat; although one parent said her son rarely uses these, finding an open classroom less easy than the hooded spaces in the library; another that her children use the library in town, or the university library. However, the new Hopkins Study Centre should alleviate matters.

The food is good: chicken and chips are popular, as are the cookies – always warm; though they have gone up 10p each due to Brexit, a student told me seriously – because the pound has gone up against the dollar. It's rather pricey: around £5 for a good lunch, and lots nip to Tescos for a £3 meal deal.

Pastoral care, well-being and discipline: 'The support service is belittled, but actually it's fantastic,' said a student who told us that if you have a problem, you can drop into the Hub (a centre developed for the 'worried well,' says the head), talk to your tutor, or any teacher. 'If you need help, look for it. You're treated like an adult – peerless, fantastic advice'.

The Hub was a response to the tsunami of low level mental health problems, such as anxiety and low mood; its aim is to increase student resilience; 'a lifesaver for my daughter', said a parent; 'cool about everything', said a student. About seven pupils drop into the Hub every day, which is staffed by one full-time mental health specialist and a team of five counsellors. They also provide classes on mindfulness and well-being, and have introduced a therapy dog: Haatchi has just three legs, looks large and vicious, and is a real poppet.

There's a nurse and sexual health clinic – 'very discreet', say students. Free condoms (six a week) and chlamydia tests available from student services, and the college can send students to a pharmacy for free emergency contraception: students here don't feel the need to titter embarrassedly about sexual health.

At this huge college, you wonder how shy introverts might fare, but they do well, insist both head and students: you quickly form bonds in your small subgroups of subject or activity. Bullying not a problem, say students; 'rare', agrees the head: 'something students have left at school'.

The independence and responsibility of college prepares pupils well for university

Parents are largely not involved, but the head says parents will be contacted early with any concerns, whether pastoral or academic.

Behaviour outside of college is only a matter of college discipline if it brings the college into disrepute; 'we're acting on bluff really', said the head thoughtfully, with few sanctions available in this quasi grown up environment; suspension is the best they can do, pupils knowing that it will be on their record and references. 'But there is little call for sanctions', he added cheerfully. Apparently troublemakers aren't terribly likely to opt for sixth form college.

The college works hard at drugs education, and second chances are possible here; but students will be asked to leave if not attending, not doing work, or behaviour is distracting others from learning (just a couple in the last few years).

Pupils and parents: Parents and students here generally reflect the white middle class make of up the Winchester area.

Communication home is mostly through students, so is reliable as your child, but they monitor attendance closely, and tell parents early if there is a problem. The parent portal shows details of homework, progress, effort and attendance.

Progress reviews show grades and effort, one parent commenting that it would be helpful to have more feedback if your child is less able. Parents are only invited to parents' evening if there's a problem, and none of those we spoke to felt this was ideal '...would like more parents' evenings, or a detailed report'; 'can go through the whole thing with seeing anyone...'.

Despite the college's proximity to the station, students say many are late to lessons because of poor public transport; the popularity of the college is such that students come from near and far, one travelling one and half hours in from the New Forest ('I spend three weeks a year on the bus – but it's absolutely worth it – unparalleled education'). For those driving in, parking is tricky: there's none at the college for students, and locals are understandably irked by students circling their streets to nab their parking spaces.

Entrance: No defined catchment area, but priority goes to those closest; offers will continue to be made in an ever increasing circle around the college until they run out of places. One hundred and fifty feeder schools, a small number from independent schools.

Base entry is five A*-C/9-4s at GCSE, but most have considerably more than this. Students at the lower end of entry will be advised to take a combination of A levels and BTecs. Students can restart and do something different if subject choices really aren't working out.

Exit: Ninety per cent of pupils go to university, 43 to Oxbridge in 2017 (in the top five Oxbridge feeder schools, in the illustrious company of Eton, Westminster and Hills Road Sixth Form College in Cambridge) and 48 medics. Around a quarter to Russell Group. One to Harvard. As with other sixth form colleges, students here are more likely to get first class and upper second degrees.

Very few drop outs – around 100 each year, students commenting on one: 'they found it too much work, so went to independent school'. Those who do drop out more often go to other sixth form colleges, agricultural college or vocational college.

Remarks: This college is a wonderful opportunity for those ready for independence, and thriving students eulogise about its greatness: 'always a step forward; always working towards where you want to be'.

It's quite academic, said a parent, who reported her children as saying 'better work harder or I'll end up at [a less academic] college...'; those who are going to struggle here are those who are have no notion of independence, aspiration or good work habits. But even these students, says the head, can come through at Peter Symonds: 'They enter a class [here] and see what it looks like to work hard and succeed'.

Reading School

12

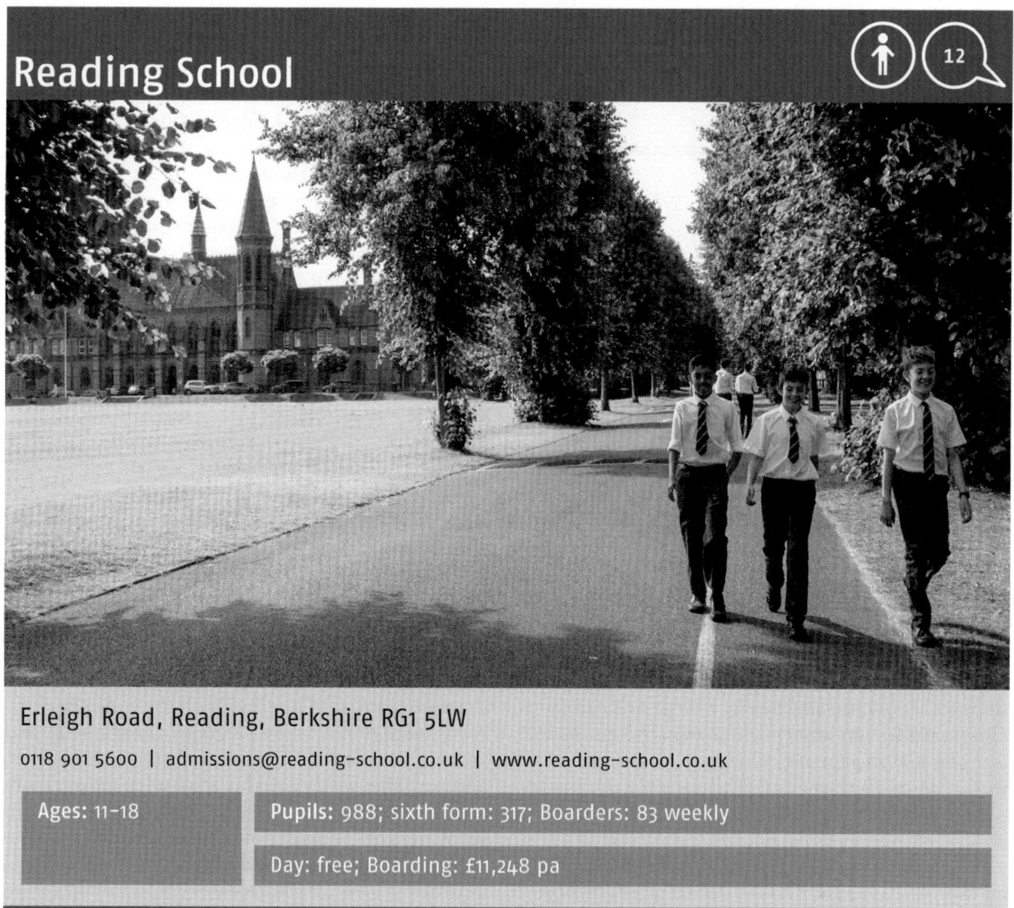

Erleigh Road, Reading, Berkshire RG1 5LW

0118 901 5600 | admissions@reading-school.co.uk | www.reading-school.co.uk

Ages: 11–18

Pupils: 988; sixth form: 317; Boarders: 83 weekly

Day: free; Boarding: £11,248 pa

Head: Since 2012, Mr Ashley Robson BA NPQH MBA, previously deputy head since 2005. History degree from Newcastle-upon-Tyne; first jobs at Princes Risborough School and Royal Grammar School, High Wycombe before becoming head of history, head of house and assistant headteacher at Aylesbury Grammar School.

With the demeanour of a jovial uncle, he's a big hit with the pupils, who describe him as 'really friendly and funny' and 'the ideal headmaster because you know he really cares about us.' And while not exactly pally with him, boys are certainly at ease in his company – doubtless helped by the fact that he teaches most of them history at one stage or another and often pops in and out of other lessons, as well as supporting sports fixtures where he can. A humble man who is big on praising staff ('This teacher is amazing,' he says, introducing us to one of them. 'How would we manage without you?' to another), he's also popular with parents – no mean feat given the sky-high expectations some of them have. 'He is an exceptional man, who is not interested in standing still, but only moving the school ahead.' 'He holds himself to very high standards and expects his staff to reflect those in everything they do. But he is also a human being and understands that boys make mistakes.' 'I've met a lot of leaders in my time and he's a real stand-out.'

No real areas of weakness thanks to combination of academic rigour and inspirational staff (whose energy and wisdom almost make you want to get stuck into the lesson yourself)

Lives an hour's drive away in Bucks with his wife, with whom he has three children – Dominic, who works at NHS England, Joseph, who's at Oxford University, and Harriett, who is studying for her A levels. Enjoys sport, particularly football, and travel.

Academic matters: For intellectually inquisitive, naturally bright and highly motivated boys, this school is likely to feel a very natural fit. And thanks to a combination of academic rigour and inspirational staff (whose sharpness, energy and wisdom almost make you want to sit down and get stuck into the lesson yourself), there are no real areas of weakness, with stand-out results across the board – including in value-added. At GCSE, 81 per cent A*-A/9-7 grades in 2017.

Setting in maths from year 8, with class sizes for top sets capped at 32, while bottom set numbers tend to hover between 10-12. No stigma 'as everyone gets A* anyway,' say pupils. New language strategy not for the fainthearted, with German, French, Spanish and Latin all studied in year 7; then Latin and two of the others in year 8; and at least one language to be taken at GCSE (Latin and German most popular). Teachers all subject specialists. 'You can't pass on what you haven't got – but even that's not good enough on its own. Teachers also need passion and the ability to inspire,' insists head, and pupils say they do this with bells on. 'Every teacher here goes the extra mile, not just in the classroom, but in terms of extra help including subject drop-in clinics and one-to-ones if you need them,' said one. Rapport between teachers and boys notably good-humoured and mutually respectful. 'I can't think of one teacher that doesn't allow you to have a joke in the class – they like making learning fun,' said one boy.

In sixth form, boys choose four A levels from a largely traditional mix, including (unusually) Latin and ancient Greek if numbers permit. In 2017, 93 per cent A*-B and nearly 76 per cent A*/A grades. Most popular subjects are maths, chemistry and economics. Boys also expected to enrich their sixth form timetable with at least one of three options, all of which demonstrate that the school's commitment to serve the wider community isn't mere lip service. First, the student charity committee, which raises around £10k for charity (past examples include Syrian refugees and partner school in Kenya). Second, the Future Stories Programme, which aims to increase social mobility by boys teaching and mentoring disadvantaged children in local primary schools ('It fits nicely with the government agenda for grammars,' says head). Third, the student-led Dementia Champions programme, whereby boys become 'dementia friends' and roll out what they've learned across the school. 'Boarders visit local care homes as part of this programme – it's great for intergenerational bonds,' one boy told us. Formal extended project qualification (EPQ) also available.

Less than 1.5 per cent with SEN (one statemented when we visited) – most on the autistic spectrum or dyslexic, whose additional help is mainly provided outside the classroom by the SENCo (who only works one day a week – she teaches the rest of the time), supported by part-time (2.5 days a week) learning support adviser and SEND governor. 'The SENCo is not backward in coming forward and really champions the boys, recognising that some staff get their needs and some don't,' one parent of a child with told us, adding, 'She is very collaborative with parents too, even letting me run a session with staff to explain what my son's condition is like to live with.' One parent with a child with dyslexia, however, told us, 'I notice it gets forgotten sometimes, for example when he needs extra time in exams.'

Games, options, the arts: For parents that treat this school as an alternative to a high performing independent school (many do), sports will be your wake-up call. With no acres of rolling green fields, rows of pristine tennis courts or swimming pool, it is fair to say that nobody is blown away by the sports facilities – or indeed successes – here. But the boys don't half do badly when they put their minds to it, holding the titles of U18 county rugby champions and KS3 and KS4 national badminton champions when we visited. As for local fixtures, there's no school they like thrashing more than Blue Coat. 'They're our local rivals and even if one of our teams draws with them, they get a rollicking in the school newspaper,' chuckles one boy. Core sports are rugby (autumn), football (spring) and cricket (summer), with lacrosse and badminton also growing in popularity. Amenities include sports field (picture perfect when we visited, with clear blue skies and boys playing in their cricket whites), refurbished gym and three pitches 400 metres away on the other side of the Royal Berkshire Hospital. There are plans to build a sports hall and multi-use games area – though nobody dares guestimate a completion date. And for the non-sporty, 'join the club,' laugh some of the boys we spoke to – although you are expected to represent your house at sports day, if not your school in fixtures. 'It's important for our identity,' says head.

Music a real strength and considered a good alternative for the non-sporty in terms of encouraging teamwork. Orchestras, ensembles and choirs galore, with the house music competition the highlight of the musical calendar. 'Last year, we sold out the town hall – this year we reckon we'll sell out the Hexagon,' one boy told us, adding that 'even if you're not mega into music, like me, it's a great night – we all love it.' 'Close your eyes and you could be listening to professionals,' gushed a parent. Peripatetic teachers cater for 220 boys.

Drama facilities nothing to write home about, but that doesn't stop it being a popular at GCSE and there were just enough boys to do A level the year we visited. Practice for a student-led extravaganza (the first in years) in full swing when we visited – We Will Rock You. Other smaller productions showcase GCSE and A level work. 'I don't know anyone who doesn't like drama here – it's not even like a lesson, but a way to express yourself and let off steam,' said one boy.

Art offered at GCSE and A level, though numbers not high and DT facilities recently scrapped to make way for a computer science block. 'Let's face it, the arts are not a big selling point – people don't come here for that. But at the same time, the school doesn't completely ignore them,' said one parent.

Copious amount of clubs, many student-led. Societies tend to run at lunchtimes, then sport and others after school. Chess (considered a sport here, albeit tongue-in-cheek) does particularly well – national schools senior chess champions when we visited. Ditto with public speaking. 'I was sent out to Hong Kong to represent the school in a public speaking competition and felt physically sick when it came to the actual moment of speaking, but I wound up reaching the finals,' one boy told us, understandably proudly. Trips aplenty, with recent examples including football tour to California, cricket tour to St Lucia, language exchanges to Germany and France, staff and student exchange to Copenhagen (longstanding partnership with a school here) and charitable trip to Kenya (where there's another school partnership). Boys on pupil premium (around 1.5 per cent when we visited) financially supported so nobody misses out.

Boarding: Two boarding houses (South House and East Wing, with some friendly rivalry between them) accommodate a maximum of six boys each per year group. Most boys' families live within the M4 corridor and because only weekly boarding is on offer here, the majority go home after school on Friday and return Sunday night or Monday morning ('although a few stay on Friday night if they've got a fixture the next day').

Décor no-frills but perfectly comfortable, with boys touchingly proud of the space spread among the eight common rooms (complete with pool tables, table football and TVs – 'particularly great fun when we all get together to watch a game'), as well as kitchens, music practice spaces and study spaces. Boys in year 7 and 8 share two or three bed dorms, while years 9 and over get their own small single rooms and sixth formers have their own slightly larger rooms, mainly in separate corridors from the younger ones. All impressively tidy when we visited (rooms are scored for tidiness daily and the weekly winner gets an extra £5 on their refectory card) – and although boys admitted 'the shared areas can quickly turn into a tip, we do tidy them up regularly.'

While boarders are by no means seen as a separate entity within the school, there's no doubt boys wear their boarding identity as a kind of badge of honour and there's a noticeable family vibe among the boarding community. 'You get great cross-year friendships that I just don't think would happen otherwise,' said one boy. 'It couldn't be further from the traditional public school boarding experience, what with the family feel and older boys taking the younger boys under their wing. My son wasn't great at maths and an older boy took such delight in helping him,' said a parent.

Boarding staff are second-to-none in terms of their 'commitment, enthusiasm, motivation, morale and belief in the boarders,' according to Ofsted – qualities that we could see for ourselves. And because both housemasters have young families, there are often young children about too. 'My first sight when I open my eyes in the morning is usually of the housemaster's 1-year-old daughter waving at me,' laughed one boy.

After-school life is – as with most boarding schools – tightly timetabled, with relaxing time from after school until 4pm, followed by clubs (at least three on offer per evening) then dinner at 5.30pm and finally shared study time from 6.30-8pm. 'I'm the kind of person that gets easily distracted, so I didn't like that aspect at first – but the teachers make sure you're on task and the good thing is you have access to everything you need and can discuss it with other classmates if you need to,' one boy told us. Much anticipated bi-annual boarding trips in summer and winter include the likes of theme park and West End theatre.

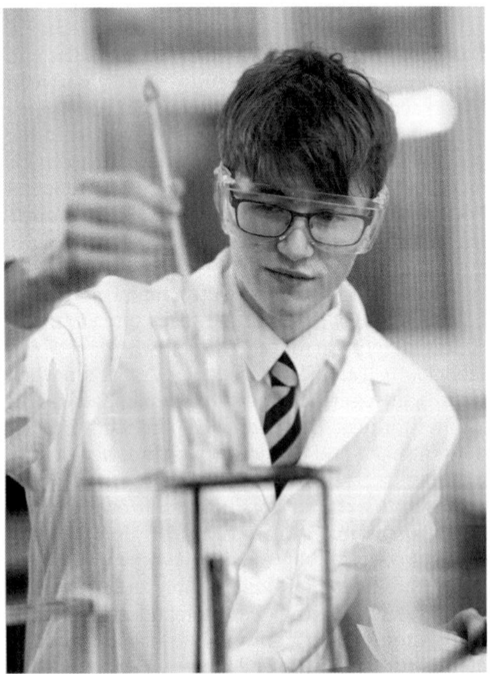

'I don't know anyone who doesn't like drama here – it's not even like a lesson, but a way to express yourself and let off steam'

Background and atmosphere: Founded as part of Reading Abbey in 1125, the school is estimated to be the 10th oldest school in England (though some argue there may have been a school running in Reading prior to this) and the 20th oldest in the world. Moved to current site in 1870, where it now consists of an attractive red-brick grade 2 listed building with two wings, in front of which sits the beautifully manicured field. Expect all the usual grammar school features – parquet flooring, green tiles on the corridor walls, windows into the classrooms etc. Other notable additions to the campus include a snazzy new science block (a joy to watch boys excitedly making benzoic acid), Page building (art, computer science, maths and IT), John Kendrick building (library plus more classrooms), the music school (far end of the field) and South House (one of the boarding houses – the other, East Wing, is attached to the main block). Around half the students bring their own packed lunch; the rest rave about the food in the newly refurbished, not to mention light and airy refectory (where they do darn good quirky cakes – beetroot and chilli among them). Also recently refurbished are four of the computer science labs (replacing the old 1950s DT room) and lecture theatre. It's a school that, say boys, never feels overcrowded and although some areas look more pristine than others, 'there's nothing we want for when it comes facilities.'

School values are excellence, integrity and leadership and refreshingly, these are brought to life not by predictable assembly orations, but by boys being given real-life responsibilities (one boy carried out a remarkably professional student survey, as just one example). And it is this, together with the scholarly yet relaxed vibe – and the leafy green campus – that gives an almost university-type feel to the place. 'Atmosphere can get a bit competitive between the boys, though,' said one boy. 'I sometimes wish there was a bit more "we're-all-in-this-together",' agreed another, though another disagreed. 'I love the friendly rivalry – trying to beat my best friend in my end-of-year marks is what's giving me that extra motivational push.' Uniform smart, 'but they're not obsessive about it,' say boys (poster states Dress for Success rather than strict lists of no-nos). Strong partnership with Kendrick

School (local girls' grammar), with joint concerts, annual prom and some societies such as the economics discussion group.

Pastoral care, well-being and discipline: Definitely more carrot than stick, with the tiered detention system rarely used. 'When boys mess up here, it's usually just a silly mistake – and the school wants us to learn from it, rather than warn us that severe punishments are waiting around every corner, which would just make us disenfranchised with school life,' one boy said. Seemingly endless (as you've probably gleaned) examples of student-led activities and policies – school believes that giving students responsibility over their own school is a better way to get them to respect it than strict rules. 'We don't force students to do things – we give them ideas and they run with them,' says head.

Anxiety can be an issue, especially at exam time – and that's just the parents. When boys get worried, their first port of call tends to be head of house (five houses in total), or – in year 12/13 – their head of year. There's also a counsellor who visits one day a week ('he's busy – and I see that as a good thing,' says head), plus there's a day matron, two boarding matrons and a new medical centre. PSHE classes, described by boys as 'insightful,' also help raise awareness of mental health issues – and there's a (student-led again) mental health action plan committee. Once-weekly visits to chapel help pupils explore moral dilemmas (as a non-denominational school, this is with a secular emphasis).

Bullying rare, although a couple of parents told us about 'a cyber-bulling incident, which the school dealt with brilliantly – getting the boys to do a presentation to parents on the dangers of social media.' No permanent exclusions since 2013 and less than a handful of temporary ones each academic year. 'The school never treats anyone unfairly – they would never get away with it,' one parent told us, explaining, 'the school works on logical argument and persuasion, which the boys are perfectly adept at using themselves to probe the senior leadership team if they don't agree with their punishment!'

Pupils and parents: If you draw the catchment area for day pupils on a map, it's by no means a neat circle, but it roughly equates to a 15 mile circumference, with the majority of day boys coming from Reading and Wokingham; furthest points reaching as far as Maidenhead, parts of Slough and Newbury. 'Most boys travel in by bus or train and the journey is under an hour,' says head. Boarders' families tend to live in the M4 corridor, within a couple of hours' drive.

Very active Reading School Parents Association (RSPA) – responsible all the usual socials and fundraising 'and many more ways to get involved in the school if you want to,' said one parent. Generally, parents a pretty vocal lot. 'Some have very, very high expectations of their sons and we have to help them manage that with the reality of the situation,' says head.

Rich ethnic mix, with white British and Indian backgrounds dominating, but plenty of others besides. Old boys include Christopher Renshaw (theatre director), Damian Green (Secretary of State for Work and Pensions), Ross Brawn (Formula 1), William Laud (Archbishop) and Joe Eyre (actor, writer and theatre director).

Entrance: Highly competitive 11+ exam, comprising of two separate multiple choice papers, each lasting around 50 minutes. Provided by the Centre for Evaluation and Monitoring (CEM) at the University of Durham, each test assesses verbal, non-verbal and numerical ability. No practice papers available (an attempt to stop over-tutoring, although you won't stop local parents giving it a go), although there is a familiarisation sheet on the school website and on the school website. Over 800 sit the entrance test for the 138 year 7 day boy places and a similar ratio for the 12 boarding spaces – you can only apply for one or the other. Having a sibling here already is no advantage and rarely do more than a handful of boys come from a single primary school (and even that's considered a lot). Registration window opens in May with a closing date around mid-June.

Boarders' good relationships with day pupils extend into informal joint weekend activities and membership of local groups and clubs

To stay on into sixth- form (or join as a newcomer) boys need the equivalent of at least 54 points across eight GCSEs, and at least a B/6 in the subjects chosen. Around 150 apply for the 70 or so additional places.

Exit: Some 85-90 per cent stay on for sixth form – 'The boys who leave after GCSE tend to go to a sixth form college nearer where they live in, say, Basingstoke or Henley, or they don't make the grades,' says head. Sixth formers almost all to university, 70 per cent to Russell Group, with Bristol, Warwick, Durham and Imperial currently featuring highly. In 2017, 22 to Oxbridge, 17 to medical school. Very strong numbers to read economics-based subjects, with second most popular course engineering, followed by medicine in third place. Also prevalent, but in smaller numbers, are history, English, classics and maths.

Remarks: Although it's been a while since the school was given the prestigious State School of the Year 2010 award by the Sunday Times, it is still recognised as one of the leading state schools in the country due to its exceptionally high academic standards and strong emphasis on personal development. What we love is that it achieves this with a good dose of merriment and 'own-your-own-learning' treatment – a testament to the teachers and leadership team who do not seem to apply undue pressure or strictness and who hand out student-led projects like Smarties. For erudite boys who want to be given wings to fly, your future starts here.

Ripon Grammar School

13

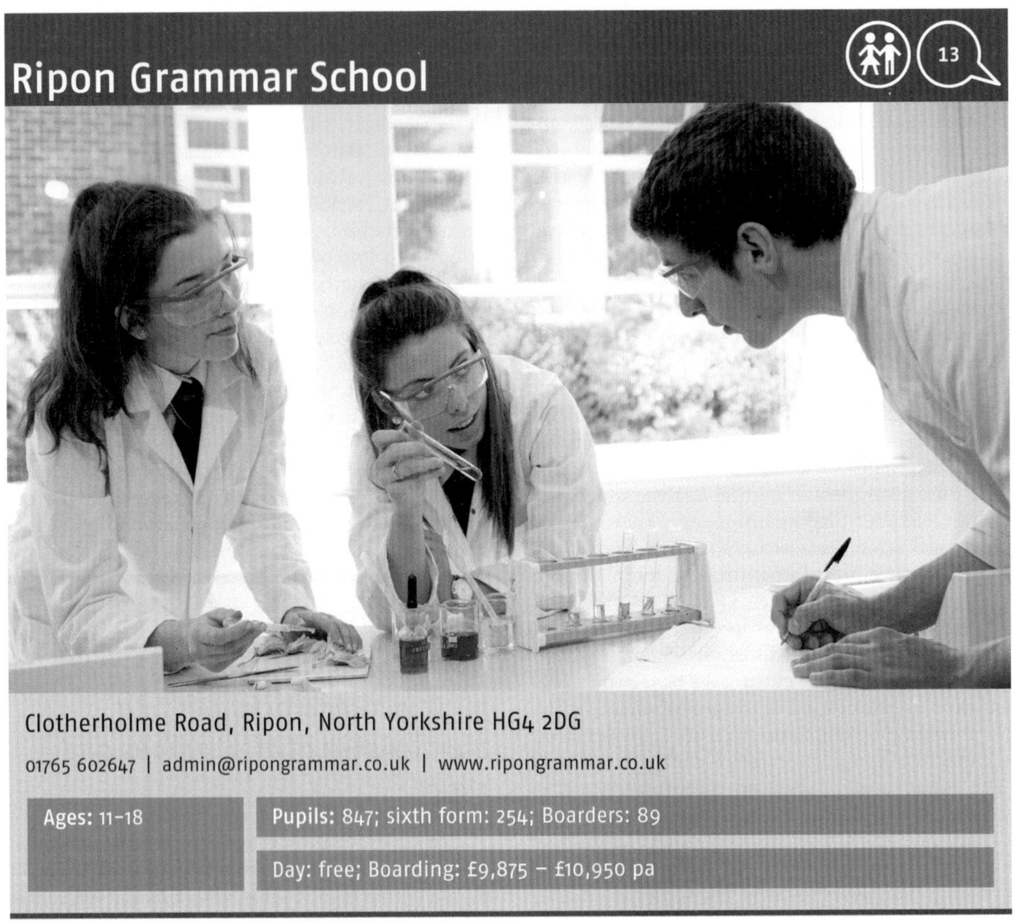

Clotherholme Road, Ripon, North Yorkshire HG4 2DG

01765 602647 | admin@ripongrammar.co.uk | www.ripongrammar.co.uk

Ages: 11–18

Pupils: 847; sixth form: 254; Boarders: 89

Day: free; Boarding: £9,875 – £10,950 pa

Headmaster: Since September 2017, Jonathan Webb MA. Previously deputy head at Durham School for five years. Educated at Batley Grammar School and has a history degree from Christ's College, Cambridge. Taught history at Pocklington School (where he was director of teaching and learning and head of history), The Manchester Grammar School and Giggleswick. He and his wife Helen live near Ripon and they have two sons. In his spare time he enjoys cricket, walking and gardening.

Academic matters: Exam results consistently very good – 79 per cent A*-B at A level in 2017, 56 per cent A*/A grades. STEM subjects unsurprisingly strong – roughly equal numbers of girls and boys take chemistry and mathematics, though physics remains a male stronghold with school working hard to change this.

Some 30 per cent take up of EPQ; good range of enrichment and community activities; pupil-led societies with weekly guest speakers. Well-drilled programme of support and encouragement for Oxbridge candidates. Strong careers and higher education advice with a week's work experience for all in year 12.

Elsewhere some evidence of girl-dominated subjects – for example in art (turning STEM to STEAM), English literature and French, compulsory at GCSE. Latin, classics, psychology, PE also available. German, though declining in many schools, still on offer, and Latin, originally started as a twilight subject, appearing by popular demand at GCSE and A level. Ancient Greek offered as an extracurricular subject at GCSE.

Sixty-four per cent A*/A at GCSE in 2017. Engineering specialism has brought astronomy, statistics and product design into the GCSE curriculum. Complete lab refurbishment in recent years.

Only setting in mathematics and French from year 8. Cross-curricular themed challenge days, off-timetable, set for years 7, 8 and 9 provide opportunities for leadership, teamwork and problem-solving, working with external advisers. Lays the groundwork for later success as regional finalists in Young Enterprise and Prince's Trust competitions.

School does a very fine job over value-added; near the top of the tree nationally. RGS is not as highly selective as some grammar schools in, for instance, Kent and Essex, being unable to draw pupils in great numbers from outside its defined catchment area.

SEN support very good – oversees provision for, eg, visual and hearing impairment and a range of special needs. In addition learning resource manager works with SENCo on intervention strategies. Paired reading with sixth formers in assembly time set up for those identified by on-line literacy assessment.

Games, options, the arts: Compulsory sport: rugby and cricket mainstay for boys, hockey for girls. Football popular for both sexes – girls have been Yorkshire junior champions – also mixed hockey, badminton, rock climbing, dance and swimming in newly refurbished swimming pool. Good representation at area and regional level in range of sports, including national U14 netball finalists. Excellent facilities, new Astroturf and sports hall paid for by independent fundraising campaign, available for local use too. 3G pitch on the way.

Music block plus performing arts facility in the new sixth form centre. Lots of enthusiastic musicians – over 100 receive tuition in school. Big band performs frequently in Ripon Cathedral, even entertained the Queen. Vocalists encouraged to join one of the three choirs. Annual drama production and joint musical production on alternate years.

Superb art on display. Visiting artists augment strong teaching team, most recently famous comic strip illustrator.

Lots of out of the classroom experiences to be had. Duke of Edinburgh, biennial World Challenge, revived music tour in Belgium, Barcelona trip for Spanish speakers, art trips to London and Paris, as well as the more local curriculum enriching visits.

Over 90 different clubs and activities on offer, ranging from the Greenpower electric car, Pageturner bookclub to philosophy – something for even the most reluctant sportsman or woman to get involved in. Pupils encouraged to take the initiative to set up and run activities and clubs. Annual charity week is just one example, sixth form led it encompasses a diverse number of activities raising money for the school's chosen charities.

Boarding: Boys' boarding house, School, is integral and has had a makeover in recent years, met with considerable approval by boarders. Light and spacious rooms, beds not bunks, a relaxed and positive environment for down time and study. Bit of a maze but the character of the building endears itself to its occupants. Johnson, girls' boarding house, recently expanded, with single rooms for some sixth formers – long overdue, by some accounts.

This is a day school with boarding, predominantly weekly boarding; pupils come from North Yorkshire and beyond, a minority from India, Africa, Caribbean and China. Boarders (room for 100 out of 800+) do well academically and the very few in residence over the weekends are well catered for. Good relationships with day pupils extend into informal joint weekend activities and membership of local groups and clubs. Demand for boarding places (14 available a year) outstrips supply, especially post-GCSE, with lots of interest in girls' boarding.

Parents have confidence that whatever their child's talents the school will help them to make the best of them. School keen to serve its local community

Boarders have a personal tutor and are in mixed age tutor groups. As majority of boarding staff are teachers, 'boarders are very well known as individuals'. Slightly at odds, the head of boarding (also deputy head) does not sleep over, maybe losing an opportunity to feel the vibes from the girls in Johnson.

Background and atmosphere: Long pedigree; there's been a grammar school in Ripon since Anglo Saxon times. School originally housed in city centre and current foundation granted a royal charter by Queen Mary in 1555. Moved to present green and pleasant 23-acre site in 1874, gift from Marquess of Ripon. Original Victorian buildings added to over the years, not always sympathetically, but more recent additions: sports hall, sixth form centre, mathematics and engineering block, state-of-the-art music facilities, observatory and girls' boarding house bring more gravitas to the school façade. The most recent addition, a humanities and modern languages block, opened in 2014.

School has remained true to North Yorkshire LA and eschewed academy status.

There is an air of purposefulness in the school; a quiet hum from classrooms and sensible movement between lessons. High profile house system in the day school involves all pupils and offers leadership opportunities. Competition in sport, rock climbing, debating, Masterchef, University Challenge and house drama competition.

Pastoral care, well-being and discipline: Very good pastoral system in operation; in addition, pupils look after each other, 'very collegiate', as one parent put it. Sixth formers are trained as peer listeners and teams of form tutors ably support heads of school. Newcomers to sixth form are 'buddied' with existing pupils to ease integration.

School says pupils interact well and both poor behaviour and exclusions are rare. At worst, usually sorted by after school detention. Genuinely good relations between staff and students throughout the school; friendly and compassionate house staff create a relaxed boarding environment. Pupils and parents cannot speak highly enough of staff, their commitment and willingness to go 'above and beyond'.

Compulsory sport: rugby and cricket mainstay for boys, hockey for girls. Football popular for both sexes – girls have been Yorkshire junior champions

Any bullying 'stamped on' and internet safety policy written by pupils, wired into PCSHE and teaching programmes.

Pupils and parents: Boarders from abroad, Yorkshire Dales and London, some from Forces, day pupils from Ripon and around. Wide range of parental backgrounds and wealth (or lack of it) though only a handful eligible for free school meals, with significant effect on pupil annual grant income. Parents feel well informed on their child's progress with regular reports three times a year and an annual parents' evening. School contact is primarily email and parents like that the termly newsletter and new sports magazine have content provided by the pupils. Very supportive PTA.

Pupils friendly, courteous, articulate and insightful; confident not arrogant, with a real pride in their school. Lots of heads up, eye contact and smiles as you walk around. This is a can do, will do school – pupils talk of friendly rivalry, pushing each to achieve. Strong protestations from both girls and boys on question of true equality: 'not an issue here'. On election of school officers, 'it's the best person for the job every time'.

Pupils friendly, courteous, articulate and insightful; confident not arrogant, with a real pride in their school

Former pupils include fashion designer Bruce Oldfield, rugby international Peter Squires, William Hague MP, David Curry MP, Guardian editor Katharine Viner, TV presenter Richard Hammond.

Entrance: Mainly from local primaries but a smattering from prep schools, about 40 schools in total. Heavily oversubscribed at 11+. Selection by verbal and non-verbal reasoning tests administered by local authority; school takes top 28 per cent of cohort.

Sixth form – around 140 external applicants for approximately 30 places for students from other schools. Numbers applying increasing. Sixth form requires minimum six B grades at GCSE but vast majority comfortably exceed this, achieving mainly A*/A grades (or numerical equivalents).

Exit: Around 10 per cent leavers at 16+ a few more at end of year 12 (two per cent in 2017). At 18 most progress to university – over half to Russell Group or 1994 Group. Five to Oxbridge in 2017, eight to study medicine. Veterinary medicine, science, engineering, art, law and economics also feature. Most popular university destinations are Durham, Newcastle, Manchester, Edinburgh and Sheffield. A number lured to London, a few overseas. Excellent careers advice has meant leading apprenticeships for students considering alternatives to university.

Money matters: Yorkshire's only state boarding school, free for day pupils, charge for boarding, but still much cheaper than independent alternatives.

Remarks: High achieving without being highly pressurised, with learning and life skill opportunities going beyond exam syllabuses. Aims to provide a blend of tradition – academic rigour and high expectations – with innovation – up-to-date technology and opportunities for the development of the whole person – and does it well. Parents have utter confidence that whatever their child's talents the school will help them to make the best of them. Keen to serve its community and clearly valued by the people of Ripon.

The Royal School Armagh

14

College Hill, Armagh, County Armagh BT61 9DH

028 3752 2807 | info@royalschool.com | royalschool.com/

Ages: 11–18

Pupils: 737; sixth form: 220; Boarders: 87

Day: £3,700 – £4,415 pa (non-EU); Boarding: £7,275 – £10,925 pa

Interim headmaster: Alan Aitken, previously deputy head (curriculum) is holding the fort. He also teaches biology to A level and psychology to GCSE and runs the badminton club. Degree in biochemistry and microbiology from Heriot-Watt University in Edinburgh. Varied teaching career has taken him from England to the Bahamas and the Middle East to Northern Ireland. He was acting principal of the British School, Riyadh, Saudi Arabia, before his appointment at the Royal School.

Academic matters: In 2017, 43 per cent of grades A*/A, 70 per cent A*-B at A level and nearly 50 per cent A*-A/9-7 at GCSE. Offers 25 subjects at GCSE. About 60 per cent take dual award in sciences, but these are also available as individual subjects. Apart from the usual subjects, also offers business studies, sports studies, psychology, home economics and music. ICT and technology both popular. Foreign nationals can sit a GCSE in their native language as independent candidates and these have included Cantonese, Irish, Finnish and Polish in recent years.

Offers 25 subjects at A level too and will run a subject with only a handful of pupils. Offer vocational subjects like health & social care and construction as well as sociology and psychology alongside more traditional subjects. Spanish, French and music available but very few takers. Software systems development recently introduced.

Everyone CAT tested on arrival at 11+ to measure innate intelligence, and teaching is based on the personalised learning programme. All students have their own online pupil dashboard, which includes their minimum attainment line and targets are set accordingly. Grades are issued every six weeks so problems can be spotted quickly and the gifted and talented can be stretched. The aim is 'to work smarter not harder,' and pupils are taught how to learn and how to be organised. If someone is underachieving the school looks at the full picture including the home situation – perhaps they have nowhere to do their homework or don't know how to revise; they need parents to be on board. All are issued with a revision booklet including tips on diet and hydration.

Four classes of 25 per year – broadly mixed ability but usually one slightly differentiated class of pupils might not take a language at GCSE so they can concentrate on English or maths. French introduced in year 8 (English year 7) with Spanish added in year 9 (English year 8).

Effective peer tutoring programme – sixth form tutors are trained each September, and as well as helping younger pupils with maths and English, they also act as confidants. Leads to increased confidence for both sides and improved organisational skills for the tutors.

School fields teams for golf and show jumping and rowing is offered at Portadown Rowing Club

Careers department of three – but eight staff involved with UCAS references. Careers guidance infused into the curriculum – careers board for each subject displayed around the school so pupils can see how a particular subject might lead into the world of work. Work experience not compulsory but about a quarter take part and school can help with placements. Pupils guided through personal statements and parents heavily involved and taken through the process by the school. School gets in outside help for interview practice.

Well-supported SEN department with head and three classroom assistants – one a dyslexia expert and one trained in autistic spectrum disorders. Range from support in the classroom, to IEPs with targets, to input from an outside agency. Five statemented children, some of whom need their own classroom assistant. The school works hard to get those with SEN into further education. The headmaster says that the job of the SEN department is to break down barriers to learning and for children to learn coping mechanisms, maybe putting notes onto podcasts if that works. A handful of pupils, all boarders, need EAL support and are progressed through IELTS – they are usually taken out of prep in the evenings.

Games, options, the arts: One compulsory two hour sports session a week with the rest extracurricular. Two term rugby and hockey school and 'rugby is almost a religion,' said a pupil, although another said that 'you don't feel excluded if it is not your thing as the school has a strong arty side too'. Teams piped onto the pitch at the beginning of a match. An old boy and ex-pro has returned as director of rugby and the school won the Medallion Shield competition in 2017. Girls' hockey and boys' rugby fixtures every Saturday – girls' hockey team were recent Ulster league champions and three of the girls are Irish hockey internationals. The girls have their own rugby team and two play for Ulster – so just to be fair the sixth form boys have formed a hockey team. The school also fields a team for golf and show jumping and rowing is offered at Portadown Rowing Club. The school has a gym and sports hall and fitness suite as well as tennis and squash courts, rugby pitches and two all-weather hockey pitches, with swimming at the local leisure centre. The CCF (with new female head) was founded in 1916 and about 100 pupils take part in either the army or air force – the air force offers the opportunity to gain a pilot's licence. Some 40-50 every year complete the Duke of Edinburgh gold award.

Modern dance very popular; the girls are recent Northern Ireland winners. The senior debaters recently won the Northern Ireland EU debate in London

All staff involved in clubs and societies and everything is a meritocracy – houseparents monitor and encourage pupils' participation. The chess club has over 20 members. Modern dance very popular; the girls are recent Norther Ireland winners and the senior debaters recently won the Northern Ireland EU debate in London. About 20 per cent of pupils learn a musical instrument and there is a range of choirs and ensembles with many getting involved in inter-school choral competitions. The two musical highlights of the year are the carol service and the spring concert held in Armagh cathedral. 'They are top-notch events', said a parent, 'and lift the hairs on the back of your neck'.

Drama offered through the junior drama club and also as an A level, and the school stages a large scale musical every other year – pupils can take part behind the scenes as well in technical lighting, costumes etc.

Art housed in two light, bright rooms and there is particular emphasis on drawing but also increasingly on ceramics, textiles, photography and multimedia. Some three or four to art college each year.

Numerous including business studies to New York, Geographers to Iceland, skiing to Italy, languages trips to France and Spain and a CCF trip to Canada or Kwa Zulu Natal.

Boarding: Boarding always oversubscribed and supposed to be no more than 10 per cent of pupils. One girls', one boys' and a sixth form boarding house. Northern Irish boarders admitted on a genuine need to board and there is usually space for the occasional ad hoc boarder in an emergency. Other boarders from all over the world. 'Boarding improves the atmosphere of the whole school and gives it more of a family feel', said a parent. The boarding areas have recently had a £2 million refurbishment and pupils are accommodated in small, light rooms of mostly two to four beds with some larger dorms for the girls, and most of the older pupils have their own study bedrooms. Younger pupils' prep carefully monitored. All houses have common rooms with a television, Xbox and a games room and boarders have their own cinema. All have to eat lunch and supper in the main school and each house has a kitchen where students can prepare breakfast and snacks.

The school has bought four houses in the Georgian mall adjacent to the school, which have been refurbished and converted into the sixth form house with a flat for the housemaster. Boys and girls share homely and comfortable communal living areas but are separated by alarmed doors at night. Sixth formers are not allowed back to their house during the day and have to swipe in and out so staff know if someone is having an unscheduled lie in.

Boarders and day pupils mix well through the house system and sport, and boarders often go to stay with friends at weekends. No Saturday school but matches and CCF on Saturday mornings. Full boarders' outings once a fortnight, maybe to Belfast, Dublin or the north coast.

Background and atmosphere: One of five Planation Schools founded in 1608 by James I to educate the sons of Scottish and English merchants and farmers who had been sent to settle in Ulster after the Irish earls had been driven out in 1607. The school moved to its current 27 acre site in 1774. It is now a voluntary grammar school and became co-ed when it amalgamated with the Armagh Girls' High School in 1986. It is officially Reformed Christian but welcomes all faiths and none. The original school is an imposing granite building with enormous windows and wide corridors, with an elegant panelled boardroom and an ancient library displaying the school's honours boards, and with computers discreetly hidden behind a glass screen. There is an impressive quad where you can . no

'Boarding improves the atmosphere of the whole school and gives it more of a family feel', said a parent. Boarders and day pupils mix well

longer park your carriage but which is now used for barbecues, and the crunchy gravel is a deterrent to illicit flits between the boys' and girls' boarding houses. There is a strong sense of history and tradition – Armagh has been the ecclesiastical capital of Ireland since the fifth century and has a Protestant and a Catholic cathedral, and an unbroken line of archbishops have been chairmen of the board of governors for the past 400 years.

There is a small prep school on site which opened in 1940.

Healthy competition between the four houses (named after previous archbishops of Armagh) gives everyone a chance to take part and 'helps pupils find their sweet spot in life,' says school. Pupils mix vertically and compete in sports, debating and photography and in the annual inter-house talent show, which often brings hidden talents to the fore. 'It's great for those who don't make the school teams,' said a parent.

The school raises £10,000-£15,000 per year for charity. Sixth form charity committee decides what to support and then how to do it. They have come up with some innovative fundraising ideas like abseiling down the side of the Europa Hotel and a colour run where everyone threw powder paint at each other. There is a strong link with the town through the local rugby club and the scouts, and pupils go carol singing in old people's homes and the hospital.

'Service learning shouldn't just be cv fodder,' says the school, 'but should be uplifting and humbling'. The Royal is involved with two schools in Uganda but the pinnacle is the ASHA Project in a slum in New Delhi, where a group of sixth formers spend a fortnight every other year working alongside the community. The (heavily subsidised) triennial rugby tour to the southern hemisphere always involves a charitable element.

Pupils wear a smart uniform of blue blazer and grey skirt or trousers all through the school, including the sixth form, with purple honours blazers for particular achievements in sports, debating or music.

Pastoral care, well-being and discipline: The five pillars of 'positive psychology' Dr Martin Seligman's well-being or PERMA (positivity, engagement, relationships, meaning and achievement) are displayed in every classroom and all are linked to the curriculum. Well thought out policies on bullying, drugs and alcohol, but school says that children refreshingly normal and generally well-behaved and low level discipline issues usually uniform related. No expulsions in 15 years. 'There are some cyber niggles but on the whole the kids get on well', and everyone knows everyone across the year groups. 'The school has a good handle on things and any issues are dealt with effectively,' said a parent. The pastoral team meets regularly and all pupils have a weekly meeting with their tutors. Children know where to go for help and information is clearly displayed on boards in the main concourse. Staff always on the lookout for signs of struggle – there are a lot of people to watch out for them, and pupils have access to an independent counsellor if needs be, very often for self-esteem issues. Parents and pupils say you are immediately made to feel part of the family and 'everyone is accessible and you can have a chat with anyone at any time'.

Pupils and parents: Parents a mixed group – from those new to the grammar system and the just about managing to the very wealthy who like the free education and don't want to send their children to the mainland; all very supportive of the school. Ulster expats want their children to have what they had and so send them back as boarders. Some 12 per cent of the total school population and 30 per cent of boarders are non-British. There is real loyalty to the school, especially among the Old Armachians, who have regular get-togethers as well as an annual dinner. Most stay in Northern Ireland but those who move away usually come back in later life.

School describes the Armachian character as 'understated excellence, disarming naturalness, modest but well rounded, articulate individuals who do not have a veneer'

Pupils generally quietly confident and modest, and the school describes the Armachian character as 'understated excellence, disarming naturalness, modest but well rounded, articulate wholesome individuals who do not have a veneer – what you get is what you see, and what you get is nice'. This is endorsed by a parent, who said, 'The school turns out well-mannered considerate children who hold doors open and stand back – very natural and not forced'.

Parents say they are always made to feel part of their children's education and 'you can ring at any time and the school knows who you are'. Parents receive the pupil dashboard three times a year and are kept informed via regular emails and parent-teacher meetings as well as a Facebook group for sport. They can get more involved through the boarding parents' group. Well-known alumni include: Irish rugby international and British and Irish Lion, Tommy Bowe; British foreign secretary, Viscount Castlereagh; politician, Sir Reg Empey; Oxford maths professor, John Lennox; Cambridge professor of ophthalmology, Keith Martin; as well as numerous senior naval and military figures.

Entrance: At 11+ via common entrance assessment exam (similar to the English 11+) – the school is oversubscribed twice over. Children come from the school's own prep school and 33 feeder primary schools in Armagh, Portadown and Lurgan. The 15 per cent of pupils who are boarders sit the school's own exam and are tested in English, maths and verbal reasoning plus a reference from their current school – the criteria for a boarding place is a genuine need for the child to board. For students whose first language isn't English, there is a minimum requirement of IELTS level 4 or equivalent.

The minimum requirement for joining the sixth form is 13 points at GCSE with at least a B/6 in subjects to be studied at A level. This applies to pupils already in the school, and if they don't achieve this they are not readmitted – the headmaster has no leeway here.

Exit: Most go to Queen's University, Belfast (Russell Group) and the University of Ulster; two off overseas in 2017. Three or four to art college most years and about one every other year to Oxbridge. Pupils encouraged to look further afield, but school understands that, for many, Northern Ireland is where they want to be – and it works out far cheaper.

Money matters: Tuition is free for EU citizens and those resident in Norther Ireland. The boarding fee is much lower than anywhere in England or Scotland – too cheap, say some parents (of day children). The annual fee for day pupils who pass the 11+ is a paltry £400.

Remarks: A compassionate and caring school where the 'holistic approach runs through the school like a stick of rock' and where the development of character is equally as important as academic achievement.

The Royal School Dungannon

15

2 Ranfurly Road, Dungannon, County Tyrone BT71 6EG

028 8772 2710 | info@rsd.dungannon.ni.sch.uk | www.royaldungannon.com

Ages: 11–18

Pupils: 639; sixth form: 144; Boarders: 52

Day: £150 – £7,800 pa (non-EU); Boarding: £7,950 – £18,000 pa (non-EU)

Headmaster: Since 2009 Dr David Burnett BA PhD NPQH (40s). Educated at Lurgan College grammar school in County Armagh and read history and politics at Queen's University, Belfast where he also took a PhD. He joined King Edward VI Grammar School in Chelmsford via the licenced teacher scheme and gained QTS (qualified teacher status) via on the job training. He became head of history and politics in 1998, moved on to Westcliff High School for boys in 2006 and spent three years as deputy headmaster before taking on the headship at Dungannon. He is married to Nicola and they have two daughters and a son. He hadn't really planned to come back to Northern Ireland but family reasons pushed him in that direction and he was offered the headship at here.

He no longer has much time for teaching, but occasionally teaches history to some senior years to keep his hand in. He has a passionate interest in sport, especially Ulster rugby, and used to be a keen player, but now confines his sporting talents to golf and tennis. Loves history and historical fiction and always has a book on the go, and says he has a bit of a weakness for computer strategy games. He says the school is about the personal development of young people and he is happy to try new and different approaches. He feels that holistic education is part of the DNA of the school and 'although exams matter and children must be pushed to do as well as they can, they will only succeed if the foundations are right..Achievement comes through effort and hard work – the best geologist is the one

who has seen the most rocks.' 'He is highly visible around the school and approachable and is well regarded, but can be quite reserved', said a parent. He wants parents to be as involved as possible and was instrumental in setting up the PTA.

Academic matters: In 2017, 75 per cent A*-B and 44 per cent A*/A at A level and 39 per cent at A*-A/9-7 at GCSE. 'Pupils are encouraged to do their best but are not pushed too hard', said a parent. Twenty-one subjects offered at A level including music and food technology. Psychology, politics, media and business studies taught at St Patrick's Academy, the local Catholic grammar and partnership school. Further maths only offered to AS level. French and Spanish offered at GCSE and A level and Hong Kong Chinese can take Cantonese GCSE, but no lessons offered and have to do the work in their own time. Science, dual award or individual subjects, is taught in well-equipped modern labs. It's popular with the girls and all the physics teachers are female. Both boys and girls choose home economics and an old boy is a pastry chef at the Ritz. Science, maths and home economics the most popular A levels, followed by history and geography, with not many takers for modern languages. Many take maths GCSE a year early and further maths GCSE in year 12 (English year 11).

Pupils are put into four mixed ability classes of 22-23 on arrival with setting in English and maths from year 10 (English year 9). Some 17-18 per class in GCSE years drops to 11-12 at A level – and this is a state school.

Full time SENCo with a team of six or seven classroom assistants. The school is wheelchair friendly and there is a handful of children with autistic spectrum disorders, but the biggest groups are dyslexics and dyspraxics who usually only need modest adjustments in class – all are given an Individual Education Plan (IEP). Three EAL teachers, with lessons after school most evenings.

School fosters a sense of public service and is determined to involve students in the wider community. Strong links with local sports clubs, churches and businesses

Well-equipped careers library, and children are taught employability skills from the first year; subject careers boards are dotted around the school. Lots of help with UCAS forms and pupils are allocated a personal careers adviser. All upper sixth take part in an interview day and former pupils who are at university come back and talk. All lower sixth have to do some work shadowing – they are supposed to find work on their own but school can help if necessary.

Good balance of well qualified teachers including one NQT and a handful in their 50s – there have been considerable changes in the last 10 years and the school now has a young and approachable team. 'The teachers want the kids to do well and they are easy to talk to – they will always ring back if there is a problem,' said a parent.

Games, options, the arts: Strong emphasis on sport, especially boys' rugby. Girls play hockey, as well as recently introduced tag rugby (Ulster champions in 2017), all play cricket and a range of minor sports are offered. Good on site facilities including rugby pitches and a floodlit all weather hockey pitch, a shooting range, two sports halls and a fitness suite which they share with the wider community. Swimming at the Dungannon leisure centre. The school has been Northern Ireland orienteering champions for three years in a row and shooting is popular with both girls and boys – the school usually has reps in the Northern Ireland teams. Hockey and rugby training three times a week with matches on Saturday mornings, but often find it hard to compete with the bigger schools in the area. Sports at lunchtime and after school and sixth form have to take some sort of exercise twice a week– the Hong Kong girls tend to prefer keep fit and zumba.

'Music is the constant heartbeat of the school,' says the headmaster. Around 200 pupils a week involved with some sort of music: junior and senior choirs, which are open to all, chamber choir, chamber orchestra, pipe band, string band – something for everyone and the music block has a computer suite for pupils to make their own compositions. The carol service and spring concert are the highlights of the musical year and there is something musical going on most lunchtimes.

Thriving drama department and the school is 'well known for putting on a good show,' said a parent. Annual play for the senior school which alternates between a musical and a more serious drama, and the lower years put on their own productions.

Busy art department – drawing and painting are particular strengths. Impressive textiles and paintings are displayed in cabinets around the school and there is an annual joint arts exhibition with St Patrick's Academy.

'Music is the constant heartbeat of the school,' says the headmaster. Around 200 pupils a week involved with some sort of music

Range of lunchtime and after-school clubs including the popular Scripture Union, and public speaking and debating societies as well as Young Enterprise and computer games design. About 20 per year achieve gold Duke of Edinburgh Award and have joint expeditions with St Patrick's Academy. Annual sports tours to Scotland and Europe and rugby and hockey tours to New Zealand or South Africa every five years. History and RE trip to Rome, art and French trips to Paris and PE and Spanish trips to Barcelona.

Boarding: About eight full and weekly boarding places in each year group. Boarders sometimes only come for a term or a year, and originate from all over the world including Irish Republic, Ukraine, Nigeria, Russia and Spain. The largest contingent is from Hong Kong – many are the relatives of former pupils who came to Dungannon in the 1970s. On the whole they integrate well and make local friends, 'although the Hong Kong Chinese can stick together', said a parent. Usually over 40 in at weekends and staff put on an activities programme, maybe baking or a trip to a shopping centre or Belfast, and children are allowed to walk into the town and go to the cinema or swimming. 'Staff are very dedicated and try to make it feel like home,' said a parent. Boarding accommodation light and airy with small dorms for the younger children and double rooms for sixth formers, together with common rooms and kitchen areas for making hot drinks and snacks. Boarders not allowed back into their rooms during the day.

Background and atmosphere: One of five Planation Schools founded in 1608 by James I to educate the sons of Scottish and English merchants and farmers who had been sent to settle in Ulster after the Irish earls had been driven out in 1607. Originally set up in Mountjoy near Lough Neagh in 1614, it moved to Dungannon town later in the century. It was founded as a boys' school but amalgamated with Dungannon High School for girls in 1986 when large parts of the campus were rebuilt and it is now a co-ed voluntary grammar. The school is set in 50 acres and the main building, built in 1789, is known as the Old Grey Mother owing to its grey cement cladding. A mix of architectural styles ranging from the Georgian buildings to the Victorian cloister, which was originally used for

PE and assemblies, as well as 20th century additions. Twenty-eight new classrooms, science labs and a sixth form centre were added in 2003. All surrounded by neat lawns and flowerbeds. The entrance hall is all blond wood and pastel colours with silverware and sporting photos lining the walls and passages. The Marshall library, which is well equipped with computers and a computerised library system, was originally the 19th century gym. It was redesigned in the 1980s and is lined with portraits and photos of worthies of the school.

The school fosters a sense of public service and is determined to involve students in the wider community, and has strong links with local sports clubs, churches and businesses and shares its facilities – primary school children come in for sports, science and creativity days. The charities committee decides how to raise and spend money – one recent popular initiative was to sell roses on Valentine's Day, and they always take part in the Christmas shoe box appeal. Sixth formers help out as classroom assistants at a local special school and other years help with sport at local primaries and go carol singing in old people's homes. The school is also involved with the Fields of Life Charity, which has set up The Bethel Royal School in Uganda; a group of sixth formers visit each year and the Ugandan children have been on a return visit to Dungannon. They raise about £12,000 a year for the school.

James Dilworth, a former pupil, left money in his will to found Dilworth School in New Zealand in 1906, and there are still close ties with gap year exchanges between the schools.

Four houses named after well-known people connected with the school. Inter-house sport and debating competitions provide leadership opportunities for senior pupils and enable children to get to know other year groups.

Pastoral care, well-being and discipline: Broadly Christian ethos provides a moral compass, but school is inter-denominational and welcomes all faiths and none. Strong focus on pastoral care with boards outside all the classrooms and children know who to turn to. 'Everyone feels valued and part of the family,' said a parent. Zero tolerance on drugs, although head says that there has not been an incident while he has been in post. Occasional issues with alcohol – 'once in a blue moon,' says the headmaster. There is one 'formal' per year but no alcohol is allowed – a hip flask was once found in the bathroom but that is about as bad as it gets. Dungannon is popular with the Hong Kong families because it is socially conservative and safe.

School very hot on anti-bullying and holds an anti-bullying week. 'The school is on top of cyber issues,' said a mother and parents can attend talks on cyber bullying and are given tips on how to keep

Food good with plenty of choice and paid for by ingenious finger print system which also enables staff to monitor what children eat. Some bring in packed lunches.

Pupils and parents: Parents mostly local and often know each other in the wider community – many attended the school themselves. Former pupils have a strong affinity with the school and are keen to give something back, and in many families several generations have attended the school.

Usually over 40 boarders in at weekends and staff put on an activities programme, maybe baking or a trip to a shopping centre or Belfast

Children 'quietly confident and believe in themselves and have great manners,' said a parent; 'they always say hello and hold the door open'. 'They are proud to be part of the school and tend to be ambitious and want to make something of themselves,' said another.

Parents say they can get as involved as they want to, are kept well informed by the data secretary and are invited to the school for regular information evenings, on topics such as how to help their children with revision techniques. Active parents' association organises social and fundraising events – they arrange quizzes and shopping trips for parents, host a welcome evening for first year pupils and have recently raised funds to buy soundboards for the stage and extra equipment for the science labs, and also help raise money for foreign trips.

Well known alumni include: open golf champion, Darren Clarke; Irish rugby captain, Paddy Johns; director general of the probation service, Eithne Birt (nee Wallis); pioneering orthopaedic surgeon, Derek McMinn and MP and life peer, Lord Maginnis of Drumglass.

Entrance: From 20-30 local primary schools – primaries very supportive of grammar schools and lots of past pupils work in local primary schools. Entry via the common entrance assessment with exams in English and maths. The tests are in the November before entry and parents can choose a school once they have the results. Sixth form entry only if there are spaces and all must achieve at least six GCSEs at B/6 or above to join or move into the sixth form.

Entry for international boarders is via the school's own tests in English and maths plus an interview and report from the current school.

Exit: Over 90 per cent go on to further education. Just over half stay in Northern Ireland and go to Queen's University, Belfast or Ulster University (where fees are less than £4,000 per annum). Others to Dublin (Trinity College and UCD, also with moderate fees), plus Hong Kong and Melbourne; some 40 per cent go to university in Scotland or England with the occasional pupil going to Oxbridge (one in 2017). The most popular subjects are engineering, food and nutrition, medicine, dentistry, geography, business/economics, teaching and physiotherapy. About two per year go to art school and about three go into nursing. Not many take a gap year – some take part in the Dilworth scholarship and spend a year in New Zealand. Good links with local businesses for those who don't want to go to university.

Money matters: Tuition is free for those within Northern Ireland and the EU and boarders only have to pay the boarding fee. Fees for those from further afield much lower than in England and Scotland.

Remarks: A charming, small, rural grammar school with a tight-knit community where everyone knows everyone. The children achieve good results but do not feel pressurised and the school experiences few of the problems common in street-savvy city schools.

St George's School (Harpenden)

16

Sun Lane, Harpenden, Hertfordshire AL5 4EY

01582 765477 | admin@stgeorges.herts.sch.uk | www.stgeorges.herts.sch.uk

Ages: 11-18

Pupils: 1,340; sixth form: 403; Boarders: 110 full

Day: free; Boarding: £11,850 pa

Head: Since September 2017, Helen Barton, previously deputy head and geography teacher here. She trained as an accountant before seeing the light, taking a PGCE and teaching at state and independent schools in Herts and Beds, joining St George's as assistant head in 2005. She studied for a masters in education and became deputy head in 2008.

Academic matters: As a totally non-selective school regularly delivering high results, parents can bank on St George's knocking it out of the park when it comes to value-added, with 49 per cent of GCSE grades A*-A/9-7 in 2017. School is clear to point out, however, that this is not just in the realm of academia, but also in 'confidence, values and esprit de corps' that the students outperform expectations, acclaiming staff's 'ability to instil a sense of can-do' in its charges. Top A level grades are similarly commonplace. In 2017, 68 per cent A*-B, 51 per cent A*/A at A level.

Ten to 11 GCSEs are the norm, with compulsory RE amongst them, leading, unusually, to a full class at A level. Parents appreciate flexible approach to timetabling at GCSE. Maths, 'without reservation', is the jewel in St George's crown and the most popular A level choice by both sexes – 'it's phenomenal to see how much they enjoy it.' Art also outstanding with school boasting the highest percentage of top grades in county at both art GCSE and A level. Setting in maths and science from end of year 7, with English set for GCSE.

French from year 7, German and Spanish from year 8 and all on offer at GCSE but, disappointingly, only French at A level. Mandarin available

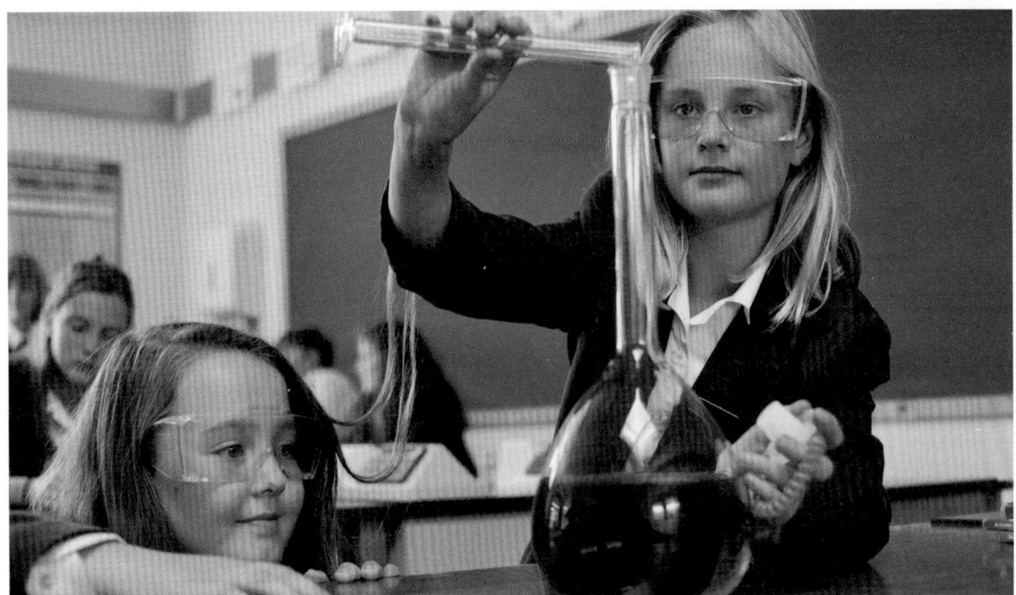

to all, although not examined, and school is one of just 45 Confucius Classrooms across the UK, meaning that it has Chinese firmly embedded in its own curriculum and strong links with China, including a popular exchange programme. Also has International School status.

SEN all in a day's work for the full time SENCo and seven teaching assistants on staff. Plenty of experience dealing with statemented children, and learning support ranges from helping with a few extra spellings to an individually planned timetable. Large percentage of cohort identified as gifted and talented, with extension work provided accordingly both on and off curriculum with Science Olympiads and Maths Challenges.

Games, options, the arts: Sport taken seriously but 'not elitist', according to school, with all abilities trained together. Rugby and cricket are main boys' sports, with A-C teams playing competitive fixtures most weeks in all year groups. It's lacrosse for the girls – St George's is the only state maintained school in the south of England to play, so all fixtures are against independents, hence often at weekends. Other popular options are netball, rounders, basketball, tennis, athletics and, to a limited extent, dance. Compulsory participation to year 13, with more casual mixed classes in sixth form that encompass table tennis, badminton and trampolining. Indoor games take place in the impressive newish sports centre, also home to an attractive and well-equipped gym and weights room.

Possibly the best art department of any school for miles around – 'the pride of the school,' say pupils. Every inch of the art corridor walls and ceilings festooned with breathtakingly creative and technically exemplary work also spilling over to cover most walls throughout school. Huge (four foot) three dimensional papier mâché masks welcome visitors into this showcase area, and from that point on it's hard to know where to look, as outstanding paintings, drawings, sculptures and installations – no two the same – assault the senses. Creative facilities also superb, with three huge DT labs – again with some wonderfully turned work on display – and two huge art rooms provide yet more exhibition space for pupils' superb creative endeavours. Textiles, photography, sculpture and graphic design all on offer.

Weekends bring Friday night football club, competitive matches on Saturdays, cinema and one big trip each term (paintballing, Thorpe Park, Brighton have featured recently)

Music provides St George's heartbeat. Choirs, orchestras and bands galore and so much talent to display that annual house music competition now takes place in Watford Colosseum. One major annual drama production – Scrooge, Fame and Hairspray in recent years – in which all year groups can participate as well as smaller shows throughout the year.

Plenty of extracurricular activities from sewing and gardening to chess or curriculum based classes take place before and after school – excellent for boarders and day pupils alike. Well-attended ATC as well as World Challenge expeditions to far flung destinations from Argentina to Mongolia. School's connection with Gansu Province, China, has yielded exchange trips and a small team led by head to lecture at University of Beijing. Other trips include educational expeditions to Washington (politics), Space Camp (maths) and a popular biennial ski trip.

Boarding: Despite the small number of boarders (maximum capacity 135, with anything between five and 15 each of boys and girls in any given year group), they are very well integrated into the school. Friendships between day and boarding pupils flourish and visits to day pupils' homes encouraged. Far from feeling like a minority group, boarders take pride in their status to the point of having requested their own, slightly different, tie. Relationships between year groups are forged through fun activities such as 'speed dating' – an in house way of getting to know newcomers.

Boarding houses have friendly family feel, thanks in no small part to the young (40s), bubbly director of boarding who lives on campus and oversees the pastoral welfare of her charges full time. 'She really understands what makes teenagers tick,' said one happy parent. Girls from years 7 to 12 are housed in the old school building – safely tucked away up what seems like 15 flights of stairs – in dorms which sleep anything from two to six: 'we tailor it according to intake from year to year and girls' individual needs,' says director of boarding. Year 13 girls have the run of a swish new house with single rooms and en suite bathrooms. Boys are in a stand-alone block with a less cosy, more practical feel – though we are assured that the sparse decorations in dorms and common room

Possibly the best art department of any school for miles around. We saw outstanding paintings, drawings and sculptures

are purely by choice ('it's not cool to have posters up,' said one of our guides). Both houses have tons of communal space – massive common rooms furnished with plenty of squashy sofas and other nooks and crannies around the house with beanbags, armchairs and computers for boys and girls to congregate outside of school hours. Both houses have well-equipped kitchen areas for boarders to make themselves snacks – and there are baskets of goodies out to keep them going after school.

Boys and girls are allowed to visit each other but only in common rooms – although apparently romantic liaisons are incredibly rare: 'There is a strong sibling-like feel amongst the boarders,' say pupils. The terms 'flexi' and 'weekly' are not used and, although some boarders go home more frequently than others, all pay the same fees (less by some stretch than most private day schools) and have the same status. Around half stay for weekends (more boys than girls), with all meals apart from weekend breakfasts taken in the main school dining room. Pupils from year 9 allowed into Harpenden with permission in twos and many attend classes such as yoga or dance in the village. Pupils grumble that school is too strict about them leaving the premises – parents breathe secret sighs of relief.

Channels of communication to home left wide open with boarders allowed phones, handed in at bedtime, although they are trusted to keep iPads and laptops 'to keep it as much like home life as possible.' Weekends bring Friday night football club, competitive matches for many on Saturdays, cinema trips and one big trip each term (paintballing, Thorpe Park, Brighton have featured recently). Boarders also have their own formal dinner or ball each term, organised by senior pupils. Younger pupils have a fixed programme of after-school activities including boarding skills – learning how cook, do their laundry, make jam etc.

Background and atmosphere: Feels more like a private school than some private schools we know – and certainly wins the prize for smartest comprehensive school uniform with its green Harris tweed blazers for the boys and pleated kilts for the girls. Situated a stone's throw from Harpenden High Street, school was founded in 1907 by the Rev Cecil Grant as a non-denominational Christian foundation with its own Anglican chaplain and weekly

Sunday chapel service, which occasionally hosts up to 400 members of the school community and their families. One of the longest established fully co-educational boarding schools in England, the school retains many of its historic traditions, with pupils taking great pride in their house competitions, formality of chapel, speech days and all the different ties awarded.

The original Victorian gothic-style building still provides the heart of the school – and girls' boarding house – with various additions and extensions which run the full gauntlet from occasionally gleaming (sports hall, language block) to downright shabby (most of the rest). Despite its somewhat down at heel sum of the parts, however, the whole hangs together with a feel of purposefulness and functionality and is actually part of the school's overall charm. Sixth form common room and study areas in dire need of a refurb, but nobody seems to mind – the overall feel of the school is welcoming and contented – 'children can grow up at their own pace,' say parents. A new link with nearby Batchwood Tennis Academy hopes to attract talented players from all over the country to boarding houses.

Pastoral care, well-being and discipline: Very little need for strong discipline – hard to believe that 'chewing gum' is the worst that happens but that was all our guides would confess to. Occasionally pupils 'don't work out' on the boarding side but in the main 'they feel very lucky to be here – there's no sense of entitlement,' says director of boarding. 'Traditional values and caring ethos,' makes school tick, according to head with strong support from parents. Pupils rewarded for demonstrating school's core values of courtesy, integrity, manners and discipline. Houses presided over by a head of house, assistant and team of tutors. The arrangement of tutor groups gives pupils very little room for manoeuvre when it comes to bad behaviour. An 'excellent' student services department supports children with welfare or emotional needs with its qualified counsellor, to whom pupils can self-refer, and a pastoral support worker.

Pupils and parents: Affluent Harpenden and its surrounding villages provide the vast majority of day pupils with boarders coming mainly from further afield, and around 55 per cent of these from overseas. Cohort is hence naturally inclined towards hard work and success upon which school can build. A highly involved and vocal parent body turns out in droves for matches, concerts and shows and the Sunday service in chapel is very well attended. Alumni include philosopher and political theorist Michael Oakeshott, classicist and writer Rex Warner, actress Laura Haddock and rugby player Owen Farrell.

Entrance: The most oversubscribed of Harpenden's three secondary schools, with a complex admissions process run by school. No academic selection but a series of priorities including catchment (currently extending to around 800 metres from school), regular church attendance for at least two years (minister's letter required), and siblings receiving priority. Genuine devoutness not put to the test – local parents can cynically choose to pray rather than pay as long as they think ahead and accept that their child will have to attend chapel at school on at least three Sundays a term. A handful each year from local prep schools.

Both houses have tons of communal space – common rooms with squashy sofas, bean-bags, armchairs and computers where pupils congregate outside school hours

Boarders must be EU resident or hold British passport and are interviewed by head and director of boarding to assess suitability, as well as provide a good reference from their previous school. 'Need' also comes into play – for example children with both parents working or in the Forces, with occasional children switching from day to boarding places to save time on the daily commute. Applications should be in a year in advance, although boarding places not currently oversubscribed. Very occasional charitable places but no bursaries offered.

Exit: Around three-quarters stay on into sixth form after GCSEs – leavers generally move to other schools and colleges. More than two-thirds to Russell Group/other top universities, with six Oxbridge places in 2017 and three medics. One off to the US.

Money matters: As a voluntary aided school, St George's buildings are owned by the school's Foundation, which has to find 10 per cent of the cost of all capital projects and on-going building maintenance from very limited funds. 'There is a lot of do-it-yourself work here'; school enlists the assistance of its active parents' association for fundraising support throughout the year.

Remarks: A real gem of a local secondary school with plenty to offer pupils whether they want to paint, study or play their way to success. Riding high as one of the top non-selective state schools in the country, St George's can boast a secure, Christian community as well as top notch results.

Sexey's School

17

Cole Road, Bruton, Somerset BA10 0DF

01749 813393 | admissions@sexeys.somerset.sch.uk | www.sexeys.somerset.sch.uk

Ages: 11–18

Pupils: 593; sixth form: 141; Boarders: 190

Day: free; Boarding: £10,125 pa

Interim Headteacher: Since October 2017, Gill Kelly, an experienced interim and consultant leader of secondary schools, most recently as interim executive principal at the Wellspring Academies Trust in Lincolnshire. She has also been principal of City Academy in Bristol for four years. She is also currently a leadership coach for Women in Leadership. She is author of Where will I do my Pineapples?, a book about building a whole new school based on her experiences.

Academic matters: Results are consistently good. At GCSE, 81 per cent got 4-9 in both maths and English, with 25 per cent of grades A*/A in 2017, and at A level, 41 per cent A*/A grades, 66 per cent A*-B. The DfE recently named Sexey's as the best performing state school in Somerset and Dorset for GCSE. Most pupils take 10 subjects at GCSE, with around 38 per cent doing triple science.

Newish deputy head (academic) has launched major focus on teaching and 'supporting students to be successful' and school continually looks at how pupils can improve. Strategy has paid dividends – school recently won two national awards for being in the top 10 per cent of schools for progress made by pupils between key stage 2 results and GCSE and in the top 10 per cent nationally for high attainment. Year 7 to 9 pupils are set for maths, science and languages (French and German). Average class sizes are 22 at key stage 3, fewer at key stage 4 and 10 to 12 in the sixth form. Good SEN provision – SENCo and her five-strong team offer literacy and numeracy support in small groups to pupils who meet county criteria. One boy increased his spelling age by 22 months after 10 weeks of specialist literacy classes.

At A level, all the usual subjects, plus business, government and politics, media studies, photography, psychology and sociology. Sport and exercise science is the only BTec available. School is continuing with AS levels and pupils must achieve three Ds in year 12 to continue into year 13. One or two opt to retake their AS exams each year. Impressive head of sixth form keeps a weather eye on all and advises on higher education and career choices. A third of sixth formers do the EPQ and all year 12s do work experience.

School is forward thinking when it comes to technology. Prep diaries have been dispensed with and students use the Show My Homework app – so pupils and parents alike can see the prep that has been set and when it's due in. School has introduced philosophy as a discrete lesson for year 7 to 9 pupils and Mandarin as an after-school enrichment subject. Younger pupils do food technology for three years (everything from nutrition and healthy eating to cooking and food safety) and the subject is offered at GCSE and A level too.

Games, options, the arts: Sport has progressed in leaps and bounds in recent years. School now plays loads of matches against independent and state schools (including two Saturday fixtures a term, one for boys, one for girls) and holds its own against the likes of Millfield and Dauntsey's. Parents contribute to a voluntary sports subs fund to help cover transport costs to matches – but there's no compulsion. When we visited, the under-15 girls' cricket team had just beaten their rivals at Millfield and King Edward's. All age groups do at least two hours of sport each week. Rugby, hockey, netball, cricket, football, equestrian pursuits, sailing – you name it, they do it. Sports hall with weights room and gym, 18m heated indoor pool, good pitches and five hard tennis courts that double up for netball and five-a-side football. Emphasis is on healthy, active lifestyles and sixth formers can also choose activities like yoga, keep fit and pilates. Dynamic director of sport says her aim is to broaden the PE curriculum for all – 'the girls want to do football and rugby and the boys want to do basketball and hockey,' she says.

Loads of weekend activities – everything from foraging to theatre trips. Younger pupils are allowed (with permission) to visit Bruton once a week, older pupils twice a week

Loads of music, drama and dance on offer. Around 130 pupils play instruments (lessons are rotated so pupils don't miss the same lessons each week). Music department is housed in former head's house and includes large classroom, recording studio and practice rooms. Reasonable numbers take music at GCSE but the subject isn't offered at A level. Performance groups include choir, wind band and folk group. Yearly drama production (Little Shop of Horrors recently) – studio space for smaller productions and traditional hall for major

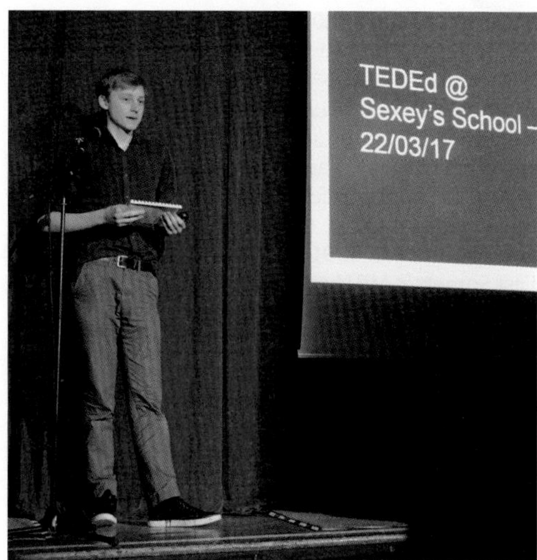

performances. Drama and theatre studies available at GCSE and A level. Art is breathtaking. We were particularly impressed by a montage of year 10 kaleidoscope paintings inspired by artist Brian Moss. The school has wisely formed close links with Hauser & Wirth Somerset, the stunning contemporary art gallery just a mile up the road.

A plethora of extracurricular activities – including circuit training, creative writing, radio club and Warhammer. Two boys who are gardening enthusiasts are developing the school's centenary garden. D of E, plus Army Cadet Force and Air Training Corps (at nearby Castle Cary). Pupils produce their own termly school magazine – recent issue included an insightful advice column on coping with exams.

Boarding: Boarders (weekly and full boarding available) account for nearly half of the school roll. They occupy three vertical, mixed boarding houses – Coombe, Lisbury and the newest, Macmillan. Boarders' dorms are mainly for two or three pupils. All well-kept and wholesome. Each house has its own houseparents, most of whom have teaching or support roles too. After-school activities between 3.40pm and 5pm every day, then boarding team takes over. Two hours of prep a night for most – year 7 to 9 boarders are supervised, older pupils can work in their rooms.

Loads of weekend activities – everything from foraging to theatre trips. Younger pupils are allowed (with permission) to visit Bruton once a week, older pupils twice a week. The mother of a year 7 boarder told us that she likes being able to drop her son off on Monday morning and pick him up on Friday afternoon. 'I feel we get the best of both worlds,' she said. 'There is no Saturday school so we get a proper family weekend.'

Background and atmosphere: School is named after Hugh Sexey, the son of poor parents who rose to become royal auditor to Elizabeth I and James I. After his death in 1619 the trustees of his will established Sexey's Hospital, which still provides care for the elderly today. The trustees later established a school for apprentices within the school grounds but it closed 200 years later. The current school was founded in 1891 and was the inspiration of East Somerset MP Hugh Hobhouse, who drafted the 1902 Education Act (his great, great grandson is a boarder at Sexey's). School later became a grammar school and then metamorphosed through voluntary controlled, grant maintained to voluntary aided. Went co-ed in 1977 and expanded its boarding provision in the 1980s to become one of the largest state boarding schools in the country, with boarding fees but free tuition.

The school's expansion over the years has resulted in a hotchpotch of architectural styles (some new, some old) squeezed into a narrow, 30-acre site, with a main road on one side and a picturesque valley on the other. Some areas of the school are slightly tired looking but the glorious countryside that bounds it on three sides more than makes up for it. In recent years Bruton, with its ancient streets of stone and stucco houses, has become one of the most sought-after places to live in the country. So many showbiz and fashion names have houses in the area – Cameron Mackintosh, Dominic West, Rhys Ifans, Sam Taylor-Wood and Mariella Frostrup to name but a few – that it's been dubbed 'the new Notting Hill' and the opening of Hauser & Wirth has added to the cachet. Mariella Frostrup was the guest of honour at a recent school speech day, cautioning students about the power of social media.

Year 7 to 11 pupils wear blazer and tie uniform (burgundy polo shirts in summer). Head recently changed dress code for sixth formers – they now wear business suits. Most like this, a few don't. 'I'd been waiting for five years to wear my own clothes,' a year 12 girl told us. Sixth form has its own common room with views over the Somerset landscape and a pervading air of studiousness when we visited at exam time. Sixth formers who have passed their driving tests are allowed to drive to school. We asked a year 12 group what they'd miss about the school when they left and they unanimously said 'Squares' – a playground game invented by Sexey's pupils. Parents praise the school's sense of community and family atmosphere and say that its size means that teachers know every child. 'Children feel proud to say they are at Sexey's,' the mother of a year 11 told us.

Food is excellent. Most have school dinners, with only a tiny handful bringing packed lunches. Everything is cooked in-house by talented chef (a former chef de partie at Heathrow) and his 20-strong team. Six hundred lunches served every day. Food is locally sourced where possible and halal, vegetarian and gluten-free options are available. Bustling canteen, with pupils allowed to sit where they want.

In recent years Bruton, with its ancient stone and stucco houses, has become one of the most sought-after places to live in the country

Pastoral care, well-being and discipline: Every pupil (day and boarding) belongs to one of four houses, each of which has a head of house and team of tutors. Lots of healthy inter-house rivalry – houses compete in sport, music, drama, enterprise, poetry and more to win the annual Bint Shield. Vertical tutor groups, with 15 minutes of tutor time every morning. School takes a huge amount of care in helping pupils' transition from primary school. Pupils due to board in year 7 come and stay for a boarding weekend in the July before they start. 'It means they're not sitting at home worrying over the summer holidays,' explains the head.

School is very keen on creating a culture of well-being and happiness. The key words at Sexey's are tolerance, respect and kindness and with that in mind the school has created The Sanctuary, a quiet place for children to go and reflect or chat about anything that's bothering them. 'The pastoral care is second to none,' a mother told us. 'The communication between teachers and parents is good too. They seem to take pride in going that extra mile.' As a C of E school, it prides itself on its close links with Diocese of Bath and Wells and St Mary's Church in Bruton (boarders regularly attend Sunday services there). School san, staffed by rotating team of three nurses, is open 24/7 for boarders. Active school council, plus head boy, head girl and raft of prefects.

Pupils and parents: A real mix. School prides itself on its diversity and pupils come from a wide variety of backgrounds – from horsey types who compete in the school equestrian team to youngsters with 'chaotic' home lives. Boarders come from all over (from Spain to Hong Kong) but must be UK nationals, hold an EU passport or be domiciled in the UK. Quite a few boarders are from army families, others from RNAS base at Yeovilton. The students we met were friendly, enthusiastic, down to earth and unpretentious. A sixth former reckoned she might have been a 'bit of a brat' if she'd gone to an independent school but said no one was like that at Sexey's.

Parents are very involved – thriving parent and staff association, with spring ball hosted in the school hall every year. Former pupils include the late Ned Sherrin, Million Dollar website creator Alex Tew and BBC wildlife film-maker James Brickell.

Entrance: Demand for day places is intense. Day admissions are handled by Somerset County Council but there's virtually no chance of a day place in years 7 to 10 unless you live within two kilometres of the school. Boarding numbers are increasing so boarding places are easier to come by. Main intakes are year 7, year 9 and sixth form. Head and head of boarding interview prospective boarders and reference from previous school required.

No new pupils admitted in year 11 and no catchment area rules for day pupils in the sixth form. Around 60 new pupils join the sixth form each year. Minimum of five GCSEs at A*-C/9-4 needed, plus some subject-specific requirements.

Exit: Up to 60 per cent leave after GCSE, mainly to take vocational courses at FE colleges in Street and Yeovil. Some to do apprenticeships.

After A level 96 per cent go to university. A wide variety of courses – from physics and biomedical science to law and history. Universities in the south west are perennially popular – Exeter, Bath, Falmouth and Plymouth – but an increasing number are going further afield, to places like Durham, Leeds, Manchester and Southampton. A few do art foundation courses and one or two go to Oxbridge most years; one medic in 2017.

Remarks: If you want your child to be a day pupil and you're lucky enough to live in the (tiny) catchment area then applying here is a no-brainer. If you want your child to board then Sexey's offers all the advantages of boarding in a small school – but without the enormous price tag or social pretentiousness.

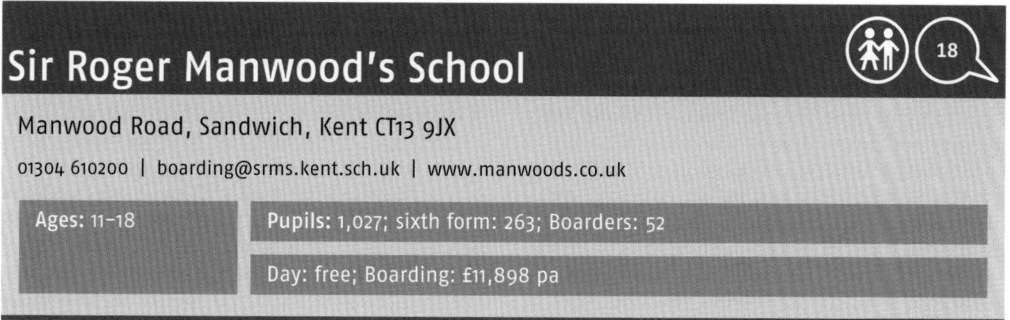

Sir Roger Manwood's School

Manwood Road, Sandwich, Kent CT13 9JX

01304 610200 | boarding@srms.kent.sch.uk | www.manwoods.co.uk

Ages: 11–18

Pupils: 1,027; sixth form: 263; Boarders: 52

Day: free; Boarding: £11,898 pa

Headteacher: Since 2013, Mr Lee Hunter, previously deputy head of Tiffin Girls' Grammar School in Surrey. A biochemist (read natural sciences at Cambridge), he first joined Tiffin Girls' as head of science in 1997. His career also includes stints as a science teacher at the Royal Grammar School in High Wycombe, the Sir James Henderson British School of Milan and Framwellgate Moor School in Durham.

Some of Mr Hunter's proudest school moments have included leading expeditions to the Indian Himalayas and introducing the Duke of Edinburgh award. Living on the Kent coast enables him to enjoy his hobbies of running, walking and cycling, as well as travelling frequently to France.

Academic matters: In 2017, 34 per cent A*/A and 63 per cent A*/B at A level, and 48 per cent A*-A/9-7 at GCSE. A quarter take history to A level. Maths is also a popular choice with more than a third of students taking A level and others taking further maths. The school has a resident maths genius who competed recently in the International Mathematics Olympiad and was placed 30th out of 548 of the world's best mathematicians. All three sciences also strongly represented at A level. The school is designated a high performing language college, and languages offered include French, German, Spanish and Mandarin Chinese (fortnightly lessons help year 7s decide whether to take it on as second language in year 8), plus Italian as a sixth form option.

If there's a weak department, it would appear to be ICT. Given that the school has computing as a specialism, it's surprising that very few candidates take it to A level. 'It's the way the lessons are taught, it needs changing,' complain sixth-formers. This cohort were among the first to take a compulsory GCSE in business and communications systems, which has appeared to turn many off computing (although it may well be a qualification they appreciate more when they are drawing up CVs). There are plans to introduce ICT courses which students will find more stimulating and relevant, following a government review of the ICT curriculum. Student requests led to A levels being introduced in film studies, psychology and sports studies, although head says that some universities' preference for traditional academic subjects seems to be turning the tide away from these newcomers.

Pupils feel they are largely taught well, 'There are one or two teachers I wouldn't employ myself, but many are the best you could get,' said one student. It's a competitive environment, but not harshly so. 'People who arrive here for the sixth form say they are pushed harder here than at other schools, but teachers work with you, they help people who are not doing so well,' one student said.

In the sixth form group, the brainy boy off to do medicine at Cambridge comes in for as much gentle joshing as the one who has found the going harder and will be reading sports sciences. 'I was one of the people who got extra help, but it didn't make me feel that everyone else was better than me,' says the latter. Another related how effective the teaching support was. 'It was spotted that I was weak at French and I got extra help. Well, then I got an A* in my French GCSE,' he said.

SEN department caters for students with dyspraxia, dyslexia and autism and provides individual support for a pupil with visual impairment.

Games, options, the arts: Sporting whizzes will be right at home here. The head reels off a long list of current and former pupils who are competing at the highest levels. 'We're very good at tennis, we've got the U14 number two in the country. We've allowed him to reduce his timetable and take time off school. One girl is representing the country in the U19 MCC ladies' cricket team. Two girls represent England in the ISF World Cross Country U18 championship. One girl competed in the national youth swimming championships, and the school has produced an international hockey player who has represented GB at two Olympic games, and a member of the England ladies' cricket team.' Such high levels of sporting success gave one parent of a boy out of this league cause for concern, but she said, 'He is not sporty and I worried about him fitting in, but he quickly found friends through the CCF and music groups.'

Boarders' weekends are filled with a mixture of organised outings and pursuing individual interests – students can take riding lessons or go for sleepovers at friends' houses

About 120 pupils get involved with the CCF, going on annual camps, shooting days and field weekends, and D of E awards are also popular. One parent wished there was more kudos for the musicians. 'Music is tiny within the life of the school, sports and languages get much more attention,' she said. However, the school counters that music has a very high profile with lots of students learning to play an instrument, and many opportunities to play music in the orchestra, various bands, choirs and concerts. Orchestral tours have recently taken pupils to Sicily and Istanbul, and the school is 'very good for musicals' according to the sixth formers. The annual big production is open to all. 'Obviously some singers are better than others, but you can still get a part if you're mediocre,' said a student.

An internationalist approach is a big part of the school's ethos, and this sees children offered exchange visits to China, India and Germany. There are language tours to Barcelona, Madrid, Paris and Berlin, a politics trip to Washington, and a visit to the Gambia every Easter, where sixth formers work at the village school.

Boarding: It's a spacious campus with lots of green space and the two boarding houses are a stone's throw from the teaching blocks. Boys have the grander accommodation with oak floors, ornate staircases and mullioned windows (33 spaces). The girls' house (23 spaces) is nondescript but cosy. All but two bedrooms are shared. Rooms have high sleepers with desks underneath and look like every teenage girls' bedroom with mates' pictures on the walls and hair straighteners lying across the beds. The housemates are 'like a family', said a boarder. The menu pinned up featured school meal standards – 'bad,' lamented a boarder when we visited, but school says there's a new catering manager, menus have changed and food is now all freshly cooked, with boarders much happier about it.

Boarders' weekends are filled with a mixture of organised outings and pursuing individual interests – students can, for example, take riding lessons or go for sleepovers at friends' houses. More staff are now on duty at weekends to organise a wider range of activities for the increasing numbers of younger boarders.

Background and atmosphere: Tucked down a quiet and leafy residential street, the school is an appealing jumble of historic buildings with modern day additions such as an IT resource centre, science blocks and Astroturf. It was founded 450 years ago by Sir Roger Manwood to bring learning to the townspeople of Sandwich. Academy status has given the school more autonomy and extra funding which has so far financed building refurbishments and an extension to the sixth form common room.

Pastoral care, well-being and discipline: Asked who is most approachable on the staff, the students rattle off a long list of names – clearly it's the majority rather than the odd one. Relationships with the staff seem unusually warm. 'The teachers are friendly, they really care and they know you on a personal level,' said one pupil. 'They care about us so much, and help us so much,' echoed another. And it would seem that treating students with kindness and respect filters down through the school. The sixth formers looked genuinely surprised when we asked about any tendency for the big kids to put the younger ones in their place, and said that would never happen. A parent concurred: 'There is no rough and tumble, there's no bullying, our child has been happy all the way through'. Another parent was worried about her child making the transition from a small independent school, but she said: 'He fitted into a family incredibly quickly.'

Pupils and parents: There's an uncommon gentleness about the school, which makes it an absolute find for parents who are concerned about how their child will deal with the hurly-burly of secondary school. A few minutes in the company of these young people is all it takes for pro-single sex school arguments to crumble. There's a warmth and naturalness between the students – no macho posturing from the boys or cliquey ring-fencing from the girls. 'Our year gets on really well,' the year 13s agree.

Sandwich regarded as posher than many of its neighbouring towns on the depressed East Kent coast and free school meal numbers lower than at nearby schools. Recently the town has been hit hard by the withdrawal of pharmaceutical giant Pfizer and the loss of 2,500 jobs, although the local council is offering enticements to businesses with the aim of creating a life sciences hub on the site. The commute to London is a slow trundle stopping at all stations; parents tend to be employed locally or stay in town for the working week.

Around half of boarders are from overseas; pupils from Nigeria, Nepal, Hong Kong, Estonia and Germany bring a healthy melée of cultures and backgrounds to the pupil mix.

Entrance: Pupils must pass the local 11+, the Kent test. Children with British or EU passports are entitled to a free education here. Out of 120 places in year 7, six are reserved for boarders. The boarding places are not usually oversubscribed, but day places are. Each year around 30 cases go to appeal, with around a further six places being awarded after appeals.

Pupils come from more than 30 feeder primary schools and the catchment is just below five miles, with the majority of pupils living in Deal, Walmer and Sandwich.

Entrance from year 8 onwards via a test administered by the school. Vast majority stays on for the sixth form; new pupils need six GCSEs at A*-C/9-4, and at least a B/6 grade in chosen subjects.

Exit: Around 15 per cent leaves after GCSEs, either for college or apprenticeships. Four to Oxbridge in 2017, others to the old guard of eg Imperial, KCL, Durham and Bristol. Creative types headed for courses in advertising, footwear design, sports journalism, dance, and musical theatre. Each year a few go on to study medicine (four in 2017, plus one vet), encouraged by the Claringbold scholarship from an old Manwoodian which provides an income of £1,000 per year during their studies.

Remarks: If you're seeking a school to move house for, this should be on your list. With a full hand of grade 1s from Ofsted it's unquestionably a good school, and the town of Sandwich offers a gorgeous beach, a golf course which regularly plays host to the Open Championship, creekside walks, and some of the best preserved medieval architecture in the country. Plus, unusually, it's a mixed sex grammar, so you can educate sons and daughters together.

If you don't want to move house, there's also the option of boarding at state school prices. Parents fighting whitened tooth and manicured nail over places in the West Kent grammars may be missing a trick here. You can get a top flight education paying only the boarding fee, a snip compared to independent day school prices in the south east.

Steyning Grammar School

19

Shooting Field, Steyning, West Sussex BN44 3RX

01903 814555 | sgs@sgs.uk.net | www.sgs.uk.net/

Ages: 11–18

Pupils: 2,206; sixth form: 451; Boarders: 117 full

Day: free; Boarding: £9,150 – £10,830 pa

Head: Since 2013, the energetic and insightful Nick Wergan (40s). He began his career in investment banking before retraining as an English teacher in 2004; then rose rapidly after being dubbed Outstanding New Teacher of the Year (2007) by the National Teaching Awards, through posts as head of English (Sackville School, East Grinstead) and deputy head (Blatchington Mill, Hove). He's resourceful and decisive, empowers his teaching team to lead and role model leadership for the pupils, and this delegation means he can also turn his powerful brain to looking at business partnerships to help with the funding crisis that dogs state schools.

He has a house on site in the Elizabethan part of the school, but also owns and lives on a vineyard nearby with his family – producing award-winning sparkling wine. This pragmatic mix of localism and global business is at the heart of his tenure. He looks to local secondaries (through Challenge Partners network) to keep Steyning Grammar striving to be its best, trumpets the school's 400 year tradition to make new legacy connections, has a conference phone on the table in one of his two offices to enable frequent management communication across two sites, and tweets and blogs avidly. He teaches English to year 7 once a week, and students say he pops in and out of classes, corridors and the canteen, working closely with the head boys and girls to take the temperature of the school too.

Academic matters: Reflections on learning are intrinsic to the school success – whether that is implicit in weekly year group assemblies (hall only holds 350); explicit in the title of the school's newsletter; or sustained through what has been created through the IB learner profile, even though the qualification is no longer on offer here. (Few state schools in the UK can afford it financially now after funding cuts.) The size of the school means that over 30 A levels and just as many GCSEs are on offer, class sizes normally 24 with 16 (restriction in practical subjects) to 20 at A level. In 2017, 24 per cent A*/A at GCSE and 74 per cent got 4-9 in both English and maths. At A level, 24 per cent A*/A and 50 per cent A*-B.

Years 7 and 8 are in the Church Street site, so their atmospheric classrooms have parquet floors and a maze of doorways leading to subject-based areas. Learning is far from low tech, though; there

Productions such as The Wedding Singer might involve 300 people in a six-night run. Pupils enthusiastic about 'Steyning's Got Talent'

are banks of computers and we saw a fizzy drink can that had been rigged to record sound. At the other end of the tech spectrum, a class loved building the rock cycle using plasticine. The library was buzzy with authors visiting and pupil volunteers, and an enterprise day involved a pitch to businessman Lord Sugar. However, by the time they have made their GCSE choices pupils are panting to get the open corridors and swell of new students in the Shooting Fields Site. The latter is dominated by the huge and successful A level specialist sixth form, which feels more like a college but with the pastoral support of a school – a real draw for the third of students who join for GCSE.

Tutorials are one-to-one and a curriculum reform means pupils now do fewer topics but more richly. Project-based learning is electric here; the pupils love it and the opportunities it provides to anchor their academic subjects in the practical and take the experience back into the classroom: a trip to the European Organisation for Nuclear Research in Cern; Kimmeridge for biology and geology; the Globe Theatre; Oviedo for Spanish.

The learning resource centre is not just about books – a remote access system means students can log on at home and avoid emailing documents back and forth. The mezzanine level is the sixth form domain and students congregate here even in break time, a sure sign of their commitment to learning – they also gather in the canteen and a learning zone behind that.

A trial period of the 'show my homework' app pleases parents as well; they like to log in and see what needs to/has been done and by when. Kahoot gamifies learning in conjuction with an interactive whiteboard; apparently a warm up to a class can get pretty heated.

Engaging teachers make for the most popular A level subjects, maths, politics and chemistry at present – science labs have loads of space for practicals, which might have 16 in each class compared to 20 in extended subjects. The school is a member of 250 Challenge Partners, in a hub with three Brighton secondaries sharing constructive collaboration and challenge to improve practice and so the education of their children – the leadership team finds it a really valuable to have such critical friends. During the GCSE years the pupils become responsible for booking their parents' appointments and act as their guides on the parents' evening itself – family feedback is that this independence works well.

The Cuthman Centre is a separate building that acts as a haven for the more vulnerable students (category 3 SEN), eight at present with specific learning difficulties; they have roll-call or more casual tea and toast there when needed, and there are NHS nurses, a counselling programme funding by pupil premium and enabled by GP referrals. In-class SEN support with learning support mentors is targeted and the impact evaluated: it ranges from laptops in exams for those with illegible writing to an SEN passport created with parent and carers. The gifted and talented (now More Able) are supported outside lesson time with book clubs and an Oxbridge programme.

Games, options, the arts: Competitive sports are netball, rugby, football, rounders and cricket, with fixtures against both independent and state schools across the county – and the Marylebone Cricket Club. The site itself has two rugby pitches and a football one hidden behind a line of trees, while sixth formers have free access to the town leisure centre adjoining the school – they can use facilities such as the pool, squash courts and dance studio (external reputation for good boys' dance). They also love the chaos of the sixth form sports day with its wheelbarrow races and Fairy Liquid slide. The equestrian team (pupil-owned horses) trains at Hickstead. We saw a game of rounders being planned using the computer suite below the boarding house – a wet weather PE lesson. If PE is not a GCSE choice, then pupils have non-competitive sport a couple of times a week.

The boarders take enormous joy in their international mix, while grounding themselves by volunteering or earning money doing shifts in the canteen

The music department is thriving with ticketed performances each season and some 20 A level students, but would love more space (who wouldn't). Logic is used for composition on Macs, there are opportunities for mixing with the use of the live room. Plenty of individual practitioners eg a boy playing the violin, guitar, piano; a ukulele and keyboard in a shared room in the boarding house.

Art and technology is exhibited throughout the halls of the school – and the drama hall is open to the public. The whole school competition is Steyning's Got Talent – some kids think it is profoundly uncool, others use it as a springboard to more public performances across the county. Full school performances such as The Wedding Singer might involve 300 people in the six-night production – set, backstage, make-up as well as performers.

The 50th school anniversary trip to the Norfolk Broads had just passed when we visited and all were proud that they are the only school still doing it, despite health and safety hobbling. Jailbreak is another riot of a challenge where the whole of year 13 is locked up and has to escape from the science department windows, source vehicles, collect permits and get to Horsham for their recapture. This, and other initiatives such as Macmillan coffee mornings, Pink Day, Comic and Sport Relief, all add up to raising around £15,000 each year for charity.

Wilton Park is nearby, the only branch of the Foreign Office outside London, and interns from there come to work with the More Able – this gives rise to a foreign affairs discussion group, tackling topics such as Syria and Ebola. For prospective medics and vets there are established links with Brighton University and timetabled prep. There are opportunities for students to become equalities, digital or eco-commissioners, do Duke of Edinburgh award and Young Enterprise, as well as lunchtime enrichment activities and independent learning working across year groups.

Boarding: On the State Boarding Schools Association committee and in the second tier of state boarding in terms of numbers. The first state boarding school to be judged outstanding by Ofsted under the new framework – in every category, with no recommendations to make. Since the school cannot make a profit, there is a limited return to invest in the boarding; the major advantage of the provision is the diversity of students. The boarders take enormous joy in their international mix, while grounding themselves by earning money on shifts in the canteen and volunteering.

Four boarding houses, two adapted and two purpose built, all with live-in houseparents. The pupils share rooms in the younger years, and are really joyful about the different cultural traditions that they get to experience, from jollof rice on Nigerian Independence Day to Chinese New Year; they promote their differences yet all order takeaways together. In the most modern house the year 13 pupils have a wet-room shower/toilet ensuite; they prop their doors open to their shared corridors and apparently are very responsive when told to turn their music down – 10.30pm curfew in the week and 11pm at weekends. The (mostly) boys watch the Premier League on their laptops; they have an ironing board and a kettle in their shared kitchen; when fending for themselves they eat toasties and pizza since health and safety dictates there is no proper oven. The houseparents lend their kitchen when a bake-a-thon is organised for charity and a list of suppliers is amended weekly to taste eg Marmite, jam, squash, milk, biscuits, bread.

The girls have photos as well as their names up on their doors – the images are taken by a photography student, whose work also features on the achievement board; this is the most obvious sign of a real sense of supportive celebration of peers. One girls' common room is huge and more homely, with desks for quiet study places too, since this is a realistic experience away from home, with scheduled time for work, although laundry returned to your cubby within a day would be unusual at home...

The ethos of the school is printed large on boards in both sites, and the children are resilient and well-supported through exam and everyday academic pressures

Facebook photos posted (eg rocket club with powder paint ejected from a parachute) and well dones handed out by the houseparents for being tidy and general good, with prizes drawn at the end of term – once it was a helicopter ride! There is chance to pitch to a 'houseparents' dragon's den' for a new piece of equipment, whether a freezer or a pool table. As elsewhere, technology is used to facilitate rather than trumpeted for its own sake: Skype interviews for prospective boarders; applications scanned and emailed in; Wifi or ethernet with hotspots means that Skyping home via an iPad is easy; WhatsApp is used to tackle awkward time differences.

Background and atmosphere: Founded in 1614, turned co-ed in 1953 and now spread over two sites in the small Sussex town of Steyning with architectural styles ranging from chocolate box Elizabethan black and white, through classic 50s secondary modern school architecture, to the super functional and crisp boarding house, not yet a decade old. It was boys only before the turn of the millennium; now it is equally co-ed and non-selective (apart from the 125 boarders), and the leading school in the country on character-based learning. The latter is now at the centre of the curriculum – teaching, assessing and reporting home on learning characteristics like grit, growth mindset, curiosity and zest.

The 'Steyning family' is made up of children who are encouraged to take risks so that they are not afraid of failure, and staff who are set on preparing the next generation to take over – 'the sooner the better!' says the head. The ethos of the school is printed large on boards in both sites, and the children are resilient and well-supported through exam and everyday academic pressures. The infrastructure for boarding, with the 125 teaching staff and 150 support staff, helps to produce excellent outcomes for disadvantaged students in particular. The staff tenure is traditionally long (30 years is not that unusual), since it is a big school with plenty of space to develop and enough room for children to escape a parent/teacher's shadow. The results are above national average, so it is really the staff's continuing challenge to find the hook to secure each student into a love of learning, demonstrate stickiness in all relationships and make sure they discover how to apply all this both in and outside the exam hall.

There are plenty of huts that deal with the overflow of lessons from this huge school; however, the head is collaborating with local industry to scratch backs and improve the school's facilities, and make those research links even stronger – funding has just been won to demolish the huts and replace them with a new classroom block.

Pupils bus in from local villages (two-thirds), are dropped off by their parents, or walk if they are lucky enough to live that close. Far from an inner city urban intake, but everyone is aware of where they stand in the wider society – boarders from the Caribbean come across occasional piercings and extensive LGBT support, the local village kids taste cultures from Barbados to Spain, and parents say, 'it opens up everyone's minds'.

Busy, big and teeming with children at break time – especially in wet weather, when they head to the gym, eat lunch in the classrooms or the school canteen. No hall large enough for a whole school gathering, but the split site means that the pupils have a real sense of progression and responsibility, from getting a key to their own locker in year 7 to wearing their own clothes in the sixth form, and using the canteen as a study space as well as one to eat in. Those with food intolerances struggle to enjoy mass meals produced within a tight budget, and the low maintenance cashless system means some parents worry about students selecting from a tempting array of sugary snacks instead of some of the healthier fruit.

Independence is highly valued here, and pupils often ask teachers for help on what suits them best in terms of learning as an individual. The staff are committed and respond swiftly and with initiative; the 400 year heritage adds gravitas when looking for aspirational connections. Ofsted, the State Boarding School Association and C of E status are all three seen as important benchmarks, but by no means the most important measure of the school's success.

Pastoral care, well-being and discipline: Both school and year councils provide feedback on issues such as uniform, the colour of leavers' hoodies, the learning resource centre, internet access to YouTube research etc. Prospective head boys and girls write a letter of application, then the school participates in an online survey, meaning year 13s get some input even though they are leaving – then they must pitch with a speech to the whole of the boarding cohort.

Horizontal pastoral system through year head and form tutor; the tutors have 12 students each and the learning mentors 10. Their aim is to personalise the school – whether that is via checking in at the Cuthman Centre and munching a piece of toast or through Pizza and Paragraphs for English Support. Growing confidence is vital, and the classes of 24 are a practical maximum to enable that.

More casually, there is supported (by the heads of year) revision in the dual purpose school canteen – peer mentors enable paired reading and might meet for breakfast in Boltons (one of the boarding houses).

Competitive sports are netball, rugby, football, rounders and cricket, with fixtures against both schools across the county – and the Marylebone Cricket Club

No truancy, no smoking on site and no drinking. If a kid impacts the learning in a classroom then they are removed from that classroom. The student could end up in the Cuthman Centre, then a follow up and reintegration. Blazers must be worn in the corridors and using of phones in classes is at teacher discretion. The range and policy of sanctions is reportedly reassuring for kids who have been beating at the boundaries at other schools; 'It's different here, you know what to expect'. The documentation and communication of the next steps is vital for everyone involved. Academic, social or emotional barriers are identified and everyone gets analysing, understanding and working together – parents and grandparents included – with reflection and using principles of restorative justice. Head says, 'we see the best of the students' behaviour at school...'

Pupils and parents: Local, rural and coastal catchment area encompasses a huge range of parental employment – multinational companies, small business owners, teachers; families will relocate and buy within the area to ensure they can get access to such a good state secondary education. A state boarding school can be a niche choice for many students – from Northern Ireland, Antigua, Denmark, to name just three.

The live Twitter feed on school trips is much more reassuring for smartphone equipped parents than interesting for the pupils back at school – likewise the Facebook page. Pupils arrange their own social lives, which is part of the independence that the school aims to build, and since so many walk, ride or bus into the school there is very little chance to of casual school gate friendships between parents.

Entrance: Strong relationships with primary schools such as Steyning Primary, Upper Beeding, Ashurst, Jolesfield in Horsham, Henfield. Catchment is 200 square kilometres encompassing Henfield to Rydon, from schools such as The Towers Covent, Shoreham College, St Andrew's High School, and Durrington High School. The local authority handles the year 7 and year 9 intake. Only boarding is selective, and that is about balancing fit and gender in a year group, aiming for 50 per cent of each sex. The sixth form is amongst the largest in the south east of England and only started marketing in 2013; before that it was just word of mouth. As a level 3 course provider (A level and equivalents), the admission is usually a B/6 or above in the subject of choice.

Exit: Up to half leave after GCSEs. After the year 13 leavers' celebration – they get into limos and head off to a club in Worthing, thrilled there is no room on site for something more low key – 70 per cent head off to higher education. Destinations and subjects range from Guildford School of Acting to history at Exeter; two to Oxbridge in 2017 and three to study medicine; others may be attracted to the reduced fees in Holland or by the established link with Harvard in the US.

Money matters: No fees for tuition, just for boarding; discounts available for up to three siblings.

Remarks: A grammar school by name only, non-selective with a huge sixth form and all the curriculum choices that size enables. Diversity of boarding provision enables the broadening of everyone's minds – from Sussex villagers to Caribbean islanders.

Welbeck, the Defence Sixth Form College

20

Forest Road, Woodhouse, Loughborough, Leicestershire LE12 8WD

01509 891712 | pa@dsfc.ac.uk | www.dsfc.ac.uk/

Ages: 16–18

Pupils: 316 (228 boys, 88 girls); Boarders: all full

£0 – £19,500 pa (means tested for MoD students)

Principal: Since 2013, Mr Peter Middleton MA. Previously deputy head at Clifton College, Mr Middleton was born in Somerset and educated at Radley before reading chemistry at Oriel College, Oxford. He began his teaching career at Cheltenham College, where he was a deputy housemaster, master in charge of rowing and first VIII coach, and an officer in the army section of the CCF. Not difficult to see the direction he was taking, confirmed by his next move, which was back to Oxford, to St Edward's, where he was a housemaster, re-formed the royal navy section, was master i/c rowing and, by now, an international rowing coach. It wasn't altogether surprising to hear that at Welbeck he likes wearing military uniform occasionally and exchanging the occasional salute. Any whisper of Apthorpe is irrelevant. Married to Clare, an educational psychologist. They have three children.

Clearly he is an ambitious man, and those who know him well speak of his drive, energy and desire to be a head. Not a ruthless man, he struck us as being like a schoolboy with a new train set. He is clearly very excited about running the school, and in his desire to share his excitement we hardly had time to exchange opening civilities before he was gesticulating wildly with something in his hand which, we realised, was being pointed at a screen nearby. The PowerPoint presentation had begun. Very informative it was, and most of what he said as introduction can be found in the prospectus bundle which will arrive when asked for.

In the course of conversations with pupils, staff and parents, it became obvious that his experience as a boarding housemaster has stood him in good stead. We heard how, shortly after his arrival, he had asked pupils to tell him how they thought the overall structure and living arrangements could be improved. As a result he has, we are told, made the boarding houses kinder establishments: they were never foot stamping, command bellowing places, but now housemasters – who, incidentally, seemed a delightful bunch – have more support,

so that boys and girls have a wider range of people to whom they can talk, gain wisdom and encouragement, seek advice and just 'chill out together.' Those connected with the boarding came over as enthusiastic and affectionate about the pupils.

Academic matters: The Defence Sixth Form College is unique. It is, as the prospectus states, a fully coeducational sixth form boarding school. Every year 175 young men and women join the college. All are destined for the military and are required to choose one from the Royal Navy, the Army, the Royal Air Force and the DESG (Defence Engineering and Science Group). Papers accompanying the prospectus tell you which grades you must have at GCSE and which subjects you have to take at A level. Always the inevitable emphasis on maths and science – everyone studies maths and the vast majority physics. Fitness tests, interviews and school reports form the basis of acceptance. They are all important. English language and the subjects required are governed by whichever branch of the military you wish to pursue. There are then lists of universities which offer places for what you wish to learn. This is where aspirants must be sure they really want to pursue these routes. Boats could be burned sooner than expected. Under good king Middleton academic aspirations have risen, but there is a limit to the breadth of A levels available. Foreign languages are taught only as enrichment AS options; for instance no Greek or Latin, no art or music A levels. Alongside maths, sciences, technology and computing you can study geography, politics or business studies, but no other humanities. In 2017, 39 per cent A*/A grades, 63 per cent A*-B. Fine for many, but be aware. This school, with all its excellence, is geared towards a specific area: engineering or technical careers in the armed forces or as a civilian within the MOD. Of course a government paid bursary of £4,000 pa would be most welcome, but there are stipulations. The school is scrupulously honest and helpful about the various permutations.

Games, options, the arts: One of the most delightful incidents of our tour was witnessing what is locally referred to as the dash for cash. This refers to the possibility of winning a bursary for university, providing your grades reach the requirements and that you are sufficiently fit to be accepted. Hence dash for cash. We watched a boy who was not, on his own admission, a natural athlete driving himself to achieve the required time. The PE staff were cheering him on, shouting encouragement, and some running with him. Passers by paused to cheer him on. It seemed the world had stopped but for those runners. And he did it by about five seconds. So he'll get his bursary. It was, he said, between gasps, 'the happiest day of my life, not so much for the bursary but because I can now go to the university of my choice.' The end of his time at Welbeck is the start of his new life.

As might be imagined there is a wide variety of activities and sport is hugely popular. All pupils are required to join the CCF for varied activities designed to prepare for different challenges and to encourage leadership.

Though we heard talk of art and music, we didn't see or hear any.

Boarding: That the general atmosphere throughout the school seems very happy must owe something to the quality and layout of the boarding accommodation. Everyone boards and the facilities are genuinely homely and in, the words of one of our guides, 'great places to live.' Those in their second and final year live, for the most part, in single ensuite bedsits; those in their first year share three in a room with ensuites. Initially we were a little surprised by having three in a room – two's company etc – but our guides assured us it worked.

Background and atmosphere: Anyone coming across the name Welbeck and thinking it sounds familiar may be thinking of Welbeck Abbey, destroyed by Henry VIII's thugs, and later adapted over the years into a huge house in Nottinghamshire in the midst of vast estates. From 1953, the year of its foundation, the college was housed in the building until 2000 when, despite its ducal associations and grandeur, it was deemed unsuitable and impractical. One snippet of history which might send a frisson of interest through the most dozy readers is that in 1913 Archduke Franz Ferdinand of Austria visited the Duke of Portland at Welbeck Abbey, and was involved in a very serious shooting accident which very nearly caused his death.

The college retains the name of Welbeck, and the specially designed and constructed buildings are excellent. Designed and built by the architectural firm HLM, the buildings are grouped in an enveloping, friendly way which creates a sense of team effort and space, housing very well laid out rooms.

Pastoral care, well-being and discipline: All the pupils we met spoke with appreciative warmth of the staff who were looking after them. They did not seem to possess any of the casual arrogance one sometimes detects in public school pupils. They were open, trusting, forthcoming and friendly. Discipline seemed easy as a result. A good touch is the presence of three serving officers and the college sergeant major, who mingle with pupils and the staff, forging useful links and running the mandatory CCF. One told us how much he was learning by being there, listening and partaking.

Not many schools can offer leavers the near certainty of going on to university to read a subject of their choice with financial aid

Pupils and parents: Pupils and parents come from all over the country and from all walks of life. Most had never boarded before but they were keen to tell us of the benefits they feel they have enjoyed during this two year spell. In amongst the literature sent in reply to parental enquiries there is a pie chart highlighting the types of feeder schools. Most come from other state schools and few from abroad. Not surprising. This is, rightly, perceived as a special school offering specific targets. Not many schools can include in their packet the near certainty of going on to university to read a subject of their choice and with such financial aid. Parents we spoke to were grateful for what the school was doing; some expressed amazed delight.

Entrance: These differ slightly according to which branch of the Forces you are aiming at, but basically include at least an A/7 and a B/6 in maths and physics plus a C/5 in English GCSE. RAF and DESG must have at least 45 GCSE points (including A/A in dual award science) and army and navy at least 40 points from their best seven subjects (at 8 for A*, 7 for A etc). You must also be medically fit and a British, Commonwealth or Irish citizen.

Exit: All those who go to university on the Defence Technical Undergraduate Scheme (DTUS) must go to one of nine universities – Aston, Birmingham, Cambridge, Loughborough, Newcastle, Northumbria, Oxford, Southampton or Strathclyde – to do an approved DTUS course. These are mostly engineering and science based, with a few management degrees. In 2017, one to Oxbridge; Aston, Southampton, Portsmouth and Birmingham are the most popular. The majority do go on to join a branch of the armed forces. They almost have to. The prospectus papers contain some delightful articles from pupils who have gone on to work with the military, taking with them the benefits they so readily acknowledge.

Money matters: The school has lots to say about money matters and offers many forms to fill in if, as is the case most of the time, parents require assistance – sponsored fees depend on family income (private self-funded students do not commit to a Forces or MOD career and may go to any university). No-one need be shy. After all, the intention of Welbeck is to help with means-testing when required and to make the seemingly impossible possible. The government, it seems, is poised to help.

Remarks: In view of the Duke of Edinburgh's connexions with Welbeck it is, perhaps, neither too fanciful nor (just) too silly to compare the school with a Battenberg cake. Both the cake and the school have different layers contributing to the whole. A number of parents and friends of the school commented on the difficulty of balancing the various facets of the school. There are the military aspects: going out on exercise, parades, map reading; the academic side: the need to work at the A level subjects in order to get to university and thence to the job; personal fitness to a pretty high standard. No doubt all these activities and the pressure they bring are perceived by many as standard. This school with its serious extras represents a very high standard and many pupils have put all their eggs in one basket. One high-ranking military man we know described Welbeck as the finest preparation not just for the armed forces but for any job in the world. But... it's not for everyone. A commitment to this excellent establishment needs careful thought and dedication.

Wymondham College

21

Golf Links Road, Morley, Wymondham, Norfolk NR18 9SZ

01953 609000 | admissions@wymondhamcollege.org | www.wymondhamcollege.org

Ages: 11–18

Pupils: 1289; sixth form: 411; Boarders: 620 full/weekly

Day: free; Boarding: £10,500 – £11,196 pa

Executive Principal: Since 2014, Mr Jonathan Taylor, formerly principal at Torch Academy Gateway Trust, Nottinghamshire. Educated at The Leys school, Cambridge, then read theology at Oxford before returning to Cambridge for a PGCE. First teaching post in nearby Cottenham, followed by assistant head at De Aston school, Market Rasen, then deputy head of Toot Hill, Nottinghamshire, before a move to the Torch Academy. A swift progress, leaving outstanding Ofsted reports in his wake. Thoughtful and immensely hard working – breakfast meetings at 7am a regular fixture with key staff- yet he hasn't disappeared in a cloud of management initiatives, preferring lots of contact with pupils and staff and teaching classes of his own. This is going down well – 'He seems to want to know us,' we were told.

In a big school, he is aware of danger of becoming out of touch and sets store by personal example. He greeted every single GCSE pupil outside the exam hall on the day of their first exam this summer to wish them luck and gets occasionally frustrated by the isolated position of his office complex – a new build under the previous principal. He is seen about the campus a lot, often accompanied by his dog, Bertie, who is, needless to say, immensely popular with pupils. Believes there is a special quality about Wymondham College, and 'the common purpose of learning for its own sake'. From personal experience he knows about boarding and understands that there is 'a lot more to a successful state boarding school than tacking a Travelodge onto a comprehensive', as has been suggested in certain quarters. Encourages pupils to contact him directly, email or in person, should they wish to, and some do. Determined to encourage the special qualities of Wymondham College and to raise standards even further – staff have fortnightly personal development sessions and are paired with a senior colleague to help share best practice and provide support. Lives on the site and is married to Julie, herself a senior education adviser.

Head of school since 2017 is Dan Browning, a history graduate from Anglia Ruskin with postgrad qualifications from UEA, the Institute of Education and Cambridge. Previous posts have included vice principal of Tendring Technology College and executive principal of St John's & King Richard School for Forces children in Cyprus.

Saturday morning school for all (though not sixth form) accepted readily enough – slightly longer holidays compensate

Academic matters: Though strictly speaking non-selective, the varied intake (50 per cent boarding) plus provision of music and sports places – and a perception in the area that 'It's for bright children' – means pupils appreciate their good fortune in being there and are motivated to work hard. Parents are a strong support and the school's results reflect all round achievement. In 2017, 83 per cent of pupils got 4-9 in both English and maths; 39 per cent A*-A/9-7 grades. Modern languages are compulsory to GCSE level (Spanish most popular). Close to 80 per cent take religious studies at GCSE – interesting for a non-faith school.

Sixth form definitely academic – despite a low bar of three B/6s and four C/5s required at GCSE for entry, most do well and higher grades are often needed for external applicants. Only four vocational courses offered in the long list of subjects to be studied, with maths taken by over half the cohort. Sciences also have a high take up. Headmaster feels this may reflect current anxieties about the need to take degrees that help lead to good jobs, but 'we are holding the line that subjects should also be studied for their own sake'. In 2017, 40 per cent A*/A grades and 65 per cent A*-B grades at A level.

As the school is regarded as 'being for bright children', there are relatively few pupils, around 12 per cent, requiring learning support, and these are milder cases of dyslexia/dyspraxia/dyscalculia, with only a small number of statemented/EHC plan pupils. Well resourced and a positive attitude about extra support. There are also breakfast and catch-up clubs run by individual departments for those needing an extra boost. All year 7s are tested on entry to the school. There is also a structured programme for teaching EFL. School has a well-established system for identifying the very bright (gifted and talented, in the jargon) early on and they spend an extra two periods a week, plus own time on an extension programme comprising a research project and an extra course chosen from space science, Russian, Latin, literature and ideas and government and politics. The presence of postgraduate fellows in the sixth form and some also resident in the houses help pupils learn good work habits – we saw a light-hearted revision session in action during GCSE study leave – and give sixth formers insider guidance with UCAS and Oxbridge entrance. A programme of visiting speakers and workshops are led by local university staff, notably from UEA and Cambridge.

Games, options, the arts: If sporty, there is plenty on offer. Usual team games – rugby included, and an extensive match schedule for the most competent though fewer games for those lower down the rankings. Games are compulsory up to sixth form, when they become optional.Pupils themselves run the five-a-side football league that operates at lunchtimes. Good facilities including swimming pool, gigantic sports hall which doubles for assemblies/concerts, Astroturf, pitches and courts galore. Keen involvement in D of E (the college runs the county scheme) and CCF also offered, though involvement in this is a voluntary activity and not timetabled.

Music important. The annual Mair cup is an opportunity for all pupils to perform in a competition between houses and is extremely popular. Over 250 have individual instrumental lessons and there are choirs and excellent jazz and concert bands that perform at events locally – including the Royal Norfolk Show. A string group has been recently established.

Flourishing art and textiles, which are taught in the Tech block, a light and airy building designed around a central atrium with good provision for display of finished efforts. Good take-up at GCSE and A level and significant numbers go on to study at degree level.

Boarding: The five boarding houses for the main school are drearily functional, though homelike enough upstairs in the dormitories. Houses are all mixed, though girls and boys have separate floors for sleeping, and day pupils as well as boarders return to houses at break and lunchtimes. Plenty of staff, matrons and resident fellows around, and pupils are cheerful and well-behaved.

A few struggle with homesickness at the beginning. Flexi or part boarding is not on offer and swapping from boarding to day is impossible, so a decision to board, taken at aged 10, has to be considered carefully. 'It's not for everyone and this is why we interview all potential boarders', we were told. Those joining in year 9 generally have fewer problems settling. The houses provide something of a refuge at break and lunchtimes when most return to base, although 'It is annoying if your friends are in another house', said one pupil. House staff around at all key times, and matrons remain on the premises at night. The majority go home at weekends but plenty remain and outings/activities are planned throughout the term. Exeats once each side of half term.

Background and atmosphere: Founded in 1951, the brainchild of Sir Lincoln Ralphs, then chief education officer for Norwich. It is the largest state boarding school in the country. The site is a former US military hospital and, despite the utilitarian nature of the buildings, it is very peaceful and in the middle of nowhere (Wymondham itself is several miles off). Some of the newer buildings – modern languages, for example – are interesting and well designed, but the most interesting of all is the single remaining Nissen hut, now listed and used, rather effectively, as the chapel. The college has a strong Christian ethos, but this is non-denominational. There is great pride in the school's history and traditions, with a memorial garden and key anniversaries celebrated regularly. Striking new sixth form centre, set around a courtyard, with boarding facilities in individual rooms with en-suite bathrooms, a refectory, working and computer areas.

One of the virtues of the site is that there is lots of 'promenade' time out in fresh air between lessons. This seems to contribute to calm and disciplined atmosphere

Traditional uniform (including ties for girls) compulsory up to year 11, but it is the cheap and cheerful sort – no Harris tweed or boaters. Pupils don't mind the slightly bleak boarding houses: 'You get used to it so quickly, and anyway, we like the people', we were told by one pupil, with nods and agreement from others. The old system of year 7s being kept in their own separate house has been discontinued and everyone is mixed up from the start. Saturday morning school for all (though not sixth form) accepted readily enough – holidays slightly longer than usual in state schools to compensate. One of the virtues of the site is that there is lots of 'promenade' time out in fresh air between lessons, and this seems to contribute to the calm and disciplined atmosphere of the school.

Pastoral care, well-being and discipline: House-based tutor groups with tutors overseeing academic and extracurricular activities from year 7 to 11. Emphasis is on good relationships. 'Work hard, be kind' is the phrase coined and we heard it quoted by year 11s quite cheerfully, if slightly tongue-in-cheek. The presence of resident fellows in the houses help with friendship and other difficulties and in addition to house staff, the school also has two counsellors and a chaplain, so there is a network of support. Looking out for younger pupils is encouraged and there is very little evidence of bad behaviour or bullying, though school is ever alert and anti-bullying strategies are in place. The parent liaison office helps to smooth communications between home and school, especially for parents of boarders.

Pupils and parents: Pupils come from Norfolk in the main (including boarders), though an increasing number are from further afield thanks, in part, to the improvements to the A11. Over 20 per cent are from overseas, a mixture of Europeans and Chinese mostly, plus those with parents working abroad. Fewer Forces families than formerly; the majority of parents are professional or managerial. 'It's an unpretentious place, not for show-offs, and we like that,' said a parent, and that is the common view. Quite a few have chosen the school because it is a state funded one and without the perceptions of privilege that independent boarding schools may possess. Pupils regard themselves as fortunate and appear straightforward and hard working.

Entrance: Main intake at 11+ but places are available at 13 (boarding only) and again in the sixth form. Day and boarding places are split roughly 50:50. Day places very oversubscribed and awarded according to the LA criteria of looked after children, siblings and distance from school. Once other categories have been dealt with, the distance from the school can be as little as 0.6 mile, though commonly up to two miles. Check carefully – despite the name, the town of Wymondham itself is not in the catchment. Eight musical aptitude and eight sporting aptitude places – four day and four boarding for each. Competition for such places is fierce.

All potential boarders are interviewed by the house heads to check that pupils are prepared for all that boarding entails (a hard call in a 10 minute chat). Places are less competitive, but still oversubscribed. It is perhaps worth adding that although you can apply for both day and boarding places, you must list them in order of preference, and if allocated a boarding place you cannot make a crafty switch to day later on. The number of places in each category is fixed.

Most remain for the sixth form, assuming they meet baseline attainment of four C/5s and three B/6s at GCSE. Not a high bar, but as numbers applying from outside exceed places available, admission is, effectively, dependant on rank order of results at GCSE for those applying from elsewhere.

Exit: Some 15 per cent leave after GCSEs Majority of sixth formers – some 75 per cent – move on to higher education. Wide range of degree subjects studied though a definite bias towards the sciences, maths, computing and business. Almost half to Russell group institutions with eight to Oxbridge in 2017 and five medics. The resident Lincoln Fellow in the sixth form is an Oxbridge graduate with a brief to dispel myths about the application process and help pupils with UCAS generally.

Money matters: Tuition is free; fees are payable for boarding provision only. Fees compare favourably with the cost of a local day independent schools. Day boarding and enhanced day boarding, for relatively modest fees, are popular option (they include meals and various after-school activities) but there are no flexible boarding arrangements.

At least one sixth form boarding scholarship a year, worth 100 per cent of fees, for a student with exceptional academic, music or sporting potential.

Remarks: Has a well deserved reputation locally, and increasingly nationally as a leading state boarding school. It is a bargain for parents who want a boarding education for their children, but without the associations of privilege or having to fork out fortunes in school fees. It is a big school and hard-working, socially outgoing types do best.

Why choose boarding for the SEN child?

A perhaps surprising number of pupils with SEN will board for at least some of their schooldays. For those with very complex or profound difficulties who require intensive support, residential care can be the best way of providing this. For other families, it's down to logistics. If the perfect specialist education is on one side of the country and work or other family commitments on the other, boarding is often the only realistic solution.

But boarding can also be an important, and valuable, part of the therapeutic process for children whose needs go beyond classroom support.

From making friends to changing duvet covers, planning and cooking meals to operating a washing machine, boarding can be an invaluable way for pupils learn the social and organisational skills that will one day allow them to lead independent lives – and do so with aplomb. It's the reason that many schools encourage pupils, even those living very close to a school, to start spending nights away. Surrounded by people who know how they tick, when to step in - and when to step back – it can be a happy, confidence-inspiring experience for both parents and children.

What to look out for in a boarding school

Boarding for the first time can be unsettling for any child. For those with SEN, the uncertainties and worries are often magnified. How good is the school at working with parents to prepare children for this new experience? Are there online or visual guides that show clearly how it works and what pupils are expected to do? What personal possessions are they able to take (pictures, duvet covers, even pets) so their room becomes their own?

- Does the school's approach get the official stamp of approval? Ofsted carries out separate accommodation inspections. What is the school's rating? (They can drop or rise rapidly.)
- How is unstructured free time after school and at

weekends organised? It may be the highlight of the week for most boarders but unsettling to those with social or communication difficulties – so is someone there to help pupils plan their time? Is there a quiet place they can retreat to if they need time out?

- An action-packed programme for boarders can sound amazing, but does it include activities your child enjoys, and are staff on hand to encourage (and keep on encouraging) pupils to try something new? If your child has a niche interest (wind turbines and George VI are two examples recently encountered) will the school be right behind them?
- How good are the staff – from subject teachers to matrons to therapists - at talking to each other? If a child is sleeping badly, has lost a prized possession or had a meltdown in a lesson, will there be a bit of unobtrusive extra support to get them through a bad time?
- What's the boarding accommodation like? Slightly scruffy isn't necessarily an issue as long as it's clean, tidy, secure, well supervised and organised, with instructions and visual timetables to make the routine easy to understand.
- Bullying happens even in the best schools but children with SEN frequently won't report it, so how is it spotted and dealt with, particularly if it happens in free time?

And finally, do boarding staff 'get' your child, understand and empathise with their quirks? Does their experience extend to pupils with similar difficulties and how have they been supported?

Are they kind, empathetic and welcoming when you visit? If a boarding school makes parents feel at home, children, whatever their learning needs, are far more likely to feel the same way.

SEN boarding schools

These are shortened versions of some of our reviews of boarding schools for children with relatively mild difficulties. Full reviews of these and other schools can be found on our website: www.goodschoolsguide.co.uk.

Appleford School, Wiltshire SP3 4HL

www.appleford.wilts.sch.uk
129 pupils, 76 boarders, aged 7-18
For children with dyslexia and other specific learning difficulties such as dyspraxia and dyscalculia

Traditional independent boarding school in every way; it looks like one and it acts like one. The new sixth form is primarily for pupils who need to retake GCSEs or who are just not quite ready go to college or sixth form elsewhere. The head agreed boarding school can be a 'bubble', so along with team building exercises, pupils are taught how to catch a bus and iron a shirt. For a specialist education, small is fantastic and without doubt pupils thrive here.

Breckenbrough School, North Yorkshire YO7 4EN

www.breckenbrough.org.uk
49 boys, 20 boarders, aged 9-19
For boys with complex learning and emotional needs including ASD and ADHD

UK's only Quaker residential special school, operating with often challenging pupils (all statemented and LA funded). Need to be academically able though won't necessarily be reflected in previous academic results. Calm, peaceful environment often transformative, one boy, previously labelled 'unteachable' going on to gain pilot's licence. Boarding sensibly tailored to needs – the boarders (full and weekly) can seek refuge in rooms before and after lessons, for example. Qualifications include GCSEs and A levels with maths and sciences a particular strength, as are fab activities, ranging from leadership to motorbike maintenance.

Bredon School, Gloucestershire GL20 6AH

http://www.bredonschool.org
249 pupils, 97 boarders, aged 7-18
For children with dyslexia, dyspraxia and other specific learning needs

Also includes mainstream pupils and more than half take GCSEs. On site is the Cisco Academy, which trains those with an interest in engineering or computer science for technical jobs or further education. It's set on a working farm, and younger pupils take their turns mucking out and feeding animals, planting and weeding vegetables. Successful clay pigeon shooting team with one former pupil now an Olympic competitor. One parent, who moved her son here after he was bullied at another school, said: 'My son is like a changed child – he is happy, relaxed, engaged.'

Bruern Abbey School, Oxfordshire OX26 1UY

www.bruernabbey.org
150 boys, 119 boarders, aged 7-13
For bright but often very dyslexic boys, some with additional needs eg Asperger's, ADHD

Top class senior school destinations reflect exceptionally hard work put in by staff (some with SpLD themselves) to give pupils skills they need to succeed in common entrance. Quirkiness a common feature. All trad subjects covered though English and maths dominate curriculum, taking up half the timetable. Dorms are large, airy, clean and tidy but in need of smartening, though bathrooms are newly kitted out. Spare cash ploughed into teaching resources, though parents show appreciation for often stellar progress made by their sons with tireless fundraising.

Frewen College, East Sussex TN31 6NL

www.frewencollege.co.uk
110 pupils, a third boarders, aged 7-18
For children with a specific learning difficulty or speech and language disorder

Pupils often arrive in a battered state. Hence there's a big focus on building confidence – often through music and drama productions – and on creating a calm, low pressure environment. 'The way in which the children learn to support each other is exceptional,' said one parent. The glorious surroundings and feeling of space are sure to ease the anxiety-ridden child. Most take five or more GCSEs, and usually around half are at least grade C/4. There's a policy of involving pupils a lot in decisions to help them feel empowered. Their proposal for less homework was adopted right up to the GCSE years.

Limpsfield Grange, Surrey RH8 0RZ

www.limpsfield-grange.surrey.sch.uk
71 girls, 24 boarders, aged 11-16
For girls with communication and interaction needs, most with autism

Rarity in sea of boys' only or boy-dominated schools – a maintained special school for girls, some too emotionally vulnerable to cope in mainstream education. Boarding time includes life skills and independence training, lessons also used to explore emotions, traditional elements (desks in rows) combined with encouragement for girls to find own ways to cope (one brings hot water bottle in class). Lack of therapy only major downside. Dogs a soothing presence (one hears readers). Most pupils will go on to take up to eight GCSEs, less academic studying for vocational qualifications.

Mark College, Somerset TA9 4NP

www.priorygroup.com/markcollege
77 pupils, 40 boarders aged 10 to 19
For children with dyslexia, dyscalculia, ASD, ADHD, speech and language difficulties, difficulties around social communication, or a history of anxiety or bullying

Children tend to be of average or above average ability. 'The classic student is the one for whom mainstream doesn't provide enough, but a local authority special school wouldn't fit their profile. We're like a mini-mainstream.' Around 50 per cent of the children will take seven or eight GCSEs. One leaver last summer achieved three As at A level. Lots of inter-school sports competitions, from football to cross-country. The benefits of boarding are immense, said one parent. 'It's made him. His communication and confidence has grown immensely, and he can now do things for himself that he never used to.'

Mary Hare School, Berkshire RG14 3BQ

www.maryhare.org.uk
244 pupils, including boarders, aged 11-19
For children with a profound and severe hearing impairment

Uses language acquisition to give best chance in later life with advanced amplification system, developed by on-site firm. Academically successful, with particularly good French and English results. A levels (20 subjects) and BTecs offered in sixth form. Huge grounds (150 acres) brilliant for mountain biking. Other sports - basketball and volleyball – also flourish, as does performing arts with plenty of soloists and groups, including school orchestra. Boarding (flexi, weekly, termly) praised for caring staff and well-implemented rewards and sanctions. Only niggle girls' accommodation - slightly less good that boys', sixth formers graduating to university-style accommodation.

More House School (Farnham), Surrey GU10 3AP

www.morehouseschool.co.uk
470 boys, 120 boarders, aged 8-18
For boys with a primary diagnosis of SpLD

Caring but no-nonsense admissions process (no to behavioural difficulties unless secondary and definitely under control with medication) ensures focus on what school does best – supporting able boys whose dyslexia has held them back. Far-flung families make boarding a necessity. Most flexi, minority full, some reluctant. School does its best – a tad more cosiness would make it even better. Education starts with confidence building - erratic spelling no bar to success. Support - extensive – is timetabled. 'Almost a bespoke education,' said parent (a view seconded by inspectors).

Northease Manor School, East Sussex BN7 3EY

www.northease.co.uk
77 pupils, 16 boarders, aged 10 to 17
For children with dyslexia, dyspraxia and dyscalculia; also ADD and social communication difficulties

Attractive school in picturesque courtyard setting with cosy boarding (flexi and weekly). Girls' rooms in particular impressively decorated, staff happy to dispense 2am reassurance if homesickness kicks in. Small classes and enthusiastic staff, many home grown (school runs own training courses) contribute to academic results. Here, assistance is in seemingly limitless supply; academic achievement against the odds the goal. While there are bright pupils here - and must be of average ability or above - complexity of needs makes acquisition of decent GCSE grades a real achievement. No plans for sixth form though work closely with local sixth form colleges Sussex Downs, Varndean, Ringmer, Plumpton, in some cases pushing to get pupils on desired courses.

Oversands School, Cumbria LA11 6SD

www.witherslackgroup.co.uk
47 boys (though co-ed since 2013), nearly all boarders, aged 8-19
For children with complex needs ranging from ASD to emotional and social difficulties

Pupils admitted if school feels it can make a difference. In ultra-out-of-town setting (mains water only since 2007). School radiates stability with plenty of encouragement to try new things. Tailored therapeutic support within what school describes as '24-hour curriculum' that extends from GCSE options (currently 12 subjects) to practical lessons in independent living, older pupils learning to manage for themselves in cottages in the woods. High standard of boarding accommodation, children, who normally go home every two weeks, choosing bedding from Argos catalogue so ready and waiting when they arrive.

Shapwick School, Somerset TA7 9NJ

www.shapwickschool.com
90 pupils, 55 boarders, aged 8-19
For dyslexic children of at least average ability

Located in beautiful Tudor manor close to sleepy village and a sanctuary for its pupils, with small classes, tailored curriculum and staff who 'get' them. Children sit eight GCSEs, English the big area where children struggle. About two-thirds are full boarders, trad model with Saturday school and two formal exeats per term, also weekly and flexi boarders, all from year 6. Boarding recently criticised by Ofsted but since improved and, while adequate rather than luxurious, praised by parents for caring staff. The sports fixture list bravely includes neighbouring titan Millfield.

Slindon College, West Sussex BN18 0RH

www.slindoncollege.co.uk
80 boys, 30 boarders, aged 8-18
For boys with dyslexia, dyspraxia, speech and language difficulties and autism spectrum conditions

Moving towards becoming a special school for autism. Visual arts particularly good here: alongside mainstream GCSEs, pupils can take GCSEs and A levels in art, textiles, graphics, photography and DT. Other subjects available as BTecs rather than A levels. Boys can take motor mechanic qualifications and build an electric car from a kit in the Greenpower club. Boarding staff are incredibly kind, dedicated and thoughtful, according to one parent. 'Yesterday they even called me about getting horse manure for my son's mushrooms - so touching, they really care,' she said.

Swalcliffe Park, Oxfordshire, OX15 5EP

www.swalcliffepark.oxon.sch.uk
47 boys, including boarders, aged 11-19
For boys with autistic spectrum conditions

Special and outstanding school in tucked away tranquil setting complete with Georgian mansion. Learning approach makes much use of 'The Four Whys' - communication, independence, self-management and achievement, to help convert troubled autistic boys into confident achievers (some excluded from previous schools). Good GCSEs no use to pupils unable to leave bedroom. Tiny class sizes with primary school environment for younger pupils – teachers come to them – pupils moving around for most lessons only in KS4. Six boarding houses, all deliberately similar, the focus for life skills acquisition and practice, from planning and shopping to cooking and clearing meals for mixed age boarding families, while individual bedrooms have en suite shower room and personal touches (including a gecko).

Sunnydown School, Surrey CR3 5ED

www.sunnydown.surrey.sch.uk
83 boys, 44 flexi boarders, aged 11-16
For boys with some form of communication and interaction need

Around 90 per cent have an autism diagnosis. They need to have mainstream academic ability, as they typically study up to eight GCSEs. Many of the boys have difficulty with processing speed 'which leads to frustration then the behaviours creep in,' head says. Various measures are used to help them get down what they want on paper, such as software which records and types speech, and which can read text to them. 'The boarding facility is second to none. I have absolutely no doubts about the care that is provided for my son, to the point I sometimes think they know him better than I do,' said one parent.

Because no-one said you have to do it alone.

Our consultants know the best schools for every type of special need.

The Good Schools Guide Education Consultants

0203 286 6824 | goodschoolsguide.co.uk/SEN | consultants@goodschoolsguide.co.uk

You may also like to read....

The Good Schools Guide 21st edition
Features independent and unbiased views of over 1,200 state and independent schools throughout Britain, written by parents for parents.

The Good Schools Guide London North
We have plundered the knowledge and experience of our North London based writers and advisers to provide not just the opinionated and unbiased school reviews for which The Good Schools Guide is renowned, but also fascinating pen portraits of the capital's diverse areas. An invaluable guide for any family considering education in the capital.

The Good Schools Guide London South
Packed with local South London knowledge, candid reviews and parent comments, not to mention a full run-down of how the English education system works.

The Good Schools Guide online subscription
Read all our reviews plus exam data, catchment maps, university entrance information, and advice on choosing a school, tutors, SEN, talented children and much more.

Uni in the USA
Written by students who have been through the US system, features in-depth descriptions of 65 US universities, plus the inside track on getting in and preparing for life across the pond.

Uni in the USA and Beyond online subscription and ebook
Also includes unis in Europe and the East, from Alberta to Abu Dhabi, and advice from SATS to visas.

The Good Schools Guide International online subscription
The one-stop educational shop for ex-pats, it reviews the best state and independent schools round the globe, plus insider knowledge on life overseas.

All available via: www.goodschoolsguide.co.uk/shop-online

Boarding schools index

School	Page

List of advertisers

Advertisers (Website) **Page**

Advertisers (Website) Page

House Ads

Notes

Notes

Notes

Notes

Notes